Hoover's Handbook of

World Business

2022

HOOVERS™

A D&B COMPANY

Austin, Texas

Hoover's Handbook of World Business 2022 is intended to provide readers with accurate and authoritative information about the enterprises covered in it. Hoover's researched all companies and organizations profiled, and in many cases contacted them directly so that companies represented could provide information. The information contained herein is as accurate as we could reasonably make it. In many cases we have relied on third-party material that we believe to be trustworthy, but were unable to independently verify. We do not warrant that the book is absolutely accurate or without error. Readers should not rely on any information contained herein in instances where such reliance might cause financial loss. The publisher, the editors, and their data suppliers specifically disclaim all warranties, including the implied warranties of merchantability and fitness for a specific purpose. This book is sold with the understanding that neither the publisher, the editors, nor any content contributors are engaged in providing investment, financial, accounting, legal, or other professional advice.

The financial data (Historical Financials sections) in this book are from a variety of sources. Mergent Inc., provided selected data for the Historical Financials sections of publicly traded companies. For private companies and for historical information on public companies prior to their becoming public, we obtained information directly from the companies or from trade sources deemed to be reliable. Hoover's, Inc., is solely responsible for the presentation of all data.

Many of the names of products and services mentioned in this book are the trademarks or service marks of the companies manufacturing or selling them and are subject to protection under US law. Space has not permitted us to indicate which names are subject to such protection, and readers are advised to consult with the owners of such marks regarding their use. Hoover's is a trademark of Hoover's, Inc.

10 9 8 7 6 5 4 3 2 1

Publishers Cataloging-in-Publication Data

Hoover's Handbook of World Business 2022

    Includes indexes.

    ISBN 978-1-64972-824-1

    ISSN 1055-7199

    1. Business enterprises — Directories. 2. Corporations — Directories.

HF3010 338.7

U.S. AND WORLD BOOK SALES

Mergent Inc.

580 Kingsley Park Drive
Fort Mill, SC
29715
Phone: 704-559-6961
e-mail: skardon@ftserussell.com
Web: www.mergentbusinesspress.com

Mergent Inc.

Executive Managing Director: John Pedernales

Publisher and Managing Director of Print Products: Thomas Wecera

Director of Print Products: Charlot Volny

Quality Assurance Editor: Wayne Arnold

Production Research Assistant: Davie Christna

Data Manager: Allison Shank

MERGENT CUSTOMER SERVICE-PRINT
Support and Fulfillment Manager: Stephanie KardonPhone: 704-559-6961
e-mail: skardon@ftserussell.com
Web: www.mergentbusinesspress.com

ABOUT MERGENT, INC.

For over 100 years, Mergent, Inc. has been a leading provider of business and financial information on public and private companies globally. Mergent is known to be a trusted partner to corporate and financial institutions, as well as to academic and public libraries. Today we continue to build on a century of experience by transforming data into knowledge and combining our expertise with the latest technology to create new global data and analytical solutions for our clients. With advanced data collection services, cloud-based applications, desktop analytics and print products, Mergent and its subsidiaries provide solutions from top down economic and demographic information, to detailed equity and debt fundamental analysis. We incorporate value added tools such as quantitative Smart Beta equity research and tools for portfolio building and measurement. Based in the U.S., Mergent maintains a strong global presence, with offices in New York, Charlotte, San Diego, London, Tokyo, Kuching and Melbourne. Mergent, Inc. is a member of the London Stock Exchange plc group of companies. The Mergent business forms part of LSEG's Information Services Division, which includes FTSE Russell, a global leader in indexes.

Abbreviations

AB – Aktiebolag (Swedish)*
ADR – American Depositary Receipts
AG – Aktiengesellschaft (German)*
AFL-CIO – American Federation of Labor and Congress of Industrial Organizations
AMEX – American Stock Exchange
A/S – Aktieselskab (Danish)*
ASA – Allmenne Aksjeselskaper (Norwegian)*
ATM – asynchronous transfer mode; automated teller machine
CAD/CAM – computer-aided design/computer-aided manufacturing
CASE – computer-aided software engineering
CD-ROM – compact disc – read-only memory
CEO – chief executive officer
CFO – chief financial officer
CMOS – complementary metal-oxide semiconductor
COMECON – Council for Mutual Economic Assistance
COO – chief operating officer
DAT – digital audio tape
DOD – Department of Defense
DOE – Department of Energy
DOT – Department of Transportation
DRAM – dynamic random-access memory
DVD – digital versatile disc/digital video disc
EC – European Community
EPA – Environmental Protection Agency
EPS – earnings per share
EU – European Union
EVP – executive vice president
FCC – Federal Communications Commission
FDA – Food and Drug Administration

FDIC – Federal Deposit Insurance Corporation
FTC – Federal Trade Commission
GATT – General Agreement on Tariffs and Trade
GmbH – Gesellschaft mit beschränkter Haftung (German)*
GNP – gross national product
HDTV – high-definition television
HMO – health maintenance organization
HR – human resources
HTML – hypertext markup language
ICC – Interstate Commerce Commission
IMF – International Monetary Fund
IPO – initial public offering
IRS – Internal Revenue Service
KGaA – Kommanditgesellschaft auf Aktien (German)*
LAN – local-area network
LBO – leveraged buyout
LNG – liquefied natural gas
LP – limited partnership
Ltd. – Limited
MFN – Most Favored Nation
MITI – Ministry of International Trade and Industry (Japan)
NAFTA – North American Free Trade Agreement
Nasdaq – National Association of Securities Dealers Automated Quotations
NATO – North Atlantic Treaty Organization
NV – Naamlose Vennootschap (Dutch)*
NYSE – New York Stock Exchange
OAO – open joint stock company (Russian)
OAS – Organization of American States

OECD – Organization for Economic Cooperation and Development
OEM – original equipment manufacturer
OOO – limited liability company (Russian)
OPEC – Organization of Petroleum Exporting Countries
OS – operating system
OTC – over-the-counter
P/E – price-to-earnings ratio
PLC – public limited company (UK)*
RAM – random-access memory
R&D – research and development
RISC – reduced instruction set computer
ROA – return on assets
ROI – return on investment
SA – Société Anonyme (French)*; Sociedad(e) Anónima (Spanish and Portuguese)*
SA de CV – Sociedad Anónima de Capital Variable (Spanish)*
SEC – Securities and Exchange Commission
SEVP – senior executive vice president
SIC – Standard Industrial Classification
SpA – Società per Azioni (Italian)*
SPARC – scalable processor architecture
SVP – senior vice president
VAR – value-added reseller
VAT – value-added tax
VC – venture capitalist
VP – vice president
WAN – wide-area network
WWW – World Wide Web
ZAO – closed joint stock company (Russian)
z o.o. – z ograniczona odpowiedzialnoscia (Polish)*

* These abbreviations are used in companies' names to convey that the companies are limited liability enterprises; the meanings are usually the equivalent of corporation or incorporated.

Contents

List of Lists

HOOVER'S RANKINGS

Companies Profiled

Companies Profiled

Companies Profiled

Companies Profiled (continued)

x

About Hoover's Handbook of World Business 2022

This edition of Hoover's Handbook of World Business is focused on its mission of providing you with premier coverage of the global business scene. Featuring 300 of the world's most influential companies based outside of the United States, this book is one of the most complete sources of in-depth information on large, non-US-based business enterprises available anywhere.

Hoover's Handbook of World Business is one of our four-title series of handbooks that covers, literally, the world of business. The series is available as an indexed set, and also includes Hoover's Handbook of American Business, Hoover's Handbook of Private Companies, and Hoover's Handbook of Emerging Companies. This series brings you information on the biggest, fastest-growing, and most influential enterprises in the world.

HOOVER'S ONLINE FOR BUSINESS NEEDS

In addition to Hoover's widely used MasterList and Handbooks series, comprehensive coverage of more than 40,000 business enterprises is available in electronic format on our Web site at www.hoovers.com. Our goal is to provide our customers the fastest path to business with insight and actionable information about companies, industries, and key decision makers, along with the powerful tools to find and connect to the right people to get business done. Hoover's has partnered with other prestigious business information and service providers to bring you all the right business information, services, and links in one place.

We welcome the recognition we have received as the premier provider of high-quality company information — online, electronically, and in print — and continue to look for ways to make our products more available and more useful to you.

We believe that anyone who buys from, sells to, invests in, lends to, competes with, interviews with, or works for a company should know all there is to know about that enterprise. Taken together, this book and the other Hoover's products and resources represent the most complete source of basic corporate information readily available to the general public.

HOW TO USE THIS BOOK

This book has four sections:

1. "Using Hoover's Handbooks" describes the contents of our profiles and explains the ways in which we gather and compile our data.

2. "A List-Lover's Compendium" contains lists of the largest, fastest-growing, and most valuable companies of global importance.

3. The company profiles section makes up the largest and most important part of the book — 300 profiles of major business enterprises, arranged alphabetically.

4. Three indexes complete the book. The first sorts companies by industry groups, the second by headquarters location. The third index is a list of all the executives found in the Executives section of each company profile.

Using Hoover's Handbooks

SELECTION OF THE COMPANIES PROFILED

The 300 profiles in this book include a variety of international enterprises, ranging from some of the largest publicly traded companies in the world — Daimler AG, for example — to Malaysia's largest and oldest conglomerate, Sime Darby Berhad. It also includes many private businesses, such as Bertelsmann AG and LEGO, as well as a selection of government-owned entities, such as Mexico's Petróleos Mexicanos. The companies selected represent a cross-section of the largest, most influential, and most interesting companies based outside the United States.

In selecting these companies, we followed several basic criteria. We started with the global giants, including Toyota and Royal Dutch Shell, and then looked at companies with substantial activity in the US, such as Vivendi and Diageo. We also included companies that dominate their industries (e.g., AB Electrolux, the world's #1 producer of household appliances), as well as representative companies from around the world (an Indian conglomerate, Tata; two firms from Finland, Nokia and Stora Enso Oyj; and two companies from Russia, OAO Gazprom and OAO LUKOIL). Companies that weren't necessarily global powerhouses but that had a high profile with consumers (e.g., IKEA) or had interesting stories (Virgin Group) were included. Finally, because of their truly global reach, we added the Big Four accounting firms (even though they are headquartered or co-headquartered in the US).

ORGANIZATION

The profiles are presented in alphabetical order. You will find the commonly used name of the enterprise at the beginning of the profile; the full, legal name is found in the Locations section. For some companies, primarily Japanese, the commonly translated English name differs from the actual legal name of the company, so both are provided. (The legal name of Nippon Steel Corporation is Shin Nippon Seitetsu Kabushiki Kaisha.) If a company name starts with a person's first name (e.g., George Weston Limited), it is alphabetized under the first name. We've also tried to alphabetize companies where you would expect to find them — for example, Deutsche Lufthansa is in the L's and Grupo Televisa can be found under T.

The annual financial information contained in the profiles is current through fiscal year-ends occurring as late as June 2019. We have included certain nonfinancial developments, such as officer changes, through September 2019.

OVERVIEW

In the first section of the profile, we have tried to give a thumbnail description of the company and what it does. The description will usually include information on the company's strategy, reputation, and ownership. We recommend that you read this section first.

HISTORY

This extended section, which is present for most companies, reflects our belief that every enterprise is the sum of its history and that you have to know where you came from in order to know where you are going. While some companies have limited historical awareness, we think the vast majority of the enterprises in this book have colorful backgrounds. We have tried to focus on the people who made the enterprises what they are today. We have found these histories to be full of twists and ironies; they make fascinating reading.

EXECUTIVES

Here we list the names of the people who run the company, insofar as space allows. We have shown age and pay information where available, although most non-US companies are not required to report the level of detail revealed in the US.

Although companies are free to structure their management titles any way they please, most modern corporations follow standard practices. The ultimate power in any corporation lies with the shareholders, who elect a board of directors, usually including officers or "insiders," as well as individuals from outside the company. The chief officer, the person on whose desk the buck stops, is usually called the chief executive officer (CEO) in the US. In other countries, practices vary widely. In the UK, traditionally, the Managing Director performs the functions of the CEO without the title, although the use of the term

CEO is on the rise there. In Germany it is customary to have two boards of directors: a managing board populated by the top executives of the company and a higher-level supervisory board consisting of outsiders.

As corporate management has become more complex, it is common for the CEO to have a "right-hand person" who oversees the day-to-day operations of the company, allowing the CEO plenty of time to focus on strategy and long-term issues. This right-hand person is usually designated the chief operating officer (COO) and is often the president of the company. In other cases one person is both chairman and president.

We have tried to list each company's most important officers, including the chief financial officer (CFO) and the chief legal officer. For companies with US operations, we have included the names of the US CEO, CFO, and top human resources executive, where available.

The people named in the Executives section are indexed at the back of the book.

The Executives section also includes the name of the company's auditing (accounting) firm, where available.

LOCATIONS

Here we include the company's full legal name and its headquarters, street address, telephone and fax numbers, and Web site, as available. We also list the same information for the US office for each company, if one exists. Telephone numbers of foreign offices are shown using the standardized conventions of international dialing. The back of the book includes an index of companies by headquarters location.

In some cases we have also included information on the geographic distribution of the company's business, including sales and profit data. Note that these profit numbers, like those in the Products/Operations section below, are usually operating or pretax profits rather than net profits. Operating profits are generally those before financing costs (interest income and payments) and before taxes, which are considered costs attributable to the whole company rather than to one division or part of the world. For this reason the net income figures (in the Historical Financials section) are usually much lower, since they are after interest and taxes. Pretax profits are after interest but before taxes.

PRODUCTS/OPERATIONS

This section lists as many of the company's products, services, brand names, divisions, subsidiaries, and joint ventures as we could fit. We have tried to include all its major lines and all familiar brand names. The nature of this section varies by company and the amount of information available. If the company publishes sales and profit information by type of business, we have included it (in US dollars).

COMPETITORS

In this section we have listed enterprises that compete with the profiled company. This feature is included as a quick way to locate similar companies and compare them. Because of the difficulty in identifying companies that only compete in foreign markets, the list of competitors is still weighted to large international companies with a strong US presence.

HISTORICAL FINANCIALS

Here we have tried to present as much data about each enterprise's financial performance as we could compile in the allocated space. Financial data for all companies is presented in US dollars, using the appropriate exchange rate at fiscal year-end.

While the information presented varies somewhat from industry to industry, it is less complete in the case of private companies that do not release data (although we have always tried to provide annual sales and employment). The following information is generally present.

A five-year table, with relevant annualized compound growth rates, covers:

- Sales — fiscal year sales (year-end assets for most financial companies)
- Net income — fiscal year net income (before accounting changes)
- Net profit margin — fiscal year net income as a percent of sales (as a percent of assets for most financial firms)
- Employees — fiscal year-end or average number of employees
- Stock price — the fiscal year close
- P/E — high and low price/earnings ratio
- Earnings per share — fiscal year earnings per share (EPS)
- Dividends per share — fiscal year dividends per share

The information on the number of employees is intended to aid the reader interested in knowing whether a company has a long-term trend of increasing or decreasing employment. As far as we know, we are the only company that publishes this information in print format.

The numbers on the left in each row of the Historical Financials section give the month and the year in which the company's fiscal year actually ends. Thus, a company with a September 30, 2018, year-end is shown as 9/18.

In addition, we have provided in graph form a stock price history for companies that trade on the major US exchanges. The graphs, covering up to five years, show the range of trading between the high and the low price, as well as the closing price for each fiscal year. For public companies that trade on the OTC or Pink Sheets or that do not trade on US exchanges, we graph net income. Generally, for private companies, we have graphed net income, or, if that is unavailable, sales.

Key year-end statistics in this section generally show the financial strength of the enterprise, including:

- Debt ratio (long-term debt as a percent of share-holders' equity)
- Return on equity (net income divided by the average of beginning and ending common share-holders' equity)
- Cash and cash equivalents
- Current ratio (ratio of current assets to current liabilities)
- Total long-term debt (including capital lease obligations)
- Number of shares of common stock outstanding
- Dividend yield (fiscal year dividends per share divided by the fiscal year-end closing stock price)
- Dividend payout (fiscal year dividends divided by fiscal year EPS)
- Market value at fiscal year-end (fiscal year-end closing stock price multiplied by fiscal year-end number of shares outstanding)
- Fiscal year sales for financial institutions.

Per share data has been adjusted for stock splits. The data for public companies with sponsored American Depositary Receipts has been provided to us by Morningstar, Inc. Other public company information was compiled by Hoover's, which takes full responsibility for the content of this section.

In the case of private companies that do not publicly disclose financial information, we usually did not have access to such standardized data. We have gathered estimates of sales and other statistics from numerous sources.

Hoover's Handbook of

World Business

A List-Lover's Compendium

The 100 Largest Global Public Companies by Sales in Hoover's Handbook of World Business 2022

Rank	Company	Sales ($ mil)	Rank	Company	Sales ($ mil)	Rank	Company	Sales ($ mil)
1	Walmart Inc	$559,151	35	Kroger Co (The)	$132,498	69	Johnson & Johnson	$93,775
2	Amazon.com Inc	$469,822	36	Home Depot Inc	$132,110	70	ITOCHU Corp (Japan)	$93,589
3	Apple Inc	$365,817	37	Allianz SE	$129,097	71	Target Corp	$93,561
4	China Petroleum & Chemical Corp	$322,004	38	JPMorgan Chase & Co	$127,202	72	CITIC Ltd	$93,328
5	PetroChina Co Ltd	$295,682	39	General Motors Co	$127,004	73	Koninklijke Ahold Delhaize N	$90,687
6	CVS Health Corp	$292,111	40	Centene Corp	$125,982	74	BNP Paribas (France)	$89,709
7	UnitedHealth Group Inc	$287,597	41	AXA SA	$125,786	75	Lowe's Companies Inc	$89,597
8	Exxon Mobil Corp	$285,640	42	Deutsche Telekom AG	$123,955	76	Citigroup Inc	$88,839
9	Volkswagen AG	$273,543	43	Bayerische Motoren Werke AG	$121,489	77	Archer Daniels Midland Co.	$85,249
10	Toyota Motor Corp	$272,933	44	TotalEnergies SE	$119,704	78	PJSC Gazprom	$84,927
11	Alphabet Inc	$257,637	45	Honda Motor Co Ltd	$118,948	79	FedEx Corp	$83,959
12	Berkshire Hathaway Inc	$245,510	46	Meta Platforms Inc	$117,929	80	Carrefour S.A.	$83,244
13	McKesson Corp	$238,228	47	China Mobile Limited	$117,437	81	Humana, Inc.	$83,064
14	Samsung Electronics Co Ltd	$217,588	48	Comcast Corp	$116,385	82	Wells Fargo & Co (New)	$82,407
15	AmerisourceBergen Corp.	$213,989	49	Mitsubishi Corp	$116,366	83	HSBC Holdings Plc	$82,026
16	Industrial and Commercial Ba	$201,209	50	Phillips 66	$114,852	84	Deutsche Post AG	$81,990
17	Costco Wholesale Corp	$195,929	51	JD.com, Inc.	$114,033	85	Sony Group Corp	$81,277
18	Hon Hai Precision Industry C	$190,662	52	Valero Energy Corp	$113,977	86	Aeon Co Ltd	$80,922
19	Mercedes-Benz AG	$189,382	53	SAIC Motor Corp Ltd	$113,472	87	Tesco PLC	$80,586
20	Shell plc	$183,195	54	Alibaba Group Holding Ltd	$109,499	88	T-Mobile US Inc	$80,118
21	China Construction Bank Corp	$180,888	55	Nippon Telegraph & Telephone	$107,871	89	Electricite de France	$80,072
22	BP PLC	$180,626	56	Stellantis NV	$106,377	90	Enel SpA	$79,755
23	AT&T Inc	$168,864	57	Japan Post Holdings Co Ltd	$105,852	91	PepsiCo Inc	$79,474
24	Microsoft Corporation	$168,088	58	Credit Agricole SA	$105,648	92	Intel Corp	$79,024
25	Cardinal Health, Inc.	$162,467	59	Federal Reserve System	$104,976	93	Hitachi, Ltd.	$78,837
26	Cigna Corp (New)	$160,401	60	Fannie Mae	$101,543	94	Munich Re Group	$78,413
27	China Railway Group Ltd	$149,039	61	Assicurazioni Generali S.p.A	$101,377	95	Prudential Plc	$77,092
28	Exor NV	$146,684	62	United Parcel Service Inc	$97,287	96	Rosneft Oil Co OJSC (Moscow)	$76,961
29	Glencore PLC	$142,338	63	Nestle SA	$96,148	97	Banco Santander SA	$76,318
30	China Railway Construction Corp	$139,188	64	China Communications Construc	$95,958	98	Procter & Gamble Co (The)	$76,118
31	Anthem Inc	$138,639	65	Hyundai Motor Co., Ltd.	$95,557	99	E.ON SE	$75,682
32	Ford Motor Co. (DE)	$136,341	66	Chevron Corporation	$94,692	100	PJSC Lukoil	$75,389
33	Verizon Communications Inc	$133,613	67	Dell Technologies Inc	$94,224			
34	Walgreens Boots Alliance Inc	$132,509	68	Bank of America Corp	$93,851			

SOURCE: MERGENT INC., DATABASE, JANUARY 2022

The 100 Largest Global Public Companies by Income
Hoover's Handbook of World Business 2022

Rank	Company	Net Income ($ mil)	Rank	Company	Net Income ($ mil)	Rank	Company	Net Income ($ mil)
1	Apple Inc	$94,680	35	Hongkong And Shanghai Bankin	$13,382	69	Allianz SE	$8,354
2	Alphabet Inc	$76,033	36	Royal Bank of Canada (Montreal)	$12,983	70	Nippon Telegraph & Telep. (Japan)	$8,274
3	Microsoft Corporation	$61,271	37	United Parcel Service Inc	$12,890	71	ConocoPhillips	$8,079
4	JPMorgan Chase & Co	$48,334	38	Home Depot Inc	$12,866	72	Regeneron Pharmaceuticals, Inc.	$8,075
5	Industrial and Commercial Ba	$48,302	39	Visa Inc	$12,311	73	American Express Co.	$8,060
6	Berkshire Hathaway Inc	$42,521	40	Freddie Mac	$12,109	74	U.S. Bancorp (DE)	$7,963
7	China Construction Bank Corp	$40,583	41	Bank of Japan	$11,933	75	CVS Health Corp	$7,910
8	Meta Platforms Inc	$39,370	42	AbbVie Inc	$11,542	76	GlaxoSmithKline Plc	$7,846
9	Amazon.com Inc	$33,364	43	Toronto Dominion Bank	$11,373	77	Texas Instruments, Inc.	$7,769
10	Bank of America Corp	$31,978	44	BHP Group Ltd	$11,304	78	Prudential Financial Inc	$7,724
11	Tencent Holdings Ltd.	$24,441	45	ThyssenKrupp AG	$11,223	79	China Life Insurance Co Ltd	$7,686
12	Novartis AG Basel	$24,021	46	Citigroup Inc	$11,047	80	Commonwealth Bank of Australia	$7,642
13	Samsung Electronics Co Ltd	$23,973	47	Morgan Stanley	$10,996	81	PepsiCo Inc	$7,618
14	Exxon Mobil Corp	$23,040	48	Cisco Systems Inc	$10,591	82	Bank Nova Scotia Halifax	$7,602
15	Alibaba Group Holding Ltd	$22,987	49	Sony Group Corp	$10,583	83	JD.com, Inc.	$7,554
16	Fannie Mae	$22,176	50	Volkswagen AG	$10,228	84	PNC Financial Services Group (The)	$7,517
17	Verizon Communications Inc	$22,065	51	Sberbank Russia	$10,175	85	Prosus N V	$7,449
18	Ping An Insurance (Group) Co	$21,880	52	Mitsubishi UFJ Financial Gro	$10,091	86	CITIC Ltd	$7,304
19	Wells Fargo & Co (New)	$21,548	53	General Motors Co	$10,019	87	Novo-Nordisk AS	$7,268
20	Johnson & Johnson	$20,878	54	Surgutneftegas PJSC	$9,931	88	Kweichow Moutai Co., Ltd.	$7,140
21	AT&T Inc	$20,081	55	Coca-Cola Co (The)	$9,771	89	Siemens AG (Germany)	$7,131
22	Intel Corp	$19,868	56	Rio Tinto Ltd	$9,769	90	Abbott Laboratories	$7,071
23	Taiwan Semiconductor Manufact	$18,429	57	Pfizer Inc	$9,616	91	Merck & Co Inc	$7,067
24	Ford Motor Co. (DE)	$17,937	58	RWE AG	$9,541	92	Northrop Grumman Corp	$7,005
25	UnitedHealth Group Inc	$17,285	59	Goldman Sachs Group Inc	$9,459	93	Bristol Myers Squibb Co.	$6,994
26	Toyota Motor Corp	$17,002	60	American International Group Inc	$9,388	94	HCA Healthcare Inc	$6,956
27	China Mobile Limited	$16,489	61	Philip Morris International Inc	$9,109	95	Unilever Plc (United Kingdom)	$6,850
28	Roche Holding AG	$16,231	62	Qualcomm Inc	$9,043	96	Broadcom Inc (DE)	$6,736
29	Sanofi	$15,113	63	Telecom Italia SpA	$8,866	97	Reliance Industries Ltd	$6,715
30	Procter & Gamble Co (The)	$14,306	64	British American Tobacco Plc (UK)	$8,734	98	ASML Holding NV	$6,659
31	Comcast Corp	$14,159	65	Mastercard Inc	$8,687	99	Mercantil Servicios Financie	$6,658
32	Nestle SA	$13,888	66	BNP Paribas (France)	$8,673	100	UBS Group AG	$6,557
33	Oracle Corp	$13,746	67	Tesco PLC	$8,552			
34	Walmart Inc	$13,510	68	Cigna Corp (New)	$8,458			

SOURCE: MERGENT INC., DATABASE, JANUARY 2022

The 100 Largest Global Public Employers
Hoover's Handbook of World Business 2022

Rank	Company	Employees	Rank	Company	Employees	Rank	Company	Employees
1	Taiwan Semiconductor Manuf.	29,847,196	35	X5 Retail Group NV	339,716	68	Panasonic Corp	243,540
2	Walmart Inc	2,300,000	36	Cognizant Technology Solutions Corp.		69	Jardine Cycle & Carriage Ltd	240,000
3	Amazon.com Inc	1,608,000			330,600	70	Continental AG (Germany, Fed	236,386
4	Volkswagen AG	662,600	37	Sumitomo Electric Industries	325,011	71	Reliance Industries Ltd	236,334
5	Accenture plc	624,000	38	Carrefour S.A.	321,383	72	Wal-Mart de Mexico S.A.B. de	231,271
6	Randstad NV	603,480	39	Fomento Economico Mexicano, S.	320,618	73	Publix Super Markets, Inc.	227,000
7	Deutsche Post AG	571,974	40	TJX Companies, Inc.	320,000	74	Deutsche Telekom AG	226,291
8	Compass Group PLC (United Ki	548,143	41	Magnit PJSC	316,001	75	P.T. Astra International TBK	226,105
9	United Parcel Service Inc	534,000	42	Walgreens Boots Alliance Inc	315,000	76	HSBC Holdings Plc	226,059
10	Home Depot Inc	504,800	43	JD.com, Inc.	314,906	77	Yamato Holdings Co., Ltd.	223,191
11	ISS	471,056	44	Fresenius SE & Co KGaA	311,269	78	Loblaw Companies Ltd	220,000
12	PJSC Gazprom	467,000	45	PepsiCo Inc	309,000	79	Dairy Farm International Hol	220,000
13	Kroger Co (The)	465,000	46	International Business Machines	307,600	80	Capgemini SE	219,314
14	China Mobile Limited	454,332	47	Siemens AG (Germany)	303,000	81	Vinci SA	217,731
15	Industrial and Commercial Ba	439,787	48	CVS Health Corp	300,000	82	Woolworths Group Ltd	215,000
16	Sodexo	422,712	49	Albertsons Companies Inc	300,000	83	Honda Motor Co Ltd	211,374
17	Koninklijke Ahold Delhaize N	414,000	50	CK Hutchison Holdings Ltd	300,000	84	Citigroup Inc	210,153
18	Target Corp	409,000	51	Concentrix Corp	290,000	85	Bank of America Corp	208,000
19	Aeon Co Ltd	408,567	52	FedEx Corp	289,000	86	AT&T Inc	203,000
20	Jardine Matheson Holdings Ltd.	403,000	53	Mercedes-Benz AG	288,481	87	Casino Guichard Perrachon S.	202,955
21	Japan Post Holdings Co Ltd	390,775	54	Costco Wholesale Corp	288,000	88	Fareast Islami Life Insuranc	200,288
22	Teleperformance SA	383,233	55	Sberbank Russia	285,600	89	McDonald's Corp	200,000
23	Starbucks Corp.	383,000	56	HCA Healthcare Inc	284,000	90	Wipro Ltd	200,000
24	Nippon Telegraph & Telephone	371,816	57	China Telecom Corp Ltd	281,192	91	Dollar Tree Inc	199,327
25	Toyota Motor Corp	370,870	58	Jabil Inc	280,000	92	Denso Corp	196,126
26	Securitas AB	370,000	59	Nestle SA	273,000	93	BNP Paribas (France)	193,319
27	Tesco PLC	367,321	60	JPMorgan Chase & Co	271,025	94	Half Robert International Inc.	191,600
28	Berkshire Hathaway Inc	360,000	61	Infosys Ltd.	259,619	95	Banco Santander SA	191,189
29	Rosneft Oil Co OJSC (Moscow)	355,900	62	China Unicom (Hong Kong) Ltd	254,702	96	Disney (Walt) Co. (The)	190,000
30	Kelly Services, Inc.	354,500	63	Alibaba Group Holding Ltd	251,462	97	Stellantis NV	189,512
31	Hitachi, Ltd.	350,864	64	JBS S.A.	250,000	98	Comcast Corp	189,000
32	UnitedHealth Group Inc	350,000	65	Aramark	248,300	99	America Movil SAB de CV	186,851
33	China Construction Bank Corp	349,671	66	Wells Fargo & Co (New)	247,848	100	Ford Motor Co. (DE)	183,000
34	Lowe's Companies Inc	340,000	67	State Bank Of India	245,652			

SOURCE: MERGENT, INC., DATABASE,JANUARY 2022

Hoover's Handbook of

World
Business

The Companies

77 Bank, Ltd. (The) (Japan)

Unlike 77 Sunset Strip 77 Bank's name doesn't denote its address but its order in the history of Japanese banking. 77 Bank was founded in 1878 as the 77th national bank in Japan. Operating more than 140 branches in the northern area of Japan's largest island Honshu 77 Bank provides the usual banking services of savings and lending as well some other operations such as temporary employment property appraisal and credit-document custody. 77 Bank also provides financial-related services that include leasing credit investigation computer-based contract services and a credit card.

EXECUTIVES

Independent Director, Seiichi Otaki
Independent Director, Masahiro Sugita
Chairman of the Board, Representative Director, Teruhiko Ujiie
President, Representative Director, Hidefumi Kobayashi
Senior Managing Director, Representative Director, Makoto Igarashi
Managing Director, Yoshikazu Onodera
Director, Koichi Suzuki
Managing Director, Atsushi Kobayashi
Managing Director, Takuji Tabata
Independent Director, Ken Nakamura
Independent Director, Masai Yamaura
Independent Director, Yoko Ushio
Independent Director, Toshio Suzuki
Independent Director, Emiko Okuyama
Independent Director, Akira Inukai
Managing Director, Atsushi Shitoh
Director, Mitsuo Chubachi
Auditors: Deloitte Touche Tohmatsu LLC

LOCATIONS

HQ: 77 Bank, Ltd. (The) (Japan)
3-3-20 Chuo, Aoba-ku, Sendai, Miyagi 980-8777
Phone: (81) 22 267 1111
Web: www.77bank.co.jp

COMPETITORS

ARAB BANK PLC   NANTO BANKLTD. THE

HISTORICAL FINANCIALS

Company Type: Public

Income Statement				FYE: March 31
	ASSETS ($ mil.)	NET INCOME ($ mil.)	INCOME AS % OF ASSETS	EMPLOYEES
03/20	80,792	168	0.2%	4,244
03/19	77,905	159	0.2%	4,296
03/18	82,101	172	0.2%	4,442
03/17	77,360	144	0.2%	4,436
03/16	76,570	141	0.2%	4,420
Annual Growth	1.4%	4.5%	—	(1.0%)

2020 Year-End Financials

Return on assets: 0.2%	Dividends
Return on equity: 3.8%	Yield: —
Long-term debt ($ mil.): —	Payout: —
No. of shares (mil.): 74	Market value ($ mil.): —
Sales ($ mil): 1,077	

A.P. Moller - Maersk A/S

A.P. Moller - Maersk is an integrated container logistics company connecting and simplifying trade to help customers grow and succeed. Operating in about 130 countries the conglomerate specializes in global container shipping and related services. It operates through Maersk Line Business (Maersk Line Safmarine and Sealand ? A Maersk company) together with the Hamburg S d brands (Hamburg S d and Alian §a) Maersk Oil Trading as well as strategic transhipment hubs under the APM Terminals brand. Other activities include marine towing and salvage through Svitzer and refrigerated containers manufactured by Maersk Container Industry. The US is the company's largest single market with some 25% of sales.

Operations

A.P. Moller ? Maersk has four segments: Ocean Logistics & Services Terminals & Towage and Manufacturing & Others.

Ocean segment which consist of approximately 70% of company's revenue Ocean includes the ocean activities of Maersk Liner Business (Maersk Line Safmarine and Sealand ? A Maersk Company) together with the Hamburg S d brands (Hamburg S d and Alian §a) as well as strategic transhipment hubs under the APM Terminals brand.

Logistics & Services segment with the logistics and supply chain management services container inland services inland haulage activities (intermodal) trade finance services and freight forwarding. It consist of over 15% of total revenue.

Terminals & Towage includes gateway terminals involving landside activities (being port activities where the customers are mainly the carriers) and towage services under the Svitzer brand. It consists of approximately 10% of revenue.

Manufacturing & others represent the remaining in the company's revenue. It includes the activities of Maersk Container Industry Maersk Supply Service and others.

Geographic Reach

Denmark-based company A.P. Moller ? Maersk operates in some 130 countries worldwide. It operates in USA Australia France Nigeria China and Hong Kong UK Germany Netherlands Brazil Singapore etc. USA is the leading country which consist of some 25% of total revenue.

Sales and Marketing

Maersk offers global and local logistics solutions to industries such as retail chemical fashion and lifestyle automotive technology and electronics as well as pharma and healthcare logistics.

Financial Performance

The company's revenue increased to $39.7 billion in 2020 from $38.9 million. Revenue increased by $850 million despite lower volumes in Ocean and gateway terminals due to the negative impacts from COVID-19.

In 2020 profit increased to $4.2 billion from $1.7 billion in 2019.

Cash held by the company at the end of 2020 increased to $5.8 billion. Operating activities provided $7.8 billion while investing and financing activities used $1.0 billion and $5.6 billion respectively. Main cash uses were for purchase of intangible assets and property plant and equipment and repayment of borrowings.

Strategy

A.P. Moller's three strategic pillars are: Creating a portfolio of end-to-end products/services; Seamless customer engagement; and Superior delivery network end-to-end.

An important element of the global integrator strategy is to strengthen the logistics product portfolio notably on the landside by improving and in-novating existing products as well as acquiring capabilities and product offerings through acquisitions. In 2020 A.P. Moller - Maersk strengthened its product offering to customers along the end-to-end value chain.

Adding more products is fundamental towards becoming the global integrator of container logistics but equally important is the ability to combine these products into tailored customer value propositions and more effectively serve the customers' needs notably through digital solutions. The COVID-19 situation accelerated A.P. Moller - Maersk's customers' need for digital engagement and services and A.P. Moller - Maersk benefited from previous investments into its technology stack including maersk.com and other online offerings.

The bedrock of the strategy of A.P. Moller - Maersk is a superior delivery network end-to-end which delivers on fundamental needs for getting goods to the right place at the right time at the right price with minimum environmental impact.

Company Background

Founded by Peter Mærsk M ller and his son Arnold Peter M ller A.P. M ller - Mærsk styles the company and family name as "Mærsk" but uses "Maersk" for the names of most of its subsidiaries. A.P. M ller - Mærsk's main shareholder is The A.P. M ller and Chastine Mc-Kinney M ller Foundation which was established by company founder A.P. M ller in 1953.

EXECUTIVES

CEO of APM Shipping Services, Morten Engelstoft, $1,528,295 total compensation
Executive Vice President, Henriette Hallberg Thygesen, $916,976 total compensation
Board of Directors, Bernard Bot
Vice Chairman, Ane Maersk Mc-Kinney Uggla
Chairman, Jim Hagemann Snabe
CEO of Ocean and Logistics, Vincent Clerc, $1,406,031 total compensation
Board of Directors, Marc Engel
Board of Directors, Arne Karlsson
Executive Vice President, Patrick Jany, $916,976 total compensation
CEO, S ren Skou, $3,056,589 total compensation
Auditors: PricewaterhouseCoopers Statsautoriseret Revisionsaktieselskab

LOCATIONS

HQ: A.P. Moller - Maersk A/S
Esplanaden 50, Copenhagen K DK-1098
Phone: (45) 33 63 33 63
Web: www.maersk.com

2017 Sales

	% of total
USA	16
China and Hong Kong	6
United Kingdom	4
Germany	3
India	3
Netherlands	3
Brazil	2
Turkey	2
Denmark	1
Singapore	1
Other countries	59
Total	**100**

PRODUCTS/OPERATIONS

2017 Sales

	$ mil.	% of total
Maersk Line	24,299	74
APM Terminals	4,138	13
Damco	2	8
Maersk Container Industry	1,016	3
Svitzer	659	2
Other businesses unallocated and eliminations	(1835)	-
Total	**30,945**	**100**

Selected Business Areas

Container shipping & related
  Damco (freight forwarding and supply chain management services)
  Maersk Container Industry (manufacturing of dry and refrigerated containers)
  Maersk Line (global container shipping)
  MCC Transport (intra-Asia container shipping)
  Safmarine (Africa Middle East and Indian subcontinent container shipping)
  Seago Line
  SeaLand
  Svitzer (specialized marine services including towing salvage and emergency response)
Terminal activities
  APM Terminals (port operations inland transportation and container repair)

COMPETITORS

ASTEC INDUSTRIES INC.
BUREAU VERITAS
CEVA GROUP PLC
ELECTROCOMPONENTS PUBLIC LIMITED COMPANY
EXPEDITORS INTERNATIONAL OF WASHINGTON INC.
GOODWIN PLC
HUNTING PLC
JD.com Inc.
JOHN WOOD GROUP PLC
NIPPON EXPRESS CO. LTD.
Petrofac Limited
REXEL
RICARDO PLC
TOUAX SCA - SGTR - CITE - SGT - CMTE - TAF - SLM TOUAGE INVE
XPO LOGISTICS INC.

HISTORICAL FINANCIALS

Company Type: Public

Income Statement   FYE: December 31

	REVENUE ($ mil.)	NET INCOME ($ mil.)	NET PROFIT MARGIN	EMPLOYEES
12/20	39,740	2,850	7.2%	83,624
12/19	38,890	(84)	—	86,279
12/18	39,019	3,169	8.1%	80,220
12/17	30,945	(1,205)	—	85,667
12/16	35,464	(1,939)	—	87,736
Annual Growth	2.9%	—	—	(1.2%)

2020 Year-End Financials

Debt ratio: 27.3%
Return on equity: 9.8%
Cash ($ mil.): 5,865
Current ratio: 1.27
Long-term debt ($ mil.): 13,224
No. of shares (mil.): 19
Dividends
  Yield: 7.3%
  Payout: 0.0%
Market value ($ mil.): 216

	STOCK PRICE ($) FY Close	P/E High/Low	PER SHARE ($) Earnings	Dividends	Book Value
12/20	11.11	0 0	145.00	0.81	1,538
12/19	7.18	— —	(4.00)	0.82	1,398
12/18	6.24	0 0	152.00	0.08	1,571
12/17	8.69	— —	(58.00)	0.07	1,474
12/16	8.00	— —	(93.00)	0.15	1,507
Annual Growth	8.6%	— —	—	53.7%	0.5%

Aareal Bank AG

Aareal Bank engages internationally in a variety of aareal estate and property-related banking and financial services for the public and private sectors. The German bank organizes its business into two primary segments. Structured property financing (its most profitable business) specializes in financing large-scale retail hotel and logistics industry properties. The consulting/services segment serves the housing property energy and waste disposal industries with specialized banking products such as electronic banking mass payment automation and downstream processes. Its Aaeron subsidiary provides IT consulting in several European countries. Aareal Bank operates in more than 20 countries in Europe North America and the Asia/Pacific region.

EXECUTIVES

Chief Lending Officer, Member of the Management Board, Dagmar Knopek, $1,025,465 total compensation
Independent Deputy Chairman of the Supervisory Board, Richard Peters, $130,921 total compensation
Member of the Management Board, Christof Winkelmann, $1,025,465 total compensation
Member of the Supervisory Board, Employee Representative, Petra Heinemann-Specht, $93,304 total compensation
Independent Member of the Supervisory Board, Hermann Wagner, $135,556 total compensation
Independent Member of the Supervisory Board, Hans-Dietrich Voigtlaender, $131,031 total compensation
Chief Financial Officer, Member of the Management Board, Marc Hess, $1,025,465 total compensation
Independent Member of the Supervisory Board, Sylvia Seignette, $102,546 total compensation
Independent Member of the Supervisory Board, Elisabeth Stheeman, $96,849 total compensation
Member of the Management Board, Chief Risk Officer, Christiane Kunisch-Wolff, $1,025,465 total compensation
Member of the Management Board, Chief Digitalization Officer, Thomas Ortmanns, $1,025,465 total compensation
Member of the Supervisory Board, Employee Representative, Thomas Hawel, $74,061 total compensation
Chairman of the Management Board, Chief Executive Officer, Hermann Merkens, $1,623,653 total compensation
Deputy Chairman of the Supervisory Board, Employee Representative, Klaus Novatius, $119,637 total compensation
Independent Chairwoman of the Supervisory Board, Marija Korsch, $301,942 total compensation
Auditors: PricewaterhouseCoopers GmbH Wirtschaftpruefungsgesellschaft

LOCATIONS

HQ: Aareal Bank AG
Paulinenstrasse 15, Wiesbaden D-65189
Phone: (49) 611 3480   **Fax:** (49) 611 3482549
Web: www.aareal-bank.com

PRODUCTS/OPERATIONS

2015 Sales

	% of total
Interest income	90
Commission income	1
Other operating income	9
Total	**100**

COMPETITORS

AOZORA BANK LTD. THE
AUSTRALIA AND NEW ZEALAND BANKING GROUP LIMITED
China Merchants Bank Co. Ltd.
HIROSHIMA BANK LTD. THE
INTERNATIONAL FINANCE CORPORATION
Industrial And Commercial Bank Of China Limited
MIZUHO BANK LTD.
NEDBANK GROUP LTD
RBC CAPITAL MARKETS LLC
RIYAD BANK
SANLAM LTD

HISTORICAL FINANCIALS

Company Type: Public

Income Statement   FYE: December 31

	ASSETS ($ mil.)	NET INCOME ($ mil.)	INCOME AS % OF ASSETS	EMPLOYEES
12/20	55,814	(90)	—	2,982
12/19	46,187	180	0.4%	2,788
12/18	48,884	256	0.5%	2,748
12/17	50,237	248	0.5%	2,800
12/16	50,374	227	0.5%	2,728
Annual Growth	2.6%	—	—	2.3%

2020 Year-End Financials

Return on assets: (-0.1%)
Return on equity: (-2.5%)
Long-term debt ($ mil.): —
No. of shares (mil.): 59
Sales ($ mil): 1,308
Dividends
  Yield: —
  Payout: —
Market value ($ mil.): —

AB Electrolux (Sweden)

AB Electrolux is a top maker of household appliances worldwide sells about 60 million products annually. Electrolux cranks out washing machines stoves refrigerators and freezers under the AEG Electrolux and Frigidaire names. Electrolux largest market is the US accounting for some 30% of its revenue. AB Electrolux was founded in 1919 by Axel Wenner-Gren.

Operations
AB Electrolux's operations are divided into four reportable segments: Europe (some 40% of sales); North America (nearly 35%); Latin America (roughly 15%) and Asia-Pacific Middle East and Africa (nearly 15%).

All these segments produces appliances for the consumer market and products comprise mainly of refrigerators freezers cookers dryers washing machines dishwashers microwave ovens vacuum cleaner and other small appliances.

Overall sales from product areas include taste with around 60% care with some 30% and well-being with about 10%.

Geographic Reach
Stockholm-based AB Electrolux boasts a global reach as its products are sold in more than 120 markets. The US is the company's biggest single market representing some 30% of sales followed by Brazil with around 10% of sales and after that no other country accounts for more than 10% of sales suggesting enviable geographic diversification.

Sales and Marketing
Electrolux sells to a substantial number of customers in the form of large retailers buying groups and independent stores.

Financial Performance
Net sales in 2020 amounted to SEK116.0 billion which is a decrease of 3%. Organic sales increased by 3% and acquisitions had a positive impact of

0.1% while currency translation had a negative impact of 6%.

In 2020 the company had a net income of SEK6.6 billion a 162% increase from the previous year's net income of SEK2.5 billion.

The company's cash at the end of 2020 was SEK20.2 billion. Operating activities generated SEK11.9 billion while investing activities used SEK5.1 billion mainly for capital expenditures. Financing activities provided another SEK2 billion.

Strategy

Electrolux focuses on consumer-relevant product innovations to drive profitable growth. Its global presence offers economies of scale and the company invests in digital transformation modularized product architectures automation and flexibility in production. Sustainability is a key business driver and a solid balance sheet facilitates profitable growth.

Mergers and Acquisitions

In mid-2021 Electrolux has agreed to acquire La Compagnie du SAV (CSAV) the main French independent service provider (ISP) specialized in repairing domestic appliances. The acquisition is fully in line with the Electrolux Group strategy to offer outstanding experiences to consumers ensuring they get the most out of their appliances during the complete lifecycle of the product. With this acquisition the company further strengthens its service network in France allowing them to meet the growing market demand in the after-sales service area in the best possible way. Financial terms were not disclosed.

HISTORY

Swedish salesman Axel Wenner-Gren saw an American-made vacuum cleaner in a Vienna Austria store window in 1910 and envisioned selling the cleaners door-to-door a technique he had learned in the US. Two years later he worked with fledgling Swedish vacuum cleaner makers AB Lux and Elektromekaniska to improve their existing designs. The two companies merged to form AB Electrolux in 1919. When the board of the new company balked at Wenner-Gren's suggestion to mass-produce vacuum cleaners he guaranteed Electrolux's sales through his own sales company.

In the 1920s the company used the "Every home — an Electrolux home" slogan as Wenner-Gren drove his sales force on and launched new sales companies in Europe and North and South America. He scored a publicity coup by securing the blessing of Pope Pius XI to vacuum the Vatican gratis for a year. By the end of the 1920s Electrolux had purchased most of Wenner-Gren's sales companies (excluding Electrolux US) and had gambled on refrigerator technology and won. By buying vacuum cleaner maker Volta (Sweden 1934) it gained retail distribution.

Despite the loss of Eastern European subsidiaries during WWII the company did well until the 1960s when it backed an unpopular refrigeration technology. Swedish electrical equipment giant ASEA controlled by Marcus Wallenberg bought a large stake in Electrolux in 1964 and in 1967 he installed Hans Werthen as chairman. Werthen slashed overhead and sold the company's minority stake in Electrolux US to Consolidated Foods. (The US Electrolux business was taken private in 1987.)

Since 1970 Electrolux has bought more than 300 companies (many of them troubled appliance makers) updated their plants and gained global component manufacturing efficiencies. Acquisitions included National Union Electric (Eureka vacuum cleaners US 1974) Tappan (appliances US 1979) Zanussi (appliances industrial products; Italy; 1984) White Consolidated Industries (appliances industrial products; US; 1986) and Lehel

(refrigerators Hungary 1991). By 1996 the company had acquired a 41% interest in Refrigera § o Paran ̄ Brazil's #2 manufacturer of appliances. (Electrolux owned it all by 1998.)

To better focus on its "white goods" (washers refrigerators etc.) in 1996 Electrolux began selling noncore businesses. In 1997 under new CEO Michael "Mike the Knife" Treschow the company launched a restructuring plan involving the closing of about 25 plants and the elimination of more than 12000 jobs mostly in Europe. The plan worked: Electrolux's profits more than quadrupled in 1998. Also that year the company launched a joint venture in India with Voltas Limited forming that country's largest refrigerator manufacturer.

Electrolux acquired the European operations of chainsaw maker McCulloch in 1999. To strengthen its Asian presence Electrolux teamed up with Toshiba for future collaboration on household appliances. Also that year the company said it would sell its vending machine unit and professional refrigeration business. That year AB Electrolux agreed to buy the major appliance business of Email Ltd. Australia's top household appliance maker.

In January 2002 it finalized the sale of its leisure appliance operations — mostly refrigerators for recreational vehicles — to private equity firm EQT Northern Europe. In April 2002 Electrolux CEO Michael Treschow resigned (but remained as a director) and was replaced by board member Hans Str ☐berg. The firm acquired Diamant Boart International a world-leading manufacturer and distributor of diamond tools and related equipment in June 2002.

As part of a restructuring effort to combat the effects of diminishing consumer demand and higher material costs Electrolux cut nearly 5000 jobs (about 6% of its workforce) during 2003.

Electrolux relaunched its flagship brand of vacuum cleaners in North America during 2004 having bought the rights from long-unaffiliated vacuum maker Electrolux LLC (now Aerus). Also that year former CEO Michael Treschow reappeared in a leadership position assuming the role of chairman. Treschow left the company again in 2007. Hans Straberg who had joined Electrolux in 1983 was appointed CEO of the business in 2002.

The firm exited its outdoor segment which consisted of chainsaws and lawn and garden equipment (Husqvarna Jonsered brands) and diamond tools (Dimas Diamant Boart names) through a spinoff in 2006.

EXECUTIVES

President, Chief Executive Officer, Director, Jonas Samuelson, $1,254,160 total compensation
Executive Vice President, Head Business Area North America, Nolan Pike
Non-Executive Independent Director, Fredrik Persson
Non-Executive Director, Petra Hedengran
Non-Executive Director, Employee Representative, Peter Ferm
Non-Executive Independent Director, Ulla Litzen
Non-Executive Independent Chairman of the Board, Staffan Bohman
Non-Executive Independent Director, David Porter
Executive Vice President, Chief Experience Officer, Ola Nilsson
Non-Executive Director, Employee Representative, Viveca Brinkenfeldt-Lever
Chief Human Resource Officer and Communications, Senior Vice President, Lars Worsoee Petersen
Executive Vice President, Head Business Area Asia Pacific, Middle East and Africa, Adam Cich
Non-Executive Director, Employee Representative, Mina Billing

Non-Executive Independent Director, Karin Overbeck
Executive Vice President, Head Business Area Europe, Anna Ohlssonleijon
Non-Executive Independent Director, Henrik Henriksson
Senior Vice President, General Counsel, Secretary of the Board of Directors, Mikael Ostman
Executive Vice President, Head Business Area Latin America, Ricardo Cons
Head of Investor Relations, Sophie Arnius
Chief Financial Officer, Therese Friberg
Chief Operations Officer and Executive Vice President, Carsten Franke
Auditors: Deloitte AB

LOCATIONS

HQ: AB Electrolux (Sweden)
S:t Goransgatan 143, Stockholm SE-105 45
Phone: (46) 8 738 60 00   **Fax:** (46) 8 738 74 61
Web: www.electroluxgroup.com

2018 Sales

	% of total
USA	31
Brazil	10
Germany	5
Australia	4
Sweden	5
Switzerland	2
Canada	2
United Kingdom	3
France	4
Italy	4
Other	30
Total	**100**

PRODUCTS/OPERATIONS

2018 Sales

	% of total
Major Appliances North America	31
Major Appliances Europe Middle East and Africa	35
Latin America	14
Asia/Pacific	7
Homecare and Small Domestic Appliances	6
Professional Products	7
Total	**100**

Selected Products and Brands

Consumer durables
  Core A
  Floorcare products
Professional products
  Foodservice equipment
  Laundry equipment

COMPETITORS

ABB Ltd	Svenska Cellulosa AB
Axel Johnson AB	SCA
Neles Oyj	TUPPERWARE BRANDS
RECKITT BENCKISER	CORPORATION
GROUP PLC	WD-40 COMPANY
SEB SA	WHIRLPOOL
CORPORATION	

HISTORICAL FINANCIALS

Company Type: Public

Income Statement				FYE: December 31
	REVENUE ($ mil.)	NET INCOME ($ mil.)	NET PROFIT MARGIN	EMPLOYEES
12/20	14,192	805	5.7%	47,543
12/19	12,790	269	2.1%	48,652
12/18	13,867	425	3.1%	54,419
12/17	14,877	700	4.7%	55,692
12/16	13,359	495	3.7%	55,400
Annual Growth	1.5%	12.9%	—	(3.8%)

Debt ratio: 1.9%	No. of shares (mil.): 287
Return on equity: 31.8%	Dividends
Cash ($ mil.): 2,471	Yield: 11.1%
Current ratio: 1.08	Payout: 216.9%
Long-term debt ($ mil.): 1,728	Market value ($ mil.): 13,249

	STOCK PRICE ($) FY Close	P/E High/Low		PER SHARE ($) Earnings	Dividends	Book Value
12/20	46.10	3	1	2.80	5.12	7.97
12/19	48.96	7	5	0.93	1.78	8.44
12/18	42.37	5	3	1.47	1.91	8.45
12/17	64.65	4	3	2.42	1.81	8.73
12/16	49.66	3	2	1.72	1.44	6.80
Annual Growth	(1.8%)	—	—	13.0%	37.2%	4.0%

ABB Ltd

ABB is a leading global technology company with a comprehensive and increasingly digitalized offering of electrification motion and automation solutions. About half of its customers are industrial customers serving production facilities and factories worldwide from process industries such as oil and gas pulp and paper as well as mining automotive food and beverage and consumer electronics. Operating for more than 130 years Zurich Switzerland-based ABB has facilities in upwards of 100 countries worldwide. The company completed its divestment of its Power Grids business to Hitachi in 2020.

Operations

ABB operates through four segments: Electrification Products Motion Industrial Automation Robotics & Discrete Automation and Corporate and Other.

Electrification Products generates over 45% of ABB's sales and manufactures products and services such as electric vehicle charging infrastructure renewable power solutions modular substation packages distribution automation products switchboard and panelboards switchgear UPS solutions circuit breakers measuring and sensing devices control products wiring accessories enclosures and cabling systems and intelligent home and building solutions designed to integrate and automate lighting heating ventilation security and data communication networks.

Motion segment produce about 25% of sales and manufactures and sells motors generators drives wind converters mechanical power transmissions complete electrical powertrain systems and related services and digital solutions for a wide range of applications in industry transportation infrastructure and utilities.

Industrial Automation accounts for more than 20% of sales and develops integrated automation and electrification systems and solutions digital solutions artificial intelligence applications for the process and hybrid industries as well as services such as remote monitoring preventive maintenance and cybersecurity services.

The Robotics & Discrete Automation division sells robotics controllers software function packages cells programmable logic controllers (PLC) industrial PCs (IPC) servo motion engineered manufacturing solutions turn-key solutions and collaborative robot solutions for a wide range of applications. It pulls in over 10% of sales. The ABB Ability digital solutions appear within all divisions that produce technical solutions for performance

and energy optimization asset health condition monitoring and cybersecurity.

Geographic Reach

Zurich Switzerland-based ABB's operations extend to more than 100 countries across Europe (more than 35% of sales) the Asia Middle East and Africa (AMEA) region and the Americas (each accounting for over 30% of sales).

ABB has properties in the US China Germany Italy Finland Sweden Switzerland Canada Poland and India.

Sales and Marketing

ABB's business areas deliver products to customers through a global network of channel partners end-customers direct sales force third-party channels as well as through system integrators and machine builders. Most of the business's revenue is derived from sales through channel partners like distributors and wholesalers as well as installers OEMs and system integrators. The company's customer base is comprised of production facilities and factories from product industries (oil and gas pulp and paper mining) discrete industries (automotive food and beverage consumer electronics) including customers that operate in the transport and infrastructure market.

Financial Performance

Note: Growth rates may differ after conversion to US Dollars.

ABB's revenue decreased by 7% or $26.1 billion in 2020 as compared to $27.9 billion in 2019. Revenues decreased across all business areas as well as across all regions with the impacts of the COVID-19 pandemic resulting in a reduction in business activity and a substantial drop in book-and-bill activities.

net income attributable to ABB in 2020 increased by $3.7 billion compared to 2019 to $5.1 billion

ABB's cash position increased to $3.9 billion at the end of 2020 compared to $3.5 billion from the prior year. The company's operating activities generated cash of $1.7 billion. Its investing activities generated $6.8 billion and its financing activities used $8.2 billion. ABB's primary cash uses were for purchases of investments and debt repayments.

Strategy

In 2020 ABB took additional steps to sustainably improve its future operating performance which included the launch of ABB Purpose. This implements the operating model ABB Way which increases accountability transparency and speed by transferring operating decisions closer to customers a review of the business portfolio as well as a review of the digital strategy. In the same year the company spent over 4% of its revenues on non-order related research and development. Within this spend the company expects that its focus on digitalization will grow. Out of its 7000 employees in research and development over 60% are focused on software and digitalization. ABB aims to grow revenues derived from software and digital services at a double-digit rate going forward.

Mergers and Acquisitions

In the same month last year the company has also completed its acquisition of a majority stake in Chargedot Shanghai New Energy Technology Co. Ltd. The acquisition sets to strengthen ABB's ties with the top Chinese electric vehicle manufacturers and expand the company's e-mobility portfolio with hardware and software developed for local requirements.

In early 2020 ABB announced an agreement to acquire Dublin-based Cylon Controls Ltd. provides building automation and HVAC control solutions for commercial and retail buildings schools and healthcare facilities. The acquisition will further to enhance its Electrification business' position in the

commercial buildings segment. The terms of the transaction were not disclosed.

HISTORY

Asea Brown Boveri (ABB) was formed in 1988 when two giants ASEA AB of Sweden and BBC Brown Boveri of Switzerland combined their electrical engineering and equipment businesses. Percy Barnevik head of ASEA became CEO.

ASEA was born in Stockholm in 1883 when Ludwig Fredholm founded Electriska Aktiebolaget to manufacture an electric dynamo created by engineer Jonas Wenstrom. In 1890 the company merged with Wenstrom's brother's firm to form Allmanna Svenska Electriska Aktiebolaget (ASEA) a pioneer in industrial electrification. Early in the 1900s ASEA began its first railway electrification project. By the 1920s it was providing locomotives and other equipment to Sweden's national railway and by the next decade ASEA was one of Sweden's largest electric equipment manufacturers. In 1962 it bought 20% of appliance maker Electrolux. ASEA created the nuclear power venture ASEA-ATOM with the Swedish government in 1968 and bought full control in 1982.

BBC Brown Boveri was formed in 1891 as the Brown Boveri and Company partnership between Charles Brown and Walter Boveri in Baden Switzerland. It made power generation equipment and produced the first steam turbines in Europe in 1900. BBC entered Germany (1893) France (1894) and Italy (1903) and diversified into nuclear power equipment after WWII.

By 1988 BBC the bigger company had a West German network that ASEA the more profitable company coveted. Both had US joint ventures. In an unusual merger ASEA (which became ABB AB) and BBC (later ABB AG) continued as separate entities sharing equal ownership of ABB. Barnevik crafted a unique decentralized management structure under which national subsidiaries were closely linked to their local customers and labor forces. In six years ABB took over more than 150 companies worldwide.

An ABB-led consortium built one of the world's largest hydroelectric plants in Iran in 1992 and in 1995 ABB merged its transportation segment into Adtranz (a joint venture with Daimler-Benz) to form the world's #1 maker of trains.

Tragedy struck in 1996. Robert Donovan CEO of ABB's US subsidiary died in a plane crash along with Commerce Secretary Ron Brown and other executives on a trade mission. Donovan's death hastened the US unit's restructuring.

In 1997 Barnevik gave up the title of CEO remaining as chairman and was succeeded by G – ran Lindahl an engineer who worked his way up the ranks at ASEA. (Barnevik remained chairman until 2001.) After 1997 profits dipped drastically Lindahl scrapped Barnevik's vaunted regional matrix structure in favor of one organized by product areas under a strong central management. Though the Asian financial crisis slowed orders ABB still pulled in large contracts including one to build the world's largest cracker plant in Texas in 1998.

In 1999 ABB acquired Elsag Bailey a Dutch maker of industrial control systems for about $1.5 billion and sold its 50% stake in Adtranz to DaimlerChrysler for about $472 million. ABB and France's ALSTOM combined their power generation businesses to form the world's largest power plant equipment maker. That year ABB AB and ABB AG were at last united under a single stock through holding company ABB Ltd.

ABB scaled back its power plant-related activities in 2000. The company sold its nuclear power business to BNFL for $485 million and its 50% stake in ABB Alstom Power to ALSTOM for $1.2 billion. (Areva acquired ALSTOM's transmission and distribution business in 2004.) In 2001 Lindahl resigned and J –rgen Centerman head of the company's automation business replaced him. Centerman promptly reorganized ABB's industrial operations into four segments based on customer type and two based on product type.

Also in 2001 ABB acquired French company Entrelec a supplier of industrial automation and control products. With economic slowdowns occurring in the company's key markets ABB announced plans in 2001 to cut 12000 jobs over 18 months. Later that year amid rising numbers of asbestos claims against US subsidiary Combustion Engineering ABB took a $470 million fourth-quarter charge to cover asbestos liabilities. The claims charged asbestos exposures stemming from products supplied before the mid-1970s by Combustion Engineering which ABB acquired in 1990.

In 2002 ABB found itself embroiled in controversy after revealing not only a record loss but also payments of large pensions to former chairman Barnevik and former chief executive Lindahl. The former executives agreed that year to return a part (about $82 million) of their pension payouts to ABB. That year the company which faced $4.4 billion in debts after industry slumps affected its sales of power systems and equipment industrial automation and controls sold part of its financial services unit to GE Commercial Finance for $2.3 billion.

The day after the company sold its structured finances unit ABB's chief executive J –rgen Centerman resigned and was replaced by the chairman J rgen Dormann. That year ABB sold its metering business to Germany-based Ruhrgas for $244 million.

In 2003 as part of its settlement with asbestos plaintiffs ABB placed Combustion Engineering into bankruptcy. Later that same year the company announced that it would sell its Sirius International reinsurance business to the Bermuda-based White Mountains; the deal was completed in 2004 for about $425 million. ABB also sold its upstream oil gas and petrochemicals unit to Candover Partners 3i and J.P. Morgan Partners for $925 million in 2004. (To clear the way for the sale ABB also agreed to pay US regulators $16 million in fines to settle bribery cases at US-based ABB Vetco Gray and Scotland-based ABB Vetco UK. The subsidiaries — part of the petroleum business that was sold — allegedly paid off government officials in Angola Kazakhstan and Nigeria in order to win oil contracts between 1998 and 2003.)

Sulzer CEO Fred Kindle succeeded Dormann as ABB's CEO in 2005. (Dormann remained chairman until his retirement in 2007.) The company made a number of small dispositions in 2005 including its Japanese control valves business its foundry business and several cable and power line businesses.

ABB ended years of litigation — and a major corporate headache — when it reached a settlement on an asbestos liability case related to US subsidiary Combustion Engineering in 2006. As part of the settlement ABB committed more than $1.4 billion to pay settled claims.

After consolidating its remaining businesses into the two areas power technologies and automation technologies ABB restructured its operations into five divisions in 2006: Power Products Power Systems Automation Products Process Automation and Robotics. It took further steps to streamline operations and position itself for growth for example by moving its main robotics operation from Detroit to Shanghai.

In 2006 ABB voluntarily disclosed to the US Department of Justice and the SEC that the company made payments in the Middle East that might have violated anti-bribery laws. The following year

ABB disclosed similar suspect payments at subsidiaries in Asia Europe and South America.

Kindle left ABB in 2008 due to what the company called "irreconcilable differences" concerning the leadership of the company; former GE Healthcare CEO Joe Hogan became CEO of ABB later that year.

In 2008 the company dug deeper into its investment purse spending $653 million to complete 12 deals. Most notably ABB purchased Kuhlman Electric a US-based transformer manufacturer from The Carlyle Group for $513 million including assumed debt. Kuhlman Electric was integrated into ABB's Power Products division in North America and deepens ABB's geographic footprint and product offerings in the industrial and electric utility sectors.

ABB's bunch of businesses has been peeled back too. Several divestitures were completed in 2008 and 2007; ABB exited its 50% interest in South Africa's ABB Powertech Transformers to Powertech owned by the Altron Group for $11 million. In 2007 ABB sold subsidiary ABB Lummus Global to Chicago Bridge & Iron Co. for some $870 million in cash as well as its Building Systems business in Germany and power plant interests in India and Morocco to Abu Dhabi National Oil. Power Lines businesses in Brazil and Mexico were also put on the sale block for $20 million.

ABB plowed in $209 million in 2009 adding eight new operations. Among them the company acquired the assets of Sinai Engineering a designer and provider of services for electrical generation and transmission systems planning as well as construction management. The transaction completed through its US ABB Inc. expanded ABB's presence in western Canada. On the other side of the world ABB picked up South Africa's Westingcorp (Pty) Ltd. The move ramped up ABB's line of power capacitors (machines that add to a system's power quality and energy efficiency) and opened the door to local and global electric utilities and mining markets.

ABB in mid-2010 acquired K-TEK a maker of level detection technology used in the oil and gas industry as well as water and other industries. Its instrumentation and sensing technologies which number more than 350000 installations enhanced ABB's slate of measurement products part of its Process Automation division. The deal garnered K-TEK's facilities in the US the Netherlands China India and South Africa.

ABB picked up US software provider Insert Key Solutions in late 2010. Its combination with the earlier acquisition of Ventyx (valued at approximately $1 billion) from Vista Equity Partners created a comprehensive portfolio of software for managing asset-intensive businesses engaged in the utility energy and communications industries. Ventyx and Insert Key Solutions joined ABB's network management business.

EXECUTIVES

President, Process Automation, Peter Terwiesch, $809,228 total compensation
Vice Chairman, Jacob Wallenberg, $455,186 total compensation
Chief Communications and Sustainability Officer, Theodor Swedjemark, $212,954 total compensation
President, Electrification Business, Tarak Mehta, $903,279 total compensation
Chairman, Peter Voser, $1,512,852 total compensation
Chief Financial Officer, Timo Ihamuotila, $960,957 total compensation
President, Motion Business, Morten Wierod, $749,775 total compensation

President, Robotics & Discrete Automation Business, Sami Atiya, $809,228 total compensation
Group General Counsel and Company Secretary, Maria Varsellona, $809,228 total compensation
Chief Executive Officer, Bjorn Rosengren, $1,601,554 total compensation
Auditors: KPMG AG

LOCATIONS

HQ: ABB Ltd
Affolternstrasse 44, P.O. Box 8131, Zurich CH-8050
Phone: (41) 43 317 7111   **Fax:** (41) 43 317 7992
Web: www.abb.com

2018 Sales

	$ mil.	% of total
Asia Middle East and Africa	9,491	34
Europe	10,129	37
The Americas	8,042	29
Total	**27,662**	**100**

PRODUCTS/OPERATIONS

2018 Sales

	$ mil.	% of total
Electrification Products	11,686	41
Robotics and Motion	9,147	32
Industrial Automation	7,394	26
Corporate and Other	273	1
Inter-segment elimination	-838	-
Total	**27,662**	**100**

Selected Products

Electrification Products
  Modular substation packages
  Distribution automation
  Measuring and sensing devices
  Circuit breakers
  Control products
  Wiring accessories
  Cabling systems
  KNX systems
Robotics and Motion
  Robots
  Robot automation solutions
  Controllers
  Electrical motors and generators
  Mechanical power transmission products
  Low- and medium-voltage drive
Industrial Automation
  Performance optimization
  Automation solutions
  System 800xA
  PLC Automation
  Decathlon Software
  Turbochargers

COMPETITORS

ASSA ABLOY AB	GKN LIMITED
Clariant AG	HITACHI EUROPE LIMITED
ENERPAC TOOL GROUP CORP.	MEGGITT PLC
	SCHNEIDER ELECTRIC SE
GENERAL ELECTRIC COMPANY	SENIOR PLC
	Siemens AG

HISTORICAL FINANCIALS

Company Type: Public

Income Statement

FYE: December 31

	REVENUE ($ mil.)	NET INCOME ($ mil.)	NET PROFIT MARGIN	EMPLOYEES
12/20	26,134	5,146	19.7%	105,600
12/19	27,978	1,439	5.1%	144,400
12/18	27,662	2,173	7.9%	146,600
12/17	34,312	2,213	6.4%	134,800
12/16	33,828	1,899	5.6%	132,300
Annual Growth	(6.2%)	28.3%	—	(5.5%)

2020 Year-End Financials

Debt ratio: 14.9%	No. of shares (mil.): 2,030
Return on equity: 35.1%	Dividends
Cash ($ mil.): 5,386	Yield: 5.7%
Current ratio: 1.25	Payout: 66.3%
Long-term debt ($ mil.): 4,828	Market value ($ mil.): 56,782

	STOCK PRICE ($) FY Close	P/E High/Low		PER SHARE ($) Earnings	Dividends	Book Value
12/20	27.96	11	6	2.43	1.61	7.72
12/19	24.09	36	27	0.67	0.79	6.34
12/18	19.01	28	18	1.02	0.81	6.54
12/17	26.82	26	20	1.03	0.76	6.93
12/16	21.07	26	18	0.88	0.73	6.26
Annual Growth	7.3%	—	—	28.9%	21.9%	5.4%

Absa Group Ltd (New)

Absa Group is one of the largest financial services groups in South Africa with operations in 12 African countries. The group offers a range of banking and financial services including deposits loans credit cards insurance financial planning and investment banking services. Its Absa Securities UK subsidiary in London launched its international operations and the group is currently working to procure licenses in the US.

Operations

Company's reportable segments are: RBB South Africa CIB South Africa ARO Head Office Treasury and other operations in South Africa; and Barclays separation.

RBB South Africa offers retail business banking and insurance products within South Africa.

CIB South Africa offers corporate and investment banking solutions in South Africa and Absa Regional Operations.

ARO offers a range of banking products to businesses as well as individual customers on the African continent outside of South Africa.

Barclays separation Barclays PLC contributed R12.1 billion to the Group in June 2017 primarily in recognition of the investments required for the Group to separate from Barclays PLC.

Geographic Reach

Headquartered in Johannesburg the company operates in 12 African countries United Kingdom United States of America. The group has majority stakes in banks in Botswana Ghana Kenya Mauritius Mozambique Seychelles South Africa Tanzania Uganda and Zambia. There are also representative offices in New York London Namibia and Nigeria as well as bank assurance operations in Botswana Kenya Mozambique South Africa and Zambia.

Sales and Marketing

The company interacts with its customers and clients through a combination of physical and electronic channels offering a comprehensive range of banking services.

Financial Performance

The company's revenue for fiscal 2020 increased to R81.6 billion compared from the prior year with R80.1 billion.

Net profit for fiscal 2020 decreased to R7.2 billion compared from the prior year with R16.0 billion.

Cash held by the company at the end of fiscal 2020 decreased to R16.8 million. Cash provided by operations was R7.0 billion while cash used for investing and financing activities were R718 million and R8.3 billion respectively. Main uses of cash were purchase of intangible assets and dividends paid.

Strategy

The company's insurance risk management objectives are to: pursue profitable growth opportunities within the financial volatility and solvency risk appetite approved by the Board; balance exposure between and within life and short-term insurance to allow for better diversification and optimal risk-adjusted returns; and leverage off the Absa presence and infrastructure across Africa.

EXECUTIVES

Independent Non-Executive Director, Chairman - Designate, Sello Moloko
Non-Executive Director, Colin Beggs
Non-Executive Independent Director, Ihron Rensburg
Group General Counsel, Charles Wheeler
Chief Executive - Corporate and Investment Bank, Charles Russon
Non-Executive Independent Director, Dhanasagree Naidoo
Chief Executive Retail and Business Banking South Africa, Acting Head People and Culture, Arrie Rautenbach
Non-Executive Independent Director, Tasneem Abdool-Samad
Non-Executive Lead Independent Director, Sipho Pityana
Non-Executive Independent Director, Rose Keanly
Deputy Chief Executive, Retail and Business Banking South Africa, Bongiwe Gangeni
Non-Executive Independent Director, Nonhlanhla Mjoli-Mncube
Interim Financial Director, Punki Modise
Non-Executive Independent Chairman of the Board, Wendy Lucasbull
Non-Executive Independent Director, Mark Merson
Non-Executive Independent Director, Francis Okomo-Okello
Non-Executive Independent Director, Alex Darko
Group Financial Director, Jason Quinn
Non-Executive Director, Rene van Wyk
Auditors: Ernst & Young Inc.

LOCATIONS

HQ: Absa Group Ltd (New)
7th Floor, Barclays Towers West, 15 Troye Street, Johannesburg 2001
Phone: (27) 11 350 4000
Web: www.absa.africa

PRODUCTS/OPERATIONS

2016 Sales

	% of total
RBB	71
CIB	22
WIMI	7
Total	**100**

2016 Sales

	% of total
Interest income	58
Non-interest income	42
Total	**100**

COMPETITORS

AMUNDI
ARES CAPITAL CORPORATION
AUSTRALIA AND NEW ZEALAND BANKING GROUP LIMITED
BANK HAPOALIM LTD.
CERBERUS CAPITAL MANAGEMENT L.P.
Credit Suisse Group AG
EATON VANCE CORP.
FIRSTRAND LTD
Julius B or Gruppe AG
NEDBANK GROUP LTD
NOMURA SECURITIES INTERNATIONAL INC.
OM RESIDUAL UK LIMITED
OVERSEA-CHINESE BANKING CORPORATION LIMITED
PUTNAM INVESTMENTS LLC
SANLAM LTD
WOODBURY FINANCIAL SERVICES INC.

HISTORICAL FINANCIALS

Company Type: Public

Income Statement — FYE: December 31

	ASSETS ($ mil.)	NET INCOME ($ mil.)	INCOME AS % OF ASSETS	EMPLOYEES
12/20	104,342	400	0.4%	36,737
12/19	99,627	1,015	1.0%	38,472
12/18	89,627	967	1.1%	40,856
12/17	94,710	1,122	1.2%	41,073
12/16	80,168	1,070	1.3%	41,241
Annual Growth	6.8%	(21.8%)	—	(2.8%)

2020 Year-End Financials

Return on assets: 0.4%	Dividends
Return on equity: 5.1%	Yield: —
Long-term debt ($ mil.): —	Payout: 87.1%
No. of shares (mil.): 828	Market value ($ mil.): —
Sales ($ mil): 9,250	

Abu Dhabi Commercial Bank

Auditors: Deloitte & Touche (M.E.)

LOCATIONS

HQ: Abu Dhabi Commercial Bank
Sheikh Zayed Bin Sultan Street, Plot C-33, Sector E-11, P.O. Box 939, Abu Dhabi
Phone: (971) 2 696 2222
Web: www.adcb.com

HISTORICAL FINANCIALS

Company Type: Public

Income Statement — FYE: December 31

	ASSETS ($ mil.)	NET INCOME ($ mil.)	INCOME AS % OF ASSETS	EMPLOYEES
12/19	110,315	1,304	1.2%	0
12/18	76,196	1,317	1.7%	0
12/17	72,158	1,164	1.6%	0
12/16	70,318	1,129	1.6%	0
12/15	62,148	1,340	2.2%	0
Annual Growth	15.4%	(0.7%)	—	—

2019 Year-End Financials

Return on assets: 1.4%	Dividends
Return on equity: 10.8%	Yield: —
Long-term debt ($ mil.): —	Payout: 53.5%
No. of shares (mil.): —	Market value ($ mil.): —
Sales ($ mil): 5,383	

Abu Dhabi Islamic Bank

Auditors: Deloitte & Touche (M.E.)

LOCATIONS

HQ: Abu Dhabi Islamic Bank
P.O. Box 313, Abu Dhabi
Phone:
Web: www.adib.co.ae

HISTORICAL FINANCIALS

Company Type: Public

Income Statement				FYE: December 31
	ASSETS ($ mil.)	NET INCOME ($ mil.)	INCOME AS % OF ASSETS	EMPLOYEES
12/19	34,305	707	2.1%	0
12/18	34,089	680	2.0%	0
12/17	33,567	625	1.9%	0
12/16	33,292	531	1.6%	0
12/15	32,229	525	1.6%	0
Annual Growth	1.6%	7.7%	—	—

2019 Year-End Financials

Return on assets: 2.0%	Dividends
Return on equity: 14.1%	Yield: —
Long-term debt ($ mil.): —	Payout: 43.3%
No. of shares (mil.): —	Market value ($ mil.): —
Sales ($ mil): 1,832	

Accenture plc

Accenture one of the world's largest consulting firms offers a portfolio of management consulting strategy digital technology interactive and business operations services to some of the top companies and government organizations in the world. Clients use Accenture's services to improve decision-making; mitigate risk and enhance security; implement modern change management programs; shape and deliver value from largescale cloud migrations; build more resilient supply chains; and reinvent manufacturing and operations with smart connected products and platforms. Accenture generates more than 45% of its revenue in North America.

Operations

Accenture's business is divided into five operating groups based on client industries: Products (consumer goods retail travel life sciences); Financial Services; Communications Media & Technology; Health & Public Service (private and public health organizations educational institutions); and Resources (chemicals energy forestry mining and metals). Revenue contributions are evenly dispersed between the five with the largest Products accounting for about 30% of sales Communications Media and Technology Health and Public Service and Financial Services with approximately 20% of sales each and the smallest Resources accounting for some 15% each.

In addition to reporting revenues by geographic markets the company also reports revenues by two types of work: consulting (some 55% of sales) and outsourcing (around 45%).

Geographic Reach

Dublin-based Accenture serves clients in more than 200 cities spanning about 50 countries. The company makes about 50% of sales from North America more than 30% from Europe and the remainder from its growth markets of the Middle East the Asia/Pacific region and Latin America.

To get close to the action Accenture has major offices in the world's leading business centers including in the US (Boston Chicago New York and San Francisco) Europe (Dublin Frankfurt London Madrid Milan Paris Rome) and the Asia/Pacific region (Bangalore Beijing Manila Mumbai Sao Paolo Shanghai Singapore Sydney and Tokyo) among others.

Sales and Marketing

Accenture's clients span the full range of industries around the world and include 89 of the Fortune Global 100 and more than three-quarters of the Fortune Global 500. It has partnerships with leading players in the tech industry including SAP ServiceNow VMWare Pegasystems Microsoft Oracle Salesforce and Workday.

The company's advertising costs were $171.8 million $57.7 million and $85.5 million for fiscal 2021 2020 and 2019 respectively.

Financial Performance

Accenture's performance for five years has continued to see an upward trend with 2021 as its highest performing year.

The company's revenue in 2021 increased by about $6.2 billion to $50.5 billion compared to about $44.3 billion in the prior year. Revenues for fiscal 2021 increased 14% in U.S. dollars and 11% in local currency compared to fiscal 2020. This included the impact of a decline in reimbursable travel costs which reduced revenues approximately 1%.

Net income for 201 also increased by about $800 million to about $6 billion compared to $5.2 billion in the prior year.

Cash held by the company at the end of 2021 amounted to $8.2 billion. Cash provided by operations was $8.9 billion. Investing and financing activities used $4.3 billion and $4.9 billion respectively. Main uses for cash were purchases of businesses and investments; and purchases of shares.

Strategy

The company is uniquely able to deliver this transformation because of its ability to bring applied innovation and deliver 360-degree value for its clients. Accenture defines 360-degree value as enabling their clients to use technology which is vital for the change in companies. The company does this by helping companies to shift to the cloud leveraging data and artificial intelligence. Operations of clients are transformed through the company's Operations services and Industry X. Accenture uses platforms such as MyWizard MyNav and SynOps to consistently offer these services to its clients.

Mergers and Acquisitions

Accenture is in a period of intense acquisition activity as it continues its pivot to digital cloud and security.

In late 2021 Accenture completes its acquisition of Tambourine an e-commerce customer experience agency with award-winning capabilities in cloud-based technologies in Japan. The agency enhances Accenture Interactive's world-class suite of sales and commerce transformation services from product and platform engineering to omnichannel delivery of commerce experiences. Terms of the transaction were not disclosed.

Also in late 2021 Accenture has acquired Germany-based T.A. Cook a consultancy specializing in asset performance management and capital projects for clients in capital-intensive industries and infrastructure. The acquisition will strengthen Accenture's capabilities for improving asset performance increasing safety and reducing environmental impact and cost in the chemicals life sciences metals and mining and oil and gas industries. Financial terms were not disclosed.

In 2021 Accenture has completed the acquisition of Experity a leading provider of cloud-based

customer experience and commerce solutions in Brazil. Experity helps businesses build greater efficiencies and agility in commerce marketing content and data through leading cloud-based platforms. Terms of the transaction were not disclosed.

HISTORY

Accenture traces its history back to the storied accounting firm of Arthur Andersen & Co. Founded by Northwestern University professor and accounting legend Arthur Andersen in 1913 the firm's expanding scope of operations led it into forensic accounting and advising clients on financial reporting processes forming the basis for a management consulting arm. Arthur Andersen led the firm until his death in 1947. His successor Leonard Spacek split off the consulting operations as a separate unit in 1954.

The consulting business grew quickly during the 1970s and 1980s thanks in part to an orgy of US corporate re-engineering. By 1988 consulting accounted for 40% of Andersen's sales. Chafing at sharing profits with the auditors (who faced growing price pressures and a rising tide of legal action due to the accounting irregularities of their clients) the consultants sought more power within the firm. The result was a 1989 restructuring that established Andersen Worldwide (later Andersen) as the parent of two independent units Arthur Andersen and Andersen Consulting (AC). The growing revenue imbalance between the operations remained unresolved however and a year later Arthur Andersen poured gas on the flames by establishing its own business consultancy.

Meanwhile AC continued to expand during the 1990s by forming practices focused on manufacturing finance and government. It addressed the shift from mainframes to PCs by forming alliances with technology heavyweights Hewlett-Packard Sun Microsystems and Microsoft. In 1996 AC teamed up with Internet service provider BBN (acquired by GTE in 1997) to form ServiceNet a joint venture to develop Internet commerce and other systems.

The Andersen family feud took a turn for the worse in 1997 with the retirement of CEO Lawrence Weinbach. A deadlocked vote for a new leader led the board to appoint accounting partner Robert Grafton as CEO angering the consulting partners. Later that year AC asked the International Chamber of Commerce to negotiate a breakup of Andersen Worldwide. George Shaheen to whom many attributed the heightened tensions between the units resigned as CEO of AC in 1999 and was replaced by Joe Forehand.

While the separation dispute dragged on the consulting business grew and diversified amid increasing consolidation in the industry. In 1999 the company moved into e-commerce venture funding with the formation of Andersen Consulting Ventures and in 2000 it inked partnership deals with Microsoft (Microsoft system implementation services) Sun Microsystems (for B2B Internet office supply sales) and BT (Internet-based human resources services).

That year an international arbitrator finally approved AC's separation from its parent ruling that the consultancy must change its name and pay Andersen Worldwide $1 billion (far less than the $15 billion demanded by the accounting partners). Renamed Accenture the company went public in 2001. While the new name (a made-up word) might have struck some as a marketing challenge having an identity distinct from that of its former parent proved to be a stroke of luck for Accenture. Andersen broke apart in 2002 after becoming embroiled in the accounting scandals of energy giant Enron.

In 2004 Accenture successfully bid on a $10 billion 10-year contract to create a system to identify visitors and immigrants coming into the country. Dubbed US-VISIT (United States Visitor and Immigrant Status Indicator Technology) the system was to be employed by the Department of Homeland Security to prevent terrorists from entering the US. However Accenture's bid nearly ran afoul of congressional critics who tried to pass spending amendments barring firms headquartered outside the US from winning security-related business.

Forehand stepped down as CEO of Accenture in 2004 and was replaced by company veteran William Green. Forehand remained chairman until he retired in 2006 when Green was named to that post as well.

Accenture acquired Capgemini's North American health practice in 2005 for $175 million in order to strengthen its offerings to hospitals and health care systems. In 2006 the firm expanded its outsourcing operations by buying NaviSys a leading provider of software for the life insurance industry along with key assets of Kansas-based accountant Savista.

In mid-2008 Accenture swallowed up ATAN an industrial and automation services provider based in Brazil that caters to the mining energy and utilities sectors. It also obtained SOPIA a Tokyo-based consulting firm specializing in Oracle systems integration. During that year Accenture added to its transportation and travel services operations (located within its Products Division) when it bought AddVal Technology. AddVal provided software and technology used for freight order management and the deal enhanced Accenture's ability to integrate and simplify its clients' freight management services capabilities.

In late 2009 Accenture looked to solidify its position in a vital market when it obtained the Symbian professional services unit of Nokia. The unit offers engineering and support services for the Symbian operating system one of the world's most widely used operating systems for smart phones. The acquired operations provided a broad range of embedded software services for mobile devices and were rebranded Accenture Embedded Mobility Services.

Accenture obtained RiskControl a consulting firm based in Brazil in early 2010. Also that year Accenture bought Beijing Genesis Interactive Technology Company an embedded software firm providing mobile software outsourcing services to companies in China. The acquisitions furthered Accenture's penetration into the cutting-edge smart phone support services market.

Focusing on beefing up its Financial Services segment in 2011 Accenture acquired Duck Creek Technologies a provider of software and tools catering to the insurance and health care sectors. At the time of the transaction Duck Creek served about 60 clients throughout North America and the UK.

At the beginning of 2011 Pierre Nanterme the former head of the company's financial services operations was promoted to become the company's newest CEO. Green remains with Accenture as chairman.

EXECUTIVES

Chief Financial Officer, K. Mcclure, $975,000 total compensation
Group Chief Executive - Growth Markets, Gianfranco Casati, $1,117,044 total compensation
Chairman of the Board, Chief Executive Officer, Director, Julie Sweet, $1,362,500 total compensation

Managing Director, Brand and Advertising, Jill Kramer
Chief Executive Officer, Europe, Jean-Marc Ollagnier, $1,097,891 total compensation
General Counsel and Corporate Secretary, Joel UnRuch
Chief Human Resource Officer, Chief Leadership Officer, Ellyn Shook
Chief Operating Officer, Johan Deblaere
Chief Executive Officer and Creative Chairman - Accenture Interactive, David Droga
Chief Accounting Officer and Corporate Controller, Richard Clark
CEO, North America, James Etheredge
Auditors: KPMG LLP

LOCATIONS

HQ: Accenture plc
 1 Grand Canal Square, Grand Canal Harbour, Dublin 2
Phone: (353) 1 646 2000
Web: www.accenture.com

2018 Sales

	% of total
North America	45
Europe	33
Growth Markets	19
Total	**100**

PRODUCTS/OPERATIONS

2018 sales

	% of total
CommunicationsMedia & Technology	19
Financial Services	20
Health & Public Service	16
Products	26
Resources	14
Reimbursement	5
Total	**100**

2018 sales

	% of total
Consulting	52
Outsourcing	43
Reimbursement	5
Total	**100**

Selected Practice Areas

Communications and high technology
 Communications
 Electronics and high technology
 Media and entertainment
Products
 Automotive
 Consumer goods and services
 Health and life sciences
 Industrial equipment
 Retail
 Transportation and travel services
Financial services
 Banking
 Capital markets
 Insurance
Resources
 Chemicals
 Energy
 Natural resources
 Utilities
Government

Selected Services

Business consulting
 Customer relationship management
 Finance and performance management
 Human performance
 Strategy
 Supply chain management
Outsourcing
 Application outsourcing
 Business process outsourcing (BPO)
 Customer contact
 Finance and accounting
 Human resources
 Learning
 Procurement

Infrastructure outsourcing
Systems integration and technology
 Enterprise architecture
 Information management
 Infrastructure consulting
 Intellectual property
Research and developmen

COMPETITORS

CAPGEMINI	MCKINSEY & COMPANY
CAPGEMINI NORTH	INC.
AMERICA INC.	RESOURCES CONNECTION
CERIDIAN CORPORATION	INC.
CGI Inc	STARPOINT SOLUTIONS
DATA AXLE INC.	LLC
INFOSYS LIMITED	WIPRO LIMITED
MAXIMUS INC.	

HISTORICAL FINANCIALS

Company Type: Public

Income Statement

FYE: August 31

	REVENUE ($ mil.)	NET INCOME ($ mil.)	NET PROFIT MARGIN	EMPLOYEES
08/21	50,533	5,906	11.7%	624,000
08/20	44,327	5,107	11.5%	506,000
08/19	43,215	4,779	11.1%	492,000
08/18	41,603	4,059	9.8%	459,000
08/17	36,765	3,445	9.4%	425,000
Annual Growth	8.3%	14.4%	—	10.1%

2021 Year-End Financials

Debt ratio: 0.1%	No. of shares (mil.): 632
Return on equity: 32.3%	Dividends
Cash ($ mil.): 8,168	Yield: 1.0%
Current ratio: 1.25	Payout: 39.3%
Long-term debt ($ mil.): 53	Market value ($ mil.): —

ACS Actividades de Construccion y Servicios, S.A.

ACS Actividades de Construcci n y Servicios IS one of Spain's largest construction and infrastructure groups. The company's activities include civil engineering installation and maintenance of energy facilities transport services and highway management. ACS has grown by investing in such firms as former construction rival Dragados and Germany-based infrastructure giant HOCHTIEF. The group is active in about 50 countries mainly in Europe and Latin America. Its largest market is North America accounting for about half of its revenue.

Operations

ACS divides its business into three segments: Infrastructure Industrial Services and Services.

ACS's infrastructure business which generates nearly 80% of the company's revenue consists of four independent multinational construction companies: Dragados HOCHTIEF Iridium and a holding in Abertis. The companies operate in a diverse range of sectors including public works (highways railways ports and airports) social value (residential buildings social facilities and installations) infrastructure services (transport communications energy resources and defense) and mining.

The Industrial Services segment brings in more than 15% of ACS' revenue and develops constructs maintains and operates energy industrial and mobility infrastructure.

The Services segment which generates almost 5% of revenue includes the business of Clece which offers comprehensive maintenance of buildings public places or organizations as well as assistance for people.

Geographic Reach

ACS is based in Madrid Spain and is active in about 50 countries. Its largest market is North America generating around 50% of revenue and followed by Asia/Pacific for some 20%. The remaining revenues are produced in Spain (almost 15%) South America (about 5%) Rest of Europe (over 5%) and Africa.

Financial Performance

Note: Growth rates may differ after conversion to US dollars.

Sales amounted to ?34.9 billion mainly the unfavorable arbitration on the Gorgon project. This is 9% less than the previous year.

In 2020 the company had a net income of ?574 million a 40% decrease from the previous year's net income of ?962 million.

Strategy

The ACS Group's context of operational decentralization requires it to adapt its strategy to the challenges and opportunities presented in a more complex and competitive sector. The group's strategy is focused on the fact that all companies share common values and culture while at the same time operating independently individually contributing a multitude of valid and profitable management formulas that generate shared knowledge and best practices.

HISTORY

In war-torn Europe in 1942 the Spanish construction company Obras y Construcciones Industriales (Ocisa) was born. The company soon began a 50-year association with Spain's hydroelectric industry marked by the completion of the dam and reservoir project Presa de Bachimana in 1950. The company built nine more dam and reservoir projects in Spain (including Presa de la Llosa completed in 1997).

As the demand for public works projects decreased and competition increased Spanish constructors began working abroad especially in Latin America where Ocisa was contracted in 1975 to create an irrigation tunnel in Venezuela's Andes.

A six-year economic expansion measured by the success of Spain's "Big Seven" construction companies including #5 Ocisa reached its end in 1992 when the Spanish government the country's biggest builder was forced to cut spending on infrastructure. This triggered consolidation in Spain's construction industry including Ocisa's 1993 acquisition of Construcciones Padros in which Ocisa held a 25% stake. Adopting the new name OCP Construcciones it also absorbed the assets of its installation and assembly subsidiary Compania de la Distribucion de Electricidad (Grupo Cobra).

The slowdown in public works projects continued and companies sought additional pooling of resources and diversification of activities at home and abroad. In 1996 OCP bought a 40% stake in the state-owned construction firm Auxini increased to 100% a year later. Also in 1997 the OCP group led by its president Florentino Perez acquired Gines Navarro Construcciones controlled (79%) by the powerful investment group led by brothers Carlos and Juan March. The two companies combined to create Spain's third-largest construction group Actividades de Construcciones y Servicios or Grupo ACS.

EXECUTIVES

Chairman and Chief Executive Officer - Industrial Services Area, Eugenio Llorente Gomez
General Secretary, Secretary of the Board, Executive Director, Jose del Valle Perez, $1,441,348 total compensation
Executive Director, Agustin Batuecas Torrego, $102,546 total compensation
Executive Vice Chairman of the Board, Antonio Garcia Ferrer, $854,554 total compensation
Executive Chairman of the Board, Florentino Perez Rodriguez, $1,960,917 total compensation
Proprietary Director, Javier Echenique Landiribar, $102,546 total compensation
Chief Executive Officer, Executive Director, Marcelino Verdes, $634,648 total compensation
Other External Director, Pedro Jose Lopez Jimenez, $415,883 total compensation
Other External Director, Miguel Roca Junyent, $102,546 total compensation
Independent Director, Emilio Garcia Gallego, $102,546 total compensation
Independent Director, Catalina Minarro Brugarolas, $102,546 total compensation
Independent Director, Antonio Botella Garcia, $102,546 total compensation
Proprietary Director, Mariano Hernandez Herreros, $102,546 total compensation
Finance and Corporate Development Manager, Cristina Aldamiz-Echevarria Gonzalez de Durana
Lead Independent Director, Jose Eladio Seco Dominguez, $102,546 total compensation
Corporate General Manager, Angel Manuel Garcia Altozano
Proprietary Director, Maria Soledad Perez Rodriguez, $102,546 total compensation
Other External Director, Joan David Grima Terre, $102,546 total compensation
Independent Director, Carmen Fernandez Rozado, $102,546 total compensation
Member of Vorstand at Hochtief AG, Chief Executive Officer of Hochtief Solutions, Nikolaus Matuschka
Auditors: KPMG Auditores, S.L.

LOCATIONS

HQ: ACS Actividades de Construccion y Servicios, S.A. Avenida de Pio XII, 102, Madrid 28036
Phone: (34) 91 343 9200   **Fax:** (34) 91 343 9456
Web: www.grupoacs.com

2017 Sales

	% of total
North America	45
Asia/Pacific	29
Spain	13
Rest of Europe	7
South Africa	5
Africa	1
Total	**100**

PRODUCTS/OPERATIONS

2017 Sales

	% of total
Construction	78
Industrial Services	18
Environment	4
Total	**100**

Selected Subsidiaries

Concessions
  Concesiones Viarias Chile S.A. (infrastructures)
  Iridium Concesiones de Infraestructuras S.A.
Construction
  Acainsa S.A. (real estate development)
  Ave Lalin
  Consorcio Tecdra S.A.
  Constructora Norte Sur S.A. (48% Chile)
  Desaladora Barcelona (28%)
  Guadarrama Iv (33%)

  Inmobiliaria Alabega S.A. (real estate development)
  Isla Verde Ute (35%)
  Soterram. Basurto Ute Tecsa-Necso (50%)
  Terminal Aeropuerto (70%)
Environment
  Consenur S.A. (management and treatment of hospital waste)
  Empordanesa de Neteja S.A. (urban solid waste management and street cleaning)
  Mapide S.A. (interior cleaning)
  Publimedia Sistemas Publicitarios S.L. (advertising services)
  RetraOil S.L. (treatment of oils and marpoles)
  Servicios Generales de Jaén S.A. (75% water)
  Somasur S.A. (intermediary company Morocco)
  Urbaser de Méjico S.A. (collection of urban solid waste and street cleaning)
  Urbaser Valencia C.A. (collection of urban solid waste and street cleaning)
  Ute Ecoparc V (20% USW treatment)
  Vertederos de Residuos S.A. (84% VERTRESA collection of urban solid waste and street cleaning)
Industrial Services
  ACS industrial Services LLC (energy production US)
  Actividades de Servicios e Instalaciones Cobra S.A. (auxiliary energy and communications distribution Guatemala)
  Andasol 1 S.A. (energy production)
  API Movilidad S.A. (road maintenance)
  BTOB Construccion Ventures S.L. (administrative management)
  Central Térmica de Mejillones S.A. (engineering supply and construction Chile)
  Cobra Ingeniería de Montajes S.A. (installations and assembly)
  Cobra Perù S.A. (auxiliary energy and communications distribution)
  Coinsal Instalaciones y Servicios S.A. de C.V. (installations and assembly El Salvador)
  Cymi Holding S.A. (securities holding company Brazil)
  Dragados Gulf Construction Ltd. (Saudi Arabia)
  Emurtel S.A. (50% electrical installations)
  Enq S.L. (electrical installations)
  Etra Catalu?a S.A. (electrical installations)
  Extresol-1 S.L. (energy production)
  Gerovitae La Guancha S.A. (senior social and health center operations)
  Humiclima Est S.A. (air conditioning)
  Incro S.A. (50% engineering)
  Infraest. Energé;ticas Medioambi. Extreme?as S.L. (services)
  Instalaciones y Servicios Codeven C.A. (air conditioning)
  Mantenimiento y Montajes Industriales S.A. (industrial maintenance and assemblies)
  Mexsemi S.A. de C.V. (99.7% assemblies Mexico)
  Opade Organizac. y Promoc de Actividades Deportivas S.A. (athletic activities organization and promotion)
  Parque Eólico Marmellar S.L. (70% energy production)
  Portumasa S.A. (manufacture and sale of electical equipment Portugal)
  Semi Maroc S.A. (99.7% assemblies)
  Serveis Catalans Serveica S.A. (electrical installations)
  SICE LLC. (design construction installation and maintenance of traffic and trade)
  Sistemas Radiantes F. Moyano S.A. (telecommunications)
  Tecnotel de Canarias S.A. (air conditioning)
  Ute C.T. Andasol 1 (80% fossil fuel plant)
  Venezolana de Limpiezas Indust. C.A. (83% VENELIN Venezuela)
Services
  Valdemingomez 2000 S.A. (34% Valdemingómez degasification)

COMPETITORS

ACCIONA SA	GROUPE CRIT
Bilfinger SE	LINDUM GROUP LIMITED
CROUDACE HOMES GRP LIMITED	SAIPEM SPA
	THE SUNDT COMPANIES
FERROVIAL SA	INC
GALLIFORD TRY LIMITED	TUTOR PERINI
GEE CONSTRUCTION LTD	CORPORATION

HISTORICAL FINANCIALS

Company Type: Public

Income Statement
FYE: December 31

	REVENUE ($ mil.)	NET INCOME ($ mil.)	NET PROFIT MARGIN	EMPLOYEES
12/20	43,349	704	1.6%	181,699
12/19	44,210	1,080	2.4%	194,036
12/18	42,243	1,047	2.5%	191,823
12/17	42,201	961	2.3%	181,527
12/16	34,242	792	2.3%	169,766
Annual Growth	6.1%	(2.9%)	—	1.7%

2020 Year-End Financials

Debt ratio: 36.3%
Return on equity: 14.4%
Cash ($ mil.): 9,917
Current ratio: 1.08
Long-term debt ($ mil.): 10,128

No. of shares (mil.): 306
Dividends
Yield: 0.3%
Payout: 1.1%
Market value ($ mil.): 2,032

	STOCK PRICE ($) FY Close	P/E High/Low		PER SHARE ($) Earnings	Dividends	Book Value
12/20	6.64	5	2	2.23	0.02	14.15
12/19	7.91	3	2	3.27	1.99	15.23
12/18	7.70	3	2	3.09	1.48	14.66
12/17	7.79	4	3	2.76	0.00	12.79
12/16	6.32	3	3	2.26	0.00	10.52
Annual Growth	1.2%	—	—	(0.3%)	—	7.7%

Adecco Group AG

Adecco is the world's largest employment agency serving about 100000 clients. The bulk of Adecco's business is providing temporary staffing permanent placement and outsourcing under the brands Adecco and Adia. The company also operates several professional staffing businesses including Badenoch + Clark Modis Spring Professional Vettery and Yoss which source IT engineering and technical finance and legal and medical and science staff. Adecco does most of its business in Europe particularly France but it has operations globally. Pontoon General Assembly and LHH is Adecco's HR outsourcing business fulfilling an organization's staffing needs. Adecco traces its roots to 1957 and has a history of growing through mergers and acquisitions.

Operations

Adecco provides staffing services under five categories: flexible placement outsourcing consulting and other services permanent placement career transition and training upskilling and reskilling.

Flexible placement is by far the company's largest operation at nearly 85% of sales focuses on deploying associates to organizations on a temporary basis providing flexibility to employers and new opportunities to candidates.

Outsourcing Consulting & Other Services (about 10% of sales) offer a full spectrum of complementary HR solutions including: Outsourcing ? staffing and managing the entirety of a labour-intensive activity such as warehouse logistics or IT support; Consulting ? providing technical experts for project-related work; Managed Service Programmes (MSPs) ? managing all parts of the flexible workforce at organisations using a large number of contingent workers; and Recruitment Process Outsourcing (RPO) ? handling the entire hiring process for employers recruiting large numbers of permanent employees.

Permanent placement accounts for less than 5% of sales and provide employers recruitment process of talents for permanent roles. It source candidates screen CVs conduct interviews and assessments and advise hiring managers. It has access to a wide range of talent including hard-to-reach professionals who are not actively looking for a new job.

Career Transition (about 5%) supports organizations and their employees through changes that require individuals to transition out of their existing roles underpinned by expert coaching and training.

Training Upskilling & Reskilling offers training upskilling and reskilling both as standalone services and in combination with other solutions such as placements or as a part of a broader workforce transformation offering. Adecco is a leading provider of work-based training.

By industry sector Adecco's Workforce Solutions business sources staff for general office and industrial settings under the brands Adecco and Adia. Adia provides on-demand staff mainly for the hospitality and events industry. Workforce Solutions generates more than 70% of sales.

Geographic Reach

Zurich Switzerland-based Adecco operates in 60 countries. France is its largest market accounting for about 20% total sales while North America generates more than 15% of sales. Adecco also trades in most countries in Western Central Northern and Eastern Europe as well as Japan India the MENA region and Australasia which account for about 10% of sales.

Sales and Marketing

Adecco provides temporary staffing permanent placement career transitioning outsourcing talent development and other services to more than 100000 clients.

Financial Performance

Note: Growth rates may differ after conversion to US Dollars.

Adecco's performance for the span of five years have fluctuated within slightly similar ranges from 2016 to 2019 which abruptly decreased in 2020.

The company's revenue for 2020 decreased by about ?3.8 billion to ?19.6 billion in 2020 compared to ?23.4 billion in 2019 due to slower market growth linked to Covid-19.

Adecco posted a net loss of ?98 million as compared to ?728 million in 2019 with the decrease driven by the lower EBITA and the impairment of goodwill.

Adecco's cash held at the end of the year totaled as at ?1.6 billion. It generated ?720 million from its operations. While the company's financing activities and investing activities used ?162 million and ?290 million respectively. Main cash uses were for capital expenditures repayment of long-term debt and dividends to shareholders.

Strategy

The Adecco Group's new strategy revolves around three core elements. These include the evolution to a brand-driven business with the establishment of three global business units namely Adecco Talent Solutions and Modis. In addition the company's strategy also revolves around the visions and clearly defined strategy to leverage the full-service offerings of the group to provide 360-degree solutions. Further the company accelerates its transformation programme with three enables superior customer experience a differentiated portfolio offering and a digitally optimized business model.

EXECUTIVES

Chief Sales and Marketing Officer, Member of the Executive Board, Valerie Beaulieu

President, Talent Solutions, Sergio Picarelli, $172,735 total compensation
Chief Executive Officer, Alain Dehaze, $1,437,430 total compensation
Chief Financial Officer, Coram Williams
President, Christophe Catoir
Chief Digital Officer, Teppo Paavola
President, Modis, Jan Gupta
Chief Information Officer, Ralf Weissbeck
Chief Human Resource Officer, Gordana Landen
Auditors: Ernst & Young Ltd.

LOCATIONS

HQ: Adecco Group AG
Bellerivestrasse 30, Zurich 8008
Phone: (41) 44 878 88 88   **Fax:** (41) 44 829 88 88
Web: www.adeccogroup.com

2018 sales

	%
France	24
North America & UK&I General Staffing	13
North America & UK&I Professional Staffing	14
Germany Austria Switzerland	9
Benelux & Nordics	9
Italy	8
Japan	5
Iberia	5
Rest of the World	11
Career Transition & Talent Development	2
Total	**100**

PRODUCTS/OPERATIONS

2018 sales

	%
General Staffing	
Office	23
Industrial	53
Professional Staffing	
IT	11
Engineering & Technical	4
Finance & Legal	4
Medical & Science	2
Solutions	
Career Transition & Talent Development	2
BPO	1
Total	**100**

Selected Brands

Adecco
Badenoch & Clark
Modis
Spring Professional

Selected Services

Career Transition
Outsourcing Talent Development and other services
Permanent Placement
Temporary Staffing

COMPETITORS

AFFILIATED MANAGERS GROUP INC.
Canadian Apartment Properties Real Estate Investment Tru
Holcim AG
IMPELLAM GROUP PLC
MANPOWERGROUP INC.
ROBERT WALTERS PLC
SEI INVESTMENTS COMPANY
Sika AG
VOLT INFORMATION SCIENCES INC.
Zurich Insurance Group AG

HISTORICAL FINANCIALS

Company Type: Public

Income Statement

FYE: December 31

	REVENUE ($ mil.)	NET INCOME ($ mil.)	NET PROFIT MARGIN	EMPLOYEES
12/20	24,007	(120)	—	30,264
12/19	26,303	816	3.1%	34,662
12/18	27,332	524	1.9%	34,774
12/17	28,362	944	3.3%	33,787
12/16	23,977	763	3.2%	33,391
Annual Growth	0.0%	—	—	(2.4%)

2020 Year-End Financials

Debt ratio: 23.3%
Return on equity: (-2.7%)
Cash ($ mil.): 1,822
Current ratio: 1.29
Long-term debt ($ mil.): 1,923

No. of shares (mil.): 161
Dividends
  Yield: 2.3%
  Payout: —
Market value ($ mil.): 5,385

	STOCK PRICE ($) FY Close	P/E High/Low		PER SHARE ($) Earnings	Dividends	Book Value
12/20	33.27	—	—	(0.75)	0.78	24.33
12/19	31.64	7	5	5.02	0.74	27.29
12/18	23.50	14	8	3.17	1.23	25.07
12/17	38.33	9	8	5.59	0.96	25.83
12/16	32.65	8	5	4.48	0.91	23.03
Annual Growth	0.5%	—	—	—	(3.9%)	1.4%

Adidas AG

adidas' broad and diverse portfolio in both the Sport Performance and Sport Inspired categories ranges from major global sports to regional grass-root events and local sneaker culture. The German sportswear company sells sports shoes apparel and equipment sporting its iconic three-stripe logo in some 160 countries. One of the top sporting goods manufacturers worldwide (along with NIKE and Under Armour) adidas focuses on football soccer basketball running and training gear and apparel as well as lifestyle goods. Its other major brand Reebok sells fitness and gym apparel. All in adidas sells adidas and Reebok-branded products through more than 2500 owned stores as well as a franchise network and via a wholesale channel. Founder Adi Dassler brother of PUMA creator Rudi began making shoes in Germany in the early 1920s. Majority of its sales were generated in Asia Pacific.

Operations

adidas operates predominantly in one industry segment ? the design distribution and marketing of athletic and sports lifestyle products.

Its ten operating segments were identified as Europe adidas North America Reebok North America Asia-Pacific Russia/CIS Latin America Emerging Markets adidas Golf Runtastic and Other centrally managed businesses. The operating segments adidas North America and Reebok North America have been aggregated to the segment North America.

Each market comprises all wholesale retail and e-commerce business activities relating to the distribution and sale of products of the adidas and Reebok brands to retail customers and end consumers. adidas Golf comprises the distribution and sale of adidas Golf branded products. Runtastic operates in the digital health and fitness space. The company provides a comprehensive ecosystem

for tracking and managing health and fitness data. Other centrally managed businesses primarily include the business activities of the Y-3 label.

The Asia pacific segment accounts for about 35% of sales followed by Europe with over 25% and North America with about 25%. Other segments account for the rest. Sales by product includes footwear (around 55% of sale) apparel (nearly 40%) and accessories and gear with approximately 5%.

Overall adidas brand generated abou 95% of sales while over 5% were generated from the Reebok brand.

Geographic Reach

Based in Bavaria Germany it sells adidas and Reebok-branded clothing through 2500 stores worldwide. Its e-commerce operation reaches customers in over 50 countries worldwide.

adidas outsources nearly all its manufacturing. Its over 130 independent manufacturing partners that were producing in 277 manufacturing facilities. The majority (roughly 70%) of its independent manufacturing partners are located in Asia. Vietnam accounts for more than 40% of its footwear manufacturing followed by Indonesia with about 30% and China with some 15%.

Financial Performance

The company's revenue for fiscal 2020 decreased by 16% to ?19.8 billion from ?23.6 billion in fiscal 2019 due to the negative effects of the coronavirus pandemic.

Net income for fiscal 2020 decreased by 78% to ?432 million compared to the prior year's net income of ?2.0 billion.

Cash held by the company at the end of fiscal 2020 increased to ?4.0 billion. Cash provided by operations and financing activities were ?1.5 billion and ?479 million respectively. Investing activities was ?115 million mainly for purchase of property plant and equipment.

Strategy

Creating the New' was the company's strategy for the period from 2015 to 2020. Adidas' ambition to drive top-and bottom-line growth by significantly increasing brand desirability was at the core of 'Creating the New' ? a strategy that proved to be very successful.

Ultimately the financial ambitions for 2020 were not met due to the impact of the global coronavirus pandemic. Aside from financials the company executed the three strategic choices of 'Creating the New' as introduced in March 2015 ? Speed Cities and Open Source ? all the way to the finish line of the strategic cycle. As a result Adidas not only established new iconic product franchises such as Ultraboost and NMD but also built and scaled innovative capabilities many of which did not previously exist in its industry. These include the groundbreaking partnerships with Parley for the Oceans and Carbon the creative collaborations with Kanye West Pharrell Williams and Beyonce the shortening of lead times through speed-enabled ranges and the creation of end-to-end consumer ecosystems in global megacities.

Company Background

adidas was founded in 1924 by Adi Dassler (hence "adi-das") in the small German town of Herzogenaurach. It found fame early on when US sprinter Jesse Owens won four gold medals at the 1936 Olympics in Berlin while wearing adidas running spikes. Adi's brother Rudolf left the company in acrimonious circumstances in 1947 and formed Puma also in Herzogenaurach; the two companies entered into an intense rivalry (later eclipsed by the adidas-NIKE rivalry). adidas became a public company in 1995 and in 2006 acquired Reebok which as of 2019 is the only non-adidas apparel brand used by the company.

HISTORY

adidas grew out of an infamous rift between German brothers Adi and Rudi Dassler who created athletic shoe giants adidas and Puma. As WWI was winding down Adi scavenged for tires rucksacks and other refuse to create slippers gymnastics shoes and soccer cleats at home. His sister cut patterns out of canvas. By 1926 the shoes' success allowed the Dasslers to build a factory. At the 1928 Amsterdam Olympics German athletes first showcased Dassler shoes to the world. In 1936 American Jesse Owens sprinted to Olympic gold in Dassler's double-striped shoes.

Business boomed until the Nazis commandeered the Dassler factory to make boots for soldiers. Although both Rudi and Adi were reportedly members of the Nazi party only Rudi was called to service. Adi remained at home to run the factory. When Allied troops occupied the area Adi made friends with American soldiers — even creating shoes for a soldier who wore them at the 1946 Olympics. Rudi came home from an American prison camp and joined his brother; together they scavenged the war-torn landscape for tank materials and tents to make shoes.

Soon a dispute between the brothers split the business. Rumors circulated that Rudi resented that Adi had failed to use his American connections to help spring him from prison camp. Rudi set up his own factory facing Adi across the River Aurach. The brothers never spoke to each other again except in court. Rudi's company was named Puma and Adi's became adidas. Adi added a third stripe to the Dassler's trademark shoe while Rudi chose a cat's paw in motion. Thus began one of the most intense rivalries in Europe. The children of Puma and adidas employees attended separate elementary schools and the employees even distinguished themselves by drinking different beers.

With Adi's innovations throughout the late 1940s and 1950s (such as the replaceable-cleat soccer shoe) adidas came to dominate the world's athletic shoe market. In the late 1950s it capitalized on the booming US market overtaking the canvas sneakers made by P.F. Flyers and Stride Rite (Keds). The company also initiated the practice of putting logos on sports bags and clothing.

adidas continued to expand globally in the 1960s and 1970s to maintain its dominant position. However a flood of new competitors following the 1972 Munich Olympics and the death of Adi in 1978 signaled the end of an era. As NIKE and Reebok captured the North American market during the 1980s adidas made one of its biggest missteps — it turned down a sneaker endorsement offer from a young Michael Jordan in 1984.

French politician and entrepreneur Bernard Tapie bought the struggling company in 1989 but he stepped down in 1992 amid personal political and business scandals. The next year Robert Louis-Dreyfus became CEO. He shifted production to Asia pumped up the advertising budget and brought in former NIKE marketing geniuses to reestablish the company's identity.

adidas became adidas-Salomon in 1997 with its $1.4 billion purchase of Salomon a French maker of skis and other sporting goods. The company also opened its first high-profile store in Portland Oregon that year. In a 1998 reorganization Louis-Dreyfus sacked Jean-Francois Gautier as Salomon's president in the wake of disappointing sales particularly from TaylorMade Golf Salomon's golf subsidiary.

Amid a 10% slide in revenue several key executives decided to leave the company in 2000 including adidas America CEO Steve Wynne. Citing poor health Louis-Dreyfus soon followed (but remained as chairman); he was replaced by the new CEO of adidas America Ross McMullin who soon after was diagnosed with cancer. Later that year the company announced it would consolidate its apparel under the Heritage label to reinforce its position in the burgeoning casual wear market.

In 2001 Louis-Dreyfus retired as chairman and in March COO Herbert Hainer became chief executive. That year adidas-Salomon opened adidas Originals retail stores in Tokyo and Berlin; that was followed with a New York City store in 2002. Despite slumping sales in the US amid deep discounting by competitors adidas announced in 2003 that it would not offer discounts and still intended to capture 20% of the country's shoe market.

Britain's Barclays Bank PLC became adidas' largest shareholder in 2004 raising its stake to 5.4%. The company changed its name in 2006 to adidas AG.

In May 2008 adidas AG won a $305 million award from a federal jury in Oregon for trademark violation of its three-stripe design by Collective Brands the operator of the Payless and Stride Rite shoe-store chains.

In November 2011 adidas acquired outdoor specialist Five Ten a leading brand in the technical outdoor markets and outdoor action sports community for $25 million.

EXECUTIVES

Chief Executive Officer and Director, Kasper Rorsted, $2,278,811 total compensation
Global Sales and Director, Roland Auschel, $1,048,253 total compensation
Chief of Finance Officer and Director, Harm Ohlmeyer, $964,855 total compensation
Deputy Chairman, Udo Mueller
Deputy Chairman, Ian Gallienne
Global Brands and Director, Brian Grevy, $835,563 total compensation
Global Operations and Director, Martin Shankland, $783,028 total compensation
Labor Director and Director, Amanda Rajkumar
Auditors: KPMG AG Wirtschaftsprüfungsgesellschaft

LOCATIONS

HQ: Adidas AG
Adi-Dassler-Strasse 1, Herzogenaurach D-91074
Phone: (49) 91 32 84 0   **Fax:** (49) 91 32 84 2241
Web: www.adidas-group.com

2018 Sales

	% of total
Asia/Pacific	33
Europe	27
North America	21
Latin America	7
Emerging Markets	5
Russia/CIS	3
Other Businesses	4
Total	**100**

PRODUCTS/OPERATIONS

2018 Sales by Product

	% of total
Footwear	58
Apparel	38
Hardware	4
Total	**100**

2018 Sales by Brand

	% of total
adidas	92
Reebok	8
Total	**100**

COMPETITORS

ASICS CORPORATION	PUMA SE
FILA U.S.A. INC.	SAUCONY INC.
NIKE INC.	SKECHERS U.S.A. INC.
PENTLAND GROUP LIMITED	TIMBERLAND LLC
POU CHEN CORPORATION	TOD'S SPA

HISTORICAL FINANCIALS
Company Type: Public

Income Statement				FYE: December 31
	REVENUE ($ mil.)	NET INCOME ($ mil.)	NET PROFIT MARGIN	EMPLOYEES
12/20	24,354	530	2.2%	62,285
12/19	26,542	2,218	8.4%	59,533
12/18	25,096	1,949	7.8%	57,016
12/17	25,435	1,315	5.2%	56,888
12/16	20,369	1,073	5.3%	57,876
Annual Growth	4.6%	(16.2%)	—	1.9%

2020 Year-End Financials

Debt ratio: 18.4%
Return on equity: 6.5%
Cash ($ mil.): 4,901
Current ratio: 1.38
Long-term debt ($ mil.): 3,046

No. of shares (mil.): 195
Dividends
Yield: 0.0%
Payout: 135.7%
Market value ($ mil.): 35,695

	STOCK PRICE ($) FY Close	P/E High/Low		PER SHARE ($)		
				Earnings	Dividends	Book Value
12/20	182.99	88	46	2.71	3.68	40.61
12/19	162.80	17	10	11.23	1.34	38.94
12/18	104.34	15	11	9.64	1.12	36.67
12/17	99.82	22	16	6.45	0.88	37.93
12/16	78.55	17	9	5.27	0.60	33.91
Annual Growth	23.5%	—	—	(15.3%)	57.2%	4.6%

Adient Plc

Auditors: PricewaterhouseCoopers LLP

LOCATIONS

HQ: Adient Plc
25-28 North Wall Quay, IFSC, Dublin 1 D01 H104
Phone: (354) 734 254 5000
Web: www.adient.com

HISTORICAL FINANCIALS
Company Type: Public

Income Statement				FYE: September 30
	REVENUE ($ mil.)	NET INCOME ($ mil.)	NET PROFIT MARGIN	EMPLOYEES
09/21	13,680	1,108	8.1%	75,000
09/20	12,670	(547)	—	77,000
09/19	16,526	(491)	—	83,000
09/18	17,439	(1,685)	—	85,000
09/17	16,213	877	5.4%	85,000
Annual Growth	(4.2%)	6.0%	—	(3.1%)

2021 Year-End Financials

Debt ratio: 34.2%
Return on equity: 61.7%
Cash ($ mil.): 1,521
Current ratio: 1.45
Long-term debt ($ mil.): 3,512

No. of shares (mil.): 94
Dividends
Yield: —
Payout: —
Market value ($ mil.): —

AEGON NV

Dutch life insurance giant Aegon serves more than 30.4 million customers worldwide. Its subsidiaries which include Transamerica and Scottish Equitable plc operates primarily in the US the Netherlands and the UK offering insurance or reinsurance business pensions asset management or services. Aegon has insurance operations in more than 20 countries in the Americas Europe and Asia and are also active in savings and asset management operations accident and health insurance general insurance and to a limited extent banking operations. Aegon stretches back all the way to 1844 where it offered loans from a converted saloon in San Francisco to help Dutch people pay for funerals.

Operations

Aegon operates through five segments: Americas Aegon the Netherlands Aegon UK Aegon International and Aegon Asset Management (AAM).

The Americas is its biggest market representing roughly 50% of revenue. It operates primarily under the Transamerica brand in the US and has operations in Brazil and Canada. Transamerica provides a wide range of life insurance long-term care (LTC) insurance and voluntary benefits (including supplemental health insurance) retirement plans recordkeeping and advisory services annuities mutual funds and other long-term savings and investment products.

Accounting for about 25% of revenue Aegon UK provides a broad range of investment retirement solutions and protection products to individuals advisers and employers. Aegon UK accesses customers through wealth advisers and the Workplace and has a market-leading position in each with 3.8 million customers and GBP 186 billion assets under administration (AUA).

Aegon the Netherlands (some 15%) provide of life non-life banking and services business. It also operates several other brands including Knab TKP Pensioen and Robidus. Aegon the Netherlands' primary subsidiaries are: Aegon Bank N.V.Aegon Cappital B.V.; Aegon Hypotheken B.V.; Aegon Levensverzekering N.V.; Aegon Schadeverzekering N.V.; and Aegon Spaarkas N.V.; among others.

Aegon International operates a diversified portfolio of both established and growing protection and retirement businesses in Southern and Eastern Europe (SEE) as well as scaling ventures and a high-net-worth insurance business in Asia. Aegon International accounts for less than 10% of revenue.

Aegon Asset Management is a global active investment manager serving institutional and private investors. It offers fixed income equities real estate absolute return liability-driven and multi-asset solutions. The segment accounts for less than 5% of total revenue.

Geographic Reach

Based in The Hague the Netherlands Aegon operates in The Netherlands UK Spain China Hong Kong Indonesia Japan Thailand Hungary Poland Romania and Turkey. It has operations in US through Transamerica while Transamerica Life Bermuda in Bermuda Hong Kong and Singapore. Its Aegon Asset Management operates from Germany Hong Kong Hungary Japan the Netherlands Spain UK and US.

Aegon also has joint ventures in Brazil China France Hong Kong India Indonesia Malaysia the Netherlands Philippines Portugal Singapore Spain Thailand and Vietnam.

Sales and Marketing

Aegon primarily sells its products and services through brokers agents independent financial advisors employee benefit consultants and banks. It also does some direct selling. Aegon's partnership with Banco Santander allows Aegon to sell products through the Spanish banking giant's branch network.

Aegon Asset Management uses several sales and distribution channels including affiliated companies direct to institutional clients independent investment advisors investment consultants joint ventures and third-party investment platforms.

Financial Performance

Note: Growth rates may differ after conversion to US Dollars.

The company had a total revenue of EUR25.657 million a 9% decrease from the previous year's EUR28.2 billion. The decrease is primarily due to a lower sales volume across all of the company's segments.

In 2020 the company had a net loss of EUR364 million a 125% decrease from the previous year's net income of EUR1.5 billion.

The company's cash at the end of 2020 was EUR8.4 billion. Operating activities used EUR2.9 billion. Investing activities and financing activities used EUR139 million and EUR778 million respectively. Main cash uses for the year were capital contributions joint ventures and associates as well as repayment of TRUPS.

Strategy

In 2020 Aegon embarked on the transformation of its organization with a new strategic focus aimed at changing its performance trajectory and increasing value for our customers shareholders and other stakeholders. As part of its new direction the company is narrowing its strategic focus to selected core and growth markets as well as one global asset management business. Aegon's three core markets are the United States the Netherlands and the United Kingdom which are among the largest retirement investment and protection markets in the world. The company's growth markets are Spain and Portugal Brazil and China. Together its core and growth markets represent more than 50% of global GDP.

As part of this focused approach the company will explore opportunities for expansion in these regions including capitalizing on local growth opportunities building strong local partnerships and pursuing promising sales and distribution channels. Alongside this Aegon Asset Management (AAM) ? a key enabler for success ? will implement a new global operating platform allowing the company to capitalize on economies of scale realize synergies and grow its third-party assets.

Within the company's core markets its strategy is to distinguish between its Financial Assets and our Strategic Assets. The company will reallocate capital from the former to the latter as well as to its growth markets.

To realize the company's transformation it will shift to an intense organizational rhythm and operate with a clear and more disciplined governance. This means that Aegon will adapt its target operating model. A prime example of this adaption is that it is establishing dedicated teams to manage the Financial Assets in the United States and in the Netherlands. The company will appoint executives to these teams who have the competencies skills and mindset to manage these books for optimal financial outcomes.

Aegon will also speed up decision-making and install clear accountabilities. It will move to a concept of 'accountability within a clear framework'. In this new model the Group sets strategy allocates capital defines risk appetite sets targets and drives strategy implementation.

HISTORY

AEGON traces its roots to 1844 when former civil servant and funeral society agent J. Oosterhoff founded Algemeene Friesche a burial society for low-income workers. The next year a similar organization Groot-Noordhollandsche was founded. These companies later became insurers and expanded nationwide. Meanwhile Olveh a civil servants' aid group was founded in 1877. The three companies merged in 1968 to form mutual insurer AGO.

AEGON's other operations came from different traditions. Vennootschap Nederland was founded in 1858 as a tontine (essentially a death pool with the survivors taking the pot) by Count A. Langrand-Dumonceau an ex-French Foreign Legionnaire from Belgium. In 1913 the company merged with Eerste Nederlandsche whose accident and health division had been previously spun off as Nieuwe Eerste Nederlandsche.

A year after Vennootschap was founded C. F. W. Wiggers van Kerchem founded a similar scheme Nillmij in the Dutch East Indies. The government promoted Nillmij to colonial civil servants and military people and for a while the company enjoyed a monopoly in the colony. Nillmij's Indonesian operations were nationalized after independence in 1957 but its Dutch subsidiaries continued to operate. All insurers were hit by fast-growing postwar government social programs. As a result industry consolidation came early to the Netherlands. In 1969 Eerste Nederlandsche Nieuwe Eerste Nederlandsche and Nillmij merged to form Ennia.

AGO demutualized in 1978 and became AGO Holding N.V. which was owned by Vereniging AGO. Meanwhile the shrinking Dutch insurance market forced companies to look overseas. AGO moved into the US in 1979 by buying Life Investors; by 1982 half of its sales came from outside the Netherlands. Ennia meanwhile expanded in Europe (it entered Spain in 1980) and the US (buying Arkansas-based National Old Line Insurance in 1981).

AGO and Ennia merged in 1983 to form AEGON. Vereniging AGO became Vereniging AEGON and received a 49% stake in the combined entity. (This stake was later reduced.) The company made more purchases at home and abroad and spent much of the rest of the decade assimilating operations.

AEGON's US units accounted for about 40% of sales in the mid-1980s and the firm increased that figure with acquisitions. In 1986 it bought Baltimore-based Monumental Corp. (life and health insurance) and expanded the company's US penetration.

This left AEGON underrepresented in Europe as deregulation paved the way for economic union and social service cutbacks spurred opportunities in private financial planning in the region. So in the 1990s AEGON began buying European companies including Regency Life (UK 1991) and Allami Biztosito (Hungary 1992). It formed an alliance with Mexico's Grupo Financiero Banamex in 1994. This reduced its reliance on US sales. It continued buying specialty operations in the US particularly asset management lines.

In 1997 AEGON began to concentrate on life insurance and financial services and shed its other operations. It bought the insurance business of Providian (now part of Washington Mutual) and sold noncore lines such as auto coverage. The next year it sold FGH Bank (mortgages) to Germany's Bayerische Vereinsbank (now Bayerische Hypotheken und Vereinsbank) and in 1999 sold auto insurer Worldwide Insurance.

That year AEGON expanded further in the US with the $9.7 billion purchase of Transamerica and

bought the life and pensions businesses of the UK's Guardian Royal Exchange. In 2000 the company sold Labouchere N.V. a Dutch banking subsidiary to Dexia. Also in 2000 AEGON acquired UK-based third-party administrator HS Administrative Services.

Following the Transamerica acquisition the company divested several assets to focus on life insurance and pensions. In 2003 and 2004 diverse parts of Transamerica Finance (including its real estate tax unit and trailer leasing business) were sold to various companies including First American GE Commercial Finance and a joint venture held by Goldman Sachs and Cerberus Capital Management.

EXECUTIVES

Independent Vice Chairman of the Supervisory Board, Corien Wortmann-Kool, $71,782 total compensation
General Counsel, Onno van Klinken
Global Chief Technology Officer, Mark Bloom
President and CEO, Transamerica, Will Fuller
CEO, Aegon International, Marco Keim
CFO, Matthew J. Rider, $1,072,181 total compensation
Independent Chairman of the Supervisory Board, William Connelly, $108,243 total compensation
Chief Risk Officer, Allegra Hovell-Patrizi
Auditors: PricewaterhouseCoopers Accountants N.V.

LOCATIONS

HQ: AEGON NV
Aegonplein 50, P.O. Box 85, The Hague 2501 CB
Phone: (31) 70 344 54 58
Web: www.aegon.com

2018 sales

	%
Europe	49
Americas	45
Asia	4
Asset Management	2
Total	**100**

PRODUCTS/OPERATIONS

2018 Sales

	% of total
Premiums	67
Investment income	24
Fees & commissions	9
Other	-
Total	**100**

COMPETITORS

ABRDN PLC
AMERICAN FINANCIAL GROUP INC.
AMERICAN INTERNATIONAL GROUP INC.
AON GLOBAL LIMITED
AVIVA PLC
AXA
Ageas
Allianz SE
Koninklijke Vopak N.V.
Louis Dreyfus Holding B.V.
MMC VENTURES LIMITED
NIPPON LIFE INSURANCE COMPANY
OM RESIDUAL UK LIMITED
PRUDENTIAL PUBLIC LIMITED COMPANY
RSA INSURANCE GROUP LIMITED
Redefine International P.L.C.
Sampo Oyj
Skandinaviska Enskilda Banken AB
The Bank of Nova Scotia
Victoria Retail Group B.V.
WILLIS TOWERS WATSON PUBLIC LIMITED COMPANY
Wolters Kluwer N.V.
Zurich Insurance Group AG

HISTORICAL FINANCIALS

Company Type: Public

Income Statement

FYE: December 31

	ASSETS ($ mil.)	NET INCOME ($ mil.)	INCOME AS % OF ASSETS	EMPLOYEES
12/20	544,688	(179)	—	22,322
12/19	494,407	1,391	0.3%	23,757
12/18	449,641	813	0.2%	26,543
12/17	474,614	2,959	0.6%	28,318
12/16	449,199	461	0.1%	29,380
Annual Growth	4.9%	—	—	(6.6%)

2020 Year-End Financials

Return on assets: (-0.0%)
Return on equity: (-0.5%)
Long-term debt ($ mil.): —
No. of shares (mil.): —
Sales ($ mil): 54,877

Dividends
Yield: 1.8%
Payout: —
Market value ($ mil.): —

	STOCK PRICE ($) FY Close	P/E High/Low		PER SHARE ($) Earnings	Dividends	Book Value
12/20	3.95	—	—	(0.11)	0.07	11.59
12/19	4.53	10	7	0.63	0.33	13.45
12/18	4.65	24	16	0.33	0.33	12.70
12/17	6.30	6	5	1.37	0.31	11.04
12/16	5.53	39	22	0.16	0.27	9.90
Annual Growth	(8.1%)	—	—	—	(28.7%)	4.0%

Aeon Co Ltd

AEON manages the companies engaged in retail business shopping mall development businesses financial service business and service businesses and related businesses. The company has about 20000 store locations 2300 supermarkets and 600 general merchandise stores. The company also operates drugstores and pharmacies and clothing and other specialty stores.

Operations

AEON's business is divided into seven primary categories. The company generates about 40% of its revenue from about supermarkets (community discount and convenience stores and small-scale supermarkets) and about 400 Sporsium and about 20 Aeon Retail general merchandise stores operating primarily under various AEON names.

The company's health and wealth business includes drugstores and pharmacies accounting for about 10% of sales. The rest of revenue is brought in by international stores (locations in China and Southeast Asian countries) as well as financial services and the development and malls and shopping centers (about 4% combined).

Geographic Reach

AEON operates in more than a dozen countries across Asia. It relies very heavily on Japan by far its largest market accounting for more than 90% of revenue. China and Southeast Asian countries and Other contribute the rest (about 8% combined).

Sales and Marketing

AEON markets its products and services such in supermarket business by online by using smartphones and roll out of advertisement distribution and digital signage. Financial services business leverage of Aeon Group's retail and e-commerce channels. The company's advertising cost or spend were 188760 million in 2019 207802 million in 2020 and 170572 million in 2021 ($1.6 billion).

Financial Performance

Net sales for 2021 totaled 7.6 trillion a 1% increase from the previous year's revenue of 7.5 trillion.

In 2021 the company had a net loss of 37.8 billion a 150% decrease from the previous year's net income of 74.9 billion.

The company's cash at the end of 2021 was 1.1 trillion. Operating activities generated 396.5 trillion while investing activities used 341.8 billion mainly for purchase of securities in banking business. Financing activities provided another 24.3 billion.

Strategy

In November 2020 Aeon revised the AEON COVID-19 Protocol for Infectious Disease Control which was instituted in June 2020. This protocol established standards for epidemic prevention measures. The November revision added measures related to the introduction of equipment to ventilate facilities and air-cleaning systems to prevent infection via airborne droplets and also added provisions regarding eradicating the risk of infection from employees in its facilities as well as measures to prevent secondary infections should a primary infection occur. The purpose of this protocol is to contribute to the realization of a society in which epidemic prevention is a part of daily life protect the health and lifestyles of customers and employees and ensure safe and secure lifestyles for people in local communities together with customers by implementing epidemic prevention measures on an ongoing basis not as a temporary initiative. Aeon will continue working to reduce transmission risk and build safe and secure store environments and workplace environments by combining a variety of epidemic prevention initiatives.

Based on a proactive management strategy the Aeon Group (Aeon Co. Ltd. and its consolidated subsidiaries) is progressing with the consolidation and decommission of its retail outlets in response to changes in the environment surrounding its locations. In FY2020 the Group made capital expenditures of 318.2 billion (USD 3002.3 million) mainly in the GMS Business the Supermarket Business and the Shopping Center Development Business.

Company Background

AEON's predecessor company Jusco was established in 1969 through a joint venture of three of other entities. It launched its retail development business that year and five years later introduced AEON's first private-brand product J-Cup.

In 1976 Jusco was listed on the Tokyo Osaka and Nagoya Stock Exchanges. The company expanded into financial services and specialty retail in the 1980s and opened its first store outside Japan (in Malaysia). By the end of the decade Jusco Group was renamed AEON Group (Jusco Co. took the AEON Co. name in 2001).

AEON became a holding company in 2008.

EXECUTIVES

Independent Director, Takashi Tsukamoto
Independent Director, Peter Child
Vice President, Representative Executive Officer, President of Subsidiary, Motohiro Fujita
Independent Director, Carrie Yu
Executive Officer, Hiroyuki Watanabe
Executive Officer, Soichi Okazaki
Executive Chairman, Representative Executive Officer, Director, Motoya Okada
Executive Vice President, Chairman of Subsidiary, Yuki Habu
President, Representative Executive Officer, Director, Akio Yoshida
Executive Officer, Manabu Oike

Vice President, Chief Financial Officer, Representative Executive Officer, Director, Akinori Yamashita
Independent Director, Kotaro Ohno
Auditors: Deloitte Touche Tohmatsu LLC

LOCATIONS

HQ: Aeon Co Ltd
1-5-1 Nakase, Mihama-ku, Chiba 261-8515
Phone: (81) 43 212 6042
Web: www.aeon.info

2018 Sales

	% of total
Japan	92
ASEAN	4
China	3
Other	1
Total	**100**

PRODUCTS/OPERATIONS

2018 Sales

	% of total
General Merchandise Stores	34
Supermarkets	36
Services and Specialty Stores	9
Health and Wellness Stores	8
Shopping Center Development	4
Financial Services	4
International Business	5
Total	**100**

Selected Store Names

Abilities Jusco (CDs DVDs and books)
Asbee (shoe stores)
Blue Grass (apparel for teenage girls)
Claire's Nippon (women's clothing)
Cox (family casual clothing)
HapYcom (drugstores)
Home Wide Corp. (home centers)
JUSCO (apparel food and household item superstores)
JUS-Photo (film developing)
Laura Ashley Japan (clothing and home furnishings)
Maxvalu (supermarkets)
Mega Sports (Sports Authority stores)
MINISTOP (convenience stores)
MYCAL Corporation (supermarkets)
My Basket (small-scale supermarkets)
Nustep (family footwear stores)
Petcity (pets & pet supplies)
Sports Authority (sporting goods)

COMPETITORS

ALFRESA HOLDINGS CORPORATION
ANA HOLDINGS INC.
BUILD-A-BEAR WORSHOP INC.
BURBERRY GROUP PLC
Brenntag Holding GmbH
CECONOMY AG
DAI-ICHI LIFE HOLDINGS INC.
FAST RETAILING CO. LTD.
FIVE BELOW INC.
FRASERS GROUP PLC

GUESS ? INC.
ISETAN MITSUKOSHI HOLDINGS LTD.
JAPAN POST HOLDINGS CO.LTD.
LAGARDERE ACTIVE
PERMIRA ADVISERS LLP
SEVEN & I HOLDINGS CO. LTD.
SOFTBANK GROUP CORP.
SOMPO HOLDINGS INC.
SUNING.COM CO.LTD.
T&D HOLDINGS INC.

HISTORICAL FINANCIALS

Company Type: Public

Income Statement

FYE: February 28

	REVENUE ($ mil.)	NET INCOME ($ mil.)	NET PROFIT MARGIN	EMPLOYEES
02/21	80,921	(668)	—	408,567
02/20	79,146	246	0.3%	420,165
02/19	76,884	213	0.3%	419,912
02/18	78,334	228	0.3%	411,104
02/17	73,139	100	0.1%	406,146
Annual Growth	2.6%	—	—	0.1%

2021 Year-End Financials

Debt ratio: 0.2%
Return on equity: (-6.9%)
Cash ($ mil.): 12,109
Current ratio: 1.04
Long-term debt ($ mil.): 18,342

No. of shares (mil.): 850
Dividends
  Yield: 0.0%
  Payout: —
Market value ($ mil.): 28,561

	STOCK PRICE ($) FY Close	P/E High/Low		PER SHARE ($) Earnings	Dividends	Book Value
02/21	33.60	—	—	(0.79)	0.34	10.75
02/20	18.17	1	1	0.29	0.32	11.57
02/19	21.33	1	1	0.25	0.29	11.75
02/18	16.75	1	1	0.27	0.28	12.79
02/17	14.76	1	1	0.12	0.26	11.99
Annual Growth	22.8%	—	—	—	6.5%	(2.7%)

AGC Inc

Auditors: KPMG AZSA LLC

LOCATIONS

HQ: AGC Inc
  1-5-1 Marunouchi, Chiyoda-ku, Tokyo 100-8405
Phone: (81) 3 3218 5603   **Fax:** 404 446-4295
Web: www.agc.com

HISTORICAL FINANCIALS

Company Type: Public

Income Statement   FYE: December 31

	REVENUE ($ mil.)	NET INCOME ($ mil.)	NET PROFIT MARGIN	EMPLOYEES
12/20	13,702	317	2.3%	60,368
12/19	13,982	409	2.9%	60,286
12/18	13,848	814	5.9%	58,853
12/17	13,007	615	4.7%	58,171
12/16	10,965	405	3.7%	55,555
Annual Growth	5.7%	(5.9%)	—	2.1%

2020 Year-End Financials

Debt ratio: 0.2%
Return on equity: 2.8%
Cash ($ mil.): 2,290
Current ratio: 1.53
Long-term debt ($ mil.): 5,171

No. of shares (mil.): 221
Dividends
  Yield: 3.2%
  Payout: 16.1%
Market value ($ mil.): 1,540

	STOCK PRICE ($) FY Close	P/E High/Low		PER SHARE ($) Earnings	Dividends	Book Value
12/20	6.95	0	0	1.43	0.22	48.82
12/19	7.11	0	0	1.84	0.22	48.10
12/18	6.56	0	0	3.62	0.20	46.69
12/17	8.70	0	0	2.67	0.17	46.57
12/16	6.77	0	0	1.75	0.15	40.50
Annual Growth	0.7%	—	—	(4.9%)	10.4%	4.8%

Ageas NV

Auditors: PwC Reviseurs d'Entreprises SRL / PwC
  Bedrijfsrevisoren BV

LOCATIONS

HQ: Ageas NV
  Rue du Marquis 1, Brussels 1000
Phone: (32) 2 557 57 11   **Fax:** (32) 2 557 57 50
Web: www.ageas.com

HISTORICAL FINANCIALS

Company Type: Public

Income Statement   FYE: December 31

	ASSETS ($ mil.)	NET INCOME ($ mil.)	INCOME AS % OF ASSETS	EMPLOYEES
12/20	136,742	1,400	1.0%	0
12/19	122,885	1,099	0.9%	10,741
12/18	116,450	926	0.8%	11,009
12/17	123,880	747	0.6%	11,260
12/16	110,121	28	0.0%	12,080
Annual Growth	5.6%	164.5%	—	—

2020 Year-End Financials

Return on assets: 1.0%
Return on equity: 9.9%
Long-term debt ($ mil.): —
No. of shares (mil.): —
Sales ($ mil): 15,181

Dividends
  Yield: 4.0%
  Payout: 30.6%
Market value ($ mil.): —

	STOCK PRICE ($) FY Close	P/E High/Low		PER SHARE ($) Earnings	Dividends	Book Value
12/20	53.39	11	5	7.44	2.16	(0.00)
12/19	59.28	12	8	5.70	1.71	66.12
12/18	44.71	13	11	4.71	1.70	55.45
12/17	48.81	16	14	3.70	1.76	57.89
12/16	39.57	343	235	0.14	1.27	49.15
Annual Growth	7.8%	—	—	(171.3%)	14.2%	—

Ahli United Bank

Ahli United Bank (AUB) is a financial services company providing a range of commercial and investment banking services in the Persian Gulf and to a lesser extent Europe Asia and the US. It owns controlling stakes in entities including The Bank of Kuwait and the Middle East Al-Ahli Bank (Qatar) Commercial Bank of Iraq Kuwait & Middle East Financial Investment Company and Ahli Bank (formerly Alliance Housing Bank Oman). AUB divides its operations into four business lines: commercial banking treasury and investments; private banking and wealth management; retail banking; and risk management. Through Ahli Bank the company began offering Islamic Sharia-compliant banking in 2007.

Auditors: Ernst & Young

LOCATIONS

HQ: Ahli United Bank
  Building 2495, Road 2832, Al-Seef District, P. O. Box 2424, Manama
Phone: (973) 17 585 858   **Fax:** (973) 17 580 569
Web: www.ahliunited.com

COMPETITORS

AKBANK TURK ANONIM SIRKETI
BANQUE SAUDI FRANSI
RIYAD BANK
TURKIYE GARANTI BANKASI ANONIM SIRKETI
UNITED OVERSEAS BANK LIMITED

HISTORICAL FINANCIALS

Company Type: Public

Income Statement   FYE: December 31

	ASSETS ($ mil.)	NET INCOME ($ mil.)	INCOME AS % OF ASSETS	EMPLOYEES
12/19	40,280	730	1.8%	0
12/18	35,507	697	2.0%	0
12/17	33,241	618	1.9%	0
12/16	31,322	570	1.8%	0
12/15	33,965	537	1.6%	0
Annual Growth	4.4%	8.0%	—	—

2019 Year-End Financials

Return on assets: 1.9%
Return on equity: 15.5%
Long-term debt ($ mil.): —
No. of shares (mil.): —
Sales ($ mil): 2,127

Dividends
  Yield: —
  Payout: 63.2%
Market value ($ mil.): —

AIA Group Ltd.

AIA Group is the largest independent publicly listed pan-Asian life insurance group. The life insurance and wealth management company operates in some 20 markets across the Asia/Pacific region. It offers life insurance credit insurance employee benefits and pension services to its corporate clients. For individuals the company provides basic life insurance along with savings investment and retirement products. Other offerings include medical insurance critical illness protection accident coverage and disability coverage. AIA was first established in Shanghai in 1919.

Operations

AIA's reportable segments are Hong Kong (including Macau) Thailand China Singapore (including Brunei) Malaysia Other Markets and Group Corporate Centre. Except for the latter segment they all provide life accident and health insurance and distribute savings plans and related financial services.

The Hong Kong segment brings in about 40% of total revenue followed by Thailand and China which bring in some 15% of revenue each.

Overall net premiums and fee income brings in some 65% of total revenue and investment return accounts for about 35% of revenue.

Geographic Reach

Hong Kong-based AIA has a presence in almost 20 markets ? wholly-owned branches and subsidiaries in Mainland China Hong Kong SAR Thailand Singapore Malaysia Australia Cambodia Indonesia Myanmar the Philippines South Korea Sri Lanka Taiwan (China) Vietnam Brunei Macau SAR and New Zealand and a 49% joint venture in India.

Sales and Marketing

Through its extensive network of agents partners and employees across the region AIA serves more than 39 million individual policyholders and more than 16 million participating members of group insurance schemes.

Financial Performance

The company's revenue for fiscal 2020 increased to $50.4 billion compared from the prior year with $47.2 billion.

Profit for fiscal 2020 decreased to $5.8 billion compared from the prior year with $6.0 billion.

Cash held by the company at the end of fiscal 2020 increased to $5.4 billion. Cash provided by operations and financing activities were $2.4 billion and $392 million respectively. Cash used for investing activities was $1.2 billion mainly for acquisition of subsidiaries.

Strategy

AIA has an unparalleled platform in Asia built up over its long history in the region and it holds leading positions in the majority of its markets. Company's focus on Asia and its corporate structure allow AIA to capture the full economics of growth for its shareholders in the world's most attractive region for life insurance. In 2020 AIA launched its new corporate strategy founded on AIA's Purpose of helping people live Healthier Longer and Better Lives.

AIA's updated strategic priorities are built on five long-term structural drivers of growth in Asia: Asia's unprecedented wealth creation; significant need for private protection; rapidly shifting consumer mindset; pervasiveness of new technologies; and embracing purpose sustainability and resilience.

Company Background

Founded in Shanghai in 1919 by Cornelius Vander Starr AIA was the original business that would later grow to become American International Group (AIG) and was a cornerstone of that company's Asia-based operations. However in 2010 AIG spun off the business through a public offering.

EXECUTIVES

Chairman, Edmund Sze-Wing Tse
Group General Counsel, Mitchell New
Group Chief Financial Officer, Garth Jones
Group Chief Investment Officer, Mark Konyn
Group Chief Strategy and Corporate Development Officer, Mark Saunders
Regional Chief Executive and Group Chief Distribution Officer, William Lisle
Group Chief Technology Officer, Biswa Misra
Group Chief Marketing Officer, Stuart Spencer
Company Secretary, Nicole Pao
Group Chief Risk Officer, Jayne Plunkett
Regional Chief Executive, Wing-shing Chan
Group Chief Human Resources Officer, Pek-san Ang
Regional Chief Executive and Group Chief Life Operations Officer, Hak Leh Tan
Group Chief Executive, President and Director, Yuan Siong Lee
Auditors: PricewaterhouseCoopers

LOCATIONS

HQ: AIA Group Ltd.
35/F, AIA Central, No. 1 Connaught Road Central,
Phone: (852) 2832 1800   **Fax:** (852) 2834 1753
Web: www.aia.com

2018 Sales by Segment

	% of total
Hong Kong	41
Thailand	14
China	13
Singapore	11
Malaysia	6
Other Markets	14
Group Corporate Centre	1
Total	**100**

PRODUCTS/OPERATIONS

2018 Sales

	$ mil.	% of total
Net premiums & fee income	31,913	88
Investment return	4,077	11
Other	30	1
Total	**36,297**	**100**

COMPETITORS

AMERICAN FINANCIAL GROUP INC.
AMERITRUST GROUP INC.
ASSURANT INC.
BROWN & BROWN INC.
Bank of Communications Co. Ltd.
China Life Insurance Company Limited
Intact Corporation Financi `re
LOCKTON INC.
Manulife Financial Corporation
NN Group N.V.
OVERSEA-CHINESE BANKING CORPORATION LIMITED
PAN-AMERICAN LIFE MUTUAL HOLDING COMPANY
QBE INSURANCE GROUP LIMITED
ROYAL LONDON MUTUAL INSURANCE SOCIETYLIMITED(THE)
SOMPO HOLDINGS INC.
Zurich Insurance Group AG

HISTORICAL FINANCIALS

Company Type: Public

Income Statement

FYE: December 31

	ASSETS ($ mil.)	NET INCOME ($ mil.)	INCOME AS % OF ASSETS	EMPLOYEES
12/20	326,121	5,779	1.8%	23,000
12/19	284,132	6,648	2.3%	23,000
12/18*	229,806	3,163	1.4%	22,000
11/17	215,691	6,120	2.8%	20,000
11/16	185,074	4,164	2.2%	20,000
Annual Growth	**15.2%**	**8.5%**	**—**	**3.6%**

*Fiscal year change

2020 Year-End Financials

Return on assets: 1.8%
Return on equity: 9.5%
Long-term debt ($ mil.): —
No. of shares (mil.): —
Sales ($ mil): 50,342

Dividends
Yield: 1.2%
Payout: 127.1%
Market value ($ mil.): —

	STOCK PRICE ($) FY Close	P/E High/Low	Earnings	Dividends	Book Value
12/20	49.13	103 66	0.48	0.61	5.23
12/19	42.09	82 57	0.55	0.63	4.76
12/18*	32.88	146 114	0.26	0.48	3.23
11/17	32.76	69 44	0.51	0.41	3.48
11/16	24.41	80 56	0.35	0.34	2.90
Annual Growth	**19.1%**	**— —**	**8.2%**	**15.6%**	**15.8%**

*Fiscal year change

AIB Gro up PLC

Allied Irish Banks (AIB) one of Ireland's largest banks and private employers is looking beyond the Emerald Isle for its proverbial pot o' gold. The company offers retail and commercial accounts and loans life insurance financing leasing pension and trust services through a network of 200 branches 74 EBS Limited offices 10 business centers and 755 ATMs. The company's capital markets division offers commercial treasury services corporate finance and investment banking services. In the US AIB specializes in financial services for the not-for-profit sector.

Operations

Over the years AIB has reorganized into a more simplified structure in which its divisions were integrated and its AIB and First Trust operations were more closely aligned. To attract additional customers the bank also introduced mobile banking services to its offerings.

HISTORY

Allied Irish Banks was formed in 1966 by the "trinity" of Provincial Bank (founded 1825) The Royal Bank (founded 1836) and Munster and Leinster (founded 1885 but with origins back to the late 1600s). Both AIB and its then-larger rival Bank of Ireland had to consolidate in order to compete with North American banks entering Ireland. From its start AIB sought to expand overseas and by 1968 it had an alliance with Canada's Toronto-Dominion Bank.

In the 1970s AIB expanded its branch network to England and Scotland. The 1980s saw AIB boost its presence in the US market (it had already debuted AIB branches) with the acquisition of First Maryland Bancorp.

The Irish Parliament's Finance Act of 1986 instituted a withholding tax known as the Deposit Interest Retention Tax (DIRT) for Irish residents. Consequently (with a wink and a nod) AIB and other banks let customers create bogus non-resident accounts to avoid paying DIRT. An investigation indicated that at one point AIB's branch in Tralee had 14700 non-resident accounts on its rolls — more than half the local population. After tax authorities began probing many of the accounts in question were reclassified as "resident" and customers had to pay the taxes on them. In 1991 AIB was reprimanded but neither the bank nor its customers have paid the remaining $100 million tax bill.

Tom Mulcahy who integrated AIB's treasury investment and international banking activities became chief executive in 1994. Mulcahy a respected leader envisioned AIB as an international Ireland-based bank.

In 1995 AIB bought UK-based investment fund manager John Govett from London Pacific Group (now Berkeley Technology Limited). Mulcahy moved AIB the same year into Eastern Europe with a stake in Poland-based Wielkopolski Bank Kredytowy (or WBK).

AIB was busy in 1999. It gained a toehold in Asia by entering a cross-marketing agreement with Singapore's Keppet TatLee bank a survivor of the region's financial crisis. Liberalized Singapore banking laws allowed AIB the right to buy one-quarter of the bank by 2001. AIB also bought an 80% stake of Bank Zachodni in Poland in 1999.

That year AIB merged First Maryland Bancorp and its other US holdings into the renamed Allfirst Financial a sizable mid-Atlantic states bank.

To consolidate its power in Eastern Europe in 2001 AIB merged its Polish banks (Wielkopolski Bank Kredytowy and Bank Zachodni) into Bank Zachodni WBK. That year Mulcahy retired but was appointed by the Irish government to take over as chairman of troubled airline Aer Lingus.

AIB lost nearly $700 million from 1996 to 2002 apparently from bogus foreign exchange transactions made by rogue trader John Rusnak who pleaded guilty to bank fraud.

In 2003 AIB sold troubled Maryland-based bank Allfirst Financial to M&T Bank Corporation. As part of the deal AIB assumed ownership of more than 20% of M&T becoming the company's largest shareholder. Under AIB's direction Allfirst had grown into a major regional player with about 250 branches in Maryland Pennsylvania Virginia and Washington DC.

In the midst of the global financial crisis the Irish government injected ?2 billion ($2.8 billion) into AIB in exchange for a 25% share in voting rights in 2008. Ireland also provided capital for Bank of Ireland and Irish Bank Resolution Corporation to help stabilize the plunging Irish financial system. AIB also sought capital from the private sector.

EXECUTIVES

Chief People Officer, Geraldine Casey
Managing Director - Corporate, Institutional & Business Banking, Cathy-Ann Bryce
Director of Corporate Affairs, Strategy & Sustainability, Mary Whitelaw
Chief Financial Officer, Executive Director, Donal Galvin
Independent Non-Executive Deputy Chairman of the Board, Brendan McDonagh
Senior Non-Executive Independent Director, Carolan Lennon
Independent Non-Executive Director, Basil Geoghegan
Independent Non-Executive Director, Elaine MacLean
Independent Non-Executive Director, Ranjit Singh
Independent Non-Executive Director, Ann O'Brien
Chief Technology Officer Designate, Fergal Coburn
Chief Operating Officer Designate, CJ Berry
Independent Non-Executive Director, Sandy Pritchard
Chief Risk Officer, Deirdre Hannigan
Chief Executive Officer, Executive Director, Colin Hunt, $569,702 total compensation
Managing Director - AIB Group (UK) plc, Robert Mulhall
Managing Director - Retail Banking, Jim O' Keeffe
Independent Non-Executive Director, Helen Normoyle
Group General Counsel, Helen Dooley
Non-Executive Independent Director, Tanya Horgan
Non-Executive Independent Director, Jan Sijbrand
Non-Executive Independent Director, Anik Chaumartin
Independent Non-Executive Director, Fergal O'Dwyer
Non-Executive Chairman of the Board, Jim Pettigrew
Auditors: Deloitte Ireland LLP

LOCATIONS

HQ: AIB Group PLC
10 Molesworth Street, Dublin 2
Phone: (353) 1 660 0311   **Fax:** 212 515-6710
Web: www.aibgroup.com

PRODUCTS/OPERATIONS

2013 Sales

	% of total
Interest and similar income	86
Fee and commission income	11
Others	3
Total	**100**

COMPETITORS

3I GROUP PLC
BANKINTER SOCIEDAD ANONIMA
Bank of Ireland
CAPITALSOURCE INC.
GENERAL ELECTRIC CAPITAL CORPORATION
KBC Groep
LLOYDS BANKING GROUP PLC
NATWEST GROUP PLC
SINOPAC FINANCIAL HOLDINGS COMPANY LIMITED
YORKSHIRE BANK PUBLIC LIMITED COMPANY

HISTORICAL FINANCIALS

Company Type: Public

Income Statement

FYE: December 31

	ASSETS ($ mil.)	NET INCOME ($ mil.)	INCOME AS % OF ASSETS	EMPLOYEES
12/20	135,474	(943)	—	9,193
12/19	110,662	367	0.3%	9,520
12/18	104,826	1,250	1.2%	9,831
12/17	107,962	1,335	1.2%	9,720
12/16	100,965	1,431	1.4%	10,376
Annual Growth	7.6%	—	—	(3.0%)

2020 Year-End Financials

Return on assets: (-0.7%)	Dividends
Return on equity: (-5.6%)	Yield: 0.0%
Long-term debt ($ mil.): —	Payout: —
No. of shares (mil.): —	Market value ($ mil.): —
Sales ($ mil): 3,451	

	STOCK PRICE ($) FY Close	P/E High/Low	PER SHARE ($) Earnings	Dividends	Book Value
12/20	4.38	— —	(0.37)	0.00	6.07
12/19	7.05	79 41	0.14	0.26	5.68
12/18	8.15	23 20	0.45	0.14	5.85
Annual Growth	(26.7%)	— —	—	—	0.9%

Aichi Bank, Ltd.

The Aichi Bank is a regional bank with an international attitude. The bank primarily serves the Aichi Prefecture of Japan but also names operations in Tokyo Osaka and the Gifu Shizuoka and Mie prefectures. Established in 1910 Aichi Bank consists of more than 100 branches and commands some $20 million in total assets. Its four subsidiaries — Aigin Business Service Aigin Lease Aigin DC Card and Aigin Computer Service — offer a variety of financial services although banking and leasing services comprise the bulk of annual revenue.

EXECUTIVES

Chairman of the Board, Representative Director, Shinichi Koide
Managing Director, Chief Director of Sales, Representative Director, Toshiyuki Suzuki
Senior Director of Sales, Director, Noboru Hayashi
Senior Managing Director, Representative Director, Katsuyuki Yazawa
Director of Main Store Sales, Director, Takashi Kozaki
Managing Director, Representative Director, Haruhiko Ando
President, Representative Director, Kenzo Haba
Senior Director of Affairs, Director, Yoshihiro Ito
Independent Director, Akio Hayashi
Managing Director, Yukinori Ito
Managing Director, Representative Director, Masato Kobayashi
Independent Director, Yasutoshi Emoto
Auditors: KPMG AZSA LLC

LOCATIONS

HQ: Aichi Bank, Ltd.
3-14-12 Sakae, Naka-ku, Nagoya, Aichi 460-8678
Phone: (81) 52 251 3211
Web: www.aichibank.co.jp

COMPETITORS

HOKKOKU BANK LTD. THE	NISHI-NIPPON
MIE BANK LTD. THE	CITYBANKLTD.

HISTORICAL FINANCIALS

Company Type: Public

Income Statement

FYE: March 31

	ASSETS ($ mil.)	NET INCOME ($ mil.)	INCOME AS % OF ASSETS	EMPLOYEES
03/21	34,212	38	0.1%	2,071
03/20	29,905	26	0.1%	2,110
03/19	28,374	42	0.1%	2,178
03/18	29,702	40	0.1%	2,260
03/17	27,815	45	0.2%	2,263
Annual Growth	5.3%	(4.0%)	—	(2.2%)

2021 Year-End Financials

Return on assets: 0.1%	Dividends
Return on equity: 1.9%	Yield: —
Long-term debt ($ mil.): —	Payout: 30.4%
No. of shares (mil.): 10	Market value ($ mil.): —
Sales ($ mil): 481	

Air France-KLM

A global giant with a strong European base the Air France-KLM Group's main areas of business are passenger transport cargo transport and aeronautical maintenance. Air France-KLM is the leading Group in terms of international traffic on departure from Europe. It offers its customers access to a network covering over 250 destinations thanks to Air France KLM Royal Dutch Airlines and Transavia. With a fleet of some 555 aircraft and 104 million passengers carried in 2019 Air France-KLM operates up to 2300 daily flights mainly from its hubs at Paris-Charles de Gaulle and Amsterdam-Schiphol. About a third of revenue comes from France.

Operations

Air France-KLM offers passenger transportation cargo transportation and aircraft maintenance services and transports over 100 million passengers and 1.1 million tons of cargo annually. It has a fleet of around 555 aircraft in operation. Some 80% of its total cargo tonnage is carried in the bellies of its passenger aircraft and around 20% in the full - freighter fleet.

The company's single operating segment consists of four businesses. Its Network business is its primary passenger and cargo business that operates under the brands Air France and KLM and domestic operators Air France HOP and KLM Cityhopper. It generates more than 80% of sales.

Its low-cost Transavia airline accounts for more than 5% of sales and flies customers in the Netherlands and France to some 130 Middle Eastern European and North African destinations. Transavia has a fleet of nearly 75 primarily B737-800 aircraft. Air France-KLM's Maintenance unit also generates over 10% of total revenue and serves both Air France-KLM and third parties with maintenance repair and overhaul services. Its three main areas or service are airframe maintenance engine maintenance and component support (electronic mechanical pneumatic and hydraulic).

Geographic Reach

The Air France-KLM network is organized around its hubs at Paris-Charles de Gaulle and Amsterdam-Schiphol airports. With these two major hubs the company links Europe to the rest of the world spanning more than 250 destinations across around 115 countries.

About 30% of its revenue comes from France and the remaining 70% comes from international operations.

Financial Performance

Note: Growth rates may differ after conversion to US Dollars.

The company's revenues amounted to ?11.1 billion a decrease of 59.2% compared to last year with Network revenues decreasing by 60.4% Maintenance revenues down by 41.6% and Transavia down by 65.3%.

The company recorded a net loss of ?1.1 billion in 2020 compared to a net income of ?290 million from the prior year.

Cash at the end of fiscal 2020 was ?6.4 billion an increase of ?2.7 billion from the prior year. Cash from operations used ?2.8 billion to the coffers and investing activities used ?1.6 billion. Financing activities provided another ?7.1 billion in the fiscal year 2020.

Strategy

KLM submitted its restructuring plan to the Netherlands Ministry of Finance. The presentation of this restructuring plan was a key condition in obtaining the aforementioned government loan and guarantees to the value of ?3.4 billion. The plan outlines how KLM intends to fulfil the conditions imposed by the Netherlands government. The presentation of the plan is a very important milestone. Substantively the plan includes elements such as the reassessment of strategy cost-cutting initiatives financial considerations and how KLM staff will contribute by way of reduced employment conditions. On November 3 2020 the ministry has approved the plan.

To face the Covid-19 crisis and forecasts expecting a return at the same level of activity of 2019 in 2024 Air France KLM must accelerate its transformation to regain its competitiveness and strengthen its leading position in terms of sustainable development. In this context Air France Group and KLM Group announced the restructuring of the company and a reduction of staff.

Air France and HOP! announced their strategic orientations and planned to adapt their workforce in the coming months. Within the framework of these strategic orientations the negotiations have been conducted by Air France and HOP! with their representatives of pilots cabin crew and ground staff.

Company Background

KLM was established in 1919 as Koninklijke Luchtvaartmaatschappij with service in the Netherlands and colonies. In 1920 it operated its first flight between London and Amsterdam and later introduced new regular routes serving Amsterdam Rotterdam Brussels Paris and London then expanded to Bremen Copenhagen and Malm ¶. KLM's fleet then consisted of the Fokker aircraft.

Air France dates back to 1933 with the merger of the five French airlines Air Union Air Orient Societe Generale de Transport Aerien (SGTA) CIDNA and Aeropostale.

The two companies merged in 2004 creating what is now Air France-KLM a holding company made up of two national airlines.

EXECUTIVES

Director, Cees 't Hart, $23,829 total compensation

Non-Executive Independent Chairman of the Board, Anne-Marie Couderc, $199,226 total compensation

Director - Representing the Employees, Karim Belabbas, $41,135 total compensation

Executive Vice President Air France-KLM Corporate Secretary, Anne-Sophie Le Lay

Director, Jian Wang, $46,422 total compensation

Director, Martin Vial, $43,286 total compensation

Director, Astrid Panosyan, $41,135 total compensation

Director, Permanent representative of Delta Air Lines, Inc., Alain Bellemare

Director, Dirk Jan van den Berg, $19,275 total compensation

Chief Executive Officer, Member of the Executive Board, Director, Benjamin Smith, $848,300 total compensation

Executive Vice President Strategy, Member of the Group Executive Committee, Angus Clarke

Chief Financial Officer, Member of the Executive Committee, Steven Zaat

Member of the Group Executive Committee, President and Chief Executive Officer, KLM, Pieter Elbers

Executive Vice President, Information Technology, Jean-Christophe Lalanne

Member of the Executive Board, Chief Revenue Officer, Pieter Bootsma

Auditors: Deloitte et Associés

LOCATIONS

HQ: Air France-KLM
2, rue Robert Esnault-Pelterie, Paris 75007
Phone: (33) 1 43 17 21 96
Web: www.airfranceklm.com

2017 Sales

	% of total
Metropolitan France	32
Benelux	15
Other Europe	19
Africa	5
Middle-Eastern Gulf and India	2
Asia-Pacific	8
North America	13
West Indies Caribbean Guyana Indian Ocean and South America	6
Total	**100**

PRODUCTS/OPERATIONS

2018 Sales

	% of total
Network	87
Transavia	6
Maintenance	7
Other	-
Total	**100**

COMPETITORS

ANDREWS SYKES GROUP PLC
AZUL SA
Deutsche Lufthansa AG
HEATHROW AIRPORT HOLDINGS LIMITED
INTERNATIONAL CONSOLIDATED AIRLINES GROUP SA
JET2 PLC
Koninklijke Luchtvaart Maatschappij N.V.
Korean Airlines Co. Ltd.
THOMAS COOK GROUP PLC
UNITED AIRLINES INC.

HISTORICAL FINANCIALS

Company Type: Public

Income Statement				FYE: December 31
	REVENUE ($ mil.)	NET INCOME ($ mil.)	NET PROFIT MARGIN	EMPLOYEES
12/20	13,608	(8,686)	—	82,132
12/19	30,526	325	1.1%	90,386
12/18	30,364	468	1.5%	88,888
12/17	30,908	(328)	—	87,312
12/16	26,234	836	3.2%	82,175
Annual Growth	**(15.1%)**	—	—	**(0.0%)**

2020 Year-End Financials

Debt ratio: 62.9%
Return on equity: —
Cash ($ mil.): 7,882
Current ratio: 0.84
Long-term debt ($ mil.): 17,391

No. of shares (mil.): 427
Dividends
  Yield: —
  Payout: —
Market value ($ mil.): 2,667

	STOCK PRICE ($) FY Close	P/E High/Low		PER SHARE ($)		
				Earnings	Dividends	Book Value
12/20	6.24	—	—	(20.32)	0.00	(15.58)
12/19	11.02	23	13	0.68	0.00	6.00
12/18	10.88	19	9	1.00	0.00	4.96
12/17	16.25	—	—	(0.97)	0.00	8.42
12/16	5.36	4	2	2.38	0.00	3.65
Annual Growth	**3.9%**			—	—	—

Airbus SE

Airbus SE (formerly European Aeronautic Defence and Space Company or EADS) is busy in the commercial and military aerospace and related markets. Europe's largest supplier it rivals Boeing in the competitive skies. The company's commercial aircraft division is the world's largest manufacturer of large commercial aircraft (seating 100-plus passengers) while its military division manufactures transport tankers and mission aircraft. Other segments include Airbus Helicopters (civil and military helicopters) and Airbus Defence and Space (satellites and launcher systems combat aircraft missile systems radar defense electronics and unmanned aerial systems).

Operations

Airbus has three operating divisions: Airbus Airbus Defence and Space and Airbus Helicopters.

The Airbus segment more than 75% of the company's revenue and manufactures passenger airliners ranging in capacity from 100 to more than 600 seats.

The Airbus Defence and Space segment (15% of revenue) is Europe's number one defense and space enterprise and among the world's top ten space businesses. Its four core business groups are Military Aircraft Space Systems Communications Intelligence & Security (CIS) and Unmanned Aerial Systems (UAS). It develops products for governments institutions and commercial customers.

Airbus Helicopters (almost 10%) is a global leader in the civil and military rotorcraft market. Its product range includes light single-engine light twin-engine medium and medium-heavy rotorcraft which are adaptable to all kinds of mission types based on customer needs.

Geographic Reach

Airbus is headquartered in the Netherlands but has its main operational base in Toulouse France. The company operates worldwide. The Commercial Aircraft division has operations in France Germany Spain and the UK as well as subsidiaries in the US China Japan India and the Middle East. Airbus Helicopters conducts its activities in four primary locations ? two in France one in Germany and one in Spain. The Defence and Space division is headquartered in Ottobrunn near in Munich Germany with main production facilities in France Germany Spain and the UK and also has engineering centers and offices in more than 80 countries.

Airbus' customer base is geographically diversified with customers in the Asia/Pacific region accounting for more than 30% of total sales Europe more than 30% North America more than 15% Middle East for about 10% and Latin America and other countries accounts the remainder.

Sales and Marketing
Airbus' customers are mostly airline companies include Avolon Jetblue Airways Moxy Vietjet Air and Scandinavian Airlines. Airbus Helicopters' principal military clients are Ministries of Defence (MoDs) in Europe Asia the US and Latin America.

Financial Performance
Consolidated revenues increased to ? 70.5 billion (2018: ? 63.7 billion) mainly driven by the higher commercial aircraft deliveries and a favourable mix at Airbus and to a lesser extent the favourable exchange rate development.

Net loss was ?1.4 billion a 56% change (?1.7 billion) from ?3.1 billion net income in 2018.

Airbus' cash balance weakened during 2019 ending the year ?114 million lower at ?9.3 billion. Its operations generated ?3.8 billion while it used ?2.9 billion in its investing activities and ?958 million in its financing activities. Airbus' main cash uses in 2019 were capital expenditures borrowing repayments and divide.

Strategy
As part of its business strategy the Company may acquire or divest businesses and/or form joint ventures or strategic alliances. Executing acquisitions and divestments can be difficult and costly due to the complexities inherent in integrating or carving out people operations technologies and products. There can be no assurance that any of the businesses that the Company intends to acquire or divest can be integrated or carved out successfully as timely as originally planned or that they will perform well and deliver the expected synergies or cost savings once integrated or separated. In addition regulatory administrative or other contractual conditions can prevent transactions from being finalized. The Company's business results of operations and financial condition may be materially affected if these transactions will not be successfully completed or do not produce the expected benefits.

Mergers and Acquisitions
In late 2019 Airbus acquires Seattle's-areas MTM an industrial automation company for an undisclosed sum. It is located in Mukilteo Washington near Seattle. The move deepens Airbus' commitment to expanding advanced robotics capabilities within its manufacturing processes. MTM perfectly fits Airbus' ambition for engineering and innovative manufacturing solutions while maintaining agility.

Company Background
Airbus dates back to the formation of Airbus Industry GIE (later Airbus SAS) in 1970 a European effort to establish a civil aviation company capable of competing with the US hegemony of Boeing Lockheed and McDonnell Douglas. It launched the A300 in 1974 and after a big win when Eastern Air Lines bought its aircraft by 1980 Airbus trailed only Boeing among the world's commercial jet makers. The European Aeronautic Defence and Space Company NV was established in the Netherlands in 2000 to consolidate various European aviation businesses including Euro-

copter Group a leader helicopter manufacturer. It changed its name to Airbus in 2014 in respect of its main subsidiary.

HISTORY

The growth of the European Aeronautic Defence and Space Company — EADS — is overshadowed by the long history of its components and by the obstacles overcome to cement the deal: The French and the Germans historically aren't overly fond of each other so how did it come to pass that Germany's DaimlerChrysler Aerospace AG (DASA) and France's Aerospatiale Matra put aside their differences to band together with Spain's Construcciones Aeron uticas SA (CASA)?

The US aerospace sector in the 1990s saw many companies consolidate scrambling to make their way in the post-Cold War era. Boeing the largest aerospace company in the world got that way by acquiring a number of operations including Rockwell International's aerospace and defense operations (1995) and most importantly McDonnell Douglas in a $16 billion deal (1997). In the same era defense giant Lockheed merged with Martin Marietta (1995) and acquired Loral (1997). These US companies had it relatively easy — they all paid taxes to Uncle Sam but acquisition deals in Europe were stymied by concerns over national security and privatization because much of Europe's defense industry was government-owned.

Spurred into action by their US rivals DASA and British Aerospace (now BAE SYSTEMS) — partners in Airbus — began merger talks in 1997. Fearful of being left out in the cold France's government-owned Aerospatiale — another Airbus partner — began talks to merge with Matra a French defense company controlled by Lagard re. Weeks after the Aerospatiale-Matra deal was announced in 1998 the chairman of DASA's parent company J rgen Schrempp met with Lagard re's CEO Jean-Luc Lagard re and proposed a three-way deal. It never occurred and in 1999 the BAE SYSTEMS and DASA deal fell through as well.

Later that year Schrempp and Lagard re met again and laid the groundwork for a merger between DASA and Aerospatiale Matra. Less than three weeks after the Aerospatiale-Matra merger was completed Lagard re found itself pitching the DASA/Aerospatiale Matra merger idea to a stunned French government (which still held a 48% stake in Aerospatiale Matra). Marathon negotiations ensued. Late in the year Spain's Construcciones Aeron uticas SA (CASA) agreed to become part of EADS.

In 2000 EADS went public and Airbus announced that it would abandon its consortium structure in favor of incorporation. The next year EADS began pushing for a consolidation of army and naval equipment manufacturing among EU countries similar to the aerospace consolidation that created EADS. For Airbus the long-sought switch from consortium to corporation finally occurred in July 2001 when Airbus S.A.S. was incorporated.

EADS bought out BAE SYSTEMS' 25% share in their Astrium joint venture in 2003. In October 2004 EADS agreed to acquire US defense electronics maker Racal Instruments as part of its plan to increase defense sales in the US. Rumors surfaced the next month that EADS was discussing a merger deal with French defense company Thales.

In December 2004 EADS and BAE SYSTEMS gave Airbus the green-light to build the superjumbo twin-deck A380 a plane that competes directly with Boeing's upcoming 787 Dreamliner. A few months later in early 2005 EADS was given preferred bidder status for the UK's Royal Air Force aerial refueling tanker contract. The program was valued at approximately $25 billion.

Claiming victory at last in 2006 Airbus beat Boeing on deliveries (434 vs. 398) but Boeing racked up a record 1004 plane orders while Airbus notched only 790. Moreover EADS' shares took a pounding in 2006 on Airbus' announcement that deliveries of the A380 would be delayed by six or seven months due to manufacturing glitches. A group of EADS shareholders cried foul and filed suit when it was revealed that co-CEO No 1 Forgeard and five other EADS directors exercised stock options weeks before an internal investigation into the delays was launched. Two weeks later Forgeard fell on his sword and resigned. Louis Gallois former chairman of Soci t Nationale des Chemins de Fer Fran ais (SNCF) France's state railway company was named to replace him. The same fate befell Airbus boss Gustav Humbert who was replaced by Christian Streiff a former executive at French building materials concern Compagnie de Saint-Gobain.

The production logjams at Airbus also prompted some of the company's airline customers to seek compensation in lieu of taking their business elsewhere (Boeing). EADS forecast that the production delays at Airbus would be a $2.5 billion drain on profits over four years. In the wake of the additional delivery delays Airbus CEO Christian Streiff was sent packing after only three months on the job. EADS Co-CEO Louis Gallois was named as his replacement.

In 2006 Daimler announced plans to gradually reduce its stake in EADS from about 30% to half that amount. Later that year EADS acquired Sofrelog of France (a maker of maritime monitoring systems). Russian bank Vneshtorgbank (100% controlled by the Russian government) also purchased a 5% stake in EADS for about $1.17 billion. The stake did not entitle Vneshtorgbank to a board seat but the move was expected to strengthen cooperation between EADS and the re-emerging Russian aerospace industry.

After long negotiations EADS shifted in 2007 to a new management structure aimed at cutting down on the damaging political bickering between its German and French management and shareholder factions. Politicians like German Chancellor Angela Merkel and French President Nicolas Sarkozy touted the compromise as a success. Others namely labor forces were more skeptical — calling the latest management shake-up just another round of musical chairs that leaves the power struggles between Paris and Munich largely unresolved.

EADS continued to expand into emerging markets especially regions including Asia the Middle East and North and South America. Deliveries included the company's (long-delayed) A380 model launched with Singapore Airlines in late 2008. Adding to Airbus's standing the all-new A350-XWB (made for the most part of lighter-weight composite materials) sliced into about two-thirds of jet demand in the Middle East. It also forged alliances and won contracts in Brazil China Japan and North America.

Airbus launched a cost-cutting initiative in 2008 that slashed some 10000 jobs. Dubbed Power8 the plan marched out cost-saving measures that aimed to reduce development cycles by two years and boost overall productivity by 20%. Central to Power8 was the spinoff of some of Airbus's manufacturing facilities to new partners. Partner funding of planes like the A350-XWB (spurred by assurances of subcontract work) plus plant sales risked an ongoing row between Airbus and unions as well as factory owners — stakeholders who feared plant divestitures and more job cuts. That year EADS captured its first big US military contract when Airbus North America was given the opportunity to make US Army light utility helicopters.

The company was awarded a contract to replace outdated KC-135 refueling tankers in conjunction with Northrop Grumman for the US Air Force — an upset protested by rival bidder Boeing. Soon after the Government Accountability Office (GAO) announced its findings of flaws in the bidding process. EADS and Northrop Grumman dropped out of the bidding in early 2010 with EADS vowing not to submit a proposal unless it was assured that it had a fair chance to win. By late summer — after US president Obama assured French president Nicolas Sarkozy that the Pentagon tanker bidding process would be fair — EADS announced that it would consider once again to enter into the bidding war. The contract to build the US tanker valued at approximately $35 billion went to Boeing in early 2011.

In September 2012 EADS (now the Airbus Group) announced it was considering a merger with UK-based BAE Systems a global provider of sensors flight controls and aircraft. However the proposed $45 billion merger — which would have created the largest global aerospace and defense player on the planet both in total sales and market value — was called off weeks later after it failed to pass European governmental and regulatory hurdles.

Preparing to capitalize on demand Airbus Group hammered out its Vision 2020 goals under which it pursues the world's #1 position in air and space platforms systems and services. Services are targeted to achieve a 25% share of the business in less than 10 years. To this end Airbus Group has been scouting deals in the services sector. In August 2011 it agreed to purchase Vizada a global satellite-based mobile communication services provider from French private-equity Apax France. The whopping ?673 million ($969 million) deal bolsters Airbus Group's subsidiary Astrium a top contractor of space-technology wares in Europe and furthers opportunities beyond Europe with maritime aerospace as well as land media and other commercial customers. Hard on its heels Airbus Group took over more than 98% of Canada-based Vector Aerospace for C$625 million (about $341 million). Vector joins Eurocopter as a stand-alone business adding a multi-platform aviation repair and overhaul business.

Auditors: Ernst & Young Accountants LLP

LOCATIONS

HQ: Airbus SE
Mendelweg 30, Leiden 2333 CS
Phone: (31) 71 5245 600   **Fax:** (31) 71 5232 807
Web: www.airbusgroup.com

2018 Sales

	% of total
Asia Pacific	37
Europe	28
North America	17
Middle East	10
Latin America	2
Other countries	6
Total	**100**

PRODUCTS/OPERATIONS

2018 Sales

	% of total
Airbus	74
Airbus Defence and Space	17
Airbus Helicopters	9
Other HQ / Consolidation	-
Total	**100**

Selected Products

Commercial Aircraft
  A series passenger aircraft
  ACJ series corporate jets
  Beluga cargo planes
Helicopters

H series helicopters
ACH corporate helicopters
Tiger attack helicopter
NH90 military helicopter
Hforce weapons system
Defence and Space
A400M airlifter aircraft
A330 MRTT tanker/transport aircraft
Eurofighter Typhoon fighter jet
Zephyr High Altitude Pseudo-Satellite (HAPS)
Unmanned aircraft systems
Earth observation
Ariane rocket launchers
Orion human spacecraft
Bartolomeo space platform

COMPETITORS

BAE SYSTEMS PLC	Koninklijke Vopak N.V.
BRITISH AIRWAYS PLC	MMC VENTURES LIMITED
Chicago Bridge & Iron Company N.V.	ROYAL DUTCH SHELL plc
	SERCO GROUP PLC
Corbion N.V.	Unilever N.V.
Expro Group Holdings N.V.	Victoria Retail Group B.V.

HISTORICAL FINANCIALS

Company Type: Public

Income Statement				FYE: December 31
	REVENUE ($ mil.)	NET INCOME ($ mil.)	NET PROFIT MARGIN	EMPLOYEES
12/20	61,256	(1,390)	—	131,349
12/19	79,130	(1,529)	—	134,931
12/18	72,956	3,497	4.8%	133,671
12/17	80,037	3,444	4.3%	129,442
12/16	70,301	1,050	1.5%	133,782
Annual Growth	**(3.4%)**	**—**	**—**	**(0.5%)**

2020 Year-End Financials

Debt ratio: 19.0%
Return on equity: (-18.1%)
Cash ($ mil.): 17,720
Current ratio: 1.17
Long-term debt ($ mil.): 17,282

No. of shares (mil.): 783
Dividends
  Yield: —
  Payout: —
Market value ($ mil.): 21,411

	STOCK PRICE ($) FY Close	P/E High/Low		PER SHARE ($) Earnings	Dividends	Book Value
12/20	27.32	—	—	(1.78)	0.00	10.09
12/19	36.75	—	—	(1.96)	0.35	8.58
12/18	23.78	8	6	4.49	0.35	14.36
12/17	24.78	7	5	4.44	1.92	20.66
12/16	16.42	13	10	1.36	1.63	5.00
Annual Growth	**13.6%**	**—**	**—**	**—**	**—**	**19.2%**

Aisin Corporation

The AISIN Group (Aisin Seiki Co. Ltd.) claims it supplies up to 15000 out of the 30000 parts that make up a car. The company's main business offers automotive-related products such as transmissions brakes and engine and car navigation systems. Its energy and home business offers items for more comfortable living with products that include heating and cooling systems and shower toilets with jet sprays. The company has approximately 215 consolidated subsidiaries and companies worldwide. Separate business segments include Aisin Seiki Group Aisin AW Group ADVICS Group and Aisin Takaoka Group. The company generates almost 55% of its revenue from its powertrain products.

Operations

AISIN operates through some 215 subsidiaries that are spread throughout four main segments.

Aisin Seiki Group is its largest segment (around 40% of total sales) and sells automotive parts as well as life and energy products. Aisin AW Group (about 40%) makes automatic transmissions and car navigation systems. The ADVICS Group (nearly 15%) is responsible for making brake components while Aisin Takaoka Group (more than 5%) manufactures the cart-iron parts for engines and brakes.

Overall the company generates almost 55% of sales from powertrain products some 20% from chassis & vehicle safety systems almost 20% from body business (power sliding door system and sunroof) and nearly 5% from the energy and home products business. The remainder of sales comes from ICT and electronics (car navigation systems and sensors) business.

Geographic Reach

Based in Japan AISIN Group has operations all over the globe. It operates almost 80 subsidiaries in Japan and over 135 internationally. The company's 13 core companies have about 20 development sites and nearly 15 advanced research facilities in Asia Europe and North America along with three test courses.

Sales and Marketing

AISIN Group's major customers for automotive products include Toyota Motor Nissan Motor Mazda General Motors and Volvo. Lifestyle-related products' customers include Toyota Housing Corp LIXIL Corp and Janis Ltd. Top customers who purchase the company's energy-related products include Tokyo Gas Saibu Gas Daikin Industries and Toho Gas.

Financial Performance

Note: Growth rates may differ after conversion to US Dollars.

The Group's revenue in 2020 decreased by 6% to 3.8 trillion compared to the prior year with 4.0 trillion.

Profit for fiscal 2020 decreased by 81% to 29.5 billion due to lower revenues while having almost the same operating expenses.

Cash held by the Group at the end of 2020 increased by 318 billion to 675.2 billion. Cash provided by operations and financing activities were 354.9 billion and 13.2 billion respectively. Cash used for investing activities was 414.5 million primarily for purchase of property plant and equipment.

Strategy

Since its establishment AISIN Group has adhered to the basic principle of "Quality First" and has sought to offer appealing products that meet customers' needs. Upholding the company's corporate principles of "Contributing to the advancement of society" and "Harmony with society and nature" the group promotes corporate behavior that helps create a sustainable society. The values and initiatives dovetail neatly with the Sustainable Development Goals (SDGs) and AISIN Group is working to contribute to the accomplishment of the SDGs through its business activities.

Mergers and Acquisitions

In early 2020 AISIN Group acquired all shares of Aisin AW Co. Ltd (AW) held by Toyota Motor Corporation for 300 billion in preparation for the merger between Aisin Seiki Group and AW.

Company Background

Aisin Seiki traces its roots to 1943 when Tokai Hikoki was founded to produce airplane engines for the Japanese war effort. After the war the company switched to manufacturing sewing machines and auto parts. Aisin Seiki took its present name in 1965 after Tokai Hikoki merged with Shinkawa Kogyo.

EXECUTIVES

Chairman of the Board, Kanshiro Toyoda
Executive Vice President, Chief Carbon Neutral Officer, Manager of Carbon Neutral Promotion Center, Toshiyuki Mizushima
Independent Director, Toshio Kobayashi
Independent Director, Tsunekazu Haraguchi
Vice Chairman of the Board, Representative Director, Kiyotaka Ise
Independent Director, Michiyo Hamada
Executive Vice President, Director, Shintaro Ito
Executive Officer, Chief Director of Group Production Technology, Masahiro Nishikawa
Executive Vice President, Chief Software & Digital Officer, Manager of DX Strategy Center, President of CSS Company, Director, Kenji Suzuki
Independent Director, Koji Kobayashi
Independent Director, Seiichi Shin
President, Executive President, Director, Moritaka Yoshida
Auditors: PricewaterhouseCoopers Aarata LLC

LOCATIONS

HQ: Aisin Corporation
  2-1 Asahi-machi, Kariya, Aichi 448-8650
Phone: (81) 566 24 8265
Web: www.aisin.co.jp

PRODUCTS/OPERATIONS

2019 Sales

	% of total
Aisin Seiki Group	39
Aisin AW Group	36
Advics Group	13
Aisin Takaoka Group	7
Other	5
Total	**100**

Selected Products

Automotive
  Chassis and vehicle safety systems
  Body products
  ICT and electronics
Energy System
  GHP
  Cogeneration system
Life and Amenity
  Bed furniture and fabric (ASLEEP)
  House remodeling service (Livelan)
  Home-use sewing machine
  Cogeneration system
  Shower-toilet seat
  Audio equipment

COMPETITORS

AB Volvo
CUMMINS INC.
DANA INCORPORATED
Dongfeng Motor Group Company Limited
JOHNSON CONTROLS INC.
Linamar Corporation
MERITOR INC.
NIDEC CORPORATION
Robert Bosch Gesellschaft mit beschr nkter Haftung
STRATTEC SECURITY CORPORATION
TENNECO INC.
TOYODA GOSEI CO. LTD.

HISTORICAL FINANCIALS

Company Type: Public

Income Statement

	REVENUE ($ mil.)	NET INCOME ($ mil.)	NET PROFIT MARGIN	EMPLOYEES
03/21	31,842	954	3.0%	139,832
03/20	34,864	221	0.6%	144,334
03/19	36,508	994	2.7%	148,359
03/18	36,811	1,267	3.4%	141,615
03/17	31,864	1,132	3.6%	135,094
Annual Growth	**(0.0%)**	**(4.2%)**	**—**	**0.9%**

FYE: March 31

2021 Year-End Financials

Debt ratio: 0.2%
Return on equity: 7.5%
Cash ($ mil.): 4,185
Current ratio: 1.55
Long-term debt ($ mil.): 7,416

No. of shares (mil.): 269
Dividends
  Yield: 0.0%
  Payout: 30.6%
Market value ($ mil.): 10,376

	STOCK PRICE ($) FY Close	P/E High	P/E Low	Earnings	Dividends	Book Value
03/21	38.50	0	0	3.54	1.08	51.45
03/20	24.22	0	0	0.82	1.38	43.76
03/19	35.78	0	0	3.69	1.35	45.13
03/18	55.52	0	0	4.62	1.41	45.78
03/17	49.73	0	0	3.97	0.00	39.59
Annual Growth	**(6.2%)**	**—**	**—**	**(2.8%)**	**—**	**6.8%**

AKBANK

Akbank provides corporate investment banking commercial banking SME banking consumer banking payment systems treasury transactions private banking and international banking services. The bank provides these services in Turkey through nearly 720 branches about 5000 ATMs and more than 600 point-of-sale terminals. Internationally Akbank operates branches in Germany and in Malta; Akbank shares is listed are listed in Borsa Istanbul (BIST). Overseas the bank's 'Level 1' ADR depository receipts are traded on the USTC market. Subsidiaries provide non-banking financial capital-market and wealth management are carried out by the Bank affiliates such as AK investment AK asset management and Aklease. The bank was founded in 1948.

EXECUTIVES

Executive Member of the Board of Directors in Charge of Credits, Ahmet Ayla
Non-Executive Member of the Board of Directors, Emre Derman
Chief Executive Officer, Executive Member of the Board of Directors, Sabri Binbasgil
Non-Executive Member of the Board of Directors, Can Paker
Executive Vice President – Commercial Banking, Mehmet Tugal
Executive Chairman of the Board of Directors, Suzan Sabanci Dincer
Executive Vice President - Corporate and Investment Banking, Levent Celebioglu
CEO of Ak Asset Management, Mehmet Ersari
Executive Vice President - Technology and Operations, N. Altintas
CEO of Ak Investment, Mert Erdogmus
Executive Vice President – Treasury, Gamze Muratoglu
CEO of Aklease, Cetin Duz
CEO of Akoede, Sitare Sezgin
Executive Vice President - Private Banking and Wealth Management, Sahin Alp Keler
Non-Executive Member of the Board of Directors, Tugrul Belli
Executive Vice President - Credit Monitoring and Collections, Ege Gueltekin
Executive Vice President – Credit Underwriting, Yunus Oezben
Akbank AG Chairman of the Managing Board and CEO, K. Oezcan
Independent Non-Executive Member of the Board of Directors, S. Toeruener
Independent Non-Executive Member of the Board of Directors, Ismail Guenter
Executive Vice President - Special Credits, Zeynep Oeztuerk
Executive Vice President - Strategy, Digital Banking and Payment Systems, Burcu Civelek Yuece
Executive Vice President – Retail Banking, Buelent Oguz
Executive Vice President - People and Culture, Pinar Anapa
Executive Vice President - CFO, Responsible for Investor Relations, Tuerker Tunali
Chief Executive Officer, Vice Chairman of the Board, Eyuep Engin
Auditors: PwC Bagimsiz Denetim ve Serbest Muhasebeci Mali Musavirlik A.S.

LOCATIONS

HQ: AKBANK
  Sabanci Center 4, Istanbul, Levent 34330
Phone: (90) 212 385 55 55   **Fax:** (90) 212 319 52 52
Web: www.akbank.com.tr

PRODUCTS/OPERATIONS

2014 Sales

	% of total
Interest income	81
Fee and commission received	16
Dividend income	-
Other operating income	3
Total	**100**

Selected Businesses

AKAssetmanagement
AKLease
AKInvestment
AKbank AG
Akbank Dubai Limited

COMPETITORS

AL RAJHI BANKING AND INVESTMENT CORPORATION
BANK VTB PAO
CAIXABANK SA
CMB WING LUNG BANK LIMITED
China Construction Bank Corporation
HDFC BANK LIMITED
Industrial And Commercial Bank Of China Limited
KEB HANA BANK CO.LTD.
QATAR NATIONAL BANK (Q.P.S.C.)
RIYAD BANK
Shanghai Pudong Development Bank Co.Ltd.
Shinhan Financial Group Co. Ltd.
VIETNAM JOINT STOCK COMMERCIAL BANK FOR INDUSTRY AND TRADE
Woori Finance Holdings Co. Ltd.

HISTORICAL FINANCIALS

Company Type: Public

Income Statement

FYE: December 31

	ASSETS ($ mil.)	NET INCOME ($ mil.)	INCOME AS % OF ASSETS	EMPLOYEES
12/20	64,340	822	1.3%	12,862
12/19	65,088	903	1.4%	13,136
12/18	67,035	1,079	1.6%	13,367
12/17	90,322	1,591	1.8%	14,253
12/16	83,469	1,375	1.6%	14,218
Annual Growth	(6.3%)	(12.1%)	—	(2.5%)

2020 Year-End Financials

Return on assets: 1.4%
Return on equity: 10.3%
Long-term debt ($ mil.): —
No. of shares (mil.): —
Sales ($ mil.): 5,140

Dividends
Yield: —
Payout: —
Market value ($ mil.): —

	STOCK PRICE ($) FY Close	P/E High/Low	PER SHARE ($) Earnings	Dividends	Book Value
12/20	1.90	199 105	0.00	0.00	0.02
12/19	2.71	261 165	0.00	0.47	0.02
12/18	2.48	297 145	0.00	0.15	0.02
12/17	5.16	377 261	0.00	0.09	0.03
12/16	4.36	413 307	0.00	0.06	0.02
Annual Growth	(18.8%)	— —	(17.7%)	—	(8.3%)

Akita Bank Ltd (The) (Japan)

Auditors: Deloitte Touche Tohmatsu LLC

LOCATIONS

HQ: Akita Bank Ltd (The) (Japan)
3-2-1 Sanno, Akita 010-8655
Phone: (81) 18 863 1212
Web: www.akita-bank.co.jp

HISTORICAL FINANCIALS

Company Type: Public

Income Statement

FYE: March 31

	ASSETS ($ mil.)	NET INCOME ($ mil.)	INCOME AS % OF ASSETS	EMPLOYEES
03/21	31,508	24	0.1%	2,011
03/20	27,920	28	0.1%	2,081
03/19	27,311	37	0.1%	2,148
03/18	29,634	44	0.2%	2,176
03/17	26,655	42	0.2%	2,191
Annual Growth	4.3%	(12.8%)	—	(2.1%)

2021 Year-End Financials

Return on assets: 0.0%
Return on equity: 1.5%
Long-term debt ($ mil.): —
No. of shares (mil.): 17
Sales ($ mil): 393

Dividends
Yield: —
Payout: —
Market value ($ mil.): —

ALD SA

Auditors: ERNST & YOUNG et Autres

LOCATIONS

HQ: ALD SA
Corosa Building, 1-3 Rue Eugene et Armand Peugeot
Corosa, Rueil-Malmaison 92800
Phone: (33) 1 58 98 79 31
Web: www.aldautomotive.com

HISTORICAL FINANCIALS

Company Type: Public

Income Statement

FYE: December 31

	REVENUE ($ mil.)	NET INCOME ($ mil.)	NET PROFIT MARGIN	EMPLOYEES
12/20	12,192	625	5.1%	6,606
12/19	10,977	633	5.8%	6,715
12/18	10,274	636	6.2%	6,520
12/17	9,909	680	6.9%	6,303
12/16	7,234	540	7.5%	5,653
Annual Growth	13.9%	3.7%	—	4.0%

2020 Year-End Financials

Debt ratio: 86.3%
Return on equity: 12.4%
Cash ($ mil.): 238
Current ratio: 0.39
Long-term debt ($ mil.): 13,784

No. of shares (mil.): 403
Dividends
Yield: —
Payout: 50.0%
Market value ($ mil.): —

ALFA SAB de CV

ALFA manages a diversified portfolio of businesses with global operations such as Sigma a leading multinational company in the food industry focused on the production marketing and distribution of quality products through well-known brands in Mexico Europe the United States and Latin America this business accounts for more than half of sales; Alpek one of the world's largest producers of polyester (PTA PET and fibers) and a leader in the Mexican market for polypropylene expandable polystyrene and caprolactam; Axtel an Information and Communication Technologies (ICT) company that serves the business and government markets in Mexico and; Newpek a company that operates in the hydrocarbon industry in Mexico. Its largest markets United States and Mexico account for around 30% of sales each.

Operations

Sigma is the leading revenue earner for ALFA bringing in more than half of annual sales. It produces commercializes and distributes cooked meats cured meats cheese yogurt other refrigerated frozen and plant-based foods Alpek (over 40% of revenue) petrochemical company in the Americas in the production of polyester (PTA PET fibers and rPET) plastics and chemicals as polypropylene expanded polystyrene and ARCEL. Axtel (around 5% sales) offers cutting-edge solutions in Information and Communication Technology (ICT) to enterprise government and mass-markets operators through its business units Alestra (services) and Axtel Networks (infrastructure) while Newpek has limited oil & gas exploration in Mexico.

Geographic Reach

Mexico-based Alfa operates more than 100 plants in nearly 20 countries. Mexico and United States are largest markets accounting for about a third of the total sales followed by Europe and other countries which contribute nearly a quarter each the remaining revenue is from Canada Central and South America.

Sales and Marketing

Alfa's businesses provide its products into different markets; Sigma (food); Alpek (containers for beverages food and consumer products packaging for electronics and appliances textiles construction and automotive); Axtel (Enterprise Government and Mass market) Newpek (Energy oil and gas). Advertising expenses were $2.5 billion and $2.6 billion for fiscal years 2020 and 2019 respectively.

Financial Performance

In 2020 ALFA's consolidated revenues were MXN $263.9 billion (US$12.3 billion) 1% higher in pesos and 9% lower in dollars compared to the amount in 2019.

Net income for fiscal 2020 increased to MXN $263.9 billion compared from the prior year with MXN $260.4 billion.

Cash held by the company at the end of fiscal 2020 increased to MXN $32.1 billion. Cash provided by operations was MXN $29.4 billion while cash used for investing and financing activities were MXN $15.6 billion and MXN $6.6 billion respectively. Main uses of cash were Cash flows in acquisition of property plant and equipment; and payments of borrowings or debt.

Strategy

The main strategic initiatives of 2020 were the functional and operative division of the company in two Business Units: Infrastructure (Axtel Networks) and Services (Alestra); and attracting proposals for the sale of its business units.

Sigma intensified efforts to pursue its four-pillar strategy in 2020 focusing on:

Growing the core business by: brand and categories diversification; technology and efficiency in operation; innovation based on design thinking; strengthening the relationship with business partners; and consumers focus.

Exploring and developing new avenues for growth by: Agile filtering analyzing incubation piloting and scaling of high potential opportunities; and Digital channels. Strengthening the organizations and Margin growth.

Company Background

In 1974 a group of businessmen led by Roberto Garza Sada founded ALFA to manage the group's interests in various businesses. A year after the company acquires Polioles (polystyrene urethanes and glycols) and Nylon de Mexico (nylon).

EXECUTIVES

Independent Director, David Martinez Guzman
Independent Director, Federico Toussaint Elosua
President of Axtel, Rolando Zubiran Shetler
President of Sigma, Rodrigo Fernandez Martinez
Independent Director, Jose Antonio Meade Kuribrena
Chairman of the Board, Armando Garza Sada
Chief Executive Officer, Director, Alvaro Fernandez Garza
Independent Director, Claudio Gonzalez Laporte
Chief Financial Officer, Eduardo Alberto Escalante Castillo
Independent Director, Alejandro Ramirez Magana
Senior Vice President - Legal, Audit and Corporate Affairs, Secretary of the Board, Carlos Jimenez Barrera
Independent Director, Enrique Luis Castillo Sanchez Mejorada
Independent Director, Guillermo Francisco Vogel Hinojosa
President of Nemak, Armando Tamez Martinez
Independent Director, Adrian Sada Gonzalez

Independent Director, Jose Fernando Calderon
Rojas
**Senior Vice President - Human Capital and
Services,** Paulino Jose Rodriguez Mendivil
President of Alpek, Jose de Jesus Valdez Simancas
Independent Director, Francisco Javier Fernandez
Carbajal
Auditors: Galaz, Yamazaki, Ruiz Urquiza, S. C.

LOCATIONS

HQ: ALFA SAB de CV
  Avenida Gomez Morin 1111 Sur, Col. Carrizalejo, San
  Pedro Garza Garcia, Nuevo Leon 66254
Phone: (52) 81 8748 2521
Web: www.alfa.com.mx

2015 Sales

	% of total
North America	68
South Central America	5
Other Countries	27
Total	**100**

PRODUCTS/OPERATIONS

2015 Sales

	% of total
Alpek	32
Sigma	36
Nemak	28
Alestra	2
Newpek	1
Others	1
Total	**100**

Selected Operations

Alpek
  Akra Polyester
  DAK Americas
  Indelpro (51% polypropylene)
  Polioles (expandable polystyrene glycol and solvents
  urethanes)
  Univex (caprolactam and ammonium sulphate)
Nemak (aluminum engine blocks and heads)
Sigma
  Sigma Alimentos (processed meats yogurt cheese
  prepared meals)
Alestra (telecommunications)
Newpek (Natural gas and oil fields)

COMPETITORS

ADVANSIX INC.
Ballard Power Systems Inc
Brenntag Holding GmbH
CARPENTER TECHNOLOGY CORPORATION
DIPLOMA PLC
FIVES
GLENCORE PLC
INDORAMA VENTURES PUBLIC COMPANY LIMITED
JOHN WOOD GROUP PLC
Methanex Corporation
RUBIS
SCHWEITZER-MAUDUIT INTERNATIONAL INC.
TOTALENERGIES SE
UFP TECHNOLOGIES INC.
Ultrapar Participacoes S/A
VALLOUREC
VISKASE COMPANIES INC.
WESFARMERS LIMITED

HISTORICAL FINANCIALS

Company Type: Public

Income Statement

FYE: December 31

	REVENUE ($ mil.)	NET INCOME ($ mil.)	NET PROFIT MARGIN	EMPLOYEES
12/20	13,280	197	1.5%	57,500
12/19	17,851	306	1.7%	83,000
12/18	18,634	668	3.6%	83,701
12/17	16,123	(104)	—	86,200
12/16	14,198	112	0.8%	81,000
Annual Growth	**(1.7%)**	**15.2%**	**—**	**(8.2%)**

2020 Year-End Financials

Debt ratio: 2.3%
Return on equity: 7.1%
Cash ($ mil.): 1,617
Current ratio: 1.52
Long-term debt ($ mil.): 5,838

No. of shares (mil.): —
Dividends
  Yield: —
  Payout: 62.5%
Market value ($ mil.): —

Alfresa Holdings Corp Tokyo

Alfresa Holdings distributes prescription drugs medical tests and devices and over-the-counter (OTC) supplements on a wholesale basis in the Japanese market. The firm is Japan's largest pharmaceuticals wholesaler holding as the third largest in the world. It also has an overseas business development arm which targets other Asian markets for growth. Its offerings also include OTC drugs diagnostic reagents and health foods. Its manufacturing division researches develops manufactures and markets these items as well as active pharmaceutical ingredients (APIs) used by other firms to make drugs.

Operations

Alfresa operates in four primary segments: Ethical Pharmaceuticals Wholesaling Self-Medication Products Wholesaling Manufacturing and Medical-Related (dispensing pharmacies).

The group's Ethical Pharmaceuticals Wholesaling segment contributes more than 85% of the group's total revenue. In addition to selling prescription drugs tests medical devices and other products it provides services to hospitals clinics pharmacies and other customers.

The Self-Medication Products Wholesaling segment provides OTC drugs health foods supplements and other items to drugstores and pharmacies. It brings in some 10% of the group's revenue.

The smallest segments are Manufacturing and Medical-Related. Manufacturing develops and manufactures drugs APIs tests medical devices and other products while Medical-Related provides dispensing pharmacy services. Each segment provides the remainder of Alfresa's total revenue.

Geographic Reach

Alfresa is headquartered in Tokyo and is ranked three as the largest pharmaceutical market in the world. The company seeks to expand in other parts of Asia particularly in China and Vietnam. In China the Group established joint venture REMEJE PHARMACEUTICALS (CHINA) CO. LTD. in 2005 as a representative office for pharmaceuticals and healthcare-related products. In Vietnam the Group established joint venture Alfresa Codupha Healthcare Vietnam Co. Ltd. (Alcopha) in 2013 to conduct import and sales mainly of medical devices and materials and diagnostic reagents and is grad-

ually setting up a stable management foundation. There are more than 200 warehouse in Japan and in overseas.

Sales and Marketing

Alfresa's customers include hospitals medical care facilities drugstores and pharmacies. Company's products and services offer to over 100000 customers throughout Japan.

Financial Performance

The Group's net sales increased 1% due to growth in sales volumes for hepatitis C therapeutic agents and anticancer drugs.

The company's net income increased by 9.7 billion to 61.2 billion compared to 51.6 billion from the prior year. The increase was primarily due to the 68% increase on their other income.

Cash held by the company in 2019 increased by 9.5 billion to 205.1 billion compared to 195.6 billion in the prior year. Cash from operations was 46.9 billion while cash used for investing and financing activities were 12.9 billion and 24.9 billion respectively.

Strategy

Alfresa's basic approach to financial and capital strategy under the 19?21 Mid-term Management Plan is to raise corporate value by pursuing the optimal balance of financial soundness capital efficiency and shareholder returns. In particular the company will press forward even further with investments and measures to promote growth based on issues identified in the previous plan.

The Alfresa Group uses capital cost as a management indicator measuring and updating provisional figures each year while referring to information from multiple external professional organizations. In addition to monitoring the profitability of existing businesses they also refer to the latest cost of capital when making investment decisions and evaluating businesses or investment securities.

Mergers and Acquisitions

Company Background

Alfresa was created in 2003 from the combination of wholesalers Azwell and Fukujin.

EXECUTIVES

Independent Director, Yoichiro Yatsurugi
Independent Director, Takashi Hara
Independent Director, Manabu Kinoshita
President of Subsidiary, Director, Yusuke Fukujin
President of Subsidiary, Director, Hisashi Katsuki
Senior Managing Executive Officer, Director,
  Seiichi Kishida
Vice President, Director, Yasuki Izumi
Chairman & President of Subsidiaries, Director,
  Koichi Shimada
Independent Director, Toshie Takeuchi
Chairman of the Board, Taizo Kubo
President, Representative Director, Ryuji Arakawa
Auditors: KPMG AZSA LLC

LOCATIONS

HQ: Alfresa Holdings Corp Tokyo
  1-1-3 Otemachi, Chiyoda-ku, Tokyo 100-0004
Phone: (81) 3 5219 5100
Web: www.alfresa.com

PRODUCTS/OPERATIONS

2018 Sales by Segment

	% of total
Ethical Pharmaceuticals Wholesaling	88
Self-Medication Products Wholesaling	10
Pharmaceutical Manufacturing	1
Medical-Related	1
Total	**100**

COMPETITORS

AEON CO. LTD.
CATALENT INC.
China National Pharmacertical Group Corporation
DECHRA PHARMACEUTICALS PLC
HIKMA PHARMACEUTICALS PUBLIC LIMITED
   COMPANY
MALLINCKRODT PUBLIC LIMITED COMPANY
MITSUBISHI CHEMICAL HOLDINGS CORPORATION
MS&AD INSURANCE GROUP HOLDINGS INC.
SEVEN & I HOLDINGS CO. LTD.
SOMPO HOLDINGS INC.
STERIS LIMITED
SUZUKEN CO. LTD.
T&D HOLDINGS INC.
TOHO HOLDINGS CO.LTD.

HISTORICAL FINANCIALS

Company Type: Public

Income Statement				FYE: March 31
	REVENUE ($ mil.)	NET INCOME ($ mil.)	NET PROFIT MARGIN	EMPLOYEES
03/21	23,511	221	0.9%	14,468
03/20	24,859	371	1.5%	14,562
03/19	23,843	376	1.6%	14,718
03/18	24,512	335	1.4%	14,629
03/17	22,824	276	1.2%	14,609
Annual Growth	0.7%	(5.4%)	—	(0.2%)

2021 Year-End Financials

Debt ratio: 0.0%
Return on equity: 5.0%
Cash ($ mil.): 1,537
Current ratio: 1.27
Long-term debt ($ mil.): 3

No. of shares (mil.): 211
Dividends
   Yield: —
   Payout: —
Market value ($ mil.): —

Alibaba Group Holding Ltd

EXECUTIVES

Independent Director, Wan Ling Martello
Director, Xiandong Jing
Chief Financial Officer, Director, Wei Wu
Chief Risk Officer, Chief Platform Governance Officer, Chief customer officer, Junfang Zheng
Chairman of the Board, Chief Executive Officer, Yong Zhang
Chief Marketing Officer, Pen-hung Tung
President, Industrial E-commerce and Community E-commerce, Shan Dai
Independent Director, Chih-Yuan Yang
Chief People Officer, Wenhong Tong
President - Alibaba Digital Media and Entertainment, Luyuan Fan
President - Taobao and Tmall, Fan Jiang
President of Alibaba Cloud Intelligence, Jianfeng Zhang
Independent Director, Chee Hwa Tung
Independent Director, E. Boerje Ekholm
Director, Kabir Misra
Independent Director, Teh-Ming Kwauk
President, Director, J. Michael Evans
Chief Technology Officer, Li Cheng
General Counsel, Sara Yu
Executive Vice Chairman, Joseph Tsai
Auditors: PricewaterhouseCoopers

LOCATIONS

HQ: Alibaba Group Holding Ltd
26/F Tower One, Times Square, 1 Matheson Street, Causeway Bay,
Phone: (852) 2215 5100   **Fax:** (852) 2215 5200
Web: www.alibabagroup.com

HISTORICAL FINANCIALS

Company Type: Public

Income Statement				FYE: March 31
	REVENUE ($ mil.)	NET INCOME ($ mil.)	NET PROFIT MARGIN	EMPLOYEES
03/21	109,499	22,986	21.0%	251,462
03/20	71,805	21,051	29.3%	117,600
03/19	56,135	13,091	23.3%	101,958
03/18	39,865	10,209	25.6%	66,421
03/17	22,979	6,341	27.6%	50,097
Annual Growth	47.7%	38.0%	—	49.7%

2021 Year-End Financials

Debt ratio: 1.3%
Return on equity: 17.6%
Cash ($ mil.): 49,042
Current ratio: 1.70
Long-term debt ($ mil.): 20,717

No. of shares (mil.): —
Dividends
   Yield: —
   Payout: —
Market value ($ mil.): —

	STOCK PRICE ($) FY Close	P/E High/Low	PER SHARE ($)		
			Earnings	Dividends	Book Value
03/21	226.73	47 29	1.04	0.00	6.66
03/20	194.48	32 20	0.98	0.00	5.01
03/19	182.45	47 32	0.62	0.00	3.59
03/18	183.54	66 38	0.49	0.00	2.86
03/17	107.83	50 33	0.31	0.00	2.02
Annual Growth	20.4%	— —	35.7%	—	34.7%

Alimentation Couche-Tard Inc

Alimentation Couche-Tard is the name of the company but you might know it through its brands like Circle K and Corner Store in the US and Statoil in Europe. The company is the second-largest convenience store operator in North America (behind 7-Eleven Inc.) and the leader in Canada where it operates under Couche-Tard banner. While most of its sales are rung up in the US it operates in Europe as well as about 15 countries in other parts of the world through license agreements. Most of the company's revenue comes from sales of fuel (it pumps about 14 billion gallons a year). Alimentation Couche-Tard which is French for "food for those who go to bed late" has expanded through acquisitions around the world.

Operations

In Couche-Tard's global operations Circle K Statoil Couche-Tard and Mac's have been its key brands.

Fuel accounts for about three-quarters of the company's revenue with merchandise and services supplying about a quarter of sales. The company also operates commercial fuel.

The company's reliance on fuel makes it sensitive to fuel prices that can fluctuate wildly. While accounting for some 72% of sales fuel supplies 46% of gross profit.

Tobacco products account for nearly 40% of the merchandise and service revenue. Couche-Tard

also sells brands of cigarettes made for the company which could expose it to legal action.

Geographic Reach

Couche-Tard operates and licenses about 16000 global sites with more than 9000 convenience stores in North America more than 2700 in Europe and 2000 around the world. The company has operations throughout the US (not including Hawaii and Alaska) in Scandinavia the Baltic states Ireland Russia and Poland. In Scandinavia Couche-Tard operates automated fuel-only sites under the Ingo brand. The company classifies as international operations its licensed stores in Asia Indonesia Central America and the Middle East.

United States generates approximately 70% of company's revenue. Europe is almost 20% and the remainder comprised of Canada's revenue.

Sales and Marketing

The company launched its Easy Pay loyalty program in all U.S markets providing everyday fuel discounts to its most loyal customer. Couche-Tard recognizes sales of merchandise and goods to certain independent operators and franchisees made from the company's distribution centers and sales of road transportation fuel upon delivery to its customers.

Financial Performance

The company's revenue decreased by $5.0 billion to $54.2 billion due to the decrease on their road transportation fuel revenues and other revenues. The decrease was primarily due to the decrease on their operations at U.S. and Europe.

Net earnings amounted to $2.4 billion for fiscal 2020 compared with $1.8 billion for fiscal 2019. The results for fiscal 2020 were affected by a pre-tax net gain of $61.5 million on the disposal of their interests in CrossAmerica Partners LP a pre-tax net gain of $41.0 million on the disposal of a portion of their U.S. wholesale fuel business as part of an asset exchange with CAPL a positive impact on income tax of $33.6 million from an adjustment to deferred tax assets pre-tax foreign exchange gain of $33.5 million acquisition costs of $6.7 million pre-tax restructuring costs of $4.5 million and an income tax expense of $2.7 million following the asset exchange transactions with CAPL.

Cash held by the company at the end of 2020 increased by $2.9 billion to $3.6 billion compared to $706.4 million in the prior year. Cash provided by operations and financing activities were $3.7 billion and $480.7 million respectively. Cash used for investing activities was $1.2 billion primarily for purchase of property and equipment intangible assets and other assets.

Strategy

Couche-Tard's five-year strategy to double again requires that they grow market share in the U.S. and expand to new growth markets and industries. Maintaining financial discipline allows them to take advantage of opportunities as they arise.

Coming into fiscal 2020 the company accelerated the pace of new store construction after a significant effort to develop their project pipelines. Couche-Tard had good momentum with the new builds until the pandemic triggered a pause in many of these projects. The company also introduced new design for their North American sites that mirrors the Holiday stores format and improves the customer journey.

The company continued to roll out their new store concept in Europe which is now at more than 300 sites with enhanced food fuel charging WIFI washrooms and parking. These stores provide a welcoming ambiance and comfortable seating area high-quality food displayed in an attractive way and improved merchandising in the rest of the store. Couche-Tard instituted learning from their initial pilots which led to improved profitability.

Mergers and Acquisitions

In early 2020 Couche-Tard acquired 17 stores from a franchise operator. These convenience stores operate under the Holiday banner in South Dakota and Minnesota within the United States.

Couche-Tard also acquired 13 company operated stores through distinct transactions. The company owns the land and building for the remaining 6 sites.

In early 2019 company acquired six company-operated stores and two commission operated retail sites through distinct transactions. The company owns the land and building for three sites and leases the land and the building for the remaining three sites. It was settled for a total cash consideration of $13.1.

EXECUTIVES

President, Chief Executive Officer, Director, Brian Hannasch, $1,308,327 total compensation

Chief Financial Officer, Claude Tessier, $490,178 total compensation

Lead Independent Director, Melanie Kau

Executive Chairman of the Board, Co-Founder, Alain Bouchard, $948,026 total compensation

Co-Founder, Corporate Director, Richard Fortin

Co-Founder, Corporate Director, Real Plourde

Executive Vice President - Development and Construction, North America, Darrell Davis, $490,803 total compensation

Executive Vice President - Operations, Europe, Hans-Olav Hoidahl

Corporate Director, Jean Bernier

Independent Director, Daniel Rabinowicz

Executive Vice President Operations - North America and Global Optimization, Timothy Miller, $573,881 total compensation

Chief Marketing Officer, Kevin Lewis, $579,924 total compensation

Independent Director, Eric Boyko

Co-Founder, Corporate Director, Jacques D'Amours

Independent Director, Monique Leroux

Chief People Officer, Ina Strand

Chief Technology Officer, Deborah Lefevre, $359,474 total compensation

Independent Director, Marie-Josee Lamothe

Independent Director, Louis Tetu

Independent Director, Janice Fields

Senior Vice President - Global Fuels, Louise Warner

Auditors: PricewaterhouseCoopers LLP

LOCATIONS

HQ: Alimentation Couche-Tard Inc
4204 Industriel Boulevard, Laval, Quebec H7L 0E3
Phone: 450 662-6632   **Fax:** 450 662-6633
Web: corpo.couche-tard.com

2018 Sales

	$ mil.	% of total
US	34,178	67
Europe	10,315	20
Canada	6,901	13
Total	**51,394**	**100**

PRODUCTS/OPERATIONS

2018 Sales

	$ mil.	% of total
Road Transportation Fuel	37,116	72
Merchandise and Services	12,976	25
Other	1,302	3
Total	**51,394**	**100**

COMPETITORS

BIM BIRLESIK MAGAZALAR PARTNERSHIP
JOHN LEWIS

ANONIM SIRKETI
CASEY'S GENERAL STORES LIMITED INC.
Companhia Brasileira de Distribuicao
EXPRESS INC.
Empire Company Limited
PLC
MARTIN MCCOLL
MURPHY USA INC.
THE KROGER CO
VILLAGE SUPER MARKET INC.

HISTORICAL FINANCIALS

Company Type: Public

Income Statement   FYE: April 25

	REVENUE ($ mil.)	NET INCOME ($ mil.)	NET PROFIT MARGIN	EMPLOYEES
04/21	45,760	2,705	5.9%	124,000
04/20	54,132	2,353	4.3%	131,000
04/19	59,117	1,833	3.1%	109,000
04/18	51,394	1,673	3.3%	0
04/17	37,904	1,208	3.2%	105,000
Annual Growth	**4.8%**	**22.3%**	**—**	**4.2%**

2021 Year-End Financials

Debt ratio: 22.5%
Return on equity: 24.3%
Cash ($ mil.): 3,015
Current ratio: 1.20
Long-term debt ($ mil.): 5,282

No. of shares (mil.): 1,079
Dividends
　Yield: 0.0%
　Payout: 9.9%
Market value ($ mil.): 36,167

	STOCK PRICE ($) FY Close	P/E High/Low	Earnings	Dividends	Book Value
04/21	33.50	15 12	2.44	0.24	11.28
04/20	28.40	32 11	2.09	0.19	9.05
04/19	59.40	37 25	1.63	0.16	7.90
04/18	43.34	36 29	1.48	0.14	6.70
04/17	47.06	48 39	1.06	0.13	5.29
Annual Growth	**(8.1%)**	**—**	**23.2%**	**17.4%**	**20.9%**

Allianz SE

One of the world's biggest insurers Allianz SE offers a range of insurance products and services ? including property-casualty life/health asset management and corporate ? through subsidiaries ventures and affiliates operating all over the globe (Allianz SE and its subsidiaries are collectively known as the Allianz Group). Based in Munich Germany the company serves more than 100 million customers in such key markets as France Morocco Italy Luxembourg Switzerland and the US. In addition to selling insurance Allianz provides retail and institutional asset management services through Allianz Asset Management private equity investment through Allianz Capital Partners.

Operations

Allianz primarily operates through three business segments ? life/health property/casualty and asset management ? which are further divided primarily by geography into 11 reportable segments.

The company offers a wide range of property-casualty and life/health insurance motor accident property general liability travel insurances and assistance services. The life/health business segment offers savings and investment products in addition to life and health policies. Allianz generates about 55% of its revenue from its life/health segment. The property/casualty segment accounts for more than 40% of revenue. These two segments do most of their business in France Germany Italy and the US.

The asset management segment which generates roughly 5% of revenue has two primary investment management businesses ? PIMCO and Allianz Global Investors (AllianzGI). The segment offers a variety of equity fixed income cash and multi-assets products as well as a strongly growing number of alternative investment products such as infrastructure debt/equity real assets liquid alternatives and solution business. It chiefly operates in Canada France Germany Italy the UK the US and the Asia-Pacific region.

Geographic Reach

Headquartered in Munich Germany Allianz operates in more than 70 countries with most of its operations in Europe. It also operates in the Asia Pacific region Africa and the Americas and operates its business from Munich and from branch offices in Rome (Italy) Casablanca (Morocco) Singapore Labuan (Malaysia) Wallisellen (Switzerland) Vienna (Austria) and Dublin (Ireland).

Sales and Marketing

Allianz has sponsorship arrangements with a collection of leading sports stadia including those occupied by Bayern Munich Juventus OGC Nice Palmeiras and Minnesota United FC (soccer) as well as Saracens FC (rugby). The company offers its products and services to more than 100 million customers in more than 70 countries.

Financial Performance

Note: Growth rates may differ after conversion to US Dollars.

Allianz' total revenue declined 1% from ?142.4 billion in 2019 to ?140.5 billion in 2020. Most of this decline was attributable to its Life/Health business in the United States and Germany.

The company's operating profit decreased by 9% mostly due to adverse impacts from COVID-19. 2020 net income attributable to shareholders was ?6.8 billion a 14% decrease from the previous year's net income of ?7.9 billion.

Allianz' cash at the end of 2020 was ?22.4 billion. Operating activities generated ?32 billion while investing activities used ?28.9 billion. Financing activities used another ?1.4 billion.

Strategy

Allianz has outlined its objectives for its medium-term strategy with the motto "Simplicity wins": outperform by moving ahead of its competitors both traditional business and disruptors; transform by becoming simpler and deeply digital; and rebalance by building market-leading positions in large profitable and fast-growing geographies as well as in new areas of business.

To implement these strategic objectives Allianz has defined a number of strategic priorities and are implementing initiatives and programs to address the five dimensions of its Renewal Agenda. These five dimensions being true customer centricity digital by default technical excellence growth engines and inclusive meritocracy.

It has also made several investments and acquisitions to further its business capabilities. Among these recent acquisitions and investments are automobile and other property/casualty business SulAmerica a strategic partnership with Virtus Investment Partners in the US retail market a bancassurance joint venture with Banco Bilbao Vizcaya Argentaria a life insurance joint venture with AEON Financial Service and an investment in ControlExpert to improve claims through artificial intelligence and automation.

Additionally under Allianz Global Corporate & Specialty a new comprehensive transformation program named "New AGCS" was launched. The program aims to regain profitability and market leadership in the corporate and specialty insurance segment. AGCS will also simplify its regional organization reducing the number of regional units from seven to six and moving from a country-centric to a more global set-up with regional delivery.

Mergers and Acquisitions

In late 2021 Allianz acquired a majority stake in Jubilee Insurance Company of Uganda Limited East Africa's largest insurance group. The stake acquired by Allianz represents 29700000 ordinary shares of Jubilee Insurance Company of Uganda. JHL will retain a 34% stake or 15300000 ordinary shares in the company. The General Business of Jubilee Insurance Company of Uganda Limited will change its name in due course to Jubilee Allianz General Insurance Company Limited subject to approvals.

Also in late 2021 Allianz acquired Aviva Italia S.p.A. the Italian property & casualty (P&C) insurance entity of the Aviva Group from Aviva Italia Holding S.p.A. The transaction which is worth about 330 million euros involved a portfolio equally distributed between motor and non-motor business segments with gross written premiums of about 400 million euros. The completion of the transaction further strengthens Allianz S.p.A.'s No.3 position in the Italian P&C insurance industry increasing the company's market share by approximately one percentage point.

In mid-2021 Allianz Australia announced the completion of the transaction to acquire Westpac's general insurance business and commenced a 20-year exclusive agreement to distribute general insurance products to Westpac customers. As part of the agreement more than 350 Westpac general insurance employees have now officially joined Allianz bringing with them a suite of talents and industry knowledge that will help Allianz to continue to grow and innovate. The agreement worth A$725 million sees the expansion of Allianz's product offering available through Westpac.

In mid-2020 Allianz acquired the automobile and other property & casualty business from SulAmerica in Brazil for approximately 3.2 billion Brazilian real (US$595 million). This completion of the transaction positions the company as the number two carrier in motor insurance and makes it one of the top three insurers in property-casualty insurance in Brazil.

Also in mid-2020 Allianz acquired Aldi logistics in Australia for A$648 million. The acquisition is a 50-50 joint venture between Charter Hall Group and Allianz Real Estate with the latter acting on behalf of several Allianz companies. "This transaction is in line with our strategy of aligning our investments to secular mega trends in the Asia Pacific region" said Rushabh Desai Asia Pacific CEO of Allianz Real Estate.

Company Background

In 1890 Allianz is founded in Munich Germany by insurance specialist Carl Thieme and banker Wilhelm Finck. In 1893 Allianz opened its office in London for international operations headed by Carl Schreiner. By the year 1938 the employee strength reached to a number of 24000. The Munich headquarters of Allianz was destroyed by bombs during the World War II. The expansions went through with the establishment of more branches in many countries of the world like Spain Brazil the Netherlands.

HISTORY

Carl Thieme founded Allianz in Germany in 1890. That year the company took part in the creation of the Calamity Association of Accident Insurance Companies a consortium of German Austrian Swiss and Russian firms to insure international commerce.

By 1898 Thieme had established offices in the UK Switzerland and the Netherlands. His successor Paul von der Nahmer expanded Allianz into the Balkans France Italy Scandinavia and the US. After a hiatus during WWI Allianz returned to foreign markets.

In WWII Allianz insured Auschwitz Dachau and other death camps. Company documents show Allianz wasn't worried about risk at the SS troop-guarded camps. After the German defeat the victors seized Allianz's foreign holdings except for a stake in Spain's Plus Ultra. In the 1950s Allianz repurchased confiscated holdings in Italian and Austrian companies.

Allianz saturated the German market and began a full-scale international drive in the late 1950s and 1960s. It became Europe's largest insurer through a series of acquisitions beginning in 1973. Allianz formed Los Angeles-based Allianz Insurance in 1977.

In 1981 Allianz launched a takeover (which turned hostile) of the UK's Eagle Star insurance company. After a 1983 bidding joust with Britain's B.A.T Industries (now part of Zurich Financial Services) Allianz withdrew.

The firm consoled itself by shopping. In 1984 it won control of Riunione Adriatica di Sicurt (Ras) Italy's second-largest insurance company. Two years later the firm bought Cornhill (now Allianz Insurance plc) on its third try. As the Iron Curtain crumbled Allianz in 1989 acquired 49% of Hungaria Biztosito. Its drang nach Osten continued the next year after national reunification when it gained control of Deutsche Versicherungs AG East Germany's insurance monopoly. Allianz that year became the first German insurer licensed in Japan; it also bought the US's Fireman's Fund Insurance.

Natural disasters led to large claims and set the company back in 1992 the first time in 20 years it lost money from its German operations. Allianz restructured operations that year; profits surged in 1993 mostly from international business.

Allianz expanded in Mexico in 1995 forming a life and health insurance joint venture with Grupo Financiero BanCrecer (now owned by Grupo Financiero Banorte). The company set up an asset management arm in Hong Kong in 1996 with an eye to further Asian expansion getting a license in China the next year. In 1997 after Holocaust survivors sued Allianz and other insurers for failing to pay on life policies after WWII Allianz agreed to participate in a repayment fund.

In 1998 Allianz bought control of Assurances Generales de France; it was the white knight that prevented Assicurazioni Generali from taking the company. In 1999 Allianz said it would restructure some of its insurance operations including spinning off its marine and aviation lines to better compete in the multinational market. That year US subsidiary Allianz Life bought Life USA Holding. In 2000 Allianz bought 70% of PIMCO Advisors Holdings to strengthen its asset management operations. That year the company continued its push into Asia buying a 12% stake in Hana Bank of South Korea and planning to boost its ownership of Malaysia British Assurance Life. Also in 2000 Allianz acquired Dutch insurer Zwolsche Algemeene.

Allianz remained acquisitive in 2001 buying US investment manager Nicholas-Applegate and taking a majority stake in ROSNO one of Russia's largest insurers. Also that year it bought a nearly 96% stake in German banking giant Dresdner and acquired the remainder the following year.

Allianz paid out claims of some $1.3 billion relating to the terrorist attacks on the World Trade Center. The company set up a terrorism insurance unit offering coverage primarily for companies within the European Union.

2018 sales

	% of total
Western & Southern Europe	32
US	11
Germany	27
Specialty insurance	16
Growth markets	9
Broker markets	4
Total	**100**

PRODUCTS/OPERATIONS

2018 sales

	% of total
Life/Health	54
Property/Casualty	41
Asset Management	5
Total	**100**

Selected Operations and Brands

Allianz
Allianz Global Corporate and Specialty
Allianz Global Investors
Allianz Worldwide Care
Euler Hermes
PIMCO

COMPETITORS

ABRDN PLC	ERGO Group AG
AEGON N.V.	ING Groep N.V.
AMERICAN INTERNATIONAL	M nchener
GROUP INC.	RSA INSURANCE GROUP
ASSICURAZIONI GENERALI	LIMITED
SPA	Talanx AG
AXA	Zurich Insurance Group
Ageas	AG
Axis Capital Holdings	
Limited	

HISTORICAL FINANCIALS

Company Type: Public

Income Statement

FYE: December 31

	ASSETS ($ mil.)	NET INCOME ($ mil.)	INCOME AS % OF ASSETS	EMPLOYEES
12/20	1,300,941	8,354	0.6%	150,269
12/19	1,135,324	8,885	0.8%	147,268
12/18	1,027,889	8,545	0.8%	142,460
12/17	1,080,437	8,155	0.8%	140,553
12/16	933,199	7,267	0.8%	140,253
Annual Growth	8.7%	3.5%	—	1.7%

2020 Year-End Financials

Return on assets: 0.6%	Dividends
Return on equity: 8.7%	Yield: 2.9%
Long-term debt ($ mil.): —	Payout: 4.0%
No. of shares (mil.): 412	Market value ($ mil.): 10,157
Sales ($ mil): 129,097	

	STOCK PRICE ($)	P/E		PER SHARE ($)		
	FY Close	High/Low	Earnings	Dividends		Book Value
12/20	24.65	2 1	20.03	0.72	240.73	
Annual Growth	—	— —	—	—	—	

Alpha Services & Holdings SA

Alpha Bank is the second-largest bank in Greece (after National Bank of Greece). It provides business and personal banking services through more than 650 branches in Greece and hundreds more in Cyprus Albania Bulgaria Romania Serbia and Ukraine as well as in New York London and Jersey in the UK Channel Islands. In addition to loans deposit accounts and credit cards the Alpha Bank group also offers retail banking asset management investment banking private banking insurance brokerage leasing and factoring. Founded in 1879 Alpha Bank has been buffeted by economic turmoil in Greece. Still it acquired Emporiki Bank S.A. from Credit Agricole in mid-2013.

EXECUTIVES

General Manager - Growth and Innovation, Executive Member of the Board of Directors, Spyros Filaretos
Non-Executive Member of the Board of Directors, Artemios Theodoridis
Chief Executive Officer, Executive Member of the Board of Directors, Vassilios Psaltis
Executive General Manager, Nicholas Chryssanthopoulos
Non-Executive Independent Member of the Board of Directors, Shahzad Shahbaz
Non-Executive Chairman of the Board of Directors, Vasileios Rapanos
Non-Executive Independent Member of the Board of Directors, Jan Vanhevel
Secretary, Georgios Triantafyllidis
Executive General Manager, Georgios Michalopoulos
Non-Executive Member of the Board of Directors, Efthymios Vidalis
Non-Executive Member of the Board of Directors, Johannes Umbgrove
Chief Risk Officer, General Manager, Spyridon Andronikakis
General Manager Retail Banking, Isidoros Passas
General Manager Wholesale Banking, Ioannis Emiris
Non-Executive Independent Member of the Board of Directors, Richard Gildea
Non-Executive Independent Member of the Board of Directors, Carolyn Dittmeier
Non-Executive Independent Member of the Board of Directors, Jean Cheval
General Manager – Chief Legal and Governance Officer, Nikolaos Salakas
Chief Financial Officer, General Manager, Lazaros Papagaryfallou
Senior Advisor to the CEO, Georgios Aronis
General Manager of International Network, Sergiu-Bogdan Oprescu
Non-Executive Independent Member of the Board of Directors, Elanor Hardwick
Chief Operating Officer, General Manager, Stefanos Mytilinaios
Non-Executive Independent Member of the Board of Directors, Dimitris Tsitsiragos
General Manager - Chief Transformation Officer, Anastasia Sakellariou
Auditors: Deloitte Certified Public Accountants S.A.

LOCATIONS

HQ: Alpha Services & Holdings SA
40 Stadiou Street, Athens GR-102 52
Phone: (30) 210 326 0000 **Fax:** (30) 210 326 5438
Web: www.alpha.gr

2015 Sales

	% of total
Greece	84
Other countries	16
Total	**100**

PRODUCTS/OPERATIONS

2015 Gross Sales

	% of total
Retail banking	47
Corporate banking	36
South Eastern Europe	14
Asset management and insurance	3
Total	**100**

2015 Sales

	% of total
Interest and similar income	87
Fee and commission income	11
Other income	2
Total	**100**

Selected Services

Bancassurance
Business Banking
Cards
Consumer Loans
Deposit Accounts
Housing Loans
Investment Products
Private Banking

COMPETITORS

BANK OF CYPRUS PUBLIC COMPANY LIMITED
BANK POLSKA KASA OPIEKI S A
CINVEN GROUP LIMITED
EMPORIKI BANK OF GREECE S.A.
EUROBANK ERGASIAS SERVICES AND HOLDINGS S.A.
Grupo Elektra S.A.B. de C.V.
LENLYN HOLDINGS LIMITED
NATIONAL BANK OF GREECE S.A.
OTP Bank Nyrt.
Steierm ɔrkische Verwaltungssparkasse
THE ROYAL BANK OF SCOTLAND PUBLIC LIMITED COMPANY
Volkswagen Bank Gesellschaft mit beschr ɔnkter Haftung

HISTORICAL FINANCIALS

Company Type: Public

Income Statement — FYE: December 31

	ASSETS ($ mil.)	NET INCOME ($ mil.)	INCOME AS % OF ASSETS	EMPLOYEES
12/20	85,979	127	0.1%	10,528
12/19	71,248	108	0.2%	10,530
12/18	69,864	60	0.1%	11,314
12/17	72,899	25	0.0%	11,727
12/16	68,497	44	0.1%	12,699
Annual Growth	**5.8%**	**30.1%**	**—**	**(4.6%)**

2020 Year-End Financials

Return on assets: 0.1%	Dividends
Return on equity: 1.2%	Yield: —
Long-term debt ($ mil.): —	Payout: —
No. of shares (mil.): 1,543	Market value ($ mil.): 440
Sales ($ mil): 3,898	

	STOCK PRICE ($)	P/E		PER SHARE ($)		
	FY Close	High/Low	Earnings	Dividends		Book Value
12/20	0.29	9 2	0.08	0.00	6.60	
12/19	0.56	9 4	0.07	0.00	6.14	
12/18	0.29	21 9	0.03	0.00	6.02	
12/17	0.57	73 44	0.01	0.00	7.45	
12/16	0.50	25 10	0.03	0.00	6.25	
Annual Growth	**(13.1%)**	**— —**	**27.0%**	**—**	**1.4%**	

Also Holding AG

EXECUTIVES

Senior Vice President of Human Resources, General Counsel, Member of the Group Management, Thomas Meyerhans
Non-Executive Member of the Board of Directors, Frank Tanski, $352,436 total compensation
Non-Executive Vice Chairman of the Board of Directors, Walter Droege, $149,066 total compensation
Non-Executive Member of the Board of Directors, Rudolf Marty, $95,828 total compensation
Non-Executive Member of the Board of Directors, Ernest-Walther Droege, $85,181 total compensation
Chief Financial Officer, Member of the Group Management, Ralf Retzko
Non-Executive Member of the Board of Directors, Peter Athanas, $106,476 total compensation
Chairman of the Board of Directors, Chief Executive Officer, Member of the Group Management, Gustavo Moeller-Hergt, $353,501 total compensation
Senior Vice President, Consumptional Business, Member of the Group Management, Jan Bogdanovich
Auditors: PricewaterhouseCoopers AG

LOCATIONS

HQ: Also Holding AG
Meierhofstrasse 5, Emmen CH-6032
Phone: (41) 41 266 18 00 **Fax:** (41) 41 266 18 70
Web: www.also-actebis.com

HISTORICAL FINANCIALS

Company Type: Public

Income Statement — FYE: December 31

	REVENUE ($ mil.)	NET INCOME ($ mil.)	NET PROFIT MARGIN	EMPLOYEES
12/20	14,602	159	1.1%	4,316
12/19	12,005	112	0.9%	4,594
12/18	10,507	92	0.9%	3,728
12/17	10,657	111	1.0%	3,870
12/16	8,430	88	1.0%	3,667
Annual Growth	**14.7%**	**16.0%**	**—**	**4.2%**

2020 Year-End Financials

Debt ratio: 10.8%	No. of shares (mil.): 12
Return on equity: 16.7%	Dividends
Cash ($ mil.): 592	Yield: —
Current ratio: 1.47	Payout: 36.9%
Long-term debt ($ mil.): 311	Market value ($ mil.): —

Aluminum Corp of China Ltd.

Auditors: Ernst & Young Hua Ming LLP

LOCATIONS

HQ: Aluminum Corp of China Ltd.
No. 62, North Xizhimen Street, Haidian District,
Beijing 100082
Phone: (86) 10 8229 8560   **Fax:** (86) 10 8229 8158
Web: www.chalco.com.cn

HISTORICAL FINANCIALS

Company Type: Public

Income Statement

FYE: December 31

	REVENUE ($ mil.)	NET INCOME ($ mil.)	NET PROFIT MARGIN	EMPLOYEES
12/20	28,438	113	0.4%	0
12/19	27,316	122	0.4%	0
12/18	26,204	126	0.5%	65,211
12/17	27	211	765.5%	64,794
12/16	20,746	57	0.3%	65,755
Annual Growth	8.2%	18.2%	—	—

2020 Year-End Financials

Debt ratio: 6.5%
Return on equity: 1.3%
Cash ($ mil.): 1,634
Current ratio: 0.74
Long-term debt ($ mil.): 7,837

No. of shares (mil.): —
Dividends
   Yield: —
   Payout: —
Market value ($ mil.): —

	STOCK PRICE ($) FY Close	P/E High/Low	PER SHARE ($) Earnings	Dividends	Book Value
12/20	8.68	353180	0.00	0.00	(0.00)
12/19	8.69	290193	0.01	0.00	(0.00)
12/18	7.82	415171	0.01	0.00	(0.00)
12/17	17.93	266123	0.01	0.00	(0.00)
12/16	10.21	583330	0.00	0.00	(0.00)
Annual Growth	(4.0%)	— —	10.4%		

America Movil SAB de CV

America M vil is Latin America's leading telecommunications services provider with about 287.5 million subscribers in some 25 countries. In Mexico the company has about 77.8 million wireless subscribers to its Telcel and Telmex brands. Its second largest market is Brazil where it has some 63.1 million subscribers through Claro. America M vil also provides fixed-line service in Central America and the Caribbean. While the company's operations are centered in Latin America it also offers service in the US through Trac-Fone and Eastern Europe through A1. The company also offers broadband Pay TV and IT services. Billionaire Carlos Slim Hel owns most of America M vil. Over 20% of its revenue is generated in Mexico.

Operations

The company provides telecommunications services which include mobile and fixed-line voice services wireless and fixed data services internet access and Pay TV over the top and other related services. The company also sells equipment accessories and computers.

Its voice services provided by the company both wireless and fixed mainly include the following: airtime local domestic and international long-distance services and network interconnection services. Data services include value added corporate networks data and internet services. Pay TV represents basic services as well as pay per view and additional programming and advertising services. AMX provides other related services to advertising in telephone directories publishing and call center services. The company also provides video audio and other media content that is delivered through the internet directly from the content provider to the end user.

Overall about 85% of sales were generated from its services while equipment accounts for the rest.

Geographic Reach

The company generates over 20% of revenue from Mexico with Brazil accounting for more than 15% and the US generates roughly 15% of revenue.

The company's other markets are the Southern Cone (Argentina Chile Paraguay and Uruguay) and Europe (Austria Belarus Bulgaria Croatia Macedonia Serbia and Slovenia). Those regions combine for approximately 15% combined of revenue. The remaining revenue (around 20% combined revenues) comes from Colombia the Andean Region (Ecuador and Peru) Central America (Costa Rica El Salvador Guatemala Honduras Nicaragua and Panama) and the Caribbean (the Dominican Republic and Puerto Rico).

Sales and Marketing

America M vil reaches customers through a network of retailers and service centers for retail customers and a dedicated sales force for corporate customers. The company counts more than 490000 points of sale and about 2900 customer service centers. America Movil's subsidiaries also sell their services and products online.

For the years ended 2018 2019 and 2020 advertising expenses were Ps.26.3 million Ps.22.8 million and Ps.19.9 million respectively.

Financial Performance

The company's revenue for fiscal 2020 increased to Ps.1.02 trillion compared from the prior year with Ps.1.01 trillion.

The company recorded a net profit of Ps.51.0 billion for 2020 a decrease of 27% or Ps.19.3 billion over 2019.

The company's revenue for fiscal 2020 increased to Ps.35.9 billion. Cash provided by operations was Ps.280.8 billion while cash used for investing and financing activities were Ps.135.6 billion and Ps.126.9 billion respectively. Main uses of cash were purchase of property plant and equipment and repayment of loans.

Strategy

America Movil continue to seek ways to optimize its portfolio including by finding investment opportunities in telecommunications and related companies worldwide including in markets where the company are already present and it often have several possible acquisitions under consideration. The company may pursue opportunities in Latin America or in other areas in the world.

Company Background

America M vil was formed in 2000 from a spin-off from Telmex which was at the time Mexico's largest local and long-distance phone service provider. In late 2006 America M vil acquired majority owner America Telecom in a move to streamline the structure of the company and to free up assets for share buybacks or dividends.

HISTORY

The company was formed in 2000 as a result of a spinoff from Telmex which was at the time Mexico's largest local and long-distance phone service provider. In late 2006 America M vil acquired majority owner America Telecom in a move to streamline the structure of the company and to free up assets for share buybacks or dividends.

The company expanded its presence in the Caribbean region in 2007 with the acquisition of Puerto Rico Telephone from Verizon Communications and a handful of other shareholders for nearly $2 billion. The next year it bought Jamaican wireless service provider Oceanic Digital Jamaica and became licenced to provide wireless services in Panama.

Also in 2008 the company rebranded its operations in Argentina Paraguay and Uruguay to its Claro brand which America M vil now uses for all of its operations in Central America and the Caribbean. That year it bought Estesa Holding a cable TV and data services provider in Nicaragua for $48 million. The acquisition of Estesa boosted America M vil's cable television and broadband offerings and gave the company greater access to the Nicaraguan market.

EXECUTIVES

President of Brazil, Jose Antonio Guaraldi Felix
Chief Financial Officer, Carlos Jose Garcia Moreno Elizondo
General Counsel, Corporate Secretary, Alejandro Cantu Jimenez
Vice Chairman of the Board, Patrick Slim Domit
Independent Director, Luis Alejandro Soberon Kuri
Independent Director, Ernesto Vega Velasco
Independent Director, Rafael Moises Kalach Mizrahi
Chief Fixed-line Operations Officer, Director, Oscar Von Hauske Solis
Chairman of the Board, Carlos Slim Domit
Director, Arturo Elias Ayub
Independent Director, Antonio Cosio Pando
Independent Director, Francisco Medina Chavez
Chief Wireless Operations Officer, Angel Alija Guerrero
Independent Director, Pablo Roberto Gonzalez Guajardo
Chief Executive Officer, Director, Daniel Hajj Aboumrad
Independent Director, David Antonio Ibarra Munoz
Chief Financial Officer of Telekom Austria, Siegfried Mayrhofer
Chief Executive Officer of Argentina, Uruguay and Paraguay, Julio Carlos Porras
Auditors: Mancera, S.C. (member of Ernst & Young Global)

LOCATIONS

HQ: America Movil SAB de CV
Lago Zurich 245, Plaza Carso/Edificio Telcel, Colonia Ampliacion Granada, Mexico City, Miguel Hidalgo 11529
Phone: (52) 55 2581 3700   **Fax:** (52) 55 2581 4422
Web: www.americamovil.com

2015 Sales

	% of total
Mexico wireless	22
Brazil	19
US	12
Mexico fixed	11
Southern cone	8
Europe	8
Colombia	7
Andean region	6
Central America	4
Caribbean	3
Total	**100**

PRODUCTS/OPERATIONS

2018 Sales

	% of total
Mexico Wireless	21
Brazil	18
US	14
Southern Cone	10
Europe	9
Telmex	9
Colombia	7
Andean Region	5
Central America	4
Caribbean	3
Total	**100**

2018 Sales

	% of total
Services	83
Equipment	17
Total	**0**

Selected Operations

Amé;rica Móvil Peru (8.3 million subscribers)
AM Wireless Uruguay (800000 subscribers)
AMX Argentina (17 million subscribers)
AMX Paraguay (500000 subscribers)
Claro Chile (3.6 million subscribers)
Claro Panama (100000 subscribers)
Codetel (Dominican Republic 4.8 million subscribers)
Comcel (Colombia 27.7 million subscribers)
Conecel (Ecuador 9.4 million subscribers)
CTE (El Salvador 800000 subscribers)
ENITEL (Nicaragua 2.2 million subscribers)
Oceanic (Jamaica 400000 subscribers)
Sercom Honduras (1.4 million subscribers)
TELPRI (Puerto Rico 1.6 million subscribers)
TracFone (US 14.4 million subscribers)
Telgua (Guatemala 1.2 million subscribers)

COMPETITORS

AMERICAN TOWER INTERNATIONAL CORPORATION	MILLICOM
AT&T INC.	CELLULAR S.A.
Altice Europe N.V.	MTN GROUP LTD
COMPUTACENTER PLC	NASPERS LTD
GLOBANT S.A.	SBA COMMUNICATIONS CORPORATION
HOMESERVE PLC	SOLOCAL GROUP
IDT CORPORATION	SYNCHRONOSS TECHNOLOGIES INC.
INMARSAT GROUP HOLDINGS LIMITED	
Intelsat Investments S.A.	

HISTORICAL FINANCIALS

Company Type: Public

Income Statement				FYE: December 31
	REVENUE ($ mil.)	NET INCOME ($ mil.)	NET PROFIT MARGIN	EMPLOYEES
12/20	51,179	2,358	4.6%	186,851
12/19	53,243	3,579	6.7%	191,523
12/18	52,797	2,673	5.1%	194,431
12/17	51,859	1,488	2.9%	191,851
12/16	47,140	418	0.9%	194,193
Annual Growth	2.1%	54.1%	—	(1.0%)

2020 Year-End Financials

Debt ratio: 1.9%
Return on equity: 21.8%
Cash ($ mil.): 1,807
Current ratio: 0.71
Long-term debt ($ mil.): 24,173

No. of shares (mil.): —
Dividends
  Yield: 2.4%
  Payout: 53.5%
Market value ($ mil.): —

AMMB Holdings BHD

From the a.m. to the p.m. AmBank Group is on the job providing financial services to customers throughout Malaysia. AMMB Holdings (which trades as AmBank Group) controls dozens of subsidiaries and affiliates providing individuals and businesses with a range of financial services and products through some 175 offices. The company operates in several segments: retail business and investment banking; insurance; and Islamic financial services. Services include asset management commercial banking futures trading leasing mortgage lending offshore banking property trust management retail financing and securities services.

EXECUTIVES

Non-Independent Non-Executive Director, Kim Wai Soo
Managing Director - Retail Banking, AmBank Group, Aaron Loo
Group Chief Financial Officer - AmBank Group, Jamie Ling
Group Chief Human Resource Officer - AmBank Group, Penelope Gan
Non-Independent Non-Executive Director, Robert Goudswaard
Chief Executive Officer - AmInvestment Bank Berhad, Wee Keng Chen
Chief Executive Officer - AmGeneral Insurance Berhad, See Dip Tan
Chief Executive Officer - AmMetLife Insurance Berhad, Jiau Jiunn Lee
Independent Non-Executive Director, Kean Yong Hong
Independent Non-Executive Director, Sooi Lin Kong
Chief Executive Officer - AmMetLife Takaful Berhad, Noor Azam bin Mohd Yusof
Group Chief Internal Auditor - AmBank Group, Shamsul Bahrom bin Mohamed Ibrahim
Senior Independent Non-Executive Director, Seng Chuan Voon
Managing Director - Business Banking, AmBank Group, Huey Wen Yap
Group Chief Compliance Officer - AmBank Group, Faradina binti Mohammad Ghouse
Independent Non-Executive Director, Farina binti Farikhullah Khan
Managing Director - Wholesale Banking, AmBank Group, Raja Teh Maimunah Raja Abdul Aziz
Group Company Secretary, Phaik Gunn Koid
Group Chief Executive Officer - AmBank Group, Sulaiman Bin Mohd Tahir, $608,611 total compensation
Independent Non-Executive Director, Yoo Lin Seow
Group Chief Risk Officer - AmBank Group, Jeroen Thijs
Group Chief Operation Officer - AmBank Group, Iswaraan Suppiah
Chief Executive Officer - AmBank Islamic Berhad, Eqhwan Mokhzanee bin Muhammad
Auditors: Messrs Ernst & Young PLT

LOCATIONS

HQ: AMMB Holdings BHD
  22nd Floor, Bangunan AmBank Group, No. 55, Jalan Raja Chulan, Kuala Lumpur 50200
Phone: (60) 3 2036 2633   **Fax:** (60) 3 2032 1914
Web: www.ambankgroup.com

COMPETITORS

AXA ADVISORS LLC &	THE DEPOSITORY TRUST
CORCENTRIC LLC	CLEARING CORPORATION
DELANCEY LIMITED	W.H. IRELAND GROUP PLC
NEWABLE INVESTMENTS LIMITED	

HISTORICAL FINANCIALS

Company Type: Public

Income Statement				FYE: March 31
	ASSETS ($ mil.)	NET INCOME ($ mil.)	INCOME AS % OF ASSETS	EMPLOYEES
03/21	41,041	(922)	—	0
03/20	39,184	310	0.8%	0
03/19	38,908	368	0.9%	0
03/18	35,679	292	0.8%	10,000
03/17	30,438	299	1.0%	10,672
Annual Growth	7.8%	—	—	—

2021 Year-End Financials

Return on assets: (-2.2%)
Return on equity: (-23.0%)
Long-term debt ($ mil.): —
No. of shares (mil.): —
Sales ($ mil): 389

Dividends
  Yield: —
  Payout: —
Market value ($ mil.): —

Ampol Ltd

Ampol Limited supplies the country's largest branded petrol and convenience network as well as refining importing and marketing fuels and lubricants. Ampol supplies fuel to around 80000 customers in diverse markets across the Australian economy including defence mining transport marine agriculture aviation and other commercial sectors. Across its retail network Ampol serves more than three million customers every week with fuel and convenience products. Its ability to service its broad customer base is supported by its robust supply chain and strategic infrastructure positions across the country which includes more than 25 terminals five major pipelines over 55 depots around 1925 branded sites and one refinery located in Lytton Queensland.

Operations

The company operates through two reportable segments: Fuels and Infrastructure and Convenience Retail.

The Fuels and Infrastructure segment (over 75%) includes revenues and costs associated with the integrated wholesale fuels and lubricants supply for the company including the nternational businesses. This includes Lytton refining Bulk Fuels sales Trading and Shipping Infrastructure and the Gull and Seaoil businesses.

The Convenience Retail segment (about 25% of revenue) includes revenues and costs associated with fuels and shop offerings at Ampol's network of stores including royalties and franchise fees on remaining franchise stores.

Overall Diesel accounted for nearly 50% the company's total revenues; petrol for about 30%; and jet fuel over 5%.

Geographic Reach

The company operates in Australia New Zealand and Singapore.

Its sourcing capabilities and geographic reach have significantly expanded in recent years with strong growth observed in third-party fuel volumes in 2020 and storage in the South East Asian region providing scope for our Trading and Shipping business to deliver strong returns on working capital in volatile market conditions.

Sales and Marketing

The recently established Houston office has been supporting Ampol's Singapore team with investigating new international markets and identifying sourcing improvement opportunities and they will continue to work together to identify further growth potential. Its Trading and Shipping operations play a key role in our success sourcing petroleum products from global markets that connect to customer needs in both Australia and other international markets.

The company has interests in associates primarily for the marketing sale and distribution of fuel products. It has interests in joint arrangements primarily for the marketing sale and distribution of fuel products and the operation of convenience stores.

Financial Performance

Revenue from the sale of goods was $15 billion in 2020 compared to $22.1 billion in the prior year. Total revenue decreased due to a 17% decline in Australian sales volumes resulting from reduced demand as a result of the COVID-19 pandemic. Australian Dollar product prices are also on average 34% lower than 2019. Lower product prices in 2020 were driven by lower weighted average Dated Brent crude oil price (2020: US$42/bbl vs 2019: US$64/bbl).

Net loss after tax attributable to equity holders of the parent entity was $484.9 million in 2020 compared to a net profit of $382.8 million in 2019. There was an inventory loss of $360 million after tax or $514 million before tax in 2020. Over time revenues will increase/decrease as the price of products changes this includes impacts from the AUD/USD exchange rate movements.

Cash at the end of fiscal year 2020 was $367.6 million. Operations and investing activities provided $267.6 million and $462.6 million respectively while financing activities used $391.8 million mainly for repayment of borrowings.

Strategy

The revitalization of the iconic Ampol brand is a key part of the company's business strategy. It provides a unique opportunity to re-engage its people reinforce its customer connections and redefine the identity of the company. As it looks towards its future and executing its strategy the reinvigoration of Ampol allows the company to enhance its market-leading position in transport fuels execute on the convenience market opportunity and reaffirm its commitment to communities.

As the company delivers the rebrand works across its retail network it is refreshing the shopfronts of its company-controlled sites to align with its format strategy. This includes transitioning its shops to its Foodary brand and the continued rollout of its Ampol Woolworths Metro format.

The company had made strong progress since it announced the return of Ampol in December 2019. It opened its first two Ampol retail sites in Sydney in August with a total of 26 sites rebranded across the country in 2020. It is on track to rebrand its entire network of more than 1900 sites by the end of 2022.

In 2020 Ampol reached several milestones in its International growth strategy with the opening of a new Trading and Shipping office in Houston and the expansion of its international storage program supported by favourable market conditions.

Company Background

Growing its business to keep up with demand in 2011 Caltex Australia dissolved the Vitalgas Pty Ltd joint venture agreement by acquiring the stake held by Origin Energy Holdings for $4.1 million. The unit then became Calgas Pty Ltd.

It also bought Graham Bailey Pty Ltd for $19.1 million. Bailey is Australia's leading provider of marine fuel remote infrastructure and related services with operations in all major Australian ports and a network of 16 sites from the south of Western Australia through to Darwin in the Northern Territories.

EXECUTIVES

Executive General Manager – Infrastructure, Andrew Brewer, $50,150 total compensation
Non-Executive Independent Director, Michael Ihlein, $92,157 total compensation
Non-Executive Independent Director, Gary Smith, $99,147 total compensation
Chief Governance and Risk Officer, Company Secretary, Michael Abbott
Non-Executive Independent Director, Elizabeth Donaghey
Non-Executive Independent Director, Mark Chellew, $135,594 total compensation
Independent Non-executive Chairman of the Board, Steven Gregg, $328,329 total compensation
Non-Executive Independent Director, Penelope Winn, $152,592 total compensation
Non-Executive Independent Director, Melinda Conrad, $135,594 total compensation
Executive General Manager – Commercial, Brent Merrick, $134,406 total compensation
Chief Financial Officer, Greg Barnes
Executive General Manager, Strategy and Corporate Development, Alan Stuart-Grant
Executive General Manager - Retail, Brand and Culture, Joanne Taylor, $607,471 total compensation
Chief Executive Officer, Managing Director, Director, Matthew Halliday, $1,068,583 total compensation
Auditors: KPMG

LOCATIONS

HQ: Ampol Ltd
29-33 Bourke Rd, Alexandria, New South Wales 2015
Phone: 800 240 398
Web: www.ampol.com.au

PRODUCTS/OPERATIONS

2011 Sales

	% of total
Refining & supply	53
Marketing	47
Total	**100**

Major Subsidiaries
Caltex Australia Petroleum Pty Ltd
Caltex Lubricating Oil Refinery Pty Ltd
Caltex Petroleum Distributors Pty Ltd
Caltex Refineries (NSW) Pty Ltd
Caltex Refineries (Qld) Pty Ltd

COMPETITORS

BUILD-A-BEAR WORKSHOP INC.	NK ROSNEFT PAO
	PETRON CORPORATION
COMPA 'IA ESPA 'OLA DE PETROLEOS SAU	PHILLIPS 66
	RELIANCE INDUSTRIES LIMITED
ESSO SOCIETE ANONYME FRANCAISE	REPSOL SA.
GS Caltex Corporation	SPRAGUE RESOURCES LP
Gibson Energy Inc	Suncor Energy Inc
IDEMITSU KOSAN CO.LTD.	THAI OIL PUBLIC COMPANY LIMITED
INDIAN OIL CORPORATION LIMITED	WINCANTON PLC

HISTORICAL FINANCIALS

Company Type: Public

Income Statement

FYE: December 31

	REVENUE ($ mil.)	NET INCOME ($ mil.)	NET PROFIT MARGIN	EMPLOYEES
12/21	15,682	406	2.6%	0
12/20	11,924	(375)	—	8,200
12/19	15,645	268	1.7%	7,644
12/18	15,338	395	2.6%	6,629
12/17	16,733	484	2.9%	4,724
Annual Growth	**(1.6%)**	**(4.3%)**	**—**	**—**

2021 Year-End Financials

Debt ratio: 11.8%	No. of shares (mil.): 238
Return on equity: 18.5%	Dividends
Cash ($ mil.): 410	Yield: 2.3%
Current ratio: 1.45	Payout: 57.3%
Long-term debt ($ mil.): 935	Market value ($ mil.): 10,349

	STOCK PRICE ($) FY Close	P/E High/Low		Earnings	PER SHARE ($) Dividends	Book Value
12/21	43.43	20	16	1.69	1.01	9.35
12/20	44.00	—	—	(1.50)	1.00	9.15
12/19	44.00	—	—	1.06	1.22	9.15
12/18	44.00	—	—	1.52	1.56	9.13
12/17	44.00	20	20	1.86	1.65	9.27
Annual Growth	**(0.3%)**	**—**	**—**	**(2.3%)**	**(11.7%)**	**0.2%**

Angang Steel Co Ltd

Angang is one of China's largest steel producers with annual output of 21mt of crude steel. Based in Liaoning it produces and sells hot-rolled products cold-rolled products medium and thick plates and other steel products mostly across China. Customers include companies in the automotive construction shipbuilding railway and pipeline construction industries. Annually Angang produces more than 20 million tons of each of its three products: iron steel and rolled steel.

Financial Performance

Revenue increased 45% to RMB 84 billion primarily due to increase in product prices and sales volume.

Net profit increased from RMB 1.6 billion in 2016 to RMB 5.6 billion the following year aided by a reduction of RMB 1 billion less in YOY impairment losses on assets.

Cash holdings increased to RMB 2.4 billion. Operations generated RMB 6.3 billion partially offset by RMB 1.4 billion outflow used in investments and RMB 4.5 billion from financing activities.

Strategy

Angang showed impressive resilience of maintaining steel margins amidst a de-stocking environment and falling margins. The market for iron and steel remains at excess capacity. Falling inventory hasn't budged high margins.

Although steel margins may continue to fall in the near term success in cost reduction (procurement and logistics) and efficiency improvements should help Angang with higher profits.

However the continuous increase in labor costs pressure of environmental protection fluctuation in prices of bulk raw materials and fuels and further trade barriers is significantly increasing costs of operations.

To tackle such grave market forces Angang seems keen to secure potential customers. In 2017 it developed 129 new direct sale customers and 60 new certifications. The company is expected to perform well in the near term with more exposure to value-added products and demand surge from mid-2018.

EXECUTIVES

Deputy General Manager, Peng Zhang
Independent Non-Executive Director, Wanglin Wang
Chairman of the Board, Executive Director, Yidong Wang
Independent Non-Executive Director, Changli Feng
Independent Non-Executive Director, Jianhua Wang
General Manager, Executive Director, Shishuai Xu
Joint Secretary of the Board, Baojun Wang
Independent Non-Executive Director, Keshi Zhu
Deputy General Manager, Hongjun Zhang
Joint Secretary of the Board, Dongzhou Zhou
Deputy General Manager, Executive Director, Zhongwu Li
Deputy General Manager, Jinsong Meng
Auditors: Ruihua Certified Public Accountants (Special General Partnership)

LOCATIONS

HQ: Angang Steel Co Ltd
Production Area of Angang Steel, Tie Xi District, Anshan City, Liaoning Province 114021
Phone: (86) 412 8417273   **Fax:** (86) 412 6727772
Web: www.ansteel.com.cn

2013 Sales

	% of total
Domestic Sales	
Northeast China	36
East China	24
South China	20
North China	8
Central South China	1
Northwest China	1
Southwest China	1
Export Sales	9
Total	**100**

PRODUCTS/OPERATIONS

Selected Products
Cold-rolled products
Cold-rolled silicon steel products
Color coated products
Galvanized products
Hot-rolled products
Plate products
Seamless steel pipe products
Wire products

COMPETITORS

AIR WATER INC.	HAYNES INTERNATIONAL
AMPCO-PITTSBURGH	INC.
CORPORATION	KOPPERS HOLDINGS INC.
AZZ INC.	MECHEL PAO
Aluminum Corporation	NLMK PAO
Of China Limited	SEVERSTAL PAO
Companhia Siderurgica	SUNCOKE ENERGY INC.
Nacional	TATA STEEL LIMITED

HISTORICAL FINANCIALS
Company Type: Public

Income Statement   FYE: December 31

	REVENUE ($ mil.)	NET INCOME ($ mil.)	NET PROFIT MARGIN	EMPLOYEES
12/20	15,428	302	2.0%	0
12/19	15,174	256	1.7%	0
12/18	15,288	1,156	7.6%	0
12/17	12,955	861	6.6%	0
12/16	8,335	232	2.8%	37,363
Annual Growth	**16.6%**	**6.8%**	—	—

2020 Year-End Financials

Debt ratio: 2.8%
Return on equity: 3.7%
Cash ($ mil.): 814
Current ratio: 0.83
Long-term debt ($ mil.): 757

No. of shares (mil.): —
Dividends
  Yield: —
  Payout: —
Market value ($ mil.): —

Anglo American Plc (United Kingdom)

Anglo American is a leading global mining company with a world class portfolio of mining and processing operations and undeveloped resources in 15 countries. Annually it produces some 20.6 million tons (Mt) of thermal coal 16.8 Mt of metallurgical coal around 37 Mt of iron ore about 647 kt of copper from two mines and some 25.1 Mct of diamond. Though present in five continents Anglo American has a major presence in Asia where it generates most of the sales. De Beers produces a third of the world's rough diamonds. Entrepreneur Ernest Oppenheimer establishes Anglo America in 1917.

Operations
The company's segments include Platinum Group Metals (more than 25% of sales) Iron Ore (nearly 25%) Copper (more than 20%) Coal (more than 10%) De Beers (about 10%) Nickel and Manganese (some 5%) and Crop Nutrients (less than 5%).

Segments predominantly derive revenue as follows ? De Beers: rough and polished diamonds; Copper: copper; Platinum Group Metals: platinum group metals and nickel; Iron Ore: iron ore; Coal: metallurgical coal and thermal coal; Nickel and Manganese: nickel manganese ore and alloys.

Geographic Reach
The company's most significant presence is in Asia accounting to about 75% of sales in which China generates some 40%. Its other productive assets can be found in South Africa Australia Botswana Brazil Canada Chile Colombia Namibia Peru and Zimbabwe among others. Anglo America is headquartered in London UK.

Sales and Marketing
The company's customers operate in some of the world's most critical and diverse industries ? from automotive to steelmaking from technology and jewelry to energy production. It engages with customers through business and industry forums.

Financial Performance
The company had a revenue of $30.9 billion in 2020 a 3% increase from the previous year's revenue of $29.9 billion. This was primarily due to a higher sales volume in the company's platinum group metals segment.

In 2020 the company had a net profit of $5.5 billion an 11% decrease from the previous year's net profit of $6.1 billion.

The company's cash at the end of 2020 was $7.5 billion. Operating activities generated $6.6 billion while investing activities used $4.7 billion mainly for expenditure on property plant and equipment. Financing activities used another $716 million primarily for repayments of bonds and borrowings.

Strategy
Guided by its Purpose ? re-imagining mining to improve people's lives ? The company's strategy is to secure develop and operate a portfolio of high quality long life resource assets. The company then applies innovative practices and technologies in the hands of its world class people to deliver sustainable value for all its stakeholders.

The company actively manages its asset portfolio to improve its overall competitive position providing products that increasingly support a fast-growing population and a cleaner greener more sustainable world.

HISTORY

In 1905 the Oppenheimers a German family with a major interest in the Premier Diamond Mining Company of South Africa began buying some of the region's richest gold-bearing land. The family formed Anglo American Corporation of South Africa in 1917 to raise money from J. P. Morgan and other US investors. The name was chosen to disguise the company's German background during WWI.

Under Ernest Oppenheimer the company bought diamond fields in German Southwest Africa (now Namibia) in 1920 breaking the De Beers hegemony in diamond production. Oppenheimer's 1928 negotiations with Hans Merensky the person credited with the discovery of South Africa's "platinum arc" led to Anglo American's interest in platinum.

The diamond monopoly resurfaced in 1929 when Anglo American won control of De Beers formed by Cecil Rhodes in 1888 with the help of England's powerful Rothschild family.

Anglo American and De Beers had become the largest gold producers in South Africa by the 1950s. They were also major world producers of coal uranium and copper. In the 1960s and 1970s Anglo American expanded through mergers and cross holdings in industrial and financial companies. It set up Luxembourg-based Minorco to own holdings outside South Africa and help the company avoid sanctions placed on firms doing business in the apartheid country.

Minorco sold its interest in Consolidated Gold Fields in 1989 and in 1990 it bought Freeport-McMoRan Gold Company (US). In 1993 Minorco bought Anglo American's and De Beers' South American European and Australian operations as part of a swap that put all of Anglo American's non-African assets except diamonds in Minorco's hands. Some analysts claimed the company had moved the assets to protect them from possible nationalization by the new black-controlled South African government. The company spun off insurer African Life to a group of black investors in 1994.

Anglo American bought a stake in UK-based conglomerate Lonrho (now Lonmin) in 1996. In 1997 Anglo American made mining acquisitions in Zambia Colombia and Tanzania and began reorganizing its gold and diamond operations. In 1998 the company's First National and Southern Life financial units merged with Rand Merchant Bank's Momentum Life Assurers to form FirstRand. (Anglo American has divested most of its interest in FirstRand.)

The company moved to the UK in 1999 and began trading on the London Stock Exchange in an effort to reach international investors. When it was based in South Africa Anglo American was unable to send its money overseas (the result of boycotts connected to that country's apartheid policies) so it bulked up on South African interests. Anglo American has evolved such that it can depend on product and geographic diversity to weather global economic turmoil. South African operations now make up less than half of the company's total sales and its base metals and platinum units each account for about a quarter of sales.

In 2000 the company bought UK building materials company Tarmac plc and later sold Tarmac America to Greece-based Titan Cement for $636 million. That year De Beers paid $590 million for Anglovaal Mining's stake in De Beers' flagship Venetia diamond mine and $900 million for Royal Dutch Shell's Australian coal mining business. On the disposal side Anglo American sold its 68% stake in LTA and its 14% stake in Li & Fung a Hong Kong trading company. Harry Oppenheimer died that year at the age of 92.

In a surprising move in early 2001 Anglo American announced that it had formed a consortium with Central Holding (the Oppenheimer family) and Debswana Diamond to acquire De Beers. In February De Beers agreed to be acquired in a deal worth about $17.6 billion. The deal — giving Anglo American and Central Holding 45% each and Debswana a 10% stake — was completed in June 2001.

In 2002 Anglo American and Japan-based conglomerate Mitsui pooled their Australian coal resources; Anglo American owns 51% of the joint venture. The company also completed a $1.3 billion deal that year for Chilean copper assets (two mines and a smelter) formerly owned by Exxon Mobil. In 2003 the company eyed the red hot iron ore market when it acquired a controlling stake in South Africa-based iron producer Kumba Resources.

Anglo American sold its 20% stake in Gold Fields to Norilsk Nickel in 2004 and reduced its stake in AngloGold Ashanti to 42% from its former 51% in 2006 then to below 20% the following year and finally entirely in 2009. In divesting its gold interests Anglo American seemed to capitulate to demands from the investor community and the idea that the gold industry is sufficiently different from the rest of the mining industry as to necessitate separate management.

The company set up new units in 2009 along product and geographical lines. The new divisions consisted of platinum (South Africa) copper (Chile) nickel (Brazil) metallurgical coal (Australia) thermal coal (South Africa) Kumba Iron Ore (of which Anglo American owned 65% South Africa) and Iron Ore Brazil. The change capped off several years of reorganization and divestment.

In 2009 the board of Anglo American rejected an offer to merge with rival Xstrata (renamed Glencore in 2014). Although Xstrata called the bid a "merger of equals" based on similar capitalization sizes Anglo American's board was not convinced of the benefits of the $68 billion all stock deal. Although Anglo American used to have a majority stake in AngloGold Ashanti it divested its remaining shares in 2009.

In 2010 Anglo American through its subsidiary Anglo Zinc completed the divestment of its zinc assets to Vedanta Resources subsidiary Sterlite Industries in a $1.3 billion deal. That year the company also sold Tarmac's aggregates businesses in France Germany Poland and the Czech Republic as well as its French and Belgian concrete products operations for $483 million.

Nicky Oppenheimer grandson of the founder retired from the board in 2011.

EXECUTIVES

Group General Counsel and Company Secretary, Richard Price
Chairman, Stuart Chambers
Group Director, Corporate Relations and Sustainable Impact, Anik Michaud
Chief Executive Officer and Director, Mark Cutifani, $1,758,390 total compensation
CEO, Base Metals, Ruben Fernandes
Technical Director and Director, Anthony O'Neill, $1,099,154 total compensation
CEO, Kumba Iron Ore, Themba Mkhwanazi
CEO, Anglo American Platinum LTD, Natascha Viljoen
Non-Executive Director, Ian Tyler
Chief Executive Officer - Kumba, Nompumelelo Zikalala
CEO, Duncan Wanblad
Group Director, People and Organisation, Didier Charreton
CFO, Stephen Pearce, $1,059,395 total compensation
Auditors: PricewaterhouseCoopers LLP

LOCATIONS

HQ: Anglo American Plc (United Kingdom)
20 Carlton House Terrace, London SW1Y 5AN
Phone: (44) 20 7968 8888   **Fax:** (44) 20 7968 8500
Web: www.angloamerican.com

PRODUCTS/OPERATIONS

2018 sales

	% of total
Coal	26
De Beers	20
Platinum Group Metals	19
Copper	17
Iron Ore	12
Nickel and Manganese	6
Corporate and other	-
Total	**100**

Selected Subsidiaries

Platinum
    Anglo Platinum Corporation Limited (75% South Africa)
Base Metals
Anglo American Sur (75% copper mines Chile)
    Empresa Minera de Mantos Blancos SA (copper Chile)
    Minera Loma de Ní;quel CA (91% nickel Venezuela)
    Minera Quellaveco SA (80% copper Peru)
    Minera Sur Andes Limitada (copper Chile)
Coal
Anglo Coal (South Africa)
    Anglo Coal (Callide) Pty Limited (Australia)
Ferrous Metals and Industries
    Kumba Resources Limited (65%; coal iron ore heavy minerals; South Africa)
Industrial Minerals
    Copebras Limitada (phosphate products Brazil)
Diamonds
    De Beers S.A. (45%)

COMPETITORS

AFRICAN DIAMONDS PLC
LIMITED
BHP GROUP PLC
Diavik Diamond Mines (2012) Inc
EUROPEAN GOLDFIELDS (SERVICES) LIMITED

FIRESTONE DIAMONDS

NEWMONT CORPORATION
SIBANYE UK LIMITED
Vale S/A

HISTORICAL FINANCIALS

Company Type: Public

Income Statement

FYE: December 31

	REVENUE ($ mil.)	NET INCOME ($ mil.)	NET PROFIT MARGIN	EMPLOYEES
12/20	30,902	2,089	6.8%	64,000
12/19	29,870	3,547	11.9%	63,000
12/18	27,610	3,549	12.9%	64,000
12/17	26,243	3,166	12.1%	69,000
12/16	21,378	1,594	7.5%	80,000
Annual Growth	**9.6%**	**7.0%**	**—**	**(5.4%)**

2020 Year-End Financials

Debt ratio: 20.7%
Return on equity: 8.2%
Cash ($ mil.): 7,521
Current ratio: 1.93
Long-term debt ($ mil.): 11,953

No. of shares (mil.): 1,238
Dividends
    Yield: 2.0%
    Payout: 20.7%
Market value ($ mil.): 20,811

	STOCK PRICE ($) FY Close	P/E High/Low		PER SHARE ($) Earnings	Dividends	Book Value
12/20	16.80	10	4	1.67	0.35	20.85
12/19	14.45	5	4	2.76	0.53	18.08
12/18	11.04	5	3	2.74	0.48	16.80
12/17	10.35	4	2	2.45	0.22	16.35
12/16	7.05	6	1	1.23	0.00	13.56
Annual Growth	**24.2%**	**—**	**—**	**7.9%**	**—**	**11.3%**

Anheuser-Busch InBev SA/NV

Auditors: Deloitte Bedrijfsrevisoren/Réviseurs d'Entreprises CVBA/SCRL

LOCATIONS

HQ: Anheuser-Busch InBev SA/NV
Brouwerijplein 1, Leuven 3000
Phone: (32) 16 27 61 11   **Fax:** (32) 16 50 61 11
Web: www.ab-inbev.com

HISTORICAL FINANCIALS

Company Type: Public

Income Statement

FYE: December 31

	REVENUE ($ mil.)	NET INCOME ($ mil.)	NET PROFIT MARGIN	EMPLOYEES
12/20	46,881	1,405	3.0%	163,695
12/19	52,329	9,171	17.5%	170,000
12/18	54,619	4,368	8.0%	172,603
12/17	56,444	7,996	14.2%	182,915
12/16	45,517	1,241	2.7%	206,633
Annual Growth	**0.7%**	**3.2%**	**—**	**(5.7%)**

2020 Year-End Financials

Debt ratio: 42.7%
Return on equity: 1.9%
Cash ($ mil.): 15,252
Current ratio: 0.82
Long-term debt ($ mil.): 93,642

No. of shares (mil.): 1,972
Dividends
    Yield: 2.0%
    Payout: 82.1%
Market value ($ mil.): 137,880

	STOCK PRICE ($) FY Close	P/E High/Low	PER SHARE ($) Earnings	Dividends	Book Value
12/20	69.91	119 50	0.69	1.45	34.49
12/19	82.04	22 14	4.53	2.01	38.65
12/18	65.81	52 30	2.17	3.30	32.96
12/17	111.56	31 26	3.98	4.08	37.54
12/16	105.44	185 139	0.71	1.70	44.37
Annual Growth	(9.8%)	—	(0.7%)	(3.9%)	(6.1%)

Anhui Conch Cement Co Ltd

Put this company to your ear and you can hear the money. Anhui Conch Cement is China's largest cement producer as measured by sales and production volume. The company has more than 15 clinker plants and 20 cement grinding mills in China. Its products include various grades of portland cement portland blast furnace slag cement compound cement and high-grade commodity clinker sold under the Conch brand. Anhui Conch Cement's products have been used in the construction of a number of large-scale infrastructure projects in Shanghai including the Oriental Pearl Television Tower and Shanghai Pudong Airport. Outside of China the company distributes its products to Europe the Americas and Southeast Asia.

EXECUTIVES

IR Contact Officer, Shui Yu
Vice Chairman of the Board, Executive Director, Jianchao Wang
Executive Director, Xiaochuan Zhou
Deputy General Manager, Qiubi Ke
Chief Engineer-Craft, Leyi Li
Deputy General Manager, Xiaobo Li
Joint Company Secretary, Pak Yue Chiu
Independent Non-Executive Director, Daguang Liang
Independent Non-Executive Director, Yunyan Zhang
General Manager, Qunfeng Li
Executive Director, Bin Wu
Independent Non-Executive Director, Xiaorong Zhang
Auditors: KPMG Huazhen LLP

LOCATIONS

HQ: Anhui Conch Cement Co Ltd
39 Wenhua Road, Wuhu City, Anhui Province 241000
Phone: (86) 553 8398976   **Fax:** (86) 553 8398931
Web: www.conch.cn

2015 Sales by Region

	% of total
Central China	31
East China	27
South China	20
West China	21
Overseas	1
Total	**100**

PRODUCTS/OPERATIONS

2015 Sales by Principal Activities

	% of total
Cliker and cement products	98
Materials and other products	1
Service income	1
Total	**100**

COMPETITORS

BUZZI UNICEM USA INC
GIANT CEMENT HOLDING INC.

HISTORICAL FINANCIALS

Company Type: Public

Income Statement

FYE: December 31

	REVENUE ($ mil.)	NET INCOME ($ mil.)	NET PROFIT MARGIN	EMPLOYEES
12/20	26,947	5,371	19.9%	0
12/19	22,567	4,827	21.4%	0
12/18	18,667	4,334	23.2%	0
12/17	11,573	2,436	21.1%	0
12/16	8,054	1,234	15.3%	44,859
Annual Growth	35.2%	44.4%	—	—

2020 Year-End Financials

Debt ratio: 0.8%
Return on equity: 23.4%
Cash ($ mil.): 9,506
Current ratio: 4.66
Long-term debt ($ mil.): 1,101
No. of shares (mil.): —
Dividends
Yield: 3.9%
Payout: 130.8%
Market value ($ mil.): —

	STOCK PRICE ($) FY Close	P/E High/Low	PER SHARE ($) Earnings	Dividends	Book Value
12/20	30.98	6 5	1.01	1.22	(0.00)
12/19	36.51	6 4	0.91	1.06	(0.00)
12/18	23.99	6 4	0.82	0.80	(0.00)
12/17	23.50	8 5	0.46	0.30	(0.00)
12/16	14.01	9 5	0.23	0.25	2.07
Annual Growth	22.0%	—	44.4%	49.1%	—

AntarChile S.A. (Chile)

AntarChile focuses on forestry fuel and fishing. As one of Chile's largest investment companies it buys shares of companies or properties that are linked to those industries. The holding company owns more than 60% of industrial conglomerate group Copec which is one of Chile's top distributors of petroleum and diesel fuel. Other holdings include investments in forestry and wood products groups Forestal Cholguan and Celulosa Arauco y Constituci n. AntarChile also is involved in the natural gas fishing forestry shipping and mining industries. Its forestry holdings produce cellulose and manufacture wood and wood panels. AntarChile is controlled by the powerful Angelini family of Chile.

EXECUTIVES

Independent Director, Jorge Desormeaux Jimenez, $170,619 total compensation
Deputy Chief Investment Officer, Ricardo Aldana Moris
Vice Chairman of the Board, Jorge Armando Andueza Fouque
Chairman of the Board, Roberto Angelini Rossi, $517,171 total compensation
Director, Andres Lyon Lyon, $404,948 total compensation
Chief Executive Officer, Andres Lehuede Bromley
Director, Juan Edgardo Goldenberg Penafiel, $404,948 total compensation
Director, Manuel Enrique Bezanilla Urrutia, $404,948 total compensation
Auditors: PricewaterhouseCoopers

LOCATIONS

HQ: AntarChile S.A. (Chile)
Avenida El Golf 150, Piso 21, Santiago, Las Condes
Phone: (56) 2 461 7710   **Fax:** (56) 2 461 7717
Web: www.antarchile.cl

COMPETITORS

CIC GROUP INC.
CK Infrastructure Holdings Limited
CLARIANT CORPORATION
CVI ENERGY CORPORATION LIMITED
ENEOS HOLDINGS INC.
FURUKAWA CO. LTD.
JFE HOLDINGS INC.
KOPPERS HOLDINGS INC.
MITSUBISHI CHEMICAL HOLDINGS CORPORATION
OJI HOLDINGS CORPORATION
OXBOW CORPORATION
SUMITOMO FORESTRY CO. LTD.
THE FIDELITY GLOBAL GROUP LTD
TIGER ROYALTIES AND INVESTMENTS PLC
TOYO SEIKAN GROUP HOLDINGS LTD.

HISTORICAL FINANCIALS

Company Type: Public

Income Statement

FYE: December 31

	REVENUE ($ mil.)	NET INCOME ($ mil.)	NET PROFIT MARGIN	EMPLOYEES
12/20	18,059	128	0.7%	0
12/19	23,716	126	0.5%	0
12/18	23,970	671	2.8%	0
12/17	20,353	399	2.0%	0
12/16	16,699	325	2.0%	31,720
Annual Growth	2.0%	(20.7%)	—	—

2020 Year-End Financials

Debt ratio: 36.1%
Return on equity: 1.9%
Cash ($ mil.): 2,186
Current ratio: 2.33
Long-term debt ($ mil.): 8,500
No. of shares (mil.): 456
Dividends
Yield: —
Payout: —
Market value ($ mil.): —

ANZ Bank

LOCATIONS

HQ: ANZ Bank
Level 9, 833 Collins Street, Docklands, Victoria 3008
Phone: (61) 3 9273 5555   **Fax:** (61) 3 8542 5252
Web: www.anz.com

HISTORICAL FINANCIALS

Company Type: Public

Income Statement

FYE: September 30

	REVENUE ($ mil.)	NET INCOME ($ mil.)	NET PROFIT MARGIN	EMPLOYEES
09/20	17,384	2,545	14.6%	38,579
09/19	20,997	4,022	19.2%	39,060
Annual Growth	(17.2%)	(36.7%)	—	(1.2%)

2020 Year-End Financials

Debt ratio: —
Return on equity: 5.8%
Cash ($ mil.): 76,810
Current ratio: —
Long-term debt ($ mil.): —
No. of shares (mil.): —
Dividends
Yield: —
Payout: 50.8%
Market value ($ mil.): —

	STOCK PRICE ($) FY Close	P/E High/Low	PER SHARE ($) Earnings	Dividends	Book Value
09/20	0.00	— —	0.84	0.43	15.36
09/19	0.00	— —	1.36	1.08	14.49
/0.00	—	—(0.00)	0.00	(0.00)	
Annual Growth	—	— —	—	—	—

Aomori Bank, Ltd. (The) (Japan)

Aomori Bank has more than a little interest in regional banking. The bank which serves the Aomori Prefecture offers commercial banking retail banking and other products and services such as credit cards leasing lending and property management. In addition to its 111 Aomori-area offices Aomori Bank also has nine subsidiaries. In an effort to better compete with big national banks operating in its region Aomori Bank joined forces with two other regional financial institutions (Akita Bank and Bank of Iwate) to launch an investment trust focusing on shares of the banks and of other local companies.

EXECUTIVES

President, Representative Director, Susumu Narita
Director, Akira Nakagawa
Vice President, Representative Director, Akihiro Kawamura
Senior Managing Executive Officer, Manager of Tokyo Office, Director, Tomohiko Sasaki
Senior Managing Executive Officer, Director, Keitaro Ishikawa
Independent Director, Mie Ishida
Independent Director, Naotake Atsumi
Independent Director, Norihisa Ishida
Independent Director, Toshisada Kushibiki
Auditors: Ernst & Young ShinNihon LLC

LOCATIONS

HQ: Aomori Bank, Ltd. (The) (Japan)
1-9-30 Hashimoto, Aomori 030-8668
Phone: (81) 17 777 1111   **Fax:** (81) 17 777 1006
Web: www.a-bank.jp

COMPETITORS

AWA BANK LTD. THE
DAISHI HOKUETSU BANK   THE
  LTD.
KAGOSHIMA BANK LTD.

HISTORICAL FINANCIALS

Company Type: Public

Income Statement   FYE: March 31

	ASSETS ($ mil.)	NET INCOME ($ mil.)	INCOME AS % OF ASSETS	EMPLOYEES
03/21	33,248	20	0.1%	2,013
03/20	29,348	13	0.0%	2,109
03/19	27,481	29	0.1%	2,182
03/18	27,411	40	0.1%	2,204
03/17	25,986	44	0.2%	2,195
Annual Growth	6.4%	(17.7%)	—	(2.1%)

2021 Year-End Financials

Return on assets: 0.0%
Return on equity: 1.9%
Long-term debt ($ mil.): —
No. of shares (mil.): 20
Sales ($ mil): 374

Dividends
Yield: —
Payout: —
Market value ($ mil.): —

Aon plc (Ireland)

Aon provides a broad range of brokerage risk retirement and health services. The company a top global insurance and reinsurance broker places policies with corporate clients and individuals on behalf of insurance companies. The Commercial Risk Solutions division provides retail property/casualty liability workers' compensation and other insurance products for groups and businesses as well as risk management services. The Reinsurance Solutions business brokers reinsurance to protect insurers from policy losses. Other units include Retirement Solutions (retirement benefits consulting) Health Solutions (health plan and benefits brokerage) and Data & Analytic Services. Aon operates in more than 120 countries; the US accounts for more than 40% of sales. Insurance commissions and client fees make up most of sales.

Operations

Aon's largest operating segment is its risk solutions segment which holds all of the insurance and reinsurance brokerage operations and accounts for about two-thirds of sales. The largest portion of that comes from the retail insurance brokerage business (operating as Aon Risk Solutions) which places policies on behalf of insurance companies for a commission. The unit also earns fees from its retail clients which include small to large corporations and other professional organizations as well as individuals. In addition Aon Risk Solutions provides risk identification and assessment cost-control and claims management affinity (professional liability) programs and other administrative services. The smaller Aon Benfield business places reinsurance policies and offers capital management and advisory services.

The Aon Hewitt division accounting for the remaining third of revenues specializes in structuring benefits programs to suit specific client needs and to control HR expenses as well as to increase employee performance and productivity measurements.

Geographic Reach

Aon provides its brokerage and consulting services from more than 500 offices in about 120 countries; the US and Europe are its largest markets. To support its international growth initiatives in emerging markets and provide for greater financial flexibility in 2012 the company converted from a US-based corporation to a UK-based public limited company. Aon moved its headquarters from Chicago to London and changed the parent entity name from Aon Corporation to Aon plc. The Chicago location continues on as the headquarters for operations in the Americas (Aon's largest geographic segment accounting for more than half of annual revenues).

Financial Performance

Aon reported revenue of $10.8 billion in 2018 an 8% increase over 2017 results. About 5% of growth came from organic measures while 2% came from acquisitions. All operating segments contributed to organic growth with the strongest improvements coming from the Commercial Risk Solutions Reinsurance Solutions and Health Solutions.

Net income attributable to shareholders dropped nearly 8% in 2018 to some $1.1 billion due to higher operating expenses (including benefits IT and general costs) and lower income from discontinued operations (related to the HR business divestiture in 2017).

The company ended 2018 with $656 million in cash down $100 million from 2017. Operating activities contributed $1.7 billion while financing activities used $1.7 billion via share repurchases and shareholder dividends.

Strategy

Aon has worked diligently over the years to expand in its core business areas. The company primarily strengthens its retail insurance brokerage network through purchases of smaller agencies. It also adds new products and services in high-growth fields such as cyber solutions and transaction liability.

The company is undergoing a multi-year restructuring program to streamline its operations for greater efficiency and insight. Through the program Aon has combined its operating units (including Aon Risk Solutions and Aon Benfield) under one segment ? Aon United. It is also eliminating about 5000 jobs. The plan has a cost of some $1.2 billion but will result in $500 million in annual savings going forward.

The restructuring program was launched after Aon sold its human resources outsourcing business (which made up the majority of its Aon Hewitt division) in 2017.

Mergers and Acquisitions

In 2017 Aon acquired Portus Consulting a UK employee benefits firm. Portus which serves small to midsized enterprises with a focus on the legal sector joined Aon's Employee Benefits division.

Company Background

To support international growth and financial flexibility in 2012 the company converted from a US-based corporation to a UK-based public limited company. Aon moved its headquarters from Chicago to London and changed the parent entity name from Aon Corporation to Aon plc. The Chicago location continued as the headquarters for operations in the Americas (Aon's largest geographic segment).

Aon spent $4.9 billion to acquire HR firm Hewitt Associates which specialized in business process outsourcing (BPO) and benefits administration for large corporations in late 2010. Hewitt Associates was combined with the existing HR business Aon Consulting Worldwide to form the Aon Hewitt entity.

Then in 2017 Aon divested the BPO and benefits administration operations (a large portion of the Aon Hewitt division) to private equity firm Blackstone Group for up to $4.8 billion. The deal helped Aon focus on its core professional services offerings as well as on areas including cybersecurity and health insurance.

HISTORY

Aon's story begins with the birth of W. Clement Stone around the turn of the 20th century. At age six he started working as a paperboy in Chicago. The young Stone devoured the optimistic messages of the 19th-century Horatio Alger novels which detailed the successes of plucky enterprising heroes.

Stone's mother bought a small Detroit insurance agency and in 1918 brought her son into the business. Young Stone sold low-cost low-benefit accident insurance underwriting and issuing policies on-site. The next year he founded his own agency the Combined Registry Co. While selling up to 122 policies per day he recruited a nationwide force of agents.

As the Depression took hold Stone reduced his workforce and improved training. Forced by his son's respiratory illness to winter in the South Stone followed the sun to Arkansas and Texas. In 1939 he bought American Casualty Insurance Co. of Dallas. It was consolidated with other purchases as the Combined Insurance Co. of America in 1947.

The company grew through the 1950s and 1960s continuing to sell health and accident policies. In the 1970s Combined expanded overseas despite being hit hard by the recession.

In 1982 after 10 years of stagnant growth under Clement Stone Jr. the elder Stone (then 79) resumed control until the completion of a merger with Ryan Insurance Co. allowed him to transfer power to Patrick Ryan.

Ryan the son of a Wisconsin Ford dealer had started his company as an auto credit insurer in 1964. In 1976 the company bought the insurance brokerage units of the Esmark conglomerate. Ryan's less-personal management style differed radically from Stone's rah-rah boosterism but the men's shared interest in philanthropy helped seal the deal.

Ryan focused on insurance brokering and added more upscale insurance products. He also trimmed staff and took other cost-cutting measures and in 1987 he changed Combined's name to Aon. In 1995 the company sold its remaining direct life insurance holdings to focus on consulting. The following year it began offering hostile takeover insurance policies to small and midsized companies.

Aon built a global presence through purchases. In 1997 it bought The Minet Group as well as troubled insurance brokerage Alexander & Alexander Services in a deal that made Aon (temporarily) the largest insurance broker worldwide. The firm made no US buys in 1998 but doubled its employee base with purchases including Spain's largest retail insurance broker Gil y Carvajal and the formation of Aon Korea the first non-Korean firm of its kind to be licensed there.

Responding to industry demands Aon announced its new fee disclosure policy in 1999 and the company reorganized to focus on buying personal line insurance firms and to integrate its acquisitions. That year it bought Nikols Sedgwick Group an Italian insurance firm and formed RiskAttack (with Zurich US) a risk analysis and financial management concern aimed at technology companies. The cost of integrating its numerous purchases however hammered profits in 1999.

Despite its troubles in 2000 Aon bought Reliance Group's accident and health insurance business as well as Actuarial Sciences Associates a compensation and employee benefits consulting company. Later in that year however the company decided to cut 6% of its workforce as part of a restructuring effort.

Aon was hit hard by the attacks on the World Trade Center (where it was headquartered) in 2001; the company lost some 175 employees. Aon announced plans to spin off its Combined Specialty Group division which offered extended consumer product warranties that year. However Aon later scrapped plans to sell this business and instead began scaling back its underwriting operations.

Aon teamed up with the Giuliani Group former New York mayor Rudolph Giuliani's consulting firm to provide business risk assessment and crisis management services in 2002.

In 2003 the company saw revenues increase primarily because of rate hikes in the insurance industry (meaning higher commissions for Aon). Also that year Endurance Specialty the company's Bermuda-based underwriting operations went public. The next year Aon sold most of its holdings in Endurance.

In 2004-05 Aon along with other brokers including Marsh & McLennan and Willis Towers Watson fell under regulatory investigation. At issue was the practice of insurance companies' payments to brokers (known as contingent commissions). The payments were thought to bring a conflict of interest swaying broker decisions on behalf of carriers rather than customers.

The bid-rigging investigation resulted in a $190 million settlement with regulators in three states and a shakeup of top management. Patrick Ryan stepped down as CEO and was replaced by McKinsey executive Gregory Case. Ryan remained as executive chairman until his retirement in 2008. Lester Knight was then elected to serve as non-executive chairman.

Aon then retrenched by launching a reorganization program. The company sold its wholesale brokerage operations Swett & Crawford (the largest in the US) to a group of investors led by Hicks Muse Tate & Furst (later HM Capital Partners) in 2005.

Aon also shed its credit warranty and property and casualty underwriting operations; it sold its Aon Warranty Group (later renamed The Warranty Group) division including Virginia Surety to Onex for $710 million in late 2006. The company concurrently sold off its Construction Program Group which was part of its property and casualty operations to Old Republic Insurance for $85 million.

In 2007 the company took steps to further simplify its operations including efforts to slim down administrative functions and consolidate some European operations. The company then exited its older but smaller insurance underwriting segment which offered supplementary health accident and life insurance and included founder W. Clement Stone's original insurance underwriting business Combined Insurance. Aon in 2008 sold the Combined Insurance unit to Chubb Limited for nearly $2.6 billion and it sold its Sterling Life Insurance underwriting unit to Munich Re for $352 million.

To expand in core business areas in 2008 Aon acquired UK-based Benfield Group in a $1.75 billion deal to strengthen its European reinsurance brokerage operations. It then merged Benfield Group with its existing Aon Re Global operations and renamed the new business Aon Benfield.

In 2009 Aon acquired 14 small insurance-brokerage agencies. The company rounded out its simplification initiatives when it sold its car insurance business AIS Management Group to Mercury General for $120 million. It also divested some runoff (inactive) property/casualty businesses sold its US premium finance loan business (Cananwill) and contracted its international premium finance operations out to third parties that year.

In 2012 the company changed its domicile moving its headquarters from Chicago to London and changing its legal name from Aon Corporation to Aon plc.

EXECUTIVES

Independent Director, Jeffrey Campbell
Chief Legal Officer, Darren Zeidel
Chief People Officer, Lisa Stevens
President, Eric Andersen, $1,000,000 total
  compensation
Chief Marketing Officer, Andy Weitz
Chief Financial Officer, Executive Vice President - Global Finance, Christina Davies, $1,000,000 total compensation
Chief Innovation Officer, New Ventures Group, Anthony Goland, $900,000 total compensation
Chief Accounting Officer and Global Controller, Michael Neller
Auditors: Ernst & Young LLP

LOCATIONS

HQ: Aon plc (Ireland)
  Metropolitan Building, James Joyce Street, Dublin 1, Ireland 60601
Phone: (353) 1 266 6000
Web: www.aon.com

2016 Sales

	% of total
United States	52
Europe Middle East & Africa	15
United Kingdom	12
Asia Pacific	12
Americas other than U.S.	9
Total	**100**

PRODUCTS/OPERATIONS

2016 Sales

	% of total
Risk Solutions	64
HR Solutions	36
Total	**100**

Selected Subsidiaries and Divisions

Risk Solutions
  Aon Benfield Inc.
  Aon Holdings International BV
  Aon Risk Services Companies Inc.
HR Solutions
  Aon Consulting Worldwide Inc.

COMPETITORS

AEGON N.V.	PRUDENTIAL PUBLIC
AVIVA PLC	LIMITED COMPANY
CNA FINANCIAL	RSA INSURANCE GROUP
CORPORATION	LIMITED
CNO FINANCIAL GROUP	Sampo Oyj
INC.	THE HARTFORD
FINANCIAL	
ING Groep N.V.	SERVICES GROUP INC.
MARSH & MCLENNAN	Zurich Insurance Group
COMPANIES INC.	AG

HISTORICAL FINANCIALS

Company Type: Public

Income Statement				FYE: December 31
	REVENUE ($ mil.)	NET INCOME ($ mil.)	NET PROFIT MARGIN	EMPLOYEES
12/21	12,193	1,255	10.3%	50,000
12/20	11,066	1,969	17.8%	50,000
12/19	11,013	1,532	13.9%	50,000
12/18	10,770	1,134	10.5%	50,000
12/17	9,998	1,226	12.3%	50,000
Annual Growth	5.1%	0.6%	—	0.0%

2021 Year-End Financials

Debt ratio: 29.4%	No. of shares (mil.): 214
Return on equity: 55.0%	Dividends
Cash ($ mil.): 544	Yield: 0.6%
Current ratio: 1.00	Payout: 50.5%
Long-term debt ($ mil.): 8,228	Market value ($ mil.): —

Aozora Bank Ltd

Aozora Bank is building its banking business to reach the blue skies above. Aozora (which means blue sky in Japanese) recently extricated itself from a multi-year government bailout and is focused on continuing its journey towards better times. Aozora has about 20 regional offices in Japan several overseas with a strong presence in its home town of

Tokyo. The bank provides a host of retail and business banking services as well as corporate banking services (loans and derivative products consulting and advisory) and specialty finance and financial markets offerings.

Operations
Aozora Bank operates several segments: Retail Banking Institutional Banking Specialized Banking and Financial Markets.

Retail Banking offers typical products and services to both consumer and commercial clients including deposit accounts checking accounts and mortgages. Through a network of branch offices internet banking phone banking and ATMs co-locating in Japan Post Bank locations it provides many avenues for its customers to transact business. This segment leverages two of the Bank's subsidiaries Aozora Securities and Aozora Investment Management.

Institutional Banking addresses the needs to corporations by offering advice on capital policy and business recovery support for overseas expansion and consultancy around management and general business activities. This segment also serves the needs of fellow Japanese financial institutions.

Specialized Banking focuses on financing for real estate deals and business recovery. It also houses the international business which works on syndicated loans corporate loans project financing and other customer needs in primarily North America and Asia.

The Financial Markets segment invests the Aozora Bank's money in such opportunities as derivatives equities and fixed income ensuring that the risk of its investments stay within the guideline risk objectives and constraints of the Aozora Bank group.

Geographic Reach
Tokyo-headquartered Aozora Bank operates 21 offices in Japan (7 in Tokyo) and one each in China (Shanghai) Hong Kong Singapore London and New York City. It extends its geographic reach through business alliance partners operating in Taiwan the Philippines Indonesia and Thailand.

Financial Performance
Note: Financial results are denoted in Japanese currency the Yen ().

Revenue declined 7% in FY2016 to 85.3 billion. The fall was due to decreases in net interest income lower fees and commissions and an almost 50% slip in other ordinary income.

Despite lower revenue favorable comparison against the prior year's deferred taxes helped net income to stay in line with the prior year about 44 billion.

Strategy
Aozora has a six-pronged strategy whose primary objective is to diversify its income sources. Its retail banking segment is looking to provide more products and services to seniors and mass affluent customers. It wants to expand its business with SMEs (small-medium enterprises) and other corporate customers. It has designs on deepening its existing relationships with regional Japanese financial institutions. Aozora wants to grow business in its Specialty Finance and its International Business segment and finally it wants to pursue diversified global investments for its own cache of cash to address its own internal risk compliance needs.

It is only a few years beyond exiting a government-funded public bail out that occurred in the late 1990's. With all the public funds now paid back Aozora has a bit more freedom of movement to pursue growth and expansion objectives.

EXECUTIVES

Independent Director, Shunsuke Takeda
Independent Director, Hiroyuki Mizuta

President, Chief Executive Officer, Representative Director, Kei Tanikawa
Vice President, Executive Officer, Chief Director of Business Corporation Sales, Representative Director, Koji Yamakoshi
Independent Director, Ippei Murakami
Independent Director, Tomonori Ito
Senior Managing Executive Officer, Chief Director of Advisory & Investment, Takeshi Ito
Chief Financial Officer, Senior Managing Executive Officer, Akira Sakai
Executive Officer, Chief Credit Risk Officer, Jun Shinozaki
Senior Managing Executive Officer, Director, Tomomi Akutagawa
Managing Executive Officer, Chief Director of Business Corporation Sales, Chief Director of Business Banking, Kazuhiro Yasuda
Vice President, Executive Officer, Chief Director of Trust Business, Chief Director of Investment Bank, Representative Director, Hideto Oomi
Auditors: Deloitte Touche Tohmatsu LLC

LOCATIONS

HQ: Aozora Bank Ltd
6-1-1 Kojimachi, Chiyoda-ku, Tokyo 102-8660
Phone: (81) 3 6752 1111
Web: www.aozorabank.co.jp

PRODUCTS/OPERATIONS

Selected affiliates
ABN Advisors
Aozora Asia Pacific Finance Limited
Aozora Europe Limited
Aozora Investments Management
Aozora Loan Services
Aozora Real Estate Investment Advisors
Aozora Regional Consulting Co. Ltd.
Aozora Securities
Aozora Trust Bank
AZB Funding
AZB Funding 2
AZB Funding 3
AZB Funding 4 Limited

COMPETITORS

AKBANK TURK ANONIM SIRKETI
AUSTRALIA AND NEW ZEALAND BANKING GROUP LIMITED
BANK OF CHINA LIMITED
BANK OF YOKOHAMALTD.THE
HDFC BANK LIMITED
Hana Financial Group Inc.
ICICI BANK LIMITED
KEYCORP
MIZUHO BANK LTD.
MIZUHO FINANCIAL GROUP INC.
QATAR NATIONAL BANK (Q.P.S.C.)
Shanghai Pudong Development Bank Co.Ltd.
UniCredit Bank AG

HISTORICAL FINANCIALS
Company Type: Public

Income Statement   FYE: March 31

	ASSETS ($ mil.)	NET INCOME ($ mil.)	INCOME AS % OF ASSETS	EMPLOYEES
03/21	53,437	261	0.5%	2,477
03/20	48,823	259	0.5%	2,433
03/19	47,452	326	0.7%	2,390
03/18	46,265	405	0.9%	2,291
03/17	41,017	392	1.0%	2,191
Annual Growth	6.8%	(9.6%)	—	3.1%

2021 Year-End Financials

Return on assets: 0.5%	Dividends
Return on equity: 6.2%	Yield: 0.0%
Long-term debt ($ mil.): —	Payout: 13.0%
No. of shares (mil.): 116	Market value ($ mil.): 693
Sales ($ mil): 1,406	

	STOCK PRICE ($) FY Close	P/E High/Low		PER SHARE ($) Earnings	Dividends	Book Value
03/21	5.94	0	0	2.24	0.29	38.27
03/20	4.69	0	0	2.22	0.35	33.75
03/19	6.13	0	0	2.79	0.39	34.74
03/18	10.18	0	0	3.47	0.44	35.20
03/17	74.11	0	0	3.36	0.41	32.10
Annual Growth	(46.8%)	—	—	(9.7%)	(8.4%)	4.5%

Aptiv PLC

Cars these days are more computer than machine and for that you've got Aptiv to thank. The company's main business is designing and assembling a car's electrical architecture including its wiring assemblies cabling and safety distribution. Aptiv also makes advanced electrical systems and software such as those involved in autonomous driving and vehicle connectivity. Aptiv has operations across the globe and counts the 25 largest auto manufacturers as customers. Aptiv formerly known as Delphi Automotive spun off its powertrain business in 2017 and renamed itself Aptiv. Its largest segment Signal and Power Solutions accounts for nearly 75% of sales. Almost 35% of sales were contributed by its US market. The company's major customers include Volkswagen Group and General Motors Company.

Operations
Aptiv's business is organized into two divisions: Signal and Power Solutions and Advanced Safety and User Experience.

The Signal and Power Solutions segment generates more than 70% of sales and designs manufactures and assembles electrical architecture for automobiles including engineered component products connectors wiring assemblies and harnesses cable management electrical centers and hybrid high voltage and safety distribution systems. Aptiv electrical systems are designed to meet the higher demands of modern computerized vehicles with integrated entertainment nagivation and other connectivity systems.

The Advanced Safety and User Experience accounts for above 25% of sales and provides hardware and software to fit out a vehicle with body controls infotainment and connectivity systems active and passive safety electronics autonomous driving software and technologies and systems integration.

Geographic Reach
Domiciled in Jersey UK Aptiv has operations in around 45 countries. It has nearly 125 manufacturing facilities and over 10 major technical centers (five in North America five in the Asia/Pacific region and two in EMEA). The company's revenue is well diversified: the US generates nearly 35% of revenue; the EMEA region brings in almost 35% and the Asia-Pacific region around 30%. Latin America accounts for the remainder.

Aptiv's regional model is set up to serve its major markets in a cost-efficient way. It serves the US from Mexico South America from Brazil Europe from Eastern Europe and the Asia/Pacific region from China.

Sales and Marketing
Aptiv's customer base includes all 25 of the largest automotive OEMs in the world; GM and

VW are Aptiv's two biggest customers and account for around 10% of the company's sales each year. Other customers include Ford Fiat-Chrysler Daimler Groupe PSA (Peugeot Citroen) Toyota and Tata Motors. On the flipside Aptiv only serves one market and is thus exposed to the fortunes of the auto industry.

Financial Performance

Aptiv has seen some growth over the years despite its recent fall. Overall the company's revenues increased 6% between 2016 and 2020. Net income increased 44% over the same five-year period despite experiencing volatility.

Aptiv's total net sales in 2020 were $13.1 billion a decrease of 9% compared to 2019. This compares to total global OEM production decreases of 16% in 2020. Aptiv experienced volume declines of 7% for the period primarily as a result of the adverse impacts of the COVID-19 pandemic on global vehicle production.

Net income increased 82% from $990 million in 2019 to $1.8 billion in 2020. SG&A expenses as well as amortization and restructuring expenses also declined that year contributing to the increase in profit despite the fall in revenue.

Cash at the end of the year was $2.9 billion a $2.4 billion increase from the year prior. Operating activities generated $1.4 billion in 2020 while financing activities contributed another $1.6 billion from public offerings of ordinary and preferred shares. Investing activities used $626 million mainly for capital expenditures.

Strategy

Aptiv believes it is well-positioned for growth from increasing global vehicle production volumes increased demand for the company's Safe Green and Connected products which are being added to vehicle content and new business wins with existing and new customers. Aptiv is focused on accelerating the commercialization of active safety autonomous driving enhanced user experiences and connected services providing the software advanced computing platforms and networking architecture required to do so.

Aptiv has successfully created a competitive cost structure while investing in research and development to grow its product offerings which are aligned with the high-growth industry mega-trends and re-aligned its manufacturing footprint into an efficient low-cost regional service model focused on increasing its profit margins.

In 2020 Aptiv continued its relentless focus on cost structure and operational optimization. The company is maximizing its operational flexibility and profitability at all points in the normal automotive business cycle by having almost all of its workforce based in best cost countries and about 20% of its hourly workforce composed of temporary employees. Aptiv is also recruiting and retaining top talent from various industries including technology.

Aptiv's key strategic priorities include commercializing the high-tech evolution of the automotive industry; leveraging its engineering and technological capabilities; targeting the right business with the right customers; capitalizing on its scale global footprint and established position in emerging markets; leveraging its lean and flexible cost structure to deliver profitability and cash flow; advancing and maintaining an efficient capital structure; and pursuing selected acquisitions and strategic investments.

Company Background

The company's return to the public markets and eventual profitability hasn't been easy. Delphi has struggled financially for years; it was only sporadically profitable for after being spun off in 1999. Delphi filed for bankruptcy in 2005 and emerged four years later as a heavily indebted private company owned by its investors Elliot Management

GM and Silver Point Capital. By that time it had laid off more than 75000 workers closed more than 70 sites reduced its products lines from 119 to 33 exited 11 businesses and had its pension (primarily for UAW workers) frozen and taken over by federal Pension Benefit Guaranty Corporation (PBGC). (In the end the union workers' pension was kept afloat by taxpayers as part of the 2009 auto industry bailout).

In 2011 Delphi was finally able to pay off GM for its $3.8 billion stake and PBGC for the $594 million it owed. The two transactions were funded with cash and $2.5 billion of new bank debt as part of a $3 billion credit facility from by investment bank J.P. Morgan Securities. The company makes about half of what it made five years ago and plans the use the proceeds from its IPO to fund operations buy equipment and repay more debt.

Paying off GM helped pave the way for the company's return to health and a new business strategy to show investors doesn't hurt either. Admittedly Delphi has much leaner operations after its restructuring and moved the bulk of its operations outside the US to emerging markets where overall costs especially labor costs are lower. Delphi no longer has any UAW employees on its payroll; outside the US it relies on non-salary and temporary workers to manage a flexible workforce.

EXECUTIVES

President, Chief Executive Officer, Director, Kevin Clark, $1,141,924 total compensation
Independent Chairman of the Board, Rajiv Gupta
Chief Accounting Officer, Vice President, Allan Brazier
Independent Director, Colin Parris
Independent Director, Nancy Cooper
Independent Director, Robert Ortberg
Independent Director, Sean Mahoney
Independent Director, Paul Meister
Independent Director, Joseph Hooley
Independent Director, Richard Clemmer
Senior Vice President, President of Signal and Power Solutions, William Presley
Chief Financial Officer, Senior Vice President - Business Operations, Joseph Massaro, $857,917 total compensation
Senior Vice President, Chief Technology Officer,Interim President Advanced Safety and User Experience, Glen De Vos
Chief Human Resource Officer, Senior Vice President, Mariya Trickett, $508,333 total compensation
Auditors: Ernst & Young LLP

LOCATIONS

HQ: Aptiv PLC
5 Hanover Quay, Grand Canal Dock, Dublin D02 VY79
Phone: (353) 1 259 7013
Web: www.delphi.com

2018 Sales

	$ mil.	% of total
United States	5,390	37
Europe Middle East & Africa	4,689	33
Asia/Pacific	3,916	27
South America	2,700	2
Total	**14,335**	**100**

PRODUCTS/OPERATIONS

2018 Sales by Segment

	$ mil.	% of total
Signal and Power Solutions	10,402	72
Advanced Safety and User Experience	4,078	28
Total	**14,435**	**100**

Selected Products

Automotive Industry
Connection Systems
Driver Interface
Electrical/Electronic Architecture
Hybrid & Electric Vehicle Products
Infotainment
Safety Electronics
Sensors

COMPETITORS

AUTOLIV INC.
AXCELIS TECHNOLOGIES INC.
ELECTROCOMPONENTS PUBLIC LIMITED COMPANY
FLEX LTD.
HALMA PUBLIC LIMITED COMPANY
HELLA GmbH & Co. KGaA
MERITOR INC.
SOGECLAIR
TENNECO INC.
TOYODA GOSEI CO. LTD.
VISTEON CORPORATION

HISTORICAL FINANCIALS

Company Type: Public

Income Statement   FYE: December 31

	REVENUE ($ mil.)	NET INCOME ($ mil.)	NET PROFIT MARGIN	EMPLOYEES
12/21	15,618	590	3.8%	155,000
12/20	13,066	1,804	13.8%	151,000
12/19	14,357	990	6.9%	141,000
12/18	14,435	1,067	7.4%	143,000
12/17	12,884	1,355	10.5%	129,000
Annual Growth	4.9%	(18.8%)	—	4.7%

2021 Year-End Financials

Debt ratio: 22.5%	No. of shares (mil.): 270
Return on equity: 7.2%	Dividends
Cash ($ mil.): 3,139	Yield: —
Current ratio: 2.01	Payout: —
Long-term debt ($ mil.): 4,059	Market value ($ mil.): —

Arab Banking Corporation (B.S.C.) (Bahrain)

ABC finds finance easy as 1-2-3. Arab Banking Corporation (Bank ABC) provides banking and financial services to a predominately Muslim clientele in the Middle East and North Africa. Offerings include retail and commercial banking investment banking portfolio management and Islamic banking. The company also provides project finance foreign exchange derivatives financial advisory services. Bank ABC operates in about 20 countries with representative and affiliate offices in Europe Asia and the Americas. The Central Bank of Libya now owns a majority of Bank ABC after acquiring about a third of the bank in two separate deals in 2010. The Kuwait Investment Authority is also a major stakeholder.

EXECUTIVES

Group Chief Credit and Risk Officer, Grant Lowen
Chief Executive Officer, Khaled Kawan

Non-Executive Independent Member of the Board, Anwar Al Mudhaf
Non-Executive / Non-independent Deputy Chairman of the Board, Hilal Al Mutairi
Deputy Group Chief Executive Officer, Sael Al Waary
Non-Executive Independent Member of the Board, Yousef Al Awadi
Non-Executive Independent Member of the Board, Farouk El Okdah
Non-Executive / Non-independent Chairman of the Board, Saddek Al Kaber
Group Chief Financial Officer, Brendon Hopkins
Non-Executive / Non-independent Member of the Board, Tarik Yousef
Non-Executive / Non-independent Member of the Board, Ahmed Ferjani
Group Head of Wholesale Banking, Jonathan Robinson
Group Chief Auditor, Johan Hundertmark
Non-Executive / Non-independent Member of the Board, Abdullah Al Humaidhi
Group Treasurer, Christopher Wilmot
Non-Executive Independent Member of the Board, Bashir Omer
Chief Operating Officer, Alex Leenen
Auditors: Ernst & Young

LOCATIONS

HQ: Arab Banking Corporation (B.S.C.) (Bahrain)
ABC Tower, Diplomatic Area, P.O. Box 5698, Manama
Phone: (973) 17 543 000   **Fax:** (973) 17 533 163
Web: www.bank-abc.com

COMPETITORS

ARAB NATIONAL BANK   UNITED OVERSEAS BANK
FIRST INTERNATIONAL   LIMITED
  BANK OF ISRAEL LTD

HISTORICAL FINANCIALS
Company Type: Public

Income Statement				FYE: December 31
	ASSETS ($ mil.)	NET INCOME ($ mil.)	INCOME AS % OF ASSETS	EMPLOYEES
12/19	30,068	194	0.6%	436
12/18	29,549	202	0.7%	394
12/17	29,499	193	0.7%	358
12/16	30,141	183	0.6%	344
12/15	28,195	180	0.6%	344
Annual Growth	1.6%	1.9%	—	6.1%

2019 Year-End Financials
Return on assets: 0.6%
Return on equity: 4.9%
Long-term debt ($ mil.): —
No. of shares (mil.): —
Sales ($ mil): 1,679

Dividends
  Yield: —
  Payout: 50.0%
Market value ($ mil.): —

Arab National Bank

Arab National Bank offers banking services for primarily commercial but also growing retail segments of the Saudi Arabia market including Shariah (Islamic) services. Its 200-plus branches (51 are women-only) provide savings and checking accounts credit and debit cards loans and investment services. Its Corporate Banking Group segment serves mid-sized and large Saudi businesses while its treasury branch offers foreign exchange services international stock trading international

bonds and margin trading accounts. Arab National Bank also owns and operates one branch located in the UK. Arab Bank owns a 40% stake in Arab National Bank which was formed in 1979.
Auditors: Ernst & Young & Co.

LOCATIONS

HQ: Arab National Bank
P.O. Box 56921, Riyadh 11564
Phone: (966) 1 402 9000   **Fax:** (966) 1 402 7747
Web: www.anb.com.sa

COMPETITORS

ARAB BANK PLC   RIYAD BANK

HISTORICAL FINANCIALS
Company Type: Public

Income Statement				FYE: December 31
	ASSETS ($ mil.)	NET INCOME ($ mil.)	INCOME AS % OF ASSETS	EMPLOYEES
12/19	48,917	806	1.6%	4,170
12/18	47,544	882	1.9%	4,132
12/17	45,787	807	1.8%	4,170
12/16	45,329	760	1.7%	4,403
12/15	45,393	789	1.7%	4,846
Annual Growth	1.9%	0.5%	—	(3.7%)

2019 Year-End Financials
Return on assets: 1.6%
Return on equity: 11.0%
Long-term debt ($ mil.): —
No. of shares (mil.): 1,500
Sales ($ mil): 2,521

Dividends
  Yield: —
  Payout: 49.5%
Market value ($ mil.): —

ArcelorMittal SA

ArcelorMittal produces a broad range of high-quality finished and semi-finished steel products. Specifically ArcelorMittal produces flat products including sheet and plate and long products including bars rods and structural shapes. It also produces pipes and tubes for various applications. ArcelorMittal sells its products primarily in local markets and to a diverse range of customers in approximately 160 countries including the automotive appliance engineering construction and machinery industries.

Operations
ArcelorMittal reports its business in the following five reportable segments corresponding to continuing activities: NAFTA Brazil Europe ACIS and Mining.

Europe accounts for about half of total revenue produces flat long and tubular products. Flat products include hot-rolled coil cold-rolled coil coated products tinplate plate and slab. These products are sold primarily to customers in the automotive general and packaging sectors.

NAFTA (nearly 25%) produces flat long and tubular products. Flat products include slabs hot-rolled coil cold-rolled coil coated steel products and plate and are sold primarily to customers in the following sectors: automotive energy construction packaging and appliances and via distributors and processors. Flat product facilities are located at seven integrated and mini-mill sites located in three countries.

Brazil (some 10%) produces flat long and tubular products. Flat products include slabs hot-rolled

coil cold-rolled coil and coated steel. Long products comprise sections wire rod bar and rebars billets and wire drawing. In 2020 shipments from Brazil totaled 9.4 million tonnes.

ACIS (around 10%) produces a combination of flat long and tubular products. It has five flat and long production facilities in three countries. In 2020 shipments from ACIS totaled 9.9 million tonnes with shipments made on a worldwide basis.

Mining generates less than 10 % of total revenue provides the company's steel operations with high quality and low-cost iron ore and coal reserves and also sells limited amounts of mineral products to third parties. The Company's mines are located in North and South America Europe Africa and CIS.

Geographic Reach
Headquartered in Luxembourg City ArcelorMittal has steel-making operations in more than 15 countries on four continents including about 40 integrated and mini-mill steel-making facilities.

The company has iron ore mines in Brazil Bosnia Canada Kazakhstan Liberia Mexico Ukraine and the US with coal mining in Kazakhstan and the US.

ArcelorMittal's logistics network includes some 15 owned or partially owned deep-water ports and linked railway sidings.

Sales and Marketing
ArcelorMittal's markets are all those that consume steel as an input including the automotive appliance engineering construction energy and machinery markets. It sells its steel products primarily in local markets and through its centralized marketing organization to a diverse range of customers in approximately 160 countries. The company prefers to sell exports through its international network of sales agencies to ensure that all ArcelorMittal products are presented to the market in a cost-efficient and coordinated manner.

Financial Performance
The company's revenue in 2020 decreased to $53.3 billion compared to $70.6 billion in 2019 primarily due to the impacts of the COVID-19 pandemic on lower steel shipments and an 8% decrease in average steel selling prices.

Net loss for fiscal 2020 decreased to $678 million compared to $2.4 billion in the prior year.

Cash held by the company at the end of fiscal 2020 increased to $6.6 billion. Cash provided by operations was $4.1 billion while cash used for investing and financing activities were $2.0 billion and $1.5 billion respectively. Main cash uses were purchase of property plant and equipment and intangibles; and payments of short-term debt.

Strategy
ArcelorMittal's success is built on its core values of sustainability quality and leadership and the entrepreneurial boldness that has empowered its emergence as the first truly global steel and mining company. Acknowledging that a combination of structural issues and macroeconomic conditions will continue to challenge returns in its sector the company has adapted its footprint to the new demand realities intensified its efforts to control costs and repositioned its operations to outperform its competitors.

Against this backdrop ArcelorMittal's strategy is to leverage four distinctive attributes that will enable it to capture leading positions in the most attractive areas of the steel industry value chain from mining at one end to distribution and first-stage processing at the other: Global scale and scope; Unmatched technical capabilities; Diverse portfolio of steel and related businesses particularly mining; and Financial capability.

HISTORY

ArcelorMittal is the product of decades of steel-making by India's Mittal family. In 1967 patriarch Mohan Mittal unsuccessfully tried to open a steel mill in Egypt. He and his four younger brothers then set up a steel company in India but squabbles pushed Mohan to chart his own course eventually giving rise to an empire that flourished under the Ispat name. Mohan's son Lakshmi began working part-time at the family steel mill while in school; he started full-time at 21 after graduating in 1971.

Mohan set up an operation in Indonesia in 1975 (Ispat Indo) and put Lakshmi in charge. The next year fueled by ambitions and held back by government regulations in India Lakshmi formed Ispat International in Jakarta Indonesia to focus on expansion through acquisitions. He spent the next decade strengthening the Indonesian operations and perfecting the minimill process using direct-reduced iron (DRI).

Ispat took advantage of the recessionary late 1980s and early 1990s by making a string of acquisitions. In 1988 it took over the management of Trinidad and Tobago's state steel companies (bought in 1994; renamed Caribbean Ispat).

In 1992 Ispat bought Mexico's third-largest (albeit bankrupt) steel and DRI producer. Two years later it acquired Canada's Sidbec-Dosco steelmaker. Also that year Lakshmi took exclusive control of international operations leaving his brothers Pramod and Vinod to control the Indian divisions.

The mid-1990s brought more acquisitions: In 1995 Ispat bought Germany's Hamburger Stahlwerks and a mill in Kazakhstan. The next year it purchased Ireland's only steelmaker Irish Steel. Lakshmi moved to London in 1996 and purchased a home on Bishops Avenue known as "millionaire's row." (Saudi Arabia's King Fahd was a neighbor.)

In 1997 the company bought the long-product (wire rod) division of Germany's Thyssen AG (renamed Ispat Stahlwerk Ruhrort and Ispat Walzdraht Hochfeld). It also completed a $776 million IPO.

Ispat acquired Chicago-based Inland Steel in 1998 (and renamed it Ispat Inland) including the steel-finishing operations of I/N Tek (60% Inland-owned joint venture with Nippon Steel) and I/N Kote (50% Inland-owned joint venture with NSC).

In 1999 Ispat formed a joint venture with Mexican steelmaker Grupo Imsa to make flat-rolled steel to sell throughout most of the Americas. It also paid $96 million for France-based Usinor's Unimétal Tréfileurope and Société Métallurgique de Révigny subsidiaries which specialize in carbon long products. That year Ispat Inland became the target of a US federal criminal grand jury investigation and a related civil lawsuit for allegedly defrauding the Louisiana Highway Department. (The case was settled for $30 million with the cost split between Ispat Inland and Contech Construction Products Inc. of Ohio.)

In 2000 the company responded to a downturn in the steel industry by starting a Web-based joint venture with Commerce One to connect buyers and sellers in the worldwide metals market. It also offered to buy VSZ Slovakia's #1 steelworks but was outbid by U.S. Steel.

After struggling with heavy debt high labor and energy costs new environmental regulations and EU steel quotas in 2001 Ispat closed down its subsidiary Irish Ispat which accounted for about 2% of the parent company's steel production.

In 2002 the company's 51%-owned pipe making subsidiary Productura Mexicana de Tuberia sold almost all of its production assets.

The present ArcelorMittal was forged in 2004 when Ispat International (of which the Mittal family owned 70%) purchased LNM Holdings (wholly owned by the Mittals) for $13 billion. In 2006 the former Mittal Steel agreed to buy rival Arcelor for about $34 billion to create ArcelorMittal.

Mittal Steel had established its hold on the world steel market through its 2005 purchase of the US-based International Steel Group (ISG) for $4.5 billion. The purchase made the company the largest steel producer (ahead of U.S. Steel and Nucor) in the US a market that had long been a targeted area for expansion for CEO Mittal. Once the deal closed the company combined ISG's operations with those of subsidiary Ispat Inland to form a single North American entity Mittal Steel USA (now ArcelorMittal USA).

Also in 2005 Mittal Steel acquired a 93% stake in Ukrainian state-run steel company KryvorizhStal with the winning $4.84 billion bid in an auction held by the Ukrainian government. The price was high but Mittal was anxious to gain a stronger foothold in the region — and to keep its rivals away from KryvorizhStal. (This fact incidentally went a long way to convincing Mittal it needed to combine with Arcelor; the competition for acquisitions was driving prices dramatically upward.)

The company also began to broaden its portfolio outside the steel industry dipping its toe into the energy business. In mid-2005 Mittal formed two joint ventures with India's government-controlled Oil & Natural Gas Corporation: one to buy stakes in foreign oil and gas projects the other involved in oil and gas trading and shipping. The ventures began to look for business in places like Indonesia Kazakhstan Angola and Trinidad and Tobago.

After consolidating his family's various steel interests in the early part of this decade Mittal began work on the steel industry as a whole and was soon the world's largest steel producer.

By 2006 Mittal Steel no longer was content to be merely the world's largest steel producer; it wanted to dominate the market. The company announced an offer to the shareholders of Arcelor then the industry's #2 player to buy that company and in the process create the world's first 100-million-ton steel producer. Arcelor and seemingly half the governments of Western Europe initially fought the attempt.

Mittal improved its proposed price however and Arcelor's board finally approved the offer when Mittal also made ownership/corporate governance concessions. The combined company is 43% owned by the Mittal family. After a few months of a transitional management team arrangement Lakshmi Mittal took over as CEO of the combined company toward the end of 2006.

In 2009 ArcelorMittal completed its acquisition of the laser-welding steel activities of Noble International a leader in the niche industry. It also acquired Mexican steel producer Sicarsta for nearly $1.5 billion an acquisition that combined with its Lazaro Cardenas created Mexico's largest steel company.

In 2011 the company spun off its stainless and specialty steels steel operations into Aperam which immediately became the world's sixth-largest stainless steel producer. ArcelorMittal made the decision in 2010 to spin off its stainless steel units in Europe and Brazil after determining that they were underperforming and would better thrive as a separate business.

After spinning its wheels in an escalating bidding war in 2011 ArcelorMittal joined rival Nunavut Iron Ore in making a joint acquisition of Canada-based Baffinland Iron Mines for $594 million. Both companies sought access to Baffinland's Mary River Project an undeveloped deposit of iron ore on sparsely populated North Baffin Island located inside the Arctic Circle as a source of raw materials. The venture faces stiff challenges including building an infrastructure around the mine's formidable location and shipping the ore out to Europe and other production sites.

Also that year the company bought a 40% stake in G Steel Public Company greatly expanding its presence in Asia. G Steel produces about 2.5 million ton of steel annually at its two slab-rolling plants in Thailand. The deal was part of ArcelorMittal's strategy of establishing a presence in emerging markets with with the potential for future growth.

In 2012 ArcelorMittal expanded its presence in China by increasing its stake in a joint venture with Valin Group known as Valin ArcelorMittal Automotive (VAMA) from 33% to 49%. VAMA is trying to enhance its position in China as a supplier of high-strength steels and products for the automotive market. The joint venture scheduled to become operational in 2014 will increase its planned capacity from 1.2 million tons to 1.5 million tons.

That year it sold New Jersey-based Skyline Steel a North American steel foundation and piling products distributor and specialty steel plate and bar producer Astralloy to US-based Nucor for $605 million.

EXECUTIVES

President, Chief Executive Officer, Member of the Management Committee, Member of the Executive Board, Aditya Mittal

Group Compliance, Data Protection Officer and Company Secretary, Henk Scheffer

Vice President, Member of the Management Board, Chief executive officer of global research and development, Gregory Ludkovsky

Vice President, Member of the Management Committee, Corporate Finance and Head of Investor Relations, Daniel Fairclough

EVP, Head of Strategy, CTO, R&D, CCM, Global Automotive, Communications and Corporate Responsibility, Brian Aranha

Vice President, Member of the Management Board, Chief executive officers, ArcelorMittal Poland, country head of Poland, head of human resources and IS/IT (ArcelorMittal Europe – Flat products) and hea, Sanjay Samaddar

Executive Vice President, Member of the Executive Board, Member of the Management Committee, Chief Executive Officer ArcelorMittal South America Long, Jefferson de Paula

Executive Vice President, Member of the Management Committee, Member of the Executive Board, Chief Executive Officer - ArcelorMittal Europe, Geert Van Poelvoorde

Vice President, Member of the Management Committee, Chief Executive Officer ArcelorMittal Europe – Long Products, Augustine Kochuparampil

Vice President - - Head of strategy and CCM (commercial coordination and marketing), Member of the Management Board, David Clarke

Vice President, Member of the Management Committee, Chief Executive Officer ArcelorMittal Mexico, Victor Cairo

Vice President, Member of the Management Board, Director of operations AM/NS India, Wim Van Gerven

Chief Financial Officer, Member of the Management Committee, Genuino Christino

Vice President, Member of the Management Board, President and chief executive officer ArcelorMittal Dofasco, Sean Donnelly

Vice President, Member of the Management Committee, Chief Executive Officer ArcelorMittal CIS (ArcelorMittal Kryvyi Rih, Ukraine and ArcelorMittal Temirtau, Kazakhstan), Vijay Goyal

Member of the Management committee, Member of the Executive committee, Chief Executive Officer of ArcelorMittal North America, John Brett

Non-Executive Independent Director, Tye Winston Burt
Non-Executive Independent Director, Etienne Schneider
Global General Counsel, Sapan Gupta
Executive Vice President, Member of the Executive Board, Member of the Management Committee, Chief Executive Officer ArcelorMittal Mining, Simon Wandke
Vice President - Head of Corporate Business Optimization, Member of the Management Committee, Chief Executive Officer ArcelorMittal North America, Brad Davey
Vice President, Member of the Management Committee, Chief Executive Officer - ArcelorMittal Europe – Flat Products, Yves Koeberle
Auditors: Deloitte Audit S.a.r.l.

LOCATIONS

HQ: ArcelorMittal SA
24-26, Boulevard dAvranches, Luxembourg L-1160
Phone: (352) 4792 1   **Fax:** (352) 4792 2235
Web: www.arcelormittal.com

2018 Sales

	$ mil.	% of total
Europe	38,263	50
Americas	29	38
Asia & Africa	8,702	12
Total	**76,033**	**100**

PRODUCTS/OPERATIONS

2018 Sales

	% of total
NAFTA	25
Europe	49
Brazil	11
ACIS	10
Mining	5
Others and eliminations	-
Total	**100**

2018 sales

Sales by type of products	% of total
Flat products	61
Long products	21
Tubular products	3
Mining products	1
Others	14
Total	**100**

Segments and Selected Products

Flat Carbon Europe
  Coated products
  Coil
  Cold-rolled
  Hot-rolled
  Plate
  Slab
  Tin plate
Flat Carbon Americas
  Coated products
  Steel
  Plate
  Coil
  Cold-rolled
  Hot-rolled
  Slabs
Long Carbon Americas & Europe
  Billets
  Blooms
  Rebar
  Sections
  Wire rod
Asia Africa & Comonwealth of Independent States
  Flat products
  Long products
  Pipes
  Tubes
ArcelorMittal Steel Solutions & Services (in-house trading and distribution arm)

COMPETITORS

DC ALABAMA INC.	SSAB AB
Gerdau S/A	TATA STEEL EUROPE
Hyundai Steel Company	LIMITED
NIPPON DENKO CO. LTD.	UNITED STATES STEEL
NLMK PAO	CORPORATION
Outokumpu Oyj	thyssenkrupp AG
Posco Co. Ltd.	

HISTORICAL FINANCIALS
Company Type: Public

Income Statement
FYE: December 31

	REVENUE ($ mil.)	NET INCOME ($ mil.)	NET PROFIT MARGIN	EMPLOYEES
12/20	53,270	(733)	—	167,743
12/19	70,615	(2,391)	—	191,248
12/18	76,033	5,149	6.8%	208,583
12/17	68,679	4,568	6.7%	197,108
12/16	56,791	1,779	3.1%	198,517
Annual Growth	**(1.6%)**	**—**		**(4.1%)**

2020 Year-End Financials

Debt ratio: 15.0%	No. of shares (mil.): 1,080
Return on equity: (-1.9%)	Dividends
Cash ($ mil.): 5,600	Yield: —
Current ratio: 1.23	Payout: —
Long-term debt ($ mil.): 9,815	Market value ($ mil.): 24,749

	STOCK PRICE ($) FY Close	P/E High/Low		PER SHARE ($) Earnings	Dividends	Book Value
12/20	22.90	—	—	(0.64)	0.00	35.42
12/19	17.54	—	—	(2.42)	0.17	38.06
12/18	20.67	7	4	5.04	0.09	41.52
12/17	32.31	7	2	4.46	0.00	38.03
12/16	7.30	5	2	1.86	0.00	29.56
Annual Growth	**33.1%**	—	—	—	—	**4.6%**

Arch Capital Group Ltd

Arch Capital Group offers property/casualty insurance and reinsurance through subsidiaries in Bermuda Canada Europe Asia and the US. Its insurance subsidiaries offer marine and aviation professional liability health care liability and other specialty lines. The company's US subsidiary Arch Insurance Group specializes in excess and surplus lines coverage. The company's Arch Re reinsurance subsidiaries focus on property/casualty coverage including catastrophe and some specialty lines. The company distributes its products through both wholesale and retail brokers.

HISTORY

Fortuitous timing helped the company as it transformed itself starting in 2000 when what was Arch-US sold off the assets of its Risk Capital Reinsurance to Folksamerica Reinsurance. It retained the core of the company and used it to form Arch Capital Group. As a freshly formed company it did not face the load of claims that hit more established insurers following the events of September 11 2001. Arch Capital Group commenced underwriting in October 2001 and capitalized on soaring rates and the need for fresh reinsurers. Earlier in that year the company had formed Arch Reinsurance Ltd (Bermuda) and had acquired other insurance operations to

As part of its transformation the company has sold off operations that no longer fit including its non-standard automobile business merchant banker Hales & Company which specialized in insurance mergers and acquisitions and property/casualty insurer American Independent Insurance.

EXECUTIVES

Independent Director, Louis Paglia
Chief Financial Officer, Executive Vice President, Treasurer, Francois Morin, $625,000 total compensation
Independent Director, Brian Posner
Independent Director, Eric Doppstadt
Chief Operations Officer of Arch Capital Services Inc, Chris Hovey
Chief Strategy and Innovation Officer at Arch Capital, Jay Rajendra
Independent Director, Moira Kilcoyne
Independent Director, Thomas Watjen
Independent Director, Laurie Goodman
Independent Director, Eugene Sunshine
Director, Eileen Mallesch
Director, Francis Ebong
Executive Vice President, Chief Human Resources Officer of Arch Capital Services Inc, Jennifer Centrone
President, Chief Underwriting Officer, Nicolas Papadopoulo, $750,000 total compensation
Senior Vice President Chief Investment Officer; President of Arch Investment Management Ltd., W. Preston Hutchings, $483,333 total compensation
Independent Director, John Bunce
President, General Counsel of Arch Capital Services Inc., Louis Petrillo, $350,000 total compensation
Independent Chairman of the Board, John Pasquesi
Auditors: PricewaterhouseCoopers LLP

LOCATIONS

HQ: Arch Capital Group Ltd
Waterloo House, Ground Floor, 100 Pitts Bay Road, Pembroke HM 08
Phone: (1) 441 278 9250   **Fax:** (1) 441 278 9255
Web: www.archcapgroup.com

COMPETITORS

AMERICAN FINANCIAL GROUP INC.	INSURANCE COMPANY OF THE WEST
AMERITRUST GROUP INC.	Maiden Holdings Ltd
AMWINS GROUP INC.	SAFECO INSURANCE
ARROWPOINT CAPITAL CORP.	COMPANY OF AMERICA
BESSO LIMITED	SEABRIGHT HOLDINGS INC.
GUY CARPENTER & COMPANY LLC	

HISTORICAL FINANCIALS
Company Type: Public

Income Statement
FYE: December 31

	ASSETS ($ mil.)	NET INCOME ($ mil.)	INCOME AS % OF ASSETS	EMPLOYEES
12/20	43,282	1,405	3.2%	4,500
12/19	37,885	1,636	4.3%	4,300
12/18	32,218	757	2.4%	3,642
12/17	32,051	619	1.9%	3,140
12/16	29,372	692	2.4%	3,250
Annual Growth	**10.2%**	**19.3%**	**—**	**8.5%**

Return on assets: 3.4%
Return on equity: 11.3%
Long-term debt ($ mil.): —
No. of shares (mil.): 406
Sales ($ mil): 8,525

Dividends
Yield: —
Payout: —
Market value ($ mil.): —

Asahi Group Holdings Ltd.

Auditors: KPMG AZSA LLC

LOCATIONS

HQ: Asahi Group Holdings Ltd.
1-23-1 Azumabashi, Sumida-ku, Tokyo 130-8602
Phone: (81) 3 5608 5116
Web: www.asahigroup-holdings.com

HISTORICAL FINANCIALS

Company Type: Public

Income Statement				FYE: December 31
	REVENUE ($ mil.)	NET INCOME ($ mil.)	NET PROFIT MARGIN	EMPLOYEES
12/20	19,673	900	4.6%	36,699
12/19	19,241	1,309	6.8%	35,996
12/18	19,280	1,373	7.1%	34,663
12/17	18,529	1,253	6.8%	38,319
12/16	14,593	762	5.2%	31,142
Annual Growth	7.8%	4.2%	—	4.2%

2020 Year-End Financials

Debt ratio: 0.3%
Return on equity: 6.7%
Cash ($ mil.): 470
Current ratio: 0.42
Long-term debt ($ mil.): 8,720

No. of shares (mil.): 506
Dividends
Yield: —
Payout: 53.9%
Market value ($ mil.): —

Asahi Kasei Corp

Auditors: PricewaterhouseCoopers Aarata LLC

LOCATIONS

HQ: Asahi Kasei Corp
1-1-2 Yuraku-cho, Chiyoda-ku, Tokyo 100-8440
Phone: (81) 3 6699 3030
Web: www.asahi-kasei.co.jp

HISTORICAL FINANCIALS

Company Type: Public

Income Statement				FYE: March 31
	REVENUE ($ mil.)	NET INCOME ($ mil.)	NET PROFIT MARGIN	EMPLOYEES
03/21	19,020	720	3.8%	44,497
03/20	19,821	957	4.8%	40,689
03/19	19,598	1,332	6.8%	39,283
03/18	19,232	1,603	8.3%	34,670
03/17	16,841	1,028	6.1%	33,720
Annual Growth	3.1%	(8.5%)	—	7.2%

2021 Year-End Financials

Debt ratio: 0.2%
Return on equity: 5.6%
Cash ($ mil.): 2,002
Current ratio: 1.62
Long-term debt ($ mil.): 3,922

No. of shares (mil.): 1,387
Dividends
Yield: 2.6%
Payout: —
Market value ($ mil.): 32,337

	STOCK PRICE ($) FY Close	P/E High/Low		PER SHARE ($) Earnings	Dividends	Book Value
03/21	23.30	0	0	0.52	0.62	9.55
03/20	14.03	0	0	0.69	0.64	9.02
03/19	20.72	0	0	0.95	0.67	8.93
03/18	26.80	0	0	1.15	0.53	8.68
03/17	19.53	0	0	0.74	0.36	7.37
Annual Growth	4.5%	—		(8.4%)	14.7%	6.7%

ASE Technology Holding Co Ltd

Advanced Semiconductor Engineering (ASE) helps chip makers wrap up production. The company is one of the world's leading providers of semiconductor packaging services; it also designs and manufactures interconnect materials and provides front-end and final chip testing services through its subsidiary ASE Test. The company provides electronic manufacturing services through Universal Scientific Industrial (USI) and it owns ISE Labs an engineering test services provider in Silicon Valley. Customers in the US account for about 65% of ASE's sales. The company has more than 240 customers around the world; some of the largest include Broadcom Microsoft NVIDIA and STMicroelectronics.

Auditors: Deloitte & Touche

LOCATIONS

HQ: ASE Technology Holding Co Ltd
26, Chin 3rd Road, Kaohsiung
Phone: (886) 2 6636 5678   **Fax:** (886) 2 2757 6121
Web: www.aseglobal.com

2016 Sales

	% of total
US	68
Taiwan	14
Asia	9
Europe	8
Others	1
Total	100

PRODUCTS/OPERATIONS

2017 Sales

	% of total
EMS	46
Packaging	43
Testing	9
Other	2
Total	100

2017 Sales

	% of total
IC Wire Bonding	49
Bumping Flip Chip WLP and SiP	30
Discrete and Other	11
Total	100

Selected Services

Material offerings
  Substrates
Packaging
  Ball grid array (BGA)
  Chip scale package (CSP)
  Dual-in-line
  Flip chip (flipping chip to connect with substrate)
  Pb free solution (lead-free)
  Pin grid array (PGA)
  Plastic-leaded chip carrier packages (PLCCs)
  Quad flat packages (QFP)
  SiP (system in package)
  Small-outline plastic J-bend packages (SOJ)
  Small-outline plastic packages (SOP)
  Thin quad flat packages (TQFP)
  Thin small-outline plastic packages (TSOP)
Testing
  Electrical design validation
  Failure analysis
  Front-end engineering testing
  Logic/mixed-signal final testing
  Memory final testing
  Reliability analysis
  Software program development
  Wafer probing
Other
  Burn-in testing
  Dry pack
  Tape and reel

Selected Subsidiaries and Affiliates

ASE Japan
ASE Korea
ASE Holding Electronics (Philippines) Incorporated
ASE Malaysia
ASE Test
Hung Ching (real estate development)
ISE Labs Inc. (engineering and testing US)
Universal Scientific Industrial Co. Ltd. (contract
  electronics manufacturing)

COMPETITORS

3D SYSTEMS CORPORATION
ELECTRONICS
ADVANTEST AMERICA
  CORPORATION (DEL)
CMC MATERIALS INC.
ELECTRO SCIENTIFIC
  INDUSTRIES INC.
LATTICE SEMICONDUCTOR
  CORPORATION
ONTO INNOVATION INC.

RENESAS

AMERICA INC.
SILICON LABORATORIES
  INC.
UNIVERSAL SCIENTIFIC
  INDUSTRIAL CO. LTD.
VENTURE

LIMITED
VERSUM MATERIALS INC.

HISTORICAL FINANCIALS

Company Type: Public

Income Statement				FYE: December 31
	REVENUE ($ mil.)	NET INCOME ($ mil.)	NET PROFIT MARGIN	EMPLOYEES
12/20	16,973	959	5.7%	101,981
12/19	13,801	569	4.1%	96,528
12/18	12,133	825	6.8%	93,891
12/17	9,795	775	7.9%	68,753
12/16	8,496	670	7.9%	0
Annual Growth	18.9%	9.4%	—	—

2020 Year-End Financials

Debt ratio: 1.1%
Return on equity: 12.9%
Cash ($ mil.): 1,833
Current ratio: 1.28
Long-term debt ($ mil.): 5,391

No. of shares (mil.): —
Dividends
Yield: 1.5%
Payout: 45.9%
Market value ($ mil.): —

	STOCK PRICE ($) FY Close	P/E High/Low		PER SHARE ($) Earnings	Dividends	Book Value
12/20	5.84	1	1	0.22	0.09	1.80
12/19	5.56	1	1	0.13	0.11	1.56
12/18	3.75	1	1	0.19	0.14	1.56
Annual Growth	24.8%	—		3.6%	(11.4%)	3.6%

ASML Holding NV

ASML Holding is one of the world's largest makers of semiconductor manufacturing equipment specializing in photolithography systems used to imprint circuitry patterns onto silicon wafers. ASML's products include EUV (extreme ultraviolet) lithography systems DUV (deep ultraviolet) lithography systems refurbished systems and metrology and inspection systems. Headquartered in Veldhoven the Netherlands ASML staffs some 60 offices in more than 15 countries. More than 70% of its revenue comes from chip manufacturers in Asia and its customers include the world's biggest chipmakers. The company was founded in 1984 and has produced versions of its flagship TWINSCAN systems since 2001.

Financial Performance

ASML has turned in steady robust growth over the past five years with revenue increasing at an average annual rate of about 17%.

In 2018 sales jumped 22% to ?10.6 billion up about ?1.7 billion in 2017 driven by a 28% rise in system sales. The company sold more systems and more high-end systems in 2018. Revenue from China was 100% higher in 2018 over 2017 as chipmakers outfitted new factories in the country.

ASML's profit advanced to about ?2.6 billion in 2018 from about ?2 billion in 2017 lifted by the stronger revenue especially the higher margins on the high-end equipment.

The company had ?3.1 billion in cash in 2018 compared to ?2.2 billion the year before. In 2018 operating activities provided ?3 billion while investing activities used ?491 million and financing activities used ?1.7 billion.

Strategy

ASML's DUV systems have been the workhorse of the company's product line providing a strong base of installed systems. And the systems are still going strong. The company sold about 190 DUV systems in 2018 a 17% increase from 2017.

ASML's more advanced EUV systems which can lay down more intricate designs on smaller pieces of silicon are just getting off the ground. ASML sold 18 EUV systems in 2018 and it expects to ship 30 in 2019. To accelerate the pace of adoption the company raised its research and development spending devoted to EUV equipment. Further the company bought about 25% of indirect interest in Carl Zeiss SMT GmbH a manufacturer of optical devices in Germany to aid continued development of EUV systems.

ASML is riding a wave of chip manufacturers moving to new processes for patterning intricate features that can only be produced economically with EUV equipment. The need for advanced chips for 5G communications networks contributes a rising demand for logic chips made with EUV systems.

ASML's sales in China doubled in 2018 from 2017 increasing the country's share of ASML sales to nearly 20%. While not substantially affected by trade tensions between China and the US in 2018 ASML could experience fallout if US-China trade tensions continue. In particular US restrictions on what technology can be sold to Chinese customers could have an impact of ASML's sales which has some operations in the US.

HISTORY

ASML Holding's pedigree is as good as its timing was bad. The company was formed in 1984 under the name ASM Lithography Holding as a joint venture between Advanced Semiconductor Materials (ASM; now ASM International) and the Scientific and Industrial Equipment Division of Philips. ASML had already begun selling a wafer stepper (a device that transfers reticle patterns onto silicon wafers) when the joint venture was announced.

Unfortunately the chip industry was headed into one of its infamous slumps. Startup costs dogged both ASM and Philips. Though the industry downturn abated by 1987 the financial stresses created by the slump led ASM to sell its 50% stake in ASML to Philips in 1988.

Philips offered a minority stake in ASML to the public in 1995. By 1998 ASML was battling Canon for the stepper industry's #2 spot. Also that year the company formed a unit to develop lithography equipment for makers of thin-film heads (used in recording and data storage) MEMS (microelectromechanical systems) and compound semiconductors.

In 1999 ASML joined with Applied Materials and Lucent Technologies (now Alcatel-Lucent) to form SCALPEL an alliance formed to speed development of electron beam lithography. Also that year the company bought MicroUnity Systems' MaskTools unit (optical proximity correction technology). In 2000 Doug Dunn a former CEO of the Philips Consumer Electronics Division became ASML's president and CEO.

ASML later agreed to acquire Silicon Valley Group (SVG) in a deal valued at about $1.6 billion. In 2001 after many delays — and opposition from some US business groups — the US government cleared the way for the merger. As part of the deal ASML and SVG were given six months to sell SVG's Tinsley unit which made highly specialized optical gear for sensitive aerospace and military applications. Late in the year ASML sold Tinsley to privately held SSG Precision Optronics (now L-3 SSG-Tinsley).

Also in 2001 Philips sold off nearly three-fourths of its remaining 24% stake in ASML. Later that year ASML cut 1400 jobs — about one-sixth of its workforce — in the face of the worst downturn yet in the worldwide chip industry. That year the company also changed its name from ASM Lithography Holding to ASML Holding.

In 2004 Dunn retired as CEO. He was succeeded by Eric Meurice a veteran executive of THOMSON Dell and Intel. ASML and Nikon reached a legal settlement on global patent litigation that year including a cross-licensing agreement. The settlement called for ASML to make an initial payment of $60 million to Nikon followed by payments of $9 million a year for three years.

Intel and Toshiba two of the biggest chip makers in the world licensed ASML's Scattering Bar Technology in 2005 technology that helped improve wafer yield results using ASML equipment. In 2007 ASML acquired Brion Technologies a developer of software for photolithography optimization for $270 million in cash. Founded in 2002 Brion became a wholly owned subsidiary of ASML.

EXECUTIVES

Chairman of the Board of Management, President, Chief Executive Officer, Peter Wennink, $1,162,194 total compensation
President, Chief Technology Officer, Vice Chairman of the Board of Management, Martin van den Brink, $1,162,194 total compensation
Executive Vice President and Chief Strategy Officer Member of the Board of Management, Frits van Hout, $790,747 total compensation
Member of the Supervisory Board, D. Durcan
Executive Vice President, Chief Operations Officer and Member of the Board of Management, Frederic Schneider-Maunoury, $790,747 total compensation

Independent Non-Executive Vice Chairman of the Supervisory Board, Douglas Grose
Independent Non-Executive Member of the Supervisory Board, Antoinette Aris
Independent Non-Executive Member of the Supervisory Board, Johannes Stork
Independent Non-Executive Member of the Supervisory Board, Carla Smits-Nusteling
Executive Vice President, Business Line EUV, Member of the Board of Management, Christophe Fouquet, $790,747 total compensation
Independent Non-Executive Member of the Supervisory Board, Terri Kelly
Member of the Supervisory Board, Warren East
Independent Non-Executive Chairman of the Supervisory Board, Gerard Kleisterlee
Independent Non-Executive Member of the Supervisory Board, Rolf-Dieter Schwalb
Chief Financial Officer, Executive Vice President, Member of the Board of Management, Roger Dassen, $790,747 total compensation
Auditors: KPMG Accountants N.V.

LOCATIONS

HQ: ASML Holding NV
 De Run 6501, Veldhoven 5504 DR
Phone: (31) 40 268 3000
Web: www.asml.com

2018 Sales

	% of total
Korea	34
Taiwan	18
United States	18
China	17
EMEA	6
Japan	5
Singapore	2
Total	**100**

PRODUCTS/OPERATIONS

2018 Sales

	% of total
Net system sales	75
Net service and field option sales	25
Total	**100**

COMPETITORS

ARD Holdings S.A.	Koninklijke Philips
ASM International N.V.	N.V.
AVAGO TECHNOLOGIES	Koninklijke Vopak N.V.
LIMITED	LATTICE SEMICONDUCTOR
BROADCOM PTE. LTD.	CORPORATION
CYMER INC.	LyondellBasell
Evonik Industries AG	Industries N.V.
Expro Group Holdings	Outokumpu Oyj
N.V.	PHOTRONICS INC.
Gemalto B.V.	SPECTRIS PLC
JENOPTIK AG	TT ELECTRONICS PLC

HISTORICAL FINANCIALS

Company Type: Public

Income Statement				FYE: December 31
	REVENUE ($ mil.)	NET INCOME ($ mil.)	NET PROFIT MARGIN	EMPLOYEES
12/21	21,065	6,658	31.6%	32,016
12/20	17,155	4,361	25.4%	28,073
12/19	13,271	2,910	21.9%	24,900
12/18	12,533	2,967	23.7%	16,647
12/17	10,852	2,539	23.4%	19,216
Annual Growth	18.0%	27.3%	—	13.6%

2021 Year-End Financials

Debt ratio: 17.1%
Return on equity: 49.0%
Cash ($ mil.): 7,868
Current ratio: 1.48
Long-term debt ($ mil.): 4,612
No. of shares (mil.): 402
Dividends
Yield: 0.4%
Payout: 21.9%
Market value ($ mil.): —

Assicurazioni Generali S.p.A.

Italy's largest insurance company (and one of the largest in Europe) Assicurazioni Generali writes insurance for risks as varied as pensions and car insurance. Present in almost 50 countries Generali's core businesses are involved in both life and property/casualty insurance (including accident health motor and home). The company targets individuals and SMEs and counts around 65.9 million customers across Europe the Asia/Pacific region and Latin America. Its home country Italy represents a third of revenue. Generali has been in business since 1831.

Operations

The company divides these into three operating segments: Life Non-Life and Asset Management.

Life segment includes saving and protection both individual and for family as well as unit linked products with investment purposes and complex plans for multinationals. It also include investment vehicles and entities supporting the activities of Life companies. Life segment accounts for about 45% of total revenue.

Non-Life segment (roughly 45% of total revenue) activities include both motor and non-motor businesses among which motor third party liabilities casualty accident and health. It includes more sophisticated covers for commercial and industrial risks and complex plans for multinationals.

Asset Management (about 10%) operates as a supplier of products and services both for the insurance companies of the Generali and for third-party customers identifying investment opportunities and sources of income for all customer simultaneously managing risks. The products include equity and fixed-income as well as alternative products.

Geographic Reach

Based in Trieste Italy Generali divides its operations into five core geographic regions. Italy accounts for about 30% of sales Germany and France generate about 15% each the ACEER (Austria Central & Eastern Europe and Russia) segment represents some 5% of revenue and other international countries (including Spain Americas Southern Europe and Asia bring in more than 5%.

Sales and Marketing

Generali serves some 65.9 million customers around the world. It sells through channels including its own global network of agents as well as financial advisors and brokers. It also sells by telephone and online.

Financial Performance

Note: Growth rates may differ after conversion to US Dollars.

The company's revenue for fiscal 2020 increased by 22% to ?993 million compared from the prior year with ?813 million.

Earnings for fiscal 2020 decreased to ?3.4 billion compared from the prior year with ?3.6 billion.

Cash held by the company at the end of fiscal 2020 increased to ?7.8 billion. Cash provided by operations was ?19.3 billion while cash used for investing and financing activities were ?16.0 billion and ?2.3 billion respectively. Main uses of cash were available for sale financial assets and other financial liabilities.

Strategy

One of the company's strategic pillars was innovation and digital transformation its digital ambition is to grant its customers agents and employees a top-level experience becoming a truly agile innovation-led digitally enabled and data driven organization.

Mergers and Acquisitions

In late 2021 Generali and Cre´dit Agricole Assurances announced that they have entered into exclusive negotiations for the acquisition of La Me´dicale Cre´dit Agricole Assurances' insurance subsidiary for healthcare professionals. The transaction also foresees the sale of Predica's death coverage portfolio marketed and managed by La Me´dicale to Generali France. La Me´dicale is a leading player in the insurance market for healthcare professionals in France. For Generali this acquisition represents a key strategic opportunity for growth enabled also by good ties with Cre´dit Agricole. The transaction is fully in line with the 'Generali 2021' strategy and it confirms the Generali's commitment to deliver profitable growth whilst creating value for customers consistent with Generali's Lifetime Partner ambition.

In 2021 Generali has signed an agreement in connection with the purchase of the majority of the shares held by AXA and Affin in the joint ventures approximately 53% of AXA Affin General Insurance Berhad (49.99% from AXA and 3% from Affin and minorities) and AXA Affin Life Insurance Berhad (49% from AXA and 21% from Affin) respectively. The total consideration for the combined transactions is of RM 1290 million (?262 million). The acquisitions will position Generali as one of the leading insurers in the Malaysian market creating the second P&C insurer by market share and entering the country's Life insurance segment.

Also in 2021 Generali has completed the acquisition of AXA Group's Greek subsidiary AXA Insurance S.A. following receipt of all necessary approvals from the relevant regulatory bodies and competition authorities. As a result of the completion of the acquisition Generali has also commenced its 20-year exclusive distribution agreement with Alpha Bank. The deal is in line with Generali's strategy to strengthen its leadership position in Europe as Generali becomes a leading player in both the P&C Health segments and strengthening its position in Life while gaining access to an important bancassurance channel in partnership with Alpha Bank.

In 2020 Generali finalized the acquisition of Seguradoras Unidas and the service company AdvanceCare (service platform operating primarily in the healthcare sector) from Calm Eagle Holdings S.a`r.l. and Calm Eagle Parent Holdings II S.a`r.l. entities majority owned by investment funds managed by certain affiliates of Apollo Global Management Inc. Seguradoras Unidas is the second largest non-life business operator in Portugal with a 15.5% market share in the segment. The acquisition of the two assets is consistent with Generali's capital redeployment strategy in disciplined M&A to support profitable growth.

HISTORY

Assicurazioni Generali was founded as Assicurazioni Generali Austro-Italiche in 1831 by a group of merchants led by Giuseppe Morpurgo in the Austro-Hungarian port of Trieste. Formed to provide insurance to the city's bustling trade industry the company offered life marine fire flood and shipping coverage. That year Morpurgo established what he intended to be Generali's headquarters in Venice. (While the company maintained offices in both cities Trieste ultimately won out.)

By 1835 Generali had opened 25 offices in Central and Western Europe; it had also expelled Morpurgo. The firm moved into Africa and Asia in the 1880s. In 1900 Generali began selling injury and theft insurance. In 1907 Generali's Prague office provided the young experimental writer Franz Kafka his first job. (He found it disagreeable and quit after a few months.)

During WWI the firm's Venice office pledged allegiance to Italy while the office in Trieste (still part of Austria-Hungary) stayed loyal to the Hapsburgs. After the war Trieste was absorbed by the new Italian republic. Under Edgardo Morpurgo Generali expanded further in the 1920s managing 30 subsidiaries and operating in 17 countries. As fascist Italy aligned itself with Germany in the 1930s adoption of anti-Semitic laws caused Morpurgo and a number of other high-ranking Jewish employees to flee the country. In 1938 Generali moved its headquarters to Rome (but moved them back to Trieste after war's end).

The firm maintained steady business both before and during Nazi occupation in WWII; in 1945 however the Soviets seized all Italian properties in Eastern Europe including 14 Generali subsidiaries. In 1950 Generali invaded the US market offering shipping and fire insurance and reinsurance. Generali established a cooperative agreement with Aetna Life and Casualty (now Aetna Inc.) in 1966 further cementing its US connections.

In 1988 Generali tried to acquire French insurer Compagnie du Midi. Foreshadowing Generali's later dealings with Istituto Nazionale delle Assicurazioni (INA) Midi escaped Generali's grasp through a merger with AXA. As the Iron Curtain frayed in 1989 Generali formed AB Generali Budapest through a joint venture with a Hungarian insurer. In 1990 the firm opened an office in Tokyo through an agreement with Taisho Marine and Fire Insurance (which became Mitsui Marine & Fire Insurance and is now Mitsui Sumitomo Insurance). By 1993 Generali had become Italy's largest insurer.

In 1997 the firm was accused along with other major European insurers of not paying on policies of Holocaust victims. (It moved to settle claims in 1999.)

EXECUTIVES

Head of General Manager Office, Bernardino Provera
Group Head of Actuarial Function, Anna Pieri
Group Head of Investor & Rating Agency Relations, Giulia Raffo
Non-Executive Independent Director, Ines Mazzilli, $119,372 total compensation
Country manager for France and CEO Generali France, Jean-Laurent Granier
Group Chief Financial Officer, Cristiano Borean
Non-Executive Vice Chairman of the Board, Clemente Rebecchini, $227,069 total compensation
Group Chief Insurance & Investment Officer, Sandro Panizza
Group Chief Executive Officer, Managing Director, Executive Director, Director in charge of the ICRMS, Philippe Donnet, $1,635,454 total compensation
Group Chief Marketing & Customer Officer, Isabelle Conner
Non-Executive Independent Director, Antonella Mei-pochtler, $104,450 total compensation
Non-Executive Chairman of the Board, Gabriele Galateri di Genola, $1,106,512 total compensation
Group Strategy & Business Accelerator Director, Bruno Andrea Scaroni
Group Compliance Officer, Maurizio Basso
Auditors: E&Y S.p.A.

LOCATIONS

HQ: Assicurazioni Generali S.p.A.
Piazza Duca degli Abruzzi 2, P.O. Box 538, Trieste
34132
Phone: (39) 40 6711   **Fax:** (39) 40 671 600
Web: www.generali.com

2018 Sales

	% of total
Italy	3
Germany	15
France	13
Austria CEE & Russia	14
International	
Spain	5
Switzerland	5
Americas and Southern Europe	2
Asia	1
Europ Assistance	2
Investments Asset & Wealth Management	10
Total	**100**

PRODUCTS/OPERATIONS

2018 Sales by Segment

	% of total
Life	57
Property/casualty	37
Holding & other	6
Total	**100**

COMPETITORS

AEGON N.V.	METLIFE INC.
AMERICAN NATIONAL	M nchener
INSURANCE COMPANY	NEW YORK LIFE
AVIVA PLC	INSURANCE COMPANY
Ageas	PRUDENTIAL FINANCIAL
Allianz SE	INC.
CNP ASSURANCES	Zurich Insurance Group
China Life Insurance	AG
Company Limited	
LINCOLN NATIONAL	
CORPORATION	

HISTORICAL FINANCIALS

Company Type: Public

Income Statement   FYE: December 31

	ASSETS ($ mil.)	NET INCOME ($ mil.)	INCOME AS % OF ASSETS	EMPLOYEES
12/20	668,517	2,140	0.3%	72,644
12/19	577,746	2,997	0.5%	71,936
12/18	590,722	2,644	0.4%	70,734
12/17	643,826	2,529	0.4%	71,327
12/16	550,309	2,197	0.4%	73,727
Annual Growth	**5.0%**	**(0.7%)**	**—**	**(0.4%)**

2020 Year-End Financials

Return on assets: 0.3%	Dividends
Return on equity: 5.9%	Yield: 0.0%
Long-term debt ($ mil.): —	Payout: 15.3%
No. of shares (mil.): 1,569	Market value ($ mil.): 13,735
Sales ($ mil): 101,376	

	STOCK PRICE ($) FY Close	P/E High/Low		PER SHARE ($) Earnings	Dividends	Book Value
12/20	8.75	10	5	1.34	0.21	23.48
12/19	10.47	6	5	1.89	0.33	20.29
12/18	8.45	7	5	1.67	0.31	17.27
12/17	9.19	7	6	1.59	0.31	19.26
12/16	7.39	6	4	1.39	0.25	16.62
Annual Growth	**4.3%**	**—**	**—**	**(1.0%)**	**(4.5%)**	**9.0%**

Associated British Foods Plc

Associated British Foods (ABF) is a highly diversified group with a wide range of food and ingredient businesses including its own low-cost high-street fashion chain Primark. ABF also makes and markets grocery products sugar ingredients and agricultural products. Some of its well-known brands include Twinings Ovomaltine Patak's Blue Dragon Kingsmill and Silver Spoon among others. Other divisions churn out sugar specialty oils and animal feed. ABF's activities span nearly 55 countries worldwide and provide its services through about 130000 employees. Roughly 40% of the company's revenue is generated within the UK.

Operations

ABF's business is divided into Retail Groceries Sugar Ingredients and Agriculture.

The Groceries segment responsible for approximately 30% of sales manufactures products such as hot beverages sugar and sweeteners vegetable oils and bread and baked goods. Its brands include hot beverages Twinings (tea) and Ovaltine (hot chocolate) Silver Spoon and Billington's (sugar) Jordans and Dorset Cereals (breakfast cereals) Mazola (corn oil) and others.

The Agriculture and Ingredients segments generate around 10% each of sales and manufacture animal feed and bakery ingredients respectively.

However despite its focus on food ABF's largest segment by revenue is Retail. The segment owns low-cost high-street chain Primark.

Geographic Reach

Based in the UK ABF has direct operations in around 55 countries across Europe Africa the Americas the Asia/Pacific region and Australia. ABF generates close to 35% of its annual sales in the UK and another nearly 35% in countries in Europe and Africa. The Asia/Pacific region the Americas the remaining more than 15% each.

The Sugar business operates about 30 factory plants in ten countries enabling the segment to produce about 4.5 million tons of sugar annually. Its operations dominate regions including Africa the UK Spain and north east China. Primark operates in about 15 countries.

Sales and Marketing

ABF's branded products are sold through supermarkets and other retail outlets and via wholesale and foodservice channels.

Financial Performance

Note: Growth rates may differ after conversion to US Dollars.

The company's performance for five years has fluctuated but overall had a downslope trend with 2021 as its lowest performing year over the five-year period.

ABF's revenue for 2021 decreased by about 53 million to about 13.8 billion compared with 13.9 billion in the prior year. All its food businesses delivered growth and in aggregate sales were 5% ahead of last year at constant currency. Primark sales in both years were impacted by trading restrictions and store closures as a result of government measures taken to contain the spread of COVID-19. The periods of closure were longer this year compared to the last financial year and sales declined by 5% at constant currency as a result.

Net income for the year ended 2021 increased by about 23 million to 478 million from 455 million in the prior year.

The company's cash for the year ended 2021 was 2.2 billion. Operating activities generated 1.4 billion. Investing activities and financing activities

used 561 million and 512 million respectively. Main cash uses were for purchases of property plant and equipment; and repayment of lease liabilities.

Strategy

Associated British Foods' strategy includes a long-term view organic and acquisition growth; a devolved operating model; entrepreneurial flair; capital discipline; prudent balance sheet management; commitment to ethical conduct; and a sustainable business practice. All these are then applied to the company's five business segments through framework for collaboration disciplined capital allocation material risk assessment and strategic engagement. As a result the efforts of Associated British Foods enabled long-term value for its customers employees investors shareholders suppliers communities and governments.

HISTORY

When Garfield Weston took over his father's company upon the elder Weston's death in 1924 George Weston Limited was one of Canada's largest bakeries. Ten years later taking advantage of the cheap prices afforded by a worldwide depression Garfield purchased a biscuit-making division from Scottish baker Mitchell & Muir and opened a factory in Edinburgh. He promptly purchased other UK bakeries and grouped them in 1935 as Allied Bakeries.

Allied went public that year with the Weston family controlling most of its shares. The company's early accomplishments included the introduction of sliced bread to the UK. By 1940 Allied had acquired more than 30 bakeries and had become Britain's largest baker by introducing inexpensive biscuits to the masses.

Garfield's son Garry joined Allied's board of directors in 1948. The following year the company acquired two Australian firms: Gold Crust Bakeries and Gartelle White. It also bought the Ryvita Company a maker of crispbread. Placed under Garry's control Ryvita eventually became a household name in the UK. Garry also helped the Burton's biscuit division launch the popular Wagon Wheels chocolate biscuits in 1951. Three years later he was sent to Australia to oversee the company's operations there.

To control the entire food-selling process Allied moved into retailing during the 1950s acquiring famous London department store Fortnum & Mason (later acquired by the Weston family). The company was renamed Associated British Foods (ABF) in 1960. During the 1960s ABF opened Primark clothing stores and bought the Fine Fare chain of supermarkets. By the time Garry returned to the UK to become CEO in 1966 his father had thrown together a number of businesses that made everything from flour to parrot food. To achieve a stronger focus Garry sold many of these.

Growth continued internally. In 1970 ABF opened the largest bakery in Western Europe in Glasgow Scotland. Frozen foods were added in 1978 the year Garfield died. The company's Twinings Tea subsidiary opened its first North American factory in 1980. Two years later ABF formed AB Ingredients to make new ingredients and additives for baked goods. The company sold the Fine Fare chain to Dee Corp. (now Somerfield) in 1986 and the following year it formed AB Technology to develop high-tech improvements for food processing.

After nearly 25 years without a major acquisition in 1991 the company purchased British Sugar one of the UK's two sugar processors from Berisford a diversified holdings firm. In 1995 the company acquired AC Humko a manufacturer of specialty oils in the US from Kraft. The next year ABF sold its supermarkets in the Irish Republic and Northern

Ireland to the UK's biggest supermarket chain Tesco. Peter Jackson was appointed CEO in 1999. That year the company acquired German baking ingredients producer Rohr Enzymes and bought several mills from Dalgety Feed.

In 2000 ABF sold its UK ice-cream business to Richmond Foods (now R&R Ice Cream). Deputy chairman Harry Bailey took over as chairman when Garry became ill. ABF sold Burtons Biscuits (Wagon Wheels) that year to investment firm HM Capital Partners (then called Hicks Muse Tate & Furst) for about $187 million and it bought several Procter & Gamble commercial shortening and oil brands. In 2001 ABF sold AB Coatings its food coatings business and Nelsons its jam and preserves business. Also that year the company agreed to buy the UK bakery ingredients business of the Kerry Group.

In 2002 ABF's subsidiary ACH Food Companies purchased 19 of Unilever's North American brands including Mazola corn oil Argo and Kingsford's corn starches Karo corn syrup and Henri's salad dressings. Also in 2002 ABF acquired the food and beverages business of Novartis with the exception of Puerto Rican and US assets. (Brands included Caotina Ovomaltine and Ovaltine.) Later in the year the company sold off its Allied Glass Containers business to management.

In 2003 ABF sold six UK flour mills to Archer Daniels Midland. In 2004 the company acquired Unilever's Mexican oils and fats brands including Inca Mazola and Capullo in a $110 million cash transaction. Later that year it acquired Irish feed ingredients companies Vistavet and Nutrition Services Ltd. ABF's subsidiary ACH Food Companies also acquired the global yeast herbs and spice businesses of Australian company Burns Philp. The acquisition included Burns Philp's Fleischmann's Yeast brand and herb and spice company Tone Brothers.

In 2004 chief executive Peter Jackson unexpectedly announced he was stepping down. A member of ABF's founding and controlling family George Weston was chosen to succeed Jackson. (The Weston family also controls Canadian food processor and supermarket operator George Weston Limited).

ABF's Allied Grain unit formed a joint venture with Banks Cargill Agriculture Frontier in 2005. Frontier's products include grains and oilseeds. The 2005 purchase of retailer Littlewoods' stores added to ABF's Primark retail department-store operations.

In 2006 AFB bought the ethnic foods business of Heinz subsidiary HP Foods; it also acquired a 51% stake in South Africa's largest sugar producer Illovo for $599 million in cash. The next year it acquired Indian food maker Patak's. Its meal-accompaniment products Blue Dragon and Westmill Foods add to ABF's other ethnic cuisine offerings. The acquisition included Patak's assets and brands in all countries with the exception of India.

Already a player in the breakfast-food sector both in the US and internationally in 2007 the company added to its branded food product offerings with the acquisition of Jordans a UK maker of breakfast cereals cereal bars muesli and oat porridge.

EXECUTIVES

Finance Director, Executive Director, John Bason, $1,015,475 total compensation
Chief Executive, Executive Director, George Weston, $1,476,806 total compensation
Non-Executive Director, Emma Adamo, $102,366 total compensation
Independent Non-Executive Director, Richard Reid, $197,908 total compensation

Independent Non-Executive Director, Dame Heather Rabbatts, $55,960 total compensation
Senior Independent Non-Executive Director, Ruth Cairnie, $163,786 total compensation
Independent Non-Executive Director, Wolfhart Hauser, $102,366 total compensation
Chairman, Michael McLintock,, $569,157 total compensation
Auditors: Ernst & Young LLP

LOCATIONS

HQ: Associated British Foods Plc
Weston Centre, 10 Grosvenor Street, London W1K 4QY
Phone: (44) 20 7399 6500   **Fax:** (44) 20 7399 6580
Web: www.abf.co.uk

2018 Sales

	% of total
UK	38
Europe & Africa	38
Asia/Pacific	14
The Americas	10
Total	**100**

PRODUCTS/OPERATIONS

2018 Sales

	%
Retail	48
Grocery	22
Sugar	12
Ingredients	9
Agriculture	9
Total	**100**

Selected Products and Brands

Agriculture
  Animal feeds (AB Agri)
Grocery
  Bread baked goods and cereal
  Allinson breads
  Burgen breads
  Jordans cereals
  Kingsmill breads
  Ryvita rye crispbread
  Speedibake bakery products
  Sunblest bread snacks and rolls
  Tip Top bread and baked goods (Australia)
  Herbs and spices
  Durkee (US)
  Gravies
  Sauces
  Seasonings
  Soup bases
  Spices
  Spice Islands (US)
  Seasonings
  Spices
  Tone's spices (US)
  Hot beverages sugar and sweeteners
  Billington's cane sugars
  Jacksons of Picadilly teas
  Karo corn syrup
  Ovaltine
  Silver Spoon sugar (UK)
  La Tisaniere teas and infusions (France)
  Twinings teas
  Meat
  Don Deligoods (Australia)
  KRC (Australia)
  Vegetable oils
  Capullo canola oil (Mexico)
  Mazola corn oil (US)
  World foods
  Blue Dragon (Asian)
  Patak's (Indian)
  Other
  Askeys ice cream and dessert accompaniments
  Baking Mad
  Baking advice
  Recipes
  Tips
  Crusha milkshake mix
Ingredients
  Specialty ingredients

Enzymes
Specialty proteins and lipids
Yeast extracts
Yeast and bakery ingredients
Argo corn starch
Retail clothing
  Primark
  Accessories
  Childrenswear
  Footwear
  Homeware
  Hosiery
  Lingerie
  Menswear
  Womenswear
Sugar
  Beet sugar

COMPETITORS

Bunge Limited
CAMPBELL SOUP COMPANY
GENERAL MILLS INC.
GREENCORE GROUP PUBLIC LIMITED COMPANY
George Weston Limited
Grupo Bimbo S.A.B. de C.V.
PARMALAT FINANZIARIA SPA
PREMIER FOODS PLC
RECKITT BENCKISER GROUP PLC
THE J M SMUCKER COMPANY

HISTORICAL FINANCIALS

Company Type: Public

Income Statement — FYE: September 18

	REVENUE ($ mil.)	NET INCOME ($ mil.)	NET PROFIT MARGIN	EMPLOYEES
09/21	19,156	659	3.4%	127,912
09/20	17,875	583	3.3%	133,425
09/19	19,704	1,093	5.5%	138,097
09/18	20,391	1,318	6.5%	137,014
09/17	20,839	1,625	7.8%	132,590
Annual Growth	(2.1%)	(20.2%)	—	(0.9%)

2021 Year-End Financials

Debt ratio: 3.3%
Return on equity: 4.8%
Cash ($ mil.): 3,138
Current ratio: 1.86
Long-term debt ($ mil.): 104
No. of shares (mil.): 791
Dividends
  Yield: 0.0%
  Payout: 7.9%
Market value ($ mil.): 20,789

	STOCK PRICE ($) FY Close	P/E High/Low	PER SHARE ($) Earnings	Dividends	Book Value
09/21	26.26	57 37	0.83	0.07	17.29
09/20	24.83	60 35	0.74	0.39	15.16
09/19	29.35	30 23	1.38	0.50	14.87
09/18	29.35	35 23	1.67	0.49	15.23
09/17	42.96	30 21	2.06	0.44	14.29
Annual Growth	(11.6%)	—	(20.2%)	(37.8%)	4.9%

AstraZeneca Plc

One of the world's major pharmaceutical firms AstraZeneca specializes in drugs for cardiovascular metabolic neurological gastrointestinal respiratory oncology and infection therapy areas. The firm's biggest sellers include cholesterol reducer Crestor cardiovascular drug Brilinta acid reflux remedy Nexium and Symbicort for asthma. AstraZeneca also markets drugs that aim to treat high cholesterol diabetes pain viral diseases and various cancers. The company has more than 30 factories globally and R&D centers in the UK US Sweden and China and its products are sold in more than 100 countries.

Operations

AstraZeneca operates as a single operating segment that researches develops manufactures and commercializes biopharmaceuticals. Its research focuses on four therapy areas: Oncology; Cardiovascular Renal & Metabolism; Respiratory & Immunology; and Other Medicines and COVID-19.

Oncology brings in more than 40% of total sales. Its major products include Faslodex for breast cancer and Zoladex for breast and prostate cancers.

The Cardiovascular Renal & Metabolism group is brings in over 25% of total sales. Its major products include Crestor for high cholesterol and Brilinta for the treatment of coronary syndromes and prevention of further coronary events. Other drugs include Farxiga Onglyza Bydureon and Byetta (for type-2 diabetes); Symlin (diabetes); Seloken/Toptol-XL and Atacand (hypertension heart failure and angina).

The Respiratory & Immunology unit brings in more than 20% of total sales largely from the sales of asthma drug Symbicort (the company's single biggest earner).

The Other Medicines and COVID-19 segment brings in about 10% of total sales produces drugs in the areas of autoimmunity infection neuroscience and gastroenterology. Its leading drugs include acid reflux medication Nexium and schizophrenia treatment Seroquel. AstraZeneca is working to defeat the COVID-19 pandemic by advancing and accelerating the development of potential medicines.

Geographic Reach

Cambridge UK-based AstraZeneca has operations in Europe North America Central America South America the Middle East Africa and the Asia/Pacific region. It manufactures products from more than 30 sites in more than 15 countries. The company has R&D centers in the US the UK Sweden Japan and China.

The Americas is AstraZeneca's most lucrative region accounting for nearly 40% of sales. The Asia/Pacific region Africa and Australasia together represent more than 35% of sales Continental Europe more than 15% and the company's native UK generate more than 5% of sales.

Sales and Marketing

AstraZeneca markets its products to physicians through sales and marketing teams who are active in more than 100 countries. It typically sells through local marketing companies which it owns as well as through distributors and local representative offices.

Financial Performance

Total Revenue for the year was up 9% (CER: 10%) to $26.6 million comprising Product Sales of $25.9 million up 10% (CER: 11%) and Collaboration Revenue of $727 million; a decrease of 11% (CER: 11%).

The company's profit increased by 156% to $3.1 billion in 2020. The increase was primarily due to lower selling general and administrative costs and research and development expense.

Cash held by the company at the end of 2020 increased by $2.3 billion to $7.5 billion from $5.2 billion in the prior year. Cash provided by operations was $4.8 billion while cash used for investing and financing activities were $285 million and $2.2 billion respectively. AstraZeneca's main cash uses in 2020 were capital expenditures and paid dividends.

Strategy

AstraZeneca's strategic priorities are focused on delivering value to patients and society.

Delivering growth and therapy area leadership by supplying medicines that can transform care and ensuring that it reaches patients who need them. Accelerating innovative science in search of

solutions that prevent treat and even cure some of the world's most serious health challenges. Being a great place to work by living its values and behaviors delivering as an enterprise team and leading in sustainability.

The fundamentals of the company's strategy are focused on innovative science and leadership in its three main therapy areas: Oncology; Cardiovascular Renal and Metabolism; and Respiratory diseases. Backed by a global presence with strength in Emerging Markets particularly China it has a portfolio of specialty and primary care medicines.

At the same time the world around is changing and the burden of disease is increasing. It is responding by increasing its focus on growth through innovation - being more patient-centric doing more with technology digital and data and advancing more cutting-edge science.

Mergers and Acquisitions

In late 2020 AstraZeneca agreed to acquire Alexion a global biopharmaceutical company for $39 billion. This acquisition allows the company to enhance its presence in immunology. The double-digit revenue growth through 2025; acquisition strengthens AstraZeneca's broad-based revenue and the company will further globalise Alexion's portfolio. The acquisition will be immediately core earnings-accretive and value-enhancing and is aligned with stated capital-allocation priorities.

HISTORY

AstraZeneca forerunner Imperial Chemical Industries (ICI) was created from the 1926 merger of four British chemical companies — Nobel Industries; Brunner Mond and Company; United Alkali; and British Dyestuffs — in reaction to the German amalgamation that created I. G. Farben. ICI plunged into research recruiting chemists engineers and managers and forming alliances with universities. Between 1933 and 1935 at least 87 new products were created including polyethylene.

Fortunes declined as competition increased after WWII. In 1980 ICI posted losses and cut its dividend for the first time. In 1982 turnaround artist John Harvey-Jones shifted ICI from bulk chemicals to high-margin specialty chemicals such as pharmaceuticals and pesticides. That business became Zeneca which ICI spun off in 1993.

The takeover specter loomed large over the company during its first year. Zeneca had several drugs in its pipeline but it also had expiring patents on others making them fair game for competitors. Bankrolled by its agrochemical business Zeneca forged alliances with other pharmaceutical firms. In 1994 it entered a marketing alliance with Amersham International (now Amersham) to sell Metastron a nuclear-medicine cancer agent. The next year Zeneca formed a joint venture with Chinese companies Advanced Chemicals and Tianli to make textile-coating chemicals.

In 1995 Glaxo was forced to sell a migraine drug candidate to complete its merger with Wellcome. Zeneca's gamble in buying the then-unproven drug (Zomig) paid off when the product gained US FDA approval two years later.

By 1997 Zeneca completed its gradual acquisition of Salick Health Care formed to create more humane cancer treatment programs. The purchase followed a trend of large drug firms moving into managed care which raised concerns that centers might be pressured to use their parent companies' drugs but Zeneca maintained that Salick would remain independent except to the extent that it offered an opportunity to evaluate treatments.

In 1998 Zeneca got the FDA's OK to sell its brand of tamoxifen (Nolvadex) to women at high risk of contracting breast cancer. In 1999 it sued Eli Lilly to protect Nolvadex against Lilly's marketing claim that its osteoporosis treatment Evista

reduced breast cancer risk a use for which it was not approved.

In 1999 Zeneca completed its purchase of Sweden's Astra to form AstraZeneca. That year the firm sold its specialty chemicals unit Zeneca Specialties to Cinven Group and Investcorp. With its agricultural business stagnated due to crippled markets in Asia and Europe AstraZeneca announced plans to merge the unit with the agrochemicals business of Novartis and spun it off as Syngenta.

In 2013 AstraZeneca sold its only non-pharma business Aptium Oncology an operator of cancer treatment centers in the US. This came on the heels of selling its other non-core units Astra Tech (medical devices) and Dentsply Sirona (dental implant systems).

EXECUTIVES

Chief Human Resource Officer, General Counsel, Jeffrey Pott
Executive Vice President - Sustainability, Chief Compliance Officer, Katarina Ageborg
Independent Non-Executive Chairman of the Board, Leif Johansson
Chief Executive Officer, Executive Director, Pascal Soriot, $1,653,220 total compensation
Non-Executive Independent Director, Michel Demare
Executive Vice President - Research & Development BioPharmaceuticals, Menelas Pangalos
Executive Vice President - BioPharmaceuticals Business, Ruud Dobber
Executive Vice President, AstraZeneca and President, AstraZeneca China, Leon Wang
Executive Vice President - Oncology Business, David Fredrickson
Non-Executive Director, Tony Mok
Non-Executive Director, Euan Ashley
Non-Executive Director, Andreas Rummelt
Executive Vice President - Operations and Information Technology, Pam Cheng
Executive Vice President - Europe and Canada, Iskra Reic
Executive Vice President - Research & Development Oncology, Jose Baselga
Executive Director and Chief Financial Officer, Aradhana Sarin
Auditors: PricewaterhouseCoopers LLP

LOCATIONS

HQ: AstraZeneca Plc
1 Francis Crick Avenue, Cambridge Biomedical Campus, Cambridge CB2 0AA
Phone: (44) 20 3749 5000   **Fax:** (44) 1223 352 858
Web: www.astrazeneca.com

2018 sales
£m %

The Americas	8,529	39
Asia Africa and Australasia	7,351	33
Continental Europe	3,820	17
UK	2,390	11
Total	**22,090**	**100**

PRODUCTS/OPERATIONS

2018 Sales

Products	$ mil.	% of total
Cardiovascular Renal & Metabolism	6,710	30
Respiratory	4,911	22
Oncology	46,028	27
Other	3,400	16
Externalization	1,041	10
Total	**22,090**	**100**

Selected Products
Cardiovascular

Atacand (angiotensin II antagonist for hypertension and heart failure)

Brilinta (acute coronary syndromes and events in high-risk post myocardial infarction)

Crestor (statin for cholesterol-lowering drug)

Onglyza (type 2 diabetes)

Plendil (calcium antagonist for hypertension and angina)

Seloken/Toprol-XL (beta-blocker for blood pressure heart failure angina)

Zestril (ACE inhibitor for hypertension other)

Gastrointestinal

Losec/Prilosec (acid reflux disease)

Nexium (acid reflux disease)

Infection and Other Products

FluMist (intranasal flu vaccine)

Merrem/Meronem (intravenous antibiotic for serious hospital infections)

Synagis (for respiratory syncytial virus or RSV in infants)

Neuroscience

Diprivan (general anesthetic)

Local anesthetics (Carbocaine Citanest Naropin Xylocaine)

Seroquel (anti-psychotic for schizophrenia and bipolar)

Zomig (migraines)

Oncology

Arimidex (aromatase inhibitor for breast cancer)

Casodex (anti-androgen for prostate cancer)

Faslodex (oestrogen receptor antagonist for breast cancer)

Iressa (kinase inhibitor for non-small cell lung cancer)

Nolvadex (breast cancer)

Zoladex (LHRH agonist for prostate and breast cancer)

Respiratory & Inflammation

Oxis (beta-agonist for asthma and chronic obstructive pulmonary disease)

Pulmicort (anti-inflammatory for asthma)

Rhinocort (topical nasal anti-inflammatory)

Symbicort (anti-inflammatory and bronchodilator in one inhaler for asthma and chronic obstructive pulmonary disease)

Selected Subsidiaries

AstraZeneca AB (Sweden)
AstraZeneca BV (The Netherlands)
AstraZeneca Canada Inc.
AstraZeneca do Brasil Limitada
AstraZeneca Farmaceutica Spain SA
AstraZeneca GmbH (Germany)
AstraZeneca KK (Japan)
AstraZeneca LP (US)
AstraZeneca Pharmaceuticals Co. Limited (China)
AstraZeneca Pharmaceuticals LP (US)
AstraZeneca Pty Limited (Australia)
AstraZeneca SAS (France)
AstraZeneca SpA (Italy)
AstraZeneca UK Limited
IPR Pharmaceuticals Inc. (Puerto Rico)
MedImmune L.L.C. (US)
Novexel SA (France)
NV AstraZeneca SA (Belgium)
Zeneca Holdings Inc. (US)

COMPETITORS

ABBVIE INC.
ADARE PHARMACEUTICALS INC.
Bausch Health Companies Inc
Boehringer Ingelheim International GmbH
ENDO INTERNATIONAL PUBLIC LIMITED COMPANY
GLAXOSMITHKLINE PLC
LES LABORATOIRES SERVIER
SANOFI
TAKEDA PHARMACEUTICAL COMPANY LIMITED
THE MEDICINES COMPANY

HISTORICAL FINANCIALS

Company Type: Public

Income Statement				FYE: December 31
	REVENUE ($ mil.)	NET INCOME ($ mil.)	NET PROFIT MARGIN	EMPLOYEES
12/20	26,617	3,196	12.0%	76,100
12/19	24,384	1,335	5.5%	70,600
12/18	22,090	2,155	9.8%	64,400
12/17	22,465	3,001	13.4%	61,100
12/16	23,002	3,499	15.2%	59,700
Annual Growth	3.7%	(2.2%)	—	6.3%

2020 Year-End Financials

Debt ratio: 29.5%	No. of shares (mil.): 1,312
Return on equity: 22.1%	Dividends
Cash ($ mil.): 7,832	Yield: 2.7%
Current ratio: 0.96	Payout: 72.1%
Long-term debt ($ mil.): 17,505	Market value ($ mil.): 65,620

	STOCK PRICE ($) FY Close	P/E High/Low		PER SHARE ($)		
				Earnings	Dividends	Book Value
12/20	49.99	25	15	2.44	1.37	11.90
12/19	49.86	49	34	1.03	1.37	10.00
12/18	37.98	24	19	1.70	1.37	9.84
12/17	34.70	15	11	2.37	1.37	11.81
12/16	27.32	12	9	2.76	1.37	11.74
Annual Growth	16.3%		—	(3.0%)	(0.0%)	0.3%

Atlas Copco AB (Sweden)

Atlas Copco is a world-leading provider of sustainable productivity solutions demanded by all types of industries enabling everything from industrial automation to reliable medical air solutions. It offers innovative compressors air treatment systems vacuum solutions industrial power tools and assembly systems machine vision and power and flow solutions .Its products are used by a wide range of industries from aerospace and automotive to infrastructure and oil and gas. Based in Stockholm Sweden Atlas Copco has customers in more than 180 countries and generates majority of its sales in Asia And Oceania.

Operations

Atlas Copco is organized into four business segments: Compressor Technique Vacuum Technique Industrial Technique and Power Technique.

Compressor Technique is the largest at over 45% of sales. It provides compressed air solutions: industrial compressors gas and process compressors and expanders air and gas treatment equipment and air management systems. The business area has a global service network and innovates for sustainable productivity mainly for the manufacturing and process industries.

The Vacuum Technique segment provides vacuum products exhaust management systems valves and related products. The main markets served are semiconductor and scientific as well as a wide range of industrial segments including chemical process industries food packaging and paper handling. Atlas Copco generates some 25% of sales from vacuum products.

Industrial Technique (around 15% of sales) provides industrial power tools assembly and machine vision solutions quality assurance products software and service through a global network. The business area innovates for sustainable productivity for customers in the automotive and general industries. The fourth segment Power Technique represents over 10% of sales. It provides air power and flow solutions such as compressors pumps light towers and generators.

Overall sales of services account for about 65% of sales and equipment around 35%.

Geographic Reach

Headquartered in Sweden Atlas Copco's global reach spans more than 180 markets in Asia/Oceania (over 35% of sales) Europe (some 30%) North America (about 25%) South America and the Middle East and Africa accounts for about 10% combined.

The company has an extensive manufacturing footprint Germany the US China India Germany and Italy.

Sales and Marketing

The company has its own sales operations (customer centers) in about 70 countries.

Atlas Copco's biggest customer industries are general manufacturing process industry electronics electronics construction automotive and service which together account for over 85% of sales.

Financial Performance

In 2020 the company's revenue decreased by 4% to SEK 99.8 billion from SEK 103.8 billion in 2019.

Profit for 2020 decreased by 11% to SEK 14.8 billion from SEK 21.6 billion in 2019.

Cash held by the company at the end of 2020 decreased to SEK 11.7 billion. Operating activities provided SEK 22.2 billion while investing and financing activities used SEK 16.3 billion and SEK 8.6 billion respectively. Main cash uses were acquisition of subsidiaries and ordinary dividend.

Strategy

The vision is to be First in Mind?First in Choice as a supplier of compressed air and gas solutions by being interactive committed and innovative and by offering customers the best value. The strategy is to further develop Atlas Copco's leading position in the selected niches and growing the business in a way that is economically environmentally and socially responsible. This should be done by capitalizing on the strong global market presence improving market penetration in mature and developing markets and continuously developing improved products and solutions to satisfy customer demands. The presence is enhanced by utilizing several commercial brands. Key strategies include growing the service business as well as developing businesses within focused areas such as air-treatment equipment blowers and compressor solutions for trains ships and hospitals. The business area is actively looking at acquiring complementary businesses.

Strategic activities include an intensified focus on research and development; Increase focus on digitalization and connected products; increase market coverage and improve presence in targeted markets/segments; develop new sustainable products and solutions offering better value and improved energy efficiency to customers; extend the product and service offering at current customers and adjacent segments and applications; perform more service on a higher share of the installed base of equipment; Increase operational efficiency; further investments in employees and their competence development; and acquire complementary businesses.

Mergers and Acquisitions

In mid-2021 Atlas Copco has acquired CPC Pumps International Inc. a Canada-based company that specializes in the design manufacturing and servicing of custom-engineered mission critical centrifugal pumps. The acquisition adds complementary assets to the company's portfolio and strengthens its market position. The purchase price is not material relative to Atlas Copco's market capitalization and is not disclosed.

Also in mid-2020 Atlas Copco has acquired Airflow Compressors & Pneumatics Ltd (Airflow) a privately owned UK company which serves mainly industrial and service companies active in the North West of England. This acquisition will enable the company to increase the footprint of its brand portfolio products and to develop the business further in the industrial hubs of Liverpool and Manchester. The purchase price is not disclosed.

The company also in 2021 has acquired the operating assets of Compressed Air Systems Inc. (CAS) a distributor of compressors located in North Carolina in the US. The acquisition will enable to reach Atlas' goal to get closer to customers. Financial terms were not disclosed.

In late 2020 Atlas Copco has completed the acquisition of Perceptron a leading supplier of automated metrology solutions headquartered in Plymouth Michigan for USD 7.00 per share corresponding to an enterprise value of MUSD 60.8 (MSEK 504). Through Perceptron's position in automated metrology and vision systems for robot guidance together with the recent acquisition of ISRA VISION Atlas Copco is creating a strong offering in machine vision solutions.

Also in 2020 Atlas Copco has agreed to acquire Ehrler and Beck GmbH. The company is a distributor of vacuum equipment and vacuum services based in Renningen Germany. This acquisition will increase its possibilities to serve Germany and neighboring countries with industrial vacuum products and services. Terms were not disclosed.

In addition Atlas Copco in 2020 has completed the acquisition of MEDGAS-Technik GmbH a manufacturer distributor installer and service provider of medical air and medical vacuum systems pipeline equipment and medical supplies headquartered in Berndroth Germany. MEDGAS will become part of the Medical Gas Solutions division in the Compressor Technique business area. Terms were not disclosed.

HISTORY

Eduard Fr □nckel chief engineer of Swedish Rail founded the company in 1873 to make railroad equipment. It had a successful start by making wagons and railroad carriages. By 1876 however competition had forced the company to diversify into producing steel bridge structures and frames for buildings and church towers. While this strategy worked for awhile by 1887 losses forced Fr □nckel to leave the company and in 1891 the business went into liquidation.

Financier A. O. Wallenberg whose financial backing had helped found the company was its largest shareholder. He restructured Atlas and provided the loans needed to keep it alive. When Wallenberg died in 1886 his son K. A. Wallenberg took his seat as a director and recruited Oscar Lamm as managing director. Lamm reversed the company's fortunes shifting it into the production of steam engines and machine tools. In 1892 Marcus Wallenberg became a board member and ran Atlas alongside Lamm.

Under Lamm and Wallenberg the company bought the Swedish rights to produce Rudolf Diesel's engine and formed a new company (with Wallenberg's brother Knut) — AB Diesels Motorer. Lamm's nephew Gunnar Jacobsson became managing director of New Atlas in 1909. Demand increased for the company's diesel engines and machine tools before and during WWI. So in 1917 the company produced its last steam locomotive and merged AB Diesels and Atlas into one company — AB Atlas Diesel — with Jacobsson as its managing director.

The diesel engine business slumped after the war. Marcus Wallenberg who had claimed chairmanship in 1933 was forced to provide loans to Atlas to keep it afloat. When Jacobsson retired in 1940 Wallenberg hired Walter Wehtje as managing director and shifted the company away from its money-losing diesel engine operations and into producing air compressors.

WWII forced Sweden to increase its farm acreage in order to sustain its population. The effort utilized the company's compressors and air tools to remove large boulders from rock-strewn fields. After the war Atlas focused on increasing exports. To compete it provided technical services with its products and by the late 1940s business had increased tenfold. The company dropped its unprofitable diesel engine line in 1948 and in 1956 it changed its name to Atlas Copco.

Developing ergonomic designs for its power tools provided rich dividends in the 1960s. In 1968 the company restructured into mining and construction airpower and tools segments. Tom Wachtmeister became CEO in 1975 and in 1980 the company made several purchases in the US to strengthen its revenues. Atlas Copco acquired Chicago Pneumatic Tool Co. (1987) and became the world's largest maker of air compressors in the process.

Michael Treschow the managing director of Atlas Copco Tools AB replaced Wachtmeister as CEO in 1991. He carried on the company's acquisition policy until he left in 1997 and was succeeded by Giulio Mazzalupi. In 1997 Atlas Copco bought Prime Service one of the US's largest equipment rental companies and in 1999 it bought US-based Rental Service Corporation (RSC) and its more than 290 equipment rental centers. The next year RSC bought 11 companies as well. In early 2001 Atlas Copco acquired Masons Holdings Ltd. a UK-based generator manufacturer and renamed the company Atlas Copco Masons.

Atlas Copco expanded its construction and mining technique business in 2002 with the acquisitions of Krupp Berco Bautechnik GmbH (a Germany-based manufacturer of hydraulic demolition equipment for the mining and construction industries) and its sister company in France from ThyssenKruppTechnologies AG. Giulio Mazzalupi was succeeded as president and CEO that year by Gunnar Brock.

In mid-2004 citing limited synergies within the manufacturing and selling of electric tools versus Atlas Copco's other businesses Atlas Copco announced the selling of Atlas Copco Electric Tools (Germany) and Milwaukee Electric Tool to Techtronic Industries for $713 million. The deal became official in January 2005.

In late 2006 Atlas Copco exited its Rental Service division when it sold most of its stake in RSC Equipment Rental to Ripplewood Holdings and Oak Hill Capital Management for about $3.4 billion. Atlas Copco retains about a 14% stake in RSC.

The decision to explore options for its Rental Service unit came in early 2006 as the company determined its rental operations were not a good strategic fit with its manufacturing activities. With operations limited to North America Rental Service needed international expansion to grow. Atlas Copco decided investing further in Rental Services was not the best strategy for the company.

While 2005 was a decent year for Atlas Copco — with high raw materials and purchased goods costs offset by price increases and improvements in operating efficiency — 2006 was the best year in the company's history. All of the company's major geographic markets turned in double-digit growth. Orders from continuing operations increased by 23%. Revenue grew by 20% and operating profit grew by 33%.

Atlas Copco grew its compressor business through targeted acquisitions in China and North America but greater still was organic growth fueled by new products improvements in its sales and distribution network and focus on the aftermarket.

The construction and mining division also grew through the acquisition of Swedish compaction and paving equipment maker Dynapac AB in early 2007. The division also experienced strong global demand for equipment as well as consumables such as drill bits and drill steel.

In 2008 the company's multiple acquisitions included mining industry service company PT Fluidcom Jaya in Indonesia and the European air compressor rental business of Aggreko. Atlas Copco also invested in the southeastern US market purchasing Industrial Power Sales a distributor of tools assembly systems and material handling equipment and Grimmer Industries' booster and portable compressor business.

CEO and president Gunnar Brock stepped down in mid-2009. Ronnie Leten assumed the position to lead the company through recovery from the economic recession. Leten previously served as president of Compressor Technique.

During 2010 Atlas Copco acquired Austria's Hartl a maker of mobile crushing and screening equipment and Netherlands-based Cirmac International which specializes in renewable energy technologies used to upgrade biogas to natural gas. More significant Atlas Copco purchased Quincy Compressor from EnPro Industries for $190 million. Quincy complements Atlas Copco's core products with a portfolio of branded compressors (reciprocating and rotary screw) and vacuum pumps as well as its presence in the US and China. Smaller acquisitions included H&F Drilling Supplies in the UK; Servis A.C. a compressor service provider in the Czech Republic; a remaining 75% stake in Indian companies Focus Rocbit and Prisma Roctools; and Compressor Engineering a UK distributor and service provider for compressed air equipment.

Among the bolt-on businesses that broaden Atlas Copco's network in fall 2010 the company took over the sales and marketing operations of its distributor in Michigan Kramer Air Tool. The deal followed acquisitions of distributors in the southern US Tooling Technologies the northwestern US American Air Products and Louisiana-based Premier Equipment.

In mid-2011 Atlas Copco acquired Spain-based GESAN S.A. a manufacturer of diesel and petrol generators. The deal gives it a better foothold with a distributor network that reaches 85 countries with Russia and other parts of Europe and Africa as principal markets

EXECUTIVES

Senior Executive Vice President, Business Area President Industrial Technique, Henrik Elmin
Chief Human Resource Officer, Senior Vice President, Cecilia Sandberg
Senior Executive Vice President, Business Area President Compressor Technique, Vagner Rego
Director, Peter Wallenberg
Independent Director, Staffan Bohman
Independent Director, Gordon Riske
Director, Johan Forssell
President, Chief Executive Officer, Director, Mats Rahmstrom, $1,693,491 total compensation
Chairman of the Board, Hans Straberg
Independent Director, Tina Donikowski
Vice President Investor Relations, Daniel Althoff
Senior Executive Vice President, Business Area President Power Technique, Andrew Walker
Senior Executive Vice President, Business Area President Vacuum Technique, Geert Follens

Independent Director, Anna Ohlssonleijon
Chief Financial Officer, Senior Vice President,
Peter Kinnart
Senior Vice President, Chief Legal Officer, Hakan
Osvald
Auditors: Ernst & Young AB

LOCATIONS

HQ: Atlas Copco AB (Sweden)
Sickla Industrivag 19, Stockholm SE-105 23
Phone: (46) 8 743 80 00   **Fax:** (46) 8 643 37 18
Web: www.atlascopco.com

2018 Sales

	% of total
Europe	31
Asia & Australia	35
North America	24
Africa & Middle East	6
South America	4
Total	**100**

PRODUCTS/OPERATIONS

2018 Sales

	% of total
Compressor Technique	46
Vacuum Technique	23
Industrial Technique	19
Power Technique	12
Total	**100**

Selected Products

Compressor Technique
  Air dryers coolers filters
  Air treatment and gas purification equipment
  Air management systems
  Compressors (gas and process)
  Compressors (oil-free and oil-injected stationary)
  Compressors (portable)
  Electric power generators
  Specialty rental services
  Turbo expanders
Construction and Mining Technique
  Construction and demolition tools
  Drilling equipment (surface)
  Drilling tools (rock)
  Exploration drilling
  Loading equipment
  Mobile crushers and screeners
  Raiseboring equipment
  Rigs (underground rock drilling)
  Rigs (surface drilling)
  Road construction equipment
  Rock reinforcement and bolting
  Tunneling and mining equipment
  Water well gas coal bed methane
Industrial Technique
  Aftermarket products software and service
  Air motors
  Air assembly tools
  Drills
  Electrical assembly tools
  Fixtured applications
  Grinding
  Hoist and trolleys
  Pneumatic power tools and systems
  Power tools (industrial)

COMPETITORS

AB Electrolux
AB Volvo
BUNZL PUBLIC LIMITED COMPANY
DCC PUBLIC LIMITED COMPANY
EATON CORPORATION PUBLIC LIMITED COMPANY
ENERPAC TOOL GROUP CORP.
GEA Group AG
HITACHI EUROPE LIMITED
HONEYWELL INTERNATIONAL INC.
JOHN CRANE INC.
PARKER-HANNIFIN CORPORATION
SANDVIK AB
SENIOR PLC
SPX CORPORATION

HISTORICAL FINANCIALS

Company Type: Public

Income Statement

FYE: December 31

	REVENUE ($ mil.)	NET INCOME ($ mil.)	NET PROFIT MARGIN	EMPLOYEES
12/20	12,213	1,808	14.8%	40,160
12/19	11,153	1,776	15.9%	38,774
12/18	10,653	11,860	111.3%	36,862
12/17	14,190	2,031	14.3%	47,599
12/16	11,181	1,316	11.8%	44,695
Annual Growth	**2.2%**	**8.3%**	**—**	**(2.6%)**

2020 Year-End Financials

Debt ratio: 2.4%
Return on equity: 27.6%
Cash ($ mil.): 1,426
Current ratio: 1.62
Long-term debt ($ mil.): 2,358

No. of shares (mil.): 1,216
Dividends
  Yield: 1.5%
  Payout: 58.5%
Market value ($ mil.): 62,123

	STOCK PRICE ($) FY Close	P/E High/Low		PER SHARE ($) Earnings	Dividends	Book Value
12/20	51.08	4	3	1.49	0.77	5.36
12/19	40.15	3	2	1.46	0.66	4.70
12/18	23.93	0	0	9.76	11.90	3.91
12/17	43.10	3	2	1.66	0.82	6.09
12/16	30.54	3	2	1.08	0.70	4.82
Annual Growth	**13.7%**	**—**	**—**	**8.3%**	**2.4%**	**2.6%**

Atos Origin

Auditors: Deloitte & Associés

LOCATIONS

HQ: Atos Origin
River Ouest, 80 Quai Voltaire, Bezons 95870
Phone: (33) 1 73 26 00 00
Web: www.atos.net

HISTORICAL FINANCIALS

Company Type: Public

Income Statement

FYE: December 31

	REVENUE ($ mil.)	NET INCOME ($ mil.)	NET PROFIT MARGIN	EMPLOYEES
12/20	13,891	675	4.9%	104,430
12/19	13,173	3,816	29.0%	108,317
12/18	14,227	721	5.1%	122,110
12/17	15,358	720	4.7%	97,267
12/16	12,459	611	4.9%	97,337
Annual Growth	**2.8%**	**2.5%**	**—**	**1.8%**

2020 Year-End Financials

Debt ratio: 25.4%
Return on equity: 7.8%
Cash ($ mil.): 4,027
Current ratio: 1.33
Long-term debt ($ mil.): 3,275

No. of shares (mil.): 109
Dividends
  Yield: 0.0%
  Payout: 17.8%
Market value ($ mil.): 1,995

	STOCK PRICE ($) FY Close	P/E High/Low		PER SHARE ($) Earnings	Dividends	Book Value
12/20	18.15	4	2	6.20	1.10	76.59
12/19	16.73	1	0	35.43	5.28	73.12
12/18	16.26	5	3	6.81	0.39	65.11
12/17	29.15	6	4	6.83	0.38	53.17
12/16	21.07	4	2	5.86	0.23	43.52
Annual Growth	**(3.7%)**	**—**	**—**	**1.4%**	**47.9%**	**15.2%**

AUDI AG

Auditors: PricewaterhouseCoopers GmbH

LOCATIONS

HQ: AUDI AG
Auto-Union-Strasse 1, Ingolstadt D-85045
Phone: (49) 841 89 0   **Fax:** (49) 841 89 325 24
Web: www.audi.com

HISTORICAL FINANCIALS

Company Type: Public

Income Statement

FYE: December 31

	REVENUE ($ mil.)	NET INCOME ($ mil.)	NET PROFIT MARGIN	EMPLOYEES
12/19	62,515	4,322	6.9%	90,640
12/18	67,850	3,873	5.7%	91,674
12/17	72,078	4,261	5.9%	90,402
12/16	62,631	2,095	3.3%	87,112
12/15	63,631	4,579	7.2%	82,838
Annual Growth	**(0.4%)**	**(1.4%)**	**—**	**2.3%**

2019 Year-End Financials

Debt ratio: 1.7%
Return on equity: 13.5%
Cash ($ mil.): 13,171
Current ratio: 1.46
Long-term debt ($ mil.): 908

No. of shares (mil.): 43
Dividends
  Yield: —
  Payout: —
Market value ($ mil.): —

Aurubis AG

   Aurubis AG is a leading global provider of non-ferrous metals and one of the largest copper recyclers worldwide. The company processes complex metal concentrates scrap metals organic and inorganic metal-bearing recycling materials and industrial residues into metals of the highest quality. Aurubis produces more than one million tons of copper cathodes annually and from them a variety of products such as wire rod continuous cast shapes profiles and flat rolled products made of copper and copper alloys. Aurubis produces a number of other metals as well including precious metals selenium lead nickel tin and zinc. The portfolio also includes additional products such as sulfuric acid and iron silicate. Founded as a stock corporation in 1866 majority of Aurubis' sales were generated in Germany.

Operations

   Aurubis operates two business segments: Metal Refining and Processing (around 90% of sales) and Flat Rolled Products (about 10%).

   The Metal Refining and Processing (MRP) segment processes complex metal concentrates copper scrap organic and inorganic metal-bearing recycling raw materials and industrial residues into metals of the highest quality. This includes the Commercial Supply Chain Management (SCM) and Operations division. The Commercial division is commissioned by plants to purchase feed materials and sell products. The SCM division is responsible to carry out production planning logistic management and sampling and to improve the group-wide metal flows and inventories. The Operations division is responsible for the ongoing optimization of the integrated smelter network and the production of all basic products and metals as well as for its future processing into other products such as continuous cast wire rod and shapes.

The Flat Rolled Products (FRP) segment processes copper and copper alloys ? primarily brass bronze and high performance alloys ? into flat rolled products and specialty wire which it then markets.

Overall around 40% of sales account from its wire rod products more than 20% comes from precious metals copper cathodes generate some 20% and the rest comes from shapes strips bars profiles and other.

Geographic Reach

Aurubis is headquartered in Hamburg Germany and has sites mostly in Europe with larger production centers in Germany Belgium Bulgaria and Spain as well as cold-rolling milling for flat rolled products slitting centers and rod plants in Germany and some part of Europe. Outside Europe Aurubis also has a production site in the US and a global sales and service network.

Germany is the largest single market and accounts for about 35% of net sales while the EU (excluding Germany) accounts for also 35%. It also generates sales from Asia Americas the rest of the Europe and other.

Sales and Marketing

Aurubis' customers include companies in the copper semis industry the cable and wire industry the electrical and electronics sector the chemical industry and suppliers for the environmental technology construction and the automotive business.

Financial Performance

The company had a revenue of ?16.3 billion a 31% increase from the previous year's revenue of ?12.4 billion. The increase is primarily due to higher sales across all of the company's segments most notably wire rod.

In 2020 the company had net earnings of ?825.3 million a 125% increase from the previous year's net earnings of ?367.3 million.

The company's cash for the year ended 2020 was ?942.4 million. Operating activities generated ?812.1 million while investing activities used ?232.1 million mainly for payments for investments in fixed assets. Financing activities used another ?96 million primarily for dividends paid.

Strategy

The company's core business is processing and metal-bearing raw materials ? concentrates as well as recycling materials. It is characterized by high productivity cost efficiency and effective sales outlets for its products. And because the world will need more and more of these metals that the company produces in the future the core business remains an essential component of the company's strategy. In light of global competition the company will secure and strengthen its core business.

For this purpose the company is continuing to expand the processing options within its group-wide smelter network. The company is executing projects in a targeted way at different sites to expand its capacities and boost multi-metal recovery. The requirement for all projects and initiatives is that they have to contribute to the company's overall strategy.

With the July 2020 acquisition of software developer azeti Aurubis has secured an Internet of Things platform to integrate and analyze production data in the long term. The azeti platform will make production process in metal production and recycling more flexible and efficient though the acquired expertise and resources open up new digital possibilities in other areas as well.

Mergers and Acquisitions

In mid-2020 Aurubis acquired Berlin software company azeti GmbH. azeti develops and markets an internet-of-things (IoT) platform that integrates and evaluates production data. The software is able to bring together large volumes of data from highly diverse sources simply and quickly allowing previously undiscovered optimization potential to be identified and utilized. Aurubis is confident that it will be able to make production processes in metal production and recycling more flexible and efficient through the azeti platform. Terms were not disclosed.

Also in mid-2020 Aurubis completed the acquisition of Metallo Group a metal recycling and refining company with sites in Belgium and Spain in a deal worth ?380 million. Metallo specializes in recovering non-ferrous metals and has annual sales of nearly ?1 billion. The acquisition of Metallo with its attractive growth potential strengthens Aurubis' metal portfolio especially in the key metals copper nickel tin zinc and lead.

EXECUTIVES

Independent Chairman of the Supervisory Board, Fritz Vahrenholt

Chief Financial Officer, Member of the Executive Board, Rainer Verhoeven, $501,956 total compensation

Member of the Supervisory Board, Employees Representative, Deniz Filiz A car

Member of the Supervisory Board, Employee Representative, Christian Ehrentraut

Chief Operating Officer, Member of the Executive Board, Heiko Arnold, $501,956 total compensation

Independent Member of the Supervisory Board, Gunnar Groebler

Chairman of the Executive Board, Chief Executive Officer, Roland Harings, $717,080 total compensation

Auditors: PricewaterhouseCoopers GmbH Wirtschaftpruefungsgesellschaft

LOCATIONS

HQ: Aurubis AG
Hovestrasse 50, Hamburg 20539
Phone: (49) 40 7883 0   **Fax:** (49) 40 7883 2255
Web: www.aurubis.com

2015 Sales

	% of total
European Union countries	37
Germany	33
Rest of Europe	2
Asia	15
America	9
Other	4
Total	**100**

PRODUCTS/OPERATIONS

2015 Sales

	% of total
Copper Products segment	76
Primary Copper segment	24
Total	**100**

Products and Services

Architectural Solutions
Bars & Profiles
Cathodes
Industrial Rolled Products
Precious Metals
Recycling
Rod & Specialty Wire
Shapes
Slitting Centers
Sulfuric Acid & Others

COMPETITORS

Andritz AG
Aperam
CHINO MINES COMPANY
Freudenberg & Co. KG
IMERYS
JX NIPPON MINING & METALS CORPORATION
Orbia Advance Corporation S.A.B. de C.V.
SEVERSTAL PAO
Umicore
voestalpine AG

HISTORICAL FINANCIALS

Company Type: Public

Income Statement

	REVENUE ($ mil.)	NET INCOME ($ mil.)	NET PROFIT MARGIN	FYE: September 30 EMPLOYEES
09/19	12,026	207	1.7%	6,853
09/18	12,146	336	2.8%	6,673
09/17	13,116	414	3.2%	6,494
09/16	10,759	136	1.3%	6,454
09/15	12,418	148	1.2%	6,321
Annual Growth	**(0.8%)**	**8.8%**	**—**	**2.0%**

2019 Year-End Financials

Debt ratio: 7.2%
Return on equity: 7.3%
Cash ($ mil.): 459
Current ratio: 2.47
Long-term debt ($ mil.): 163

No. of shares (mil.): 44
Dividends
Yield: —
Payout: 29.4%
Market value ($ mil.): —

Australia & New Zealand Banking Group Ltd

Auditors: KPMG

LOCATIONS

HQ: Australia & New Zealand Banking Group Ltd
ANZ Centre Melbourne, Level 9, 833 Collins Street, Docklands, Victoria 3008
Phone: (61) 3 9273 5555   **Fax:** (61) 3 8542 5252
Web: www.anz.com

HISTORICAL FINANCIALS

Company Type: Public

Income Statement

	ASSETS ($ mil.)	NET INCOME ($ mil.)	INCOME AS % OF ASSETS	FYE: September 30 EMPLOYEES
09/20	741,812	2,545	0.3%	38,579
09/19	662,905	4,022	0.6%	39,060
09/18	679,851	4,615	0.7%	39,924
09/17	703,341	5,021	0.7%	44,896
09/16	696,998	4,349	0.6%	46,554
Annual Growth	**1.6%**	**(12.5%)**	**—**	**(4.6%)**

2020 Year-End Financials

Return on assets: 0.3%
Return on equity: 5.8%
Long-term debt ($ mil.): —
No. of shares (mil.): —
Sales ($ mil): 19,938

Dividends
Yield: 5.6%
Payout: 85.7%
Market value ($ mil.): —

	STOCK PRICE ($) FY Close	P/E High/Low		PER SHARE ($) Earnings	Dividends	Book Value
09/20	12.46	16	8	0.84	0.71	15.36
09/19	19.21	9	7	1.36	1.11	14.49
09/18	20.20	10	9	1.53	1.12	14.87
09/17	23.36	12	9	1.65	1.22	15.73
09/16	21.25	11	9	1.44	1.26	15.10
Annual Growth	(12.5%)	—		(12.6%)	(13.5%)	0.4%

Aviva Plc (United Kingdom)

The company's services and products includes Investments Savings & Retirement UK Life General Insurance. Its long-term comprises life insurance long-term health and accident insurance savings pensions and annuity business written by the life insurance subsidiaries including managed pension fund business. While the general insurance provides insurance cover to individuals and to small and medium-sized businesses for risks associated mainly with motor vehicles property and liability such as employers' liability and professional indemnity liability and medical expenses. In addition fund management business invests policyholders' and shareholders' funds. Its Aviva Investors arm provides asset management globally. The company also offers private medical insurance through employers. All of the company's businesses operate under the Aviva banner. The group traces its history back to 1696.

Operations

Aviva divides its business into the following segments: UK & Ireland Life (about 55%) General Insurance (some 15%) Aviva Investors (less than 5%) Manage-for-Value (about 30%).

The United Kingdom comprises two operating segments ? Life and General Insurance. The principal activities of the UK Life operations are life insurance long-term health and accident insurance savings pensions and annuity business.

The principal activity of the operation in Canada is general insurance. In particular it provides personal and commercial lines insurance products principally distributed through insurance brokers. The principal activities of the operations in France are long-term business and general insurance. Activities in Poland comprise long-term business and general insurance and includes long-term business in Lithuania.

The operations in Italy are in the life and non-domestic insurance markets. The Ireland segment also includes Friends First.

Aviva Investors operates in most of the markets in which the group operates in particular the UK France North America and Asia Pacific. Aviva Investors manages policyholders' and shareholders' invested funds provides investment management services for institutional pension fund mandates.

Net earned premiums are by far Aviva's biggest revenue source at nearly 55% with most of the rest arising from fees and commission income and net income.

Geographic Reach

The UK which accounts for 55% of sales primary markets include France Italy Ireland and Poland.

Sales and Marketing

Aviva distributes its products through many channels — including direct sales forces and independent brokers partners and bank representatives — tailored to each market in which it operates. In the UK Aviva has an exclusive arrangement with Santander for the Spanish bank and ING to sell life insurance through its UK branch network. Moreover the company has over 3.5 million customers in the UK registered on MyAviva allowing them to manage their policies online.

Financial Performance

Note: Growth rates may differ after conversion to US Dollars.

Aviva's total revenue varies hugely year-by-year due to fluctuations in investment income. Profits have risen steadily over the last five years but ending it with a decrease for 2020.

The company's revenue for 2020 decreased by 1.1 billion to 27.2 billion as compared to the previous year's revenue of 28.3 billion.

Net income also decreased 30% to 1.9 billion in 2020 as compared to 2019's net income of 2.5 billion.

Aviva's cash on hand decreased 2.1 billion during 2020 ending the year at 17.1 billion. The company used 2.7 billion in its operations. The company used 165million through its investing activities with another 884 billion used in its financing.

Strategy

Aviva's strategy is to prioritize focusing the portfolio transform performance and financial strength. In focusing the portfolio the company was able to complete the disposals in Aviva Singapore and plans to dispose the entire business in France the joint venture in Turkey and the remaining Life and General Insurance business in Italy. The company aims to transform performance through simplifying digitizing and automating the business. Lastly the company focuses on their financial strength capitalizing on its strong solvency and liquidity and reducing debt.

HISTORY

When insurers hiked premiums after the 1861 Great Tooley Street Fire of London merchants formed Commercial Union Fire Insurance (CU). It opened offices throughout the UK and in foreign ports and soon added life (1862) and marine (1863) coverage.Over the next 20 years CU's foreign business thrived. The firm had offices across the US by the 1880s. In the 1890s CU entered Australia India and Southeast Asia. Foreign business eventually accounted for some 75% of CU's sales.

CU went shopping in the 20th century adding accident insurer Palatine Insurance Co. of Manchester in 1900 and rescuing two companies ruined by San Francisco's 1906 earthquake and fire. CU recovered from the Depression with the help of a booming auto insurance market and spent most of the 1930s and WWII consolidating operations to cut costs.

Profits suffered in the 1950s as CU faced increased competition in the US. To boost sales it merged with both multi-line rival North British and Mercantile and life insurer Northern and Employers Assurance in the early 1960s. While US business continued to lag in the 1970s the company's European business grew.

From 1982 to 1996 CU cut its operations in the US entered new markets (Poland 1992; South Africa and Vietnam 1996) and sold its New Zealand subsidiaries (1995). As competition in the UK increased the company in 1997 reorganized and merged with General Accident in 1998.

General Accident & Employers Liability Assurance Association (GA) was formed in 1885 in Perth Scotland to sell workers' compensation insurance. Within a few years GA had branches in London and Scotland. It diversified into insurance for train accidents (1887) autos (1896) and fire (1899); in 1906 its name changed to General Accident Fire and Life Assurance.

GA expanded into Australia Europe and Africa at the turn of the century. After WWI the company's auto insurance grew along with car ownership. During the 1930s the company entered the US auto insurance market. WWII put a stop to GA's growth.

The company expanded after the war forming Pennsylvania General Fire Insurance Association (1963) and acquiring the UK's Yorkshire Insurance Co. (1967). By the 1980s about one-third of its sales came from the US.

After 1986 GA acquired some 500 real estate brokerage agencies to cross-sell its home and life insurance. To increase presence in Asia and the Pacific the company in 1988 acquired NZI Corp. a New Zealand banking and insurance company whose failing operations cost GA millions. At the same time new US government regulations and a series of damaging storms hammered the company.

In response GA cut costs posting a profit by 1993. As the industry consolidated the company bought nonstandard auto insurer Sabre (1995) life insurer Provident Mutual (1996) and General Insurance Group Ltd. in Canada (1997). Unable to compete on its own GA merged with CU to form CGU in 1998.

After the merger CGU added personal pension plans and entered alliances to sell insurance in Italy and India. Merger costs and exceptional losses for 1998 hit operating profits hard. In 1999 CGU upped its stake in French bank Societe Generale to about 7% to help it fend off a hostile takeover attempt by Banque Nationale de Paris (now BNP Paribas).

In 2000 CGU merged with rival Norwich Union to form CGNU and made plans to exit the Canadian life and the US general insurance businesses. In 2001 CGNU sold its US property/casualty operations to White Mountains Insurance.

In an attempt to strengthen its brand name the company changed its name to Aviva in 2002. Following the name change the company merged and rebranded many of its subsidiaries. Aviva also made changes to its Asian operations in 2004 selling its general insurance business in Asia to Mitsui Sumitomo Insurance.

Back home Aviva acquired UK-based automotive service company RAC in 2005 (sold to The Carlyle Group in 2011) to gain access to its auto insurance and loan businesses. To get to the meaty middle Aviva stripped off RAC's non-core businesses including its fleet services which it sold to VT Group in 2006. At around the same time the company also divested its 50% ownership in Lex Vehicle Leasing to HBOS (which later merged with Lloyds TSB to become Lloyds Banking Group).

As part of an effort to focus on the Aviva brand the company changed the long-time UK brand name of Norwich Union to Aviva UK in 2009.

EXECUTIVES

Group General Counsel and Company Secretary, Kirstine Cooper

Independent Non-Executive Director, Patricia Cross, $180,841 total compensation

Senior Independent Non-Executive Director, Patrick Flynn, $219,317 total compensation

Non-Executive Chairman of the Board, George Culmer, $502,763 total compensation

Group CEO and Director, Amanda Blanc, $714,385 total compensation

Independent Non-Executive Director, Mohit Joshi, $11,543 total compensation
Independent Non-Executive Director, Jim McConville, $19,238 total compensation
Independent Non-Executive Director, Pippa Lambert
Non-Executive Independent Director, Martin Strobel
Non-Executive Independent Director, Shonaid Jemmett- Page
Chief Financial Officer and Director, Jason Windsor, $865,728 total compensation
Independent Non-Executive Director, Michael Mire, $164,167 total compensation
Independent Non-Executive Director, Belen Garcia, $211,622 total compensation
Auditors: PricewaterhouseCoopers LLP

LOCATIONS

HQ: Aviva Plc (United Kingdom)
St. Helen's, 1 Undershaft, London EC3P 3DQ
Phone: (44) 20 7283 2000
Web: www.aviva.com

2018 sales

	%
United Kingdom	38
France	20
Canada	11
Poland	3
Italy Ireland Spain and other	23
Asia/Pacific	4
Aviva Investors	1
Total	**100**

PRODUCTS/OPERATIONS

2018 Sales

	% of total
Net earned premiums	92
Fees & commissions	8
Total	**100**

COMPETITORS

ABRDN PLC	LEGAL & GENERAL GROUP
AEGON N.V.	PLC
AON GLOBAL LIMITED	Sampo Oyj
AXA	THE HARTFORD
FINANCIAL	
Ageas	SERVICES GROUP INC.
ERGO Group AG	Zurich Insurance Group
ING Groep N.V.	AG

HISTORICAL FINANCIALS

Company Type: Public

Income Statement				FYE: December 31
	ASSETS ($ mil.)	NET INCOME ($ mil.)	INCOME AS % OF ASSETS	EMPLOYEES
12/20	654,865	3,818	0.6%	28,930
12/19	607,515	3,364	0.6%	31,181
12/18	549,617	2,001	0.4%	31,703
12/17	597,930	2,021	0.3%	30,021
12/16	541,777	864	0.2%	29,530
Annual Growth	4.9%	45.0%	—	(0.5%)

2020 Year-End Financials

Return on assets: 0.5%
Return on equity: 14.9%
Long-term debt ($ mil.): —
No. of shares (mil.): —
Sales ($ mil): 63,553

Dividends
Yield: 3.3%
Payout: 33.0%
Market value ($ mil.): —

	STOCK PRICE ($)	P/E		PER SHARE ($)		
	FY Close	High/Low		Earnings	Dividends	Book Value
12/20	8.82	16	8	0.95	0.30	6.80
12/19	11.02	18	15	0.83	0.72	5.97
12/18	9.44	37	24	0.48	0.92	5.73
12/17	13.78	28	24	0.47	0.63	6.03
12/16	11.81	83	57	0.19	0.50	5.49
Annual Growth	(7.0%)	—		50.5%	(11.9%)	5.5%

Awa Bank, Ltd.

When it comes to serving customers in the Tokushima Prefecture few financial institutions go "way back" like Awa Bank. Established in 1896 the bank serves both private and corporate customers offering the typical array of banking products such as savings foreign and domestic exchanges credit cards and ATM maintenance. Its lending operations includes loans for houses cars and education while its leasing segment provides equipment leasing services to small and midsized businesses. Awa Bank operates through a network of more than 90 branches and four subsidiaries.
Operations
The Bank has two business segments. Its Banking segment is engaged in deposit loan securities investment and domestic exchange and foreign exchange businesses as well as the sale of public bond investment trust and insurance products. The Leasing segment offers leasing services.

EXECUTIVES

Managing Executive Officer, Director of Main Sales Unit, Manager of Ryogoku Bridge Office, Manager of Kachidoki Bridge Office, Director, Hiroshi Ishimoto
Managing Executive Officer, Manager of Osaka Office, Director, Masahiro Yamashita
Independent Director, Hiroshi Sonoki
Independent Director, Hiroshi Fujii
Independent Director, Seiko Noda
Director, Yasuhiko Sumitomo
Independent Director, Takeshi Yabe
President, Representative Director, Susumu Nagaoka
Chairman of the Board, Yoshifumi Okada
Managing Director, Shiro Yamato
Managing Director, Atsunori Miura
Independent Director, Akira Yonebayashi
Managing Director, Yamato Nishi
Director, Yasuo Ohnishi
Senior Managing Director, Representative Director, Takehisa Fukunaga
Auditors: KPMG AZSA LLC

LOCATIONS

HQ: Awa Bank, Ltd.
2-24-1 Nishisemba-cho, Tokushima 770-8601
Phone: (81) 88 623 3131
Web: www.awabank.co.jp

COMPETITORS

AOZORA BANK LTD. THE	HANG SENG BANK
LIMITED	
CHINA MINSHENG BANKING	OITA BANKLTD.
THE	
CORP. LTD.	
China Construction	
Bank Corporation	

HISTORICAL FINANCIALS

Company Type: Public

Income Statement				FYE: March 31
	ASSETS ($ mil.)	NET INCOME ($ mil.)	INCOME AS % OF ASSETS	EMPLOYEES
03/21	34,916	76	0.2%	1,821
03/20	31,102	102	0.3%	1,874
03/19	30,076	98	0.3%	1,880
03/18	30,932	111	0.4%	1,890
03/17	28,673	111	0.4%	1,909
Annual Growth	5.0%	(8.9%)	—	(1.2%)

2021 Year-End Financials

Return on assets: 0.2%
Return on equity: 3.1%
Long-term debt ($ mil.): —
No. of shares (mil.): 42
Sales ($ mil): 592

Dividends
Yield: —
Payout: —
Market value ($ mil.): —

AXA SA

Auditors: Mazars

LOCATIONS

HQ: AXA SA
25, Avenue Matignon, Paris 75008
Phone: (33) 1 40 75 48 43
Web: www.axa.com

HISTORICAL FINANCIALS

Company Type: Public

Income Statement				FYE: December 31
	ASSETS ($ mil.)	NET INCOME ($ mil.)	INCOME AS % OF ASSETS	EMPLOYEES
12/20	987,463	3,883	0.4%	114,625
12/19	876,743	4,330	0.5%	120,869
12/18	1,065,827	2,450	0.2%	104,065
12/17	1,043,069	7,443	0.7%	95,728
12/16	942,674	6,154	0.7%	97,707
Annual Growth	1.2%	(10.9%)	—	4.1%

2020 Year-End Financials

Return on assets: 0.4%
Return on equity: 4.4%
Long-term debt ($ mil.): —
No. of shares (mil.): —
Sales ($ mil): 125,786

Dividends
Yield: 3.4%
Payout: 58.6%
Market value ($ mil.): —

	STOCK PRICE ($)	P/E		PER SHARE ($)		
	FY Close	High/Low		Earnings	Dividends	Book Value
12/20	23.95	25	12	1.53	0.83	36.83
12/19	28.15	19	14	1.70	1.50	32.89
12/18	21.39	40	27	0.90	1.50	30.00
12/17	29.67	13	11	2.98	2.78	35.01
12/16	25.20	11	8	2.43	2.30	30.81
Annual Growth	(1.3%)	—		(10.8%)	(22.6%)	4.6%

BAE Systems Plc

BAE Systems is one of the leading military contractors and major foreign players in the US defense market. BAE's main products and services provide land air and sea combat and support vehicles; weapons systems; cyber defense; and electronic sensors and systems. Based in the UK BAE has close ties with the UK Government but its biggest market is the US which it supplies through BAE Systems Inc one of the biggest suppliers to the US Department of Defense. BAE's fighter aircraft include the Hawk Tornado and the next-generation Eurofighter Typhoon.

Operations

BAE Systems operates through five primary segments: Electronic Systems Cyber & Intelligence Platforms & Services (US) Air and Maritime.

Air is the largest segment bringing in more than 35% of sales. It designs upgrade and builds fixed-wing military and training aircraft and provides training support and information services to the Royal Air Force and other customers worldwide. Its primary airframes are the Eurofighter Typhoon the Hawk Advanced Jet Trainer and the Tornado.

Electronic Systems generates over 20% of sales and produces commercial and defense electronics for flight and engine control electronic warfare systems electro-optical sensors precision guidance and seeker solutions persistent surveillance capabilities communication systems and hybrid-electric drive systems.

Platforms and Services (US) accounts for more than 15% of sales and carries out the production and service support of armored combat and tactical vehicles military and commercial ships major and minor caliber naval guns and missile launchers canisters artillery systems intelligent munitions and armor systems.

Maritime generates about 15% of sales and designs and manufactures naval ships and submarines and compatible combat systems and equipment. The segment also provides an array of associated services including training maintenance and modernization programs to support ships and equipment.

Cyber & Intelligence accounts nearly 10% of sales and covers the company's cyber security secure government and commercial financial security activities.

Overall BAE generates nearly 40% of sales from Military and technical services support over 35% from Platforms more than 20% from Electronic Systems and about 5% from Cyber.

Geographic Reach

UK-based BAE Systems has major operations in the UK US Australia and Saudi Arabia.

The US generates about 45% of sales Other International Markets about 20% the UK almost 20% Saudi Arabia close to 15% and Australia less than 5%.

Sales and Marketing

BAE's largest customers are the US UK and Saudi Arabia governments. As well as governments BAE also sells to large prime contractors and commercial businesses. The company engages third parties to assist sales and marketing activities of BAE.

Financial Performance

BAE's sales started to recover in 2019 after seeing a continued decline from 2016 to 2018. Profit has fluctuated over the last five years.

BAE's sales grew about 5% from 18.3 billion in 2019 to 19.3 billion in 2020. The growth is due to the increase in sales on all of the company's segments.

2020's net income fell 10% to 1.4 billion compared to 1.5 billion in 2019.

BAE Systems cash at the end of 2020 was 2.7 billion. Operating activities generated 1.2 billion. Investing activities used 2 billion. Financing activities generated 973 million.

Strategy

BAE's strategy is comprised of five key long-term areas of focus that will help the company to achieve its vision and mission. It is centered on maintaining and growing its core franchises and securing growth opportunities through advancing its three strategic priorities and demonstrating the company's behaviors.

The five key long-term areas consist of maintaining and growing the company's defense business; Continuing to grow business in adjacent markets; developing and expanding international business; inspiring and developing a diverse workforce to drive success; and Enhancing financial performance and deliver sustainable growth in shareholder value.

BAE's three strategic priorities which are embedded throughout the company provides the link between its longer term strategy and near term business objectives for all its employees.

Mergers and Acquisitions

In mid-2020 BAE acquired Raytheon's Airborne Tactical Radios for $275 million. Raytheon based in Massachusetts US is one of the industry's leading providers of battle-tested products and capabilities that will expand the company's Electronic Systems Portfolio.

In early 2020 BAE entered into an agreement to acquire Collins Aerospace's Military Global Positioning System for $1.9 billion. Collins Aerospace based in Florida US is one of the leading providers of mission critical military GPS receiver solutions. The acquisition will also contribute to the company's Electronic Systems Portfolio.

Also in 2020 BAE completed the acquisition of Techmodal Limited (Techmodal) a UK-based consultancy and digital services company for cash consideration of 38 million. Techmodal has a number of long-term contracts with the UK Ministry of Defence and complements the Group's existing digital data and technical service capabilities.

Company Background

Post-Wright brothers and pre-WWII a host of aviation companies sprang up to serve the British Empire — too many to survive after the war when the empire contracted. Parliament took steps in 1960 to save the industry by merging companies to form larger stronger entities — Hawker-Siddeley Aviation and British Aircraft Corporation (BAC).

Hawker-Siddeley made up of aircraft and missiles divisions was created by combining A.V. Roe Gloster Aircraft Hawker Aircraft Armstrong Whitworth and Folland Aircraft. It attained fame in the 1960s for developing the Harrier "jump jet."

BAC was formed from the merger of Bristol Aeroplane English Electric and Vicker-Armstrong. In 1962 it joined France's Aerospatiale to build the supersonic Concorde and became a partner in ventures to develop the Tornado and Jaguar fighters. The cost of these ventures plus the commercial failure of the Concorde was more than the company could bear. Realizing British aviation was again in trouble the British government nationalized BAC and Hawker-Siddeley in 1976 and merged them in 1977 with Scottish Aviation to form British Aerospace (BAe).

HISTORY

Post-Wright brothers and pre-WWII a host of aviation companies sprang up to serve the British Empire — too many to survive after the war when the empire contracted. Parliament took steps in 1960 to save the industry by merging companies to form larger stronger entities — Hawker-Siddeley Aviation and British Aircraft Corporation (BAC).

Hawker-Siddeley made up of aircraft and missiles divisions was created by combining A.V. Roe Gloster Aircraft Hawker Aircraft Armstrong Whitworth and Folland Aircraft. It attained fame in the 1960s for developing the Harrier "jump jet."

BAC was formed from the merger of Bristol Aeroplane English Electric and Vicker-Armstrong. In 1962 it joined France's Aerospatiale to build the supersonic Concorde and became a partner in ventures to develop the Tornado and Jaguar fighters. The cost of these ventures plus the commercial failure of the Concorde was more than the company could bear. Realizing British aviation was again in trouble the British government nationalized BAC and Hawker-Siddeley in 1976 and merged them in 1977 with Scottish Aviation to form British Aerospace (BAe).

EXECUTIVES

Chief Executive, Executive Director, Charles Woodburn, $1,260,757 total compensation
Non-Executive Independent Director, Stephen Pearce
Non-Executive Independent Director, Nicole Piasecki
Group Finance Director, Executive Director, Bradley Greve, $587,412 total compensation
Non-Executive Independent Director, Jane Griffiths
Non-Executive Independent Director, Nicholas Anderson
Senior Vice President - Government Relations, Shelly Stoneman
Non-Executive Director, Ewan Kirk
Non-Executive Director, Crystal Ashby
Non-Executive Director, Carolyn Fairbairn
Non-Executive Independent Chairman of the Board, Roger Carr
Auditors: Deloitte LLP

LOCATIONS

HQ: BAE Systems Plc
6 Carlton Gardens, London SW1Y 5AD
Phone: (44) 1252 373232
Web: www.baesystems.com

2018 Sales

	% of total
US	46
UK	22
Saudi Arabia	15
Rest of Europe	7
Rest of Middle East	4
Australia	3
Canada	3
Rest of Asia and Pacific	-
Total	**100**

PRODUCTS/OPERATIONS

2018 Sales

	% of total
Air	33
Electronic Systems	23
Maritime	17
Platforms & Services (US)	17
Cyber & Intelligence	10
Total	**100**

COMPETITORS

AEROVIRONMENT INC.	RAYTHEON COMPANY
COBHAM LIMITED	RAYTHEON
TECHNOLOGIES	
DASSAULT AVIATION	CORPORATION
INSITU INC.	TEXTRON INC.
LEONARDO SPA	

HISTORICAL FINANCIALS

Company Type: Public

Income Statement

FYE: December 31

	REVENUE ($ mil.)	NET INCOME ($ mil.)	NET PROFIT MARGIN	EMPLOYEES
12/20	26,307	1,772	6.7%	89,600
12/19	24,172	1,949	8.1%	87,800
12/18	21,476	1,276	5.9%	78,000
12/17	24,747	1,153	4.7%	76,000
12/16	21,884	1,123	5.1%	76,000
Annual Growth	4.7%	12.1%	—	4.2%

2020 Year-End Financials

Debt ratio: 26.8%
Return on equity: 25.7%
Cash ($ mil.): 3,777
Current ratio: 1.00
Long-term debt ($ mil.): 6,764
No. of shares (mil.): —
Dividends
Yield: 4.3%
Payout: 220.8%
Market value ($ mil.): —

	STOCK PRICE ($) FY Close	P/E High/Low		PER SHARE ($) Earnings	Dividends	Book Value
12/20	27.15	90	54	0.55	1.17	1.97
12/19	30.28	67	50	0.61	1.11	2.23
12/18	23.42	112	73	0.40	1.11	2.22
12/17	31.18	138	110	0.36	1.13	2.01
12/16	29.03	106	79	0.35	1.01	1.33
Annual Growth	(1.7%)	—	—	11.9%	3.8%	10.3%

2020 Year-End Financials

Debt ratio: 3.4%
Return on equity: 12.9%
Cash ($ mil.): 5,471
Current ratio: 2.68
Long-term debt ($ mil.): 9,225
No. of shares (mil.): —
Dividends
Yield: —
Payout: —
Market value ($ mil.): —

	STOCK PRICE ($) FY Close	P/E High/Low		PER SHARE ($) Earnings	Dividends	Book Value
12/20	216.24	27	11	1.24	0.00	10.43
12/19	126.40	3	2	8.04	0.00	679.86
12/18	158.60	0	0	113.44	0.00	677.91
12/17	234.21	1	0	80.54	0.00	509.11
12/16	164.41	1	0	45.88	0.00	382.65
Annual Growth	7.1%	—	—	(59.4%)	(59.4%)	

Baloise Holding AG

Founded in 1863 as a fire insurance company Baloise-Holding today is a general insurer that sells such standardized products as group and individual life policies and accident property and health insurance to small firms and individuals. The company is one of the leading insurers in Switzerland operating primarily there and in Germany; together the countries account for over 65% of its sales. Through subsidiaries it also operates in other nearby countries including Belgium and Luxembourg. Baloise also provides banking pension plans and other financial services through its Baloise Bank SoBa. The company uses its own sales force as well as partner distributors and independent brokers to sell its wares.

Operations

Baloise operates through four segments: Non-Life Life Banking (including asset management) and Other Activities. Its Non-Life segment offers accident and health coverage as well as liability motor property and marine products which are primarily targeted towards retail clients. Life provides individuals and companies with endowment policies term insurance investment-linked products and private placement life insurance. Baloise's Banking segment includes subsidiaries Baloise Bank SoBa in Switzerland while the group's Other Activities segment comprises investment companies real estate companies and financing firms.

Life insurance accounts for nearly 45% of revenue while another more than 35% accounts in non life insurance and the remaining accounts the rest.

Geographic Reach

Switzerland accounts for more than 50% of Baloise's revenues while the remaining accounts in Germany Belgium and Luxembourg. The group also has operations in Germany (including the regional branch of Basler versicherungs). In Luxembourg the company operates Baloise Assurance.

Its head office is located in Basel.

Sales and Marketing

The company sells its products through its own sales department as well as partners and outside brokers. It serves private and corporate end customers at all Baloise locations.

Financial Performance

Baloise has reported increasing revenue from 2015 to 2017 a fall in revenue in 2018 and a rise again in 2019. Revenue increased by 24% for the past five years. Net income followed a similar trend reporting a 36% increase for the past five years.

Revenue increased from CHF 7.3 billion in 2018 to CHF 11 billion in 2019. Revenue increase resulted from an increase in premiums earned and policy fees realized gains and losses on investments and premiums earned and policy fees offset by a decrease in investment income and income from services rendered.

Net income was CHF 689.5 million a 32% increase from the previous year.

Strategy

Last year Baloise sharpened its strategic focus. It used its insights from the first three years of the Simply Safe strategic phase to set priorities for its digital initiatives. Baloise had initially experimented in various different areas gaining invaluable experience but is now concentrating on the 'Home' and 'Mobility' ecosystems. This is where it sees the greatest opportunities for building on its robust core business by expanding the portfolio of services for its customers.

Baloise also made huge progress with strengthening optimizing and diversifying its core business. In the life business it is continuing to improve the business mix by focusing on risk and unit-linked products. The company also capitalized on the opportunities for growth in Switzerland presented by the withdrawal of a competitor. The strategic reallocation of the non-life portfolio in Germany is having a positive impact. The German business's turnaround is reflected in a considerable increase in new customers.

The 2019 results for the Luxembourg business unit were also robust. Baloise unlocked opportunities and possibilities in Belgium's attractive non-life insurance market when it acquired insurance company Fidea NV in the first half of the year. The announced acquisition of Athora's non-life insurance portfolio will also markedly strengthen the market position of the Belgian business. These two acquisitions will underpin Belgium's role as a second key pillar within the Baloise Group alongside the Swiss business. They will also help to diversify the business. The Athora portfolio will significantly strengthen Baloise's position in the Wallonia region of Belgium.

Mergers and Acquisitions

In 2020 As part of a strategic partnership Baloise Asset Management is acquiring a stake in Zurich-based asset manager Tolomeo Capital AG. With this transaction Baloise Asset Management will further strengthen its position as one of Switzerland's leading rule-based asset managers. In addition it will exploit synergies and complementary capabilities in areas such as automated investment solutions and alternative investments. Terms were not disclosed.

In 2020 Baloise has acquired two plots of land as part of the Giessen development in D bendorf. Plans for the approximately 35000 square metre site include the construction of 500 new homes as well as commercial units and green spaces by 2026. The acquisition of the land and the planned development expands Baloise's investment portfolio of rented property in highly attractive locations. Terms were not disclosed.

In 2019 As part of its Simply Safe strategy Baloise Asset Management part of the Baloise Group has acquired a stake in business start-up Brainalyzed a specialist in machine learning and artificial intelligence (AI). Following a two-year partnership and its first experiences with swarm-based artificial intelligence Baloise has decided to invest in the company. Brainalyzed's innovative approach to AI will help Baloise Asset Management to successfully expand its third-party asset management business.

Company Background

The Basler Versicherungs-Gesellschaft gegen Feuerschaden (Baloise Insurance Company for Fire Damage) is founded in 1863. Today it is

Baidu Inc

EXECUTIVES

Chief Financial Officer, Rong Luo
Co-Founder, Chairman and Chief Executive Officer, Robin Li
Chief Technology Officer, Haifeng Wang
Independent Director, Jixun Foo
Senior Vice President, General Counsel, Zhixiang Liang
Chief Strategy Officer, Herman Yu
Executive Vice President, Dou Shen
Senior Vice President, Shanshan Cui
Auditors: Ernst & Young Hua Ming LLP

LOCATIONS

HQ: Baidu Inc
Baidu Campus, No. 10 Shangdi 10th Street, Haidian District, Beijing 100085
Phone: (86) 10 5992 8888   **Fax:** (86) 10 5992 0000
Web: www.baidu.com

HISTORICAL FINANCIALS

Company Type: Public

Income Statement

FYE: December 31

	REVENUE ($ mil.)	NET INCOME ($ mil.)	NET PROFIT MARGIN	EMPLOYEES
12/20	16,371	3,435	21.0%	41,000
12/19	15,436	295	1.9%	37,779
12/18	14,869	4,008	27.0%	45,887
12/17	13,032	2,812	21.6%	39,343
12/16	10,159	1,675	16.5%	45,887
Annual Growth	12.7%	19.7%	—	(2.8%)

known as the Baloise Group and operates in four countries under the umbrella of Baloise Holding Ltd. At the time of its greatest geographical expansion around 1938 it had offices in about 50 countries worldwide.

HISTORY

In 1863 15 business leaders in Basel Switzerland formed the Baloise Fire Insurance Company. This was followed in 1864 by the formation of the Baloise transportation and life insurance companies.

Baloise-Holding was created in 1962 as a holding company for the previously independent insurance entities. In 1971 it merged all of its non-life companies into the Baloise Insurance Group.

Under its then-new chairman and president Rolf Sch¤uble Baloise-Holding began in 1993 to re-organize its operations as it implemented a new corporate strategy. Key components of the strategy included a focus on the company's core European markets and a pattern of discarding less-profitable businesses. In 1998 Baloise-Holding sold off its US operations.

Strengthening its position as a full-fledged financial services company in 2000 Baloise acquired Swiss bank Solothurner (now Baloise Bank SoBa).

The same year it purchased Belgian bank HBK-Spaarbank Belgian insurer Amazon Insurance N.V. and Swiss regional bank Solothurner Bank SoBa.

EXECUTIVES

Non-Executive Chairman of the Board, Andreas Burckhardt, $1,405,487 total compensation
Non-Executive Independent Vice Chairman of the Board, Andreas Beerli, $133,095 total compensation
Non-Executive Independent Director, Thomas Pleines, $133,095 total compensation
Non-Executive Independent Director, Christoph Gloor, $133,095 total compensation
Member of the Executive Board, Head of Corporate Division Asset Management, Matthias Henny, $532,381 total compensation
Non-Executive Independent Director, Hugo Lasat, $133,095 total compensation
President of the Corporate Executive Committee, Group Chief Executive Officer, Gert De Winter, $1,011,525 total compensation
Chief Financial Officer, Member of the Corporate Executive Committee, Carsten Stolz, $532,381 total compensation
Member of the Executive Board, Head of Corporate Division Switzerland, Michael Mueller, $745,334 total compensation
Chief Technology Officer, Member of the Corporate Executive Committee, Alexander Bockelmann, $638,857 total compensation
Non-Executive Independent Director, Thomas von Planta, $133,095 total compensation
Non-Executive Independent Director, Marie-Noelle Zen-Ruffinen, $133,095 total compensation
Non-Executive Independent Director, Hans-Joerg Schmidt-Trenz, $133,095 total compensation
Non-Executive Independent Director, Christoph Mader, $133,095 total compensation
Non-Executive Independent Director, Markus Neuhaus, $133,095 total compensation
Auditors: Ernst & Young Ltd.

LOCATIONS

HQ: Baloise Holding AG
Aeschengraben 21, Basel CH-4002
Phone: (41) 58 285 89 42   **Fax:** (41) 58 285 70 70
Web: www.baloise.com

2014 Sales

	% of total
Switzerland	48
Germany	18
Belgium	17
Luxembourg	16
Other	1
Total	**100**

PRODUCTS/OPERATIONS

2014 Sales

	% of total
Non-life insurance	47
Life	53
Total	**100**

Selected Subsidiaries

Austria
 Basler Versicherungen (insurance and pension products for private and business clients)
Belgium
 Mercator Verzekeringen (personal and property insurance for individuals and small to mid-sized businesses)
Germany
 Basler Versicherungen (personal and property insurance for individuals small and mid-sized enterprises and selected industrial clients)
 Deutscher Ring (insurance and pension products for individuals)
Luxembourg
 Bâloise Assurances (life personal and property insurance for private and business clients)
Switzerland
 Bâloise Bank SoBa (banking products and services)
 Basler Versicherungen (insurance and pension products for individuals and small to mid-sized enterprises)

COMPETITORS

ABRDN PLC
AMUNDI
Canadian Apartment Properties Real Estate Investment Tru
Credit Suisse Group AG
GROUPE CRIT
Holcim AG
LEGAL & GENERAL GROUP PLC
LIVERPOOL VICTORIA FRIENDLY SOCIETY LTD
MAPFRE SA
SYNERGIE
Sampo Oyj
Sika AG
Swiss Life Holding AG
Talanx AG

HISTORICAL FINANCIALS

Company Type: Public

Income Statement   FYE: December 31

	ASSETS ($ mil.)	NET INCOME ($ mil.)	INCOME AS % OF ASSETS	EMPLOYEES
12/20	100,330	493	0.5%	7,693
12/19	90,015	718	0.8%	7,646
12/18	82,193	531	0.6%	7,203
12/17	86,605	561	0.6%	7,286
12/16	79,196	525	0.7%	7,270
Annual Growth	**6.1%**	**(1.6%)**	**—**	**1.4%**

2020 Year-End Financials

Return on assets: 0.4%
Return on equity: 6.3%
Long-term debt ($ mil.): —
No. of shares (mil.): 45
Sales ($ mil): 9,855
Dividends
 Yield: 0.0%
 Payout: 3.8%
Market value ($ mil.): 648

	STOCK PRICE ($) FY Close	P/E High/Low		PER SHARE ($) Earnings	Dividends	Book Value
12/20	14.38	2	2	10.93	0.42	176.01
12/19	18.13	1	1	15.51	0.36	152.44
12/18	14.92	1	1	11.30	0.32	130.30
12/17	15.24	1	1	11.76	0.31	136.98
12/16	12.48	1	1	11.02	0.28	118.74
Annual Growth	**3.6%**	**—**	**—**	**(0.2%)**	**10.8%**	**10.3%**

Banco Bilbao Vizcaya Argentaria SA (BBVA)

Auditors: KPMG Auditores, S.L.

LOCATIONS

HQ: Banco Bilbao Vizcaya Argentaria SA (BBVA)
Plaza San Nicolas 4, Bilbao 48005
Phone: (34) 91 537 7000   **Fax:** (34) 91 537 6766
Web: www.bbva.com

HISTORICAL FINANCIALS

Company Type: Public

Income Statement   FYE: December 31

	ASSETS ($ mil.)	NET INCOME ($ mil.)	INCOME AS % OF ASSETS	EMPLOYEES
12/20	903,501	1,601	0.2%	123,174
12/19	784,465	3,943	0.5%	126,973
12/18	774,940	6,097	0.8%	125,627
12/17	827,211	4,218	0.5%	131,856
12/16	772,754	3,669	0.5%	134,792
Annual Growth	**4.0%**	**(18.7%)**	**—**	**(2.2%)**

2020 Year-End Financials

Return on assets: 0.1%
Return on equity: 2.7%
Long-term debt ($ mil.): —
No. of shares (mil.): —
Sales ($ mil): 41,040
Dividends
 Yield: 5.7%
 Payout: 114.5%
Market value ($ mil.): —

	STOCK PRICE ($) FY Close	P/E High/Low		PER SHARE ($) Earnings	Dividends	Book Value
12/20	4.94	47	19	0.17	0.28	8.22
12/19	5.58	14	10	0.53	0.29	8.22
12/18	5.29	12	7	0.87	0.30	8.15
12/17	8.50	20	15	0.58	0.36	8.35
12/16	6.77	14	10	0.53	0.39	7.62
Annual Growth	**(7.6%)**	**—**	**—**	**(24.5%)**	**(7.3%)**	**1.9%**

Banco Bradesco SA

Auditors: KPMG Auditores Independentes

LOCATIONS

HQ: Banco Bradesco SA
Cidade de Deus S/N, Vila Yara, Sao Paulo, Osasco 06029-900
Phone: (55) 11 3684 4011   **Fax:** (55) 11 3684 3213
Web: www.bradesco.com.br

HISTORICAL FINANCIALS

Company Type: Public

Income Statement
FYE: December 31

	ASSETS ($ mil.)	NET INCOME ($ mil.)	INCOME AS % OF ASSETS	EMPLOYEES
12/20	308,970	3,049	1.0%	89,575
12/19	342,942	5,229	1.5%	97,329
12/18	336,383	4,272	1.3%	98,605
12/17	369,587	5,158	1.4%	98,808
12/16	366,250	5,498	1.5%	108,793
Annual Growth	(4.2%)	(13.7%)	—	(4.7%)

2020 Year-End Financials

Return on assets: 1.0%
Return on equity: 11.2%
Long-term debt ($ mil.): —
No. of shares (mil.): —
Sales ($ mil): 25,298

Dividends
Yield: 2.1%
Payout: 28.7%
Market value ($ mil.): —

	STOCK PRICE ($) FY Close	P/E High/Low		PER SHARE ($) Earnings	Dividends	Book Value
12/20	5.26	4	2	0.33	0.10	3.17
12/19	8.95	5	3	0.56	0.40	3.80
12/18	9.89	6	4	0.46	0.17	3.62
12/17	10.24	6	4	0.61	0.19	4.41
12/16	8.71	5	3	0.59	0.19	3.66
Annual Growth	(11.8%)			— —(13.7%)(14.1%)		
(3.5%)						

Banco BTG Pactual S.A.

LOCATIONS

HQ: Banco BTG Pactual S.A.
Av. Brigadeiro Faria Lima, 3477, Sao Paulo
Phone: (55) 11 3383 2159   **Fax:** (55) 11 3383 2001
Web: www.btgpactual.com

HISTORICAL FINANCIALS

Company Type: Public

Income Statement
FYE: December 31

	ASSETS ($ mil.)	NET INCOME ($ mil.)	INCOME AS % OF ASSETS	EMPLOYEES
12/20	47,159	765	1.6%	0
12/19	41,382	1,000	2.4%	0
12/18	34,008	624	1.8%	0
12/17	35,460	719	2.0%	0
12/16	34,229	1,454	4.2%	0
Annual Growth	8.3%	(14.8%)	—	—

2020 Year-End Financials

Return on assets: 1.9%
Return on equity: 16.4%
Long-term debt ($ mil.): —
No. of shares (mil.): —
Sales ($ mil): 4,629

Dividends
Yield: —
Payout: —
Market value ($ mil.): —

Banco Comercial Portugues SA

Auditors: Deloitte & Associados, SROC S.A.

LOCATIONS

HQ: Banco Comercial Portugues SA
Praca D. Joao I, 28, Porto 4000-295
Phone: (351) 21 321 1081   **Fax:** (351) 21 321 1079
Web: www.millenniumbcp.pt

HISTORICAL FINANCIALS

Company Type: Public

Income Statement
FYE: December 31

	ASSETS ($ mil.)	NET INCOME ($ mil.)	INCOME AS % OF ASSETS	EMPLOYEES
12/19	91,666	339	0.4%	18,585
12/18	86,946	344	0.4%	15,929
12/17	86,237	223	0.3%	15,727
12/16	75,247	25	0.0%	15,807
12/15	81,565	256	0.3%	17,252
Annual Growth	3.0%	7.2%	—	1.9%

2019 Year-End Financials

Return on assets: 0.3%
Return on equity: 5.0%
Long-term debt ($ mil.): —
No. of shares (mil.): —
Sales ($ mil): 3,303

Dividends
Yield: —
Payout: —
Market value ($ mil.): —

Banco de Chile

Banco de Chile proffers a place for pesos. Chile's second-largest bank after Banco Santander Chile it has some 300 branches and 1400 ATMs in its home country as well as operations in Argentina Brazil China Mexico and the US. In addition to corporate and retail banking the company offers (through subsidiaries) mutual funds brokerage insurance financial planning factoring and other services. The Luksic family through such entities as Quiñenco and Sociedad Matriz Banco de Chile controls a majority of the bank. In 2008 Citigroup bought a 10% stake in the bank (with an option to acquire more) from Quiñenco and merged its Chilean operations into Banco de Chile.

EXECUTIVES

Manager - Operations and Technology Division, Esteban Kemp Kemp De La Hoz
Director, Samuel Libnic
Controller, Oscar Mehech Castellon
Chief Executive Officer, Eduardo Ebensperger Orrego
Manager - Global Compliance Division, Felipe Echaiz Bornemann
Independent Director, Jaime Estevez Valencia, $78,304 total compensation
Director, Andres Ergas Heymann, $78,304 total compensation
Chairman of the Board, Pablo Jose Granifo Lavin, $755,257 total compensation
Independent Director, Alfredo Cutiel Ergas Segal, $78,304 total compensation
Director, Jean Paul Luksic Fontbona, $78,304 total compensation
CEO of Banchile Corredores de Bolsa, Hernan Arellano Salas
Director, Jose Francisco Perez Mackenna, $78,304 total compensation
People and Organization Division Manager, Cristian Lagos Contardo
Chief Financial Officer, Rolando Arias Sanchez
General Counsel, Secretary to the Board, Alfredo Villegas Montes
Marketing and Digital Banking Division, Claudia Herrera Garcia
Commercial Banking Division Manager, Jose Vizcarra Villalobos
Corporate Banking Division Manager, Axel Romero
Manager - Cyber Security Division, Salvador Danel
Efficiency and Productivity Division Manager, Nicolas Burr De la Huerta

Vice Chairman of the Board, Andronico Luksic Craig, $234,912 total compensation
Director, Raul Anaya Elizalde, $12,629 total compensation
Vice Chairman of the Board, Julio Santiago Figueroa
Manager - Wholesale Credit Risk Division, Paola Alam Auad
Manager - Retail Credit Risk Division, Interim Global Risk Control Division Manager, Julio Cesar Cubillo Navarro
Auditors: EY Audit SpA

LOCATIONS

HQ: Banco de Chile
Paseo Ahumada 251, Santiago
Phone: (56) 2 637 1111   **Fax:** (56) 2 653 5156
Web: www.bancochile.cl

COMPETITORS

AUSTRALIA AND NEW ZEALAND BANKING GROUP LIMITED
BANCO DE GALICIA Y BUENOS AIRES S.A.U.
BANCO POPULAR ESPA 'OL SA (EXTINGUIDA)
BANCO SANTANDER RIO S.A.
Bolivar Banco C.A.
CHANG HWA COMMERCIAL BANK LTD.
METROPOLITAN BANK & TRUST COMPANY

HISTORICAL FINANCIALS

Company Type: Public

Income Statement
FYE: December 31

	ASSETS ($ mil.)	NET INCOME ($ mil.)	INCOME AS % OF ASSETS	EMPLOYEES
12/20	64,084	565	0.9%	13,134
12/19	55,648	819	1.5%	13,562
12/18	51,320	869	1.7%	13,831
12/17	52,945	930	1.8%	14,023
12/16	47,026	862	1.8%	14,611
Annual Growth	8.0%	(10.0%)	—	(2.6%)

2020 Year-End Financials

Return on assets: 0.9%
Return on equity: 10.1%
Long-term debt ($ mil.): —
No. of shares (mil.): —
Sales ($ mil): 2,896

Dividends
Yield: 3.0%
Payout: 13,094.4%
Market value ($ mil.): —

	STOCK PRICE ($) FY Close	P/E High/Low		PER SHARE ($) Earnings	Dividends	Book Value
12/20	20.38	6	4	0.01	0.63	0.06
12/19	20.99	5	4	0.01	0.79	0.05
12/18	28.60	15	5	0.01	0.77	0.05
12/17	96.53	17	13	0.01	0.75	0.06
12/16	70.45	13	11	0.01	0.76	0.05
Annual Growth	(26.7%)			— — (9.3%) (4.8%) 3.6%		

Banco De Sabadell SA

Founded in 1881 Banco de Sabadell (also known as BancoSabadell) is one of the top banking groups in Spain offering corporate commercial and private banking through more than 2000 branches mostly in Spain as well as in France Morocco the UK and the US. The company operates TSB Banking Group PLC (TSB) which operates in the UK; ActivoBank for online banking; SabadelMexico a full-service bank and Sabadel-lUrquijo for private banking. BancoSabadell also offers insurance products through bancassurance along with asset management and securities brokerage services.

Operations

With total asset of ?235.8 million BancoSabadell offers a range of financial services to over 12 million customers through more than 2000 branches. BancoSabadell operates the following main business segments: Business Banking Personal Banking Private Banking Institutional Banking Asset Management and Bancassurance.

Banco Sabadell was founded as a corporate bank hence its specialization and lasting leadership in corporate banking. Through more than 1500 branches the bank manages Personal Banking customers who are locals of Spain as well as over 800000 foreigners. It also operates with the specific brand SabadellUrquijo Private Banking which specializes in sports and entertainment. Institutional banking is the Group's Division that deals with institutional clients which is structured into three work teams: the first one deals with public institutions that are part of the General State Government; the second team works with financial organizations and insurers; and the third team deals with religious institutions. In 2020 a strategic partnership was formed with Amundi Asset Management Europe's leading asset manager in terms of assets under management. The specialized bancassurance business provides a wide range of products (savings and risk life and pensions and general insurance) for individuals and businesses sold by the Bank's network tailored to the needs of each organization and their brands and different channels through which they operate.

In terms of shareholder structure retail shareholders account for 56% of over 240000 shareholders while institutional shareholders account for 44%. Majority of the bank's shareholders are under the 12000 shareholding tranche.

Geographic Reach

Banco Sabadell operates in over 20 countries throughout the world and has commercial banks in Spain the UK and Mexico.

Sales and Marketing

In 2020 BancoSabadell adopted new ways of working and relating to customers through digital channels leveraging the work that had been done in the past while guaranteeing business continuity at all times and supporting its customers in their search for financial solutions to the problems caused by the pandemic.

Progress with digitalization is focused on efficiency and commercial activity. In 2020 93% of service transactions of the company in Spain happened through distance channels. Of which nearly 40% of loans were sold digitally and over 70% of sales were made through digital channels.

BancoSabadell provides its foreign customers Online Banking its App and 24/7 Call Center support in several languages.

Financial Performance

Note: Growth rates may differ after conversion to US dollars.

BancoSabadell's net profit was at ?2 million which was impacted by the effects of managing the COVID-19 crisis. Net income excluding TSB was at ?222 million while TSB alone recorded a net loss of ?220 million in 2020. The bank's net interest income fell by nearly 6% to ?884 million ($1 billion) in 2020 compared to ?833 million ($1 billion) from the prior year.

Strategy

Banco Sabadell's business model focuses on customer service digitization the strength and geographical diversification of its balance sheet our solvency and on generating long-term value for is shareholders is employees and society in general.

Sustainability is at the heart of Banco Sabadell's corporate strategy. The transformation process

carried out in recent years based on digitalization and new information technologies has incorporated the changes entailed by the transition towards a sustainable economy and sustainable development. The Bank has made sustainability a key element of its strategy through a policy that frames all the Bank's activity within ESG parameters. A sustainable finance plan has been set in motion and the Bank placed its first issue of sustainable bonds.

In 2020 Banco Sabadell launched its framework for the issuance of bonds linked to the Sustainable Development Goals. It identifies sustainable goals that Banco Sabadell is currently promoting as well as those that it aims to promote in the future.

Sabadell will launch a new strategic plan that will prioritize its Spanish domestic business with the goal of increasing efficiency and profitability in order to create value for its shareholders.

Company Background

Previously BancoSabadell acquired Miami-based Mellon United National Bank (which it rebranded Sabadell United Bank) and its 15 branches from The Bank of New York Mellon in 2010. The following year it acquired the assets and branches of the failed Lydian Private Bank further adding to its operations in the region. In 2007 the company acquired TransAtlantic Bank and BBVA's private banking business also both based in Miami.

Closer to home BancoSabadell acquired smaller rival Banco Guipuzcoano in 2010. The following year it acquired savings bank Caja de Ahorros del Mediterraneo (CAM) which had been seized by the government for a symbolic ?1. That brought some 5 million additional customers to the bank increased its assets by around 75% and upped its branch numbers by more than 900. CAM is now SabadellCAM.

EXECUTIVES

Independent Director, Aurora Cata Sala, $189,141 total compensation
Lead Independent Director, Anthony Elliott Ball, $170,910 total compensation
Independent Director, Pedro Fontana Garcia, $225,602 total compensation
Independent Director, Jose Ramon Martinez Sufrategui, $159,516 total compensation
Deputy General Manager, Ramon de la Riva Reina
Non-Member Secretary of the Board, Miguel Roca Junyent
Chief Risk Officer, Executive Director, David Vegara Figueras, $113,940 total compensation
General Manager - Operations and People, Miguel Montes Guell
General Manager - Sabadell Spain, Carlos Ventura Santamans
Deputy General Manager, Enric Rovira Masachs
Executive Director, Secretary General, Maria Jose Garcia Beato, $113,940 total compensation
Independent Director, Jose Manuel Martinez Martinez, $157,238 total compensation
Chief Financial Officer, General Manager, Tomas Varela Muina
Independent Director, George Johnston, $214,208 total compensation
Independent Director, Manuel Valls Morato, $182,304 total compensation
Deputy General Manager, Manuel Tresanchez Montaner
Independent Director, Mireya Gine Torrens, $44,436 total compensation
Independent Director, Alicia Reyes Revuelta
Chief Executive Officer, Executive Director, Jaime Guardiola Romojaro, $113,940 total compensation
Independent Vice Chairman of the Board, Javier Echenique Landiribar, $235,857 total compensation

Director, David Martinez Guzman, $113,940 total compensation
Executive Chairman of the Board, Jose Oliu Creus, $266,620 total compensation
Auditors: KPMG Auditores, S.L.

LOCATIONS

HQ: Banco De Sabadell SA
  Avenida Oscar Espla, 37, Alicante 03007
Phone: (34) 93 902 323 000
Web: www.bancsabadell.com

PRODUCTS/OPERATIONS

2013 Sales

	% of total
Net interest income	44
Income from trading and exchange differences	38
Fee and Commission income	18
Total	**100**

2014 Sales

	%
Commercial Banking	83
Corporate Banking	10
Sabadell Urquijo Banking	2
Investment Managment	2
Real Estate Asset Management	3
Total	**100**

COMPETITORS

AKBANK TURK ANONIM SIRKETI
BANCO BILBAO VIZCAYA ARGENTARIA SOCIEDAD ANONIMA
BANCO BPI S.A.
BANCO SANTANDER SA
BANKINTER SOCIEDAD ANONIMA
Banco Santander Brasil S/A
Banco do Brasil S/A
Bank of Communications Co. Ltd.
Landesbank Baden-W rttemberg
NATIXIS
NORINCHUKIN BANK THE
SLM CORPORATION
STATE BANK OF INDIA
Shinhan Financial Group Co. Ltd.
ZIONS BANCORPORATION

HISTORICAL FINANCIALS

Company Type: Public

Income Statement   FYE: December 31

	ASSETS ($ mil.)	NET INCOME ($ mil.)	INCOME AS % OF ASSETS	EMPLOYEES
12/20	289,349	2	0.0%	24,089
12/19	251,222	862	0.3%	25,349
12/18	254,602	8	0.0%	15,319
12/17	265,342	4	0.0%	15,374
12/16	224,383	5	0.0%	26,022
Annual Growth	**6.6%**	**(19.1%)**	**—**	**(1.9%)**

2020 Year-End Financials

Return on assets: 0.0%   Dividends
Return on equity: 0.0%   Yield: 3.6%
Long-term debt ($ mil.): —   Payout: —
No. of shares (mil.): —   Market value ($ mil.): —
Sales ($ mil): 8,282

	STOCK PRICE ($) FY Close	P/E High/Low	PER SHARE ($) Earnings	Dividends	Book Value
12/20	0.84	— —	(0.01)	0.03	2.73
12/19	2.42	20 12	0.15	0.02	2.58
12/18	2.44	87 47	0.06	0.11	2.42
12/17	4.10	31 24	0.17	0.08	2.76
12/16	3.01	27 18	0.14	0.03	2.41
Annual Growth	**(27.4%)**	**— —**	**—**	**0.8%**	**3.1%**

Banco Santander Brasil SA

The bank part of Spain's Banco Santander provides financial services through 3564 branches primarily in Brazil's south and southeast with a major presence in the states of S o Paulo and Rio Grande do Sul. Santander Brasil also offers wholesale banking to large corporations. Additional services include asset management private banking and insurance.

Operations

Banco Santander operates through two business segments: Commercial Banking (more than 90% of total revenue) and Global Wholesale Banking (nearly 10%).

Commercial Banking segment provides services and products to individuals and companies (except for global corporate customers). The revenue from this segment is derived from the banking and financial products and services available to its account and non-account holders.

Global Wholesale Banking offers a wide range of national and international tailored financial services and structured solutions corporate customers comprised mostly of local and multinational corporations.

Geographic Reach

Banco Santander operates four major administrative operational centers all of which are owned properties. Additionally it owns more than 400 properties for the activities of its banking network and rents some 2280 properties for the same purpose.

Sales and Marketing

Banco Santander serves its products and services to nearly 28 million active customers through traditional media such as television and printed media but also the internet mobile advertising and social networks.

The company offers its financial services and products to its customers through multichannel distribution networks composed of physical channels such as branches mini-branches and ATMs; call centers; and digital channels such as Internet banking and mobile banking. The company has over 2150 branches over 1400 mini-branches nearly 13000 own ATMs and nearly 23800 shared ATMs.

Financial Performance

Total income amounted to R$48.2 billion in 2020 a decrease of 18% in comparison with the year ended 2019 primarily due to the impact of the COVID-19 pandemic on the Brazilian economy.

Consolidated profit for 2020 totaled R$13.4 billion a decrease of 19% over the year ended 2019 mainly impacted by the performance of gains/losses on financial assets and liabilities (net) and exchange differences (net) line.

Cash and cash equivalent for fiscal year 2020 was about R$28.4 billion compared to R$21.4 billion in 2019. Cash generated by operating activities was R$42.3 billion while investing and financing activities used R$1.2 billion and R$34.2 billion respectively.

Strategy

Banco Santander uses a range of strategies and instruments including entering into derivative and other transactions to hedge our exposure to market credit and operational risks. Its strategy is to endeavor to grow in a profitable recurring and sustainable manner by providing services with excellence and to consistently strive to enhance customer satisfaction levels expand its customer base and increase the loyalty of its customers.

To achieve this goal the company has been deeply focused on understanding how the Brazilian market works to address its demands effectively. In line with this approach it has sought to identify its different types of customers and their specific needs. Accordingly it adopted a strategy that is based on serving its customers wherever and whenever they want through multi-channel (digital and/or physical) solutions that provide a customized and innovative portfolio of services and products.

Company Background

The parent company listed approximately 15% of its shares of its Brazilian unit on the New York Stock Exchange in a 2009 IPO. It turned out to be the world's largest IPO that year raising some R$13 billion ($8 billion). The proceeds from the offering have been used to drive growth by funding new branches and lending. It is also growing its insurance and credit card businesses; the company recently began offering its Santander-Ferrari credit card.

In late 2010 Santander rebranded its Brazilian brands — Banco Real and Santander Brasil — under the same name and platform. (It completed similar restructuring efforts in the UK and Mexico.) The parent company has high hopes for its Latin American operations especially in the high-growth markets of Brazil and Mexico. As such Santander is committed to investing in those units as it solidifies its position as a leading global bank.

Santander Brasil is the result of the 2006 merger of Banco Santander banks Banco Santander Brasil Banco Santander Meridional and Banco do Estado de S o Paulo. The company added to its Brazilian bank empire when it acquired Banco Real in 2008. At the time Banco Real was the fourth largest non government-owned Brazilian bank. The acquisition boosted Santander Brasil into the top three of banks in Brazil (along with Banco Bradesco and Ita Uni-banco)

Brazil is a promising region of the world for banking. The country was a resilient market during the economic downturn. Employment levels rose and a new middle class emerged. As the Brazilian economy expands Santander Brasil expects lending and overall demand for banking services to grow.

Auditors: PricewaterhouseCoopers Auditores Independentes

LOCATIONS

HQ: Banco Santander Brasil SA
Avenida Presidente Juscelino Kubitschek, 2041 and 2235 Bloco A, Vila Olimpia, Sao Paulo 04543-011
Phone: (55) 11 3174 8589   **Fax:** (55) 11 3174 6751
Web: www.santander.com.br

PRODUCTS/OPERATIONS

2013 Sales

	% of total
Interest and similar income	82
Fee and commission income	17
Gains on financial transactons	1
Total	**100**

COMPETITORS

ABN AMRO Bank N.V.
BANCA MONTE DEI PASCHI DI SIENA SPA
BANCO BILBAO VIZCAYA ARGENTARIA SOCIEDAD ANONIMA
BANCO DE SABADELL SA
BANCO POPULAR ESPA 'OL SA (EXTINGUIDA)
BANCO SANTANDER SA
BANK VTB PAO
BNP PARIBAS
Banco Bradesco S/A
Banco Latinoamericano de Comercio Exterior S.A.
CLYDESDALE BANK PLC
COMMONWEALTH BANK OF AUSTRALIA
Danske Bank A/S
GRUPO SUPERVIELLE S.A.
INTESA SANPAOLO SPA
ITAU UNIBANCO HOLDING SA
KEYCORP
NATWEST GROUP PLC
SBERBANK PAO
The Bank of Nova Scotia
ZIONS BANCORPORATION

HISTORICAL FINANCIALS

Company Type: Public

Income Statement

FYE: December 31

	REVENUE ($ mil.)	NET INCOME ($ mil.)	NET PROFIT MARGIN	EMPLOYEES
12/20	13,661	2,583	18.9%	44,599
12/19	22,879	4,081	17.8%	47,819
12/18	21,040	3,241	15.4%	48,012
12/17	26,651	2,693	10.1%	47,404
12/16	30,100	2,253	7.5%	0
Annual Growth	(17.9%)	3.5%	—	—

2020 Year-End Financials

Debt ratio: —
Return on equity: 13.2%
Cash ($ mil.): 3,879
Current ratio: —
Long-term debt ($ mil.): —

No. of shares (mil.): —
Dividends
  Yield: 6.8%
  Payout: 178.3%
Market value ($ mil.): —

	STOCK PRICE ($) FY Close	P/E High/Low		PER SHARE ($) Earnings	Dividends	Book Value
12/20	8.64	6	3	0.33	0.56	5.36
12/19	12.13	6	5	0.52	0.47	6.32
12/18	11.13	7	4	0.41	0.46	6.16
12/17	9.67	10	6	0.34	0.44	6.86
12/16	8.89	10	4	0.29	0.24	6.75
Annual Growth	(0.7%)	—	—	3.7%	23.5%	(5.6%)

Banco Santander Chile

A majority-owned indirect subsidiary of Spanish financial services giant Grupo Santander Banco Santander Chile is the largest bank in its home country. From more than 460 branches throughout Chile (including about 100 Banafe bank locations catering to middle-income clients) the bank offers consumer banking residential mortgage financing credit cards auto loans and investment management services for approximately 2.3 million customers. The bank also has about 40 payment centers operating as Santander SuperCaja. Corporate banking services include commercial lending and leasing trade financing financial advisory services and cash management.

EXECUTIVES

Chief Risk Officer, Franco Rizza
Director of Technology and Operation, Ricardo Bartel Jeffery
Director Clients and Service Quality, Carlos Volante Neira
Chief Executive Officer, Miguel Mata Huerta

President of the Board, Group Country Head, Claudio Melandri Hinojosa
Independent Director, Juan Pedro Santa Maria Perez
Second Independent Vice Chairman of the Board, Orlando Poblete Iturrate
Director, Lucia Santa Cruz Sutil
Director, Ana Dorrego de Carlos
First Independent Vice Chairman of the Board, Rodrigo Vergara Montes
General Counsel, Cristian Florence Kauer
Director of Retail Banking, Matias Sanchez Garcia
Independent Director, Felix de Vicente Mingo
Corporate Financial Controller, Guillermo Sabater Maroto
Independent Director, Alfonso Gomez Morales
Chief Financial Officer, Emiliano Muratore Raccio
Chief Administrative and Costs Officer, Sergio Avila Salas
Director of Human Resources and Communications, Maria Eugenia de la Fuente Nunez
Director of Corporate Products, Cristian Peirano Novoa
Director of Internal Audit, Oscar Gomez Llorente
Director of Middle-Market Banking, Jose Manuel Manzano Tagle
Chief Accounting Officer, Jonathan Covarrubias
Director, Rodrigo Echenique Gordillo
Director of Corporate and Investment Banking, Fred Meller Sunkel
Auditors: PricewaterhouseCoopers Consultores Auditores SpA

LOCATIONS

HQ: Banco Santander Chile
Bandera 140, 20th Floor, Santiago
Phone: (11) 562 2320 8284   **Fax:** (11) 562 696 1679
Web: www.santander.cl

COMPETITORS

BANCA ANTONVENETA SPA
BANK OF THE JAMES FINANCIAL GROUP INC.
CITIBANK NATIONAL ASSOCIATION
CREDIT INDUSTRIEL ET COMMERCIAL
FIRST COMMONWEALTH FINANCIAL CORPORATION
HMN FINANCIAL INC.
NIBDAN LIMITED
National Bank of Canada
QNB CORP.
Slovensk sporitelna a.s.
Taishin Financial Holding Co. Ltd.

HISTORICAL FINANCIALS

Company Type: Public

Income Statement			FYE: December 31
	ASSETS ($ mil.)	NET INCOME ($ mil.)	INCOME AS % OF ASSETS	EMPLOYEES
12/20	78,367	770	1.0%	10,470
12/19	68,620	840	1.2%	11,200
12/18	56,385	857	1.5%	11,305
12/17	58,249	915	1.6%	11,068
12/16	55,533	713	1.3%	11,354
Annual Growth	9.0%	1.9%	—	(2.0%)

2020 Year-End Financials

Return on assets: 1.0%   Dividends
Return on equity: 15.5%   Yield: 3.4%
Long-term debt ($ mil.): —   Payout: 18,059.4%
No. of shares (mil.): —   Market value ($ mil.): —
Sales ($ mil): 3,326

	STOCK PRICE ($) FY Close	P/E High/Low		PER SHARE ($) Earnings	Dividends	Book Value
12/20	18.99	9	5	0.00	0.65	0.03
12/19	23.07	9	7	0.00	0.83	0.02
12/18	29.90	10	9	0.00	1.12	0.02
12/17	31.27	11	8	0.00	0.90	0.03
12/16	21.87	9	7	0.00	0.85	0.02
Annual Growth	(3.5%)	—	—	1.9%	(6.5%)	3.9%

Banco Santander Mexico SA, Institucion de Banca Multiple, Grupo Financiero Santander Mexico

Grupo Financiero Santander which operates primarily through Banco Santander (Mexico) bank is among the top five largest financial services firms in Mexico based on net income assets and deposits. It offers retail and commercial banking as well as asset management brokerage and custody services (through subsidiary Casa de Bolsa Santander) and securities underwriting. Banco Santander Mexico serves more than 12 million customers with approximately 1300 branches across the country. Grupo Financiero Santander is 75%-owned by Spanish banking giant Grupo Santander.

Operations

The company's retail banking segment is its largest bringing in about 85% of total revenue. Wholesale banking which includes the broker-dealer operations brings in most of the rest.

Auditors: PricewaterhouseCoopers, S.C.

LOCATIONS

HQ: Banco Santander Mexico SA, Institucion de Banca Multiple, Grupo Financiero Santander Mexico
Avenida Prolongacion Paseo de la Reforma 500, Col. Lomas de Santa Fe, Delegacion Alvaro Obregon, Mexico City 01219
Phone: (52) 55 5257 8000   **Fax:** (52) 55 5269 2701
Web: www.santander.com.mx

PRODUCTS/OPERATIONS

2014 Sales

	%
Retail Banking	85
Global Wholesale Banking	13
Corporate Activities	2
Total	**100**

2014 Sales

	%
Interest income and similar income	75
Fee and commission income	21
Gains/(losses) on financial assets and liabilities (net)	3
Other operating income	1
Total	**100**

COMPETITORS

Grupo Financiero Banorte S.A.B. de C.V.

Grupo Financiero Inbursa S.A.B. de C.V.

HISTORICAL FINANCIALS

Company Type: Public

Income Statement			FYE: December 31
	ASSETS ($ mil.)	NET INCOME ($ mil.)	INCOME AS % OF ASSETS	EMPLOYEES
12/20	92,501	954	1.0%	21,183
12/19	77,567	1,077	1.4%	15,857
12/18	71,639	984	1.4%	16,016
12/17	67,471	948	1.4%	15,116
12/16	65,291	797	1.2%	16,976
Annual Growth	9.1%	4.6%	—	5.7%

2020 Year-End Financials

Return on assets: 1.1%   Dividends
Return on equity: 13.1%   Yield: —
Long-term debt ($ mil.): —   Payout: —
No. of shares (mil.): —   Market value ($ mil.): —
Sales ($ mil): 7,439

	STOCK PRICE ($) FY Close	P/E High/Low		PER SHARE ($) Earnings	Dividends	Book Value
12/20	5.15	3	1	0.14	0.00	1.14
12/19	6.78	3	2	0.16	0.33	1.05
12/18	6.16	3	2	0.14	0.29	0.92
12/17	7.31	4	3	0.14	0.00	0.86
12/16	7.19	4	3	0.12	0.00	0.76
Annual Growth	(8.0%)	—	—	4.7%	—	10.5%

Banco Santander SA (Spain)

Spain's Banco Santander offers retail banking and consumer finance in Portugal the UK and other parts of Europe as well as the US. Subsidiaries such as Banco Santander Chile Banco Santander (Brasil) Santander R o in Argentina and Grupo Financiero Santander (Mexico) make it a top banking group in Latin America (generating over 45% of the group's revenue). Other units offer asset management private banking corporate and investment banking and insurance. All told the company has some ?1.5 trillion in assets about 148 million customers and around 11235 branch locations.

Operations

Banco Santander has operations in retail banking and consumer finance commercial and wholesale banking private banking asset management and insurance.

The bank is organized principally along geographic lines where its primary geographies constitute separate segments: South America (over 40% of sales) Europe (more than 35%) North America (around 20%) and Santander Global Platform accounts for the rest.

The company also operates its secondary segments which includes: Retail Banking (around 80% of sales) Corporate and Investment Banking (over 10%) Wealth Management and Insurance (some 5%) and Santander Global Platform.

Retail Banking covers all customer banking businesses including consumer finance except those of corporate banking which are managed through Santander Corporate & Investment Banking asset management private banking and insurance which are managed by Wealth Management & Insurance. Corporate & Investment Banking (SCIB) business reflects revenue from global corporate banking investment banking and markets worldwide including treasuries managed globally (always after the appropriate distribution with Retail Banking customers) as well as equity business. Wealth Management & Insurance includes the asset management business (Santander Asset Management) the corporate unit of Private Banking and International Private Banking in Miami and Switzerland and the insurance business (Santander Insurance). Santander Global Platform which comprises its global digital services under a single business unit (breakdown in the primary segment definition) as well as 50% of the results generated by these services in the commercial network.Net interest income accounts for over 70% of total revenue followed by net fee income with over 20%. Its loan portfolio remained balanced: individuals (some 45%) consumer credit (over 15%) SMEs and corporates (around 25%) and SCIB (nearly 15%).

Geographic Reach

Madrid-based Banco Santander is well diversified between mature economies and emerging markets making financial results more predictable. Its main geographies are Brazil (generating some 30% of profits) US (some 10%) and the UK (approximately 10%) and Mexico (around 10%). Its other main territories are Chile Argentina Spain Portugal and Poland which account for around 5% of sales each.

Sales and Marketing

Santander has about 148 million customers and some 22.8 million of what it terms 'loyal customers' i.e. customers it has deeper relationships with either via online or multiple accounts. Santader has around 100000 people talking to our customers every day. Advertising expenses totaled EUR 517 million EUR 685 million and EUR 646 million for the years 2020 2019 and 2018 respectively.

Financial Performance

The company had a net interest income of ?32 billion in 2020 a 9% decrease from the previous year's net interest income of ?35.3 billion.

In 2020 the company had a net loss of ?7.7 billion a ?15.8 billion decrease from the previous year's net income of ?8.1 billion.

The company's cash at the end of 2020 was ?153.8 billion. Operating activities generated ?66.2 billion while investing activities used ?7.2 billion. Financing activities used another ?1.9 billion.

Strategy

In mid-2021 Santander Bank N.A. through its Santander Universities program ("Santander") is pleased to announce a partnership with the Colin Powell School of Civic and Global Leadership at the City College of New York to create the Santander Finance Boot Camp and the Santander Fellows program. The three-year $300000 initiative fully supported by Santander is designed to prepare Colin Powell School students for careers in banking and finance by providing them with the tools they need to apply for analyst and internship experiences in their junior years. The initiative will also contribute to the diversification of the financial sector by supplying it with historically underrepresented groups including racial and ethnic minorities immigrants and first generation students.

Mergers and Acquisitions

In mid-2021 Banco Santander announced that Santander Holdings USA the bank's US holding company has reached an agreement to acquire Amherst Pierpont Securities a market-leading independent fixed-income broker dealer through the acquisition of its parent holding company Pierpont Capital Holdings LLC for a total consideration of approximately $600 million. Amherst Pierpont will

become part of Santander Corporate & Investment Banking (Santander CIB) global business line. Amherst Pierpont is a leading independent broker-dealer based in the US with a premier fixed-income and structured product franchise. Completion of the acquisition significantly enhances Santander CIB's infrastructure and capabilities in market making of US fixed income capital markets provides a platform for self-clearing of fixed income securities for the group globally grows its institutional client footprint and expands its structuring and advisory capabilities for asset originators in the real estate and specialty finance markets.

Company Background

In 2017 Banco Santander acquired failing Spanish bank Banco Popular for one euro. While Santander has quite the mess to sort out — Popular is saddled with ?37 billion in toxic real estate loans — the purchase made Santander the #1 bank in Spain and Portugal and has the potential to make a solid contribution to profits. The acquisition included various asset sales including a ?30 billion property sale — the largest in Spanish history.

HISTORY

In 1857 a group of Basque businessmen had formed Banco Santander to finance Latin American trade. The emergence of Cantabria as a leading province after WWI helped the bank expand first regionally and then nationally.

The Bot n family has been closely identified with the bank for decades. Emilio Bot n served first as a board member and then for a few years as chairman before his death in 1923. The post was held by his son Emilio Bot n-Sanz de Sautuola from 1950 to 1986 when his son Emilio Bot n Sanz de Sautuola y Garc a de los R os (known as Don Emilio) took over.

Spanish banks were spared the worst of the Great Depression (thanks to their isolation and the country's shunning the gold standard) but Spain's civil war was draining. In the early 1940s Santander expanded into Madrid and other major Spanish cities and merged with a few rivals. In the 1950s and 1960s as interest rates were controlled and mergers halted banks competed by building branch networks and investing overseas particularly in Latin America. In 1965 Santander joined with Bank of America to form Bankinter (it divested most of its stake by the mid-1990s).

Tight economic controls were relaxed in the 1970s after Franco's death. Despite global recession Santander continued to invest in Latin America through the mid-1980s.

In the late 1980s Santander prepared to compete in a deregulated Spain and Europe forming alliances with Royal Bank of Scotland Kemper (now part of Zurich Financial Services) and Metropolitan Life Insurance. In 1989 the bank jumpstarted competition by introducing Spain's first high-interest account.

Santander focused on home in the 1990s. Spurned by Banco Hispano Americano (BHA) Santander acquired a 60% stake in the ailing Banco Español de Credito (Banesto) which became wholly owned in 1998. The bank took a hit when Latin America plunged into an economic crisis that year. With profit margins falling the bank merged with BCH in 1999.

BCH was formed by the 1991 merger of Banco Central and BHA. BHA had been established in 1900 by investors in Latin America; Central had been founded in 1919. The mixed banks offered both commercial and investment banking; they funded industrialization and investment in Latin America and became two of Spain's largest banks before the civil war.

After the war BHA sold its Latin American assets when the currency dried up while Central used

mergers and acquisitions to expand across Spain. Isolated from WWII by Franco the two banks used their dual strategies to fund overseas investment and domestic-branch growth.

After Franco's death the banks faced increased competition at home and abroad. Central bought BHA in 1991 to remain competitive as Spain entered the European Economic Community (now the EU) in 1992.

Following the merger BCH trimmed 20% of its branches fired some 10000 employees and sold unprofitable holdings. Focused on Latin America the bank took small stakes in small banks. Losing its edge BCH merged with Santander in 1999.

In 2000 the newly merged BSCH focused on expanding in Europe and Latin America. Among its European moves was its alliance with Societe Generale to buy investment-fund management firms particularly in the US. In Latin America the bank bought Brazil's Banco Meridional Banco do Estado de S o Paulo (Banespa) and Grupo Financiero Serfin Mexico's #3 bank. Critics questioned the $5 billion price tag BSCH paid for Banespa charging that the formerly state-run bank was overvalued in 2001. Executive in-fighting saw ex-Santander chairman Emilio Bot n triumph over ex-BCH chairman Jose Mar a Amus tegui for control of BSCH's helm. Soon after the bank started doing business as simply Santander Central Hispano. The following year the bank sold off its shares of Germany's Commerzbank and France's Societe Generale.

In one of Europe's largest cross-border bank mergers ever Santander paid more than ?12 billion ($15 billion) for British bank Abbey National in 2004. It solidified its UK operations through the approximately ?1.25 billion ($2.6 billion) purchase of Alliance & Leicester. Abbey then acquired the retail deposit business of Bradford & Bingley after it was nationalized in 2008.

Another acquisition helped Santander grow in South America. In 2007 the company along with Royal Bank of Scotland and Fortis acquired the Netherlands-based ABN AMRO (the international retail banking giant with more than 4350 branches) for around ?71 billion ($87 billion). As part of the bid Banco Santander took ABN AMRO's Brazilian operations doubling its market share in Brazil. Also a part of the ABN AMRO deal Santander became the largest non-government-owned bank in Uruguay.

In 2009 the Venezuelan government took over Banco Santander subsidiary Banco de Venezuela the third-largest bank in the country. The government paid some ?755 million ($1 billion) to nationalize the bank.

Also that year Santander acquired the approximately three-quarters of Sovereign it didn't already own. Santander then purchased a more than ?3 billion ($4 billion) US car loan portfolio and a loan servicing platform from HSBC.

In 2010 Santander took full control of its Mexico unit by acquiring Bank of America's 25% stake in Grupo Financiero Santander for ?2 billion ($2.5 billion) as well as the rest of Puerto Rican unit Santander BanCorp it didn't already own. It then acquired GE Capital's $2 billion consumer mortgage business in Mexico for $162 million plus the assumption of debt. The company has also been opening new branches in the region. While the financial downturn and the European sovereign debt crisis has been rough for Spain and Portugal Mexico holds promise for growth. Hoping to cash in on some of that growth Banco Santander spun off nearly 25% of Grupo Financiero Santander in a public offering worth more than $4 billion.

Banco Santander also made a big move into Eastern Europe. In 2011 it paid ?4 billion (nearly $6 billion) for Poland's Bank Zachodni. The acquisition may signal more acquisitions for Santander in neighboring Eastern European countries.

In 2010 Santander bought a ?2.5 billion ($3 billion) auto loan portfolio from Citigroup.

Banco Santander also operates Santander UK the result of the 2010 merger of Abbey National Bradford & Bingley and the former Alliance & Leicester (all of which were acquired by Santander). Santander's acquisitions in the UK helped bump up profits from the region in 2009 and 2010 but in 2011 profits slipped as a result of remediation charges related to mis-sold payment protection insurance.

EXECUTIVES

Goup Head of Costs, Javier Maldonado Trinchant
Group Chief Audit Executive, Juan Guitard Marin
Group head of Supervisory and Regulatory Relations, Monica Lopez-Monis Gallego
Non-Executive Independent Director, Homaira Akbari, $87,164 total compensation
Group Head of Accounting and Financial Control, Jose Francisco Doncel Razola
Non-Executive Independent Director, Alvaro Antonio Cardoso de Souza, $154,959 total compensation
Global Head of Corporate & Investment Banking, Jose Maria Linares Perou
Non-Executive Independent Director, Belen Romana Garcia, $111,711 total compensation
Non-Executive Independent Director, Ramiro Mato Garcia-Ansorena, $135,589 total compensation
Non-Executive Independent Director, Henrique de Castro, $87,164 total compensation
Non-Executive Independent Director, Pam Walkden, $130,409 total compensation
Group Chief Compliance Officer, Marjolien van Hellemondt-Gerdingh
Group Head of Technology and Operations, Dirk Marzluf
Non-Executive Director, Luis Isasi Fernandez de Bobadilla, $50,577 total compensation
Non-Executive Independent Director, Gina Lorenza Diez Barroso Azcarraga, $2,248 total compensation
Regional Head of Europe, Antonio Simoes
Non-Executive Independent Director, Ramon Martin Chavez Marquez, $9,213 total compensation
Group Chief Risk Ofcer, Keiran Foad
Chief Digital and Innovation Officer, Lindsey Argalas
Group Head of Strategy And Corporate Development And Of Consumer Finance (Santander Consumer Finance), Jose Luis de Mora Gil-Gallardo
CEO, Santander Brazil, Sergio Rial
Group Head of Communications, Corporate Marketing and Research, Juan Manuel Cendoya Mendez de Vigo
Group Chief Financial Officer, Jose Antonio Garcia Cantera
Head of Santander Global Payments, Francisco Javier San Felix Garcia, $87,164 total compensation
Executive Chairman of the Board, Ana Botinsanz De Sautuola O'shea, $87,164 total compensation
Group Head of General Secretariat and Human Resources, Secretary, Jaime Perez Renovales
Non-Executive Independent Director, Sol Daurella Comadran, $87,164 total compensation
Head, Santander Spain, Rami Aboukhair Hurtado
Vice Chairman of the Board and Lead Independent Non-Executive Director, Bruce Carnegie-brown, $371,879 total compensation
Auditors: PricewaterhouseCoopers Auditores, S.L.

LOCATIONS

HQ: Banco Santander SA (Spain)
Santander Group City, Avenida Cantabria s/n, Madrid, Boadilla del Monte 28660
Phone: (34) 91 259 65 20
Web: www.santander.com

2018 sales

	%
Continental Europe	32
United Kingdom	11
Latin America	43
United States	14
Eliminations	-
Total	**100**

PRODUCTS/OPERATIONS

2018 sales

	%
Retail Banking	87
Corporate & Investment Banking	10
Wealth Management	3
Eliminations	-
Total	**100**

2018 sales

	%
Net interest income	70
Net fee and commission income	24
Other	6
Total	**100**

COMPETITORS

AGFIRST FARM CREDIT BANK
BANCO DE SABADELL SA
BANKIA SA (EXTINGUIDA)
CAIXA GERAL DE DEP "SITOS S.A.
CAIXABANK SA
FEDERAL HOME LOAN BANK OF DALLAS
FEDERAL HOME LOAN MORTGAGE CORPORATION
HSBC HOLDINGS PLC
NATWEST GROUP PLC
NORINCHUKIN BANK THE
SLM CORPORATION
STANDARD CHARTERED PLC
UNICREDIT SPA

HISTORICAL FINANCIALS

Company Type: Public

Income Statement				FYE: December 31
	ASSETS ($ mil.)	NET INCOME ($ mil.)	INCOME AS % OF ASSETS	EMPLOYEES
12/20	1,851,059	(10,764)	—	191,189
12/19	1,709,630	7,314	0.4%	196,419
12/18	1,671,150	8,943	0.5%	202,713
12/17	1,731,366	7,934	0.5%	202,251
12/16	1,413,959	6,550	0.5%	191,635
Annual Growth	**7.0%**	**—**		**(0.1%)**

2020 Year-End Financials

Return on assets: (-0.5%)
Return on equity: (-9.6%)
Long-term debt ($ mil.): —
No. of shares (mil.): —
Sales ($ mil): 76,317
Dividends
Yield: 3.1%
Payout: —
Market value ($ mil.): —

	STOCK PRICE ($) FY Close	P/E High/Low	PER SHARE ($) Earnings	Dividends	Book Value
12/20	3.05	— —	(0.66)	0.10	5.78
12/19	4.14	14 10	0.41	0.19	6.76
12/18	4.48	15 10	0.51	0.20	6.80
12/17	6.54	19 15	0.48	0.55	7.02
12/16	5.18	13 8	0.43	0.37	6.58
Annual Growth	**(12.4%)**	**— —**	**—**	**(28.9%)**	**(3.2%)**

BanColombia SA

Bancolombia has a wealth of services for wealthy and average Colombians alike. Serving more than 6.4 million customers Bancolombia is the #1 bank in Colombia with more than 700 branches and some 2300 ATMs throughout the country. Its Banagr cola division has another 100 branches located in El Salvador. The bank provides traditional commercial and retail banking services including deposit accounts loans and mortgages credit and debit cards and cash management. It also offers asset management insurance investment banking and brokerage services. In addition to its core Colombia and El Salvador operations the bank is also present in the US Panama and Peru. Bancolombia traces its roots back to 1945.

EXECUTIVES

Independent Director, Andres Felipe Mejia Cardona
Chief Financial Officer, Financial Vice President, Jose Humberto Acosta Martin
Vice President of Corporate Services, Jaime Alberto Villegas Gutierrez
Independent Director, Luis Fernando Restrepo Echavarria
Corporate Vice President, Mauricio Rosillo Rojas
Vice President - Risk Management, Rodrigo Prieto Uribe
Chief Executive Officer of Banco Agricola SA, Rafael Barraza Dominguez
Chief Executive Officer, Juan Carlos Mora Uribe
Non Independent Member, Gonzalo Alberto Perez Rojas
Vice President - Business, Maria Cristina Arrastia Uribe
Independent Director, Arturo Condo Tamayo
Chief Executive Officer of Banistmo, Aimee Sentmat de Grimaldo
Chief Legal Officer and General Counsel, Claudia Echavarria Uribe
Innovation Vice President, Cipriano Lopez Gonzalez
Non Independent Member, Juan David Escobar Franco
Independent Member, Sylvia Gomez
Independent Director, Silvina Vatnick
Vice President of Internal Audit, Jose Mauricio Rodriguez
Auditors: PricewaterhouseCoopers Ltda.

LOCATIONS

HQ: BanColombia SA
Cra. 48 # 26-85, Medellin
Phone: (57) 1 488 5371
Web: www.grupobancolombia.com

PRODUCTS/OPERATIONS

2013 Sales

	% of total
Interest income	
Loans	65
Financial leases	9
Investment sercurities	5
Fees and other service income	
Credit and debit card fees	7
Commissions from banking services	4
Collections and payment fees	3
Trust activities	2
Checking fees	1
Others	4
Total	**100**

Selected Subsidiaries

Banca de Inversion Bancolombia S.A. (investment banking)

Bancolombia (Panamá;) S.A.
Bancolombia Puerto Rico
Factoring Bancolombia S.A. (99.97%)
Fiduciaria Bancolombia S.A. (trust services 98.8%)
Inversiones Financieras Banco Agricola S.A.
(investments 98.4%)
Leasing Bancolombia S.A.
Patrimonio Autonomo CV Sufinanciamiento (loan management)
Valores Bancolombia S.A. (securities brokerage)

COMPETITORS

ARAB BANK PLC
BANCO BPI S.A.
Banque de Montreal
CREDITO BERGAMASCO SPA
DIME COMMUNITY BANCSHARES INC.
EUROBANK ERGASIAS SERVICES AND HOLDINGS S.A.
ISRAEL DISCOUNT BANK OF NEW YORK
METROPOLITAN BANK & TRUST COMPANY
MUFG AMERICAS HOLDINGS CORPORATION
The Bank of Nova Scotia
The Toronto-Dominion Bank

HISTORICAL FINANCIALS

Company Type: Public

Income Statement				FYE: December 31
	ASSETS ($ mil.)	NET INCOME ($ mil.)	INCOME AS % OF ASSETS	EMPLOYEES
12/20	74,672	80	0.1%	30,633
12/19	71,879	949	1.3%	31,075
12/18	67,799	818	1.2%	31,040
12/17	68,325	876	1.3%	31,061
12/16	65,376	954	1.5%	31,598
Annual Growth	3.4%	(46.1%)	—	(0.8%)

2020 Year-End Financials

Return on assets: 0.1%
Return on equity: 1.0%
Long-term debt ($ mil.): —
No. of shares (mil.): 509
Sales ($ mil): 6,794
Dividends
Yield: 3.8%
Payout: 1,675.0%
Market value ($ mil.): 20,480

	STOCK PRICE ($) FY Close	P/E High/Low		PER SHARE ($) Earnings	Dividends	Book Value
12/20	40.18	0	0	0.10	1.54	15.22
12/19	54.79	0	0	1.01	1.24	16.06
12/18	38.10	0	0	0.87	1.35	15.02
12/17	39.66	0	0	0.93	1.26	15.19
12/16	36.68	0	0	1.01	1.17	13.90
Annual Growth	2.3%	—	—	(43.7%)	7.2%	2.3%

Bangkok Bank Public Co., Ltd. (Thailand)

Bangkok Bank wants to protect the baht you've got. One of the largest commercial banks in Thailand Bangkok Bank provides a variety of banking services to individual and commercial clients including checking and savings accounts loans Internet banking and treasury and investment banking services. It operates about 1200 branches serving 16 million customers throughout Thailand about a dozen other Southeast Asian countries the UK and the US. The bank was founded in 1944 in response to the difficulty Thai businessmen encountered in receiving credit facilities from foreign banks; it has since had a hand in developing its homeland's industry and agriculture.

EXECUTIVES

Chairman of the Board of Executive Directors, Executive Director, Deja Tulananda
Independent Director, Prachet Siridej
Independent Director, Kovit Poshyananda
Executive Vice President - Corporate Cash Management Services and Trade Services, Pipat Assamongkol
Executive Vice President - Foreign Exchange Trading, Treasury Front Office, Treasury Division, Paisarn Lertkowit
Executive Vice President, Manager - Corporate Finance Department, Merchant Banking Division, Prasert Deejongkit
Executive Vice President - Micro Segment Management, Customer Segment Management, Consumer Banking, Voraporn Vidhayasirinun
Executive Vice President - Public Relations Department, Executive Director, Member of the Board of Executive Directors, Thaweelap Rittapirom
Executive Vice President - Special Projects in Technology, Office of the President, Thantika Bodhisompon
Executive Vice President - Conglomerate 2, Financial Institution, Agro Industry and Heavy Industry, Corporate Banking, Yaowadee Nakhata
Senior Executive Vice President, Executive Director, Member of the Board of Executive Directors, Chansak Fuangfu
Senior Executive Vice President, Chong Toh
Senior Executive Vice President, Member of the Board of Executive Directors, Executive Director, Suvarn Thansathit
Executive Vice President, Manager - Research Department, Piyapan Tayanithi
Senior Executive Vice President, Manager of Treasury Division, Director, Boonsong Bunyasaranand
Executive Vice President - Treasury Front Office, Treasury Division, Sa-ard Theerarojanawong
Senior Executive Vice President, Siridej Aungudomsin
Executive Vice President - Construction, Property Development, Telecommunication, Manager of Telecommunication and Corporate Banking, Panit Dunnvatanachit
Executive Vice President, Corporate Secretary, Apichart Ramyarupa
Executive Vice President of Accounting and Finance Division, Benjaporn Prisuwanna
Independent Director, Mongkolchaleam Yugala
Executive Vice President - Credit Management, Thawat Treewannakul
Executive Vice President - Application Support, Technology Division, Kajornvut Tayanukorn
Executive Vice President - Risk Management, Secretary to the Risk Oversight Committee, Kirati Laisathit
Executive Vice President - Automobile and Heavy Equipment, Electronics and Computer Parts, Textile and Garment, Conglomerate 1, Service Industry Conglomerate 4 and Sugar Industry, Corporate Banking, Thongchai Ananthothai
Executive Vice President - Credit Approval and Business Banking, Than Siripokee
Senior Executive Vice President - General Management and Human Resources Division, Secretary to the Nomination and Remuneration Committee, Ruchanee Nopmuang
Independent Director, Gasinee Witoonchart
Member of the Board of Executive Directors, Executive Director, Singh Tangtatswas
Executive Vice President, Co-Head of International Banking Group, Nutthaporn Luangsuwan

Executive Vice President of International Banking Group, Suwatchai Songwanich
Independent Director, Phornthep Phornprapha
President, Member of the Board of Executive Directors, Executive Director, Chartsiri Sophonpanich
Non-Executive Chairman of the Board, Piti Sithi-Amnuai
Member of the Board of Executive Directors, Executive Director, Amorn Chandarasomboon
Independent Director, Chokechai Niljianskul
Executive Vice President, Manager of Loan Recovery and Legal, Credit Management, Kraisorn Barameeauychai
Senior Executive Vice President - Corporate Banking, Niramarn Laisathit
Senior Executive Vice President, Suteera Sripaibulya
Executive Vice President, Manager, Shared Operation and Securities Service Department, Pornnit Dunnvatanachit
Senior Executive Vice President, Manager - Technology Division, Kukkong Ruckphaopunt
Executive Vice President - Relationship and Sales Management, Consumer Banking, Pochanee Kongkalai
Senior Executive Vice President, Rushda Theeratharathorn
Executive Vice President, Manager - Credit Card Division, Shoke Na Ranong
Senior Executive Vice President - Chemical and Petrochemical 1, 2 & 3, Chinese Corporate, Multinational 1 & 2 and Special Business, Corporate Banking, Kanit Si
Member of the Board of Executive Directors, Executive Director, Charamporn Jotikasthira
Executive Vice President - Office of the President, Piyada Sucharitkul
Senior Executive Vice President, Head of International Banking Group & Manager, International Branch Division, Chaiyarit Anuchitworawong
Executive Vice President, Manager - Chemical and Petrochemical 2, Corporate Banking, Suchada Sukpantavorn
Independent Director, Arun Chirachavala
Senior Executive Vice President - Special Projects in Technology, Office of the President, Ian Gillard
Executive Vice President, Manager - Research and Analytics, Consumer Banking, Athita Pureetip
Independent Director, Siri Jirapongphan
Independent Director, Pichet Durongkaveroj
Executive Vice President, Hong Kong and China, in charge of Business Expansion and IT (China), Cheng Leo Lin
Executive Vice President, Manager, Mutual Fund Product, Consumer Product Development, Consumer Banking, Suyanee Puripanyawanich
Auditors: Deloitte Touche Tohmatsu Jaiyos Audit Co., Ltd.

LOCATIONS

HQ: Bangkok Bank Public Co., Ltd. (Thailand)
333 Silom Road, Bangrak, Bangkok 10500
Phone: (66) 0 2231 4333   **Fax:** (66) 0 2231 4890
Web: www.bangkokbank.com

COMPETITORS

ARAB BANK PLC
BANK OF AYUDHYA PUBLIC COMPANY LIMITED
COMMONWEALTH BANK OF AUSTRALIA
FB FINANCIAL CORPORATION
FIRST NATIONAL BANK OF ALASKA
HANG SENG BANK LIMITED
STANDARD CHARTERED PLC
UniCredit Bank AG
VIETNAM TECHNOLOGICAL AND COMMERCIAL JOINT STOCK BANK

HISTORICAL FINANCIALS

Company Type: Public

Income Statement				FYE: December 31
	ASSETS ($ mil.)	NET INCOME ($ mil.)	INCOME AS % OF ASSETS	EMPLOYEES
12/20	127,696	573	0.4%	0
12/19	107,988	1,202	1.1%	0
12/18	96,345	1,092	1.1%	25,287
12/17	94,428	1,013	1.1%	0
12/16	82,252	888	1.1%	0
Annual Growth	11.6%	(10.4%)	—	—

2020 Year-End Financials

Return on assets: 0.4%
Return on equity: 3.9%
Long-term debt ($ mil.): —
No. of shares (mil.): 1,908
Sales ($ mil): 5,466

Dividends
Yield: 0.0%
Payout: —
Market value ($ mil.): 39,294

	STOCK PRICE ($) FY Close	P/E High/Low		PER SHARE ($)		
				Earnings	Dividends	Book Value
12/20	20.59	3	2	0.30	0.70	7.86
12/19	27.50	2	1	0.63	0.85	7.52
12/18	32.00	2	2	0.57	0.81	6.69
12/17	33.14	2	1	0.53	0.81	6.46
12/16	22.25	2	1	0.47	0.73	5.55
Annual Growth	(1.9%)		—	(10.4%)	(1.1%)	9.1%

Bank Audi SAL

Auditors: BDO, Semaan, Gholam & Co.

LOCATIONS

HQ: Bank Audi SAL
Bank Audi Plaza, Omar Daouk Street, Bab Idriss, Beirut
Phone: (961) 1 994000   **Fax:** (961) 1 990555
Web: www.bankaudigroup.com

HISTORICAL FINANCIALS

Company Type: Public

Income Statement				FYE: December 31
	ASSETS ($ mil.)	NET INCOME ($ mil.)	INCOME AS % OF ASSETS	EMPLOYEES
12/19	39,535	(605)	—	6,288
12/18	47,201	499	1.1%	6,306
12/17	43,751	538	1.2%	6,541
12/16	44,249	445	1.0%	7,017
12/15	42,253	389	0.9%	6,891
Annual Growth	(1.6%)	—	—	(2.3%)

2019 Year-End Financials

Return on assets: (-1.4%)
Return on equity: (-18.3%)
Long-term debt ($ mil.): —
No. of shares (mil.): 278
Sales ($ mil): 3,525

Dividends
Yield: —
Payout: —
Market value ($ mil.): —

Bank Hapoalim B.M. (Israel)

The largest bank in Israel Bank Hapoalim caters to individual commercial and corporate clients at home and abroad. Within Israel the Bank Hapoalim Group has more than 270 full-service branches and business centers. Another 30 express branches are in the works. Overseas it has about 45 branches correspondent offices and financial subsidiaries in Asia Australia Europe Latin America and North America; its international focus is on private banking and the corporate sector. Bank Hapoalim provides investment banking services including the underwriting of and investment in companies; it also provides trust services to individuals and businesses.

EXECUTIVES

External Director, Dalia Lev
Chief Financial Officer, Member of the Management Board, Ram Gev
Head of Human Resources, Member of the Management Board, Amit Oberkovich
Chief Accountant, Member of the Management Board, Guy Kalif
Director, Israel Trau
Director, Stanley Fischer
Executive Vice President, Member of the Management Board & Head of Financial Markets and International Banking, Yadin Antebi, $485,904 total compensation
President, Chief Executive Officer, Member of the Management Board, Dov Kotler, $703,283 total compensation
Executive Vice President, Head of Corporate Banking, Member of the Management Board, Tsahi Cohen, $464,108 total compensation
Director, David Zvilichovsky
External Independent Director, Noam Hanegbi
Executive Vice President, Member of the Management Board, Head of Information Technology, Eti Ben-zeev, $469,630 total compensation
Chief Internal Auditor & Executive Vice President, Zeev Hayo, $423,240 total compensation
Director, Richard Kaplan
Executive Vice President, Chief Legal Advisor, Member of the Management Board, Yael Almog, $464,108 total compensation
Chief Marketing Officer, Asaf Azulay
Executive Vice President, Chief Risk Officer, Member of the Management Board, Amir Bachar
Corporate Secretary, Gilad Bloch
External Director, David Avner
External Director, Ronit Abramson Rokach
Chairman of the Board, External Independent Director, Ruben Krupik, $462,946 total compensation
Executive Vice President, Head of Innovation and Corporate Strategy, Member of the Management Board, Golan Scherman, $300,778 total compensation
Member of the Management Board, Head of Retail Banking, Dalit Raviv
Auditors: Ziv Haft

LOCATIONS

HQ: Bank Hapoalim B.M. (Israel)
50 Rothschild Blvd., Tel-Aviv 66883
Phone: (972) 3 567 3333   **Fax:** (972) 3 560 7028
Web: www.bankhapoalim.com

COMPETITORS

AUSTRALIA AND NEW ZEALAND BANKING GROUP LIMITED
CITIZENS SOUTH BANKING CORPORATION
FIDELITY FINANCIAL CORPORATION
FIRST INTERNATIONAL BANK OF ISRAEL LTD
HFB FINANCIAL CORPORATION
METROPOLITAN BANK & TRUST COMPANY
Nottingham Building Society
PEOPLE'S UNITED FINANCIAL INC.
SALISBURY BANCORP INC.
SI FINANCIAL GROUP INC.

HISTORICAL FINANCIALS

Company Type: Public

Income Statement				FYE: December 31
	ASSETS ($ mil.)	NET INCOME ($ mil.)	INCOME AS % OF ASSETS	EMPLOYEES
12/20	167,801	639	0.4%	0
12/19	134,203	520	0.4%	8,964
12/18	122,844	691	0.6%	9,427
12/17	130,908	766	0.6%	11,173
12/16	116,667	684	0.6%	11,628
Annual Growth	9.5%	(1.7%)	—	—

2020 Year-End Financials

Return on assets: 0.4%
Return on equity: 5.2%
Long-term debt ($ mil.): —
No. of shares (mil.): —
Sales ($ mil): 4,555

Dividends
Yield: 0.0%
Payout: 82.8%
Market value ($ mil.): —

	STOCK PRICE ($) FY Close	P/E High/Low		PER SHARE ($)		
				Earnings	Dividends	Book Value
12/20	32.44	30	16	0.48	0.40	(0.00)
12/19	40.25	31	25	0.39	0.78	8.28
12/18	31.00	20	16	0.49	0.68	7.15
12/17	37.00	19	16	0.55	0.64	7.38
12/16	29.70	16	12	0.49	0.44	6.33
Annual Growth	2.2%		—	(0.5%)	(2.7%)	—

Bank Leumi Le-Israel B.M.

Bank Leumi le-Israel looms large as one of Israel's largest financial institutions. The company whose name translates as National Bank of Israel offers retail banking (for consumers and small businesses) commercial banking (middle-market businesses) corporate banking (large companies) and private banking (wealthy clients) through deposits mortgages and other loans credit cards trust services and investments.It hasabout 235 branches in Israel and more than 80 locations (including branches agencies and representative offices) in some 20 countries including the US. Subsidiary Leumi Partners provides corporate investment banking services and makes direct investments in nonbanking businesses.

HISTORY

At the beginning of the 20th century a group of prominent Jewish men led by Austrian Zionist Theodor Herzl founded the Jewish Colonial Trust (which would later become known as Otzar Hitsyashvut Hayehudim or OHH). An advocate of the

Jewish settlement of Palestine the trust recognized the need for a financial institution to promote colonization in the region which was then part of the Ottoman Empire. In 1902 it established the Anglo-Palestine Company the forerunner of Bank Leumi le-Israel. A year later the London-based company opened its first Palestinian office in Jaffa (now Tel Aviv).

As WWI began the company had half a dozen branches. The outbreak of hostilities between Great Britain and the Ottoman Empire forced the London-based bank to close its offices but it continued to operate from the Spanish Consulate in Jerusalem. By the mid-1920s the company was known as the Anglo-Palestine Bank and was playing a significant role in the development of local agriculture.

During the following decade Palestine saw an influx of refugees from Nazism in Europe. The bank assisted in transferring assets to Palestine and anchored the area's economy through WWII. When Israel gained independence in 1948 the Anglo-Palestine Bank became the nation's fiscal agency and printed monetary notes for the new government. It began to focus its efforts on international operations and in 1950 opened its first US office in New York City. But even though it was the national bank of the newly formed Israeli state the bank was still based in London. In 1951 a company named Ieumi Le'Israel was founded in Tel Aviv and assumed control of the bank which took the name Bank Leumi le-Israel (National Bank of Israel) in 1954. Also that year the government formed the Bank of Israel and Bank Leumi resumed its commercial banking activities.

Bank Leumi maintained its status as Israel's leading bank until the 1980s when triple-digit inflation hit the country. The bottom fell out in 1983 when investors pulled out of the stock market fearing devaluation of the shekel. As they had done for several years Bank Leumi and Israel's other major banking groups reacted by taking out massive loans to buy their own stock and shield against losses in share price. The artificially inflated bank stocks crashed and thousands of individual investors lost their savings. The Israeli government intervened paying some $7 billion to bail out the banks. Though the state now held most of Bank Leumi's stock the OHH maintained voting rights.

In 1986 following a government inquiry into the stock scandal chairman Ernst Japhet and the company's board were forced to resign prompting more contention. On their way out Japhet and his officers received millions of dollars in severance pay and monthly pensions. The ramifications of what became known as "Leumigate" resulted in the company's next two chairmen also being ousted over the next two years. Rival Bank Hapoalim wrested the mantle of Israel's #1 bank from Bank Leumi in 1987.

The government sold off 10% of its interest in the firm to a unit of Deutsche Bank in 1993 and in 1995 mandated that banks sell their nonfinancial holdings. That year Galia Maor became CEO as the first woman head of an Israeli bank and Eitan Raff became chairman (he announced his retirement in 2010).

Controversy continued however. In 1997 Bank Leumi sold a majority stake in Migdal Insurance to Assicurazioni Generali which amplified questions regarding the buyer's handling of life insurance policies of Jewish Holocaust victims. The inquiry spread to Bank Leumi which released information about dormant accounts the next year but nonetheless faced government scrutiny and lawsuits from descendants of Holocaust victims.

In 2006 an Israeli law established a company to collect restitution for property deemed abandoned by Holocaust victims who had made bank deposits and bought real estate and bank shares in Israel in anticipation of the establishment of a Jewish homeland in Palestine. After years of wrangling The Company for Restitution of Holocaust Victims Assets in mid-2009 filed suit against Bank Leumi considered to be the holder of the most Jewish Holocaust assets; the lawsuit asked for NIS 300 million ($75 million) in restitution for more than 3500 victims. Denying any financial culpability the bank later that year offered NIS 20 million ($5 million). In 2010 it agreed to arbitration.

EXECUTIVES

President, Chief Executive Officer, Member of the Management Board, Hanan Friedman, $803,835 total compensation
External Independent Director, Yedidia Stern
First Executive Vice President, Chief Internal Auditor and Head of the Internal Audit Division, Sharon Gur, $356,582 total compensation
External Independent Director, Shmuel Ben-Zvi
First Executive Vice President, Chief Risk Officer, Head of the Risk Management Division, Member of the Management Board, Liat Shuv
External Independent Director, Tamar Gottlieb
Director, Ester Dominissini
First Executive Vice President, Head of Capital Markets Division, Member of the Management Board, Bosmat Ben Zvi
First Executive Vice President, Head of Finance and Accounting Division, Chief Accounting Officer, Member of the Management Board, Omer Ziv, $461,493 total compensation
External Independent Director, Ytzhak Edelman
First Executive Vice President, Head of Banking Division, Member of the Management Board, Shmuel Arbel, $369,114 total compensation
Director, Irit Shlomi
External Independent Director, Ohad Marani
External Independent Director, Yoram Gabbay
Chairman of the Board, Samer Haj-Yehia, $789,595 total compensation
First Executive Vice President, Head of Corporate Division, Member of the Management Board, Ronen Agassi, $431,662 total compensation
Auditors: Kost Forer Gabbay & Kasierer

LOCATIONS

HQ: Bank Leumi Le-Israel B.M.
34 Yehuda Halevi Street, Tel-Aviv 65546
Phone: (972) 3 514 8111   **Fax:** (972) 3 566 1872
Web: www.bankleumi.com

COMPETITORS

BANK OF CHINA LIMITED	NATIONAL BANK OF
Bank of Ireland	GREECE S.A.
COMMONWEALTH BANK OF	SANTANDER HOLDINGS USA
AUSTRALIA	INC.
DEPFA BANK PUBLIC	UniCredit Bank AG
LIMITED COMPANY	WESTPAC BANKING
DEUTSCHE BANK AG	CORPORATION
KfW	
NATIONAL AUSTRALIA	
BANK LIMITED	

HISTORICAL FINANCIALS

Company Type: Public

Income Statement   FYE: December 31

	ASSETS ($ mil.)	NET INCOME ($ mil.)	INCOME AS % OF ASSETS	EMPLOYEES
12/19	135,779	1,019	0.8%	9,239
12/18	122,772	868	0.7%	9,740
12/17	129,875	913	0.7%	11,201
12/16	114,193	726	0.6%	11,636
12/15	106,484	724	0.7%	12,528
Annual Growth	6.3%	8.9%	—	(7.3%)

Return on assets: 0.7%	Dividends
Return on equity: 9.9%	Yield: —
Long-term debt ($ mil.): —	Payout: 40.2%
No. of shares (mil.): 1,524	Market value ($ mil.): —
Sales ($ mil): 4,780	

Bank Muscat S.A.O.G

EXECUTIVES

Member of the Shariah Supervisory Board, Majid Al Kindi
Non-Executive Non-Independent Member of the Board, Khalid Al Shamsi, $24,122 total compensation
Chief Executive Officer, Walid Al Hashar
Non-Executive Non-Independent Member of the Board, Said Al Harthy, $23,407 total compensation
Non-Executive Independent Director, Representative Of A Shareholding Juristic Person, Saud Al Mashani, $10,338 total compensation
Member of the Shariah Supervisory Board, Esam Ishaq
Non-Executive Independent Director, Nasser Bin Mohammed Al Harthy, $25,747 total compensation
Chief Corporate Banking Officer, Ahmed bin Faqir Al Balushi
Member of the Shariah Supervisory Board, Walid Bin Sulaiman Al-Qurri
Member of the Shariah Supervisory Board, Mufti Irshad Ahmed Aijaz
Chief Strategy and Corporate Services Officer, Sheikha Yousuf Al Farsi
Non-Executive Vice Chairman of the Board, Ahmed Bin Hamed bin Hilal Al Sadi, $22,496 total compensation
Chief Personal Banking Officer, K. Gopakumar
Chief Financial Officer, Thangavel Ganesh
Chairman of the Shariah Supervisory Board, Ali Al Quradaghi
Non-Executive Independent Chairman of the Board, Khalid Bin Mustahail Al Mashani, $23,407 total compensation
Non-Executive Independent Member of the Board, representing Ministry of Defense Pension Fund, Saif Bin Salim Al Harthy, $25,487 total compensation
Auditors: PricewaterhouseCoopers LLC

LOCATIONS

HQ: Bank Muscat S.A.O.G
Building No. 120/4, Block No. 311, Street No. 62, Airport Heights, Seeb PC 112
Phone: (968) 24 795555   **Fax:** (968) 2470 7806
Web: www.bankmuscat.com

HISTORICAL FINANCIALS
Company Type: Public

Income Statement				FYE: December 31
	ASSETS ($ mil.)	NET INCOME ($ mil.)	INCOME AS % OF ASSETS	EMPLOYEES
12/19	31,965	482	1.5%	3,818
12/18	31,958	467	1.5%	3,779
12/17	28,996	459	1.6%	3,712
12/16	28,100	458	1.6%	3,747
12/15	32,578	455	1.4%	3,712
Annual Growth	(0.5%)	1.4%	—	0.7%

2019 Year-End Financials
Return on assets: 1.5%
Return on equity: 9.4%
Long-term debt ($ mil.): —
No. of shares (mil.): —
Sales ($ mil): 1,751

Dividends
Yield: —
Payout: 187.4%
Market value ($ mil.): —

Bank of Ayudhya Public Co Ltd

Bank of Ayudhya is bahting more than a billion. The bank also known as Krungsri has more than 550 branches throughout Thailand; almost half are in the Bangkok area. It also operates overseas branches in Hong Kong Laos and the Cayman Islands. Serving individuals and small to midsized businesses the bank offers deposit lending insurance and investment services. For corporations it performs investment banking and trading services as well. The bank also provides deposit trade and investment services to other financial institutions. Bank of Ayudhya was founded in 1945 in Thailand's Ayudhya province. The bank is a subsidiary of The Bank of Tokyo-Mitsubishi UFJ (BTMU) owned by Mitsubishi UFJ.

EXECUTIVES

First Executive Vice President, Head of Internal Audit Group, Puntipa Hannoraseth
Senior Vice President, Head of Corporate Secretariat Department, Corporate Secretary and Secretary to the Board of Directors, Thidarat Sethavaravichit
Non-Executive Director, Nopporn Tirawattanagool
Independent Director, Tongurai Limpiti
Independent Director, Potjanee Thanawaranit
Independent Chairman of the Board, Karun Kittisataporn
First Executive Vice President - Office of the President and Chief Executive Officer, Nuttawit Boonyawat
First Executive Vice President, Head of JPC/MNC Banking, Yoshiyuki Horio
Executive Vice President, Office of the President and Chief Executive Officer, Dominic Notario
First Executive Vice President, Head of Retail and Consumer Banking, Acting Head of High Net-Worth Division, Acting Head of Retail Banking and Distribution Group, Phonganant Thanattrai
Non-Executive Director, Pornsanong Tuchinda
Independent Director, Virat Phairatphiboon
Senior Executive Vice President, Chief Risk Officer, Chandrashekar Krishoolndmangalam
President, Chief Executive Officer, Executive Director, Seiichiro Akita
Executive Vice President, Deputy Head of Global Markets Group, Shinichiro Namiki
Executive Vice President, Head of Transaction Banking Group, Yingluk Kongkasai
Executive Vice President, Head of Financial Governance Risk and Compliance Division, Finance Group, Acting Head of Internal Control Department, Finance Group, Acting Head of Related Party Transaction, Jiraporn Popairoj
Non-Executive Director, Toru Matsuda
First Executive Vice President, Chief Strategy Officer, Pairote Cheunkrut
Executive Vice President, Head of Operations Group, Wirote Chuenratanakul
Executive Vice President, Head of Krungsri Auto Finance and Strategy Division, Krungsri Auto Group, Congsin Congcar
Executive Vice President, Head of Financial Planning and Analysis – Retail and Consumer Department, Finance Group, Akanit Mattison
First Executive Vice President, Chief Information and Digital Officer, Sayam Prasitsirigul
Executive Vice President, Head of Accounting Division, Finance Group, Kriangsak Jongsukkigparnich
Executive Vice President, Chief Credit Officer, Yoshio Ueyama
Deputy Head of JPC/MNC Banking, Head of Multinational Corporate Banking Division, JPC/MNC Banking, Executive Vice President, Yoichiro Tsukamoto
Chief Financial Officer, First Executive Vice President - Finance, Executive Director, Duangdao Wongpanitkrit
Executive Vice President, Head of Krungsri Auto Group, Kittiya Srisanit
Executive Vice President, Office of the President and Chief Executive Officer, Somwang Toraktrakul
Executive Vice President, Head of Financial Planning and Analysis - Commercial Banking JPC/MNC and Global Markets Department, Finance Group, Pornnapa Patarasatienkul
Non-Executive Director, Junko Kawano
Executive Vice President, Head of Financial Planning and Analysis Division - Finance Group, Pisara Pattanasiri
Independent Director, Jamlong Atikul
Executive Vice President, Deputy Head of Transaction Banking Group, Masahiro Matsumoto
Executive Vice President, Deputy Head of Retail and Consumer Banking, Kotaro Kato
Executive Vice President, Head of Legal Group, Thitivorn Chothayaphorn
First Executive Vice President, Chief Human Resource Officer, Vasin Udomratchatavanich
Executive Vice President, Office of the President and CEO, Chayathip Phanmanee
Executive Vice President, Office of the President and Chief Executive Officer, Saisunee Hanprathueangsil
First Executive Vice President, Head of Global Markets Group, Kenichi Nishii
Executive Vice President, Chief Compliance Officer, Data Protection Officer, Saengchart Wanichwatphibun
Auditors: Deloitte Touche Tohmatsu Jaiyos Audit Co., Ltd.

LOCATIONS
HQ: Bank of Ayudhya Public Co Ltd
1222 Rama III Road, Bang Phongphang Subdistrict, Yannawa District, Bangkok 10120
Phone: (66) 2 296 2000   **Fax:** (66) 2 683 1304
Web: www.krungsri.com

COMPETITORS
HACHIJUNI BANK LTD. THE
NATIONAL BANK OF KUWAIT S.A.K.P.

VIETNAM JOINT STOCK COMMERCIAL BANK FOR INDUSTRY AND TRADE

HISTORICAL FINANCIALS
Company Type: Public

Income Statement				FYE: December 31
	ASSETS ($ mil.)	NET INCOME ($ mil.)	INCOME AS % OF ASSETS	EMPLOYEES
12/20	87,159	769	0.9%	0
12/19	79,213	1,099	1.4%	0
12/18	67,191	767	1.1%	0
12/17	64,115	712	1.1%	0
12/16	52,610	597	1.1%	0
Annual Growth	13.5%	6.5%	—	—

2020 Year-End Financials
Return on assets: 0.9%
Return on equity: 8.2%
Long-term debt ($ mil.): —
No. of shares (mil.): —
Sales ($ mil): 4,943

Dividends
Yield: —
Payout: —
Market value ($ mil.): —

Bank of Canada (Ottawa)

Whether you say "bank" or "banque" the Bank of Canada is the country's central bank. It is responsible for setting monetary policy (by setting interest rates) issuing and safeguarding currency from counterfeiting managing the Canadian banking system and managing funds for the government and other clients. The Bank of Canada works through six regional offices including one in New York City. The Board of Directors provides general oversight of the management and administration of the Bank.

EXECUTIVES

Governor, Tiff Macklem
Chief Human Resource Officer, Managing Director, Alexis Corbett
Chief Financial Officer, Managing Director, Coralia Bulhoes
Deputy Governor, Timothy Lane
Director, Monique Jerome-Forget
Chief Operating Officer, Filipe Dinis
Chief Information Officer, Managing Director, Sylvain Chalut
Director, Claire Kennedy
Deputy Governor, Lawrence Schembri
Auditors: KPMG LLP

LOCATIONS
HQ: Bank of Canada (Ottawa)
234 Wellington Street, Ottawa, Ontario K1A 0G9
Phone: 800 303 1282   **Fax:** 613 782-7713
Web: www.bankofcanada.ca

COMPETITORS
ALLIED IRISH BANKS PUBLIC LIMITED COMPANY
BANK OF ENGLAND
BANK OF GREECE S.A.
DZ BANK AG Deutsche
FEDERAL RESERVE BANK OF ATLANTA
FEDERAL RESERVE BANK OF DALLAS
FEDERAL RESERVE BANK OF KANSAS CITY
FEDERAL RESERVE BANK OF NEW YORK

FEDERAL RESERVE BANK OF PHILADELPHIA (INC)
NATIONAL BANK OF ROMANIA
RESERVE BANK OF INDIA

HISTORICAL FINANCIALS
Company Type: Public

Income Statement				FYE: December 31
	ASSETS ($ mil.)	NET INCOME ($ mil.)	INCOME AS % OF ASSETS	EMPLOYEES
12/19	121,150	1,318	1.1%	1,800
12/18	117,517	1,138	1.0%	1,750
12/17	112,500	988	0.9%	1,700
12/16	107,443	1,078	1.0%	1,700
12/15	102,421	1,190	1.2%	1,600
Annual Growth	4.3%	2.6%	—	3.0%

2019 Year-End Financials
Return on assets: 1.1%
Return on equity: 246.6%
Long-term debt ($ mil.): —
No. of shares (mil.): 0
Sales ($ mil): 2,316
Dividends
Yield: —
Payout: —
Market value ($ mil.): —

Bank of East Asia Ltd.

Bank of East Asia provides retail and commercial banking services in Hong Kong and mainland China. Its offerings include deposit accounts consumer loans mortgages business loans credit cards private banking and investment management. Bank of East Asia has some 60 branches locations in Hong Kong and about 50 SupremeGold Centers and 10 i-Financial Centers throughout the city and more than 40 outlets in mainland China. The bank has established a presence in Southeast Asia the United Kingdom and the United States. Bank of East Asia's subsidiary Blue Cross (Asia-Pacific) Insurance Limited serves as underwriter of general insurance products.

EXECUTIVES

Non-Executive Director, Francisco Serrado Trepat
Independent Non-Executive Director, Tak-yeung Mong
Non-Executive Deputy Chairman of the Board, Kwok Cheung Li
Independent Non-Executive Director, William Doo
Independent Non-Executive Deputy Chairman of the Board, Chi-Yun Wong
Non-Executive Director, Kwok-sze Li
Non-Executive Director, Yau-lai Lo
Independent Non-executive Director, Lai Tai Fan Hsu
Non-Executive Director, Win-kong Ng
Company Secretary, Chun-tak Law
Non-Executive Director, Kwok Sing Li
Co-Chief Executive, Executive Director, Man Bun Li, $1,005,606 total compensation
Co-Chief Executive, Executive Director, Man-kiu Li, $1,005,606 total compensation
Deputy Chief Executive Officer, Chief Operating Officer, Hon-shing Tong
Deputy Chief Executive Officer, Chief Investment Officer, Kai-cheong Li
Independent Non-Executive Director, Ying-yen Tang
Independent Non-Executive Director, Kwok-wing Li
Executive Chairman of the Board, Kwok Po Li, $1,521,302 total compensation

Independent Non-Executive Director, Delman Lee
Non-Executive Director, Masayuki Oku
Auditors: KPMG

LOCATIONS
HQ: Bank of East Asia Ltd.
10 Des Voeux Road Central,
Phone: (852) 3608 3608   **Fax:** (852) 3608 6000
Web: www.hkbea.com

PRODUCTS/OPERATIONS

2014 Sales

	% of total
Interest income	83
Non-interest income	17
Total	**100**

COMPETITORS

BANK OF AYUDHYA PUBLIC COMPANY LIMITED
BANK OF CYPRUS PUBLIC COMPANY LIMITED
BANK OF THE PHILIPPINE ISLANDS
CIMB GROUP HOLDINGS BERHAD
DBS GROUP HOLDINGS LTD
HACHIJUNI BANK LTD. THE
KB Financial Group Inc.
OGAKI KYORITSU BANK LTD. THE
OVERSEA-CHINESE BANKING CORPORATION LIMITED
PUBLIC FINANCIAL HOLDINGS LIMITED
SHIZUOKA BANK LTD. THE
UNITED OVERSEAS BANK LIMITED

HISTORICAL FINANCIALS
Company Type: Public

Income Statement				FYE: December 31
	ASSETS ($ mil.)	NET INCOME ($ mil.)	INCOME AS % OF ASSETS	EMPLOYEES
12/20	114,077	466	0.4%	9,539
12/19	111,110	418	0.4%	9,846
12/18	107,180	831	0.8%	9,796
12/17	103,508	1,196	1.2%	9,978
12/16	98,742	480	0.5%	10,389
Annual Growth	3.7%	(0.7%)	—	(2.1%)

2020 Year-End Financials
Return on assets: 0.4%
Return on equity: 3.2%
Long-term debt ($ mil.): —
No. of shares (mil.): —
Sales ($ mil): 3,612
Dividends
Yield: 2.7%
Payout: 46.3%
Market value ($ mil.): —

	STOCK PRICE ($) FY Close	P/E High/Low		PER SHARE ($) Earnings	Dividends	Book Value
12/20	2.13	2	2	0.13	0.06	4.99
12/19	2.18	4	2	0.11	0.10	4.83
12/18	3.18	2	1	0.26	0.12	4.52
12/17	4.22	1	1	0.41	0.11	4.55
12/16	3.80	4	2	0.16	0.09	3.98
Annual Growth	(13.5%)	—	—	(5.4%)	(10.1%)	5.8%

Bank of Ireland Group plc

Auditors: KPMG

LOCATIONS
HQ: Bank of Ireland Group plc
40 Mespil Road, Dublin 4
Phone:
Web: www.bankofireland.com

HISTORICAL FINANCIALS
Company Type: Public

Income Statement				FYE: December 31
	ASSETS ($ mil.)	NET INCOME ($ mil.)	INCOME AS % OF ASSETS	EMPLOYEES
12/20	164,154	(910)	—	9,782
12/19	148,073	433	0.3%	10,440
12/18	141,625	710	0.5%	10,367
12/17	146,912	795	0.5%	10,892
12/16	130,009	837	0.6%	11,208
Annual Growth	6.0%	—	—	(3.3%)

2020 Year-End Financials
Return on assets: (-0.5%)
Return on equity: (-7.7%)
Long-term debt ($ mil.): —
No. of shares (mil.): 1,073
Sales ($ mil): 6,200
Dividends
Yield: 0.0%
Payout: —
Market value ($ mil.): 4,241

	STOCK PRICE ($) FY Close	P/E High/Low		PER SHARE ($) Earnings	Dividends	Book Value
12/20	3.95	—	—	(0.89)	0.00	10.92
12/19	5.40	19	10	0.40	0.18	10.06
12/18	5.62	17	9	0.66	0.13	9.84
Annual Growth	(16.2%)	—	—	—	—	2.6%

Bank of Iwate, Ltd. (The) (Japan)

Operating on the island of Honshu The Bank of Iwate is certainly nothing to sneeze at. The bank boasts about 110 branches more than 90 of them in its home Iwate prefecture on the island of Honshu. Besides the usual banking services such as deposits and credit cards Bank of Iwate also provides leasing and clerical outsourcing. It has been focusing on lending to small and midsized firms and enhancing customer convenience. Ever on guard against the encroachment of major banks Bank of Iwate has teamed with two other regional banks Aomori Bank and Akita Bank to create an investment trust. The Bank of Iwate was founded in 1932 as Iwate Shokusan Bank. It took on its present name in 1960.

EXECUTIVES

Managing Director, Keiji Iwata
Senior Managing Director, Masahiro Saito
Director of Main Store Sales, Director, Yasuyuki Aramichi
Independent Director, Atsushi Takahashi
President, Representative Director, Sachio Taguchi
Managing Director, Yuichi Kato
Chairman of the Board, Representative Director, Masahiro Takahashi
Independent Director, Fumio Ube
Director of Tokyo Sales, Director, Katsuya Sato
Independent Director, Hiroshi Miura

Director of General Planning, Manager of Public Relations CSR Office, Director, Shigeki Miura
Managing Director, Osamu Sakamoto
Auditors: KPMG AZSA LLC

LOCATIONS

HQ: Bank of Iwate, Ltd. (The) (Japan)
  1-2-3 Chuodori, Morioka, Iwate 020-8688
Phone: (81) 19 623 1111   **Fax:** (81) 19 652 6751
Web: www.iwatebank.co.jp

COMPETITORS

BANGKOK BANK PUBLIC   Portigon AG
  COMPANY LIMITED   UniCredit Bank AG
Erste Group Bank AG

HISTORICAL FINANCIALS

Company Type: Public

Income Statement   FYE: March 31

	ASSETS ($ mil.)	NET INCOME ($ mil.)	INCOME AS % OF ASSETS	EMPLOYEES
03/21	34,689	26	0.1%	1,939
03/20	32,109	34	0.1%	1,994
03/19	31,689	37	0.1%	2,057
03/18	33,495	52	0.2%	2,116
03/17	31,773	90	0.3%	2,128
Annual Growth	2.2%	(26.7%)	—	(2.3%)

2021 Year-End Financials

Return on assets: 0.0%
Return on equity: 1.4%
Long-term debt ($ mil.): —
No. of shares (mil.): 17
Sales ($ mil): 409

Dividends
  Yield: —
  Payout: 36.5%
Market value ($ mil.): —

Bank of Japan

Founded in 1882 as Japan's central bank the Bank of Japan primarily issues banknotes and acts as a treasurer for the government. It operates 30-plus branches more than a dozen local offices and a handful of overseas offices. The bank is responsible for implementing lending rate changes as well as maintaining fluctuations in reserve requirements. It also compiles data and performs research and analysis pertaining to the overall economy. The bank's policy board meets more than a dozen times each year to make decisions on monetary policies. The policies are carried out by the Bank of Japan's providing and absorbing funds into the market. The Bank of Japan's first banknotes were issued in 1885.

Geographic Reach

Tokyo-based Bank of Japan boasts 32 branches and 14 local offices in Japan plus 7 representative offices abroad.

Strategy

As the central bank for the land of the rising sun the Bank of Japan is in charge of monetary policy and the sustainability of the country's currency with the goal of keeping inflation low while ensuring the highest rate of employment by preventing deflation. It also is the sole issuer of the country's currency the Bank of Japan notes employing a range of measures to prevent counterfeiting including watermarks special inks and micro-lettering.

The bank stands by a handful of organizational principles to keep the public's trust and confidence. These principles are: to promote the public interest by fulfilling the core purposes outlined in the Bank of Japan Act demonstrate accountability of policies and operations via its various external networks; ensure excellence in central banking services and respond to changes in environment; ensure integrity and high standards of morality through every officer and employee of the organization; and make effective and efficient use of management resources when it comes to operations and organizational management.

Company Background

The Bank of Japan's first banknotes were issued in 1885 with konnyaku powder being mixed with the paper in order to discourage counterfeiting. One minor glitch however was that the konnyaku powder attracted rats; consequently the initial banknotes were removed from circulation in 1899.

EXECUTIVES

Vice President, Hiroshi Nakaso
President, Haruhiko Kuroda
Vice President, Kikuo Iwata
Auditors: Ryota Yanagihara; Yoji Onozawa; Hirokazu Fujita

LOCATIONS

HQ: Bank of Japan
  2-1-1 Nihonbashi Hongoku-cho, Chuo-ku, Tokyo 103-0021
Phone: (81) 3 3279 1111
Web: www.boj.or.jp

COMPETITORS

BANCO DE SABADELL SA
BANK OF GREECE S.A.
BARCLAYS PLC
BOARD OF GOVERNORS OF THE FEDERAL RESERVE
  SYSTEM
DZ BANK AG Deutsche
FEDERAL RESERVE BANK OF ATLANTA
FEDERAL RESERVE BANK OF CHICAGO
FEDERAL RESERVE BANK OF PHILADELPHIA (INC)
NATIONAL BANK OF ROMANIA
Portigon AG
RESERVE BANK OF INDIA
UNITED STATES DEPT OF TREASURY
UniCredit Bank AG

HISTORICAL FINANCIALS

Company Type: Public

Income Statement   FYE: March 31

	REVENUE ($ mil.)	NET INCOME ($ mil.)	NET PROFIT MARGIN	EMPLOYEES
03/20	20,642	11,932	57.8%	4,636
03/19	21,612	5,300	24.5%	4,636
03/18	17,312	7,202	41.6%	4,653
03/17	14,707	4,531	30.8%	4,646
03/16	14,222	3,660	25.7%	4,646
Annual Growth	9.8%	34.4%	—	(0.1%)

2020 Year-End Financials

Debt ratio: 0.0%
Return on equity: 30.9%
Cash ($ mil.): 1,889
Current ratio: 0.88
Long-term debt ($ mil.): 73

No. of shares (mil.): —
Dividends
  Yield: —
  Payout: —
Market value ($ mil.): —

Bank of Kyoto Ltd (Japan)

For financial services in Kyoto proper protocol might involve a visit to The Bank of Kyoto. The regional bank serves Kyoto and neighboring prefectures through some 165 branch offices. The bank serves businesses particularly small and medium-sized local companies as well as individual consumers. In addition to traditional deposit banking and lending The Bank of Kyoto and its subsidiaries offer credit cards leasing stock brokerage and business consulting services. The bank has worked to expand its operations beyond its home base and has opened branches to the north in the Kinki Region. Founded in 1941 the bank has about $81 billion in assets and ranks as Kyoto Prefecture's largest retail bank.

Geographic Reach

The Bank of Kyoto operates 110 branches in Kyoto Prefecture 28 in Osaka Prefecture a dozen in Shiga eight in Hyogo and seven branches in Nara.

Strategy

The Bank of Kyoto is aggressively opening branches to expand its reach beyond Kyoto Prefecture. Since opening its first branch at Kusatsu in Shiga Prefecture in 2000 the bank has opened branches in five neighboring prefectures (Kyoto Osaka Shiga Nara and Hyogo).

EXECUTIVES

President, Representative Director, Nobuhiro Doi
Senior Managing Director, Representative Director, Masaya Anami
Managing Director, Toshiro Iwahashi
Managing Director, Director, Mikiya Yasui
Managing Director, Hiroyuki Hata
Non-Executive Independent Director, Junko Otagiri
Independent Director, Chiho Oyabu
Non-Executive Independent Director, Eiji Ueki
Auditors: Deloitte Touche Tohmatsu LLC

LOCATIONS

HQ: Bank of Kyoto Ltd (Japan)
  700 Yakushimae-cho, Karasuma-dori Matsubara-Agaru, Shimogyo-ku, Kyoto 600-8652
Phone: (81) 75 361 2211   **Fax:** (81) 75 343 1276
Web: www.kyotobank.co.jp

COMPETITORS

AICHI BANKLTD. THE
NISHI-NIPPON
  CITYBANKLTD.

HISTORICAL FINANCIALS

Company Type: Public

Income Statement   FYE: March 31

	ASSETS ($ mil.)	NET INCOME ($ mil.)	INCOME AS % OF ASSETS	EMPLOYEES
03/20	92,846	187	0.2%	3,969
03/19	87,274	286	0.3%	4,092
03/18	89,263	181	0.2%	4,154
03/17	79,596	166	0.2%	4,099
03/16	72,614	189	0.3%	4,052
Annual Growth	6.3%	(0.3%)	—	(0.5%)

Bank of Montreal (Quebec)

Auditors: KPMG LLP

LOCATIONS

HQ: Bank of Montreal (Quebec)
129 rue Saint-Jacques, Montreal, Quebec H2Y 1L6
Phone: 416 867-7366   **Fax:** 416 867-6793
Web: www.bmo.com

HISTORICAL FINANCIALS

Company Type: Public

Income Statement   FYE: October 31

	ASSETS ($ mil.)	NET INCOME ($ mil.)	INCOME AS % OF ASSETS	EMPLOYEES
10/21	799,970	6,079	0.8%	43,863
10/20	713,601	3,645	0.5%	43,360
10/19	646,973	4,211	0.7%	45,513
10/18	589,502	4,150	0.7%	45,454
10/17	552,342	4,162	0.8%	45,200
Annual Growth	9.7%	9.9%	—	(0.7%)

2021 Year-End Financials

Return on assets: 0.7%
Return on equity: 13.1%
Long-term debt ($ mil.): —
No. of shares (mil.): 648
Sales ($ mil): 26,523
Dividends
Yield: 0.0%
Payout: 36.6%
Market value ($ mil.): 28,460

	STOCK PRICE ($) FY Close	P/E High/Low		PER SHARE ($) Earnings	Dividends	Book Value
10/21	43.91	37	2	9.37	3.43	71.85
10/20	175.26	32	4	5.68	3.19	65.87
10/19	39.59	6	3	6.57	3.08	60.66
10/18	46.80	11	5	6.22	2.88	54.47
Annual Growth	(2.1%)	—	—	10.8%	4.5%	7.2%

Bank of Nagoya, Ltd.

Camrys and Corollas aren't the only "big wheels" you'll find in Nagoya. The prefecture is home to The Bank of Nagoya as well as automaker Toyota and other vehicle manufacturers. The regional bank has more than 105 branches in and around its home area as well as locations in other major Japanese cities and two representative offices in China. The Bank of Nagoya focuses on serving the businesses of the region as well as individual consumers. In addition to deposit banking and lending the bank and its subsidiaries offer such products and services as leasing credit cards and securities trading. The Bank of Nagoya was established in 1949.

EXECUTIVES

President, Representative Director, Ichiro Fujiwara
Director, Naoto Sugita
Managing Director, Chief Director of Sales, Representative Director, Shinichi Yokota
Managing Director, Director, Masao Minamide
Director of Sales in Main Office, Director, Katsutoshi Yamamoto
Chairman of the Board, Kazumaro Kato
Director of Human Resources Development, Manager of Shining Reform Promotion Office , Director, Seiji Inagaki
Director of Market Sales, Director, Kenji Suzuki
Managing Director, Satoru Hattori
Independent Director, Takehisa Matsubara
Independent Director, Takao Kondo
Director of Business, Director, Mitsuru Yoshihashi
Independent Director, Masatoshi Sakaguchi
Independent Director, Nobuyoshi Hasegawa
Independent Director, Hisako Munekata
Auditors: KPMG AZSA LLC

LOCATIONS

HQ: Bank of Nagoya, Ltd.
3-19-17 Nishiki, Naka-ku, Nagoya, Aichi 460-0003
Phone: (81) 52 951 5911   **Fax:** (81) 52 961 6605
Web: www.meigin.com

COMPETITORS

BANK OF IWATE LTD. THE
BANK OF THE RYUKYUS LIMITED

HISTORICAL FINANCIALS

Company Type: Public

Income Statement   FYE: March 31

	ASSETS ($ mil.)	NET INCOME ($ mil.)	INCOME AS % OF ASSETS	EMPLOYEES
03/21	44,369	96	0.2%	2,394
03/20	36,250	42	0.1%	2,396
03/19	35,191	55	0.2%	2,445
03/18	36,103	54	0.2%	2,486
03/17	32,802	53	0.2%	2,534
Annual Growth	7.8%	16.2%	—	(1.4%)

2021 Year-End Financials

Return on assets: 0.2%
Return on equity: 4.4%
Long-term debt ($ mil.): —
No. of shares (mil.): 18
Sales ($ mil): 682
Dividends
Yield: —
Payout: 11.8%
Market value ($ mil.): —

Bank of Nova Scotia Halifax

Scotiabank is a leading bank in the Americas that provides personal and commercial banking wealth management and private banking corporate and investment banking and capital markets. Through its Canadian Banking it serves customers through its network of about 955 branches more than 3765 automated banking machines (ABMs) and the internet mobile telephone banking and specialized sales teams. Canadian Banking also provides an alternative self-directed banking solution to over 2 million Tangerine Bank customers. The bank services include deposit accounts loans insurance brokerage asset management wealth management foreign exchange services equity underwriting and trust services. The majority of its total revenue (about 60%) comes from customers in Canada.

Operations

Scotiabank has its business lines: Canadian Banking International Banking Global Banking and Markets and Global Wealth Management.

The International Banking business (about 20% of the revenue) provides products and services similar to the Canadian Banking segment but with nearly 10 million Retail Corporate and Commercial customers.

Canadian Banking serves more than 10 million retail small business and commercial banking clients. It interacts with its customers through a network of over 950 physical branches and more than 3765 ATMs along with mobile and digital banking platforms. The segment provides financial advice and solutions such as debit & credit cards checking accounts home mortgages and insurance products. The segment generates above 40% of all revenue and earnings.

Global Banking and Markets (GBM) (above 20%) provides corporate clients with lending and transaction services investment banking advice and access to capital markets. GBM is a full-service wholesale bank in the Americas with operations in about 20 countries serving clients across Canada the US Latin America Europe and Asia-Pacific.

Global Wealth Management (more than 15%) is focused on delivering comprehensive wealth management advice and solutions to clients across Scotiabank's footprint. Global Wealth Management serves over 2 million investment fund and advisory clients across 13 countries ? managing over $500 billion in assets.

Geographic Reach

Toronto Canada-based Scotiabank generates over 50% of its revenue from Canada. Its southern neighbor the US accounts for less than 5% of revenue while its major South American markets such as Mexico Peru Chile Brazil and Colombia combine to bring in some 45%.

It also has operations in Europe and the Caribbean with a relatively large presence in Panama Costa Rica and Dominican Republic. Within Asia it runs its business in China India Hong Kong Japan Thailand Singapore and others.

Sales and Marketing

Scotiabank serves nearly 50% of its loans to residential mortgages and more than 35% from business and government. Canadian Banking serves customers through its network of branches automated banking machines online mobile and telephone banking and specialized sales teams. Its business clients operate in several industries including real estate & construction financial services wholesale & retail energy automotive healthcare technology media agriculture and others.

Financial Performance

In the past five years Scotiabank's revenue rose 13% to C$21.3 billion in fiscal 2021 (ended October) from C$27.2 billion in fiscal 2017. Its net income increased by 17% to C$9.9 billion in fiscal 2021 from C$8.2 billion in fiscal 2017.

In fiscal 2021 the company posted a total revenue of C$31.3 billion a decrease of C$84 million from the prior year. Net interest income was C$16.9 billion a decrease of C$359 million or 2%. The negative impact of foreign currency translation of 3% together with lower margins and the impact of divested operations more than offset positive increases from strong asset growth in Canadian Banking and higher contribution from asset/liability management activities. Non-interest income was up C$275 billion or 2% to C$14.3 billion.

Net income was C$9.9 billion in fiscal 2021 up 45% from C$6.8 billion in fiscal 2020 due primarily to lower provision for credit losses as a result of a more favorable credit and macroeconomic outlook.

Cash at the end of fiscal 2021 was C$9.7 billion down by C$1.4 million from the prior year. Operating activities used C$12.8 billion while financing activities used another C$2.8 billion. Investing activities generated C$14.7 billion. Main cash uses were cash dividends paid and distribution paid redemption of preferred shares and payment of lease liabilities.

Strategy

As economies in the region rebounded throughout the year International Banking launched a series of initiatives to strengthen the business recover profitability and invest across its footprint to develop its full potential.

Underpinning the long-term strategy is the focus on being the preferred choice for customers leveraging digital engagement to deliver superior customer experiences while driving operational efficiency and outpacing the competition in priority businesses enabled by a diverse and talented winning team.

EXECUTIVES

President, Chief Executive Officer, Director, Brian Porter, $966,424 total compensation
Executive Vice President and Country Head, Scotiabank Peru, Miguel Uccelli Labarthe
Executive Vice President and Country Head, Scotiabank Mexico, Adrian Rosiles, $698,186 total compensation
Executive Vice President - Canadian Wealth Management, Alex Besharat
Independent Director, Lynn Patterson
Executive Vice President - Customer Insights, Data & Analytics, Philp Thomas
Independent Director, Calin Rovinescu
Executive Vice President - Retail Distribution, John Doig
Executive Vice President - Finance, Maria Theofilaktidis
Independent Director, Susan Segal
Independent Director, Guillermo Babatz
Independent Chairman of the Board, Aaron Regent
Executive Vice President - Enterprise Risk Governance, Michael Henry
Independent Director, Scott Bonham
Co-Group Head, Global Banking and Markets, Head, Global Capital Markets, Jake Lawrence, $371,701 total compensation
Executive Vice President, General Counsel, Ian Arellano
Group Head, Technology & Operations, Michael Zerbs
Executive Vice President, Caribbean, Central America and Uruguay, Anya Schnoor
Co-Group Head, Global Banking and Markets, James Neate
Executive Vice President, President & Chief Executive Officer, Tangerine, Gillian Riley
Independent Director, Nora Aufreiter
Group Head - International Banking and Digital Transformation, Ignacio Deschamps, $446,042 total compensation
Independent Director, Una Power
Group Head and Chief Risk Officer, Daniel Moore
Executive Vice President and Country Head, Scotiabank Chile, Francisco Sardon de Taboada

Group Head and Chief Human Resources Officer, Barbara Mason
Group Head, Canadian Banking, Dan Rees, $446,042 total compensation
Executive Vice President, Chief Digital Officer, Shawn Rose
Independent Director, Benita Warmbold
EVP and Global CIO, Business Technology, Ashley Veasey
Group Head, Global Wealth Management, Glen Gowland
Group Head and Chief Financial Officer, Rajagopal Viswanathan, $408,871 total compensation
Executive Vice President, Treasurer, Tom McGuire
Executive Vice President and Chief Auditor, Paul Baroni
EVP, Global Operations, Tracy Bryan
EVP and COO, Global Banking and Markets, Loretta Marcoccia
EVP, Canadian Commercial Banking, Kevin Teslyk
Auditors: KPMG LLP

LOCATIONS

HQ: Bank of Nova Scotia Halifax
  1709 Hollis Street, Halifax, Nova Scotia B3J 3B7
Phone: 416 866-3672   **Fax:** 416 866-7767
Web: www.scotiabank.com

PRODUCTS/OPERATIONS

FY2017 Revenue

	% of total
Interest	
Loans	62
Securities & Deposits with financial institutions	5
Non-interest	
Banking	11
Wealth management	9
Trading	4
Underwriting and other advisory	2
Non-trading foreign exchange	2
Net gain on sale of investment securities	2
Insurance underwriting income net of claims	2
Net income from investments in associated corporations	1
Others	3
Total	**100**

FY2017 Revenue

	% of total
Canadian Banking	46
International Banking	37
Global Banking and Markets	17
Total	**100**

Selected Canadian Subsidiaries

BNS Capital Trust
BNS Investment Inc.
  Montreal Trust Company of Canada
  Scotia Merchant Capital Corporation
Dundee Bank of Canada
Maple Trust Company
National Trustco Inc.
  The Bank of Nova Scotia Trust Company
  National Trust Company
RoyNat Inc.
Scotia Capital Inc.
  1548489 Ontario Limited
  Scotia iTrade Corp.
Scotia Asset Management L.P.
Scotia Capital Inc.
Scotia Dealer Advantage Inc.
Scotia Insurance Agency Inc.
Scotia Life Insurance Company
Scotia Mortgage Corporation
Scotia Securities Inc.
Scotiabank Capital Trust
Scotiabank Subordinated Notes Trust.
Scotiabank Tier 1 Trust

Selected International Subsidiaries

The Bank of Nova Scotia Berhad (Malaysia)
The Bank of Nova Scotia International Limited
  (Bahamas)
  The Bank of Nova Scotia Asia Limited (Singapore)

The Bank of Nova Scotia Trust Company (Bahamas) Ltd.
Scotiabank & Trust (Cayman) Ltd. (Cayman Islands)
BNS (Colombia) Holdings Limited
Grupo BNS de Costa Rica S.A.
Scotia Insurance (Barbados) Limited
Scotiabank (Bahamas) Limited
Scotiabank (British Virgin Islands) Limited
Scotiabank Caribbean Treasury Limited (Bahamas)
Scotiabank (Hong Kong) Limited
Scotiabank (Ireland) Limited
Scotia Group Jamaica Limited (72%)
  The Bank of Nova Scotia Jamaica Limited
  Scotia DBG Investments Limited (77% Jamaica)
Grupo Financiero Scotiabank Inverlat S.A. de C.V. (97% Mexico)
Nova Scotia Inversiones Limitada (Chile)
  Scotiabank Chile S.A.
Scotia Capital (USA) Inc.
Scotia Holdings (US) Inc.
  The Bank of Nova Scotia Trust Company of New York
  Scotiabanc Inc. (US)
Scotia International Limited (Bahamas)
  Scotiabank Anguilla Limited
Scotiabank de Puerto Rico
Scotiabank El Salvador S.A.
Scotiabank Europe plc (UK)
Scotiabank Peru S.A.A.
Scotiabank Trinidad and Tobago Limited

COMPETITORS

AEGON N.V.
ARGOSY INVESTMENT PARTNERS L.P.
Agricultural Bank of China Limited
BANK OF INDIA
BARCLAYS BANK PLC
BPCE
Banco Bradesco S/A
Banco do Brasil S/A
Bank of Communications Co. Ltd.
China Construction Bank Corporation
Gemalto B.V.
HSBC Bank Canada
ITAU UNIBANCO HOLDING SA
Industrial And Commercial Bank Of China Limited
MMC VENTURES LIMITED
MUFG AMERICAS HOLDINGS CORPORATION
NATIONAL AUSTRALIA BANK LIMITED
NATIONAL WESTMINSTER BANK PUBLIC LIMITED COMPANY
SBERBANK PAO
Shinhan Financial Group Co. Ltd.
TD BANK NATIONAL ASSOCIATION
THE PNC FINANCIAL SERVICES GROUP INC

HISTORICAL FINANCIALS

Company Type: Public

Income Statement				FYE: October 31
	ASSETS ($ mil.)	NET INCOME ($ mil.)	INCOME AS % OF ASSETS	EMPLOYEES
10/21	959,182	7,602	0.8%	89,488
10/20	854,331	4,947	0.6%	92,001
10/19	824,596	6,231	0.8%	101,813
10/18	760,435	6,367	0.8%	97,629
10/17	712,455	6,130	0.9%	55,645
Annual Growth	**7.7%**	**5.5%**	**—**	**12.6%**

2021 Year-End Financials

Return on assets: 0.8%
Return on equity: 13.5%
Long-term debt ($ mil.): —
No. of shares (mil.): 1,215
Sales ($ mil): 31,796

Dividends
Yield: 0.0%
Payout: 46.7%
Market value ($ mil.): 79,678

STOCK PRICE ($)		P/E		PER SHARE ($)		
	FY Close	High/Low		Earnings	Dividends	Book Value
10/21	65.56	9	6	6.23	2.91	47.16
10/20	41.56	11	6	3.98	2.71	42.27
10/19	57.33	9	7	5.07	2.62	42.15
10/18	53.71	9	8	5.19	2.55	40.49
10/17	64.52	10	8	5.05	2.33	38.97
Annual Growth	0.4%	—	—	5.4%	5.7%	4.9%

Bank of Queensland Ltd

Auditors: KPMG

LOCATIONS

HQ: Bank of Queensland Ltd
Level 6, 100 Skyring Terrace, Newstead, Queensland 4006
Phone: (61) 7 3212 3333   **Fax:** (61) 7 3212 3399
Web: www.boq.com.au

HISTORICAL FINANCIALS

Company Type: Public

Income Statement				FYE: August 31
	ASSETS ($ mil.)	NET INCOME ($ mil.)	INCOME AS % OF ASSETS	EMPLOYEES
08/21	66,989	270	0.4%	2,218
08/20	41,710	84	0.2%	2,021
08/19	37,412	200	0.5%	2,098
08/18	38,260	242	0.6%	2,039
08/17	40,704	277	0.7%	2,031
Annual Growth	13.3%	(0.6%)	—	2.2%

2021 Year-End Financials

Return on assets: 0.5%	Dividends
Return on equity: 7.0%	Yield: 0.0%
Long-term debt ($ mil.): —	Payout: 82.9%
No. of shares (mil.): 639	Market value ($ mil.): 8,167
Sales ($ mil): 1,353	

STOCK PRICE ($)		P/E		PER SHARE ($)		
	FY Close	High/Low		Earnings	Dividends	Book Value
08/21	12.77	20	12	0.46	0.38	7.10
08/20	8.47	56	24	0.18	0.39	6.85
08/19	12.31	20	16	0.47	0.87	6.41
08/18	16.01	23	16	0.59	1.16	7.02
08/17	20.10	23	17	0.69	1.02	7.63
Annual Growth	(10.7%) (1.8%)	—	—	(9.8%)	(21.9%)	

Bank of the Philippine Islands

Bank of the Philippine Islands is one of that country's largest lenders. The universal bank has more than 800 branches in its homeland as well as locations in Hong Kong Italy and the US. It provides asset management and trust services mutual funds electronic banking and brokerage services in addition to standard commercial and consumer deposits loans and credit cards. The bank also performs investment banking services such as corporate finance and advisory. Giant Philippine conglomerate Ayala controls the Bank of the Philippine Islands which sells insurance provided by other Ayala divisions.

EXECUTIVES

Independent Director, Octavio Espiritu
Non-Executive Director, Romeo Bernardo
President, Chief Executive Officer, Executive Director, Cezar Consing
Non-Executive Director, Ramon Del Rosario
Independent Director, Cesar Purisima
Non-Executive Director, Jose Teodoro Limcaoco
Senior Vice President, Chief Audit Executive, Rosemarie Cruz
Independent Director, Ignacio Bunye
Vice President, Corporate Secretary, Angela Pilar Maramag
Executive Vice President, Head - Mass Retail Products, Marie Josephine Ocampo
Senior Vice President, Chief Risk Officer, Head - Risk Management Office, Marita Socorro Gayares
Senior Vice President, Chief Marketing Officer, Mary Catherine Elizabeth Santamaria
Senior Vice President, Head - Branch Sales and Service Channels, Angelie King
Senior Vice President, Chief Credit Officer, Joseph Anthony Alonso
Senior Vice President, Head of Business Banking, Eric Roberto Luchangco
Senior Vice President - Global Markets, Treasurer, Dino Gasmen
Non-Executive Chairman of the Board, Jaime Augusto Zobel De Ayala
Non-Executive Vice Chairman of the Board, Fernando Zobel De Ayala
Chief Operating Officer, Executive Vice President, Head of Enterprise Services Segment, Ramon Jocson
Senior Vice President - Corporate Banking, Roland Gerard Veloso
Independent Director, Maria Dolores Yuvienco
President - BPI Family Savings Bank, Maria Cristina Go
Executive Vice President, Head - Corporate Clients Segment and Corporate Banking, Juan Carlos Syquia
Chief Compliance Officer, Vice President, Head - Bank's Compliance Division, Noravir Gealogo
Independent Director, Eli Remolana
Independent Director, Janet Ang
Chief Finance Officer, Executive Vice President, Chief Sustainability Officer, Head of Strategy and Finance, Maria Theresa Marcial Javier
Auditors: Isla Lipana & Co.

LOCATIONS

HQ: Bank of the Philippine Islands
Ayala North Exchange Tower 1, Ayala Ave. Corner Salcedo St., Legaspi Village, Makati City 1229
Phone: (63) 2 246 5902
Web: www.bpi.com.ph

COMPETITORS

ARAB BANK PLC   RIYAD BANK

HISTORICAL FINANCIALS

Company Type: Public

Income Statement				FYE: December 31
	ASSETS ($ mil.)	NET INCOME ($ mil.)	INCOME AS % OF ASSETS	EMPLOYEES
12/20	46,485	445	1.0%	19,952
12/19	43,546	568	1.3%	21,429
12/18	39,703	439	1.1%	18,911
12/17	38,220	449	1.2%	17,047
12/16	34,853	445	1.3%	15,201
Annual Growth	7.5%	0.0%	—	7.0%

2020 Year-End Financials

Return on assets: 0.9%	Dividends
Return on equity: 7.7%	Yield: 0.0%
Long-term debt ($ mil.): —	Payout: 470.4%
No. of shares (mil.): —	Market value ($ mil.): —
Sales ($ mil): 2,621	

STOCK PRICE ($)		P/E		PER SHARE ($)		
	FY Close	High/Low		Earnings	Dividends	Book Value
12/20	35.48	8	5	0.10	0.46	1.29
12/19	39.86	6	5	0.13	0.66	1.18
12/18	37.89	—	—	0.10	0.21	1.05
12/17	37.89	7	6	0.11	0.44	0.92
12/16	39.70	7	7	0.11	0.67	0.85
Annual Growth	(2.8%)	—	—	(3.4%)	(8.7%)	11.1%

Bank Polska Kasa Opieki SA

Bank Polska Kasa Opieki better known as Bank Pekao (from its initials P.K.O.) offers retail corporate and investment banking services primarily in Poland. It also provides leasing and asset management services. Branches can also be found in France and the Ukraine. In addition to traditional deposit products Bank Pekao offers loans leasing and factoring services custodial services currency exchange and foreign trade facilitation. Originally founded as a state-owned bank to provide banking services to Polish emigrants Bank Pekao is now controlled by Italian bank UniCredit which holds approximately 53% of its shares.

EXECUTIVES

Vice President of the Management Board supervising the Private Banking and Investment Products Division, Jaroslaw Fuchs, $209,559 total compensation
Vice Chairwoman of the Supervisory Board, Joanna Dynysiuk
Member of the Supervisory Board, Malgorzata Sadurska
Vice President of the Management Board supervising the Corporate Banking and MIB Division, Jerzy Kwiecinski
Vice President of the Management Board, Pawel Straczynski
Independent Member of the Supervisory Board, Michal Kaszynski
Independent Member of the Supervisory Board, Sabina Bigos-Jaworowska
Vice President of the Management Board supervising the SME Banking Division, Magdalena Zmitrowicz, $239,569 total compensation

Independent Member of the Supervisory Board, Justyna Glebikowska-Michalak

Secretary of the Bank's Supervisory Board, Stanislaw Kaczoruk

Independent Member of the Supervisory Board, Marian Majcher

Vice President of the Management Board supervising the Risk Management Division, Marcin Gadomski, $192,887 total compensation

President of the Management Board, Leszek Skiba, $174,162 total compensation

Chairwoman of the Supervisory Board, Beata Kozlowska-chyla

Vice President of the Management Board supervising Banking Operations and IT Division, Blazej Szczecki

Vice President of the Management Board supervising the Retail Banking Division, Wojciech Werochowski

Member of the Supervisory Board, Marcin Izdebski

Auditors: KPMG Audyt Spolka z ograniczona odpowiedzialnoscia sp. k.

LOCATIONS

HQ: Bank Polska Kasa Opieki SA
53/57 Grzybowska Street, Warsaw 00-950
Phone: (48) 22 656 00 00   **Fax:** (48) 22 656 00 04
Web: www.pekao.com.pl

COMPETITORS

BANCOLOMBIA S A
CREDITO BERGAMASCO SPA
DEUTSCHE BANK LTD.
EXTRACO CORPORATION
KAS BANK N.V.
SITIBANK AO
THE ROYAL BANK OF SCOTLAND PUBLIC LIMITED COMPANY

HISTORICAL FINANCIALS

Company Type: Public

Income Statement				FYE: December 31
	ASSETS ($ mil.)	NET INCOME ($ mil.)	INCOME AS % OF ASSETS	EMPLOYEES
12/19	53,593	570	1.1%	15,678
12/18	50,910	609	1.2%	16,714
12/17	53,251	710	1.3%	17,339
12/16	41,650	544	1.3%	17,757
12/15	43,122	585	1.4%	18,327
Annual Growth	5.6%	(0.6%)	—	(3.8%)

2019 Year-End Financials

Return on assets: 1.1%
Return on equity: 9.3%
Long-term debt ($ mil.): —
No. of shares (mil.): 262
Sales ($ mil): 2,594

Dividends
Yield: —
Payout: 63.0%
Market value ($ mil.): 8,294

	STOCK PRICE ($) FY Close	P/E High/Low		PER SHARE ($)		
				Earnings	Dividends	Book Value
12/19	31.60	—	—	2.17	1.37	23.49
12/18	31.60	—	—	2.32	1.69	23.14
12/17	31.60	—	—	2.71	2.03	25.45
12/16	31.60	4	3	2.08	1.61	20.86
12/15	58.75	—	—	2.23	1.94	22.79
Annual Growth	(14.4%)	—	—	(0.6%)	(8.3%)	0.8%

Bank Sarasin & Co

Bank Sarasin one of Switzerland's largest and most reputable private banks specializes in asset management investment funds securities trading and investment counseling catering to both private and corporate clients. Established in 1841 the bank also offers complementary services such as corporate finance and brokerage analysis. The bank's financial services businesses are run through several subsidiaries including Sarasin Funds Management and Sarasin Investment Management which manages the bank's fund advisement activities in the UK. Safra Group acquired control of Bank Sarasin from Netherlands-based Rabobank in 2012.

Auditors: Deloitte AG

LOCATIONS

HQ: Bank Sarasin & Co
Elisabethenstrasse 62, Basel, Postfach 4002
Phone: (41) 58 317 44 44   **Fax:** (41) 58 317 44 00
Web: www.jsafrasarasin.com

COMPETITORS

ARBUTHNOT LATHAM & CO.   MIZUHO TRUST & BANKING
LIMITED   CO. LTD.

HISTORICAL FINANCIALS

Company Type: Public

Income Statement				FYE: December 31
	ASSETS ($ mil.)	NET INCOME ($ mil.)	INCOME AS % OF ASSETS	EMPLOYEES
12/19	37,889	393	1.0%	2,178
12/18	35,814	353	1.0%	2,151
12/17	36,036	323	0.9%	2,155
12/16	21,433	118	0.6%	0
12/15	21,644	136	0.6%	0
Annual Growth	15.0%	30.3%	—	—

2019 Year-End Financials

Return on assets: 1.0%
Return on equity: 9.0%
Long-term debt ($ mil.): —
No. of shares (mil.): 0
Sales ($ mil): 1,634

Dividends
Yield: —
Payout: —
Market value ($ mil.): —

Bankinter, S.A.

Founded in 1965 as a joint venture between what is now Grupo Santander and Bank of America Bankinter is among the top six banks in Spain. The company offers a variety of consumer and business banking services through about 360 branch locations agents telephone services mobile banking and the Internet. A pioneer in Internet stock trading Bankinter conducts more than half of its transactions online. It serves corporations individuals and small enterprises. Bankinter provides mutual and pension funds mortgages leasing and securities brokerage focusing on convenient low-cost delivery and customer service. Investment firm Cartival S.A. owns about 23% of Bankinter.

HISTORY

In 1962 Franco tried to end mixed banks in Spain with a decree that prevented banks from taking part in both commercial and investment operations. The banks circumvented this through cosmetic compliance spending the next decade nominally spinning off operations. In 1965 Banco Santander (now Grupo Santander) and Bank of America created Banco Intercontinental Espanol (Bankinter) in Madrid to specialize in industrial banking.

From 1970 to 1985 Bankinter evolved into a retail bank; it introduced credit cards personal loans and other services and offered financing to larger corporations. Bankinter was not consumed by the great branch race that defined banking-industry competition in Franco-era Spain; the bank had only 150 branches by 1985.

The bank became independent as both Bank of America (in 1987) and Santander (1994) reduced their stock holdings. Bankinter began diversifying its operations opening branches and gaining more clients. Bankinter's successful 1987 introduction of a high-interest special deposit account was dulled when other banks followed suit slowing growth. The bank took its current name in 1990 and in 1991 introduced some of Spain's first mutual funds. Within a recession-hammered economy Bankinter worked to cut costs through the introduction of telephone banking (1992) and other innovative conveniences.

Attracted by the low-cost liquidity of private banking Bankinter entered that segment in 1995. It took a step in the allfinanz direction that year creating an auto and home insurance alliance with Royal Bank of Scotland subsidiary Direct Line; the UK bank already had insurance ventures with Bankinter sibling Santander. Two years later Bankinter began BKNet Spain's first online stock-trading service.

In 1998 the bank opened a Mexican office to explore the possibility of transferring its high-tech operations into that country. As the financial industry's global consolidation continued the bank in 1999 said it was seeking a foreign ally possibly one that could help expand Bankinter's online technology.

The bank found willing partners later that year inking deals to form an Internet bank in Spain with a joint venture of US Web portal Lycos (now part of Terra Networks) and German media giant Bertelsmann as well as another Internet bank with Portugal's Banco Espirito Santo.

Although Bankinter recorded 2004 as a particularly profitable year with income up nearly 25% it also suffered the death of a deputy manager Jose Garcia in the March 11 terrorist attacks against Madrid.

In 2007 the bank sold 50% of its life insurance division to Spanish insurer Mapfre. The sale boosted Bankinter's capital.

In 2008 Credit Agricole increased its ownership in the bank to about 20%. It became the bank's largest shareholder edging out former chairman Jaime Bot n.

EXECUTIVES

Independent Director, Fernando Jose Frances Pons, $82,140 total compensation

Executive Vice Chairman of the Board, Representative of Cartival SA, Alfonso Botin-Sanz De Sautuola Y Naveda, $209,572 total compensation

Non-Executive Chairman of the Board, Other External Director, Pedro Guerrero Guerrero, $215,921 total compensation

Proprietary Director, Marcelino Botin-Sanz de Sautola Naveda, $107,961 total compensation

Independent Director, Maria Teresa Pulido Mendoza, $107,961 total compensation
Independent Director, Rafael Mateu De Ros Cerezo, $127,013 total compensation
Chief Financial Officer, Jacobo Diaz Garcia
Independent Director, Teresa Martin-Retortillo Rubio, $122,250 total compensation
Proprietary Director, Fernando Maria Masaveu Herrero, $107,961 total compensation
Chief Executive Officer, Executive Director, Maria Dolores Dancausa Trevino, $190,520 total compensation
Independent Director, Alvaro Alvarez-Alonso Plaza, $122,250 total compensation
Independent Director, Maria Luisa Jorda Castro, $122,250 total compensation
Auditors: PricewaterhouseCoopers Auditores, S.L.

LOCATIONS

HQ: Bankinter, S.A.
Paseo de la Castellana, 29, Madrid 28046
Phone: (34) 91 339 75 00   **Fax:** (34) 91 339 83 23
Web: www.bankinter.com

PRODUCTS/OPERATIONS

2014 Sales

	% of total
Interest and similar income	54
Fee and commission income	14
Other revenues	32
Total	**100**

Selected Subsidiaries

Aircraft S.A.
Bankinter Consultoria Asesoramiento y Atencion Telefonica S.A.
Bankinter Gestion de Seguros S.A.
Bankinter International B.V. (Netherlands)
Bankinter Seguros de Vida S.A.
Gesbankinter S.A.
Hispamarket S.A.
Intergestora S.A.
Intergestora Nuevas Tecnologias S.C.R. S.A.
Intermobiliaria S.A.

COMPETITORS

BANCO DE SABADELL SA
BANKIA SA (EXTINGUIDA)
CAIXABANK SA
DEUTSCHE BANK AG
NATWEST GROUP PLC
NORINCHUKIN BANK THE
Nordea Bank AB
SLM CORPORATION
SYNOVUS FINANCIAL CORP.
UniCredit Bank AG

HISTORICAL FINANCIALS

Company Type: Public

Income Statement			FYE: December 31
	ASSETS ($ mil.)	NET INCOME ($ mil.)	INCOME AS % OF ASSETS	EMPLOYEES
12/20	118,129	389	0.3%	8,668
12/19	94,011	618	0.7%	8,531
12/18	87,609	602	0.7%	5,605
12/17	85,510	593	0.7%	5,578
12/16	70,936	517	0.7%	5,486
Annual Growth	**13.6%**	**(6.9%)**	**—**	**12.1%**

2020 Year-End Financials

Return on assets: 0.3%
Return on equity: 6.4%
Long-term debt ($ mil.): —
No. of shares (mil.): 898
Sales ($ mil): 2,638
Dividends
 Yield: 0.0%
 Payout: 24.2%
 Market value ($ mil.): 4,719

STOCK PRICE ($)	P/E	PER SHARE ($)		
FY Close	High/Low	Earnings	Dividends	Book Value
12/20	5.25	24 10	0.41	0.10	6.78
12/19	7.54	13 9	0.67	0.27	6.00
12/18	8.25	19 14	0.65	0.27	5.72
12/17	9.32	19 16	0.65	0.24	5.81
12/16	8.05	15 11	0.57	0.18	4.81
Annual Growth(10.1%)	— —	(8.2%)(13.9%)	8.9%

Banque Cantonale Vaudoise

Banque Cantonale Vaudoise (BCV) provides a variety of financial services primarily to customers in the canton of Vaud in southwestern Switzerland. With about 70 retail locations it offers commercial corporate and private banking services as well as wealth management and securities brokerage. The bank is dedicated to the canton's development and in fact does business with some two-thirds of Vaud's small and midsized enterprises. The Vaud government owns more than half of BCV which was originally founded in 1845.

EXECUTIVES

Member of the Executive Board, Chief Financial Officer, Head of the Finance & Risks Division, Thomas Paulsen
Independent Vice Chairman of the Board, Jean-Francois Schwarz
Chief Executive Officer, Member of the Executive Board, Pascal Kiener, $965,934 total compensation
Member of the Executive Board, Head of the Credit Management Division, Chief Credit Officer, Bertrand Sager
Member of the Executive Board, Head of the Private Banking Division, Gerard Haeberli
Member of the Executive Board, Head of the Retail Banking, Jose Sierdo
Independent Director, Ingrid Deltenre
Member of the Executive Board, Head of the Business Support, Christian Meixenberger
Independent Chairman of the Board of Directors, Jacques de Watteville
Independent Director, Peter Ochsner
Independent Director, Fabienne Freymond Cantone
Independent Director, Jack Clemons
Member of the Executive Board, Head of the Corporate Banking Division, Andreas Diemant
Auditors: KPMG

LOCATIONS

HQ: Banque Cantonale Vaudoise
Place Saint-Francois 14, P.O. Box 300, Lausanne 1001
Phone: (41) 21 212 10 10   **Fax:** (41) 21 212 12 22
Web: www.bcv.ch

COMPETITORS

BANK OF GEORGIA   CADENCE BANCORP LLC

HISTORICAL FINANCIALS

Company Type: Public

Income Statement			FYE: December 31
	ASSETS ($ mil.)	NET INCOME ($ mil.)	INCOME AS % OF ASSETS	EMPLOYEES
12/20	60,388	375	0.6%	1,909
12/19	50,017	375	0.8%	1,921
12/18	48,655	355	0.7%	1,896
12/17	46,533	328	0.7%	1,922
12/16	43,309	304	0.7%	1,943
Annual Growth	**8.7%**	**5.4%**	**—**	**(0.4%)**

2020 Year-End Financials

Return on assets: 0.6%
Return on equity: 9.2%
Long-term debt ($ mil.): —
No. of shares (mil.): 86
Sales ($ mil): 1,220
Dividends
 Yield: —
 Payout: —
 Market value ($ mil.): —

Baoshan Iron & Steel Co Ltd

Auditors: Deloitte Touche Tohmatsu Certified Public Accountants Limited

LOCATIONS

HQ: Baoshan Iron & Steel Co Ltd
Baosteel Command Center, No. 885, Fujin Road, Baoshan District, Shanghai 201900
Phone: (86) 21 26647000   **Fax:** (86) 21 26646999
Web: www.baosteel.com/plc/

HISTORICAL FINANCIALS

Company Type: Public

Income Statement			FYE: December 31
	REVENUE ($ mil.)	NET INCOME ($ mil.)	NET PROFIT MARGIN	EMPLOYEES
12/20	43,490	1,938	4.5%	0
12/19	41,972	1,785	4.3%	0
12/18	44,372	3,135	7.1%	0
12/17	44,487	2,945	6.6%	0
12/16	26,743	1,291	4.8%	0
Annual Growth	**12.9%**	**10.7%**		**—**

2020 Year-End Financials

Debt ratio: 1.5%
Return on equity: 6.9%
Cash ($ mil.): 2,582
Current ratio: 1.13
Long-term debt ($ mil.): 3,419
No. of shares (mil.): —
Dividends
 Yield: —
 Payout: —
 Market value ($ mil.): —

Barclays Bank Plc

Barclays Bank PLC known as Barclays International is the international and investment banking unit of Barclays PLC. The company s comprised primarily of the Banking Corporate Banking and Markets businesses aiding money managers financial institutions governments supranational organizations and corporate clients to manage their funding financing strategic and risk management needs. Barclays International's diversified business portfolio provides balance resilience and exciting growth opportunities. The division has strong global market positions and continues to invest in people and technology in order to deliver sustainable improved returns. Barclays International offers customers and clients a range of products and services spanning consumer and wholesale banking.

Operations

Barclays Bank PLC comprises two units Corporate and Investment Bank (CIB; about 80% of sales) and Consumer Cards and Payments (CCP; around 20%).

The CIB segment comprises Barclay's Banking Corporate Banking and Markets businesses which aid money managers institutions governments and corporate clients in managing their funding financing and risk management needs.

The CCP segment consists of US Consumer Bank Barclays Payments Barclaycard Germany and Private Bank. Barclays Payments enables businesses of all sizes to make and receive payments. It also has a partnership-focused business model offering credit cards to consumers through its partners such as American Airlines and Wyndham Hotels & Resorts as well as online retail savings products. In addition it offers r multiple consumer products in Germany including credit cards online loans installment purchase financing electronic Point of Sale (ePOS) financing and deposits. Its Private Bank offers banking credit and investment capabilities to meet the needs of its clients across the UK Europe the Middle East and Africa and Asia.

Overall net trading income accounts for about 45% of Barclays Bank's total revenue with net fee commission and other income and net interest income contributing around 35% and approximately 20% respectively.

Geographic Reach

The company is based in London UK.

Financial Performance

The company's net interest income decreased 14% from ?9.4 billion in 2019 to ?8.1 billion in 2020.

In 2020 the company had a net income of ?3.1 billion a 30% decrease from the previous year's net income of ?4.4 billion.

The company's cash at the end of 2020 was ?210.1 billion. Operating activities generated ?57.5 billion while investing activities used ?18.4 billion mainly for purchase of financial assets at fair value through other comprehensive income. Financing activities provided another ?2.7 billion.

Strategy

Barclays has transformed over the past few years. The company has evolved to respond to the needs of customers and clients and adapted to changes in the economic and regulatory environment. The company's four strategic pillars consist of:

Focus on customers and clients. Putting them at the heart of the decisions the company make about running its business and shaping it for the future;

Continue digitalizing. Enabling its customers and clients to engage with the company in the way they want to and making its business more efficient;

Strengthen its diversification. Diversify the company's organization by business geography and income type to be more resilient to economic headwinds and future trends; and

Protect and strengthen its culture. Draw on the company's Purpose and Values to guide its choices as colleagues and as an organization

Each of these components is complementary with benefits from improvements in one reinforcing progress across the others. For example the company better meets client needs by focusing on digitalization which in turn expands its product sets and strengthens diversification. This improves the resilience of the Group increases efficiency and reduces cost and operational risk while providing an improved experience and faster capability for customers.

Auditors: KPMG LLP

LOCATIONS

HQ: Barclays Bank Plc
 1 Churchill Place, London E14 5HP
Phone: (44) 20 7116 3170
Web: www.barclays.com

2018 sales

	%
United Kingdom	33
Americas	51
Europe	11
Asia	4
Africa and Middle East	1
Total	**100**

PRODUCTS/OPERATIONS

2018 sales

	%
Corporate and Investment Bank	70
Consumer Cards and Payments	30
Head Office	-
Total	**100**

2018 sales

	%
Net Interest Income	23
Net Fee and Commission Income	41
Net Trading Income	32
Net Investment Income	3
Other Income	1
Total	**100**

COMPETITORS

BANCO BBVA ARGENTINA S.A.
BANCO BPI S.A.
BANK VTB PAO
BPCE
Banco Bradesco S/A
Banque Lombard Odier & Cie SA
CREDIT INDUSTRIEL ET COMMERCIAL
China Construction Bank Corporation
FEDERAL RESERVE BANK OF ATLANTA
FEDERAL RESERVE BANK OF CHICAGO
FEDERAL RESERVE BANK OF PHILADELPHIA (INC)
HSBC Bank Canada
ICICI BANK LIMITED
KEYCORP
NATIONAL AUSTRALIA BANK LIMITED
NATIONAL BANK HOLDINGS CORPORATION
NEDBANK GROUP LTD
National Bank Financial & Co Inc
National Bank of Canada
SANTANDER UK GROUP HOLDINGS PLC
SBERBANK PAO
Swedbank AB
THE CO-OPERATIVE BANK P.L.C.
THE ROYAL BANK OF SCOTLAND PUBLIC LIMITED
 COMPANY
The Bank of New York Mellon SA/NV
The Bank of Nova Scotia
UMB FINANCIAL CORPORATION
Woori Finance Holdings Co. Ltd.
ZIONS BANCORPORATION

HISTORICAL FINANCIALS

Company Type: Public

Income Statement

	ASSETS ($ mil.)	NET INCOME ($ mil.)	INCOME AS % OF ASSETS	EMPLOYEES
12/20	1,446,224	2,420	0.2%	20,900
12/19	1,157,699	2,799	0.2%	20,500
12/18	1,120,613	1,066	0.1%	22,400
12/17	1,525,392	(1,753)	—	79,900
12/16	1,493,335	4,088	0.3%	119,300
Annual Growth	**(0.8%)**	**(12.3%)**	**—**	**(35.3%)**

FYE: December 31

2020 Year-End Financials

Return on assets: 0.1%
Return on equity: 3.3%
Long-term debt ($ mil.): —
No. of shares (mil.): —
Sales ($ mil): 27,997

Dividends
 Yield: —
 Payout: —
 Market value ($ mil.): —

	STOCK PRICE ($) FY Close	P/E High/Low		Earnings	PER SHARE ($) Dividends	Book Value
12/20	16.79	—	—	(0.00)	0.00	31.29
12/19	15.12	—	—	(0.00)	0.00	28.53
12/18	46.99	—	—	(0.00)	0.00	26.00
Annual Growth	**(40.2%)**			**—**	**—**	**4.7%**

Barclays PLC

Raising the bar for global finance Barclays PLC owns one of Europe's largest banks a top market-making investment bank the top UK credit card and a British universal bank. Its flagship Barclays Bank UK has nearly 860 branches in the UK reaching around 10 million digitally-active customers and some 9 million active mobile banking users. Barclays International has retail operations throughout Europe UK and the Americas as well as extensive investment banking and wealth management activities. Barclays provides consumer lending and payment processing services. The UK accounts for more than half of Barclays' revenue.

Operations

Barclays operates two businesses: Barclays International and Barclays UK.

Barclays International generates around two thirds of revenue and consists of its corporate and investment bank; and consumer cards and payments. Barclays International's diversified business portfolio provides balance resilience and exciting growth opportunities. The division has strong global market positions and continues to invest in people and technology in order to deliver sustainable improved returns. Barclays International offers customers and clients a range of products and services spanning consumer and wholesale banking.

Barclays UK (accounts for around a third of revenue) a ring fenced bank comprised largely of UK Personal and Business Banking and Barclaycard Consumer UK businesses. UK Personal Banking offers retail solutions to help customers with their day-to-day banking needs. UK Business Banking serves business clients from high growth start-ups to small and medium-sized enterprises with specialist advice for their business banking needs. Barclaycard Consumer UK is a leading credit card provider offering flexible borrowing and payment solutions while delivering a leading customer experience.

Geographic Reach

Barclays operates in around 55 countries. In the UK it has nearly 860 retail banking branches. The UK accounts for more than 50% of Barclays' revenue the Americas nearly 35% and Europe nearly 10%. It also generates a small amount in the Asia-Pacific region and Africa and the Middle East.

Barclays' head office is located in London United Kingdom.

Sales and Marketing

Barclays UK's customers and clients consists of high growth and small and medium-sized companies. Barclays International's customers and clients consists of consumers; corporates; financial institutions; and money managers and institutional investors.

Barclays spent some 330 million on marketing and advertising in 2020 from some 425 million and nearly 495 million in 2019 and 2018.

Financial Performance

Note: Growth rates may differ after conversion to US Dollars.

Barclays' financial performance has been underwhelming during the last five years. Net interest income and non-interest income have both fluctuated over the period causing total revenue to be similarly uneven.

In 2020 Barclays' revenue increased 1% to 21.7 billion thanks to a 22% increase in Barclays International's CIB income due to strong Markets income reflecting market share gains in a buoyant trading environment as well as strong Banking income resulting in the best ever year on a comparable basis for both businesses. CC&P income of 3.4 billion down 22% driven by lower credit card balances margin compression and reduced payments activity.

Barclays had an decrease of 38% in profits from .4 billion in 2019 to 1.5 billion in 2020 primarily due to the profit loss in Consumer Cards and Payments and head office division offset by the increase profit in Corporate Investment Bank.

The bank's cash balance grew during 2020 ending the year 43.5 billion higher at 210.1 billion. Barclays' operations used cash of 57.5 billion. Its investing activities used 18.3 billion while financing activities generated 2.7 billion. The bank's primary cash uses were purchase of financial assets and redemption of subordinated debt.

Strategy

As a purpose-driven organization Barclays aspires to create opportunities to rise for all of its stakeholders. Its strategy has been developed to balance the needs of customers and clients colleagues investors and wider society. Barclays has transformed over the last four years responding to changes in the economic and regulatory environment and to the changing needs of customers and clients.

Barclays' four strategic pillars consists of: focusing on customers and clients; becoming more digital; protecting and strengthening its culture; and maintaining and increasing its diversification.

The company's strategy builds on its strengths and will steer it through those challenges.

Company Background

Legal troubles have caused headwinds for Barclays's bottom line in recent years. In mid-2012 the company admitted to manipulating the London Interbank Offered Rate (LIBOR) a benchmark for daily global short-term interest rates. The bank repeatedly manipulated the LIBOR in order to make its funding position look stronger than it actually was; the rigging also helped the bank make money on credit derivatives. Chairman Martin Agius and CEO Bob Diamond both resigned as a result of the developments and the company paid US and UK regulators some 290 million ($453 million) in settlement fines. Shortly after the LIBOR scandal the UK's Serious Fraud Office launched an inquiry

into payments Barclays made to sovereign investor Qatar Holding in 2008. At the behest of regulators Barclays ringfenced its UK consumer bank from its riskier investment banking assets in 2018.

HISTORY

Barclays first spread its wings in 1736 when James Barclay united his family's goldsmithing and banking businesses. As other family members joined the London enterprise it became known as Barclays Bevan & Tritton (1782).

Banking first became regulated in the 19th century. To ward off takeovers 20 banks combined with Barclays in 1896. The new firm Barclay & Co. began preying on other banks. Within 20 years it bought 17 including the Colonial Bank chartered in 1836 to serve the West Indies and British Guiana (now Guyana). The company renamed Barclays Bank Ltd. in 1917 weathered the Depression as the UK's #2 bank.

Barclays began expanding again after WWII and by the late 1950s it had become the UK's top bank. It had a computer network by 1959 and in 1966 it introduced the Barclaycard in conjunction with Bank of America's BankAmericard (now Visa).

In 1968 the UK's Monopolies Commission barred Barclays' merger with two other big London banks but had no objections to a two-way merger so Barclays bought competitor Martins.

Barclays moved into the US consumer finance market in 1980 when it bought American Credit 138 former Beneficial Finance offices and Bankers Trust's branch network.

During the 1980s London banks faced competition from invading overseas banks local building societies and other financial firms. Banking reform in 1984 led to formation of a holding company for Barclays Bank PLC.

To prepare for British financial deregulation in 1986 Barclays formed Barclays de Zoete Wedd (BZW) by merging its merchant bank with two other London financial firms. Faced with sagging profits Barclays sold its California bank in 1988 and its US consumer finance business in 1989.

In 1990 Barclays bought private German bank Merck Finck & Co. and Paris bank L'Europeenne de Banque. The company countered 1992's bad-loan-induced losses by accelerating a cost-cutting program begun in 1989. To appease stockholders chairman and CEO Andrew Buxton (a descendant of one of the bank's founding families) gave up his CEO title hiring Martin Taylor (previously CEO of textile firm Courtaulds) for the post.

The company sold its Australian retail banking business in 1994 then began trimming other operations including French corporate banking and US mortgage operations. However it bought the Wells Fargo Nikko Investment Company to boost Asian operations.

Barclays' piecemeal sale of BZW signaled its failure to become a global investment banking powerhouse. In 1997 it sold BZW's European investment banking business to Credit Suisse First Boston retaining the fixed-income and foreign exchange business. (Credit Suisse bought Barclays' Asian investment banking operations in 1998.)

Losses in Russia and a $250 million bailout of US hedge fund Long-Term Capital Management hit Barclays Capital in 1998. Taylor resigned that year in part because of his radical plans for the bank. Sir Peter Middleton stepped in as acting CEO; Barclays later tapped Canadian banker Matthew Barrett for the post. (Middleton also became chairman upon Buxton's retirement.)

Barclays in 1999 started a move toward online banking at the expense of traditional branches. The company announced free lifetime Internet access for new bank customers.

In 2000 the bank ruffled feathers when it announced the closure of about 170 mostly rural UK branches. Also in 2000 the company sold its Dial auto leasing unit to ABN AMRO and bought Woolwich plc. The following year Barclay's closed its own life insurance division opting instead to sell the life insurance and pension products of London-based Legal & General Group.

In 2004 chief executive Barrett was named Barclays' chairman succeeding Peter Middleton who became chairman of Centre for Effective Dispute Resolution (CEDR) and later chancellor of the University of Sheffield.

After exiting the South African market in 1987 over apartheid concerns Barclays returned in a big way in 2005 buying a majority stake (about 57%) in the Absa Group one of the country's largest retail banks. The deal also represented the largest-ever direct foreign investment there. The next year Barclays sold its South African businesses including corporate international retail and commercial operations to Absa.

The company entered the US credit card market when it bought Juniper Financial (now Barclays Bank Delaware) from Canadian Imperial Bank of Commerce (CIBC) in 2004. In a previous hook-up with CIBC Barclays merged its Caribbean banking business with CIBC's to create an 85-branch regional bank FirstCaribbean International Bank with each company owning 44%; Barclays sold its stake to CIBC in 2006.

In 2005 the bank sold its vendor finance businesses in the UK and Germany to CIT Group. Barclays said that the sale will allow it to focus on its commercial leasing business.

The bank moved to assimilate its Woolwich acquisition in 2006 when it closed 200 branches and consolidated Woolwich branches into existing Barclays locations. It retained the Woolwich mortgage brand but switched account holders to Barclays accounts.

The company and HSBC formed a joint venture that manages their cash handling operations in the UK. Named Vaultex the joint venture acquired Loomis Cash Management in 2007.

Marcus Agius succeeded the retiring Matthew Barrett as chairman in 2007.

Although the company withdrew its bid for Dutch banking giant ABN AMRO (narrowly escaping that troubled deal) in 2008 it bought Russian bank Expobank from Petropavlovsk Finance. Expobank was one of the largest ATM networks in Russia and part of the booming consumer banking industry there. Also that year Barclays sold noncore business Barclays Life and its portfolio of some 760000 life and pension policies to Swiss Re for 753 million ($1.5 billion).

The group chose not to participate in the UK's bank bailouts as the global financial crisis intensified in late 2008 but pursued its own capital-raising plan. Through the deal sovereign investment fund Qatar Investment Authority became the bank's largest shareholder with a 5% stake.

In 2009 it shut down US-based subprime mortgage lender EquiFirst which it had purchased from Regions Financial before it fell victim to the mortgage bust.

Later that year it sold a majority of Barclays Global Investors to American money manager BlackRock for 9.5 billion ($15 billion). In exchange it gained a 20% stake in the new BlackRock with some $3 trillion under management for institutional clients around the world. The deal provided the bank with much-needed cash and cleared the way for a commercial partnership with BlackRock.

Another major transaction was the 1 billion ($1.8 billion) acquisition of Lehman Brothers' North American operations a deal which made Barclays Capital one of the world's largest investment banks.

EXECUTIVES

CEO, Consumer Banking and Payments, Ashok Vaswani
Chairman, Barclays Bank UK PLC, Crawford Gillies
Group Chief Executive, C.S. Venkatakrishnan
Group Chief Compliance Officer, Laura Padovani
Non-Executive Independent Director, Mohamed El-Erian
Non-Executive Independent Director, Diane Schueneman
Vice Chairman, Investment Banking Europe, Laurent Meyer
Auditors: KPMG LLP

LOCATIONS

HQ: Barclays PLC
  1 Churchill Place, London E14 5HP
Phone: (44) 20 7116 3170
Web: www.barclays.com

2018 Sales

	% of total
UK	52
Americas	36
Europe	8
Africa and Middle East	3
Asia	1
Total	**100**

PRODUCTS/OPERATIONS

2018 Sales

	% of total
Barclays International	66
Barclays UK	34
Head Office	-
Total	**100**

COMPETITORS

BANK OF ENGLAND
BARCLAYS SLCSM (NO.1) LIMITED
Bank of Canada
FEDERAL RESERVE BANK OF PHILADELPHIA (INC)
HSBC HOLDINGS PLC
LLOYDS BANKING GROUP PLC
NATWEST GROUP PLC
Schweizerische Nationalbank

HISTORICAL FINANCIALS

Company Type: Public

Income Statement			FYE: December 31
	ASSETS ($ mil.)	NET INCOME ($ mil.)	INCOME AS % OF ASSETS	EMPLOYEES
12/20	1,841,694	3,252	0.2%	83,000
12/19	1,505,743	4,323	0.3%	80,800
12/18	1,446,931	2,739	0.2%	83,500
12/17	1,530,666	(1,732)	—	79,900
12/16	1,492,316	2,558	0.2%	119,300
Annual Growth	**5.4%**	**6.2%**	**—**	**(8.7%)**

2020 Year-End Financials

Return on assets: 0.1%
Return on equity: 3.6%
Long-term debt ($ mil.): —
No. of shares (mil.): —
Sales ($ mil): 37,705

Dividends
Yield: 1.8%
Payout: 11.6%
Market value ($ mil.): —

STOCK PRICE ($)	P/E	PER SHARE ($)		
FY Close	High/Low	Earnings	Dividends	Book Value
12/20	7.99	115 49	0.12	0.14	5.17
12/19	9.52	70 50	0.19	0.35	4.91
12/18	7.54	119 78	0.12	0.24	4.66
12/17	10.90	— —	(0.14)	0.16	5.06
12/16	11.00	112 63	0.13	0.22	4.70
Annual Growth	**(7.7%)**	**— —**	**(2.1%)**	**(9.9%)**	**2.4%**

Basellandschaftliche Kantonalbank (Switzerland)

EXECUTIVES

Member of the Executive Board, Head of Private Customers & Direct Banking, Kaspar Schweizer
Non-Executive Independent Director, Kurt Strecker, $101,518 total compensation
Member of the Executive Board, Head of Corporate Customers & Loans, Daniel Braendlin
Non-Executive Independent Director, Marco Primavesi, $101,518 total compensation
Non-Executive Independent Director, Erica Spiegler, $71,063 total compensation
Non-Executive Independent Director, Nadine Jermann, $71,063 total compensation
Non-Executive Independent Chairman of the Board, Elisabeth Schirmer-Mosset, $197,961 total compensation
Non-Executive Independent Director, Stephan Naef, $71,063 total compensation
Non-Executive Independent Director, Doris Greiner, $71,063 total compensation
Member of the Executive Board, Head of IT & Services, Simon Leumann
Non-Executive Vice Chairman of the Board, Anton Lauber, $50,759 total compensation
Member of the Executive Board, Head of Private Banking & Investment Services, Jean-Daniel Neuenschwander
Non-Executive Independent Director, Dieter Voellmin, $101,518 total compensation
Member of the Executive Board, Head of Finance & Risk Management, Herbert Kumbartzki
Chief Executive Officer, Chairman of the Executive Board, John Haefelfinger
Non-Executive Independent Director, Frenk Mutschlechner, $71,063 total compensation
Auditors: Ernst & Young Ltd

LOCATIONS

HQ: Basellandschaftliche Kantonalbank (Switzerland)
  Rheinstrasse 7, Liestal CH-4410
Phone: (41) 61 925 94 94
Web: www.blkb.ch

HISTORICAL FINANCIALS

Company Type: Public

Income Statement			FYE: December 31
	ASSETS ($ mil.)	NET INCOME ($ mil.)	INCOME AS % OF ASSETS	EMPLOYEES
12/20	33,800	156	0.5%	710
12/19	28,219	141	0.5%	687
12/18	25,760	136	0.5%	685
12/17	24,808	136	0.6%	673
12/16	23,272	131	0.6%	657
Annual Growth	**9.8%**	**4.6%**	**—**	**2.0%**

2020 Year-End Financials

Return on assets: 0.4%
Return on equity: 10.9%
Long-term debt ($ mil.): —
No. of shares (mil.): 0
Sales ($ mil): 412

Dividends
Yield: —
Payout: —
Market value ($ mil.): —

BASF SE

The company's portfolio is divided into the Chemicals Materials Industrial Solutions Surface Technologies Nutrition & Care and Agricultural Solutions segments and serves nearly all sectors. Based in Germany BASF's manufacturing footprint spans more than 90 countries and around 250 production sites worldwide. From basic chemicals to high value-added products and system solutions — serves around 100000 customers globally.

Operations

The company operates through 11 divisions grouped into six segments: Surface Technologies (Catalysts and Coatings) Materials (Performance Materials and Monomers) Chemicals (Petrochemicals and Intermediates) Industrial Solutions (Dispersions & Pigments and Performance Chemicals) Agricultural Solutions Nutrition & Care (Care Chemicals and Nutrition & Health) and Others.

The Surface Technologies segment products includes catalysts and battery materials for the automotive and chemical industries surface treatments colors and coatings. This segment accounts for over 20% of the total revenue. The Materials segment (generates some 20%) offers advanced materials and its precursors for new applications and systems. Its product portfolio includes isocyanates and polyamides as well as inorganic basic products and specialties for plastics and plastics processing. The Chemicals segment brings in around 15% of sales and makes basic chemicals and intermediates contributing to the organic growth of key value chains. Alongside internal transfers customers include the chemical and plastics industries.

The Industrial Solutions segment develops and markets ingredients and additives for industrial applications such as polymer dispersions pigments resins electronic materials antioxidants and additives. The segment represents around 15% of total sales.

Agricultural Solutions (nearly 15% of revenue) provides fungicides herbicides insecticides and biological crop protection and seed treatment. It offers farmers innovative solutions including those based on digital technologies combined with practical advice.

Geographic Reach

BASF is based in the industrial city of Ludwigshafen Germany and has operations in around 90 countries. It manages its vast activities through around 10 operating divisions which are further divided into some 75 strategic business units.

Six of BASF's manufacturing sites are highly efficient "Verbund" sites including its Ludwigshafen sitewhich is the world's largest chemicals plant. BASF's total production footprint totals around 240 sites worldwide.

BASF's R&D activities focus on three key sites in Europe Asia and North America: Process Research & Chemical Engineering (Ludwigshafen Germany); Advanced Materials & Systems Research (Shanghai China); and Bioscience Research (Research Triangle Park North Carolina).

Germany is BASF's largest single market at roughly 15% of total sales the rest of the Europe were about 40%. North America accounts for more than 20 % and Asia over 20% of sales.

Sales and Marketing

BASF boasts a global base of around 100000 customers ranging from major global customers and medium-sized businesses to end consumers.

BASF established its five global service units. The five global units are Global Procurement Global Engineering Services and Global Digital Services Global Business Services and the European Site & Verbund Management.

Financial Performance

Note: Growth rates may differ after conversion to US Dollars. BASF SE's performance for the span of five years have fluctuated with 2017 as the company's highest performing year. Revenue for 2020 decreased by ?167 million to ?59.1 billion as compared to 2019's revenue of ?59.3 billion. The company recorded a net loss of ?1.1 billion in 2020 as compared to the prior year's net income of ?8.4 billion. BASF's cash at the end of the year ?1.9 billion higher at ?4.3 billion. The company's operations produced a cash inflow of ?5.4 billion. Investing activities used another ?1.9 billion while financing activities used ?1.6 billion.

Strategy

BASF is passionate about chemistry and its customers. To be the world's leading chemical company for its customers BASF will grow profitably and create value for society. Thanks to its expertise its innovative and entrepreneurial spirit and the power of its Verbund integration it makes a decisive contribution to changing the world for the better. Creating chemistry for a sustainable future is what drives BASF and what it does best.

Its aspiration is to be the world's leading chemical company and achieve profitable growth. Its strategic focus are primarily close cooperation between research and business units strong customer focus and further development of innovation strategies. In 2020 the company invested ?2.1 billion to research and development while operating divisions accounted for more than 80% of total research and development expenses.

Company Background

Originally named Badische Anilin & Soda-Fabrik BASF AG was founded in Mannheim Germany by jeweler Frederick Englehorn in 1861. Unable to find enough land for expansion in Mannheim BASF moved to nearby Ludwigshafen in 1865. The company was a pioneer in coal tar dyes and it developed a synthetic indigo in 1897. Its synthetic dyes rapidly replaced more expensive organic dyes. BASF scientist Fritz Haber synthesized ammonia in giving BASF access to the market for nitrogenous fertilizer. The company moved into petrochemicals and became a leading manufacturer of plastic and synthetic fiber.

HISTORY

Originally named Badische Anilin & Soda-Fabrik BASF AG was founded in Mannheim Germany by jeweler Frederick Englehorn in 1861. Unable to find enough land for expansion in Mannheim

BASF moved to nearby Ludwigshafen in 1865. The company was a pioneer in coal tar dyes and it developed a synthetic indigo in 1897. Its synthetic dyes rapidly replaced more expensive organic dyes.

BASF scientist Fritz Haber synthesized ammonia in 1909 giving BASF access to the market for nitrogenous fertilizer (1913). Haber received a Nobel Prize in 1918 but was later charged with war crimes for his work with poison gases. Managed by Carl Bosch another Nobel Prize winner BASF joined the I.G. Farben cartel with Bayer Hoechst and others in 1925 to create a German chemical colossus. Within the cartel BASF developed polystyrene PVC and magnetic tape. Part of the Nazi war machine I.G. Farben made synthetic rubber and used labor from the Auschwitz concentration camp during WWII.

After the war I.G. Farben was dismantled. BASF regained its independence in 1952 and rebuilt its war-ravaged factories. Strong postwar domestic demand for basic chemicals aided its recovery and in 1958 BASF launched a US joint venture with Dow Chemical. (BASF bought out Dow's half in 1978.) The company moved into petrochemicals and became a leading manufacturer of plastic and synthetic fiber.

In the US the company purchased Wyandotte Chemicals (1969) Chemetron (1979) and Inmont (1985) among others. To expand its natural gas business in Europe in 1991 the company signed deals with Russia's Gazprom and France's Elf Aquitaine. BASF bought Mobil's polystyrene-resin business and gained almost 10% of the US market.

BASF bought Imperial Chemical's polypropylene business in 1994 and became Europe's second-largest producer of the plastic. The next year the company paid $1.4 billion for the pharmaceutical arm of UK retailer Boots.

In 1997 BASF formed a joint venture with PetroFina (now TOTAL); in 2001 the venture opened the world's largest liquid steam cracker in Port Arthur Texas.

BASF made seven major acquisitions in 1998 including the complexing business of Ciba Specialty Chemicals. It also made six divestitures which included its European buildings-paints operations sold to Nobel N.V.

In 1999 the US fined the company $225 million for its part in a worldwide vitamin price-fixing cartel (in 2001 the European Commission fined it another $260 million bringing the total expected cost of fines out-of-court settlements and legal expenses to about $800 million). BASF also faced a class-action suit as a result of the scheme. That year the company moved into oil and gas exploration in Russia through a partnership agreement with Russia's Gazprom. BASF also merged its textile operations into Bayer and Hoechst's DyStar joint venture forming a $1 billion company that is a world-leading dye maker.

BASF completed its acquisition of Rohm and Haas' industrial coatings business in 2000 and bought the Cyanamid division (herbicides fungicides and pesticides) of American Home Products (now Wyeth). That year BASF expanded its superabsorbents business by paying $656 million for US-based Amcol International's Chemdal International unit.

Rather than attempt to compete in the rapidly consolidating pharmaceutical industry in 2001 BASF sold its midsized Knoll Pharmaceutical unit to Abbott Laboratories for about $6.9 billion. It also announced that it was closing 10 plants and cutting about 4000 jobs (4% of its workforce).

BASF sold its fibers unit in 2003 to focus on core chemical operations which it added to throughout the next few years. For example it bought a portion of Bayer's agchem businesses

for $1.3 billion when European antitrust regulators mandated the Bayer divestment following its acquisition of Aventis CropScience. BASF also acquired Honeywell Specialty Materials' engineering plastics business in exchange for its fibers division. BASF's acquisition later that year of MSA's Callery Chemical Division strengthened BASF's line of inorganics which it planned to focus on providing to the pharmaceutical industry. Other acquisitions included Ticona's nylon 66 business and Sunoco's plasticizers unit.

That year also brought chairman J rgen Hambrecht's announcement that the company would push forward with a restructuring of its North American business. The focus of the plan was to save more than $250 million over the next three years. Included among the steps were job cuts of approximately 1000 and the relocation of its North American headquarters (though remaining in New Jersey) in late 2004. (The move to smaller facilities was enabled by the sale of Knoll Pharmaceuticals in 2001 which reduced operations at the home base.)

BASF sold Basell its petrochemical JV with Shell in 2005. The two companies had announced in 2004 that they planned to exit the polyolefins business with the sale of Basell. The deal was finalized late the next year. Investment group Access Industries came in with the winning bid of about $5.7 billion. That company's name was changed to LyondellBasell after its 2007 acquisition of Lyondell Chemical Company.

The company opened two Verbund sites in Asia — one in Nanjing China and the other in Kuantan Malaysia. The Chinese site delivered its first product in early 2005 and began operating fully in the middle of that year. It's the centerpiece and primary operation of BASF-YPC a joint venture with Sinopec that was formed in 2000. BASF's goal is to achieve 70% of its sales in the region from local production by 2015; that figure hovered at about 60% in 2008.

The company also legally changed its name from BASF Aktiengesellschaft to BASF SE in 2008. The move made formal BASF's transition to a European company as opposed to one organized in Germany.

In 2009 BASF spent about $4 billion to acquire Swiss chemicals giant Ciba. Following a review phase of Ciba's operations and their fit within the structure of BASF the company began integrating Ciba into its performance products segment; this entailed the sale or closure of almost half of Ciba's 55 manufacturing facilities and the loss of about 3700 of its employees. As part of that strategy BASF SE sold the Regulatory and Safety Testing businesses of Ciba's Expert Services unit to London-based Intertek Group in 2010.

Also in 2010 BASF acquired specialty chemicals company Cognis GmbH in a $3.8 billion deal. Cognis gave BASF a boost in entering several high-margin business lines such as personal care and cosmetics.

EXECUTIVES

LOCATIONS

HQ: BASF SE
Carl-Bosch-Strasse 38, Ludwigshafen D-67056
Phone: (49) 621 60 0 **Fax:** (49) 621 602525
Web: www.basf.com

2018 Sales

	% of total
Europe	
Germany	29
Other Countries	16
North America	27
Asia Pacific	22
South America Africa Middle East	6
Total	**100**

PRODUCTS/OPERATIONS

2018 Sales

	% of total
Functional Materials & Solutions	34
Performance Products	25
Chemicals	26
Agricultural Solutions	10
Other	5
Total	**100**

Selected Products

Chemicals
 Inorganics
 Ammonia
 Formaldehyde
 Melamine
 Sulfuric acid
 Urea
 Intermediates
 Performance chemicals
 Water-based resins
 Petrochemicals
 Feedstocks
 Industrial gases
 Plasticizers
 Specialty chemicals
Plastics
 Engineering plastics
 Foams
 Polyamides and intermediates
 Polyurethanes
 Styrenics
Functional Solutions
 Catalysts
 Battery materials
 Chemical catalysts
 Coatings
 Automotive coatings
 Decorative paints
 Industrial coatings
 Pigments
 Construction chemicals
Performance Products
 Automotive fluids
 Care chemicals
 Paper chemicals
 Pharma ingredients
 Textile chemicals
Agricultural Solutions
 Crop protection
 Fungicides
 Herbicides
 Insecticides

COMPETITORS

ALTANA AG	SIGMA-ALDRICH
AMERICAN PACIFIC	CORPORATION
CORPORATION	Solvay
ASPEN AEROGELS INC.	THE CHEMOURS COMPANY
Akzo Nobel N.V.	THE DOW CHEMICAL
Clariant AG	COMPANY
Evonik Industries AG	WARWICK INTERNATIONAL
FUCHS PETROLUB SE	GROUP LIMITED

HISTORICAL FINANCIALS

Company Type: Public

Income Statement

	REVENUE ($ mil.)	NET INCOME ($ mil.)	NET PROFIT MARGIN	EMPLOYEES
12/20	72,592	(1,300)	—	110,302
12/19	66,597	9,454	14.2%	117,628
12/18	71,775	5,390	7.5%	118,371
12/17	77,289	7,286	9.4%	114,333
12/16	60,766	4,282	7.0%	111,975
Annual Growth	**4.5%**	**—**	**—**	**(0.4%)**

2020 Year-End Financials

Debt ratio: 32.4%
Return on equity: (-2.8%)
Cash ($ mil.): 5,314
Current ratio: 1.83
Long-term debt ($ mil.): 20,719

No. of shares (mil.): 918
Dividends
 Yield: 3.3%
 Payout: —
Market value ($ mil.): 18,076

	STOCK PRICE ($) FY Close	P/E High/Low		PER SHARE ($) Earnings	Dividends	Book Value
12/20	19.68	—	—	(1.41)	0.67	45.07
12/19	18.72	2	2	10.27	0.64	50.73
12/18	17.59	5	3	5.85	0.66	43.71
12/17	27.47	17	4	7.92	0.66	44.16
12/16	92.57	21	14	4.66	0.57	36.57
Annual Growth	**(32.1%)**	**—**	**—**	**—**	**4.1%**	**5.4%**

BAWAG Group AG

Putting your money in BAWAG beats hiding your money in a mattress. As one of the largest banks in Austria BAWAG P.S.K. (for short) operates a network of more than 150 BAWAG branches and some 1300 P.S.K. post office outlets around the country. It focuses on small and mid-sized business and retail customers. The BAWAG P.S.K. Group includes more than 50 companies in Austria and abroad. Among its Austrian bank subsidiaries are easybank and –VKB. The company also has banking units in Malta Slovenia Hungary and Libya. BAWAG P.S.K. is owned by Cerberus Capital Management.
Auditors: KPMG Austria Wirtschaftspruefungs-und Steuerberatungsgesellschaft

LOCATIONS

HQ: BAWAG Group AG
 Wiedner Gurtel 11, Vienna A-1100
Phone: (43) 5 99 05 0
Web: www.bawaggroup.com

COMPETITORS

Ageas	Sampo Oyj
MEDIOLANUM SPA PLC	THOMAS COOK GROUP
NATWEST GROUP PLC	Talanx AG
RSA INSURANCE GROUP LIMITED	

HISTORICAL FINANCIALS

Company Type: Public

Income Statement

	ASSETS ($ mil.)	NET INCOME ($ mil.)	INCOME AS % OF ASSETS	EMPLOYEES
12/20	65,203	348	0.5%	4,071
12/19	51,267	515	1.0%	3,696
12/18	51,187	499	1.0%	3,474
12/17	55,227	559	1.0%	3,437
12/16	41,963	510	1.2%	2,951
Annual Growth	**11.6%**	**(9.1%)**	**—**	**8.4%**

2020 Year-End Financials

Return on assets: 0.5%
Return on equity: 6.9%
Long-term debt ($ mil.): —
No. of shares (mil.): 87
Sales ($ mil): 1,896

Dividends
 Yield: —
 Payout: 171.1%
 Market value ($ mil.): —

Bayer AG

Bayer one of the leading life science companies around the world makes prescription products and works in oncology hematology ophthalmology through its Pharmaceuticals division; OTC products like Claritin and Canesten via its Consumer Health division; and crop protection and pest control via its Crop Science division. Its top selling pharmaceuticals include oral anticoagulant Xarelto and eye disease medicine Eylea. Also known as Bayer Group the company has approximately 385 operating subsidiaries worldwide and operates in the US through Bayer Corporation. About 30% of the company's revenue is generated from the US.

Operations

Bayer operates in three reportable segments: Crop Science Pharmaceuticals and Consumer Health.

The Crop Science segment does business in seeds and plant traits crop protection digital solutions and customer services. Main products and brands include Adengo Asgrow BioAct Dekalb Fox Maxforce Seminis Climate FieldView and Deltapine.

Pharmaceuticals division includes development production and marketing of prescription products especially for cardiology and women's health; specialty therapeutics in the areas of oncology hematology ophthalmology and ? in the medium term ? cell and gene therapy; diagnostic imaging equipment and the necessary contrast agents. Among its products and brands are Adalat Betaferon Cipr Eylea Medrad Stellant Nexavar and Visanne.

The Consumer Health business includes development production and marketing of mainly nonprescription (over-the-counter) products in the dermatology nutritional supplements digestive health allergy cough and cold and pain and cardiovascular risk prevention categories. In addition to Alka-Seltzer Bepanthen and Canesten its main products and brands also include Elevit Iberogast Redoxon Supradyn and One A Day.

Geographic Reach

Bayer headquartered in Leverkusen Germany generates approximately 35% of sales from North America its largest geographical segment. It also generates significant revenue in Europe the Middle East and Africa (around 30%) and the Asia/Pacific region (roughly 20%). Latin America brings in nearly 15% of sales. The US is Bayer's single largest geography at around 30% of sales.

Most of Bayer's core manufacturing facilities are in Germany and the US. The company also has operations in the Americas Africa Asia Pacific and the Middle East. Overall Bayer comprises approximately 385 consolidated companies operating in about 85 countries around the world.

Sales and Marketing

Bayer's pharmaceuticals products are distributed primarily through wholesalers pharmacies and hospitals while Crop Science products are sold through wholesalers and retailers or directly to farmers and it markets pest and weed control products and services to professional users outside the agriculture industry. The Consumer Health division's well-known and established brands are sold through pharmacies and pharmacy chains supermarkets online retailers and other large and small retailers.

Financial Performance

Note: Growth rates may differ after conversion to US Dollars.

Sales of the Bayer Group came in level with the previous year in 2020 at ?41.4 billion a 5% decrease from the previous year's revenue of ?43.5 billion. Sales at Crop Science advanced by 1% (Fx & portfolio adj.) to ?18.8 billion. The company's businesses in Latin America and Asia / Pacific contributed to the increase while sales receded in North America.

In 2020 the company had a net loss of ?10.5 billion a 357% decrease from the previous year's net income of ?4.1 billion.

The company's cash at the end of 2020 was ?4.2 billion. Operating activities generated ?4.6 billion while investing activities used ?4.1 billion mainly for cash outflows for current financial assets as well as additions to property plant equipment and intangible assets. Financing activities provided another ?423 million.

Strategy

Bayer's strategy as a diversified life science company remains unchanged especially in the current situation with the systemic relevance and resilience of its businesses becoming particularly evident in the face of the global COVID-19 pandemic. At the same time the pandemic has accelerated a number of trends meaning that the company needs to execute its strategy and implement the transformation of its company at a faster pace.

Bayer focuses on four strategic levers to deliver attractive returns for shareholders while also making a positive contribution to society and the environment:

It develops innovative products and solutions and leverage cutting-edge research to address unmet societal challenges. As part of these endeavors the company is improving its access to innovation by collaborating with third parties. In addition it is working on disruptive technologies for example through its Leaps by Bayer activities while also continuing to drive the digitalization of the entire value chain.

Bayer drives the operational performance of its business by optimizing its resource allocation. Alongside its ongoing efficiency and structural measures the company has also launched a program to accelerate its transformation.

Sustainability is an integral part of Bayer's business strategy operations and compensation system. It makes a positive contribution to society and the environment. The company's ambitious targets for 2030 are fully in step with the United Nations' Sustainable Development Goals and the climate targets of the Paris Agreement.

As a global leader in health and nutrition Bayer continues to develop its business. The company creates value with strategy-based resource allocation focused on profitable growth. It is active in regulated and highly profitable sectors that are driven by innovation and in which we have the objective to grow ahead of the competition.

Mergers and Acquisitions

In late 2020 Bayer acquired Asklepios BioPharmaceutical (AskBio) a US-headquartered biopharmaceutical company specializing in the research development and manufacturing of gene therapies across different therapeutic areas. AskBio's development portfolio includes investigational pre-clinical and clinical stage candidates for the treatment of neuromuscular central nervous system cardiovascular and metabolic diseases. The acquisition fuels Bayer's cell and gene therapy platform with potential to bring urgently needed treatments to patients across multiple disease areas with high unmet need. Under the terms of the agreement Bayer will pay an upfront consideration of approximately $2 billion and potential success-based milestone payments of up to approximately $2 billion.

HISTORY

Friedrich Bayer founded Bayer in Germany in 1863 to make synthetic dyes. Research led to such discoveries as Antinonin (synthetic pesticide 1892) aspirin (1897) and synthetic rubber (1915).

Under Carl Duisberg Bayer allegedly made the first poison gas used by Germany in WWI. During the war the US seized Bayer's US operations and trademark rights and sold them to Sterling Drug.

In 1925 Bayer BASF Hoechst and other German chemical concerns merged to form I.G. Farben Trust. Their photography businesses combined as Agfa also joined the trust. Between wars Bayer developed polyurethanes and the first sulfa drug Prontosil (1935).

During WWII the trust took over chemical plants of Nazi-occupied countries used slave labor and helped make Zyklon B gas used to kill people at Auschwitz. At war's end Bayer lost its 50% of Winthrop Laboratories (US) and Bayer of Canada (to Sterling Drug). The 1945 Potsdam Agreement called for the breakup of I.G. Farben and Bayer AG emerged in 1951 as an independent company with many of its original operations including Agfa.

After rebuilding in West Germany Bayer AG and Monsanto formed a joint venture (Mobay 1954); Bayer AG later bought Monsanto's share (1967). In the 1960s the company offered more dyes plastics and polyurethanes and added factories worldwide. Agfa merged with Gevaert (photography Belgium) in 1964; Bayer AG retained 60%. Over the next 25 years it acquired Miles Labs (Alka-Seltzer US 1978) the rest of Agfa-Gevaert (1981) Compugraphic (electronic imaging US 1989) and Nova's Polysar (rubber Canada 1990).

Bayer AG integrated its US holdings under the name Miles in 1992 (renamed Bayer Corporation in 1995). The next year it introduced its first genetically engineered product Kogenate hemophilia treatment. It regained US rights to the Bayer brand and logo in 1994 by paying SmithKline Beecham $1 billion for the North American business of Sterling Winthrop.

EXECUTIVES

Chairman of the Supervisory Board, Norbert Winkeljohann, $415,883 total compensation
Chief Transformation and Talent Officer, Sarena Lin
CFO and Head, North America, Wolfgang Nickl, $906,966 total compensation
Chairman, CEO and Chief Sustainability Officer, Werner Baumann, $1,900,529 total compensation
President, Crop Science and Head, Latin America and Africa, Liam Condon, $1,094,969 total compensation
President, Consumer Health and Head, APAC, Heiko Schipper, $906,966 total compensation
Head, Pharmaceuticals and Head, Europe and Middle East, Stefan Oelrich, $967,355 total compensation
Auditors: Deloitte GmbH

LOCATIONS

HQ: Bayer AG
Kaiser-Wilhelm-Allee 1, Leverkusen 51368
Phone: (49) 214 30 1   **Fax:** (49) 214 30 71985
Web: www.bayer.com

2017 Sales

	% of total
Europe/Middle East/Africa	38
North America	29
Asia/Pacific	22
Latin America	11
Total	**100**

2017 Sales

	% of total
United States	24
Germany	10
China	7
Brazil	5
Other	54
Total	**100**

PRODUCTS/OPERATIONS

2017 Sales

	% of total
Pharmaceuticals	50
Crop Science	28
Consumer Health	17
Animal Health	5
Total	**100**

Selected Operations and Products

HealthCare
Animal health products
Diabetes care products
Consumer care products (over-the-counter drugs)
Pharmaceuticals
CropScience
BioScience (biotechnology and seeds)
Crop protection (insecticides and herbicides)
Environmental science (lawn care and non-agricultural pesticides)

Selected Brands

HealthCare
Adalat (cardiovascular medication)
Advantage (animal health)
Aleve/Flanax (analgesic)
Alka-Seltzer (analgesic and antacid)
Aspirin (analgesic)
Aspirin Cardio (cardiovascular)
Avalox/Avelox (antibiotic)
Bepanthen/Bepanthol (skin care treatment)
Betaferon/Betaseron (multiple sclerosis medication)
Baytril (animal health infections)
Breeze/Contour (diabetes care glucose meters)
Canesten (antifungal)
Cipro/Ciprobay (antibiotic)
Glucobay (diabetes treatment)
Iopamiron (diagnostic imaging)
Kogenate (hematology/cardiology)
Levitra (impotence drug)
Magnevist (diagnostic imaging)
Mirena (contraceptive)
Nexavar (oncology)
One-A-Day (vitamins)
Supradyn (multivitamin)
Ultravist (diagnostic imaging)
Yasmin/Yasminelle/YAZ (contraceptive)
CropScience
Confidor/Gaucho/Admire/Merit (insecticides/seed treatment)
Flint/Stratego/Sphere/Nativo (fungicides)
Poncho (seed treatment)
Ficam/Maxforce/Esplanade/K-Othrine (Environmental Science)

COMPETITORS

ALLERGAN LIMITED
Apotex Inc
BAYER CORPORATION
BRISTOL-MYERS SQUIBB COMPANY
Bausch Health Companies Inc
CIPLA LIMITED
DECHRA PHARMACEUTICALS PLC
DR.REDDY'S LABORATORIES LIMITED
EISAI CO. LTD.
HIKMA PHARMACEUTICALS PUBLIC LIMITED
 COMPANY
MERCK & CO. INC.
Roche Holding AG
SUMITOMO DAINIPPON PHARMA CO. LTD.
TEVA PHARMACEUTICAL INDUSTRIES LIMITED

HISTORICAL FINANCIALS

Company Type: Public

Income Statement

FYE: December 31

	REVENUE ($ mil.)	NET INCOME ($ mil.)	NET PROFIT MARGIN	EMPLOYEES
12/20	50,809	(12,880)	—	101,459
12/19	48,890	4,593	9.4%	107,435
12/18	45,333	1,941	4.3%	110,838
12/17	41,974	8,794	21.0%	99,762
12/16	49,382	4,784	9.7%	115,688
Annual Growth	0.7%	—	—	(3.2%)

2020 Year-End Financials

Debt ratio: 42.3%
Return on equity: (-26.8%)
Cash ($ mil.): 5,143
Current ratio: 0.97
Long-term debt ($ mil.): 39,084

No. of shares (mil.): 982
Dividends
 Yield: 3.5%
 Payout: —
Market value ($ mil.): 14,579

	STOCK PRICE ($) FY Close	P/E High/Low	PER SHARE ($) Earnings	Dividends	Book Value
12/20	14.84	— —	(13.11)	0.53	38.13
12/19	20.28	5 4	4.68	1.51	54.10
12/18	17.57	18 10	2.06	0.96	56.46
12/17	31.09	18 4	10.08	0.59	53.35
12/16	104.28	22 17	5.74	0.49	38.73
Annual Growth	(38.6%)	— —	—	2.1%	(0.4%)

Bayerische Motoren Werke AG

Bayerische Motoren Werke better known as BMW is the leading automaker in the premium segment worldwide. It manufactures and sells around 2.5 million premium-brand cars and off-road vehicles each year under the BMW MINI and Rolls-Royce names. Spare parts and accessories are also offered. Its vehicles and products are sold worldwide through company branches independent dealers subsidiaries and importers. In addition the company also offers car leasing and credit financing for both retail and corporate fleet customers as well as dealer financing and insurance. BMW also makes motorcycles. BMW generates majority of sales internationally.

Operations

The BMW Group comprises three main segments: Automotive Motorcycles and Financial Services. An "Other Entities" segment consists of holding companies and group financing companies.

The Automotive segment contributes about 70% of total group revenue and sells BMW-branded cars MINI-branded cars and the 100-year-old luxury Rolls-Royce line. Motorcycles (less than 5%% of sales) are geared toward premium markets with models in the sport tour roadster heritage adventure and urban mobility categories.

Financial Services which account for over 25%of sales offers financing and leasing to retail customers through nearly 60 entities as well as through co-operation agreements with local financial services providers and importers.

Geographic Reach

Based in Munich Germany BMW operates 30-plus production and assembly plants in about 15 countries and racks up sales in more than 110 countries. The company also operates almost 45 dedicated sales subsidiaries and financial services locations and nearly 15 R&D centers worldwide.

BMW's cars are popular worldwide pulling in billions in sales from Europe North America Asia and other major markets. It generates nearly 45% of its revenue in Europe and over 30% in Asia (primarily in China). The US contributes almost 25% of revenue. The MINI brand is particularly popular in its spiritual home of the UK where the majority of MINIs are manufactured.

Sales and Marketing

BMW sells around 2.5 million cars for fiscal year 2020. Its sales network comprises around 3500 BMW 1600 MINI and some 150 Rolls-Royce dealerships. In Germany cars are sold through BMW branches and independent dealerships. Outside Germany vehicles are distributed through subsidiaries and independent importers. Motorcycles are sold by more than 1200 dealerships and importers in over 90 countries.

Financial Performance

Note: Growth rates may differ after conversion to US Dollars.

The company's revenue has fluctuated over the last five years. Net income has grown towards 2017 but recorded a decline the following year until the most recent fiscal year in 2020.

The company's revenue decreased by 5% to ?99 billion compared to ?104.2 billion in the prior year. The decline was primarily due to the decrease on sales in their automotive and motorcycles division.

Net income fell 23% to ?3.9 billion due to higher cost of sales and other operating expenses.

BMW's cash position improved during 2020 ending the year ?1.5 billion higher at ?13.5 billion representing a healthy level of cash reserves. Its operating activities produced ?13.3 billion while its financing and investing activities used ?8.3 billion and ?3.6 billion respectively.

Strategy

The BMW Group's strategy comprises four key elements which are summarized in a strategy arrow that points towards the future. These four elements are position direction strategic approach and collaboration.

Individual mobility as the BMW Group understands it is inextricably linked with conserving the world's natural resources. The BMW Group bases its contribution to the sustainable development of its planet on scientifically derived criteria. With this principle in mind it combines ecological and social aspects with securing its long-term future in all its activities.

Sustainability is intrinsic to the BMW Group's strategic orientation. At the end of July 2020 the Board of Management of BMW AG announced the first details of this strategy and presented targets to which the enterprise will remain committed for the period up to 2030. By 2030 the carbon emissions generated by BMW Group vehicles are to be reduced by more than 40% per kilometre driven. The BMW Group has been working successfully for many years to reduce the level of carbon emissions of its new vehicle fleet worldwide.

HISTORY

BMW's logo speaks to its origin: a propeller in blue and white the colors of Bavaria. In 1913 Karl Rapp opened an aircraft-engine design shop near Munich. He named it Bayerische Motoren Werke (BMW) in 1917. The end of WWI brought German aircraft production to a halt and BMW shifted to making railway brakes until the 1930s. BMW debuted its first motorcycle the R32 in 1923 and the company began making automobiles in 1928 after buying small-car company Fahrzeugwerke Eisenach.

In 1933 BMW launched a line of larger cars. The company built aircraft engines for Hitler's Luftwaffe in the 1930s and stopped all auto and motorcycle production in 1941. BMW chief Josef Popp resisted and was ousted. Under the Nazis the company operated in occupied countries built rockets and developed the world's first production jet engine.

With its factories dismantled after WWII BMW survived by making kitchen and garden equipment. In 1948 it introduced a one-cylinder motorcycle which sold well as cheap transportation in postwar Germany. BMW autos in the 1950s were large and expensive and sold poorly. When motorcycle sales dropped the company escaped demise in the mid-1950s by launching the Isetta a seven-foot three-wheeled "bubble car."

In the 1970s BMW's European exports soared and the company set up a distribution subsidiary in the US. The company also produced larger cars that put BMW on par with Mercedes-Benz.

EXECUTIVES

Member of the Board of Management of BMW AG, Production, Milan Nedeljkovic, $911,524 total compensation
Member of the Board of Management of BMW AG, Human Resources, Labour Relations Director, Ilka Horstmeier, $911,524 total compensation
Chairman, Oliver Zipse, $2,050,930 total compensation
Member of the Board of Management of BMW AG, Finance, Nicolas Peter, $1,082,435 total compensation
Member of the Board of Management of BMW AG, Purchasing and Supplier Network, Andreas Wendt, $911,524 total compensation
Member of the Board of Management of BMW AG, Customer, Brands, Sales, Pieter Nota, $911,524 total compensation
Auditors: PricewaterhouseCoopers GmbH

LOCATIONS

HQ: Bayerische Motoren Werke AG
Aktiengesellschaft, Munich 80788
Phone: (49) 89 382 0   **Fax:** (49) 89 3895 5858
Web: www.bmwgroup.com

2018 Sales

	% of total
Europe	
Germany	14
Rest of Europe	32
Americas	
US	17
Rest of Americas	4
Asia	
China	19
Rest of Asia	11
Other Regions	3
Total	100

PRODUCTS/OPERATIONS

2018 Sales

	% of total
Automotive	74
Financial services	24
Motorcycles	2
Elimination	
Total	**100**

Selected Products

Automobiles
  BMW
  1 Series
  3 Series
  5 Series
  6 Series
  7 Series
  X3 X5 X6 sports utility vehicles
  M Models
  Z4
  MINI Electric
  MINI Cooper
  MIMI Hatch
  MIMI Clubman
  Rolls-Royce Phantom
  Rolls-Royce Wraith
  Rolls-Royce Dawn
Motorcycles
  BMW

COMPETITORS

ALLISON TRANSMISSION HOLDINGS INC.
Dongfeng Motor Group Company Limited
GENERAL MOTORS COMPANY
HONDA MOTOR CO. LTD.
Hyundai Motor Company
LCI INDUSTRIES
MANN+HUMMEL FILTRATION TECHNOLOGY
  INTERMEDIATE HOLDINGS
MOTORCAR PARTS OF AMERICA INC.
Magna International Inc
PEUGEOT SA
Rheinmetall AG
Robert Bosch Gesellschaft mit beschr onkter Haftung
TOYOTA BOSHOKU CORPORATION
VOLKSWAGEN AG

HISTORICAL FINANCIALS

Company Type: Public

Income Statement

FYE: December 31

	REVENUE ($ mil.)	NET INCOME ($ mil.)	NET PROFIT MARGIN	EMPLOYEES
12/20	121,489	4,633	3.8%	120,726
12/19	117,003	5,518	4.7%	133,778
12/18	111,633	8,150	7.3%	134,682
12/17	118,290	10,333	8.7%	129,932
12/16	99,425	7,246	7.3%	124,729
Annual Growth	5.1%	(10.6%)	—	(0.8%)

2020 Year-End Financials

Debt ratio: 37.5%
Return on equity: 6.2%
Cash ($ mil.): 16,613
Current ratio: 1.14
Long-term debt ($ mil.): 59,501

No. of shares (mil.): 602
Dividends
  Yield: 2.1%
  Payout: 10.2%
Market value ($ mil.): 17,669

	STOCK PRICE ($) FY Close	P/E High/Low		Earnings	PER SHARE ($) Dividends	Book Value
12/20	29.35	5	3	7.03	0.64	124.14
12/19	27.12	4	3	8.39	0.93	110.64
12/18	26.97	3	2	12.39	1.13	109.50
12/17	34.67	3	2	15.73	1.01	107.75
12/16	31.01	3	2	11.03	0.00	82.63
Annual Growth	(1.4%)	—	—	(10.7%)	—	10.7%

BAYWA Bayerische Warenvermittlung Landwirtschaftlicher Genossenschaften AG

BayWa develops leading projects and solutions for the basic human needs of food energy and building. The Germany commodities trader (pronounced bay-vah) deals in agricultural produce (grain and oilseed fertilizers feed seed fresh fruit production) agricultural equipment building materials (building components and equipment) renewable energy products and services (wind solar) and energy (gas heating oil lubricants mineral oils). BayWa's trades mainly in New Zealand Asia and South America but it has operations in over 45 countries in total including the US. The company was founded in 1923. Germany generates most of BayWa's sales.

Operations

BayWa operates three principal segments: Agriculture Energy and Building Materials.

The Agriculture segment generates about 65% of total sales and consists of four businesses: Agri Supply & Trade "BAST" (grain and oilseeds trading); Agricultural Trade & Services (grain and oilseed marketing); Global Produce (fresh fruit and vegetable trading); and Agricultural Equipment (buys and sells machinery equipment and systems for agriculture).

The Energy segment generates some 25% of annual sales and consists of a Conventional Energy (sale of oils fuels lubricants wood pellets) and Renewable Energies (development and project planning of wind solar and biomass systems). BayWa is one of Europe's largest renewable energy plant manufacturers and one of the top-ten solar developers worldwide.

Building Materials generates some 10% of sales and consists of building materials trading of the company.

BayWa also operates a nascent Innovation & Digitalization segment that employs technology to bring down costs for agricultural producers.

Overall more than 95% of sales were generated from the sales of goods.

Geographic Reach

Based in Munich Germany BayWa has operations in over 45 countries. Germany accounts for about 40% of total sales followed by Austria which gives in roughly 15% Netherlands generate about 10% of total sales and rest comes from other countries.

The company's Building Materials division trades materials in Germany and Austria. It operates about 130 locations in Germany and more than 30 in Austria.

Sales and Marketing

BayWa's customers include producers of starch and feedstuffs malt houses breweries and biofuel manufactures as well as agriculture and forestry local government and industrial customers.

The company's advertising costs were ?47.3 million and ?55.9 million in 2020 and 2019 respectively.

Financial Performance

The revenues of the BayWa Group rose by 1% or ?96.4 million to ?17.2 billion in the financial year 2020.

In 2020 the company had a gross profit of ?2.3 billion a 17% increase from the previous year's gross profit of ?2 billion.

The company's cash at the end of 2020 was ?168.4 million. Operating activities generated ?674.8 million while investing activities used ?274.8 million primarily for investments in intangible assets property plant and equipment and investment property. Financing activities used another ?458.2 million mainly for payments for financing loans.

Strategy

BayWa is taking two market-driven approaches regarding its further strategic development: ensuring business continuity by enhancing competitive strength as well as growth in new business areas by developing innovative customer-focused business models. The group's growth ambitions focus on Renewable Energies BAST and Global Produce business units.

The objective in the Energy segment is to further advance the global expansion of renewable energies. Another focus is on the scale continued internationalization and expanding the service business as well as on the provision of integrated energy solutions. Examples include the combination of installations for generating renewable energy with efficient energy storage systems as well as the cross-segment development of innovative products and services.

The Conventional Energy business unit continuously promotes the expansion of mobility solutions in the fields of charging infrastructure for e-mobility LNG filling stations and digital mobility. Furthermore BayWa also offers e-mobility solutions created based on comprehensive fleet analysis and targeted at fleet operators.

In the Agriculture segment BayWa aims to deepen existing customer ties and attract new customers by seizing opportunities to export to international markets expanding agricultural products range through the addition of specialties.

HISTORY

BayWa was founded in 1923 when the Bavarian Trading Company separated from the Bavarian Savings & Loan Bank amid the hyperinflation that swept Germany in the 1920s.

Despite the economic turmoil of the 1920s and 1930s the co-operative established itself helping Bavarian farmers cope with rampant inflation. During WWII and thereafter BayWa helped stabilize the Bavarian economy by catering to the agricultural sector.

As part of Germany's postwar economic miracle BayWa innovated in tractor and combine manufacturing. The company also diversified into construction materials the house and garden markets and mineral oils.

In the 1970s BayWa opened its first retail stores followed by gas stations and heating oil depots. In 1972 the original name of Bayerischewarenhandelsgesellschaft was shortened to BayWa.

After German reunification in 1990 BayWa expanded in the East. Former East German companies looked for partners willing to transfer technology.

Spurred by regional and international competition in the 1990s BayWa expanded abroad starting in neighboring Austria.

EXECUTIVES

Member of the Supervisory Board, Joachim Rukwied
Vice Chairman of the Supervisory Board, Klaus Buchleitner

Member of the Management Board, Chief Financial Officer, Andreas Helber, $1,907,023 total compensation
Member of the Supervisory Board, Wilhelm Oberhofer
Member of the Supervisory Board, Wolfgang Altmueller
Member of the Supervisory Board, Monika Hohlmeier
Chairman of the Supervisory Board, Manfred Nuessel
Member of the Supervisory Board, Michael Kuffner
Member of the Management Board, Marcus Pollinger, $899,674 total compensation
Member of the Supervisory Board, Andrea Busch
Member of the Supervisory Board, Johann Lang
Vice Chairman of the Supervisory Board, Werner Waschbichler
Chairman of the Management Board, Chief Executive Officer, Klaus Lutz, $5,031,957 total compensation
Member of the Management Board, Reinhard Wolf, $1,373,326 total compensation
Member of the Management Board, Matthias Taft, $1,845,039 total compensation
Member of the Supervisory Board, Renate Glashauser
Member of the Supervisory Board, Monique Surges
Member of the Supervisory Board, Theo Bergmann
Auditors: Deloitte GmbH Wirtschaftspruefungsgesellschaft

LOCATIONS

HQ: BAYWA Bayerische Warenvermittlung Landwirtschaftlicher Genossenschaften AG Arabellastrasse 4, Munich D-81925
Phone: (49) 89 9222 3887   **Fax:** (49) 89 9212 3887
Web: www.baywa.de

Sales 2018

	%
Germany	43
Austria	14
Netherlands	10
Other International	33
Total	**100**

PRODUCTS/OPERATIONS

2018 Sales

	% of total
Agriculture	66
Energy	24
Building materials	10
Innovation & Digitalisation	-
Other activities	-
Total	**100**

COMPETITORS

ASSYSTEM	GOODWIN PLC
Andritz AG	Grupo Carso S.A.B. de
BODYCOTE PLC	C.V.
Brenntag Holding GmbH	MARUBENI CORPORATION
CNIM GROUPE	REPSOL SA.
ENERPAC TOOL GROUP	RUBIS
CORP.	TECNICAS REUNIDAS SA
GENERAC HOLDINGS INC.	Uniper SE
GENUIT GROUP PLC	

HISTORICAL FINANCIALS

Company Type: Public

Income Statement

FYE: December 31

	REVENUE ($ mil.)	NET INCOME ($ mil.)	NET PROFIT MARGIN	EMPLOYEES
12/20	21,265	44	0.2%	21,207
12/19	19,419	41	0.2%	19,193
12/18	19,300	36	0.2%	17,864
12/17	19,134	47	0.2%	17,323
12/16	16,349	32	0.2%	16,711
Annual Growth	**6.8%**	**8.1%**	**—**	**6.1%**

2020 Year-End Financials

Debt ratio: 45.4%
Return on equity: 3.7%
Cash ($ mil.): 206
Current ratio: 1.12
Long-term debt ($ mil.): 1,388

No. of shares (mil.): 35
Dividends
  Yield: —
  Payout: 147.0%
Market value ($ mil.): —

BBMG Corp

EXECUTIVES

General Manager, Executive Director, Yingwu Jiang
Deputy General Manager, Wenyan Liu
Deputy General Manager, Staff Elected Director, Zhaojia Wang
Deputy General Manager, Changlu Jiang
Independent Director, Weifeng Wei
Executive Director, Secretary of the Board, Baojin Zheng
Deputy General Manager, Zhiqiang An
Executive Director, Dong Wu
Auditors: Ernst & Young Hua Ming LLP

LOCATIONS

HQ: BBMG Corp
Tower D, Global Trade Center, No. 36, North Third Ring East Road, Dongcheng District, Beijing 100013
Phone: (86) 10 66411587   **Fax:** (86) 10 66412086
Web: www.bbmg.com.cn

HISTORICAL FINANCIALS

Company Type: Public

Income Statement

FYE: December 31

	REVENUE ($ mil.)	NET INCOME ($ mil.)	NET PROFIT MARGIN	EMPLOYEES
12/20	16,513	434	2.6%	0
12/19	13,197	530	4.0%	0
12/18	12,083	474	3.9%	0
12/17	9,785	435	4.5%	0
12/16	6,874	386	5.6%	49,721
Annual Growth	**24.5%**	**3.0%**	**—**	**—**

2020 Year-End Financials

Debt ratio: 6.0%
Return on equity: 4.5%
Cash ($ mil.): 4,379
Current ratio: 1.54
Long-term debt ($ mil.): 10,603

No. of shares (mil.): —
Dividends
  Yield: —
  Payout: —
Market value ($ mil.): —

BCE Inc

BCE is Canada's largest provider of telecommunications services. The company (formerly Bell Canada Enterprises) owns Bell Canada the incumbent provider of long-distance and local telephone access in Ontario and Quebec as well as the Atlantic provinces with more than 33 million subscribers. It also provides broadband internet access to about 3.9 million subscribers and TV subscriptions to more than 2.9 million viewers. BCE's mobile holdings include wireless carrier Bell Mobility and subsidiary Virgin Mobile Canada. The company's brands include Bell Fibe (internet protocol TV) AlarmForce (home security) TSN (sports network) and CraveTV.

Operations

Bell Wireline which generates more than half of BCE's sales provides data internet access TV and local and long distance telephone as well as well as other communications services and products. It serves Bell's residential small and medium-sized business and enterprise customers in Ontario's and Quebec's metro areas.

Bell Wireless accounts for more than a third of BCE's revenue with wireless voice and data communication products and services to Bell's residential small and medium-sized business and large enterprise customers across Canada.

Bell Media brings in about an eighth of BCE's revenue. The segment encompasses 30 conventional TV stations; 30 specialty TV channels including TSN Space Discovery and RDS; four national pay-TV services including The Movie Network (TMN); and more than 100 licensed radio stations in 54 markets across Canada. The unit also offers out-of-home advertising with billboards and digital formats.

Geographic Reach

BCE provides local access network in Ontario Quebec the Atlantic provinces and Manitoba as well as in Canada's Northern Territories.

The company's broadband fiber network consists of fiber-to-the-node (FTTN) and fiber-to-the-premise (FTTP) locations covers 9.5 million homes and businesses in Ontario Quebec the Atlantic provinces and Manitoba.

Sales and Marketing

BCE has an extensive retail network with more than 2360 retail locations across Canada including 1360 Bell-branded stores and The Source stores and Glentel-operated stores. It also sells through third-party dealers and retailers.

Financial Performance

(Figures are in Canadian dollars and might differ from other sources due to exchange rates).

BCE's revenue has risen for seven years in a row reaching a company high in 2018.

The company's sales hit $23.4 billion in 2018 a 3% increase from 2017 driven by BCE revenues increased by 3.1% in 2018 compared to last year driven by growth in its three segments. Service revenue rose about 2% and product revenue was about 14% higher in 2018 compared to 2017. The MTS acquisition also contributed to the revenue gain.

BCE's earnings dipped 2.5% to $2.9 billion due to higher expenses including impairment charges of $200 million related to the Bell Media segment higher depreciation and amortization expense and higher finance costs.

The company's coffers held $3.3 billion in cash and equivalents in 2018 compared to $4.8 billion in 2017. In 2018 BCE had $5.7 billion generated from operations while investing and financing activities used $3.4 billion and $2.5 billion respectively.

Strategy

Just because BCE is the biggest telecom company in Canada doesn't mean it can't get bigger. In 2018 the company began new services to attract new customers and hold on to current customers.

In phone service BCE rolled out a prepaid wireless service called Lucky. The company said the service should keep its postpaid customers who want to change to a prepaid plan. Lucky's rate plan of $20 give BCE a service to pitch to price-conscious consumers. The plan helped drive 480000 net wireless subscribers a 44% increase year-to-year.

Also in 2018 BCE started an over-the-top (OTT) service that offers premium channels from the US that include HBO Showtime Starz and Hulu to help it to keep cord-cutters as customers and attract non-pay-TV subscribers. Additionally BCE started an OTT version of its TSN sports network.

BCE expanded its wireless capabilities setting the goal of it wireless-to-the-home program to reach 1.2 million homes up from 800000 homes. The increase was driven by a Canadian government program which allows for an acceleration of the company's capital cost allowance.

The company continues to lose customers of its traditional residential lines. The number of subscribers fell to 2.9 million in 2018 from 3.2 million in 2017 a 7.5% decrease.

Mergers and Acquisitions

In 2018 BCE acquired Axia NetMedia Corp. the Calgary-based operator of SuperNet. The broadband network in Alberta provides service to provincial and municipal offices Indigenous communities schools libraries healthcare institutions businesses and internet service providers.

In 2018 BCE bought AlarmForce Industries the second biggest home security company in Canada for $166 million. The deal positions BCE in the smart home automation market and extends its reach deeper into the home.

BCE acquired Manitoba Telecom Services (MTS) for $3.1 billion) in 2017. The deal expanded BCE's operations in the west of Canada adding around 490000 Manitoba Telecom subscribers. BCE intends to invest in building out wireless and internet networks in Manitoba.

Company Background

Alexander Graham Bell experimented with the telephone in his native Canada before moving to the US in the mid-1870s. His father sold his Canadian patent rights to National Bell Telephone which combined with Canada's Hamilton District Telegraph to form Bell Telephone Company of Canada. Known as Bell Canada it received a charter in 1880 and settled in Montreal. By 1882 it had 40 exchanges. AT&T owned 48% of the company in 1890 but by 1925 Canadians owned 95% of Bell Canada. (AT&T severed all ties in 1975.)

HISTORY

Alexander Graham Bell experimented with the telephone in his native Canada before moving to the US in the mid-1870s. His father sold his Canadian patent rights to National Bell Telephone which combined with Canada's Hamilton District Telegraph to form Bell Telephone Company of Canada. Known as Bell Canada it received a charter in 1880 and settled in Montreal. By 1882 it had 40 exchanges. AT&T owned 48% of the company in 1890 but by 1925 Canadians owned 95% of Bell Canada. (AT&T severed all ties in 1975.)

EXECUTIVES

President, Bell Media and Vice Chair, BCE and Bell, Wade Oosterman, $671,208 total compensation

Group President, Bell Mobility, Bell Residential and Small Business, Blaik Kirby, $559,340 total compensation

Independent Director, Sheila Murray

President, Bell Business Markets, Thomas Little, $521,671 total compensation

Group President, Customer Experience, John Watson, $559,340 total compensation

Independent Director, Robert Simmonds

President and CEO, BCE and Bell Canada, Mirko Bibic, $969,523 total compensation

Independent Director, David Denison

EVP, Corporate Services and CHRO, Bernard le Duc

Independent Director, Ian Greenberg

Chief Financial Officer and Vice Chair, Atlantic Canada, Glen LeBlanc, $503,406 total compensation

President, Bell Residential and Small Business, Rizwan Jamal

Independent Director, Monique Leroux

Independent Director, Calin Rovinescu

President, Bell Mobility, Claire Gillies

Senior Vice-President, Content Development and News and Vice Chair, Quebec Bell Canada, Karine Moses

Independent Director, Jennifer Tory

Independent Director, Cornell Wright

Independent Director, Louis Pagnutti

Executive Vice-President, Chief Technology Officer, Bell Canada, Stephen Howe, $489,716 total compensation

Independent Director, Robert Dexter

Chair of the Board BCE Inc. and Bell Canada, Gordon Nixon

Chief Information Officer, Michael Cole

Independent Director, Karen Sheriff

Auditors: Deloitte LLP

LOCATIONS

HQ: BCE Inc
1, Carrefour Alexander-Graham-Bell, Building A, 7th Floor, Verdun, Quebec H3E 3B3
Phone: 514 786-8424   **Fax:** 514 766-8161
Web: www.bce.ca

PRODUCTS/OPERATIONS

2018 Sales

	% of total
Bell Wireline	52
Bell Wireless	35
Bell Media	13
Total	**100**

2018 Sales

	% of total
Services:	
Data	32
Wireless	27
Voice	14
Media	11
Other services	1
Products:	
Wireless	9
Data	2
Wireless	2
Total	**100**

COMPETITORS

1&1 AG	SPRINT CORPORATION
AT&T INC.	Swisscom AG
CHARTER COMMUNICATIONS INC.	TELECOM ITALIA SPA
MTS PAO	TELUS Corporation
SBA COMMUNICATIONS CORPORATION	VODAFONE GROUP PUBLIC LIMITED COMPANY

HISTORICAL FINANCIALS

Company Type: Public

Income Statement

	REVENUE ($ mil.)	NET INCOME ($ mil.)	NET PROFIT MARGIN	EMPLOYEES
12/20	17,972	1,961	10.9%	50,704
12/19	18,402	2,334	12.7%	52,100
12/18	17,233	2,045	11.9%	52,790
12/17	18,122	2,222	12.3%	51,679
12/16	16,116	2,147	13.3%	48,090
Annual Growth	**2.8%**	**(2.2%)**	**—**	**1.3%**

FYE: December 31

2020 Year-End Financials

Debt ratio: 34.0%
Return on equity: 11.8%
Cash ($ mil.): 175
Current ratio: 0.69
Long-term debt ($ mil.): 18,775

No. of shares (mil.): 904
Dividends
  Yield: 5.8%
  Payout: 120.6%
Market value ($ mil.): 38,709

	STOCK PRICE ($) FY Close	P/E High/Low	PER SHARE ($) Earnings	Dividends	Book Value
12/20	42.80	19 13	2.17	2.50	18.23
12/19	46.35	15 12	2.59	2.39	17.90
12/18	39.53	14 12	2.28	2.31	16.65
12/17	48.01	16 15	2.48	2.29	16.96
12/16	43.24	14 12	2.47	2.03	14.95
Annual Growth	**(0.3%)**	**— —**	**(3.2%)**	**5.4%**	**5.1%**

BDO Unibank Inc.

BDO could stand for "Big Darn Operation" but instead it's short for Banco de Oro Unibank the latest iteration of a merger that took place in 2007 between two Filipino entities Banco de Oro Universal Bank and Equitable PCI Bank. Since 1968 Banco de Oro has provided corporate commercial retail and investment banking services throughout the country. Established in 1938 Equitable PCI brings to the coupling its commercial banking small and middle market lending trust leasing and remittances expertise. Combined BDO operates a network of more than 680 branches and some 1200 ATMs in Metro Manila as well as the Luzon Mindanao and Visayas provinces.

EXECUTIVES

Executive Vice President, Treasurer, Dalmacio Martin

President, Chief Executive Officer, Executive Director, Nestor Tan, $53,578 total compensation

Executive Vice Chairman of the Board, Jesus Jacinto, $53,578 total compensation

Executive Vice President, Julie Chua

Senior Executive Vice President, Head - Branch Banking Group, Jaime Yu

Executive Vice President, Chief Risk Officer, Head - Risk Management Group, Evelyn Villanueva

Senior Vice President - Information Technology Group, Alexander Francis Deato

Senior Vice President - Internal Audit, Carol Warner

Executive Vice President, Comptroller, Lucy Dy

Independent Director, Vipul Bhagat

Non-Executive Director, Christopher Bell-Knight, $111,677 total compensation

Executive Vice President, Stella Cabalatungan

Non-Executive Director, Josefina Tan, $53,578 total compensation

Corporate Secretary, Edmundo Tan
Executive Vice President, Jeanette Javellana
Senior Executive Vice President, Head -
 Institutional Banking Group, Walter Wassmer
Assistant Corporate Secretary, Sabino Acut
Independent Director, Dioscoro Ramos, $109,663
 total compensation
Senior Vice President, Montiel Delos Santos
Senior Credit Executive, Nilo Pacheco
Senior Vice President, Andre Flores
Senior Vice President, Carlo Nazareno
Executive Vice President, Deputy Head of
 Institutional Banking Group, Cecilia Luz Tan
Senior Vice President, Sharon Mae Vicente
Senior Vice President, Jose Eduardo Quimpo
Senior Vice President, Gerardo Clemente Rivera
Non-Executive Chairperson of the Board, Teresita
 Sy, $204,645 total compensation
Senior Executive Vice President and Head of
 Central Operations Group, Joseph Gotuaco
Independent Director, George Barcelon, $106,865
 total compensation
Independent Director, Vicente Perez, $110,446
 total compensation
Senior Vice President, Gina Marie Galita
Senior Vice President, Head – Information
 Technology Group, Frederic Mark Gomez
Senior Vice President, Paul John Siy
Lead Independent Director, Jones Castro, $113,468
 total compensation
Independent Director, Jose Buenaventura,
 $111,453 total compensation
Senior Vice President, Frederico Rafael Ocampo
Senior Vice President, Richard Grau
Senior Vice President, Jonathan Go
Senior Vice President, Angelita Manulat
Senior Vice President, Edwin Tajanlangit
Senior Vice President and Region Head of Branch
 Banking Group/Region 1 - Northern Luzon, Ma.
 Theresa Simbul
Executive Vice President, Maria Corazon Mallillin
Senior Vice President, BDO Unibank Inc, Lazaro
 Jerome Guevarra
Senior Vice President, Belinda Fernandez
Senior Executive Vice President, Head -
 Consumer Lending Group, Rolando Tanchanco
Senior Vice President, Melanie Belen
Senior Vice President, Roberto Santos
Senior Vice President, Jose Alfredo Pascual
Head, Legal Services Group and Assistant
 Corporate Secretary, Alvin Go
Executive Vice President, Albert Yeo
Senior Vice President, Dante Tinga
Senior Vice President, Noel Sugay
Senior Vice President, Maria Rhoda Orsolino
Senior Vice President, Jaime Nasol
Senior Vice President, Maria Nannette Regala
Senior Vice President, Maria Carina Antonio
Senior Vice President, Head - Human Resources
 Group, Evelyn Salagubang
Senior Vice President, Sonia Maribel Go
Executive Vice President, Head - Investor
 Relations and Corporate Planning Group, Luis
 Reyes
Senior Vice President, Tomas Mendoza
Senior Vice President, Geneva Gloria
Senior Vice President, Deputy Treasurer, Marilyn
 Go
Executive Vice President, Gerard Lee Co
Senior Vice President and Officer-in-Charge, to
 BDO Finance Corporation, BDO Leasing and
 Finance, Inc. and BDO Rental, Inc., Manuel
 Locsin
Executive Vice President, President/Director -
 BDO Capital and Investment Corporation,
 Eduardo Francisco
Senior Vice President, Romeo Co
Senior Vice President, Rogel Raya
Senior Vice President, Aurea Imelda Montejo
Senior Vice President, Myla Untalan

Senior Credit Executives, Member of the
 Executive Committee and Management Credit
 Committee, Edmundo Soriano
Senior Vice President, General Manager - BDO
 Insurance Brokers, Inc., Maria Theresa Tan
Senior Vice President, Susan Audrey Rivera
Senior Vice President, Ramon David
Senior Vice President, Gabriel Lim
Senior Vice President, Manuel Patricio Malabanan
Senior Vice President, Reynaldo Tanjangco
Senior Vice President, Enrico Hernandez
Senior Credit Executive, Mario Palou
Senior Vice President, Chief Compliance Officer,
 Federico Tancongco
Senior Vice President, Trust Officer, Rafael Ayuste
President and Chief Executive Officer & Director
 of BDO Life Assurance Company, Inc., Renato
 Vergel de Dios
Senior Vice President, Ferdinand Bacungan
Senior Vice President, Gwyneth Entao
Senior Vice President, Cristina Ngo
Senior Vice President, Jonathan Cua
Executive Vice President, Group Head for the
 Transaction Banking Group, Edwin Romualdo
 Reyes
Senior Vice President, Ramon Militar
Senior Vice President, Roy Allan Magturo
Senior Vice President, Chief Internal Auditor,
 Estrellita Ong
Senior Vice President, Noel Andrada
Executive Vice President, President/Director of
 One Network Bank, Inc. (A Rural Bank of BDO),
 Jesus Itchon
Auditors: Punongbayan & Araullo

LOCATIONS

HQ: BDO Unibank Inc.
 BDO Corporate Center, 7899 Makati Avenue, Makati
 City 0726
Phone: (63) 2 840 7000
Web: www.bdo.com.ph

COMPETITORS

ARAB BANK PLC
BANCO BILBAO VIZCAYA ARGENTARIA SOCIEDAD
 ANONIMA
BANCO POPULAR ESPA 'OL SA (EXTINGUIDA)
BANK OF AYUDHYA PUBLIC COMPANY LIMITED
FUNDACION CAJA MEDITERRANEO
HANG SENG BANK LIMITED
ITAU UNIBANCO HOLDING SA
QNB FINANSBANK ANONIM SIRKETI

HISTORICAL FINANCIALS
Company Type: Public

Income Statement				FYE: December 31
	ASSETS ($ mil.)	NET INCOME ($ mil.)	INCOME AS % OF ASSETS	EMPLOYEES
12/20	70,243	587	0.8%	38,756
12/19	62,975	872	1.4%	38,510
12/18	57,545	622	1.1%	36,387
12/17	53,560	563	1.1%	33,747
12/16	46,956	526	1.1%	31,443
Annual Growth	10.6%	2.8%	—	5.4%

2020 Year-End Financials

Return on assets: 0.8%
Return on equity: 7.4%
Long-term debt ($ mil.): —
No. of shares (mil.): —
Sales ($ mil): 4,417
Dividends
 Yield: 0.6%
 Payout: 106.6%
Market value ($ mil.): —

	STOCK PRICE ($)	P/E		PER SHARE ($)		
	FY Close	High/Low		Earnings	Dividends	Book Value
12/20	22.24	5	3	0.13	0.14	1.86
12/19	32.08	3	2	0.20	0.13	1.66
12/18	25.32	4	3	0.14	0.13	1.43
12/17	31.78	5	4	0.13	0.13	1.37
12/16	20.33	3	3	0.14	0.14	1.20
Annual Growth	2.3%	—	—	(1.8%)	(0.1%)	11.6%

Beijing Shougang Co Ltd

EXECUTIVES

Independent Director, Wenxian Gu
Auditors: Grant Thornton

LOCATIONS

HQ: Beijing Shougang Co Ltd
 No. 99, Shijingshan Road, Beijing 100041
Phone: (86) 10 88293727   Fax: (86) 10 68873028
Web: www.sggf.com.cn

HISTORICAL FINANCIALS
Company Type: Public

Income Statement				FYE: December 31
	REVENUE ($ mil.)	NET INCOME ($ mil.)	NET PROFIT MARGIN	EMPLOYEES
12/20	12,224	273	2.2%	0
12/19	9,938	179	1.8%	0
12/18	9,562	349	3.7%	0
12/17	9,258	339	3.7%	0
12/16	0	0	—	0
Annual Growth	—	—	—	—

2020 Year-End Financials

Debt ratio: 6.1%
Return on equity: 6.3%
Cash ($ mil.): 962
Current ratio: 0.39
Long-term debt ($ mil.): 3,537
No. of shares (mil.): —
Dividends
 Yield: —
 Payout: —
Market value ($ mil.): —

BHP Group Ltd

BHP Group (formerly BHP Billiton) mines copper and iron ore by the ton. The UK half of dual-listed Anglo-Australian BHP is among the world's biggest mining companies (BHP Billiton Limited is Australia-listed). Beyond iron ore its activities include exploration and development of untapped resources extraction and electrowinning processing of commodities as well as rehabilitation and closure of operational sites primarily in Australia and the Americas. BHP has significant annual productions of iron ore (about 250 Mt) petroleum (some 110 MMBoe) coal (around 40 Mt) and copper (about 1724 Kt). The company's largest market is China with over 60% of total sales.

Operations

BHP has four reportable segments? Iron Ore (about 50% of sales) Copper (some 25%) Coal (around 15%) and Petroleum (nearly 10% The Iron Ore segment's principal activity is mining of iron ore. The Copper segment includes mining of copper silver zinc molybdenum uranium and gold. The Coal segment's principal activity is mining of metallurgical coal and energy coal. The Petroleum segment includes exploration development and production of oil and gas.

Geographic Reach

Headquartered in London BHP has presence in Chile Peru Brazil Colombia and Canada the US Australia Trinidad and Tobago the UK and Algeria. China is the company's largest market with over 60% of total sales followed by Japan with about 10%.

In Australia its operated mineral assets include Western Australia Iron Ore Queensland Coal (BMA and BMC) New South Wales Energy Coal Olympic Dam and Nickel West. Olympic Dam is one of the world's largest ore bodies. In the Americas its operated mineral assets are comprised of Escondida Pampa Norte and Jansen along with non-operated assets Antamina Cerrej "n and Samarco. BHP also has petroleum operated assets like Shenzi Angostura Pyrenees and Macedon. Additionally it has non-operated assets of Atlantis Mad Dog Bass Strait and North West Shelf.

Sales and Marketing

The company has over 9000 suppliers around the world.

Financial Performance

BHP's revenue (year ended June 2020) decreased 3% to $42.9 billion in 2020. This decrease was primarily attributable to lower average realized prices for coal petroleum and copper and lower volumes due to natural field decline at Petroleum and lower grade at Escondida and Spence combined with planned maintenance across a number of its assets. This was partially offset by higher average realized prices for iron ore record production at WAIO record average concentrator throughput at Escondida and improved operational stability.

Profit of the company for the year was $8 billion lower by 4% compared to profit the year prior. Lower revenue and high expenses contributed to the decrease in profit.

Cash and cash equivalents at end of the year were $13.4 billion. Operations provided $15.7 billion in 2020 while investing activities used $7.6 billion and financing activities used another $9.8 billion. The main cash uses for the year were for purchases of property and equipment and dividends payment.

Strategy

BHP's strategy is to have the best capabilities best commodities and best assets to create long-term value and high returns. Its strategy is underpinned by its disciplined approach to capital allocation and risk management and its overriding commitment to generating social value for its stakeholders. Social value is at the core of its approach and purpose ? to bring people and resources together to build a better world. It underpins its decisions and actions from the positive contribution it makes to the environment and society to support the needs of its workforce partners customers economies and communities. The longevity of BHP's assets means it must think and plan in decades. The long-term health of its business is dependent on the long-term health of its society and a sustainable natural environment.

As it looks to the future BHP and its products will play an essential role as the world's population continues to grow improved living standards are pursued and momentum towards decarbonization increases.

It has secured and will continue to grow options in copper and nickel where increasing demand and its capability gives it competitive opportunities. It is moving to concentrate its coal portfolio on higher-quality coking coals with greatest potential upside for quality premiums as steelmakers seek to improve blast furnace utilization and reduce emissions intensity and will pursue options to divest its interests in BMC New South Wales Energy Coal (NSWEC) and Cerrej n. In oil and gas it will continue to invest in opportunities that are resilient under a range of price scenarios and which are aligned to its strengths. It will seek to divest oil and gas assets that are mature or which are likely to realize greater value under different ownership. This approach to actively managing its portfolio for value risk and returns over multiple time horizons will yield superior returns for its investors and greater value for its partners and communities.

Mergers and Acquisitions

In late 2020 BHP has completed the transaction to acquire an additional 28% working interest in Shenzi a six-lease development in the deepwater Gulf of Mexico from Hess Corporation (Hess) for US$505 million. The transaction brings BHP's working interest to 72% and adds approximately 11000 barrels of oil equivalent per day of production (90% oil).

In mid-2020 BHP has agreed to acquire the Honeymoon Well Nickel Project comprising the Honeymoon Well development project and a 50% interest in the Albion Downs North and Jericho exploration joint ventures from MPI Nickel Pty Ltd a wholly owned subsidiary of Norilsk Nickel Australian Holdings BV. The combined tenement package is located in the northern Goldfields region of Western Australia. Terms were not disclosed.

Company Background

From two small mining companies founded in the mid-1800s to the eventual merger of Broken Hill Proprietary and Billiton in 2001 today BHP is a leader in the resources industry. BHP began as a silver lead and zinc mining company in Broken Hill Australia in 1885. Billiton goes back further to 1851 as a tin mining company in the island of Belitung in Indonesia. Over the next century it expanded into businesses like oil & gas nickel diamond mining and marketing and potash businesses with varying success stories. In 2015 BHP decided to simplify its vast portfolio by spinning off some of its metals and mining businesses into a global company South32.

HISTORY

After starting out on its own in 1860 Billiton was subsequently bought first by Royal Dutch Shell and then by Gencor only to end up on its own once again. In 1860 a group of Dutch shareholders formed Billiton NV. The company bought the rich tin deposits of Billiton island (now part of Indonesia) for which it was named. The business grew to include tin and lead smelting in the Netherlands. Billiton NV began mining bauxite in the 1940s but WWII caused a production slowdown.

While demand for petroleum products exploded in the 1950s and 1960s in 1970 the industry nosedived. Royal Dutch Shell (formed from the merger of Royal Dutch and Shell Transport and Trading) responded by diversifying buying Billiton NV which it renamed Billiton International. Shell had gotten its start in commodities in the 1880s selling Russian oil of the Rothschilds to the Far East. Royal Dutch formed in 1890 after buying the rights to drill for oil in the Dutch East Indies. The two companies merged in 1907.

The 1970 Billiton purchase helped Royal Dutch Shell make up for the 1970s oil shortage and rationing that had resulted from OPEC's crude oil price hikes. Slow worldwide economic growth a major recession and oil and chemicals overcapacity impacted the company in the late 1970s and early 1980s.

Royal Dutch Shell sold Billiton in 1994 to Gencor which had been formed in 1980 by the merger of General Mining and Finance Corporation and Union Corporation. General Mining began mining gold in South Africa in the 1890s and Gencor continued its predecessors' metals and manufacturing operations. Gencor however spent the early 1980s focused on manufacturing because it anticipated a downturn in base metals. But the recession inflation and high interest rates stifled Gencor's success and the company became known as an unfocused conglomerate. In 1986 a newly appointed chairman separated Gencor's manufacturing and mining interests.

By 1989 Gencor had cut its staff and reorganized. That year it bought 31% of South Africa's Richards Bay aluminum smelter. Within two years Gencor had become a holding company with a primary interest in mining. In 1993 the firm unbundled its non-mining activities. With the end of apartheid in 1994 Gencor was able to expand abroad. Its purchase of Billiton catapulted its presence into 13 countries but in 1996 the metals market spiraled downward.

Billiton was spun off by Gencor in 1997. It took over all of Gencor's nonprecious metal interests including its aluminum titanium ferroalloy and coal assets. That year Billiton combined its nickel interests with QNI of Australia. Making good on its plan to buy new base metals assets Billiton entered a joint venture in 1998 to explore for lead and zinc with Ireland's Ennex. Billiton also sold its metals brokerage subsidiary to Metallgesellschaft AG (Germany).

In 1999 Billiton announced that it would invest in smaller companies with promising properties and limit its own in-house exploration operations. It entered joint ventures with PT Taraco Mining to explore for coal in Indonesia and with Comet Resources to develop the Ravensthorpe Nickel Project in Western Australia.

Billiton's offer for a 21% stake in the Gove bauxite-alumina project in Australia was bested by Alcan in 2000. The company agreed to pay Alcoa about $1.5 billion for its majority stake in the Worsley alumina refinery in Australia. With Anglo American and Glencore International (now Glencore Xstrata) it acquired a 50% stake in Colombia's Cerrejon Zona Norte coal mine for $384 million; it then bought Canadian mining company Rio Algom (copper molybdenum uranium and coal) for $1.2 billion.

In 2001 Billiton closed the purchase of Alcoa's share of the Worsley smelter. The same year Billiton agreed to be acquired by Aussie natural resources company BHP Ltd. to form a dual-listed entity — known collectively as BHP Billiton — consisting of BHP Billiton Limited (run from Melbourne) and BHP Billiton plc (run from London). The deal closed in June 2001.

Auditors: Ernst & Young

LOCATIONS

HQ: BHP Group Ltd
Nova South, 160 Victoria Street, London SW1E 5LB
Phone: (44) 20 7802 4000   **Fax:** (44) 20 7802 4111
Web: www.bhp.com

2015 Sales

	% of total
Australia	5
United Kingdom	1
Rest of Europe	5
China	36
Japan	11
Rest of Asia	11

North America			17
South America			3
Southern Africa			1
Rest of world			1
India			4
South Korea			6
Total			**100**

PRODUCTS/OPERATIONS

2015 Sales

	% of total
Iron Ore	33
Petroleum and Potash	26
Copper	26
Coal	13
Group and unallocated items	2
Total	**100**

COMPETITORS

ANGLO PACIFIC GROUP PLC
ASA RESOURCE GROUP PLC
BARRICK TZ LIMITED
BHP GROUP LIMITED
FREEPORT-MCMORAN INC.
VEDANTA RESOURCES LIMITED
Vale S/A
WEATHERLY INTERNATIONAL PUBLIC LIMITED
COMPANY

HISTORICAL FINANCIALS

Company Type: Public

Income Statement   FYE: June 30

	REVENUE ($ mil.)	NET INCOME ($ mil.)	NET PROFIT MARGIN	EMPLOYEES
06/21	60,817	11,304	18.6%	34,478
06/20	42,931	7,956	18.5%	31,589
06/19	44,288	8,306	18.8%	28,926
06/18	43,638	3,705	8.5%	27,161
06/17	38,285	5,890	15.4%	26,146
Annual Growth	12.3%	17.7%	—	7.2%

2021 Year-End Financials

Debt ratio: 16.5%
Return on equity: 22.7%
Cash ($ mil.): 15,246
Current ratio: 1.63
Long-term debt ($ mil.): 15,348

No. of shares (mil.): —
Dividends
  Yield: 4.2%
  Payout: 209.8%
Market value ($ mil.): —

	STOCK PRICE ($) FY Close	P/E High/Low	PER SHARE ($) Earnings	Dividends	Book Value
06/21	72.83	36 21	2.23	3.12	10.14
06/20	49.73	37 20	1.57	2.86	9.48
06/19	58.11	36 27	1.60	6.60	9.34
06/18	50.01	75 52	0.69	2.94	10.44
06/17	35.59	38 25	1.10	1.08	10.76
Annual Growth	19.6%	— —	19.2%	30.4%	(1.5%)

Bid Corp Ltd

Auditors: PricewaterhouseCoopers Inc.

LOCATIONS

HQ: Bid Corp Ltd
  2nd floor, North Wing, 90 Rivonia Road, Postnet Suite
  136, Sandton 2196
Phone: (27) 10 592 2150
Web: www.bidcorpgroup.com

HISTORICAL FINANCIALS

Company Type: Public

Income Statement   FYE: June 30

	REVENUE ($ mil.)	NET INCOME ($ mil.)	NET PROFIT MARGIN	EMPLOYEES
06/20	15,009	150	1.0%	23,427
06/19	16,017	508	3.2%	25,858
06/18	14,791	439	3.0%	26,448
06/17	16,224	496	3.1%	25,613
06/16	16,796	406	2.4%	24,064
Annual Growth	(2.8%)	(22.0%)	—	(0.7%)

2020 Year-End Financials

Debt ratio: 2.1%
Return on equity: 4.3%
Cash ($ mil.): 870
Current ratio: 1.07
Long-term debt ($ mil.): 565

No. of shares (mil.): 334
Dividends
  Yield: —
  Payout: 90.7%
Market value ($ mil.): —

Blom Bank SAL

Auditors: BDO, Semaan, Gholam & Co.

LOCATIONS

HQ: Blom Bank SAL
  Verdun, Rachid Karami Street, BLOM Bank Bldg., P.O.
  Box 11-1912, Beirut, Riad El Solh 1107 2807
Phone: (961) 1 743 300   **Fax:** (961) 1 738 946
Web: www.blombank.com

HISTORICAL FINANCIALS

Company Type: Public

Income Statement   FYE: December 31

	ASSETS ($ mil.)	NET INCOME ($ mil.)	INCOME AS % OF ASSETS	EMPLOYEES
12/19	33,295	109	0.3%	4,853
12/18	36,740	507	1.4%	0
12/17	32,544	482	1.5%	0
12/16	29,506	448	1.5%	4,673
12/15	29,087	386	1.3%	4,818
Annual Growth	3.4%	(27.0%)	—	0.2%

2019 Year-End Financials

Return on assets: 0.3%
Return on equity: 3.4%
Long-term debt ($ mil.): —
No. of shares (mil.): 206
Sales ($ mil): 2,841

Dividends
  Yield: —
  Payout: 197.2%
Market value ($ mil.): —

	STOCK PRICE ($) FY Close	P/E High/Low	PER SHARE ($) Earnings	Dividends	Book Value
12/19	0.00	— —	0.51	1.01	15.04
12/18	9.45	0 0	2.37	1.01	15.60
12/17	8.10	— —	2.25	0.94	14.31
12/16	8.10	— —	2.20	0.78	14.01
Annual Growth	—	— —	(30.6%)	6.6%	1.8%

BNP Paribas (France)

Ask this company "O est la banque?" and the answer is virtually everywhere. One of Europe's largest banks BNP Paribas and its many subsidiaries offer a wide range of retail and corporate and investment banking services across Europe North America Africa and the Asia/Pacific region. Additional services include corporate vehicle leasing digital banking and investment services and private banking and wealth management. BNP Paribas operates in Italy through BNL banca commerciale and in Belgium via BNP Paribas Fortis. In the US the company owns BancWest. BNP Paribas earns roughly 75% of its revenue from customers in Europe (mainly in France Belgium Italy and Luxembourg). BNP has more than ?2 trillion in assets.

Operations

BNP Paribas operates two core businesses: Retail Banking & Services and Corporate & Institutional Banking.

Retail Banking & Services operates more than 7000 branches in more than 70 countries and accounts for around 75% of the bank's total revenue. The segment consists of its domestic retail banking networks in France Italy (BNL bc) Belgium (BNP Paribas Fortis) and Luxembourg (BGL BNP Paribas) as well as certain specialized retail banking divisions (Personal Investors Leasing Solutions Arval and New Digital Businesses). BNP Paribas is the leading private bank in France and #1 for cash management and professional equipment financing in Europe. BNL bc holds a residential mortgage market share of around 7% in Italy and a 4% household current account market share.

International Financial Services consists of all BNP Paribas Group's retail banking businesses outside the euro zone split between Europe-Mediterranean and BancWest in the United States. It also includes personal finance insurance and wealth and asset management activities.

Corporate and Institutional Banking generates the remaining 25% of revenue. It consists of three divisions. Corporate Banking provides services in Europe the Middle East Africa the Asia/Pacific region and Americas as well as corporate finance activities. Global Markets offers fixed income currency and commodities and equity and prime services. Securities Services caters to management companies financial institutions and other corporations.

Broadly speaking the company makes more than 45% of its net revenue from interest (after interest expense). Net commission income brings in more than 20% and the rest arises from gains on financial instruments and available-for-sale financial assets insurance and other activities that generate more than 30% of revenues combined.

Geographic Reach

While it caters to more than 70 countries Paris-based BNP focuses mainly on four domestic markets where it holds leading positions: Belgium France Italy and Luxembourg. Europe is the bank's largest market accounting for more than 75% of revenue. North America contributed more than 10% while the Asia/Pacific and Africa region and other countries each contributed more than 5%.

In France BNP Paribas' retail network consists of more than 1800 branches and more than 5000 ATMs. Its private banking network consists of numerous centers throughout France 2 wealth management offices more than 20 general business centers approximately 80 SME centers and more than 60 We Are Innovation (WAI) start-up support locations.

In Italy through BNL banca commerciale BNP Paribas operates more than 720 branches 1800 ATMs more than 35 private banking centers 45 small business centers around 45 branches dealing with SMEs large corporates local authorities and public sector organizations and a few trade centers for cross-border activities and investment desks that assist local and international companies with direct investments in Italy.

BNP Paribas' Belgium unit operates around 600 branches more than 2700 ATMs around 20 small business centers 270 Fintro franchises around 660 retail outlets in partnership with Bpost Bank.

In Luxembourg it supports its 183000 customers via more than 40 branches about 130 ATMs and five private banking centers.

BancWest is active in some 25 Western and Mid-Western US states. It operates around 535 branches.

The Europe-Mediterranean segment operates a network in more than 1910 branches across 14 countries including Turkey Poland Ukraine Morocco Tunisia Algeria and seven countries in Sub-Saharan Africa.

Sales and Marketing

BNP Paribas has a deep sponsorship relationship with tennis. Led by its long-term sponsorship of the Roland Garros French Open tennis tournament held each summer in Paris the company also sponsors the Davis Cup the Fed Cup the BNP Paribas Masters and more. The company also has a number of cultural sponsorships across music theater film and dance.

Financial Performance

Note: Growth rates may differ after conversion to US dollars.

BNP Paribas has recorded sluggish revenue growth in the past five years due to a lackluster interest rate and market environment. Meanwhile net income has trended slowly but consistently upwards and BNP's profit margins are among the highest out of Europe's leading commercial banks.

In 2019 BNP Paribas' revenue rose 5% to ?44.6 billion. Revenues in the operating divisions rose by 6% with an increase in all the divisions: a 1% increase in Domestic Markets 7% in International Financial Services and 12% in CIB which posted strong revenue growth with very good performance by Global Markets and Corporate Banking.

The Group's net income attributable to equity holders came at ?8.2 billion up 9% compared to ?7.5 billion in the prior year. Operating income rose by 10% to ?10.1 billion mostly from the increase in its operating divisions.

BNP's cash balance weakened during 2019 ending the year ?30.3 billion lower at ?152.2 billion. The bank's operations used ?50.8 billion while investing activities used another ?323 million. Financing activities generated ?20.1 billion. Operating activities were net cash negative due to a ?75.6 billion net decrease in cash related to operating assets and liabilities.

Strategy

BNP Paribas' 'Road to 2020' plan rests on four pillars: grow the business provide a new customer experience accelerate digitization and improve operating efficiency. BNP Paribas is investing ?3 billion to make better use of data implement new customer journeys adapt information systems and upgrade its operational model. The shift to digital also includes the closure of hundreds of its traditional (and more expensive) branches; in total the bank expects the initiative to produce cost savings of ?3.4 billion.

The exceptional transformation costs under the 2020 plan totalled ?2.7 billion in three years. The Group will no longer have transformation costs in 2020 which will enable it to reduce spending by ?7 million in 2020 compared to 2019. The recurring savings generated by the plan at the end of 2019 totalled ?1.8 billion in line with the objectives. The Group expects to generate an additional ?1.5 billion in additional recurring savings in 2020 thereby attaining the target of ?3.3 billion in cumulative recurring cost savings.

In 2020 the Group anticipates continuing to grow business in all the operating divisions by leveraging a strong business drive and the contribution of the diversified and integrated model. The reinforcement of the franchises within the integrated model should continue in particular for CIB with the ongoing development of its businesses and the strengthening of its businesses and the strengthening of its European leadership.

Mergers and Acquisitions

In early 2020 BNP Paribas acquired the depository unit of Spain-based Banco Sabadell for 115 million euros. Soledad Lecube head of BNP Paribas Securities Services Spain commented: "The acquisition of Sabadell's depositary banking business consolidates our position as a leading asset servicing provider in Spain where we are the first depositary bank for independent asset managers."

HISTORY

BNP Paribas Group's predecessor Banque Nationale de Paris (BNP) is the progeny of two state banks with parallel histories; each was set up to jump-start the economy after a revolution in 1848.

For a century Paris-based Comptoir National d'Escompte de Paris (CNEP) bounced between private and public status depending on government whim. It was the #3 bank in France from the late 19th century through the 1950s.

Banque National pour le Commerce et l'Industrie (BNCI) started in Alsace a region that was part of Germany from the Franco-Prussian War until WWI. BNCI served as an economic bridge between Germany and France which had to give the bank governmental resuscitation during the Depression. By the 1960s BNCI had passed CNEP in size.

French leader Charles de Gaulle expected banking to drive post-WWII reconstruction and in 1945 CNEP and BNCI were nationalized. In 1966 France's finance minister merged them and they became BNP. That year the company started an association with Dresdner Bank of Germany under which the two still operate joint ventures primarily in Eastern Europe.

By 1993 privatization was again in vogue and BNP was cut loose by the government. It expanded outside France to ameliorate the influences of the French economy and government. Even before it was privatized BNP was involved in such politically charged actions as the bailout of OPEC money repository Banque Arabe and the extension of credit to Algeria's state oil company Sonatrach.

The privatized BNP looked overseas in the late 1990s. In 1997 alone it won the right to operate in New Zealand bought Laurentian Bank and Trust of the Bahamas took control of its joint venture with Egypt's Banque du Caire and opened a subsidiary in Brazil.

BNP bought failed Peregrine Investment's Chinese operations in 1998. That year the bank also expanded in Peru opened an office in Algeria opened a representative office in Uzbekistan set up an investment banking subsidiary in India and bought Australian stock brokerage operations from Prudential.

After a decade of globe-trotting BNP brought it on home in 1999 and set off a year of tumult in French banking. As France's other two large banks (Societe Generale and Paribas) made plans to merge BNP decided it would absorb both banks as a means to get a bigger chunk of the to-be-privatized Credit Lyonnais and to protect France from Euro-megabank penetration by creating the globe's largest bank.

Executives at Societe Generale (SG) had other ideas forming a cartel called "Action Against the BNP Raid." Meanwhile BNP tried to boost to controlling stakes its holdings in the two banks. (In Europe's cross-ownership tradition the target banks also owned part of BNP.) France's central bank tried unsuccessfully to negotiate a deal (the government supported the triumvirate merger). A war of words was played out in the media and finally shareholders had to vote on the proposals. In the end BNP won control of Paribas but not SG. As BNP prepared to integrate a reluctant Paribas into its operations regulators ordered BNP to relinquish its stake in SG. The newly merged company was dubbed BNP Paribas Group.

In 2000 BNP Paribas and Avis Group launched a fleet-management joint venture. BNP also bought 150 shopping centers from French retailer Carrefour and the 40% of merchant bank Cobepa that it didn't already own. In 2001 BNP Paribas took full control of US-based BancWest. The company bought United California Bank from UFJ Holdings (now part of Mitsubishi UFJ Financial Group) the following year.

The bank opened up a second "home market" when it bought Italy's Banca Nazionale del Lavoro (BNL) for $11 billion in 2006.

Two of the French bank's most transformative acquisitions included the deal to buy Italian bank Banca Nazionale del Lavoro in 2006 and the 75% purchase of Fortis Bank (which also included a 25% stake in Fortis Insurance). Both deals boosted BNP Paribas' retail banking business across Europe. Retail banking is now responsible for more than 60% of BNP Paribas' revenues.

In addition to the Fortis and BNL acquisitions BNP Paribas looked to grow in new markets. BNP Paribas acquired Sahara Bank in Libya and a 51% stake in UkrSibbank one of Ukraine's leading banks.

In 2008 as the world's economies struggled to stay afloat the French government agreed to inject ?10.5 billion ($14 billion) into the nation's top six banks including BNP Paribas. The government didn't receive shares in the banks it assisted; rather the capital injections were meant to help reenergize lending activities in France. A year after receiving the cash BNP Paribas announced plans to repay the government's aid.

In 2009 after a couple of false starts and a seven-month saga BNP Paribas acquired control of Fortis Banque (also known as Fortis Bank). Fortis' Dutch operations were excluded from the transaction. The deal further cemented BNP Paribas as a top European bank. Fortis Bank was nationalized in October 2008 to prevent its collapse and the takeover by BNP Paribas was delayed and revised to satisfy Fortis shareholders and other interested parties. Upon the closing of the deal BNP Paribas became the market leader in Belgium and Luxembourg. The Belgian government gained more than 10% of BNP Paribas in the transaction.

BNP Paribas complimented its 2009 acquisition of Fortis with the purchase of private bank Insinger de Beaufort.

In 2011 BNP Paribas continued its strategy of expanding in high growth markets and acquired a majority of South Africa's Cadiz Securities. BNP Paribas also owns Banque Internationale pour le Commerce et l'Industrie which is active in six African nations and a majority of T rk Ekonomi Bankasi in Turkey. BNP Paribas has been expanding in China Egypt Israel and Russia as well.

In 2012 the company sold the bulk of its controlling stake in real estate firm Klepierre to US mall owner Simon for some ?1.5 billion (around $2 billion) to further raise its capital levels.

EXECUTIVES

Chief Executive Officer, Jean-Laurent Bonnafe, $1,779,752 total compensation
CEO, BNP Paribas Personal Finance, Charlotte Dennery
Head, CIB Global Banking EMEA, Yannick Jung
Chief Information Officer, Bernard Gavgani
Head, Corporate and Institutional Banking Global Markets, Olivier Osty
CEO, BNP Paribas Cardif, Pauline Leclerc-Glorieux
Chief Executive Officer and Chairman, BNP Paribas Fortis, Maxime Jadot
Head, International Retail Banking, Stefaan Decraene
COO and Head, Retail Banking, Thierry Laborde
COO and Head, Corporate and Institutional Banking, Yann Gerardin
Group Chief Risk Officer, Member of the Executive Committee, Franck Roncey
Chairman of the Board, Jean Lemierre, $1,082,435 total compensation
Deputy Chief Operating Officer, Operational Efficiency, Laurent David
Chairman, BNL, Andrea Munari
Deputy COO and Head, Investment and Protection Services, Renaud Dumora
Head, Compliance, Nathalie Hartmann
Head, Corporate Engagement, Antoine Sire
CEO, BNL, Elena Goitini
Head of Territory - India, Aymar De Liedekerke Beaufort
Chief Executive Officer of India, Sanjay Singh
Auditors: Mazars

LOCATIONS

HQ: BNP Paribas (France)
16, Boulevard des Italiens, Paris 75009
Phone: (33) 1 40 14 45 46 **Fax:** (33) 1 42 98 21 22
Web: www.bnpparibas.com

2018 Sales

	% of total
Europe	75
North America	11
Asia & Pacific	7
Others	7
Total	**100**

PRODUCTS/OPERATIONS

2018 Sales

	% of total
Retail Banking & Services:	
Domestic Markets	
French Retail Banking	14
Belgian Retail Banking	8
BNL banca commerciale	7
Other Domestic Markets activities	7
International Financial Services	
Personal Finance	13
International Retail Banking	
BancWest	6
Wealth and Asset Management	6
EuropeMediterranee	8
Insurance	6
Corporate & Institutional Banking:	
Global Markets	11
Corporate Banking	9
Securities Services	5
Other Activities	-
Total	**100**

2018 Sales

	% of total
Net interest income	49
Net commission income	22
Net gain on financial instruments at fair value through profit or loss	14
Net gain on available-for-sale financial assets and other financial assets not measured at fair value	1
Net income from insurance activities	10
Net income from other activities	4

Total	100

COMPETITORS

ABN AMRO Bank N.V.	HSBC HOLDINGS PLC
Banque de Montreal	NATWEST GROUP PLC
COMMONWEALTH BANK OF AUSTRALIA	Royal Bank of Canada
	STANDARD CHARTERED PLC
Co ¶peratieve Rabobank U.A.	Svenska Handelsbanken AB
Credit Suisse Group AG	UBS AG
Danske Bank A/S	

HISTORICAL FINANCIALS

Company Type: Public

Income Statement

FYE: December 31

	ASSETS ($ mil.)	NET INCOME ($ mil.)	INCOME AS % OF ASSETS	EMPLOYEES
12/20	3,054,099	8,673	0.3%	193,319
12/19	2,430,466	9,176	0.4%	198,816
12/18	2,337,155	8,618	0.4%	202,625
12/17	2,349,860	9,301	0.4%	196,128
12/16	2,193,026	8,132	0.4%	192,418
Annual Growth	**8.6%**	**1.6%**	**—**	**0.1%**

2020 Year-End Financials

Return on assets: 0.3%
Return on equity: 6.4%
Long-term debt ($ mil.): —
No. of shares (mil.): 1,249
Sales ($ mil): 89,708

Dividends
Yield: 0.0%
Payout: 20.9%
Market value ($ mil.): 33,238

	STOCK PRICE ($) FY Close	P/E High/Low		PER SHARE ($) Earnings	Dividends	Book Value
12/20	26.61	6	3	6.52	1.36	110.83
12/19	29.69	5	4	6.97	1.68	96.59
12/18	22.54	7	4	6.56	1.76	93.03
12/17	37.35	7	5	7.25	1.62	97.95
12/16	31.85	5	3	6.34	1.24	85.29
Annual Growth	**(4.4%)**	**—**	**—**	**0.7%**	**2.4%**	**6.8%**

Boc Hong Kong Holdings Ltd

BOC Hong Kong (Holdings) is the parent of Bank of China (Hong Kong) which has more than 190 branches 280 automated banking centers and over 1000 self-service machines in Hong Kong. The bank serves retail customers small entrepreneurs and corporate customers providing loans trade related products and other credit facilities investment and insurance products. It also operates banknote printing business. Bank of China which is controlled by the Chinese government owns about two-thirds of BOC Hong Kong.

Operations

BOC Hong Kong (Holdings) operates under four operating segments: Personal Banking Corporate Banking Treasury and Insurance.

Both Corporate Banking (about 40% of revenue) and Personal Banking (about 30% of revenue) provide general banking services including various deposit products overdrafts loans and other credit facilities investment and insurance products and foreign currency and derivative products. Corporate Banking serves corporate clients while Personal Banking serves retail customers.

Treasury (about 30% of revenue) manages the funding and liquidity interest rate and foreign exchange positions of the bank in addition to proprietary trades. The Insurance segment represents the business mainly relating to life insurance products including individual life insurance and group life insurance products.

Overall BOC Hong Kong (Holdings) generates more than 50% of its revenue from interest income followed by insurance premiums for about 25% of revenue and commissions about for 15%.

Geographic Reach

Hong Kong-based BOC Hong Kong (Holdings) has operations in the US Singapore and China. It also has branches in Thailand Malaysia Vietnam the Philippines Indonesia Cambodia Laos and Brunei.

Sales and Marketing

BOC Hong Kong (Holdings)'s five largest customers accounted less than 30% of total interest income and other operating income of the bank in 2019.

Financial Performance

In 2019 BOCHK's annual profit hit a new high of HK$34.1 billion representing a growth of 4% year-on-year.

Cash held by the company at the end of 2019 decreased to HK$331.7 billion compared to HK$626.1 billion in the prior year. Cash used for operations investing activities and financing activities were HK$268.7 billion HK$3.3 billion and HK$18.5 billion respectively.

Strategy

BOCHK's strategic goal is to "Build a Top-class Full-service and Internationalised Regional Bank". Capitalising on its advantages as a major commercial banking group in Hong Kong BOCHK aims to increase local market penetration and actively expand its business in the Southeast Asian region. The company strive to provide customers with comprehensive professional and high-quality services. As one of the three note-issuing banks and the sole clearing bank for Renminbi ("RMB") business in Hong Kong BOCHK has strong market positions in all major businesses. Its strong RMB franchise has made the company the first choice for customers in RMB business.

EXECUTIVES

Deputy Chief Executive, Bing Wang
Chief Financial Officer, Yang Sui
Independent Non-Executive Director, Eva Cheng
Non-Executive Director, Jingzhen Lin
Chief Operating Officer, Xiangqun Zhong
Deputy Chief Executive, Shu Yuan
Independent Non-executive Director, Wai-Hok Tung
Deputy Chief Executive, Qi Wang
Independent Non-Executive Director, Koon Shum Choi
Non-Executive Chairman of the Board, Liange Liu
Independent Non-executive Director, Beng Seng Koh
Independent Non-Executive Director, Yee Kwan Quinn Law
Deputy Chief Executive, Yun Chi Kung Yeung
Chief Risk Officer, Xin Jiang
Executive Vice Chairman of the Board, Chief Executive, Yu Sun, $18,049 total compensation
Non-Executive Vice Chairman of the Board, Jin Liu
Auditors: Ernst & Young

LOCATIONS

HQ: Boc Hong Kong Holdings Ltd
53rd Floor, Bank of China Tower, 1 Garden Road,
Phone: (852) 2846 2700 **Fax:** (852) 2810 5830
Web: www.bochk.com

PRODUCTS/OPERATIONS

2014 Sales

	% of total
Interest income	58
Fee and commission income	17
Gross earned premiums	20
Net trading gain	3
Others	2
Total	**100**

COMPETITORS

AKBANK TURK ANONIM SIRKETI
BANK OF INDIA
CHINA MINSHENG BANKING CORP. LTD.
China Merchants Bank Co. Ltd.
HSBC HOLDINGS PLC
HSBC USA INC.
MALAYAN BANKING BERHAD
OVERSEA-CHINESE BANKING CORPORATION
 LIMITED
The Bank of Nova Scotia
Woori Finance Holdings Co. Ltd.

HISTORICAL FINANCIALS

Company Type: Public

Income Statement				FYE: December 31
	ASSETS ($ mil.)	NET INCOME ($ mil.)	INCOME AS % OF ASSETS	EMPLOYEES
12/20	428,358	3,416	0.8%	14,915
12/19	388,613	4,133	1.1%	14,668
12/18	377,025	4,085	1.1%	14,046
12/17	338,538	3,975	1.2%	13,050
12/16	300,182	7,157	2.4%	12,836
Annual Growth	9.3%	(16.9%)	—	3.8%

2020 Year-End Financials

Return on assets: 0.8%	Dividends
Return on equity: 8.5%	Yield: 6.1%
Long-term debt ($ mil.): —	Payout: 1,135.5%
No. of shares (mil.): —	Market value ($ mil.): —
Sales ($ mil): 11,952	

	STOCK PRICE ($) FY Close	P/E High/Low	PER SHARE ($) Earnings	Dividends	Book Value
12/20	60.13	30 21	0.32	3.67	3.83
12/19	69.18	30 21	0.39	3.70	3.67
12/18	73.94	35 24	0.39	3.28	3.39
12/17	101.57	35 24	0.38	3.22	2.94
12/16	71.55	15 9	0.68	4.95	2.74
Annual Growth	(4.3%)	—	(16.9%)	(7.2%)	8.7%

BOE Technology Group Co Ltd

BOE Technology Group is an IoT company that provides smart ports and professional services for information interaction and human health. The company makes semiconductor display is the key driver of the company's business growth and has taken up the leading position on the industrial chain thanks to core technical capability reserves. The business has the intellectual capital and resource reserves to propel the fast growth of other businesses. BOE specializes in thin-film transistor liquid-crystal display (TFT-LCD) panels which appear brighter and sharper than traditional LCD. It also makes light-emitting diode (LED) and high-brightness LCD modules and LED backlights. Majority of its sales were generated in the Chinese Mainland.

Operations

The company operates segments including Display Business (about 95%) Smart systems innovation business Smart medicine & engineering integration business Sensor and application solutions business and others (generated the rest).

The display business integrates design and manufacturing of display devices and strives to offer TFT-LCD AMOLED Microdisplay and other intelligent interface devices which develops a platform that integrates panels modules whole widget and services. This business focuses on providing high-quality smartphones tablet PCs laptops monitors TVs vehicles electronic shelf label (ESL) tiled display screens industrial control wearable devices VR/AR devices electronic tags white goods healthcare mobile payment interactive whiteboards and other intelligent display devices for customers.

The smart systems innovation business integrates designs of system solutions. Supported by AI and big data technologies this business focuses on soft and hard products and services and offers integrated IoT solutions of smart government affairs urban beautification smart transportation smart finance smart education smart park and smart energy.

The smart medicine and engineering business provides professional healthcare services and features the innovative integration of medical and engineering by integrating technology and medical science.

The sensor and application solutions business integrates design and manufacturing of B2B system solutions. This business focuses on medical detection household detection communication and transportation smart homes and other fields to provide customers with integrated design and manufacturing services of sensor devices.

The Mini-LED business integrates design and manufacturing of devices and provides Mini-LED backlight products with strong reliability and high dynamic range that allow precisely brightness adjustment for smartphones tablet PCs laptops monitors TVs and other products. Other service mainly includes technical development service and patent maintenance service.

Geographic Reach

Based in China BOE customers in China generate about 50%% of revenue and customers in other Asia account for another 40%. Europe and the Americas are responsible for over 10% of revenue.

Sales and Marketing

The company's five biggest customers generate about 35% of its revenue.

Financial Performance

The company's revenue for fiscal 2020 increased by 17% to RMB135.6 trillion compared with RMB116.1 trillion.

Profit for fiscal 2020 increased to RMB5.0 trillion up about 162% compared to RMB1.9 trillion in the prior year.

Cash held by the company at the end of fiscal 2020 increased to RMB68.1 trillion. Cash provided by operations and financing activities were RMB39.3 trillion and RMB23.8 trillion respectively. Investing activities used RMB43.4 trillion mainly for payment for the acquisition of fixed assets intangible assets and other long-term assets.

Strategy

To establish a group-level capabilities system appropriate to the IoT transformation strategy BOE launched Phase II innovative transformation of SOPIC in 2020. It has built a "three vertical and three horizontal" operation management mechanism with high efficiency and collaboration an organizational system for agile response capabilities reuse and efficient operation and a vertical management system with strategy process and performance as the core and integration the front middle and back offices. As a result organizational efficiency has notably improved.

Besides with confidence in its future development prospects and high recognition of its value the company issued its first medium- and long-term equity incentive plan in 2020 which was implemented by buying back some social public shares with proprietary funds. Beneficiaries of the plan are the core technical team and key management members. The implementation of the first equity incentive plan has further improved the corporate governance structure to the interest of shareholders the company and core personnel and will facilitate the realization of the company's long-term business objectives and the creation of value for all stakeholders.

Company Background

Founded as Beijing Orient Electronics Group in 1993 the company changed its name to BOE Technology in 2001.

EXECUTIVES

Executive Vice President, Chief Lawyer, Liqiong Feng
Executive Vice President, Zhaohong Zhang
Vice Chairman of the Board, Jinfeng Pan
Chief Human Resource Officer, Vice President, Yu Zhang
Independent Director, Shoulian Tang
Executive Vice President, Director, Wenbao Gao
Vice President, Chief Cultural Officer, Chuanbin Miao
Chairman of the Board, Yanshun Chen
Independent Director, Xuan Li
Independent Director, Xiaolin Hu
Independent Director, Huacheng Wang
Senior Vice President, Chief Audit Officer, Chief Risk Officer, Zhongdong Xie
Executive Vice President, Chief Performance Management Officer, Huifeng Zhong
Chief Financial Officer, Executive Vice President, Executive Director, Yun Sun
Director, Jie Song
Executive Vice President, Xiangjun Yao
Vice President, Secretary of the Board, Hongfeng Liu
President, Vice Chairman of the Board, Xiaodong Liu
Auditors: KPMG Huazhen LLP

LOCATIONS

HQ: BOE Technology Group Co Ltd
 12 Xihuan Middle Road, Beijing Economic-
 Technological Development Area, Beijing 100176
Phone: (86) 10 64318888   Fax: (86) 10 64366264
Web: www.boe.com

2013 Sales

	% of total
PRC	54
Other Asian Regions	39
America	5
Europe	2
Total	**100**

PRODUCTS/OPERATIONS

2013 Sales

	% of total
TFT-LCDs	79
Display System	11
Backlight Products	5
Others	5
Total	**100**
Products and Services	

Display Device
For Mobile
For TPC
For NB
For MNT
For TV
For DID
Electronic Material
Smart System Product
Display System
Environment Lighting
Photovoltaic System
ODM/OEM
Smart Healthcare Service

COMPETITORS

ADVANCED ENERGY INDUSTRIES INC.
ALTERA CORPORATION
AU Optronics Corp.
BROADCOM INC.
CALAMP CORP.
CLEARONE INC.
COMTECH TELECOMMUNICATIONS CORP.
DIALOG SEMICONDUCTOR LIMITED
DIODES INCORPORATED
EXAR CORPORATION
HARMONIC INC.
KOPIN CORPORATION
KVH INDUSTRIES INC.
LG Electronics Inc.
LITE-ON TECHNOLOGY CORPORATION
MAXAR TECHNOLOGIES INC.
MONOLITHIC POWER SYSTEMS INC.
MOTOROLA SOLUTIONS INC.
PLANAR SYSTEMS INC.
QUALCOMM INCORPORATED
Quanta Computer Inc.
RUCKUS WIRELESS INC.
SEACHANGE INTERNATIONAL INC.
SHARP CORPORATION
SILICON IMAGE INC.
SKYWORKS SOLUTIONS INC.
Samsung Electronics Co. Ltd.
TDK CORPORATION
VICOR CORPORATION

HISTORICAL FINANCIALS

Company Type: Public

Income Statement				FYE: December 31
	REVENUE ($ mil.)	NET INCOME ($ mil.)	NET PROFIT MARGIN	EMPLOYEES
12/20	20,725	769	3.7%	0
12/19	16,679	275	1.7%	0
12/18	14,118	499	3.5%	0
12/17	14,414	1,162	8.1%	0
12/16	9,921	271	2.7%	49,151
Annual Growth	20.2%	29.8%	—	—

2020 Year-End Financials

Debt ratio: 5.9%	No. of shares (mil.): —
Return on equity: 5.0%	Dividends
Cash ($ mil.): 11,267	Yield: —
Current ratio: 1.23	Payout: —
Long-term debt ($ mil.): 20,312	Market value ($ mil.): —

Bouygues S.A.

Bouygues (pronounced "bweeg") operates in three primary business areas: construction telecommunications and media. Its road buildings and property development contracting services operate through Bouygues Construction road builder Colas and property developer Bouygues Immo-

bilier. The group also owns around 95% stake in Bouygues Telecom (France's #3 mobile phone carrier) and nearly 15% of industrial group AL-STOM. Bouygues' principal owners are brothers Martin and Oliver Bouygues and the company's employees. Bouygues generates majority of sales from France.

Operations

Bouygues SA is a diversified industrial group with five main business segments: Bouygues Construction Bouygues Immobilier Colas Bouygues Telecom and TF1.

Colas generates the biggest sale accounting for around 35%. Its three main activities are: roads construction materials and railways. It also includes transport of water and energy in France. Colas has significant additional construction materials production and recycling activities which it operates via a network of quarries as well as emulsion asphalt and ready-mix concrete plants.

Bouygues Construction which accounts for almost 35% of sales is a benchmark player in sustainable construction through the construction of many eco-neighborhoods low-carbon buildings and structures certified against the best world eco-standards as well as through rehabilitation of sites to reach positive-energy status.

Bouygues Telecom accounts for more than 15% of sales and has been providing the best technology to make its customer's digital lives richer and more intense. Its vocation is to provide high-quality networks products and services adapted to the needs and expectations of its 25 million customers.

Bouygues Immobilier produces more than 5% of sales and is one of France's leading property developers developing residential commercial and office buildings.

TF1 which generates over 5% of sales offers unique range if unencrypted and pay-TV content and services that responds to the people's new ways of consuming media.

Geographic Reach

Paris-based Bouygues' largest market is France which accounts for nearly 60% of its total sales. Europe excluding France contributes almost 20% of total sales and Americas more than 10%. The firm is also active in Africa the Asia Pacific region Central America and the Middle East. While the company does business in around 80 countries worldwide it is mainly active in developed nations.

Financial Performance

Note: Growth rates may differ after conversion to US dollars.

Company's revenue for fiscal 2020 decreased by 9% to ?34.7 billion compared from the prior year with ?37.9 billion.

Profit for fiscal 2020 decreased by ?488 million to ?696 million compared from the prior year with ?1.2 billion.

Strategy

The Bouygues group creates and shares value over the long term with its stakeholders. In order to accomplish this core objective it draws on a stable ownership structure and a strategic framework through which its five business segments roll out their own operational strategies.

Company's business segments drive growth over the long term because they meet essential needs for housing transportation communication information and entertainment.

The diversity of its business segments helps cushion the impact of the less positive business cycles. In 2020 the company proved how resilient it is during the health crisis.

Mergers and Acquisitions

In 2021 Bouygues Group signs purchase agreement with Engie to acquire Equans. The acquisition will accelerate Bouygues' development in the strong growth potential multi-technical services

sector at the convergence between the energy digital and industrial transitions.

Company Background

HISTORY

With the equivalent of $1700 in borrowed money Francis Bouygues son of a Paris engineer started Entreprise Francis Bouygues in 1952 as an industrial works and construction firm in the Paris region of France. Within four years his firm had expanded into property development.

By the mid-1960s Bouygues had entered the civil engineering and public works sectors and developed regional construction units across France. In 1970 it was listed on the Paris stock exchange. Four years later the company established Bouygues Offshore to build oil platforms.

In 1978 the firm built Terminal 2 of Paris' Charles de Gaulle airport. Three years later it won the contract to construct the University of Riyadh in Saudi Arabia (then the world's largest building project at 3.2 million sq. ft.) which was completed in 1984. That year Bouygues acquired France's #3 water supply company Saur and power transmission and supply firm ETDE.

Expansion continued in 1986 with the purchase of the Screg Group which included Colas France's top highway contractor. The next year the company led a consortium to buy 50% of newly privatized network Societe Television Fran Şaise 1 (TF1). Bouygues became the largest shareholder with a 25% stake (increased to 40% by 1999). In 1988 the company began building the Channel Tunnel (completed 1994) and moved into its new ultramodern headquarters dubbed Challenger in Saint-Quentin-en-Yvelines outside Paris.

After rumors of failing health Francis Bouygues resigned as chairman in 1989. His son Martin took over as chairman and CEO although the patriarch called France's "Emperor of Concrete" remained on the board until his death in 1993.

Despite fears that the group would suffer without its founder's leadership Bouygues continued to grow with the 1989 acquisition of a majority interest in Grands Moulins de Paris France's largest flour milling firm (sold 1998). In 1990 it purchased Swiss construction group Losinger.

The company entered the telecom industry in 1993 with a national paging network and added a mobile phone license a year later. In 1996 the group listed 40% of Bouygues Offshore's shares on the New York and Paris stock exchanges. Also that year it launched mobile phone operator Bouygues Telecom and entered a partnership with Telecom Italia.

By 1999 Bouygues Telecom had reached 2 million customers and Bouygues bought back a 20% share held by the UK's Cable and Wireless to increase its stake to nearly 54%. That year Bouygues Offshore bought Norwegian engineering firm Kvaerner and the group spun off its construction sector creating Bouygues Construction.

After word circulated that Deutsche Telekom wanted to acquire the group's telecom unit Bouygues became the target of takeover rumors. Francois Pinault France's richest businessman became Bouygues' largest non-family shareholder when he increased his stake to 14% (later reduced to about 2%). Pinault's biggest rival Bernard Arnault upped his stake to more than 9% of the group fueling speculation of a battle over control of the board.

In 2001 the company pulled out of France's auction for a third-generation wireless license and remained the only European incumbent mobile carrier without a major domestic investment in 3G technology (until 2009). The next year the company agreed to buy Telecom Italia's stake in Bouygues Telecom increasing Bouygues' ownership in the mobile operator from 54% to more than 65%. In 2002 the company sold its 51% stake in oil field platform construction unit Bouygues Offshore to Italian oil services group Saipem which announced plans to bid for the remaining shares.

However talks with German utility giant E.ON over the sale of Bouygues' Saur subsidiary failed that year after E.ON decided to focus instead on its electricity and gas operations.

In 2005 Bouygues was more successful when it sought to sell Saur piecemeal. It sold several divisions of the subsidiary (Coved Saur France Saur International and Stereau) to French private equity firm PAI Partners but retained the African and Italian (Sigesa-Crea) divisions of the firm.

Bouygues bought the French government's 21% stake in ALSTOM for $2.5 billion in 2006. The deal was approved on the condition that it not try to control the company for at least three years. Bouygues did build up its holding after the acquisition though eventually holding 29% of the shares.

In 2008 property developer Bouygues Immobilier expanded with the acquisition of Urbis a French rival. That year Colas bought the Gouyer Group of companies (distribution of construction materials) in Martinique and Guadeloupe while Bouygues Telecom acquired a fixed-line network that allowed it to launch the Bbox broadband router and Internet services that include VoIP email Internet access and television; the telecom unit also gained the previously denied right to offer the iPhone 3G.

EXECUTIVES

Deputy Chief Executive Officer, Chief Financial Officer, Pascal Grange
Senior Vice President of Human Resources, Jean Soussan
Director, Employee Representative, Beatrice Besombes
Director, Employees Representative, Bernard Allain
Chairman and Chief Executive Officer of Bouygues Telecom, Richard Viel
Chairman of the Board, Martin Bouygues, $1,048,253 total compensation
Director, Olivier Bouygues, $379,801 total compensation
Chief Executive Officer, Olivier Roussat, $1,424,257 total compensation
Chairman and Chief Executive Officer of TF1, Gilles Gerard Pelisson
Independent Director, Charlotte Bouygues
Chairman and CEO, Pascal Minault
Chairman and Chief Executive Officer of Colas, Frederic Gardes
Independent Director, Benoit Maes
Auditors: Mazars

LOCATIONS

HQ: Bouygues S.A.
32 avenue Hoche, Paris 75008
Phone: (33) 1 44 20 10 00
Web: www.bouygues.com

2018 Sales

	% of total
Europe	
France	61
European Union	11
Other countries	5
North America	11
Asia-Pacific	5
Africa	3
Central and South America	1
Middle East	1
Oceania	3
Total	**100**

PRODUCTS/OPERATIONS

2018 Sales

	% of total
Colas	37
Bouygues Construction	34
Bouygues Telecom	15
Bouygues Immobilier	8
TF1	6
Total	**100**

Selected Subsidiaries and Affiliates

Construction
  Autoroute de liaison Seine-Sarthe SA (33%)
  Bouygues Bâtiment Ile-de-France SA (99.9%)
  Bati-Ré;nov SA (99.3%)
  Bouygues Bâtiment International SA (99.9%)
  Bouygues Thaï Ltd (49%)
  DTP Singapour Pte Ltd (99.9%)
  Kohler Investment SA (Luxembourg 99.9%)
  Bouygues Construction SA (99.9%)
  ETDE SA (99.9%)
  Exprimm IT (99.9%)
  Icel Maidstone Ltd (UK 99.9%)
  Quille SA (99.9%)
  Westminster Local Education Partnership Ltd (UK 80%)
Media
  Mé;tro France Publications (15%)
  Té;lé;vision Française 1 SA (TF1 43%)
  TF1 Vidé;o (43%)
  TV Breizh (43%)
Property
  Bouygues Immobilier
  Parque Empresearial Cristalia SL
  SNC Bouygues Immobilier Entreprises Île-de-France
Roads
  Cofiroute (16%)
  Colas Guadeloupe (97%)
  Colas Hungaria (97%)
  Colas Polska (97%)
  Colas SA (96%)
  Spac (97%)
Telecommunications
  Bouygues Telecom SA (90%)

COMPETITORS

ACS ACTIVIDADES DE CONSTRUCCION Y SERVICIOS SA
CAPGEMINI
COMPUTACENTER PLC
EDP - ENERGIAS DE PORTUGAL S.A.
FERROVIAL SA
FOMENTO DE CONSTRUCCIONES Y CONTRATAS SA
HOCHTIEF AG
ORANGE
SOFTBANK GROUP CORP.
STRABAG SE
TELECOM ITALIA SPA
VINCI

HISTORICAL FINANCIALS

Company Type: Public

Income Statement   FYE: December 31

	REVENUE ($ mil.)	NET INCOME ($ mil.)	NET PROFIT MARGIN	EMPLOYEES
12/20	42,660	854	2.0%	129,018
12/19	42,676	1,329	3.1%	130,450
12/18	40,929	1,501	3.7%	129,275
12/17	39,623	1,300	3.3%	119,836
12/16	33,682	772	2.3%	122,615
Annual Growth	**6.1%**	**2.5%**	**—**	**1.3%**

2020 Year-End Financials

Debt ratio: 18.7%
Return on equity: 6.6%
Cash ($ mil.): 5,184
Current ratio: 0.98
Long-term debt ($ mil.): 6,804
No. of shares (mil.): 380
Dividends
  Yield: 0.0%
  Payout: 11.7%
Market value ($ mil.): 3,236

	STOCK PRICE ($) FY Close	P/E High/Low		PER SHARE ($) Earnings	Dividends	Book Value
12/20	8.50	5	4	2.25	0.26	33.33
12/19	8.40	3	2	3.56	0.23	30.76
12/18	7.94	3	2	4.07	0.24	29.94
12/17	6.56	—	—	3.61	0.24	28.98
12/16	6.56	—	—	2.22	0.21	24.22
Annual Growth	**6.7%**	—	—	**0.3%**	**6.2%**	**8.3%**

BP PLC

BP is one of the largest oil and gas companies in the world. BP explores produces and sells oil and gas fuels lubricants wind power and biofuels. BP's main brands include the eponymous BP brand which appears on rigs offices and gas stations gas station-specific brands Amoco (US) and Aral (Germany) lubricant brand Castrol and gas station convenience store brands ampm and Wild Bean Cafe. It has operations throughout the world but generates most of its revenue from outside of US. In 2021 the company's reportable segments changed consistent with a change in the way that resources are allocated and performance. Its reportable segments are now gas & low carbon energy oil production & operations customers & products and Rosneft.

Operations

BP has two major operating segments: Downstream and Upstream. Rosneft is also reported as its segment.

The downstream segment is BP's primary earner bringing in some 90% of total sales. BP manages the refining manufacturing marketing transportation and supply and trading of crude oil petroleum petrochemicals products lubricants and related services to wholesale and retail customers.

Upstream activities (about 10% of revenue) include oil and natural gas exploration field development and production transportation storage and processing. BP also markets and trades LNG and natural gas liquids.

BP's interest in Rosneft is accounted for using the equity method the biggest oil producer in Russia and although reported as a separate operating segment it does not contribute to sales.

Other businesses and corporate comprises the biofuels and wind businesses the group's shipping and treasury functions and corporate activities worldwide.

Geographic Reach

Headquartered in London BP has LNG activities are located in Abu Dhabi Angola Australia Indonesia and Trinidad. In Europe BP is active in the North Sea and the Norwegian Sea. BP also has activities in Abu Dhabi Azerbaijan China India Indonesia Iraq Kuwait Oman Russia Australia and Eastern Indonesia.

Its upstream activities in Americas are located in deepwater Gulf of Mexico the Lower 48 states Canada Mexico Argentina Brazil and Trinidad & Tobago and through PAEG a joint venture that is owned by BP (50%) and Bridas Corp. (50%) in Argentina Bolivia and Uruguay. It also has activities in Africa are located in Algeria Angola C ´te d'Ivoire Egypt The Gambia Libya Mauritania S o Tome & Pr ncipe and Senegal.

In terms of revenue US is the company's largest market generating some 30% of total revenue.

Sales and Marketing

BP primarily sells oil and gas through pipelines and by ship truck and rail serving 11.5 million retail customer every day.

Major company brands include eponymous BP as well as AMOCO ampm Aral and Castrol. With more than 2.5 million customers visit an Aral service station Aral is one of the most recognized brands in Germany while BP and Castrol are leading brands of motor oil and lubricants. US retail brand ampm has more than 950 locations throughout the US west coast.

Financial Performance

The company's revenue decreased to $180.4 billion compared from the prior year with $278.4 billion.

The loss for the year ended 31 December 2020 attributable to BP shareholders was $20.3 billion compared with a profit of $4.0 billion in 2019.

Cash held by the company at the end of fiscal 2020 increased to $31.1 billion. Cash provided by operations and financing activities were $12.2 billion and $4.0 billion respectively. Cash used for investing activities was $7.9 billion mainly for expenditure on property plant and equipment intangible and other assets.

Strategy

The company focuses on three areas of activity: low carbon electricity and energy convenience and mobility and resilient and focused hydrocarbons. Each focus area represents an attractive opportunity in its own right. Taken individually they are not unique to BP. But the company plan to leverage three sources of differentiation to help BP amplify value: integrating energy systems partnering with countries cities and industries and driving digital and innovation.

Company Background

BP's history dates back to efforts of British companies to capitalize on discoveries of rich oil deposits in Middle East in the late 19th and early 20th Centuries. These included the Anglo-Persian Oil Company (later the Anglo-Iranian Oil Company) in which the British Government took a majority share in 1914. It became British Petroleum in 1954 and following a number of other acquisitions became BP in 2000. BP's modern history is marked by the 2010 Deepwater Horizon disaster a massive spill in the Gulf of Mexico that resulted in the highest fines and penalties in the history of the US.

EXECUTIVES

Non-Executive Independent Director, Brendan Nelson

Chief Executive Officer and Director, Bernard Looney, $1,514,703 total compensation

EVP, Gas and Low Carbon Energy, Dev Sanyal

Senior Non-Executive Independent Director, Paula Reynolds

EVP, People and Culture, Kerry Dryburgh

Executive Vice President, Legal, Eric Nitcher

Non-Executive Independent Director, Pamela Daley

Chief Financial Officer, Murray Auchincloss, $446,330 total compensation

EVP, Innovation and Engineering, David Eyton

EVP, Regions, Cities, and Solutions, William Lin

EVP, Strategy and Sustainability, Giulia Chierchia

Executive Vice President - Communications and Advocacy, Geoff Morell

Executive Vice President, Customers and Products, Emma Delaney

Executive Vice President, Trading and Shipping, Carol-Lee Howle

Non-Executive Independent Director, Tushar Morzaria

Non-Executive Independent Director, Johannes Teyssen

Non-Executive Independent Director, Karen Richardson

Non-Executive Independent Director, John Sawers

EVP, Production and Operation, Gordon Birrell

Non-Executive Independent Director, Melody Meyer

Non-Executive Independent Chairman of the Board, Helge Lund

Auditors: Deloitte LLP

LOCATIONS

HQ: BP PLC
1 St. James's Square, London SW1Y 4PD
Phone: (44) 20 7496 4000   **Fax:** (44) 20 7496 4630
Web: www.bp.com

2018 Sales

	% of total
US	33
Other countries	67
Total	**100**

PRODUCTS/OPERATIONS

2018 Sales

	% of total
Downstream	91
Upstream	9
Other businesses and corporate	-
Total	**100**

Major Operations

Refining and marketing
  Marketing
  Refining
  Supply and trading
  Transportation and shipping
Exploration and production
  Field development
  Gas processing and marketing
  Oil and gas exploration
  Pipelines and transportation
Gas and power
  Natural gas marketing and trading
  Natural gas liquids
Chemicals
  Chemical intermediates
  Feedstock
  Performance products
  Polymers
Other
  Coal mining
  Solar power

Selected Subsidiaries

Atlantic Richfield Co
BP America Inc. (US)
BP Amoco Chemcal Company (US)
BP Oil Australia
BP Exploration Operating Company
BP Espóa (Spain)
BP International
BP Norge (Norway)
BP Oil New Zealand
BP Shipping
BP Southern Africa (South Africa)
Burmah Castrol
The Standard Oil Company (US)

COMPETITORS

Archer Limited
Brenntag Holding GmbH
CHIYODA CORPORATION
China National Offshore Oil Corporation
ENEOS HOLDINGS INC.
ENI SPA
HELLENIC PETROLEUM S.A. HOLDING
HUNTING PLC
KINDER MORGAN INC
LUKOIL PAO
Louis Dreyfus Holding B.V.
LyondellBasell Industries N.V.
MARATHON OIL CORPORATION
Metal rgica Gerdau S/A
OSAKA GAS CO. LTD.
PHILLIPS 66
ROYAL DUTCH SHELL plc
RUBIS
SASOL LTD
SURGUTNEFTEGAZ PAO

HISTORICAL FINANCIALS

Company Type: Public

Income Statement				FYE: December 31
	REVENUE ($ mil.)	NET INCOME ($ mil.)	NET PROFIT MARGIN	EMPLOYEES
12/20	180,626	(20,305)	—	63,600
12/19	282,423	4,026	1.4%	70,100
12/18	303,282	9,383	3.1%	73,000
12/17	243,372	3,389	1.4%	74,000
12/16	185,474	115	0.1%	74,500
Annual Growth	(0.7%)	—	—	(3.9%)

2020 Year-End Financials

Debt ratio: 27.1%
Return on equity: (-23.8%)
Cash ($ mil.): 31,111
Current ratio: 1.22
Long-term debt ($ mil.): 63,305

No. of shares (mil.): —
Dividends
  Yield: 9.1%
  Payout: —
Market value ($ mil.): —

	STOCK PRICE ($) FY Close	P/E High/Low		PER SHARE ($) Earnings	Dividends	Book Value
12/20	20.52	—	—	(1.00)	1.87	3.52
12/19	37.74	228	182	0.20	2.44	4.86
12/18	37.92	102	78	0.47	2.41	4.95
12/17	42.03	244	194	0.17	2.38	4.97
12/16	37.38	613	14531	0.01	2.38	4.90
Annual Growth	(13.9%)	—	—	—	(5.9%)	(8.0%)

Brenntag SE

EXECUTIVES

Chairman of the Supervisory Board, Doreen Nowotne, $193,699 total compensation

Independent Deputy Chairman of the Supervisory Board, Andreas Rittstieg, $170,910 total compensation

Chief Financial Officer, Member of the Management Board, Georg Mueller, $740,613 total compensation

Chief Transformation Officer, Member of the Management Board, Ewout Van Jarwaarde

Independent Member of the Supervisory Board, Stefanie Berlinger, $136,728 total compensation

Chief Operating Officer - Brenntag Specialties, Member of the Management Board, Henri Nejade, $598,187 total compensation

Independent Member of the Supervisory Board, Ulrich Harnacke, $136,728 total compensation

Independent Member of the Supervisory Board, Wijnand Donkers, $136,728 total compensation

Chairman of the Management Board, Chief Executive Officer, Christian Kohlpaintner, $1,139,406 total compensation

Chief Operating Officer - Brenntag Essentials, Member of the Management Board, Steven Terwindt, $236,996 total compensation

Auditors: PricewaterhouseCoopers GmbH Wirtschaftsprüfungsgesellschaft

LOCATIONS

HQ: Brenntag SE
 Messeallee 11, Essen 45131
Phone: (49) 201 6496 1141   **Fax:** (49) 201 6496 2003
Web: www.brenntag.de

HISTORICAL FINANCIALS

Company Type: Public

Income Statement   FYE: December 31

	REVENUE ($ mil.)	NET INCOME ($ mil.)	NET PROFIT MARGIN	EMPLOYEES
12/20	14,452	572	4.0%	17,237
12/19	14,395	524	3.6%	17,492
12/18	14,372	527	3.7%	16,616
12/17	14,077	432	3.1%	15,416
12/16	11,085	380	3.4%	14,826
Annual Growth	6.9%	10.8%	—	3.8%

2020 Year-End Financials

Debt ratio: 24.7%	No. of shares (mil.): 154
Return on equity: 13.1%	Dividends
Cash ($ mil.): 891	Yield: 1.1%
Current ratio: 1.69	Payout: 5.3%
Long-term debt ($ mil.): 1,825	Market value ($ mil.): 2,435

	STOCK PRICE ($) FY Close	P/E High/Low		PER SHARE ($) Earnings	Dividends	Book Value
12/20	15.76	5	2	3.71	0.18	28.20
12/19	10.80	4	3	3.39	0.17	25.55
12/18	8.71	4	3	3.41	0.17	24.29
12/17	12.60	6	4	2.81	0.16	23.07
12/16	11.10	5	4	2.46	0.14	20.16
Annual Growth	9.2%	—	—	10.8%	7.5%	8.8%

Bridgestone Corp (Japan)

Auditors: Deloitte Touche Tohmatsu LLC

LOCATIONS

HQ: Bridgestone Corp (Japan)
 3-1-1 Kyobashi, Chuo-ku, Tokyo 104-8340
Phone: (81) 3 6836 3162   **Fax:** 615 937-3621
Web: www.bridgestone.co.jp

HISTORICAL FINANCIALS

Company Type: Public

Income Statement   FYE: December 31

	REVENUE ($ mil.)	NET INCOME ($ mil.)	NET PROFIT MARGIN	EMPLOYEES
12/20	29,053	(226)	—	138,036
12/19	32,473	2,695	8.3%	143,589
12/18	33,192	2,652	8.0%	143,509
12/17	32,380	2,562	7.9%	142,669
12/16	28,531	2,270	8.0%	143,616
Annual Growth	0.5%	—	—	(1.0%)

2020 Year-End Financials

Debt ratio: 0.1%	No. of shares (mil.): 704
Return on equity: (-1.0%)	Dividends
Cash ($ mil.): 7,864	Yield: 3.6%
Current ratio: 1.97	Payout: —
Long-term debt ($ mil.): 3,997	Market value ($ mil.): 11,548

	STOCK PRICE ($) FY Close	P/E High/Low		PER SHARE ($) Earnings	Dividends	Book Value
12/20	16.40	—	—	(0.32)	0.59	29.62
12/19	18.49	0	0	3.72	0.74	29.98
12/18	19.19	0	0	3.52	0.74	28.81
12/17	23.24	0	0	3.33	0.62	27.73
12/16	18.05	0	0	2.89	0.58	24.96
Annual Growth	(2.4%)	—	—	—	0.6%	4.4%

British American Tobacco Plc (United Kingdom)

British American Tobacco (BAT) is a leading multi-category consumer goods business. The company rolls more than 5200 billion cigarettes a year sold in around 180 markets across 50-plus countries. BAT sells five global cigarette brands (including Dunhill Kent Rothmans Lucky Strike and Pall Mall). The company is a leading FTSE company with truly international credentials. Spread across six continents its regions are the United States of America; Americas and Sub-Saharan Africa; Europe and North Africa; and Asia-Pacific and Middle East. Additionally BAT owns Reynolds American. Most of BAT's revenue comes from the US.

Operations

British American Tobacco (BAT) offers combustible portfolio (including but not limited to Kent Dunhill Lucky Strike Pall Mall Rothmans Camel (US) Newport (US) Natural American Spirit (US)) which accounts for about 90% of sales; New Category portfolio (being Vapour THP and Modern Oral) which accounts for some 5%) and the group's Traditional Oral portfolio (around 5%) and the group's operations in the United States Europe and North Africa Americas and Sub-Saharan Africa and Asia-Pacific and Middle East.

Geographic Reach

Based in London UK BAT operates some 45 factories in about 45 countries. The US is its largest market accounting for about 45% of sales followed by Europe and North Africa at about a quarter of sales Asia/Pacific and Middle East at about a fifth of sales and Americas and Sub-Saharan Africa at approximately 15% of sales.

Sales and Marketing

BAT sells its products through some 180 markets with 11 million points of sale reaching 150 million consumers daily.

Financial Performance

Revenue was marginally lower than 2019 down 0.4% with 2020 at 25.8 billion while 2019 was 25.9 billion. An increase in revenue from New Categories (up 14.9%) and a good performance in Combustibles driven by price mix of 7% in 2020 (compared to 9% in 2019) was more than offset by a translational foreign exchange headwind of 3.5% due to the relative strength of sterling (2019: tailwind of 0.6%).

Profit for fiscal 2020 increased to 6.4 billion compared with 5.7 billion.

Cash held by the company at the end of fiscal 2020 increased to 2.9 billion. Cash provided by operations was 9.8 billion while cash used for investing and financing activities were 783 million and 7.9 billion respectively. Main cash uses were purchases of property plant and equipment; and reductions in and repayments of borrowings.

Strategy

BAT has set ambitious targets to reach 50 million consumers of its non-combustible products by 2030 and more than triple its revenue from New Categories from 1.3 billion in 2019 to 5 billion by 2025. These ambitions will be met through the delivery of its three clear strategic priorities: ?to drive a step change in New Categories to accelerate growth supported by increased investment; ?to generate value through Combustibles to provide the capabilities and funding; and ?to simplify the company to create a stronger faster more agile organization.

Mergers and Acquisitions

In late 2020 British American Tobacco p.l.c. announces that the US business of the BAT Group (BAT) has acquired the nicotine pouch product assets of Dryft Sciences LLC (Dryft) a US-based Modern Oral nicotine product company. This acquisition expands BAT's Modern Oral portfolio in the US expanding from 4 to 28 product variants. It follows the acceptance of Dryft's recent Pre-Market Tobacco Product Application (PMTA) submission for filing by the US Food and Drug Administration. Terms were not disclosed.

Company Background

In fall 2011 it purchased Colombia's second-largest cigarette maker Productora Tabacalera de Colombia (Protabaco) for $452 million. Protabaco's brands include Mustang (the country's #2 selling cigarette) Premier and President. The deal elevates BAT from third place to second in Colombia's cigarette market.

HISTORY

After a year of vicious price-cutting between Imperial Tobacco (UK) and James Buchanan Duke's American Tobacco in the UK Imperial counterattacked in the US. To end the cigarette price war in the UK the firms created British American Tobacco (BAT) in 1902. The truce granted Imperial the British market American the US market and they jointly owned BAT in the rest of the world.

With Duke in control BAT expanded into new markets. In China it was selling 25 billion cigarettes a year by 1920. When the Communist revolution ended BAT's operations in China the company lost more than 25% of its sales (although China later reemerged as a major export market for the company's cigarettes).

A 1911 US antitrust action forced American to sell its interest in BAT and opened the US market to the company. BAT purchased US cigarette manufacturer Brown & Williamson in 1927 and continued to grow through geographic expansion until the 1960s. In 1973 BAT and Imperial each regained control of its own brands in the UK and Continental Europe. Imperial sold the last of its stake in BAT in 1980.

Fearing that mounting public concern over smoking would limit the cigarette market BAT acquired nontobacco businesses; it changed its name to B.A.T Industries in 1976. The acquisitions of retailers Saks (1973) Argos (UK 1979) Marshall Field (1982) and later insurance firms diversified the company's sales base. After a 1989 hostile takeover bid from Sir James Goldsmith it sold its retail operations and retained its tobacco and financial services.

In 1994 B.A.T acquired the former American Tobacco for $1 billion. In 1997 the company acquired Cigarrera de Moderna (with 50% of Mexico's cigarette sales) and formed a joint venture with the Turkish tobacco state enterprise Tekel.

B.A.T's tobacco operations were spun off in 1998 as British American Tobacco (BAT). The financial services operations were merged with Zurich Insurance in a transaction that created two holding companies: Allied Zurich (UK) and Zurich Allied (Switzerland). With the changes Martin Broughton became chairman of BAT.

The company in 1999 paid $8.2 billion to buy Dutch cigarette company Rothmans International (Rothmans Dunhill) from Switzerland's Compagnie Financiere Richemont and South Africa's Rembrandt Group — both controlled by Anton Rupert. With the purchase BAT received a controlling stake in Canada's Rothmans Benson & Hedges (RBH).

In early 2000 BAT bought the 58% of Canada's Imasco it didn't already own. Imasco sold off its financial services and BAT received Imasco's Imperial Tobacco unit (not related to the UK's Imperial Brands) in the deal. (Formerly called Imperial Tobacco Company of Canada Imasco was created in 1908 with help from BAT.) BAT also unloaded its share of RBH via a public offering.

In 2001 BAT bought the 40.5% of its BAT Australasia subsidiary (formed in 1999 through the Rothmans merger) it didn't already own. Broughton announced that year that the Chinese government had approved development plans that would allow the company to build a factory in China. The company also announced it would build the first foreign-owned cigarette factory in South Korea at that time the world's #8 tobacco market.

Increasing its Latin American regional presence BAT purchased a controlling stake in Peru's top tobacco company Tabacalera Nacional and several of its suppliers in 2003. However two months later BAT said it would not make the million-dollar investment in the company. The announcement came soon after Peru raised taxes on cigarettes. By the end of the year BAT had purchased tobacco manufacturer Ente Tabacchi Italiani S.p.A. from the Italian government. BAT sold the distribution end of its Italian business to Compañ a de Distribuci n Integral Logista in 2004 the same year that Broughton retired; the company named Jan du Plessis as chairman and Paul Adams as CEO.

In June 2009 the company acquired an 85% stake in Indonesia's fourth largest cigarette maker PT Bentoel Internasional Investama Tbk for 303 million ($494 million) from Rajawali Group. Later that year Richard Burrows became chairman; he replaced du Plessis who had become chairman of Rio Tinto. Replacing Adams Nicandro Durante became CEO in early 2011. BAT in fall 2011 acquired Colombia's second-largest cigarette maker Productora Tabacalera de Colombia (Protabaco) for $452 million.

EXECUTIVES

Chief Executive Officer and Director, Jack Bowles, $1,614,743 total compensation
Regional Director, Europe and North Africa, Johan Vandermeulen
Director, Scientific Research, David O'Reilly
Director, New Categories, Paul Lageweg
Finance and Transformation Director, Tadeu Marroco, $993,984 total compensation
Chief Marketing Officer, Kingsley Wheaton
Director, Legal and External Affairs and General Counsel, Jerome Abelman
Senior Non-Executive Independent Director, Dimitri Panayotopoulos
Non-Executive Independent Director, Susan Farr
Non-Executive Independent Director, Marion Helmes
Non-Executive Independent Director, Holly Koeppel
Chairman of the Board, Luc Jobin
Regional Director, Americas and Sub-Saharan Africa, Luciano Comin

Director, Digital and Information, Marina Bellini
Director, Talent, Culture and Inclusion, Hae Kim
Regional Director, Asia-Pacific and Middle East, Michael Dijanosic
Non-Executive Independent Director, Karen Guerra
Director, Operations, Zafar Khan
Non-Executive Independent Director, J. Darrell Thomas
President and CEO, Reynolds American Inc., Guy Meldrum
Non-Executive Independent Director, Savio Kwan
Auditors: KPMG LLP

LOCATIONS

HQ: British American Tobacco Plc (United Kingdom) Globe House, 4 Temple Place, London WC2R 2PG
Phone: (44) 20 7845 1000 **Fax:** (44) 20 7240 0555
Web: www.bat.com

2018 sales

	%
US	39
Europe and North Africa	24
Asia/Pacific and Middle East	20
Americas	17
Total	**100**

PRODUCTS/OPERATIONS

2018 sales

	%
Combustible Portfolio	63
Potentially Risk-Reduced Products	
Vapor	1
THP	2
Modern Oral	-
Traditional Oral	4
Other	30
Total	**100**

Selected Brands

Benson & Hedges
Camel Snus
Craven 'A'
Dunhill
glo
Granit
Grizzly
John Player Gold Leaf
Kent
Kool
Lucky Strike
Lyft
Kodiak
Mocca
Pall Mall
Peter Stuyvesant
Player's Gold Lead
Rothmans
State Express 555
Viceroy
VIP
Vogue
Vuse
Vype

COMPETITORS

INCHCAPE PLC
JAPAN TOBACCO INC.
Koninklijke Ahold Delhaize N.V.
PORTMEIRION GROUP PUBLIC LIMITED COMPANY
PYXUS INTERNATIONAL INC.
RALLYE
RECKITT BENCKISER GROUP PLC
Reemtsma Cigarettenfabriken Gesellschaft mit besc
SIBANYE UK LIMITED
TARKETT

HISTORICAL FINANCIALS

Company Type: Public

Income Statement

				FYE: December 31
	REVENUE ($ mil.)	NET INCOME ($ mil.)	NET PROFIT MARGIN	EMPLOYEES
12/20	35,176	8,734	24.8%	89,182
12/19	34,172	7,532	22.0%	94,846
12/18	31,270	7,701	24.6%	95,239
12/17	27,408	50,695	185.0%	91,402
12/16	18,145	5,717	31.5%	85,335
Annual Growth	18.0%	11.2%	—	1.1%

2020 Year-End Financials

Debt ratio: 43.5%
Return on equity: 10.0%
Cash ($ mil.): 4,283
Current ratio: 0.88
Long-term debt ($ mil.): 54,488

No. of shares (mil.): —
Dividends
  Yield: 7.1%
  Payout: 76.1%
Market value ($ mil.): —

	STOCK PRICE ($) FY Close	P/E High/Low		PER SHARE ($) Earnings	Dividends	Book Value
12/20	37.49	17	12	3.81	2.68	37.38
12/19	42.46	17	13	3.29	2.58	36.92
12/18	31.86	25	12	3.36	2.52	36.43
12/17	66.99	7	3	24.72	3.07	35.81
12/16	112.67	49	35	3.07	1.94	4.97
Annual Growth	(24.1%)	—	—	5.6%	8.4%	65.6%

Brookfield Asset Management Inc

Brookfield Asset Management (BAM) has over $600 billion in assets under management including real estate renewable power infrastructure credit and private equity. It owns a global portfolio of commercial retail residential and development properties. Brookfield is also one of the world's largest investors in renewable power owning more than 5200 power-generating facilities including wind and solar plants with a total of approximately 20000 megawatts of generating capacity. The company's private equity business invests in high-quality companies with high barriers to entry. Most of the company's revenue were generated from the US with about 30% of sales.

Operations

Brookfield Asset Management has seven core business segments: Private Equity Real Estate Infrastructure Renewable Power Residential Development Asset Management and Corporate Activities.

The Private Equity segment invests in a broad range of industries with a focus on business services infrastructure services and industrial operations. It accounts for more than 55% of total revenue.

The Infrastructure segment develops owns and operates the company's infrastructure assets including utility transport energy data infrastructure and sustainable resource holdings. It accounts for some 15% of revenue.

The Real Estate segment develops owns and operates the company's retail office core retail LP investments and other properties. It holds 226 million sq. ft. of space around the world. The segment brings in nearly 15% of total revenue.

Renewable Power assets include wind solar water storage and other power-generation facilities in the Americas and Europe. It brings in more than 5% of revenue.

The Asset Management operations (about 5%) include managing listed partnerships private funds and public securities on behalf of the company's investors as well as share of the asset management activities of Oaktree.

Residential Development is engaged in land condominium and home development in North America and Brazil. It also accounts for less than 5% of revenue.

The Corporate Activities segment manages investment of cash and financial assets as well as the management of corporate leverage including corporate borrowings and preferred equity.

Geographic Reach

Toronto-based BAM has a wide variety of holdings around the world with operations in the Asia/Pacific region Europe the Middle East North America and South America. About 30% of its revenue comes from its business in the US. Its next-largest markets are the UK (some 25% of revenue) Australia Asia Canada Europe (about 10% each) Brazil (some 5%) and Colombia (less than 5%).

Sales and Marketing

BAM's investors include sovereign wealth funds and other institutional investors and individuals.

Financial Performance

The company's revenue for fiscal 2020 decreased to $62.8 billion compared from the prior year with $67.8 billion.

Net income for fiscal 2020 decreased to $707 million compared from the prior year with $5.4 billion.

Cash held by the company at the end of fiscal 2020 increased to $9.9 billion. Cash provided by operations and investing activities were $8.3 billion and $8.7 billion respectively. Cash used for financing activities was $13.9 billion mainly for financial assets and other.

Strategy

The company predominantly invest in real assets across real estate infrastructure renewable power and private equity and hold a significant investment in Oaktree Capital Management ("Oaktree") which is a leading global alternative investment management firm with an expertise in credit.

Brookfield Asset Management's invest where it can bring its competitive advantages to bear such as its strong capabilities as an owner-operator its large-scale capital and its global reach.

Company Background

Brookfield Asset Management was established in 1899 as the S o Paulo Railway Light and Power Company. In the 1950s the company began investing in real assets and in the 1990s it scooped up major commercial properties in New York and Boston. It also invested in renewable energy holdings. The group established its first third-party fund in 2001 launching its asset management operations.

In 2017 Brookfield Renewable Partners partnered with other investors to acquire 51% of TerraForm Power a portfolio of solar and wind power assets for a total commitment of $656 million. Later that year the investors acquired all of TerraForm Global another renewable power portfolio with assets in Brazil China and India for a total of $750 million. Also in 2017 the company acquired a portfolio of manufactured housing communities in the US for $768 million.

EXECUTIVES

Independent Director, Marcel Coutu

Chief Executive Officer, Managing Partner, Director, James Flatt, $770,400 total compensation
Managing Partner, Samuel Pollock, $522,480 total compensation
Vice Chairman of the Board, Jeffrey Blidner, $492,274 total compensation
Vice Chairman of the Board, Managing Partner, Brian Lawson, $452,280 total compensation
Affiliated Director, Jack Cockwell
Managing Partner, Cyrus Madon, $522,480 total compensation
Managing Partner, Chief Operating Officer, Lori Pearson
Independent Chairman of the Board, Frank Mckenna
Managing Partner, Chief Investment Officer, Sachin Shah, $522,480 total compensation
Managing Partner, Brian Kingston, $750,000 total compensation
Independent Director, Diana Taylor
Independent Director, Angela Braly
Independent Director, Rafael Miranda
Affiliated Director, Howard Marks
Independent Director, Ngee Huat Seek
Managing Partner, Chief Financial Officer, Nicholas Goodman, $447,840 total compensation
Managing Partner, Head of Corporate Strategy and Chief Legal Officer, Justin Beber
Managing Partner, Chief Executive Officer of Alternative Investments, Craig Noble
Independent Director, Hutham Olayan
Independent Director, Janice Fukakusa
Auditors: Deloitte LLP

LOCATIONS

HQ: Brookfield Asset Management Inc
Suite 300, Brookfield Place, 181 Bay Street, P.O. Box 762, Toronto, Ontario M5J 2T3
Phone: 416 363-9491   **Fax:** 416 365-2856
Web: www.brookfield.com

2017 Sales

	$ mil.	% of total
UK	15,106	37
US	8,284	20
Canada	5,883	14
Australia	4,405	11
Brazil	3,206	8
Other	3,902	10
Total	**40,786**	**100**

PRODUCTS/OPERATIONS

2017 Sales by Segment

	$ mil.	% of total
Private Equity	24,220	60
Real Estate	6,824	17
Infrastructure	3,859	10
Renewable Power	2,788	7
Residential Development	2,447	6
Corporate Activities	362	-
Asset Management	286	-
Total	**40,786**	**100**

Selected Subsidiaries

Brookfield Infrastructure Partners L.P. (70%)
Brookfield Office Properties Inc. (32%)
Brookfield Renewable Partners L.P. (40%)
Brookfield Residential Properties (31%)
Norbord Inc. (40%)

COMPETITORS

DIGITALBRIDGE GROUP INC.
First Capital Realty Inc
GOODMAN LIMITED
HEIWA REAL ESTATE CO.LTD.
INDUS REALTY TRUST
MITSUI FUDOSAN CO. LTD.
OPPENHEIMER HOLDINGS INC.
PROLOGIS INC.
Power Corporation of Canada
SILVER MERGER SUB 1
INC.
MITSUBISHI ESTATE COMPANY LIMITED
LLC
SUMITOMO REALTY & DEVELOPMENT CO. LTD.

HISTORICAL FINANCIALS

Company Type: Public

Income Statement

FYE: December 31

	REVENUE ($ mil.)	NET INCOME ($ mil.)	NET PROFIT MARGIN	EMPLOYEES
12/20	62,752	(134)	—	150,000
12/19	67,826	2,807	4.1%	151,000
12/18	56,771	3,584	6.3%	100,000
12/17	40,786	1,462	3.6%	80,750
12/16	24,411	1,651	6.8%	55,700
Annual Growth	**26.6%**	**—**	**—**	**28.1%**

2020 Year-End Financials

Debt ratio: 43.1%
Return on equity: (-0.3%)
Cash ($ mil.): 9,933
Current ratio: —
Long-term debt ($ mil.): 148,401

No. of shares (mil.): 1,510
Dividends
Yield: 1.1%
Payout: —
Market value ($ mil.): 62,347

	STOCK PRICE ($) FY Close	P/E High/Low		Earnings	PER SHARE ($) Dividends	Book Value
12/20	41.27	—	—	(0.12)	0.48	23.72
12/19	57.80	33	21	1.73	0.43	23.20
12/18	38.35	19	16	2.27	0.40	20.81
12/17	43.54	48	36	0.89	0.37	19.64
12/16	33.01	34	26	1.03	0.35	18.41
Annual Growth	**5.7%**			**—**	**8.5%**	**6.6%**

Brookfield Business Partners LP

Auditors: Deloitte LLP

LOCATIONS

HQ: Brookfield Business Partners LP
73 Front Street, 5th Floor, Hamilton HM 12
Phone: (441) 294 3309
Web: www.brookfield.com

HISTORICAL FINANCIALS

Company Type: Public

Income Statement

FYE: December 31

	REVENUE ($ mil.)	NET INCOME ($ mil.)	NET PROFIT MARGIN	EMPLOYEES
12/20	37,635	(91)	—	67,315
12/19	43,032	43	0.1%	67,030
12/18	37,168	74	0.2%	46,651
12/17	22,823	(58)	—	26,900
12/16	7,960	(32)	—	20,400
Annual Growth	**47.5%**	**—**	**—**	**34.8%**

2020 Year-End Financials

Debt ratio: 43.8%
Return on equity: (-4.4%)
Cash ($ mil.): 2,743
Current ratio: 1.19
Long-term debt ($ mil.): 22,059

No. of shares (mil.): 148
Dividends
Yield: 0.6%
Payout: —
Market value ($ mil.): —

BT Group Plc

BT Group is one of the world's leading communications services companies. The company provides solutions for its customers in over 180 countries such as broadband mobile TV networking IT services and related services and applications. BT operates through four customer-facing units: Consumer Global Enterprise and Openreach. BT also builds owns and operates the UK's largest fixed and mobile networks which support the country's digital ambition. BT designs markets sells and supports differentiated innovative and compelling solutions to their customers. The company generates nearly 90% of its total revenue from the UK.

Operations

BT divides its operations into four segments: Consumer Enterprise Global and Openreach.

The BT Consumer segment generates over 45% of sales and provides consumer mobile fixed and converged communications solutions.

The Enterprise segment (25% of sales) keeps around 1.2m UK and Republic of Ireland businesses and public sector organizations connected. It provides network solutions to more than 1400 UK communications providers.

The Global segment (nearly 20% of sales) integrates secures and manages network and cloud infrastructure and services for multinational corporations.

Openreach (more than 10% of sales) runs the UK's main fixed connectivity access network connecting homes mobile phone masts schools shops banks hospitals libraries broadcasters governments and big and small businesses to the world.

Overall BT generates around 40% of sales from its Fixed-Access Subscriptions followed by its Mobile subscriptions for more than 20% of sales. ICT & Managed Networks and Equipment and Other services account for almost 40% of sales combined.

Geographic Reach

Based in London BT generates nearly 90% of its revenue at home in the UK. The company has customers in around 180 countries. The firm also has a presence in high-growth regions in Asia Pacific Latin America the Middle East and Africa.

Sales and Marketing

BT operates in wholesale and retail markets. Its customers are consumers businesses multinational corporations public sector organizations and other communications providers. Consumers buy solutions from its BT EE and Plusnet brands.

It includes landline mobile broadband and TV services coupled with supplementary propositions like handsets accessories and insurance. Businesses buy similar solutions from BT but with more focus on complex managed network solutions IT services and cyber security.

Most customers buy BT products and services on monthly recurring subscriptions or contracts. Individuals households and small and medium-sized enterprises (SMEs) are typically on 12?24 month contracts. Larger UK and international business customers usually buy managed solutions on multi-year contracts. Wholesale customers buy contracts ranging from one month to five or more years.

Financial Performance

Reported revenue was 21.3 billion down 7% in 2021. This was due primarily to the impact of Covid-19 on Consumer and their enterprise units ongoing legacy product declines and divestments but was partially offset by higher equipment revenue and Openreach bases in fibre and Ethernet.

The company reported a comprehensive income loss of 3.1 billion in 2021.

BT's cash on hand fell 513 million during fiscal 2021 ending the year at 896 million. The company's operations generated 6.3 billion partially offset by its financing which used 3.2 billion and another 3.2 billion used in its investing activities.

Strategy

BT Group plans to grow value for all their stakeholders through three strategic pillars: build the strongest foundations; create standout customer experiences; and lead the way to a bright sustainable future. For the company's first strategic pillar they plan to build the best converged networks; build a simpler more dynamic BT; and build a culture where their people can be their best. BT will continue to invest in fiber 5G edge core and extended access to build the best converged smart network so their customers can do more. For the second strategic pillar the company will relentlessly focus on creating standout customer experiences by connecting more people and moving from products to better smarter outcomes. For the last strategic pillar the company will leverage new tech-driven growth engines that support great outcomes for customers and country and by operating a sustainable and responsible business.

Company Background

BT Group dates back to the 1840s and the early days of the telegraph. The UK government took control of the multitude of companies that sprang up and housed them under the Post Office government branch — then a major department of government. The Post Office telecommunications activities were renamed British Telecom (BT) in 1980 and separated out from the Post Office — by that point a nationalized industry rather than government department — in 1981. BT was privatized in 1984 and the telecom market was opened to competition. British Telecom became BT in 1991. In 2005 Ofcom the regulator ordered the creation of Openreach a BT Group company tasked with the management of the UK's telecom infrastructure and allowing unbiased access for rival telecom companies. The company acquired EE in 2016 and became the UK's biggest mobile network.

HISTORY

In 1879 the British Post Office (now known as Royal Mail and formerly Consignia) got the exclusive right to operate telegraph systems. When private firms tried to offer phone service the government objected arguing in court that its telegraph monopoly was imperiled. The courts agreed and the Post Office was empowered to license private phone companies collect a 10% royalty and operate its own systems.

The private National Telephone Company emerged as the leading phone outfit competing with the Post Office. When National's license expired in 1911 the Post Office took over and became the monopoly phone company. In 1936 the phone system introduced its familiar red phone booths designed for King George V's jubilee.

Under a 1981 law telecommunications were split from the Post Office and placed under the new British Telecommunications (BT). The government also allowed competitor Mercury Communications — formerly One 2 One and now known as T-Mobile (UK)— to compete. The Thatcher government soon called for BT's privatization.

EXECUTIVES

Independent Non-Executive Director, Allison Kirkby, $161,889 total compensation

Independent Non-Executive Director, Leena Nair, $151,445 total compensation

Independent Non-Executive Director, Ian Cheshire, $157,973 total compensation

Non-Independent Non-Executive Director, Adel Al-Saleh

Independent Non-Executive Director, Sara Weller, $110,973 total compensation

CEO, Enterprise, Rob Shuter

Chief Digital and Innovation officer, Harmeen Mehta

Chairman of the Board, Adam Crozier

Chief Executive Officer, Global Services, Bas Burger

Group General Counsel, Company Secretary and Director, Regulatory Affairs, Sabine Chalmers

Chief Executive Officer and Director, Philip Jansen, $1,436,121 total compensation

Independent Non-Executive Director, Matthew Key, $174,945 total compensation

General Counsel, Enterprise, Rachel Canham

Chief Technology and Information Officer, Howard Watson

Chief Financial Officer and Director, Simon Lowth, $959,589 total compensation

Chief Executive Officer, Consumer, Marc Allera

Corporate Affairs Director, Ed Petter

Chief Executive Officer, Openreach, Clive Selley

Auditors: KPMG LLP

LOCATIONS

HQ: BT Group Plc
  81 Newgate Street, London EC1A 7AJ
Phone:
Web: www.btplc.com

2018 Sales

	% of total
Europe Middle East & Africa (ecxl. UK)	11
UK	83
Americas	4
Asia Pacific	2
Total	**100**

PRODUCTS/OPERATIONS

2019 Sales

	% of total
Consumer	45
Enterprise	25
Global Services	20
Openreach	10
Total	**100**

2019 Sales by Market

	%
Fixed-Access Subscriptions	39
Mobile Subscriptions	23
Equipment and Other Services	17
ICT & Managed Networks	21
Total	**100**

Selected Subsidiaries and Affiliates

Basilica Computing Limited (IT services)
British Telecommunications plc (telecommunication related services and products)
BT Americas Inc. (telecommunication related services and products US)
BT Australasia Pty Limited (telecommunication related services and products Australia)
BT Centre Nominee 2 Limited (property holding company)
BT Communications Ireland Limited (telecommunications services)
BT Conferencing Inc. (Audio video and Web conferencing services US)
BT Convergent Solutions Limited (communications related services and products)
BT ESPAÑA Compóí;a de Servicios Globales de Telecomunicaciones S.A. (telecommunication related services and products Spain)
BT Fleet Limited (fleet management)
BT France SA (telecommunication related services and products)
BT Frontline Pte Ltd (communications related services and products Singapore)
BT (Germany) GmbH & Co. oHG (telecommunication related services and products)

BT Global Services Limited (international telecommunications network systems)

BT Holdings Limited (investment holding company)

BT Hong Kong Limited (telecommunication related services and products)

BT Infrastructures Critiques (IT systems and network services France)

BT INS Inc (Information telecommunication consulting and software US)

BT Italia SpA (telecommunications related services and products Italy 97%)

BT Limited (international telecommunication network systems provider)

BT Nederland NV (telecommunication related services and products The Netherlands)

BT US Investments Limited (investments holding company US)

Communications Global Network Services Limited (telecommunication related services and products Bermuda)

Communication Networking Services (UK) (telecommunication related services and products)

Infonet Services Corporation (global managed network services provider US)

Infonet USA Corporation (global managed network services provider US)

Radianz Americas Inc. (global managed network services provider US)

COMPETITORS

AT&T INC.	TELEFONICA SA
CISCO SYSTEMS INC.	TELSTRA CORPORATION
COMPUTACENTER PLC	LIMITED
IDT CORPORATION	Telefon AB LM Ericsson
SPRINT CORPORATION	VERIZON COMMUNICATIONS
Shaw Communications	INC.
Inc	XO HOLDINGS INC
TELECOM ITALIA SPA	

HISTORICAL FINANCIALS

Company Type: Public

Income Statement   FYE: March 31

	REVENUE ($ mil.)	NET INCOME ($ mil.)	NET PROFIT MARGIN	EMPLOYEES
03/21	29,365	2,026	6.9%	99,700
03/20	28,296	2,142	7.6%	0
03/19	30,690	2,828	9.2%	106,700
03/18	33,335	2,855	8.6%	105,800
03/17	30,040	2,382	7.9%	106,400
Annual Growth	(0.6%)	(4.0%)	—	(1.6%)

2021 Year-End Financials

Debt ratio: 45.1%   No. of shares (mil.): —
Return on equity: 11.1%   Dividends
Cash ($ mil.): 1,376   Yield: —
Current ratio: 1.15   Payout: —
Long-term debt ($ mil.): 21,715   Market value ($ mil.): —

Bunzl Plc

Bunzl bundles miscellaneous non-food items to provide a comprehensive offer for clients in the foodservice grocery safety cleaning and hygiene retail and healthcare sectors. It sources and distributes an eclectic range of items ranging from packaging catering equipment and hygiene supplies to PPE chemicals latex gloves and medical supplies that are essential to the smooth functioning of business. Based in London serves customers in North America Bunzl's biggest market Europe the UK and the Asia/Pacific region via its own fleet and via third-party carriers. Overall it has operations in more than 30 countries.

Operations

Bunzl serves six main customer markets with a range of non-food products. These include food packaging disposable tableware guest amenities catering equipment cleaning products and safety items (the Foodservice market); films labels bags and cleaning and hygiene supplies (Grocery); PPE gloves boots hard hats ear and eye protection and other workwear (Safety); cleaning and hygiene materials chemicals and hygiene paper (Cleaning & Hygiene); bags packaging receipt paper (Retail); and gloves swabs bandages stethoscopes IV drips and medical tape (Healthcare).

Geographic Reach

London-based Bunzl operates in more than 30 countries in total. Its most lucrative market is North America representing nearly 60% of sales followed by Europe at 20% and the UK and Ireland at nearly 15%. All other countries generate nearly 10% of sales.

Most of Bunzl's suppliers are in China.

Sales and Marketing

Bunzl sells through direct store delivery crossdock and warehouse replenishment programs on a local regional national and international basis. In addition the company uses multinational and local supplier relationships. The company supplies products to customers via its own fleet of vehicles as well as third party carriers.

Bunzl employs some 3200 sales staff supported by 2600 locally based customer service employees.

Bunzl serves a diversified industry base. Food services is the most valuable industry to the company representing 30% of sales followed by grocery (more than 25%) safety (about 15%) and cleaning & hygiene (more than 10%) Retail healthcare other sectors generate the remaining revenue.

Financial Performance

Note: Growth rates may differ after conversion to US Dollars.

Revenue increased to 9.3 billion (2018: 9.1 billion) up 1.0% at constant exchange rates (up 3% at actual exchange rates) reflecting the benefit of acquisitions partly offset by the impact of disposals in 2018 and a small decrease in organic revenue which was down 0.2%.

Cash held by the company at the end of 2019 decreased by 3.4 million to 140.8 million compared from the prior year with 144.2 million. Cash provided by operations was 669.3 million while cash used for investing and financing activities were 162.6 million and 492.2 million respectively. Main uses for cash were purchase of business dividends paid repayment of borrowings and payment of lease liabilities.

Strategy

Bunzl continues to pursue its consistent and proven strategy of developing the business through organic growth consolidating the markets in which the company competes through focused acquisitions and continuously improving the quality of its operations thereby making its businesses more efficient and sustainable.

The company looks to achieve organic growth by applying its extensive resources and specialist knowledge and expertise to enable our customers to reduce or eliminate the hidden costs of sourcing and distributing a broad range of goods-not-for-resale and to make their businesses more sustainable. By offering an efficient and cost-effective one-stop-shop to meet their product demands combined with the provision of a variety of value-added innovative sustainable and customized service solutions its customers can focus on their core businesses and achieve purchasing efficiencies and savings while freeing up working capital improving their distribution capabilities reducing carbon emissions and simplifying their own internal administration processes.

Although Bunzl purchased fewer businesses in 2019 than in recent years growth through acquisitions remains a key element of its strategy which has enabled the company to build leading positions in a number of market sectors in the Americas Europe and the Asia Pacific.

Mergers and Acquisitions

In mid-2020 Bunzl announced to acquire Tennessee-based MCR Safety a company engaged in distribution of a variety of largely own brand personal protection equipment and other safety products for an undisclosed amount. The acquisition complement Bunzl's existing product range and significantly strengthen and expand its safety operations both in the US and elsewhere.

In early 2020 Bunzl acquired Birmingham-based Bodyguard Workwear a distributor of afety workwear and other personal protection equipment for an undisclosed sum. It also acquired Sao Paulo-based Medcorp a distributor of healthcare related products for an undisclosed amount. The acquisition expanded its existing healthcare business in Brazil and complements and strengthens its product offering in healthcare sector.

In early 2020 Bunzl acquired Cleveland-based Joshen Paper & Packaging a distributor of packaging and other goods not for resale to customers operating principally in the grocery sector for an undisclosed amount. The acquisition will help Bunzl to enhance its operations in the US.

In 2019 it acquired Coolpack a Dutch distributor of specialist packaging to supermarkets pharmaceuticals food processors and foodservice companies.

HISTORY

Bunzl's earliest predecessor was a Czechoslovakian haberdashery that opened its doors in 1854. The company moved its operations to Austria in 1883 and expanded into rag trading and textile and paper manufacturing. The firm went by Bunzl & Biach but it was run by the Bunzl family. In the late 1920s the company began making cigarette filters from crepe paper.

Hitler annexed Austria in 1938 but the Jewish Bunzl family had planned ahead by moving the headquarters from Vienna to Switzerland in 1936. The firm also had a subsidiary in London that served as an alternate base; when the company's Austrian assets were seized during Nazi occupation family members sought refuge in the UK Switzerland and the US. Hugo Bunzl who had championed the idea of making cigarette filters wound up in the UK. In 1940 he founded Tissue Papers Ltd. to make tissue crepe paper and cigarette filters. The family regained its Austrian operations in 1946 and Tissue Papers began distributing the Austrian paper products. Its name was changed to Bunzl Pulp & Paper Ltd. in 1952.

Filter-tipped cigarettes became more popular after the war and Eastman Kodak soon developed cellulose acetate tow filters. Bunzl began using the material in 1954 the same year it set up American Filtrona Corporation its US subsidiary. Medical research began to identify cigarette smoking as a health risk and filters soared in popularity. Bunzl stepped up production and soon became the world leader in cigarette filters. Its paper and packaging business also grew and the company went public in 1957.

Bunzl continued to grow steadily thanks to cigarette filter sales. Growth slowed however and governments began restricting cigarette advertising. The company began to diversify in the late 1960s; through product development and acquisitions it was able to offer self-adhesive labels tapes plastic tubes and polythene film and bags.

In 1970 Bunzl Pulp & Paper took over its Austrian progenitor Bunzl & Biach. The purchase brought Bunzl more fully into papermaking and reduced its dependence on cigarette filters. By the latter half of the decade many cigarette companies were making their own filters and competition from Eastern Europe was hurting the company's paper margins. To compensate Bunzl expanded its plastics operations into pipes; it also had a disastrous foray into data processing.

In 1980 Bunzl sold its Austrian paper business and the waning filter business once again made up the lion's share of profits. The company bought into the specialized paper and plastic distribution business through acquisitions during the early 1980s. By the end of 1984 sales had more than quintupled with filters responsible for less than 20% of profits. Bunzl made about 70 more purchases between 1985 and 1987 but it had integration problems and began to sell companies even as it was picking them up.

The company focused on its core operations in the 1990s although goodwill charges related to divestitures and a reassessment of past charges led to a loss in 1994. In 1997 Bunzl created Bunzl Extrusion with the reacquisition of American Filtrona (it had operated separately since 1984). Bunzl also bought Grocery Supply Systems (supermarket disposables) that year. In the first half of 1998 Bunzl spent about $60 million on acquisitions that included UK paper distributor The Paper Company and Netherlands-based extruded-plastics maker Enitor BV. In 1999 Bunzl bought Provend Group PLC a leading provider of vending supplies (beverage-vending machines) and catering disposables in the UK. The following year the company enhanced its outsourcing holdings by acquiring Shermond Products Limited a UK-based health care and hygiene product supplier.

In an effort to diversify its product offerings in 2001 Bunzl expanded its food supplies business (utensils catering supplies) in the US and Europe. In 2002 Bunzl further expanded its European food outservices business with its acquisition of Lockhart (catering supplies) from Sodexo whose client base complements Bunzl's in the UK.

Bunzl split off its Filtrona operations in 2005 (since renamed Essentra) creating two publicly traded companies where there previously had been only one.

In 2010 Bunzl purchased Clean Care A/S a supplier of cleaning and hygiene consumable products based in Denmark. A few months later it snatched up Weita Holding a similar firm catering to Switzerland. The previous year Bunzl bought W.K. Thomas an airlines and catering foodservices distributor and Industrial Supplies cleaning and hygiene products distributor. Part of the King UK group W.K. Thomas and Industrial Supplies were in administration (the UK's bankruptcy program).

In August 2011 the company sold its vending business in the UK (acquired in 1999) at a loss (Å 56 million).

EXECUTIVES

Chief Executive Officer, Executive Director, Frank van Zanten, $1,138,016 total compensation
Chief Financial Officer, Executive Director, Richard Howes, $746,449 total compensation
Independent Non-Executive Director, Vinodka Murria
Chairman, Peter Ventress
Auditors: PricewaterhouseCoopers LLP

LOCATIONS

HQ: Bunzl Plc
York House, 45 Seymour Street, London W1H 7JT
Phone: (44) 20 7725 5000   **Fax:** (44) 20 7725 5001
Web: www.bunzl.com

2018 Sales

	% of total
North America	58
Europe	
Continental	20
UK & Ireland	14
Rest of world	8
Total	**100**

PRODUCTS/OPERATIONS

2018 Sales by Market

	% of total
Food service	29
Grocery	26
Cleaning & hygiene	12
Retail	11
Safety	12
Health care	7
Other	3
Total	**100**

COMPETITORS

ASSA ABLOY AB
DCC PUBLIC LIMITED
  COMPANY
DOMTAR CORPORATION
DS SMITH PLC
GOINDUSTRY-DOVEBID
  LIMITED
INNERWORKINGS INC.

MANUTAN INTERNATIONAL
Ontex Group
RECKITT BENCKISER
  GROUP PLC
RENTOKIL INITIAL PLC
Svenska Cellulosa AB
  SCA

HISTORICAL FINANCIALS

Company Type: Public

Income Statement				FYE: December 31
	REVENUE ($ mil.)	NET INCOME ($ mil.)	NET PROFIT MARGIN	EMPLOYEES
12/20	13,798	586	4.3%	19,239
12/19	12,316	461	3.7%	18,984
12/18	11,592	416	3.6%	18,846
12/17	11,590	419	3.6%	17,595
12/16	9,138	327	3.6%	16,285
Annual Growth	**10.9%**	**15.7%**	**—**	**4.3%**

2020 Year-End Financials

Debt ratio: 44.1%
Return on equity: 23.4%
Cash ($ mil.): 1,288
Current ratio: 1.42
Long-term debt ($ mil.): 2,204

No. of shares (mil.): 337
Dividends
  Yield: 1.9%
  Payout: 39.9%
Market value ($ mil.): 11,458

	STOCK PRICE ($) FY Close	P/E High/Low		PER SHARE ($)		
				Earnings	Dividends	Book Value
12/20	34.00	28	13	1.75	0.66	7.77
12/19	27.80	33	24	1.38	0.58	6.84
12/18	30.72	32	25	1.25	0.58	6.43
12/17	28.34	35	29	1.26	0.55	5.82
12/16	25.80	37	27	0.98	0.42	4.81
Annual Growth	**7.1%**	**—**	**—**	**15.6%**	**11.9%**	**12.7%**

Bupa Finance plc

Auditors: KPMG LLP

LOCATIONS

HQ: Bupa Finance plc
1 Angel Court, London EC2R 7HJ
Phone:

HISTORICAL FINANCIALS

Company Type: Public

Income Statement				FYE: December 31
	REVENUE ($ mil.)	NET INCOME ($ mil.)	NET PROFIT MARGIN	EMPLOYEES
12/20	16,537	522	3.2%	77,586
12/19	16,264	(159)	—	79,986
12/18	15,141	506	3.3%	77,706
12/17	16,544	765	4.6%	62,412
12/16	13,590	579	4.3%	64,980
Annual Growth	**5.0%**	**(2.6%)**	**—**	**4.5%**

2020 Year-End Financials

Debt ratio: —
Return on equity: 5.7%
Cash ($ mil.): 2,328
Current ratio: —
Long-term debt ($ mil.): —

No. of shares (mil.): 200
Dividends
  Yield: —
  Payout: —
Market value ($ mil.): —

BYD Co Ltd

Battery manufacturer BYD has seen its sales go vroom after it entered the automobile business. BYD was once the second-largest rechargeable battery producer in the world after Energizer. But now the company gets juiced from selling its line of midsize gas and hybrid vehicles in China. BYD manufactures about a dozen models including a handful of sedans a couple of minivans an SUV and a convertible coupe. With its background in batteries BYD is also on track to produce its first plug-in all-electric car the E6. The company still manufactures electronic components for mobile phones nickel batteries and lithium-ion batteries. Berkshire Hathaway subsidiary MidAmerican Energy Holdings owns a 10% stake in BYD.

EXECUTIVES

Independent Non-Executive Director, Zi-dong Wang
Vice President, Lin Ren
Independent Non-Executive Director, Min Zhang
Independent Non-Executive Director, Hongping Cai
Independent Non-Executive Director, Yan bo Jiang
Executive Chairman of the Board, President, Chuan-Fu Wang, $769,755 total compensation
Non-Executive Director, Zuo-quan Xia
Vice President, Long He
Vice President, Yu-bo Lian
Vice President, Zhi-qi He
Vice President, Chuan-fang Wang
Non-Executive Vice Chairman of the Board, Xiang-yang Lv
Senior Vice President, Hong-bin Luo
Vice President, Huan-ming Liu
Vice President, Jie Wang
Vice President, Ke Li
Secretary to the Board, Company Secretary and Chief Investment Officer, Qian Li
Chief Financial Officer, Ya-Lin Zhou
Auditors: Ernst & Young Hua Ming (LLP)

LOCATIONS

HQ: BYD Co Ltd
Unit 1712, 17th Floor, Tower 2, Grand Central Plaza, No. 138 Shatin Rural Commmittee Road, New Territories,
Phone:
Web: www.byd.com.cn

2014 Sales

	% of total
China	86
USA	4
Europe	3
India	1
Other	6
Total	**100**

PRODUCTS/OPERATIONS

Product Selected

Automobiles Photovoltaic
Handset and Assembly Services
Rechargeable Battery

2014 Sales

	% of total
Automobiles and related products	47
Handset components & assembly services	44
Rechargeable batteries & photovoltaic business	9
Total	**100**

COMPETITORS

BRILLIANCE CHINA AUTOMOTIVE HOLDINGS
LIMITED
C&D TECHNOLOGIES INC.
CROWN BATTERY MANUFACTURING COMPANY
ENER1 INC.
ENERSYS
GEELY AUTOMOBILE HOLDINGS LIMITED
NEW ENERGY SYSTEMS GROUP
VARTA AG

HISTORICAL FINANCIALS

Company Type: Public

Income Statement   FYE: December 31

	REVENUE ($ mil.)	NET INCOME ($ mil.)	NET PROFIT MARGIN	EMPLOYEES
12/20	23,943	647	2.7%	0
12/19	18,357	232	1.3%	0
12/18	18,908	404	2.1%	0
12/17	16,275	624	3.8%	0
12/16	14,430	727	5.0%	194,000
Annual Growth	13.5%	(2.9%)	—	—

2020 Year-End Financials

Debt ratio: 3.9%
Return on equity: 7.4%
Cash ($ mil.): 2,208
Current ratio: 1.05
Long-term debt ($ mil.): 3,612

No. of shares (mil.): —
Dividends
  Yield: 0.0%
  Payout: 6.4%
Market value ($ mil.): —

	STOCK PRICE ($) FY Close	P/E High/Low		PER SHARE ($) Earnings	Dividends	Book Value
12/20	52.77	36	6	0.22	0.01	(0.00)
12/19	9.92	28	19	0.07	0.05	(0.00)
12/18	12.60	20	11	0.14	0.03	(0.00)
12/17	17.48	15	8	0.22	0.04	(0.00)
12/16	10.41	7	4	0.27	0.08	2.71
Annual Growth	50.0%	—	—	(4.5%)	(36.7%)	—

C.P. All Public Co Ltd

EXECUTIVES

Vice Chairman of Executive Committee, Executive Director, Pittaya Jearavisitkul

Independent Director, Padoong Techasarintr
Director, Adirek Sripratak
Chairman of the Board, Soopakij Chearavanont
Vice President - Purchasing, Phaphatsorn Thanasorn
Independent Director, Pridi Boonyoung
Executive Vice Chairman of the Board, Chairman of the Executive Committee, Korsak Chairasmisak
Vice Chairman of Executive Committee, Executive Director, Piyawat Titasattavorakul
Vice Chairman of the Executive Committee, Tanin Buranamanit
Executive Director, Umroong Sanphasitvong
Director, Prasert Jarupanich
Director, Narong Chearavanont
Vice President - Accounting and Finance, Company Secretary, Supot Shitgasornpongse
Chief Financial Officer, Senior Vice President - Accounting and Finance, Taweesak Kaewrathtanapattama
General Manager - Accounting and Taxation, Aphaporn Wisitkamthorn
Independent Director, Nampung Wongsmith
Vice Chairman of the Board, Suphachai Chearavanont
Senior Vice President - Accounting and Finance, Kriengchai Boonpoapichart
Independent Director, Prasobsook Boondech
Independent Director, Phatcharavat Wongsuwan
Acting Chief Executive Officer, Member of the Executive Committee, Yuthasak Poomsurakul
Member of the Executive Committee, Wisade Wisidwinyoo
Senior Vice President - Corporate Asset and Facilities Management, Vichien Chuengviroj
Senior Vice President - Distribution Center Function, Ampa Yongpisanpop
Vice President - Corporate Strategy, Ronnakitt Pojamarnpornchai
Vice President - Internal Audit, Kidsada Euapiyachart
Vice President - Information Technology, Wiwat Pongritsakda
Senior Vice President - Human Resource, Lawan Tienghongsakul
Compliance Manager, Arthit Paladja
Managing Director and in charge of Operation, Vichai Janjariyakun
Auditors: KPMG Phoomchai Audit Ltd.

LOCATIONS

HQ: C.P. All Public Co Ltd
  313 C.P. Tower, 24th Floor, Silom Road, Kwang Silom, Khet Bangrak, Bangkok 10500
Phone: (66) 2 677 9000   **Fax:** (66) 2 679 0050
Web: www.cpall.co.th

HISTORICAL FINANCIALS

Company Type: Public

Income Statement   FYE: December 31

	REVENUE ($ mil.)	NET INCOME ($ mil.)	NET PROFIT MARGIN	EMPLOYEES
12/20	18,257	537	2.9%	0
12/19	19,172	750	3.9%	0
12/18	16,317	646	4.0%	0
12/17	15,022	611	4.1%	0
12/16	12,625	465	3.7%	0
Annual Growth	9.7%	3.7%	—	—

2020 Year-End Financials

Debt ratio: 1.5%
Return on equity: 16.8%
Cash ($ mil.): 1,355
Current ratio: 0.66
Long-term debt ($ mil.): 7,398

No. of shares (mil.): —
Dividends
  Yield: —
  Payout: —
Market value ($ mil.): —

Canadian Imperial Bank Of Commerce (Toronto, Ontario)

Canadian Imperial Bank of Commerce (CIBC) has assets worth more than $770 billion and is one of Canada's "Big 5" banks. It serves about 10 million clients in Canada the US and around the world. Through four strategic business units CIBC provides a range of financial products and services to individuals small businesses and commercial corporate and institutional customers.

Operations

CIBC organizes its operations into four main business segments. The largest Canadian Personal and Small Business Banking generates about half of the company's total revenues and provides financial advice products and services through a team of advisors to personal and small business clients.

The Canadian Commercial Banking and Wealth Management division (more than 20% of revenues) and U.S. Commercial Banking and Wealth Management (10%) both offer relationship-oriented commercial and private banking and wealth management services to middle-market companies entrepreneurs and high-net-worth individuals and families.

Capital Markets (more than 20%) sells integrated global markets products and services investment banking advice corporate banking and research to corporate government and institutional clients globally.

Geographic Reach

CIBC does about 80% of its business in Canada (plans are in the works for a new global headquarters CIBC Square to be built in Toronto Ontario).

Although working to increase its footprint in the US US operations currently represent more than 10% of sales. The company also does business in the Caribbean (close to 10% of total revenues). It generates less just about 1% of sales in other countries.

Sales and Marketing

CIBC provides financial products and services to 10 million individual small business commercial corporate and institutional clients from Canada and around the world.

The bank has been increasing its advertising spend over the past few years for strategic initiatives and for developing its enhanced travel rewards program. It spent more than $270 million toward advertising and business development in fiscal 2020.

Financial Performance

Note: Growth rates may differ after conversion to US dollars.

CIBC's financial performance for the span of five years have seen steady growth and growing year by year with 2020 as its highest performing year.

The company's revenue increased by C$130 million to $18.7 billion as compared to 2019's revenue of C$18.6 million.

Net income decreased by 35% to C$3.8 billion in 2020 as compared to the previous year's net income of C$5.1 million.

Cash held by the bank at the end of the year was C$43.5 billion. Operation activities provided C$60.3 billion. Financing activities and investing activities used C$1.2 billion and C$19.4 billion.

Strategy

The company aims on delivering superior client experience and top-tier shareholder returns while maintain their financial strength. CIBC focuses on their strategies to enable them to achieve these goals namely focusing on key client segments simplifying and transforming to deliver a modern relationship-banking proposition and advancing the company's purpose-driven culture.

HISTORY

In 1858 Bank of Canada was chartered; Toronto financier William McMaster bought the charter in 1866 when investors failed to raise enough money to open it and changed the name to Canadian Bank of Commerce.

The firm opened in 1867 bought the Gore Bank of Hamilton (1870) and expanded within seven years to 24 branches in Ontario as well as Montreal and New York. Led by Edmund Walker the bank spread west of the Great Lakes with the opening of a Winnipeg Manitoba branch in 1893 and joined the Gold Rush with branches in Dawson City Yukon Territory and Skagway Alaska in 1898.

As the new century began the bank's purchases spanned the breadth of Canada from the Bank of British Columbia (1901) to Halifax Banking (1903) and the Merchants Bank of Prince Edward Island (1906). More buys followed in the 1920s; the bank's assets peaked in 1929 and then plunged during the Depression. It recovered during WWII.

In 1961 Canadian Bank of Commerce merged with Imperial Bank of Canada to become Canadian Imperial Bank of Commerce (CIBC). Imperial Bank was founded in 1875 by Henry Howland; it went west to Calgary and Edmonton and became known as "The Mining Bank." It bought Barclays Bank (Canada) in 1956.

As the energy and agriculture sectors declined in the early 1980s two of CIBC's largest borrowers Dome Petroleum and tractor maker Massey-Ferguson defaulted on their loans. Deregulation opened investment banking to CIBC which in 1988 bought a majority share of Wood Gundy one of Canada's largest investment dealers; CIBC also purchased Merrill Lynch Canada's retail brokerage business.

In 1992 CIBC added substantially to its loss reserves (resulting in an earnings drop of 98%) to cover real estate losses from developer Olympia & York and others. This launched more cost-cutting as the company reorganized by operating segments.

Deregulation allowed CIBC to begin selling insurance in 1993; the company built a collection of life credit personal property/casualty and nonmedical health companies.

In 1996 the bank formed Intria a processing and technical support subsidiary. The next year CIBC Wood Gundy became CIBC World Markets and CIBC bought securities firm Oppenheimer & Co. and added its stock underwriting and brokerage abilities to CIBC World Markets.

In 1998 increasing foreign competition prompted CIBC and Toronto-Dominion to plan a merger (as did Royal Bank of Canada and Bank of Montreal); the government halted both plans citing Canada's already highly concentrated banking industry.

Spurned the bank overhauled its operations to spark growth in the late 1990s. To cut costs it eliminated some 4000 jobs and sold its more than $1-billion real estate portfolio. It teamed with the Winn-Dixie (1999) and Safeway (2000) supermarket chains to operate electronic branches in the US. The firm scaled back its disappointing international operations and began selling its insurance units.

In 2000 CIBC created Amicus as a holding company for CIBC World Markets' retail electronic banking business. The following year the bank sold its merchant card services business to US-based Global Payments.

In 2002 the company snagged US-based Merrill Lynch's Canadian retail brokerage asset management and securities operations renaming it CIBC Asset Management Inc. That same year CIBC merged its Caribbean banking business with that of UK-based Barclays to create FirstCaribbean Bank.

The next year CIBC sold the Oppenheimer private client and asset-management divisions to Fahnestock Viner (now Oppenheimer Holdings). It sold Juniper Financial a Delaware-based credit card issuer to Barclays for some $293 million in 2004.

In 2004 and again in 2006 CIBC was sued by creditors of Internet telecommunications company Global Crossing stating that the bank had engaged in insider trading to the tune of $2 billion. Creditors demanded a return of the proceeds. CIBC denied the claims but in 2006 two units of the bank agreed to pay $17.4 million to investors in the ill-fated telecom.

More trouble came in 2005 when CIBC agreed to pay some $2.4 billion in an investor class-action suit to resolve claims that the company helped notorious energy trader Enron to conceal losses.

EXECUTIVES

Independent Director, Katharine Stevenson
Senior Executive Vice President, Group Head - Capital Markets and Direct Financial Services, Harry Culham, $371,701 total compensation
Independent Director, Barry Zubrow
Independent Director, Michelle Collins
President, Chief Executive Officer, Director, Victor Dodig, $743,403 total compensation
Independent Director, Patrick Daniel
Independent Director, Luc Desjardins
Independent Director, Nicholas Le Pan
Independent Director, Jane Peverett
Senior Executive Vice President, Group Head, CIBC U.S. Region, President, Chief Executive Officer of CIBC Bank USA, Michael Capatides, $749,517 total compensation
Senior Executive Vice President, Group Head - Technology, Infrastructure and Innovation, Christina Kramer
Independent Director, Kevin Kelly
Senior Executive Vice President, Group Head - People, Culture and Brand, Sandy Sharman
Senior Executive Vice President, Group Head - Commercial Banking and Wealth Management, Canada, Jon Hountalas
Independent Director, Martine Turcotte
Independent Director, Christine Larsen
Independent Director, Nanci Caldwell
Senior Executive Vice President, Chief Financial Officer and Enterprise Strategy, Hratch Panossian, $371,701 total compensation
Independent Director, Charles Brindamour
Auditors: Ernst & Young LLP

LOCATIONS

HQ: Canadian Imperial Bank Of Commerce (Toronto, Ontario)
Commerce Court, Toronto, Ontario M5L 1A2
Phone: 416 813-3743
Web: www.cibc.com

2017 Sales

	% of total
Canada	83
Caribbean	8
US	7
Other Countries	2
Total	**100**

PRODUCTS/OPERATIONS

2017 Sales

	% of total
Canadian Personal and Small Business Banking	52
Canadian Commercial Banking and Wealth Management	22
Capital Markets	17
US Commercial Banking and Wealth Management	5
Corporate and other	4
Total	**100**

PRODUCT CATEGORIES

Financial advice
Mobile banking
Online banking
Mobile investment consulting
Mobile wallets
Business Plus credit cards
Digital cart
Simplii Financial
Wealth management services
CIBC Integrated Payments service
CIBC Active Global Currency Pool
Commercial banking services
CIBC Global Money Transfer service
International Student Pay

COMPETITORS

BANK OF AMERICA CORPORATION	ING Groep N.V.
BARCLAYS PLC	KEYCORP
COMMONWEALTH BANK OF AUSTRALIA	NATWEST GROUP PLC
Credit Suisse Group AG	SUNTRUST BANKS INC.
HSBC HOLDINGS PLC	U.S. BANCORP
HUNTINGTON BANCSHARES INCORPORATED	UBS AG

HISTORICAL FINANCIALS

Company Type: Public

Income Statement

	ASSETS ($ mil.)	NET INCOME ($ mil.)	INCOME AS % OF ASSETS	FYE: October 31 EMPLOYEES
10/21	678,140	5,204	0.8%	0
10/20	578,505	2,849	0.5%	43,853
10/19	494,687	3,868	0.8%	45,157
10/18	454,740	4,011	0.9%	44,220
10/17	440,006	3,657	0.8%	44,928
Annual Growth	**11.4%**	**9.2%**	—	—

2021 Year-End Financials

Return on assets: 0.8%	Dividends
Return on equity: 14.8%	Yield: 0.0%
Long-term debt ($ mil.): —	Payout: 41.9%
No. of shares (mil.): 450	Market value ($ mil.): 54,668
Sales ($ mil): 18,859	

	STOCK PRICE ($) FY Close	P/E High/Low		PER SHARE ($) Earnings	Dividends	Book Value
10/21	121.26	9	6	11.28	4.73	81.97
10/20	74.62	11	6	6.18	4.38	69.22
10/19	85.26	8	7	8.50	4.21	65.45
10/18	86.32	8	7	8.87	4.10	60.10
10/17	88.05	8	7	8.75	3.88	54.99
Annual Growth	**8.3%**	—	—	**6.6%**	**5.1%**	**10.5%**

Canadian Natural Resources Ltd

Canadian Natural is a Canadian based senior independent energy company engaged in the acquisition exploration development production marketing and sale of crude oil natural gas and NGLs. The company's principal core regions of operations are western Canada the UK sector of the North Sea and Offshore Africa. In addition the company has major interests in oil sands production in Canada. Canadian Natural Resources has reported proved reserves of more than 11.9 billion barrels of oil bitumen and natural gas liquids including about 7.0 billion barrels of synthetic crude oil and approximately 9.4 trillion cu. ft. of natural gas and produced an average of nearly 1 million barrels of oil equivalent per day. The company was founded in 1989.

Operations

Canadian Natural Resources generates more than half of its revenue through three geographic segment activities. These include the exploration development production and marketing of crude oil natural gas liquids and natural gas. The company's Oil Sands Mining and Upgrading activities account for about 45% of revenue are reported in a separate segment from exploration and production activities. Midstream and Refining activities include the company's pipeline operations an electricity co-generation system and NWRP.

Geographic Reach

Canadian Natural Resources' exploration and production activities are conducted in three geographic segments: North America (accounts for about 50% of total revenue); North Sea (around 5%); and Offshore Africa (less than 5%).

The company is headquartered in Calgary Alberta with about 15 domestic operating locations. It also has nearly 5 international offices in Central Africa the UK and West Africa.

Sales and Marketing

Canadian Natural Resources customers are mainly in the crude oil and natural gas industry.

Financial Performance

Note: Growth rates may differ after conversion to US Dollars.

The company's revenue for 2020 was C$16.9 billion a 26% decrease from the previous year's revenue of C$22.9 billion. Product sales decreased 28% to $17.5 billion for 2020 from $24.4 billion for 2019. The decrease in product sales was primarily a result of lower WTI benchmark pricing due to decreased demand for refined products as a result of COVID-19.

For 2020 the company reported a net loss of $435 million compared with net earnings of $5.4 billion for 2019 (2018 ? net earnings of $2.6 billion). The net loss for 2020 included net after-tax income of $321 million related to the effects of share-based compensation risk management activities fluctuations in foreign exchange rates the foreign exchange gain on the settlement of the cross currency swaps the gain on acquisition disposition and revaluation the loss from investments and a provision relating to the Keystone XL pipeline project.

The company's cash at the end of 2020 was C$184 million. Operating activities generated C$4.7 billion while financing activities used C$1.9 billion mainly for dividends on common shares. Investing activities used another C$2.8 billion primarily for net expenditures on property plant and equipment.

Strategy

Canadian Natural Resources' objectives are to increase crude oil and natural gas production reserves cash flow and net asset value on a per common share basis through the economic and sustainable development of its existing crude oil and natural gas properties and/or acquisition of new reserves. The company strives to meet these objectives in a sustainable and responsible way maintaining a commitment to environmental stewardship and safety excellence.

The company strives to meet these objectives by having a defined growth and value enhancement plan for each of its products and segments. The company takes a balanced approach to growth and investments and focuses on creating long-term shareholder value.

The company's three-phase crude oil marketing strategy includes: blending various crude oil streams with diluents to create more attractive feedstock; supporting and participating in pipeline expansions and/or new additions; and supporting and participating in projects that will increase the downstream conversion capacity for heavy crude oil and bitumen (thermal oil).

Strategic accretive acquisitions are a key component of the company's strategy. The company has used a combination of internally generated cash flows and debt and equity financing to selectively acquire properties generating future cash flows in its core areas. The company's financial discipline commitment to a strong balance sheet and capacity to internally generate cash flows provides the means to responsibly and sustainability grow in the long term.

Mergers and Acquisitions

In late 2020 Canadian Natural Resources completed the acquisition of all the issued and outstanding common shares of Painted Pony Energy Ltd. Painted Pony has Northeast British Columbia and Calgary head office. The company will also assume Painted Pony's total debt of approximately $350 million. This acquisition further strengthens Canadian Natural's natural gas assets and production base in key operating areas and complements the company's diversified portfolio. This transaction also allows to further insulate against natural gas costs in oils sands operations and has minimal impact on the low overall corporate decline rate.

Company Background

The company was founded in 1989.

EXECUTIVES

Senior Vice President - Corporate Development and Land, Ronald Laing
Senior Vice President - Safety, Risk Management and Innovation, Pamela McIntyre
Senior Vice President - Thermal, Trevor Cassidy
Senior Vice President - Canadian Conventional Field Operations, Troy Anderson
Independent Director, M. Elizabeth Cannon
Chief Financial Officer, Senior Vice President - Finance, Mark Stainthorpe, $184,539 total compensation
Senior Vice President - Development Operations, William Peterson
Senior Vice President - Exploration, Kendall Stagg
Chief Operating Officer - Oil Sands, Scott Stauth, $278,379 total compensation
Senior Vice President - Production, Allan Frankiw
Independent Director, Frank Mckenna
Independent Director, Wilfred Gobert
Chief Operating Officer - Exploration and Production, Darren Fichter, $248,576 total compensation
Vice President - Legal, General Counsel, Corporate Secretary, Paul Mendes
Independent Director, Christopher Fong

Senior Vice President of Marketing, Bryan Bradley
Senior Vice-President - Oil Sands Mining and Upgrading, Jay Froc
Vice President - Land, Betty Yee
Independent Director, Annette Verschuren
Independent Director, David Tuer
Executive Chairman of the Board, Norman Edwards, $0 total compensation
Director, Steve Laut, $127,407 total compensation
President, Director, Tim McKay, $387,764 total compensation
Independent Director, Catherine Best
Lead Independent Director, Gordon Giffin
Auditors: PricewaterhouseCoopers LLP

LOCATIONS

HQ: Canadian Natural Resources Ltd
2100, 855 - 2 Street S.W., Calgary, Alberta T2P 4J8
Phone: 403 514-7605   **Fax:** 403 517-6975
Web: www.cnrl.com

2015 Sales

	% of total
Exploration and Production	
North America	68
North Sea	5
offshore Africa	4
Oil sands mining and upgrading	22
Midstream	1
Total	**100**

COMPETITORS

BATTALION OIL CORPORATION
Baytex Energy Corp
CIMAREX ENERGY CO.
Cenovus Energy Inc
ENQUEST PLC
EOG RESOURCES INC.
EVOLUTION PETROLEUM CORPORATION
Enerplus Corporation
GULFPORT ENERGY OPERATING CORPORATION
MRC ENERGY COMPANY
NOBLE ENERGY INC.
PDC ENERGY INC.
SANDRIDGE ENERGY INC.

HISTORICAL FINANCIALS

Company Type: Public

Income Statement

FYE: December 31

	REVENUE ($ mil.)	NET INCOME ($ mil.)	NET PROFIT MARGIN	EMPLOYEES
12/20	13,267	(341)	—	9,993
12/19	17,563	4,159	23.7%	10,180
12/18	15,440	1,902	12.3%	9,709
12/17	13,282	1,912	14.4%	9,973
12/16	7,808	(151)	—	7,270
Annual Growth	14.2%	—	—	8.3%

2020 Year-End Financials

Debt ratio: 22.3%
Return on equity: (-1.2%)
Cash ($ mil.): 144
Current ratio: 0.86
Long-term debt ($ mil.): 15,794

No. of shares (mil.): 1,183
Dividends
  . Yield: 5.2%
  Payout: —
Market value ($ mil.): 28,472

	STOCK PRICE ($) FY Close	P/E High/Low		PER SHARE ($) Earnings	Dividends	Book Value
12/20	24.05	—	—	(0.29)	1.26	21.48
12/19	32.35	7	5	3.49	1.13	22.64
12/18	24.13	17	10	1.56	1.02	19.54
12/17	35.72	18	14	1.62	0.88	20.65
12/16	31.88	—	—	(0.14)	0.70	17.54
Annual Growth	(6.8%)	—	—	—	15.9%	5.2%

Canadian Tire Corp Ltd

Don't be fooled by its name: Canadian Tire sells much more than tires. About 490 Canadian Tire general merchandise stores run by a network of associate dealers across Canada sell automotive home and sports and leisure products including bicycles. The company's 90-plus PartSource auto parts stores cater to automotive do-it-yourselfers and professionals while its roughly 385-location Mark's Work Wearhouse chain offers work and casual apparel and footwear for men and women. Its Canadian Tire Petroleum subsidiary runs 300 gas bar locations making it one of the country's largest independent gasoline retailers. Established in 1922 Canadian Tire also owns Canada's largest sporting goods retailer FGL Sports.

Operations

Canadian Tire operates three business segments: Retail CT REIT and Financial Services.

The Retail segment (which made up 89% of Canadian Tire's total revenue in fiscal 2015 ended January) includes the business from its Canadian Tire PartSource Canadian Tire Petroleum (CTP) Mark's and various FGL Sports stores. Its Canadian Tire stores make up about half of its total revenue and are operated by independent business owner dealers. Its CTP stores sell fuel and related products from about 300 agent operated gas bars that boast 296 convenience stores and over 80 car wash stations. The company's 415 FGL Sports stores sell sports-related footwear apparel and equipment under the Sport Chek Hockey Experts Sports Experts National Sports Intersport Pro Hockey Life and Atmosphere banners.

The Financial Services segment (8% of revenue) markets a range of Canadian Tire-branded credit cards through its subsidiary Canadian Tire Financial Services (CTFS). (One in five Canadian households had a Canadian Tire credit card in 2014.) CTFS's subsidiary Canadian Tire Bank offers personal loans and lines of credit; high-interest and tax-free savings accounts; insurance plans; and warranty products. Scotiabank acquired a 20% stake in the company's financial services business in October 2014 which raised nearly $477 million in net proceeds for Canadian Tire.

The CT REIT segment (3% of revenue) owned 273 properties spanning 20 million square feet of gross leasable area across all provinces and two territories in Canada as of early 2015. Its property portfolio included Canadian Tire stores retail centers anchored by Canadian Tire stores company distribution centers a mixed-use commercial property and devleopment lands where future Canadian Tire stores could be built.

Geographic Reach

Canadian Tire's retail outlets blanket the country with a store network that served about 90% of Canada's population in 2014. The company has representative offices in the Pacific Rim related to product sourcing logistics and vendor management. Its four distribution facilities are in Brampton Ontario; Calgary Alberta; and Montreal Quebec.

Sales and Marketing

Canadian Tire's supply chain partners include common carrier trucking companies third-party logistics companies ocean carriers and railways.

Financial Performance

Note: Growth rates may differ after conversion to US dollars. This analysis uses financials from the company's annual report.

Canadian Tire's annual revenues and profits have been trending higher since 2009 with a growing total store base and rising same-store sales.

The company's revenue climbed 6% to C$12.5 billion ($10.7 billion) in fiscal 2015 (ended January

3 2015) mostly thanks to a combination of 6% Retail sales growth from strong performance from its Canadian Tire and FGL Sports stores; and 5% Financial Services business growth as credit card sales and balances grew. Its Retail business grew for a variety of factors: its Canadian Tire's retail sales improved with enhanced assortments and new products; its automotive business posted strong results through the year; its FGL Sports sales grew thanks to strong same-store sales at its Sport Chek locations and new store openings; and Mark's sales grew thanks to new marketing campaigns that promoted new assortments and national brands in men's casual wear and footwear.

Revenue growth in FY2015 drove Canadian Tire's net income up 13% to C$639.3 million ($548 million) for the year. The company's operating cash levels fell 36% to C$574.8 million ($492.5 million) despite higher earnings due to unfavorable working capital changes mostly related to merchandise inventories.

Strategy

Canadian Tires' President and CEO laid out a handful of priorities in late 2015 as the company's strategy for growth. These included: continuing to strengthen the company's brands; growing its relationships with its independently-owned Canadian Tire Dealers; embracing the new world of retail by utilizing in-store digital and digital marketing practices and building its e-commerce channel; becoming more productive and efficient; and continuing to look for inorganic growth opportunities building upon its successful acquisitions of the Forzani Group (now FGL Sports) and Mark's Work Wearhouse it made in the past.

Some of the company's other priorities outlined in 2015 included: renovating its Canadian Tire stores with expanded Living categories and better store design; building Mark's market share in the overall casual apparel and casual footwear market with a specific focus on menswear in the jeans outwear and casual footwear categories; and expanding its FGL Sports' Sport Check store network — especially adding new large urban flagship concept stores — while closing over 100 other retail locations by 2017.

To boost traffic and customer retention within its existing stores Canadian Tires has been pushing its "My Canadian Tire Money" card and mobile app loyalty program. The program launched in October 2014 not only gives customers reward points for shopping at the Canadian Tire-affiliated stores but also provides allows the company to leverage customer shopping data to build new retail strategies and personalized relationships over the long term.

HISTORY

In 1922 brothers John and Alfred Billes bought Hamilton Tire and Garage in Toronto a city with 40000 cars at the time. In addition to the usual repair parts tires and batteries the brothers also provided a homemade brand of antifreeze. They fired up earnings even more by renting spaces in their heated garage so drivers in that cold land wouldn't have trouble starting their cars in the morning.

Five years after buying the garage the Billes brothers incorporated as Canadian Tire. Aptly named the company began fielding requests for auto parts from across the country. In 1928 Canadian Tire published a French-English bilingual catalog that is still distributed to 9 million homes.

The Great Depression had little effect on the company as more Canadians sought to hold on to their cars (numbering a million in 1930) rather than buy new ones. For these many do-it-yourself auto mechanics Canadian Tire introduced the super-lastic tire guarantee the first time in the country a tire was guaranteed for other than the

manufacturers' defects. Also in the 1930s the company opened its first associate store in Hamilton Ontario forming the pattern for many such stores to come.

The 1950s saw Canadian Tire roll out a chain of gas stations and introduce a cash bonus coupon called Canadian Tire Money that gas-buying customers could redeem on store merchandise. In the early 1960s customers could earn Tire Money at retail stores as well as gas stations.

Tiring of its core product the company began diversifying its line selling small appliances and other housewares. In the early 1970s tires and other auto supplies accounted for half of Canadian Tire's sales; by 1978 those products accounted for about 35%.

In the next decade the company found itself going south. In 1982 it bought the Texas-based White Stores chain. After disappointing results however Canadian Tire had sold all its US stores by 1986.

In 1994 Canadian Tire introduced its Next Generation stores with expanded offerings and a more customer-friendly format. In another innovation five years later the company announced plans to launch a chain of 200 PartSource stores aimed at garage professionals and advanced do-it-yourselfers. In 2000 Canadian Tire launched an e-commerce site that now markets 15000 products.

In order to focus on its own credit card the company sold its credit card management operations to Citigroup-owned Associates Financial Services of Canada in 2001. Also that year Canadian Tire acquired the Mark's Work Wearhouse apparel chain.

In 2002 the company built and opened 20 stores; in 2003 19 stores were opened.

Tom Gauld formerly president of Canadian Tire Financial Services succeeded Wayne Sales and president and CEO of Canadian Tire in April 2006. Sales remained on the board of directors as vice chairman.

In September 2008 Canadian Tire sold 11 of its retail properties to two commercial real estate firms for a combined $164 million and change. The sale is part of the company's plan to sell and lease back a dozen of its properties for $174 million.

In January 2009 Gauld retired and was succeeded as CEO by director Stephen Wetmore.

In August 2011 Canadian Tire acquired Canada's largest sporting goods retailer The Forzani Group for C$771 million (nearly US$800 million). Forzani which owns the Sport Chek and Athletes World chains among others will operate as a separate business unit as part of the acquisition.

The 2011 acquisition of the Forzani Group — the first major purchase by CEO Stephen Wetmore — was designed to shore up the retailer's position in sporting goods and apparel and give it more competitive heft as it prepared for the 2013 arrival of the US's #2 discounter Target Corp in Canada.

EXECUTIVES

Non Independent Director, J. Owens
Executive Vice President, Chief Financial Officer, Gregory Craig, $436,761 total compensation
President, Chief Executive Officer and Director, Greg Hicks, $695,590 total compensation
Non Independent Director, Owen Billes
Independent Director, Martha Billes
Non-Executive Independent Chairman of the Board, Maureen Sabia
Independent Director, John Furlong
Executive Vice President - CTC, Strategic Advisor, General Counsel, James Christie, $531,859 total compensation
Chief Brand and Customer Officer, Susan O'Brien
Independent Director, David Court

Non Independent Director, Donald Murray
Independent Director, Eric Anderson
Executive Vice President - CTC, President - Canadian Tire Financial Services, President, Chief Executive Officer of Canadian Tire Bank, Mahes Wickramasinghe, $494,135 total compensation
Independent Director, Patrick Connolly
Independent Director, Mark Derbyshire
Independent Director, Cynthia Trudell
Independent Director, Norman Jaskolka
Auditors: Deloitte LLP

LOCATIONS

HQ: Canadian Tire Corp Ltd
 2180 Yonge Street, Toronto, Ontario M4P 2V8
Phone: 416 480-8725   **Fax:** 416 480-8763
Web: www.investors.canadiantire.ca

PRODUCTS/OPERATIONS

2015 Stores

	No.
Canadian Tire Stores	493
FGL Sports	436
Mark's Work Wearhouse	383
Gas bars	297
PartSource	91
Total	**1,700**

2015 Revenue

	% of total
Canadian Tire Retail	89
Financial services	8
CT Reit	3
Eliminations	-
Total	**100**

Selected Products

Automotive
 Batteries and accessories
 Car radio and video systems and parts
 Car security systems
 Emergency road kits
 Lighting and electrical products
 Test and tune supplies and equipment
 Tires
 Truck and trailer accessories
 Wiper blades
Garden and patio
 Barbecues and accessories
 Fertilizers
 Garden tools
 Garden wear
 Patio furniture
 Pest control supplies
 Sheds
 Wheelbarrows and carts
Home products
 Bathroom cabinets and other supplies
 Batteries
 Cleaning supplies
 Electrical
 Electronics
 Home décor
 Kitchen products
 Laundry products
 Lighting products
 Mailboxes
 Pet supplies
 Plumbing supplies
 Safety and security products
 Storage and organization products
Sports and recreation
 Baseball
 Bicycles
 Camping equipment and supplies
 Curling
 Fishing equipment and supplies
 Golf equipment and supplies
 Skateboard and scooters
 Snowshoeing
 Sport and duffel bags
Workshop
 Carpentry tools
 Electrical products

Generators
Power tool accessories
Shop vacuums
Welding and soldering equipment and supplies

COMPETITORS

BRIDGESTONE RETAIL OPERATIONS LLC	HIBBETT INC.
CARQUEST CORPORTION	KEYSTONE AUTOMOTIVE OPERATIONS INC.
COSTCO WHOLESALE CORPORATION	O'REILLY AUTOMOTIVE INC.
DESTINATION XL GROUP INC.	SPARTANNASH COMPANY

HISTORICAL FINANCIALS
Company Type: Public

Income Statement
FYE: January 1

	REVENUE ($ mil.)	NET INCOME ($ mil.)	NET PROFIT MARGIN	EMPLOYEES
01/22	12,791	885	6.9%	33,892
01/21*	11,673	590	5.1%	31,786
12/19	11,100	594	5.4%	31,574
12/18	10,453	514	4.9%	31,686
12/17	10,716	586	5.5%	29,710
Annual Growth	**4.5%**	**10.9%**	**—**	**3.3%**

*Fiscal year change

2022 Year-End Financials

Debt ratio: 25.5%
Return on equity: 23.5%
Cash ($ mil.): 1,375
Current ratio: 1.72
Long-term debt ($ mil.): 4,299

No. of shares (mil.): 60
Dividends
 Yield: 0.0%
 Payout: 25.5%
Market value ($ mil.): 8,632

	STOCK PRICE ($) FY Close	P/E High/Low		PER SHARE ($) Earnings	Dividends	Book Value
01/22	143.52	9	7	14.43	3.69	66.89
01/21*	131.85	11	4	9.66	3.57	58.08
12/19	105.57	9	8	9.61	3.17	52.02
12/18	102.57	13	9	7.91	2.68	51.61
12/17	128.95	12	10	8.51	2.07	56.99
Annual Growth	**2.7%**	**—**	**—**	**14.1%**	**15.5%**	**4.1%**

*Fiscal year change

Canadian Western Bank

Auditors: KPMG LLP

LOCATIONS

HQ: Canadian Western Bank
 Suite 3000, 10303 Jasper Avenue N.W., Canadian Western Bank Place, Edmonton, Alberta T5J 3X6
Phone: 780 423-8888   **Fax:** 780 423-8897
Web: www.cwb.com

HISTORICAL FINANCIALS
Company Type: Public

Income Statement
FYE: October 31

	ASSETS ($ mil.)	NET INCOME ($ mil.)	INCOME AS % OF ASSETS	EMPLOYEES
10/21	30,214	288	1.0%	2,789
10/20	25,512	203	0.8%	2,505
10/19	23,856	217	0.9%	2,278
10/18	22,102	200	0.9%	2,178
10/17	20,586	177	0.9%	2,174
Annual Growth	**10.1%**	**12.9%**	**—**	**6.4%**

2021 Year-End Financials

Return on assets: 1.0%
Return on equity: 10.4%
Long-term debt ($ mil.): —
No. of shares (mil.): 89
Sales ($ mil): 1,167

Dividends
 Yield: 0.0%
 Payout: 31.1%
Market value ($ mil.): 2,859

	STOCK PRICE ($) FY Close	P/E High/Low		PER SHARE ($) Earnings	Dividends	Book Value
10/21	31.98	9	6	3.02	0.94	32.00
10/20	18.36	9	4	2.15	0.86	28.75
10/19	25.67	8	6	2.31	0.81	25.63
10/18	23.51	11	8	2.12	0.77	22.14
10/17	26.63	11	8	1.88	0.72	21.65
Annual Growth	**4.7%**	**—**	**—**	**12.5%**	**6.7%**	**10.3%**

Canon Inc

Auditors: Deloitte Touche Tohmatsu LLC

LOCATIONS

HQ: Canon Inc
 30-2, Shimomaruko 3-chome, Ohta-ku, Tokyo 146-8501
Phone: (81) 3 3758 2111   **Fax:** (81) 3 5482 9680
Web: www.global.canon/en

HISTORICAL FINANCIALS
Company Type: Public

Income Statement
FYE: December 31

	REVENUE ($ mil.)	NET INCOME ($ mil.)	NET PROFIT MARGIN	EMPLOYEES
12/20	30,661	808	2.6%	181,897
12/19	33,096	1,152	3.5%	187,041
12/18	35,936	2,298	6.4%	195,056
12/17	36,260	2,150	5.9%	197,776
12/16	29,082	1,288	4.4%	197,673
Annual Growth	**1.3%**	**(11.0%)**	**—**	**(2.1%)**

2020 Year-End Financials

Debt ratio: 0.0%
Return on equity: 3.1%
Cash ($ mil.): 3,955
Current ratio: 1.35
Long-term debt ($ mil.): 46

No. of shares (mil.): 1,045
Dividends
 Yield: 5.7%
 Payout: 200.7%
Market value ($ mil.): 20,298

	STOCK PRICE ($) FY Close	P/E High/Low		PER SHARE ($) Earnings	Dividends	Book Value
12/20	19.41	0	0	0.77	1.12	23.89
12/19	27.35	0	0	1.08	1.47	23.31
12/18	27.60	0	0	2.13	1.52	23.81
12/17	37.40	0	0	1.98	1.33	23.63
12/16	28.14	0	0	1.18	1.28	21.79
Annual Growth	**(8.9%)**	**—**	**—**	**(10.1%)**	**(3.3%)**	**2.3%**

Capgemini SE

Auditors: KPMG S.A.

LOCATIONS

HQ: Capgemini SE
 Place de l'Etoile 11 rue de, Paris, Tilsitt 75017
Phone: (33) 1 47 54 50 00   **Fax:** (33) 1 47 54 50 25
Web: www.capgemini.com

HISTORICAL FINANCIALS

Company Type: Public

Income Statement

FYE: December 31

	REVENUE ($ mil.)	NET INCOME ($ mil.)	NET PROFIT MARGIN	EMPLOYEES
12/19	15,859	961	6.1%	219,314
12/18	15,113	835	5.5%	211,313
12/17	15,334	982	6.4%	199,698
12/16	13,239	972	7.3%	193,077
12/15	12,977	1,224	9.4%	180,639
Annual Growth	5.1%	(5.9%)	—	5.0%

2019 Year-End Financials

Debt ratio: 20.3%
Return on equity: 10.7%
Cash ($ mil.): 2,763
Current ratio: 1.28
Long-term debt ($ mil.): 2,878

No. of shares (mil.): 169
Dividends
Yield: 1.5%
Payout: 6.8%
Market value ($ mil.): 4,119

	STOCK PRICE ($) FY Close	P/E High/Low		PER SHARE ($) Earnings	Dividends	Book Value
12/19	24.36	5	3	5.61	0.38	55.93
12/18	19.53	6	4	4.87	0.40	51.33
12/17	23.74	5	4	5.71	0.75	49.70
12/16	16.82	9	3	5.54	0.29	44.76
12/15	46.32	7	5	6.89	0.27	43.57
Annual Growth	(14.8%)	—	—	(5.0%)	9.7%	6.4%

Carrefour S.A.

Carrefour (which means "crossroads" in French) is a retailer and operates in approximately 12225 stores under various banners including hypermarkets (Carrefour) supermarkets (Carrefour Market) convenience stores (including City Contact and Express) and cash-and-carry outlets (Promocash) in 30 countries in Europe Latin America Africa-Middle-East and Asia. Besides France Carrefour's core markets are Belgium Italy Poland Romania and Spain. Nearly half of the company's total sales is generated from France.

Operations

Carrefour's store network consists of around 1200 hypermarkets an assortment of 20000 to 80000 product references for a sales area ranging from 2400 to 23000m2. With surfaces of between 1000 and 3500m2 the Carrefour Market banner offers a wide choice of fresh and local products as well as an assortment of non-food products adapted to its customers. The company's convenience stores sales areas ranging from 200 to 900m2 Proxi Carrefour Bio Carrefour Contact Carrefour Express and Carrefour City are the company's daily living brands. Nearly 415 cash and carry outlets and it is developing particularly in Brazil under the Atacadao brand and in France under the Promocash brand. The cash & carry format offers traders restaurateurs and professionals a wide range of food and non-food products presented on pallets individually or in multipack at wholesale prices.

In addition the company has strongly developed local services around e-commerce: click & collect drive home delivery - including delivery in one hour.

Geographic Reach

France (including its overseas territories) is Carrefour's largest market accounting for 50% of sales. As well as its mainline Carrefour-branded hypermarkets and supermarkets its convenience store network consists of the Carrefour City Carrefour Contact Carrefour Express and Carrefour Bio banners. Its cash and carry businesses operate as Promocash.

The rest of Europe particularly Belgium Poland Italy Spain and Romania generates more than 30% of sales and has around 4300 stores Carrefour is also present in other European countries via partnerships including in Turkey via Sabanci which operates more than 640 stores in the country.

Latin America accounts for around 20% of total sales. Carrefour is the leading retailer in both Brazil and Argentina. In the Asia/Pacific region (less than 5% of sales) Carrefour is active in China. Taiwan as well as Indonesia via franchising. It has 475 stores in the region.

Carrefour also has around 460 stores spread across Africa the Middle East and the Dominican Republic.

Carrefour has separate retail websites in each of its geographies.

Sales and Marketing

In France Carrefour has improved its price positioning. Strengthening loyalty schemes with the new "Market Loyalty Premium" launched in early 2020 in supermarkets (approximately 10% discount every day on fresh products such as fruits and vegetables butcher fishmonger flowers and plants; approximately 15% discount for Pass card-holders).

The company is outperforming the market in food e-commerce. Sizeable investments in digital are again reflected in an increase of more than 30% in food e-commerce sales in 2019.

Financial Performance Note: Growth rates may differ after conversion to US Dollars.

Carrefour's sales have been on a general upward track for the last five years but the company's profits have declined steeply in the past years with consecutive losses in 2017 and 2018 before recovering in 2019.

In 2019 revenue fell ?24 million to ?74.1 billion due to changes in exchange rates which reduced net sales by ?2.4 billion almost exclusively attributable to the Latin America region.

Net income was ?1.3 billion a vast improvement from the ?344 million loss of the prior year. The company sold 80% of its equity interest in Carrefour China to Chinese group Suning.com which took effect in September of 2019 at ?615 million. A disposal gain of around ?1.1 billion was recognized from discontinued operations.

Carrefour's cash on hand grew ?166 million during 2019 ending the year at ?4.5 billion. The company's operations generated ?3.2 billion. Its financing activities used ?1.9 billion and its investing activities used another ?1 billion. Carrefour's main cash uses in 2019 were acquisitions while the company issued bonds to support liquidity.

Strategy

The company's "Carrefour 2022" strategy is wide-ranging and touches most if not all parts of its business. Launched in 2018 Carrefour 2022 has four main pillars the company is focused on: deploying a simplified and open organization gaining in productivity to reinforce its attractiveness creating an omni-channel universe of reference and making "eating better" accessible to everyone.

Carrefour is investing ?2.8 billion in e-commerce with the goal of generating ?5 billion from online by 2022. The company overhauled all of its interfaces and applications to offer a comprehensive range of services accessible from a single site in each country which includes drive-up walk-up click and collect next-day delivery and express delivery. It also plans on opening 3000 convenience stores by 2022 in addition to the opening of 200 drive pick-up points in 2018.

It has also established a partnership with Spanish start-up Glovo which enables Carrefour to offer home delivery services in only 30 minutes in France Spain Italy and Argentina. Carrefour Brazil has also posted strong growth in e-commerce sales from its successful collaboration with the Rappi delivery application among others. The aim is to roll out home delivery of Carrefour products in all French cities with more than 10000 inhabitants by 2022.

Additionally Carrefour is forming partnerships to boost its competitiveness and operational efficiency. Carrefour was chosen by Google to be its first global food partner in 2019 applying artificial intelligence and machine learning techniques by applying these to concrete cases such as anticipating stock shortages. In an effort to combat waste and address environmental challenges Carrefour has collaborated with the Too Good To Go application which helps its customers identify unsold food at low prices.

Mergers and Acquisitions

n mid-2020 Carrefour Italy inaugurated a new Carrefour Express Via Fumagalli in Milan. The endpoint of a major challenge consisted of integrating 25 Conad points of sale into the Carrefour network 21 under the Express banner and 4 Market stores. This operation strengthens Carrefour's presence in Italy in a highly strategic region and segment.

Also in the same year Carrefour has entered into an agreement with Dairy Farm to acquire Wellcome Taiwan consolidating its position as the leading multi-format food retailer in that market. The transaction's enterprise value is 97 million euros1. Wellcome Taiwan posted net sales of around 390 million euros in 2019.

HISTORY

Although its predecessor was actually a supermarket opened by Marcel Fournier and Louis Defforey in a Fournier's department store basement in Annecy France the first Carrefour supermarket was founded in 1963 at the intersection of five roads (Carrefour means "crossroads"). That year Carrefour opened a vast store dubbed a "hypermarket" by the media in Sainte-Genevi¨ve-des-Bois outside Paris.

The company opened additional outlets in France and moved into other countries including Belgium (1969) Switzerland (1970 — the year it went public) Italy and the UK (1972) and Spain (1973). Carrefour stepped up international expansion during the mid-1970s after French legislation limited its growth within the country.

Carrefour exported its French-style hypermarkets to the US (Philadelphia) in 1988. Scant advertising limited selection and a union strike led Carrefour to close its US operations in 1993. Carrefour opened its first hypermarket in Taiwan in 1989. The next year it formed Carma a 50-50 joint venture with Groupama to sell insurance. Carrefour paid over $1 billion for two rival chains (the bankrupt Montlaur chain and Euromarche) in 1991.

Daniel Bernard replaced Michel Bon the hard-charging expansion architect in 1992 after a 50% drop in first-half profits. A year later Carrefour partnered with Mexican retailer Gigante to open a chain of hypermarkets in Mexico. (In 1998 Carrefour bought Gigante's share of the joint venture.) In 1996 the company bought a 41% stake in rival GMB (Cora hypermarket chain) and sold its 11% stake in US warehouse retailer Costco (it now owns 20% of Costco UK). The next year Carrefour allowed 16 hypermarkets owned by Guyenne et Gascogne Coop Atlantique and Chareton to operate under the Carrefour name. It expanded into Poland in 1997 and the Czech Republic in 1998.

Its biggest acquisition (at the time) came in 1998 when Carrefour acquired French supermarket operator Comptoirs Modernes (with about 800 stores under the Stoc Comod and Marche Plus flags). Carrefour also entered the Indonesian market that year.

In August 1999 Carrefour announced a deal even bigger than the one for Comptoirs Modernes — a $16.3 billion merger with fellow French grocer Promod¨s which operated more than 6000 hypermarkets supermarkets convenience stores and discount stores in Europe. Paul-Auguste Halley and Leonor Duval Lemonnier founded Promod¨s in Normandy France in 1961. Initially a wholesale food distributor Promod¨s opened its first supermarket in 1962. This was followed by a cash-and-carry wholesale outlet (1964) a hypermarket (1970) and convenience stores (Shopi and 8 Huit during the 1970s). To gain regulatory approval for the acquisition Carrefour divested its stake in the Cora chain and sold nearly 40 other stores in France and Spain. The Promod¨s acquisition was completed in 2000.

The company joined with US retailer Sears and software maker Oracle among others to form internet-based supply exchange GlobalNetXchange in early 2000. Also that year Carrefour bought Belgian retailer GB (about 500 stores).

In 2001 Carrefour sold its 74% stake in Picard Surgeles (frozen food stores). Carrefour also opened its first Japanese grocery store near Tokyo that year.

The grocer sold its 10% stake in PetSmart Inc. in a public offering in July 2002. That December Carrefour acquired the remaining 20% of the shares of Centro Comerciales Carrefour its Spanish subsidiary it didn't already own in a public tender offer.

In February 2003 Carrefour acquired two hypermarkets in Italy from Hyparlo. In October it entered the Scandinavian market through a franchise partnership and supply agreement with Norwegian grocer NorgesGruppen. Soon after Carrefour Poland acquired two hypermarkets there from troubled Dutch retailer Royal Ahold. In late 2003 Carrefour's discount chain Ed acquired 44 Treff Marche shops in France from German retailer Edeka.

The company sold its seven-hypermarket Chilean division in January 2004 to Distribuci n Y Servicio. In April Carrefour opened its first Champion supermarket in Beijing. In September it entered Norway with six Meny Champion discount supermarkets in Oslo in partnership with Norway's NorgesGruppen.

In February 2005 Luc Vandevelde the former chairman of troubled British retailer Marks and Spencer succeeded Daniel Bernard as nonexecutive chairman of Carrefour. Bernard had been with Carrefour for 13 years. No stranger to the company Vandevelde was chief executive of Promod¨s when it merged with Carrefour in 1999. Concurrently ex-CFO Jose-Luis Dur n was named CEO. In March Carrefour sold its 29 hypermarkets in Mexico to Grupo Comercial Chedraui for an undisclosed sum. Also in March Carrefour exited the Japanese market with the sale of its eight hypermarkets there to Japanese retail giant AEON CO. On the plus side Carrefour completed the acquisition of Chris Cash & Carry of Cyprus through its Greek subsidiary Carrefour Marinopoulos. In November the French retailer acquired full ownership of three of its Chinese hypermarket joint ventures from its local partners: Kunming Department Store Co. a unit of China's Kunming Sinobright (Group) Co.; Hunan Yiyou Commercial Trade Co.; and Xinjiang Grandscape Investment Co. Also in 2005 Carrefour swapped 15 of its hypermarkets in Slovakia and the Czech Republic for five outlets in

Taiwan operated by rival Tesco exiting both countries.

Carrefour increased its ownership stake in Groupe Hyparlo in late 2005 to 49% (up from 20% in 2004).

In 2006 the company pulled out of South Korea where it held a relatively weak market position. Carrefour sold its 32 stores there to local fashion retailer E.Land for about $1.9 billion. In July Carrefour acquired 98% of the share capital and 99% of the voting rights of Hyparlo which operates stores under the Carrefour banner in France and Romania. The retailer launched its own mobile phone service Carrefour Mobile at all 218 of its hypermarkets in France in late 2006. (Rival Auchan launched a similar product earlier in the year.)

Vandevelde resigned his position in 2007 as non-executive chairman after a falling out with the controlling Halley family. In July Carrefour acquired 250 Spanish discount supermarkets trading under the PLUS banner for about $275 million. About the same time it sold a dozen hypermarkets in Portugal to Sonae the country's largest retailer for about $920 million. In October Carrefour added to its holdings in Romania with the purchase of the Artima supermarket chain there from Polish-based private equity firm Enterprise Investors for about $87 million.

In March 2008 the Halley family split its 13% stake in Carrefour into two separate holding companies — Halley Participations SAS and Comet BV — thereby ceding control of the French retail giant to Blue Capital. In May Robert Halley stepped down as chairman of the company's supervisory board and was replaced by the deputy chairman Amaury de Seze. Blue Capital which recently was granted two seats on the company's supervisory board won a third with the appointment of Bernard Arnault.

Duran stepped down in January 2009 and Lars Olofsson took over as top executive. In June the company opened its first location in Russia: a hypermarket in Moscow. A second Russian store debuted in September.

In November 2010 Carrefour sold its 42 stores in Thailand to Casino Guichard-Perrachon's Big C affiliate there for some ?868 million ($1.17 billion).

At Carrefour's annual meeting in June 2011 chairman Amaury de Seze stepped down and Olofsson added the chairman's title. Olofsson retired in May 2012 and was succeeded by Georges Plassat who joined Carrefour as COO in April 2012.

EXECUTIVES

Member of the Executive Board, Executive Director, Communication for the Group and France, Charles Hufnagel
Independent Director, Claudia Almeida E Silva
Director, Alexandre Arnault
Member of the Group Executive Committee, Executive Director, Merchandise, Supply and Formats, Guillaume De Colonges
Member of the Executive Board, Executive Director, France, Rami Baitieh
Member of the Group Executive Committee, Executive Director, Northern and Eastern Europe (Belgium, Poland and Romania) and Chief Executive Officer of Carrefour Belgium, Francois Melchior De Polignac
Member of the Executive Board, Executive Director, Spain, Alexandre de Palmas
Member of the Executive Committee, Executive Director, Strategy & Transformation for the Group and France, Morgane Weill
Executive Director - Italy, Member of the Executive Board, Christophe Rabatel

Member of the Executive Board, E-Commerce Data, Digital Transformation Director, Elodie Perthuisot
Chairman of the Board, Chief Executive Officer, Chairman of the Executive Committee, Alexandre Bompard, $1,637,896 total compensation
Member of the Group Executive Committee, General Secretary, Laurent Vallee
Member of the Group Executive Committee, Chief Financial Officer, Matthieu Malige
Member of the Group Executive Committee, Executive Director, Human Resources and Assets for the Group and France, Jerome Nanty
Executive Director, Argentina, Stéphane Maquaire
Auditors: Mazars

LOCATIONS

HQ: Carrefour S.A.
33, avenue Emile-Zola, TSA 55555, Boulogne-Billancourt 92100
Phone: (33) 1 41 04 26 00   **Fax:** (22) 1 41 04 26 01
Web: www.carrefour.com

2018 Sales

	% of total
France	47
Europe	28
Latin America	18
Asia	7
Total	**100**

PRODUCTS/OPERATIONS

2018 Stores

	No.
Convenience	7,029
Supermarkets	3,319
Hypermarkets	1,384
Cash & Carry	379
Total	**12,111**

Selected Operations and Banners

Hypermarkets
  Carrefour
Supermarkets
  Champion
  GB
  Globi
  GS
  Marinopoulos
  Norte
  Super GB
  Super GS
  Unic
Hard discount stores
  Ed
  Minipreco
Other stores
  Cash-and-carry stores
  Docks Market
  Promocash
  Puntocash
Convenience stores
  8 à Huit
  Di per Di
  GB Express
  Marché; Plus
  Proxi
  Shopi
Other Operations
Carfuel (petroleum products)
Comptoirs Modernes (supermarkets)
Costco UK (20% warehouse club)
Erteco (hard-discount stores)
Financiera Pryca (46% consumer credit Spain)
Fourcar B.V. (investments The Netherlands)
GlobalNetXchange (Internet-based supply exchange joint venture)
Ooshop (online shopping)
Prodirest (catering)
Providange (auto centers)
S2P (60% consumer credit)

ELO
H & M Hennes & Mauritz
AB
INDUSTRIA DE DISE 'O
  TEXTIL SA
J SAINSBURY PLC
KERING

KINGFISHER PLC
REWE - Zentral-AG
Tengelmann
WM MORRISON
  SUPERMARKETS LIMITED
WOOLWORTHS GROUP
  LIMITED

HISTORICAL FINANCIALS

Company Type: Public

Income Statement   FYE: December 31

	REVENUE ($ mil.)	NET INCOME ($ mil.)	NET PROFIT MARGIN	EMPLOYEES
12/19	83,244	1,267	1.5%	321,383
12/18	89,230	(642)	—	363,862
12/17	97,069	(636)	—	378,923
12/16	83,176	787	0.9%	372,330
12/15	85,891	1,067	1.2%	380,920
Annual Growth	(0.8%)	4.4%	—	(4.2%)

2019 Year-End Financials

Debt ratio: 28.3%
Return on equity: 11.8%
Cash ($ mil.): 5,014
Current ratio: 0.82
Long-term debt ($ mil.): 9,116

No. of shares (mil.): 807
Dividends
  Yield: 3.1%
  Payout: 6.4%
Market value ($ mil.): 2,658

	STOCK PRICE ($) FY Close	P/E High/Low		PER SHARE ($) Earnings	Dividends	Book Value
12/19	3.29	3	2	1.59	0.10	13.82
12/18	3.32	—	—	(0.84)	0.11	13.47
12/17	4.34	—	—	(0.84)	0.17	15.80
12/16	4.84	—	—	1.07	0.00	14.74
12/15	5.72	5	4	1.47	0.09	14.42
Annual Growth	(12.9%)	—	—	2.0%	3.0%	(1.1%)

Casino Guichard Perrachon S.A.

One of the world's leading food retailers Casino Group owns and operates more than 10800 stores including hypermarkets (mostly Geant) supermarkets (Casino and Monoprix to name a few) restaurants (Casino Shop) and discount stores (Leader Price). It is the top European group retail sector recognized by Vigeo Eris the ESG rating agency and world's leading food retailer recognized by the Wall Street Journal and the #1 convenience store operator in France (primarily as Petit Casino but other banners include Franprix Vival and Spar). Most of its stores are in France but it has outlets in Cameroon Uruguay Brazil Colombia and Argentina.

Operations

Its retail operations bring revenue from France of about 48% from Latam retail about 46% and 6% revenue from e-commerce.

Of its 10800 stores 5206 are convenience stores 872 are Franprix 810 are Leader Price 419 Casino supermarkets and 105 Casino hypermarkets. It also operates 233 stores in other business.

Geographic Reach

Casino is headquartered in France. It has more than 244 affiliated stores and 155 stores operating in North Africa and Middle East and 37 more in Sub-Saharan Africa and in 22 countries including France Colombia Brazil Argentina Uruguay Senegal Cote d'Ivoire Cameroon Madagascar and Mauritius.

Sales and Marketing

Casino deals in physical and digital retail and e-commerce.

Financial Performance

Note: Growth rates may differ after conversion to US Dollars.

The company's revenue for fiscal 2020 decreased to ?31.9 billion compared from the prior year with ?34.6 billion.

Net loss for fiscal 2020 decreased to ?886 million compared from the prior year with ?1.4 billion.

Strategy

The "Customer service of the year" award put Floa at the top of the lending institution category. This trophy pays tribute to the digital strategy of Floa and its teams which simplifies banking and makes customers' lives easier.

The company have made this a strategic priority in and of itself. In 2020 the company was recognized for its commitments and actions in this area such as being ranked the top European group in the retail sector by Vigeo Eiris the ESG rating agency and Moody's subsidiary and the world's leading food retailer by the Wall Street Journal. The company has long been recognized for its initiatives to promote diversity and equal opportunity.

Company Background

Casino is controlled by Euris which is controlled by Jean-Charles Naouri Casino's chairman and CEO.

HISTORY

Frenchman Geoffroy Guichard married Antonia Perrachon a grocer's daughter in 1889 in Saint-tienne France. Three years later Geoffroy took over his father-in-law's general store (a converted "casino" or musical hall). In 1898 the company became Societe des Magasins du Casino. By 1900 when it became a joint stock company Casino had 50 stores; it opened its 100th store in 1904. That year the company introduced its first private-label product: canned sardines. In 1917 Guichard named his two sons Mario and Jean as managers.

By WWI there were about 215 branches more than 50 in Saint- tienne. From 1919 to the early 1920s the company opened several factories to manufacture goods such as food soap and perfumes. In 1925 the elder Guichard retired leaving the day-to-day operations of Casino to his two sons. (Geoffroy died in 1940.) WWII took a heavy toll on the company: About 70 Casino stores were leveled and another 450 were damaged.

The company began opening cafeterias in 1967 and in 1976 it formed Casino USA to run them. Casino USA bought an interest in the California-based Thriftimart volume retailer in 1983 renaming the company after Thriftimart's Smart & Final warehouse stores.

Casino grew by acquiring companies across France including CEDIS (16 hypermarkets 116 supermarkets and 722 smaller stores in eastern France; 1985) and La Ruche Meridionale (18 hypermarkets and 112 supermarkets in southern France 1990). Casino bought nearly 300 hypermarkets and supermarkets from Rallye SA in 1992 giving Rallye about 30% of the company. The company opened its first hypermarket in Warsaw Poland in 1996.

Rival Promod ¨s made a roughly $4.5 billion hostile takeover bid for Casino in 1997. Guichard family members voted against the Promod ¨s offer instead backing a $3.9 billion friendly offer from Rallye (increasing their stake to nearly 50%). Casino also launched a massive counterattack —

buying more than 600 Franprix and Leader Price supermarket stores from food manufacturer TLC Beatrice and acquiring a 21% stake in hypermarket chain Monoprix. Promod ¨s withdrew its bid four months later.

Casino expanded internationally in the late 1990s acquiring stakes in food retailers in Argentina (Libertad) Uruguay (Disco) Colombia (Almacenes Exito SA) Brazil (Companhia Brasileira de Distribui § o) and Thailand (Big C the country's largest retailer). It also opened its first hypermarket in Taichung Taiwan.

Expansion in France included a joint venture (called Opera) formed in 1999 with retailer Cora SA to buy food and nonfood goods for the Casino and Cora stores and the acquisition of 100 convenience stores (converted to the Petit Casino banner) in southwest France from retailer Guyenne et Gascogne.

Casino acquired 100 Proxi convenience stores in southeast France in 2000 from Montagne (most became Vival franchises) and more than 400 convenience stores (Eco Service and others) from Auchan. Casino also bought 51% of French online retailer Cdiscount.com (CDs videos CD-ROMs and DVDs) and upped its ownership in several of its international supermarket operations including gaining 100% ownership of Libertad. It also increased its ownership of Monoprix to 49%.

In July 2002 Casino bought a 38% stake in Laurus NV its financially troubled Dutch rival. Laurus operates nearly 2000 supermarkets in the Netherlands Spain and Belgium. (Soon after Casino sold Laurus's unprofitable stores in Spain and Belgium.) Also in 2002 the company sold its wine division Les Chais Beaucairois to wine and spirits company Marie Brizard for $22 million.

Chief executive Pierre Bouchut unexpectedly left Casino in March 2005. Jean-Charles Naouri the company's chairman and controlling shareholder replaced him. In May Casino took joint control of Brazil's leading food retailer Companhia Brasileira de Distribui § o along with the family of Ab lio Diniz. Previously Casino held a minority stake in the supermarket chain. Casino spun off some of its shopping center assets in an October IPO for part of its real estate assets in France including shopping mall properties adjacent to its hypermarket and supermarkets as well as the land under its cafeterias.

In 2006 the French supermarket operator spun off its property company Mercialys. (Following the IPO Casino holds about a 60% stake in Mercialys.) In January 2006 Casino increased its stake in Colombia's biggest retailer Exito to nearly 39%. The company in July sold its 19 hypermarkets in Poland to METRO AG its German rival for about $1.1 billion as part of its asset disposal program. In September Casino sold its 50% stake in its Taiwanese subsidiary Far Eastern Geant to its joint venture partner Far Eastern Department Stores.

Real estate sales continued in late 2007 with the announcement that Casino plans to sell nearly $930 million in assets including 255 grocery stores in France. The retailer says it plans to use the proceeds from the sale of these "mature" assets for high-potential projects in France and abroad. In May 2007 Casino sold its 55% stake of the California-based Smart & Final warehouse grocery chain to Apollo Management for $813 million thereby exiting the US market.

Casino acquired in July 2008 about 90% of the French textile maker International Textiles Associes (or INTEXA) from members of the Broyer family. Also Casino exercised its option in 2008 to increase its share in Dutch supermarket operator Super de Boer (formerly Laurus acquired in 2002) to a majority stake. However in December 2009 Casino sold its 57% stake in Super de Boer to

Dutch rival Jumbo Groep Holding for ?552.5 (nearly $800 million).

In November 2009 Casino acquired the remaining shares of Leader Price and Franprix chains from the Baud family bringing its ownership stake up to 100% in both chains.

EXECUTIVES

Independent Director, Maud Bailly
Director, Permanent representative of Saris, Josseline de Clausade
Lead Independent Director, Thierry Billot
Director, Permanent representative of Fimalac, Thomas Piquemal
Independent Director, Beatrice Dumurgier
Chairman of the Board, Chief Executive Officer, Member of the Executive Committee, Jean-Charles Naouri, $524,126 total compensation
Director, Frederic Saint-Geours
Director, Permanent representative of Matignon Diderot, Odile Muracciole
Director, David de Rothschild
Director, Permanent Representative of Euris, Jacques Dumas
Independent Director, Nathalie Andrieux
Independent Director, Christiane Feral-Schuhl
Director, Permanent Representative of Finatis, Didier Leveque
Director, Permanent Representative of Fonciere Euris, Michel Savart
Auditors: ERNST & YOUNG et Autres

LOCATIONS

HQ: Casino Guichard Perrachon S.A.
1, Cours Antoine Guichard, Saint-Etienne, Cedex 1 42008
Phone: (33) 4 77 45 31 31   **Fax:** (33) 4 77 45 38 38
Web: www.groupe-casino.fr

PRODUCTS/OPERATIONS

2015 Stores

	No.
France	10,627
International	
Argentina	27
Uruguay	65
Brazil	2,181
Colombia	1,668
Thailand	734
Vietnam	42
Total	**15,344**

2015 type of Stores (France)

	No.
Casino hypermarket	128
Supermarkets	441
Monoprix	698
Franprix	867
Leader price	810
Convenience stores	6,916
Indian ocean	146
Other Activities	621
Total	**10,627**

2015 Sales

	% of Total
France Retail	41
Latam Retail	32
Latam Electronics	11
Asia	9
E-Commerce	7
Total	**100**

Selected Operations

Banque du Groupe Casino (60% financial services)
Big C (36% Thailand)
Casino Enterprise (non-food operations)
Cativen (66% Venezuela)
Cdiscount.com (67% e-commerce)
Companhia Brasileira de Distribuição (34% Brazil)
Devoto (97% supermarkets Uruguay)

Exito Colombia SA (55% supermarkets)
Franprix (supermarkets)
Gé;ant (hypermarkets)
Imagica (photo and digital imaging processing)
Leader Price (supermarkets)
Libertad (hypermarkets Argentina)
Vindé;mia (supermarkets; Madagascar Mauritius Ré;union)

COMPETITORS

ACCOR
COMPAGNIE FINANCIERE RICHEMONT SA
FOOT LOCKER INC.
Grupo Comercial Chedraui S.A.B. de C.V.
INDUSTRIA DE DISE 'O TEXTIL SA
KERING
KINGFISHER PLC
REWE - Zentral-AG
Victoria Retail Group B.V.

HISTORICAL FINANCIALS

Company Type: Public

Income Statement

FYE: December 31

	REVENUE ($ mil.)	NET INCOME ($ mil.)	NET PROFIT MARGIN	EMPLOYEES
12/20	39,899	(1,087)	—	202,955
12/19	39,644	(1,607)	—	209,696
12/18	42,527	(61)	—	214,458
12/17	45,339	143	0.3%	226,606
12/16	38,043	2,828	7.4%	227,842
Annual Growth	**1.2%**	**—**	**—**	**(2.9%)**

2020 Year-End Financials

Debt ratio: 32.3%
Return on equity: (-22.0%)
Cash ($ mil.): 3,367
Current ratio: 0.82
Long-term debt ($ mil.): 8,219

No. of shares (mil.): 107
Dividends
  Yield: —
  Payout: —
Market value ($ mil.): 666

	STOCK PRICE ($) FY Close	P/E High/Low		PER SHARE ($) Earnings	Dividends	Book Value
12/20	6.18	—	—	(10.48)	0.00	37.15
12/19	9.70	—	—	(15.28)	0.35	49.75
12/18	7.96	—	—	(1.09)	0.72	70.87
12/17	12.01	22	18	0.76	0.75	82.00
12/16	9.51	0	0	24.91	0.86	80.46
Annual Growth	**(10.2%)**	**—**	**—**	**—**	**—**	**(17.6%)**

Cathay Financial Holding Co

One of the largest financial services firms in Taiwan Cathay Financial Holding Co. owns companies involved in banking insurance brokerage and more. Its holdings include life accident and health insurer Cathay Life; property/casualty coverage provider Cathay Century; and Cathay United Bank which offers consumer banking services such as deposit accounts loans and credit cards as well as international banking. Cathay Financial Group also has units devoted to venture capital investing. All told the company has more than 700 locations and claims a customer base of more than 13 million customers. Cathay Financial Holding Co. was founded in 1962.

Operations

Cathay Financial Holdings Co. is composed of insurance securities banking and other diversified financial institutions. Primary subsidiaries of the company include Cathay Life Cathay United Bank Cathay Century Insurance Cathay Securities and Investment Trust and Cathay Venture.

Geographic Reach

Taiwan-based Cathay Financial Holdings Co. operates more than 630 offices across Taiwan. It also operates branches in Hong Kong Japan Vietnam Indonesia Philippines Cambodia Singapore and China among others.

Financial Performance

Cathay FHC's revenue increased from $1.8 billion in 2018 to $2.2 billion in 2019.

Net income was $2.1 billion 25% higher compared to $1.7 billion in the previous year.

Cash and cash equivalents at the end of the year were $13.2 million in contrast to $14.6 million in 2019. Cash provided by operating activities was $16.6 million. Investing activities used $314.5 million primarily for acquisition of investments accounted for using the equity method while financing activities provided $296.2 million primarily from proceeds from issuance of bonds.

Strategy

For its 2020 strategy Cathay FHC plans to continue to implement regional strategies and achieve the vision of becoming a leading financial institution in the Asia Pacific region; promote digital transformation and build an ecosystem of digital financial services; and optimize asset/liability allocation and management and create a solid foundation for sustainable operations.

EXECUTIVES

Chairman of the Board, Hong-Tu Tsai
General Manager, Director, Chang-Ken Lee
Director, Tiao-Kuei Huang
Director, Cheng-Ta Tsai
Director, Cheng-Chiu Tsai
Senior Deputy General Manager, David Sun
Independent Director, Li-Ling Wang
Deputy General Manager, Ming-Chiao Liang
Vice Chairman of the Board, Tsu-Pei Chen
Chief Financial Officer, Grace Chen
Independent Director, Tang-Chieh Wu
Deputy General Manager, Pei-Ching Lin
Director, Ming-Ho Hsiung
Director, Ming-Jian Kuo
Deputy General Manager, Hua-Ben Miao
Deputy General Manager, Jui-Reui Hung
Deputy General Manager, Kuang-Hsueh Chen
Chief Investment Officer, Sophia Cheng
Director, Chi-Wei Joong
Deputy General Manager, Ching-Yuan Kung
Independent Director, Feng-Chiang Miau
Deputy General Manager, Deh-Yen Weng
Deputy General Manager, Shu-Ying Wu
Chief Compliance Officer, Judie Hsu
Chief Risk Officer, Ching-Lu Huang
Chief Information Officer, Senior Deputy General Manager, Jian-Hsing Wu
Deputy General Manager, Ta-Ching Hung
Senior Deputy General Manager, Chung-Yi Teng
Deputy General Manager, Fu-Min Wang
Deputy General Manager, Yu-Mei Lee
Senior Deputy General Manager, Xu-Jie Yao
Senior Deputy General Manager, Hsiang-Hsin Tsai
Senior Deputy General Manager, Tsung-Hsien Tsai
Independent Director, Edward Y. Way
Auditors: Deloitte & Touche

LOCATIONS

HQ: Cathay Financial Holding Co
No. 296, Jen Ai Road, Section 4, Taipei
Phone: (886) 2 2708 7698 **Fax:** (886) 2 2325 2488
Web: www.cathayholdings.com

COMPETITORS

Assante Corporation
Bank of Communications Co. Ltd.
CITIZENS FINANCIAL GROUP INC.
COMMUNITY BANK SYSTEM INC.
FIRST HORIZON CORPORATION
FIRSTRAND LTD
Manulife Financial Corporation
OVERSEA-CHINESE BANKING CORPORATION
LIMITED
SANTANDER UK GROUP HOLDINGS PLC
STANDARD BANK GROUP LTD
Shinhan Financial Group Co. Ltd.
UNITED OVERSEAS BANK LIMITED
W.H. IRELAND GROUP PLC
WEBSTER FINANCIAL CORPORATION

HISTORICAL FINANCIALS

Company Type: Public

Income Statement				FYE: December 31
	ASSETS ($ mil.)	NET INCOME ($ mil.)	INCOME AS % OF ASSETS	EMPLOYEES
12/20	389,666	2,653	0.7%	0
12/19	336,204	2,096	0.6%	0
12/18	301,604	1,682	0.6%	0
12/17	298,176	1,898	0.6%	0
12/16	251,457	1,471	0.6%	0
Annual Growth	11.6%	15.9%	—	—

2020 Year-End Financials

Return on assets: 0.7%
Return on equity: 8.9%
Long-term debt ($ mil.): —
No. of shares (mil.): —
Sales ($ mil): 12,454
Dividends
Yield: —
Payout: —
Market value ($ mil.): —

Cathay Pacific Airways Ltd.

Auditors: KPMG

LOCATIONS

HQ: Cathay Pacific Airways Ltd.
33rd Floor, One Pacific Place, 88 Queensway,
Phone: (852) 2747 5210 **Fax:** (852) 2810 6563
Web: www.cathaypacific.com

HISTORICAL FINANCIALS

Company Type: Public

Income Statement				FYE: December 31
	REVENUE ($ mil.)	NET INCOME ($ mil.)	NET PROFIT MARGIN	EMPLOYEES
12/19	13,737	217	1.6%	34,200
12/18	14,180	299	2.1%	32,400
12/17	12,448	(161)	—	32,700
12/16	11,960	(74)	—	33,800
12/15	13,203	774	5.9%	26,833
Annual Growth	1.0%	(27.2%)	—	6.3%

2019 Year-End Financials

Debt ratio: 5.8%
Return on equity: 2.6%
Cash ($ mil.): 1,908
Current ratio: 0.48
Long-term debt ($ mil.): 9,825
No. of shares (mil.): —
Dividends
Yield: 2.9%
Payout: 388.8%
Market value ($ mil.): —

	STOCK PRICE ($) FY Close	P/E High/Low		PER SHARE ($) Earnings	Dividends	Book Value
12/19	7.23	21	14	0.06	0.21	2.05
12/18	7.01	16	10	0.08	0.08	2.08
12/17	7.83	—	—	(0.04)	0.01	1.99
12/16	6.53	—	—	(0.02)	0.18	1.81
12/15	8.62	9	5	0.20	0.30	1.57
Annual Growth	(4.3%)	—	—	(27.2%)	(7.8%)	6.9%

Ceconomy AG

Ceconomy (formerly Metro) is Europe's leading consumer electronics retailer. Through the retail brands Media Markt and Saturn Ceconomy sells thousands of electronic items such as gaming household appliances smart home telecommunications computer photo as well as an option to rent rather than buy appliances for more than 1000 stores in around 15 European countries including its home market of Germany. Its other businesses includes digital advertising company Retail Media Group and Deutsche Technikberatung which offers installation assistance connection and troubleshooting of electronic devices at home. Ceconomy separated out Metro its grocery retail business as a standalone entity in 2017. Ceconomy holds some 25% stake in Fnac Darty France's largest electronics retailer.

Operations

Subsidiary MediaMartkt Saturn Retail Group holds Ceconomy's main interests Media Market Saturn Media Markt is Ceconomy's biggest business operating more than 850 stores in some 15 countries. In addition to physical and online retail Media Markt offers after-sales services such as delivery assembly and installation and repairs. It also offers appliance rental. Saturn operates more than 170 stores in three European countries. Most of its stores are host to "SmartBars" which offer repair and other services.

Subsidiary Retail Media Group develops advertising campaigns based on impersonal visitor and purchase statistics. Lastly Deutsche Technikberatung offers professional assistance with home installation networking and troubleshooting of electronic appliances.

The company generates approximately 13% of total sales from online.

Geographic Reach

Germany is home to more than 430 of Dusseldorf-based Ceconomy's total base of some 1050 stores. Its second biggest presence is in Italy with over 115 stores while its remaining stores are relatively well diversified across some 15 other countries in Western/Southern Europe Eastern Europe and Central Europe as well as Turkey.

Ceconomy reports sales under three regions: DACH (Germany Austria Switzerland and Hungary) which accounts for nearly 60% of the sales; Western Europe (more than 30%); and Eastern Europe and other countries (the rest).

Sales and Marketing

Ceconomy operates two customer loyalty programs Media Markt Club and Saturn Card. The special feature is that customers can work their way up the levels of the customer card by collecting "bits" which allows them to claim certain advantages.

Financial Performance

After dropping in 2016 Ceconomy's revenue has been declining gradually with the exception of 2019. Its net income has been fluctuating in the same period.

In the past financial year 2018/19 CECONOMY's Group sales increased slightly by 0.2 per cent compared with the prior-year period to ?21.5 billion.

The company's net income resurfaced from a loss of ?212 million in 2018 to a profit of ?122 million in 2019.

Ceconomy's cash position rose during 2019 ending the year at ?1.1 billion. The company's operating activities generated ?86 million and its financing activities used ?178 million while investing activities generated ?118 million.

Strategy

Ceconomy's strategic approach consists of:

Customer orientation. With its omnichannel business model CECONOMY is guided by customers' expectations and requirements. The full customer focus allows customers to shop wherever whenever and however they want. In addition we continuously and systematically measure our customers' satisfaction using the net promoter score (NPS) in order to permanently enhance our service quality.

Sustainability. Sustainability and climate awareness are of enormous and increasing importance both for CECONOMY and for customers. For this reason measures to increase sustainability are very important. For example there is now a pilot project enabling customers to recycle old mobile phones by depositing them in innovative recycling machines in selected stores. The customers are paid back the residual value of the phones in the form of a voucher.

Centralization. Ceconomy's development is closely tied to lean efficient and effective structures and processes that are being incrementally established throughout the Group. The Group is therefore also defining what Group-wide cooperation will look like in the future: more centralized and with clear responsibilities at all levels.

Digitalization. One of Ceconomy's main strengths is to set digital trends systematically adjust the portfolio on that basis and promote innovation. The areas in which digital trends can be used are diverse and constantly provide new opportunities to make the shopping experience even more enjoyable.

Services. Ceconomy does more than merely sell products: the Group delivers solutions in the digital world and is constantly expanding its range of services. In recent financial years for example the service portfolio of Deutsche Technikberatung has been expanded and SmartBars rolled out to all stores.

HISTORY

Otto Beisheim founded METRO SB-Grossmarkte in the German town of Mulheim in 1964. A wholesale business serving commercial customers it operated under the name METRO Cash & Carry. Three years later Beisheim received backing from the owners of Franz Haniel & Cie (an industrial company founded in 1756) and members of the Schmidt-Ruthenbeck family (also in wholesaling). This allowed METRO to expand rapidly in Germany and in 1968 into the Netherlands under the name Makro Cash & Carry via a partnership with Steenkolen Handelsvereeniging (SHV). During the 1970s the company expanded its wholesaling operations within Europe and moved into retailing.

METRO's foray into retailing was aided during the next decade by the acquisition of department store chain Kaufhof AG. By the 1980s the rise of specialty stores had many department stores on the defensive and Kaufhof's owners sold it to METRO and its investment partner Union Bank of Switzerland.

As METRO's ownership interest in Kaufhof rose above 50% the chain began converting some of its stores from department stores into fashion and sporting goods sellers. Kaufhof began acquiring a stake in computer manufacturer and retailer Vobis in 1989. In 1993 METRO now operating as METRO Holding AG acquired a majority interest in supermarket company Asko Deutsche Kaufhaus which owned the Praktiker building materials chain. The reclusive Beisheim retired from active management the following year.

To cut costs and prepare for expansion into Asia in 1996 METRO Holding merged its German retail holdings — Kaufhof; Asko; another grocery operation Deutsche SB Kauf; and its German cash-and-carry operations — into one holding company METRO AG.

EXECUTIVES

Chief Financial Officer, Florian Wieser, $298,783 total compensation

Deputy Chairman, Sylvia Woelke, $183,253 total compensation

Chairman, Thomas Dannenfeldt, $179,270 total compensation

Member of the Supervisory Board, Employee Representative, Thomas Fernkorn

Member of the Supervisory Board, Employee Representative, Lasse Putz

Independent Member of the Supervisory Board, Katrin Adt

CEO and Labour Director, Karsten Wildberger, $268,905 total compensation

Auditors: KPMG AG Wirtschaftsprüfungsgesellschaft

LOCATIONS

HQ: Ceconomy AG
  Kaistrasse 3, Duesseldorf 40221
Phone: (49) 211 5408 7125
Web: www.ceconomy.de

2018 Sales

	% of total
DACH (Germany Austria Switzerland Hungary)	58
Western/Southern Europe	32
Eastern Europe	8
Others	2
Total	**100**

2018 stores

	Number
Germany	432
Austria	52
Switzerland	27
Hungary	29
Belgium	28
Greece	12
Italy	115
Luxembourg	2
Netherlands	49
Portugal	10
Spain	86
Poland	86
Turkey	71
Sweden	28
Others	28
Total	**1,022**

PRODUCTS/OPERATIONS

Selected Operations
Consumer Electronics
  Media Markt

Saturn
Other OperationsiBoodJukeRetail Media GroupDeutsche Teknikberatung

COMPETITORS

A123 SYSTEMS LLC
ARLINGTON INDUSTRIES INC.
DAIWABO INFORMATION SYSTEM CO. LTD.
FACILITY SOLUTIONS GROUP INC.
GAMES WORKSHOP GROUP PLC

HOUSTON WIRE & CABLE COMPANY
MANUTAN INTERNATIONAL
METCASH LIMITED
SONEPAR MANAGEMENT US INC.
WESCO INTERNATIONAL INC.

HISTORICAL FINANCIALS

Company Type: Public

Income Statement   FYE: September 30

	REVENUE ($ mil.)	NET INCOME ($ mil.)	NET PROFIT MARGIN	EMPLOYEES
09/20	24,390	(271)	—	47,727
09/19	23,404	133	0.6%	55,259
09/18	24,807	(245)	—	61,827
09/17	26,175	1,301	5.0%	68,804
09/16	65,211	668	1.0%	226,053
Annual Growth	**(21.8%)**	—	—	**(32.2%)**

2020 Year-End Financials

Debt ratio: 27.1%
Return on equity: (-37.0%)
Cash ($ mil.): 1,737
Current ratio: 0.89
Long-term debt ($ mil.): 2,166

No. of shares (mil.): 356
Dividends
  Yield: —
  Payout: —
Market value ($ mil.): 342

	STOCK PRICE ($) FY Close	P/E High/Low		PER SHARE ($) Earnings	Dividends	Book Value
09/20	0.96	—	—	(0.76)	0.00	1.60
09/19	1.09	4	2	0.37	0.00	2.33
09/18	1.35	—	—	(0.74)	0.04	2.23
09/17	2.30	2	1	3.98	4.25	2.44
09/16	5.94	4	3	2.04	0.14	18.32
Annual Growth	**(36.6%) (45.7%)**	—	—	—	—	—

Cemex S.A.B. de C.V.

CEMEX is a leading vertically integrated heavy building materials company focused on four core businesses?Cement Ready-Mix Concrete Aggregates and Urbanization Solutions. It is a global building materials company that provides high-quality products and reliable services to customers and communities in more than 50 countries. The majority of its sales come from cement; the company has about 65 cement plants and an annual production capacity of some 92 million tons. CEMEX operates in North America as well as in Africa Asia Europe the Middle East and South America. The US is the company's largest market with around 30% of sales.

Operations

Cemex has over 90 million tons of installed cement capacity. It also produces over 45 million cu. meters of ready-mix concrete and nearly 135 million tons of aggregates each year.

Its core businesses have included Cement a binding agent when mixed with aggregates and water produces either ready-mix concrete or mortar; Ready-Mix Concrete a combination of cement aggregates admixtures and water; Aggregates ob-

tained from land-based sources or by dredging marine deposits; and Urbanization Solutions which leverages its competitive advantages to capture new urbanization business opportunities with a value proposition based on sustainability.

Cemex generates about 40% of sales from cement over 30% from ready-mix and nearly 15% from aggregates.

Geographic Reach

Based in Monterrey Mexico Cemex has production facilities in around 20 countries around the globe.

Cemex's revenue is well diversified geographically with the US generating around 30% of sales and Mexico with over 20%. The Europe Asia Middle East and Africa region accounts for about 35% while South Central America and the Caribbean region pulls in some 10%.

Sales and Marketing

The company serves some 42000 customers.

Financial Performance

The company's revenue for fiscal 2020 decreased to $13.0 billion compared to the prior year's $13.1 billion.

Net loss for fiscal 2020 was $1.3 billion compared to the prior year's net income of $91 million.

Cash held by the company at the end of fiscal 2020 increased to $950 million. Cash provided by operations and investing activities were $1.6 billion and $88 million respectively. Cash used for investing activities was $1.5 billion mainly for debt repayments.

Strategy

In September 2020 CEMEX announced Operation Resilience the company's medium-term strategy that responds to the changes in its outlook for its business due to the COVID-19 pandemic and lays out a plan to enhance EBITDA growth over the next three years. It allows CEMEX to optimize its portfolio for profitable growth while securing its position as a vertically integrated leading heavy building materials company with a focus on four core businesses: cement ready-mix aggregates and urbanization solutions.

CEMEX's Alternative Fuels Strategy helps the company confront climate change by enabling it to rely less on fossil fuels and thereby reduce the CO_2 intensity of clinker manufacturing. Concurrently by co-processing waste as an alternative fuel in its cement operations CEMEX can help decrease the amount of waste society sends to landfill reduce public investment in new dedicated waste management facilities and foster local business creation and employment by developing alternative fuel supply chains.

HISTORY

The foundation of CEMEX began with — what else? — cement. Lorenzo Zambrano founded Cementos Hidalgo in northern Mexico in 1906. In 1931 the company merged with Cementos Portland Monterrey and was renamed Cementos Mexicanos from which its current name CEMEX is derived.

During the 1960s the company expanded into the cities of Ciudad Valles and Torre n by building plants; it moved into Merida in 1966 by acquiring Cementos Maya. The founder's grandson also named Lorenzo Zambrano joined the company in 1968. CEMEX became a true national force during the 1970s by acquiring more plants including one in central Mexico.

CEMEX went public in 1976. With its acquisition of Cementos Guadalajara and its three plants it became Mexico's top cement maker. After serving in several engineering positions and as VP of operations Zambrano was named CEO in 1985. He had worked at CEMEX as a teenager in the early 1960s and claims he knew he wanted to work for CEMEX since he was 14.

Zambrano set about making CEMEX an international player. Already an exporter the company boosted its exporting business by purchasing Cementos An̄huac in 1987. Two years later CEMEX sealed its position as the top Mexican cement maker by acquiring that country's #2 cement company Cementos Tolteca. CEMEX then bought its first non-Mexican operations in 1992 adding Valenciana de Cementos and Sanson Spain's largest cement makers. Two years later CEMEX added Vencemos (Venezuela's top cement business) Cemento Bayano (Panama) and a plant in Texas.

The globalization of CEMEX helped the company weather several peso devaluations during the 1990s including one in late 1994. The company continued to expand abroad adding Cementos Nacionales (Dominican Republic) in 1995 and Cementos Diamante and Samper (both in Colombia) in 1996. Those deals made the company the world's third-largest cement producer.

After claiming more of the European and Latin American cement markets CEMEX turned its attention to the Pacific Rim where it made investments in Rizal Cement Company in the Philippines in 1997 and PT Semen Gresik in Indonesia in 1998 (it sold its 25% stake in 2006).

A booming US economy fueled residential and commercial construction in fiscal 1999 lifting CEMEX to record sales. In 2000 CEMEX gained significant size when it acquired US cement maker Southdown for $2.8 billion. The company sold its Kentucky and Missouri operations to Rinker Materials a unit of Australia's CSR Ltd in 2001.

In mid-2002 CEMEX bought Puerto Rican Cement Company (PRCC) for around $180 million. The next year CEMEX acquired Mineral Resource Technologies and Dixon-Marquette Cement in the US. In 2005 CEMEX added extensive European operations with the acquisition of UK-based ready-mix cement giant RMC Group. The deal worth about $5.8 billion instantly made CEMEX a leader in Europe.

The company also acquired Rinker Australia's biggest building material manufacturer for more than $14 billion in 2007. In 2008 CEMEX sold most of its stake in telecom company Axtel and later its Canary Islands operations garnering a combined $474 million for debt payments. In 2009 CEMEX (still struggling under the weight of debt and facing declining sales) sold its Australian operations to Holcim for nearly $2 billion. In 2011 CEMEX bought Ready Mix USA's interest in the companies' two joint ventures which have operations in the Southeast US.

EXECUTIVES

Chief Executive Officer, Director, Fernando Angel Gonzalez Olivieri
President for CEMEX Europe, Middle East, Africa & Asia, Sergio Medina
Independent Director, Isabel Maria Aguilera Navarro
President of CEMEX USA, Jaime Muguiro Dominguez
Executive Chairman of the Board of Directors, Rogelio Zambrano Lozano
Chief Financial Officer, Executive Vice President - Finance and Administration, Maher Al-Haffar
Executive Vice President of Sustainability, Commercial and Operations Development, Juan Romero Torres
Executive Vice President of Strategic Planning and Business Development, Jose Antonio Gonzalez Flores
Executive Vice President of Corporate Affairs, Enterprise Risk Management and Social Impact, Mauricio Doehner Cobian

Company Secretary, Roger Saldana Madero
Executive Vice President of Digital and Organization Development, Luis Hernandez Echavez
Independent Director, Gabriel Jaramillo Sanint
Independent Director, Everardo Elizondo Almaguer
President for CEMEX in South, Central America and the Caribbean, Jesus Gonzalez Herrera
Executive Vice President of Investor Relations, Corporate Communications and Public Affairs, Louisa Rodriguez
President, CEMEX Mexico, Ricardo Barba
Auditors: KPMG Cardenas Dosal S.C. (member of KPMG International)

LOCATIONS

HQ: Cemex S.A.B. de C.V.
Avenida Ricardo Margain Zozaya 325, Colonia Valle del Campestre, San Pedro Garza Garcia, Nuevo Leon 66265
Phone: (52) 81 8888 8888   **Fax:** (52) 81 8888 4417
Web: www.cemex.com

2018 Sales

	% of total
United States	26
Europe	26
Mexico	24
South Central America & Caribbean	14
Asia Middle East and Africa	10
Total	**100**

PRODUCTS/OPERATIONS

2018 Sales

	% of total
Cement	45
Ready mix	39
Aggregates	16
Total	**100**

Selected Subsidiaries

CEMEX Mé;xico S. A. de C.V.
  CEMEX Espóa S.A. (Spain)
  Assiut Cement Company (Egypt)
  Cement Bayano S.A. (Panama)
  CEMEX Asia Holdings Ltd. (Singapore)
  APO Cement Corporation (Philippines)
  CEMEX (Thailand) Co. Ltd.
  Solid Cement Corporation (Philippines)
  CEMEX Colombia S.A.
  CEMEX (Costa Rica) S.A.
  CEMEX de Puerto Rico Inc
  CEMEX Dominicana S.A. (Dominican Republic)
  CEMEX France Gestion (S.A.S.)
  CEMEX Corp. (US)
  CEMEX Venezuela S.A.C.A.
CEMEX U.K.
  CEMEX Austria AG
  CEMEX Czech Republic s.r.o.
  CEMEX Deutschland AG. (Germany)
  CEMEX Holdings (Israel) Limited
  CEMEX Investments Limited (UK)
  CEMEX Polska sp. Z.o.o. (Poland)
  CEMEX SIA (Latvia)
  Readymix plc (Ireland)

COMPETITORS

AGGREKO LIMITED
Dyckerhoff GmbH
HOLCIM (US) INC.
Holcim AG
JAMES HARDIE INDUSTRIES PUBLIC LIMITED COMPANY
LOMA NEGRA COMPA ̄IA INDUSTRIAL ARGENTINA S.A.
Resolute Forest Products Inc
SEKISUI CHEMICAL CO. LTD.
SOJITZ CORPORATION
TAIHEIYO CEMENT CORPORATION
TITAN AMERICA LLC
VISCOFAN SA

HISTORICAL FINANCIALS

Company Type: Public

Income Statement

FYE: December 31

	REVENUE ($ mil.)	NET INCOME ($ mil.)	NET PROFIT MARGIN	EMPLOYEES
12/20	12,970	(1,467)	—	41,663
12/19	13,130	143	1.1%	40,640
12/18	14,079	532	3.8%	42,024
12/17	13,103	772	5.9%	40,878
12/16	12,126	678	5.6%	41,853
Annual Growth	**1.7%**	**—**	**(0.1%)**	

2020 Year-End Financials

Debt ratio: 37.2%
Return on equity: (-16.8%)
Cash ($ mil.): 950
Current ratio: 0.79
Long-term debt ($ mil.): 9,160

No. of shares (mil.): —
Dividends
  Yield: —
  Payout: —
Market value ($ mil.): —

	STOCK PRICE ($) FY Close	P/E High/Low	PER SHARE ($) Earnings	Dividends	Book Value
12/20	5.17	— —	(0.03)	0.00	0.18
12/19	3.78	1797932	0.00	0.10	0.21
12/18	4.82	36 22	0.01	0.00	0.21
12/17	7.50	30 20	0.02	0.00	0.20
12/16	8.03	27 11	0.02	0.00	0.19
Annual Growth	**(10.4%)**	**— —**	**—**	**—**	**(1.3%)**

Cencosud SA

Cencosud is one of the largest and most prestigious retail conglomerates in Latin America. The company's five major business units are supermarkets home improvements department stores shopping centers and financial services. The company trademark brands registered in Chile Argentina Colombia Brazil and Peru are Jumbo Easy Santa Isabel Disco and more. In addition the company continues to develop own brands such as Krea URB Alpes Outdoors and more. Cencosud has signed licensing agreements with well-known international brands such as American Eagle Carter's Women'Secret Topshop Topman Aerie and Miss Selfridge.

Operations
Cencosud operations are spread across different lines of business such as supermarkets home improvement department stores shopping centers and financial services.

Geographic Reach
Based in Chile Cencosud has some 1125 stores in Argentina Brazil Chile Columbia and Peru.

Sales and Marketing
Cencosud markets its products and services through an e-commerce channel. Expanded its coverage by opening two online shopping alternatives in Chile supermarkets through the Santa Isabel website and Brazil Supermarkets. In addition Cencosud and Cornershop signed an agreement for supermarkets and home improvements operations in Chile Peru Colombia and Brazil allowing Corners shop customers to shop at supermarkets without service charge. In addition Uber and Uber Eats users can access Rincon Jumbo Products and prepared meals from supermarkets through the App (Including Argentina). The company launched the Jumbo Prime Program membership that includes free and unlimited delivery online purchase over CLP 30000.

Financial Performance

The company's revenue in 2020 increased by 6% to CLP 10.1 trillion from CLP 9.5 trillion in 2019.

Strategy

Cencosud forged a new strategic alliance with Cornershop. Through it Jumbo Easy and Paris were integrated into the app. The agreement will allow the development of e-commerce channels for all business units in Chile Brazil Peru and Colombia and also includes technological integration. The strategic alliance was highlighted as a positive move by Moody's rating agency.

Cencosud's strategic focuses presented in 2019 and updated in the guidance published on January 14 2021 aim to position the Company as a leading player in the sustainable food business integrating environmental social and governance dimensions into its model. This includes a three-year strategic look where the main focuses are: Increase market share in Supermarkets e-commerce and Home Improvement in the most profitable markets; Maximize Cencosud's return on capital through more efficient use of the Company's existing assets such as land and stores for the development of new retail stores Shopping Centers and investments to deepen market penetration in e-commerce channels; and Accelerate the e-commerce strategy that allows customers to access an increasingly complete and efficient omnichannel proposition.

EXECUTIVES

Chief Executive Officer, Corporate General Manager, Matias Videla Sola
Legal Affairs and Institutional Relations Corporate Manager, Sebastian Rivera
Shopping Centers Division Manager, German Cerrato
Director, Julio Moura Neto, $151,824 total compensation
Department Stores Corporate Manager, Ricardo Bennett
Director, Heike Paulmann Koepfer
Independent Director, Mario Valcarce Duran
Director, Peter Paulmann Koepfer
Director, Alejandro Perez Rodriguez
Director, Jorge Perez Alati
Director, Felipe Bascunan
Chairman of the Board, Horst Npaulmann M
Auditing Corporate Manager, Bronislao Jandzio
Auditors: PricewaterhouseCoopers

LOCATIONS

HQ: Cencosud SA
Avenida Kennedy 9001, Piso 4, Santiago, Las Condes 4144
Phone: (56) 22 959 0545   **Fax:** (56) 22 959 0368
Web: www.cencosud.com

2016 Sales

	% of total
Chile	42
Argentina	24
Brazil	15
Peru	10
Colombia	9
Total	**100**

2016 Store locations

	Nos
Chile	384
Argentina	356
Brazil	211
Peru	105
Colombia	115
Total	**1,171**

PRODUCTS/OPERATIONS

2016 Sales

	% of total
Supermarkets	72
Home Improvement	13
Department Stores	11
Shopping Centers	2
Financial Services	2
Total	**100**

COMPETITORS

ABERTIS INFRAESTRUCTURAS SA
ALDI GmbH & Co. KG Essen
BOSCOV'S DEPARTMENT STORE LLC
DAIMARU MATSUZAKAYA DEPARTMENT STORES CO. LTD.
EL CORTE INGLES SA
El Puerto de Liverpool S.A.B. de C.V.
FONCIERE EURIS
Falabella S.A.
ISETAN MITSUKOSHI LTD.
KORBER SUPPLY CHAIN US INC.
MARKET AMERICA INC.
OZBURN-HESSEY HOLDING COMPANY LLC
SIERRA TRADING POST INC.
STEIN MART INC.
The North West Company Inc
Wal-Mart Canada Corp

HISTORICAL FINANCIALS

Company Type: Public

Income Statement				FYE: December 31
	REVENUE ($ mil.)	NET INCOME ($ mil.)	NET PROFIT MARGIN	EMPLOYEES
12/20	13,838	32	0.2%	117,638
12/19	12,955	154	1.2%	125,269
12/18	13,898	275	2.0%	133,846
12/17	17,003	715	4.2%	135,821
12/16	15,496	581	3.8%	139,093
Annual Growth	**(2.8%)**	**(51.5%)**	**—**	**(4.1%)**

2020 Year-End Financials

Debt ratio: 0.0%
Return on equity: 0.5%
Cash ($ mil.): 959
Current ratio: 1.09
Long-term debt ($ mil.): 3,321
No. of shares (mil.): —
Dividends
Yield: —
Payout: 400.0%
Market value ($ mil.): —

Cenovus Energy Inc

Cenovus Energy is the third-largest Canadian oil and natural gas producer. The company is also known as the second-largest Canadian- based refiner and upgrader. The company's major operations include oil sands plays of Alberta; thermal and crude oil and natural gas projects across Western Canada; crude oil production in Newfoundland and Labrador; and natural gas and liquids production in China and Indonesia. Cenovus' upstream assets produce an average of more than 470000 barrels of oil per day. In 2020 the company acquired Husky in order to create a resilient Canadian-based integrated energy company.

Operations

The company's segments include Oil Sands Conventional and Refining & Marketing.

Its Oil Sands segment contribute to more than 50% of the company's revenues and operates the development and production of bitumen in northeast Alberta. The company's bitumen assets include Foster Creek Christina Lake and Narrow lake.

The company's refining and marketing segment (more than 40% of company's revenue) transports sells and refines crude oil into petroleum and chemical products. The company currently owns two refineries in the US with Phillips 66. The company's conventional segment accounts for about 5% of the industry revenue includes interests in a number of natural gas processing facilities.

Geographic Reach

Alberta-based Cenovus operates in Canada the US and the Asia Pacific Region. The company's major operations include oil sands plays of Alberta; thermal and crude oil and natural gas projects across Western Canada; crude oil production in Newfoundland and Labrador; and natural gas and liquids production in China and Indonesia.

Financial Performance

The company's performance for the past five years has fluctuated ending with 2020 having a significant decrease from 2019.

Cenovus' revenue decreased by about $7 billion to $13.2 billion in 2020 as compared to 2019's revenue of about $20.2 billion. The decrease in the company's revenue decrease was largely due to the impact of the COVID-19 pandemic on crude oil prices.

The company also noted a net loss of about $2.4 billion as compared to the prior year's net income of $2.2 billion. The net loss also included a $100 million loss related to the Keystone XL pipeline project.

Cenovus' cash held at the end of the year amounted to $378 million. The company's operating activities provided $273 million in 2020. The company's investing activities used $863 million while its financing activities provided about $837 million. Main cash uses were capital expenditures and repayment of long-term debt.

Strategy

Cenovus' strategy remains focused on maximizing shareholder value through cost leadership as well as realizing the best margins for its products. The company believes that its diverse and integrated portfolio will help the company to deliver and maintain its operations. The company's 2021 budget focuses on sustaining capital and generating free funds for its operations.

Company Background

Cenovus Energy was formed in late 2009 as a spinoff from major Canada-based oil and gas player EnCana.

The split allowed EnCana to focus almost exclusively on natural gas exploration and development in North America while Cenovus took on responsibilities as an integrated oil company with the intent of boosting its production and refining capacities. An expansion at the Wood River refinery in Illinois is placed Cenovus among the leading heavy oil refiners in the US. The coker and refinery upgrade (completed in late 2011) increased its crude oil refining capacity and more than doubled its heavy crude oil refining capacity.

In 2010 Cenovus reported an improvement in revenues and income as the result of global economy bouncing back from a recession which produced higher commodity prices and demand driving up sales of the company's products.

EXECUTIVES

Executive Vice President, Upstream - Thermal, Major Projects & Offshore, Norrie Ramsay
Independent Director, Keith Casey
Non-Independent Director, Frank Sixt
Executive Vice President - Safety & Operations Technical Services, P. Andrew Dahlin
Independent Director, Eva Kwok
Senior Vice President - Stakeholder Engagement, Chief Sustainability Officer, Rhona Delfrari

Independent Director, Wayne Shaw
Chief Financial Officer, Executive Vice President, Jeffrey Hart
Non-Independent Director, Canning Fok
Independent Director, Richard Marcogliese
Independent Director, Rhonda Zygocki
Independent Director, Jane Mongeau
Chief Executive Officer, President, and Director, Alexander Pourbaix, $717,043 total compensation
Executive Vice President and Chief Operations Officer, Jonathan McKenzie, $438,150 total compensation
Executive Vice President, Upstream - Conventional & Integration, J. Drew Zieglgansberger, $426,559 total compensation
Executive Vice President - Downstream, Keith Chiasson
Executive Vice President - Corporate Services, Sarah Walters
Senior Vice President - Legal, General Counsel & Corporate Secretary, Gary Molnar
Independent Director, Jane Kinney
Independent Chairman of the Board, Keith MacPhail
Independent Director, Harold Kvisle
Executive Vice President - Strategy & Corporate Development, Karamjit Sandhar
Auditors: PricewaterhouseCoopers LLP

LOCATIONS

HQ: Cenovus Energy Inc
  4100, 225 6 Avenue S.W., Calgary, Alberta T2P 1N2
Phone: 403 766-3770
Web: www.cenovus.com

PRODUCTS/OPERATIONS

2014 Sales

	% of total
Refining & marketing	62
Upstream	
Oil sands	23
Conventional	15
Total	**100**

2014 Sales

	% of total
Canada	52
United States	48
Total	**100**

COMPETITORS

Advantage Oil & Gas Ltd
Athabasca Oil Corporation
BERRY PETROLEUM COMPANY LLC
CIVITAS RESOURCES INC.
Canadian Natural Resources Ltd
Cequence Energy Ltd
EXTRACTION OIL & GAS INC.
GULFPORT ENERGY OPERATING CORPORATION
Inter Pipeline Ltd
MARATHON OIL CORPORATION
NUSTAR ENERGY L.P.
Ovintiv Canada ULC
TALOS PETROLEUM LLC
Tourmaline Oil Corp

HISTORICAL FINANCIALS

Company Type: Public

Income Statement   FYE: December 31

	REVENUE ($ mil.)	NET INCOME ($ mil.)	NET PROFIT MARGIN	EMPLOYEES
12/21	36,397	460	1.3%	5,938
12/20	10,388	(1,868)	—	2,413
12/19	15,497	1,684	10.9%	2,361
12/18	15,306	(1,959)	—	2,264
12/17	13,594	2,685	19.8%	2,882
Annual Growth	**27.9%**	**(35.6%)**	—	**19.8%**

2021 Year-End Financials

Debt ratio: 18.0%	No. of shares (mil.): 2,001
Return on equity: 2.9%	Dividends
Cash ($ mil.): 2,255	Yield: 0.5%
Current ratio: 1.64	Payout: 32.4%
Long-term debt ($ mil.): 9,724	Market value ($ mil.): 24,575

	STOCK PRICE ($) FY Close	P/E High/Low		PER SHARE ($) Earnings	Dividends	Book Value
12/21	12.28	48	21	0.21	0.07	9.26
12/20	6.04	—	—	(1.52)	0.13	10.68
12/19	10.15	6	4	1.37	0.16	12.00
12/18	7.03	—	—	(1.59)	0.15	10.44
12/17	9.13	5	2	2.43	0.16	12.97
Annual Growth (8.1%)	**7.7%**			—	**(45.7%)**	**(18.8%)**

Centrica Plc

Centrica is centered on supplying the energy needs of its more than 9 million customer accounts mainly in the UK Ireland and North America via five major brands? British Gas Bord G is Energy Centrica Business Solutions Centrica Energy Marketing & Trading and Upstream. It is one of the largest electricity and gas supplier in the UK. It also offers related installation repair and maintenance services digital smart technologies (the Hive) and energy hedging and optimization strategies (Neas). The company holds a 69% interest in Spirit Energy an exploration and production company that is a joint venture with Bayerngas Norge which the company intended to exit by the end of 2020.

Operations

The company operates through five operating segment: British Gas Bord Gais Energy Energy Marketing & Trading Centrica Business Solutions and Upstream.

British Gas supplies energy to residential customers in England Scotland and Wales. British Gas Services provides services and solutions to residential customers in England Scotland and Wales.

Bord G is provides energy supply services and solutions to residential and business customers in the Republic of Ireland.

Centrica Business Solutions provides energy supply to business customers in England Scotland and Wales and low-carbon energy solutions for business customers internationally.

Energy Marketing & Trading is the trading and optimization arm of Centrica and is also responsible for managing commodity risk and sourcing energy on behalf of the group's energy supply activities in the UK.

Upstream includes its oil and gas E&P assets Centrica's 20% interest in the UK's nuclear power generation fleet and the Rough field. The company have announced its intention to sell Spirit Energy and its interest in nuclear.

Geographic Reach

The company is headquartered in Windsor UK.

Financial Performance

The company's revenue for fiscal 2020 decreased to 24.4 billion compared from the prior year with 26.8 billion.

Cash held by the company at the end of fiscal 2020 increased to 1.4 billion. Cash provided by operations was 1.4 billion while cash used for investing and financing activities were 285 million and 482 million respectively. Main uses of cash were for purchase of property plant and equipment and intangible assets and financing interest paid.

Strategy

In 2019 Centrica evolved its focus on five key priorities to deliver its strategy and the company

---

align performance and risk management processes around these including its Key Performance Indicators. Centrica's group priorities are underpinned by safety compliance and conduct. The five key priorities are: customer obsession operational excellence most competitive provider cash flow growth and empowered colleague

Company Background

Centrica traces its roots back to British Gas which is one of the oldest companies in the world with a history stretching back over 200 years. However the company as it stands today only dates back to 1986 when the gas industry was privatized and British Gas Plc was formed with a "tell Sid" campaign encouraging customers to buy shares in the company.

In 1997 Centrica was founded when British Gas was split into two separate companies.

HISTORY

William Murdock invented gas lighting in 1792. In 1812 the Gas Light and Coke Company of London was formed as the world's first gas supplier to the public and by 1829 the UK had 200 gas companies.

In the second half of the 19th century the gas industry began looking for new uses for the fuel. Gas stoves were introduced in 1851 the geyser water heater was invented in 1868 and in 1880 the first gas units to heat individual rooms were developed.

Gas companies countered the emerging electricity industry by renting gas stoves at low prices and installing gas fittings (stove pipe and lights) in poor homes with no installation charges or deposits. By 1914 the UK had 1500 gas suppliers.

The electricity industry soon made major strikes against the gas industry's dominance. In 1926 the government began reorganizing the fragmented electricity supply industry building a national power grid and establishing the Central Electricity Generating Board to oversee it.

The gas industry was nationalized in 1949 and 1050 gas suppliers were brought under the control of the British Gas Council. Still the gas industry was losing. Supplying gas was more expensive than generating electricity: Gas was seen as a power supply of the past. The Gas Council sought to change that image through an aggressive marketing campaign in the 1960s touting gas as a modern clean fuel. Other factors played a part in its re-emergence: The Clean Air Act of 1956 steadily reduced the use of coal for home heating liquefied natural gas was discovered in the North Sea and OPEC raised oil prices in the 1970s. When natural gas was introduced most of the old gasworks were demolished and the British Gas Council (which became the British Gas Corp. in 1973) set about converting free of charge every gas appliance in the UK to natural gas.

As Margaret Thatcher's government began privatizing state industries the British Gas Corp. was taken public in 1986. Freed from government control British Gas expanded its international exploration and production activities. When the US gas industry began deregulating British Gas formed joint venture Accord Energy in 1994 with US gas trader Natural Gas Clearinghouse (now NGC) to sell gas on the wholesale market.

With the opening of the UK gas-supply market (which began regionally in 1996 and went nationwide in 1998) British Gas split into two public companies to avoid a conflict of interest between its supply business and its monopoly transportation business. In 1997 it spun off Centrica the retail operations and BG (now BG Group) which received the transportation business and the international exploration and production operations.

The UK electricity supply market began opening up to competition in 1998 and Centrica won

750000 UK electricity customers most of them also gas customers. In 1999 it bought The Automobile Association which it sold to venture capitalists in 2004. In 2000 Centrica began offering telecom services in the UK.

Centrica moved into North America in 2000 by purchasing two Canadian companies: natural gas retailer Direct Energy Marketing and gas production company Avalanche Energy. It gained a 28% stake in US marketing firm Energy America through the Direct Energy transaction and purchased the remaining 72% from US firm Sempra Energy the next year. Continuing its non-domestic strategy Centrica bought a 50% interest in Belgium energy supplier Luminus.

The firm purchased 60% of the 1260-MW Humber Power station in 2001 its first domestic power plant interest. It also acquired the UK operations of Australia's One.Tel and it bought Enron's European retail supply business Enron Direct for $137 million.

In 2002 Centrica purchased the retail energy services business of Canadian pipeline company Enbridge for $637 million; it also agreed to acquire another Enron-controlled company US retail energy supplier NewPower Holdings for $130 million. But Centrica withdrew its offer to buy NewPower a month after the deal was announced because of concerns about NewPower's potential Enron-related liabilities. Later that year Centrica acquired 200000 retail customer accounts in Ohio and Pennsylvania from NewPower.

In 2004 the company brought all its UK upstream activities together under Centrica Energy.

In 2005 Centrica acquired Oxxio the Netherlands #4 energy supplier.

To pursue green energy options in 2007 British Gas launched British Gas New Energy.

In 2007 Centrica acquired Newfield Exploration's North Sea assets for $486 million and in 2008 it acquired its first gas and oil assets in the Norwegian North Sea for $375 million (from Marathon Oil).

Growing it retail business in 2008 Centrica acquired Electricity Direct a UK commercial retail supplier serving nearly 1 million customers.

In 2008 Centrica's British Gas unit acquired 40000 small and mid-sized business customers from UK retail energy provider BizzEnergy in the wake of the latter's sudden financial collapse.

Centrica began in 2012 a program to save 500 million ($788 million) in costs over the next two years by identifying efficiencies. Although the company plans to continue investing for further growth it has already started cutting 2300 positions company-wide as well as implementing a pay freeze across much of the group. It set out to develop a better relationship with its customers by simplifying the purchase of gas and electricity. It also decided to make the cost of delivery more transparent by giving its customers a breakdown on their bill of the actual costs of providing the energy.

Through its aggressive acquisition strategy in North America the company has gained more than 6 million retail power and gas supply customers in less than a decade as part of its Direct Energy operations. Building on its portfolio of offerings in 2011 it acquired Illinois-based Home Warranty of America (HWA) for 30 million ($48 million). HWA provides whole home warranty plans to more than 70000 customers through a network of 4000 contractors.

Direct Energy also made three acquisitions in 2011 for its residential energy supply business in North America: Gateway Energy Services First Choice Power and Vectren Retail. The deals part of the company's strategy of acquiring smaller suppliers and buying in deregulated markets added more than 750000 customers.

In a major move to grow its upstream business and its Norwegian operations Centrica completed a 936 million ($1.5 billion) deal in 2012 to acquire Norwegian assets from Statoil and ConocoPhillips. Combined the new assets will increase the company's reserves by almost 40% and its production by more than 30%. The acquisition includes proved and probable reserves of 117 million barrels of oil equivalent and production of 34000 barrels of oil evalent per day. The buy also makes Centrica one of Norway's fastest growing companies with a third of its gas and oil production originating from that region. The company's upstream operations also have a presence in Trinidad and the Netherlands.

In spite of the growth of Centrica's gas assets the company decided to raise its gas and electricity prices by 17% in late 2011 to cover the rising wholesale commodity prices in the first half of the year. Mild weather that year led to a decline per household averaging 21% less in gas and 4% less in electricity consumption. With lower residential demand customer bills were 4% lower on average in 2011. Consumer complaints over higher prices for heating homes in the UK led to protests at the offices of utility companies and at town halls early in 2012.

EXECUTIVES

Non-Executive Director, Amber Rudd
Auditors: Deloitte LLP

LOCATIONS

HQ: Centrica Plc
Millstream, Maidenhead Road, Windsor, Berkshire SL4 5GD
Phone:
Web: www.centrica.com

PRODUCTS/OPERATIONS

2017 Sales by Geography

	% of total
UK	48
US	34
Rest of Europe	12
Others	6
Total	**100**

2017 Sales by Segment

	% of total
Centrica Business	54
Centrica Consumer	43
Exploration & Production	2
Centrica Storage	1
Total	**100**

COMPETITORS

DYNEGY INC.
EDF ENERGY LIMITED
EXELON CORPORATION
ITALGAS RETI SPA
KINDER MORGAN ENERGY
  PARTNERS L.P.

NISOURCE INC.
PHOENIX NATURAL GAS
  LIMITED
SEMPRA ENERGY
SSE PLC

HISTORICAL FINANCIALS

Company Type: Public

Income Statement | | | | FYE: December 31

	REVENUE ($ mil.)	NET INCOME ($ mil.)	NET PROFIT MARGIN	EMPLOYEES
12/20	16,716	55	0.3%	25,753
12/19	29,942	(1,350)	—	29,147
12/18	37,901	233	0.6%	31,780
12/17	37,850	449	1.2%	34,901
12/16	33,339	2,056	6.2%	38,278
Annual Growth	(15.9%)	(59.4%)	—	(9.4%)

2020 Year-End Financials

Debt ratio: 42.8%
Return on equity: 3.7%
Cash ($ mil.): 2,483
Current ratio: 1.36
Long-term debt ($ mil.): 6,262

No. of shares (mil.): —
Dividends
  Yield: 2.7%
  Payout: —
Market value ($ mil.): —

	STOCK PRICE ($) FY Close	P/E High/Low	PER SHARE ($) Earnings	Dividends	Book Value
12/20	2.47	732243	0.01	0.07	0.23
12/19	4.86	—	(0.24)	0.48	0.28
12/18	6.87	257197	0.04	0.60	0.71
12/17	7.43	214123	0.08	0.63	0.65
12/16	11.53	38 29	0.38	0.58	0.60
Annual Growth (21.6%)	(32.0%)	—	— (60.3%)	(41.5%)	

Changlin Co Ltd

Auditors: ShineWing Certified Public Accountants

LOCATIONS

HQ: Changlin Co Ltd
No. 10, Changlin Road, Changzhou, Jiangsu Province 213002
Phone: (86) 519 86781168   **Fax:** (86) 519 86750025
Web: www.changlin.com.cn

HISTORICAL FINANCIALS

Company Type: Public

Income Statement | | | | FYE: December 31

	REVENUE ($ mil.)	NET INCOME ($ mil.)	NET PROFIT MARGIN	EMPLOYEES
12/20	15,074	83	0.6%	0
12/19	12,124	63	0.5%	0
12/18	11,915	66	0.6%	0
12/17	11,384	55	0.5%	0
12/16	7,225	29	0.4%	0
Annual Growth	20.2%	29.4%	—	—

2020 Year-End Financials

Debt ratio: 2.1%
Return on equity: 10.8%
Cash ($ mil.): 911
Current ratio: 1.05
Long-term debt ($ mil.): 213

No. of shares (mil.): —
Dividends
  Yield: —
  Payout: —
Market value ($ mil.): —

Charoen Pokphand Foods Public Co., Ltd. (Thailand)

Charoen Pokphand Foods Public Company (CPF) operates integrated agro-industrial and food business including livestock and aquaculture such as swine broiler layer duck shrimp and fish. The businesses are categorized into three categories namely Feed Farm and Food. The company also operates retail and foods outlets. The company has about 210 subsidiaries including chicken farms in Turkey; feed production and aquaculture operations in China Laos Malaysia and Russia; and a fast-food restaurant in Shanghai. Parent Charoen Pokphand Group owns over 45% of CPF. Majority of its sales were generated from the Asia. The company was founded in 1978.

Operations

The company operates in two segments: Livestock business (nearly 90% of sales) and Aquaculture business (over 10%).

The livestock business comprises chicken duck and pigs while the aquaculture business comprises shrimp and fish. Its two main businesses are vertically integrated starting from sourcing of raw materials for animal feed production manufacturing animal feed breeding animals farming animals for commercial purposes processing meat producing ready-to-eat food products and including operating food retail outlets and restaurants.

Its three main categories include animal farm products (over 45% of sales) animal fees (more than 35%) and processed foods and ready meals (around 15%).

Geographic Reach

Headquartered in Bangkok Thailand it has presence and sales offices in China India Laos Malaysia Philippines Russia Turkey UK Vietnam as well as Australia Belgium Denmark France Germany Italy Japan Singapore South Africa Spain UAE and the US. The company generates around 60% of sales from Asia around 25% in Thailand nearly 10% in Europe and nearly 5% in America.

Sales and Marketing

The company operates various distribution channels for easy access to products including: traditional trade channels such as fresh markets; wholesale and modern trade channels such as convenience stores supermarket hypermarkets and wholesale distribution center; food services such as hotel restaurants general restaurants fast food restaurants food centers and catering business etc. In addition the company has established its own product distribution channels covering stores which are distribution centers restaurants and food courts.

The company's advertising public relationship and sale promotion expenses were 3.7 million baht and 3.2 million baht in 2020 and 2019 respectively.

Financial Performance

The company's revenue for fiscal 2020 increased to 607.8 billion baht compared from the prior year with 544.9 billion baht.

Profit for fiscal 2020 increased to 44.1 billion baht compared from the prior year with 24.1 billion baht.

Cash held by the company at the end of fiscal 2020 increased to 54.4 billion baht. Cash provided by operations and financing activities were 71.0 billion baht and 28.8 billion baht respectively. Cash used for investing activities was 75.9 billion baht mainly for payment for acquisition of investments.

Strategy

The company focuses on operating businesses according to strategic region and modern production process with international standards. With the aim of competing in the front line of the food industry the company use resources properly and environmental friendly. The company also takes into account the appropriate return to shareholders and interests of all stakeholders to ensure sustainable growth.

To push forward the company's vision and aforementioned mission to fulfill its goals the board of directors reviews and approves the company's strategies annually. The strategies for 2021 have been defined into 3 main strategies which include 'Sustainable growth aiming for excellence and building solid foundation+ along with building a corporate value called the CPF Way under good management framework including corporate governance structure internal audits and enterprise-wide comprehensive risks management.

EXECUTIVES

Independent Director, Rungson Sriworasat
Independent Director, Vatchari Vimooktayon
Chairman of the Board, Soopakij Chearavanont
Executive Vice President - Quality Assurance Unit, Sommai Tachasirinugune
Executive Director, Chief Operating Officer - Livestock Business and Chief Operating Officer - Sausage & Ready Meal Business, Siripong Aroonratana
Vice Chairman of the Board, Phongthep Chiaravanont
Chairman of the Executive Board, Vice Chairman of the Board, Adirek Sripratak
Chief Financial Officer, Executive Director, Paisan Chirakitcharern
Vice Chairperson of the Executive Board, Executive Director, Arunee Watcharananan
Head of CPF Finance & Accounting Shared Service Center, Santi Vitayapipopskul
Executive Director, Chief Operating Officer - Aquaculture Business, Sujint Thammasart
Independent Director, Pongsak Angkasith
Company Secretary, Member of Executive Committee and Senior Vice President - Investor Relations and Capital Market, Kobboon Srichai
Vice Chairman of the Board, Suphachai Chearavanont
Independent Director, Vinai Vittavasgarnvej
Independent Director, Phatcharavat Wongsuwan
Chief Operating Officer - Five Star and Restaurant Business, Sathit Sangkanarubordee
Chief Executive Officer, Executive Director, Prasit Boondoungprasert
Auditors: KPMG Phoomchai Audit Ltd.

LOCATIONS

HQ: Charoen Pokphand Foods Public Co., Ltd. (Thailand)
313 C.P. Tower, Silom Road, Silom, Bangrak, Bangkok 10500
Phone: (66) 2 766 8000   **Fax:** (66) 2 638 2139
Web: www.cpfworldwide.com

2015 sales

	% of total
Asia	57
Thailand	33
Europe	8
America	1
Other	1
Total	**100**

PRODUCTS/OPERATIONS

Selected Brands

Livestock feed products
CP
Hi-Gro
Hogtonal
Hyprovite
Anvipro
Star Feed
Novo
Safe Feed
Erawan
Aquatic Animal Feed
Star Feed
Hi-Grade
Blanca
Stargate
Safe Fish
Safe Fo

2015 Sales

	% of total
Livestock business	85
Aquaculture business	15
Total	**100**

Selected Products

Swine feed
Chicken feed
Duck feed
Shrimp feed
Fish feed
Farming Products
Swine
Broilers
Layers
Ducks
Shrimps
Fish

COMPETITORS

ARYZTA AG	SALMOLUX INC.
Marfrig Global Foods S/A	SMITHFIELD FOODS INC.
	STARKIST CO.
NIPPON SUISAN KAISHALTD.	TRI-MARINE INTERNATIONAL INC.
OCEAN BEAUTY SEAFOODS LLC	WELBILT INC.
	WESFARMERS LIMITED
PECO FOODS INC.	WH Group Limited

HISTORICAL FINANCIALS

Company Type: Public

Income Statement				FYE: December 31
	REVENUE ($ mil.)	NET INCOME ($ mil.)	NET PROFIT MARGIN	EMPLOYEES
12/20	19,697	869	4.4%	0
12/19	17,878	619	3.5%	0
12/18	16,752	480	2.9%	0
12/17	15,393	468	3.0%	0
12/16	12,975	410	3.2%	0
Annual Growth	11.0%	20.6%	—	—

2020 Year-End Financials

Debt ratio: 1.6%	No. of shares (mil.): —
Return on equity: 14.4%	Dividends
Cash ($ mil.): 1,917	Yield: —
Current ratio: 0.95	Payout: 32.2%
Long-term debt ($ mil.): 8,156	Market value ($ mil.): —

Chiba Bank, Ltd

Auditors: Ernst & Young ShinNihon LLC

LOCATIONS

HQ: Chiba Bank, Ltd
1-2 Chiba-Minato, Chuo-ku, Chiba 260-8720
Phone: (81) 43 245 1111
Web: www.chibabank.co.jp

HISTORICAL FINANCIALS

Company Type: Public

Income Statement				FYE: March 31
	ASSETS ($ mil.)	NET INCOME ($ mil.)	INCOME AS % OF ASSETS	EMPLOYEES
03/21	161,645	448	0.3%	6,917
03/20	143,803	442	0.3%	6,884
03/19	135,123	455	0.3%	6,942
03/18	135,438	506	0.4%	7,090
03/17	126,072	471	0.4%	7,122
Annual Growth	6.4%	(1.3%)	—	(0.7%)

2021 Year-End Financials

Return on assets: 0.3%
Return on equity: 5.0%
Long-term debt ($ mil.): —
No. of shares (mil.): 742
Sales ($ mil): 2,103

Dividends
  Yield: —
  Payout: 29.9%
  Market value ($ mil.): —

China Coal Energy Co Ltd

China Coal Energy as its name suggests operates in China and produces coal used to create energy that powers utilities and steel companies. In addition to coal production and trading the company also provides coking operations manufactures coal mining equipment like conveyors and roof supports and provides design and consulting services to coal miners. Still the coal operations are by far its largest business providing some 80% of total sales. China Coal Energy was formed in 2006 by China's largest coal company China National Coal Group Corporation which owns a 57% stake. It is the country's #2 coal producer and the largest coal mining equipment maker in China.

EXECUTIVES

Non-Executive Director, Rongzhe Zhao
Non-Executive Director, Qian Xu
Independent Non-Executive Director, Chengjie Zhang
Vice Chairman of the Board, Executive Director, Yi Peng
Independent Non-Executive Director, Chuangshun Liang
Chief Financial Officer, Qiaolin Chai
Vice President, Jiayu Ni
Independent Non-Executive Director, Ke Zhang
Secretary of the Board, Qun Jiang
Auditors: PricewaterhouseCoopers

LOCATIONS

HQ: China Coal Energy Co Ltd
No. 1, Huangsidajie, Chaoyang District, Beijing 100120
Phone: (86) 10 82236028   **Fax:** (86) 10 82256479
Web: www.chinacoalenergy.com

2014 Sales

	% of total
Domestic markets	99
Asia Pacific markets	1
Total	**100**

PRODUCTS/OPERATIONS

2014 Sales

	% in total
Coal operations	82
Coal mining equipment operations	8
Coal chemicals operations	6
Other operations	4
Total	**100**

Main Business

Coal Production Sales
And Trading
Coal-based Chemicals
Coal Mining Equipment
Manufacturing
Power Generation
Subsidiaries

China Coal Pingshuo Industry Coal Limited Liability Corporation
Shanghai Datun Energy Resources Co. Ltd.
China Coal & Coke Holdings Ltd.
China National Coal Mining Equipment Co. Ltd.
Xi an Engineering Design Co. Ltd. China Coal
China Coal Handan Design Engineering Co.，Ltd.
China National Coal Development Co. Ltd.
China Coal Tendering Co.，Ltd.
China National Coal Industry Qinhuangdao Imp. & Exp. Co. Ltd.
Shanghai ChinaCoal East China Co. Ltd.
China Coal Energy Shandong Co. Ltd.
China National Coal Imp. & Exp. （Tianjin）Co. Ltd.
Huajin Coking Coal Co. Ltd.
Chinacoal Energy(Heilongjiang) Company Limited
Zhongtian Synergetic Energy Company Limited
China Coal Energy Company Limited Xinjiang Branch
Sunfield Resources Co. Ltd.

COMPETITORS

GS Caltex Corporation
Lotte Chemical Corporation
RENTECH INC.

WALTER COKE INC.
Yankuang Energy Group Co. Ltd.

HISTORICAL FINANCIALS

Company Type: Public

Income Statement   FYE: December 31

	REVENUE ($ mil.)	NET INCOME ($ mil.)	NET PROFIT MARGIN	EMPLOYEES
12/20	21,552	902	4.2%	0
12/19	18,581	808	4.4%	0
12/18	15,140	499	3.3%	0
12/17	12,466	371	3.0%	0
12/16	8,731	246	2.8%	47,113
Annual Growth	**25.3%**	**38.3%**		

2020 Year-End Financials

Debt ratio: 5.1%
Return on equity: 5.9%
Cash ($ mil.): 5,496
Current ratio: 0.90
Long-term debt ($ mil.): 11,040

No. of shares (mil.): —
Dividends
  Yield: 5.7%
  Payout: —
  Market value ($ mil.): —

China Communications Constructions Group Ltd

Auditors: PricewaterhouseCoopers Zhong Tian LLP

LOCATIONS

HQ: China Communications Constructions Group Ltd
85 De Sheng Men Wai Street, Xicheng District, Beijing 100088
Phone: (86) 10 8201 6562   **Fax:** (86) 10 8201 6524
Web: www.ccccltd.cn

HISTORICAL FINANCIALS

Company Type: Public

Income Statement   FYE: December 31

	REVENUE ($ mil.)	NET INCOME ($ mil.)	NET PROFIT MARGIN	EMPLOYEES
12/20	95,957	2,477	2.6%	0
12/19	79,731	2,889	3.6%	0
12/18	71,365	2,861	4.0%	0
12/17	74,192	3,162	4.3%	0
12/16	62,174	2,411	3.9%	0
Annual Growth	**11.5%**	**0.7%**	**—**	**—**

2020 Year-End Financials

Debt ratio: 4.8%
Return on equity: 6.8%
Cash ($ mil.): 19,579
Current ratio: 1.00
Long-term debt ($ mil.): 48,583

No. of shares (mil.): —
Dividends
  Yield: —
  Payout: —
  Market value ($ mil.): —

China Construction Bank Corp

Auditors: Ernst & Young

LOCATIONS

HQ: China Construction Bank Corp
No. 25, Financial Street, Xicheng District, Beijing 100033
Phone: (86) 10 6621 5533   **Fax:** (86) 10 6621 8888
Web: www.ccb.com

HISTORICAL FINANCIALS

Company Type: Public

Income Statement   FYE: December 31

	ASSETS ($ mil.)	NET INCOME ($ mil.)	INCOME AS % OF ASSETS	EMPLOYEES
12/20	4,301,405	40,583	0.9%	349,671
12/19	3,655,564	37,764	1.0%	347,156
12/18	3,376,230	36,450	1.1%	345,971
12/17	3,399,862	37,068	1.1%	352,621
12/16	3,018,937	33,465	1.1%	362,482
Annual Growth	**9.3%**	**4.9%**	**—**	**(0.9%)**

2020 Year-End Financials

Return on assets: 0.9%
Return on equity: 11.5%
Long-term debt ($ mil.): —
No. of shares (mil.): —
Sales ($ mil): 180,887

Dividends
  Yield: 5.0%
  Payout: 508.2%
  Market value ($ mil.): —

	STOCK PRICE ($) FY Close	P/E High/Low		PER SHARE ($) Earnings	Dividends	Book Value
12/20	15.02	18	13	0.16	0.76	1.45
12/19	17.30	17	14	0.15	0.75	1.27
12/18	16.30	21	15	0.15	0.74	1.15
12/17	18.45	19	16	0.15	0.72	1.09
12/16	15.17	16	11	0.13	0.66	0.91
Annual Growth	**(0.2%)**	**—**	**—**	**5.2%**	**3.5%**	**12.3%**

China Evergrande Group

Evergrande is a residential real estate developer based in Shenzhen Guangdong Province China. One of China's leading developers the company has more than 870 housing projects active in more than 280 Chinese cities. The Evergrande Tourism Group is focusing to developing two flagship theme-park products that are the first of their kind in the world namely Evergrande Fairyland and Evergrande Water World. It also operates large-scale theme parks including the under construction Ocean Flower Island resort off the coast of Hainan. Evergrande Health builds and operates health resorts that provide all-age and elderly care including through its Boao Evergrande International Hospital. Evergrande has total assets of around 2.2billion. Founded in 1996 the company began trading on the Hong Kong Stock Exchange in late 2009.

Operations

The group is organized into four business segments: property development property management property investment and other businesses. Other businesses mainly include new energy vehicle business hotel operations internet business health industry business and investment business.

The property development accounts for over 95% of sales. The remaining were generated from property management property investment and other businesses.

Geographic Reach

Headquartered in Shenzhen Guangdong Province China the company has more than 870 housing projects active in more than 280 Chinese cities.

Sales and Marketing

Digital technology mobile Internet big data and other cutting-edge technologies have been widely used in the company's marketing activities matching with flexible and aggressive sales strategies and strong execution of all staff on marketing. The group's five largest customers and suppliers accounted for less than 30% of the group's total turnovers and purchases.

The company's selling and marketing costs were RMB23.3 billion in 2019 RMB18.1 billion in 2018 and RMB17.2 billion in 2017 respectively.

Financial Performance

Note: Growth rates may differ after conversion to US Dollars.

Evergrande's figures have consistently grown in the past five years. Revenues rose about 260% between 2015 and 2019. Net income has also risen by about 63% in the same period despite fluctuations throughout the years.

In 2019 revenue was RMB477.6 billion representing a year-over-year growth of 2% compared with 2018. The rise was mainly due to increases in revenues in the property development segment property management segment and investment properties.

Net income fell 116% to RMB17.3 billion in 2019 from RMB37.4 billion the prior year. This was due to a decrease in the group's gross profit attributable to the delivery and settlement of revenue of the lower-priced clearance stock properties in 2019. Selling and marketing costs as well as administrative expenses also increased by 29% and 34% respectively.

Cash at the end of the year was RMB150.1 billion a RMB20.7 billion increase from the prior year. Operating activities used RMB67.4 billion due to an increase in interest paid and lower net cash from operations compared to 2018. Investing activities used RMB55.3 billion mainly for acquisition of subsidiaries and purchases of property plant and equipment. Meanwhile financing activities generated RMB143.2 billion from proceeds of corporate bonds and cash advances from joint ventures.

Strategy

Evergrande is fully implementing the development strategy of "growing sales controlled scale and reduced leverage." The group will leverage its abundant land reserves and its huge advantage of online channels to achieve rapid sales growth. It plans to steadily reduce overall land reserves with average reduction of 30 million sq.m. per year. The group also plans to significantly reduce its total debt and lower its net gearing ratio.

In 2019 the group further strengthened the real estate business and continued to maintain abundant high-quality land reserves in order to facilitate quality development.

The group acquired 153 new pieces of land and further acquired the land surrounding 39 existing projects during the year. The group also launched 178 new projects for sale in several dozens of cities including Shanghai Shenzhen and Nanjing among others. There were a total of 1012 projects for sale which were at different stages ranging from being completed to under construction distributed in 254 cities.

The group also invested in Guanghui Group the world's largest automobile distributor. Together the group has established a large offline-sales network. Leveraging more than 14 million part-time salespersons on the vast online sales network on "Heng Fang Tong" Platform the group has further expanded its online sales network served by both full-time and part-time salespersons.

Mergers and Acquisitions

In the 4th quarter of 2019 through the acquisition of NEVS the Group acquired some new energy vehicles business with an aggregate consideration of RMB1960 million. The group also acquired equity interest of HangFa Investment Management Co. Ltd. at total consideration of about 10400 Million.

Also in 2019 the group acquired equity interest of KJTC at total consideration of about 3600 Million.

In early 2019 the group entered into a Sale and Purchase Agreement with a third party in relation to the acquisition of 100% equity interest of Mini Minor Limited with a consideration of US$1130 million (equivalent to approximately RMB7755 million). Mini Minor held 51% shareholding of National Energy Vehicle Sweden AB ("NEVS"). NEVS with its headquarters based in Sweden is a global electric vehicle company focused on intelligent automobiles. Mini Minor subsequently acquired additional 17% equity interest of NEVS 2019.

EXECUTIVES

Independent Non-Executive Director, Chengyan Zhou
Vice President, Zhaohua Chen
Executive Director, Chairman of Evergrande New Energy Vehicle Group, Shawn Siu
Chairman- Fairyland group, Shengli Duan
Company Secretary, Kar Chun Fong
President- Evergrande New Energy Vehicle Group and Chairman of New Energy Technology Group, Yongzhuo Liu
Executive Chairman of the Board, Ka Yan Hui
Independent Non-Executive Director, Hongxi Xie
Chief Executive Officer, Executive Vice President of the Board, Haijun Xia, $23,900,000 total compensation
Executive Director, Chairman of Evergrande Bao Group, Junping Shi, $1,648,277 total compensation
Vice President, Chen Min

Executive Vice President, Zhaohui Tan
Independent Non-Executive Director, Qi He
Chief Financial Officer, Executive Director, Darong Pan, $1,076,355 total compensation
Vice President, Xuefei Liu
Executive President and Chairman of the Property group, Litao Zhen
Executive Vice President, Weikang Liang
Executive President, Peng Ke
Executive Vice President, Jialin Zhu
Non-Executive Director, Senlin Liang
Auditors: PricewaterhouseCoopers

LOCATIONS

HQ: China Evergrande Group
No. 1126 Haide 3rd Road, Nanshan District, Shenzhen, Guangdong Province 518054
Phone: (852) 2287 9226
Web: www.evergrande.com

COMPETITORS

BELLWAY P L C	GREAT PORTLAND ESTATES
CANCOM SE	P L C
DEXUS PROPERTY	NEWRIVER REIT PLC
SERVICES PTY LIMITED	QUINTAIN LIMITED
EURAZEO	U AND I GROUP LIMITED

HISTORICAL FINANCIALS

Company Type: Public

Income Statement   FYE: December 31

	REVENUE ($ mil.)	NET INCOME ($ mil.)	NET PROFIT MARGIN	EMPLOYEES
12/19	68,632	2,483	3.6%	133,123
12/18	67,777	5,435	8.0%	131,694
12/17	47,794	3,745	7.8%	125,526
12/16	30,449	733	2.4%	89,250
12/15	20,498	1,610	7.9%	83,372
Annual Growth	**35.3%**	**11.4%**	**—**	**12.4%**

2019 Year-End Financials

Debt ratio: 5.2%	No. of shares (mil.): —
Return on equity: 12.4%	Dividends
Cash ($ mil.): 21,565	Yield: —
Current ratio: 1.37	Payout: 50.0%
Long-term debt ($ mil.): 61,470	Market value ($ mil.): —

China Fortune Land Development Co Ltd

Auditors: Zhejiang Pan-China Certified Public Accountants Co., Ltd.

LOCATIONS

HQ: China Fortune Land Development Co Ltd
Zhongtang, Baiguan Town, Shangyu, Zhejiang Province 312300
Phone: (86) 575 2158191   **Fax:** (86) 575 2151888
Web: www.ekingair.com

HISTORICAL FINANCIALS

Company Type: Public

Income Statement
FYE: December 31

	REVENUE ($ mil.)	NET INCOME ($ mil.)	NET PROFIT MARGIN	EMPLOYEES
12/20	15,474	560	3.6%	0
12/19	15,120	2,099	13.9%	0
12/18	12,183	1,707	14.0%	0
12/17	9,164	1,349	14.7%	0
12/16	7,750	934	12.1%	0
Annual Growth	18.9%	(12.0%)	—	—

2020 Year-End Financials

Debt ratio: 4.3%
Return on equity: 6.5%
Cash ($ mil.): 4,127
Current ratio: 1.54
Long-term debt ($ mil.): 16,953

No. of shares (mil.): —
Dividends
　Yield: —
　Payout: —
Market value ($ mil.): —

China Gezhouba Group Co., Ltd.

Auditors: Daxin Certified Public Accountants

LOCATIONS

HQ: China Gezhouba Group Co., Ltd.
　7/F., Block B, Gezhouba Hotel, No. 558, Jiefang
　Avenue, Wuhan, Hubei Province 430033
Phone: (86) 27 83790455　　**Fax:** (86) 27 83790755
Web: www.cggc.cn

HISTORICAL FINANCIALS

Company Type: Public

Income Statement
FYE: December 31

	REVENUE ($ mil.)	NET INCOME ($ mil.)	NET PROFIT MARGIN	EMPLOYEES
12/20	17,218	654	3.8%	0
12/19	15,800	782	4.9%	0
12/18	14,629	677	4.6%	0
12/17	16,413	719	4.4%	0
12/16	14,437	488	3.4%	0
Annual Growth	4.5%	7.6%	—	—

2020 Year-End Financials

Debt ratio: 4.5%
Return on equity: 7.4%
Cash ($ mil.): 3,954
Current ratio: 1.10
Long-term debt ($ mil.): 6,834

No. of shares (mil.): —
Dividends
　Yield: —
　Payout: —
Market value ($ mil.): —

China Grand Automotive Services Co Ltd

EXECUTIVES

Director, Ren Wang
Independent Director, Yongming Liang

Vice President, Secretary of the Board, Director, Xing Xu
Independent Director, Xiaoming Cheng
Chairman of the Board, Wei Lu
Director, Jian Zhang
Vice President, Yongfan Wang
Independent Director, Kuanyun Xia
President, Director, Xinming Wang
Chief Financial Officer, Vice President, Director, Ao Lu
Independent Director, Jinjun Shen
Auditors: Zon Zun Certified Public Accountants Office Ltd.

LOCATIONS

HQ: China Grand Automotive Services Co Ltd
　No. 18, Qixianling Jingxian Street, High-Tech Zone,
　Dalian, Liaoning Province 116025
Phone: (86) 411 84820297　　**Fax:** (86) 411 84820297
Web: www.merro.com.cn

HISTORICAL FINANCIALS

Company Type: Public

Income Statement
FYE: December 31

	REVENUE ($ mil.)	NET INCOME ($ mil.)	NET PROFIT MARGIN	EMPLOYEES
12/20	24,225	231	1.0%	0
12/19	24,497	373	1.5%	0
12/18	24,159	473	2.0%	0
12/17	24,696	596	2.4%	0
12/16	19,501	403	2.1%	0
Annual Growth	5.6%	(13.0%)	—	—

2020 Year-End Financials

Debt ratio: 6.1%
Return on equity: 3.8%
Cash ($ mil.): 4,435
Current ratio: 1.17
Long-term debt ($ mil.): 2,843

No. of shares (mil.): —
Dividends
　Yield: —
　Payout: —
Market value ($ mil.): —

China Hongqiao Group Ltd

Auditors: ShineWing (HK) CPA Limited

LOCATIONS

HQ: China Hongqiao Group Ltd
　Huixian One Road, Zouping Economic Development
　District, Zouping City, Shandong
Phone: (852) 2815 1080　　**Fax:** (852) 2815 0089
Web: www.hongqiaochina.com

HISTORICAL FINANCIALS

Company Type: Public

Income Statement
FYE: December 31

	REVENUE ($ mil.)	NET INCOME ($ mil.)	NET PROFIT MARGIN	EMPLOYEES
12/19	12,097	875	7.2%	43,734
12/18	13,112	786	6.0%	47,584
12/17	14,339	786	5.5%	50,500
12/16	8,841	986	11.2%	60,537
12/15	6,791	561	8.3%	65,076
Annual Growth	15.5%	11.7%	—	(9.5%)

2019 Year-End Financials

Debt ratio: 6.2%
Return on equity: 9.9%
Cash ($ mil.): 6,015
Current ratio: 1.43
Long-term debt ($ mil.): 6,705

No. of shares (mil.): —
Dividends
　Yield: —
　Payout: 48.7%
Market value ($ mil.): —

China International Marine Containers Group Ltd.

Auditors: PricewaterhouseCoopers Zhong Tian CPAs Limited Company

LOCATIONS

HQ: China International Marine Containers Group Ltd.
　8/F., CIMC R&D Center, 2 Gangwan Avenue, Shekou,
　Nanshan District, Shenzhen, Guangdong Province
　518067
Phone: (86) 755 2669 1130　　**Fax:** (86) 755 2682 6579
Web: www.cimc.com

HISTORICAL FINANCIALS

Company Type: Public

Income Statement
FYE: December 31

	REVENUE ($ mil.)	NET INCOME ($ mil.)	NET PROFIT MARGIN	EMPLOYEES
12/20	14,396	817	5.7%	0
12/19	12,332	221	1.8%	0
12/18	13,593	491	3.6%	0
12/17	11,725	385	3.3%	0
12/16	7,360	77	1.1%	0
Annual Growth	18.3%	80.1%	—	—

2020 Year-End Financials

Debt ratio: 5.0%
Return on equity: 12.8%
Cash ($ mil.): 1,862
Current ratio: 1.10
Long-term debt ($ mil.): 3,922

No. of shares (mil.): —
Dividends
　Yield: —
　Payout: —
Market value ($ mil.): —

China Life Insurance Co Ltd

China Life Insurance Company also known as China Life provides long-term individual and group life insurance policies annuity contracts and long-term health insurance policies in force. It also provides both individual and group accident and short-term health insurance policies and services. It has more than 300 million individual and group policies in force. China Life sells its individual products primarily through its own network comprised of exclusive agents direct sales representatives and dedicated and non-dedicated agencies. In addition to life insurance the company provides asset management services and health and accident insurance. The company is a life insurance company established in Beijing China on 30 June 2003.

Operations

China Life operates in four primary segments: Life Insurance (more than 80% of total revenue) Health Insurance (around 15% of revenue) Accident Insurance and Other (less than 5% combined).

Life Insurance business relates primarily to the sale of life insurance policies including those life insurance policies without significant insurance risk transferred.

The Health Insurance business relates primarily to the sale of health insurance policies including those health insurance policies without significant insurance risk transferred.

Accident Insurance business relates primarily to the sale of accident insurance policies.

China Life also controls China Life Asset Management Company making it one of the largest insurance asset managers in the nation.

Geographic Reach

Based in Beijing China Life has branches in nearly all of China's geographic regions.

Sales and Marketing

China Life has an extension distribution network of exclusive agents direct sales representatives and dedicated and non-dedicated agencies. Sales are also conducted through individual business bank and phone sales channels

The company kept in close contact with investors by various means such as phone and internet corresponded with them through more than 1700 emails answered more than 350 calls and emails and recorded a click-through rate of 40000 viewers for the internet broadcast of results briefings and open days.

Financial Performance

Except in 2018 China Life's total revenue has been on an upward trend for the last five years while its net income has fluctuated.

The company's total revenue rose 16% from RMB 627.4 billion in 2018 to RMB 729.5 billion in 2019.

Net income skyrocketed from RMB 11.4 billion in 2018 to RMB 58.3 billion in 2019.

China Life's cash at the end of 2019 totaled RMB 53.3 billion. Operating activities provided RMB 286 billion while investing and financing activities used RMB 247.5 billion and RMB 36.1 billion respectively.

Strategy

In 2019 despite the complicated situation of increased risks and challenges at home and abroad China Life concentrated on the strategic goal of "China Life Revitalization" with "Dual Centers and Dual Focuses" as its strategic core adhered to the overall keynote of making steady progress and upheld the operational guideline of "prioritizing business value strengthening sales force achieving stable growth upgrading technology optimizing services and guarding against risks."

The company accelerated the establishment of a development system of "Yi Ti Duo Yuan" with strengthened individual agent channel in coordination with other channels as well as a market-oriented investment management system strengthened technological empowerment focused on the transformation of sales and the development of protection-oriented business reformed its sales models investment and services systems constantly improved the efficiency of risk prevention and control and achieved the coordinated growth of business scale and value.

Company Background

China Life's history goes back to 1949 when its predecessor People's Insurance Company of China (PICC) was established. The unified national insurer was created just 20 days after the founding of new China. In 2003 PICC was dissolved and re-

placed by four state-owned firms including China Life. The company went public that year listing on the Hong Kong Stock Exchange and the New York Stock Exchange. It listed on the Shanghai Stock Exchange in 2007.

HISTORY

China Life listed on the NYSE in what would become one of the largest IPOs of 2003 valued at more than $3 billion. The company's IPO however was tarnished by subsequent revelations of improper accounting prior to the company's going public; several US lawsuits were filed but in 2006 the SEC's investigation came to an end with no action taken.

EXECUTIVES

President, Executive Director, Hengxuan Su, $32,186 total compensation
Non-Executive Director, Junhui Wang
Finance Director, Vice President, Executive Director, Xiumei Huang
Vice President, Qi Ruan
Chief Marketing Officer, Vice President, Zhong Zhan
Vice President, Secretary of the Board, Chief Actuary, Executive Director, Mingguang Li
Chief Compliance Officer, Chongmiao Xu
Independent Director, Haitao Zhai
Operation Director, Hong Yang
Auditors: Ernst & Young Hua Ming LLP

LOCATIONS

HQ: China Life Insurance Co Ltd
16 Financial Street, Xicheng District, Beijing 100033
Phone: (86) 10 63631191   **Fax:** (86) 10 66575112
Web: www.e-chinalife.com

PRODUCTS/OPERATIONS

2017 Sales by Segment

	% of total
Life Insurance	86
Health Insurance	11
Accident Insurance	2
Other	1
Total	**100**

COMPETITORS

AMERICAN NATIONAL INSURANCE COMPANY
CNO FINANCIAL GROUP INC.
GIBRALTAR LIFE INSURANCE CO. LTD. THE
Kyobo Life Insurance Co. Ltd.
NIPPON LIFE INSURANCE COMPANY
Picc Property And Casualty Company Limited
SOMPO HOLDINGS INC.
Samsung Life Insurance Co. Ltd.
UNUM GROUP

HISTORICAL FINANCIALS

Company Type: Public

Income Statement   FYE: December 31

	ASSETS ($ mil.)	NET INCOME ($ mil.)	INCOME AS % OF ASSETS	EMPLOYEES
12/20	650,190	7,685	1.2%	0
12/19	535,586	8,376	1.6%	0
12/18	473,141	1,656	0.4%	102,817
12/17	445,273	4,956	1.1%	102,297
12/16	388,382	2,754	0.7%	99,739
Annual Growth	13.7%	29.2%	—	—

2020 Year-End Financials

Return on assets: 1.2%	Dividends
Return on equity: 11.7%	Yield: 4.0%
Long-term debt ($ mil.): —	Payout: 176.2%
No. of shares (mil.): —	Market value ($ mil.): —
Sales ($ mil): 31,774	

	STOCK PRICE ($) FY Close	P/E High/Low	PER SHARE ($) Earnings	Dividends	Book Value
12/20	11.06	9 5	0.27	0.44	(0.00)
12/19	13.83	7 5	0.27	0.08	(0.00)
12/18	10.49	41 26	0.06	0.26	(0.00)
12/17	15.61	16 13	0.17	0.14	(0.00)
12/16	12.87	23 15	0.10	0.25	1.55
Annual Growth	(3.7%)	— —	29.9%	14.9%	—

China Merchants Shekou Industrial Zone Holdings Co Ltd

Auditors: Shinewing Certified Public Accountants (Special General Partnership)

LOCATIONS

HQ: China Merchants Shekou Industrial Zone Holdings Co Ltd
3rd Building, Nanhai E Cool, No. 6, Xinghua Road, Shekou, Nanshan District, Shenzhen, Guangdong Province 518067
Phone: (86) 755 26819600   **Fax:** (86) 755 26818666
Web: www.cmsk1979.com

HISTORICAL FINANCIALS

Company Type: Public

Income Statement   FYE: December 31

	REVENUE ($ mil.)	NET INCOME ($ mil.)	NET PROFIT MARGIN	EMPLOYEES
12/20	19,818	1,873	9.5%	0
12/19	14,036	2,304	16.4%	0
12/18	12,834	2,215	17.3%	0
12/17	11,595	1,877	16.2%	0
12/16	9,154	1,379	15.1%	0
Annual Growth	21.3%	7.9%	—	—

2020 Year-End Financials

Debt ratio: 3.2%	No. of shares (mil.): —
Return on equity: 12.4%	Dividends
Cash ($ mil.): 13,654	Yield: —
Current ratio: 1.54	Payout: —
Long-term debt ($ mil.): 15,344	Market value ($ mil.): —

China Mobile Limited

China Mobile Limited sees unlimited potential. The company is one of China's largest wireless operator by subscribers which total some 1 billion. China Mobile currently puts in an all-out effort to drive the "5G+" plan forward to pursue and promote 5G+4G coordinated development. In general the company provides mobile telecommunications related services such as data and voice services. In addition to its flagship postpaid GoTone brand the company targets the youth and budget-conscious markets with M-Zone and Easy Own prepaid services. State-controlled China Mobile Communications Corporation (CMCC) indirectly holds a majority stake of less than 75% through intermediary subsidiary China Mobile (Hong Kong) Group Limited. The company was founded in 1997.

Operations

China Mobile provides telecommunications services (such as voice and data services) telecommunication related products (such as handsets) customer point rewards and/or other promotional goods/services.

In terms of the company's sales telecommunications services accounts for more than 90% while sales of products and others account for almost 10%.

China Mobile's Telecommunications service is divided in voice services which accounts for over 12% of total sales and data services which is further divided in: wireless data traffic (more than 50% of total sales); applications and information services (some 10%); wireline broadband (almost 10%); and SMS & MMS.

The company has three popular brands: "GoTone" "M-zone" and "Easy Own". In addition it works further on the integrated development of "network+ cloud+ DICT" for its business line.

The company also accelerated the implementation of "5G+" by formulating well-coordinated development of 5G and 4G. It constructed and began operating more than 50000 5G base stations and launched 5G commercial services in 50 cities.

Geographic Reach

Hong Kong based China Mobile has its presence in approximately 50 cities in China.

Sales and Marketing

The majority of China Mobile operating revenue is from contracts with the customers. In general the company serves individual and corporate customers. Its five largest customers generates less than 30% of total revenue.

Financial Performance

China Mobile recorded operating revenue of RMB745.9 billion for the 2019 financial year up by 1% compared to last year. Of this telecommunications services revenue amounted to RMB674.4 billion or a growth of 1% year-on-year.

Cash held by the company at the end of 2019 increased by RMB 118.6 billion to RMB 175.9 billion compared from the previous year with RMB 57.3 billion. Cash provided by operations was RMB 247.6 billion while cash used for investing and financing activities were RMB 64.2 billion and RMB 64.9 billion respectively. Main uses for cash was payment for property plant and equipment.

Strategy

Coupled with this was the impact of government policies including the continued implementation of the "speed upgrade and tariff reduction". Against this backdrop China Mobile joined together to overcome these hurdles and work towards its ultimate goal of becoming a world-class enterprise by building a dynamic "Powerhouse". This was centered on the key strategy of high-quality development supported by a value-driven operating system that leverages its advantages of scale to drive further convergence integration and digitization across the board. China Mobile structured its organization to enable effective and synergetic capability building and collaborative growth while nurturing internal vitality. In addition the company further implemented its "5G+" plan to spearhead the development of "four growth engines" comprising the "customer" "home" "business" and "new" markets. These measures have

helped China Mobile obtain positive momentum in overall operating results which was a hard-earned achievement for it in a tough year.

Company Background

China Mobile Limited was incorporated in Hong Kong on 3 September 1997. The Company was listed on the New York Stock Exchange ("NYSE") and The Stock Exchange of Hong Kong Limited ("HKEX" or the "Stock Exchange") on 22 October 1997 and 23 October 1997 respectively.

EXECUTIVES

Vice President, Huidi Li
Vice President, Dachun Zhao
Chief Financial Officer, Executive Director, Ronghua Li, $15,857 total compensation
Executive Director, Yuhang Wang, $97,595 total compensation
VP, CFO and Director, Xin Dong, $106,877 total compensation
Independent Non-Executive Director, Kin Wah Yiu
Independent Non-Executive Director, Mo chi Cheng
Independent Non-Executive Director, Qiang Yang
Executive Chairman of the Board, Jie Yang, $107,006 total compensation
Vice President, Qin Jian
Vice President, Tongqing Gao
Independent Non-Executive Director, Man Yiu Chow
Auditors: PricewaterhouseCoopers Zhong Tian LLP

LOCATIONS

HQ: China Mobile Limited
   60/F, The Center, 99 Queens Road Central,
Phone: (852) 3121 8888   **Fax:** (852) 3121 8809
Web: www.chinamobileltd.com

PRODUCTS/OPERATIONS

2015 Sales

	% of total
Telecommunication Services	
Voice Services	56
Data Services	33
Other	5
Other products & services	6
Total	100

2015 Sales

	% of total
Revenue from telecommunications services	87
Revenue from sales of products and others	13
Total	100

COMPETITORS

AT&T INC.
BT GROUP PLC
China Telecom Corporation Limited
FORESCOUT TECHNOLOGIES INC.
IOMART GROUP PLC
ORANGE
Oi S A Em Recuperacao Judicial
Restricted Data - Order Investigation 654703487
SA ESKER
SPRINT CORPORATION
STARHUB LTD.
Shaw Communications Inc
Sierra Wireless Inc
TELEPERFORMANCE SE
VOCERA COMMUNICATIONS INC.
VODACOM GROUP LTD

HISTORICAL FINANCIALS

Company Type: Public

Income Statement

	REVENUE ($ mil.)	NET INCOME ($ mil.)	NET PROFIT MARGIN	EMPLOYEES
				FYE: December 31
12/20	117,437	16,489	14.0%	454,332
12/19	107,199	15,325	14.3%	464,656
12/18	107,122	17,123	16.0%	459,152
12/17	113,795	17,561	15.4%	464,656
12/16	102,018	15,659	15.3%	460,647
Annual Growth	3.6%	1.3%	—	(0.3%)

2020 Year-End Financials

Debt ratio: —	No. of shares (mil.): —
Return on equity: 9.5%	Dividends
Cash ($ mil.): 32,526	Yield: 0.0%
Current ratio: 1.12	Payout: 251.0%
Long-term debt ($ mil.): —	Market value ($ mil.): —

	STOCK PRICE ($) FY Close	P/E High/Low		PER SHARE ($) Earnings	Dividends	Book Value
12/20	28.54	9	5	0.81	2.02	8.58
12/19	42.27	10	7	0.74	1.70	7.75
12/18	48.00	9	7	0.84	1.89	7.47
12/17	50.54	11	9	0.86	3.57	7.40
12/16	52.43	11	9	0.76	1.49	6.89
Annual Growth	(14.1%)	—	—	1.3%	8.0%	5.7%

China Molybdenum Co Ltd

EXECUTIVES

Vice Chairman of the Board, Chief Investment Officer, Executive Director, Chaochun Li
Vice Chairman of the Board, Non-Executive Director, Yimin Guo
Independent Non-Executive Director, Ye Yan
President, Ruiwen Sun
Joint Company Secretary, Sau Mei Ng
Chief Financial Officer, Vice President, Yiming Wu
Chairman of the Board, Non-Executive Director, Honglin Yuan
Independent Non-Executive Director, Yougui Wang
Non-Executive Director, Yunlei Cheng
Independent Non-Executive Director, Shuhua Li
Vice President, Jun Zhou
Auditors: Deloitte Touche Tohmatsu Certified Public Accountants LLP (Special General Partnership)

LOCATIONS

HQ: China Molybdenum Co Ltd
   North of Yihe, Huamei Shan Road, Chengdong New District, Luanchuan County, Luoyang City, Henan Province 471500
Phone: (86) 379 6865 8017   **Fax:** (86) 379 6865 8030
Web: www.chinamoly.com

HISTORICAL FINANCIALS

Company Type: Public

Income Statement				FYE: December 31
	REVENUE ($ mil.)	NET INCOME ($ mil.)	NET PROFIT MARGIN	EMPLOYEES
12/20	17,274	356	2.1%	0
12/19	9,869	266	2.7%	0
12/18	3,774	673	17.9%	0
12/17	3,710	419	11.3%	0
12/16	1,000	143	14.4%	0
Annual Growth	103.8%	25.5%	—	—

2020 Year-End Financials

Debt ratio: 4.9%
Return on equity: 5.8%
Cash ($ mil.): 2,591
Current ratio: 1.35
Long-term debt ($ mil.): 2,903

No. of shares (mil.): —
Dividends
  Yield: —
  Payout: —
Market value ($ mil.): —

China Overseas Land & Investment Ltd

China Overseas Land & Investment (COLI) builds upon its bricks-and-mortar aspirations both in Hong Kong and mainland China. The company specializes in property development and commercial property management operation. Other businesses include construction design and property management. The company targets its investment and development efforts in about 50 major cities including Beijing Guangzhou Hong Kong and Shanghai. Hua Dong Region accounts for its largest geographic market which accounts for more than 25% of total revenue.

Operations

Known as China Overseas Property in mainland China the company operates through three primary segments: Property Development Property Investments and Other Operations (revenue from hotel operation provision of construction and building design consultancy services). The largest segment Property Development accounts for more than 95% of total revenue and the remaining accounts the rest.

Geographic Reach

COLI has a strong presence in the Hua Dong and Hua Bei regions which brought in more than 25% and more than 20% of revenues respectively. To a lesser extent it also operates in the Northern Region Hua Bei Region Western Region Macau and Hong Kong.

Its head office is located in Hong Kong.

Sales and Marketing

The five largest customers of the Group accounted for less than 30% of the Group's revenue while the five largest suppliers of the Group accounted for less than 30% of the Group's total purchases.

Financial Performance

NOTE: Growth rates may differ after conversion to US dollars.

During the year the revenue of the company increased to RMB163.7 billion (2018: RMB144.0 billion) representing an increase of 14% as compared to last year.

Profit attributable to equity shareholders of the company amounted to RMB41.6 billion (2018: RMB37.7 billion) representing an increase of 10%.

Cash held by the company at the end of 2019 increased to RMB 92.9 billion compared to RMB 84.0 billion in the prior year. Cash provided by operations and financing activities were RMB 9.9 billion and RMB 1.5 billion respectively. Cash used for investing activities was RMB 2.6 billion mainly for capital contributions to joint ventures.

Strategy

In 2019 the company maintained its prudent investment strategy targeting the efficient replenishment of high-quality land reserves. Through strategies of "going smart" and industrialization the company strengthened research and development and application of smart communities smart homes and green technologies to rapidly transform it into product advantages for the company and boost customer satisfaction.

Company Background

COLI was incorporated in Hong Kong in 1979.

EXECUTIVES

Executive Chairman of the Board, Jianguo Yan, $631,082 total compensation
Vice Chairman of the Board, Chief Operating Officer, Executive Vice President, Executive Director, Chief Architect, Liang Luo, $311,866 total compensation
Independent Non-Executive Director, Ka Keung Chan
Independent Non-Executive Director, Man Bun Li
Vice President, Executive Director, Guanghui Guo, $255,398 total compensation
Vice President, Feng Xu
Assistant President, Xin Xu
Vice President, Xianyong Liu
Vice President, Yi Zhang
Independent Non-Executive Director, Lai Tai Fan Hsu
Vice President, Dapeng Qi
Assistant President, Wendong Xu
Chief Executive Officer, Executive Director, Zhichao Zhang, $230,129 total compensation
Vice President, Guoxin Ouyang
Vice President, Deyou Chen
Company Secretary, Wai Sang Chong
Chief Financial Officer, Sai Kit Lui
Non-Executive Vice Chairman of the Board, Yong Zhuang
Vice President, Huiming Liu
Non-Executive Director, Wenhai Zhao
Auditors: PricewaterhouseCoopers

LOCATIONS

HQ: China Overseas Land & Investment Ltd
  10/F., Three Pacific Place, 1 Queens Road East,
Phone: (852) 2988 0666   **Fax:** (852) 2865 7517
Web: www.coli.com.hk

PRODUCTS/OPERATIONS

2014 Sales

	% of total
Property development	97
Property investment	1
Other operations	2
Total	**100**

Operations

Property development
Property investment
Property-related business
  Construction design
  Property management

COMPETITORS

ARMADA/HOFFLER PROPERTIES L.L.C.
COUNTRYSIDE PROPERTIES (UK) LIMITED
GREAT PORTLAND ESTATES P L C
HELICAL PLC
LAING O'ROURKE PLC.
WHARF (HOLDINGS) LIMITED THE

HISTORICAL FINANCIALS

Company Type: Public

Income Statement				FYE: December 31
	REVENUE ($ mil.)	NET INCOME ($ mil.)	NET PROFIT MARGIN	EMPLOYEES
12/19	23,519	5,981	25.4%	6,200
12/18	21,892	5,732	26.2%	5,900
12/17	21,246	5,216	24.6%	5,600
12/16	21,157	4,774	22.6%	5,500
12/15	19,104	4,297	22.5%	5,300
Annual Growth	5.3%	8.6%	—	4.0%

2019 Year-End Financials

Debt ratio: 3.7%
Return on equity: 14.7%
Cash ($ mil.): 13,717
Current ratio: 2.17
Long-term debt ($ mil.): 22,690

No. of shares (mil.): —
Dividends
  Yield: 0.0%
  Payout: 94.0%
Market value ($ mil.): —

	STOCK PRICE ($) FY Close	P/E High/Low		PER SHARE ($) Earnings	Dividends	Book Value
12/19	19.50	5	4	0.55	0.51	3.68
12/18	16.87	29	3	0.52	0.46	3.30
12/17	92.25	31	21	0.48	0.48	3.10
12/16	79.10	30	21	0.47	0.47	2.62
12/15	103.27	35	22	0.47	0.52	2.51
Annual Growth	(34.1%)	—	—	4.1%	(0.2%)	10.1%

China Pacific Insurance (Group) Co., Ltd.

Auditors: PricewaterhouseCoopers

LOCATIONS

HQ: China Pacific Insurance (Group) Co., Ltd.
  1 South Zhongshan Road, Huangpu, Shanghai 200010
Phone: (86) 21 58767282   **Fax:** (86) 21 68870791
Web: www.cpic.com.cn

HISTORICAL FINANCIALS

Company Type: Public

Income Statement				FYE: December 31
	REVENUE ($ mil.)	NET INCOME ($ mil.)	NET PROFIT MARGIN	EMPLOYEES
12/20	64,059	3,758	5.9%	110,940
12/19	54,997	3,986	7.2%	111,247
12/18	51,335	2,619	5.1%	107,741
12/17	49,083	2,253	4.6%	101,887
12/16	38,317	1,736	4.5%	0
Annual Growth	13.7%	21.3%	—	—

2020 Year-End Financials

Debt ratio: —
Return on equity: 12.4%
Cash ($ mil.): 3,192
Current ratio: —
Long-term debt ($ mil.): —

No. of shares (mil.): —
Dividends
  Yield: —
  Payout: 49.4%
Market value ($ mil.): —

China Petroleum & Chemical Corp

China Petroleum and Chemical Corporation (Sinopec Corp.) is China's largest producer and supplier of refined oil products and its second-largest crude oil producer. It is also China's largest petrochemicals producer and distributor and the world's fourth-largest ethylene producer. Operations include oil and gas exploration and production; crude oil processing; oil products trading transportation distribution and marketing; and petrochemicals manufacturing. In 2010 it reported proved reserves of 2.9 billion barrels of oil and 6.5 trillion cu. ft. of natural gas; it also owns more than 29600 gas stations and 34 refineries. China's government controls about 76% of the company through Sinopec Group.

EXECUTIVES

Senior Vice President, Ge Chen
Senior Vice President, Director, Yiqun Ling
Chief Financial Officer, Dongua Shou
Vice President, Secretary of the Board, Wensheng Huang
Non-Executive Chairman of the Board, Yongsheng Ma
Vice President, Rifeng Zhao
Independent Non-Executive Director, Min Tang
Independent Non-Executive Director, Jianing Wu
Independent Non-Executive Director, Hongbin Cai
Senior Vice President, Director, Hongbin Liu
President, Director, Baocai Yu
Director, Shaofeng Zhang
Vice President, Xizhi Yu
Auditors: PricewaterhouseCoopers Zhong Tian LLP

LOCATIONS

HQ: China Petroleum & Chemical Corp
No. 22 Chaoyangmen North Street, Chaoyang District, Beijing 100728
Phone: (86) 10 5996 0028   **Fax:** (86) 10 5996 0386
Web: www.sinopec.com

2015 Sales

	% of total
Mainland China	78
Others	22
Total	**100**

PRODUCTS/OPERATIONS

2015 Sales

	% of total
Marketing and distribution	34
Refining	28
Chemicals	10
Exploration and production	4
Corporate and others	24
Total	**100**

COMPETITORS

Bankers Petroleum Ltd
Bp (China) Holdings Limited
Cenovus Energy Inc
China National Offshore Oil Corporation
JAPAN PETROLEUM EXPLORATION CO.LTD.
KUWAIT PETROLEUM CORPORATION S.A.K
NOVATEK PAO
OIL AND NATURAL GAS CORPORATION LIMITED
PetroChina Company Limited
PetroKazakhstan Inc
QATAR ENERGY
SPINDLETOP OIL & GAS CO.

SURGUTNEFTEGAZ PAO
TransAtlantic Petroleum Corp

HISTORICAL FINANCIALS
Company Type: Public

Income Statement

FYE: December 31

	REVENUE ($ mil.)	NET INCOME ($ mil.)	NET PROFIT MARGIN	EMPLOYEES
12/20	322,003	5,034	1.6%	0
12/19	426,285	8,276	1.9%	402,206
12/18	420,333	9,172	2.2%	423,543
12/17	362,691	7,855	2.2%	446,225
12/16	278,066	6,721	2.4%	451,611
Annual Growth	3.7%	(7.0%)	—	—

2020 Year-End Financials

Debt ratio: 0.9%
Return on equity: 4.4%
Cash ($ mil.): 28,196
Current ratio: 0.87
Long-term debt ($ mil.): 12,815
No. of shares (mil.): —
Dividends
  Yield: 7.4%
  Payout: 7,854.3%
Market value ($ mil.): —

	STOCK PRICE ($) FY Close	P/E High/Low		PER SHARE ($) Earnings	Dividends	Book Value
12/20	44.60	243	143	0.04	3.30	(0.00)
12/19	60.15	176	117	0.07	4.99	0.88
12/18	70.60	196	134	0.08	7.72	0.86
12/17	73.37	212	168	0.06	3.66	0.92
12/16	71.02	194	123	0.06	1.78	0.85
Annual Growth	(11.0%)	—	—	(6.9%)	16.7%	

China Railway Construction Corp Ltd

EXECUTIVES

Vice President, Lixin Wang
Vice President, Chengjun Liu
Chairman of the Board, Executive Director, Jianping Wang
Executive Director, Ruchen Liu
President, Executive Director, Shangbiao Zhuang
Vice President, Zhen Ni
Vice President, Wenzhong Wang
Vice President, Ning Li
Chief Accounting Officer, Chief Compliance Officer, Xiuming Wang
Independent Non-Executive Director, Xiaoqiang Lu
Independent Non-Executive Director, Huacheng Wang
Independent Non-Executive Director, Wen Cheng
Independent Non-Executive Director, Patrick Sun
Executive Director, Dayang Chen
Auditors: Ernst & Young Hua Ming LLP

LOCATIONS

HQ: China Railway Construction Corp Ltd
East, No. 40 Fuxing Road, Haidian District, Beijing 100855
Phone: (86) 10 5268 8600   **Fax:** (86) 10 5268 8302
Web: www.crcc.cn

HISTORICAL FINANCIALS
Company Type: Public

Income Statement

FYE: December 31

	REVENUE ($ mil.)	NET INCOME ($ mil.)	NET PROFIT MARGIN	EMPLOYEES
12/20	139,188	3,423	2.5%	0
12/19	119,348	2,902	2.4%	0
12/18	106,148	2,607	2.5%	0
12/17	104,646	2,467	2.4%	0
12/16	90,628	2,016	2.2%	0
Annual Growth	11.3%	14.2%	—	—

2020 Year-End Financials

Debt ratio: 2.3%
Return on equity: 9.6%
Cash ($ mil.): 28,744
Current ratio: 1.12
Long-term debt ($ mil.): 20,967
No. of shares (mil.): —
Dividends
  Yield: 0.0%
  Payout: 110.0%
Market value ($ mil.): —

	STOCK PRICE ($) FY Close	P/E High/Low		PER SHARE ($) Earnings	Dividends	Book Value
12/20	5.19	8	4	0.22	0.24	(0.00)
12/19	10.93	10	7	0.19	0.24	(0.00)
12/18	13.54	11	7	0.18	0.22	(0.00)
12/17	11.56	14	10	0.17	0.19	(0.00)
12/16	13.01	14	8	0.15	0.17	(0.00)
Annual Growth	(20.5%)	—	—	10.9%	9.6%	

China Railway Group Ltd

China Railway Group keeps its infrastructure construction projects on the right track. A subsidiary of state-owned China Railway Engineering Corporation the company designs and constructs railways roads bridges tunnels subways and other structures. It also offers related consulting and engineering services as well as property development and construction services for commercial and residential buildings and other projects. In addition to its core transportation-related projects the company pursues projects from municipal and energy entities in China and abroad. Some of those projects have included hydroelectricity facilities ports and docks.

Operations

China Railway Group operates through five main segments. Its Infrastructure Construction segment generated 82% of its total sales in 2014 and works on railways highways bridges railways irrigation works dams docks airports and municipal works among other projects. Its Property Development segment (5% of revenue) is its next largest and sells or manages residential and commercial properties. The other segments include Survey Design and Consulting Services (2%); Engineering Equipment and Component Manufacturing (2%); and other (9%).

Geographic Reach

Beyond China the group has worked on construction projects in the Americas Europe Africa and the Asia Pacific. Still the group generated 96% of its total revenue from China in 2014.

Sales and Marketing

China Railway Group's largest customer is the China Railway Corporation which accounted for 32% of its total revenue in 2014. Its four next largest customers combined made up another 2.5% of its total revenue.

Financial Performance

Note: Growth rates may differ after conversion to US dollars. This analysis uses financials from the company's annual report.

China Railway Group's annual revenues and profits have grown more than 30% since 2011 thanks mostly to increased demand for infrastructure construction in China with the growing economy.

The group's revenue climbed 9% to RMB$590.2 billion ($95.9 billion) during 2014 mostly driven by double-digit growth in its infrastructure construction business with more demand for railways highways building construction and urban rail work. The group's Survey Design and Consulting Services business grew 12% due to a rise in infrastructure project activity while its manufacturing and property development businesses each grew by 6% during the year.

Strong revenue growth in 2014 drove China Railway Group's net income higher by 9% to RMB$10.26 billion ($1.67 billion). The group's operating cash levels more than doubled to RMB$19.4 billion ($3.16 billion) in FY2014 mostly as it was able to collect more of its trade receivables with stronger management initiatives.

Strategy

Buoyed by an influx of infrastructure funds from the Chinese government's "One Belt and One Road" policy the group in 2015 planned to build a new China brand for high speed rail and expand its construction projects globally (through its "Go Global" campaign) in new infrastructure markets such as Russia and Israel. The group also planned to invest more in Research Development and Technological Achievements creating some 957 new research projects during 2014 with support from national funds amounting to nearly RMB$29 million.

Despite a strategy to expand internationally most of China Railway Group' work still originates in China. Recent projects include new light rail systems and highways in some of China's larger cities. Ultimately a state-owned company China Railway Group receives much of its funding for projects from the Chinese government which has been pushing to expand the country's public transportation infrastructure.

Company Background

China Railway Group traces its roots back to the 1950s. It has completed hundreds of infrastructure projects in more than 50 countries since the 1970s.

EXECUTIVES

Executive Chairman of the Board, Yun Chen
Non-Executive Director, Zonglin Ma
Vice President, Tengqun Yu
Vice President, Hui Liu
Chief Financial Officer, Chief Accounting Officer, Cui Sun
Auditors: Deloitte Touche Tohmatsu CPA LLP

LOCATIONS

HQ: China Railway Group Ltd
918, Block 1, No. 128 South 4th Ring Road West, Fengtai District, Beijing 100070
Phone:
Web: www.crec.cn

PRODUCTS/OPERATIONS

2015 Sales

	% of total
Infrastructure Construction	85
Property Development	5
Survey Design and Consulting Services	2
Engineering Equipment and Component Manufacturing	2
Other Businesses	6
Total	**100**

COMPETITORS

BECHTEL GROUP INC.
CARILLION PLC
CHIYODA CORPORATION
China Communications Construction Company Limited
China Railway Construction Group Co. Ltd.
Crrc Corporation Limited
FLUOR CORPORATION
FUELCELL ENERGY INC.
HELIX ENERGY SOLUTIONS GROUP INC.
HOCHTIEF AG
HYDER CONSULTING GROUP HOLDINGS LIMITED
KBR INC.
LARSEN AND TOUBRO LIMITED
ORION GROUP HOLDINGS INC.

HISTORICAL FINANCIALS

Company Type: Public

Income Statement

FYE: December 31

	REVENUE ($ mil.)	NET INCOME ($ mil.)	NET PROFIT MARGIN	EMPLOYEES
12/20	149,038	3,851	2.6%	0
12/19	122,284	3,402	2.8%	0
12/18	107,648	2,500	2.3%	0
12/17	106,549	2,469	2.3%	0
12/16	92,648	1,801	1.9%	0
Annual Growth	**12.6%**	**20.9%**	**—**	**—**

2020 Year-End Financials

Debt ratio: 3.0%
Return on equity: 10.5%
Cash ($ mil.): 26,721
Current ratio: 1.05
Long-term debt ($ mil.): 24,720
No. of shares (mil.): —
Dividends
Yield: —
Payout: —
Market value ($ mil.): —

China Resources Land Ltd

China Resources Land does more than dabble in property development investment and management. The company which is part of China Resources (Holdings) Company primarily develops properties in urban areas of China such as Beijing Shanghai Shenzhen and Chengdu. It specializes in mid-range and upscale residential and commercial properties. China Resources Land also also offers property management services. Other divisions are involved in interior design and furniture manufacturing. The company owns major properties in the country including the Beijing China Resources Building China Resources Times Square and Shenzhen City Crossing.

Operations

The company operates in four segments: sale of developed properties property investments and management hotel operations and construction and decoration services.

Geographic Reach

In 2013 China Resources Land's geographic reach expanded to 42 cities with over 70 projects under development.

EXECUTIVES

Independent Non-Executive Director, Andrew Yan
President, Executive Director, Xin Li, $230,644 total compensation

Executive Vice Chairman of the Board, Chief Operating Officer, Dawei Zhang, $230,644 total compensation
Senior Vice President, Executive Director, Chief Strategy Officer, Ji Xie, $187,068 total compensation
Independent Non-Executive Director, Hin Ngai Ho
Senior Vice President, Chairman of the East and North-East China Region, Xiaokai Kong
Independent Non-Executive Director, Kam To Wan
Chief Human Resource Officer, Senior Vice President, Executive Director, Bingqi Wu, $187,068 total compensation
Senior Vice President, Liqiang Zhang
Company Secretary, Chi Lik Lo
Independent Non-Executive Director, Zhe Sun
Independent Non-Executive Director, Wei Zhong
Non-Executive Chairman of the Board, Xiangming Wang
Executive Director, Shiqing Guo, $3,738 total compensation
Non-Executive Director, Liang Zhang
Non-Executive Director, Jian Dou
Non-Executive Director, Hong Cheng
Non-Executive Director, Xiaoyong Liu
Auditors: Ernst & Young

LOCATIONS

HQ: China Resources Land Ltd
46th Floor, China Resources Building, 26 Harbour Road, Wanchai,
Phone: (852) 2877 2330   **Fax:** (852) 2877 9068
Web: www.crland.com.hk

PRODUCTS/OPERATIONS

2015 sales

	% of total
Sales of developed properties	90
Property investment & management	6
Hotel operations	1
Construction decoration services & others	3
Total	**100**

COMPETITORS

AGILE GROUP HOLDINGS LIMITED
CHINA MOTOR BUS COMPANY LIMITED
Citycon Oyj
HANG LUNG GROUP LIMITED
MITSUBISHI ESTATE COMPANY LIMITED
RESTART SPA IN FORMA ABBREVIATA RESTART SPA
THE GALE COMPANY L L C
TOKYU LAND CORPORATION
YANLORD LAND GROUP LIMITED

HISTORICAL FINANCIALS

Company Type: Public

Income Statement

FYE: December 31

	REVENUE ($ mil.)	NET INCOME ($ mil.)	NET PROFIT MARGIN	EMPLOYEES
12/20	27,458	4,557	16.6%	48,414
12/19	21,231	4,120	19.4%	51,976
12/18	17,619	3,523	20.0%	46,518
12/17	15,173	2,945	19.4%	38,087
12/16	14,098	2,514	17.8%	33,524
Annual Growth	**18.1%**	**16.0%**	**—**	**9.6%**

2020 Year-End Financials

Debt ratio: 2.9%
Return on equity: 15.3%
Cash ($ mil.): 13,676
Current ratio: 1.29
Long-term debt ($ mil.): 19,791
No. of shares (mil.): —
Dividends
Yield: 3.8%
Payout: —
Market value ($ mil.): —

China Resources Pharmaceutical Group Ltd

Auditors: Ernst & Young

LOCATIONS

HQ: China Resources Pharmaceutical Group Ltd
Room 4104-05, 41/F, China Resources Building, 26
Harbour Road, Wanchai,
Phone:
Web: www.crpharm.com

HISTORICAL FINANCIALS

Company Type: Public

Income Statement   FYE: December 31

	REVENUE ($ mil.)	NET INCOME ($ mil.)	NET PROFIT MARGIN	EMPLOYEES
12/19	26,256	422	1.6%	67,000
12/18	24,219	515	2.1%	62,000
12/17	22,076	445	2.0%	56,000
Annual Growth	9.1%	(2.7%)	—	9.4%

2019 Year-End Financials

Debt ratio: 2.6%
Return on equity: 8.2%
Cash ($ mil.): 1,608
Current ratio: 1.25
Long-term debt ($ mil.): 1,187

No. of shares (mil.): —
Dividends
  Yield: —
  Payout: 21.1%
Market value ($ mil.): —

	STOCK PRICE ($) FY Close	P/E High/Low	PER SHARE ($) Earnings	Dividends	Book Value
12/19	0.00	— —	0.07	0.01	0.83
12/18	0.00	— —	0.08	0.02	0.80
Annual Growth	—	— —	(9.6%)	(7.7%)	2.0%

China Shenhua Energy Co., Ltd.

China Shenhua Energy Company (CSEC) is principally engaged in the production and sale of coal and electricity railway port and shipping transportation and coal-to-olefins businesses in China. CSEC operates five major mines. The Shendong Mines account for close to two-thirds of its total coal production which is about 185 million tons a year. It is the largest listed coal company in China and globally with the sales volume of coal reaching more than 447 million tonnes and commercial coal production volume reaching approximately 282.7 million tonnes. CSEC owns and operates four railway lines and port facilities for the transportation of its coal. The company also operates some 15 power plants total installed capacity of close to 30245 MW. Almost all of its sales account to China.

Operations

The company operates six segments: Coal (over 70% of sales) Power (over 20%) Railway Port Shipping and Coal Chemical (accounts for the remaining).

Coal operations produce coal from surface and underground mines and the sale of coal to external customers the power operations segment and the coal chemical operations segment.

Power operations use coal from the coal operations segment and external suppliers thermal power wind power water power and gas power to generate electric power for the sale to coal operations segment and external customers.

Railway operations provide railway transportation services to the coal operations segment the power operations segment the coal chemical operations segment and external customers.

Port operations provide loading transportation and storage services to the coal operations segment and external customers. The company charges service fees and other expenses which are reviewed and approved by the relevant government authorities.

Shipping operations provide shipment transportation services to the power operations segment the coal operations segment and external customers.

Coal chemical operations use coal from the coal operations segment to first produce methanol and further process into polyethylene and polypropylene together with other by-products for sale to external customers.

Geographic Reach

The company is headquartered in China where it generates almost all of it sales.

Sales and Marketing

The company sells its coal under long-term supply contracts which allow periodical price adjustments and at spot market. It also sells its polyethylene at spot market.

The total revenue from the top five customers of the group accounts for some 35% of the revenue of the group including the revenue of the group from its largest customer accounting for around 25% of the revenue of the group. The largest customer of the group was China Energy (including its subsidiaries) the controlling shareholder of the company. The group mainly sells coal products and provides coal transportation service to the company.

Financial Performance

Except in 2019 the company's revenue has been rising in the last few years. It has an overall growth of 37% between 2015 and 2019.

The company had a revenue of RMB 241.9 billion an 8% decrease from the previous year. The decrease was primarily due to lower sales volume in the company's Power Port and Coal Chemical Segments.

Profit for the year ended 2019 totaled RMB 49.8 billion.

The company's cash for the year ended 2019 was RMB 41.8 billion. Operating activities generated RMB 63.1 billion while investing activities used RMB 46.3 billion primarily for purchases of wealth management products included in prepaid expenses and other current assets. Financing activities used another RMB 37.2 billion primarily for dividends paid to equity holders of the company.

Strategy

Over the past year guided by the overall development strategy requirement of "One Target Three Models and Five Strategies and Seven First-class" of China Energy the company took active measures to identify its strategic positioning defined its development goals and organized the promotion of strategy research for development the development of world-class demonstration enterprises and the preparation of the "14th five-year" plan which charted the course and laid a solid foundation for the long-term development of the company.

EXECUTIVES

Deputy General Manager, Staff Elected Director, Xingzhong Wang
Chairman of the Board, Executive Director, Xiangxi Wang
Secretary of the Board, Qing Huang
Non-Executive Director, Jinzhong Jia
Chief Accounting Officer, Shancheng Xu
Deputy General Manager, Executive Director, Mingjun Xu
Independent Non-Executive Director, Guoqiang Yuan
Independent Non-Executive Director, Hanwen Chen
Independent Non-Executive Director, Chong'en Bai
General Manager, Zhiren Lu
Auditors: Deloitte Touche Tohmatsu Certified Public Accountants LLP

LOCATIONS

HQ: China Shenhua Energy Co., Ltd.
22 Andingmen Xibinhe Road, Dongcheng District, Beijing 100011
Phone: (86) 10 5813 3399   **Fax:** (86) 10 5813 1804
Web: www.csec.com

2008 Sales

	% of total
China	91
Other countries	9
Total	**100**

COMPETITORS

ADANI ENTERPRISES LIMITED
COAL INDIA LIMITED
DOMINION ENERGY INC.
FLORIDA POWER & LIGHT COMPANY
GREAT PLAINS ENERGY INCORPORATED

L&L ENERGY INC.
THE SOUTHERN COMPANY
U.S. CHINA MINING GROUP INC.
WEC ENERGY GROUP INC.

HISTORICAL FINANCIALS

Company Type: Public

Income Statement   FYE: December 31

	REVENUE ($ mil.)	NET INCOME ($ mil.)	NET PROFIT MARGIN	EMPLOYEES
12/20	35,665	5,989	16.8%	0
12/19	34,760	6,215	17.9%	0
12/18	38,396	6,377	16.6%	0
12/17	38,224	6,920	18.1%	0
12/16	26,371	3,270	12.4%	0
Annual Growth	7.8%	16.3%	—	—

2020 Year-End Financials

Debt ratio: 1.6%
Return on equity: 10.9%
Cash ($ mil.): 19,488
Current ratio: 2.48
Long-term debt ($ mil.): 8,178

No. of shares (mil.): —
Dividends
  Yield: 13.5%
  Payout: 213.1%
Market value ($ mil.): —

	STOCK PRICE ($) FY Close	P/E High/Low	PER SHARE ($) Earnings	Dividends	Book Value
12/20	7.47	5 3	0.30	1.01	(0.00)
12/19	8.33	5 3	0.31	0.42	(0.00)
12/18	8.64	5 4	0.32	0.47	(0.00)
12/17	10.38	5 4	0.35	1.64	(0.00)
12/16	7.39	8 4	0.16	0.14	(0.00)
Annual Growth	0.3%	— —	16.3%	63.7%	—

China Southern Airlines Co Ltd

One of China's top three airline companies along with China Eastern Airlines and Air China China Southern Airlines operates a fleet of over 865 passenger and cargo transport aircraft including Boeing models 787777 747& 737 and Airbus models A380 330 320 350 from its hub in Guangzhou and around 15 branches regional bases. China Southern Airlines has over 4000 daily flights. The company generates most of its sales domestically.

Operations

China Southern Airlines' scope of business includes: provision of services of domestic regional and international scheduled and unscheduled air transportation of passenger cargo mail and baggage; provision of services of general aviation; provision of services of aircraft maintenance; acting as an agency of domestic and foreign airlines; offering airlines catering services (operated by branch office only); and conducting other aviation and relevant businesses among others.

The company generates vast majority of sales from traffic activities. The remaining is from other operating activities including commission general aviation and hotel and tour operations.

The company has two reportable operating segments; Airline Transportation Operations (around 95% of sales) and other segments (about 5%) according to internal organization structure managerial needs and internal reporting system. Airline transportation operations comprises the Group's passenger and cargo and mail operations. Other segments includes hotel and tour operation air catering services ground services cargo handling and other miscellaneous services.

Geographic Reach

China Southern Airlines headquarters is located in Guangzhou. It has about 15 branches in Beijing Shenzhen and other cities and around 10 holding aviation subsidiaries including Xiamen Airlines. The company has set up SAGA in Zhuhai and has set up nearly 25 domestic offices in Hangzhou Qingdao and other places and approximately 55 overseas offices in Sydney New York and other places. It generates some 70% of total sales from domestic operations about 30% from international and the rest were generated from Hong Kong Macau & Taiwan.

Sales and Marketing

The company's top 5 customers account for less than 30%% of the company's total revenue. Its advertising and promotion expenses were RMB 121 million and RMB 314 million in 2020 and 2019 respectively.

Financial Performance

The company's total operating revenue decreased by RMB61.8 billion or 40% from RMB154.3 billion in 2019 to RMB92.6 billion in 2020.

The net loss attributable to equity shareholders of the company of RMB10.8 billion was recorded in 2020 as compared to the net profit attributable to equity shareholders of the company of RMB2.6 billion in 2019.

Cash held by the company at the end of fiscal 2020 increased to RMB25.4 billion. Cash provided by operations and financing activities were RMB2.7 billion and RMB28.9 billion respectively. Cash used for investing activities was RMB8.0 billion mainly for acquisition of property plant and equipment and other assets.

Strategy

China's development strategy and macro policies are conducive to the development of aviation industry The development strategies implemented in China has greatly expanded the development space for the aviation industry.

Guided by the development goals of the "14th Five-Year Plan" and the Long-Range Objectives Through the Year 2035 the company will further focus on quality and efficiency and have determined the overarching approach for quality development being "adhering to five concepts of development implementing five strategies promoting six campaigns and achieving six transformations".

The company adheres to the "five development" concepts of safety high quality innovation cooperation and sharing; focuses on the "five strategies" in relation to hub network ecosystem innovation-driven lean management and control and brand management; carries out "six campaigns" on promoting safety production grasping major strategic opportunities deepening reforms in key areas enhancing management to first class optimizing and adjusting five major structures improving service quality; and strives for "six transformations" from speed-oriented to quality-oriented from comprehensive market expansion to exploring key areas from a relatively single industry to high relevance and diversified industries from planning management and control to market operation from the traditional business model to digitalization and ecological circle and from extensive management to refined management.

Auditors: PricewaterhouseCoopers Zhong Tian LLP

LOCATIONS

HQ: China Southern Airlines Co Ltd
278 Ji Chang Road, Guangzhou, Guangdong Province 510405
Phone: (86) 20 8612 4462   **Fax:** (86) 20 8665 9040
Web: www.csair.com

2014 Sales

	% of total
Domestic	- 77
International	21
Hong Kong Macau & Taiwan	2
Total	**100**

PRODUCTS/OPERATIONS

2014 Sales

	% of total
Traffic revenue	96
Other	4
Total	**100**

Selected Services

Excess baggage
Carry-on baggage
Delayed/damaged/lost baggage
Checked Baggage
Restrictions on baggage transportation
Special baggage

COMPETITORS

AIR PARTNER PLC
ANA HOLDINGS INC.
ATLAS AIR WORLDWIDE HOLDINGS INC.
AerCap Holdings N.V.
Air Canada
BRISTOW GROUP INC.
CATHAY PACIFIC AIRWAYS LIMITED
Crrc Corporation Limited
Deutsche Lufthansa AG
Fraport AG Frankfurt Airport Services Worldwide
INTELSAT INFLIGHT LLC
JAPAN AIRLINES CO.LTD.
Koninklijke Luchtvaart Maatschappij N.V.
QANTAS AIRWAYS LIMITED

SPIRIT AIRLINES INC.
THAI AIRWAYS INTERNATIONAL PUBLIC COMPANY LIMITED
UNITED AIRLINES HOLDINGS INC.
UNITED AIRLINES INC.

HISTORICAL FINANCIALS

Company Type: Public

Income Statement   FYE: December 31

	REVENUE ($ mil.)	NET INCOME ($ mil.)	NET PROFIT MARGIN	EMPLOYEES
12/20	14,152	(1,657)	—	0
12/19	22,178	380	1.7%	0
12/18	20,880	433	2.1%	0
12/17	19,591	908	4.6%	0
12/16	16,530	727	4.4%	0
Annual Growth	(3.8%)	—	—	—

2020 Year-End Financials

Debt ratio: 4.1%
Return on equity: (-16.2%)
Cash ($ mil.): 3,948
Current ratio: 0.41
Long-term debt ($ mil.): 5,830

No. of shares (mil.): —
Dividends
  Yield: —
  Payout: —
Market value ($ mil.): —

	STOCK PRICE ($) FY Close	P/E High/Low	Earnings	Dividends	Book Value
12/20	29.65	— —	(0.12)	0.00	(0.00)
12/19	33.60	226 128	0.03	0.31	(0.00)
12/18	30.36	231 93	0.04	0.68	(0.00)
12/17	51.82	91 47	0.09	0.67	(0.00)
12/16	25.71	70 47	0.07	0.50	(0.00)
Annual Growth	3.6%	— —	—	—	—

China Taiping Insurance Holding Co., Ltd.

EXECUTIVES

Independent Non-Executive Director, Dajian Zhu
Executive Chairman of the Board, Sidong Wang, $51,182 total compensation
Executive Director, Xing Xiao, $26,945 total compensation
Independent Non-Executive Director, Zhichun Xie
Independent Non-Executive Director, Ting Yuk Wu
Executive Director, Bo Hong, $26,945 total compensation
Chief Internal Auditor, Yanjun Jiao
Non-Executive Director, Changgui Yang
Non-Executive Director, Cui Zhang
Non-Executive Director, Xingguo Hu
Non-Executive Director, Zhaoxu Guo
Executive Vice Chairman of the Board, General Manager, Zhaojun Yin
Chief Financial Officer, Company Secretary, Ruohan Zhang
Independent Non-Executive Director, Fan Chiu Fun Law
Deputy General Manager, Kedong Li
Auditors: PricewaterhouseCoopers

LOCATIONS

HQ: China Taiping Insurance Holding Co., Ltd.
25/F., 18 King Wah Road, North Point,
Phone: (852) 2854 6100   **Fax:** (852) 2544 5269
Web: www.ctih.cntaiping.com

HISTORICAL FINANCIALS

Company Type: Public

Income Statement   FYE: December 31

	ASSETS ($ mil.)	NET INCOME ($ mil.)	INCOME AS % OF ASSETS	EMPLOYEES
12/19	118,074	1,156	1.0%	65,957
12/18	96,028	878	0.9%	75,341
12/17	85,279	785	0.9%	77,472
12/16	65,175	615	0.9%	60,270
12/15	62,964	818	1.3%	53,682
Annual Growth	17.0%	9.0%	—	5.3%

2019 Year-End Financials

Return on assets: 1.0%
Return on equity: 12.6%
Long-term debt ($ mil.): —
No. of shares (mil.): —
Sales ($ mil): 31,628

Dividends
  Yield: —
  Payout: 12.2%
Market value ($ mil.): —

China Telecom Corp Ltd

LOCATIONS

HQ: China Telecom Corp Ltd
31 Jinrong Street, Xicheng District, Beijing 100033
Phone: (86) 10 5850 1800   **Fax:** (86) 10 6601 0728
Web: www.chinatelecom-h.com

HISTORICAL FINANCIALS

Company Type: Public

Income Statement   FYE: December 31

	REVENUE ($ mil.)	NET INCOME ($ mil.)	NET PROFIT MARGIN	EMPLOYEES
12/20	60,175	3,187	5.3%	281,192
12/19	53,998	2,948	5.5%	281,215
12/18	54,828	3,083	5.6%	280,747
12/17	56,278	2,860	5.1%	284,206
12/16	50,731	2,592	5.1%	287,076
Annual Growth	4.4%	5.3%	—	(0.5%)

2020 Year-End Financials

Debt ratio: 1.1%
Return on equity: 5.8%
Cash ($ mil.): 3,621
Current ratio: 0.31
Long-term debt ($ mil.): 3,703

No. of shares (mil.): —
Dividends
  Yield: 0.0%
  Payout: —
Market value ($ mil.): —

	STOCK PRICE ($) FY Close	P/E High/Low	PER SHARE ($) Earnings	Dividends	Book Value
12/20	27.55	170 106	0.04	1.58	0.69
12/19	41.19	220 152	0.04	1.43	0.63
12/18	50.73	210 146	0.04	1.23	0.62
12/17	47.47	236 206	0.04	1.28	0.62
12/16	46.13	236 185	0.03	1.05	0.56
Annual Growth	(12.1%)	— —	5.8%	11.0%	5.2%

China Unicom (Hong Kong) Ltd

China Unicom (Hong Kong) Limited has brought competition to the world's largest telecommunications market. The Chinese government set up China Unicom in 1994 as the first competitor to another government-owned telecommunications monopoly. The state-controlled company provides 437 million subscribers long-distance broadband data and mobile communications services in 31 provinces cities and other regions throughout China. It is the country's #2 mobile phone operator behind former monopoly China Mobile Communications. China Unicom (Hong Kong) Limited operates primarily in the Chinese northern provinces; major cities served include Beijing and Tianjin.

EXECUTIVES

Senior Vice President, Yanzhou Mai
Executive Director, Junzhi Wang
Senior Vice President, Yongbo Tang
President, Executive Director, Zhongyue Chen
Executive Chairman of the Board, Chief Executive Officer, Liehong Liu
Senior Vice President, Baojun Liang
Independent Non-Executive Director, Wai Ming Wong
Independent Non-Executive Director, Shui Ming Chung
Independent Non-Executive Director, Fan Chiu Fun Law
Independent Non-Executive Director, Wing Lam Cheung
Senior Vice President, Biao He
Company Secretary, Shun Loy Yung
Auditors: KPMG Huazhen LLP

LOCATIONS

HQ: China Unicom (Hong Kong) Ltd
75th Floor, The Center, 99 Queen's Road Central,
Phone: (852) 2121 3220   **Fax:** (852) 2121 3232
Web: www.chinaunicom.com.hk

PRODUCTS/OPERATIONS

2013 Sales

	% of total
Mobile	51
Fixed-line	30
Telecommunication products	19
Total	**100**

COMPETITORS

CABLE & WIRELESS WORLDWIDE LIMITED
China Telecom Corporation Limited
Deutsche Telekom AG
NIPPON TELEGRAPH AND TELEPHONE CORPORATION
PCCW LIMITED
TATA COMMUNICATIONS LIMITED
TELSTRA CORPORATION LIMITED
Tele2 AB
Telekom Austria Aktiengesellschaft
Telenor ASA

HISTORICAL FINANCIALS

Company Type: Public

Income Statement   FYE: December 31

	REVENUE ($ mil.)	NET INCOME ($ mil.)	NET PROFIT MARGIN	EMPLOYEES
12/20	46,456	1,910	4.1%	254,702
12/19	41,751	1,628	3.9%	256,385
12/18	42,289	1,482	3.5%	260,964
12/17	42,233	280	0.7%	267,590
12/16	39,486	90	0.2%	270,484
Annual Growth	4.1%	114.6%	—	(1.5%)

2020 Year-End Financials

Debt ratio: 0.3%
Return on equity: 3.8%
Cash ($ mil.): 3,529
Current ratio: 0.49
Long-term debt ($ mil.): 837

No. of shares (mil.): —
Dividends
  Yield: 0.0%
  Payout: 327.1%
Market value ($ mil.): —

	STOCK PRICE ($) FY Close	P/E High/Low	PER SHARE ($) Earnings	Dividends	Book Value
12/20	5.68	24 14	0.06	0.21	1.63
12/19	9.36	35 23	0.05	0.18	1.50
12/18	10.66	42 32	0.05	0.07	1.49
12/17	13.53	240 170	0.01	0.01	1.53
12/16	11.55	416 319	0.00	0.22	1.37
Annual Growth	(16.3%)	— —	95.2%	(1.8%)	4.5%

China United Network Communications Ltd

Auditors: PricewaterhouseCoopers Zhongtian Certified Public Accountants Co., Ltd.

LOCATIONS

HQ: China United Network Communications Ltd
29th Floor, No. 1033, Changning Road, Changning District, Shanghai 200050
Phone: (86) 21 52732228   **Fax:** (86) 21 52732220
Web: www.chinaunicom-a.com

HISTORICAL FINANCIALS

Company Type: Public

Income Statement   FYE: December 31

	REVENUE ($ mil.)	NET INCOME ($ mil.)	NET PROFIT MARGIN	EMPLOYEES
12/20	46,456	844	1.8%	0
12/19	41,751	716	1.7%	0
12/18	42,289	593	1.4%	0
12/17	42,233	65	0.2%	0
12/16	39,486	22	0.1%	0
Annual Growth	4.1%	148.4%	—	—

2020 Year-End Financials

Debt ratio: 0.5%
Return on equity: 3.7%
Cash ($ mil.): 5,384
Current ratio: 0.49
Long-term debt ($ mil.): 837

No. of shares (mil.): —
Dividends
  Yield: —
  Payout: —
Market value ($ mil.): —

China Vanke Co Ltd

Vanke is one of the largest mainland residential real estate developer in China. It operates logistics and warehousing services through VX Logistic Properties that manages a total of some 150 projects in about 45 cities. The company also holds some 25 operating hotel properties covering core cities such as Shenzhen Guangzhou Suzhou Hangzhou etc. and certain travel destinations. Vanke has developed more than 46.6 million square meters of properties and also expanded its business to commercial development rental housing logistics and warehouse services ski resorts and education. Furthermore the company also looks out for investment opportunities in overseas markets. It has already entered eight cities overseas namely New York San Francisco Los Angeles Seattle London Moscow Singapore and Kuala Lumpur etc.

Sales and Marketing

Vanke established a digital platform for real estate development and also for digital marketing tools through its subsidiary Wanyi Technology. Online applications such as "Your home purchase APP" "My home online" "Best to share" "Sales expert" and "E house selection" provide millions of customers with comprehensive services from house inspection to delivery. The revenue from the top five customers was approximately RMB 2.02 billion representing 1% of the revenue of the Group for the year and the percentage of which is less than 30%.

The company's selling and marketing expenses were RMB 9.0 billion and RMB 7.9 billion in 2019 and 2018 respectively.

EXECUTIVES

Chairman of the Board, Liang Yu
Finance Director, Executive Vice President, Huihua Han
Secretary of the Board, Xu Zhu
Independent Director, Jianing Wu
Independent Director, Dian Kang
Independent Director, Shuwei Liu
Director, Guobin Hu
Director, Jie Xin
Director, Shaojie Tang
Independent Director, Yichen Zhang
Non-Executive Director, Jiangsong Lei
President, Chief Executive Officer, Director, Jiusheng Zhu
Chief Operating Officer, Executive Vice President, Xiao Liu
Chief Operating Officer, Executive Vice President, Director, Haiwu Wang
Auditors: KPMG Huazhen Certified Public Accountants

LOCATIONS

HQ: China Vanke Co Ltd
Vanke Center, No. 33, Huanmei Road, Dameisha, Yantian District, Shenzhen, Guangdong Province 518083
Phone: (86) 755 25606666   **Fax:** (86) 755 25531696
Web: www.vanke.com

PRODUCTS/OPERATIONS

2015 Sales

	% of total
Property development	97
Property service	2
Other	1
Total	**100**

COMPETITORS

BELLWAY P L C
Country Garden Holdings Company Limited
Evergrande Real Estate Group Co. Ltd.
FRASERS PROPERTY (UK) LIMITED
GOODMAN LIMITED
NEW WORLD CHINA LAND LIMITED

HISTORICAL FINANCIALS

Company Type: Public

Income Statement   FYE: December 31

	REVENUE ($ mil.)	NET INCOME ($ mil.)	NET PROFIT MARGIN	EMPLOYEES
12/20	64,081	6,347	9.9%	0
12/19	52,871	5,586	10.6%	0
12/18	43,278	4,910	11.3%	0
12/17	37,326	4,310	11.5%	0
12/16	34,630	3,027	8.7%	0
Annual Growth	**16.6%**	**20.3%**	—	—

2020 Year-End Financials

Debt ratio: 2.1%
Return on equity: 20.0%
Cash ($ mil.): 29,850
Current ratio: 1.17
Long-term debt ($ mil.): 26,851
No. of shares (mil.): —
Dividends
  Yield: —
  Payout: —
Market value ($ mil.): —

Chong Qing Changan Automobile Co Ltd

Auditors: Ernst & Young Hua Ming LLP (Special General Partnership)

LOCATIONS

HQ: Chong Qing Changan Automobile Co Ltd
No. 260, East Jianxin Road, Jiangbei District, Chongqing 400023
Phone: (86) 23 67594008   **Fax:** (86) 23 67866055
Web: www.changan.com.cn

HISTORICAL FINANCIALS

Company Type: Public

Income Statement   FYE: December 31

	REVENUE ($ mil.)	NET INCOME ($ mil.)	NET PROFIT MARGIN	EMPLOYEES
12/20	12,930	508	3.9%	0
12/19	10,145	(380)	—	0
12/18	9,638	98	1.0%	0
12/17	12,295	1,096	8.9%	0
12/16	11,310	1,481	13.1%	41,173
Annual Growth	**3.4%**	**(23.5%)**	—	—

2020 Year-End Financials

Debt ratio: 0.2%
Return on equity: 6.8%
Cash ($ mil.): 4,893
Current ratio: 1.16
Long-term debt ($ mil.): 146
No. of shares (mil.): —
Dividends
  Yield: —
  Payout: —
Market value ($ mil.): —

Chubb Ltd

Chubb Limited sells commercial and personal property and casualty insurance personal accident and supplemental health insurance (A&H) reinsurance and life insurance to a diverse group of clients. The world's largest publicly traded property/casualty insurer Chubb primarily provides those lines of insurance to commercial and personal customers in some 55 nations and territories. Policies offered include general liability homeowners auto accident workers' compensation and specialty crop and marine coverage. It also offers services such as risk management loss control and complex claims management programs. The company's Chubb Tempest Re businesses provide reinsurance to property/casualty insurers in North America and Europe. Chubb holds total assets of approximately $191 billion.

Operations

Chubb operates through six primary business segments: North America Commercial P&C Insurance Overseas General Insurance North America Personal P&C (property and casualty) Insurance Life Insurance North America Agricultural Insurance and Global Reinsurance.

The largest segments are North America Commercial P&C Insurance (about 40% of net premiums earned) and Overseas General Insurance (about 25% of net premiums earned).

North America Commercial P&C Insurance serves large institutional customers corporations and small- and mid-sized companies in the US Canada and Bermuda. It also includes the company's Westchester and Chubb Bermuda wholesale and specialty units.

Overseas General Insurance is composed of Chubb International and Chubb Global Markets the company's international specialty and excess and surplus business. Chubb International operates in Europe the Asia Pacific region Far East Eurasia and Africa and Latin America. It offers property and casualty accident and health specialty and personal lines products. Chubb Global Markets offers specialty insurance and includes Chubb's Lloyd's of London Syndicate 2488.

North America Personal P&C Insurance (about 15% of net premiums) provides affluent and high-net-worth consumers in the US and Canada with property liability travel and recreational marine coverage insurance and services.

The Life Insurance segment (more than 5% of net premiums) operates through Chubb Life Chubb Tempest Life Re and the North American supplemental A&H and life business of Combined Insurance. It offers individual life and group benefit insurance primarily in developing markets.

North America Agricultural Insurance also active in the US and Canada provides a variety of coverage including crop insurance primarily Multiple Peril Crop Insurance (MPCI) and crop-hail insurance through Rain and Hail Insurance Service (Rain and Hail) as well as farm and ranch and specialty P&C commercial insurance products and services through its Chubb Agribusiness unit. It accounts for approximately 5% of net premiums.

Global Reinsurance is the company's smallest segment bringing in less than 5% of net earned premiums. It includes Chubb Tempest Re Bermuda Chubb Tempest Re USA Chubb Tempest Re International and Chubb Tempest Re Canada.

Geographic Reach

Chubb has offices around the world including North America (Philadelphia Pennsylvania; Wilmington Delaware; Whitehouse Station New Jersey; and Simsbury Connecticut) Europe (including its headquarters in Switzerland) Bermuda Latin

America Asia Pacific and the Far East. It generates around 55% of net premiums from North America. Chubb Global Markets operates out of Lloyd's of London the world-renowned specialty insurance market.

Sales and Marketing

Chubb's customers range from individuals (including wealthy individuals) and small businesses to multi-national corporations and other insurance companies. Most of the company's business is conducted through company agents or third-party insurance brokers or agents.

Chubb's products are generally offered through a North American network of independent agents and brokers as well as eTraditional which are digital platforms where the company electronically quote bind and issue for agents and brokers. An example of this is the Chubb Marketplace.

Chubb has counted most of the Fortune 1000 as clients for many years.

Financial Performance

Total revenue for the year was $36 billion a 5% increase from the previous year's total revenue of $34.2 billion. The increase was primarily due to higher net premiums earned throughout the year.

In 2020 the company had a net income of $3.5 billion a 21% decrease from the previous year's net income of $4.5 billion.

The company's cash at the end of 2020 was $1.8 billion. Operating activities generated $9.8 billion while investing activities used $7.5 billion mainly for purchases of fixed maturities available for sale. Financing activities used another $2.1 billion primarily for repayment of repurchase agreements.

Strategy

In early 2021 Chubb announced the launch of BLINKS by Chubb a new brand focused on delivering easy effortless and affordable insurance products for digitally savvy consumers.

Blink is a suite of Chubb-backed consumer insurance products that the company's affinity and digital broker partners will be able to offer to their customers supplementing their own products and services with relevant offerings that can deepen customer relationships and loyalty. The first Blink product available now in 25 states is personal cyber protection.

With the financial strength product breadth and underwriting excellence offered by Chubb the world's largest publicly traded property and casualty insurer Blink offers more than just a new digital insurance option. With Blink customers get Chubb's deep insurance expertise world-class claims service as well as an end-to-end digital experience to make the purchase and service experience effortless.

Blink offers flexible customizable coverage options. Policies are modular and written in plain understandable language. In short the coverage is crafted for consumers who are just beginning to identify their insurance needs and for those who know exactly what coverages they want.

Mergers and Acquisitions

In recent years Chubb has focused its geographic expansion on smaller acquisitions in emerging global marketplaces. In 2011 it entered two new markets for life insurance in North Asia after acquiring New York Life 's life insurance operations in Hong Kong and South Korea for about $425 million.

In 2012 Chubb acquired Indonesian general insurance firm Asuransi Jaya Proteksi for some $130 million. It closed its purchase of Mexican surety insurer Fianzas Monterrey from New York Life for $285 million in 2013 as well as its purchase of another Mexican insurance firm ABA Seguros from Ally Financial for $865 million.

In 2015 the company acquired the Fireman's Fund US personal lines business catering to high-

net-worth customers. The deal valued at $365 million and providing access to more than 120000 premier personal lines customers expanded Chubb's position as one of the largest personal lines insurers catering to wealthy individuals.

Later that year the company announced a much larger deal with plans to acquire insurer Chubb which specialized in serving wealthy clients for $28.3 billion. The combined company which operates under the Chubb name became one of the world's largest property/casualty firms. ACE shareholders own 70% of the new company.

Company Background

In early 2016 the former ACE Limited acquired the US's Chubb Corporation for $28 billion and took the Chubb name.

EXECUTIVES

President and Chief Operating Officer, John Keogh, $1,032,692 total compensation
Vice Chairman, Chubb Group and President, North America Insurance, John Lupica, $895,385 total compensation
Executive Vice President, Chubb Group and Chief Digital Officer and Chief Risk Officer, Sean Ringsted, $575,000 total compensation
Executive Vice President, Chubb Group and Chief Investment Officer, Timothy Boroughs
Executive Vice President, Construction Industry Practice Leader, Lyndsey Christofer
Executive Vice President, Chubb Group and Chief Financial Officer, Peter Enns
Property and Casualty Chief Underwriting Officer, United Kingdom, Ireland and South Africa, Hilda Toh
Vice Chairman, Chubb Group Global Underwriting and Claims, Paul Krump, $895,385 total compensation
Executive Vice President, Chubb Group and General Counsel, Joseph Wayland
Chairman and Chief Executive Officer, Chubb Limited and Chubb Group, Evan Greenberg, $1,400,000 total compensation
Auditors: PricewaterhouseCoopers LLP

LOCATIONS

HQ: Chubb Ltd
Baerengasse 32, Zurich CH-8001
Phone: (41) 43 456 7600
Web: www.acegroup.com

PRODUCTS/OPERATIONS

2018 Sales by Segment

	$ mil.	% of total
Net premiums earned		
North America Commercial P&C Insurance	12,402	37
Overseas General Insurance	8,612	26
North America Personal P&C Insurance	4,593	14
Life Insurance	2,218	6
North America Agricultural Insurance	1,569	5
Global Reinsurance	670	2
Net investment income	3,305	10
Net realized gains	(652)	-
Total	**32,717**	**100**

COMPETITORS

AIG EUROPE (SERVICES) LIMITED
AMERICAN NATIONAL INSURANCE COMPANY
AXA UK PLC
BRITISH UNITED PROVIDENT ASSOCIATION LIMITED(T
CARDTRONICS INC.
CHRISTIE GROUP PLC
JELF LIMITED
MILESTONE CAPITAL PARTNERS LLP
PLANET PAYMENT INC.
PRISM TECHNOLOGIES GROUP INC.

STATE STREET CORPORATION
UNIVERSAL INSURANCE HOLDINGS INC.
XL GROUP PUBLIC LIMITED COMPANY
Zurich Insurance Group AG

HISTORICAL FINANCIALS
Company Type: Public

Income Statement
FYE: December 31

	ASSETS ($ mil.)	NET INCOME ($ mil.)	INCOME AS % OF ASSETS	EMPLOYEES
12/20	190,774	3,533	1.9%	31,000
12/19	176,943	4,454	2.5%	33,000
12/18	167,771	3,962	2.4%	32,700
12/17	167,022	3,861	2.3%	31,000
12/16	159,786	4,135	2.6%	31,000
Annual Growth	4.5%	(3.9%)	—	0.0%

2020 Year-End Financials

Return on assets: 1.9%
Return on equity: 6.1%
Long-term debt ($ mil.): —
No. of shares (mil.): 450
Sales ($ mil): 35,994

Dividends
Yield: 2.0%
Payout: 61.4%
Market value ($ mil.): —

Chubu Electric Power Co Inc

Chubu Electric Power is Japan's an electric utility. The company supplies power to about 16 million people in central Japan's Chubu region a manufacturing region in Japan that includes Nagoya. The company has biomass hydroelectric nuclear wind and solar power generating facilities and it has a capacity of more than 33400 MW. In addition the company offers services utilizing renewable energy that align with customer needs towards the realization of a low-carbon society including the CO_2-free menu service. In response to deregulation Chubu Electric Power has moved into newer industries including IT natural gas supply real estate management and overseas consulting.

Operations

The company operate its business into three reportable segment: Customer Service & Sales Power Network and JERA.

Customer Service & Sales focuses on expansion of total energy services centered on gas & electric power. Power Network is focus on provision of power network services and JERA focuses on fuel upstream and procurement to power generation and wholesale of electricity and gas.

Electricity (90% of total revenue) has about 210 power generation facilities in Japan a transmission line that runs more than 12200 kilometers a distribution line that runs more than 133300 kilometers and nearly 930 transformer substations.

Other (15%) provides energy services such as the sale of gas and liquefied natural gas (LNG) and the provision of co-generation systems.

Geographic Reach

The company's headquarter is located in Higashi-shincho Higashi-ku Nagoya.

In addition to Japan the company has offices in Australia Mexico UAE The Netherlands India Canada Indonesia Philippines Mexico Oman Thailand Taiwan Qatar Vietnam and the US.

Sales and Marketing

The company supplies electricity to residential commercial and industrial customers via transmission and distribution lines.

Moreover the company created new forms of community which are connected home service Korekara Denki (energy services based on customer participation) smart pole service and regional information bank.

Financial Performance

Note: Growth rates may differ after conversion to US Dollars.

In 2019 consolidated operating revenue increased by 1% from the previous consolidated fiscal year to 3.1 trillion yen mainly due to an increase in fuel cost adjustment charge and increase in surcharge and grant based on Act on Special Measures Concerning Procurement of Electricity from Renewable Energy Sources by Electric Utilities.

The company's net income in 2019 fell by 3.9 billion yen to 62.2 billion yen from 66 billion yen in the prior year.

Cash held by the company at the end of 2019 decreased by 402.5 billion yen to 147.6 billion yen compared to 550.1 billion yen in the prior year. Cash provided by operations was 255.9 billion while cash used for investing and financing activities were 647.6 billion yen and 5.9 billion yen respectively.

Strategy

In April 2020 the Chubu Electric Power Group split off their power transmission and distribution business. At the same time the company split off their sales business and put into practice business model that separates power generation from sales. With each of their businesses dealing with customers and society and developing independently they are more certain to deliver good-quality environmentally friendly energy that is essential for their daily lives and business in a safer more affordable and more stable manner.

Building on this foundation along with energy the company will provide new services that exceed the expectations of their customers and society while utilizing digital technology through the creation of community support infrastructure. Through these activities they will contribute to the resolution of social issues including the achievement of a low-carbon society which is an urgent issue worldwide.

Mergers and Acquisitions

In 2019 Mitsubishi Corporation and Chubu Electric Power Co. Inc. were selected as the preferred buyers in a bid for the Dutch Energy Company "Eneco".

Both MC and Chubu have since been completing the acquisition procedures. The total value of this acquisition is 4.1 billion euros (500 billion yen).

Eneco is an integrated energy company that is actively engaged in renewable power generation projects.

EXECUTIVES

Independent Director, Kurihara Mitsue
Chairman of the Board, Representative Director, Satoru Katsuno
Executive Vice President, Chief Director of Business Creation, Yoshinori Masuda
President, Executive President, Representative Director, Kingo Hayashi
Independent Director, Takayuki Hashimoto
Executive Vice President, Manager of Hamaoka Nuclear Power General Business Center, Hiromu Masuda
Independent Director, Tadashi Shimao
Executive President of Subsidiary, Director, Shinya Otani

Chief Financial Officer, Executive Vice President, Chief Director of Business Administration, Representative Director, Hitoshi Mizutani
Senior Managing Executive Officer, Chief Information Officer, Chief Director of Business Strategy, Director, Hisanori Ito
Senior Managing Executive Officer, Chief Nuclear Officer, Chief Director of Nuclear Power, Director of Nuclear Power, Representative Director, Ichiro Ihara
Auditors: KPMG AZSA LLC

LOCATIONS

HQ: Chubu Electric Power Co Inc
  1 Higashi-Shincho, Higashi-ku, Nagoya, Aichi 461-8680
Phone: (81) 52 951 8211
Web: www.chuden.co.jp

PRODUCTS/OPERATIONS

2016 Sales

	% of total
Electric power	90
Energy	3
Other	7
Total	**100**

COMPETITORS

ALLETE INC.
AMERESCO INC.
EnBW Energie Baden-Württemberg AG
GENERAC HOLDINGS INC.
GOOD ENERGY GROUP PLC
KANSAI ELECTRIC POWER COMPANY INCORPORATED THE
KYUSHU ELECTRIC POWER COMPANY INCORPORATED
Korea Electric Power Corporation
NATURGY ENERGY GROUP SA.
NRG ENERGY INC.
PPL CORPORATION
TUCSON ELECTRIC POWER COMPANY

HISTORICAL FINANCIALS

Company Type: Public

Income Statement				FYE: March 31
	REVENUE ($ mil.)	NET INCOME ($ mil.)	NET PROFIT MARGIN	EMPLOYEES
03/21	26,510	1,329	5.0%	28,238
03/20	28,244	1,505	5.3%	28,448
03/19	27,406	717	2.6%	30,321
03/18	26,870	700	2.6%	30,554
03/17	23,286	1,025	4.4%	30,635
Annual Growth	**3.3%**	**6.7%**	**—**	**(2.0%)**

2021 Year-End Financials

Debt ratio: 0.3%	No. of shares (mil.): 756
Return on equity: 7.5%	Dividends
Cash ($ mil.): 1,593	Yield: —
Current ratio: 0.59	Payout: —
Long-term debt ($ mil.): 16,696	Market value ($ mil.): —

Chugoku Bank, Ltd. (The)

Chugoku Bank hopes to attract individuals and businesses who are looking to bank on the sunny side. The Japanese regional bank serves the Okayama prefecture (known as 'the sunny land') and the neighboring areas of Ehime Hiroshima Hyogo Kagawa and Tottori through some 150 offices and a network of ATMs. The bank also boasts overseas operations with offices in China Hong Kong Singapore and the US. Chugoku Bank subsidiaries and affiliates are involved in such businesses as asset management credit cards credit guarantees financing leasing and pre-paid cards. Japan Trustee Services Bank Ltd. owns a majority stake in the bank.

EXECUTIVES

Chairman of the Board, Masato Miyanaga
Director, Hiromichi Ando
President, Representative Director, Sadanori Kato
Senior Managing Director, Representative Director, Koji Terasaka
Senior Managing Director, Representative Director, Yasuhide Harada
Independent Director, Toshihide Saito
Director, Kotaro Kogame
Managing Director, Hiromichi Kato
Independent Director, Akira Kodera
Independent Director, Hiromichi Furuya
Independent Director, Yoshiro Sato
Independent Director, Kazuhiro Tanaka
Managing Director, Tatsuo Hiramoto
Managing Director, Shinichi Taniguchi
Managing Director, Hiroyuki Ohara
Independent Director, Yukiyo Seino
Auditors: KPMG AZSA LLC

LOCATIONS

HQ: Chugoku Bank, Ltd. (The)
  1-15-20 Marunouchi, Kita-ku, Okayama 700-8628
Phone: (81) 86 223 3111   **Fax:** 212 371-7173
Web: www.chugin.co.jp

PRODUCTS/OPERATIONS

Selected Subsidiaries

CBS Company Limited
Chugin Asset Management Company Limited
Chugin Securities Co. Ltd.
The Chugin Card Company Limited
The Chugin Credit Guarantee Co. Limited
The Chugin Lease Company Limited
The Chugin Operation Center Co. Limited

COMPETITORS

DAISHI HOKUETSU BANK NANTO BANKLTD. THE LTD.
HACHIJUNI BANK LTD. THE

HISTORICAL FINANCIALS

Company Type: Public

Income Statement				FYE: March 31
	ASSETS ($ mil.)	NET INCOME ($ mil.)	INCOME AS % OF ASSETS	EMPLOYEES
03/20	75,056	109	0.1%	4,885
03/19	74,530	146	0.2%	4,933
03/18	79,739	200	0.3%	5,012
03/17	74,092	181	0.2%	5,132
03/16	69,459	242	0.3%	5,134
Annual Growth	**2.0%**	**(18.0%)**	**—**	**(1.2%)**

2020 Year-End Financials

Return on assets: 0.1%	Dividends
Return on equity: 2.2%	Yield: —
Long-term debt ($ mil.): —	Payout: 34.7%
No. of shares (mil.): 188	Market value ($ mil.): —
Sales ($ mil): 1,172	

CIMB Group Holdings Bhd

CIMB Group is the second-largest financial services firm in Malaysia behind Maybank. It is the holding company for CIMB Bank CIMB Investment Bank and CIMB Islamic which provide retail and commercial banking and financial services to 13 million customers throughout Southeast Asia. While it has a presence in 17 countries (including a CIMB Securities office in New York City) the bank's main markets are Malaysia Indonesia Singapore Thailand and Cambodia. Altogether the group has more than 1050 branches. CIMB Group's offerings include corporate and consumer banking investment banking Islamic banking stock brokerage asset management and insurance. It was established in 1924 as Bian Chiang Bank.

Mergers and Acquisitions

CIMB Investment Bank became one of the largest investment banking franchises in Asia in 2012 with the acquisition of most of the Asian investment banking business of the Royal Bank of Scotland. The acquisition gave CIMB a presence in Taiwan and Australia and expanded its operations in Hong Kong India and China. RBS kept its business in South Korea.

EXECUTIVES

Non-Executive Independent Director, Shulamite Khoo

Chief Executive Officer, Executive Director, Abdul Rahman bin Ahmad

Independent Member of the Shariah Supervisory Board, Mohamed Fairooz Abdul Khir

Country Head, Thailand President and Chief Executive Officer, CIMB Thai Bank PCL, Chee Kin Wong

Non-Executive Non-Independent Director, Mei Shwen Tan

Non-Executive Independent Director, Didi Syafruddin Yahya

Independent Member of the Shariah Supervisory Board, Aishath Muneeza

Chief Executive Officers, CIMB Digital Asset, Group Chief Executive Officer, Touch'n Go Group, Effendy Hamid

Independent Chairman of the Shariah Supervisory Board, Shafaai Musa

Independent Member of the Shariah Supervisory Board, Yousef abdullah Al Shubaily

Non-Executive Independent Chairman of the Board, Mohd Nasir ahmad

Group Chief Legal and Compliance Officer, Keen Yew Kwan, $28,964 total compensation

Senior Non-Executive Independent Director, Su Yin Teoh

Chief Executive Officer - Group Consumer Banking, Samir Gupta

Non-Executive Independent Director, Mohamed Ross Mohd Din

Non-Executive Independent Director, Robert Coombe

Group Chief People Officer, Gurdip Sidhu

Non-Independent Non-Executive Director, Kok Kwan Lee

Chief Executive Officer, Group Transaction Banking, Chief Executive Officers CIMB Foundation, Group Chief Sustainability Officer, Rafe Haneef

Country Head, Indonesia President Director and Chief Executive Officer, PT Bank CIMB Niaga Tbk, Tigor Siahaan

Group Chief Financial Officer, Khairul Rifaie

Chief Executive Officer, Group Islamic Banking, Chief Executive Officer/Executive Director, CIMB Islamic Bank Berhad, Ahmad Shahriman Mohd Shariff

Group Chief Internal Auditor, Amran Mohamad

Independent Member of the Shariah Supervisory Board, Ahmed Baqar Rehman

Country Head, Singapore, Chief Executive Officer, CIMB Bank Singapore, Chief Executive Officer, Group Commercial Banking, Meng Teck Lee

Group Company Secretary, Rossaya mohd Nashir

Independent Member of the Shariah Supervisory Board, Ahmad Sufian Che Abdullah

Group Chief Risk Officer, David Thomas

Non-Executive Independent Director, Afzal Abdul Rahim

Auditors: PricewaterhouseCoopers PLT

LOCATIONS

HQ: CIMB Group Holdings Bhd
Level 13, Menara CIMB, Jalan Stesen Sentral 2, Kuala Lumpur Sentral, Kuala Lumpur 50470
Phone: (60) 3 2261 8888   **Fax:** (60) 3 2261 0099
Web: www.cimb.com

COMPETITORS

AEGON N.V.
ARAB BANKING CORPORATION B S C
AUSTRALIA AND NEW ZEALAND BANKING GROUP LIMITED
Allianz SE
DBS GROUP HOLDINGS LTD
Grupo Financiero Banorte S.A.B. de C.V.
HACI OMER SABANCI HOLDING ANONIM SIRKETI
ING Groep N.V.
NATWEST GROUP PLC
OVERSEA-CHINESE BANKING CORPORATION LIMITED
PIRAEUS FINANCIAL HOLDINGS S.A.
PUBLIC BANK BHD
SAVILLS PLC
W stenrot & W rttembergische AG

HISTORICAL FINANCIALS

Company Type: Public

Income Statement				FYE: December 31
	ASSETS ($ mil.)	NET INCOME ($ mil.)	INCOME AS % OF ASSETS	EMPLOYEES
12/20	149,599	296	0.2%	34,183
12/19	140,118	1,114	0.8%	35,265
12/18	129,222	1,350	1.0%	36,104
12/17	124,778	1,102	0.9%	37,597
12/16	108,285	794	0.7%	38,945
Annual Growth	8.4%	(21.8%)	—	(3.2%)

2020 Year-End Financials

Return on assets: 0.2%
Return on equity: 2.1%
Long-term debt ($ mil.): —
No. of shares (mil.): —
Sales ($ mil): 6,320

Dividends
Yield: —
Payout: —
Market value ($ mil.): —

CITIC Ltd

CITIC Limited is one of China's largest conglomerates and a constituent of the Hang Seng Index. CITIC has grown in step with the country's rise and modernization. It has built a remarkable portfolio of businesses in comprehensive financial services advanced intelligent manufacturing advanced materials new consumption and new-type urbanization. CITIC Limited is now 58% owned by CITIC Group and the rest is held by independent shareholders. About 85% of its revenue comes from mainland China.

Operations

CITIC operates through five reportable segments: Comprehensive financial services; Advanced Materials; New Consumption; New-type urbanizations; and Advanced intelligent manufacturing.

Comprehensive financial services segment accounts for about 40% of total revenue includes banking trust asset management securities and insurance services.

Advanced materials segment (around 35%) includes exploration processing and trading of resources and energy products including crude oil coal and iron ore as well as manufacturing of special steels.

New consumption segment (nearly 15%) includes motor and food and consumer products business telecommunication services publication services modern agriculture and others.

New-type urbanization segment includes development sale and holding of properties contracting and design services infrastructure services environmental services and others. The segment generates less than 10% of total revenue.

Advanced intelligent manufacturing segment (nearly 5%) includes manufacturing of heavy machineries specialized robotics aluminium wheels aluminium casting parts and other products.

Geographic Reach

Headquartered in Hong Kong CITIC earned some 85% of revenue from mainland China while Hong Kong Taiwan and Macau and other countries generate about 15% of combined revenue.

Financial Performance

In 2020 the group achieved revenue of HK$552.9 million up by 5% year on year on a comparable basis of which 41% came from the financial segment and 59% from the non-financial segments. After the COVID-19 pandemic was brought under control the group resumed business and production and in the second half of 2020 recorded an increased net profit attributable to ordinary shareholders of 45% year on year. This enabled the group as a whole to achieve a profit growth rate of 5% year on year that reached HK$56.6 billion of which 2% was in the financial segment and 15% in the non-financial segments.

In 2020 the company had a net income of HK$97.7 billion a 2% increase from the previous year's net income of HK$96 billion.

The company's cash at the end of 2020 was HK$452.7 million. Operating activities generated HK$193.2 billion while investing activities used HK$256.2 billion mainly for payments for purchase of financial investments. Financing activities provided another HK$36 billion.

Strategy

CITIC Pacific Special Steel adheres to the business strategy "domestic trade to supplement foreign trade and midrange products to supplement high-end products. In 2020 13.99 million tonnes of steel products were sold of which 1.36 million tons were export sales that accounted for 10% of total sales. Xingcheng Special Steel posted record sales volumes as premium crankshaft steel sales directly supplying BMW and Hyundai doubled; sales doubled for Daye Special Steel's high-performance flat spring steel with a 1550 MPa standard; steel for automobile standard parts produced by Qingdao Special Steel tripled and Jingjiang Special Steel's cylinder pipe continued to hold the largest market share in China.

EXECUTIVES

Non-Executive Director, Kangle Song
Independent Non-Executive Director, Anthony Neoh
Independent Non-Executive Director, Jinwu Xu
Company Secretary, Wing Kay Choy
Non-Executive Director, Yanxiang Peng
Non-Executive Director, Lin Zhang
Non-Executive Director, Jiang Tang
Independent Non-Executive Director, Wai Keung Siu
Vice President of the Company and a member of the executive committee, Guoquan Wang
Executive Chairman of the Board, Hexin Zhu, $34,809 total compensation
Vice President, Member of the Executive Board, Zuo Xu
President, Executive Vice Chairman of the Board, Guohua Xi, $23,206 total compensation
Non-Executive Director, Yang Yu
Vice President , Member of the Executive Committee, Heying Fang
Vice chairman of the executive committee, Shengjun Ren
Member of the Executive Board, Jun Cui
Vice President and member of the executive committee, Zhengjun Liu
Independent Non-Executive Director, Gregory Curl
Non-Executive Director, Xiaoping Yang
Vice President, Member of the Executive Committee, Qingping Li, $51,569 total compensation
Auditors: PricewaterhouseCoopers

LOCATIONS

HQ: CITIC Ltd
32nd Floor, CITIC Tower, 1 Tim Mei Avenue, Central,
Phone: (852) 2820 2111   **Fax:** (852) 2877 2771
Web: www.citic.com

2015 Sales

	% of total
Mainland China	87
Hong Kong and Macau	6
Overseas	7
Total	**100**

PRODUCTS/OPERATIONS

2015 Sales

	% of total
Financial Services	49
Manufacturing	14
Resources and energy	11
Real estate	7
Engineering contracting	4
Others	15
Total	**100**

COMPETITORS

BANK OF CHINA LIMITED
BOC HONG KONG (HOLDINGS) LIMITED
Bank of Communications Co. Ltd.
DBS GROUP HOLDINGS LTD
GLENCORE PLC
Gerdau S/A
HANWA CO.LTD.
INVESTCORP HOLDINGS B.S.C
KASIKORNBANK PUBLIC COMPANY LIMITED
KOBE STEEL LTD.
NATIONAL AUSTRALIA BANK LIMITED
NLMK PAO
NOVELIS INC.
OVERSEA-CHINESE BANKING CORPORATION LIMITED
UNITED OVERSEAS BANK LIMITED
YAPI VE KREDI BANKASI ANONIM SIRKETI

HISTORICAL FINANCIALS

Company Type: Public

Income Statement

	REVENUE ($ mil.)	NET INCOME ($ mil.)	NET PROFIT MARGIN	EMPLOYEES
				FYE: December 31
12/20	93,327	7,304	7.8%	135,304
12/19	94,188	6,922	7.3%	287,910
12/18	88,459	6,414	7.3%	273,344
12/17	76,207	5,617	7.4%	243,036
12/16	65,760	5,560	8.5%	127,610
Annual Growth	**9.1%**	**7.1%**	**—**	**1.5%**

2020 Year-End Financials

Debt ratio: —
Return on equity: 8.9%
Cash ($ mil.): 97,433
Current ratio: —
Long-term debt ($ mil.): —

No. of shares (mil.): —
Dividends
 Yield: 0.0%
 Payout: 87.6%
Market value ($ mil.): —

	STOCK PRICE ($) FY Close	P/E High/Low		Earnings	PER SHARE ($) Dividends	Book Value
12/20	3.46	3	2	0.25	0.22	2.99
12/19	6.62	4	3	0.24	0.25	2.61
12/18	7.68	5	4	0.22	0.22	2.45
12/17	6.90	5	5	0.19	0.19	2.42
12/16	7.14	6	4	0.19	0.17	2.17
Annual Growth	**(16.6%)**	**—**	**—**	**7.1%**	**6.7%**	**8.3%**

CK Hutchison Holdings Ltd

Auditors: PricewaterhouseCoopers

LOCATIONS

HQ: CK Hutchison Holdings Ltd
48th Floor, Cheung Kong Center, 2 Queen's Road Central,
Phone: (852) 2128 1188   **Fax:** (852) 2128 1705
Web: www.ckh.com.hk

HISTORICAL FINANCIALS

Company Type: Public

Income Statement

	REVENUE ($ mil.)	NET INCOME ($ mil.)	NET PROFIT MARGIN	EMPLOYEES
				FYE: December 31
12/19	38,400	5,115	13.3%	300,000
12/18	35,383	4,979	14.1%	300,000
12/17	31,798	4,491	14.1%	300,000
12/16	33,508	4,256	12.7%	290,000
12/15	21,514	15,297	71.1%	270,000
Annual Growth	**15.6%**	**(24.0%)**	**—**	**2.7%**

2019 Year-End Financials

Debt ratio: 3.6%
Return on equity: 8.5%
Cash ($ mil.): 17,610
Current ratio: 1.36
Long-term debt ($ mil.): 39,206

No. of shares (mil.): —
Dividends
 Yield: 3.7%
 Payout: —
Market value ($ mil.): —

	STOCK PRICE ($) FY Close	P/E High/Low		Earnings	PER SHARE ($) Dividends	Book Value
12/19	9.53	1	1	1.33	0.35	15.88
12/18	9.48	1	1	1.29	0.33	15.18
12/17	12.56	2	1	1.16	0.30	15.24
12/16	11.35	2	1	1.10	0.29	14.20
12/15	13.44	1	0	4.76	8.92	14.33
Annual Growth	**(8.2%)**	**—**	**—**	**(27.3%)**	**(55.3%)**	**2.6%**

Clydesdale Bank PLC (United Kingdom)

Founded in 1838 Clydesdale is a full-service Scotland-based financial institution. Along with standard personal and commercial services such as deposit accounts lending credit cards and financial advice the bank also dabbles in agribusiness and private banking. Clydesdale Bank has over 60 retail branches in Scotland. It is one of the only banks in Scotland that issues its own notes.

Operations

The bank is a strong low risk bank focused on providing residential mortgages personal and business current accounts savings personal loans and credit cards loans for small and medium businesses and payment and transaction services.

Overall net interest income generates some 90% of total revenue.

Geographic Reach

The company operates across its core regional markets: Scotland North East England North West England Yorkshire and the Humber.

Financial Performance

Revenue for fiscal 2021 increased to 1.6 billion compared from with 1.5 billion.

Profit for fiscal 2021 increased to 416 million compared with a loss of 173 million.

Cash held by the company at the end of fiscal 2021 increased to 10.3 billion. Cash provided by operations and investing activities were 582 million and 465 million respectively. Financing activities used 608 million mainly for amounts repaid under the TFS.

Strategy

The company has continued to make good progress delivering its strategy and benefiting from an improving economic backdrop. The company has delivered strong financial results with improved performance and momentum on most key metrics. A recovery in income reduced costs a significant reduction in the level of expected credit loss (ECL) provisions and robust common equity tier 1 (CET1) accretion all leave the bank well placed to accelerate its digital strategy and deliver profitable growth.

Auditors: Ernst & Young LLP

LOCATIONS

HQ: Clydesdale Bank PLC (United Kingdom)
30 St. Vincent Place, Glasgow, Scotland G1 2HL
Phone: (44) 0141 248 7070   **Fax:** (44) 0141 204 0828
Web: www.cbonline.co.uk

COMPETITORS

AKBANK TURK ANONIM SIRKETI
ASSOCIATED BANC-CORP
AXIS BANK LIMITED
BANCO DE SABADELL SA

BANK OF THE WEST
Banco Bradesco S/A
Banco do Brasil S/A
Bank of Communications Co. Ltd.
CAPITAL ONE FINANCIAL CORPORATION
COLUMBIA BANKING SYSTEM INC.
Danske Bank A/S
FINANCIAL INSTITUTIONS INC.
HDFC BANK LIMITED
HSBC Bank Canada
Laurentian Bank of Canada
M&T BANK CORPORATION
NATIONAL BANK HOLDINGS CORPORATION
NATIONAL WESTMINSTER BANK PUBLIC LIMITED
  COMPANY
Nordea Bank AB
PINNACLE FINANCIAL PARTNERS INC.
REGIONS FINANCIAL CORPORATION
Royal Bank of Canada
The Bank of Nova Scotia
U.S. BANCORP
WEBSTER FINANCIAL CORPORATION
YORKSHIRE BANK PUBLIC LIMITED COMPANY

HISTORICAL FINANCIALS
Company Type: Public

Income Statement   FYE: September 30

	ASSETS ($ mil.)	NET INCOME ($ mil.)	INCOME AS % OF ASSETS	EMPLOYEES
09/19	112,156	(262)	—	8,703
09/18	56,841	(311)	—	5,769
09/17	58,002	(393)	—	6,040
09/16	51,777	(722)	—	6,718
09/15	58,740	(377)	—	4,616
Annual Growth 17.5%		—	—	17.2%

2019 Year-End Financials

Return on assets: (-0.3%)	Dividends
Return on equity: (-5.0%)	Yield: —
Long-term debt ($ mil.): —	Payout: —
No. of shares (mil.): —	Market value ($ mil.): —
Sales ($ mil): 3,311	

CNH Industrial NV

Auditors: Ernst & Young LLP

LOCATIONS

HQ: CNH Industrial NV
 25 St. James's Street, London SW1A 1HA
Phone: (44) 1268 533000   **Fax:** 630 887-2344
Web: www.cnhindustrial.com

HISTORICAL FINANCIALS
Company Type: Public

Income Statement   FYE: December 31

	REVENUE ($ mil.)	NET INCOME ($ mil.)	NET PROFIT MARGIN	EMPLOYEES
12/20	26,032	(493)	—	64,016
12/19	28,079	1,422	5.1%	63,499
12/18	29,706	1,068	3.6%	64,625
12/17	27,361	295	1.1%	63,356
12/16	24,872	(252)	—	62,828
Annual Growth 1.1%		—	—	0.5%

2020 Year-End Financials

Debt ratio: 53.4%	No. of shares (mil.): 1,353
Return on equity: (-8.9%)	Dividends
Cash ($ mil.): 9,629	Yield: —
Current ratio: 5.45	Payout: —
Long-term debt ($ mil.): 26,053	Market value ($ mil.): —

CNOOC Ltd

CNOOC Limited boasts itself as an upstream company specializing in oil and natural gas exploration development and production. In addition the company is also one of the major oil and natural gas producers in offshore China. In 2020 the company had net proved reserves of about 5.37 billion BOE. Further the company had a net production of about 1.4 million BOE per day which included a net production of about 53700 BOE per day in the company's equity method investees. The company operates in both China and overseas. In their operations in China the company engages in oil and natural gas exploration while its overseas operations hold interest in numerous world-class oil and gas projects through their diversified portfolio of high-quality assets.

Operations
The company operates in three reportable segments: E&P which accounts for more than 90% of total revenue; Trading Business (about 10%) and Corporate.

Geographic Reach
The company operates in both China and overseas. In their operations in China the company engages in oil and natural gas exploration while its overseas operations hold interest in numerous world-class oil and gas projects through their diversified portfolio of high-quality assets.

In addition CNOOC Limited also engages in exploration development production and sale of crude oil and natural gas in Canada the United Kingdom Nigeria Argentina Indonesia Uganda Iraq Brazil Guyana Russia and Australia.

Sales and Marketing
CNOOC Limited's major customers in China are China National Offshore Oil Corporation CNPC Sinopec Group. Its customers also includes some local private refineries.

Financial Performance
CNOOC Limited's performance has seen growth from 2016 to 2019 but abruptly decreased in 2020.

The company's revenue decreased by RMB 77.8 billion to RMB 155.3 billion in 2020 as compared to 2019's revenue of RMB 233.2 billion.

The company's net income in 2020 decreased by RMB 36 billion to RMB 24.9 billion as compared to 2019's net income of RMB 61 billion.

CNOOC Limited's cash held amounted to RMB 24 billion at the end of the year. The company's operating activities provided about RMB 82 billion. Its investing activities and financing activities used RMB 50.9 billion and RMB 38.7 billion respectively. Main cash uses were capital expenditures dividends paid and purchase of other financial assets.

Strategy
The company's goals as one of the largest independent oil and gas exploration and production companies focus on its strategy to focus on reserve and production growth; and developing its natural gas business. The company continues to focus on independent exploration efforts in major operating segments. As for its overseas operations the company strives to acquire more high-quality exploration blocks and improve exploration efficiency. In addition the company also adopts a low-carbon development concept and actively expands its natural gas business.

EXECUTIVES

Vice President, Chenggang Duan
Non-Executive Director, Dongfen Wen
Independent Non-Executive Director, Zhi Zhong Qiu, $122,523 total compensation

Non-Executive Chairman of the Board, Dongjin Wang
Independent Non-Executive Director, Hau Yin Tse, $150,909 total compensation
Joint Company Secretary, Sik Yu Tsue
Chief Financial Officer, Weizhi Xie
Executive Vice President, General Manager - CNOOC China Limited Tianjin Branch, Xinjian Cao
Non-Executive Vice Chairman of the Board, Yong Li
Deputy Chief Exploration Engineer, Yunhua Deng
Independent Non-Executive Director, Juen-Yee Lau, $122,523 total compensation
Compliance Officer, General Counsel, Joint Company Secretary, Xiaonan Wu
Vice President, General Manager of CNOOC China Limited Hainan Branch, Yun Yang
Executive Director, Qinglong Xia
Vice President, Fujie Sun
Chief Executive Officer, Executive Director, Keqiang Xu, $34,613 total compensation
Auditors: Deloitte Touche Tohmatsu

LOCATIONS

HQ: CNOOC Ltd
 65th Floor, Bank of China Tower, One Garden Road,
Phone: (852) 2213 2500   **Fax:** (852) 2525 9322
Web: www.cnoocltd.com

2007 Sales

	% of total
China	86
Other countries	14
Total	**100**

PRODUCTS/OPERATIONS

2015 Sales

	% of total
Exploration and Production	87
Trading business	13
Total	**100**

2015 Sales

	% of Total
Oil and gas sales	86
Marketing revenues	12
Other income	2
Total	**100**

Selected Subsidiaries
CNOOC China Limited (China)
CNOOC Finance (2002) Limited (British Virgin Islands)
CNOOC Finance (2003) Limited (British Virgin Islands)
CNOOC International Limited (British Virgin Islands)
CNOOC Offshore Oil (Singapore) Pte. Ltd.

COMPETITORS

ADAMS RESOURCES & ENERGY INC.	OIL AND NATURAL GAS CORPORATION LIMITED
Athabasca Oil Corporation	PETROBRAS AMERICA INC.
CRESTWOOD EQUITY PARTNERS LP	Paramount Resources Ltd
Canadian Natural Resources Ltd	PetroChina Company Limited
Equinor ASA	Petroleo Brasileiro S A Petrobras
GAZPROM NEFT PAO	RS ENERGY K.K.
GAZPROM PAO	SPRAGUE RESOURCES LP
Husky Energy Inc	Suncor Energy Inc
INDIAN OIL CORPORATION LIMITED	WORLD FUEL SERVICES CORPORATION
NGL ENERGY PARTNERS LP	

HISTORICAL FINANCIALS
Company Type: Public

Income Statement				FYE: December 31
	REVENUE ($ mil.)	NET INCOME ($ mil.)	NET PROFIT MARGIN	EMPLOYEES
12/20	23,756	3,815	16.1%	18,353
12/19	33,514	8,773	26.2%	18,703
12/18	32,997	7,660	23.2%	18,312
12/17	28,642	3,792	13.2%	19,030
12/16	21,095	91	0.4%	19,718
Annual Growth	3.0%	154.0%	—	(1.8%)

2020 Year-End Financials

Debt ratio: 2.8%
Return on equity: 5.6%
Cash ($ mil.): 10,065
Current ratio: 2.18
Long-term debt ($ mil.): 19,114

No. of shares (mil.): —
Dividends
Yield: 0.0%
Payout: 9,397.7%
Market value ($ mil.): —

	STOCK PRICE ($) FY Close	P/E High/Low	PER SHARE ($) Earnings	PER SHARE ($) Dividends	PER SHARE ($) Book Value
12/20	91.65	340 154	0.09	8.05	1.49
12/19	166.67	136 105	0.20	8.40	1.44
12/18	152.45	170 109	0.17	6.58	1.36
12/17	143.56	266 205	0.08	5.04	1.31
12/16	123.96	135 488 088	0.00	4.04	1.23
Annual Growth	(7.3%)	—	—177.7%	18.8%	4.8%

Co-operative Bank plc

The Co-operative Bank is the first UK high street bank to introduce a customer-led Ethical Policy which sets out the way it does business. It provides a full range of banking products and services to almost 5 million retail and SME (Small and Medium Sizes Enterprises) customers. The bank also offers insurance (through sister firm Co-operative Insurance Society) and investments such as ISAs unit trusts pensions and trust funds. The company was founded in 1872 as the Loans and Deposits department of Co-operative Wholesale Society.

Operations

The company offers products to both retail and business banking customers which together are referred to as its core customer segments. The Retail segment accounts for over 80% while SME generated nearly 20%.

The Retail segment offers high street telephony and online services including current accounts savings mortgages personal loans and credit cards. The SME segment offers banking services for small and medium-sized businesses charities and social enterprises including current accounts savings loans overdrafts and credit cards. In addition it also has a treasury function which manages the bank's portfolio of liquid assets interest rate risk and wholesale funding to meet liquidity and capital requirements as well as leading the day-to-day cash clearing and collateral management for the bank.

Geographic Reach

The company is headquartered in Manchester UK.

Sales and Marketing

The company caters to almost 5 million retail and SME (Small and Medium Sizes Enterprises) customers.

Financial Performance

The company's revenue for fiscal 2020 decreased to 315.3 million compared from the prior year with 386.6 million.

Loss for fiscal 2020 decreased to 95.7 million compared from the prior year with 153 million.

Cash held by the company at the end of fiscal 2020 increased to 4.2 billion. Cash provided by operations investing and financing activities were 481.2 million 1.1 billion and 168.7 million respectively.

Strategy

In December 2018 the company launched its five-year strategy. Its strategy reflects three phases: fix the basics which is now complete and provides a platform to enable the future and to create a sustainable competitive advantage as a successful bank differentiated by values and ethics with a customer first focus as a proud North West employer. The company continues to execute its strategic plan; however as a result of COVID-19 the company has revisited its operational priorities to react to changes in the environment.

Auditors: Ernst & Young LLP

LOCATIONS

HQ: Co-operative Bank plc
P.O. Box 101, 1 Balloon Street, Manchester M60 4EP
Phone: (44) 161 832 3456   **Fax:** (44) 161 829 4475
Web: www.co-operativebank.co.uk

PRODUCTS/OPERATIONS

2016 Sales

	% of total
Interest receivable and similar income	86
Fee and commission income	14
Total	**100**

COMPETITORS

BARCLAYS BANK PLC
BPCE
Banco Bradesco S/A
CAPITAL ONE FINANCIAL CORPORATION
CHINA MINSHENG BANKING CORP. LTD.
CONSUMERS BANCORP INC.
CREDITO EMILIANO SPA
CTBC Financial Holding Co. Ltd.
FIRST NATIONAL CORPORATION
FIRSTRUST SAVINGS BANK
NATIONAL BANK HOLDINGS CORPORATION
OLD POINT FINANCIAL CORPORATION
SANTANDER UK GROUP HOLDINGS PLC
SBERBANK PAO
THE CITIZENS NATIONAL BANK OF MERIDIAN (INC)
UNION BANK OF INDIA
VIRGIN MONEY UK PLC
ZIONS BANCORPORATION

HISTORICAL FINANCIALS
Company Type: Public

Income Statement				FYE: December 31
	ASSETS ($ mil.)	NET INCOME ($ mil.)	INCOME AS % OF ASSETS	EMPLOYEES
12/20	34,935	(130)	—	2,890
12/19	30,948	(202)	—	3,357
12/18	29,496	(87)	—	3,547
12/17	33,078	314	1.0%	3,965
12/16	33,937	(515)	—	4,766
Annual Growth	0.7%	—	—	(11.8%)

2020 Year-End Financials

Return on assets: (-0.3%)
Return on equity: (-6.1%)
Long-term debt ($ mil.): —
No. of shares (mil.): —
Sales ($ mil): 670

Dividends
Yield: —
Payout: —
Market value ($ mil.): —

Co-Operative Group (CWS) Ltd.

The Co-operative Group feels a duty of care to its customers from cradle to grave. The assortment of businesses run by Britain's largest cooperative society include principally grocery retail insurance and funeralcare alongside other businesses such as financial and legal advice and electrical goods retail. The company is one of the UK's largest grocery retailers with about 2775 food stores and is Britain's largest funeral service provider with over 1000 funeral homes. Established in 1863 the Co-op is owned by its 4 million members. Anyone can become a member of the Group granting the member cashback voting rights and a share of profits by subscribing for 1.

Operations

The Co-operative Group operates five businesses: Food Funeralcare Insurance Electrical and Legal Services. Food generates around 75% of sales each year while Funeralcare and Insurance generate less than 5% each. The majority of the remainder around 15% is brought in by joint-buying activities operated by the Co-operative for itself and other independent co-operative societies.

The Food segment sells groceries at 2775 stores up and down the UK. It also sells fuel at certain sites.

Funeralcare offers pre-need and at-need funerals (meaning planning ahead and after-the-fact funerals) through 1000 funeral homes across the UK. Insurance offers car young driver breakdown home travel pet business and van insurance. The Legal Services business offers will services family law personal injury employment solicitors and conveyancing. The Electrical segment sells a range of dishwashers fridges freezers ovens small appliances vacuum cleaners and more from big name brands such as Indesit Dyson Sony and Samsung.

Geographic Reach

Manchester-based Co-operative Group's reach covers much of the UK.

Financial PerformanceNote: Growth rates may differ after conversion to US Dollars.

Co-operative Group nearly collapsed in 2013 due to the frenzied competitive environment in the UK food retail sector particularly from discounters like Aldi and Lidl (Aldi overtook Co-op Food as the UK's fifth largest grocery retailer in 2017) as well as pressure from the advance of e-commerce. Since then thanks to an aggressive sell off strategy that saw the company dispose its banking farming travel and pharmacy businesses the company has paid down debt and returned its core Food business to growth.

In fiscal 2016 revenue increased 2% to 9.5 billion thanks to growth in food and insurance. Food was up despite weakness at the pump which had a negative effect on revenue of around 200 million thanks to its store opening program. Most of Co-op's revenue growth came from the 112 store openings in the year while the 155 refitted stores also had a positive impact. The Insurance segment grew 28% to 439 million due to improvements in pricing and distribution capabilities. Funeralcare was able to grow revenue around 8 million despite a lower death rate during the year thanks to an expansion of its services particularly into a lower price point.

The company lost 134 million during the year as higher operating profit was offset by an increase in finance costs and losses in joint ventures.

Cash from operations fell 13% to 247 million due mostly to an increase in receivables.

Strategy

After its near-collapse in 2013 Co-operative Group has been selling off a number of its businesses to raise cash and give it space to invest in its main businesses of Food Funeralcare and Insurance. In 2014 the company sold its Pharmacy business to Bestway Group for 620 million its Farms business to the Wellcome Trust its Sunwin Services Group business to Cardtronics for 41.5m and Co-operative Estates sold the former Co-operative Food regional distribution center at Halesowen to Dawn Meats.It also sold its Motor business in 2015 its Travel business in 2016 and in 2017 it completed the sale of its entire banking operations.

With its finances stabilized in 2016 Co-operative Group began investing in its businesses once more. It has been opening new convenience stores at a rate of knots (in 2016 it opened 112) and has been refurbishing many more (155 in 2016). The company's strategy is based on owning the convenience market where prices are of less importance than convenience and which offers protection against the likes of Aldi and Lidl who have less of a hold in the market.

It also penned a deal in 2018 to become the exclusive wholesale supplier of Costcutter's 2200 stores and will acquire co-operative-like organization Nisa which has revenue of around 1.2 billion.

Mergers and Acquisitions

In 2017 Co-operative Group agreed to acquire Nisa a brand and buying group of independent retailers and wholesalers active in the UK. The company fought off Sainsbury's for the company's signature and the deal will add some 1.25 billion to Co-operative Group's annual revenue.

HISTORY

Co-operative Group originally was known as the North of England Co-operative Society with 300 members located mostly in Lancashire and Yorkshire. The society used its collective strength to buy goods in bulk at favorable prices reflecting the retail consumer co-operative movement sweeping across Europe in the mid-1800s. Social responsibility profit sharing and honesty about products were guiding principles.

The North of England Co-operative Society changed its name to the Co-operative Wholesale Society (CWS) in 1872 and started diversifying into financial services. The Co-operative Bank was created as an arm of CWS as was Co-operative Insurance Society.

John Mitchell was elected chairman in 1874 and led an expansion into manufacturing to provide more control over the goods required by customers. Boots soap and biscuits were made in CWS factories. Tea was imported from India where CWS owned plantations and brought to Britain in the co-op's ships.

By 1904 CWS owned a convalescent home for sick members and the Co-operative Insurance Society started offering death benefits. Within weeks of the outbreak of WWI in 1914 CWS was turning out 10000 uniforms a day for the army. In WWII CWS officials served on advisory boards for food and nonfood goods.

CWS moved into the era of the modern supermarket in 1942 when a member of the London Co-operative Society adopted the American idea of taking away the shop counter and letting customers select their own goods.

CWS merged with the Scottish Co-operative Wholesale Society in 1973.

Chief executive Graham Melmoth took the helm in 1996 after rising through CWS over 22 years. He spearheaded the merger with Co-operative Retail Services in 2000 and the name change to Co-operative Group the next year. In 2001 Co-operative Group began a major reorganization and revamped its membership rules to meet the competition from leading retailers such as Tesco.

Melmoth retired in September 2002 and was succeeded by board member Martin Beaumont. In October 2002 the Co-operative Group acquired rival convenience store operator Alldays for 131 million. In 2002 the co-op switched all of its private-label chocolate to the Fairtrade label. (The Co-op pioneered Fairtrade in the UK with bananas.)

In 2003 Co-operative Group acquired the Balfour chain of convenience stores and newsstands for 31 million. The travel group bought Sunshare Vacations.

In May 2004 Co-operative Group acquired 64 convenience stores under the Spar and Local Plus banners in southwest England from Conveco further reinforcing its position as the UK's largest convenience store operator. That month chairman Keith Darwin retired and was succeeded by Bob Burlton a board member for 11 years. In August the co-op sold its dairy business Associated Co-operative Creameries (ACC) to now defunct Dairy Farmers of Britain for 75 million. Falling profits at the co-op's supermarkets and convenience stores led to the resignation in September of Malcolm Hepworth head of the Food Retail Group after seven years with the company.

In 2005 the Co-operative Group sold its Priority Motors Group to Reg Vardy to concentrate on its core financial and food retailing businesses. Later in the year the co-op announced plans to sell or shut down its loss-making department store unit selling off what it can and then closing whatever is left by February 2007.

In July 2007 Co-operative Group merged with its smaller rival United Co-operatives to create a group with about 4500 outlets including 2300 food stores nationwide. The tie-up formed the world's largest cooperative retailer. Following the merger Beaumont retired as chief executive allowing Peter Marks the chief executive of United to run the combined business. In September the co-op sold its retail shoe business Shoefayre to the Shoe Zone Group for an undisclosed sum.

In 2008 the Co-op remodeled 700 of its food stores as part of a 200 million refurbishment program.

In March 2009 the Co-operative Group acquired Somerfield Group for about 1.5 billion ($3 billion). The purchase increased its grocery store count to some 3000 shops with about 8% of the UK grocery market.

In 2010 the Co-op acquired funeral provider Plymouth and South West Co-operative Society (PSW) the operator of 30-plus funeral homes.

In 2012 it grew its food retailing business with the addition of 83 convenience stores opened or acquired including the purchase of Scottish chain David Sands. It also opened 27 new funeral homes refurbished a crematorium and invested in new vehicles. Also in 2012 the Co-op disposed of some of its auto dealerships and its clothing business.

Meanwhile the Co-op's big name in travel retailing has diminished as tough economic times hammer the travel and tourism market. In a move to reduce its exposure the Co-op in 2011 merged its retail travel business which boasts 400-plus outlets across the UK with travel service scion Thomas Cook and independent retailer Midlands Co-operative Society. The deal created the largest retail travel operation in the UK with more than 1200 outlets. (However Thomas Cook is expected to shutter as many as 200 locations post merger.) The merged entity is 66.5%-owned by Thomas Cook 30%-owned by the Co-op with the remainder owned by Midlands.

In a major expansion in 2012 it reached a deal with Lloyds to acquire more than 630 Cheltenham and Gloucester and Lloyds TSB branches (an estimated 4.8 million Lloyds customers). The European Commission has ruled that Lloyds sell part of itself by the end of 2013 in order to increase competition in the banking sector.

EXECUTIVES

Non-Executive Director, Paul Chandler
Counsel, Company Secretary, Helen Grantham, $446,625 total compensation
Non-Executive Independent Director, Victor Adebowale
Non-Executive Independent Director, Rahul Powar
Non-Executive Director, Hazel Blears
Member Nominated Director, Sarah Mccarthy-fry
Chief Executive Officer, Jo Whitfield, $829,447 total compensation
Chief People & Services Officer, Helen Webb, $574,232 total compensation
Member Nominated Director, Margaret Casely-Hayford
Non-Executive Independent Director, Stevie Spring
Chief Financial Officer, Executive Director, Shirine Khoury-haq, $796,269 total compensation
Chief Executive Officer, Steve Murrells, $957,054 total compensation
Deputy Chief Executive Officer, Pippa Wicks, $902,488 total compensation
Non-Executive Independent Director, Simon Burke
Senior Non-Executive Independent Director, Christopher Kelly
Independent Non-Executive Chairman of the Board, Allan Leighton
Auditors: Ernst & Young LLP

LOCATIONS

HQ: Co-Operative Group (CWS) Ltd.
1 Angel Square, Manchester M60 0AG
Phone:
Web: www.co-operative.coop

PRODUCTS/OPERATIONS

2016 Sales

	% of total
Food	75
federal	17
funeral	3
Insurance	4
Other	1
Total	**100**

2016 Stores

	No.
Food stores	2,774
Funeral homes	1,026
Total	**3,800**

COMPETITORS

ACE HARDWARE CORPORATION
C&S WHOLESALE GROCERS INC.
CENTRAL ENGLAND CO-OPERATIVE LIMITED
EDEKA ZENTRALE Stiftung & Co. KG

MARKS AND SPENCER GROUP P.L.C.
TARGET CORPORATION
TESCO PLC
TRUE VALUE COMPANY L.L.C.
WAKEFERN FOOD CORP.

HISTORICAL FINANCIALS
Company Type: Public

Income Statement				FYE: January 5
	REVENUE ($ mil.)	NET INCOME ($ mil.)	NET PROFIT MARGIN	EMPLOYEES
01/19	12,759	(195)	—	62,786
01/18*	12,828	94	0.7%	65,887
12/16	11,651	(164)	—	70,399
01/16	13,730	22	0.2%	69,078
01/15	14,562	333	2.3%	80,957
Annual Growth	(3.3%)	—	—	(6.2%)

*Fiscal year change

2019 Year-End Financials
Debt ratio: 13.8%
Return on equity: (-5.0%)
Cash ($ mil.): 354
Current ratio: 0.98
Long-term debt ($ mil.): 1,260

No. of shares (mil.): —
Dividends
  Yield: —
  Payout: —
Market value ($ mil.): —

Coca-Cola Europacific Partners plc

Auditors: Ernst & Young LLP

LOCATIONS
HQ: Coca-Cola Europacific Partners plc
  Pemberton House, Bakers Road, Uxbridge UB8 1EZ
Phone: (44) 1895 231 313
Web: www.ccep.com

HISTORICAL FINANCIALS
Company Type: Public

Income Statement				FYE: December 31
	REVENUE ($ mil.)	NET INCOME ($ mil.)	NET PROFIT MARGIN	EMPLOYEES
12/20	13,016	611	4.7%	22,000
12/19	13,492	1,223	9.1%	17,498
12/18	13,190	1,040	7.9%	23,500
12/17	13,260	824	6.2%	23,500
12/16	9,643	579	6.0%	19,100
Annual Growth	7.8%	1.3%	—	3.6%

2020 Year-End Financials
Debt ratio: 44.1%
Return on equity: 8.1%
Cash ($ mil.): 1,869
Current ratio: 0.98
Long-term debt ($ mil.): 7,502

No. of shares (mil.): 454
Dividends
  Yield: —
  Payout: —
Market value ($ mil.): —

Colas SA Boulogne

Colas a subsidiary of the Bouygues Group undertakes more than 60000 projects every year via a network of 800 construction units and 3000 material production and recycling sites in some 50 countries worldwide on five continents. Colas operates in the segments ? Roads Construction Materials and Railways. Roads operates in the construction and maintenance of roads industrial platforms logistics and retail hubs recreational facilities and environmental projects including Road safety and signaling (Aximum) services. Colas also provides civil engineering services (small and large structures) and operates in the building sector (construction rehabilitation deconstruction) in certain regions. Construction Materials operates in the production distribution sales and recycling of construction materials (aggregates emulsions and binders asphalt mixes ready-mix concrete bitumen) including bitumen storage. Railways includes the design and engineering of large complex projects the construction renewal and maintenance of railway networks including track laying and maintenance electrification (catenaries and substations) signaling and security systems as well as rail freight activity.

EXECUTIVES
Group Human Resources Director, Member of the Executive Committee, Philippe Tournier
Director, Olivier Bouygues
Director - Permanent Representative of Bouygues SA, Pascal Grange
General Manager - Bitumen, Member of the Executive Committee, Louis Gabanna
Independent Director, Colette Lewiner
Independent Director, Catherine Ronge
General Secretary, Member of the Executive Committee, Eric Haentjens
Chairman of the Board, Chief Executive Officer, Member of the Executive Committee, Frederic Gardes, $968,494 total compensation
Director, Olivier Roussat, $170,910 total compensation
Director, Arnauld Van Eeckhout
General Manager, Mainland France/Overseas France and Indian Ocean territories, Member of the Executive Committee, Thierry Meline
Auditors: Mazars

LOCATIONS
HQ: Colas SA Boulogne
  1 rue du Colonel Pierre Avia, Paris, Cedex 75730
Phone: (33) 1 47 61 75 00   **Fax:** (33) 1 47 61 76 00
Web: www.colas.com

2017 Sales
	% of total
France	52
North America	22
Europe (excluding France)	17
Rest of the world	9
Total	**100**

PRODUCTS/OPERATIONS

2017 Sales
	% of total
Roads Mainland France	37
Roads Europe	14
Roads North America	22
Roads Rest of the World	10
Specialized Activities	17
Total	**100**

COMPETITORS
COLAS INC.
CONTI ENTERPRISES INC.
Chicago Bridge & Iron Company N.V.
EIFFAGE
GRIFFITH COMPANY
HILL & SMITH INFRASTRUCTURE PRODUCTS GROUP LIMITE
HeidelbergCement AG
KOKOSING CONSTRUCTION COMPANY INC.
KUMAGAI GUMI CO. LTD.
Ledcor Holdings Inc
MORO CORPORATION
PHILLIPS & JORDAN INCORPORATED
STERLING CONSTRUCTION COMPANY INC.
TAKENAKA CORPORATION

HISTORICAL FINANCIALS
Company Type: Public

Income Statement				FYE: December 31
	REVENUE ($ mil.)	NET INCOME ($ mil.)	NET PROFIT MARGIN	EMPLOYEES
12/20	15,104	115	0.8%	59,397
12/19	15,385	293	1.9%	59,853
12/18	15,121	258	1.7%	57,997
12/17	14,049	393	2.8%	58,273
12/16	11,632	374	3.2%	58,803
Annual Growth	6.7%	(25.5%)	—	0.3%

2020 Year-End Financials
Debt ratio: 8.1%
Return on equity: 3.4%
Cash ($ mil.): 743
Current ratio: 1.00
Long-term debt ($ mil.): 424

No. of shares (mil.): 32
Dividends
  Yield: —
  Payout: 100.6%
Market value ($ mil.): —

Coles Group Ltd (New)

Auditors: Ernst & Young

LOCATIONS
HQ: Coles Group Ltd (New)
  800-838 Toorak Road, Hawthorn East, Victoria 3123
Phone: (61) 3 9829 5111
Web: www.colesgroup.com.au

HISTORICAL FINANCIALS
Company Type: Public

Income Statement				FYE: June 27
	REVENUE ($ mil.)	NET INCOME ($ mil.)	NET PROFIT MARGIN	EMPLOYEES
06/21	29,558	763	2.6%	0
06/20	25,971	672	2.6%	0
06/19	26,949	1,005	3.7%	0
06/18	28,904	1,165	4.0%	0
Annual Growth	0.7%	(13.2%)	—	—

2021 Year-End Financials
Debt ratio: 4.7%
Return on equity: 37.1%
Cash ($ mil.): 597
Current ratio: 0.59
Long-term debt ($ mil.): 867

No. of shares (mil.): 1,334
Dividends
  Yield: —
  Payout: 81.0%
Market value ($ mil.): —

	STOCK PRICE ($)	P/E		PER SHARE ($)		
	FY Close	High/Low	Earnings	Dividends	Book Value
06/21	0.00	— —	0.57	0.46	1.60
Annual Growth	—		—	—	—

Commercial Bank of Qatar

EXECUTIVES

Non-Independent & Executive Chairman of the Board, Abdullah Bin Ali Bin Jabor Al Thani

Managing Director, Non-Independent & Executive Member of the Board, Omar Al Fardan

Executive General Manager, Treasury & Strategy, Parvez Khan

Non-Independent & Executive Vice Chairman of the Board - Representative of Alfardan Investment Company, Hussain Ibrahim Al Fardan

Executive General Manager, Chief International Banking, Fahad Badar

Independent Non-Executive Member of the Board - Representative of Qatar Insurance Company, Khalaf Ahmad Al Mannai

Executive General Manager, Chief Internal Audit Officer, Rana Salatt

Independent Non-Executive Member of the Board, Faisal bin Fahad bin Jassim Al Thani

Chief Operating Officer, Executive General Manager, Leonie Lethbridge

Executive General Manager, Chief Wholesale Banking, Rajbhushan Buddhiraju

Executive General Manager, Consumer Banking, Amit Sah

Chief Financial Officer, Executive General Manager, Rehan Khan

Independent Non-Executive Member of the Board, Saleh Abdulla Mohamed Al Ibrahim Al Mannai

Independent Non-Executive Member of the Board, Mohd Ismail Mandani Al Emadi

Chief Compliance Officer, Senior AGM, Abdulla Ahmed Al-Fadli

Executive General Manager, Chief Marketing Officer, Hussein Ali Al-Abdulla

Non-Independent & Executive Member of the Board, Abdul Rahman Bin Hamad Al Attiyah

Chief Human Capital Officer, Executive General Manager, Jassim Saud Abdulaziz Hamad Al Thani

Acting Chief Risk Officer, Executive General Manager, Paul Gossiaux

Independent Non-Executive Director of the Board, Bader Omar Al Dafa

Group Chief Executive Office, Joseph Abraham

Auditors: Ernst & Young

LOCATIONS

HQ: Commercial Bank of Qatar
P.O. Box 3232, Doha
Phone: (974) 4449 0000   **Fax:** (974) 4449 0070
Web: www.cbq.com.qa

HISTORICAL FINANCIALS

Company Type: Public

Income Statement				FYE: December 31
	ASSETS ($ mil.)	NET INCOME ($ mil.)	INCOME AS % OF ASSETS	EMPLOYEES
12/19	40,532	555	1.4%	0
12/18	37,107	456	1.2%	0
12/17	38,035	165	0.4%	0
12/16	35,805	137	0.4%	2,138
12/15	33,902	391	1.2%	2,286
Annual Growth	4.6%	9.1%	—	—

2019 Year-End Financials

Return on assets: 1.4%
Return on equity: 9.6%
Long-term debt ($ mil.): —
No. of shares (mil.): —
Sales ($ mil): 2,347

Dividends
Yield: —
Payout: 5.4%
Market value ($ mil.): —

Commerzbank AG

Auditors: Ernst & Young GmbH
Wirtschaftspruefungsgesellschaft

LOCATIONS

HQ: Commerzbank AG
Kaiserplatz, Frankfurt am Main 60261
Phone: (49) 69 136 20   **Fax:** (49) 69 28 53 89
Web: www.commerzbank.com

HISTORICAL FINANCIALS

Company Type: Public

Income Statement				FYE: December 31
	ASSETS ($ mil.)	NET INCOME ($ mil.)	INCOME AS % OF ASSETS	EMPLOYEES
12/20	622,132	(3,522)	—	46,724
12/19	520,554	723	0.1%	48,512
12/18	529,502	990	0.2%	49,410
12/17	542,427	187	0.0%	49,417
12/16	507,299	294	0.1%	49,941
Annual Growth	5.2%	—	—	(1.7%)

2020 Year-End Financials

Return on assets: (-0.5%)
Return on equity: (-10.0%)
Long-term debt ($ mil.): —
No. of shares (mil.): 1,252
Sales ($ mil): 11,201

Dividends
Yield: —
Payout: —
Market value ($ mil.): 8,078

	STOCK PRICE ($)	P/E		PER SHARE ($)		
	FY Close	High/Low		Earnings	Dividends	Book Value
12/20	6.45	—	—	(2.86)	0.00	26.93
12/19	6.07	18	10	0.57	0.14	26.33
12/18	6.66	23	9	0.79	0.23	25.80
12/17	14.93	128	71	0.14	0.00	27.64
12/16	7.65	46	25	0.23	0.19	24.12
Annual Growth	(4.2%)	—	—	—	—	2.8%

Commonwealth Bank of Australia

Commonwealth Bank of Australia (CBA) one of Australia's Four banks offers retail private business and institutional banking services funds management insurance and investment services. CBA's brands include Bankwest Colonial First State on-line brokerage CommSec and ASB Bank which provides banking investment and financial services . CBA serves over 15 million customers via about 1000 branch offices and nearly 2500 ATMs in Australia. In addition CBA operates in Australia New Zealand United Kingdom the United States China Japan Europe Singapore Hong Kong and Indonesia. CBA offers life insurance and a provider of home loans in Australia. It has total assets of A$1.1 trillion.

Operations

Broadly speaking Commonwealth Bank of Australia (CBA) generates around 80% of its revenue from interest income from its various banking divisions and New Zealand operations. Other banking income provides about 20% of total revenue. Income from fund management and insurance income account for the remainder.

CBA operates six divisions.

Its Retail Banking unit which generates some 55% of its revenue provides deposit home loan and consumer loan products to retail customers and small businesses. The Business Banking division (over 30% of revenue) provides personalized banking services to Agribusiness customers and high-net-worth individuals as well as margin lending through CommSec and retail banking products and servicing to non-relationship managed small business customers.

Institutional Banking and Markets (about 10% of revenue) provides debt and equity capital raising financial and commodities price risk management and transactional banking services to corporate institutional and government clients. Its Wealth Management division provides superannuation investment retirement and insurance products and services including financial planning. The rest of its revenue comes from its operations in New Zealand (almost 15% of revenue).

Geographic Reach

Commonwealth Bank of Australia generates around 85% of its revenue from customers in Australia and more than 10% in New Zealand. The bank operates retail banks in New Zealand (ASB) and Indonesia (Commonwealth Bank of Indonesia). It has minority investments in China and Vietnam. It also has banking branch offices in London New York Japan Singapore Malta Hong Kong New Zealand Beijing and Shanghai.

Sales and Marketing

Commonwealth Bank of Australia provides financial education to school children in Australia through its Start Smart program which has reached more than three million pupils since its inception. It also funds the Commonwealth Bank Teaching Awards and Evidence For Learning.

CBA has 7.6 million active digital customers. CBA uses CommBank app and the Customer Engagement Engine which uses artificial intelligence to analyze data and serve customers with the information and services that are most relevant to them.

Advertising marketing and loyalty costs were A$412 million A$424 million and A$443 million for the years 2021 2020 and 2019 respectively.

Financial Performance

Note: Growth rates may differ after conversion to US dollars.

Commonwealth Bank of Australia (CBA) has steadily grown its revenue between 2019 and 2021 after declining in the couple of years prior. Net profit has fluctuated over the last five years.

The group's statutory net profit after tax for the financial year 2021 (ended June) was A$10.2 billion an increase of A$589 million or 6% on the prior year.

CBA used A$42.3 billion in operating activities in 2021. Net cash provided by investing activities was A$871 million. Net cash provided in financing activities was A$18.3 billion and cash at the end of the year was A$87.4 billion. It increased by about 220% compared to 2020.

Strategy

CBA's strategy is to become a simpler better bank that delivers balanced and sustainable outcomes for the customers community people and shareholders. CBA is becoming a simpler bank by focusing on the core banking businesses and simplifying the organization to reduce costs and create the capacity to invest while also reducing risk and making it easier for the customers and people to get things done. Becoming a better bank is about being more capable and reliable acting transparently and doing the right thing and consistently delivering better outcomes for the stakeholders.

The four execution priorities are: Leadership in Australia's recovery and transition; Reimagined products and services; Global best digital experiences and technology; and Simpler better foundations.

As part of the Bank's strategic priorities it has committed to playing a leadership role in supporting Australia's economic recovery and transition to a sustainable economy. In addition to considering the risks of climate change its strategy also seeks to harness the significant existing and emerging opportunities to help its customers reduce their emissions and adapt to climate change.

Mergers and Acquisitions

HISTORY

The Commonwealth Bank Act of 1911 allowed banks to conduct both savings bank and central bank functions and paved the way for the founding of the Commonwealth Bank of Australia the next year. The bank initially operated through a single main office and in nearly 500 post offices in Victoria; it spread out through the entire country over the next few years.

The young bank was drafted during WWI to help the federal government organize war loans and a merchant shipping fleet. In 1919 the bank took over responsibility for issuing notes from the Federal Treasury. In 1928 it created the Commonwealth Savings Bank from its savings department.

Australia — heavily indebted to British lenders — was devastated by the Great Depression. As banks failed the Commonwealth Bank picked up several other institutions including the state banks in Western Australia and New South Wales. During those years Commonwealth took on more and more of the functions of a central bank.

During WWII the bank again came to the aid of its country acting as an agent for the federal government. After the war when the Australian economy stabilized the bank began offering home loans.

After years of controversy in 1959 two bank acts formally separated the Commonwealth Bank's central bank and savings functions. The Reserve Bank of Australia took over the central bank functions in 1960 and the trading and savings operations were taken over by the new Commonwealth Development Bank later renamed the Commonwealth Banking Corporation (a subsidiary of Commonwealth Bank of Australia).

The bank concentrated on expansion and diversification in the 1970s establishing travel home insurance and financing (CBFC 1978); it set its sights on technology in the 1980s expanding its credit card offerings and introducing electronic banking.

The US's 1987 stock market crash again affected Australia's banks which spent almost a decade recovering. Luckily for Commonwealth Bank it wasn't the hardest hit.

In 1988 Commonwealth Bank moved into life insurance and investment services forming subsidiaries Commonwealth Life and Commonwealth Management Services (now together known as CBA Financial Services). In 1989 the bank bought 75% of New Zealand-based ASB Bank.

Commonwealth faced a bevy of challenges including banking deregulation that began in 1982 foreign competition and 1990's banking-law amendments allowing banks to be publicly traded. All of these factors influenced Commonwealth's decision to reorganize. The government sold approximately 30% of its stake in 1991 in part to help Commonwealth fund its acquisition of the State Bank of Victoria. The government sold the rest of its stake in 1996.

That year the company's push into electronic banking bore fruit — some 60% of all its banking transactions were online; that figure later rose to 80%. The company moved into e-commerce in 1999 putting out a call for an overseas partner; Commonwealth's stated goal was to generate one-quarter of its income outside Australia. Also that year Commonwealth and a division of The Bank of Nova Scotia joined forces to form a commodities trading group specializing in metals. In 2000 the company bought Australian financial services firm Colonial Limited.

In late 2008 the company acquired Australia-based BankWest from British bank HBOS (now part of Lloyds Banking Group). The US$1.5 billion deal included insurer and asset manager St. Andrew's (which was later sold) and bolstered CBA's presence in western Australia. Its 2008 acquisitions of BankWestfrom HBOS bolstered its position in western Australia.

In 2010 CBA entered the Chinese insurance market with the launch of a joint venture with Bank of Communications.

In 2011 the bank opened branches in China India and Indonesia and bought a 20% sake in Vietnam International Bank. Also that year the bank continued to strengthen its ties to China signing a referral agreement with Agricultural Bank of China to capture potential customers.

EXECUTIVES

Group Executive - Enterprise Services and Chief Information Officer, Pascal Boillat, $1,147,107 total compensation

Group Executive, Institutional Banking and Markets, Andrew Hinchliff, $796,630 total compensation

Group Executive, Human Resources, Sian Lewis, $643,762 total compensation

Chief Executive Officer, Managing Director, Executive Director, Matt Comyn, $1,698,921 total compensation

Non-Executive Independent Chairman of the Board, Catherine Livingstone

Group Executive - Financial Services and Chief Financial Officer, Alan Docherty, $777,987 total compensation

Group Executive, Retail Banking Services, Angus Sullivan, $953,225 total compensation

Group Chief Risk Officer, Nigel Williams, $1,065,080 total compensation

General Manager, Governance, Risk & Compliance and Company Secretary, Kristy Huxtable

Group Executive, Program Delivery, Scott Wharton

General Counsel, Joint Company Secretary, Carmel Mulhern

Chief Executive and Managing Director - ASB Bank Ltd, Vittoria Shortt, $721,157 total compensation

Deputy Chief Executive Officer, David Cohen, $915,941 total compensation

Group Executive Business and Private Banking, Mike Vacy-Lyle, $837,643 total compensation

Independent Non-Executive Director, Genevieve Bell A.O

Independent Non-Executive Director, Simon Moutter

Independent Non-Executive Director, Peter Harmer

Non-Executive Independent Director, Julie Galbo

Auditors: PricewaterhouseCoopers

LOCATIONS

HQ: Commonwealth Bank of Australia
Ground Floor, Tower 1, 201 Sussex Street, Sydney, New South Wales 2000
Phone: (61) 2 9378 2000   **Fax:** (61) 2 9118 7192
Web: www.commbank.com.au

2017

	%
Australia	83
New Zealand	11
Other locations	5
Total	**100**

PRODUCTS/OPERATIONS

2017

	%
Interest income	60
Other banking income	19
Premiums from insurance contracts	10
Funds management income	8
Investment revenue (funds management	2
Investment revenue (insurance	1
Total	**100**

2017 Sales by Segment

	% of total
Retail banking services	43
Business & private banking	16
Institutional banking & markets	12
Wealth Management	10
New Zealand	9
Bankwest	8
IFS and Other Divisions	4
Total	**100**

Selected Brands
ASB (New Zealand)
Bankwest
Colonial First State
CommInsure
CommSec
FirstChoice
Sovereign

COMPETITORS

AUSTRALIA AND NEW ZEALAND BANKING GROUP LIMITED
BANK OF CHINA LIMITED
Bank of Communications Co. Ltd.
Canadian Imperial Bank Of Commerce
DEUTSCHE BANK AG
ING Groep N.V.
KEYCORP
NATWEST GROUP PLC
Nordea Bank AB
QATAR NATIONAL BANK (Q.P.S.C.)
STANDARD CHARTERED PLC
Skandinaviska Enskilda Banken AB
UniCredit Bank AG
WESTPAC BANKING CORPORATION

HISTORICAL FINANCIALS

Company Type: Public

Income Statement				FYE: June 30
	ASSETS ($ mil.)	NET INCOME ($ mil.)	INCOME AS % OF ASSETS	EMPLOYEES
06/21	819,639	7,641	0.9%	50,278
06/20	694,916	6,602	1.0%	48,167
06/19	684,170	6,005	0.9%	48,238
06/18	720,056	6,888	1.0%	45,753
06/17	750,192	7,628	1.0%	45,614
Annual Growth	2.2%	0.0%	—	2.5%

2021 Year-End Financials

Return on assets: 0.9%	Dividends
Return on equity: 13.5%	Yield: 2.4%
Long-term debt ($ mil.): —	Payout: 44.0%
No. of shares (mil.): 1,772	Market value ($ mil.): 132,986
Sales ($ mil): 22,693	

	STOCK PRICE ($) FY Close	P/E High/Low		PER SHARE ($) Earnings	Dividends	Book Value
06/21	75.03	14	8	4.05	1.80	33.33
06/20	48.13	11	7	3.59	2.74	27.91
06/19	58.19	12	9	3.28	2.97	27.58
06/18	54.13	12	9	3.82	3.08	28.29
06/17	63.77	12	9	4.30	3.16	28.12
Annual Growth	4.1%	—		(1.5%)	(13.2%)	4.3%

Compagnie De L Odet

Holding company Financière de l'Odet controls a two-thirds stake in Bollore a diversified company with operations in the transportation and logistics manufacturing fuel distribution and communications and media sectors. Bollore's transportation and logistics operations consist mainly of freight forwarding and port operations. Its manufacturing businesses produce plastic films and specialty papers. Bollore also has interests in oil palm and rubber tree plantations. Chairman Vincent Bollore holds a controlling stake in Financière de l'Odet through his company Sofibol and other entities.

Auditors: Constantin Associés

LOCATIONS

HQ: Compagnie De L Odet
Odet, Ergue-Gaberic 29500
Phone: (33) 1 46 96 44 33　　**Fax:** (33) 1 46 96 44 22
Web: www.financiere-odet.com

2016 Sales

	% of total
France and overseas departments and territories	39
Africa	22
Europe excluding France	17
Americas	13
Asia/Pacific	9
Total	100

PRODUCTS/OPERATIONS

2016 Sales

	% of total
Transportation and logistics	54
Communications	23
Oil logistics	19
Electricity storage and solutions	3
Other activities	1
Total	100

2016 Sales

	% of total
Provision of services	77
Sale of goods	21
Income from associated activities	2
Total	100

COMPETITORS

China Baowu Steel Group Corporation Limited
Econosto N.V.
FIVES
GEODIS
HES Beheer B.V.
J. & J. DENHOLM LIMITED
SONEPAR
UNIPART GROUP OF COMPANIES LIMITED
YAMATO HOLDINGS CO.LTD.

HISTORICAL FINANCIALS
Company Type: Public

Income Statement　　　　　　　　　　FYE: December 31

	REVENUE ($ mil.)	NET INCOME ($ mil.)	NET PROFIT MARGIN	EMPLOYEES
12/19	27,918	136	0.5%	83,801
12/18	26,393	139	0.5%	81,003
12/17	22,148	442	2.0%	74,828
12/16	10,682	241	2.3%	58,023
12/15	11,813	323	2.7%	55,383
Annual Growth	24.0%	(19.4%)	—	10.9%

2019 Year-End Financials

Debt ratio: 23.7%	No. of shares (mil.): 4
Return on equity: 3.2%	Dividends
Cash ($ mil.): 3,304	Yield: —
Current ratio: 0.82	Payout: 3.4%
Long-term debt ($ mil.): 10,585	Market value ($ mil.): —

Compagnie de Saint-Gobain

Auditors: KPMG Audit

LOCATIONS

HQ: Compagnie de Saint-Gobain
Tour Saint-Gobain, 12, place de l'Iris, Courbevoie 92400
Phone: (33) 1 47 62 30 00
Web: www.saint-gobain.com

HISTORICAL FINANCIALS
Company Type: Public

Income Statement　　　　　　　　　　FYE: December 31

	REVENUE ($ mil.)	NET INCOME ($ mil.)	NET PROFIT MARGIN	EMPLOYEES
12/20	46,810	559	1.2%	167,552
12/19	47,826	1,578	3.3%	170,643
12/18	47,873	480	1.0%	181,001
12/17	48,960	1,877	3.8%	179,149
12/16	41,310	1,384	3.4%	172,063
Annual Growth	3.2%	(20.3%)	—	(0.7%)

2020 Year-End Financials

Debt ratio: 31.6%	No. of shares (mil.): 530
Return on equity: 2.4%	Dividends
Cash ($ mil.): 10,362	Yield: 0.0%
Current ratio: 1.45	Payout: —
Long-term debt ($ mil.): 12,492	Market value ($ mil.): 4,845

	STOCK PRICE ($) FY Close	P/E High/Low		PER SHARE ($) Earnings	Dividends	Book Value
12/20	9.14	12	5	1.04	0.00	41.43
12/19	8.17	3	2	2.90	0.30	40.21
12/18	6.59	14	8	0.87	0.31	37.76
12/17	11.01	4	4	3.37	0.30	40.15
12/16	9.22	4	3	2.48	0.27	35.76
Annual Growth	(0.2%)	—		— (19.5%)	—	3.7%

Compagnie Financiere Richemont SA

Compagnie Financiere Richemont is the owner of prestigious Maisons recognized for its excellence in jewelry watches fashion and accessories and distinguished by their craftsmanship and creativity. It markets Cartier jewelry Piaget and Baume & Mercier watches Montblanc pens and Chloe haute coture. Richemont also owns jeweler Van Cleef & Arpels. Customers can get their hands on Richemont's finery at its over 2245 boutiques scattered across five continents as well as online. Richemont was founded in Switzerland in 1940s by South African Johann Rupert. Majority of its sales were generated in the Asia-Pacific.

Operations

The company operates in three segments: Jewellery Maisons (around 55% of sales) Specialist Watchmakers (over 15%) and Online Distributors (more than 15%). Others account for the rest of the sales.

The Jewellery Maisons designs manufactures and distributes jewellery products; these comprise Buccellati Cartier and Van Cleef & Arpels.

The Specialist Watchmakers' primary activity includes the design manufacture and distribution of precision timepieces. The group's Specialist Watchmakers comprise A. Lange & Söhne Baume & Mercier IWC Schaffhausen Jaeger-LeCoultre Panerai Piaget Roger Dubuis and Vacheron Constantin.

The Online Distributors' primary activity is the online sale of luxury goods. This segment comprises Watchfinder and YNAP.

Other operating segments include Alaïa Chloe dunhill Montblanc Peter Millar Purdey Serapian AZ Factory investment property companies and other manufacturing entities.

By product Richemont generates over 40% of its sales from jewelry and around 30% from watches. Clothing and leather goods account for around 10% each. Other items such as writing instruments bring in the remainder.

Richemont's maisons are supported by regional and central functions structured around the world to provide specialized support in terms of distribution finance legal IT and administration.

Geographic Reach

Headquartered in Geneva Switzerland Richemont generates some 45% of its sales from the Asia/Pacific region its biggest geography. Europe accounts for nearly 25% the Americas with nearly 20% and Japan and the Middle East and Africa with over 5% each. It has over 2245 mono-brand boutiques in around 35 locations.

Sales and Marketing

Richemont generates around 55% of sales through its retail channel and the rest from its wholesale and online retail channels.

Financial Performance

The company's revenue for fiscal 2021 decreased to ?13.1 billion compared with ?14.2 billion in the prior year due to a sharp decline in the first half of the financial year as the health crisis spread across the globe.

Net profit for fiscal 2021 increased to ?1.3 billion compared with ?931 million in the prior year.

Cash held by the company at the end of fiscal 2021 increased to ?3.8 billion. Operating and financing activities contributed ?3.2 billion and ?906 million respectively. Investing activities used ?2.2 billion mainly for investment in money market and externally managed funds.

Strategy

The company's innovative practices range from new materials to new distribution models and from new ways to collaborate internally to new ways to improve customer service.

The primary objective of the company's compensation strategy is to align variable compensation paid to senior executives to total shareholder returns over the long term while attracting and retaining key talent in the face of competition from other multinational groups.

Mergers and Acquisitions

In mid-2021 Richemont has acquired 100% of Delvaux the renowned Belgian luxury leather goods Maison in a private transaction. Delvaux is the oldest luxury leather goods Maison in the world. It has a unique heritage expressed through the richness of its archives and distinguishes itself through its exceptional savoir faire and creativity. Delvaux's leather pieces are crafted by skilled artisans in its workshops across Belgium and France and mostly sold across a highly qualitative network of 50 boutiques worldwide. Richemont's acquisition will position Delvaux for its next stage of development by enabling Delvaux to leverage the Group's global presence and digital capabilities to develop its omnichannel opportunities and customer engagement. Terms were not disclosed.

HISTORY

Anton Rupert started a tobacco company in the late 1940s that eventually became the Rembrandt Group a tobacco and liquor giant in South Africa with other diverse holdings. To avoid possible antiapartheid sanctions in 1988 Rupert and his son Johann spun off Rembrandt's non-South African holdings.

Those holdings included 33% of UK-based tobacco firm Rothmans International (Benson & Hedges). Rothmans had a controlling stake in Dunhill Holdings (tobacco and accessories) and it had acquired piecemeal a major stake in jeweler Cartier in the 1970s and 1980s. The Rembrandt spin off based in Zug Switzerland and named Compagnie Financi"re Richemont went public in 1988.

Richemont increased its stake in Rothmans in 1990 to about 63% by purchasing Philip Morris' shares. The next year Richemont expanded into new areas buying South African pay-TV station M-Net and through a joint venture acquiring 49% of Horn & Hardart (which became Hanover Direct in 1993). Dunhill acquired the Karl Lagerfeld fashion house in 1992.

In part to shelter the company from UK taxes in 1993 Richemont's assets were split into two publicly traded companies: Rothmans International (tobacco) and Vend´me Luxury Group which combined Dunhill's fashion holdings and Cartier. (Vend´me is a square in Paris where many expensive Cartier items are sold.) Richemont retained majority interests in both firms.

In 1995 Richemont acquired the shares of Rothmans it didn't already own and merged it with Rembrandt's South African tobacco holdings. Richemont also merged M-Net with two other television companies to form Network Holdings (NetHold) in exchange for a 50% stake in that firm.

The next year Richemont bought Swiss luxury watchmaker Vacheron Constantin and it sold most of NetHold to French pay-TV operator Canal+ in exchange for 15% of Canal+ (now owned by Vivendi Universal). (It sold that stake in 1999.) The company in 1997 bought French leather goods company Lancel and sold Karl Lagerfeld SA to the designer. Richemont increased its stake in Hanover Direct that year by purchasing the shares of its joint venture it didn't own. It also bought out Vend´me's minority shareholders in

1997 making the company a wholly owned subsidiary.

Richemont exited tobacco in 1999 by merging its tobacco holdings with British American Tobacco (BAT) the world's #2 cigarette company in exchange for a 35% stake in BAT (including the shares owned by Remgro formerly Rembrandt). That year Richemont also purchased 60% of Van Cleef & Arpels a manufacturer and retailer of watches and jewelry with over 40 stores. It wrapped up the year by taking a 20% stake in online jewelry retailer Adornis.com (which shut down in late 2000).

In 2000 Richemont bought Swiss luxury watch dial manufacturer Stern Group and later Mannesmann AG's Les Manufactures Horlogeres SA luxury watch unit. Beating a host of rivals (including LVMH) Richemont acquired the Jaeger-LeCoultre IWC and A. Lange & S ¶hne luxury watch brands; the purchase positioned the company to control the market for watches costing more than $1500.

Chloe designer Stella McCartney left the company in 2001 to launch her own label with Gucci. Also in 2001 the company purchased an additional 20% of Van Cleef & Arpels raising its stake in the company to 80%. Additionally that year Richemont wrote down to zero its investment in catalog marketer Hanover Direct's (Domestications Silhouettes) common stock.

The company spun off its jointly held 30% stake in BAT in October 2008. The spinoff was timed to coincide with a potentially penalizing change in Luxembourg tax law that would have left Richemont vulnerable to the ebbs and flows in upscale purchasing.

After five years at the helm CEO Norbert Platt retired at the end of 2009. He cited health concerns as the reason for his retirement.

In June 2010 Richemont completed its acquisition of more than 93% of the shares in Net-A-Porter Limited. NET-A-PORTER operates as an independent entity alongside Richemont's other luxury goods businesses.

Auditors: PricewaterhouseCoopers SA

LOCATIONS

HQ: Compagnie Financiere Richemont SA
50 chemin de la Chenaie, CP 30, Geneva, Bellevue Ch-1293
Phone: (41) 22 721 3500   **Fax:** (41) 22 721 3550
Web: www.richemont.com

2018 Sales

	% of total
Asia-Pacific	40
Europe	27
Americas	16
Middle East and Africa	8
Japan	9
Total	**100**

PRODUCTS/OPERATIONS

2018 Sales

	% of total
Jewelry Maisons	59
Specialist Watchmakers	25
Other businesses (apparel & leather & accessories)	17
Total	**100**

2018 Sales

	% of total
Retail	63
Wholesale	37
Total	**100**

2018 Sales

	% of total
Jewelry	41
Watches	40
Leather goods	7
Clothing	4
Writing instruments	4
Other	4
Total	**100**

Major Brands

A. Lange & Söhne (watches)
Alaia
Alfred Dunhill (menswear and accessories)
Baume & Mercier (watches)
Cartier (jewelry and watches)
Chloé (womenswear jewelry fragrances and accessories)
Dunhill
Giampiero Bodino (jewelry)
IWC (watches)
Jaeger-LeCoultre (watches)
Lancel (leather goods)
Montblanc (writing instruments)
Officine Panerai (watches)
Peter Millar
Piaget (watches)
Purdey (firearms)
Roger Dubuis (watches)
Vacheron Constantin (watches)
Van Cleef & Arpels (jewelry and watches)

COMPETITORS

CHRISTIAN DIOR	LVMH MOET HENNESSY
FOSSIL GROUP INC.	LOUIS VUITTON
FRASERS GROUP PLC	MOVADO GROUP INC.
HERMES INTERNATIONAL	MULBERRY GROUP PLC
INCHCAPE PLC	RALLYE
INVESTCORP HOLDINGS	Signet Jewelers
B.S.C	Limited
Koninklijke Ahold	TIFFANY & CO.
Delhaize N.V.	The Swatch Group AG
LAURA ASHLEY HOLDINGS	
PLC	

HISTORICAL FINANCIALS

Company Type: Public

Income Statement   FYE: March 31

	REVENUE ($ mil.)	NET INCOME ($ mil.)	NET PROFIT MARGIN	EMPLOYEES
03/21	15,418	1,526	9.9%	34,760
03/20	15,598	1,022	6.6%	34,728
03/19	15,710	3,129	19.9%	35,640
03/18	13,534	1,505	11.1%	28,740
03/17	11,375	1,292	11.4%	28,580
Annual Growth	7.9%	4.2%	—	5.0%

2021 Year-End Financials

Debt ratio: 33.2%	No. of shares (mil.): 513
Return on equity: 7.4%	Dividends
Cash ($ mil.): 9,240	Yield: 1.0%
Current ratio: 2.61	Payout: 3.5%
Long-term debt ($ mil.): 6,964	Market value ($ mil.): 4,913

	STOCK PRICE ($) FY Close	P/E High/Low		PER SHARE ($) Earnings	Dividends	Book Value
03/21	9.57	4	2	2.69	0.10	40.60
03/20	5.37	5	3	1.80	0.12	36.60
03/19	7.26	2	1	5.53	0.11	37.14
03/18	8.95	5	4	2.66	0.11	35.20
03/17	7.86	4	2	2.29	0.10	32.36
Annual Growth	5.0%		—	4.2%	(0.9%)	5.8%

Compagnie Generale des Etablissements Michelin SCA

Auditors: Deloitte & Associés

LOCATIONS

HQ: Compagnie Generale des Etablissements Michelin SCA
23, place des Carmes-Dechaux, Clermont-Ferrand 63000
Phone: (33) 4 73 32 20 00
Web: www.michelin.com

HISTORICAL FINANCIALS

Company Type: Public

Income Statement   FYE: December 31

	REVENUE ($ mil.)	NET INCOME ($ mil.)	NET PROFIT MARGIN	EMPLOYEES
12/20	25,121	775	3.1%	123,642
12/19	27,097	1,965	7.3%	127,187
12/18	25,226	1,920	7.6%	117,393
12/17	26,324	2,037	7.7%	114,069
12/16	22,075	1,769	8.0%	111,708
Annual Growth	3.3%	(18.6%)	—	2.6%

2020 Year-End Financials

Debt ratio: 29.9%
Return on equity: 4.8%
Cash ($ mil.): 5,825
Current ratio: 1.83
Long-term debt ($ mil.): 7,571

No. of shares (mil.): 178
Dividends
Yield: 1.7%
Payout: 11.3%
Market value ($ mil.): 4,587

	STOCK PRICE ($) FY Close	P/E High/Low		PER SHARE ($) Earnings	Dividends	Book Value
12/20	25.72	8	5	4.31	0.45	86.94
12/19	24.45	3	2	10.85	0.83	83.13
12/18	19.60	3	2	10.59	0.83	77.33
12/17	28.62	3	3	11.20	0.78	74.96
12/16	22.21	2	2	9.53	0.59	62.15
Annual Growth	3.7%	—	—	(18.0%)	(6.7%)	8.8%

Compal Electronics Inc

Compal Electronics is one of the world's largest notebook computer manufacturers counting Dell Lenovo and Acer as customers. Compal also makes mobile phone handsets LCD and 3D TVs and computer displays as well as a growing list of server computers tablets and media players. The Taiwan-based company operates in China as well as in other countries including Vietnam and India. The US is its biggest single market accounting for about 45% of sales.

Operations

Compal operates two segments: the Information Technology product segment (over 95% of sales) which is primarily engaged in the development manufacture and sale of information technology products and mobile communication products; and the Strategy Integrate Product segment (nearly 5%) is primarily engaged in the research development manufacture and sale of networking products.

It gets virtually all of its revenue from its 5C segment.

Geographic Reach

Based in Taiwan Compal has sites in China the US Vietnam and Brazil as well as in Poland and India. In terms of sales US accounts for about 45% followed by China with over 10%.

Sales and Marketing

Compal's customers are Sony Hitachi Vodafone Dell and Lenovo for which it makes notebooks and servers. Acer is also a customer.

Financial Performance

The company's revenue for fiscal 2020 increased to NT$1.0 trillion compared from the prior year with NT$980.4 billion.

Profit for fiscal 2020 increased to NT$13.1 billion compared from the prior year with NT$10.0 billion.

Cash held by the company at the end of fiscal 2020 increased to NT$89.1 billion. Cash provided by operations and financing activities were NT$14.3 billion and NT$18.8 billion respectively. Cash used for investing activities was NT$7.9 billion mainly for acquisition of property plant and equipment.

Company Background

Established in 1984 Compal has grown to its present scale with outstanding management and solid R&D capacity. To meet client needs from design to manufacturing Compal manufacture 5C products such as notebook computers tablets wearable devices smart phones. In 2007 Compal established its second offshore manufacturing base in Vietnam in light of prospective emerging market demand the company proceeded to set up an NB service center in Poland and another NB manufacturing plant in Brazil. In order to achieve the objective of optimized production capacity and high product quality.

EXECUTIVES

Vice Chairman of the Board, Chief Strategy Officer, Jui-Tsung Chen
Deputy General Manager, Head of Finance, Guo-Dung Yu
Deputy General Manager, Yau-De Chiou
Deputy General Manager, Peng Kuee Lau
Director, Chieh-Li Hsu
Director, Wen-Being Hsu
Independent Director, Wen-Chung Shen
Director, Chiung-Chi Hsu
General Manager, Director, Chung-Pin Wong
Chairman of the Board, Sheng-Hsiung Hsu
Deputy General Manager, Tzong-Ming Wang
Deputy General Manager, Jui-Chun Shyur
Senior Deputy General Manager, Min-Tung Weng
Deputy General Manager, Ta-Chun Wang
Deputy General Manager, Hsin-Kung Mao
Senior Deputy General Manager, Chung-Hsing Tan
General Counsel, Peng-Hong Chan
Executive Deputy General Manager, Director, Ming-Chih Chang
Senior Deputy General Manager, Hsi-Kuan Chen
Senior Deputy General Manager, Kuo-Chuan Chen
Director, Anthony Bonadero
Director, Charng-Chyi Ko
Deputy General Manager, Yi-Yun Chang
Director, Sheng-Chieh Hsu
Senior Deputy General Manager, Sheng-Hung Li
Deputy General Manager, Jen-Liang Lin
Director, Yen-Chia Chou
Deputy General Manager, Hsin-Hsiung Huang
Independent Director, Min Chih Hsuan
Deputy General Manager, Chih-Chuan Cheng
Deputy General Manager, Fu-Chuan Chang
Senior Deputy General Manager, Chun-De Shen
Deputy General Manager, Yung-Nan Chang
Deputy General Manager, Yi-Chiang Chiu
Executive Deputy General Manager, Chen-Chang Hsu
Executive Deputy General Manager, Director, Sheng-Hua Peng
Senior Deputy General Manager, Wen-Da Hsu
Deputy General Manager, Ching-Hsiung Lu
Independent Director, Duei Tsai
Deputy General Manager, Tu-Chuan Tu
Deputy General Manager, Chiao-Lie Huang
Deputy General Manager, Po-Tang Wang
Deputy General Manager, Jyh-Shyan Liang
Deputy General Manager, Cheng-Hui Su
Deputy General Manager, Chang-Chieh Tien
Deputy General Manager, Wei-Chia Wang
Senior Deputy General Manager, Lo-Chun Lee
Senior Deputy General Manager, Chi-Wai Wan
Deputy General Manager, Yong-Ho Su
Deputy General Manager, Head of Accounting, Cheng-Chiang Wang
Senior Deputy General Manager, Bor-Heng Chen
Senior Deputy General Manager, Chyou-Jui Wei
Deputy General Manager, Shih-Hong Huang
Auditors: KPMG

LOCATIONS

HQ: Compal Electronics Inc
No. 581 & 581-1, Ruiguang Road, Neihu District, Taipei 11492
Phone: (886) 2 8797 8588   **Fax:** (886) 2 2659 1566
Web: www.compal.com

2017 Sales

	% of total
United States	38
Mainland China	13
Netherlands	11
Germany	4
UK	4
Others	30
Total	**100**

PRODUCTS/OPERATIONS

2017 Sales

	% of total
IT Product Segment	98
Strategically Integrated Product Segment	2
Total	**100**

2017 Sales

	% of total
5C Electronic Products	100
Others	-
Total	**100**

COMPETITORS

Amap Software Co. Ltd.
CODEMASTERS SOFTWARE COMPANY LIMITED(THE)
HON HAI PRECISION INDUSTRY CO. LTD.
INVENTEC CORPORATION
LANYON SOLUTIONS INC.
MICRO ELECTRONICS INC.
QUARK SOFTWARE INC.
Quanta Computer Inc.
SHI INTERNATIONAL CORP.
Samsung Electronics Co. Ltd.

HISTORICAL FINANCIALS

Company Type: Public

Income Statement   FYE: December 31

	REVENUE ($ mil.)	NET INCOME ($ mil.)	NET PROFIT MARGIN	EMPLOYEES
12/20	37,325	333	0.9%	0
12/19	32,748	232	0.7%	0
12/18	31,640	291	0.9%	0
12/17	29,935	193	0.6%	0
12/16	23,702	251	1.1%	0
Annual Growth	12.0%	7.3%		

Debt ratio: 0.8%
Return on equity: 8.7%
Cash ($ mil.): 3,171
Current ratio: 1.27
Long-term debt ($ mil.): 405

No. of shares (mil.): —
Dividends
  Yield: —
  Payout: —
Market value ($ mil.): —

Compania de Distribucion Integral Logista Holdings SA

Auditors: Ernst & Young, S.L

LOCATIONS

HQ: Compania de Distribucion Integral Logista
Holdings SA
Calle Trigo 39, Poligono Industrial Polvoranca,
Madrid, Leganes 28914
Phone: (34) 91 481 98 00
Web: www.grupologista.com

HISTORICAL FINANCIALS

Company Type: Public

Income Statement

	REVENUE ($ mil.)	NET INCOME ($ mil.)	NET PROFIT MARGIN	EMPLOYEES
09/21	12,520	201	1.6%	5,851
09/20	12,363	184	1.5%	5,956
09/19	11,070	179	1.6%	5,980
09/18	10,976	181	1.7%	5,803
09/17	11,216	181	1.6%	5,599
Annual Growth	2.8%	2.6%	—	1.1%

FYE: September 30

2021 Year-End Financials

Debt ratio: —
Return on equity: 33.5%
Cash ($ mil.): 198
Current ratio: 0.89
Long-term debt ($ mil.): —

No. of shares (mil.): 131
Dividends
  Yield: —
  Payout: —
Market value ($ mil.): —

Compass Group PLC (United Kingdom)

Look in almost any direction and you'll likely see a foodservice operation run by this company. Compass Group is the world's largest contract foodservices provider with operations in in around 45 countries and manage the business across three geographic regions and five main sectors including its largest market the US. It provides hospitality and foodservice for a variety of businesses and such public-sector clients as cultural institutions hospitals and schools. The company also provides operations in sporting and leisure venues exhibit centers visitor attractions and major events as well as support services to major companies in the oil gas mining and construction industries. Its food-service brands include Chartwells Crothall and Levy Restaurants.

Operations

Compass Group trades under some 15 brands. These include Eurest Restaurant Associates Flik Canteen and Bon Appetit (business and industry); medirest morrison and crothall (healthcare and seniors); Chartwells Flik and Bon Appetit (education); Levy (sports and leisure); and ESS (defense offshore and remote).

Business & Industry accounts for nearly 40% of sales provides nutritious foods while healthcare and seniors generates about nearly 30% of sales provides public and private sectors with quality assurance of food and some support services.

Education (about 20% of sales) provides dining solutions and support in academic fields from kindergarten to college.

Other segment includes Sports & Leisure (about 10% of sales) operates at some sporting and leisure venues exhibition centres visitor attractions and major events. Defense Offshore and Remote (about 10% of sales) provides food and some support services to major companies in the oil gas mining and construction industries.

Geographic Reach

UK-Based Compass Group operates primarily in North America Europe and other regions worldwide. North America is the company's biggest territory accounting for some 65% of sales. Europe (Western Europe Scandinavia and Russia and Turkey) generates 25% of sales. Other countries which stretch from most of South America to Africa South Asia and China brings in the remaining some 10% of sales.

The company also has a very strong presence in Australia and Japan while China and India have strong long-term growth potential being the high growth economies of emerging markets.

Sales and Marketing

Compass Group operates in five sectors: business & industry (more than 35% of sales) healthcare & seniors (roughly 30%) education (more than 15%) sports & leisure (about 10%) and defense offshore & remote (less than 10%).

Compass Group has a roughly 10% share of the global foodservice market.

Financial Performance

Note: Growth rates may differ after conversion to US Dollars.

Compass Group has delivered revenue growth for the past five years but was disrupted by a decrease in 2020. Consequently net income was stable since 2017 but dropped in 2020.

Total revenue declined by nearly 20% to 19.9 billion from the previous year primarily due to the impacts of COVID-19.

Net income fell 88% to 133 million from 1.1 billion in 2019 due to a decrease in revenue.

Compass Group's cash position strengthened in 2020 ending the year 1.1 billion higher at 1.5 billion. It generated 845 million from its operations and 1.3 billion from its financing activities while investing activities used 1.0 billion. The company's primary cash uses in 2020 were acquisitions capital expenditures borrowing repayments and dividend payouts.

Strategy

While the company makes the occasional bolt-on acquisition Compass Group's priority is driving organic revenue growth. The company is intent on expanding its 10% global share of the food services market believing that as economic conditions and regulatory burdens put pressure on organizations' budgets the benefits of food service outsourcing will become more apparent. Compass Group's scale allows the company to operate more efficiently providing a competitive advantage. In the Defence Offshore & Remote market segment the company's approach is to build lasting strategic relationships with large local and international operators.

In response to the pandemic the company is innovating and evolving its operating model. By innovating and adapting its offer and operations to the 'new normal' this will allow the business to reduce costs and increase flexibility so that it can provide clients and consumers an exciting offer that is delivered safely and provides great value. The three main areas of strategic focus are: digital labour and central production units.

Mergers and Acquisitions

In early 2020 Compass acquired Fazer Food Services for an initial consideration of 363 million (?414 million) net of cash acquired. Fazer Food Services is a leading food service business in the Nordic region with operations in Finland Sweden Norway and Denmark across several sectors including Business & Industry Education Healthcare & Seniors and Defence. Fazer Food Services' clear focus on food and culinary innovation will further strengthen Compass Group's existing offer and will enable Compass to create more compelling and innovative solutions for its clients and consumers.

EXECUTIVES

Group Chief Commercial Officer, Shelley Roberts
Group Chief Operating Officer, North America and Director, Gary Green, $1,482,759 total compensation
Managing Director, UK & Ireland, Robin Mills
Chairman, Ian Meakins
Group Chief Financial Officer, Palmer Brown
Group Chief Executive Officer and Director, Dominic Blakemore, $1,367,859 total compensation
Regional Managing Director, Asia Pacific, Mark van Dyck
Regional Managing Director, Latin America, James Meaney
Non-Executive Director, Sundar Raman
Group General Counsel and Company Secretary, Alison Yapp
Group Chief People Officer, Deborah Lee
Auditors: KPMG LLP

LOCATIONS

HQ: Compass Group PLC (United Kingdom)
Compass House, Guildford Street, Chertsey, Surrey
KT16 9BQ
Phone: (44) 1932 573 000
Web: www.compass-group.com

20187 sales

	%
North America	59
Europe	25
Rest of the World	16
Total	**100**

PRODUCTS/OPERATIONS

2018 sales

	%
Business & Industry	39
Healthcare & Seniors	24
Education	18
Sports & Leisure	12
Defence Offshore and Remote	7
Total	**100**

Selected Operating Units

All Leisure (sports and leisure venues)
Bon Appé;tit Management Company (on-site dining services)
Canteen (vending services)
Chartwells (education foodservices)
Crothall (health care facilities management)
ESS (offshore and remote foodservices)

Eurest (corporate foodservice)
FLIK (upscale foodservices)
Levy Restaurants (fine dining sports and leisure events)
Medirest (health care services)
Morrison Management Specialists (health care foodservice)
Restaurant Associates Managed Services (corporate dining and sporting and leisure events)
Scolarest (education foodservices)

COMPETITORS

ALTEN
DAILY MAIL AND GENERAL TRUST P L C
EMPRESARIA GROUP PLC
GOODWIN PLC
HYVE GROUP PLC
MAPFRE SA
NASPERS LTD
R P S GROUP PLC
REXEL
STHREE PLC

HISTORICAL FINANCIALS

Company Type: Public

Income Statement				FYE: September 30
	REVENUE ($ mil.)	NET INCOME ($ mil.)	NET PROFIT MARGIN	EMPLOYEES
09/20	25,580	170	0.7%	548,143
09/19	30,627	1,366	4.5%	596,452
09/18	29,949	1,467	4.9%	595,841
09/17	30,221	1,554	5.1%	588,112
09/16	25,400	1,285	5.1%	527,180
Annual Growth	0.2%	(39.6%)	—	1.0%

2020 Year-End Financials

Debt ratio: 32.9%
Return on equity: 3.2%
Cash ($ mil.): 1,903
Current ratio: 0.94
Long-term debt ($ mil.): 4,712

No. of shares (mil.): 1,785
Dividends
  Yield: 3.1%
  Payout: 312.9%
Market value ($ mil.): 26,942

	STOCK PRICE ($) FY Close	P/E High/Low	PER SHARE ($) Earnings	Dividends	Book Value
09/20	15.09	334 152	0.10	0.47	3.44
09/19	25.75	38 27	0.86	0.46	2.58
09/18	22.62	32 26	0.93	0.42	2.15
09/17	21.62	33 25	0.95	0.45	1.77
09/16	19.41	33 22	0.78	0.41	1.96
Annual Growth	(6.1%)	— —	(39.8%)	3.6%	15.1%

Continental AG (Germany, Fed. Rep.)

Continental AG is the parent company of the Continental Group. The company offers safe efficient intelligent and affordable solutions for vehicles machines traffic and transportation. It is divided into three group sectors: Automotive Technologies Rubber Technologies and Powertrain Technologies. Each sector is comprised of five business areas with a total of 21 business units. Customers outside Germany generate some 80% of company's total revenue. The Continental-Caoutchouc- und Gutta-Percha Compagnie is founded in Hanover in 1871 as a joint stock company. Manufacturing at the main factory in Vahrenwalder Street includes soft rubber products rubberized fabrics and solid tires for carriages and bicycles.

Operations

Continental operates through Automotive Technologies Rubber Technologies and Powertrain Technologies.

Continental's Automotive Technologies sector generates over 40% of the company's total sales. The sector has two business areas: the Autonomous Mobility and Safety area which develops produces and integrates active and passive safety technologies and controls vehicle dynamics; and the Vehicle Networking and Information area which develops and integrates components and end-to-end systems for connected mobility ? architecture hard-ware software and services.

The Rubber Technologies generates more than 40% of the company's consolidated sales and is made of two business areas: Tires (more than 25% of total sales) which stands for innovative top performance in tire technology provides services for dealers and fleet management as well as digital tire monitoring and management systems are further areas of focus and offers premium portfolio in the car truck bus two-wheel and specialty tire segment; and ContiTech business area (some 15% of sales) which focuses on smart and sustainable solutions beyond rubber and develops digital and intelligent solutions in future-oriented sectors.

The Powertrain Technologies generates nearly 20% of the company's total sales. The Powertrain business area brings together the full spectrum of Continental's expertise in drivetrain technology. Its portfolio includes 48-volt electrification solutions electric drives and power electronics for hybrid and battery electric vehicles. Powertrain also develops and produces high-voltage boxes electronic controls sensors actuators turbo-charges.

Geographic ReachWith some 550 locations in about 60 countries Continental does half of its business in Europe (about 20% in Germany) while the other half is divided between North America and Asia. Continental AG is headquartered in Hanover Germany.

Sales and Marketing

With about 70% total revenue automotive manufacturers are Continental's most important customer group. This industry is accordingly important for the growth of the Automotive Technologies and Powertrain Technologies group sectors. In the Tires business area of the Rubber Technologies group sector sales to dealers and end customers represent the largest share of the tire-replacement business. In the ContiTech business area important customers come from both the automotive industry and other key industries such as railway engineering machine and plant construction mining and the replacement business.

Financial Performance

Continental's revenue fell by 15% or ?37.7 billion in 2020 compared to the prior year. All three group sectors posted significantly lower sales due to the COVID-19 pandemic.

The company's net income fell to ?961.9 million in 2020. The primary reasons for this were the weaker operating performance due to COVID-19 and the negative impact of special effects totaling ?1.87 billion which mainly comprised impairment and restructuring in the third and fourth quarters of 2020.

Cash at the end of fiscal 2020 was ?2.9 billion a ?403 million decrease from 2019. Operating activities provided ?2.7 billion in cash and investing activities used ?1.8 billion for capital expenditures. Financing activities used another ?1.1 billion for debt payments.

Strategy

Continental aims to capitalize on the opportunities brought by the transformation in the mobility industry. To do this the company adopted a realigned strategy based on three cornerstones; strengthening operational performance differenti-ating the portfolio and turning change into opportunity.

The company is aligning its cost structure to global market conditions. Measures for this purpose were introduced in September 2019 and part of the company's Transformation 2019-2029 structural program. In addition to this the company continues to improve productivity for example by increasing the level of automation and digitalization in their production environment.

To differentiate the company's product portfolio in a more targeted way the company is focusing on its growth and value areas to establish a strong position in innovative fields featuring highly dynamic growth and to address saturated markets with stable but low growth.

To support the company's third cornerstone turning change into opportunity it has laid a solid foundation for sustainability like practically no other company in the supplier industry at the end of 2020. By 2022 Continental will make its global business with zero-tailpipe-emission vehicles completely carbon-neutral.

HISTORY

A group of financiers and industrialists with interests in the rubber industry founded Continental-Caoutchouc und Gutta-Percha Compagnie in Hanover Germany in 1871. The company's products included solid tires for carriages and bicycles rubberized fabrics and various consumer items.

In 1892 Continental was the first German maker of pneumatic bicycle tires. During this period the budding automobile and motorcycle industries created fresh demand for solid tires. Continental began producing pneumatic tires for automobiles in 1898. By 1904 Continental was first to develop a treaded tire. Between 1905 and 1913 Continental expanded into Australia Denmark Italy Norway Romania Sweden and the UK by forming marketing subsidiaries. However the onset of WWI caused a shift to military production and the overseas sales network dissolved.

Poor overall economic conditions atrophied postwar tire industry growth and by the late 1920s the company merged several German rubber firms to create a much larger and stronger Continental. In 1929 the company changed its name to Continental Gummi-Werke AG.

EXECUTIVES

Chairman, Nikolai Setzer
Chairman of the Supervisory Board, Wolfgang Reitzle
Auditors: KPMG AG

LOCATIONS

HQ: Continental AG (Germany, Fed. Rep.)
  Vahrenwalder Strasse 9, Hanover D-30165
Phone: (49) 511 938 01   **Fax:** (49) 511 938 81 770
Web: www.continental.com/en

2017 Sales

	% of total
Europe	
Germany	20
Europe excluding Germany	29
North America	25
Asia	22
Other cegions	4
Total	**100**

PRODUCTS/OPERATIONS

2017 Sales

	% of total
Automotive Group	
Chassis & safety	22
Interior	21
Powertrain	17
Rubber Group	
Tires (passenger & light truck)	26
ContiTech	14
Total	**100**

Selected Automotive Group Products

Chassis and Safety
  Chassis components
  Electronic brake systems
  Hydraulic brake systems
  Passive safety and ADAS
  Sensors
Interior
  Body and security
  Commercial vehicles and aftermarket
  Connectivity
  Instrumentation and displays
  Interior modules
  Multimedia
Powertrain
  Engine systems
  Fuel supply
  Hybrid electric vehicle
  Sensors and actuators
  Transmissions

Selected Rubber Group Products

ContiTech
  Air spring systems
  Benecke-Kaliko group
  Conveyor belt group
  Elastomer coatings
  Fluid technology
  Power transmission group
  Vibration control
Tires
  Commercial vehicles
  Off-road vehicles
  Passenger and light truck
  Motorcycles
  Bicycles

COMPETITORS

APTIV PLC	HELLA GmbH & Co. KGaA
BARNES GROUP INC.	NHK SPRING CO. LTD.
DENSO CORPORATION	STRATTEC SECURITY
Dongfeng Motor Group	CORPORATION
Company Limited	TENNECO INC.
Dᴜrr AG	TOYODA GOSEI CO. LTD.
Freudenberg & Co. KG	TOYOTA BOSHOKU
GENTHERM INCORPORATED	CORPORATION
GKN LIMITED	ZF Friedrichshafen AG

HISTORICAL FINANCIALS

Company Type: Public

Income Statement — FYE: December 31

	REVENUE ($ mil.)	NET INCOME ($ mil.)	NET PROFIT MARGIN	EMPLOYEES
12/20	46,296	(1,180)	—	236,386
12/19	49,938	(1,375)	—	241,458
12/18	50,851	3,317	6.5%	243,226
12/17	52,756	3,577	6.8%	230,656
12/16	42,815	2,959	6.9%	216,019
Annual Growth	**2.0%**	—	—	**2.3%**

2020 Year-End Financials

Debt ratio: 20.7%
Return on equity: (-6.9%)
Cash ($ mil.): 3,606
Current ratio: 1.16
Long-term debt ($ mil.): 6,313
No. of shares (mil.): 200
Dividends
  Yield: 1.5%
  Payout: —
Market value ($ mil.): 2,992

	STOCK PRICE ($) FY Close	P/E High/Low		PER SHARE ($) Earnings	Dividends	Book Value
12/20	14.96	—	—	(5.90)	0.24	75.25
12/19	12.83	—	—	(6.88)	0.37	86.42
12/18	13.78	4	1	16.59	0.39	102.21
12/17	53.88	4	3	17.89	0.37	94.87
12/16	38.50	3	2	14.79	0.29	75.34
Annual Growth	**(21.0%)**	—	—	—	**(4.7%)**	**(0.0%)**

Corporacion Nacional del Cobre de Chile

Codelco is a different kind of high-energy copper top. State-owned Corporaciᴏn Nacional del Cobre de Chile (Codelco) is one of the world's top producers of copper its reserves represents around 5% of global copper reserves. Its core business is exploring developing and exploiting mineral resources processing them to produce refined copper and by-products and then marketing them to customers around the world. The company operates through seven mining divisions: Chuquicamata Ministro Hales Radomiro Tomic Gabriela Mistral Salvador Andina El Teniente as well as the Ventanas Smelter and Refinery. It produces and markets refined products such as copper cathodes with 99.9% purity which are obtained in its electrorefining and electrowinning processes unrefined products including copper concentrates roasted copper concentrates anodes and blister (metallic material with a purity of around 99.5% which is used as raw material for the production of copper cathodes) and by-products which includes molybdenum its main by-product a key input in the manufacture of special steels; sulfuric acid which has the property of dissolving various types of metals and substances; gold silver and rhenium.

EXECUTIVES

Chairman of the Board, Juan Feliu
Director, Paul Shiodtz Obilinovich
Director, Juan Enrique Morales Jaramillo
Vice President - Smelters and Refineries, Jose Sanhueza Reyes
Vice President - Projects, Gerhard von Borries Harms
Chief Executive Officer, Executive Director, Octavio Araneda Oses
Director, Isidoro Palma Penco
Director, Blas Tomic Errazuriz
Director, Ghassan Dayoub Pseli
Auditors: Deloitte Auditores y Consultores Limitada

LOCATIONS

HQ: Corporacion Nacional del Cobre de Chile Calle Huerfanos 1270, Casilla 150-D, Santiago
Phone: (56) 2 690 3000   **Fax:** (56) 2 690 3288
Web: www.codelco.com

PRODUCTS/OPERATIONS

2015 Sales

	% of total
El Teniente	21
Chuquicamata	18
R. Tomic	14
M. Hales	14
Andina	9
G. Mistral	6
Ventanas	5
Salvador	4
Other	9
Total	**100**

2015 Sales

	% of total
Asia	
China	25
Other	18
America	16
Europe	12
Other	29
Total	**100**

COMPETITORS

ASARCO LLC	Mountain Boy Minerals
First Quantum Minerals	Ltd
Ltd	Nexa Resources
Inmet Mining	THOMPSON CREEK
METALS	
Corporation	COMPANY USA
Lundin Mining	Vale S/A
Corporation	
MONTERRICO METALS	
LIMITED	

HISTORICAL FINANCIALS

Company Type: Public

Income Statement — FYE: December 31

	REVENUE ($ mil.)	NET INCOME ($ mil.)	NET PROFIT MARGIN	EMPLOYEES
12/20	14,173	242	1.7%	15,267
12/19	12,524	6	0.1%	16,726
12/18	14,308	155	1.1%	18,036
12/17	14,641	569	3.9%	18,562
12/16	11,536	(275)	—	18,605
Annual Growth	**5.3%**	—	—	**(4.8%)**

2020 Year-End Financials

Debt ratio: 43.2%
Return on equity: 2.2%
Cash ($ mil.): 2,107
Current ratio: 2.26
Long-term debt ($ mil.): 17,735
No. of shares (mil.): —
Dividends
  Yield: —
  Payout: —
Market value ($ mil.): —

COSCO Shipping Holdings Co Ltd

Auditors: Ruihua Certified Public Accountants, LLP

LOCATIONS

HQ: COSCO Shipping Holdings Co Ltd
  2nd Floor, 12 Yuanhang Business Centre, Central Boulevard and East Seven Road Junction, Tianjin Port Free Trade Zone, Tianjin 300461
Phone: (86) 22 66270898   **Fax:** (86) 22 66270899
Web: www.chinacosco.com

HISTORICAL FINANCIALS
Company Type: Public

Income Statement
FYE: December 31

	REVENUE ($ mil.)	NET INCOME ($ mil.)	NET PROFIT MARGIN	EMPLOYEES
12/20	26,185	1,517	5.8%	0
12/19	21,709	972	4.5%	0
12/18	17,566	178	1.0%	0
12/17	13,901	409	2.9%	0
12/16	10,247	(1,426)	—	0
Annual Growth	26.4%	—	—	—

2020 Year-End Financials

Debt ratio: 5.0%
Return on equity: 24.9%
Cash ($ mil.): 8,080
Current ratio: 0.97
Long-term debt ($ mil.): 9,708

No. of shares (mil.): —
Dividends
  Yield: —
  Payout: —
Market value ($ mil.): —

Cosmo Energy Holdings Co Ltd

Auditors: KPMG AZSA LLC

LOCATIONS

HQ: Cosmo Energy Holdings Co Ltd
1-1-1 Shibaura, Minato-ku, Tokyo 105-8302
Phone: (81) 3 3798 3128
Web: ceh.cosmo-oil.co.jp

HISTORICAL FINANCIALS
Company Type: Public

Income Statement
FYE: March 31

	REVENUE ($ mil.)	NET INCOME ($ mil.)	NET PROFIT MARGIN	EMPLOYEES
03/21	20,169	775	3.8%	10,390
03/20	25,223	(259)	—	10,155
03/19	25,015	479	1.9%	9,700
03/18	23,761	685	2.9%	9,842
03/17	20,502	476	2.3%	9,880
Annual Growth	(0.4%)	13.0%	—	1.3%

2021 Year-End Financials

Debt ratio: 0.3%
Return on equity: 30.4%
Cash ($ mil.): 478
Current ratio: 0.81
Long-term debt ($ mil.): 3,420

No. of shares (mil.): 84
Dividends
  Yield: —
  Payout: 9.2%
Market value ($ mil.): —

Country Garden Holdings Co Ltd

Country Garden builds residential properties in China. The group primarily develops large-scale apartment communities and townhouses in China's suburbs. Its more than 170 projects boast an aggregate completed gross floor area (GFA) of 45.7 million square meters. Country Garden manages 20 completed properties and has 45 more under construction totaling 48000 units. The company also owns nine hotels with more under construction. It was founded in 1997 in Guangdong Province by Chairman and CEO Yang Guoqiang (also known as Yeung Kwok Keung). His daughter Yang Huiyan a director with the firm owns 59% of Country Garden and is China's richest woman. Country Garden listed on the Hong Kong Stock Exchange in 2007.
Auditors: PricewaterhouseCoopers

LOCATIONS

HQ: Country Garden Holdings Co Ltd
Suite 1702, 17/F., Dina House, Ruttonjee Centre, 11 Duddell Street, Central,
Phone:
Web: www.countrygarden.com.cn

PRODUCTS/OPERATIONS

2016 Sales

	% of total
Property development	97
Construction fitting & decoration	1
Property management	1
Hotel operation	1
Total	**100**

2016 Sales

	% of total
Guangdong	29
Jiangsu	17
Anhui	7
Zhejiang	5
Hubei	4
Hebei	4
Hunan	4
Fujian	3
Henan	3
Others	24
Total	**100**

Selected Projects

Country Garden - Galaxy Palace
Country Garden - Grand Garden
Country Garden - Springs City
Country Garden - Ten Miles Coast
Country Garden City Garden
Country Garden Grand Lake
Country Garden Phoenix City
Dalang Country Garden
Heshan Country Garden
Holiday Island
Malaysia Project
Tianjin Country Garden

COMPETITORS

ACANTHE DEVELOPPEMENT
AGILE GROUP HOLDINGS LIMITED
CHINESE ESTATES HOLDINGS LIMITED
HYSAN DEVELOPMENT COMPANY LIMITED
ICADE
K. WAH INTERNATIONAL HOLDINGS LIMITED
SRE GROUP LIMITED
THE HOWARD HUGHES CORPORATION
TIAN AN CHINA INVESTMENTS COMPANY LIMITED
TOMSON GROUP LIMITED

HISTORICAL FINANCIALS
Company Type: Public

Income Statement
FYE: December 31

	REVENUE ($ mil.)	NET INCOME ($ mil.)	NET PROFIT MARGIN	EMPLOYEES
12/20	70,770	5,354	7.6%	93,899
12/19	69,832	5,683	8.1%	101,784
12/18	55,112	5,032	9.1%	131,387
12/17	34,867	4,005	11.5%	124,837
12/16	22,045	1,658	7.5%	94,450
Annual Growth	33.9%	34.0%	—	(0.1%)

2020 Year-End Financials

Debt ratio: 2.4%
Return on equity: 21.3%
Cash ($ mil.): 25,557
Current ratio: 1.17
Long-term debt ($ mil.): 35,204

No. of shares (mil.): —
Dividends
  Yield: 5.7%
  Payout: 826.2%
Market value ($ mil.): —

	STOCK PRICE ($) FY Close	P/E High/Low		PER SHARE ($) Earnings	Dividends	Book Value
12/20	32.15	23	19	0.24	0.08	1.23
12/19	35.80	22	16	0.26	1.82	1.01
12/18	30.49	33	16	0.23	0.07	0.81
12/17	48.68	40	22	0.19	0.86	0.68
12/16	13.92	27	17	0.08	0.42	0.47
Annual Growth	23.3%	—	—	33.7%	(34.3%)	27.4%

Covestro AG

Auditors: KPMG AG

LOCATIONS

HQ: Covestro AG
Building K12, Kaiser-Wilhelm-Allee 60, Leverkusen D-51373
Phone: (49) 214 6009 2000   **Fax:** (49) 214 6009 3000
Web: www.covestro.com

HISTORICAL FINANCIALS
Company Type: Public

Income Statement
FYE: December 31

	REVENUE ($ mil.)	NET INCOME ($ mil.)	NET PROFIT MARGIN	EMPLOYEES
12/20	13,139	563	4.3%	16,501
12/19	13,935	619	4.4%	17,201
12/18	16,738	2,087	12.5%	16,770
12/17	16,947	2,408	14.2%	16,176
12/16	12,569	839	6.7%	15,579
Annual Growth	1.1%	(9.5%)	—	1.4%

2020 Year-End Financials

Debt ratio: 21.0%
Return on equity: 8.4%
Cash ($ mil.): 1,723
Current ratio: 2.62
Long-term debt ($ mil.): 2,720

No. of shares (mil.): 193
Dividends
  Yield: 1.6%
  Payout: 17.0%
Market value ($ mil.): 5,920

	STOCK PRICE ($) FY Close	P/E High/Low		PER SHARE ($) Earnings	Dividends	Book Value
12/20	30.65	13	6	3.04	0.50	35.63
12/19	22.77	10	7	3.39	0.98	31.97
12/18	25.00	6	3	10.83	0.98	33.48
12/17	51.90	5	4	11.90	0.58	31.84
12/16	34.70	9	8	4.15	1.43	21.84
Annual Growth	(3.1%)	—	—	(7.5%)	(23.1%)	13.0%

CrediCorp Ltd.

Auditors: Gaveglio, Aparicio y Asociados S.C.R.L

LOCATIONS

HQ: CrediCorp Ltd.
Calle Centenario 156, La Molina, Lima 12
Phone: (51) 1 313 2014   **Fax:** (51) 1 313 2121
Web: www.credicorpnet.com

HISTORICAL FINANCIALS
Company Type: Public

Income Statement				FYE: December 31
	ASSETS ($ mil.)	NET INCOME ($ mil.)	INCOME AS % OF ASSETS	EMPLOYEES
12/20	65,582	95	0.1%	36,806
12/19	56,649	1,286	2.3%	35,828
12/18	52,450	1,178	2.2%	34,024
12/17	52,606	1,262	2.4%	33,636
12/16	46,578	1,046	2.2%	33,282
Annual Growth	8.9%	(45.0%)	—	2.5%

2020 Year-End Financials

Return on assets: 0.1%
Return on equity: 1.3%
Long-term debt ($ mil.): —
No. of shares (mil.): 79
Sales ($ mil): 5,077

Dividends
Yield: 6.8%
Payout: 929.0%
Market value ($ mil.): —

Credit Agricole SA

Auditors: ERNST & YOUNG et Autres

LOCATIONS

HQ: Credit Agricole SA
12 place des Etat-Unis, Montrouge, Cedex 92127
Phone: (33) 1 43 23 52 02
Web: www.credit-agricole.com

HISTORICAL FINANCIALS
Company Type: Public

Income Statement				FYE: December 31
	ASSETS ($ mil.)	NET INCOME ($ mil.)	INCOME AS % OF ASSETS	EMPLOYEES
12/20	2,721,530	5,754	0.2%	142,159
12/19	1,984,649	5,438	0.3%	75,423
12/18	1,860,248	5,038	0.3%	73,346
12/17	1,858,408	4,374	0.2%	73,707
12/16	1,609,410	3,737	0.2%	137,871
Annual Growth	14.0%	11.4%	—	0.8%

2020 Year-End Financials

Return on assets: 0.2%
Return on equity: 5.1%
Long-term debt ($ mil.): —
No. of shares (mil.): —
Sales ($ mil): 105,647

Dividends
Yield: 0.1%
Payout: —
Market value ($ mil.): —

	STOCK PRICE ($)	P/E		PER SHARE ($)		
	FY Close	High/Low		Earnings	Dividends	Book Value
12/20	6.24	—	—	(0.00)	0.98	50.31
12/19	7.23	5	3	1.66	0.39	24.49
12/18	5.33	6	4	1.59	0.37	23.53
12/17	8.22	8	6	1.35	0.36	24.47
12/16	6.14	6	3	1.18	0.32	21.64
Annual Growth	0.4%	—	—	—	32.4%	23.5%

Credit Suisse Group AG

Credit Suisse is one of Switzerland's top financial services firms. The group provides investment management and advice private banking and asset management services to clients worldwide. Its investment banking offerings include debt and equity underwriting of public securities offerings and private placements. The group also provides wealth management services and asset management services to individual institutional and government clients. With around 110 retail branches in Switzerland it operates in about 50 countries.

Operations

Credit Suisse operates three divisions with a regional focus: Swiss Universal Bank International Wealth Management and Asia Pacific. These regional businesses are supported by the Investment Bank division.

The Investment Bank division delivers client-centric sales and trading products services and solutions across all asset classes and regions as well as advisory underwriting and financing services. The company's range of products and services includes global securities sales trading and execution prime brokerage capital raising and comprehensive corporate advisory services. Investment bank division accounts for 40% of revenue.

Swiss Universal Bank offers financial advice and solutions to private corporate and institutional clients primarily in Switzerland. The Private Clients business serves high- and ultra-high-net-worth individuals (UHNWIs). Corporate & Institutional Clients serves large businesses SMEs institutional clients external asset managers and financial institutions. It generates more than 25% of sales.

Through its Private Banking business the International Wealth Management segment offers comprehensive advisory services and tailored investment and financing solutions to rich people in Europe the Middle East Africa and Latin America. It serves pension funds governments foundations and endowments corporations and individuals. It generates around 20% of total sales.

In the Asia Pacific division delivers an integrated wealth management financing underwriting and advisory offering to its target ultra-high-net-worth entrepreneur and corporate clients. The company provide a comprehensive suite of wealth management products and services to its clients in Asia Pacific and provide a broad range of advisory services related to debt and equity underwriting of public offerings and private placements as well as mergers and acquisitions (M&A). The segment accounts for around 10% of revenue.

Geographic Reach

Zurich Switzerland-based Credit Suisse has operations in about 50 countries. It generates around 30% of sales from the Americas while approximately 30% comes from Switzerland itself. The Asia/Pacific region and EMEA accounts for 20% of sales each.

Sales and Marketing

Credit Suisse serves global corporates SMEs rich people governments institutions institutional investors such as pensions and hedge funds and private individuals.

Financial Performance

Compared to 2019 net revenues of CHF 22.4 billion were stable primarily reflecting higher net revenues in the Investment Bank offset by lower net revenues in International Wealth Management. The increase in net revenues in the Investment Bank was driven by broad-based growth across all businesses. The decrease in net revenues in International Wealth Management was primarily driven by the impairment loss from York reflected in other revenues lower transaction-based and performance-based revenue and lower net interest income.

Net income for fiscal 2020 decreased by 22% to CHF2.7 billion compared with CHF3.4 billion in the prior year.

Cash held by the company at the end of fiscal 2020 increased to CHF139.1 billion. Cash used for operations was CHF6.5 billion while investing and financing activities provided CHF16.7 billion and CHF29.7 billion respectively.

Strategy

Credit Suisse's strategy has driven its operational success as the company has transformed Credit Suisse since 2015. During its restructuring phase between 2015 and 2018 the company lowered its break-even point through a significant reduction in its cost base successfully de-risked its investment banking activities and strengthened its capital base. Since then Credit Suisse has implemented a series of structural refinements intended to improve effectiveness drive efficiencies and capture future growth opportunities.

Credit Suisse is now focused on the growth phase of its strategic journey proactively investing to capture growth opportunities across all its businesses and its ambition to be a leader in sustainability.

Mergers and Acquisitions

Company Background

The bank has been plagued by litigation charges in recent years. In 2012 Credit Suisse handed over information to the US government as part of an investigation into hidden Swiss bank accounts that are used by wealthy Americans to evade taxes. Credit Suisse was among other Swiss banks that were being investigated. Swiss privacy laws have typically protected wealthy individuals who funnel money through offshore accounts.

HISTORY

In 1856 shortly after the creation of the Swiss federation Alfred Escher opened Credit Suisse (CS) in Zurich. Primarily a venture capital firm CS helped fund Swiss railroads and other industries. It later opened offices in Italy and helped establish the Swiss Bank Corporation.

CS shifted its focus to commercial banking in 1867 and sold most of its stock holdings. By 1871 it was Switzerland's largest bank buoyed by the nation's swift industrialization. In 1895 CS helped create the predecessor of Swiss utility Electrowatt. Foreign activity grew in the 1920s. A run on banks in the Depression forced CS to sell assets at a loss and dip into reserves of unreported retained profits.

Trade declined in WWII but neutrality left Switzerland's institutions intact and made it a major banking center partly due to CS's role as a conduit for the Nazis' plundered gold. Foreign exchange and gold trading became important activities for CS after WWII. Mortgage and consumer credit acquisitions fueled domestic growth in the 1970s.

In 1978 the bank took a stake in US investment bank First Boston and with it formed London-based Credit Suisse-First Boston (CSFB). CS created 44%-owned holding company Credit Suisse First Boston to own First Boston CSFB and Tokyo-based CS First Boston Pacific.

The stock market crash of 1987 led a damaged First Boston to merge with CSFB the next year. In 1990 CS (renamed CS Holding) injected $300 million into CSFB and shifted $470 million in bad loans from its books becoming the first foreign owner of a major Wall Street investment bank.

In the early 1990s CS Holding strengthened its insurance business with a Winterthur Insurance alliance. In 1993 and 1994 acquisitions helped it gain share in its overbanked home market.

In 1996 CS Holding reorganized as Credit Suisse Group and grew internationally including further merging the daredevil US investment banking operations into Credit Suisse's more staid and relationship-oriented corporate banking. It bought Winterthur (Switzerland's #2 insurer) in 1997 as well as Barclays' European investment banking business.

Credit Suisse and other Swiss banks came under fire in 1996 for refusing to relinquish assets from Jewish bank accounts from the Holocaust era and for gold trading with the Nazi regime. In 1997 the banks agreed to establish a humanitarian fund for Holocaust victims. A stream of lawsuits by American heirs and boycott threats from US states and cities led in 1998 to a tentative $1.25 billion settlement (unpopular in Switzerland) with Credit Suisse on the hook for about a third of that.

CS in 1998 expanded its investment banking by buying Brazil's Banco de Investimentos Garantia; it also moved to expand US money management operations by allying with New York-based Warburg Pincus Asset Management. By 1999 that joint venture — which was to give the investment firm access to CS's mutual fund distribution channels in Europe and Asia — had morphed into CS's $650 million purchase of Warburg Pincus Asset Management.

Japan revoked the license of the company's financial products unit for obstructing an investigation (the harshest penalty ever given to a foreign firm at the time); it also accused the company of helping 60 others hide losses and cover up evidence.

In 2000 the company started a mortgage and home-buying Web site and decided to allow searches of Holocaust-era accounts. The next year as a part of its European expansion Credit Suisse acquired Spanish broker and asset manager General de Valores y Cambios.

Under former chairman and CEO Lukas M hlemann the company expanded Credit Suisse First Boston when it bought US investment firm Donaldson Lufkin & Jenrette in 2000 and renamed it Credit Suisse First Boston (USA).

The collapse of Credit Suisse's share price along with what proved to be an over-ambitious acquisition strategy brought about the downfall of M hlemann who was pressured out by shareholders in 2002.

In 2005 Credit Suisse merged with its Credit Suisse First Boston subsidiary creating a global Credit Suisse brand and in 2006 reorganized into three distinct operating segments — investment banking private banking and asset management along with insurance.

Credit Suisse sold insurance subsidiary Winterthur to AXA in 2006 for nearly $10 billion. A Winterthur sale had been on Credit Suisse's agenda for a while as a plan to divest noncore operations. Also that year Credit Suisse and General Electric jointly acquired a 50% stake in London City Airport which serves about 2 million travelers a year. The following year as a cost-saving measure Credit Suisse combined four private banks and one securities dealer into Clariden Leu.

The company named Brady Dougan CEO in 2007. Dugan was the first non-German speaker to hold the position.

Globally the investment banking industry was hit hard by the US subprime mortgage crisis and Credit Suisse was no exception. The company reported a net loss of ?5.4 billion in 2008 the worst in its history. Credit Suisse turned down a bailout offer from the Swiss government in 2008 but it did receive a capital injection of CHF10 billion ($8.7 billion) from private investors. However the capital infusion couldn't prevent losses as global credit markets froze and consumer and shareholder confidence fell.

The company cut more than 5000 jobs or some 11% of its workforce mostly from its investment banking unit. It also reviewed its results for 2007 and among its findings discovered rogue traders in its ranks la the beleaguered Soci t G n rale. Credit Suisse reduced its results accordingly.

In 2008 it bought an 80% stake in US firm Asset Management Finance Corporation a division of National Bank of Canada. Also in 2008 it expanded its Middle East franchise when it bought majority ownership in joint venture Saudi Swiss Securities which it renamed Credit Suisse Saudi Arabia. It has added Shariah-compliant banking for Islamic clients and has expanded in other markets including Brazil Kazakhstan and Turkey.

The following year Credit Suisse sold certain fund management assets and businesses to Aberdeen Asset Management in exchange for about 25% of Aberdeen's shares.

Auditors: KPMG AG

LOCATIONS

HQ: Credit Suisse Group AG
Paradeplatz 8, Zurich 8001
Phone: (41) 44 333 1111 **Fax:** (41) 44 333 1790
Web: www.credit-suisse.com

2018 sales

	% total
Switzerland	36
Americas	42
Asia Pacific	14
EMEA	8
Total	**100**

PRODUCTS/OPERATIONS

2018 sales

	% of total
Commissions & fees	57
Net interest income	33
Trading revenues	3
Other	7
Total	**100**

2018 sales

	% of total
Swiss Universal Bank	26
International Wealth Management	25
Global Markets	23
Asia Pacific	16
Investment Banking & Capital Markets	10
Strategic Resolution Unit	-
Corporate Center	-
Total	**100**

COMPETITORS

AMUNDI	Royal Bank of Canada
Baloise Holding AG	SEI INVESTMENTS
DEUTSCHE BANK AG	COMPANY
EATON VANCE CORP.	UBS AG
ING Groep N.V.	WISDOMTREE
INVESTMENTS	INC.
Julius B r Gruppe AG	
NOMURA HOLDINGS INC.	

HISTORICAL FINANCIALS

Company Type: Public

Income Statement

FYE: December 31

	ASSETS ($ mil.)	NET INCOME ($ mil.)	INCOME AS % OF ASSETS	EMPLOYEES
12/20	914,941	3,030	0.3%	48,770
12/19	814,416	3,536	0.4%	47,860
12/18	781,647	2,057	0.3%	45,680
12/17	815,899	(1,007)	—	46,840
12/16	805,441	(2,662)	—	47,170
Annual Growth	**3.2%**	**—**		**0.8%**

2020 Year-End Financials

Return on assets: 0.3%	Dividends
Return on equity: 6.1%	Yield: 1.7%
Long-term debt ($ mil.): —	Payout: 24.7%
No. of shares (mil.): —	Market value ($ mil.): —
Sales ($ mil): 25,420	

	STOCK PRICE ($) FY Close	P/E High/Low		Earnings	PER SHARE ($) Dividends	Book Value
12/20	12.80	14	7	1.20	0.30	20.14
12/19	13.45	11	8	1.37	0.26	18.53
12/18	10.86	24	13	0.78	0.74	17.51
12/17	17.85	—	—	(0.42)	1.21	16.84
12/16	14.31	—	—	(1.30)	0.69	19.69
Annual Growth	**(2.7%)**			**—**	**(18.9%)**	**0.6%**

Credito Emiliano Spa Credem Reggio Emilia

Being in the middle isn't always such a bad thing. Just ask Credito Emiliano one of Italy's leading midsized bank holding companies. Through its 20 financial subsidiaries and affiliates Credito Emiliano (also known as Credem) offers a host of retail commercial and institutional banking services through some 590 branches across Italy. In addition to its lending and deposit products the financial group offers life and liability insurance pensions asset management leasing and various corporate financial services. Credem Holding owned by the Maramotti family (known in fashion circles for its design house Max Mara) controls the company.

EXECUTIVES

Non-Executive Director, Giorgio Ferrari, $311,226 total compensation
Executive Vice Chairman of the Board, Enrico Corradi, $67,542 total compensation
General Manager, Nazzareno Gregori
Non-Executive Director, Giovanni Viani, $49,001 total compensation
Joint General Manager, Angelo Campani
Non-Executive Chairman of the Board, Lucio Zanon di Valgiurata, $58,272 total compensation
Executive Vice Chairman of the Board, Luigi Maramotti, $59,596 total compensation
Auditors: Ernst & Young S.p.A.

LOCATIONS

HQ: Credito Emiliano Spa Credem Reggio Emilia
Via Emilia San Pietro 4, Reggio Emilia 42100
Phone: (39) 522 5821 **Fax:** (39) 522 433969
Web: www.credem.it

2008 Sales

Italy	% of total
North-central	63
Southern & islands	35
Other countries	2
Total	**100**

PRODUCTS/OPERATIONS

2008 Sales

	% of total
Retail banking	59
Corporate loans	16
Investment banking	-
Wealth management	5
Other	20
Total	**100**

COMPETITORS

BPCE
KEYCORP
THE NATIONAL BANK OF INDIANAPOLIS
 CORPORATION

HISTORICAL FINANCIALS

Company Type: Public

Income Statement				FYE: December 31
	ASSETS ($ mil.)	NET INCOME ($ mil.)	INCOME AS % OF ASSETS	EMPLOYEES
12/19	53,477	226	0.4%	6,201
12/18	49,435	213	0.4%	6,195
12/17	49,849	223	0.4%	6,140
12/16	41,780	139	0.3%	6,068
12/15	40,796	180	0.4%	5,516
Annual Growth	7.0%	5.7%	—	3.0%

2019 Year-End Financials

Return on assets: 0.4%	Dividends
Return on equity: 3.0%	Yield: —
Long-term debt ($ mil.): —	Payout: —
No. of shares (mil.): 330	Market value ($ mil.): —
Sales ($ mil): 2,038	

CRH Plc

Through subsidiaries (including Oldcastle in North America) the Ireland-based international company makes and distributes cement concrete aggregate glass and asphalt for commercial residential and infrastructure projects across the globe. CRH has over 3100 operating locations and a presence in around 30 countries CRH has become the top supplier of building materials in North America and the largest heavyside materials business in Europe. It operates as Tarmac in the UK. The largest Irish company CRH was formed in 1970 and has grown quickly in recent years thanks to a relentless acquisition program.

Operations

CRH operates in three operating segments: Americas materials (around 40% of revenue) Europe materials (about 35%) and Building products (25%).

Americas Materials Division is a vertical integrated supplier of building materials used widely in construction projects throughout North America. Typically these materials are resource-backed in mineral deposits found within their extensive network of quarry locations where they are processed for supply as aggregates asphalt cement and ready-mixed concrete.

Europe Materials Division manufactures and supplies a broad range of materials for use in construction projects including aggregates cement lime asphalt ready-mixed concrete and cement products. With an extensive in the strong and stable markets of Western Europe a strong footprint in growing Eastern European markets and an attractive position in Asia the Division is geographically balanced and has broad exposure to residential non-residential and infrastructure sectors.

Building products is a new division established by CRH in 2019 as part of their strategy to create a more simplified and focused business which is better positioned to exploit opportunities presented by economic development changing demographics sustainability and other evolving trends in construction markets globally. The Division brings together related products businesses in Europe North America and Asia Pacific across four strategic product groups for growth: Architectural Products Building Envelope Infrastructure Products and Construction Accessories.

Geographic Reach

Ireland-based CRH operates in more than 30 countries on four continents. CRH operates from around 1475 locations in the Americas (around 45 US states six Canadian provinces and Southeast Brazil) and over 1150 across Europe.

Sales and Marketing

CRH markets its products to infrastructure residential and non-residential demand for repair maintenance and new build construction projects.

Financial Performance

Note: Growth rates may differ after conversion to US dollars.

CRH's revenue has seen growth in past years but declined in the most recent fiscal year. Net income has fluctuated over the last five years.

In 2020 revenue from continuing and discontinued operations fell by 2% to ?27.6 billion primarily driven by decline in the company's Americas Materials and Europe Materials division.

Net income fell by about 30% to ?1.1 billion compared to ?1.6 billion from the previous year.

At the end of the fiscal year 2020 the company's cash held increased by 83% to ?7.7 billion from ?4.2 billion from the prior year. Cash from operations provided ?3.9 billion cash from investing activities used ?1.1 billion and cash provided for financing activities were ?287 million.

Strategy

CRH's strategy is to grow and improve its business in a sustainable and responsible way through a relentless focus on performance improvement focused growth and value creation for the benefit of all its stakeholders. The company's strategy is underpinned by four strategic objectives including Continuous Improvement; Focused Growth; Benefits of Scale and Integrations; and Developing Leaders.

Through a range of commercial excellence initiatives its Europe Materials Division delivered $42 million of benefits in 2020 through the use of new digital tools assessment processes training and planning-related initiatives aimed at improving commercial performance.

In 2020 CRH brought its Construction Accessories businesses together globally under one new brand 'Leviat' to allow them to benefit from the synergies that come from being part of an integrated global construction accessories company including collaboration on sales marketing and product development.

Company Background

The Group resulted from the merger in 1970 of two leading Irish public companies Cement Limited (established in 1936) and Roadstone Limited (incorporated in 1949). Cement Limited manufactured and supplied cement while Roadstone Limited was primarily involved in the manufacture and supply of aggregates readymixed concrete mortar coated macadam asphalt and contract surfacing to the Irish construction industry.

EXECUTIVES

Non-Executive Director, Badar Khan
Chief Executive, Executive Director, Albert
 Manifold, $1,673,787 total compensation
Group General Counsel, Isabel Foley
Group Finance Director, Jim Mintern
President, Europe Materials, Onne Van der Weijde
**President, Global Strategy & Business
 Development,** David Dillon
Group Executive, Strategic Operations, Randy
 Lake
Senior Non-Executive Independent Director,
 Gillian Platt, $94,570 total compensation
Chairman, Richard Boucher, $94,570 total
 compensation
Non-Executive Independent Director, Mary
 Rhinehart, $94,570 total compensation
Non-Executive Independent Director, Siobhan
 Talbot, $94,570 total compensation
Non-Executive Independent Director, Johan
 Karlstrom, $94,570 total compensation
Non-Executive Independent Director, Shaun Kelly,
 $94,570 total compensation
Non-Executive Independent Director, Richard
 Fearon, $7,975 total compensation
Non-Executive Independent Director, Lamar
 Mckay, $7,975 total compensation
Chief Innovation & Sustainability Officer, Juan
 Pablo San Agustin
President, Building Products, Nathan Creech
Non-Executive Director, Caroline Dowling
Chief Human Resource Officer, Gina Jardine
President, Americas Materials, Dan Stover
Auditors: Deloitte Ireland LLP

LOCATIONS

HQ: CRH Plc
 Stonemason's Way, Rathfarnham, Dublin D16 KH51
Phone: (353) 1 404 1000   **Fax:** (353) 1 404 1007
Web: www.crh.com

2018 sales

	%
United States	45
Rest of Europe	25
UK	12
Benelux	9
Ireland	2
Rest of the World	7
Total	**100**

2018 Sales

	% of total
Europe	
Heavyside	28
Distribution	14
Lightside	6
Americas	
Materials	33
Distribution	9
Asia	2
Total	**100**

PRODUCTS/OPERATIONS

2018 sales

	%
Cement lime and cement products	12
Aggregates asphalt and readymixed products	27
Construction contract activities	21
Construction accessories	2
Perimeter protection shutters & awnings and network access products	2
Architectural and precast products	17
Architectural glass and glazing systems and wholesale hardware distribution	6
General Builders Merchants DIY and Sanitary Heating & Plumbing	14
Total	**100**

Selected Activities and Products

Materials
  Aggregates
  Agricultural and chemical lime
  Asphalt
  Cement
  Concrete products
  Ready-mixed concrete
Products
  Architectural concrete
  Building products
  Building envelope products
  Construction accessories
  Clay facing bricks pavers and blocks
  Structural concrete
Distribution
  Builders merchants
  DIY stores

COMPETITORS

ARKEMA	HALMA PUBLIC LIMITED
ASTEC INDUSTRIES INC.	COMPANY
Evonik Industries AG	Holcim AG
FLETCHER BUILDING	MARUBENI CORPORATION
LIMITED	SEVERFIELD PLC
GENUIT GROUP PLC	SIGMAROC PLC
GIBRALTAR INDUSTRIES	THE ALUMASC GROUP PLC
INC.	TYMAN PLC
GOODWIN PLC	

HISTORICAL FINANCIALS

Company Type: Public

Income Statement   FYE: December 31

	REVENUE ($ mil.)	NET INCOME ($ mil.)	NET PROFIT MARGIN	EMPLOYEES
12/20	27,587	1,122	4.1%	77,099
12/19	28,213	2,165	7.7%	86,951
12/18	30,679	2,882	9.4%	89,831
12/17	30,232	2,271	7.5%	89,213
12/16	28,618	1,312	4.6%	86,778
Annual Growth	(0.9%)	(3.8%)	—	(2.9%)

2020 Year-End Financials

Debt ratio: 27.1%	No. of shares (mil.): 795
Return on equity: 6.1%	Dividends
Cash ($ mil.): 7,721	Yield: 2.1%
Current ratio: 2.01	Payout: 64.0%
Long-term debt ($ mil.): 10,958	Market value ($ mil.): 33,857

	STOCK PRICE ($) FY Close	P/E High/Low	PER SHARE ($) Earnings	Dividends	Book Value
12/20	42.58	30 13	1.42	0.91	24.72
12/19	40.33	17 11	2.68	0.80	23.79
12/18	26.35	12 8	3.45	0.81	22.51
12/17	36.09	18 15	2.70	0.80	20.72
12/16	34.38	23 15	1.57	0.68	17.61
Annual Growth	5.5%	— —	(2.6%)	7.6%	8.8%

CRRC Corp Ltd

Auditors: Deloitte Touche Tohmatsu Certified
  Public Accountants LLP

LOCATIONS

HQ: CRRC Corp Ltd
  No. 16 Central West Fourth Ring Road, Haidian
  District, Beijing 100036
Phone: (86) 10 5186 2188   **Fax:** (86) 10 6398 4785
Web: www.crrcgc.cc

HISTORICAL FINANCIALS

Company Type: Public

Income Statement   FYE: December 31

	REVENUE ($ mil.)	NET INCOME ($ mil.)	NET PROFIT MARGIN	EMPLOYEES
12/20	34,808	1,732	5.0%	0
12/19	32,912	1,695	5.2%	0
12/18	31,851	1,643	5.2%	0
12/17	32,426	1,659	5.1%	0
Annual Growth	2.4%	1.4%	—	—

2020 Year-End Financials

Debt ratio: 1.0%	No. of shares (mil.): —
Return on equity: 8.1%	Dividends
Cash ($ mil.): 5,120	Yield: —
Current ratio: 1.26	Payout: —
Long-term debt ($ mil.): 1,024	Market value ($ mil.): —

	STOCK PRICE ($) FY Close	P/E High/Low	PER SHARE ($) Earnings	Dividends	Book Value
12/20	0.00	—	0.06	0.00	(0.00)
Annual Growth	—	—	—	—	—

Currys plc

Auditors: Deloitte LLP

LOCATIONS

HQ: Currys plc
  1 Portal Way, London W3 6RS
Phone: (44) 203 110 3251
Web: www.dixonscarphone.com

HISTORICAL FINANCIALS

Company Type: Public

Income Statement   FYE: May 1

	REVENUE ($ mil.)	NET INCOME ($ mil.)	NET PROFIT MARGIN	EMPLOYEES
05/21	14,386	16	0.1%	36,087
05/20*	12,746	(204)	—	42,209
04/19	13,458	(412)	—	42,990
04/18	14,493	228	1.6%	43,760
04/17	13,699	381	2.8%	45,461
Annual Growth	1.2%	(54.3%)	—	(5.6%)

*Fiscal year change

2021 Year-End Financials

Debt ratio: 0.1%	No. of shares (mil.): 1,166
Return on equity: 0.5%	Dividends
Cash ($ mil.): 243	Yield: —
Current ratio: 0.75	Payout: 300.0%
Long-term debt ($ mil.): —	Market value ($ mil.): —

Dah Sing Banking Group Ltd

Dah Sing Banking Group (DSBG) wants to help you sing all the way to the bank. The banking division of Hong Kong's Dah Sing Group DSBG operates three subsidiaries (Dah Sing Bank Banco Comercial de Macau and MEVAS Bank) a securities trading company and a joint venture private banking business with SG Hambros Bank which provides offshore private banking services. The bank's services include savings accounts credit cards loans and e-banking. Dah Sing Bank has nearly 50 branches in Hong Kong more than a dozen branches in Macau and a handful of locations in China. It also owns about 20% of China's Bank of Chongqing with 70 locations. Fellow Dah Sing Group subsidiary Dah Sing Financial Group owns DSBG.

Auditors: PricewaterhouseCoopers

LOCATIONS

HQ: Dah Sing Banking Group Ltd
  36th Floor, Everbright Centre, 108 Gloucester Road,
  Wanchai,
Phone: (852) 2507 8866   **Fax:** (852) 2598 5052
Web: www.dahsing.com

COMPETITORS

First Financial Holding Co. Ltd.
HUA NAN FINANCIAL HOLDINGS CO.LTD.
Hana Financial Group Inc.
ITAU UNIBANCO HOLDING SA
SINOPAC FINANCIAL HOLDINGS COMPANY LIMITED

HISTORICAL FINANCIALS

Company Type: Public

Income Statement   FYE: December 31

	ASSETS ($ mil.)	NET INCOME ($ mil.)	INCOME AS % OF ASSETS	EMPLOYEES
12/19	31,258	287	0.9%	2,970
12/18	29,401	316	1.1%	2,899
12/17	28,053	279	1.0%	2,825
12/16	26,463	276	1.0%	2,751
12/15	25,291	283	1.1%	2,619
Annual Growth	5.4%	0.3%	—	3.2%

2019 Year-End Financials

Return on assets: 0.9%	Dividends
Return on equity: 8.2%	Yield: —
Long-term debt ($ mil.): —	Payout: 30.1%
No. of shares (mil.): 1,405	Market value ($ mil.): —
Sales ($ mil): 1,255	

Dah Sing Financial Holdings Ltd.

Dah Sing Financial Holdings (DSFH) owns subsidiaries active in banking insurance investments and other financial services. Part of Hong Kong's Dah Sing Group the company has operations in Hong Kong and mainland China. It owns a majority stake in Dah Sing Banking Group itself the parent of about a half-dozen banking private banking and securities trading entities. Other DSFH holdings include insurance companies Dah Sing Life Assurance and Dah Sing General Insurance as well as a 20% stake in Great Wall Life Insurance. The group has expanded through numerous acquisitions with a particular focus on Macau and Hong Kong.

EXECUTIVES

Non-Executive Director, Eiichi Yoshikawa
**Group General Manager, Vice Chairman, Managing
  Director and Chief Executive of Dah Sing Bank
  Limited,** Tsu-Hing Wong

Chief Financial Officer, Chi-Leung Chow
Chief Executive Officer, Managing Director,
 Executive Director, Hon-Hing Wong, $1,123,959
 total compensation
Executive Chairman of the Board, Shou-Yeh
 Wong, $766,581 total compensation
Independent Non-Executive Director, Paul
 Winkelmann
Independent Non-Executive Director, Kwan-Yuen
 Leung
Company Secretary, Wai-Nar Wong
Independent Non-Executive Director, Paul
 Kennedy
Non-Executive Director, Yoshikazu Shimauchi
Alternate Director, Nakamura Shinkichi
**Deputy Chief Executive Officer, Executive
 Director,** Pak-Ling Wang, $792,108 total
 compensation
Auditors: PricewaterhouseCoopers

LOCATIONS

HQ: Dah Sing Financial Holdings Ltd.
36th Floor, Everbright Centre, 108 Gloucester Road,
Wanchai,
Phone: (852) 2507 8866   **Fax:** (852) 2598 5052
Web: www.dahsing.com

COMPETITORS

AUSTRALIA AND NEW ZEALAND BANKING GROUP
 LIMITED
BOC HONG KONG (HOLDINGS) LIMITED
CIMB GROUP HOLDINGS BERHAD
GREAT EASTERN HOLDINGS LIMITED
HSBC HOLDINGS PLC
OCBC Wing Hang Bank Limited
PRUDENTIAL PUBLIC LIMITED COMPANY

HISTORICAL FINANCIALS

Company Type: Public

Income Statement				FYE: December 31
	ASSETS ($ mil.)	NET INCOME ($ mil.)	INCOME AS % OF ASSETS	EMPLOYEES
12/19	32,145	219	0.7%	3,097
12/18	30,298	244	0.8%	3,027
12/17	28,858	691	2.4%	2,949
12/16	28,788	243	0.8%	2,999
12/15	27,453	251	0.9%	2,830
Annual Growth	4.0%	(3.3%)	—	2.3%

2019 Year-End Financials

Return on assets: 0.7%
Return on equity: 6.5%
Long-term debt ($ mil.): —
No. of shares (mil.): 319
Sales ($ mil): 1,317

Dividends
 Yield: —
 Payout: 27.8%
Market value ($ mil.): —

Dai Nippon Printing Co Ltd

A leading commercial printer Dai Nippon Printing (DNP) has diversified beyond the business of
spreading ink on paper. The global firm still produces books and magazines dictionaries catalogs
and business forms and it has added items such
as CD-ROMs holograms and smart cards to the
mix while subsidiary CHI Group sells e-books.
DNP's business consists of two business areas.
One is the Printing Business area which includes

the Information Communication segment Lifestyle
and Industrial Supplies segment and Electronics
segment. The other is the Beverages Business area
undertaken through Hokkaido Coca-Cola Bottling
Co. Ltd.

Operations

DNP's business consists of two business areas:
Printing Business area which includes Information
Communication segment Lifestyle and Industrial
Supplies segment and Electronics segment; and
Beverages Business area.

The Information Communication segment consists of the Publishing Business responsible for
publishing media and publishing logistics Information Innovation Business responsible for marketing and information security and Imaging Communication Business that creates "products and
experience" including photo prints. The segment
accounts for around 55% of the revenue.

The Lifestyle and Industrial Supplies segment
consists of businesses in three fields: Packaging
Living Spaces and Industrial High-performance
Materials. Segment accounts for more than a quarter of revenue.

The Electronics segment has developed display
related products and electronic device businesses
both in Japan and overseas. Segment accounts for
more than 10% of revenue.

The Beverages Business area undertaken
through Hokkaido Coca-Cola Bottling Co. Ltd. The
DNP Group's Hokkaido Coca-Cola Bottling Co.
Ltd. undertakes the Beverages business. In addition to developing new products leveraging the
Coca-Cola brand name we are also engaging in
the vending machine business and sales promotion
activities targeting mass retailing outlets. Business
area accounts for about 5% of revenue.

Geographic Reach

Headquartered in Tokyo Japan the company operates more than 75 production sites which more
than 60 of the production sites was in Japan.

Financial Performance

Net sales for fiscal 2021 decreased by 5% to 1.3
trillion compared from the prior year with 1.4 trillion.

DNP's net income for fiscal 2021 decreased to
27.8 billion compared from the prior year with
72.1 billion.

Cash held by the company at the end of fiscal
2021 decreased to 304.2 billion. Cash provided by
operations was 61.9 billion while cash used for investing and financing activities were 56.3 billion
and 78.3 billion respectively. Main uses of cash
were payments for purchases of property plant
and equipment; and payments for purchases of
treasury stock.

Strategy

DNP will strive to achieve its operating income
target of 75 billion yen and secure stable ROE of
5.0% or higher five years from now in the fiscal
year ending March 31 2025 to realize "What the
DNP Group Aims To Be."

To achieve this the company has newly formulated a three-year medium-term management plan
that started from the fiscal year ending March 31
2021 and DNP have commenced various related
activities. This plan has two basic strategies consisting of Create value through "P&I Innovations"
and Strengthen business infrastructure to support
growth and the company will implement specific
measures under the plan.

HISTORY

In 1876 Shueisha the predecessor to Dai Nippon
Printing (DNP) was established in central Tokyo.
As the only modern printing firm in Japan it was
well-positioned to attract the business of the
emerging newspaper and book industries. The
company originally used a movable-type hand

printer but became the first private industry to use
steam power in Japan when it updated its presses
in 1884.

Following Japanese victories over China and
Russia at the turn of the century Japan embarked
on a period of military and economic expansion.
This was matched by a growing demand for printing. In 1927 Japan published 20000 book titles
and 40 million magazines. The country's first four-
color gravure printing system was inaugurated the
following year. In 1935 Shueisha changed its name
to Dai Nippon Printing following its merger with
Nisshin Printing.

The 1930s and 1940s were lean times for printers; Japan's repressive military government sup-
pressed publishers and banned books. WWII devastated the publishing industry along with the rest
of the Japanese economy but the publishing industry recovered soon after the end of the war.
DNP was assisted in its recovery by government
contracts; in 1946 it was designated by the Ministry of Finance to print 100-yen notes. In 1949
the company entered the securities printing business and in 1951 it expanded into packaging and
decorative interiors production. DNP reemerged
in 1958 as Japan's largest printing firm.

In 1963 DNP followed Toppan in setting up an
office in Hong Kong. Both Hong Kong and Singapore had become havens for Shanghai printing
entrepreneurs who had emigrated in the face of
the Communist takeover of China in 1949. These
cities became centers for low-cost high-quality
color printing for British and American book publishers. In 1973 DNP overtook R. R. Donnelley as
the world's largest printer. The next year the company set up a subsidiary in the US DNP (America)
Inc.

DNP moved into the information processing
business in the 1980s developing a credit card-
sized calculator in 1985 a digital color printer system in 1986 and a Japanese-language word
processor in 1987. The company launched Hi-Vi-
sion Static Pictures in 1989 to market a process
that converted data into a form used by high-definition TV. In 1990 DNP bought a controlling stake
in Tien Wah Press the #1 printer in Singapore.

The next year DNP completed the first construction stage of its Okayama plant dedicated to information media supplies (mainly transfer ribbons for
color printers). The second stage specializing in
interior decorative materials was completed in
1993.

In 1994 the company launched its Let's Go to
an Amusement Park! virtual reality software system. Two years later DNP produced an integrated
circuit card for about a tenth of current costs giving
it a major competitive edge in the magnetic card
market.

In 1999 the company began selling CD-ROMs
online through subsidiary TransArt. The following
year Dai Nippon formed partnerships or joint ventures with Toshiba (to develop printed circuit
boards) Microsoft (to develop Windows-based
smart cards) and Numerical Technologies (to develop advanced phase-shifted photomasks). In
2002 the company joined with Toshiba and Takara
to develop and promote a lightweight educational
computer called an Ex-Pad.

In 2006 the company renamed its Industrial
Supplies operation to become Lifestyle Materials
and made plans to expand that business. The following year it purchased a stake in bookstore chain
Maruzen and invested in TRC Inc. a provider of li-
brary operation services. In 2008 TRC became a
wholly owned subsidiary of DNP.

The company ramped up efforts to revitalize
Japan's ailing book market through investments
and acquisitions in 2009. Aiming to boost education and publishing operations DNP acquired a
majority stake in bookseller Junkudo which oper-

ates about 30 shops in major Japanese cities. It also invested in Shufunotomo Co. a women's magazine publisher. DNP combined its resources and influence with three other Japanese publishers agreeing to acquire a roughly 30% stake in secondhand bookseller Bookoff. The chain operates through about 1000 stores across Japan.

EXECUTIVES

President, Representative Director, Yoshinari Kitajima

Senior Managing Executive Officer, Motoharu Kitajima

Chairman of the Board, Representative Director, Yoshitoshi Kitajima

Senior Managing Executive Officer, Sakae Hikita

Senior Managing Director, Representative Director, Masato Yamaguchi

Senior Managing Director, Representative Director, Kenji Miya

Managing Director, Satoru Inoue

Independent Director, Tsukasa Miyajima

Director, Minako Miyama

Managing Director, Masafumi Kuroyanagi

Independent Director, Ryuichi Tomizawa

Managing Director, Hirofumi Hashimoto

Independent Director, Kazuyuki Sasajima

Independent Director, Ikuo Morita

Auditors: ARK LLC

LOCATIONS

HQ: Dai Nippon Printing Co Ltd
 1-1-1 Ichigaya-Kagacho, Shinjuku-ku, Tokyo 162-8001
Phone: (81) 3 6735 0129
Web: www.dnp.co.jp

2016 Sales

	% of total
Japan	84
Asia	10
Other countries	6
Total	**100**

PRODUCTS/OPERATIONS

2016 Sales

	% of total
Information Communication	56
Lifestyle & Industrial Supplies	26
Electronics	14
Beverages	4
Total	**100**

Selected Products and Services

Information Communication
 Bank notes
 Books
 Business forms
 Catalogs
 CD-ROMs and DVDs
 Direct mail
 Magazines
 Plastic cards
 Promotional publications
Lifestyle and Industrial Supplies
 Decorative materials
 Packaging
Electronics
 Color filters for liquid crystal displays
 Photomasks
 Projection TV screens
 Shadowmasks for color TVs
Beverages

COMPETITORS

CECONOMY AG	MPAC Industries
COLOREDGE INC.	Corporation
COMPUTACENTER PLC	PANTONE LLC
DS SMITH PLC	QUAD/GRAPHICS INC.
Heidelberger	TOPPAN INC.
Druckmaschinen AG	VERICO TECHNOLOGY LLC

ITOCHU CORPORATION	XEROX CORPORATION
MACDERMID INCORPORATED	

HISTORICAL FINANCIALS
Company Type: Public

Income Statement   FYE: March 31

	REVENUE ($ mil.)	NET INCOME ($ mil.)	NET PROFIT MARGIN	EMPLOYEES
03/21	12,060	226	1.9%	54,817
03/20	12,914	640	5.0%	48,192
03/19	12,655	(322)	—	47,449
03/18	13,299	258	1.9%	46,523
03/17	12,612	225	1.8%	45,836
Annual Growth	**(1.1%)**	**0.1%**	**—**	**4.6%**

2021 Year-End Financials

Debt ratio: 0.0%   No. of shares (mil.): 280
Return on equity: 2.5%   Dividends
Cash ($ mil.): 2,719   Yield: 2.8%
Current ratio: 1.97   Payout: 35.5%
Long-term debt ($ mil.): 1,039   Market value ($ mil.): 2,962

	STOCK PRICE ($) FY Close	P/E High	P/E Low	PER SHARE ($) Earnings	PER SHARE ($) Dividends	PER SHARE ($) Book Value
03/21	10.55	0	0	0.81	0.30	33.57
03/20	10.48	0	0	2.17	0.30	30.03
03/19	11.97	—	—	(1.07)	0.29	29.80
03/18	10.47	0	0	0.85	0.30	32.87
03/17	10.88	0	0	0.73	0.29	30.04
Annual Growth	**(0.8%)**	**—**	**—**	**2.5%**	**0.6%**	**2.8%**

Dai-ichi Life Holdings Inc

Auditors: KPMG AZSA LLC

LOCATIONS

HQ: Dai-ichi Life Holdings Inc
 1-13-1 Yuraku-cho, Chiyoda-ku, Tokyo 100-8411
Phone: (81) 3 3216 1222
Web: www.dai-ichi-life-hd.com

HISTORICAL FINANCIALS
Company Type: Public

Income Statement   FYE: March 31

	REVENUE ($ mil.)	NET INCOME ($ mil.)	NET PROFIT MARGIN	EMPLOYEES
03/21	67,746	3,285	4.8%	64,823
03/20	57,965	298	0.5%	63,719
03/19	59,981	2,032	3.4%	62,938
03/18	61,108	3,427	5.6%	62,943
03/17	54,689	2,068	3.8%	62,606
Annual Growth	**5.5%**	**12.3%**	**—**	**0.9%**

2021 Year-End Financials

Debt ratio: —   No. of shares (mil.): 1,114
Return on equity: 8.4%   Dividends
Cash ($ mil.): 27,230   Yield: 0.0%
Current ratio: —   Payout: 19.2%
Long-term debt ($ mil.): —   Market value ($ mil.): —

	STOCK PRICE ($) FY Close	P/E High	P/E Low	PER SHARE ($) Earnings	PER SHARE ($) Dividends	PER SHARE ($) Book Value
03/21	0.00	0	0	2.94	0.57	38.97
03/20	12.10	1	0	0.26	0.54	30.71
Annual Growth	**—**	**—**	**—**	**82.9%**	**1.1%**	**6.1%**

Daikin Industries Ltd

Founded in 1924 Daikin Industries is the #1 air conditioning company in the world. Daikin makes air conditioning and refrigeration products for residential and industrial use. Residential products include heat pumps gas furnaces and air conditioners; industrial products range from infrared ceramic space heaters to marine vessel air conditioners. Daikin also sells chemicals (fluorocarbons surfactants and mold-release agents) oil hydraulics for machinery and products such as aircraft parts for defense organizations. The US is its largest markets each generating more than 25% of net sales.

Operations

Daikin operates in three reportable business segments?Air Conditioning Chemicals and Others.

Daikin's Air Conditioning business accounts for more than 90% of total revenue and offers a wide range of air conditioning products such as room air conditioning systems air purifiers heat pump hot water and room heating systems water chillers and industrial dust collectors to name a few.

The Chemicals business offers fluorine compounds with distinctive characteristics such as fluoropolymers fluoroelastomers and fluorocarbon gas which are developed to support a variety of industries including the semiconductor and automotive markets. This segment accounts for more than 5% of total revenue.

The Others segment includes four divisions and generates less than 5% of total revenue. The filter business represents the sale of air filters for air conditioning systems. The oil hydraulics business comprises the manufacture of equipment that facilitates the smooth movement of various types of machinery such as industrial and construction machinery and vehicles. Its defense systems business manufactures artillery shells warheads and fuses as well as aircraft parts; processing technologies for these products are also used for home-use oxygen therapy equipment such as respiration synchronizers and oxygen concentrators. The electronics systems business includes database systems and product development.

Geographic Reach

The company's corporate headquarters is located in Osaka Japan. Daikin utilizes a market-centered local production strategy that places its manufacturing facilities close to its target markets. The number of production bases totals around 100 global locations in over 150 countries and regions.

United States is largest market representing more than quarter of total sales. Other major markets include Japan generating over 20%. Asia and Oceania and Europe account for more than 15%. China and other regions produce the remaining less than 20%.

Sales and Marketing

The company advertises through its website as well as in the Japanese financial publication the Nikkei Shimbun. The company sells its products through its own network of dealers online customer support is also available anytime.

Financial Performance

Note: Growth rates may differ after conversion to US Dollars.

Daikin's net sales as well as profits have increased steadily over the past several consecutive years. Net sales and net income increased 25% between 2016 and 2020.

Revenue in fiscal 2020 (ended March 31) was 2.6 trillion a 3% increase from 2.5 trillion in 2019 due in part to the company's solid performance up to the third quarter. In the fourth quarter however the global economy slowed sharply due to the COVID-19 pandemic. In response to this Daikin worked to minimize the impact on its business and management including sales production and procurement.

Net income decreased 10% to 170.7 billion in 2020 partly due to the effect of recording of an impairment loss despite a gain on sales of investment securities.

Daikin's cash and cash equivalents for fiscal 2020 amounted to 46 billion a decrease of 56.2 billion from the previous fiscal year. Cash from operating activities was 302.2 billion an increase of 52.2 billion from the year prior due to a decrease in the amount of increase in trade receivables. Investing activities used 156.2 billion a decrease of 9.6 billion from the year prior as expenditures for the acquisition of consolidated subsidiaries decreased. Daikin's financing activities used 169.9 billion an increase of 101.2 billion from the year prior mainly due to a decrease in short-term borrowings.

Strategy

Daikin has a strategic management plan FUSION 20 focused on co-creating new value in the air and environment fields. This strategy was 13 Group-wide Core Strategy Themes encompassing approaches to new business structures and existing domains technologies and monozukuri corporate management and a unique corporate philosophy.

The key aspects of FUSION center on the company's ability to thoroughly execute initiatives in line with the planned strategy and maintain its commitment to achieving quantitative targets while at the same time promoting the advancement of flexibility in management. Even amid a tough operating environment Daikin focused in fiscal 2020 on achieving the goals outlined in the FUSION 20 plan through the implementation of 176 business division themes and ten Group-wide follow-up themes.

In fiscal 2021 the final year of FUSION 20 Daikin will work to enhance its financial structure through both defensive and offensive measures to reach the plan's targets despite severe conditions caused by COVID-19. Daikin's market capitalization has grown by around 20 times over the 25 years between end-March 1995 and end-March 2020 being ranked eighth in market cap growth over the 30 years of the Heisei Era (1989-2019).

Daikin is spending the current year formulating its next strategic management plan FUSION 25. To achieve further growth the company believes it necessary to not only maintain its current initiatives but also develop and implement new measures with the future in mind. Daikin expects its mainstay air conditioner business which includes the service and solutions business as well as the air quality-related business to be a growth business even after COVID-19 is brought under control. Daikin also believes it to be a business that can contribute to the needs of society and the resolution of social issues by supporting the health and safety of all.

Company Background

Daikin Industries traces its roots back to 1924. Founded in Osaka Japan as Osaka Kinzolu Kogyosho Limited Partnership the company began as a town factory with no more than 15 employees making radiator tubes for aircraft. In 1933 the company began doing research on flourine refrigerants and later began manufacturing a methyl chloride type refrigerator dubbed the Mifujirator. With the successful development of fluorocarbon gas the company began mass-producing the Mifujirator starting in 1942. It introduced Japan's first packaged air conditioner for commercial use and began marketing the first residential window air conditioner in 1958. The company was renamed

Daikin Kogyo Co. Ltd. in 1963 and later to the current Daikin Industries Ltd. in 1982.

EXECUTIVES

President, Chief Executive Officer, Representative Director, Masanori Togawa
Chairman of the Board, Global Group Representative Executive Officer, Noriyuki Inoue
Executive Vice President, Director, Takashi Matsuzaki
Executive Vice President, Chairman of Subsidiary, Representative Director, Ken Tayano
Executive Officer, Yasushi Yamada
Executive Vice President, Chairman of Subsidiary, Director, Masatsugu Minaka
Senior Managing Executive Officer, Chief Director of Accounting & Finance, Koichi Takahashi
Senior Managing Executive Officer, Masayuki Moriyama
Executive Vice President, Director, Yoshihiro Mineno
Independent Director, Akiji Makino
Independent Director, Shingo Torii
Managing Executive Officer, President and Chief Executive Officer of Subsidiary, Director, Kanwal Jawa
Independent Director, Tatsuo Kawada
Independent Director, Yuko Arai
Auditors: Deloitte Touche Tohmatsu LLC

LOCATIONS

HQ: Daikin Industries Ltd
Umeda Center Bldg., 2-4-12 Nakazaki-Nishi, Kita-ku, Osaka 530-8323
Phone: (81) 6 6373 4356
Web: www.daikin.co.jp

2018 sales

	% of total
Japan	24
USA	24
China	17
Asia and Oceania	15
Europe	14
Other regions	6
Total	**100**

PRODUCTS/OPERATIONS

2018 Sales

	% of total
Air conditioning	89
Chemicals	9
Other	2
Total	**100**

Selected Products and Operations

Air Conditioning and Refrigerator Division
  Split/multi-split type air conditioners
  Unitary (ducted split)
  Air to water heat pump systems
  Heating systems
  Air purifiers
  Medium/low temperature refrigeration
  Sky/air (packaged air conditioners for shops and small offices)
  Ventilation products
  Control systems
  Commercial air cleaners
  Commercial air conditioners
  Container refrigeration
  Large-scale refrigerators
  Marine vessel air conditioners and refrigerators
  Marine-type container refrigeration units
  Room air cleaners
  Room air conditioners
Chemical Division
  Equipment and systems
  Fluorocarbon gas
  Synthesized products
Oil Hydraulics Division

Centralized lubrication units and systems
Oil hydraulic products for industrial machinery
Oil hydraulic products for mobile equipment
Defense Systems Division
  Aircraft components
  Ammunition
  Warheads for aerial torpedoes

COMPETITORS

AAON INC.
AIR PRODUCTS AND CHEMICALS INC.
DOVER CORPORATION
ENERPAC TOOL GROUP CORP.
GARDNER DENVER INC.
GENUIT GROUP PLC
Gree Electric Appliances Inc. Of Zhuhai
HAYNES INTERNATIONAL INC.
MIGAMI INC.
Piller Blowers & Compressors GmbH
REVCOR INC.
SEKISUI CHEMICAL CO. LTD.
TECOGEN INC.
TECUMSEH PRODUCTS COMPANY LLC
TRANE INC.
VERTIV CORPORATION
WELBILT INC.

HISTORICAL FINANCIALS

Company Type: Public

Income Statement

FYE: March 31

	REVENUE ($ mil.)	NET INCOME ($ mil.)	NET PROFIT MARGIN	EMPLOYEES
03/21	22,518	1,411	6.3%	93,102
03/20	23,494	1,572	6.7%	89,957
03/19	22,404	1,707	7.6%	86,472
03/18	21,571	1,780	8.3%	78,837
03/17	18,281	1,376	7.5%	75,543
Annual Growth	5.4%	0.6%	—	5.4%

2021 Year-End Financials

Debt ratio: 0.1%
Return on equity: 10.0%
Cash ($ mil.): 6,648
Current ratio: 2.26
Long-term debt ($ mil.): 4,956

No. of shares (mil.): 292
Dividends
  Yield: 0.7%
  Payout: 2.9%
Market value ($ mil.): 5,914

	STOCK PRICE ($) FY Close	P/E High/Low		PER SHARE ($) Earnings	Dividends	Book Value
03/21	20.21	0	0	4.82	0.15	51.47
03/20	11.98	0	0	5.37	0.16	45.24
03/19	11.69	0	0	5.83	0.13	43.77
03/18	11.07	0	0	6.08	0.13	41.80
03/17	201.72	0	0	4.71	0.12	34.04
Annual Growth	(43.7%)	—	—	0.6%	6.8%	10.9%

Daito Trust Construction Co., Ltd.

You can trust Daito to land on the right side of a property deal. Daito Trust Construction provides a unique service to Japanese landowners ? the ability to develop a tailored business plan to unlock long-term value in their land. In Japan it is customary to pass land to succeeding generations. Passing it to heirs triggers tax consequences and sometimes places it in the hands of people who don't know what to do with it. Daito and its subsidiaries designs a plan to develop the land ? such as building a high-rise apartment complex ? and then constructs the building recruits tenants manages the property remits payment to the landowner and keeps a little for its own profit. Since the inception of this business model in 1980 it has built more than 170000 buildings worked with 80000 landowners and exceeded 1 million units under management.

Operations

Daito Trust Construction's core business model is comprised of two segments construction and real estate. The construction segment diagnoses potential land uses designs a building & funding plan proposes the plan to the landowner and once agreed to constructs the building. The real estate segment recruits tenants and manages leases and the property for a 35-year term.

Much of the group's operations occur within three companies: Daito Trust Construction Daito Kentaku Leasing and Daito Kentaku Partners. Other subsidiaries provide tangential services Daito Energy installs solar power panels on the roofs its buildings (> 13000); Gaspal Group designs builds and delivers natural gas to nearly households (> 300000); and Care Partner operates elderly & nursery care facilities. It also owns finance and insurance businesses.

Geographic Reach

Tokyo-headquartered Daito performs much of its business in Japan's major cities. It has branched out in recent years into Malaysia where it owns the Le Meridien Kuala Lumpur Hotel and into the US where it owns an apartment building co-developed with a US-based partner.

Financial Performance

Note: Financial results are denoted in Japanese currency the Yen ().

Daito Construction has produced consistently upward revenue for over a decade rising each year from 2007 to 2017 from 564 billion to 1.5 trillion. Net income over that same period nearly doubled increasing from 42 million to more than 80 million.

In FY2017 (ended March 31 2017) Daito generated 1.5 trillion (about US$13.8 billion). Revenue for the year improved in all categories ? completed construction contracts real estate sales and other business revenue ? resulting in a 6% rise year-over-year.

Net income jumped 22% to 82.5 billion (about US$760 million). The company managed expenses well improving its gross margin two percentage points. With the increased revenue and lower expenses the firm registered a nice earnings boost compared to FY2016.

Cash at the end of the year was 200 million an increase of 18 million. Operating activities contributed 124 million to cash most of it from net income. Investing activities used 33 million to purchase tangible assets (property plant equipment) investment securities and intangible assets. Financing activities depleted cash by 72 million mostly to issue stock dividends to shareholders and to repurchase company stock.

Strategy

Daito Construction's strategy is slow and steady. It operates somewhat like a real estate investment trust generating stable revenue and income year after year spinning off a large portion of earnings to shareholders and investing the rest into growing its portfolio of properties. The company's business model varies however in that it works with existing landowners to determine what kind of property to build and that it limits its time frame by instituting a 35-year leases with its landowners.

The group is enjoying nice economic tailwinds brought about by a growing economy low interest rates brought about in early 2015 by the Bank of Japan and increasing demand for single-person

households. Demand for rental housing is expected to be brisk in coming years.

From business perspective Daito's core competencies in construction and real estate will continue to aid the expansion of its portfolio. Its trajectory of units under management has been impressive growing from 600000 in 2010 to 8000000 in 2013 and exceeding 1000000 in 2017.

The group also expects to expand its other operations in energy nursing care childcare and overseas investments.

EXECUTIVES

President, Chief Executive Officer, Representative Director, Katsuma Kobayashi
Managing Director, Chief Director of Business Administration, Chief Director of Related Business, Shuji Kawai
Director of Main Related Business Unit, Director, Kanitsu Uchida
President of Subsidiary, Director, Yoshihiro Mori
Independent Director, Toshiaki Yamaguchi
Independent Director, Takashi Shoda
Senior Director of Design, Director, Masafumi Tate
Independent Director, Mami Sasaki
Managing Director, Chief Director of Real Estate Business, President of Subsidiary, Koji Sato
Managing Director, Chief Director of Construction Business, Kei Takeuchi
Independent Director, Atsushi Iritani
Auditors: Deloitte Touche Tohmatsu LLC

LOCATIONS

HQ: Daito Trust Construction Co., Ltd.
2-16-1 Konan, Minato-ku, Tokyo 108-8211
Phone: (81) 3 6718 9111
Web: www.kentaku.co.jp

COMPETITORS

COUNTRYWIDE GROUP LIMITED	MAPELEY ESTATES LIMITED
FLETCHER KING PLC	PIRES INVESTMENTS PLC
FORESTAR GROUP INC. CORP.	REALOGY HOLDINGS
INVITATION HOMES INC.	

HISTORICAL FINANCIALS

Company Type: Public

Income Statement | | | | FYE: March 31

	REVENUE ($ mil.)	NET INCOME ($ mil.)	NET PROFIT MARGIN	EMPLOYEES
03/21	13,447	562	4.2%	21,549
03/20	14,613	832	5.7%	21,916
03/19	14,368	812	5.7%	21,754
03/18	14,662	827	5.6%	20,834
03/17	13,390	734	5.5%	19,556
Annual Growth	0.1%	(6.5%)	—	2.5%

2021 Year-End Financials

Debt ratio: 0.1%	No. of shares (mil.): 68
Return on equity: 21.2%	Dividends
Cash ($ mil.): 1,919	Yield: 4.4%
Current ratio: 1.70	Payout: 15.0%
Long-term debt ($ mil.): 753	Market value ($ mil.): 2,007

	STOCK PRICE ($) FY Close	P/E High/Low		PER SHARE ($) Earnings	Dividends	Book Value
03/21	29.15	0	0	8.21	1.29	39.89
03/20	23.02	0	0	12.03	1.43	37.99
03/19	34.93	0	0	10.94	1.36	37.16
03/18	42.75	0	0	10.97	1.36	36.82
03/17	34.89	0	0	9.59	0.78	31.93
Annual Growth	(4.4%)	—	—	(3.8%)	13.6%	5.7%

Daiwa House Industry Co Ltd

Daiwa House Industry is one of the leading companies in housing construction and real estate industries. Its businesses build lease sell and manage rental properties single-family houses condominiums and commercial buildings. Daiwa's other businesses include energy efficiency and construction support services as well as operation of hotels and sports clubs. Daiwa has more than 35 offices located in Hokkaido Fukushima Saitama-higashi Yokohama Kawasaki Nagoya and Hiroshima among others and more than 30 branches. It also owns and operates nine factories and manages autonomous group companies in about 25 countries. The company was founded by Nobuo Ishibashi in 1955 with "industrialization of construction" as a corporate philosophy.

Operations

Daiwa House Industry's revenue is diversified across seven business segments.

Through its Rental Housing segment (nearly 25% of net sales) Daiwa manages about 611875 (mostly Japanese) housing units.

The company designs and builds constructions in Japan ranging from medical buildings and elderly welfare and housing facilities to food processing facilities and offices under its Logistics Business and Corporate Facilities segment (about 25%).

Daiwa's Commercial Facilities business (roughly 20%) constructs commercial buildings including retail properties hotels and residential facilities that include retail stores. It constructs about 915 projects.

In its Single-Family Houses division (more than 10%) Daiwa has constructed and sold about 5180 single-family homes. The company also builds entire housing subdivisions.

Via its Condominiums segment (about 10%) Daiwa has sold around 2940 condominium units and manages about 376170 in Japan.

The company conducts renovations principally for single-family houses condominiums and rental housing through its Existing Homes business (less than 5%).

Daiwa's Other Businesses division (more than 10%) includes operations in construction and construction materials logistics interior design home products energy efficiency services hotels sports clubs and parking lots.

Geographic Reach

Headquartered in Osaka Japan Daiwa House Industry has more than 35 offices in Japan over 30 branches nine factories and research and training centers in Nara Osaka and Tokyo. The company also has international offices in China Taiwan Indonesia Philippines Vietnam Myanmar and Mexico.

Sales and Marketing

Daiwa House Industry is emphasizing constructions that ameliorate societal needs in Japan including nursing homes environmentally friendly housing food-industry facilities offices hotels fitness health and leisure and medical buildings among others.

Financial Performance

Note: Growth rates may differ after conversion to US dollars.

During the pandemic the company's top priority was to safeguard all of its stakeholders' lives and health. While affected by restrictions on face-to-face sales activities the company worked quickly to roll out new products and services adapted to the New Normal and sales using its websites. As a result the company had net sales of 4.1 trillion a 6% decrease from the previous year's net sales of 4.4 trillion.

Net income attributable to owners of the parent was 195.1 billion.

Operating activities generated 430.3 billion while investing activities used 390 billion. Financing activities provided 102.7 billion.

Strategy

Strategies and initiatives in Housing segment consists of:

Development and roll out of customer and local needs-oriented products; Ideas on housing adapted for working at home; Uptake of ZEH; Initiatives for combination housing (housing combined with those for other uses); Diversification of revenue streams from large-scale multi-use development redevelopment and rebuilding projects leveraging Group strengths.

Strategies and initiatives in Business segment consists of:

Diversification of tenants reflecting social trends and local attributes; Development of high-performance logistics facilities and promotion of digitalization; Development of data centers; Propose capital investments and a review on the network of bases to transform our supply chain; Seize demand for the "cold chain" market.

Company Background

Founded in 1955 by Nobuo Ishibashi Daiwa House Industry first developed homes that could be quickly built using steel pipe frameworks to withstand natural disasters. The technique was first used for warehouses depots and offices primarily for the Japanese National Railways and the Japanese government. The company went on to develop study rooms that that could be built in three hours larger prefabricated houses targeting newlyweds and eventually large-scale residential complexes.

EXECUTIVES

Vice President, Representative Director, Tamio Ishibashi

Independent Director, Yukinori Kuwano

Independent Director, Miwa Seki

President, Chief Executive Officer, Chief Operating Officer, Representative Director, Keiichi Yoshii

Independent Director, Kazuyoshi Kimura

Independent Director, Yutaka Shigemori

Managing Executive Officer, Chief Director of Overseas Business, Director, Nobuya Ichiki

Chief Financial Officer, Vice President, Chief Director of Business Administration, Chief Director of Relation Business, Representative Director, Takeshi Kosokabe

Managing Executive Officer, Chief Director of Distribution Store Business, Director of Business Promotion in Distribution store Business Unit, Director, Keisuke Shimonishi

Managing Executive Officer, Chief Director of Compliance & Quality Assurance Promotion, Director, Yoshinori Ariyoshi

Independent Director, Yukiko Yabu

Managing Executive Officer, Chief Director of Construction Business, Director, Tatsuya Urakawa

Managing Executive Officer, Chief Director of Housing Complex Business, Director of Business Promotion in Housing Complex Business Unit, Director, Kazuhito Dekura

Managing Executive Officer, Chief Director of Housing Business, Director, Hirotsugu Ohtomo

Auditors: Ernst & Young ShinNihon LLC

LOCATIONS

HQ: Daiwa House Industry Co Ltd
   3-3-5 Umeda, Kita-ku, Osaka 530-8241
Phone: (81) 6 6225 7804   **Fax:** (81) 6 6342 1399
Web: www.daiwahouse.co.jp

PRODUCTS/OPERATIONS

2017 Sales

	% of total
Rental housing	26
Logistics Business and Corporate Facilities	22
Commercial Facilities	16
Single-Family Housing	10
Condominiums	7
Existing Homes	3
Other Businesses	16
Total	**100**

COMPETITORS

CAVCO INDUSTRIES INC.
ENVOLVE CLIENT SERVICES GROUP LLC
FLETCHER BUILDING LIMITED
INVITATION HOMES INC.
KEEPMOAT HOMES LIMITED
KENNEDY-WILSON HOLDINGS INC.
LIXIL CORPORATION
LLANMOOR DEVELOPMENT CO. LIMITED
MIRVAC LIMITED
MITSUI FUDOSAN CO. LTD.
SANCTUARY HOUSING ASSOCIATION
SHEPHERD BUILDING GROUP LIMITED
SHIMIZU CORPORATION
STOCKLAND (UK) LIMITED
SUMITOMO REALTY & DEVELOPMENT CO. LTD.
THE ST JOE COMPANY
TRANSWESTERN COMMERCIAL SERVICES L.L.C.

HISTORICAL FINANCIALS

Company Type: Public

Income Statement

	REVENUE ($ mil.)	NET INCOME ($ mil.)	NET PROFIT MARGIN	EMPLOYEES
03/21	37,270	1,761	4.7%	71,299
03/20	40,351	2,152	5.3%	70,344
03/19	37,415	2,144	5.7%	67,174
03/18	35,748	2,225	6.2%	64,402
03/17	31,419	1,804	5.7%	60,539
Annual Growth	**4.4%**	**(0.6%)**	**—**	**4.2%**

FYE: March 31

2021 Year-End Financials

Debt ratio: 0.2%
Return on equity: 10.9%
Cash ($ mil.): 3,847
Current ratio: 1.84
Long-term debt ($ mil.): 9,579

No. of shares (mil.): 654
Dividends
  Yield: 3.5%
  Payout: —
Market value ($ mil.): 19,329

	STOCK PRICE ($) FY Close	P/E High	/Low	PER SHARE ($) Earnings	Dividends	Book Value
03/21	29.54	0	0	2.68	1.04	25.33
03/20	24.62	0	0	3.24	1.10	23.96
03/19	31.82	0	0	3.22	1.02	21.71
03/18	38.59	0	0	3.35	0.91	20.85
03/17	28.83	0	0	2.72	0.79	17.57
Annual Growth	**0.6%**	**—**	**—**	**(0.3%)**	**7.2%**	**9.6%**

Danone

Danone is one of the largest dairy food and water producers in the world. The company is organized around three core activities: Essential Dairy and Plant Based Waters and Specialized Nutrition. The #1 maker of fresh dairy products worldwide Danone sells dozens of global and regional yogurt brands including top-sellers Dannon and Activia functional brands like Actimel and Danonino and Greek yogurt brands Oikos and Danio. The company's evian Volvic Aqua water brands (among others) make it #3 worldwide in bottled water and Danone is also the world's #2 baby nutrition company. Its medical nutrition products are #1 in Europe. It also owns US organic food company WhiteWave Foods. The company generates more than half of its revenue in Europe and NORAM region.

HISTORY

In 1965 Antoine Riboud replaced his uncle as chairman of family-run Souchon-Neuvesel a Lyons France-based maker of glass bottles. Antoine quickly made a mark in this field — he merged the firm with Boussois a major French flat-glass manufacturer creating BSN in 1966.

Antoine enlarged BSN's glass business and filled the company's bottles by acquiring well-established beverage and food concerns. In 1970 BSN purchased Brasseries Kronenbourg (France's largest brewer) Societe Europeenne de Brasseries (another French brewer) and Evian (mineral water France). The 1972 acquisition of Glaverbel (Belgium) gave BSN 50% of Europe's flat-glass market. The next year BSN merged with France's Gervais Danone (yogurt cheese Panzani pasta; founded in 1919 and named after founder Isaac Carasso's son Daniel). This moved the company into pan-European brand-name foods.

Increasing energy costs depressed flat-glass earnings so BSN began divesting its flat-glass businesses. In the late 1970s it acquired interests in brewers in Belgium Spain and Italy.

BSN bought Dannon the leading US yogurt maker (co-founded by Daniel Carasso who had continued making Danone yogurt in France until WWII) in 1982. It established a strong presence in the Italian pasta market by buying stakes in Ponte (1985) and Agnesi (1986). BSN also purchased Generale Biscuit the world's #3 biscuit maker (1986) and RJR Nabisco's European cookie and snack-food business (1989).

In a series of acquisitions starting in 1986 BSN took over Italy and Spain's largest mineral water companies and several European pasta makers and other food companies. Adopting the name of its leading international brand BSN became Groupe Danone in 1994.

Antoine's son Franck succeeded him as chairman in 1996 and restructured the company to focus on three core businesses: dairy beverages (specifically water and beer) and biscuits. By 1997 Danone had begun shedding non-core grocery products. The company simultaneously stepped up acquisitions of dairy beer biscuit and water companies in developing markets.

The 1998 purchase of AquaPenn Spring Water for $112 million doubled its US water-bottling production capacity. Danone in 1999 completed a merger and subsequent sale of part of its BSN Emballage glass-packaging unit to UK buyout firm CVC Capital Partners for $1.2 billion; Danone retained 44% ownership. Thirsty for the #2 spot in US bottled water sales Danone gulped down McKesson Water (the #3 bottled water firm in the

US after Nestle and Suntory) for $1.1 billion in 2000.

Also in 2000 Danone's joint venture Finalrealm (which includes several European equity firms) along with Burlington Biscuits Nabisco and HM Capital Partners (then called Hicks Muse Tate & Furst) acquired 87% of leading UK biscuit maker United Biscuits. Danone then bought Naya (bottled water Canada) and sold its brewing operations (#2 in Europe) to Scottish & Newcastle (later acquired by Heineken and Carlsberg) for more than $2.6 billion.

During 2001 Danone announced restructuring would shutter two LU biscuit plants and eliminate about 1800 jobs; the move met with strikes and legal battles. That same year having been bumped to the #2 spot in the US yogurt market (after General Mills' Yoplait brand) Danone acquired 40% of Stonyfield Farm the #4 yogurt brand in the US and ultimately came to own 84% of the company.

The company launched 2002 with a series of beverage acquisitions including Frucor (New Zealand) and Zywiec Zdroj (the top brand of water in Poland). Danone then struck a deal handing Coca-Cola the distribution and marketing of Evian in North America and formed a joint venture with Coke to distribute its lower-end water brands. Antoine Riboud died that same year at the age of 83.

Danone divested noncore companies during 2002 including the sale of its Italian meat and cheese business Galbani and its Kro Beer Brands (Kronenbourg 1664 brands) to Scottish & Newcastle. Then typical of its consolidation strategy later in 2002 Danone acquired the home and office water delivery companies Chateau'd'eau (France) Patrimoine des Eaux du Quebec (Canada) and Canada's Sparkling Spring (now Aquaterra).

In 2004 Danone sold its 10% interest in the Australian dairy firm National Foods. Later that year it announced an alliance with Japanese dairy group Yakult Honsha to focus both companies' efforts with probiotics. Danone is a 20% shareholder of Yakult and has agreed not to increase its share holdings of Yakult for five years and not to pursue majority control for another five. Also in 2004 Danone acquired the Mexican bottled water company Arco Iris.

While its dairy and water businesses bubbled along nicely Danone found its cookies crumbling. Opting for a new recipe in 2004 it joined with Argentine food giant ARCOR Group to merge both companies' biscuits operations in South America. Later that same year Danone sold off its W&R Jacob Ltd. biscuits operations in Ireland to local company Fruitfield Foods. It also sold Italaquae its Italian bottled water business to LGR Holding.

Long after its departure from brewing in 2004 Danone was fined ?1.5 million for forming a beer distribution cartel along with Heineken in 1996. In 2005 Danone and Coca-Cola ended their 2002 water-distribution joint venture with Coke buying out Danone's 49% share for about $100 million.

In 2005 Danone got out of the brewing business altogether with the sale of its 33% stake in Spanish brewer Mahou. It sold its HP Foods Group including Amoy Lea & Perrins and HP sauce brands to Heinz and its biscuits businesses in the UK and Ireland. That year it sold its US home and office water-delivery company DS Waters of America to investment firm Kelso & Company. Danone has increased its ownership of Russian dairy and beverage company Wimm-Bill-Dann Foods to almost 20%.

Due to slow sales for its chilled products and competition from lower-priced brands in 2006 Danone introduced Senj (a soy-based yogurt) in France. It acquired Egyptian fresh dairy products company Olait (which it renamed Danone Dairy Egypt) and Algerian bottled water company Tessala. On the Asian front Danone acquired 23% of

fruit-drink company China Huiyuan Juice Group and 51% of Wahaha. (It sold its interest in Huiyuan Juice in 2010.) In the Ukraine it bought fresh dairy company JSC Molochnyi Zavod. In the US it launched the Activia brand yogurt.

Because it wants to introduce more organic products in Europe in 2006 Danone announced the spending of $66 million on the expansion of its subsidiary Stonyfield Farm's New Hampshire production plant. (That year Stonyfield bought a 34% interest in Irish organic dairy Glenisk.)

In 2006 Danone sold its Amoy Asian sauce and chilled foods business to Ajinomoto exiting the sauce business altogether. It then sold virtually all of its grocery activities glass-container business its cheese and cured meat activities (Galbani) and its beer activities in Europe. It also sold New Zealand biscuits maker Griffins Food to investment firm Pacific Equity Partners.

Danone paid ?12 billion (about $16 billion) for Numico maker of infant food and medical nutrition (nutritional bars and shakes) in 2007. The Numico products (Cow & Gate Dumex Mellin milupa NUTRICIA) joined Danone's bledina baby-food brand to create a wide array of well-known nutritional products for babies and adults. The purchase made Danone the largest baby-food maker in Europe.

Prior to announcing the Numico purchase Danone announced the sale of its cookie business to Kraft Foods; that deal closed in late 2007. At the time some analysts saw Danone as ripe for a takeover; hence the Numico deal was construed as a way for Danone to remain independent. (The acquisition was viewed as helping ward off predators who might have been attracted to the cash that Danone accrued as a result of the Kraft deal.) As part of its strategy to divest itself of all biscuit/cookie activities in 2009 the company ended its Indian joint venture with the Wadia Group. Danone sold its 50% interest in the operation ABI Holdings to Wadia.

Strengthening its business in Asia in 2007 Danone acquired all of the Japanese joint venture with Ajinomoto and Calpis that it did not already own. Renamed Danone Japan the operation manufactures fresh products for the expanding Japanese dairy market.

Saying it wanted to "regain room for maneuver[ing]" in 2007 it sold off its 20% stake in and terminated its distribution agreement with Shanghai-based Bright Dairy. Danone cited no specifics surrounding the move but the company has had legal disputes with various joint-venture partners in China and India recently relating to how its brands are marketed and produced.

In late 2007 the company exited its joint venture with Chinese company Mengniu Dairy Group citing time frame and other condition difficulties. (Both companies agreed to the termination of the venture which was initiated in 2006.) Turning to South America that same year Danone acquired a 70% holding in Chile's fresh dairy company Vialat.

Among its divestments in 2008 in order to fulfill European Union requirements for its acquisition of Numico the company sold off its French baby milk and baby drinks businesses to Groupe Lactalis. That year it also sold its subsidiary Frucor a maker of non-alcoholic beverages in New Zealand and Australia as well as its international brands V and Mizone (with the exception of in China and Indonesia) to Suntory for some ?600 million ($780 million).

Danone took full control of its South African joint venture Danone Clover in 2009. It purchased Clover's 45% stake for R1085 ($145 million). (Clover is one of South Africa's largest dairy companies.) Other partnerships include a joint venture with Weight Watchers formed in 2008. The 51% Weight Watchers-49% Danone operation provides

weight-management services to the People's Republic of China.

Following its acquisition of a controlling interest in a venture with Russia's Unimilk in 2010 Danone sold its 18.4% stake in Wimm-Bill-Dann Foods back to the Russian dairy and juice producer for $470 million.

EXECUTIVES

Executive Vice-President, Chief Financial, Technology and Data Officer, Juergen Esser
Director Representing Employees, Frederic Boutebba
Independent Director, Jean-Michel Severino
Non-Executive Vice Chairwoman of the Board, Cecile Cabanis
Executive Vice President of Human Resources, Member of the Executive Committee, Bertrand Austruy
Independent Director, Lionel Zinsou-Derlin
Director, Representing Employees, Bettina Theissig
Independent Director, Gaelle Olivier
Independent Director, Serpil Timuray
Independent Director, Clara Gaymard
Non-Executive Chairman of the Board, Gilles Schnepp
Lead Independent Director, Michel Landel
Independent Director, Guido Barilla
Chief Executive Officer - International, Member of the Executive Board, Veronique Penchienati-Bosetta
Chief Executive Officer, Antoine de Saint-Affrique
Chief Human Resource Officer, Roberto Di Bernardini
Chief Sustainability and Strategic Business Development Officer, Henri Bruxelles
EVP, Growth and Innovation, Nigyar Makhmudova
EVP and CEO, Danone Noth America, Shane Grant
Auditors: PricewaterhouseCoopers Audit

LOCATIONS

HQ: Danone
17, Boulevard Haussmann, Paris 75009
Phone: (33) 1 44 35 20 20   Fax: (33) 1 44 35 26 95
Web: www.danone.com

2018 Sales

	% of total
Asia-Pacific Latin America Middle East Africa & CIS	45
Europe and NORAM	55
Total	100

PRODUCTS/OPERATIONS

2018 sales

	%
Essential Dairy & Plant-Based (North America)	20
Essential Dairy & Plant-Based (International)	33
Specialized Nutrition	29
Waters	18
Total	100

COMPETITORS

COCA-COLA AMATIL PTY LTD
Grupo Lala S.A.B. de C.V.
MONDELEZ INTERNATIONAL INC.
Nestle S.A.
PARMALAT FINANZIARIA SPA

PREMIER FOODS PLC
RECKITT BENCKISER GROUP PLC
SUNTORY HOLDINGS LIMITED
UNILEVER PLC

HISTORICAL FINANCIALS

Company Type: Public

Income Statement FYE: December 31

	REVENUE ($ mil.)	NET INCOME ($ mil.)	NET PROFIT MARGIN	EMPLOYEES
12/20	28,988	2,400	8.3%	101,911
12/19	28,391	2,165	7.6%	102,449
12/18	28,230	2,690	9.5%	105,783
12/17	29,581	2,940	9.9%	104,843
12/16	23,170	1,816	7.8%	99,187
Annual Growth	5.8%	7.2%	—	0.7%

2020 Year-End Financials

Debt ratio: 46.0%	No. of shares (mil.): 649
Return on equity: 11.6%	Dividends
Cash ($ mil.): 727	Yield: 3.6%
Current ratio: 1.03	Payout: 14.1%
Long-term debt ($ mil.): 15,061	Market value ($ mil.): 8,512

	STOCK PRICE ($) FY Close	P/E High/Low		PER SHARE ($) Earnings	Dividends	Book Value
12/20	13.10	6	4	3.67	0.48	30.61
12/19	16.49	6	5	3.31	0.43	29.83
12/18	13.98	5	4	4.16	0.44	28.92
12/17	16.77	4	4	4.69	0.42	27.49
12/16	12.58	5	4	2.95	0.33	22.43
Annual Growth	1.0%	—	—	5.6%	9.4%	8.1%

Danske Bank A/S

Danske Bank is a Nordic bank serving 3.3 million personal and business customers as well as more than 2300 corporate and institutional customers in 12 countries. The bank has over 180 branches and serves its core markets including Denmark Finland Norway and Sweden. The bank offers a wide range of services in the fields of banking mortgage finance insurance pension real-estate brokerage asset management and trading in fixed income products foreign exchange and equities. Danske Bank's roots go back to 1871 when Den Danske Landmandsbank was founded.

Operations

Danske Bank operates five business units a Non-core unit and an Other Activities unit.

Banking DK which accounts for more than 30% of the bank's revenue serves retail and commercial customers in Denmark. The unit offers tailored financial advice to customers aside from daily banking home financing investment and retirement planning solutions. For commercial customers the unit provides targeted advice and solutions based on the size and situation of the customers' business. Services include strategic advice on for instance international expansion and acquisitions. The unit offers digital solutions to facilitate daily operations including cross-border transfers and cash management.

Banking Nordic (25% of revenue) serves retail and commercial customers in Sweden Norway and Finland providing customer offerings similar to those of Banking DK. In addition the unit encompasses the group's global asset finance activities such as lease activities.

Corporates & Institutions (25% of revenue) is the wholesale banking division of the group. It serves all of the group's corporate and institutional customers by offering expertise within financing financial markets general banking investment serv-

ices and corporate finance advisory services. In addition the unit operates globally supported by global product areas and local customer coverage and acts as a bridge to the world for Nordic customers as well as a gateway into the Nordics for international customers. The unit is organized in four areas: a customer unit named General Banking and three product areas; named Capital Markets Fixed Income & Currencies (FI&C) and Transaction Banking & Investor Services.

Wealth Management (almost 15% of revenue) serves companies and institutional investors in the markets in which the Group operates. The unit offers a broad range of products and services within wealth and asset management investments pension savings and insurance.

Northern Ireland (less than 5%) serves retail and commercial customers through a network of branches and business centres in Northern Ireland alongside digital channels.

Non-core includes certain customer segments that are no longer considered part of the core business. Other Activities encompasses group treasury group support functions and eliminations including the elimination of returns on own shares and issues as well as interest on additional tier 1 capital which is reported as an interest expense in the business units.

Geographic Reach

Denmark accounts for more than 70% of Copenhagen-based Danske Bank's total revenue. Norway brings in almost 10% followed by Sweden and Finland with more than 5% each.

As well as the four Nordic countries and Northern Ireland Danske operates in Ireland the UK Lithuania Luxembourg Germany Poland the US China and India.

Sales and Marketing

Danske Bank serves retail and commercial customers as well as companies and institutional investors through a network of branches business centres and digital channels.

Financial Performance

Note: Growth rates may differ after conversion to US dollars.

Danske Bank's revenues have been fluctuating over the past five years. The bank has an overall revenue growth of had a decline of more than 10% from 2016 to 2020.

In 2020 the bank's total income fell by 6% or DKK42.4 billion compared to the prior year. Net profit decreased by 70% or DKK4.6 billion in 2020 versus the prior year. The net profit in 2020 was affected mainly by loan impairment charges of DKK 7 billion reflecting expected credit losses due to the corona crisis.

Net interest income was stable at DKK 21.9 billion. There were positive effects from deposit and lending volumes higher deposit margins and an increase in amortization of loan origination fees.

Danske Bank ended 2020 with total cash and cash equivalents of DKK400.9 billion. Operating activities provided DKK186.5 billion while investing activities used DKK1.3 billion. Financing activities generated DKK18.3 billion.

Strategy

Danske Bank launched the Better Bank transformation in late 2020 and announced clear ambitions towards 2023 for all of its stakeholder groups: customers employees society and shareholders. The bank started its multi-year transformation to become a simpler and more competitive bank to continue its journey towards becoming more integrated into the lives of its customers and the Nordic societies as well as to address a number of industry- and Danske Bank-specific challenges.

The bank's 2023 ambitions for its key stakeholders include: to be among the top two in customer satisfaction in everything they do; to engage at least 90% of their employees; to operate sus-

tainably ethically and transparently and have a positive impact on the societies they are part of; and achieve a 9% to 10% return on shareholders' equity and a cost per income ratio in the low 50s.

Mergers and Acquisitions

In 2021 Danske Bank has entered into an agreement with OP Financial Group in Finland and the consortium of banks behind Vipps in Norway to merge the three mobile payment providers MobilePay Vipps and Pivo. The ambition is to create Europe's best and most comprehensive digital wallet. Serving 11 million users and over 330000 shops and web shops the company will be one of the largest bank-owned mobile payment providers in Europe. In addition the parties plan to invest heavily in e-commerce which has been growing rapidly in recent years and to ensure users access to mobile cross-border payments. The banks behind Vipps will own 65% of the new parent company Vipps AS Danske Bank will own 25% and the OP Financial Group will own 10%.

HISTORY

Leathersmith-turned-stock trader Gottlieb Gedalia founded Den Danske Landmandsbank Hypothek- og Vexelbank i Kj benhavn (The Danish Farmer's Bank Mortgage and Exchange Bank of Copenhagen. It would change its name four times before finally settling on the less-verbose Danske Bank.

Even in its early years Danske Bank never restricted itself to purely agricultural concerns preferring to offer a wide range of banking services that appealed to farmers merchants and businessmen alike. Isak Gl ckstadt who managed the bank from 1872 until his death in 1910 guided the bank to prominence in Copenhagen's corporate landscape where it became a leading commercial bank. Gl ckstadt's son Emil succeeded his father as managing director in 1910. Despite his best efforts Danske Bank could not cope with the strains of WWI and the Depression; the Danish government had to rescue the firm from bankruptcy. But the bank survived German occupation during WWII mostly unscathed.

During the 1960s and 1970s Denmark's government encouraged Danish banks to expand internationally. Danske Bank pounced on the opportunity by forming consortium banks with such Nordic neighbors as Skandinaviska Enskilda Banken (aka S-E-Banken). Danske Bank stayed ahead of its competitors through acquisitions including the purchase of two large Danish banks in 1990 making it Denmark's largest bank.

By 1990 the bank also had made its presence felt worldwide but Asian economic crises in the early 1990s caused the bank's international subsidiaries to fall short of expectations. After restructuring its international business the bank focused more energy on its Nordic customers. It bought Sweden's –stg ¶ta Enskilda in 1998 and Norway's Fokus Bank in 1999. In 2000 Danske bought fellow Danish Bank BG Bank. Danske also added a Finnish asset management company and a majority interest in Pol-Can Bank of Poland in the same year. In 2001 Danske and BG trimmed down redundant branches.

Danske Bank bought the banking operations of Finnish insurer Sampo for more than $5 billion in 2007. The acquisition brought in more than 150 branches in Finland Estonia Latvia and Lithuania. It followed Danske Bank's 2005 acquisitions of National Irish Bank and Northern Bank from National Australia Bank for some $1.8 billion.

EXECUTIVES

Head of Large Corporates and Institutions, Member of the Executive Leadership Team, Berit Behring, $1,192,812 total compensation
Chief Administrative Officer, Member of the Executive Leadership Team, Philippe Vollot, $1,351,854 total compensation
Independent Director, Raija-Leena Hankonen-Nybom
Vice Chairman of the Board, Jan Nielsen
Director, Lars-Erik Brenoee
Director, Employee Representative, Bente Bang
Director, Employee Representative, Thorbjoern Lundholm Dahl
Director, Employee Representative, Kirsten Brich
Independent Vice Chairman of the Board, Carol Sergeant
Independent Director, Bente Avnung Landsnes
Head of Personal and Business Customers, Member of the Executive Leadership Team, Glenn Soderholm, $1,351,854 total compensation
Director, Employee Representative, Charlotte Hoffmann
Auditors: Deloitte Statsautoriseret Revisionspartnerselskab

LOCATIONS

HQ: Danske Bank A/S
Holmens Kanal 2-12, Copenhagen K DK-1092
Phone: (45) 45 44 00 00   **Fax:** 212 370-9564
Web: www.danskebank.com

PRODUCTS/OPERATIONS

2017 Sales

	% of total
Net interest income	49
Net fee income	32
Net trading income	16
Other income	3
Total	**100**

2017 Sales by Segment

	% of total
Personal Banking	25
Business Banking	23
Corporate & Institutions	23
Wealth Management	17
Northern Ireland	4
Other Activities	5
Eliminations (2)	
Reclassification	3
Total	**100**

COMPETITORS

Banco do Brasil S/A
CLYDESDALE BANK PLC
COMMONWEALTH BANK OF AUSTRALIA
Co ¶peratieve Rabobank U.A.
DEUTSCHE BANK AG
KEYCORP
Landesbank Baden-W rttemberg
NATIONAL WESTMINSTER BANK PUBLIC LIMITED COMPANY
Svenska Handelsbanken AB
The Toronto-Dominion Bank
U.S. BANCORP
UniCredit Bank AG

HISTORICAL FINANCIALS

Company Type: Public

Income Statement

FYE: December 31

	ASSETS ($ mil.)	NET INCOME ($ mil.)	INCOME AS % OF ASSETS	EMPLOYEES
12/20	677,814	666	0.1%	22,376
12/19	565,216	2,146	0.4%	22,006
12/18	548,802	2,132	0.4%	20,683
12/17	569,917	3,238	0.6%	19,768
12/16	494,783	2,726	0.6%	19,303
Annual Growth	**8.2%**	**(29.7%)**	**—**	**3.8%**

2020 Year-End Financials

Return on assets: 0.1%	Dividends
Return on equity: 2.3%	Yield: 0.0%
Long-term debt ($ mil.): —	Payout: 42.5%
No. of shares (mil.): 853	Market value ($ mil.): 7,008
Sales ($ mil): 22,514	

	STOCK PRICE ($) FY Close	P/E High/Low		PER SHARE ($) Earnings	Dividends	Book Value
12/20	8.21	2	1	0.78	0.33	32.59
12/19	8.05	1	0	2.51	0.43	30.02
12/18	9.99	1	1	2.53	0.56	29.29
12/17	19.55	1	1	3.56	0.49	30.30
12/16	15.18	1	1	2.87	0.37	25.30
Annual Growth	**(14.2%)**	**—**	**—**	**(27.9%)**	**(3.0%)**	**6.5%**

Datang International Power Generation Co Ltd

Datang Power is a powerful player in the Chinese power market. Datang International Power Generation (Datang Power) formerly Beijing Datang Power Generation operates and develops power plants (primarily coal-fired) sells electricity and provides power equipment maintenance services. One of China's top independent power producers with a generating capacity of 39190 MW (coal-fired wind powered and hydroelectric facilities) Datang Power owns and operates four power plants and manages more than 50 power and power-related companies in 18 provinces. In 2013 it added 1240 MW of renewable energy capacity. Government-owned China Datang Corp. owns about 35% of Datang Power (which also has chemical and coal assets).

EXECUTIVES

Non-Executive Director, Zheng Xiao
Chief Accounting Officer, Joint Company Secretary, Jinming Jiang
Independent Non-Executive Director, Jizhen Liu
Director, Xianguo Zhao
Director, Xin Cao
General Manager, Executive Director, Yongpan Liang
Director, Shengxiang Jin
Director, Xuejun Ying
Director, Shaowen Zhu
Director, Yongxing Sun
Independent Non-Executive Director, Dongxiao Niu

Non-Executive Director, Jianlong Liu
Non-Executive Independent Director, Baoquan Kou
Non-Executive Independent Director, Fengqi Si
Non-Executive Independent Director, Wenlong Zong
Secretary of the Board, Baowen Mai
Non-Executive Director, Min Su
Auditors: ShineWing (HK) CPA Limited

LOCATIONS

HQ: Datang International Power Generation Co Ltd
No. 9 Guangningbo Street, Xicheng District, Beijing 100033
Phone: (86) 10 88008800   **Fax:** (86) 10 88008111
Web: www.dtpower.com

PRODUCTS/OPERATIONS

2015 Sales

	% of total
Sales of electricity	90
Sales of chemical products	3
Heat supply	2
Sales of coal	-
Others	5
Total	**100**

2015 Sales

	% of total
Power generation Segment	93
Chemical segment	3
Coal segment	-
Other segments	4
Total	**100**

COMPETITORS

Brookfield Renewable Power Inc
COGENTRIX ENERGY POWER MANAGEMENT LLC
INTERGEN SERVICES INC.
TAIWAN POWER COMPANY

HISTORICAL FINANCIALS

Company Type: Public

Income Statement

FYE: December 31

	REVENUE ($ mil.)	NET INCOME ($ mil.)	NET PROFIT MARGIN	EMPLOYEES
12/20	14,619	464	3.2%	0
12/19	13,718	153	1.1%	0
12/18	13,577	179	1.3%	33,483
12/17	12,936	229	1.8%	0
12/16	8,250	(396)	—	22,966
Annual Growth	**15.4%**	**—**	**—**	**—**

2020 Year-End Financials

Debt ratio: 8.0%	No. of shares (mil.): —
Return on equity: 4.4%	Dividends
Cash ($ mil.): 1,265	Yield: —
Current ratio: 0.43	Payout: —
Long-term debt ($ mil.): 15,004	Market value ($ mil.): —

DBS Group Holdings Ltd.

Founded in 1968 DBS is a leading financial services group in Asia with a presence in about 20 markets. Headquartered and listed in Singapore DBS has a growing presence in the three key Asian axes of growth: Greater China (less than 10% of total income) Southeast Asia and South Asia (roughly 10%). The bank serves 10.7 million customers for a full range of services in consumer banking wealth management and institutional banking. DBS has a SGD 646 billion of total assets.

Operations

DBS Group reports in four major business segments are: consumer banking/ wealth management institutional banking treasury markets and others.

Consumer Banking/ Wealth Management (over 40% of total income) provides individual customers with a diverse range of banking and related financial services. The products and services available to customers include current and savings accounts fixed deposits loans and home finance cards payments investment and insurance products.

Institutional Banking (nearly 40%) provides financial services and products to institutional clients including bank and non-bank financial institutions government-linked companies large corporates and small and medium-sized businesses. The business focuses on broadening and deepening customer relationships. Products and services comprise the full range of credit facilities from short-term working capital financing to specialized lending. It also provides global transactional services such as cash management trade finance and securities and fiduciary services treasury and markets products corporate finance and advisory banking as well as capital markets solutions.

Treasury Markets' activities (some 15%) primarily include structuring market-making and trading across a broad range of treasury products. The Others segment (some 5%) encompasses the results of corporate decisions that are not attributed to business segments as well as the contribution of LVB as its activities have not been aligned with the Group's segment definitions.

Geographic Reach

DBS generates majority of its income from Singapore (about 70%) where its head office is located while 20% comes from Hong Kong. The rest of greater China South and Southeast Asia and the rest of the world generate less than 5% each.

Hong Kong comprises mainly DBS Bank (HK) Limited and DBS HK branch. Rest of Greater China comprises mainly DBS Bank (China) Ltd DBS Bank (Taiwan) Ltd and DBS Taipei branch. South and Southeast Asia comprises mainly PT Bank DBS Indonesia DBS Bank India Limited (including LVB balances post-amalgamation) and DBS Labuan branch.

Sales and Marketing

Throughout the year DBS maintained active engagement of its stakeholders with enhanced content and contextualized marketing. It interacts with customers through multiple channels including digital banking call centers and branches to better understand their requirements so that it can propose the right financial solutions for them. It communicates with its employees using multiple channels to ensure they are aligned with its strategic priorities. This also allows the company to be up to date with their concerns.

Financial Performance

Total income was stable at SGD 14.6 billion. Net interest income fell to SGD 9.1 million from SGD 9.6 million the prior year due to a fall in net interest margin but offset by gains from investment securities. Total deposits rose significantly by 15% to SGD 465 billion reflecting its leading savings deposit and cash management franchises enhanced by digitalization capabilities.

Net profit declined 26% to SGD 4.8 million in 2020 from SGD 6.4 million in 2019 due to higher total allowances set aside to buffer against potential risks arising from the pandemic.

Cash at the end of the fiscal year 2020 was SGD 42 million compared to SGD 20 million in 2019. Operating activities generated SGD 24.9 million while investing activities used SGD 415 thousand. Financing activities also used SGD 2.4 million primarily for dividends paid to shareholders.

Strategy

Over the past five years DBS' transformation strategy has been focused on three pillars: being digital to the core embedding ourselves in the customer journey and thinking and acting like a startup. While the company has seen rising digital adoption over the years Covid-19 accelerated these trends. In 2020 almost three in four customers applied for a mortgage online compared to over one in three the previous year. DBS PayLah! usage also saw exponential growth.

DBS's strategy is predicated on Asia's megatrends including the rising middle class growing intra-regional trade urbanization and the rapid adoption of technology that is fueling new innovations.

EXECUTIVES

Group Head of Consumer Banking and Wealth Management, Sim Seng Lim
Chief Information Officer, Head of Group Technology and Operations at DBS Bank, Jimmy Ng
Non-Executive Independent Director, Weng Kin Lim
Non-Executive Independent Director, Punita Lal
Non-Executive Non-Independent Director, Kai Fong Chng
Non-Executive Independent Director, Judy Lee
Non-Executive and Non-Independent Director, Tian Yee Ho
Group Corporate Treasurer, Philip Fernandez
Head of Group Strategic Marketing and Communications, Ngui Karen
Head of Treasury and Markets at DBS Bank, Wai Hung Ng
Chief Risk Officer - DBS Group, Teck Long Tan
Group Head - Capital Markets, Eng-kwok Seat Moey
Non-Executive Independent Director, Sai Choy Tham
Country Head, Tse Koon Shee
Non-Executive Non-Independent Chairman of the Board, Lim Huat Seah
Head - Group Human Resources, Yan Hong Lee
Chief Financial Officer, Sok Hui Lim
Chief Executive Officer of DBS Bank India Limited, Surojit Shome
Non-Executive Independent Director, Bonghan Cho
Non-Executive and Lead Independent Director, Tse Ghow Lim
Group Head - Legal, Compliance and Secretariat, Chee Kin Lam
Head, Institutional Banking Group, Su Shan Tan
Group Head of Audit, Derrick Goh
Chief Executive Officer of DBS Bank Taiwan, Lim Him Chuan
Chief Executive Officer, Executive Director, Piyush Gupta, $869,966 total compensation
Chief Executive Officer of DBS Bank (Hong Kong), Sebastian Paredes
Chief Executive Officer of DBS Bank (China) Limited, Neil Ge
President Director of P.T. Bank DBS Indonesia, Paulus Sutisna
Group Head, Strategy and Planning, Kwee Juan Han
Auditors: PricewaterhouseCoopers LLP

LOCATIONS

HQ: DBS Group Holdings Ltd.
12 Marina Boulevard, Marina Bay Financial Centre Tower 3, 018982
Phone: (65) 6878 8888   **Fax:** 213 627-0228
Web: www.dbs.com

2016 Sales

	% of total
Singapore	66
Hong Kong	18
Rest of the greater China	7
South and Southeast Asia	6
Rest of the world	3
Total	**100**

PRODUCTS/OPERATIONS

2016 Sales

	% of total
Institutional Banking	45
Consumer Banking/wealth management	37
Treasury	10
Others	8
Total	**100**

2016 Sales

	% of total
Interest income	64
Net fee and commission income	20
Net Trading income	12
Net income from investment securities	3
Other income	1
Total	**100**

Selected Subsidiaries

DBS Bank
  Bank of the Philippines Islands (20.3%)
  Cholamandalam DBS Finance Limited (37.4%)
  DBS Asia Capital Limited
  DBS Asset Management Ltd
  DBS Diamond Holdings Ltd
  DBS Bank (Hong Kong) Limited
  Hutchison DBS Card Ltd (50%)
  DBSN Services Pte. Ltd.
  DBS Vickers Securities (Singapore) Pte Ltd
  The Islamic Bank of Asia Limited (50%)
  PT Bank DBS Indonesia (99%)

COMPETITORS

AUSTRALIA AND NEW ZEALAND BANKING GROUP LIMITED
Agricultural Bank of China Limited
BANK OF EAST ASIA LIMITED THE
BANK OF THE PHILIPPINE ISLANDS
BANK VTB PAO
Bank of Communications Co. Ltd.
CHINA MINSHENG BANKING CORP. LTD.
CIMB GROUP HOLDINGS BERHAD
CITIC Securities International Company Limited
China Construction Bank Corporation
China Merchants Bank Co. Ltd.
HDFC BANK LIMITED
ICICI BANK LIMITED
IYO BANK LTD. THE
NATIONAL AUSTRALIA BANK LIMITED
PUBLIC BANK BHD
QATAR NATIONAL BANK (Q.P.S.C.)
RESONA HOLDINGS INC.
SBERBANK PAO
SINOPAC FINANCIAL HOLDINGS COMPANY LIMITED
The Bank of Nova Scotia
UNITED OVERSEAS BANK LIMITED

HISTORICAL FINANCIALS
Company Type: Public

Income Statement   FYE: December 31

	ASSETS ($ mil.)	NET INCOME ($ mil.)	INCOME AS % OF ASSETS	EMPLOYEES
12/20	491,731	3,571	0.7%	29,000
12/19	430,307	4,750	1.1%	28,000
12/18	404,457	4,095	1.0%	0
12/17	387,534	3,271	0.8%	24,174
12/16	333,271	2,932	0.9%	22,194
Annual Growth	10.2%	5.1%	—	6.9%

2020 Year-End Financials
Return on assets: 0.7%	Dividends
Return on equity: 8.9%	Yield: 3.5%
Long-term debt ($ mil.): —	Payout: 210.3%
No. of shares (mil.): —	Market value ($ mil.): —
Sales ($ mil): 13,409	

	STOCK PRICE ($) FY Close	P/E High/Low	PER SHARE ($) Earnings	Dividends	Book Value
12/20	76.05	44 28	1.37	2.73	16.21
12/19	77.16	34 28	1.83	4.16	14.84
12/18	69.73	42 31	1.58	4.98	14.12
12/17	74.66	45 31	1.27	1.79	13.89
12/16	47.75	31 22	1.15	1.56	12.17
Annual Growth	12.3%	— —	4.5%	15.0%	7.4%

DCC Plc

DCC offers international sales marketing and support services across four divisions: Liquid Petroleum Gas (LPG) Retail & Oil Technology and Healthcare. It distributes to end users or resellers in 20 countries sourcing product wholesale from refineries and manufacturers. DCC operates through dozens of subsidiaries including Butagaz Exertis Certas and Flogas. It also trades under the Esso brand under license in Norway. Most revenue comes from the UK. DCC was founded in 1976 as a venture capital company before expanding into commodity distribution.

Operations
DCC operates under four reportable segments: DCC Retail & Oil DCC Technology. DCC LPG and DCC Healthcare.

Retail & Oil generate about 60% of revenue. The group is the leading operator of retail petrol stations in Europe and is the leading reseller of fuel cards in Britain and leading oil distributor in Europe.

Technology brings up more than 25% of revenue. It is a leading route-to-market and supply chain partner for global technology brands and customers.

LPG gives in more than 10% of revenue. The group markets its LPG in Europe North America and Asia. It also involves in retailing of natural gas and electricity as well as the sales and distribution of industrial gases including refrigerants.

Healthcare generate about 5% of revenue. It provides products and services to healthcare providers and health and beauty brand owners.

Geographic Reach
Dublin-based DCC generate more than 45% of its revenue from Europe followed France which gives in about 20% Ireland brings up more than 5% and the rest comes from other countries.

Sales and Marketing
DCC has a diverse customer base. Its hydrocarbon businesses serve domestic agriculture commercial aviation and marine customers and gas stations. The Technology division's customers are physical and online retailers resellers and value added retailers. The Heathcare segment serves health & beauty brand owners specialist retailers and direct sales/mail order companies.

Financial Performance
Note: Growth rates may differ after conversion to US Dollars.

Overall the company's revenue decreased by 3% to 14.8 billion primarily driven by the lower oil price that prevailed during 2019.

The company's profit decreased by 1% to 254.2 million compared from 271.1 million in the prior year. The decrease was due to lower revenue while having a higher finance cost.

Cash held by the company at the end of 2019 increased by 218.7 million to 1.7 billion compared to the prior year with 1.5 billion. Cash provided by operations and financing activities were 529.1 million and 427.0 million respectively. Cash used for investing activities was 319.5 million primarily for acquisition of subsidiaries and purchase of property plant and equipment.

Strategy
In September 2019 DCC Healthcare completed the disposal of DCC Vital's UK generic pharma activities and related manufacturing facility in Ireland (Kent Pharma and Athlone Laboratories). The disposal sharpens the strategic focus of DCC Vital allowing it to concentrate on those areas where it has market-leading positions and sustainable competitive advantage in particular in the sales marketing and distribution of medical products in Britain and Ireland. Whilst part of the DCC the cash flows generated by the disposed business more than recovered its acquisition cost however the transaction resulted in a loss on disposal of 34.7 million principally representing a non-cash impairment of the goodwill recognized on the initial acquisition of the business.

DCC Healthcare made considerable strategic progress during the year in generating very good profit growth significantly expanding its presence in the US nutrition market with two substantial acquisitions and strengthening its position in the primary and secondary healthcare sectors in Britain with a number of small bolt-on acquisitions.

Mergers and Acquisitions
DCC uses acquisitions as its primary source of growth making numerous every year. In 2017 and 2018 these have included: Medisource and Elite One Source (Health & Beauty); Hammer MTR Hypertec Stampede and Jam Industries (Technology); Dansk Fuels Esso Retail Norway and SNAP (Retail & Oil); and Shell Hong Kong & Macau Countrywide LPG TEGA and Retail West (Liquefied Petroleum Gas).

Company Background
In early 2020 DCC Healthcare acquired Minnesota based Amerilab Technologies Inc. a specialist provider of contract manufacturing and related services in effervescent nutritional products for $85 million. The acquisition is part of the company's step to build a business of scale in the world's largest health supplements and nutritional products market.

In late 2019 DCC Healthcare acquired Florida-based Ion Labs Inc. a contract manufacturer of nutritional products for $60 million. This acquisition represented a significant step in DCC Health & Beauty Solutions' strategy to build a material presence in the attractive US health supplements and nutritional products market.

EXECUTIVES
Non-Executive Director, Alan Ralph
Chief Executive, Executive Director, Donal Murphy, $998,303 total compensation
Managing Director - DCC Healthcare, Conor Costigan
Chief Information Officer, Peter Quinn
Non-Executive Independent Director, Tufan Erginbilgic
Non-Executive Director, Laura Angelini
Managing Director - DCC Retail & Oil, Eddie O'Brien
General Counsel, Company Secretary, Darragh Byrne
Chief Financial Officer, Executive Director, Kevin Lucey, $368,102 total compensation
Managing Director - DCC LPG, Henry Cubbon
Senior Non-Executive Independent Director, Caroline Dowling
Non-Executive Chairman of the Board, Mark Breuer
Managing Director - DCC Technology, Tim Griffin
Head of Group Human Resources, Nicola McCracken
Non-Executive Director, Liu Lily
Non-Executive Independent Director, Pamela Kirby
Non-Executive Independent Director, David Jukes
Auditors: KPMG

LOCATIONS
HQ: DCC Plc
DCC House, Leopardstown Road, Foxrock, Dublin 18
Phone: (353) 1 279 9400   **Fax:** (353) 1 283 1017
Web: www.dcc.ie

2018 sales
	$ mil	%
United Kingdom	7,741	54
France	2,712	19
Ireland	927	6
Other	2,884	21
Total	**14,264**	**100**

PRODUCTS/OPERATIONS

2018 Sales
	% of total
Retail & Oil	65
Technology	22
LPG	10
Healthcare	4
Total	**100**

COMPETITORS
ABB Ltd	MRC GLOBAL INC.
ASSA ABLOY AB	N L INDUSTRIES INC.
BUNZL PUBLIC LIMITED COMPANY	REXEL
Brenntag Holding GmbH	SIG PLC
HITACHI EUROPE LIMITED	SSP GROUP PLC
INNERWORKINGS INC.	TUBOS REUNIDOS SA

HISTORICAL FINANCIALS
Company Type: Public

Income Statement   FYE: March 31

	REVENUE ($ mil.)	NET INCOME ($ mil.)	NET PROFIT MARGIN	EMPLOYEES
03/21	18,464	402	2.2%	13,199
03/20	18,228	303	1.7%	12,773
03/19	19,946	343	1.7%	12,418
03/18	20,044	367	1.8%	10,430
03/17	15,318	269	1.8%	10,848
Annual Growth	4.8%	10.5%	—	5.0%

2021 Year-End Financials

Debt ratio: 30.3%	No. of shares (mil.): 98
Return on equity: 11.4%	Dividends
Cash ($ mil.): 2,459	Yield: —
Current ratio: 1.40	Payout: 53.8%
Long-term debt ($ mil.): 2,138	Market value ($ mil.): —

Dekabank Deutsche Girozentrale

EXECUTIVES

Vice Chairman of the Management Board, Matthias Danne

Member of the board of directors, Martin Muller

Chairman of the Board Of Directors, Georg Stocker

Chief Financial Officer, Member of the board of directors, Daniel Kapffer

Chief Risk Officer, Member of the board of directors, Birgit Gasoline

Auditors: KPMG AG Wirtschaftspruefungsgesellschaft

LOCATIONS

HQ: Dekabank Deutsche Girozentrale
 Mainzer Landstrasse 16, Frankfurt 60325
Phone: (49) 69 71 47 0 **Fax:** (49) 69 71 47 13 76
Web: www.dekabank.de

HISTORICAL FINANCIALS

Company Type: Public

Income Statement				FYE: December 31
	ASSETS ($ mil.)	NET INCOME ($ mil.)	INCOME AS % OF ASSETS	EMPLOYEES
12/20	104,944	260	0.2%	4,711
12/19	109,224	235	0.2%	4,723
12/18	115,027	327	0.3%	4,716
12/17	112,371	313	0.3%	4,419
12/16	90,758	278	0.3%	4,283
Annual Growth	3.7%	(1.7%)	—	2.4%

2020 Year-End Financials

Return on assets: 0.2%	Dividends
Return on equity: 3.8%	Yield: —
Long-term debt ($ mil.): —	Payout: —
No. of shares (mil.): —	Market value ($ mil.): —
Sales ($ mil): 4,760	

Denso Corp

DENSO Corporation is the number 2 global automotive parts manufacturer (behind Bosch). The Japan-based company supplies OEM and aftermarket components and systems for most of the world's carmakers (Toyota Motor accounts for roughly half of DENSO's total revenue). DENSO products include powertrain systems vehicle electronics electrification systems and cockpit systems as well as advanced safety and automated driving technologies. The company has expanded recently into industrial and consumer products such as bar code readers industrial robots and home energy management systems. About half of its sales are generated in Japan.

Operations

DENSO is divided into five product groups: thermal systems powertrain systems mobility electronics electrification systems and sensor & semiconductor (less than 5%).

The thermal systems business (about 25% of sales) provides air conditioning systems for cars and buses truck refrigeration units radiators and cooling systems. It also develops products for interior thermal management that monitor the driver's physical condition and adjust for temperature humidity and even fragrance.

Powertrain systems (nearly 25%) manufactures engine-related products such as variable cam timing (VCT) systems exhaust gas sensors and products for drive systems such as oil pressure control valves.

Mobility electronics (more than 20%) encompasses DENSO's connected car offerings for advanced safety and automated driving systems.

The electrification systems segment (more than 15%) is focused on products that provide more energy-efficient powertrains and moreeco-friendly technologies. This segment makes hybrid and electric car drive systems steering and braking control products and power supply and starting system products.

Other Automotive which is more than 5% of total revenue supplies automotive parts and service tools.

Geographic Reach

Based in Japan DENSO operates in about 35 countries and regions. Approximately 45% of the company's revenue is generated in Japan and more than 20% in other Asian countries. The company does more than 20% of its business in North America (with minor operations through subsidiaries in South America) and about 10% in Europe.

Sales and Marketing

Sales to original equipment manufacturers (OEMs) account for about 90% of DENSO's sales with the remaining revenue coming from aftermarket and non-automotive activities. Its largest customer Toyota Motor Group accounts for roughly half of sales.

Financial Performance

Note: Growth rates may differ after conversion to US Dollars.

DENSO's revenue has been increasing steadily over the past five years except for 2020.

Although sales volume remained flat until the third quarter revenue of the Group decreased by 209.3 billion or 4% to 5.2 billion for the year ended March 31 2020 due to a significant market contraction caused by the COVID-19 pandemic in the fourth quarter and exchange rate fluctuations.

Profit attributable to owners of the parent company decreased by 186.4 billion or 73% to 68.1 billion. Primarily due toa provision for quality costs in the second half of the fiscal year and reduction in production volume reflecting lower sales.

Cash at the end of fiscal 2020 was 597.8 billion a decrease of 113.8 billion from the prior year. Cash from operations contributed 595.3 billion to the coffers while investing activities used 447.4 billion mainly for purchases of property and equipment. Financing activities used another 240.9 billion for loan payments dividends to stockholders and the company's stock repurchase program.

Strategy

DENSO aims to achieve sustainable growth in a changing environment by remaining alert to the needs of society. The company have identified four priority areas: electric vehicles advanced safety/autonomous vehicles connectivity and factory automation/agriculture. They will continue to create new value by using their accumulated technology and experience to drive further progress in new mobility-related fields by contributing to the advancement of manufacturing through their factory automation business and by applying DENSO technology to their agriculture business.

DENSO has been developing mass-production process technologies to their plants around the worlds to achieve the same high "Monozukuri (manufacturing)" level globally. Hirose Plant has been establish development and mass-production process as Electrification Global Mother with EIC. They will developing good mass-production line to all over the global production plants.

Mergers and Acquisitions

In 2019 DENSO purchased a stake in Infineon Technologies one of the top manufacturers of in-vehicle semiconductor products. DENSO will combine Infineon Technologies' advanced semiconductor technologies with its own in-vehicle technologies and expertise to accelerate the development of new and emerging mobility solutions.

Company Background

Originally the in-house parts supplier for Toyota Nippondenso Co. (the predecessor to DENSO) was spun off by Toyota in 1949. Nippondenso remained dependent upon Toyota for sales as it still does today.

In 1966 Nippondenso established sales offices in the US then turned to Europe establishing a branch office Germany in 1970. It later went on to establish subsidiaries in the US Canada Europe and Asia. In 1984 Nippondenso joined with Allen Bradley Co. (US) to develop factory automation equipment. The company changed its name to DENSO CORPORATION in 1996. In 2001 the company merged its industrial equipment subsidiaries (bar code scanners and factory automation robots) and spun them off as majority-owned subsidiary DENSO Wave (now part of the company's non-automotive business segment). In 2006 DENSO added four new Chinese production facilities that make navigation systems air conditioner compressors instrument panels and oil filters. It has also established technical centers in China and Thailand.

Over the years DENSO has partnered with rival parts suppliers Bosch and Aisin Seiki and carmaker Toyota Motor forming joint ventures and alliances to collaborate on the development of emerging technologies such as advanced safety features and automated driving.

HISTORY

Originally the in-house parts supplier for Toyota Nippondenso Co. (the predecessor to DENSO) was spun off by Toyota in 1949 because Toyota no longer wanted the burden of Nippondenso's troubled financial performance. Nippondenso remained dependent upon Toyota for sales and members of Toyota's controlling family the Toyodas remained involved in management. Nippondenso established a technological partnership with Germany's Robert Bosch in 1953.

As part of its plan to become a major supplier to North American carmakers in 1966 Nippondenso established a sales office in Chicago and branch offices in Los Angeles and Detroit. It then turned to Europe establishing a branch office in Stuttgart Germany in 1970. The following year the company established its first overseas subsidiary Nippondenso of Los Angeles (now DENSO Sales California). In 1972 the company established three more foreign subsidiaries in Australia Canada and Thailand. A European subsidiary (now DENSO Europe) was established in the Netherlands in 1973.

Nippondenso began consignment production for what is now known as Asmo Co. a maker of electric motors in 1978. In 1984 the company joined with Allen Bradley Co. (US) to develop factory automation equipment. That year the predecessor to DENSO Manufacturing Michigan one of the company's largest international subsidiaries was established. Nippondenso expanded into Spain in 1989 by opening a plant in Barcelona.

In 1990 the company formed NDM Manufacturing (now DENSO Manufacturing UK) a joint venture (25%-owned) with Magneti Marelli of Italy for the manufacture of automotive air conditioning and heating systems. The following year Nippondenso and AT&T formed a joint venture for the development of integrated circuit (IC) cards.

Nippondenso established several Chinese manufacturing joint ventures during the mid-1990s. In 1994 the company was recognized by the Guinness Book of Records as the maker of the world's smallest car the DENSO Micro Car.

The company changed its name to DENSO CORPORATION in 1996. In 1999 it acquired the rotating machines business of Magneti Marelli. The next year DENSO agreed to buy out Magneti Marelli's share in the companies' automotive air conditioning and heating joint venture (the deal was completed in 2001).

In 2001 DENSO ceased production of wireless phones in order to focus on making onboard car information systems. Also in 2001 the company merged its industrial equipment subsidiaries (bar code scanners and factory automation robots) and spun them off as majority-owned subsidiary DENSO Wave.

DENSO joined forces with Robert Bosch GmbH in 2003 to form a joint venture for the development of car navigation and multimedia systems.

In 2006 DENSO added four new Chinese production facilities that make navigation systems air conditioner compressors instrument panels and oil filters. It has also established technical centers in China and Thailand.

EXECUTIVES

President and CEO, Koji Arima
Senior Executive Officer and Head, OEM Sales and Marketing Group, Solution Sales and Marketing Group, Kazuaki Fujitani
Senior Executive Officer and CTO; Head, Research Development Center, Advanced Mobility Systems Business Development, Solution Planning, Smart City, AD Business, Mobility Systems Business Group; President, MIRISE Technologies, Yoshifumi Kato
Senior Executive Officer and Chief Corporate Revolution Officer and Chief Quality Officer; Head, Safety, Quality & Environment Center, Environment Neutral Systems Development, FC System Business Development and CV&OH, Yukihiro Shinohara
Senior Executive Officer and CHRO; Head, General Administration and HR Center, Korea, Kenichiro Ito
Senior Executive Officer, CFO and Chief Risk Officer; Head, Corporate Strategy Center, Group Companies of Japan, Yasushi Matsui
Director, Akio Toyoda
Independent Director, Yuko Mitsuya
Independent Director, Shigeki Kushida
EVP and Chief Customer Officer, Toshiyuki Kato
Auditors: Deloitte Touche Tohmatsu LLC

LOCATIONS

HQ: Denso Corp
1-1 Showa-cho, Kariya, Aichi 448-8661
Phone: (81) 566 61 7910
Web: www.denso.co.jp

2019 Sales

	% of total
Japan	43
Asia	23
North America	22
Europe	11
Others	1
Total	**100**

PRODUCTS/OPERATIONS

2019 Sales

	% of total
Thermal Systems	26
Powertrain Systems	24
Mobility Systems	17
Electrification Systems	15
Electronic Systems	12
Other Automotive	2
FA-New Business	4
Total	**100**

Products & Services
Electronics
Powertrain ECU (electronic control unit) designSemiconductor sensorPower cardsAcoustic vehicle alerting systemsBody control computers
Powertrain
VCTCommon rail systemsSpark plugExhaust gas sensorHigh pressure pumps
Thermal
CondensersRadiatorsBus air-conditionersRefrigeration unitsWater cooled intercoolers
Mobility
Milimeter-wave radarIntegrated cockpit systems

COMPETITORS

AUTOCAM CORPORATION
EATON CORPORATION PUBLIC LIMITED COMPANY
HELLA GmbH & Co. KGaA
HILITE INTERNATIONAL INC.
JOHNSON CONTROLS INC.
JTEKT CORPORATION
LEAR CORPORATION
MOTORCAR PARTS OF AMERICA INC.
SUMITOMO ELECTRIC INDUSTRIES LTD.
TENNECO INC.
VALEO

HISTORICAL FINANCIALS
Company Type: Public

Income Statement				FYE: March 31
	REVENUE ($ mil.)	NET INCOME ($ mil.)	NET PROFIT MARGIN	EMPLOYEES
03/21	44,585	1,129	2.5%	196,126
03/20	47,475	627	1.3%	202,363
03/19	48,424	2,298	4.7%	206,521
03/18	48,106	3,018	6.3%	204,314
03/17	40,490	2,304	5.7%	185,134
Annual Growth	2.4%	(16.3%)	—	1.5%

2021 Year-End Financials

Debt ratio: 0.1%
Return on equity: 3.4%
Cash ($ mil.): 8,104
Current ratio: 1.86
Long-term debt ($ mil.): 6,826

No. of shares (mil.): 774
Dividends
  Yield: 1.9%
  Payout: —
Market value ($ mil.): 25,839

	STOCK PRICE ($) FY Close	P/E High/Low		PER SHARE ($) Earnings	Dividends	Book Value
03/21	33.35	0	0	1.46	0.66	45.35
03/20	15.86	0	0	0.81	0.64	40.39
03/19	19.52	0	0	2.95	0.61	41.90
03/18	27.71	0	0	3.87	0.59	43.46
03/17	22.08	0	0	2.92	0.54	37.70
Annual Growth	10.9%	—	—	(15.9%)	5.4%	4.7%

Desjardins Group

Auditors: PricewaterhouseCoopers LLP/s.r.l./s.e.n.c.r.l.

LOCATIONS

HQ: Desjardins Group
100 Des Commandeurs Street, Levis, Quebec G6V 7N5
Phone: 514 281-7000   **Fax:** 418 833-5873
Web: www.desjardins.com

HISTORICAL FINANCIALS
Company Type: Public

Income Statement				FYE: December 31
	REVENUE ($ mil.)	NET INCOME ($ mil.)	NET PROFIT MARGIN	EMPLOYEES
12/20	18,575	1,641	8.8%	48,930
12/19	18,177	1,781	9.8%	47,849
12/18	14,493	1,542	10.6%	46,200
12/17	15,109	1,563	10.3%	45,547
12/16	12,598	1,180	9.4%	47,655
Annual Growth	10.2%	8.6%	—	0.7%

2020 Year-End Financials

Debt ratio: 0.3%
Return on equity: 7.4%
Cash ($ mil.): 9,523
Current ratio: —
Long-term debt ($ mil.): 1,172

No. of shares (mil.): —
Dividends
  Yield: —
  Payout: —
Market value ($ mil.): —

Deutsche Bank AG

Deutsche Bank AG is one of the leading financial groups in the world and in Germany. It operates around 1890 retail branch locations in some 60 countries across five continents. Deutsche Bank serves private individuals corporate customers and institutional clients with a wide variety of investment financial and related products and services. The bank's asset management business holds over ?790 billion in assets under management. Deutsche Bank generates most of its revenue from outside of Germany. The company was founded in 1870.

Operations

The company operates in six operating segments: Investment Bank (IB) Private Bank (PB) Corporate Bank (CB) Asset Management (AM) Capital Release Unit (CRU) and Corporate & Other (C&O).

IB previously part of the former Corporate & Investment Bank includes Deutsche Bank's Origination & Advisory businesses generates over 35% of sales. It also includes Fixed Income Currency (FIC) Sales & Trading which includes their Global Credit Trading Foreign Exchange Rates and Emerging Markets Debt businesses.

PB accounts for about 35% of net revenue. It serves personal and private clients wealthy individuals entrepreneurs and families. In our international businesses we also focus on commercial clients. We are organized along two business divisions: Private Bank Germany and International Private Bank. Our product range includes payment and account services credit and deposit products as well as investment advice including a range of

Environmental Social and Governance (ESG) products.

CB made around 20% of total revenue includes the Global Transaction Bank which was previously part of the former Corporate & Investment Bank as well as the German Commercial Clients division formerly part of the Private & Commercial Business (Germany).

The Asset Management operates under the DWS brand. It is unchanged from Deutsche Bank's previous segmentation and provides investment solutions to individual investors and institutions with a diversified range of Active Passive and Alternative Asset Management products and services. It generates roughly 10% of net sales.

New Capital Release Unit's (CRU) principal objectives are to liberate capital consumed by low return assets and businesses that earn insufficient returns or activities that are no longer core to its strategy by liberating capital in an economically rational manner. In addition the CRU is focused on reducing costs.

Overall net interest income accounts for about 50% of Deutsche's total net revenue. Net fee and commission income represents about 40% of sales.

Geographic Reach

Headquartered in Frankfurt the financial capital of Germany (and continental Europe) Deutsche is active in around 60 countries worldwide. It derives nearly 40% of sales from its home market of Germany while its other major markets are the US (some 20%) and the Rest of Europe Middle East and Africa and Asia/Pacific (around 15%).

Sales and Marketing

The global coverage function in the Corporate Bank focuses on international Large Corporate Clients and is organized into two units: Coverage and Risk Management Solutions. Coverage includes multi-product generalists covering headquarter level and subsidiaries via global regional and local coverage teams.

Coverage of the IB's clients is provided by the Institutional Client Group which houses their debt sales team and works in conjunction with Finance Solutions Group in the Corporate Bank covering capital markets and Treasury solutions.

Private Bank Germany business and Private & Commercial Business International have similar distribution channels. Those include branch network supported by customer call centers and self-service terminals; advisory centers of the Deutsche Bank brand in Germany Italy and Spain which connects branch network with digital offerings; online and mobile banking including Digital Platform through which they provide a transaction platform for banking brokerage and self-services combined with a multi-mobile offering for smartphones and tablets; and lastly financial advisors as an additional service channel in collaboration with self-employed financial advisors as well as sales and cooperation partners.

Financial Performance

Net revenues were ? 24 billion in 2020 an increase of ? 864 million or 4 % compared to 2019. The main drivers for the increase were significantly higher revenues in Investment Bank (IB) driven by benefits of underlying market activity and strong client engagement following its strategic re-positioning.

The bank reported a net profit of ? 624 million in 2020 compared to a net loss of ? 5.3 billion in 2019.

Cash held by the company at the end of fiscal 2020 increased to ?156.3 billion. Cash provided by operations was ?30.7 billion while cash used for investing and financing activities were ?1.9 billion and ?311 million respectively. Main cash uses were financial assets at fair value through other comprehensive income and repayments and extinguishments of subordinated long-term debt.

Strategy

In July 2019 the company announced a strategic transformation of Deutsche Bank designed to significantly improve sustainable returns to shareholders. This strategy is underpinned by four specific objectives. First to refocus Deutsche Bank around four core businesses focusing on key areas of strength and more predictable revenue sources while exiting business areas unlikely to produce adequate returns. Second to reduce its adjusted costs and improve the efficiency and effectiveness of its infrastructure. Third to reinvigorate the leadership and spirit of the bank by enabling faster decision-making increasing discipline in execution and unleashing Deutsche Bank's entrepreneurial culture. Finally Deutsche Bank established the Capital Release Unit to liberate capital consumed by low return assets and businesses that earn insufficient returns or that are no longer core to its strategy by winding those down in an economically rational manner.

Mergers and Acquisitions

In 2021 Deutsche Bank acquires Berlin-based payment service provider Better Payment. Through the acquisition Deutsche Bank will expand its market share in payment processing and acceptance. Better Payment operates a service for the technical processing of online payments. For this purpose the company uses a payment platform ("online payment gateway") to carry out and receive online payments. Terms were not disclosed.

Company Background

Deutsche Bank was founded in 1870 in Berlin by Adelbert Delbr ck a private banker and Ludwig Bamberger a politician and currency expert. Shortly after it opened its first international branches in China (Shanghai and Yokohama) and the UK (London). In its first century of activity significant events included financing steel company Krupp (which became ThyssenKrupp) the Northern Pacific Railroad and film company UFA (which made films including Fritz Lang's Metropolis). Deutsche dipped its toe into investment banking in the late 1980s and by the late 1990s the bank was dead-set on taking on global leaders in investment banking such as JPMorgan and Goldman Sachs. Deutsche responded slowly to the 2008 financial crisis stumbling from net loss to net loss before CEO Christian Sewing in 2019 cut a fifth of its workforce and retrenched the bank with downwardly revised investment banking ambitions.

HISTORY

Georg von Siemens opened Deutsche Bank in Berlin in 1870. Three years later the firm opened an office in London and was soon buying other German banks. In the late 1800s Deutsche Bank helped finance Germany's electrification (carried out by Siemens AG) and railroad construction in the US and the Ottoman Empire. Von Siemens ran the bank until his death in 1901.

The bank survived post-WWI financial chaos by merging with Disconto-Gesellschaft and later helped finance the Nazi war machine. After the war the Allies split the company into 10 banks; it became extinct in Soviet-controlled East Germany.

The bank was reassembled in 1957 and primarily engaged in commercial banking often taking direct interests in its customers. It added retail services in the 1960s. In 1975 to prevent the Shah of Iran from gaining a stake in Daimler-Benz (now Daimler) the bank bought 29% of that company.

The firm opened an investment banking office in the US in 1971 and a branch office in 1978. In the 1980s it expanded geographically buying Bank of America's Italian subsidiary (1986) and UK merchant bank Morgan Grenfell (1989); it also moved

into insurance creating life insurer DB Leben (1989).

Terrorists killed chairman Alfred Herrhausen a symbol of German big business in 1989. After German reunification in 1990 successor Hilmar Kopper oversaw the bank's reestablishment in eastern Germany.

In 1994 Deutsche Bank bought most of ITT's commercial finance unit. That year the company suffered scandal when real estate developer Jurgen Schneider borrowed more than DM1 billion and disappeared; he was later found and returned to Germany.

The company grew its global investment banking operations in 1995 under its Morgan Grenfell subsidiary. Corporate culture clashes prompted Deutsche Bank to take greater control of the unit and restructure it in 1998.

Deutsche Bank's global aspirations suffered a setback in 1998 when losses on investments in Russia trimmed its bottom line. Still trying to put WWII behind it the bank accepted responsibility for its wartime dealing in gold seized from Jews but has rejected liability to compensate victims of Nazi forced labor who toiled in industrial companies in which it holds stakes.

In 1999 the bank acquired Bankers Trust. Despite a decision to divest its industrial portfolio that year the company bought Tele Columbus the #2 cable network in Germany and Piaggio the Italian maker of the famed Vespa motor scooter. On the banking front Deutsche Bank bought Chase Manhattan's Dutch auction business and sought a foothold in Japan through alliances with Nippon Life Insurance and Sakura Bank (now part of Sumitomo Mitsui Banking).

In 2000 the company agreed to merge with Dresdner Bank (after which they would spin off their retail banking businesses) but the merger collapsed in part over the fate of investment banking subsidiary Dresdner Kleinwort Benson. German mega-insurer Allianz bought Dresdner in 2001. Deutsche Bank's reorganization plans the same year saw the bank eliminate 2600 jobs worldwide and realign its businesses into two divisions. Deutsche Bank also bought Banque Worms from French insurer AXA.

Looking for a steady supply of cash in 2001 Deutsche Bank's Morgan Grenfall Private Equity bought 3000 English pubs owned by UK-based conglomerate Whitbread plc. In 2002 more shuffling of the executive board members allowed Deutsche Bank to grow in the international Anglo-American style rather than as a domestic player.

In 2004 Deutsche Bank acquired Berkshire Mortgage (now Deutsche Bank Berkshire Mortgage) one of the top multifamily residential lenders in the US. The next year it bought Russian financial services company United Financial Group and combined its depositary business with its own.

The year 2006 was a bad year for the company from a public relations standpoint. Fallout from former chairman Rolf Breuer's remarks regarding the financial stability of banking client Kirch Holding led to a shake-up in the executive suite and the board that year. Later UK financial regulators charged the bank an $11.1 million fine for market misconduct related to trading activity in 2004. In the US the IRS investigated the bank for alleged abusive tax shelters.

The bank also took a public relations hit when its CEO Josef Ackermann went on trial for illegal bonuses during his tenure at Mannesmann.

To boost its lending operations in the US the company bought MortgageIT a real estate investment trust for some ?285 million ($430 million) in 2007. The timing wasn't great: the subsidiary suffered a major loss a victim of the US subprime mortgage crisis. Also that year Deutsche Bank acquired Abbey Life from Lloyds Banking Group for some ?1 billion ($2 billion.) This acquisition fared better than MortgageIT finishing out the year in the black.

Deutsche Bank's expansion was slowed in 2008 when its proposed acquisition of some of ABN AMRO's assets — including corporate and commercial units parts of Hollandische Bank Unie and a factoring company — from Fortis was canceled.

On the heels of a global expansion which began in earnest in 2002 Deutsche Bank was hit hard by the worldwide financial crisis. The company reported a fourth-quarter loss of ?4.8 billion in 2008 largely due to declines in its trading and asset management businesses. Its Americas business primarily the US operations was hit the hardest by far.

But in 2009 Deutsche Bank's growth seemed to pick back up again as it acquired Dresdner Bank's global agency securities lending business from Commerzbank. The business was merged with Deutsche's trust and securities services unit. The deal expanded Deutsche Bank's custody platform.

EXECUTIVES

Chief Risk Officer, Stuart Lewis, $2,601,642 total compensation
Head, Corporate Bank and Investment Bank, Fabrizio Campelli, $2,506,692 total compensation
Chief Executive Officer, Christian Sewing, $3,551,148 total compensation
President, Karl von Rohr, $3,133,365 total compensation
Deputy Chairman, Detlef Polaschek
Chief Technology, Data and Innovation Officer, Bernd Leukert, $2,506,692 total compensation
Chief Executive Officer, Americas, Christiana Riley, $2,499,638 total compensation
Auditors: KPMG AG Wirtschaftspruefungsgesellschaft

LOCATIONS

HQ: Deutsche Bank AG
Taunusanlage 12, Frankfurt am Main 60325
Phone: (49) 69 910 00   **Fax:** (49) 69 910 34 225
Web: www.db.com

2018 Sales

	% of total
Germany	38
Americas	22
UK	14
Rest of Europe Middle East and Africa	13
Asia/Pacific	13
Other	.
Total	**100**

PRODUCTS/OPERATIONS

2018 Sales

	% of total
Corporate & Investment Bank	51
Private & Commercial Bank	40
Asset Management	9
Other	.
Total	**100**

COMPETITORS

AUSTRALIA AND NEW ZEALAND BANKING GROUP LIMITED
COMMONWEALTH BANK OF AUSTRALIA
Credit Suisse Group AG
DZ BANK AG Deutsche
Erste Group Bank AG
ING Groep N.V.
Raiffeisen Zentralbank –sterreich Aktiengesellschaft
STANDARD CHARTERED PLC
UBS AG
WESTPAC BANKING CORPORATION

HISTORICAL FINANCIALS

Company Type: Public

Income Statement

FYE: December 31

	ASSETS ($ mil.)	NET INCOME ($ mil.)	INCOME AS % OF ASSETS	EMPLOYEES
12/20	1,626,111	592	0.0%	84,659
12/19	1,456,984	(6,051)	—	87,597
12/18	1,543,879	305	0.0%	91,737
12/17	1,767,841	(900)	—	97,733
12/16	1,679,430	(1,480)	—	99,744
Annual Growth	**(0.8%)**	—	—	**(4.0%)**

2020 Year-End Financials

Return on assets: 0.0%
Return on equity: 0.8%
Long-term debt ($ mil.): —
No. of shares (mil.): 2,065
Sales ($ mil): 37,329
Dividends
Yield: —
Payout: —
Market value ($ mil.): —

Deutsche Lufthansa AG (Germany, Fed. Rep.)

Germany's air ambassador Deutsche Lufthansa rivals the world's largest airlines. Operating in about 530 subsidiaries and affiliated companies the global aviation group runs Europe's largest passenger airline. Lufthansa Passenger Airlines operates a global route network of more than 315 destinations in over 100 countries with a fleet of almost 750 aircrafts. The company's logistics is also a market leader in international airfreight transportation through Lufthansa Cargo. Lufthansa is also comprised of AirPlus Lufthansa Aviation Training and offers IT services through Lufthansa Systems. The majority of Lufthansa's sales come from Europe.

Operations
Lufthansa operates five business segments Network Airlines MRO (maintenance repair and overhaul) Catering Logistics and Eurowings.

Network airlines segment consists of Lufthansa's multi-hub airlines Lufthansa Germany Airlines SWISS and Austrian Airlines. It offers premium and high-quality products and services comprehensive route networks combined with highest level of travel flexibility. The segment generates more than 40% of sales.

Doing business as Lufthansa Technik the MRO segment is one of the leading global providers of maintenance repair and overhaul services for civilian commercial aircraft. It accounts for nearly 25% of sales.

Catering provides in-flight food for more than 300 airlines with nearly 140 plants in over 45 countries primarily under the LSG Sky Chefs brand. It accounts for almost 20 % of sales.

Logistics generates more than 5% of Lufthansa's revenue. It consists of the airfreight container management specialist Jettainer group the time:matters subsidiary which specializes in particularly urgent consignments and the equity investment in the cargo airline AeroLogic.

The Eurowings segment (less than 5% of sales) holds Lufthansa's budget airline operations providing low-cost direct services under the Eurowings Germanwings and Eurowings Europe banners. It also includes Brussels Air and Lufthansa's equity investment in SunExpress.

Overall Traffic generates more than 65% of Lufthansa's Revenue.

Geographic Reach
Cologne Germany-based Lufthansa's largest market is Europe which generates nearly 60% of total revenue. North America generates nearly 20% and the Asia/Pacific region more than 15%. Lufthansa also generates revenue in Central and South America the Middle East and Africa.

Sales and Marketing
Lufthansa sells flight tickets and related ancillary services primarily via agents websites or other airlines in the course of interlining. The number of passengers it carries declined to about 36 million from more than 140 million passengers in 2019 due to a decline of over 67% in the number of flights.

Financial Performance
Note: Growth rates may differ after conversion to US Dollars.

Lufthansa's sales have been fluctuating over the last five years. Net income followed the same trend with a recorded net loss in the most recent fiscal year.

In 2020 the airline saw a decline in its sales by 63% to ?13.6 billion. This was due to the decline in all its business segments except in Logistics. Traffic revenue for the Lufthansa Group airlines fell by 68% year-on-year to ?9.1 billion in the financial year 2020.

Net result attributable to shareholders of Deutsche Lufthansa AG fell to a net loss of ?6.7 billion compared to a net income of ?1.2 billion in the prior year. It was burdened by impairment losses on the fleet and goodwill as well as the negative changes in the market value of fuel hedging instruments.

Lufthansa's cash position increased in 2020 ending the year ?389 million higher at ?1.8 billion. Lufthansa's operating activities used cash of ?2.3 billion and its investing activities used ?962 million and its financing activities provided ?5.1 billion. Main cash uses were for purchase of securities and capital expenditures.

Strategy
Lufthansa Group's strategy consists of:

Market position as a leading European airline group to be strengthened by coping successfully with the coronavirus crisis; Airlines form the core of the Lufthansa Group; Focus is on restructuring consistent attention to customer needs and long-term increases in profitability and cash flow; and Sustainability and corporate responsibility.

The financial strategy of the Lufthansa Group seeks to increase its company value in a sustainable manner. It will concentrate on three dimensions: improving profitability focusing capital allocation and maintaining financial stability.

HISTORY

The Weimar government created Deutsche Luft Hansa (DLH) in 1926 by merging private German airlines Deutscher Aero Lloyd (founded 1919) and Junkers Luftverkehr (formed in 1921 by aircraft manufacturer Junkers Flugzeugwerke). DLH built what would become Europe's most comprehensive air route network by 1931. It served the USSR through Deruluft (formed 1921; dissolved 1941) an airline jointly owned by DLH and the Soviet government. In 1930 DLH and the Chinese government formed Eurasia Aviation Corporation to develop air transport in China.

DLH established the world's first trans-Atlantic airmail service from Berlin to Buenos Aires in 1934 and went on to develop air transport throughout South America. The outbreak of WWII ended operations in Europe and the Chinese government seized Eurasia Aviation in 1941. Klaus Bonhoeffer head of DLH's legal department led an unsuccessful coup against the Nazi leadership and was executed in 1945. Soon afterward all DLH operations ceased.

In 1954 the Allies allowed the recapitalization of Deutsche Lufthansa. The airline started with domestic routes returned to London and Paris (1955) and then re-entered South America (1956). In 1958 it made its first nonstop flight between Germany and New York and initiated service to Tokyo and Cairo. Meanwhile it started a charter airline with several partners in 1955. Lufthansa bought out its partners in 1959 and renamed the unit Condor two years later.

The carrier resumed service behind the Iron Curtain in 1966 with flights to Prague. The stable West German economy helped Lufthansa maintain profitability through most of the 1970s. The reunification of Germany in 1990 ended Allied control over Berlin airspace allowing Lufthansa which had bought Pan Am's Berlin routes to fly there under its own colors for the first time since the end of WWII.

EXECUTIVES

Member of the Executive Board and Head of Commercial Passenger Airlines, Harry Hohmeister, $881,899 total compensation

Member of the Execuitve Board and Chief Officer Airline Resources & Operations Standard, Detlef Kayser, $881,899 total compensation

Chief Financial Officer and Director, Remco Steenbergen

Member of the Supervisory Board, Erich Clementi, $50,133 total compensation

Chairman of the Board and CEO, Carsten Spohr, $1,676,066 total compensation

Auditors: Ernst & Young GmbH Wirtschaftpruefungsgesellschaft

LOCATIONS

HQ: Deutsche Lufthansa AG (Germany, Fed. Rep.) Lufthansa Aviation Center (LAC), Airportring, Frankfurt D-60546

Phone: (49) 69 696 0   **Fax:** (49) 69 696 33022
Web: www.lufthansagroup.com

2018 Sales

	% of total
Europe	62
North America	18
Asia/Pacific	13
Central and South America	3
Middle East	2
Africa	2
Total	**100**

PRODUCTS/OPERATIONS

2018 Sales

	% of total
Network Airlines	57
Eurowings	11
MRO	15
Catering	8
Logistics	7
Other	2
Total	**100**

COMPETITORS

AEROFLOT PAO
AIR FRANCE - KLM
ALASKA AIR GROUP INC.
ANA HOLDINGS INC.
CATHAY PACIFIC AIRWAYS LIMITED
China Southern Airlines Company Limited
DELTA AIR LINES INC.
INTERNATIONAL CONSOLIDATED AIRLINES GROUP SA
Koninklijke Luchtvaart Maatschappij N.V.
QANTAS AIRWAYS LIMITED
SINGAPORE AIRLINES LIMITED

HISTORICAL FINANCIALS

Company Type: Public

Income Statement

FYE: December 31

	REVENUE ($ mil.)	NET INCOME ($ mil.)	NET PROFIT MARGIN	EMPLOYEES
12/20	16,892	(8,253)	—	110,065
12/19	41,664	1,361	3.3%	138,353
12/18	41,656	2,477	5.9%	135,534
12/17	42,777	2,833	6.6%	129,424
12/16	33,529	1,875	5.6%	124,306
Annual Growth	(15.8%)	—	—	(3.0%)

2020 Year-End Financials

Debt ratio: 40.9%
Return on equity: (-116.7%)
Cash ($ mil.): 2,216
Current ratio: 0.68
Long-term debt ($ mil.): 12,357

No. of shares (mil.): 597
Dividends
  Yield: —
  Payout: —
Market value ($ mil.): 7,848

	STOCK PRICE ($) FY Close	P/E High/Low		Earnings	PER SHARE ($) Dividends	Book Value
12/20	13.13	—	—	(15.35)	0.00	2.77
12/19	18.15	10	6	2.86	0.64	23.82
12/18	22.95	8	4	5.24	0.67	22.80
12/17	36.80	7	3	6.03	0.43	24.15
12/16	12.90	4	3	4.02	0.37	15.90
Annual Growth (35.4%)	0.4%	—	—	—	—	

Deutsche Post AG

Deutsche Post AG (operating as Deutsche Post DHL Group) is Europe's largest postal service the company is also one of the world's leading providers of express delivery freight transport supply chain management and e-commerce solutions. Deutsche Post trades under two brand names Deutsche Post and DHL. The company does business in Europe (its largest market) the Americas and Asia Pacific. Its Post & Parcel Germany division deliver around 6 million parcels about 50 million letter per working day. Deutsche Post can trace its lineage back to the earliest days of centralized post in Germany when Maximilian I established reliable postal links across the Holy Roman Empire.

Operations

Deutsche Post operates through five divisions: Express; Post and Parcel Germany; Global Forwarding Freight; Supply Chain and e-Commerce solutions.

The Express division (about 30% of sales) delivers urgent documents through its core product Time Definite International (TDI) which offers predefined delivery times.

Post and Parcel Germany contributes about 25% of total revenues and represents the company's mail and package delivery services primarily in Germany where it owns more than 60% of the market. Deutsche Post's Global Forwarding and Freight division (more than 20%) brokers transport services between customers and freight carriers by air ocean and ground transportation.

The Supply Chain segment (about 20%) offers warehousing and logistics services such as planning sourcing and production activities primarily to the automotive technology and life sciences and healthcare sectors.

Lastly the eCommerce solutions generating more than 5% of the total revenue geared towards providing high-quality solutions particularly to customers in the rapid growing e-commerce sector. Its core activities include national last-mile parcel delivery in selected countries. It also supplies cross-border non-TDI services.

Geographic Reach

Based in Bonn Germany Deutsche Post delivers to almost everywhere in the world. Germany accounts for about 30% of total sales; wider Europe contributes a similar amount again. The rest arises mainly from the Americas and the Asia Pacific region.

Sales and Marketing

The company's products and services are targeted towards both private and business customers and range from physical and hybrid letters to special products for merchandise delivery and include additional services as registered mail cash on delivery and insured items. The company markets through retail outlets post boxes mail centers paketshops salespoints letter and parcel delivery parcel centers packstations.

Financial Performance

Note: Growth rates may differ after conversion to US Dollars.

Deutsche Post's performance has been increasing and growing year by year for the span of five years and ending with 2020 as its highest performing year.

In 2020 consolidated revenue rose by ?3.4 billion to ?66.8 billion although currency effects reduced by ?1.6 billion. The proportion of revenue generated abroad increased from 69.9% to 70.3%.

Consolidated net profit showed sharp improvement in 2020 rising from ?2.8 billion to ?3.2 billion.

The company had cash and cash equivalents of ?4.5 billion at the end of 2020. Operating activities provided ?7.7 billion while investing activities used ?3.6 billion. Financing activities used another ?2.2 billion mainly for dividends paid.

Strategy

Deutsche Post's Strategy 2025 is used by the company to focus on a sustained execution of the company's goals of becoming an employer provider and investment of choice.

The company's divisions form the core of the group. Since all five divisions have distinct profiles and service offerings Deutsche Post's group strategy is structured along multi-divisional lines. The company focuses upon the specific growth drivers that will strengthen the profitable core of the company's business units with the goal of achieving industry-leading margins in all segments.

As part of the company's Accelerated Digitalization Strategy DHL has collaborated with Locus Robotics and plans to use up to 2000 robots.

HISTORY

The German postal system was established in the 1490s when German emperor Maximilian I ordered a reliable and regular messenger service to be set up between Austria (Innsbruck where the emperor had his court) and the farther reaches of his Holy Roman Empire: the Netherlands France and Rome. The von Tassis (later renamed Taxis) family of Italy was responsible for running the network. Family members settled in major cities across Europe to expand the postal business.

Although the family operated what was officially an exclusively royal mail service by the early 1500s the company was also delivering messages for private patrons. In 1600 a family member who served as general postmaster was authorized to collect fees for private mail deliveries. By the early 19th century Thurn und Taxis as the company was then called was the leading postal service in the Holy Roman Empire serving more than 11 million people.

The dissolution of the Holy Roman Empire prompted by Napoleon's military adventures led to the creation of a federation of 39 independent German states. Thurn und Taxis had to make agreements with members of the separate states including Austria and Prussia. After Austria's defeat in 1866 by Prussia the confederation was dissolved and all Thurn und Taxis postal systems were absorbed by Prussia. When Bismarck's Prussian-led German Reich was established in 1870 the new postal administration (Reichspostverwaltung) began issuing postage stamps valid across Germany.

After Germany was defeated in WWII and split into two nations in 1949 two postal systems were established: Deutsche Post (East Germany) and Deutsche Bundespost (West Germany). The fall of the Berlin Wall in 1989 preceded a reunion of the two German states in 1990. That year Deutsche Post led by chairman Klaus Zumwinkel was integrated into Deutsche Bundespost.

EXECUTIVES

Chairman of the Management Board, Chief Executive Officer, responsible for Global Business Services, Frank Appel, $2,347,955 total compensation

Member of the Management Board, Finance, Melanie Kreis, $1,068,478 total compensation

Member of the Management Board, Express, John Pearson, $814,675 total compensation

Member of the Management Board, Global Forwarding and Freight, Tim Scharwath, $1,026,414 total compensation

Member of the Management Board, eCommerce Solutions, Ken Allen, $1,146,008 total compensation

Member of the Management Board, Human Resources, Thomas Ogilvie, $1,006,475 total compensation

Member of the Management Board, Supply Chain, Oscar De Bok, $814,675 total compensation

Auditors: PricewaterhouseCoopers GmbH

LOCATIONS

HQ: Deutsche Post AG
Zentrale - Investor Relations, Bonn 53250
Phone: (49) 228 182 6 3636   **Fax:** (49) 228 182 6 3199
Web: www.dpdhl.de

2018 Sales

	% of total
Europe	
Germany	30
Europe (excluding Germany)	30
Americas	18
Asia/Pacific	18
Other regions	4
Total	**100**

PRODUCTS/OPERATIONS

2018 Sales

	% of total
PeP	29
Express	25
Global Forwarding Freight	23
Supply Chain	21
Corporate Center/Other	2
Total	**100**

Selected Services

Mail and package delivery
Dialogue marketing services
Time Definite International (TDI) express delivery
Air freight
Freight forwarding services
Contract logistics
Ocean freight
Outsourcing and system solutions for the mail business

COMPETITORS

AEGIS COMMUNICATIONS GROUP LLC
APAC CUSTOMER SERVICES INC.
Clariant AG
Deutsche Telekom AG
JOHN MENZIES PLC
NEXT FIFTEEN COMMUNICATIONS GROUP PLC
ORANGE
Otto (GmbH & Co KG)
PLANET PAYMENT INC.
SIG PLC
SSP GROUP PLC
Securitas AB
TELEFONICA SA
VIAD CORP

HISTORICAL FINANCIALS

Company Type: Public

Income Statement

	REVENUE ($ mil.)	NET INCOME ($ mil.)	NET PROFIT MARGIN	EMPLOYEES
				FYE: December 31
12/20	81,990	3,656	4.5%	571,974
12/19	71,117	2,945	4.1%	546,924
12/18	70,486	2,376	3.4%	547,459
12/17	72,457	3,252	4.5%	513,338
12/16	60,538	2,786	4.6%	498,459
Annual Growth	7.9%	7.0%	—	3.5%

2020 Year-End Financials

Debt ratio: 15.4%
Return on equity: 21.3%
Cash ($ mil.): 5,500
Current ratio: 1.05
Long-term debt ($ mil.): 8,530

No. of shares (mil.): 1,239
Dividends
Yield: 2.1%
Payout: 37.4%
Market value ($ mil.): 61,755

	STOCK PRICE ($) FY Close	P/E High/Low		PER SHARE ($) Earnings	Dividends	Book Value
12/20	49.84	21	10	2.90	1.05	13.65
12/19	37.82	18	12	2.35	1.24	12.83
12/18	27.33	28	16	1.90	1.37	12.62
12/17	47.59	22	16	2.58	1.23	12.37
12/16	32.74	15	10	2.22	0.87	9.66
Annual Growth	11.1%	—	—	6.9%	4.9%	9.0%

Deutsche Telekom AG

Deutsche Telekom (DT) is one of the world's leading integrated telecommunications companies with some 242 million mobile customers 27 million fixed-network lines and 22 million broadband lines. Operating as T-Mobile in the US and in certain other European countries the company offers fixed-network and mobile communications services and products as well as information and communication technology (ICT). It offers its consumers fixed-network/ broadband mobile internet and internet-based TV products and services as well as ICT solutions for our business and corporate customers. DT generates majority of sales in North America.

Operations

Deutsche Telekom is divided into five segments: three geographic-based segments (US Germany and Europe) Systems Solutions segment and Group Development.

The US Deutsche Telekom operates in the mobile communications market as T-Mobile US and is the largest 5G network provider in the country.

T-Mobile US is Deutsche Telekom's biggest business accounting for about 60% of total sales.

Deutsche Telekom's Germany segment operates fixed-network and mobile telecoms infrastructure for businesses and consumers in the country. It accounts for over 20% of the company's total sales. The Europe segment consists of all fixed-network and mobile operations of the national companies in Greece Romania Hungary Poland the Czech Republic Croatia Slovakia Austria North Macedonia and Montenegro and generates around 10% of sales.

The Systems Solutions segment which accounts for about 5% of sales offers business customers a portfolio of integrated products and solutions. With offerings for connectivity digital solutions cloud and infrastructure and security in addition to strategic partnerships it offers its customers help and guidance to implement digital business models. The remaining sales are from Group Development and Group Headquarters & Group services.

Overall DT generates some 95% of sales from Telecommunications and around 5% from ICT solutions.

Geographic Reach

Deutsche Telekom (DT) headquartered in Bonn Germany operates in more than 50 countries worldwide. The company gets approximately 75% of its revenue from outside Germany mostly in North America but also in other European countries.

Sales and Marketing

Deutsche Telekom is known for its recognizable hot pink corporate color scheme. The company sponsors a number of high-profile venues and organizations particularly within sports such as the Telekom Baskets Bonn. Deutsche Telekom also sponsors Bayern Munich Germany's most successful soccer team.

It also has some 242 million mobile customers 27 million fixed-network lines and 22 million broadband customers.

Financial Performance

The company's revenue for fiscal 2020 increased to ?101.0 million compared from the prior year with ?80.5 million.

Net profit for fiscal 2020 increased to ?4.2 million compared from the prior year with ?3.9 million.

Cash held by the company at the end of fiscal 2020 increased to ?12.9 billion. Cash provided by operations and financing activities was ?23.7 billion and ?7.6 billion respectively. Cash used for investing activities was ?22.6 billion mainly for Property plant and equipment.

Strategy

Consistent with its efforts to systematically implement the Group strategy pillar "Lead in business productivity" with effect from July 1 2020 TC Services and Classified ICT portfolio units previously assigned to the Systems Solutions operating segment as well as Telekom Global Carrier (TGC) and Network Infrastructure (NWI) which had formerly been disclosed under the Europe operating segment and the Group Headquarters & Group Services segment respectively have been combined in the Germany operating segment.

This strategy has proved very successful: In terms of market capitalization the company is Europe's highest-value telecommunications company (as of December 31 2020). The company raised its full-year guidance for 2020 in the course of the year despite the coronavirus pandemic. Nevertheless the pandemic has not left the company unscathed. For example temporary travel restrictions have resulted in lower roaming and visitor revenues. Deutsche Telekom's terminal equipment business also felt the squeeze as did its corporate customer business. While it is impossible to quantify the long-term impact of the coronavirus pandemic the company see it as both a risk and an opportunity: One the one hand the company expect to see appreciable effects on the economy as a whole while on the other the pandemic has given a boost to the digitalization trend.

Mergers and Acquisitions

In early 2020 Deutsche Telecom completed the merging of T-Mobile US with US telecom carrier Sprint (the third- and fourth-largest carriers in the US). The combined company would boast around 125 million subscribers closing the gap to rivals AT&T (141 million) and Verizon (150 million). The deal is worth $26 billion.

HISTORY

Deutsche Telekom was formed by the 1989 separation of West Germany's telecommunications services from the nation's postal system Deutsche Post. Dating back to the 15th century (when the Thurn und Taxis private postal system was created for German principalities) the service expanded to cover Austria France the Netherlands and most of Germany by the 1850s. After the 1866 Austro-Prussian War it became part of the North German Postal Confederation. When the German Empire was formed in 1871 the postal operation became the Deutsche Reichspost (later the Bundespost). Shortly thereafter the newly invented telephone was introduced in Germany.

Post-WWI inflation shook the Bundespost and the government allowed it to try new organizational structures. A 1924 law allowed the state-run service to operate as a quasi-commercial company. After WWII the American-British zone returned postal authority to Germans and in 1949 the USSR established the state of East Germany.

Only by the 1960s did West Germany's postal and phone services meet modern standards. Privatization of the Bundespost became a political cause when many complained about the monopoly's cost and inefficiency. Efforts to privatize the agency (named Deutsche Telekom in 1989) intensified with the 1990 German reunification. Faced with updating the antiquated phone system of the former East Germany however political opposition to taking Deutsche Telekom public faded.

The company began operating T-D1 its mobile phone network in 1992 and the next year it launched T-Online now Germany's largest online service provider. In 1996 Deutsche Telekom finally went public and raised more than $13 billion in Europe's largest IPO. It also launched Global One with France Telecom (renamed Orange) and Sprint (now Sprint Nextel); as part of the partnership Deutsche Telekom took a 10% stake in Sprint.

In 1998 European Union (EU) member countries opened their phone markets to competition and Deutsche Telekom's long-distance market share quickly eroded. Under EU pressure in 1999 the company said it would sell its cable network which it divided into nine regional units.

EXECUTIVES

Board Member for Technology and Innovation, Claudia Nemat, $1,025,465 total compensation

Board Member for Finance, Christian Illek, $1,025,465 total compensation

Board Member for Germany and Managing Director, Telekom Deutschland GmBH, Srini Gopalan, $1,025,465 total compensation

Board Member, Adel Al-Saleh, $1,025,465 total compensation

Board Member for Europe, Dominique Leroy, $170,910 total compensation

Member of the Supervisory Board, Employee Representative, Kerstin Marx, $125,334 total compensation

CEO, Timotheus Hoettges, $1,709,108 total compensation

Board Member for Human Resources and Legal Affairs, Labor Director, Birgit Bohle, $797,583 total compensation

Board Member for USA and Group Development Deutsche Telekom AG, Thorsten Langheim, $1,025,465 total compensation

Auditors: PricewaterhouseCoopers GmbH Wirtschaftpruefungsgesellschaft

LOCATIONS

HQ: Deutsche Telekom AG
Friedrich-Ebert-Allee 140, Bonn D-53113
Phone: (49) 228 181 49494   **Fax:** (49) 228 181 94004
Web: www.telekom.com

2017 Sales

	% of total
US	48
Europe	
Germany	28
Other European countries	15
System Solutions	7
Group Development	2
Total	**100**

PRODUCTS/OPERATIONS

2017 Sales

	% of total
Telecommunications	90
ICT solutions	9
Other	1
Total	**100**

COMPETITORS

AT&T INC.	TDC Holding A/S
BT GROUP PLC	TELEFONICA SA
Deutsche Post AG	TELSTRA CORPORATION
IDT CORPORATION	LIMITED
LEVEL 3 PARENT LLC	Telenor ASA
OOREDOO Q.P.S.C	Telia Company AB
Proximus	VODAFONE GROUP PUBLIC
SPRINT CORPORATION	LIMITED COMPANY

HISTORICAL FINANCIALS

Company Type: Public

Income Statement				FYE: December 31
	REVENUE ($ mil.)	NET INCOME ($ mil.)	NET PROFIT MARGIN	EMPLOYEES
12/20	123,955	5,103	4.1%	226,291
12/19	90,417	4,341	4.8%	210,533
12/18	86,640	2,480	2.9%	215,675
12/17	89,843	4,148	4.6%	217,349
12/16	77,179	2,824	3.7%	218,341
Annual Growth	12.6%	15.9%	—	0.9%

2020 Year-End Financials

Debt ratio: 47.4%
Return on equity: 12.2%
Cash ($ mil.): 15,879
Current ratio: 1.00
Long-term debt ($ mil.): 111,253

Dividends
No. of shares (mil.): —
Yield: 3.5%
Payout: 65.6%
Market value ($ mil.): —

	STOCK PRICE ($) FY Close	P/E High/Low		PER SHARE ($) Earnings	Dividends	Book Value
12/20	18.27	23	15	1.08	0.65	9.29
12/19	16.29	22	19	0.92	1.49	7.48
12/18	16.98	39	32	0.53	0.74	7.43
12/17	17.66	29	24	0.89	0.70	7.74
12/16	17.10	30	26	0.61	0.56	6.62
Annual Growth	1.7%	—	—	15.2%	3.8%	8.9%

Dexia SA

Auditors: DELOITTE Bedrijfsrevisoren CVBA / Reviseurs d'Entreprises SCRL

LOCATIONS

HQ: Dexia SA
Place du Champ de Mars, 5, Brussels B-1050
Phone: (32) 2 213 50 81
Web: www.dexia.com

HISTORICAL FINANCIALS

Company Type: Public

Income Statement				FYE: December 31
	ASSETS ($ mil.)	NET INCOME ($ mil.)	INCOME AS % OF ASSETS	EMPLOYEES
12/19	135,097	(1,008)	—	606
12/18	181,861	(541)	—	773
12/17	216,900	(553)	—	996
12/16	224,661	372	0.2%	1,148
12/15	250,824	177	0.1%	1,203
Annual Growth	(14.3%)	—	—	(15.8%)

2019 Year-End Financials

Return on assets: (-0.6%)
Return on equity: (-12.1%)
Long-term debt ($ mil.): —
No. of shares (mil.): 420
Sales ($ mil): 7,489

Dividends
Yield: —
Payout: —
Market value ($ mil.): —

	STOCK PRICE ($) FY Close	P/E High/Low	PER SHARE ($) Earnings	Dividends	Book Value
12/19	0.00	— —	(0.00)	0.00	19.51
12/18	1.58	— —	(1.29)	0.00	20.45
12/17	1.58	— —	(18.74)	0.00	
3,070.41					
12/16	1.58	0 0	12.07	0.00	
2,246.68					
Annual Growth (69.5%)		— —	—	—	—

Diageo Plc

Diageo is the first name on the guest list for many a party. The UK-based company is a global leader in spirits and liqueurs boasting a portfolio of world-renowned brands such as Smirnoff vodka Captain Morgan rum Johnnie Walker whisky Baileys Irish cream and Tanqueray gin. It also makes beer including Guinness and wine. With more than 200 global local and luxury brands it owns some two dozen of the world's top 100 premium spirits labels. Diageo rings up sales in virtually every country in the world and has 150-plus production sites globally. North America is its largest market accounting for more than a third of total sales.

Operations

Diageo groups its products into three main alcohol types: spirits beer and ready-to-drink.

Spirits comprise most of the company's revenue generating some 80%. Beer accounts for about 15% of sales and ready-to-drink products (such as premixed gin and tonic) generate about 5%. Other products including wine bring in the remaining sales.

Breaking it down further scotch accounts for about 25% of sales followed by beer (about 15%) and vodka (more than 10%).

Its brands are also split into categories such as Global (brands available in most of the world such as Smirnoff and Johnnie Walker) Local Stars (individual to one market and providing a platform for growth) and Reserve (luxury exclusive brands at the above-premium price point such as Ciroc and Casamigos).

Geographic Reach

Diageo divides its operations along geographic lines to more easily cater to variations in consumer tastes through location-specific brand strategy accounts marketing and corporate functions.

The company generates about 40% of sales in North America with Europe & Turkey and the Asia/Pacific region each adding another 20%-25%. Diageo generates more than 10% of sales in Africa and nearly 10% in Latin America and the Caribbean.

Diageo has offices and production facilities in North America Latin America and Caribbean Europe Africa and the Asia/Pacific region. It sells products in more than 180 markets in these regions. The company's broad geographic footprint protects it from instability in one or multiple of its operating environments.

Sales and Marketing

The company works with a wide range of customers including big and small customers on- and off-trade and digital and e-commerce.

Financial Performance

Note: Growth rates may differ after conversion to US Dollars.

Over the past years Diageo's revenue and profits have been on the rise but experienced a 9% decline 2020. Overall revenue is up about 12% since fiscal 2016 to 2020 (ended June).

In fiscal 2020 the company reported a revenue of 11.7 billion down 9% from the prior year. The downturn was primarily driven by a decline in organic net sales. Organic net sales were down 8.4% with growth in North America offset by declines in all other regions.

Net income fell 56% to 1.4 billion that year driven by a decline in revenue and finance charges among other items.

Cash at the end of fiscal 2020 was 3.2 billion an increase of 2.5 billion from the prior year. Cash from operations contributed 2.3 billion to the coffers while investing activities used 805 million mainly for capital expenditures. Financing activities used another 1.0 billion for proceeds from bonds and dividends to stockholders.

Strategy

Like many of its peers in the alcohol industry Diageo is pursuing a policy of premiumization in its mature and emerging markets. In mature markets the company leverages its premium core and reserve brands which position customers to trade up into luxury categories. In emerging markets Diageo's approach is to use accessible price points to introduce customers and potential customers to the world of higher-priced premium spirits. Globally the company is betting on some 750 million new customers being able to afford international premium spirits over the next ten years.

Diageo continues to invest in its giant brands to build them for the future. It has announced 150 million in Scotch whisky tourism including a new Johnnie Walker Experience in Edinburgh and $130 million for expansion of the Bulleit distillery in Kentucky. In addition Diageo increased its stake in Sichuan Shuijingfang Co. its super-premium baijiu business in China to 63%.

From a product standpoint the company is focused on attracting new customers (more than 50% of product innovations in fiscal 2019 were focused on new customers compared to about 30% four years ago). Recent launches that illustrate that point include White Walker by Johnnie Walker a limited-edition whisky introduced in collaboration with HBO's behemoth Game of Thrones and Ketel One Botanical spirit drink infused with real fruit.

Mergers and Acquisitions

In late 2020 Diageo agreed to acquire Chase Distillery the owner of Chase GB Gin and the award-winning Chase Original Potato Vodka. Dayalan Nayager Managing Director Diageo Great Britain commented: "We are excited about the growth opportunity within the premium plus segment and are very much looking forward to working with the Chase team to build on the portfolio's considerable potential."

In 2020 Diageo has completed the acquisition of Aviation Gin LLC and Davos Brands LLC ('Davos Brands'). This acquisition supports its participation in the super premium gin segment in the United States and is in line with Diageo's strategy to acquire high growth brands with attractive margins that support premiumisation.

Company Background

Diageo was created by Guinness and GrandMet's 1997 merger.

Guinness began business in 1759 when Arthur Guinness leased a small brewery in Dublin Ireland. Guinness began specializing in porters in 1799. Managed by the third generation of Guinnesses the company went public as a London-based firm in 1886.

GrandMet was established by Maxwell Joseph. In 1931 he began acquiring properties for resale but WWII slowed his progress. He started buying hotels in 1946 and by 1961 GrandMet had gone public.

HISTORY

Diageo — from the Latin word for "day" and the Greek word for "world" — was born from Guinness and GrandMet's 1997 merger to fight flat liquor sales and spirited competitors.

Guinness began business in 1759 when Arthur Guinness leased a small brewery in Dublin Ireland. Guinness began specializing in porters in 1799. Managed by the third generation of Guinnesses the company went public as a London-based firm in 1886.

In the 1950s managing director Hugh Beaver was credited with conceiving the Guinness Book of Records . During the 1970s Guinness bought more than 200 companies with disappointing results. Guinness refocused on brewing and distilling operations in the late 1980s by selling noncore businesses and acquiring firms such as Schenley (Dewar's). In 1988 and 1989 it bought 24% of LVMH Mo «t Hennessy Louis Vuitton (later exchanged for 34% of LVMH's wine and spirits business). More acquisitions followed in the 1990s capped by Guinness' 1997 announcement of its $19 billion merger with Grand Metropolitan.

GrandMet was established by Maxwell Joseph. In 1931 he began acquiring properties for resale but WWII slowed his progress. He started buying hotels in 1946 and by 1961 GrandMet had gone public.

Diversification began in 1970 with the purchases of catering firms restaurants and betting shops. In the early 1970s in what was the largest British takeover to that time GrandMet bought brewer Truman Hanburg followed by Watney Mann which owned International Distillers & Vintners makers of Bailey's Bombay Gin and J&B.

GrandMet looked overseas through the 1970s taking over the Liggett Group a US cigarette maker (sold 1986) whose Paddington unit was the US distributor of J&B Scotch. In 1987 it bought Heublein (Smirnoff Lancers Jose Cuervo). Two years later it bought The Pillsbury Company (Burger King and Green Giant) in a hostile takeover.

In 1997 Guinness and GrandMet combined creating Diageo and dividing the companies and brands among four divisions: The Pillsbury Company Burger King Guinness and United Distillers & Vintners.

In 2000 COO Paul Walsh a former Pillsbury CEO took over as CEO of both Diageo and its newly combined alcoholic beverage division Guinness/UDV. Also that year Diageo along with fellow wine and spirits producer Pernod Ricard agreed to pay $8.2 billion to Vivendi for the Seagram's drinks business that holds several brands including Crown Royal VO Canadian whiskies and Sterling Vineyards.

In 2001 Diageo sold its Guinness World Records business to media company Gullane Entertainment for $63 million. That year the company also completed its sale of Pillsbury to General Mills. After months of wrangling with the FTC Diageo finally won regulatory approval for the Seagram's drinks purchase from Vivendi in 2001. The company gained the Crown Royal and VO Canadian brands through this purchase.

In 2002 Diageo completed the sale of its Malibu rum brand to Allied Domecq for about $796 million; the deal also sealed Diageo's ownership of the Captain Morgan rum brand as Allied Domecq agreed to drop its lawsuit involving Captain Morgan. Diageo discontinued marketing its Captain Morgan Gold rum drink in the US later that year because of disappointing sales.

Also in 2002 Diageo sold Burger King for $1.5 billion to a group composed of Texas Pacific Group Bain Capital and Goldman Sachs Capital Partners. Diageo's decision to sell its Pillsbury unit and its Burger King business (the #2 burger chain after McDonald's) was part of the company's new focus on its spirits wine and beer businesses. The Pillsbury divestiture gave the company a 33% stake in General Mills (Diageo sold nearly half of its shares in October 2004). Also in 2002 Diageo and Pernod Ricard which together own rights to the Seagram's brand sold Seagram's line of nonalcoholic mixers to The Coca-Cola Company.

In 2003 Diageo and Jose Cuervo said they would jointly sell Don Julio and Tres Magueyes tequilas. Diageo also joined with Heineken to purchase 30% of InBev's (now Anheuser-Busch InBev's) Namibia Breweries in southern Africa. The brewery will make Heineken and Beck's beer.

Diageo said in 2003 that it would launch a low-alcohol version of its highly popular Baileys Irish Cream. Known as Baileys Glide the drink is made with Irish whiskey but Diageo said it would be manufactured in Germany. Also that year Diageo reopened the George Dickel distillery in Tullahoma Tennessee. In addition Diageo cut 150 jobs in 2003 from its Guinness operation amid declining sales of the well-known stout.

In 2005 Diageo and Heineken formed a partnership for the production and distribution of Guinness in Russia. The company also acquired The Chalone Wine Group in 2005 for about $260 million. It added the winery into Diageo's current US wine operations which are organized under Diageo Chateau & Estate Wines. Diageo also acquired Netherlands distiller Ursus Vodka for an undisclosed amount and added Bushmills Irish whiskey to its stable with the purchase of the brand from Pernod Ricard for $363 million. It also agreed to stay out of any negotiations regarding the takeover of Allied Domecq. (In 2005 Pernod Ricard acquired Allied Domecq.) That year it also disposed of its 4% holdings in General Mills saying the investment was not congruent with its business strategy.

In 2007 the company acquired about a 45% stake in Quanxing which distills the traditional premium Chinese liquor baijiu.

In 2008 Diageo formed a 50-50 joint venture with Dutch vodka maker Ketel One paying ?610 million ($900 million) for its interest. The partnership followed Diageo's abandoned plans to bid on Absolut vodka maker V&S Group. (Ultimately the V&S Group was auctioned off to Pernod Ricard by its owner the Swedish government.) Also that year Diageo took full ownership of D Distribution the Russian distributor of the Smirnoff and Smirnov brands. It paid about $30 million for the remaining 25% stake held by Alfa Group.

Diageo saw its leadership change in 2008 when Lord James Blyth of Rowington stepped down as chairman. He was replaced by Franz Humer who previously served as CEO of F. Hoffmann-La Roche.

Meanwhile Diageo has signaled an interested in acquiring Moet Hennessy the spirits and wine subsidiary of French luxury conglomerate LVMH; however LVMH is not inclined to sell. Diageo owns about 35% of Mo t Hennessy. Undeterred from building its liqueurs portfolio Diageo in mid-2010 increased its interest in the London Group which supplies the premium NUVO brand of liqueurs to a little more than 70%. London Group was created through a joint venture between Diageo and New York entrepreneur Raphael Yakoby.

EXECUTIVES

General Counsel, Company Secretary, Tom Shropshire
Non-Executive Independent Director, Nicola Mendelsohn
President, Global Supply and Procurement and Chief Sustainability Officer, Ewan Andrew
Chief Financial Officer, Lavanya Chandrashekar
Chief Executive and Director, Ivan Menezes, $1,655,393 total compensation
Non-Executive Chairman of the Board, Javier Larraz
President, Diageo Africa & Beer, John O'Keeffe
President, Europe and India, John Kennedy
Non-Executive Independent Director, Alan Stewart
President, Asia Pacific and Global Travel, Sam Fischer
Chief Marketing Officer, Cristina Diezhandino
Director, Global Corporate Relations, Daniel Mobley
Chief HR Officer, Mairéad Nayager
Senior Non-Executive Independent Director, Susan Kilsby
President, North America and Global Supply, Debra Crew
Non-Executive Independent Director, Melissa Bethell
Managing Director and CEO, United Spirits Limited, Hina Nagarajan
Non-Executive Independent Director, John Manzoni
Non-Executive Independent Director, Ireena Vittal
Non-Executive Independent Director, Valerie Chapoulaud-Floquet
President, Latin America and Caribbean, Alvaro Cardenas
Auditors: PricewaterhouseCoopers LLP

LOCATIONS

HQ: Diageo Plc
Lakeside Drive, Park Royal, London NW10 7HQ
Phone: (44) 20 8978 6000
Web: www.diageo.com

2019 Sales

	% of total
North America	35
Europe & Turkey	23
Asia-Pacific	21
Africa	12
Latin America & Caribbean	9
Total	**100**

PRODUCTS/OPERATIONS

2019 Sales

	% of sales
Spirits	69
Beer	16
Ready-to-drink	6
Other	9
Total	**100**

Selected Brands

Strategic brands
Baileys Original Irish Cream liqueur
Buchanan's De Luxe Scotch whiskey
Captain Morgan rum
Ciroc vodka
Crown Royal Canadian whisky
Don Julio
Guinness stout
J&B Scotch whiskey
Johnnie Walker Scotch whisky
Ketel One vodka
Smirnoff vodka
Tanqueray London Dry and Tanqueray No. TEN gin
Windsor Premier Scotch whisky

COMPETITORS

Anheuser-Busch InBev	MGP INGREDIENTS INC.
BEAM SUNTORY INC.	MOLSON COORS BEVERAGE
BROWN-FORMAN	COMPANY
CORPORATION	NAKED WINES PLC
CAMPARI AMERICA LLC	NATIONAL WINE &
CASTLE BRANDS INC.	SPIRITS INC.
DISTELL INTERNATIONAL	PERNOD RICARD
LIMITED	RADICO KHAITAN LIMITED
FOSTER'S GROUP PTY LTD	THE EDRINGTON GROUP
MARTIN MILLER'S GIN	LIMITED
LIMITED	

HISTORICAL FINANCIALS

Company Type: Public

Income Statement				FYE: June 30
	REVENUE ($ mil.)	NET INCOME ($ mil.)	NET PROFIT MARGIN	EMPLOYEES
06/21	17,656	3,688	20.9%	27,650
06/20	14,418	1,728	12.0%	27,775
06/19	16,324	4,009	24.6%	28,420
06/18	15,993	3,973	24.8%	29,917
06/17	15,640	3,455	22.1%	30,433
Annual Growth	**3.1%**	**1.6%**	**—**	**(2.4%)**

2021 Year-End Financials

Debt ratio: 63.9%
Return on equity: 38.9%
Cash ($ mil.): 3,811
Current ratio: 1.60
Long-term debt ($ mil.): 17,839

No. of shares (mil.): —
Dividends
  Yield: 1.9%
  Payout: 242.0%
Market value ($ mil.): —

	STOCK PRICE ($) FY Close	P/E High/Low	PER SHARE ($) Earnings	Dividends	Book Value
06/21	191.69	171 118	1.57	3.71	3.74
06/20	134.39	297 178	0.73	3.43	3.24
06/19	172.32	133 97	1.65	3.35	4.48
06/18	144.01	121 99	1.59	3.35	4.85
06/17	119.83	118 97	1.37	3.02	4.86
Annual Growth	**12.5%**	**— —**	**3.5%**	**5.3%**	**(6.4%)**

DiDi Global Inc

LOCATIONS

HQ: DiDi Global Inc
No. 1 Block B, Shangdong Digital Valley, No. 8 Dongbeiwang West Road, Beijing, Haidian District
Phone: (86) 10 8304 3181

HISTORICAL FINANCIALS

Company Type: Public

Income Statement				FYE: December 31
	REVENUE ($ mil.)	NET INCOME ($ mil.)	NET PROFIT MARGIN	EMPLOYEES
12/20	21,671	(1,607)	—	15,914
12/19	22,245	(1,398)	—	14,214
12/18	19,668	(2,177)	—	13,563
Annual Growth	**5.0%**	**—**		**8.3%**

2020 Year-End Financials

Debt ratio: 0.7%
Return on equity: (-8.7%)
Cash ($ mil.): 2,961
Current ratio: 2.61
Long-term debt ($ mil.): 222

No. of shares (mil.): 108
Dividends
  Yield: —
  Payout: —
Market value ($ mil.): —

	STOCK PRICE ($) FY Close	P/E High/Low	PER SHARE ($) Earnings	Dividends	Book Value
12/20	0.00	— —	(15.31)	0.00	160.07
12/19	0.00	— —	(13.89)	0.00	179.20
Annual Growth	**—**		**—**	**—**	**(5.5%)**

DKSH Holding Ltd

DKSH Holding provides logistics and supply chain management services to companies looking to do business in Asia. Its consumer goods unit markets luxury fashion food and lifestyle products while its food and ingredients business markets and sources the stuff of which consumable products are made. Its health care unit distributes pharmaceuticals and medical equipment and its specialty chemicals unit provides raw materials sourcing and brokering services to manufacturers. Its technology unit provides products and services to a variety of industries. Formed in 2002 DKSH operates in more than 35 countries across Asia Europe and the Americas.

Operations
The company operates through several primary segments: Consumer Goods (42% of net sales) Healthcare (46%) Performance Materials (8%) Technology (4%) and Other (non-Business Unit).

Geographic Reach
DKSH is based in Zurich and operates in 35 countries through a network of 720 business locations in Asia Pacific and 30 business locations in Europe and the US.

Sales and Marketing
The company serves specialty chemicals food and beverage pharmaceutical and personal care industries.

Financial Performance
DKSH's revenues climbed 3% from 2013 to 2014. The growth was mainly fueled by a 7% spike in Healthcare sales and an 11% rise in sales from Greater China. Its net income decreased by 16% from 2013 to 2014 mainly due to an uptick in

goods and materials purchased and consumables used.

Strategy

One way DKSH grows is by opening new facilities in select markets. In 2015 the company opened a new distribution center in Kota Kinabalu. The distribution center represented a capacity upgrade in its Malaysian consumer goods and healthcare infrastructure and is part of its growth plans within the Sabah region.

EXECUTIVES

Non-Executive Director, Andreas Keller, $159,714 total compensation

Non-Executive Chairman of the Board, Adrian Keller, $399,286 total compensation

Non-Executive Independent Director, Frank Gulich, $159,714 total compensation

Chief Financial Officer, Member of the Executive Board, Bernhard Schmitt

Member of the Group Management, Chief Information Officer, Michael Hutab

Member of the Group Management, Co-Head Business Unit Performance Materials, Thomas Sul

General Counsel, Secretary of the Board of Directors, Member of the Executive Committee, Laurent Sigismondi

Non-Executive Independent Director, Hans Tanner, $159,714 total compensation

Member of the Group Management, Co-Head Business Unit Performance Materials, Natale Capri

Head Corporate Affairs & Strategic Investments, Member of the Executive Committee, Stephen Ferraby

Chief Executive Officer, Member of the Executive Board, Stefan Butz, $1,064,763 total compensation

Non-Executive Independent Director, Annette Koehler, $159,714 total compensation

Member of the Group Management, Head Business Unit Healthcare, Bijay Singh

Member of the Group Management, Head Business Unit Technology, Hanno Elbraechter

Non-Executive Independent Director, Eunice Zehnder-Lai, $159,714 total compensation

Non-Executive Independent Director, Wolfgang Baier, $159,714 total compensation

Non-Executive Independent Director, Jack Clemons, $159,714 total compensation

Non-Executive Independent Director, Marco Gadola, $559,000 total compensation

Head Business Unit Consumer Goods and Member of the Executive Committee, Terry Seremetis

Auditors: Ernst & Young Ltd

LOCATIONS

HQ: DKSH Holding Ltd
Wiesenstrasse 8, P.O. Box 888, Zurich 8034
Phone: (41) 44 386 7272 **Fax:** (41) 44 386 7282
Web: www.dksh.com

PRODUCTS/OPERATIONS

2014 Sales

	% of total
Consumer goods	42
Healthcare	46
Performance Materials	8
Technology	4
Total	**100**

2014 Sales

	% of total
Thailand	34
Greater China	30
Malaysia/Singapore	20
Other	16
Total	**100**

COMPETITORS

APTARGROUP INC.
BODYCOTE PLC CORPORATION
BUREAU VERITAS
BayWa AG
COMPASS GROUP PLC
DCC PUBLIC LIMITED COMPANY
KION GROUP AG

MITSUBISHI CHEMICAL HOLDINGS
RENOLD PUBLIC LIMITED COMPANY
TERNIUM S.A.
TITON HOLDINGS PLC
UNIVAR SOLUTIONS INC.

HISTORICAL FINANCIALS

Company Type: Public

Income Statement

	REVENUE ($ mil.)	NET INCOME ($ mil.)	NET PROFIT MARGIN	EMPLOYEES
12/20	12,196	178	1.5%	32,447
12/19	11,978	178	1.5%	33,353
12/18	11,532	259	2.2%	32,996
12/17	11,277	212	1.9%	31,973
12/16	10,320	204	2.0%	30,318
Annual Growth	4.3%	(3.4%)	—	1.7%

2020 Year-End Financials

Debt ratio: 7.5%	No. of shares (mil.): 65
Return on equity: 8.9%	Dividends
Cash ($ mil.): 772	Yield: —
Current ratio: 1.48	Payout: 80.9%
Long-term debt ($ mil.): 246	Market value ($ mil.): —

FYE: December 31

DNB BANK ASA

DNB is Norway's largest financial services group and one of the largest in the Nordic region in terms of market capitalization. The Group offers a full range of financial services including loans savings advisory services insurance and pension products for retail and corporate customers. DNB's bank branches in Norway in-store postal and banking outlets post office counters Internet banking mobile services and international offices ensure that the bank is present where its customers are. It is a major operator in a number of industries for which it also has a Nordic or international strategy

Operations

As Scandinavia's largest financial services group DNB offers financial services through mobile solutions the internet bank customer service centers real estate broking branch offices and international offices. It has 233 000 corporate customers and 2.1 million personal customers. 1.5 million personal customers use its internet bank and 1.2 million use its mobile bank.

According to DNB's management model the operating segments are independent profit centers that are fully responsible for their profit after tax and for achieving the targeted returns on allocated capital. DNB has the following operating segments: Personal customers Corporate customers Risk management and Traditional pension products.

Personal customer (30% of total income) include the Group's total products and activities to private customers in all channels both digital and physical with the exception of home mortgages recorded under Traditional pension products where returns accrue to the policy- holders.

Corporate customers (nearly 55% of total income) include all of the Group's business customers both in Norway and abroad. Customers in the segment include everything from small business customers and start-ups to large Norwegian and international corporate customers.

The Risk management and Traditional pension products segments generated over 15% of DNB's total income.

Geographic Reach

DNB has around 4 400 suppliers 114 of which accounted for approximately 80% of the Group's purchasing costs. Most its suppliers are from the Nordic countries Western Europe and North America.

With a strong position and knowledge about the Nordic markets and 700 employees spread around the globe DNB offers tailored solutions within a broad specter of products. DNB offers its corporate clients financial services from our offices around the globe ? countries in Europe the US and Asia Pacific.

Majority of DNB's international investors are based in the US (nearly 20% of shares) and the UK (nearly 10%).

Sales and Marketing

The open chat service was launched on TV and social media the same weekend. The bank's own people both managers and advisers at the customer service center spoke directly to you and me on prime-time television. A review of all marketing and digital sales activities is carried out annually the purpose of which is to identify any possible risks in connection with marketing activities relating to products and services.

DNB's customer centers received nearly 3 million calls from personal customers and 365000 calls from corporate customers. Personal customer market share in Norway alone has exceeded 40% in 2020 and corporate customer market share for deposits reached nearly 40%.

For personal customers DNB offers a wide range of products through Norway's largest distribution network comprising mobile banking digital banking branch offices customer centres and real estate broking. In addition external distribution of credit cards and car financing in Sweden is included in the business area. External distribution through the cooperation with Posten Norway AS (the Norwegian postal service) was phased out in the third quarter of 2020 with the transition to a solution based on the payment app Vipps. For corporate customers are served by offices both in Norway and abroad. In addition customers are offered access to corporate online and mobile banking services as well as other digital services.

DNB spent NOK 693 million for marketing and public relations in 2020 compared to NOK 821 million in the prior year.

Financial Performance

DNB's profit fell for nearly 23% to NOK 19.8 million in 2020 from NOK 25.7 million in 2019.

Cash at the end of fiscal year 2020 was at NOK 289.1 million compared to NOK 307.8 million in the prior year. Operating activities generated NOK 84.6 million while investing activities used NOK 4.7 million primarily for acquisition of fixed assets. Financing activities also used NOK 102.2 million in 2020.

Strategy

DNB's strategy sets the course for the Group's development within the waters it navigates. This applies to everything from initiatives by traditional players and market entrants regulation and technological advances to the macroeconomic situation around it and customer expectations. It has proven to be competitive and financially sound during a difficult year.

To succeed DNB needs to accelerate its pace of innovation while balancing scarce resources such as capital development funds and people. It has therefore identified four areas as essential for creating the best customer experiences: increase innovative power; increase the use of customer in-

sight; drive skills enhancement and; incorporate corporate responsibility in all processes.
Auditors: Ernst & Young AS

LOCATIONS

HQ: DNB BANK ASA
  Dronning Eufemias gate 30, Oslo 0191
Phone: (47) 915 03000
Web: www.dnb.no/en

2013 Sales

	% of total
Norway	80
Other international operations	15
Baltics and Poland	5
Total	**100**

PRODUCTS/OPERATIONS

2013 Sales

	% of total
Large corporate and international customers	36
Personal customers	37
Small and medium-sized enterprises	16
Trading	6
Traditional pension products	5
Total	**100**

COMPETITORS

BANK VTB PAO
CENKOS SECURITIES PLC
CREDITO EMILIANO SPA
FIRST INTERNATIONAL BANK OF ISRAEL LTD
HARGREAVES LANSDOWN PLC
ISRAEL DISCOUNT BANK OF NEW YORK
LEGAL & GENERAL GROUP PLC
METROPOLITAN BANK HOLDING CORP.
NATIONAL AUSTRALIA BANK LIMITED
POSTE ITALIANE SPA
SANTANDER UK GROUP HOLDINGS PLC
SBERBANK PAO
SMITH & WILLIAMSON HOLDINGS LIMITED
STANDARD BANK GROUP LTD
STARTEK INC.
Shinhan Financial Group Co. Ltd.
THANACHART CAPITAL PUBLIC COMPANY LIMITED
THE WESTERN UNION COMPANY
VIRGIN MONEY HOLDINGS (UK) PLC
Woori Finance Holdings Co. Ltd.

HISTORICAL FINANCIALS

Company Type: Public

Income Statement				FYE: December 31
	ASSETS ($ mil.)	NET INCOME ($ mil.)	INCOME AS % OF ASSETS	EMPLOYEES
12/20	342,600	2,196	0.6%	9,311
12/19	317,848	2,799	0.9%	9,336
12/18	303,559	2,686	0.9%	9,638
12/17	329,086	2,544	0.8%	9,561
12/16	308,372	2,168	0.7%	11,459
Annual Growth	**2.7%**	**0.3%**	**—**	**(5.1%)**

2020 Year-End Financials

Return on assets: 0.6%	Dividends
Return on equity: 7.6%	Yield: —
Long-term debt ($ mil.): —	Payout: —
No. of shares (mil.): 1,550	Market value ($ mil.): —
Sales ($ mil): 9,111	

Doosan Heavy Industries & Construction Co Ltd

Doosan Heavy Industries & Construction is engage in manufacturing of a range of power generation equipment including boilers turbines and generators. The engineering procurement and construction contractor provides the equipment for nuclear coal-fired and combined-cycle power plant projects worldwide. Doosan Heavy also provides water treatment facility technology for power plants and wastewater plants. Through various other divisions it also supplies casting and forging products and materials handling systems. Founded in 1962 Doosan Heavy is partially owned by the Doosan Corporation and is headquartered in Changwon South Korea.

Operations

Doosan Heavy manufactures an expansive selection of heavy industrial products. It builds a range of thermal and nuclear power generation equipment including boilers turbines and generators. The company manufactures earthmoving equipment such as forklifts and bobcats constructs highway and rail lines creates crankshafts for large ships and builds wind turbine generators. It also engages in engineering procurement and construction of thermal power plants including nuclear coal-fired and combined-cycle project. Doosan Heavy also provides water treatment facility technology for power plants seawater desalination facilities urban drinking water and wastewater plants.

Its business segments include Power Generation Water Industrial Plants Castings & Forgings and Construction among others. It is part owner of other affiliated Doosan Corporation subsidiaries the most notable being Doosan Infracore.

Geographic Reach

Changwon South Korea-headquartered Doosan Heavy is manufacturing a range of power generation equipment including boilers turbines and generators. It also engages in engineering procurement and construction of thermal power plants. It is also engages in general construction seawater desalination and etc.

It operates in five European subsidiaries: Doosan Power Systems Doosan Babcock Doosan Skoda Power Doosan Lentjes Doosan and Enpure.

The company has four subsidiaries in Asia and the Middle East: Doosan Power Systems India Doosan Vina Doosan Heavy Industries Japan and Doosan Power Systems Arabia.

In the Americas Doosan Heavy operates subsidiaries Doosan HF Controls Doosan Heavy Industries America Doosan GridTech and Doosan Power Services America.

Sales and Marketing

Doosen Heavy Industries and Construction markets its products and services through its affiliate company such Hancomm an advertising agency and Vogue Doosan Magazine.

Financial Performance

Note: Financial results are denominated in the company's home currency the Korean Won.

The company's revenue for fiscal 2020 decreased to 15.1 trillion won compared from the prior year with 15.7 trillion won.

Loss for fiscal 2020 increased to 838.4 billion won compared from the prior year with 104.4 billion won.

Cash held by the company at the end of fiscal 2020 increased to 2.3 trillion won. Cash provided by operations and financing activities were 1.3 trillion won and 1.2 trillion won respectively. Cash used for investing activities was 526.0 billion won mainly increase in short-term loans.

EXECUTIVES

Non-Executive Independent Director, Yik Hyeon Nam
Non-Executive Independent Director, Dae Gi Kim
President, Co-Chief Executive Officer, Director, Yeon Yin Jung
Auditors: KPMG Samjong Accounting Corp.

LOCATIONS

HQ: Doosan Heavy Industries & Construction Co Ltd
  22, Doosanvolvo-ro Seongsan-gu, Changwon-si, Gyeongsangnam-do 51711
Phone: (82) 55 278 6114   **Fax:** (82) 55 264 5551
Web: www.doosanheavy.com

PRODUCTS/OPERATIONS

2016 Sales by Segment (incl. Intersegment)

	% of total
Power generation	79
Water	6
Industrial Plants	1
Castings & Forgings	7
Construction	7
Wholesale & Retail	-
Total	**100**

Selected Subsidiaries

America
  Doosan GridTech
  Doosan Heavy Industries America
  Doosan HF Controls
  Doosan Hydro Technology
  Doosan Power Services Americas
Asia
  Doosan Power Systems India
  Doosan Heavy Industries Japan
  Doosan Power Systems Arabia
  Doosan VINA
  Doosan DCS VINA
Europe
  Doosan Babcock
  Doosan Enpure
  Doosan Lentjes
  Doosan IMGB
  Doosan Power Systems
  Doosan Skoda Power

COMPETITORS

BRIGHTSOURCE ENERGY INC.
CIC GROUP INC.
China Communications Construction Company Limited
China Railway Engineering Group Co. Ltd.
DOOSAN BABCOCK LIMITED
Doosan Corporation
FLUOR CORPORATION
GEMMA POWER SYSTEMS LLC
Hyundai Doosan Infracore Co. Ltd.
Korea Shipbuilding & Offshre Engineering Co. Ltd.
LARSEN AND TOUBRO LIMITED
ORION GROUP HOLDINGS INC.
S & B ENGINEERS AND CONSTRUCTORS LTD.
SNC-LAVALIN CONSTRUCTORS INC.
WARTSILA NORTH AMERICA INC.
WEBUILD SPA

HISTORICAL FINANCIALS
Company Type: Public

Income Statement
FYE: December 31

	REVENUE ($ mil.)	NET INCOME ($ mil.)	NET PROFIT MARGIN	EMPLOYEES
12/19	13,562	(342)	—	0
12/18	13,239	(469)	—	7,294
12/17	13,622	(273)	—	7,609
12/16	11,564	(142)	—	7,728
12/15	13,772	(882)	—	7,771
Annual Growth	(0.4%)	—	—	—

2019 Year-End Financials

Debt ratio: 0.0%
Return on equity: (-14.7%)
Cash ($ mil.): 1,248
Current ratio: 0.68
Long-term debt ($ mil.): 2,204

No. of shares (mil.): 202
Dividends
  Yield: —
  Payout: 0.68
Market value ($ mil.): —

DSV AS

EXECUTIVES

Chief Financial Officer, Member of the Executive Board, Michael Ebbe
Director, Niels Smedegaard
Independent Director, Marie-Louise Aamund
Independent Director, Birgit Noergaard
Independent Chairman of the Board, Thomas Plenborg
Independent Director, Beat Walti
Deputy Chairman of the Board, Jorgen Moeller
Independent Director, Annette Sadolin
Group Chief Operating Officer, Member of the Executive Board, Jens Lund, $1,726,973 total compensation
Chief Executive Officer, Member of the Executive Board, Jens Andersen, $2,323,008 total compensation
Auditors: PricewaterhouseCoopers Statsautoriseret Revisionsaktieselskab

LOCATIONS

HQ: DSV AS
  Hovedgaden 630, Hedehusene 2640
Phone: (45) 43 20 30 40
Web: www.dsv.com

HISTORICAL FINANCIALS
Company Type: Public

Income Statement
FYE: December 31

	REVENUE ($ mil.)	NET INCOME ($ mil.)	NET PROFIT MARGIN	EMPLOYEES
12/20	19,122	701	3.7%	56,621
12/19	14,231	556	3.9%	61,216
12/18	12,123	613	5.1%	47,394
12/17	12,060	479	4.0%	45,636
12/16	9,622	236	2.5%	44,779
Annual Growth	18.7%	31.2%	—	6.0%

2020 Year-End Financials

Debt ratio: 1.7%
Return on equity: 8.7%
Cash ($ mil.): 669
Current ratio: 1.05
Long-term debt ($ mil.): 1,454

No. of shares (mil.): 226
Dividends
  Yield: 0.0%
  Payout: 45.0%
Market value ($ mil.): 18,991

	STOCK PRICE ($) FY Close	P/E High/Low		PER SHARE ($) Earnings	Dividends	Book Value
12/20	84.02	5	2	3.04	1.37	34.58
12/19	57.83	3	2	2.77	1.12	32.46
12/18	32.95	2	1	3.31	1.02	12.54
12/17	39.47	3	2	2.54	0.96	12.98
12/16	22.13	3	2	1.27	0.80	10.27
Annual Growth	39.6%	—	—	24.4%	14.2%	35.5%

Dubai Islamic Bank Ltd

Auditors: Deloitte & Touche (M.E.)

LOCATIONS

HQ: Dubai Islamic Bank Ltd
  P.O. Box 1080, Dubai
Phone: (971) 4 295 3000   **Fax:** (971) 4 295 4111
Web: www.alislami.ae

HISTORICAL FINANCIALS
Company Type: Public

Income Statement
FYE: December 31

	ASSETS ($ mil.)	NET INCOME ($ mil.)	INCOME AS % OF ASSETS	EMPLOYEES
12/20	78,844	896	1.1%	0
12/19	63,116	1,365	2.2%	0
12/18	60,907	1,338	2.2%	0
12/17	56,456	1,176	2.1%	0
12/16	47,635	979	2.1%	0
Annual Growth	13.4%	(2.2%)	—	—

2020 Year-End Financials

Return on assets: 1.2%
Return on equity: 9.0%
Long-term debt ($ mil.): —
No. of shares (mil.): —
Sales ($ mil): 3,854

Dividends
  Yield: —
  Payout: 52.6%
Market value ($ mil.): —

E.ON SE

E.ON is one of Europe's largest operators of energy networks and energy infrastructure and a provider of innovative customer solutions for 50 million customers. The company's operations are energy networks and customer solutions. Its non-strategic operations are reported under non-core Business. These include power and gas distribution customer service sales and farms. With customers in Germany Denmark Sweden Italy the UK Czech Republic Hungary Romania Slovakia and Turkey E.ON boasts not more than 4100 GWh per commodity 705000 kilometers of energy networks in Germany and about 15.1 million connection points for power in its service territory. About 55% of E.ON's total revenue comes from Germany.

Operations

E.ON operates through two segments: Energy Networks and Customer Solutions.

Energy Networks (about 70% of annual sales) consists of E.ON's power and gas distribution networks and related activities. It is subdivided into three regional markets: Germany Sweden and East-Central Europe/Turkey (which consists of the Czech Republic Hungary Romania Poland Croatia Slovakia and the stake in Enerjisa Enerji in Turkey).

Customer solutions brings in around 25 of the annual net sales. It serves municipal public industrial commercial and residential customers through a portfolio of products and services that focus on distributed generation and storage and sustainable mobility solutions. The segment also includes E.ON Business Solutions and the eMobility business.

Overall electricity generates around 75% of total revenue while gas for nearly 20% and other for less than 10% of total revenue.

Geographic Reach

E.ON's corporate headquarters is in Essen Germany. E.ON has a presence in Germany Norway Denmark the Netherlands the United Kingdom Belgium France Poland Czech Republic Italy Austria Slovakia Croatia Slovenia Romania Hungary and Italy.

About 55% of E.ON's total revenue comes from Germany.

Sales and Marketing

The company's customers are across all categories: residential small and medium-sized enterprises large commercial and industrial and public entities.

Financial Performance

Note: Growth rates may differ after conversion to US Dollars.

The company's revenue for fiscal 2020 increased by 48% to ?60.9 billion compared from the prior year with ?41.3 billion.

Net income for fiscal 2020 decreased by 34% to ?1.0 billion compared from the prior year with ?1.6 billion.

Cash held by the company at the end of fiscal 2020 increased to ?2.7 billion. Cash provided by operations was ?5.3 billion while cash used for investing and financing activities were ?1.9 billion and ?2.6 billion respectively. Main uses of cash were purchases of investments and repayments of financial liabilities.

Strategy

E.ON's objective is to systematically focus the company on the new energy world of increasingly empowered and proactive customers. It will create new markets for its customers by providing them with new products services and technologies. The company's efforts will be guided by its principles of integration focus efficiency and growth.

The company began integrating its innogy SE last year and after the squeeze-out and acquisition of its remaining stock will accelerate this process in the current year. Its focus is on combining the respective organizational entities in line with its Target Operating Model. After the transaction is completed the new E.ON will be the first European player to focus exclusively on municipal commercial and residential customers and will generate a large part of its EBIT with regulated business.

In addition to strengthening its core businesses the innogy takeover will enable it to leverage substantial synergies of about ?740 million by 2022 thereby making important progress toward its efficiency targets. It expects the systematic optimization and digitization of its business processes to deliver additional efficiency gains.

As its growth strategy calls for extensive investments in both business segments the main focus will be on Energy Networks in which it will invest about ?3.2 billion in 2020. It also plans to invest about ?0.9 billion in Customer Solutions.

HISTORY

VEBA (originally Vereinigte Elektrizitats-und Bergwerks AG) was formed in 1929 in Berlin to consolidate Germany's state-owned electricity and mining interests. These operations included PreussenElektra an electric utility formed by the German government in 1927; Hibernia a coal mining firm founded in 1873; and Preussag a mining and smelting company founded in 1923.

In the 1930s VEBA produced synthetic gasoline (essential to the German war machine) from coal at its Hibernia plant. In 1938 the company and chemical cartel I. G. Farben set up Chemische Werke H ls to make synthetic rubber. After WWII VEBA's assets in western Germany were transferred to the government and several executives were arrested. Preussag was spun off in 1959.

In 1965 the government spun off VEBA to the public. That year the company entered trading and transportation by buying Stinnes one of West Germany's largest industrial companies. In 1969 VEBA transferred its coal mining interests to Ruhrkohle and a few years later moved into oil exploration and development. The company shortened its name to VEBA in 1970.

The West German government sold its remaining stake in VEBA in 1987. In a changed regulatory environment large investors were able to accumulate big portions of stock and their dissatisfaction with the company's lackluster results made it a takeover target. In response new chairman Ulrich Hartmann began cutting noncore businesses and reducing staff.

In 1990 VEBA began accumulating mobile communications networking and cable TV companies. It allied with the UK's Cable and Wireless (C&W) in 1995 to develop a European mobile phone business but in 1997 C&W sold its interest to VEBA (as part of the deal VEBA gained a 10% stake in C&W which it sold in 1999). In anticipation of the 1998 deregulation of the German telecom market VEBA and RWE merged their German telecom businesses in 1997.

VEBA acquired a 36% stake in Degussa a specialty chemicals company in 1997; two years later Degussa merged with H ls to form a separately traded chemical company called Degussa-H ls in which VEBA took a 62% stake. VEBA sold a 30% stake in Stinnes to the public in 1999. The company's telecom venture sold its fixed-line telephone business its cable TV unit and its stake in mobile phone operator E-Plus.

These moves however were just the prelude to a bigger deal: a $14 billion merger agreement between VEBA and fellow German conglomerate VIAG. The partners announced plans to dump noncore businesses and beef up their energy and chemicals holdings. VEBA and VIAG completed their merger in 2000 and the combined company adopted the name E.ON. The companies' utilities businesses were combined into E.ON Energie and their chemicals units were brought together as Degussa.

To gain regulatory approval to form E.ON VEBA and VIAG agreed to sell their stakes in German electric utilities Bewag and VEAG and coal producer LAUBAG. E.ON sold its VEAG and LAUBAG interests along with semiconductor and electronics distribution units in 2000 and sold Bewag in 2001.

In 2001 E.ON agreed to acquire UK electricity generator Powergen (now E.ON UK) and it sold off nonutility operations including Degussa and Veba Oel. E.ON swapped a 51% stake in Veba Oel for BP's 26% stake in German natural gas supplier Ruhrgas (now E.ON Ruhrgas). E.ON also sold Kl ¶ckner to UK steel trader Balli and sold its stake in silicon wafer maker MEMC to buyout firm Texas Pacific Group.

In 2002 E.ON sold its VAW Aluminum unit to Norwegian conglomerate Norsk Hydro in a $2.8 billion deal. Regulators moved to prevent E.ON from acquiring BP's stake in Ruhrgas in 2002 but BP agreed to pay for the Veba Oel stake in cash if necessary and the swap was completed later that year. E.ON also acquired Vodafone and ThyssenKrupp's stakes in Ruhrgas in 2002 and it sold its remaining stake in Veba Oel to BP.

Also in 2002 E.ON completed its purchase of Powergen (which included its US subsidiary LG&E Energy) for about $8 billion and it sold its 65% stake in logistics company Stinnes to German railroad operator Deutsche Bahn. In late 2002 E.ON acquired the UK energy supply and generation businesses of TXU Europe in a $2.5 billion deal.

The following year E.ON swapped its majority stake in chemical maker Degussa with coal group RAG for RAG's 18% interest in Ruhrgas. It completed its acquisition of Ruhrgas by purchasing the combined 40% stake held by Royal Dutch Shell Exxon Mobil and TUI (formerly Preussag). It also sold subsidiary Viterra's energy services unit (gas and water meters) to CVC Capital Partners.

In 2005 the company acquired the Enfield power station in the UK for $250.2 million.

In 2007 E.ON acquired Ireland-based wind farm company Airtricity for $1.4 billion.

Pursuing growth in new geographic markets in 2007 E.ON acquired Russia-based power utility OGK-4 for almost $6 billion. Outmaneuvered by its rivals in 2008 it dropped its $56 billion bid to buy Endesa S.A. Spain's largest electric utility settling for the purchase of a number of Endesa's generation assets in Spain and Italy.

In 2009 to counter EDF's acquisition of British Energy E.ON and RWE formed a joint venture to develop 6000 MW of nuclear power capacity in the UK.

That year prompted by the regulatory requirements of the European Commission E.ON and GDF SUEZ agreed to swap generating assets to allow for more competition in their major markets. It sold 860 MW of Germany-based conventional power plants 132 MW of hydroelectric plants and access to 770 MW of nuclear power. In return GDF SUEZ sold to E.ON a similar amount of power generation capacity in France and the Benelux countries. In 2010 also to meet EU anti-monopoly regulations it sold grid operator Transpower to Dutch giant TenneT for $1.1 billion and it swapped 5000 MW of generation capacity with EDF and EnBW.

In 2010 the company sold E.ON U.S. which operates Kentucky's two major utilities for $7.6 billion. Its US assets were no longer considered a core part of its growth strategy and the sale helped to pay down debt. To raise cash that year it also sold its 3.5% stake in Gazprom to Russian investment bank Vnesheconombank for $4.4 billion.

EXECUTIVES

Chairman and Chief Executive Officer, Leonhard Birnbaum, $911,524 total compensation
Chief Financial Officer, Marc Spieker
Chairman of the Supervisory Board, Karl-Ludwig Kley
Chief Operating Officer, Networks, Thomas König, $797,583 total compensation
Chief Operating Officer, Digital, Victoria Ossadnik
Deputy Chairman, Supervisory Board, Christoph Schmitz
Auditors: PricewaterhouseCoopers GmbH Wirtschaftspruefungsgesellschaft

LOCATIONS

HQ: E.ON SE
Bruesseler Platz 1, Essen D-45131
Phone: (49) 211 184 00   **Fax:** (49) 211 45 79 5 01
Web: www.eon.com

2016 Sales

	% of total
Germany	57
United Kingdom	20
Europe (other)	16
Sweden	6
Other	1
Total	**100**

PRODUCTS/OPERATIONS

2016 Sales

	% of total
Customer Solutions	53
Energy Networks	38
Renewables	3
Non-Core Business	3
Corporate Functions/Other	3
Total	**100**

2016 Sales

	% of total
Electricity	78
Gas	17
Other	5
Total	**100**

COMPETITORS

BERKSHIRE HATHAWAY ENERGY COMPANY
ELECTRICITE DE FRANCE
ENDESA SA
ENEL SPA
EXELON CORPORATION
Fortum Oyj

IBERDROLA SOCIEDAD ANONIMA
INTERNATIONAL POWER LTD.
SSE PLC
Uniper SE

HISTORICAL FINANCIALS

Company Type: Public

Income Statement				FYE: December 31
	REVENUE ($ mil.)	NET INCOME ($ mil.)	NET PROFIT MARGIN	EMPLOYEES
12/20	75,682	1,248	1.6%	78,126
12/19	46,443	1,758	3.8%	78,948
12/18	34,327	3,690	10.8%	43,302
12/17	46,143	4,705	10.2%	42,699
12/16	40,873	(8,922)	—	43,138
Annual Growth	**16.7%**	—	—	**16.0%**

2020 Year-End Financials

Debt ratio: 42.2%	No. of shares (mil.): —
Return on equity: 14.4%	Dividends
Cash ($ mil.): 5,884	Yield: 3.4%
Current ratio: 0.81	Payout: 86.9%
Long-term debt ($ mil.): 36,110	Market value ($ mil.): —

	STOCK PRICE ($) FY Close	P/E High/Low		PER SHARE ($)		
				Earnings	Dividends	Book Value
12/20	11.06	36	25	0.48	0.38	2.32
12/19	10.67	17	13	0.76	0.35	3.91
12/18	9.87	8	6	1.71	0.26	3.04
12/17	10.88	7	4	2.21	0.19	2.22
12/16	7.05	—	—	(4.57)	1.43	(0.57)
Annual Growth	**11.9%**	—	—	—	**(28.4%)**	—

East Japan Railway Co.

If you want to ride the rails into Tokyo you could find yourself cruising at 168 mph aboard a bullet train operated by East Japan Railway better known as JR East. The company serves more than 15 million people daily and carries passengers on more than 7400 km of track in the eastern half of the Japanese mainland including the Tokyo area. JR East's Shinkansen (bullet-train) lines connect metropolitan Tokyo with other major cities. Besides its transportation-related operations JR East generates revenue from leasing restaurant and retail space in its stations and from managing shopping centers and office buildings on property that has been developed near its stations.

Operations

East Japan Railway has four operating segments: Transportation Retail & Services Real Estate & Hotels and Other.

The Transportation segment includes passenger transportation operations which are centered on railway operations as well as travel agency services cleaning services station operations facilities maintenance operations and railcar manufacturing and maintenance. The segment accounts for almost 70% of the company's total revenue.

The Retail & Services segment consists of JR East's life-style service business that includes retail sales and restaurant operations wholesale businesses a truck transportation business and advertising and publicity. The segment accounts for more than 15% of revenue.

The Real Estate & Hotels segment encompasses JR East's life-style service business that includes shopping center operations leasing of office buildings and other properties and hotel operations. This segment accounts for more than 10% of total revenue.

JR East's Other segment consists of IT & Suica which includes credit cards and information processing among other businesses. The segment accounts for nearly 5% of total revenue.

Geographic Reach

The railway business of JR East spans the eastern half of the Hons Shinkansen network which connects Tokyo with regional cities in five directions.

The company is headquartered in Tokyo Japan. It also has offices internationally located in New York Paris London and Singapore.

Sales and Marketing

JR East major customers was omitted as no single outside customer contributes about 10% or more to company's total sales.

The average number of passengers per day is about 17 million.

Financial Performance

Note: Growth rates may differ after conversion to US Dollars.

As a result of the company's initiatives during the fiscal year under review operating revenues increased 2% year on year to 3.0 trillion ($27.0 billion).

JR East profit attributable to owners of parent increased 2% to 295.2 billion ($2660 million) mainly due to higher income before income taxes.

In fiscal 2019 net cash provided by operating activities totaled 663.8 billion ($6.0 billion) 40.4 billion less than in the previous fiscal year. This result was mainly due to an increase in major receivables. Net cash used in investing activities amounted to 594.4 billion ($5.3 billion) 52.6 billion more than in the previous fiscal year. This result was mainly due to an increase in payments for purchases of fixed assets. Net cash used in financing activities came to 120.7 billion ($1.1 billion) 14.4 billion less than in the previous fiscal year. This result was mainly due to an increase in proceeds from procurement of interest-bearing debt.

Strategy

In July 2018 the company announced the Group Management Vision "Move Up 2027" and entered the second year.

The goal of "Move Up 2027" is to create a service that integrates transportation services lifestyle services and IT/Suica starting from "people". This is a service that only JR East has because it has a multi-layered "real" network that supports the living infrastructure. The group will build an ecosystem centered on "people" who continue to create new value by fusing technological innovation and big data.

"Move Up2027" will finally enter the full-scale execution phase. Following the lifestyle service business growth vision "NEXT10" formulated in 2017 in 2018 the company started "Medium-term Vision for Service Quality Reforms 2020" and "Group Safety Plan 2023" and newly established "Technology Innovation Promotion Division". JR East have steadily laid the foundation for the strong promotion of "Reform 2027". In the future based on these JR East will put the transition from the "railway infrastructure starting point" to the "human starting point" on track. To realize the future depicted in "Move Up 2027" it will concretely accelerate measures in line with the three focus points of "safety" "life" and "happiness of employees and their families."

EXECUTIVES

Chairman of the Board, Tetsuro Tomita
President, Chief Executive Officer, Representative Director, Yuji Fukasawa
Vice President, Chief Director of Technology Innovation Promotion, Representative Director, Katsumi Ise
Managing Executive Officer, Deputy Chief Director of International Business, Yoshihiro Kumamoto
Managing Executive Officer, Ikuju Asami
Independent Director, Motoshige Ito
Independent Director, Reiko Amano
Managing Director, Chief Director of General Planning, Kiwamu Sakai
Vice President, Chief Director of Business Creation, Representative Director, Yoichi Kise
Managing Executive Officer, Chief Director of International Business, Hitoshi Saiaki
Independent Director, Hiroko Kawamoto
Managing Director, Atsuko Itoh
Vice President, Chief Director of Railway Business, Representative Director, Totaro Ichikawa
Managing Director, Deputy Chief Director of Technology Innovation Promotion, Atsushi Ouchi
Auditors: KPMG AZSA LLC

LOCATIONS

HQ: East Japan Railway Co.
2-2-2 Yoyogi, Shibuya-ku, Tokyo 151-8578
Phone: (81) 3 5334 1111   **Fax:** (81) 3 5334 1320
Web: www.jreast.co.jp

PRODUCTS/OPERATIONS

2017 Sales

	% of total
Transportation	64
Retail & Services	18
Real Estate & Hotels	11
Other	7
Total	**100**

COMPETITORS

AUTOGRILL SPA
CSX CORPORATION
Compagnie des Chemins de Fer Nationaux du Canada
FIRSTGROUP PLC
HASEKO CORPORATION
LONDON UNDERGROUND LIMITED
N.V. Nederlandse Spoorwegen
NATIONAL RAILROAD PASSENGER CORPORATION
RZHD PAO
UNION PACIFIC CORPORATION

HISTORICAL FINANCIALS

Company Type: Public

Income Statement

FYE: March 31

	REVENUE ($ mil.)	NET INCOME ($ mil.)	NET PROFIT MARGIN	EMPLOYEES
03/21	15,936	(5,219)	—	98,158
03/20	27,145	1,827	6.7%	98,415
03/19	27,107	2,665	9.8%	99,034
03/18	27,782	2,721	9.8%	99,584
03/17	25,765	2,485	9.6%	98,544
Annual Growth	**(11.3%)**	—	—	**(0.1%)**

2021 Year-End Financials

Debt ratio: 0.3%	No. of shares (mil.): 377
Return on equity: (-20.3%)	Dividends
Cash ($ mil.): 1,789	Yield: 1.7%
Current ratio: 0.44	Payout: —
Long-term debt ($ mil.): 27,899	Market value ($ mil.): 4,490

	STOCK PRICE ($) FY Close	P/E High/Low		PER SHARE ($) Earnings	Dividends	Book Value
03/21	11.89	—	—	(13.84)	0.21	60.63
03/20	12.61	0	0	4.84	0.24	76.76
03/19	16.05	0	0	6.98	0.22	72.60
03/18	15.64	0	0	7.06	0.21	69.88
03/17	14.52	0	0	6.39	0.20	61.00
Annual Growth	**(4.9%)**	—	—	—	**0.7%**	**(0.1%)**

Eaton Corp plc

Auditors: Ernst & Young LLP

LOCATIONS

HQ: Eaton Corp plc
Eaton House, 30 Pembroke Road, Dublin 4 44114-2584
Phone: (353) 1 637 2900
Web: www.eaton.com

HISTORICAL FINANCIALS

Company Type: Public

Income Statement

FYE: December 31

	REVENUE ($ mil.)	NET INCOME ($ mil.)	NET PROFIT MARGIN	EMPLOYEES
12/21	19,628	2,144	10.9%	86,000
12/20	17,858	1,410	7.9%	92,000
12/19	21,390	2,211	10.3%	101,000
12/18	21,609	2,145	9.9%	99,000
12/17	20,404	2,985	14.6%	96,000
Annual Growth	**(1.0%)**	**(7.9%)**	—	**(2.7%)**

2021 Year-End Financials

Debt ratio: 25.2%	No. of shares (mil.): 398
Return on equity: 13.6%	Dividends
Cash ($ mil.): 297	Yield: 1.7%
Current ratio: 1.04	Payout: 59.0%
Long-term debt ($ mil.): 6,831	Market value ($ mil.): —

Ecopetrol SA

Ecopetrol performs crude oil and natural gas exploration production refining and transportation. The largest company in Colombia (where it accounts for 60% of national production and is one of the world's 40 largest oil companies) Ecopetrol has two large refineries (Barrancabermeja and Cartagena) strategically located to supply the domestic market and to export oil and oil products to the southern US. Ecopetrol explores for oil and gas across Colombia and is expanding internationally through exploration partnerships in Brazil Peru and the US Gulf of Mexico. In 2013 the company reported proved reserves of more than 1.4 billion barrels of oil equivalent.

Geographic Reach
Headquartered in Bogota Colombia the company has exploration and production activities in Brazil Peru and the US (Gulf of Mexico). In 2013 it derived almost 40% of its revenues from Colombia and nearly 30% from the US.

Sales and Marketing
The company's crude oil export sales are made both in the spot market and through long-term contracts primarily to refiners in the US Gulf Coast Far East Europe and the U. West Coast. It sell natural gas to distribution companies through take-or-pay or swing contracts.

Strategy
The company has ambitious expansion plans including the doubling of refining capacity and the emergence of Ecopetrol as a leader in biofuels production. The company's goal is to produce 1 million barrels of oil equivalent per day by 2015 and 1.3 million of oil equivalent per day in 2020.

Ecopetrol's strategy is focused on supplying the local market and exporting crude oil refined products petrochemical products and natural gas to end-users including refineries and wholesalers in order to improve its margins. It also intends to increase its market participation in crude oil and refined products in Asia and Europe.

In an effort to enhance the strategic and logistical framework of Colombia's oil industry in response to the increase in hydrocarbon production and higher sales of crudes and refined products both within Colombia and on the international markets in 2012 the company established Cenit as a wholly-owned subsidiary specializing in logistics and transportation of hydrocarbons within Colombia.

During 2012 the company acquired 23908 kilometers of additional seismic equivalent which includes 13908 kilometers in the US Gulf Coast and 10000 kilometers in Brazil. During the first quarter of 2013 it drilled five stratigraphic wells out of which two exhibited evidence of hydrocarbons (Segua 1 and Circe 1).

EXECUTIVES

Independent Director, Hernando Ramirez Plazas
General Secretary, Monica Jimenez Gonzalez
Vice President of Human Resources, Alejandro Arango Lopez
Vice President of Legal Affairs and General Counsel, Fernan Ignacio Bejarano Arias
Vice President - Development and Production, Jorge Elman Osorio Franco
Vice President of Commercial and Marketing, Pedro Fernando Manrique Gutierrez
Independent Director, Luis Guillermo Echeverri Velez
Vice President of Projects and Engineering, Jurgen Gerardo Loeber Rojas
Director, German Eduardo Quintero Rojas
Director of the Colombian Petroleum Institute, Andres Eduardo Mantilla Zarate
Independent Director, Santiago Perdomo Maldonado
Independent Director, Juan Emilio Posada Echeverri
Vice President - Digital, Ernesto Gutierrez de Pineres
Independent Director, Sergio Restrepo Isaza

Compliance Officer, Vice President of Corporate Compliance, Maria Juliana Alban Duran
Vice President - Gas, Yeimy Baez
Vice President of Health, Safety and Environment, Mauricio Jaramillo Galvis
Independent Director, Cecilia Velez White
Vice-President of Sustainable Development, Diana Hoyos
Vice President - Strategy and New Businesses, Nicolas Ramirez
Chief Executive Officer of Cenit S.A.S, Hector Manosalva Rojas
Independent Director, Esteban Piedrahita Uribe, $14,315 total compensation
Vice President of Refining and Industrial Processes, Walter Canova
Vice President of Exploration, Elsa Jaimes
Chief Executive Officer, Felipe Bayon Pardo
Chief Operating Officer, Alberto Consuegra Granger
Chief Financial Officer, Jaime Caballero Uribe
Vice President of Supply and Services, Carlos Andres Santos Nieto
Independent Director, Carlos Gustavo Cano Sanz
Auditors: Ernst & Young Audit S.A.S.

LOCATIONS

HQ: Ecopetrol SA
Carrera 13 No. 36-24, Bogota
Phone: (57) 1 234 4000   **Fax:** (57) 1 234 5628
Web: www.ecopetrol.com.co

2013 Sales

	% of total
Colombia	38
US	29
Asia	16
Europe	7
Central America and Caribbean	5
South America	3
Others	2
Total	**100**

PRODUCTS/OPERATIONS

2013 Sales

	% of total
Exploration & production	59
Refining activities	34
Transportation & logistics	7
Total	**100**

COMPETITORS

COMPA IA ESPA OLA DE PETROLEOS SAU
China National Offshore Oil Corporation
ENEOS HOLDINGS INC.
ISRAMCO INC.
LUKOIL PAO
MARATHON OIL CORPORATION
OMV Aktiengesellschaft
PETROBRAS AMERICA INC.
Petr leos Mexicanos E.P.E.
REPSOL SA.

HISTORICAL FINANCIALS

Company Type: Public

Income Statement				FYE: December 31
	REVENUE ($ mil.)	NET INCOME ($ mil.)	NET PROFIT MARGIN	EMPLOYEES
12/20	14,674	463	3.2%	13,977
12/19	21,765	4,184	19.2%	15,157
12/18	21,131	3,505	16.6%	12,228
12/17	18,749	2,405	12.8%	11,682
12/16	16,151	815	5.0%	10,920
Annual Growth	(2.4%)	(13.2%)	—	6.4%

2020 Year-End Financials

Debt ratio: 0.0%
Return on equity: 3.0%
Cash ($ mil.): 1,484
Current ratio: 1.25
Long-term debt ($ mil.): 12,215

No. of shares (mil.): —
Dividends
Yield: 10.0%
Payout: 8,233.5%
Market value ($ mil.): —

	STOCK PRICE ($) FY Close	P/E High/Low		PER SHARE ($)		
				Earnings	Dividends	Book Value
12/20	12.91	1	0	0.01	1.30	0.35
12/19	19.96	0	0	0.10	1.78	0.40
12/18	15.88	0	0	0.09	0.61	0.41
12/17	14.63	0	0	0.06	0.15	0.38
12/16	9.05	0	0	0.02	0.01	0.34
Annual Growth	9.3%	—	—	(13.1%)	260.7%	1.0%

EDP Energias de Portugal S.A.

EDP - Energias de Portugal is a multinational and vertically integrated utility company that generates transmits distributes and supplies electricity and gas to nearly 10 million customers. EDP is one of the largest wind energy production company in the world and almost 75% of its energy is produced from renewable resources. Other operations include a majority stake in Spanish utility HC Energ a. EDP (a major wind energy player) which has a combined generating capacity of about 25 GW from its domestic hydroelectric coal solar and wind-powered plants. About half of the company's sales were generated in Portugal.

Operations
EDP operates through three segments: Client Solutions & Energy Management (about 60% of sales) Networks (approximately 30%) and Renewables (nearly 10%).

The Client Solutions & Energy Management segment includes activities such as generation of electricity from non-renewable sources mainly coal and gas; electricity and gas supply and related energy solutions services to clients; and energy management businesses responsible for management of purchases and sales of energy in Iberian and Brazilian markets and also for the related hedging transactions. This operates under subsidiaries such as EDP - Comercializa § o e Servi §os de Energia Ltda.; EDP España S.A.U; EDP Comercial - Comercializa § o de Energia S.A.; Porto do Pecem Gera § o de Energia S.A.; UNGE - Unidade de Neg cio de Gest o de Energia Iberica (EDP S.A.); and EDP - Gest o da Produ § o de Energia S.A.

The Networks segment corresponds to the activities of electricity distribution and transmission including last resort suppliers. This segment includes but not limited to E-Redes ? Distribui § o de Eletricidade S.A.; SU Eletricidade S.A. S.A.; Viesgo Distribuci n Electrica S.L.; EDP G s Servi §o Universal S.A.; EDP Transmiss o Alian §a SC S.A.; and EDP S o Paulo Distribui § o de Energia S.A among others.

The Renewables segment corresponds to the activity of generation of electricity from renewable sources mainly hydro wind and solar which operates under EDP - Gest o da Produ § o de Energia S.A.; EDP España S.A.U; EDP Renov veis S.A. and all subsidiaries of the EDPR Group; Enerpeixe S.A.; Investco S.A.; and Lajeado Energia S.A.

Overall about 85% of the company's sales were generated by its electricity and network access.

Geographic Reach

Headquartered in Lisbon the company has facilities in about 20 countries in four continents including Portugal Spain France Belgium Italy Brazil Poland Mexico the US Canada the UK China and Nigeria among others. Portugal accounts for around 50% of EDP's sales followed by Spain bringing in more than 20% Brazil approximately 20% US some 5% and other countries account for the rest.

Sales and Marketing

The company distributes about 75 TWh of electricity through overhead and underground lines to nearly 9 million electricity customers of which more than 4 million customers are in liberalized market and more than 4 million customers are in last resort. It also serves nearly 700000 gas customers.

Financial Performance

Note: Growth rates may differ after conversion to US Dollars.

The company's revenue for fiscal 2020 decreased to ?12.4 billion compared form the prior year with ?14.3 billion.

Profit for fiscal 2020 increased to ?1.5 billion compared from the prior year with ?1.2 billion.

Cash held by the company at the end of fiscal 2020 increased to ?3 billion. Cash provided by operations was ?2.5 billion while cash used for investing and financing activities were ?285.5 million and ?593.8 billion respectively. Main uses of cash were property plant and equipment and intangible assets; and payments relating to financial debt.

Strategy

The company's 2021-25 strategic plan is underpinned by three axes: Accelerated and Sustainable Growth; a Future-Proof Organization powered by increased investment in innovation and digital transformation; and ESG Excellence and Attractive Returns.

EDP will accelerate its renewables growth namely in Europe and North America seeking to double its installed capacity in wind and solar in the next 5 years adding 4 GW per year. The company will continue to grow and create value in its low-risk networks portfolio in Portugal Spain and Brazil ? a critical enabler of the energy transition ? investing more than ?3 billion to maximize value through grid modernization and operational excellence in distribution and superior execution of projects in transmission in Brazil.

Mergers and Acquisitions

In late 2020 EDP completed the acquisition of Viesgo for an enterprise value (100%) of ?2.7 billion. This transaction includes the establishment of a long-term partnership with Macquarie Super Core Infrastructure Fund SD Holdings S. .R.L. (MSCIF) for electricity distribution business in Spain which will be 75.1% owned by EDP and 24.9% by MSCIF. This partnership will own three electricity distribution companies: E-Redes (previously 100% owned by EDP) Viesgo Distribuci n and Begasa (currently 100% owned by Viesgo). This enlarged electricity distribution operation in Spain.

HISTORY

EDP - Energias de Portugal has its roots in the several power enterprises that sprouted throughout the country during the infancy of electricity. The first recorded event in Portugal's electrification was the import of six voltaic arc lamps in 1878. The nation's first large-scale project saw the light in 1893 when the city of Braga was illuminated by the Sociedade de Electricidade do Norte de Portugal.

Electricity grew throughout the 1900s in the form of municipal concession contracts for distribution and government-licensed power plants.

Large-scale power stations were not in effect in Portugal until after 1947 when Companhia Nacional de Electricidade was formed to interconnect the small generating systems dotting the nation. From the 1950s to mid-1970s new companies were formed to bring electricity to various parts of Portugal.

The original Electricidade de Portugal was founded in the wake of a leftist revolution during the 1970s in Portugal. In what became known as the Captain's Revolution military officers overthrew the Portuguese government which had been a dictatorship since 1933. The new government dominated by Marxists nationalized Portugal's industries including its generation transmission and distribution companies in 1975. The next year the Portuguese government created Electricidade de Portugal to unify the recently nationalized companies.

A new Social Democrat government came to power in 1987 and decided to denationalize Portuguese industry including EDP. The company reorganized into four major sectors in 1994: production (headed by its CPPE subsidiary) transmission distribution and services (led by its REN subsidiary which operated the national grid four regional utilities and 10 services units). EDP was the holding company.

Seeking opportunities opened up by the privatization of Brazil's state-owned electricity distributor EDP joined a consortium with Spain's Endesa and Chile's Chilectra to buy 70% of Rio de Janeiro distributor CERJ in 1996. The next year EDP gained a license to help build a hydro plant in Brazil. By 1998 the Endesa-led consortium had gained control of another Brazilian distributor Coelce.

The Portuguese government floated 30% of EDP in 1997 raising $1.76 billion. In a joint venture with the UK's PowerGen and Germany's Siemens EDP formed Turbog´s to operate a power plant that would produce 20% of Portugal's electricity.

In 1998 EDP forged an alliance with Spain's Iberdrola and bought 80% of Guatemalan utility EEGSA. That year EDP and S o Paulo utility CPFL gained control of S o Paulo distributor Bandeirante. In 1999 EDP acquired stakes in two other Brazilian distributors. It also joined the UK's Thames Water to develop projects in Portugal Chile and Brazil and bought 45% of Chilean water and sewage company Essel. (EDP exchanged its stake in Essel for Thames Water's interest in the Portuguese joint venture in 2002.) The Portuguese state reduced its stake in EDP to about 50% in 1999.

Stepping up its telecommunications activities in 2000 EDP made its telecom unit Onitelecom (ONI) fully operational and agreed to share a fiber-optic network on the Iberian Peninsula with Spain's Iberdrola. (In 2006 however the company sold its stake in ONI.) Also in 2000 the Portuguese government acquired a majority stake in EDP's REN unit and EDP combined its four power distribution utilities into one unit (EDP Distribui § o).

In 2001 EDP and Spanish savings bank Cajastur jointly bid to buy Hidrocant ¯brico one of Spain's leading utilities. EDP won control of 20% of Hidrocant ¯brico while German utility Energie Baden-W rttemberg (EnBW) won control of 60%. The following year after a fierce bidding war the two companies agreed that EDP would control the majority share (40%) while EnBW would own only 35%.

The company changed its name from EDP - Electricidade de Portugal to EDP - Energias de Portugal in 2004.

Since 2007 the company has sold much of its holdings in other firms to pay down debt. Divestment deals include a 30% stake in Portugal's national transmission grid operator Rede Electrica Nacional (REN); a 40% stake in TURBOG S - Produtora Energetica the company behind the construction of gas power station Tapada do Outeiro; and a 27% stake in PORTUGEN - Energia which is in charge of operating Tapada do Outeiro. In 2011 it sold a 7.7% stake in Brazil's Ampla Energia to a subsidiary of Spain's Endesa for ?85 million ($121 million).

EXECUTIVES

Independent Member of the General and Supervisory Board, Vasco Joaquim Rocha Vieira, $76,340 total compensation

Vice Chairman of the General and Supervisory Board, Representative of China Three Gorges Corporation, Dingming Zhang, $40,173 total compensation

Member of the Executive Board of Directors, Global Head for Energy Distribution Networks, Miguel Nuno Simoes Nunes Ferreira Setas, $320,991 total compensation

Chief Financial Officer of EDP and EDP Renovaveis, Member of the Executive Board of Directors, Rui Manuel Rodrigues Lopes Teixeira, $644,268 total compensation

Member of the Executive Board and Company Secretary and General Secretary, Maria Teresa Isabel Pereira, $663,279 total compensation

Independent Member of the General and Supervisory Board, Ilidio da Costa Leite de Pinho, $64,946 total compensation

Independent Member of the General and Supervisory Board, Maria del Carmen Fernandez Rozado, $79,758 total compensation

Independent Member of the General and Supervisory Board, Augusto Carlos Serra Ventura Mateus, $76,340 total compensation

Independent Chairman of the General and Supervisory Board, Luis Filipe Marques Amado, $586,793 total compensation

Member of the General and Supervisory Board, Representative of Senfora BV, Mohammed Issa Khalfan Al Huraimel Al Shamsi, $10,703 total compensation

Member of the General and Supervisory Board, Representative of Banco Comercial Portugues, S.A., Nuno Manuel da Silva Amado, $38,486 total compensation

Member of the Executive Board of Directors, Joao Manuel Verissimo Marques da Cruz, $337,440 total compensation

Member of the Executive Board, Antonio Fernando Melo Martins da Costa, $633,406 total compensation

Member of the General and Supervisory Board, Fernando Maria Masaveu Herrero, $76,340 total compensation

Independent Member of the General and Supervisory Board, Joao Carvalho das Neves, $131,031 total compensation

Independent Member of the General and Supervisory Board, Maria Celeste Ferreira Lopes Cardona, $91,152 total compensation

Member of the General and Supervisory Board, Representative of China Three Gorges (Portugal), Sociedade Unipessoal, Lda., Shengliang Wu, $39,930 total compensation

Independent Member of the General and Supervisory Board, Jorge Avelino Braga de Macedo, $76,340 total compensation

Chief Executive Officer of EDP and EDP Renovaveis, Member of the Executive Board of Directors, Miguel Stilwell de Andrade, $752,439 total compensation

Member of the General and Supervisory Board, Representative of Draursa, S.A., Felipe Fernandez, $39,930 total compensation

Member of the General and Supervisory Board, Representative of China Three Gorges (Portugal), Sociedade Unipessoal, Lda.), Eduardo de Almeida Catroga, $63,811 total compensation

Independent Member of the General and Supervisory Board, Luis Palha da Silva, $79,758 total compensation

Independent Member of the General and Supervisory Board, Laurie Lee Fitch, $64,946 total compensation

Independent Member of the General and Supervisory Board, Clementina Maria Damaso De Jesus Silva Barroso, $79,758 total compensation

Member of the General and Supervisory Board, representation of China Three Gorges (Europe), S.A, Ignacio Herrero Ruiz

Member of the General and Supervisory Board, Representative of Sonatrach, Karim Djebbour

Member of the Executive Board of Directors, In Charge of Conventional Generation, Ana Paula Marques

Member of the Executive Board of Directors, Global Marketing Head, Vera de Morais Pinto Pereira Carneiro, $663,279 total compensation

Auditors: PriceWaterHouseCoopers & Associados, SROC, Lda.

LOCATIONS

HQ: EDP Energias de Portugal S.A.
Avenida 24 de Julho, 12, Lisbon, Poente 1249-300
Phone: (351) 21 001 25 00 **Fax:** (351) 21 001 28 99
Web: www.edp.pt

2014 Sales

	% of total
Portugal	51
Spain	27
Brazil	18
US	2
Other	2
Total	**100**

PRODUCTS/OPERATIONS

2014 Sales

	% of total
Electricity and Network access	87
Gas and Network access	10
Revenue from assets assigned to concessions	3
Sales of CO2 licences	0
Other	0
Total	**100**

COMPETITORS

ELECTRICITE DE FRANCE	RWE AG
ENEL SPA	TELEFONICA SA
FUTUREN	THE AES CORPORATION
Fortum Oyj	UNITED UTILITIES GROUP
NATIONAL GRID PLC	PLC
REXEL	VINCI

HISTORICAL FINANCIALS

Company Type: Public

Income Statement   FYE: December 31

	REVENUE ($ mil.)	NET INCOME ($ mil.)	NET PROFIT MARGIN	EMPLOYEES
12/20	15,277	982	6.4%	11,610
12/19	16,092	574	3.6%	11,660
12/18	17,496	594	3.4%	11,631
12/17	18,875	1,334	7.1%	11,657
12/16	15,410	1,014	6.6%	11,992
Annual Growth	(0.2%)	(0.8%)	—	(0.8%)

2020 Year-End Financials

Debt ratio: 46.5%
Return on equity: 8.6%
Cash ($ mil.): 3,625
Current ratio: 1.06
Long-term debt ($ mil.): 17,211

No. of shares (mil.): —
Dividends
 Yield: 4.8%
 Payout: 1,354.7%
Market value ($ mil.): —

	STOCK PRICE ($) FY Close	P/E High/Low	PER SHARE ($) Earnings	Dividends	Book Value
12/20	65.64	309181	0.26	3.18	2.98
12/19	43.08	314239	0.16	2.13	2.74
12/18	34.85	291217	0.16	2.27	2.83
12/17	34.66	131103	0.37	2.34	3.15
12/16	30.65	135105	0.27	1.24	2.73
Annual Growth	21.0%	— —	(1.6%)	26.5%	2.2%

Eiffage SA

French construction firm Eiffage is responsible for some of France's biggest and most recognizable landmarks including the Channel Tunnel the Louvre pyramid and through an ancestor company the Eiffel Tower from which Eiffage takes its name. Today the company operates through dozens of subsidiaries that build infrastructure and commercial projects primarily in Western Europe. Active in around 50 countries and almost every construction vertical the group consists of four business lines: Concessions Construction Energy Systems and Infrastructures. One of Europe's largest construction firms completes some 100000 projects annually split between private and public sector contracts. France accounts for the vast majority of Eiffage's business.

Operations

Eiffage's participation in infrastructure projects accounts for some 30% of its annual revenue. It consists of a road and motorway construction business a metal-based construction arm (structures shells and facades) and Eiffage Génie Civil a general constructor covering a large range of projects and works including viaducts and tunnels.

The Construction and Energy Systems businesses both bring in some 25% of sales. Construction is active in urban and property development construction maintenance and works and services. Energy Systems designs builds and operates electrical industrial HVAC and energy equipment and systems.

Operating mostly under public-private partnership models the Concessions business brings in 20% of total sales and operates toll roads and builds and manages public facilities (such as prisons sports stadia schools power plants and high-speed rail lines.

Geographic Reach

Eiffage drums up business in around 50 countries worldwide mostly in Europe. France is Eiffage's single largest market accounting for 80% of total revenue. The rest of Europe accounts for nearly 20% of sales while a few percent comes from outside Europe.

Sales and Marketing

Eiffage often works under a public-private partnership arrangement usually with the French government. To pay down debt Eiffage has since 2011 sold off €1.5 billion in PPP contracts.

Financial Performance

Note: Growth rates may differ after conversion to US Dollars.

In fiscal 2017 Eiffage's revenue increased 7% or around €1 billion to €15.3 billion.

The company grew both its contracting and concessions revenue while non-France revenue grew a strong 15%. An increase in light and heavy goods vehicle traffic helped motorway concession revenue grow 4% while the Energy Systems business rose 9% on the back of growth internationally in addition to contributions from acquisitions.

Net income also grew 7% thanks to higher revenue and lower debt payments. The company has been selling off public-private partnership (PPP) contracts and using the proceeds to pay off debt. Between 2011 and 2017 the company realized €1.5 billion in PPP proceeds.

Eiffage's cash position was largely unchanged on prior year as stronger cash generation from operations and lower investment expenditure were offset by higher debt repayments as the company continued its deleveraging program.

Strategy

Eiffage partnered with Carillion and Kier on a number of significant rail infrastructure projects in the UK including the HS2 London-Birmingham link and the Cross Rail lines. Carillion went bust in 2018 and to keep the under-pressure projects from stalling Eiffage took the decision to partner 50:50 with Kier and offer laid-off Carillion workers employment.

The company has also been deleveraging by selling off public-private partnership contracts and using the proceeds to pay off debt.

Mergers and Acquisitions

In 2018 advanced its European expansion strategy through a number of acquisitions. Eiffage agreed to acquired Kropman a Netherlands-based specialist in electrical and mechanical engineering contamination control and measurement. It also acquire Priora a Swiss-based construction firm for €340 million and Spanish construction firm Ingenieria y Montajes for €25 million.

In 2017 Eiffage acquired Saipem's maritime works business which is active mainly in Kuwait Congo and Panama.

HISTORY

Fougerolle made its name in construction during the 1840s with the completion of the Nivernaise canal. Co-founded by Philippe and Jacques Fougerolle in 1844 the company went on to begin construction of Saint Gothard tunnel in the Swiss Alps which was completed in 1882.

By 1890 the company expanded its operations in France to include work on the metro line between Porte de Clichy and Place de la Trinite and internationally with construction of the Namur fortifications in Belgium. It completed the Adolphe bridge in Luxembourg in 1903 and was granted a contract to construct the Rio Grande do Sul port in Brazil in 1908.

During WWI the company was enlisted to help keep the flow of supplies steady between Paris and Amiens with the construction of a second railroad. After the war the company returned to its previous operations under the name Le Soliditit Fran Sais. It completed several airship hangars in Orly France in 1921.

During the 1920s and 1930s the company expanded its operations into French colonies building the port in Dakar (1927) and the Deir Ez Zor bridge over the Euphrates River on the Iraq-Syria border. Domestically the company constructed a series of fortifications making up the Maginot line to try to deter a German invasion. It also managed to complete one arm of the Parisian Metro before the Germans invaded in 1940.

The company resumed its operations and helped rebuild war-torn France. It bought up subsidiaries but remained a family-led company with a decentralized management — during a time when the French construction industry was beginning a shift toward larger government-influenced public conglomerates.

In 1954 it completed the Bin el Ouidane dam in Morocco and the Serre-Pon §on dam in the French Alps in 1960. The company reorganized under the name Societe des Entreprises Fougerolle Limousin in 1970. Aided by 20 years of economic growth in France the company acquired construction specialist Societe Nouvelle de Constructions et de Travaux (1973) and foundation specialist Gifor (1974).

A series of losses on projects in Iraq and Nigeria coupled with the collapse of the French construction market in the early 1980s nearly bankrupted the company. It was spared with the help of investment banking firm Paribas and oil company TOTALI in 1982. A third major investor Generale des Eaux attempted to acquire Fougerolle in the late 1980s but its efforts were thwarted by an employee-led buyout of the company headed by CEO Jean-Fran §ois Roverato in 1989.

Fougerolle bolstered is operations with the acquisition of France's second largest-construction firm Societe Auxiliaire d'Entreprise (SAE) in 1992 and the combined companies were renamed Eiffage in 1993. The group began to consolidate the complementary operations of the two companies. In 1999 Fougerolle Quillery and SAE combined to form Eiffage Construction and Norelec and Forclum were formed into the group's electrical contracting arm. Eiffage's road construction operations were brought together as Appia in 2000. The next year Eiffage shareholders agreed to merge with its holding company Financi "re SAE-Fougerolle in order to reduce the company's debt.

In 2001 the company completed a leveraged management buyout that had begun in 1990. Employee ownership of the company was reduced to 23%. The next year Eiffage along with French construction giant VINCI acquired a stake in ASF Europe's second-largest toll road operator. In 2002 the group also gained control of Polish construction company Mitex.

That year EIFFAGE and rival French construction giant VINCI grabbed nearly 20% of Autoroutes du Sud de la France when it was partly privatized.

The company reorganized in 2004 shedding excess baggage and streamlining operations. It sold its stake in ASF to VINCI.

Spanish construction group Sacyr Vallehermoso acquired more than 30% of EIFFAGE in 2006 but — after a nearly two-year-long dispute between the rivals —- sold that stake to a group of French investors (including Caisse des D p "ts and Groupama) in 2008.

EXECUTIVES

Director, Jean-Francois Roverato
Director, Dominique Marcel
Director, Philippe Vidal
Independent Director, Jean Guenard
Chief Financial Officer, Member of the Executive Committee, Christian Cassayre
Chairman of Motorway Concessions in France, Member of the Executive Committee, Philippe Nourry
Director - Representative of Employee Shareholders, Laurent Dupont
Independent Director, Marie Lemarie
Independent Director, Carol Xueref
Independent Director, Isabelle Salaun
Chairman of the Board, Chief Executive Officer, Chairman of the Energy Systems Division, Member of the Executive Committee, Benoit De Ruffray, $982,737 total compensation
Independent Director, Odile Georges-Picot

Chairman of the Construction Division, Member of the Executive Committee, Olivier Genis
Director - Representing Employees, Michele Grosset
Auditors: KPMG Audit IS

LOCATIONS

HQ: Eiffage SA
Campus Pierre Berger, 3-7, place de l'Europe, Velizy-Villacoublay 78140
Phone: (33) 1 34 65 89 89
Web: www.eiffage.com

2013 Sales

	% of total
France	84
Rest of Europe	14
Other countries	2
Total	**100**

PRODUCTS/OPERATIONS

2017 Sales

	% of total
Infrastructures	31
Energy	25
Construction	25
Concessions	20
Metal	.
Property development (2)	
Total	**100**

Major Subsidiaries

Clemessy
Eiffage Concessions (highway and other infrastructure operations)
Eiffage Construction (building industry and property development)
Eiffage Energie
Eiffage Travaux Publics (road and railway construction civil engineering and earthworks)
Eiffel (metallic construction and glass facades)
Forclum (electrical contracting and facilities management)

COMPETITORS

AMEC FOSTER WHEELER LIMITED
ARCADIS N.V.
BOUYGUES
Bilfinger SE
COLAS SA
DRAGADOS SOCIEDAD ANONIMA
FERROVIAL SA
FOMENTO DE CONSTRUCCIONES Y CONTRATAS SA
HOCHTIEF AG
OBAYASHI CORPORATION
WS ATKINS LIMITED

HISTORICAL FINANCIALS

Company Type: Public

Income Statement

FYE: December 31

	REVENUE ($ mil.)	NET INCOME ($ mil.)	NET PROFIT MARGIN	EMPLOYEES
12/19	20,990	814	3.9%	51,252
12/18	19,348	720	3.7%	50,051
12/17	18,302	653	3.6%	49,203
12/16	15,109	501	3.3%	49,439
12/15	15,320	339	2.2%	50,854
Annual Growth	**8.2%**	**24.4%**	**—**	**0.2%**

2019 Year-End Financials

Debt ratio: 51.3%	No. of shares (mil.): 97
Return on equity: 14.4%	Dividends
Cash ($ mil.): 4,962	Yield: —
Current ratio: 0.94	Payout: 37.8%
Long-term debt ($ mil.): 12,011	Market value ($ mil.): —

Electricite de France

State-owned Electricite de France (EDF) has been quick to expand into global deregulated markets. One of the world's top electric utilities (as well as one of the last major state-controlled energy giants in Europe) EDF has a generating capacity of over 500 TWh (primarily from nuclear sources) and provides power to approximately 38 million customers 28 million of which are in France. EDF generates majority of its total sales from France.

Operations

EDF operates in nine segments: France ? Generation and Supply France ? Regulated Activities Framatome United Kingdom Italy Other International EDF Renewables Dalkia and Other activities.

France ? Generation and Supply Activities segment generates about 40% of total sales. The segment includes EDF's energy production and sales activities commodity trading and other activities.

France ? Regulated Activities which accounts for over 20% of total sales consists of distribution transmission EDF's island activities and the activities of Electricite de Strasbourg.

The UK Italy Dalkia and Framatone segments include entities of its subgroups. The segments generate about 35% of sales combined.

The remaining sales are from Other International EDF Renewables and Other Activities.

Geographic Reach

EDF is headquartered in Paris France which also generates about 60% of the company's sales.

Financial Performance

Note: Growth rates may differ after conversion to US Dollars.

The company's revenue for fiscal 2020 decreased to ?69 billion compared from the prior year with ?71.3 billion.

Net income for fiscal 2020 decreased to ?615 million compared from the prior year with ?5.2 billion.

Cash held by the company at the end of fiscal 2020 increased to ?6.3 billion. Cash provided by operations and financing activities were ?12.9 billion and ?2.6 billion respectively. Cash used for investing activities was ?12.9 billion mainly for investments in intangible assets and property plant and equipment.

Mergers and Acquisitions

In the early 2020 EDF acquired Pod Point one of the UK's largest electric vehicle (EV) charging company. The acquisition is the largest investment of EDF in the EV market in line with its plan to become the leading energy company for electric mobility in France the UK Italy and Belgium.

HISTORY

The French government nationalized hundreds of regional private firms to form Electricit de France (EDF) in 1946 as part of an effort to rebuild the nation's badly shaken post-war economy. This was a marked difference from the notoriously complex and inefficient pre-war electrical industry.

By the 1950s EDF had taken advantage of the centralized control and developed massive hydroelectric projects. Hydroelectric power would account for more than 70% of EDF's power.

But in France as elsewhere hydro wasn't enough to keep up with the growing demand for electricity and fossil fuels became an increasingly important power source. Then came the oil shortages of the 1970s and France — with limited domestic supplies of oil and gas — began searching for alternatives to fossil-fueled plants. Nuclear power was determined to be the answer.

The government moved to invest billions of dollars in developing its relatively small nuclear power production facilities. Muddled with Malthusian predictions of power shortages and a preoccupation with having enough energy to be self-reliant France found its nuclear operations left the government with more energy than it could use and more debt than it wanted. The company began to build a cable connecting the Continent to the UK in 1981. With the power grids of the two countries connected in 1986 EDF was finally able to start exporting its power to the Brits.

The 1990s brought with them deregulation. EDF fought to keep the UK-France grid closed to other energy sellers. After the government forbade the utility from diversifying into areas other than electricity in 1995 the company turned its attention to foreign investment especially in Latin America.

The company faced increasing deregulatory pressures from without in the late 1990s. The newly formed European Union required open competition from member states. Begrudgingly and behind schedule EDF opened about 30% of its market to competition in 2000.

Other members of the EU complained that EDF was trying to play it both ways: It was making aggressive acquisitions in the UK liberalized market (it bought London Electricity in 1999) while resisting a competition-enabling breakup or even allowing a foreign competitor to buy a stake in the French market.

EDF in 2001 expanded its stake in Italy's Montedison a conglomerate with substantial energy holdings by forming a consortium (Italenergia) with Italian automaker Fiat and some Italian banks to wrest control of Montedison from Italian bank MEDIOBANCA. Although the consortium owns 94% of Montedison EDF has only 2% of voting rights. (Montedison changed its name to Edison in 2002.)

EDF also purchased a 35% interest in German utility Energie Baden-W rttemberg in 2001 and it merged its energy services unit with Dalkia a unit of Vivendi Environnement (now Veolia Environnement) taking a 34% stake in Dalkia (which will eventually be increased to 50%). EDF subsidiary London Electricity agreed to buy $2.4 billion in UK assets from TXU Europe that year including a 2000 MW power plant TXU's Eastern Electricity distribution unit and its interest in TXU/EDF joint venture 24seven; the deals were completed in 2001 and 2002.

In 2002 EDF increased its stake in Brazilian utility Light Servi os de Eletricidade to 88% by swapping Light's interest in S o Paulo utility Eletropaulo for AES's 24% interest in Light. Later that year EDF purchased UK electric and gas utility SEEBOARD (1.9 million customers) from US utility AEP in a $2.2 billion deal.

Deregulation of 70% of the French market took effect in July 2004. Between 2000 and 2004 only 30% of the market was deregulated just more than the percentage required by European Union (EU) rulings.

EDF acquired Edison SpA (Italy's second-largest power group) in partnership with Italian utility company AEM SpA in 2005 for an estimated $15.4 billion.

Expanding its presence and its position as a nuclear power provider in the US in 2009 EDF unit EDF Development acquired 49.99% of Constellation Energy's Constellation Energy Nuclear Group LLC for $4.5 billion. (However another joint venture between these two parties aimed at developing new nuclear power plants in the US was terminated in 2010 after strategic disagreements between the principals).

In a move to boost its position as both a major energy and a nuclear power player in Europe in 2009 EDF acquired British Energy with its 1.1 million customer accounts for about $18 billion.

In 2010 EDF signed two new agreements with China National Nuclear Corporation and China Guangdong Nuclear Power Holding Company solidifying its role as a long term partner in China's nuclear development program. (The company has worked in China for 25 years).

To help pay down debt to pay for its expansion in 2010 Hong Kong's Cheung Kong Infrastructure and Hongkong Electric both controlled by Hong Kong-based billionaire Li Ka-shing acquired EDF's three UK distribution UK grids in a deal valued at about $9 billion. In 2011 EDF sold its 45% stake in German power utility Energie Baden-W rttemberg for $6.1 billion.

In 2012 EDF acquired the Italy-based energy group Edison by purchasing Delmi's entire investment (50%) in Transalpina Di Energia for a total of ?784 million. Following this acquisition the Group held 78.96% of the capital and 80.64% of the voting rights in Edison.

Not to be left out in the competitive renewable energy market EDF is seeking to boost its wind and solar energy output from a few hundred MW in 2008 to 4000 MW (in 2012) and higher in 2013.

The company is working on a ?6 billion Flamanville EPR construction project in France. In early 2013 the civil engineering work was 94% complete and 39% of the electro-mechanical equipment was in place. Its other projects included French offshore projects at Saint-Nazaire Courseulles-sur-Mer and F camp.

EXECUTIVES

Director - Employee Representative, Jean-Paul Rignac
Director - Employee Representative, Jacky Chorin
Director, Marie-Christine Lepetit, $52,122 total compensation
Chairman of the Board, Chairman of the Executive Committee, Chief Executive Officer, Jean-Bernard Levy, $512,732 total compensation
Group Senior Executive Vice-President, Innovation, Corporate Responsibility and Strategy, Member of Executive Committee, Alexandre Perra
Director - Employee Representative, Christian Taxil
Independent Director, Colette Lewiner, $58,122 total compensation
Independent Director, Laurence Parisot, $40,121 total compensation
Group Senior Executive Vice President, Group General Secretary, Member of the Executive Committee, Pierre Todorov
Group Senior Executive Vice President, New Nuclear Projects and Engineering, Member of the Executive Committee, Xavier Ursat
Director - Representative of the French State, Martin Vial, $44,788 total compensation
Independent Director, Claire Pedini, $50,787 total compensation
Group Senior Executive Vice President, Group Finance, Member of the Executive Committee, Xavier Girre
Group Senior Executive Vice President, Human Resources, Member of the Executive Committee, Christophe Carval
Group Senior Executive Vice President - Customers, Services and Regions, Member of Executive Committee, Marc Benayoun
Group Senior Executive Vice-President, Nuclear and Thermal, Member of Executive Committee, Cedric Lewandowski

Group Senior Executive Vice President, Transformation and Operational Effectiveness, Member of the Executive Committee, Veronique Lacour
Group Senior Executive Vice President, Chief Executive Officer of EDF Energy, Member of the Executive Committee, Simone Rossi
General Representative for Industrial Quality and Nuclear Skills, Member of the Executive Committee, Alain Tranzer
Independent Director, Philippe Petitcolin, $32,120 total compensation
Director, Francois Delattre, $32,120 total compensation
Independent Director, Bruno Cremel, $39,455 total compensation
Director - Employee Representative, Vincent Rodet
Director, Gilles Denoyel, $39,455 total compensation
Director - Employee Representative, Claire Bordenave
Group Senior Executive Vice-President, International Division, Member of Executive Committee, Beatrice Buffon
Director - Employee Representative, Karine Granger
Director, Veronique Bedague-Hamilius, $12,261 total compensation
Director, Michele Rousseau, $42,788 total compensation
Senior Executive President, Renewable Energies and CEO, EDF Energies Nouvelles, Bruno Bensasson
Auditors: KPMG S.A

LOCATIONS

HQ: Electricite de France
22/30 avenue Wagram, Paris, Cedex 08 75382
Phone: (33) 1 40 42 22 22   **Fax:** (33) 1 40 42 32 17
Web: www.edf.com

PRODUCTS/OPERATIONS

2018 Sales

	%
France-Regulated Activities	22
France-Generation and Supply Activities	35
UK	12
Italy	12
Dalkia	6
Framatone	4
International	3
EDF Renewables	2
Other Activities	4
Total	**100**

COMPETITORS

DYNEGY INC.	ENERGIA GROUP NI
E.ON SE	HOLDINGS LIMITED
E.ON UK PLC	IBERDROLA SOCIEDAD
EDF ENERGY LIMITED	ANONIMA
ENDESA SA	THE AES CORPORATION
ENEL SPA	Uniper SE

HISTORICAL FINANCIALS

Company Type: Public

Income Statement				FYE: December 31
	REVENUE ($ mil.)	NET INCOME ($ mil.)	NET PROFIT MARGIN	EMPLOYEES
12/19	80,072	5,787	7.2%	161,552
12/18	78,990	1,347	1.7%	162,208
12/17	83,471	3,803	4.6%	152,033
12/16	75,182	3,010	4.0%	154,845
12/15	81,697	1,292	1.6%	159,112
Annual Growth	(0.5%)	45.5%	—	0.4%

2019 Year-End Financials

Debt ratio: 24.9%
Return on equity: 11.3%
Cash ($ mil.): 4,416
Current ratio: 1.30
Long-term debt ($ mil.): 63,218

No. of shares (mil.): —
Dividends
  Yield: 3.1%
  Payout: 4.1%
Market value ($ mil.): —

	STOCK PRICE ($)	P/E		PER SHARE ($)		
	FY Close	High/Low	Earnings	Dividends		Book Value
12/19	2.17	2 1	1.68	0.07		16.84
12/18	3.02	18 11	0.23	0.11		16.94
12/17	2.44	3 2	1.17	0.23		16.96
12/16	1.98	2 2	1.21	0.22		17.26
12/15	2.94	17 8	0.35	0.41		19.74
Annual Growth	(7.3%)	— —	48.3%	(36.1%)		(3.9%)

Empire Co Ltd

Empire Company Limited (Empire) comprises an empire of supermarkets food distribution and real estate investments. The company operates through wholly-owned subsidiary Sobeys a chain of more than 1500 food and drug stores across Canada under names such as Sobeys Safeway FreshCo and IGA as well as more than 350 retail fuel locations. Additionally the company distributes food to its own stores and other retailers. Empire invests in commercial real estate through stakes in real estate investment trust Crombie REIT and residential property developer Genstar. Empire and its subsidiaries franchisees and affiliates employ approximately 127000 people.

Operations

Empire's business is organized in two reportable segments?Food Retailing and Investments and Other Operations.

Empire's Food Retailing business consists of wholly-owned subsidiary Sobeys Inc. Banners include Foodland Thrifty Foods and Lawton's Drug. The segment consists of company-owned franchised and affiliated stores and locations. Virtually all of Empire's revenue is generated by this segment.

The Investments and Other Operations segment (less than 1% of sales) principally consists of real estate investments and various other corporate operations. It includes a more than 40% stake in both Crombie REIT and Genstar.

Geographic Reach

Headquartered in Stellarton Nova Scotia Empire operates retail stores and fuel locations in every province in Canada. Its stake in real estate investment trust Crombie REIT allows the company to profit from income-producing properties such as shopping centers freestanding stores and mixed-use developments in urban and suburban markets in Canada. Its Genstar California-based hasoperations in Ontario Western Canada and the US.

Sales and Marketing

The company has AIR MILES loyalty program for its customers. AIR MILES are earned by Sobeys customers based on purchases in stores. The company pays a per point fee under the terms of the agreement with AIR MILES.

Financial Performance

Empire Company's revenue for the last five years was in the $23 billion to $26 billion range. Revenue increased by 12% for the last five years. Net income has increased steadily for the last five years with the company suffering a net loss only in 2016.

Revenue in 2020 amounted to $26.6 billion a 6% increase from the previous year which resulted from an increase in sales across all formats except for fuel. Fuel sales for the quarter decreased by approximately 40% due to a combination of lower demand and a sharp decrease in fuel prices.

Net income increased 51% to $583.5 million compared to $387.3 million in 2019.

Cash and cash equivalents at the end of the year were $1 billion 82% higher than the previous year. Cash provided by operating activities was $2.1 billion. Investing activities used $376.3 million while financing activities used $1.3 billion. Main cash uses were purchases of property and equipment advances on credit facilities and payments of lease liabilities.

Strategy

Empire has invested in people to create a more diverse and inclusive workforce that enables the company to build healthy communities through programs such as the Community Action Fund and the Strengthening Our Inclusive Leadership program. As a result the company received 5 industry leading inclusion awards.

The company has reduced its environmental impact and enhanced resilience to climate change to protect the planet for future generations.

The company has also put its focus on sustainable sourcing of products which won the company a Business Innovator of the Year award.

Company Background

J. W. Sobey started a butcher shop and meat delivery business in Nova Scotia in 1907 later expanding to a full-service grocery operation in 1924. By 1939 Sobeys had six grocery stores in Nova Scotia and continue to grow by promising low prices and introducing new products and concepts into the Sobey grocery business. On a trip through the US in the 1940s Sobey executives witnessed first-hand the operation of a new type of grocery store?the supermarket. Sobeys introduced the first supermarket in Nova Scotia in 1947.

While continuing to build its grocery operation Sobeys began investing in real estate carried out as the Empire Company. Empire went public on the Toronto Stock Exchange in 1983. At the same time the Sobeys chain was folded into Empire. In 1987 Sobeys opened its first store in Ontario; by the early 1990s Sobeys had expanded in Ontario and into Quebec.

The 1998 acquisition of The Oshawa Group (owner of the IGA and Price Chopper grocery chains) tripled the size of Sobeys and made its food service distributorship the largest in Canada. Later that year Empire took Sobeys public again retaining a majority stake in the grocery business. In 2000 Empire sold its 25% stake in US-based grocery retailer Hannaford Bros. Co. to Delhaize America for more than $800 million in cash and stock.

In 2013 Sobeys bought more than 200 Safeway stores in Western Canada for a whopping $5.8 billion. An anti-competition ruling against the company in 2014 prompted Sobeys to sell off its one remaining Price Chopper store to the North West Company.

EXECUTIVES

Independent Director, Karl Sobey
Independent Director, Paul Sobey
Independent Director, Frank Sobey
Independent Director, John Sobey
Independent Director, Robert Sobey
Independent Director, Martine Turcotte
Independent Director, Cynthia Devine
Independent Director, William Linton
Independent Director, Susan Lee
Independent Director, Gregory Josefowicz
Independent Director, Sharon Driscoll
Independent Chairman of the Board, James Dickson
Independent Director, Martine Reardon
Senior Vice President, General Counsel, Corporate Secretary, Douglas Nathanson
Executive Vice President - Human Resources, Simon Gagne, $404,767 total compensation
Independent Director, Michelle Banik
President, Chief Executive Officer, Director, Michael Medline, $859,187 total compensation
Chief Financial Officer, Michael Vels, $534,602 total compensation
Auditors: PricewaterhouseCoopers LLP

LOCATIONS

HQ: Empire Co Ltd
  115 King Street, Stellarton, Nova Scotia B0K 1S0
Phone: 902 752-8371   **Fax:** 902 238-7124
Web: www.empireco.ca

PRODUCTS/OPERATIONS

Related Businesses

Pharmacy
Wholesale
Fuel/Convenience
Liquor
Private Label Brands
Loyalty Reward Programs
Real Estate

COMPETITORS

AMIRA C FOODS INTERNATIONAL DMCC	GROCERY OUTLET INC.
Alimentation Couche-Tard Inc	ITOCHU CORPORATION
C.P. POKHPHAND CO. LTD.	SPARTANNASH COMPANY
DOLLAR GENERAL CORPORATION	UNITED NATURAL FOODS INC.
DOMINO'S PIZZA INC.	VRANKEN-POMMERY MONOPOLE

HISTORICAL FINANCIALS

Company Type: Public

Income Statement
FYE: May 1

	REVENUE ($ mil.)	NET INCOME ($ mil.)	NET PROFIT MARGIN	EMPLOYEES
05/21	23,107	571	2.5%	134,000
05/20	19,074	416	2.2%	63,000
05/19	18,780	287	1.5%	60,000
05/18	18,917	123	0.7%	120,000
05/17	17,374	115	0.7%	62,000
Annual Growth	7.4%	49.3%	—	21.2%

2021 Year-End Financials

Debt ratio: 6.5%
Return on equity: 16.9%
Cash ($ mil.): 725
Current ratio: 0.92
Long-term debt ($ mil.): 960

No. of shares (mil.): 265
Dividends
  Yield: 0.0%
  Payout: 20.0%
Market value ($ mil.): 8,371

	STOCK PRICE ($)	P/E		PER SHARE ($)	
	FY Close	High/Low	Earnings	Dividends	Book Value
05/21	31.54	13 9	2.12	0.42	13.42
05/20	21.60	12 8	1.53	0.34	10.41
05/19	22.21	16 12	1.05	0.33	10.60
05/18	19.48	34 25	0.46	0.33	10.60
05/17	15.70	28 19	0.42	0.30	9.76
Annual Growth	19.1%	— —	49.8%	9.2%	8.3%

Empresas COPEC SA

Everything is copasetic at Copec as long as the gas and oil keep flowing. Empresas Copec (formerly known as Compañ a de Petr leos de Chile) is the country's #1 importer and distributor of gasoline and petroleum by-products sold through several channels including its more than 600 gas stations. Copec's interests aren't single-minded though: The industrial conglomerate owns Celulosa Arauco y Constituci n (whose subsidiaries and affiliates cover the spectrum of forestry and wood products manufacturing) and fisheries businesses Corpesca and SouthPacific Korp or SPK. Other interests include mining electricity and retail holdings. Chile's Angelini family (through AntarChile) controls some 60% of Copec.

EXECUTIVES

Chief Executive Officer of Celulosa Arauco y Constitucion S.A., Matias Jorge Domeyko Cassel
Chief Financial Officer, Rodrigo Huidobro Alvarado
Chief Executive Officer of Compania de Petroleos de Chile Copec S.A., Lorenzo Gazmuri Schleyer
Director of Finance and Investor Relations, Cristian Gonzalo Palacios Gonzalez
Director, Arnaldo Gorziglia Balbi
Chief Executive Officer of Orizon S.A., Rigoberto Rojo Rojas
Chief Executive Officer of Abastible S.A., Joaquin Cruz Sanfiel
Chief Executive Officer of Inmobiliaria Las Salinas Ltda, Arturo Natho Gamboa
Chief Executive Officer, Eduardo Navarro Beltran
Director, Andres Bianchi Larre
Chairman of the Board, Roberto Angelini Rossi
Vice Chairman of the Board, Jorge Armando Andueza Fouque
Director, Juan Edgardo Goldenberg Penafiel
Independent Director, Gabriel Amos Bitran Dicowsky
Corporate Counsel and Secretary of the Board of Directors, Jose Tomas Guzman Rencoret
Director of Communications, Francisca Riveros Novoa
Chief Executive Officer of Aprovisionadora Global de Energía S.A., Klaus Luhrmann
Director of Business Development, Sebastian Dittborn Errazuriz
Chief Executive Officer of Mina Invierno S.A., Guillermo Hernandez
Chief Executive Officer of Alxar Mineria S.A., Erwin Kaufmann Salinas
Director of Corporate Affairs, Pamela Harris Honorato
Chief Development Officer, Jorge Ferrando Yanez
Auditors: PricewaterhouseCoopers

LOCATIONS

HQ: Empresas COPEC SA
Avenida El Golf 150, Piso 17, Santiago, Las Condes
Phone: (56) 2 461 7000 **Fax:** (56) 2 461 7070
Web: www.copec.cl

PRODUCTS/OPERATIONS

2007 Sales

	% of total
Fuels	73
Forestry	26
Fisheries	1
Total	**100**

COMPETITORS

Antarchile S.A.	Neles Oyj
BP P.L.C.	RENOLD PUBLIC LIMITED
DYNACTION	COMPANY
Grupo Carso S.A.B. de	TERNIUM S.A.
C.V.	Ultrapar Participacoes
IRPC PUBLIC COMPANY	S/A
LIMITED	VALLOUREC

HISTORICAL FINANCIALS
Company Type: Public

Income Statement   FYE: December 31

	REVENUE ($ mil.)	NET INCOME ($ mil.)	NET PROFIT MARGIN	EMPLOYEES
12/20	18,059	190	1.1%	0
12/19	23,716	172	0.7%	0
12/18	23,970	1,070	4.5%	0
12/17	20,353	639	3.1%	0
12/16	16,699	554	3.3%	31,714
Annual Growth	2.0%	(23.4%)	—	—

2020 Year-End Financials

Debt ratio: 36.0%	No. of shares (mil.): 1,299
Return on equity: 1.7%	Dividends
Cash ($ mil.): 2,146	Yield: —
Current ratio: 2.39	Payout: —
Long-term debt ($ mil.): 8,432	Market value ($ mil.): —

Enbridge Inc

Canada-based Enbridge is one of the biggest pipeline operators in North America. It serves approximately 75% of Ontario residents via approximately 3.8 million meter connections and generates approximately 1750 megawatts (MW) of net renewable power in North America and Europe. As well as fossil fuels the company also invests in renewable energy with investments in North American and European renewable energy totaling 1750 MW of installed capacity. In all the US accounts for 60% of Enbridge's revenue.

Operations
Enbridge divides its operations into five reportable segments: Liquids Pipelines Gas Transmission and Midstream Gas Distribution and Storage Renewable Power Generation and Energy Services.

Energy Services segment accounts for about half of total revenue provides energy supply and marketing services to North American refiners producers and other customers.

Liquids Pipelines (around 25%) consists of pipelines and related terminals in Canada and the United States that transport various grades of crude oil and other liquid hydrocarbons. It includes Canadian Mainline the Lakehead System Regional Oil Sands System Bakken System and other feeder pipelines.

Gas Transmission and Midstream maintains natural gas pipelines and gathering and processing facilities including US Gas Transmission Canadian Gas Transmission US Midstream and other assets. The segment brings in more than 10% of revenue.

Gas Distribution and Storage consists of natural gas utility operations the core of which is Enbridge Gas Inc. which serves residential commercial and industrial customers throughout Ontario and maintains natural gas distribution business in Quebec and New Brunswick. This business segment also includes natural gas distribution activities in Quebec and an investment in Noverco Inc. (Noverco). It represents about 10% of revenue.

Renewable Power Generation (around 5% of revenue) consists primarily of investments in wind and solar assets as well as geothermal waste heat recovery and transmission assets. The segment includes the Montana-Alberta Tie-Line (MATL) a 300 MW transmission line which runs from Great Falls Montana to Lethbridge Alberta. The segment's investments represent approximately 1977 MW of net generation capacity.

Geographic Reach
Headquartered in Calgary Alberta Canada Enbridge's core businesses include Liquids Pipelines which transports approximately 25% of the crude oil produced in North America; Gas Transmission and Midstream which transports approximately 20% of the natural gas consumed in the US; Gas Distribution and Storage which serves approximately 75% of Ontario residents via approximately 3.8 million meter connections; and Renewable Power Generation which generates approximately 1750 megawatts (MW) of net renewable power in North America and Europe.

Sales and Marketing
Enbridge Gas' principal source of revenue arises from distribution of natural gas to customers. The services provided to residential small commercial and industrial heating customers are primarily on a general service basis without a specific fixed term or fixed price contract. The services provided to larger commercial and industrial customers are usually on an annual contract basis under firm or interruptible service contracts. Under a firm contract Enbridge Gas is obligated to deliver natural gas to the customer up to a maximum daily volume. The service provided under an interruptible contract is similar to that of a firm contract except that it allows for service interruption at Enbridge Gas' option primarily to meet seasonal or peak demands.

Customers have a choice with respect to natural gas supply. Customers may purchase and deliver their own natural gas to points upstream of the distribution system or directly into Enbridge Gas' distribution system or alternatively they may choose a system supply option whereby customers purchase natural gas from Enbridge Gas' supply portfolio. To acquire the necessary volume of natural gas to serve its customers Enbridge Gas maintains a diversified natural gas supply portfolio acquiring supplies on a delivered basis in Ontario as well as acquiring supply from multiple supply basins across North America.

Financial Performance
Enbridge's revenue has been rising over the last five years but declined in fiscal year 2020 still recording an overall growth of 13%. The company's net income has been following a similar trend with an overall growth of almost 62.5%.

In 2020 Enbridge's sales fell 22% to C$39.1 billion from C$50.1 billion from the prior year.

Net income fell 41% from C$5.7 billion in 2019 to C$3.4 billion in 2020.

Enbridge's cash balance fell by C$186 million to C$490 million during 2020. Operating activities generated C$9.8 billion while investing activities used C$5.2 billion with C$4.8 billion for financing activities.

Strategy
The company's strategic priorities for the business continue to focus on enhancing the value of its existing assets executing on its secured growth program and investing in organic in-franchise opportunities to modernize extend and expand its network with a particular emphasis on increasing its connections to global export markets.

Enbridge plans to continue to enhance the performance safety and returns of its existing infrastructure through productivity efficiencies optimization of its throughput and embedded tariff and revenue inflators. Its Technology + Innovation Labs plays a key role to drive business improvement and return on capital by bringing its operations and commercial people together with technology specialists to find ways to improve business and operating performance.

Through 2023 Enbridge secured capital program and growth embedded in the business give the company high visibility to 5 ? 7% distributable cash flow growth per share on average. Beyond 2023 the strength of its organic growth opportunity set along with its ability to further enhance returns on existing assets gives the company confidence that it can continue to grow the business profitably over the medium term.

Environment Social and Governance (ESG) leadership is an important element of the company's strategy. Its commitment to reducing its carbon footprint building lasting relationships in the communities it serves and promoting equality inclusiveness and transparency play a role in our ability to operate its assets and thus generate cash flow over the long term.

Mergers and Acquisitions

In 2020 NextDecade and Enbridge announced that they have entered into a definitive agreement whereby Enbridge will acquire Rio Bravo Pipeline Company LLC (RBPL) from NextDecade for a cash purchase price not to exceed $25 million with $15 million paid at closing and the balance paid upon NextDecade's reaching a positive final investment decision (FID) on its Rio Grande LNG export facility in the Port of Brownsville Texas. Upon closing of the transaction Enbridge will own one hundred percent of RBPL and assume all responsibility for the development financing construction and operations of the Rio Bravo Pipeline.

Company Background

Enbridge is an early pioneer in the development of oil production in Western Canada. The company was born in 1949 when crude oil was discovered in Leduc No. 1. Starting life as the Interprovincial Pipe Line Company it was conceived as a pipeline that will carry Alberta crude to refineries in Regina.

In 1950 it sold some 3 million barrels of oil. By 2018 the company will sell close to that volume every day.

Enbridge merged with Spectra in early 2017 to create one of the largest energy infrastructure company in North America with an enterprise value of approximately US $126 billion.

EXECUTIVES

Independent Director, Dan Tutcher
President, Chief Executive Officer and Director, Albert Monaco, $1,153,091 total compensation
Independent Director, James England
Executive Vice President and Chief Financial Officer, Vernon Yu, $460,002 total compensation
Executive Vice President and Chief Legal Officer, Bob Rooney, $415,697 total compensation
Executive Vice President, President, Gas Transmission and Midstream, William Yardley, $522,064 total compensation
Independent Director, Pamela Carter
Independent Director, Susan Cunningham
Independent Director, Teresa Madden
Independent Director, Stephen Poloz
Independent Non-Executive Chairman of the Board, Gregory Ebel
Executive Vice President & President, Liquids Pipelines, Colin Gruending, $437,832 total compensation
Independent Director, Jane Rowe
Independent Director, Mayank Ashar
Independent Director, Guardie Banister
Auditors: PricewaterhouseCoopers LLP

LOCATIONS

HQ: Enbridge Inc
200, 425 - 1st Street S.W., Calgary, Alberta T2P 3L8
Phone: 403 231-3900   **Fax:** 403 231-5929
Web: www.enbridge.com

2018 Sales

	% of total
US	59
Canada	41
Total	**100**

PRODUCTS/OPERATIONS

2018 Sales

	% of total
Commodity sales	60
Transportation and other services	31
Gas distribution	9
Total	**100**

Selected Subsidiaries and Affiliates

Gas Pipelines Processing and Energy Services
  Aux Sable Liquids Products Inc. (43%)
  Alliance Pipeline Limited Partnership (50%)
  Tlbury Solar Project
  Vector Pipeline Limited Partnership (60%)
Gas Distribution
  Enbridge Gas Distribution
  Enbridge Gas New Brunswick (63%)
  Gazifère Inc.
  Niagara Gas Transmission Limited
Liquids Pipelines
  Chicap Pipe Line Company (44%)
  Enbridge Energy Partners L.P. (13%)
  Enbridge Pipelines (Athabasca) Inc.
  Enbridge Pipelines (North Dakota) Inc.
  Enbridge Pipelines (NW) Inc.
  Enbridge Pipelines (Toledo) Inc.
  Enbridge Pipelines Inc.
  Frontier Pipeline Company (78%)
  Mustang Pipe Line Partners (30%)
  Olympic Pipe Line (85%)
Sponsored Investments
  Enbridge Income Fund (72%)
  Enbridge Energy Partners L.P. (25.5%)
Corporate
  Noverco Inc. (39%)
  Gaz Mé;tropolitain and Company Limited Partnership (71%)
  Vermont Gas Systems Inc.

COMPETITORS

AltaGas Ltd	OGE ENERGY CORP.
ENERGY TRANSFER LP	PLAINS GP HOLDINGS
ENTERPRISE PRODUCTS	L.P.
PARTNERS L.P.	TC Energy Corporation
GENESIS ENERGY L.P.	TRANSMONTAIGNE
NOBLE MIDSTREAM	PARTNERS LLC
PARTNERS LP	

HISTORICAL FINANCIALS

Company Type: Public

Income Statement   FYE: December 31

	REVENUE ($ mil.)	NET INCOME ($ mil.)	NET PROFIT MARGIN	EMPLOYEES
12/21	36,957	4,859	13.1%	10,900
12/20	30,698	2,641	8.6%	11,200
12/19	38,449	4,381	11.4%	11,300
12/18	34,056	2,116	6.2%	12,000
12/17	35,399	2,280	6.4%	12,700
Annual Growth	**1.1%**	**20.8%**	**—**	**(3.7%)**

2021 Year-End Financials

Debt ratio: 35.1%	
Return on equity: 10.1%	Dividends
Cash ($ mil.): 251	Yield: 6.8%
Current ratio: 0.49	Payout: 149.3%
Long-term debt ($ mil.): 53,359	Market value ($ mil.): 79,176

	STOCK PRICE ($) FY Close	P/E High/Low	PER SHARE ($) Earnings	Dividends	Book Value
12/21	39.08	15 11	2.25	2.68	23.57
12/20	31.99	30 18	1.16	2.42	23.79
12/19	39.77	15 13	2.02	2.22	25.05
12/18	31.08	26 19	1.07	2.08	(0.00)
12/17	39.11	28 21	1.32	1.92	27.36
Annual Growth	**(0.0%)**	**— —**	**14.4%**	**8.6%**	**(3.7%)**

Endesa S.A.

Endesa provides power to some 10.6 million electricity customers and approximately 1.6 million gas customers. A subsidiary of Italian power giant Enel Endesa is a leading electric utility in Spain and has a gross installed capacity of some 24230 MW from nuclear hydroelectric and renewable energy plants. Endesa is the primary electricity company in Chile Argentina Colombia and Peru and also operates in Brazil. The company is also investing heavily in renewable energy to meet Spain's commitment to greenhouse gas reduction. Spain accounts for the Majority of the company's sales.

Operations

The company's segments include Generation and Supply (about 85% of sales) Distribution (about 15%) and Structure (nearly 5%) which mainly includes balances and transactions of holding companies and financing and service provision companies.

Geographic Reach

Its registered offices and headquarters are at Madrid. About 90% of sales were generated in Spain Portugal with some 5% and France Germany Italy UK Netherlands and Other accounts for the rest.

Sales and Marketing

ENDESA maintains relationships with a large number of customers 10.6 million electricity customers and 1.6 million gas customers.

Financial Performance

Income in 2019 totaled ?20.2 billion ?37 million (-0.2%) less than that of 2018.

The company's net income for 2019 decreased to ?180 million compared to ?1.4 billion in the prior year.

Cash held by the company at the end of 2019 increased by ?18 million to ?31 million compared to ?13 million in the prior year. Cash provided by operations was ?2.2 billion while cash used for investing and financing activities were ?30 million and ?2.1 billion respectively.

Strategy

Development of the electricity grid has long been a fundamental pillar of ENDESA's strategy. Projected investment driven by the electrification of demand and the inclusion of renewable energies aims to improve grid quality and efficiency reducing operating costs and increasing the value of assets through investments in smart grids and the pursuit of excellence.

To this end ENDESA continues with its investment effort aimed at becoming the reference digital operator and for this it will allocate Euros 1100 million in the 2019-2022 period to the development automation and modernization of the network. This amount represents approximately 55% of the Euros 2000 million total investment envisaged for this business in the plan.

HISTORY

When dictator Francisco Franco set about rebuilding Spain after the Civil War Empresa Nacional de Electricidad (Endesa) was formed in 1944 under the state-run Instituto Nacional de Industria (INI). The nation's lack of power facilities sparked the company into building hydroelectric plants. In the 1950s the US fighting the Cold War financed Spain's industrial boom which Endesa aided by building coal-fired plants including Compostilla (on line in 1961).

When inflation plagued Spain in the late 1950s the government cut off INI's funding. INI and its companies then borrowed heavily from banks. Spain then passed the Stabilization Act in 1959 to make INI companies self-financing though they were still government-owned. In the 1960s many of Spain's rural areas were undeveloped so the government instituted and funded a plan to build power infrastructure.

In 1972 Endesa acquired the As Pontel and Teruel facilities where it began constructing fossil fuel plants. However the energy crisis of the early 1970s kept the plants from operating until 1976 and 1979 respectively.

After Franco's death in 1975 King Juan Carlos moved Spain into Europe's free market union. In preparation for the liberalization of the energy markets INI and Endesa reorganized in 1983 and shifted INI's holdings in regional electric utilities (Eneco Enher Gesa and Unelco) to Endesa.

After the government halted its nuclear power program in 1984 many private electric companies were left with bad investments. Endesa was brought in to bail them out by taking over power plants; to repay Endesa they were forced to buy Endesa's electricity. The 1985 asset swaps also brought regional power companies Erz and Fecsa into Endesa's grasp.

In 1986 Spain joined the European Community; two years later the government sold 20% of Endesa to the public. In the early 1990s Endesa went into coal production when it purchased ENCASUR (1990) and it continued buying interests in private power companies including Viesgo and Sevillana.

The government floated more of the company in 1997 and the utility became Endesa S.A. Its eye on Latin American opportunity Endesa bought a 29% stake in Chile's largest power company Enersis. It also branched into telecommunications by grabbing a small stake in Retevisi n.

Endesa was fully privatized in 1998 the year Spain's deregulation process began. The next year Endesa paid some $2.6 billion to buy the outstanding shares of its regional units and merge them into the company as part of its larger effort to reorganize and cut its costs and workforce. Endesa also increased its stake in Enersis to more than 60%.

In 2000 Endesa began restructuring its regional electric utilities into separate generation and distribution units. Also that year Endesa Telecom Italia and Uni n Fenosa combined their Spanish telecom holdings to form the Auna joint venture. (Telecom Italia later sold its stake to Santander Central Hispano.) Endesa also agreed to acquire rival Spanish utility Iberdrola but the companies cancelled the transaction in 2001.

In 2001 Endesa completed the purchase of a 30% interest in French generation company SNET. The company also acquired one of Italian utility Enel's power production units (Elettrogen). Endesa sold its New Viesgo unit (a spinoff composed of regional electric utility Electra de Viesgo which served 500000 customers and had 2400 MW of generation assets) to Enel in 2002.

Endesa branched out into new territories to prepare for the deregulation of Spain's electric utility market which took full effect in 2003.

In 2005 Endesa sold its major stake in Auna to France Telecom (since renamed Orange).

The company found itself the target of takeover bids by other European power companies seeking to bulk up in the wake of the deregulation of the European power and gas markets. In 2007 E.ON and Gas Natural made bids of $47-plus billion and $26-plus billion respectively for Endesa. That year Enel and Acciona jumped into the fray buying about 70% and 25% of the company respectively when Gas Natural dropped out of the bidding. E.ON dropped out in 2008 in return for buying some power plants and shareholdings in Italy Spain and France from Endesa. In 2009 Enel bought Acciona's stake.

In 2009 Endesa had a generating capacity of more than 3700 MW of wind power or about 10% of the Spanish wind power market. In another major move to promote renewable energy in 2010 the company agreed to develop about 550 recharging locations in Barcelona Madrid and Seville to power electric cars.

EXECUTIVES

Independent Director, Alejandro Echevarria Busquet, $214,208 total compensation

General Manager - People and Organisation, Paolo Bondi

Vice Chairman of the Board, Francesco Starace

Director, Alberto De Paoli

General Manager - Media, Pablo Azcoitia Lorente

Independent Non-Executive Chairman of the Board, Juan Sanchez Calero Guilarte, $688,200 total compensation

General Secretary to the Board of Directors and General Manager - Legal Counsel and Corporate Affairs, Francisco Borja Acha Besga

Independent Director, Ignacio Garralda Ruiz de Velasco, $227,881 total compensation

General Manager - Energy Management, Juan Maria Moreno Mellado

Director, Maria Patrizia Grieco, $214,208 total compensation

General Manager Institutional Relations and Regulation, Jose Casas Marin

Chief Executive Officer, Executive Director, Jose Damian Bogas Galvez, $1,058,508 total compensation

General Manager Sustainability, Maria Malaxechevarria Grande

Independent Director, Francesco de Lacerda, $217,626 total compensation

Director, Antonio Cammisecra

Auditors: KPMG Auditores, S.L.

LOCATIONS

HQ: Endesa S.A.
Calle Ribera Del Loira 60, Madrid 28042
Phone: (34) 91 213 10 00   **Fax:** (34) 91 563 81 81
Web: www.endesa.es

2009 Sales

	% of total
Europe	
Spain & Portugal	68
Latin America	32
Total	**100**

COMPETITORS

E.ON SE	NATIONAL GRID PLC
ELECTRICITE DE FRANCE	REXEL
ENEL SPA	RWE AG
Fortum Oyj	STRABAG SE
KOC HOLDING ANONIM	UNITED UTILITIES GROUP
SIRKETI	PLC

HISTORICAL FINANCIALS

Company Type: Public

Income Statement

FYE: December 31

	REVENUE ($ mil.)	NET INCOME ($ mil.)	NET PROFIT MARGIN	EMPLOYEES
12/20	21,574	1,710	7.9%	9,591
12/19	22,632	191	0.8%	9,952
12/18	23,127	1,622	7.0%	9,763
12/17	24,043	1,753	7.3%	9,706
12/16	20,039	1,489	7.4%	9,694
Annual Growth	1.9%	3.5%	—	(0.3%)

2020 Year-End Financials

Debt ratio: 27.9%
Return on equity: 18.5%
Cash ($ mil.): 494
Current ratio: 0.73
Long-term debt ($ mil.): 7,286

No. of shares (mil.): 1,058
Dividends
Yield: 4.2%
Payout: 39.7%
Market value ($ mil.): 15,277

	STOCK PRICE ($) FY Close	P/E High/Low		PER SHARE ($) Earnings	Dividends	Book Value
12/20	14.43	12	9	1.62	0.61	8.48
12/19	13.86	89	75	0.18	0.57	8.15
12/18	11.62	9	8	1.53	0.56	9.77
12/17	11.66	11	8	1.65	0.57	10.30
12/16	11.07	10	6	1.40	0.50	8.93
Annual Growth	6.9%	—	—	3.6%	5.4%	(1.3%)

Enel Americas SA

Latin America's largest power holding company Enel Americas (formerly Enersis Americas) gives Chile (and its neighbors) plenty of heat. Its distribution companies provide power to almost 14.3 million customers (45 million people) in regions of Chile (Chilectra Chile) Argentina (Edesur) Brazil (Ampla Energ a e Servicos and Coelce) Colombia (Codensa) and Peru (Edelnor). Its 60%-owned Enel Generaci n Chile is Chile's largest power generator with 15846 MW of capacity. Endesa Americas merged with Chilectra Americas (Enel's pan-American power distribution holding company) in late 2016 and became Enel Americas.

EXECUTIVES

Chairman of the Board, Francisco de Borja Acha Besga

Independent Director, Patricio Gomez Sabaini

Head, Investor Relations, Rafael De la Haza

Vice Chairman of the Board, Jose Antonio Vargas Lleras

Independent Director, Domingo Cruzat Amunategui

Independent Director, Hernan Somerville Senn

General Counsel and Secretary, Domingo Valdes Prieto

Chief Executive Officer, Maurizio Bezzecheri

Internal Audit Officer, Raffaele Cutrignelli

Chief Financial Officer, Aurelio Bustilho de Oliveira

Planning and Control Officer, Francisco Ruz

Head of Enel X South America, Simone Tripepi

Auditors: KPMG Auditores Consultores Ltda.

LOCATIONS

HQ: Enel Americas SA
Avenida Santa Rosa 76, Piso 16, Santiago
Phone: (56) 2 353 4639   **Fax:** (56) 2 378 4790
Web: www.enelamericas.com

PRODUCTS/OPERATIONS

2016 Sales

	% of total
Distribution	67
Generation and Transmission	33
Total	**100**

2016 Sales

	% of total
Brazil	36
Colombia	30
Peru	17
Argentina	17
Total	**100**

Selected Subsidiaries

Ampla Energí;a e Serviços (distribution generation and transmission Brazil)
Centrais Elé;tricas Cachoeira Dourada (distribution generation and transmission Brazil)
Chilectra (distribution)
Compóí;a Americana de Multiservicios (CAM electricity support services and engineering)
Edelnor (distribution Peru)
Edesur (distribution Argentina)
Endesa Brasil Consolidated (distribution generation and transmission Brazil)
Endesa Chile (generation)
Endesa Fortaleza (distribution generation and transmission Brazil)
Inmobiliaria Manso de Velasco (IMV real estate)
Synapsis (information and telecommunications)

COMPETITORS

CMS ENERGY CORPORATION
EDP ESPA 'A SAU
EDP ESPIRITO SANTO DISTRIBUICAO DE ENERGIA SA
EVERGY INC.
Enel Generacion Chile S.A.
Grupo Mexico S.A.B. de C.V.
PUBLIC SERVICE ENTERPRISE GROUP INCORPORATED
SCANA CORPORATION
TRANSPORTADORA DE GAS DEL SUR S.A.

HISTORICAL FINANCIALS

Company Type: Public

Income Statement

				FYE: December 31
	REVENUE ($ mil.)	NET INCOME ($ mil.)	NET PROFIT MARGIN	EMPLOYEES
12/20	12,192	825	6.8%	16,731
12/19	14,314	1,614	11.3%	17,295
12/18	13,184	1,201	9.1%	18,364
12/17	10,540	709	6.7%	11,393
12/16	7,794	574	7.4%	10,324
Annual Growth	11.8%	9.5%	—	12.8%

2020 Year-End Financials

Debt ratio: 21.0%
Return on equity: 9.1%
Cash ($ mil.): 1,506
Current ratio: 0.85
Long-term debt ($ mil.): 3,837

No. of shares (mil.): —
Dividends
  Yield: 6.4%
  Payout: 4,974.9%
Market value ($ mil.): —

	STOCK PRICE ($)	P/E	PER SHARE ($)		
	FY Close	High/Low	Earnings	Dividends	Book Value
12/20	8.22	1028501	0.01	0.53	0.11
12/19	10.98	447312	0.02	0.38	0.13
12/18	8.92	573338	0.02	0.29	0.12
12/17	11.17	905650	0.01	0.22	0.11
12/16	8.21	2 1	0.01	0.31	0.11
Annual Growth	0.0%	— —	(1.5%)	14.6%	(0.4%)

Enel Societa Per Azioni

Enel is the largest private renewable energy operator in the world with 49 GW of managed capacity and the largest private electricity distribution company globally with 74 million end users connected to the world's most advanced digitalized grids. It manages the largest customer base in the world among private companies with approximately 70 million customers. Enel's portfolio of power stations includes hydroelectric wind thermal electricity and other renewables. About 20% of Enel's revenue comes from its home country Italy. Enel was founded in 1962 with the fusion of more than a thousand energy producers.

Operations

Enel reports six business segments three of which are its leading revenue earners ? End-user markets (more than 35%) Thermal generation and trading (more than 25% of total revenue) Infrastructure and Networks (around 25%) and Enel Green Power (about 10%). The two other segments Enel X and Services bring in a combined less than 5% of revenue.

Geographic Reach

Based in Italy Enel is primarily present in more than 30 countries from Europe to Latin America North America Africa Asia and Oceania.

Enel's largest market Italy bringing in nearly 40% of total sales while other European market generates roughly 40% and Americas with about 25%.

Financial Performance

The company's revenue for fiscal 2020 decreased by 19% to ?65.0 billion compared with ?80.3 billion in the prior year.

Profit for fiscal 2020 increased by 20% to ?2.6 billion compared to ?2.2 billion in the prior year.

Cash held by the company at the end of fiscal 2020 ?6.0 billion. Cash provided by operations was ?11.5 billion while cash used for investing and financing activities were ?10.1 billion and ?4.0 billion respectively. Main cash uses were investments in property plant and equipment; and repayments of borrowings.

Strategy

With the new Strategic Plan the company has indicated its direction for the next ten years mobilizing approximately ?190 billion between direct and third-party investments in order to achieve its objectives in a decade that promises to be full of opportunities to be seized through two complementary business models: the traditional ownership model based on direct investments to support long-term sustainable development in which platforms contribute to business growth and value maximization; and a new Stewardship model in which the use of platforms enables new services products and know-how by catalyzing third-party investments.

The 2021-2023 Strategic Plan is ideally placed as the first step in a growth path that spans the entire coming decade. The group's ambitions are reflected in a marked increase in investments both direct and indirect to enable the acceleration of trends in decarbonization and electrification.

HISTORY

Italy's energy consumption doubled in the 1950s as the country experienced a period of rapid industrialization and urbanization. A tight-knit oligopoly controlled the electric power industry and included Edison SADE La Centale SME and Finelettrica. The economic boom pushed into the 1960s and the Italian government created Enel (Ente Nazionale per l'Energia Elettrica) in 1962 to nationalize the power industry. In 1963 Enel began gradually buying some 1250 electric utilities. About 160 municipal utilities and the larger independents such as Edison were left out of the takeover.

The company spent the late 1960s and early 1970s connecting Italy's unwieldy transmission network and building new power plants including the La Spezia thermoelectric plant (600 MW). Construction costs coupled with the high prices Enel was required to pay for its takeover targets caused the utility to become steeped in debt. The Arab oil embargoes of the early 1970s made matters worse and the Italian government helped Enel with an endowment in 1973.

The energy crisis also prompted Enel to build its first nuclear power plant Caorso which came on line in 1980. However nuclear power was short-lived in Italy: After the 1986 Chernobyl accident a national referendum forced Enel to deactivate its nukes in 1987. The firm also stepped up its development of renewable energy sources in the 1980s.

Meanwhile Enel opened its Centro Nazionale de Controllo (CNC) in Rome in 1985 to supervise Italy's power grid. The next year the company turned its first profit.

To begin disassembling Enel's monopoly the Italian government in 1992 opened the power generation market to outside producers and converted Enel into a joint stock company (with the state holding all of the shares). Following the European Union's 1997 directive to deregulate Europe's power industry Enel unbundled its utility activities and began trimming its staff.

Italy's Bersani Decree (passed in 1999) outlined the restructuring process: Enel was ordered to divest 25% of its capacity (15000 MW) and turn over a portion of its municipal distribution networks to local governments to enhance competition in the country's power market. Accordingly it transferred management of the national transmission grid to an independent government-owned operator Gestore della Rete di Trasmissione Nazionale (GRTN) and reduced its customer count by approximately 1 million through municipal distribution asset sales.

Enel had already begun to diversify. It started Wind Telecomunicazioni a joint venture with France Telecom — later renamed Orange— and Deutsche Telekom in 1998. (Deutsche Telekom sold its stake to the other partners in 2000.) Wind first offered fixed-line and mobile telecom services to corporations; it extended the services to residential users in 1999. In addition Enel began building water infrastructure to serve local distributors and purchased three water operations in southern Italy.

Also in 1999 the government floated 32% of Enel in one of the world's largest IPOs at the time. The next year the company bought Colombo Gas (a northern Italian gas distributor with about 75000 customers) and it transferred control of its transmission network to Gestore della Rete di Trasmissione Nazionale (an independent government-owned operator) while retaining ownership of the assets.

Enel bought fixed-line telephone company Infostrada from Vodafone in 2001 acquired two more Italian gas distributors and sold its 5400-MW Elettrogen generation unit to Spain's Endesa for $2.3 billion. That year Enel put its 7000-MW Eurogen generation unit on the auction block. The high bidder with a $2.6 billion offer was a consortium backed by Fiat and lectricite de France; the sale was completed in 2002.

Also in 2002 Enel merged Infostrada into Wind Telecomunicazioni to create one of Italy's top telecom companies it purchased Camuzzi Gazometri's gas distribution business (Italy's second-largest) for $870 million from Mill Hill Investments and it bought Endesa's Viesgo unit (2400 MW of generating capacity and 500000 power customers) for about $1.8 billion.

Enel sold its final generation divestment company Interpower (2600 MW) to a consortium of utilities (including Belgian utility Electrabel and Italian utility ACEA) for about $880 million in 2003.

That year Enel purchased France Telecom's 27% stake in Wind for $1.4 billion making the unit a wholly owned subsidiary. (Enel had flirted with the idea of taking Wind public but instead sold the unit in 2006 to the Egypt-based Weather Investments consortium which had the backing of Orascom Telecom's chairman and CEO Naguib Sawiris.)

The Italian government began the second round of Enel's privatization process in 2003 by selling a 7% stake to Morgan Stanley for more than $2.3 billion. In 2004 the government further reduced its stake by nearly 20% through a public offering of shares.

In 2005 it acquired power distribution and sales businesses in Romania and in 2006 in Slovakia.

With Italian regulators requiring that Enel divest 80% of its Terna subsidiary (which holds the company's power transmission assets) by 2007 Enel spun off 50% of the unit in an IPO in 2004. The following year it divested another 44% and the company reduced its holding to about 5% by January 2006. Grid management and operational functions were also transferred from GRTN back to Terna.

In 2008 the company set Enel Green Power to develop wind solar geothermal and biomass projects. By 2009 it was operating alternative energy plants worldwide with a generating capacity of 4700 MW. In 2010 Enel Green Power acquired Pagoda Wind Power which is developing 4000 MW of wind projects in California.

In what could have been a large cross-border deal Enel considered making a bid for France's SUEZ (now GDF SUEZ) utility company. Perhaps in reaction to the news of Enel's interest France's Gaz de France made a bid for SUEZ (consummated in 2008) a move that Italy called protectionist.

Unperturbed by its failure to secure SUEZ the company took control of Spain's power giant Endesa in 2007 increasing its market share as a European power player. Hoping to pay down what had become a heavy debt load the company in 2009 sold an 80% stake in gas distributor Enel Rete Gas for $666 million.

In 2012 Enel Green Power consolidated its position in the Greek renewable industry through the launching of two new plants - a wind farm and a photovoltaic plant - both located in the Peloponnese region.

EXECUTIVES

Head of Latin America, Maurizio Bezzeccheri

Non-Executive Independent Director, Anna Svelto
Chief Financial Officer, Alberto De Paoli
Chief Innovability Officer, Ernesto Ciorra
Head, North America, Enrico Viale
Head of Global Power Generation, Head of Africa, Asia and Oceania, Salvatore Bernabei
Head of Audit Function, Silvia Fiori
Head of Global Digital Solutions, Carlo Bozzoli
Head of Iberia, Jose Bogas Galvez
Head of Legal and Corporate Affairs, Giulio Fazio
Chief Executive Officer - Enel X, Francesco Venturini
Non-Executive Chairman of the Board, Michele Crisostomo
Non-Executive Independent Director, Mirella Pellegrini
Non-Executive Independent Director, Mariana Mazzucato
Non-Executive Independent Director, Costanza De Villeneuve
Head of People and Organization, Guido Stratta
Non-Executive Independent Director, Cesare Calari
Head of Global Energy and Commodity Management, Claudio Machetti
Head of Communications, Roberto Deambrogio
Head of Global Procurement, Francesca Di Carlo
Head of Europe and Euro-Mediterranean Affairs, Simone Mori
Head of Italy, Carlo Tamburi
Chief Executive Officer, General Manager, Executive Director, Francesco Starace
Auditors: KPMG S.p.A.

LOCATIONS

HQ: Enel Societa Per Azioni
  Viale Regina Margherita, 137, Rome 00198
Phone: (39) 6 8509 3184   **Fax:** (39) 6 8509 5810
Web: www.enel.com

2018 sales

	%
Italy	50
Iberia	26
South America	19
Europe and Euro-Mediterranean Affairs	3
North and Central America	2
Africa Asia and Oceania	-
Total	**100**

PRODUCTS/OPERATIONS

2018 Sales

	% of total
Thermal Generation and Trading	41
End-user markets	35
Infrastructure and Networks	16
Enel Green Power	4
Enel X	1
Services	3
Total	**100**

2018 sales

	%
Sale of electricity	57
Transport of Electricity	14
Fees from network operators	1
Transfers from institutional market operators	2
Sales of gas	6
Transport of gas	1
Sale of fuel	11
Other	8
Total	**100**

COMPETITORS

BOOZ ALLEN HAMILTON HOLDING CORPORATION
COAL INDIA LIMITED
CORERO NETWORK SECURITY PLC
ELECTRICITE DE FRANCE

IBERDROLA SOCIEDAD ANONIMA
INTERNATIONAL POWER LTD.
MANAGEMENT CONSULTING GROUP PLC

ENDESA SA
FALCK SPA
FRANKLIN COVEY CO.

SNAM SPA
THE HACKETT GROUP INC

HISTORICAL FINANCIALS

Company Type: Public

Income Statement

FYE: December 31

	REVENUE ($ mil.)	NET INCOME ($ mil.)	NET PROFIT MARGIN	EMPLOYEES
12/20	79,755	3,203	4.0%	66,717
12/19	90,188	2,440	2.7%	68,253
12/18	86,659	5,484	6.3%	69,272
12/17	89,473	4,530	5.1%	62,900
12/16	74,536	2,713	3.6%	62,080
Annual Growth	**1.7%**	**4.2%**	**—**	**1.8%**

2020 Year-End Financials

Debt ratio: 44.3%	No. of shares (mil.): —
Return on equity: 8.8%	Dividends
Cash ($ mil.): 7,248	Yield: 2.1%
Current ratio: 0.81	Payout: 74.0%
Long-term debt ($ mil.): 60,774	Market value ($ mil.): —

	STOCK PRICE ($) FY Close	P/E High/Low	PER SHARE ($)		
			Earnings	Dividends	Book Value
12/20	10.15	40 25	0.32	0.22	3.42
12/19	7.85	38 27	0.24	0.18	3.36
12/18	5.81	13 10	0.54	0.16	3.57
12/17	6.11	18 12	0.44	0.12	4.10
12/16	4.37	17 14	0.27	0.10	3.61
Annual Growth	**23.5%**	**—**	**3.8%**	**22.3%**	**(1.4%)**

Eneos Holdings Inc

ENEOS (formerly JXTG) is an integrated energy holding company that combines the businesses of two of Nippon Oil and Nippon Mining Holdings in petroleum refining and marketing oil and natural gas exploration and production and metals. In addition the company supplies electricity and hydrogen. With a unified sales system for nationwide network of approximately 13000 service stations and a nationwide network of more than 10 refineries and plants in Japan the company processes approximately 1.87 million bbl per day. Based in Japan the company was established in 2010.

Operations

ENEOS operates through three major segments: Energy Oil and Natural Gas Exploration & Production and Metals.

The company's Energy business is engaged in core businesses that include petroleum products and petrochemicals as well as businesses that will be mainstays of the future including electric power gas hydrogen renewable energy and materials.

Its Metals business includes non-ferrous metal resources development and mining copper gold silver sulfuric acid copper foils materials for rolling and processing thin film materials non-ferrous metal recycling and industrial waste treatment transportation by ships non-ferrous metal products titanium and electric wires.

Its Oil and Natural Gas Exploration & Production business is engaged in long-term oil and gas field operations to maintain a stable supply of oil and gas resources while also conducting basic research and developing systems.

With power generation capacity of approximately 1.59 million kW the company has a crude oil processing capacity of 1.87 million bbl/day. It also has approximately 450000 tons of refined copper production capacity in Japan per year.

Geographic Reach

Based in Tokyo Japan ENEOS markets refined products across Japan is engaged in exploration development and production of oil and gas in some 10 countries around the world and has stake in a copper mine in Chile.

Financial Performance

Note: Growth rates may differ after conversion to US Dollars.

Company's revenue for fiscal 2020 decreased to 7.7 trillion yen compared from the prior year with 10.0 trillion yen.

Net income for fiscal 2020 was 114.0 billion yen compared from the prior year with a net loss of 187.9 billion yen.

Strategy

The ENEOS Group announced its Long-Term Vision to 2040 in 2019 and is now moving forward with measures to achieve the envisioned goals in this vision. As an energy and materials company group contributing to the development of a low-carbon recycling-oriented society is one of its top priorities. The company are accelerating its efforts to strengthen its management foundation and reform its business structure by strengthening the competitiveness of its base businesses and developing and strengthening ENEOS' growth businesses.

In the second Medium-Term Management Plan the company aim to maximize cash flows by strengthening the competitiveness of our base businesses and accelerate development and strengthening of its growth businesses through the use of digital technology and collaboration with different industries and areas while capitalizing on its strengths.

Mergers and Acquisitions

In late 2021 ENEOS has acquired all Japan Renewable Energy's (JRE) issued shares for a $1.7bn consideration. The company's subsidiary Eneos Corporation will acquire the shares from Goldman Sachs Asset Management and an affiliate of Singapore-based sovereign wealth fund GIC Private Limited. JRE will become a wholly owned subsidiary of Eneos Holdings following the deal's completion. The company is based in Tokyo.

Company Background

The merger of Nippon Oil and Nippon Mining in 2010 was spurred on by changes in the Japanese oil industry including excess refining capacity due to the continued decline in domestic demand for refined petroleum products a growing consumer awareness of environmental issues and alternative energy options and a sluggish Japanese economy. Such trends prompted the two to consider restructuring and integrating their businesses to strengthen competitiveness. Following the merger JX Nippon set up upstream oil business JX Nippon Oil & Gas Exploration and metals unit JX Nippon Mining and Metals as operating subsidiaries.

Petroleum refining and marketing will continue to be a core segment that JX Holdings plans to expand further throughout Asia and arpund the world. However it may also look for future opportunities to engage in new energy markets such as fuel cells and photovoltaic power generation to keep up with the growing green trend.

In 2012 the company's wholly owned subsidiary JX Nippon Exploration and Production (U.K.) Limited signed sale and purchase agreements to acquire an extensive portfolio of non-operated oil and gas assets in the UK Continental Shelf from ENI. The assets give JX a substantial long-term oil and gas production base in the UK.

EXECUTIVES

Chairman of the Board, Group Chief Executive Officer, Representative Director, Tsutomu Sugimori
President, Executive President, President & Executive President of Subsidiary, Representative Director, Katsuyuki Ohta
Independent Director, Hiroko Ohta
Independent Director, Yoshiiku Miyata
Independent Director, Seiichiro Nishioka
President & Executive President of Subsidiary, Non-Executive Director, Hiroshi Hosoi
Director, Yoshiaki Ohuchi
Independent Director, Yuko Mitsuya
President & Executive President of subsidiary, Non-Executive Director, Seiichi Murayama
Executive Vice President, Director, Yasushi Yatabe
Executive Vice President, Director, Junichi Iwase
Executive Vice President, Director, Yoshikazu Yokoi
Independent Director, Toshiko Oka
Director, Shingo Nishimura
Independent Director, Yasumi Kudo
Executive Vice President, CDO, Director, Takeshi Saito
Auditors: Ernst & Young ShinNihon LLC

LOCATIONS

HQ: Eneos Holdings Inc
1-1-2 Otemachi, Chiyoda-ku, Tokyo 100-8162
Phone: (81) 3 6257 7075
Web: www.hd.eneos.co.jp

2014 Sales

	% of total
Japan	74
China	19
Other countries	7
Total	**100**

PRODUCTS/OPERATIONS

2014 Sales

	% of total
Energy	87
Metals	8
Oil & natural gas exploration & production	2
Other	3
Total	**100**

COMPETITORS

ABU DHABI NATIONAL ENERGY COMPANY - PJSC
CLEAN TECH ASSETS LIMITED
CVI ENERGY CORPORATION LIMITED
Canadian Natural Resources Ltd
ESSAR ENERGY LIMITED
Evonik Industries AG
FURUKAWA CO. LTD.
JFE HOLDINGS INC.
MARATHON OIL CORPORATION
MITSUBISHI CHEMICAL HOLDINGS CORPORATION
OJI HOLDINGS CORPORATION
PROSPEX ENERGY PLC
PTT PUBLIC COMPANY LIMITED
Riverstone Energy Limited
SASOL LTD
SURGUTNEFTEGAZ PAO
TOKYO ELECTRIC POWER COMPANY HOLDINGS INCORPORATED
TOYO SEIKAN GROUP HOLDINGSLTD.

HISTORICAL FINANCIALS

Company Type: Public

Income Statement

FYE: March 31

	REVENUE ($ mil.)	NET INCOME ($ mil.)	NET PROFIT MARGIN	EMPLOYEES
03/21	69,162	1,029	1.5%	55,114
03/20	92,231	(1,731)	—	55,359
03/19	100,498	2,910	2.9%	54,978
03/18	97,008	3,408	3.5%	54,956
03/17	62,832	1,341	2.1%	47,777
Annual Growth	**2.4%**	**(6.4%)**	—	**3.6%**

2021 Year-End Financials

Debt ratio: 0.2%
Return on equity: 4.9%
Cash ($ mil.): 3,772
Current ratio: 1.14
Long-term debt ($ mil.): 12,827

No. of shares (mil.): —
Dividends
Yield: 0.0%
Payout: 123.9%
Market value ($ mil.): —

	STOCK PRICE ($) FY Close	P/E High/Low		PER SHARE ($) Earnings	Dividends	Book Value
03/21	9.21	0	0	0.32	0.40	6.52
03/20	7.21	—	—	(0.53)	0.41	6.61
03/19	9.00	0	0	0.86	0.36	7.36
03/18	11.80	0	0	1.00	0.32	6.99
03/17	9.82	0	0	0.54	0.30	6.13
Annual Growth	**(1.6%)**	—	—	**(12.3%)**	**7.6%**	**1.5%**

Engie SA

Engie is a European and world leader in low-carbon electricity production centralized and decentralized energy networks and associated services. The company relies on its key business lines (Renewables Decentralized infrastructure Client Solutions Thermal Generation and Energy Supply) to offer its customers competitive high value-added solutions that enable them to achieve their carbon-neutrality targets. Engie operates electricity power plants natural gas terminals and storage facilities in over 40 countries.

Operations

Engie has four Global Business Lines (GBLs): Client Solutions Networks Renewables and Thermal which are designed to support the local teams and encourage cross-cutting performance by proposing an inter-BU strategy for their business contributing to decisions on the allocation of resources between BUs identifying and managing the key cross-cutting digital and excellence programs identifying and implementing worldwide partnerships and supporting measuring and presenting the global performance of their business activities.

Client solutions encompasses services and service packages such as design engineering works operation installation maintenance and facility management as well as asset management activities such as heating and cooling networks dedicated energy generation assets (decentralized energy delivered directly to the client).

Networks comprises the company's electricity and gas infrastructure activities and projects. These activities include the management and development of (i) gas and electricity transportation networks in Europe and Latin America and natural gas distribution networks in Europe Asia and the American continent (ii) natural gas underground storage in Europe and (iii) regasification infrastructure in France and Chile.

Renewables comprises all centralized renewable energy generation activities including financing construction and operation of renewable energy facilities using various energy sources such as hydroelectric onshore wind photovoltaic solar biomass offshore wind geothermal and biogas.

Thermal encompasses all the company's centralized energy generation activities using thermal assets whether contracted or not. It includes the operation of power plants fueled mainly by gas and coal as well as pump-operated storage plants.

Engie's 25 business units have been regrouped into seven reportable segments reflecting the geographic areas where the company operates: USA & Canada (less than 10% of the revenue) France excluding infrastructures (nearly 30%) France infrastructures (more than 10%) Rest of Europe (more than 30%) Latin America (less than 10%) Middle East Asia & Africa (less than 5%).

Geographic Reach

Engie has activities in over 40 countries. Europe accounts for about 75% of sales with France alone accounts for about 40%. North America South America Asia Middle East and Africa accounts for the remaining of sales. Its headquarters are located in France.

Sales and Marketing

ENGIE provides gas and electricity to end-customers worldwide with around 21 million contracts. Nearly half of its customers are located outside France.

Engie records relatively light R&D spend at nearly ?190 million in 2020.

Financial Performance

The company's revenue decreased by 7% to ?55.7 billion in 2020 compared to ?60 billion in the prior year. The decrease was primarily driven by the Covid-19 crisis impacting mainly Supply and Client Solutions activities across all geographies. The company reported a net loss of ?893 million.

Cash held by the company at the end of 2020 was ?2.5 billion higher than the prior year with ?12.9 billion. Cash provided by operations was ?7.6 billion. Cash used by investing and financing activities was ?4 billion and ?562 million respectively.

Strategy

ENGIE launched a renewed strategic focus on its core businesses and skills bringing value-added for the transition. The refocusing was based on a simplification of the business areas around strategic objectives structured by business lines: for Renewables to develop green power generation resources within an integrated system; for Networks to invest in high-performance networks for the energy transition supporting balanced carbon neutral energy mixes; decentralized energy networks and energy services: to propose large-scale integrated solutions based on long-term contracts; for Thermal production and energy supply to develop low-carbon capacity and support the transition of existing power systems; and energy management and nuclear.

Mergers and Acquisitions

In November 2021 Engie and Credit Agricole Assurances announced an agreement to acquire a 97.33% stake of Eolia Renovables from Canada-based Alberta Investment Management Corporation. The transaction includes the ownership and operation of 899 MW of operating assets and a 1.2 GW pipeline of renewable projects. The acquisition is set to boost the company's presence in the Spanish renewables market and accelerate the company's growth and reach its target of 50 GW of renewable capacity by 2025. The transaction will have a ?0.4 billion net financial debt impact for ENGIE.

HISTORY

The first canal in Egypt was dug in the 13th century BC but it was Napoleon who revived the idea of a shorter trade route to India: a canal through Egypt linking the Gulf of Suez with the Mediterranean. Former French diplomat and engineer Ferdinand de Lesseps formed Compagnie Universelle du Canal Maritime de Suez in 1858 to build and eventually operate the canal which opened 11 years later. Egypt's modernization had pushed it into debt and increased its ties to the British government which by 1875 had acquired a 44% stake in the company.

For more than 80 years the Suez Canal was a foreign enclave protected by the British Army since 1936. After Egypt's puppet government fell and as Gamal Abd Al-Nasser assumed power in 1956 British troops exited the Canal Zone which Egypt quickly nationalized. Israel Britain and France attacked but the UN arranged a truce and foreign forces withdrew leaving the Suez in Egypt's control.

With no canal to operate Universelle du Canal Maritime de Suez became Compagnie Financi re de Suez in 1958. A year later it created a bank (which became Banque Indosuez in 1974).

In 1967 Financi re de Suez became the largest shareholder in Soci t Lyonnaise des Eaux et de L'Eclairage a leading French water company. Formed in 1880 Lyonnaise des Eaux had stakes in water (Northumbrian Water) and energy (Elyo). After France's energy firms were nationalized in 1946 Lyonnaise des Eaux dipped deeper into the water industry by acquiring Degr mont (now Ondeo-Degr mont) in 1972. It also purchased stakes in waste management (SITA 1970) and heating systems (Cofreth 1975).

In the 1980s Lyonnaise des Eaux expanded in Spain the UK and the US and diversified into cable TV (1986) and broadcast TV (1987). It merged with construction firm Dumez in 1990.

Meanwhile Financi re de Suez became a financial power when it won a controlling stake in Soci t G n rale de Belgique (SGB) in 1988 and bought Groupe Victoire in 1989. But the two buys left the firm (renamed Compagnie de Suez in 1990) deeply in debt.

Losing money Compagnie de Suez disposed of Victoire (1994) and then the valuable Banque Indosuez (1996). In 1996 the company bought a controlling stake in Belgium's top utility Tractebel (now SUEZ-TRACTEBEL). Compagnie de Suez and Lyonnaise des Eaux merged in 1997 to create Suez Lyonnaise des Eaux. The following year Suez Lyonnaise acquired the rest of SGB and bought the European and Asian operations of waste management giant Browning-Ferris Industries; it also began divesting noncore operations.

Suez Lyonnaise in 1999 expanded its core businesses primarily in the US. The company bought Calgon (water treatment US) and Nalco Chemical (water treatment chemicals US) then merged Calgon into Nalco to form Ondeo Nalco. (The company's name was changed back to Nalco when it was divested in 2003.)

In 2000 Suez Lyonnaise bought United Water Resources (now United Water) and acquired the rest of SITA. Through its Elyo subsidiary Suez Lyonnaise bought out minority shareholders in US-based Trigen Energy. The company also merged its construction unit Groupe GTM with French construction rival VINCI; Suez Lyonnaise then sold the VINCI shares that it received from the transaction.

The next year the company shortened its name to Suez (later modified to SUEZ) as part of a global rebranding effort. It also united its water services operations under the ONDEO brand. In 2002 SUEZ made Tractebel a wholly owned subsidiary

by purchasing the remaining publicly held shares. Also in 2002 SUEZ sold minority stakes in communications equipment manufacturer Sagem (now SAFRAN) steelmaker Arcelor and motorway operator Autopistas Concesionaria Espa 'ola (ACESA).

SUEZ divested most of its 11% stake in Belgian insurance firm Fortis for nearly $2 billion in 2003. It also sold its 79% stake in cable company Coditel that year. In 2003 the company merged Tractebel and SGB (Tractebel's former holding company) to form SUEZ-TRACTEBEL.

Gaz de France was founded in 1946 by the French government to consolidate the more than 500 (mostly coal-fired) gas works that had existed before WWII. From 1949 on Gaz de France focused on upgrading gas plants and local transmission networks. Its first long-distance pipeline was built in 1953 linking Paris to the Lorraine coal gas fields. With the development of the Lacq gas field in southwestern France annual gas sales increased by 300% between 1957 and 1962.

By 1965 nearly half of the French population was supplied with natural gas. Spurred on by the loss of its Algerian colony which held major oil and gas assets the French government pushed for new gas supplies to supplement its Lacq resources. Gaz de France was able to secure a contract with Algerian natural gas supplier Sonatrach in 1965 and in 1967 it signed an import contract with Dutch supplier Gasunie. The company also diversified in the 1960s helping to build a natural gas liquefaction plant in Algeria and a receiving terminal in Le Havre. It also helped pioneer gas storage engineering.

Following the price shock of the Arab oil embargo of the early 1970s Gaz de France stepped up its search for alternative suppliers including contracts with Russia's largest gas producer Soyouzgazexport (in 1976 1980 and 1984) and four separate Norwegian producers Efofisk (1977) Stafjord (1985) Heimdal (1986) and Gullfaks (1987). The company also renewed contracts with its Dutch and Algerian suppliers.

During the 1990s Gaz de France expanded its international operations as deregulation in the industry accelerated. In 1994 the company gained a foothold in eastern Germany's gas sector by buying gas production and storage company Erdgas Erdol GmbH (EEG). Three years later Gaz de France acquired Italian heating and related services firm Agip Servizi and was awarded a joint venture contract to distribute gas in Berlin in 1997 and in the suburbs of Mexico City in 1998.

Through contracts for North Sea oil and gas with Elf Aquitaine (now owned by TOTAL FINA ELF) British-Borneo and Ruhrgas in 1999 the company increased its natural gas supplies. It also established new gas supply contracts with Nigeria and Qatar.

For the first time in its history Gaz de France became an offshore field operator in 2000 by acquiring exploration and production company TransCanada International Netherlands and a 39% stake in Noordgastransport BV an offshore gas pipeline operator.

In 2001 through the purchase of a 10% interest in Petronet LNG Gaz de France embarked on a project to import liquefied natural gas from Qatar to India.

France's energy and environmental services giants came together when SUEZ merged with Gaz de France in 2008 to form GDF SUEZ. As part of the merger agreement and in order to clear hurdles set up by the EU competition policy SUEZ then spun off its waste and water unit SUEZ Environnement.

Following the 2008 merger of Gaz de France with SUEZ in a move to expand geographically GDF SUEZ acquired a 90% stake in Izmit Gaz

Dagitim San Ve Tic AS (Turkey's third-largest natural gas distributor) for $232 million.

In 2009 the company made further geographic realignments prompted by the regulatory requirements of the European Commission for GDF SUEZ and Germany's E.ON to allow for more competition in their major markets by swapping some generation capacity. It acquired from E.ON 860 MW of Germany-based conventional power plants 132 MW of hydroelectric plants and through subsidiary Electrabel access to 770 MW of nuclear power. In return GDF SUEZ sold to E.ON a similar amount of power generation capacity in France and the Benelux countries.

Ramping up its nuclear assets in 2011 GDF SUEZ formed a joint venture with IBERDROLA and Scottish and Southern Energy. NuGeneration planned to develop up to 3600 MW of nuclear power in the UK. Late in 2011 SSE announced plans to sell its 25 percent in NuGen to GDF SUEZ and IBERDROLA and return to its renewable energy strategy.

EXECUTIVES

Director - Representative of the Employees, Alain Beullier

Director - Representative of the French State, Isabelle Bui

Director - Representative of the Employees, Christophe Aubert

Chief Executive Officer, Catherine Macgregor

Independent Director, Fabrice Bregier, $104,255 total compensation

Independent Director, Francoise Malrieu, $171,480 total compensation

Executive Vice President in charge of Networks activities, Member of the Executive Committee, Edouard Sauvage

Director - Representative of the Employees, Philippe Lepage

Independent Director, Marie-Jose Nadeau, $189,584 total compensation

Director - Representative of the French State, Marie-noelle Jego-laveissiere, $85,421 total compensation

Director - Representative of the French State, Patrice Durand, $88,617 total compensation

CFO, EVP, United Kingdom and Ireland, Paulo Almirante

Executive Vice President in charge of Communications and Brand, Member of the Executive Board, Ana Busto

Independent Director, Peter Ricketts of Shortlands, $111,288 total compensation

Executive Vice President in charge of Strategy & Innovation, Industrial Development, Research & Technology, and Purchasing, and in charge of the Africa BU, Member of the Executive Board, Shankar Krishnamoorthy

EVP, Elengy, GRDF, GRTgaz, Storengy, China, and APAC; Head, Gas and Power Networks Global Business Line, Didier Holleaux

Executive Vice President supervising the UK and LATAM (Latin America), Member of the Executive Board, Franck Bruel

Executive Vice President in charge of the Cities & Local Authorities, Industries, Tertiary & Proximity BUs, Member of the Executive Board, Wilfrid Petrie

Director - Representative of the Employees, Christophe Agogue

Executive Vice President in charge of the GEM (Global Energy Management), Generation Europe, BtoC France and Benelux BUs, and head of the Thermal Global Business Line, Member of the Executive Board, Pierre Chareyre

Independent Director, Ross Mcinnes, $171,480 total compensation

Executive Vice President in charge of Digital and Information Systems, Member of the Executive Board, Yves Le Gelard

Independent Chairman of the Board, Jean-Pierre Clamadieu, $256,750 total compensation

Auditors: ERNST & YOUNG et Autres

LOCATIONS

HQ: Engie SA
1, Place Samuel de Champlain, Courbevoie 92400
Phone: (33) 1 44 22 00 00
Web: www.engie.com

2018 Sales

	% of total
Europe	
France	41
Belgium	10
Other EU countries	26
Other European countries	1
Asia Middle East and Oceania	8
North America	6
South America	7
Africa	1
Total	**100**

COMPETITORS

CLP HOLDINGS LIMITED
ENABLE OKLAHOMA INTRASTATE TRANSMISSION LLC
ETP LEGACY LP
Electrabel
Fortum Oyj
IBERDROLA SOCIEDAD ANONIMA
Infraestructura Energetica Nova S.A.P.I. de C.V.
NORTHERN NATURAL GAS COMPANY
OMV Aktiengesellschaft
PNM RESOURCES INC.
TECHNIP
VINCI

HISTORICAL FINANCIALS

Company Type: Public

Income Statement
FYE: December 31

	REVENUE ($ mil.)	NET INCOME ($ mil.)	NET PROFIT MARGIN	EMPLOYEES
12/20	68,422	(1,885)	—	172,703
12/19	67,431	1,104	1.6%	171,103
12/18	69,394	1,182	1.7%	249,795
12/17	77,953	1,705	2.2%	155,128
12/16	70,363	(438)	—	153,090
Annual Growth	(0.7%)	—	—	3.1%

2020 Year-End Financials

Debt ratio: 28.8%
Return on equity: (-4.9%)
Cash ($ mil.): 15,930
Current ratio: 1.11
Long-term debt ($ mil.): 34,609

No. of shares (mil.): —
Dividends
Yield: 0.0%
Payout: —
Market value ($ mil.): —

	STOCK PRICE ($) FY Close	P/E High/Low	PER SHARE ($) Earnings	Dividends	Book Value
12/20	15.30	— —	(0.87)	0.65	14.70
12/19	16.17	50 41	0.38	1.26	15.39
12/18	14.32	46 35	0.42	0.84	16.88
12/17	17.17	35 25	0.54	1.03	18.39
12/16	12.74	— —	(0.24)	1.04	17.43
Annual Growth	4.7%	— —	—	(11.0%)	(4.2%)

ENI S.p.A.

Eni is one of the world's major oil and gas suppliers engaging in exploration development production and trading activities worldwide. Downstream its portfolio of refineries transmission networks and power generation plants sell fuels/biofuels chemical products lubricants and gas & power. Outside its home country of Italy Eni is active Africa Europe and North America as well as other productive gas regions such as Kazakhstan and Venezuela. Europe which accounts for most of Eni's sales is home to more than 5400 service stations. The company has 4.7 GW of installed energy generation capacity and more than 7 billion barrels of oil equivalent proved hydrocarbon reserves.

Operations

Eni has four reporting segments: Gas & Power; Exploration & Production; Refining & Marketing and Chemicals; and Corporate and Other activities.

Gas & Power generates more than 50% of Eni's total sales. The segment consists of Eni's supply and marketing of natural gas and LNG and the supply production and marketing of power. Natural gas and power reach wholesale and retail customers while LNG is sold to businesses/other entities only.

The Refining & Marketing and Chemicals segment accounts for around 25% of sales and comprises Eni's manufacturing supply and distribution and marketing activities of oil and chemical products.

Exploration & Production generates about 25% of sales. Explores for develops and produces crude oil LNG and natural gas including the construction and operations of liquefaction plants.

Corporate and other activities generates more than 1% of sales. It provide services to the operating subsidiaries comprising holding financing and treasury IT HR real estate legal assistance captive insurance as well as the results of the Group environmental.

Taking an Upstream-Downstream view of Eni the company's Upstream units have onshore and offshore projects that pick oil exploration blocks drill wells and manage the whole hydrocarbon production operations. In the Midstream and Downstream sectors Eni manages the transportation and storage of hydrocarbons as well as the refining marketing and distribution of oil products.

Geographic Reach

Based in Rome Italy Eni is active in more than 65 countries worldwide across Europe (Italy Norway and the UK) Africa (Algeria Angola Congo Egypt Ghana Libya Mozambique Nigeria) the US Venezuela and Kazakhstan. Of Eni's 5400 service stations in Europe about 4200 are in Italy.

Europe accounts for nearly 70% of annual sales Africa generates about 15% of sales Asia more than 10% of sales and the Americas gives in roughly 5% of sales.

Sales and Marketing

Eni spent ?176 million ?161 million and ?102 million in marketing expense for fiscal years 2019 2018 and 2017 respectively.

Financial Performance

Note: Growth rates may differ after conversion to US Dollars.

Total revenues amounted to ?71.0 billion reporting a decrease of 8%. Sales from operations in the full year of 2019 (?70.0 billion) decreased by ?5.9 billion or down by 8% from 2018.

In the full year 2019 the group reported net profit attributable to Eni's shareholders of ?148 million (?4.1 billion in the full year 2018). The reported operating profit was ?6.4 billion approximately 36% lower than in 2018 down by ?3.6 billion; approximately 80% of the decline is related to the E&P segment.

Eni's cash on hand fell during 2019 ending the year ?4.9 billion higher at ?6.0 billion. The company's operations generated ?12.4 billion while its investing activities used ?11.4 billion and its financing used ?5.8 billion. Its biggest cash uses were investments in tangible assets long-term debt repayments and dividends.

Strategy

Eni's business model is focused on creating value for its stakeholders and shareholders through a strong presence along the whole value chain.

Firstly Eni's business is constantly focused on the operational excellence. A continuous commitment to the valorization of people and in HSE to the safeguard of health and safety and environmental protection; the efficiency and resilience of operations thanks to which Eni has accelerated projects' time-to-market reducing its break-even; a solid financial discipline; and the maximum attention to the integrity and respect for human rights.

Secondly Eni's business model envisages a path to decarbonization with the ambition to lead the company to become carbon neutral in the long-term.

Lastly Eni's value creation will leverage on the alliances for the promotion of local development in its countries of operation. Eni is not only committed to address the valorization of resources of producing countries allocating its unity initiatives - from diversification of local economies to health projects education access to water and hygiene. This distinctive approach called Dual Flag is based on collaborations with institutions cooperation agencies and local stakeholders in order to identify certain necessary actions to meet the needs of communities in line with the National Development Plans and the 2030 UN Agenda.

Mergers and Acquisitions

Eni completed its merger of its Eni Norge AS with Point Resources and HitecVision to form Var Energi which will operate as an independent exploration and production energy company of hydrocarbons in Norway. Eni owns 69.6 percent of Var Energu with 30.4 percent belonging to HitecVision. The newly formed company will have 17 oil and gas fields stretching from the Barents Sea to the North Sea and reserves around 1250 mboe.

HISTORY

Although the Italian parliament formed Ente Nazionale Idrocarburi (National Hydrocarbon Agency) in 1953 Enrico Mattei is the true father of Eni. In 1945 Mattei a partisan leader during WWII was appointed northern commissioner of Agip a state-owned petroleum company founded in 1926 by Mussolini and ordered to liquidate the company. Mattei instead ordered the exploration of the Po Valley where workers found methane gas deposits in 1946.

When Eni was created in 1953 Mattei was named president. His job was to find energy resources for an oil-poor country. He initiated a series of joint ventures with several Middle Eastern and African nations offering better deals than his large oil company rivals which he dubbed the Seven Sisters.

Mattei didn't stick to energy: By the time he died in a mysterious plane crash in 1962 Eni had acquired machinery manufacturer Pignone finance company Sofid Milan newspaper Il Giorno and textile company Lane Rossi. Eni grew during the 1960s partly because of a deal made for Soviet crude in 1958 and a joint venture with Esso in 1963. It also expanded its chemical activities.

By the early 1970s losses in Eni's chemical and textile operations the oil crisis and the Italian government's dumping of unprofitable companies on Eni hurt its bottom line. Former finance minister Franco Reviglio took over in 1983 and began cutting inefficient operations.

EniChem merged with Montedison Italy's largest private chemical company in 1988 but clashes between the public agency and the private company made Montedison sell back its stake in 1990. Eni became a joint stock company in 1992 but the government retained a majority stake.

Franco Bernabe took over Eni following a 1993 bribery scandal and began cutting noncore businesses. The Italian government began selling Eni stock in 1995. In 1996 Eni signed on to develop Libyan gas resources and build a pipeline to Italy. A year later the company merged its Agipa exploration and production subsidiary into its main operations. Eni also took a 35% stake in Italian telecom company Albacom (which has since been sold to British Telecom Group).

The government cut its stake in Eni from 51% to 38% in 1998. That year Vittorio Mincato a company veteran succeeded Bernabe as CEO. In 1999 Eni and Russia's RAO Gazprom the world's largest natural gas production firm agreed to build a controversial $3 billion natural gas pipeline stretching from Russia to Turkey. Eni agreed to invest $5.5 billion to develop oil and gas reserves in Libya; it also sold interests in Saipem and Nuovo Pignone as well as some of its Italian service stations.

In 2000 Eni paid about $910 million for a 33% stake in Galp a Portuguese oil and gas company that also has natural gas utility operations. Also that year Eni bought British-Borneo Oil & Gas in a $1.2 billion deal and in 2001 it paid $4 billion for UK independent exploration and production company LASMO topping a bid by US-based Amerada Hess.

The Italian government sold off another 5% of Eni in 2001 reducing its stake to about 30% and announced that it was considering selling its entire investment. In an effort to reduce noncore holdings the company sold property management subsidiary Immobiliare Metanopoli to Goldman Sachs. Also that year Eni sold a minority stake in its gas pipeline unit Snam Rete Gas to the public.

In 2002 Eni entered discussions to acquire Enterprise Oil but lost out to a rival bid from Royal Dutch Shell. Later that year Eni's oil field services unit Saipem gained control of Bouygues Offshore.In 2006 Eni and Gazprom formed an international alliance to launch joint mid and downstream gas projects and collaborate in upstream and in technological activities.

EXECUTIVES

Non-Executive Independent Director, Filippo Giansante
Non-Executive Independent Director, Nathalie Tocci
Non-Executive Independent Director, Ada Lucia De Cesaris
Head of Investor Relations, Martina Opizzi
Technology, R&D & Digital Director, Francesca Zarri
Non-Executive Independent Director, Raphael Louis Vermeir
External Communication Director, Erika Mandraffino
Chief Executive Officer, Director and General Manager, Claudio Descalzi, $428,416 total compensation
Chairman, Lucia Calvosa
Director Corporate Affairs and Governance, Roberto Ulissi
Legal Affairs & Commercial Negotiation Director, Stefano Speroni
Internal Audit Director, Marco Petracchini
Non-Executive Independent Director, Karina Litvack, $94,506 total compensation
Non-Executive Independent Director, Pietro Guindani, $94,506 total compensation
Human Capital & Procurement Coordination Director, Claudio Granata
Chief Operating Officer - Natural Resources, Alessandro Puliti
Chief Financial Officer, Francesco Gattei
Chief Operating Officer - Energy Evolution, Giuseppe Ricci
Public Affairs Director, Lapo Pistelli
Executive Vice President, Integrated Compliance, Luca Franceschini
Non-Executive Independent Director, Emanuele Piccinno
Auditors: PricewaterhouseCoopers SpA

LOCATIONS

HQ: ENI S.p.A.
 1, piazzale Enrico Mattei, Rome 00144
Phone: (39) 2 52061632   **Fax:** (39) 6 59822575
Web: www.eni.com

2018 Sales

	% of total
Europe	
Italy	33
Other EU countries	27
Other countries	9
Asia	13
Africa	11
Americas	7
Total	**100**

PRODUCTS/OPERATIONS

2018 Sales

	% of total
Gas & power	57
Refining & marketing and chemicals	30
Exploration & production	13
Corporate & other activities	-
Total	**100**

Selected Subsidiaries and Affiliates

Distrigas NV (gas Belgium)
EniPower SpA (power generation)
Italgas SpA (natural gas supply)
Saipem SpA (42.9% oil field services)
Snam Rete Gas SpA (52.5% gas pipeline)
Snamprogetti SpA (contracting and engineering)

COMPETITORS

CHEVRON CORPORATION
COSMO OIL CO. LTD.
EXXON MOBIL CORPORATION
Equinor ASA
GAZPROM NEFT PAO
INDIAN OIL CORPORATION LIMITED
LUKOIL PAO
MOL Magyar Olaj- es G zipari Nyilv nosan M k ¶d
Petroleo Brasileiro S A Petrobras

HISTORICAL FINANCIALS
Company Type: Public

Income Statement   FYE: December 31

	REVENUE ($ mil.)	NET INCOME ($ mil.)	NET PROFIT MARGIN	EMPLOYEES
12/20	55,163	(10,597)	—	31,495
12/19	79,762	166	0.2%	32,053
12/18	88,109	4,725	5.4%	31,701
12/17	85,083	4,044	4.8%	32,934
12/16	59,861	(1,545)	—	33,536
Annual Growth	(2.0%)	—	—	(1.6%)

2020 Year-End Financials

Debt ratio: 29.8%	No. of shares (mil.): —
Return on equity: (-20.2%)	Dividends
Cash ($ mil.): 11,552	Yield: 4.1%
Current ratio: 1.39	Payout: —
Long-term debt ($ mil.): 26,871	Market value ($ mil.): —

	STOCK PRICE ($) FY Close	P/E High/Low	PER SHARE ($) Earnings	Dividends	Book Value
12/20	20.60	— —	(2.97)	0.85	12.85
12/19	30.96	895 726	0.04	1.33	15.03
12/18	31.50	33 26	1.32	1.37	16.22
12/17	33.19	40 33	1.13	1.39	15.99
12/16	32.24	— —	(0.43)	1.21	15.55
Annual Growth	(10.6%)	— —	—	(8.3%)	(4.7%)

Equinor ASA

Auditors: Ernst & Young AS

LOCATIONS

HQ: Equinor ASA
Forusbeen 50, Stavanger N-4035
Phone: (47) 51 99 00 00   **Fax:** (47) 51 99 00 50
Web: www.statoil.com

HISTORICAL FINANCIALS
Company Type: Public

Income Statement   FYE: December 31

	REVENUE ($ mil.)	NET INCOME ($ mil.)	NET PROFIT MARGIN	EMPLOYEES
12/20	45,818	(5,510)	—	20,245
12/19	64,357	1,843	2.9%	21,412
12/18	79,593	7,535	9.5%	20,525
12/17	61,187	4,590	7.5%	20,245
12/16	45,873	(2,922)	—	20,539
Annual Growth	(0.0%)	—	—	(0.4%)

2020 Year-End Financials

Debt ratio: 27.6%	No. of shares (mil.): —
Return on equity: (-14.6%)	Dividends
Cash ($ mil.): 6,757	Yield: 4.3%
Current ratio: 1.58	Payout: —
Long-term debt ($ mil.): 29,118	Market value ($ mil.): —

	STOCK PRICE ($) FY Close	P/E High/Low	PER SHARE ($) Earnings	Dividends	Book Value
12/20	16.42	— —	(1.69)	0.71	10.43
12/19	19.91	43 29	0.56	1.01	12.36
12/18	21.17	13 9	2.27	0.91	12.91
12/17	21.42	15 12	1.40	0.76	12.04
12/16	18.24	— —	(0.91)	0.69	10.85
Annual Growth	(2.6%)	— —	—	0.9%	(1.0%)

Ericsson

Auditors: Deloitte AB

LOCATIONS

HQ: Ericsson
Torshamnsgatan 21, Kista, Stockholm SE-164 83
Phone: (46) 10 719 0000
Web: www.ericsson.com

HISTORICAL FINANCIALS
Company Type: Public

Income Statement   FYE: December 31

	REVENUE ($ mil.)	NET INCOME ($ mil.)	NET PROFIT MARGIN	EMPLOYEES
12/20	28,443	2,139	7.5%	100,824
12/19	24,425	238	1.0%	99,417
12/18	23,553	(729)	—	95,359
12/17	24,535	(4,291)	—	100,735
12/16	24,558	189	0.8%	111,464
Annual Growth	3.7%	83.4%	—	(2.5%)

2020 Year-End Financials

Debt ratio: 1.3%	No. of shares (mil.): —
Return on equity: 20.6%	Dividends
Cash ($ mil.): 5,337	Yield: 1.3%
Current ratio: 1.31	Payout: 24.7%
Long-term debt ($ mil.): 2,719	Market value ($ mil.): —

	STOCK PRICE ($) FY Close	P/E High/Low	PER SHARE ($) Earnings	Dividends	Book Value
12/20	11.95	3 1	0.64	0.16	3.19
12/19	8.78	16 12	0.07	0.11	2.68
12/18	8.87	— —	(0.22)	0.12	2.95
12/17	6.68	— —	(1.31)	0.07	3.69
12/16	5.83	17 9	0.06	0.27	4.72
Annual Growth	19.7%	— —	83.0%	(12.3%)	(9.3%)

Erste Group Bank AG

Erste Group Bank is the holding company of Erste Bank Austria's first savings bank founded in 1819. However the company has grown beyond its home country to number about 2195 branches throughout Central and Eastern European that serve some 16 million customers. The company has operating subsidiaries in Austria Croatia the Czech Republic Hungary Slovakia Serbia and Romania as well as an indirect presence in four other countries in the region. Erste Group banks provide financial services such as savings and lending to individuals and small to medium-size businesses. Half of its sales were generated from Austria.

Operations

The company operates in two geographic segments: Austria and Central and Eastern Europe both generated half of the company's sales.

Its Austria segment comprises of the Erste Bank Oesterreich & Subsidiaries (EBOe & Subsidiaries) which includes the Erste Bank der oesterreichischen Sparkassen AG (Erste Bank Oesterreich) and its main subsidiaries (e.g. sBausparkasse Salzburger Sparkasse Tiroler Sparkasse Sparkasse Hainburg); the Savings Banks segment which includes those savings banks that are members of the Haftungsverbund (cross-guarantee system) of the Austrian savings banks sector; and other Aus-

tria segment comprises Erste Group Bank AG (Holding) with its Corporates and Group Markets business Erste Group Immorent GmbH Erste Asset Management GmbH and Intermarket Bank AG.

Its Central and Eastern Europe (CEE) consists of the following six operating segments covering Erste Group's banking subsidiaries located in the respective CEE countries: Czech Republic (comprising Cesk ̈ sporitelna Group) Slovakia (comprising Slovensk ̈ sporitelna Group) Romania (comprising Banca Comerciala Romana Group) Hungary (comprising Erste Bank Hungary Group) Croatia (comprising Erste Bank Croatia Group) and Serbia (comprising Erste Bank Serbia Group).

Overall net interest income generated over 65% of sales net fee & commission income with nearly 30% and net trading result and gains/losses from financial instruments at FVPL with roughly 5%.

Geographic Reach

Vienna Austria-based Erste Bank is home to some 845 branches in Austria the most of any country. The Czech Republic has nearly 440 Erste branches Romania some 370 Slovakia around 205 Croatia about 140 Hungary over 105 and Serbia nearly 90.

Sales and Marketing

The company serves some 3.8 million customers in Austria 4.5 million in Czech Republic 2.2 million in Slovakia 0.9 million in Hungary 2.9 million in Romania 0.5 million in Serbia and 1.3 in Croatia.

Its advertising and marketing expenses for the years 2020 and 2019 were ?154.6 million and ?200.1 million respectively.

Financial Performance

The company's revenue for fiscal 2020 increased to ?6.8 billion compared from the prior year with ?6.7 billion.

Profit for fiscal 2020 decreased to ?783.1 million compared from the prior year with ?1.5 billion.

Cash held by the company at the end of fiscal 2020 increased to ?35.8 billion. Cash provided by operations and financing activities were ?24.5 billion and ?1.1 billion respectively. Cash used for investing activities was ?351.6 million mainly for acquisition of property and equipment and intangible assets.

Strategy

Erste Group strives to be the leading retail and corporate bank in the eastern part of the European Union including Austria. To achieve this goal Erste Group aims to support its retail corporate and public sector customers in realizing their ambitions and ensuring financial health by offering excellent financial advice and solutions lending responsibly and providing a safe harbor for deposits. Erste Group's business activities will continue to contribute to economic growth and financial stability and thus to prosperity in its region. Erste Group's strategy is based on three pillars: efficiency; digital transformation; and growth.

HISTORY

In 1819 a bank was born and its name was Erste oesterreichische Spar-Cassa. Called Die Erste for short the bank was Austria's first commercial and savings bank. Unlike Austria's community savings banks Die Erste was independent — not backed by government guarantees.

For more than 150 years Die Erste operated as a local savings bank serving Vienna. Then in 1979 the Austrian government passed a law that would alter the face of the banking industry in that country. The Banking Act of 1979 placed banks and savings institutions in direct competition with each other by allowing them both to take part in all aspects of the banking business. As a result of the enhanced competition Die Erste began expanding its domestic branch network.

Meanwhile the Austrian savings banks had established their own central institution in 1937 and called it Girovereinigung der –sterreichischen Sparkassen or Girozentrale for short. Girozentrale focused on managing the liquidity reserves of the savings banks and helping them with their syndication and securities businesses. The bank also endeavored to improve the non-cash payment system and to promote mortgage savings. Concentrating on international and investment banking rather than retail banking Girozentrale eventually became the country's third-largest bank.

Throughout the late 1980s and into the 1990s rumors began to spread about a possible merger between Girozentrale and Die Erste (both were associated with the nation's conservative People's Party). In 1992 Girozentrale merged with –sterreichisches Credit-Institut (–CI) to create GiroCredit giving the central savings bank a branch network for the first time. But it also made GiroCredit a direct competitor with its two largest shareholders — Bank Austria (now part of HypoVereinsbank) and Die Erste who were also fierce competitors with each other.

Between 1992 and 1994 Die Erste and Bank Austria struggled to find a solution to the problem of GiroCredit's ownership. In 1994 Bank Austria emerged the victor by winning the majority stake in GiroCredit in a move that was characterized by Die Erste as "unfriendly."

Throughout the next two years Die Erste attempted to secure a stake in Creditanstalt Austria's second-biggest bank as the Austrian government began moves to privatize it. Die Erste acted as a part of a consortium of Austrian German and Italian entities interested in obtaining stakes in the bank. But in 1997 Bank Austria won that battle too managing to take over Creditanstalt. In turn Die Erste bought Bank Austria's majority stake in GiroCredit. The resulting company was given the name Erste Bank which went public that year in the largest stock issue in Austrian history. In 1998 it became the first major Austrian company to allow for the election of small shareholder representatives to its supervisory board.

In 2000 Erste Bank bought a majority stake in Cesk Sporitelna the largest retail bank in the Czech Republic from the Czech government. Later in the year the Slovak government allowed Erste Bank to become a major shareholder in the previously state-owned Slovensk sporitel'na. Erste Bank was also one of several Austrian banks to be accused by the European Commission of fixing foreign exchange fees.

In 2001 Erste Bank took control of Slovensk Sporitel'na and acquired majority ownership of Tiroler Sparkasse Bank AG. The following year Erste Bank took full control of Czech Republic-based Czeska Sporitelna. Ever acquisitive in 2005 the company completed its acquisition of Serbia's Novosadska banka.

Erste in 2006 acquiered Romanian bank Banca Comerciala Romana the largest bank in that country and previously state-owned.

Erste switched to a holding company structure in 2008. That year the company also sold most of its insurance business to Vienna Insurance Group.

EXECUTIVES

Independent Member of the Supervisory Board, Matthias Bulach

Independent Member of the Supervisory Board, Henrietta Egerth-Stadlhuber

Chief Risk Officer, Member of the Management Board, Alexandra Habeler-Drabek, $391,827 total compensation

Independent Second Vice Chairman of the Supervisory Board, Maximilian Hardegg

Independent Member of the Supervisory Board, Employee Representative, Andreas Lachs

Independent Member of the Supervisory Board, Employee Representative, Karin Zeisel

Independent Member of the Supervisory Board, Employee Representative, Barbara Pichler

Independent Member of the Supervisory Board, Employee Representative, Jozef Pinter

Independent Member of the Supervisory Board, Marion Khuny

Independent Member of the Supervisory Board, Elisabeth Krainer Senger-Weiss

Chairman of the Supervisory Board, Friedrich Roedler

Independent Member of the Supervisory Board, Employee Representative, Markus Haag

Independent Member of the Supervisory Board, Employee Representative, Regina Haberhauer

Chief Corporates and Capital Markets Officer, Member of the Management Board, Ingo Bleier, $391,827 total compensation

Chief Operating Officer, Member of the Management Board, David O'Mahony

Chief Financial Officer, Member of the Management Board, Stefan Dorefler, $391,827 total compensation

Independent Member of the Supervisory Board, Michele Sutter Ruedisser

Independent Member of the Supervisory Board, John Stack

First Vice Chairman of the Supervisory Board, Jan Homan

Chairman of the Management Board, Chief Executive Officer, Bernhard Spalt, $391,827 total compensation

Auditors: Sparkassen-Prufungsverband (Prufungsstelle)

LOCATIONS

HQ: Erste Group Bank AG
  Am Belvedere 1, Vienna A-1100
Phone: (43) 5 0100 10100
Web: www.erstegroup.com

PRODUCTS/OPERATIONS

2017 Sales

	% of total
Net interest income	67
Net fee & commission income	36
Net trading result	1
Total	**100**

Selected Subsidiaries

Banca Comerciala Romana S.A. (BCR)
Ceská Sporitelna (Czech Republic)
Erste Bank a.d. Novi Sad (Serbia)
Erste Bank Croatia (Erste & Steiermärkische Bank d.d.)
Erste Bank der oesterreichen Sparkassen AG
  Autoleasing EBV
  Sparkasse Salzburg
  Wohnbaubank
Erst Bank Hungary Nyrt.
Erste Bank Ukraine (formerly Bank Prestige)
Slovenská sporitelna a.s. (Slovakia)

COMPETITORS

BANK OF CHINA LIMITED
Bank Leumi le-Israel Ltd.
Bayerische Landesbank
COMMONWEALTH BANK OF AUSTRALIA
DZ BANK AG Deutsche
KBC Groep
KfW
Nordea Bank AB
Portigon AG
Raiffeisen Zentralbank –sterreich Aktiengesellschaft
UNICREDIT SPA
WESTPAC BANKING CORPORATION

HISTORICAL FINANCIALS

Company Type: Public

Income Statement

	ASSETS ($ mil.)	NET INCOME ($ mil.)	INCOME AS % OF ASSETS	EMPLOYEES
12/20	340,442	961	0.3%	45,690
12/19	275,855	1,650	0.6%	47,284
12/18	271,172	2,053	0.8%	47,397
12/17	264,516	1,577	0.6%	47,702
12/16	219,863	1,335	0.6%	47,034
Annual Growth	11.6%	(7.9%)	—	(0.7%)

FYE: December 31

2020 Year-End Financials

Return on assets: 0.3%	Dividends
Return on equity: 4.7%	Yield: —
Long-term debt ($ mil.): —	Payout: —
No. of shares (mil.): 405	Market value ($ mil.): 6,147
Sales ($ mil): 9,866	

	STOCK PRICE ($) FY Close	P/E High/Low		PER SHARE ($) Earnings	Dividends	Book Value
12/20	15.16	14	6	1.93	0.00	52.48
12/19	18.76	7	5	3.63	0.76	42.97
12/18	16.53	6	4	4.60	0.68	40.29
12/17	21.80	8	6	3.52	0.57	40.64
12/16	14.62	5	3	3.09	0.25	32.13
Annual Growth	0.9%	—	(11.2%)	—	13.1%	

Essity Aktiebolag (Publ)

Auditors: Ernst & Young AB

LOCATIONS

HQ: Essity Aktiebolag (Publ)
  P.O. Box 200, Stockholm SE-101 23
Phone: (46) 8 788 51 00
Web: www.essity.com

HISTORICAL FINANCIALS

Company Type: Public

Income Statement

	REVENUE ($ mil.)	NET INCOME ($ mil.)	NET PROFIT MARGIN	EMPLOYEES
12/20	14,901	1,251	8.4%	46,084
12/19	13,864	990	7.1%	45,980
12/18	13,238	880	6.7%	47,000
12/17	13,317	989	7.4%	47,700
12/16	11,168	419	3.8%	0
Annual Growth	7.5%	31.5%	—	—

FYE: December 31

2020 Year-End Financials

Debt ratio: 2.8%	No. of shares (mil.): 702
Return on equity: 18.8%	Dividends
Cash ($ mil.): 609	Yield: —
Current ratio: 1.05	Payout: 46.3%
Long-term debt ($ mil.): 4,342	Market value ($ mil.): —

Eurobank Ergasias Services & Holdings SA

Eurobank Ergasias has a lot of branches for shaking the money tree. The bank operates some 500 branches business centers and ATMs in its home country Greece and about 1250 more in about half-a-dozen other central and southeastern European countries. In addition to traditional retail banking and consumer lending Eurobank offers business banking factoring insurance leasing investment banking and wealth management services. The bank was founded in 1990 as Euromerchant Bank. Swiss-based EFG Bank European Financial Group owns about 44% of Eurobank.

EXECUTIVES

Non-Executive Member of the Board of Directors, Bradley Martin
Deputy Chief Executive Officer, Group Chief Operating Officer and International Activities, Member of the Executive Board; Executive Member of the Board of Directors, Stavros Ioannou
Chairman of the Executive Board, Chief Executive Officer, Executive Member of the Board of Directors, Fokion Karavias
General Manager Group Risk Management, Group Chief Risk Officer, Member of the Executive Board, Christos Adam
Independent Non-Executive Member of the Board of Directors, Jawaid Mirza
Independent Non-Executive Member of the Board of Directors, Rajeev Kakar
Deputy Chief Executive Officer, Head of Group Corporate and Investment Banking, Member of the Executive Board, Executive Member of the Board of Directors, Konstantinos Vassiliou
General Manager of Group Finance, Group Chief Financial Officer, Member of the Executive Board, Harris Kokologiannis
Independent Non-Executive Member of the Board of Directors, Rena Panou
Independent Non-Executive Member of the Board of Directors, Alice Gregoriadi
Non-Executive Vice Chairman of the Board, Georgios Chryssikos
Independent Non-Executive Member of the Board of Directors, Cinzia Basile
Non-Executive Chairman of the Board, Georgios Zanias
Independent Non-Executive Member of the Board of Directors, Irene Rouvitha-panou
Auditors: KPMG Certified Auditors S.A.

LOCATIONS

HQ: Eurobank Ergasias Services & Holdings SA
8 Othonos Street, Athens 105 57
Phone: (30) 214 40 61000   **Fax:** (30) 210 323 3866
Web: www.eurobank.gr

COMPETITORS

BANCOLOMBIA S A
BANK OF CYPRUS PUBLIC COMPANY LIMITED
BARCLAYS BANK PLC
Banque de Montreal
Cesk   sporitelna a.s.
Grupo Elektra S.A.B. de C.V.
Grupo Financiero Banorte S.A.B. de C.V.
MIZRAHI TEFAHOT BANK LTD
NORTHERN BANK LIMITED
ORIENTAL BANK OF COMMERCE
STANDARD CHARTERED PLC
W   stenrot & W   rttembergische AG

HISTORICAL FINANCIALS
Company Type: Public

Income Statement   FYE: December 31

	ASSETS ($ mil.)	NET INCOME ($ mil.)	INCOME AS % OF ASSETS	EMPLOYEES
12/20	83,121	(1,488)	—	11,501
12/19	72,711	142	0.2%	13,456
12/18	66,403	104	0.2%	13,162
12/17	71,960	124	0.2%	15,816
12/16	70,103	242	0.3%	16,285
Annual Growth	4.4%	—	—	(8.3%)

2020 Year-End Financials

Return on assets: (-1.8%)   Dividends
Return on equity: (-20.3%)   Yield: 0.7%
Long-term debt ($ mil.): —   Payout: —
No. of shares (mil.): —   Market value ($ mil.): —
Sales ($ mil): 3,880

	STOCK PRICE ($) FY Close	P/E High/Low		PER SHARE ($) Earnings	Dividends	Book Value
12/20	0.35	—	—	(0.41)	0.00	1.74
12/19	0.48	14	6	0.04	0.00	2.02
12/18	0.25	15	6	0.05	0.00	2.64
12/17	0.52	12	6	0.06	0.00	3.92
12/16	0.35	6	2	0.12	0.00	3.25
Annual Growth	(0.3%)	—	—	—	—	(14.5%)

Everest Re Group Ltd

Everest Re Group is the holding company for Everest Reinsurance Company (Everest Re) an underwriter of property/casualty reinsurance and insurance. Everest Re markets its reinsurance products to US and international insurance companies both directly and through independent brokers. Under the reinsurance arrangements Everest Re assumes the risks on policies written by its clients. The company offers specialized underwriting in several areas including property/casualty marine aviation and surety and accident and health.

Operations
Effective January 1 2020 Everest Re revised it reporting segments to Insurance Operations and Reinsurance Operations.

The Insurance operation generates roughly 70% of gross written premiums and writes property and casualty insurance directly and through brokers surplus lines brokers and general agents within the US Canada and Europe through its offices in the US Canada Ireland and a branch located in Zurich. The Reinsurance operation (about 30% of gross written premium) writes worldwide property and casualty reinsurance and specialty lines of business on both a treaty and facultative basis through reinsurance brokers as well as directly with ceding companies. Business is written in the US Bermuda and Ireland offices as well as through branches in Canada Singapore and the United Kingdom.

The company generates some 90% from premiums while net investment income with more than 5% and net realized capital gains account for the rest.

Geographic Reach
Everest Re is co-headquartered in Bermuda and New Jersey. It has offices in Bermuda Brussels Atlanta Boston Houston Indianapolis Los Angeles California Pennsylvania Connecticut Florida Chicago Dublin London Miami New York Sao Paulo Singapore Toronto and Zurich.

The company's international business is conducted through its Everest Re units in Canada Brazil and Singapore as well as through its Bermuda Re and Everest International units. Everest Re Group's traditional insurance offerings are provided in the US through Everest Security Everest Denali Everest Premier Everest National Insurance and Everest Indemnity Insurance.

Sales and Marketing
The company writes business on a worldwide basis for many different customers and lines of business thereby obtaining a broad spread of risk. The company is not substantially dependent on any single customer small group of customers line of business or geographic area. For the 2020 calendar year no single customer (ceding company or insured) generated about 5% of the company's gross written premiums. Approximately 65% 30% and 5% of the company's 2020 gross written premiums were written in the broker reinsurance insurance and direct reinsurance markets respectively.

Financial Performance
The company had a total revenue of $9.6 billion a 17% increase from the previous year.

In 2020 the company had a net income of $514.2 million a 49% decrease from the previous year's net income of $1 billion.

The company's cash at the end of 2020 was $801.7 million. Operating activities generated $2.9 billion while investing activities used a $3.7 billion primarily for cost of fixed maturities. Financing activities provided another $800.2 million.

Strategy
Everest Re's business strategy is to sustain its leadership position within targeted reinsurance and insurance markets provide effective management throughout the property and casualty underwriting cycle and thereby achieve an attractive return for its shareholders. The company's underwriting strategies seek to capitalize on its financial strength and capacity global franchise stable and experienced management team diversified product and distribution offerings underwriting expertise and disciplined approach efficient and low-cost operating structure and effective enterprise risk management practices.

The company offers treaty and facultative reinsurance and admitted and non-admitted insurance. Its products include the full range of property and casualty reinsurance and insurance coverages including marine aviation surety errors and omissions liability directors' and officers' liability medical malpractice other specialty lines accident and health and workers' compensation.

The company's underwriting strategies emphasize underwriting profitability over premium volume. Key elements of this strategy include careful risk selection appropriate pricing through strict underwriting discipline and adjustment of its business mix in response to changing market conditions. The company focuses on reinsuring companies that effectively manage the underwriting cycle through proper analysis and pricing of underlying risks and whose underwriting guidelines and performance are compatible with its objectives.

Commencing in 2015 the Everest Re initiated a strategic build out of its insurance platform through the investment in key leadership hires which in turn has brought significant underwriting talent and stronger direction in achieving its insurance program strategic goals of increased premium volume and improved underwriting results. Recent growth is coming from highly diversified areas including newly launched lines of business as well as product and geographic expansion in existing lines of business. The company is building a world-class insurance platform capable of offering products across lines and geographies complementing its leading global reinsurance franchise.

As part of this initiative the company launched a new syndicate through Lloyd's of London and formed Ireland Insurance providing access to additional international business and new product opportunities to further diversify and broaden its insurance portfolio going forward.

EXECUTIVES

Chairman of the Board, Joseph Taranto
Chief Operating Officer, Executive Vice President, Head of the Everest Reinsurance Division, James Williamson
Group Chief Financial Officer, Executive Vice President, Mark Kociancic, $201,923 total compensation
Senior Vice President and Group Chief Transformation and Shared Services Leader, Anne Rocco
Independent Director, John Amore
Independent Director, Meryl Hartzband
Independent Director, John Graf
President, Chief Executive Officer, Director, Juan Andrade, $1,298,077 total compensation
President and Chief Executive Officer of the Everest Insurance, Michael Karmilowicz
Independent Director, Roger Singer
Independent Director, John Weber
Executive Vice President, General Counsel, Corporate Secretary, Sanjoy Mukherjee, $632,307 total compensation
Auditors: PricewaterhouseCoopers LLP

LOCATIONS

HQ: Everest Re Group Ltd
Seon Place - 4th Floor, 141 Front Street, P.O. Box HM 845, Hamilton HM 19
Phone: (1) 441 2950006   **Fax:** (1) 441 2954828
Web: www.everestre.com

PRODUCTS/OPERATIONS

2017 Gross Written Premiums by Segment

	% of total
US Reinsurance	36
Insurance	29
International	18
Bermuda	17
Total	**100**

COMPETITORS

AON GLOBAL LIMITED
BRIT LIMITED
Enstar Group Limited
FARADAY HOLDINGS LIMITED
FEDNAT HOLDING COMPANY
GUY CARPENTER & COMPANY LLC
Hiscox Ltd
Industrial Alliance Insurance and Financial Services In
JLT GROUP HOLDINGS LIMITED
Maiden Holdings Ltd
ODYSSEY RE HOLDINGS CORP.
SCOR SE
Talanx AG
XL GROUP PUBLIC LIMITED COMPANY

HISTORICAL FINANCIALS

Company Type: Public

Income Statement				FYE: December 31
	ASSETS ($ mil.)	NET INCOME ($ mil.)	INCOME AS % OF ASSETS	EMPLOYEES
12/20	32,788	514	1.6%	1,746
12/19	27,324	1,009	3.7%	1,603
12/18	24,794	103	0.4%	1,415
12/17	23,591	468	2.0%	1,276
12/16	21,321	996	4.7%	1,121
Annual Growth	11.4%	(15.2%)	—	11.7%

2020 Year-End Financials

Return on assets: 1.7%
Return on equity: 5.4%
Long-term debt ($ mil.): —
No. of shares (mil.): 39
Sales ($ mil): 9,598

Dividends
Yield: 2.6%
Payout: 48.5%
Market value ($ mil.): —

Evonik Industries AG

Evonik is one of the world leaders in specialty chemicals. The company produces a diverse range specialty chemicals used in manufacturing processes to enhance the properties of a vast array of products broadly under the categories nutrition and care resource efficiency and performance materials. It include tires insulating materials detergents tablets and wind turbines to name a few. Based in Essen Germany Evonik has operations in more than 100 countries and has production facilities in some 25 including Germany Belgium the US and China. Majority of its sales were generated in the EMEA region which accounts for about 50% of total.

Operations

Evonik recently implemented a new segment structure which includes Special Additives Nutrition & Care Smart Materials Performance Materials and Services.

The Specialty Additives segment accounts for about 25% of company revenue. The segment combines the company's business of high-performance additives and versatile crosslinkers. The company's nutrition and care segment (around 25% of company revenue) apply all products directly on or in humans or animals.

The Performance materials segment account for more than 25% of the company's revenue and supplies high-performance materials for environment-friendly and energy-efficient systems to the automotive paints coatings adhesives and construction industries. The company's other segments also includes performance materials (some 15%) and Services (about 5%).

Geographic Reach

Essen Germany-based Evonik has operations in more than 100 countries and factories in some 25 countries. Europe Middle East and Asia region accounts for about 50% of sales North America with over 20% Asia/Pacific around 25% and Central America with the remaining.

Financial Performance

Note: Growth rates may differ after conversion to US Dollars.

Evonik's performance for the span of five years have fluctuated with revenues seeing a downward trend since 2017 and ending 2020 as its lowest performing year.

Revenues declined by 7% or ?909 million to ?12.2 billion as compared to previous year's revenue of ?13.1 billion.

In 2020 the company's net income significantly decreased as well by about ?1.6 billion to ?465 million as compared to previous year's net income of ?2.1 billion.

Evonik's cash on hand at the end of the year was at ?563 million. The company's operations generated ?1.7 billion while investing activities also provided ?386 million. The company's financing activities used ?1.7 billion mainly for dividends paid.

Strategy

Evonik's strategy focuses in sustainability which is a vital part in their business strategy. The company has set goals which are systematically imple-

mented. In addition the company focuses in actively managing its portfolio in the growth driven by innovation and sustainability ambitious financial targets and its performance-oriented culture.

Mergers and Acquisitions

Evonik has been on an acquisition spree as it reshapes its portfolio.

In mid-2020 Evonik is acquiring the Porocel Group for US$210 million to accelerate the growth of its catalysts business. Based in Houston Texas Porocel offers a technology for highly efficient rejuvenation of desulfurization catalysts which are in increasing demand to produce low-sulfur fuel.

Evonik in early 2020 acquires biotechnology company innovativeHealth Group. Headquartered at the Scientific Park of Madrid (Spain) innoHealth's technology platforms screen and combine natural ingredients and extracts to generate novel dermocosmetic products with synergistic activities. The company becomes part of Evonik's Care Solutions Business Line. The acquisition of innoHealth further strengthens Evonik's Health & Care growth engine and allows Evonik to expand its product development for unique active ingredients.

Also in early 2020 Evonik has successfully closed the acquisition of the US company PeroxyChem for US$640 million after the responsible court in Washington D.C. dismissed the lawsuit filed by the Federal Trade Commission (FTC) to block the acquisition. The acquired business isintegrated into the Resource Efficiency segment.

In late 2019 Evonik acquired Endexo the surface modification business of Interface Biologics a privately-held material science company located in Toronto Canada. The acquisition strengthens the capabilities of Evonik's Heath & Care segment.

In early2019 Evonik Industries acquired Structured Polymers an Austin-based startup which comes with a new patented technology that expands its portfolio of specialty polymer powders in the additive manufacturing market. Evonik leverages the acquisition to capture more of the rapidly growing 3D-printing market.

HISTORY

The RAG Foundation planned an IPO for Evonik in 2011 but decided to postpone the launch until 2012 because of uncertainty in financial markets. A dip in the blue-chip DAX index has delayed other IPOs but Evonik's listing was expected to be one of Germany's largest. The company could raise as much as $ 6.3 billion for its owners. However in 2012 the company postponed its IPO plans again because of uncertainty in the markets.

Evonik divested 51% of its STEAG unit to a consortium of municipal utilities in Germany's Rhine-Ruhr region. The $900 million deal included an option for the consortium to acquire up to 100% of the shares by 2014. The company put STEAG on the chopping block in 2010 in a move to focus on Degussa its specialty chemicals unit. STEAG operates power generation plants in Germany as well as in Colombia the Philippines and Turkey.

To focus on its chemicals portfolio the company decided to divest businesses that may have limited growth potential. Subsequently Evonik exited the carbon blacks business in 2011 which generated more than $1.3 billion the previous year. The company has set a goal of achieving $650 million in cost savings each year starting in 2012 and has started implementing measures to meet that goal. The company also divested the colorants operations of its Coatings and Additives unit in 2012 selling it to US-based private equity firm Arsenal Capital Partners for an undisclosed price.

In 2011 Evonik acquired the hanse chemie Group a Hamburg-based firm that produces components and raw materials for sealants and adhesives moldings and casting compounds. Its products are used in the construction industry automotive manufacturing dental technology windpower and photovoltaic plants.

Later that year the company acquired the pharmaceuticals business (the polymer and formulation services) of US-based SurModics which will widen Evonik's presence in North America. SurModics Pharmaceuticals which was an affiliate of SurModics Inc. develops injectable drug delivery systems. The acquisition further expands Evonik's Pharma Polymers business and its health care operations after its purchase of the Resomer business of Boehringer Ingelheim Pharma GmbH. That deal completed in March 2011 transferred the entire Resomer product portfolio including standard and customer-specific polymers for medical applications and pharmaceutical formulations to Evonik's Pharma Polymers strengthening that business line.

As part of its global growth strategy based on new technologies for its hydrogen peroxide operations the company acquired the hydrogen peroxide unit of Kemira Chemicals Canada. The acquisition complements the company's hydrogen peroxide operations in China and bolsters Evonik's position as one of the leading suppliers of hydrogen peroxide to the North American market. It boosts its capacity for hydrogen peroxide production in North America to more than 200000 metric tons per year. Evonik also operates hydrogen peroxide sites in Alberta Canada and in Alabama in the US.

In 2010 the company made a couple of small acquisitions. Evonik bought the metals catalysts business of H.C. Starck which serves the pharmaceutical building materials and automotive sectors. That year it acquired the UK company Membrane Extraction Technology Ltd. and Methacrylate Specialty Esters from Arkema both of which will slot into Evonik's high performance polymers unit.

The company has also been integrating the operations of its 2010 acquisition in the US Tippecanoe Laboratories with those of its global synthesis operations. The Indiana company produces active ingredients and intermediates for the pharmaceutical industry.

As part of its global growth strategy in 2010 the company began operating a production plant at full capacity for high-quality polymers and coating systems in Shanghai in a project it calls MATCH (methacrylates to China).

Evonik subsidiary SFW Energia bought a mine gas cogeneration plant in the Upper Silesia region of Poland in 2010. The acquisition of the plant which produces 40 MW of thermal power and 5 MW of electricity will bolster Evonik's position in the renewable energy market.

Evonik was founded in 2007.

EXECUTIVES

Independent Chairman of the Supervisory Board, Bernd Tonjes, $284,851 total compensation
Member of the Supervisory Board; Employee Representative, Anke Strueber-Hummelt, $113,940 total compensation
Independent Member of the Supervisory Board, Ulrich Weber, $113,940 total compensation
Member of the Supervisory Board, Frank Loellgen, $113,940 total compensation
Deputy Chairwoman of the Supervisory Board, Karin Erhard, $142,425 total compensation
Member of the Supervisory Board, Martin Kubessa, $113,940 total compensation
Member of the Supervisory Board, Jens Barnhusen, $113,940 total compensation
Member of the Supervisory Board; Employee Representative, Martin Albers, $113,940 total compensation

Independent Member of the Supervisory Board, Michael Ruediger, $113,940 total compensation
Chief Financial Officer, Member of the Executive Board, Ute Wolf, $911,524 total compensation
Independent Member of the Supervisory Board, Aldo Belloni, $113,940 total compensation
Independent Member of the Supervisory Board, Siegfried Luther, $113,940 total compensation
Chairman of the Executive Board, Christian Kullmann, $1,595,168 total compensation
Independent Member of the Supervisory Board, Volker Trautz, $113,940 total compensation
Member of the Supervisory Board, Thomas Sauer, $113,940 total compensation
Independent Member of the Supervisory Board, Peter Spuhler, $113,940 total compensation
Chief Human Resource Officer and Member of the Executive Board, Thomas Wessel, $911,524 total compensation
Independent Member of the Supervisory Board, Barbara Albert, $113,940 total compensation
Independent Member of the Supervisory Board, Barbara Grunewald, $113,940 total compensation
Independent Member of the Supervisory Board, Angela Titzrath, $113,940 total compensation
Deputy Chairman of the Executive Board, Harald Schwager, $1,287,528 total compensation
Auditors: PricewaterhouseCoopers GmbH Wirtschaftspruefungsgesellschaft

LOCATIONS

HQ: Evonik Industries AG
Rellinghauser Strasse 1-11, Essen D-45128
Phone: (49) 201 177 3315   **Fax:** (49) 201 177 3053
Web: www.evonik.de

2018 sales

	%
Western Europe	43
North America	23
Asia/Pacific North	15
Asia/Pacific South	6
Eastern Europe	6
Central and South America	4
Middle East and Africa	3
Total	**100**

PRODUCTS/OPERATIONS

2018 sales

	%
Resource Efficiency	38
Nutrition & Care	31
Performance Materials	26
Services	5
Total	**100**

COMPETITORS

ALTANA AG
BODYCOTE PLC
Borealis AG
Brenntag Holding GmbH
Clariant AG
DIPLOMA PLC
FERROGLOBE PLC
GOODWIN PLC
LANXESS AG
LANXESS SOLUTIONS US INC.
Orbia Advance Corporation S.A.B. de C.V.
SASOL LTD
SEKISUI CHEMICAL CO. LTD.

HISTORICAL FINANCIALS

Company Type: Public

Income Statement   FYE: December 31

	REVENUE ($ mil.)	NET INCOME ($ mil.)	NET PROFIT MARGIN	EMPLOYEES
12/20	14,971	570	3.8%	33,106
12/19	14,717	2,364	16.1%	32,423
12/18	17,205	1,067	6.2%	36,201
12/17	17,284	859	5.0%	35,803
12/16	13,443	891	6.6%	33,905
Annual Growth	2.7%	(10.5%)	—	(0.6%)

2020 Year-End Financials

Debt ratio: 17.8%   No. of shares (mil.): 466
Return on equity: 5.4%   Dividends
Cash ($ mil.): 690   Yield: —
Current ratio: 1.70   Payout: 115.0%
Long-term debt ($ mil.): 3,721   Market value ($ mil.): —

Exor NV

LOCATIONS

HQ: Exor NV
Gustav Mahlerplein 25, Amsterdam, North Holland 1082 MS
Phone: (31) 20 240 2 220   **Fax:** (31) 20 240 2 738
Web: www.exor.com

HISTORICAL FINANCIALS

Company Type: Public

Income Statement   FYE: December 31

	REVENUE ($ mil.)	NET INCOME ($ mil.)	NET PROFIT MARGIN	EMPLOYEES
12/20	146,684	(36)	—	23
12/19	161,403	3,427	2.1%	23
12/18	164,099	1,542	0.9%	22
12/17	171,937	1,668	1.0%	21
12/16	147,895	621	0.4%	0
Annual Growth	(0.2%)	—	—	—

2020 Year-End Financials

Debt ratio: —   No. of shares (mil.): 231
Return on equity: (-0.2%) Dividends
Cash ($ mil.): 43,643   Yield: —
Current ratio: —   Payout: —
Long-term debt ($ mil.): — Market value ($ mil.): —

Fairfax Financial Holdings Ltd

Fairfax Financial Holdings is a holding company whose corporate objective is to build long term shareholder value by achieving a high rate of compound growth in book value per share over the long term. Its subsidiaries including Odyssey Group Allied World and Crum & Forster focus on property/casualty coverage and associated investment management. The company also offers reinsurance and specialty insurance policies. Its operations span countries in Southeast Asia Eastern Europe

Middle East and Brazil. Chairman and CEO Prem Watsa control nearly 45% of the voting rights of Fairfax Financial. Majority of its sales were generated in the US.

Operations
Fairfax Financial's operating segments are largely represented by its subsidiaries: Allied World Odyssey Group (formerly OdysseyRe) Crum & Forster Brit Northbridge Zenith National Fairfax Asia Runo Other Insurance and Reinsurance and Other (non-insurance operations).

Allied World (roughly 25% of sales) provides property/casualty and specialty insurance and reinsurance worldwide (including on the Lloyd's exchange).

US-based Odyssey Group accounting for about 25% of sales underwrites property/casualty reinsurance worldwide. It also underwrites specialty insurance primarily in the US and the UK including through the Lloyd's of London market.

Crum & Forster (more than 15% of sales) provides commercial and specialty insurance in the US market.

Other segments include Brit (about 15%) a market-leading global Lloyd's of London specialty insurer and reinsurer; Northbridge (about 10%) a national commercial property and casualty insurer in Canada providing property and casualty insurance products through its Northbridge Insurance and Federated subsidiaries; Zenith National (about 5%) an insurer primarily engaged in workers' compensation business in the US; and Fairfax Asia (less than 5%) which includes the company's operations that underwrite insurance and reinsurance coverages in Hong Kong (Falcon) Malaysia (Pacific Insurance) Indonesia (AMAG Insurance) and Sri Lanka (Fairfirst Insurance).

About 55% of sales came from casualty insurance while property accounts for about 35% and specialty accounts for about 10%. In addition insurance products account for some three-quarters of sales while reinsurance accounts for the rest.

Geographic Reach
The company corporate office is located in Toronto Canada. It also has operations in the US in which the US accounts for over 60% of sales while international accounts for about 20% and the remaining accounts for Canada and Asia.

Sales and Marketing
The company uses brokers to distribute its business and in some instances will distribute through agents or directly to customers. The company may also conduct business through third parties such as managing general agents where it is cost effective to do so and where the company can control the underwriting process to ensure its risk management criteria are met. Each of these channels has its own distinct distribution characteristics and customers.

Financial Performance
The decrease in income to $19.8 billion in 2020 from $21.5 billion in 2019 principally reflected decreased net gains on investments and other revenue share of loss of associates in 2020 compared to share of profit of associates in 2019 and decreased interest and dividends.

Net earnings for fiscal 2020 decreased to $37.4 million compared with $2.0 billion in the prior year.

Cash held by the company at the end of fiscal 2020 increased to $4.5 billion. Cash provided by operations and financing activities were $139.8 million and $436.9 million respectively. Investing activities used $46.8 million mainly for purchases of premises and equipment and intangible assets.

Strategy
The company may periodically and opportunistically acquire other insurance and reinsurance companies or execute other strategic initiatives developed by management. Although the company

undertakes due diligence prior to the completion of an acquisition it is possible that unanticipated factors could arise and there is no assurance that the anticipated financial or strategic objectives following an integration effort or the implementation of a strategic initiative will be achieved which could adversely affect the company's financial condition profitability or cash flows. The company may periodically explore opportunities to make strategic investments in all or part of certain businesses or companies. Acquisitions may involve a number of special risks including failure to retain key personnel unanticipated events or circumstances and legal liabilities some or all of which could have a material adverse effect on the company's business results of operations and financial position.

Mergers and Acquisitions
In 2020 Fairfax Financial Holdings Limited has acquired through its subsidiaries ownership and control of $330000000 aggregate principal amount of 1.75% unsecured subordinated convertible debentures of BlackBerry Limited representing approximately 90% of BlackBerry's private placement of an aggregate principal amount of $365000000 of Debentures. BlackBerry's head and registered office is located in Waterloo Ontario.

Company Background
Fairfax was founded in 1985 by Chairman and CEO V. Prem Watsa.

EXECUTIVES

Independent Director, Brandon Sweitzer
Chief Operating Officer, Vice President, Peter Clarke, $745,787 total compensation
Vice President - Corporate Affairs, Corporate Secretary, Eric Salsberg, $400,139 total compensation
Vice President - Strategic Investments, Bradley Martin, $452,940 total compensation
Lead Independent Director, Anthony Griffiths
Director, David Johnston
Independent Director, Robert Gunn
Vice President - Corporate Development, John Varnell, $376,704 total compensation
Independent Director, Timothy Price
Chief Financial Officer, Vice President, Jennifer Allen, $447,472 total compensation
Independent Director, Karen Jurjevich
Independent Director, Lauren Templeton
Director, Benjamin Watsa
Director, Christine McLean
Independent Director, R. William McFarland
Director, William Weldon
Auditors: PricewaterhouseCoopers LLP

LOCATIONS

HQ: Fairfax Financial Holdings Ltd
95 Wellington Street West, Suite 800, Toronto, Ontario M5J 2N7
Phone: 416 367-4941   **Fax:** 416 367-4946
Web: www.fairfax.ca

Sales 2016

	% of total
United States	62
Canada	13
Asia	11
International	14
Total	**100**

PRODUCTS/OPERATIONS

2016 Sales

	% of total
Casualty	56
Property	32
Specialty	12
Total	**100**

2016 Sales

	% of total
OdysseyRe	24
Crum & Forster	21
Brit	20
Northbridge	11
Zenith National	8
Fairfax Asia	7
Runoff	2
Other	7
Total	**100**

Selected Subsidiaries
Insurance
  Asian Insurance
  Falcon Insurance Company (Hong Kong) Ltd.
  First Capital Insurance Limited (Singapore)
  Canadian Insurance
  Northbridge Financial Corporation
  Commonwealth Insurance Company
  Federated Holdings of Canada Limited
  Lombard General Insurance Company of Canada
  Markel Insurance Company of Canada
  U.S. Insurance
  Crum & Forster Holdings Corporation
Reinsurance
  CRC (Bermuda) Reinsurance Limited
  Odyssey Re Holdings Corp.
  Polish Re (Poland)
  Wentworth Insurance Company Ltd. (Barbados)
Runoff
  nSpire Re Limited
  RiverStone Group LLC
  RiverStone Holdings Limited
  TRG Holding Corporation

COMPETITORS

AMERICAN NATIONAL INSURANCE COMPANY
AON GLOBAL LIMITED
Aspen Insurance Holdings Limited
Enstar Group Limited
Everest Re Group Ltd.
ING Groep N.V.
MAPFRE SA
METLIFE INC.
NUMIS CORPORATION PLC
OLD REPUBLIC INTERNATIONAL CORPORATION
PRUDENTIAL FINANCIAL INC.
REINSURANCE GROUP OF AMERICA INCORPORATED
RenaissanceRe Holdings Ltd.
Sampo Oyj
Talanx AG

HISTORICAL FINANCIALS

Company Type: Public

Income Statement

FYE: December 31

	ASSETS ($ mil.)	NET INCOME ($ mil.)	INCOME AS % OF ASSETS	EMPLOYEES
12/20	74,054	218	0.3%	41,044
12/19	70,508	2,004	2.8%	44,043
12/18	64,372	376	0.6%	39,043
12/17	64,090	1,740	2.7%	38,040
12/16	43,384	(512)	—	31,134
Annual Growth	14.3%	—	—	7.2%

2020 Year-End Financials

Return on assets: 0.3%
Return on equity: 1.5%
Long-term debt ($ mil.): —
No. of shares (mil.): 26
Sales ($ mil): 19,794

Dividends
  Yield: 0.0%
  Payout: 158.9%
Market value ($ mil.): 9,197

	STOCK PRICE ($) FY Close	P/E High/Low		PER SHARE ($) Earnings	Dividends	Book Value
12/20	340.94	72	35	6.29	10.00	513.67
12/19	469.11	7	6	69.79	10.00	520.37
12/18	440.08	49	35	11.65	10.00	467.76
12/17	530.34	8	6	64.98	10.00	483.75
12/16	486.70	—	—	(24.18)	10.00	411.01
Annual Growth	(8.5%)	—	—	—	(0.0%)	5.7%

Far East Horizon Ltd.

Auditors: Ernst & Young

LOCATIONS

HQ: Far East Horizon Ltd.
Suite 6305, 63/F, Central Plaza, 18 Harbour Road,
Wanchai,
Phone: (852) 2588 8688   **Fax:** (852) 2511 8660
Web: www.fehorizon.com

HISTORICAL FINANCIALS

Company Type: Public

Income Statement   FYE: December 31

	ASSETS ($ mil.)	NET INCOME ($ mil.)	INCOME AS % OF ASSETS	EMPLOYEES
12/19	37,447	623	1.7%	17,903
12/18	38,668	571	1.5%	12,813
12/17	34,952	496	1.4%	11,558
12/16	23,986	415	1.7%	8,184
12/15	21,450	385	1.8%	6,084
Annual Growth	14.9%	12.8%	—	31.0%

2019 Year-End Financials

Return on assets: 1.6%
Return on equity: 11.1%
Long-term debt ($ mil.): —
No. of shares (mil.): —
Sales ($ mil): 4,012

Dividends
Yield: —
Payout: 28.9%
Market value ($ mil.): —

Fast Retailing Co., Ltd.

Fast Retailing is the world's third-largest apparel retailer behind Inditex (owner of the ZARA brand) and H&M. Since 1963 the company has been working to fill the gap in Japan's casual wear market. Through its UNIQLO brand (a combination of the words unique and clothing) the company operates more than 2000 stores in Japan and in foreign markets including Greater China Southeast Asia and Oceania Europe and the US and Canada. Fast Retailing along with its subsidiaries markets functional basics for men women and children under the LifeWear concept of everyday comfort. The company's GU and Global Brands retail divisions also operate almost 1400 other stores selling products under the GU Theory Comptoir des Cotonniers J Brand and Princesse tam.tam brand names. .

Operations

The company operates in four business segments: UNIQLO Japan UNIQLO International GU and Global Brands.

UNIQLO is Fast Retailing's mainstay brand offering basic casualwear at reasonable prices. UNIQLO Japan operates about 830 stores and contributes more than 40% of the company's total revenue. UNIQLO International (more than 40%) operates about 1250 stores.

GU is considered to be the company's more low-priced "fun" fashion brand and generates about 10% of sales through almost 400 stores. Its Global Brands business (more than 5%) operates through close to 1000 stores and features clothing under the Theory Comptoir des Cotonniers Princesse tam.tam and J Brand names.

Fast Retailing is a specialty store retailer of private label apparel (SPA) using a business model where the company controls the entire process from design through manufacture and retail sales.

Geographic Reach

Based in Tokyo Japan Fast Retailing operates through about 3400 stores in Japan Greater China Southeast Asia and Oceania the US and Canada Europe and Russia. Its product development centers are located in the cities of Tokyo New York London Paris Shanghai and Los Angeles.

Sales and Marketing

Fast Retailing's UNIQLO divisions sell products via stores and e-commerce channels and market core products via TV commercials promotional flyers and through email and social media. Online sales in the US account for about 20% of UNIQLO's overall revenue and in China about 15%. In Japan more than 7% of UNIQLO's business is conducted online; the company is hoping to increase online sales in Japan by allowing customers to collect online purchases from nearby UNIQLO stores.

Financial Performance

Fast Retailing has seen an upward trend in revenue over the last five years with double-digit growth in 2018. Sales increased by 14% to 2130 billion in 2018 (ended August) compared with 1812 million the previous year.

Along with higher sales net income also increased by 30% to 154.8 billion in 2018. Athough improving UNIQLO North America posted a profit loss in 2018 with brand visibility still low in the US and Canada.

Cash at the end of fiscal 2018 was 69.4 billion an increase of 9.6 billion from the prior year. Cash from operations contributed 176.4 billion to the coffers while investing activities used 57.2 billion mainly for purchases of property and equipment related to building out store networks. Accounting for dividends to stockholders financing activities provided 198.2 billion primarily from the inflow from a corporate bond issue.

Strategy

Already Asia's largest apparel retailer Fast Retailing seeks no less than to become #1 in the world by 2020. To succeed it plans to leverage its successful model of combining quality and aggressive pricing of its private-label apparel with the international expansion of its UNIQLO chain. It is also looking to integrate its physical stores and e-commerce operations to give customers a seamless experience.

The company is focused on producing reasonably-priced yet high-quality clothing designed for relaxed everyday comfort?a concept it calls LifeWear. To increase sales the company has recently developed several new products including its cold-weather HEATTECH innerwear Ultra Light Down and its 3D Knit fabric that uses technology to produce a whole garment seamlessly.

Fast Retailing aims to change the entire consumer retail industry by transforming its supply chain with an information-driven digital approach to managing and integrating design planning production distribution and retail sales. Dubbed the Ariake Project the company is working to build a supply chain that uses advanced information technology to create links between the company's partner factories warehouses and stores worldwide. It's using a new partnership with Google and its own vast amounts of information to analyze big data such as colors and design features popular with consumers. Fast Retailing is also using technology such as artificial intelligence and advanced algorithms to more accurately predict fluctuating production volumes. The company has incorporated RFID tags on all products and working with logistics partner Daifuku Co. Ltd. opened its first fully automated warehouse dedicated to online sales in 2018.

In 2018 UNIQLO International surpassed UNIQLO Japan in sales for the first time. The company has seen rapid growth in Greater China Southeast Asia South Korea and India. It plans to open more large-format stores in prime urban locations (and promote its GU brand) in Asian markets in the future. Plans are underway to expand in Europe as well; its first store opened in Sweden in 2018. To become profitable in the US Fast Retail also is planning new large-format stores in prime locations versus smaller stores in declining American shopping malls.

EXECUTIVES

Independent Director, Nobumichi Hattori
Independent Director, Masaaki Shintaku
Chief Financial Officer, Group Senior Executive Officer, Director, Takeshi Okazaki
Independent Director, Takashi Nawa
Independent Director, Naotake Ohno
Group Senior Executive Officer, Director, Koji Yanai
Group Senior Executive Officer, Chairman of Subsidiaries, Director, Kazumi Yanai
Independent Director, Kathy Matsui
Chairman of the Board, President, Group Chief Executive Officer, Chairman & President of Subsidiaries, Representative Director, Tadashi Yanai
Auditors: Deloitte Touche Tohmatsu LLC

LOCATIONS

HQ: Fast Retailing Co., Ltd.
Midtown Tower, 9-7-1 Akasaka, Minato-ku, Tokyo 107-6231
Phone: (81) 3 6865 0050
Web: www.fastretailing.com

PRODUCTS/OPERATIONS

2018 sales

	% of total
UNIQLO International	42
UNIQLO Japan	41
GU	10
Global Brands	7
Total	100

COMPETITORS

AEON CO. LTD.
CECONOMY AG
CHICO'S FAS INC.
DENTSU GROUP INC.
FRASERS GROUP PLC
GAMES WORKSHOP GROUP PLC
ISETAN MITSUKOSHI HOLDINGS LTD.
J.FRONT RETAILING CO.LTD.
MANUTAN INTERNATIONAL
MEDIPAL HOLDINGS CORPORATION

SEVEN & I HOLDINGS CO. LTD.
SOFTBANK GROUP CORP.
SOMPO HOLDINGS INC.
SONY GROUP CORPORATION
SUNTORY HOLDINGS LIMITED
UNY GROUP HOLDINGS CO.LTD.
V.F. CORPORATION
ZUMIEZ INC.

HISTORICAL FINANCIALS

Company Type: Public

Income Statement   FYE: August 31

	REVENUE ($ mil.)	NET INCOME ($ mil.)	NET PROFIT MARGIN	EMPLOYEES
08/20	19,070	857	4.5%	128,492
08/19	21,542	1,529	7.1%	137,281
08/18	19,222	1,397	7.3%	124,679
08/17	16,840	1,078	6.4%	76,143
08/16	17,296	465	2.7%	69,921
Annual Growth	2.5%	16.5%	—	16.4%

2020 Year-End Financials

Debt ratio: —
Return on equity: 9.5%
Cash ($ mil.): 10,381
Current ratio: 2.56
Long-term debt ($ mil.): —

No. of shares (mil.): 102
Dividends
  Yield: 0.7%
  Payout: 5.4%
Market value ($ mil.): 6,113

	STOCK PRICE ($) FY Close	P/E High/Low		PER SHARE ($) Earnings	Dividends	Book Value
08/20	59.87	0	0	8.39	0.44	88.94
08/19	58.49	0	0	14.96	0.45	86.49
08/18	46.58	0	0	13.67	0.34	76.33
08/17	28.65	0	0	10.56	0.31	64.90
08/16	35.18	0	0	4.56	0.31	54.55
Annual Growth	14.2%	—	—	16.5%	9.1%	13.0%

Faurecia SE (France)

Faurecia is one of the world's largest automotive seat makers. In addition to car seats it also manufactures emission control systems vehicle interiors and doors and front-end systems. Although Europe accounts for over 45% of overall revenue it supplies most major carmakers including GM Ford and Volkswagen. Faurecia is a global leader in its four areas of business: seating interiors Clarion Electronics and clean mobility. The company's strong technological offering provides carmakers with solutions for the cockpit of the future and sustainable mobility. Faurecia was formed in 1997 with the takeover of Bertrand Faure by PSA-owned ECIA to create a global automotive player. In 2021 with the merger of PSA and FCA and the creation of Stellantis a new chapter began in Faurecia's history.

Operations

Faurecia operates four business units. Seating (roughly 40% of revenue) design and manufacture of complete vehicle seats seating frames and adjustment mechanisms; Interiors (about 30%) design manufacture and assembly of instrument panels and complete cockpits door panels and modules and acoustic systems; Clean Mobility (more than 25%) design and manufacture of exhaust systems solutions for fuel cell electric vehicles and after treatment solutions for commercial vehicles; and Clarion Electronics (about 5%) design and manufacture of display technologies driver assistance systems and cockpit electronics.

Geographic Reach

Faurecia has around 265 industrial sites and roughly 40 R&D centers in some countries around the world. Europe is the company's largest market at more than 45% of overall revenue followed by North America and Asia at some 25% of revenue each. South America and rest of the world accounts for the remaining 5% of revenue.

Sales and Marketing

Faurecia works with some of the biggest names in the automotive industry. Its five main customers represent about 55% of revenue. VW leads the way with more than 15% followed by Ford (over 10%) PSA Peugeot Citroen (about 10%) Renault-Nissan (about 10%) and FCA (around 5%).

Financial Performance

Note: Growth rates may differ after conversion to US Dollars.

Sales for fiscal 2020 decreased to ?14.7 billion compared from the prior year with ?17.8 billion.

The net income is a loss of ?321.5 million compared from the prior year with ?664.7 million.

Cash held by the company at the end of fiscal 2020 increased to ?3.1 billion. Cash provided by operations and financing activities were ?1.1 billion each. Cash used for investing activities was ?1.4 billion mainly for capitalized development costs.

Strategy

Faurecia's mission is to develop technologies for sustainable mobility and to create personalized experiences for the Cockpit of the Future. At the same time the company offer solutions to meet the challenges of future generations. This mission guides its transformation strategy and its investment. In 2019 the company created its fourth Business Group Faurecia Clarion Electronics accelerated its investment in fuel cell technologies for zeroemissions mobility and launched its ambitious program to be CO2 neutral by 2030.

Mergers and Acquisitions

In 2021 Faurecia has acquired designLED. The Scotland-based company specialized in advanced backlighting technologies will strengthen Faurecia's offer for display technologies and enrich its immersive experiences for the Cockpit of the Future. Combined with the IRYSTec's strength in image experience and processing designLED will enable Faurecia to develop new types of advanced backlighting for use cases that promote safety personalization and convenience. This will give Faurecia Clarion Electronics greater design freedom for new generations of displays that are easy to integrate in any type of cockpit configuration.

Also in 2021 Faurecia with its wholly owned subsidiary Faurecia Participations GmbH as bidding entity published the offer document for its voluntary public takeover offer in cash for all outstanding shares of Hella a major automotive player in lighting and electronics based in Lippstadt Germany. The combined company will become a major technology player focused on six activities. Five of which Electronics Lighting Seating Interiors Clean Mobility will each exceed ?3 billion of sales. The newly created Business Group Life Cycle Value Management will quickly grow to reach a leading position.

In early 2021 Faurecia successfully completed the final closing of its acquisition of CLD one of the leading Chinese manufacturers of hydrogen tanks. Headquartered in ShenYang CLD has around 200 employees and 2 plants in Liaoning with a capacity of 30000 tanks per year. Through the acquisition of CLD and thanks to the certification of Type IV tanks Faurecia will further energize its momentum for hydrogen mobility in China.

HISTORY

Bertrand Faure opened his workshop in Levallois-Perret France in 1914 to manufacture cushions and spring backs for automotive seats; spring pads were developed in 1929. The company diversified into bedding in 1954. The following year it opened a factory near Etampes.

Throughout the 1960s and 1970s Bertrand Faure continued to grow through geographic and product-line expansion. The company boosted its metal and foam seat-making operations in France and in 1971 it expanded into Germany with the purchase of automotive seating component manufacturer Schmitz. Faure bought French bedding maker Merinos in 1973 and then changed its company name to Epeda-Bertrand Faure. Between 1977 and 1978 Epeda-Bertrand Faure expanded its automotive seating business through acquisitions in Spain and Portugal.

Epeda-Bertrand Faure diversified into the luggage business with the 1982 purchase of Delsey. That year the company was floated on the French stock exchange. In 1983 Epeda-Bertrand Faure further strengthened its car-seat business in France with the purchase of Autocoussin (structures and foam) and Cousin Fr"res (mechanisms). Another plant in Germany was opened in 1986 to supply BMW. That year Epeda-Bertrand Faure invested in Canadian CASE a leading North American maker of car-seat mechanisms. The company also reorganized its automotive activities under the name Bertrand Faure Automobile.

Epeda-Bertrand Faure acquired Luchaire a defense materials and aerospace and automotive equipment manufacturer in 1987. The following year the company bought automotive seating structures maker Sicam (Italy) and seating foam and structures firm Molaflex (Portugal). In 1989 the company forged joint ventures in the UK Japan and Canada for the manufacture of car seating.

By 1990 the company had reorganized into four product segments: automotive seats bedding luggage and aerospace equipment. The automotive seating business was conducted under the name Bertrand Faure while the rest of the group changed its name to EBF. Bertrand Faure purchased RHW a leading German maker of car seats in 1991.

The following year EBF's board of directors decided to focus the company on automotive seating and initiated a vast restructuring plan. EBF sold its bedding concerns in 1994. As part of its restructuring EBF changed its name back to Bertrand Faure. Two years later Bertrand Faure opened offices in Beijing and S o Paulo.

Peugeot S.A. subsidiary ECIA and Bertrand Faure merged in 1999 to form Faurecia. In 2000 Faurecia bolstered its North American presence by purchasing US-based automotive exhaust system maker AP Automotive Systems; it renamed the subsidiary Faurecia Exhaust Systems. The company acquired Sommer Allibert's car interiors business early in 2001.

Expanding in Asia Faurecia purchased Chang Heung Precision Co. Ltd. a Korean maker of exhaust systems in 2003.

Since 2004 the headcount at high-cost Western European locations has been reduced while headcount in low-cost regions has increased.

In 2006 the company opened a new plant in China for the manufacture of automotive seats and interior modules for Ford.

In 2006 CEO Pierre Levi stepped down amid a corruption scandal involving Faurecia employees who allegedly offered kickbacks to managers at customers including Volkswagen and BMW. CFO Frank Imbert was named interim CEO then director Gregoire Olivier followed as CEO. Yann Delabri"re succeeded him in early 2007.

In 2007 sales in North America grew by 42%. The company opened seven new plants in the US in 2006 and 2007 — in Michigan (seats interior modules front end modules) Ohio (interior modules and exhaust systems) and South Carolina (seats).

In Asia Faurecia's sales grew by 21% in 2007 over the previous year. To keep up momentum Faurecia continues to invest in the region.

EXECUTIVES

Independent Director, Linda Hasenfratz
Independent Director, Peter Mertens
Independent Director, Jean-Bernard Levy
Executive Vice President, Group Human Resources, Member of the Executive Committee, Jean-Pierre Sounillac
Director, Robert Peugeot
Executive Vice President, Group Communications, Member of the Executive Committee, Kate Philipps
Executive Vice President, Group Chief Financial Officer; Member of the Executive Committee, Michel Favre

Executive Vice President - SAS Interior Modules, Member of the Executive Board, Hagen Wiesner
Independent Director, Penelope Herscher
Independent Director, Odile Desforges
Director representing the employees, Daniel Bernardino
Director Representing the Employees, Emmanuel Pioche
Executive Vice President, Faurecia Seating, Member of the Executive Board, Eelco Spoelder
Executive Vice President - China, Member of the Executive Committee, Francois Tardif
Independent Director, Valerie Landon
Executive Vice President, Sales & Program Management; Member of the Executive Committee, Thorsten Muschal
Executive Vice President, Faurecia Clarion Electronics, Member of the Executive Committee, Jean-Paul Michel
Independent Director, Denis Mercier
Independent Director, Yan Mei
Chief Executive Officer, Member of the Executive Committee, Director, Patrick Koller, $974,191 total compensation
Independent Chairman of the Board, Michel De Rosen, $287,061 total compensation
Executive Vice President - Group Operations, Member of the Executive Committee, Christophe Schmitt
Auditors: Mazars

LOCATIONS

HQ: Faurecia SE (France)
23-27, avenue des Champs-Pierreux, Nanterre 92000
Phone: (33) 1 72 36 70 00   Fax: (33) 1 72 36 70 07
Web: www.faurecia.com

2016 Sales

	% of total
Europe	52
North America	28
Asia	16
South America	3
Rest of the World	1
Total	100

PRODUCTS/OPERATIONS

2016 Sales

	% total
Clean Mobility	39
Automotive Seating	35
Interior Systems	26
Total	100

2016 Sales by Customer

	% of total
VW Group	15
Ford group	14
Renault-Nissan	12
Peugeot S.A.	11
GM	8
Daimler	6
BMW	4
Others	30
Total	100

COMPETITORS

ADIENT PUBLIC LIMITED COMPANY	Rheinmetall AG
CIE AUTOMOTIVE SA	SPECTRIS PLC
GEA Group AG	TARKETT
GKN LIMITED	TOWER INTERNATIONAL INC.
INCHCAPE PLC	TOYOTA BOSHOKU CORPORATION
JENOPTIK AG	
LEAR CORPORATION	

HISTORICAL FINANCIALS

Company Type: Public

Income Statement   FYE: December 31

	REVENUE ($ mil.)	NET INCOME ($ mil.)	NET PROFIT MARGIN	EMPLOYEES
12/20	17,984	(464)	—	113,931
12/19	19,949	662	3.3%	115,496
12/18	20,069	802	4.0%	114,693
12/17	24,192	731	3.0%	109,275
12/16	19,756	673	3.4%	98,608
Annual Growth	(2.3%)	—	—	3.7%

2020 Year-End Financials

Debt ratio: 34.4%	No. of shares (mil.): 137
Return on equity: (-10.0%)	Dividends
Cash ($ mil.): 3,794	Yield: —
Current ratio: 0.99	Payout: —
Long-term debt ($ mil.): 5,182	Market value ($ mil.): —

FAW Car Co., Ltd.

EXECUTIVES

Director, Changqing Liu
Independent Director, Fangming Han
Chairman of the Board, Hanjie Hu
General Manager, Director, Qixin Zhu
Director, Xiao Yang
Independent Director, Zhihong Mao
Independent Director, Zhonglang Dong
Auditors: RSM China Certified Public Accountants (Special Ordinary Partnership)

LOCATIONS

HQ: FAW Car Co., Ltd.
No. 4888, Weishan Road, High New Technology Industrial Development Zone, Changchun, Jilin Province 130012
Phone: (86) 431 85781108   Fax: (86) 431 85781100
Web: www.fawcar.com.cn

HISTORICAL FINANCIALS

Company Type: Public

Income Statement   FYE: December 31

	REVENUE ($ mil.)	NET INCOME ($ mil.)	NET PROFIT MARGIN	EMPLOYEES
12/20	17,381	408	2.4%	0
12/19	3,975	7	0.2%	0
12/18	3,815	22	0.6%	0
12/17	4,287	43	1.0%	0
12/16	3,270	(137)	—	0
Annual Growth	51.8%	—	—	—

2020 Year-End Financials

Debt ratio: —	No. of shares (mil.): —
Return on equity: 16.3%	Dividends
Cash ($ mil.): 2,853	Yield: —
Current ratio: 1.33	Payout: —
Long-term debt ($ mil.): —	Market value ($ mil.): —

Ferguson PLC (New)

Ferguson PLC is one of the world's largest distributors of heating and plumbing supplies to professional contractors. The company distributes heating and cooling equipment plumbing supplies pipes valves safety equipment and fire protection products as well as building materials in North America and Europe. Key customers include building contractors plumbing and heating engineers and industrial and mechanical contractors. In 2019 the company announced it was spinning off its Wolseley subsidiary as a separate public company. Wolseley will focus on the UK market while Ferguson will concentrate solely on customers in the UK.

HISTORY

In the late 1800s Irishman Frederick Wolseley immigrated to Australia where he developed the world's first mechanical sheep shearer. In 1889 he formed Wolseley Sheep Shearing Machine Company. Herbert Austin a young engineer who perfected Wolseley's machine moved back to England and became manager of the company's Birmingham factory when the company relocated there in 1893.

In 1895 Austin amazed by an automobile exhibition he attended in Paris obtained an advance from the company to develop an automobile; it went into production in 1901. The car manufacturing operations were separated from the company's other machinery operations and soon were bought by Vickers. (Austin went out on his own in 1905 and began producing cars under his own name — the venerable Austin line.)

By the middle of the century Wolseley Sheep Shearing had grown to include central heating and plumbing products distribution. In 1958 it joined with Geo. H. Hughes to form Wolseley-Hughes. At the time the company was a small manufacturer with 11 distribution depots.

The company's watershed transition began in 1976 when Jeremy Lancaster took over the chairmanship from his father. (In the 20 years that Lancaster was chairman profits rose from about $6 million in 1976 to more than $350 million in 1996.) In the late 1970s the company began expanding rapidly through acquisitions. In 1982 it went public and acquired Ferguson Enterprises a leading distributor of plumbing supplies on the US's East Coast. The acquisition marked the company's first substantial US purchase. Three years later the company formed Wolseley Centers which distributed building products under the names Plumb Center Controls Center and Pipeline Center. In 1986 the company changed its name to Wolseley plc. Acquisitions that year included Carolina Builders Corporation and M.P. Harris & Co. Late 1980s acquisitions included Familian (1987) the largest plumbing supplier on the US's West Coast and Familian Northwest (1988).

Wolseley then looked across the English Channel. In 1992 it bought Brossette France's largest specialist distributor of plumbing supplies. The company moved further eastward in 1994 acquiring –AG Group (now Wolseley Austria) Austria's largest wholesale plumbing supply business. In addition to 40 Austrian branches –AG also had five branches in both Hungary and Germany and four in the Czech Republic. The –AG deal solidified Wolseley's position as the world's #1 plumbing and heating merchant.

Wolseley turned its attention back to the US in the mid-1990s buying a half-dozen companies including Building Material Supply. John Young became CEO that year when Jeremy Lancaster retired from the company.

In 1998 the company began integrating California-based Familian and Virginia-based Ferguson Enterprises — together responsible for more than half of Wolseley's US distribution revenues — under Ferguson's management. The company continued making acquisitions that year and the next including its first Italian company (Manzardo plumbing and heating supplies); it also grew by opening new outlets. Wolseley sold some of its burner and boiler manufacturing operations in 1999.

Chairman Richard Ireland became acting chief executive in June 2000 with the retirement of Young for health reasons. That year the company sold most of its manufacturing businesses. It sold its remaining boiler and burner manufacturing businesses in early 2001. In May 2001 Ferguson Enterprises CEO Charles Banks was named group chief executive.

Also in 2001 Wolseley bought the heating and plumbing operations of Westburne Group (from France-based Rexel a distributor of electrical equipment) for $356 million to further expand in the US. In 2002 Wolseley bought Clayton Acquisition a Florida-based wholesale distributor of waterworks for $110 million. Additionally in 2002 the company bought Wasco a Dutch heating-equipment supplier for $58 million to expand in Europe. In December of that year Ireland was replaced as chairman by deputy chairman John Whybrow.

In July 2003 Wolseley bought Pinault Bois & Materiaux (now PB & M) which distributes lumber and building supplies in France from Pinault-Printemps-Redoute. Wolseley acquired three North American businesses JM Lumber Liberty Equipment & Supply and Nuroc Plumbing and Heating Supplies in September 2003.

The company acquired Tobler Management [now Wolseley (Schweiz)] a Swiss HVAC wholesaler from CapVis in December 2003. PB & M acquired Groupe Simoni a French building materials distributor in January 2004. Wolseley expanded its Irish business through the August 2004 acquisition of Brooks Group an Irish building supply company from UPM-Kymmene. Capping an acquisitive year Wolseley also acquired Parnell-Martin Management and Record Supply Company in the US and TAPS Wholesale Bath Centre in Canada in December 2004.

Overall in the fiscal year ended July 2005 the company spent 431 million on 26 acquisitions.

In April 2006 Wolseley acquired Brandon Hire for 72 million. The acquisition of DT Group in September brought Wolseley into new markets in Denmark Finland Norway and Sweden. In October the company purchased Woodcote - stavebni materialy a.s. a general builders merchant with operations in the Czech Republic Croatia Hungary Poland Romania and Slovakia. Overall in fiscal 2006 the company added 279 new locations.

In August 2007 Wolseley purchased Davidson Pipe Company in the US thereby gaining access to the New York metropolitan market.

In 2008 the company acquired Gama Myjava in Slovakia.

In May 2009 Wolseley sold a 51% stake in BMC Stock to The Gores Group LLC a US private equity firm. In June Ian Meakins joined Wolseley as CEO. He succeeded Claude "Chip" Hornsby who resigned from the position after three years.

In July 2011 the company sold its Electric Center business to Edmundson Electrical. In November Wolseley sold its remaining 49% stake in Stock Building Supply to Gores Group.

In 2017 the company changed its name from Wolseley PLC to Ferguson PLC.

EXECUTIVES

Group Chief Executive Officer, Executive Director, Kevin Murphy, $1,118,300 total compensation
Non-Executive Independent Director, Brian May
Non-Executive Independent Director, Catherine Halligan
Non-Executive Independent Director, Thomas Schmitt
Non-Executive Independent Chairman of the Board, Geoffrey Drabble
Non-Executive Independent Director, Suzanne Wood
Group General Counsel, Ian Graham
Group Chief Financial Officer, Executive Director, Bill Brundage, $552,500 total compensation
Non-Executive Independent Director, Kelly Baker
Group Chief Information Officer, Mike Sajor
Auditors: Deloitte LLP

LOCATIONS

HQ: Ferguson PLC (New)
1020 Eskdale Road, Winnersh Triangle, Wokingham RG41 5TS
Phone: (44) 0118 927 3800   **Fax:** (44) 118 929 8701
Web: www.fergusonplc.com

2011 Sales

	% of total
North America	
US	40
Canada	6
UK	18
Nordic region	16
France	14
Central Europe	6
Total	**100**

PRODUCTS/OPERATIONS

2011 Sales by Market

	% of total
Residential repair maintenance & improvement	36
Non-residential repair maintenance & improvement	21
Residential new construction	20
Non-residential new construction	16
Civil infrastructure	7
Total	**100**

2011 Sales by Product

	% of total
Plumbing heating & air conditioning	40
Building materials	30
Civil/waterworks commercial & industrial	28
Other	2
Total	**100**

Selected Products

Building materials
  Beams and trusses
  Bricks blocks and aggregates
  Cement
  Doors and frames
  Glass
  Insulation
  Plaster and plasterboard
  Roofing materials
  Tiles and flooring
  Timber products
Civil/waterworks industrial and commercial
  Carbon and stainless steel pipes valves and fittings
  Drainage pipes
  Underground pressure pipes
Plumbing heating and air conditioning
  Air conditioning equipment
  Baths and showers
  Boilers and burners
  Brassware
  Control equipment
  Copper tubing
  Heat pumps
  Hot water cylinders
  Plastic pipes and fittings
  Radiators and valves
  Sanitaryware
  Solar equipment
  Ventilation equipment
Other
  Electrical cables
  Lighting
  Wiring
Services
  Customer inventory management
  Installation
  Maintenance

Selected Subsidiaries

CFM
  Heating appliances Luxembourg
DT Group
  Building materials Denmark
Ferguson Enterprises Inc.
  Wholesale distribution of plumbing heating and piping products US
Manzardo SpA
  Heating and plumbing equipment Italy
OAG AG
  Heating and plumbing products Austria
PB&M
  Building materials and wood distribution France
Tobler
  Heating and plumbing products Switzerland
Wasco Holding BV
  Heating equipment The Netherlands
Wolseley Canada
  Wholesale distribution of plumbing heating and ventilation products Canada
Wolseley France
  Building materials plumbing and heating products France
Wolseley UK Limited
  Construction products UK
Woodcote Group
  Construction materials Czech Republic

COMPETITORS

INTERLINE BRANDS INC.
SID HARVEY INDUSTRIES INC.

HISTORICAL FINANCIALS

Company Type: Public

Income Statement   FYE: July 31

	REVENUE ($ mil.)	NET INCOME ($ mil.)	NET PROFIT MARGIN	EMPLOYEES
07/21	22,792	1,508	6.6%	29,538
07/20	21,819	961	4.4%	34,637
07/19	22,010	1,108	5.0%	35,939
07/18	20,752	1,267	6.1%	34,056
07/17	19,971	1,027	5.1%	33,511
Annual Growth	3.4%	10.1%	—	(3.1%)

2021 Year-End Financials

Debt ratio: 20.1%
Return on equity: 32.8%
Cash ($ mil.): 1,335
Current ratio: 1.67
Long-term debt ($ mil.): 2,528

No. of shares (mil.): 222
Dividends
  Yield: —
  Payout: 35.7%
Market value ($ mil.): —

FIH Mobile Ltd

EXECUTIVES

Senior Director, Finance Division, Hui Chung Chen
Independent Non-Executive Director, Daniel Mehan
Director - Business Development, Nai-Pin Hsiung

Independent Non-Executive Director, Yun Chih Tao

Acting Executive Chairman of the Board, Chief Executive Officer, Yu Yang Chih, $91,000 total compensation

Executive Director, Wen-Yi Kuo, $444,000 total compensation

Company Secretary, Kin Yan Wong

Chief Financial Officer, Kam Wah Tam

Chief Operating Officer, Executive Director, Hsiao-Yi Meng, $25,000 total compensation

Auditors: Deloitte Touche Tohmatsu

LOCATIONS

HQ: FIH Mobile Ltd
No. 369 Jianshe South Road, Anci District, Langfang City, Hebei Province
Phone:
Web: www.fihmb.com

HISTORICAL FINANCIALS

Company Type: Public

Income Statement   FYE: December 31

	REVENUE ($ mil.)	NET INCOME ($ mil.)	NET PROFIT MARGIN	EMPLOYEES
12/19	14,378	(12)	—	85,729
12/18	14,929	(857)	—	97,484
12/17	12,080	(525)	—	92,779
12/16	6,233	138	2.2%	74,652
12/15	7,450	229	3.1%	81,013
Annual Growth	17.9%	—	—	1.4%

2019 Year-End Financials

Debt ratio: 8.6%
Return on equity: (-0.5%)
Cash ($ mil.): 1,545
Current ratio: 1.18
Long-term debt ($ mil.): —

No. of shares (mil.): —
Dividends
  Yield: —
  Payout: —
  Market value ($ mil.): —

	STOCK PRICE ($) FY Close	P/E High/Low	PER SHARE ($) Earnings	Dividends	Book Value
12/19	3.91	— —	(0.00)	0.00	0.26
12/18	2.11	— —	(0.11)	0.00	0.26
12/17	5.86	— —	(0.07)	0.36	0.39
12/16	6.16	489 348	0.02	0.55	0.45
12/15	7.73	410 257	0.03	0.49	0.47
Annual Growth	(15.7%) (14.4%)	— —	—	—	—

First Abu Dhabi Bank PJSC

Auditors: KPMG Lower Gulf Limited

LOCATIONS

HQ: First Abu Dhabi Bank PJSC
FAB Building, Khalifa Business Park 1 Al Qurum, P. O. Box 6316, Abu Dhabi
Phone:
Web: www.bankfab.com

HISTORICAL FINANCIALS

Company Type: Public

Income Statement   FYE: December 31

	ASSETS ($ mil.)	NET INCOME ($ mil.)	INCOME AS % OF ASSETS	EMPLOYEES
12/19	223,817	3,409	1.5%	5,451
12/18	202,620	3,270	1.6%	0
12/17	182,156	2,486	1.4%	0
12/16	114,537	1,441	1.3%	0
12/15	110,691	1,424	1.3%	0
Annual Growth	19.2%	24.4%	—	—

2019 Year-End Financials

Return on assets: 1.6%
Return on equity: 11.9%
Long-term debt ($ mil.): —
No. of shares (mil.): —
Sales ($ mil): 9,095

Dividends
  Yield: —
  Payout: 67.2%
  Market value ($ mil.): —

Flex Ltd

Flex Ltd. a top contract manufacturer offers solutions that span from initial design through ramp-up and volume manufacturing as well as through end of life and circularity offerings. Flex's services range from design engineering to manufacturing and assembly to logistics to innovation services and power modules. It makes and assembles printed circuit board assembly and assembly of systems and subsystems that incorporate printed circuit boards and complex electromechanical components. Flex covers a lot of ground around the world operating more than 100 locations in approximately 30 countries. Majority of the company's revenue are generated from international markets.

Operations

The company recently made changes in its organizational structure to further drive efficiency and productivity. As a result the company's financial performance is based on two reportable segments: Flex Agility Solutions (FAS) and Flex Reliability Solutions (FRS).

FAS segment comprises about 60% of the company's revenue. It is optimized for longer product lifecycles requiring complex ramps with specialized production models and critical environments.

The FRS segment is optimized for longer product lifecycles requiring complex ramps with specialized production models and critical environments. It contributes more than 40% of the revenue.

Geographic Reach

Flex operates a network of more than 100 facilities in approximately 30 countries. Its extensive network of innovation labs design centers manufacturing and services sites in the world's major consumer and enterprise products markets are located in Asia the Americas and Europe.

The company's headquarters is located in Changi South Lane Singapore and its headquarters in US is located in San Jose California.

Customers in China account for about 25% of sales with customers in Mexico generating nearly 20% of sales and US customers supplying some 15%. Brazil Malaysia India and other countries account for the rest.

Sales and Marketing

Flex delivers technology innovation supply chain and manufacturing solutions to various industries such as automotive and healthcare.

Financial Performance

Flex's performance for the span of five years have fluctuated with an upward trend from 2017 to 2019 then having a downward trend for the following years of 2020 and 2021.

Net sales for fiscal year 2021 decreased less than 1% or $0.1 billion to $24.1 billion from the prior year. The decrease in sale was most notable in its FAS segment down $0.6 billion or 4.0% from the prior year driven by lower demand in its Consumer Devices business due to the impact of COVID-19 and more significantly its continued strategic shift away from high volatility short cycle businesses that we initiated in the prior years.

Its net income totaled $613 million representing an increase of $525 million or 597% compared to fiscal year 2020 due to the factors explained above further impacted by higher impairment charges incurred in fiscal year 2020.

Flex held about $2.6 billion in cash in 2021 compared to about $1.9 billion the year before. The company's operating activities provided $144 million. The company's investing activities used $202 million while financing activities provided $743 million. Main cash uses were for purchase of property and equipment and repayments of bank borrowings and long-term debt.

Strategy

Flex helps customers responsibly build products that create value and improve people's lives. It does this by providing its customers with product development lifecycle services from innovation design and engineering to manufacturing supply chain solutions logistics and circularity offerings. Its strategy is to enable and scale innovation for customers maintain its leadership in its capabilities and build extended offerings in high-growth industries and markets.

Flex focuses on hiring and retaining the world's best talent to maintain the company's competitiveness and world-class capabilities. It has taken steps to attract the best engineering functional and operational leaders and have accelerated efforts to develop the future leaders of the company.

Flex believes that building strong partnerships with customers and delivering on its commitments strengthens trust and customer retention. Its customers come first and it has a relentless focus on delivering distinctive products and services in a cost-effective manner with fast time to market. Flex is highly collaborative and leverages its global system and processes to operate with speed and responsiveness to provide customers with a reliant supply chain partner.

Flex focuses on companies that are leaders in their industry and value the company's superior capabilities in design manufacturing and supply chain services. It focuses on high growth industries and markets where it has distinctive competence and compelling value propositions. Flex's market-focused approach to managing business increases customers' competitiveness by leveraging its deep vertical industry and cross-industry expertise as well as global scale regional presence and agility to respond to changes in market dynamics.

The company continues to invest in maintaining the leadership of its world-class manufacturing and services capabilities including automation new product introduction and large-scale manufacturing.

HISTORY

Flextronics International formed in 1990 followed two earlier contract manufacturers named Flextronics formed in 1969 and 1980. The latter iteration used acquisitions to expand throughout Asia and the US. In 1988 it opened the first US-managed contract electronics plant in China and that year sales topped $200 million.

But acquisitions burdened Flextronics with debt and left it with disparate operations. It divested its US-based manufacturing operations and laid off 75% of its workforce. The company brought in a management team to sell its healthy Asian operations to pay off debt. These operations formed the current incarnation of Flextronics International.

A revitalized Flextronics based in Singapore went public in 1994. It quickly joined the industry rush toward consolidation and globalization. Acquisitions included nCHIP (California 1996) FICO Plastics (Hong Kong 1997) Neutronics Electronic Industries (Austria 1997) and Kyrel EMS Oyj (Finland and France 1999).

In 2000 Flextronics acquired rival The DII Group which propelled the company to the #4 spot in contract manufacturing (behind Solectron SCI Systems and Celestica). The company was also selected by Microsoft to build the software juggernaut's Xbox video game console. Later that year Motorola and Flextronics signed one of the largest outsourcing deals ever worth an estimated $30 billion over five years. The company expanded further in Asia when it acquired JIT Holdings a Singapore-based electronics manufacturer.

In 2001 Flextronics announced a deal with telecommunications giant Ericsson; under the pact Flextronics assumed management of Ericsson's mobile phone manufacturing operations worldwide. Later that year the company announced that it would cut its workforce by about 10% and that the multibillion-dollar deal with Motorola unraveled due to a continuing market slowdown. Flextronics also repurchased Motorola's 5% stake in the company.

Also that year Flextronics bought Telcom Global Solutions a supplier of planning and design services for telecommunications providers. Flextronics later announced a deal with Xerox to acquire Xerox facilities in Brazil Canada Malaysia and Mexico for about $220 million and to provide manufacturing services to Xerox for five years. Later that year the company laid off 10000 workers — about 15% of its staff — in a cost-cutting move. Flextronics also acquired a 91% stake in Orbiant a telephone network services spinoff of Swedish telecom giant Telia for $100 million in cash (along with future payments pegged to the unit's performance).

In 2002 the company made a deal with CASIO COMPUTER under which Flextronics bought two CASIO plants in Asia then supplied the Japanese electronics maker with finished products in a three-year pact. Also that year the company significantly expanded its presence in southern China with the purchase of Hong Kong-based NatSteel Broadway (printed circuit boards plastic and metal components) for about $367 million.

In 2004 Flextronics took over optical wireless and enterprise manufacturing as well as optical design operations from Nortel Networks in a four-year supply deal generating about $2.5 billion in annual revenues. Flextronics later closed several former Nortel facilities in Canada France and Northern Ireland.

Flextronics also acquired a majority ownership stake in India-based software services provider Hughes Software Systems (HSS) in 2004. The following year Flextronics purchased Agilent's mobile communications camera module business. The company sold its semiconductor division to AMIS Holdings (now part of ON Semiconductor) and its Flextronics Network Services division was merged with a company called Telavie and renamed Relacom; Flextronics retained a 30% stake.

Flextronics set plans in 2005 to build an industrial park in Chennai India to supplement its existing operations on the subcontinent where it previously employed more than 5000 people. The development added to the two manufacturing facilities and three design centers Flextronics had in India.

To focus on its core electronics manufacturing services business in 2006 Flextronics sold its Flextronics Software Systems business (renamed Aricent) to an affiliate of KKR for about $900 million in cash and notes. Flextronics retained a 15% equity interest in the software development business which was primarily based in India (it sold the remaining stake in 2009). Divestitures of its software and semiconductor businesses took a small chunk out of the company's revenues — $278 million in fiscal 2006.

Flextronics then acquired International Display-Works a contract manufacturer of small LCDs and LCD modules for cell phones and other consumer electronics for stock valued at approximately $243 million. International DisplayWorks became a wholly owned subsidiary of Flextronics operating within the company's Components Group. Also in 2006 nLight Corp. acquired the assets of Flextronics Photonics including a line of fiber-coupled and hybrid microelectronic devices.

In 2007 Flextronics purchased rival contract manufacturer Solectron in a deal valued at $3.6 billion. The combination vaulted the company into the position of the second-largest contract electronics manufacturer in the world trailing only Hon Hai Precision Industry the maker of products for Apple Dell and many other companies.

The next year it bought contract disposable device maker Avail Medical Products a private company with around $250 million in sales to further the expansion of its Flextronics Medical segment. Also in 2008 Flextronics inked a deal to acquire Elcoteq's ZAO Elcoteq subsidiary and plant in St. Petersburg Russia. Flextronics however later terminated the transaction and was forced to pay a fee for noncompletion.

In 2009 it sold its stake in Aricent a privately held communications software company to investment firms KKR and CPP Investment Board for about $250 million. The sale was part of a plan to sell noncore assets as Flextronics tried to bolster its balance sheet during the economic downturn. At the end of the year it bought SloMedical S.R.O. a leading maker of disposable medical devices for the European market. In addition to adding disposable devices for the medical and surgical market in Eastern Europe SloMedical (based in Slovenia) gave Flextronics an FDA-compliant clean room-enabled production site with low production costs.

In 2012 Flextronics acquired Stellar Microelectronics an EMS provider based in California that specializes in custom packaging services for the aerospace defense and medical manufacturing markets as part of a plan to expand services for the highly regulated markets. Also that year Flextronics sold its Vista Point camera module business to Tessera Technologies' subsidiary DigitalOptics; the sale included the brand intellectual property and China-based manufacturing assets.

EXECUTIVES

Independent Director, Erin McSweeney
Chief Financial Officer, Paul Lundstrom, $390,833 total compensation
Independent Director, John Harris
President - Global Operations and Components, Francois Barbier, $603,500 total compensation
Independent Director, Michael Hurlston
Director, Patrick Ward
President of Flex Agility Solutions, Michael Hartung, $514,023 total compensation
Chief Accounting Officer, David Bennett
Independent Chairman of the Board, Michael Capellas

Executive Vice President, General Counsel, Scott Offer, $534,820 total compensation
Chief Executive Officer, Director, Revathi Advaithi, $862,500 total compensation
Auditors: DELOITTE & TOUCHE LLP

LOCATIONS

HQ: Flex Ltd
2 Changi South Lane, 486123
Phone: (65) 6876 9899
Web: www.flex.com

2018 Sales

	$ mil.	% of total
China	6,649	25
Mexico	4,539	17
US	3,106	12
Brazil	2,181	8
Malaysia	1,996	8
India	1,805	7
Other countries	5,935	23
Total	**26,211**	**100**

PRODUCTS/OPERATIONS

2018 Sales

	$ mil.	% of total
Communications & Enterprise Compute	8,336	32
Consumer Technologies Group	6,836	26
Industrial & emerging industries	6,813	24
High reliability solutions	4,829	18
Total	**26,211**	**100**

Selected Services

Assembly and manufacturing
  Box build (complete systems)
  Complex electromechanical components
  Printed circuit boards (PCBs)
  Subsystems (including those that incorporate PCBs)
Engineering
  Design
  Prototyping
  Test development
Materials procurement and management
  Planning
  Purchasing
  Warehousing
Network support
  Installation and maintenance of telecommunications systems and corporate networks
Packaging
Plastic and metal components
Product distribution
Recycling and refurbishment
Testing of PCBs subsystems and systems
Warranty repair

COMPETITORS

ARROW ELECTRONICS INC.	LIKEWIZE CORP.
BRIGHTPOINT INC.	RESIDEO TECHNOLOGIES
Celestica Inc	INC.
FILTRONIC PLC	TAITRON COMPONENTS
Huawei Investment &	INCORPORATED
Holding Co. Ltd.	TESSCO TECHNOLOGIES
JABIL INC.	INCORPORATED

HISTORICAL FINANCIALS

Company Type: Public

Income Statement   FYE: March 31

	REVENUE ($ mil.)	NET INCOME ($ mil.)	NET PROFIT MARGIN	EMPLOYEES
03/21	24,124	613	2.5%	167,201
03/20	24,209	87	0.4%	160,000
03/19	26,210	93	0.4%	200,000
03/18	25,441	428	1.7%	200,000
03/17	23,862	319	1.3%	200,000
Annual Growth	**0.3%**	**17.7%**	**—**	**(4.4%)**

2021 Year-End Financials

Debt ratio: 23.8%	No. of shares (mil.): 492
Return on equity: 19.5%	Dividends
Cash ($ mil.): 2,637	Yield: —
Current ratio: 1.45	Payout: —
Long-term debt ($ mil.): 3,515	Market value ($ mil.): —

Fomento Economico Mexicano, S.A.B. de C.V.

Fomento Econ mico Mexicano or FEMSA is a top soft drink bottler and convenience store operator in Latin America. Its Coca-Cola FEMSA subsidiary is the world's largest Coca-Cola bottler. FEMSA bottles Coca-Cola Sprite other soft drinks juices and water in around 10 Latin American countries. The company operates about 560 service stations located in more than 15 states throughout Mexico and it also owns about 19565 OXXO convenience stores in Colombia Chile Mexico and Peru primarily in the northern part of the country through its FEMSA Comercio subsidiary.

Operations

In addition to its beverage operations and retail holdings (the OXXO chain is the largest and fastest-growing in the Americas) FEMSA also provides logistics refrigeration services and plastics to internal and external customers.

The company's business units include Coca-Cola FEMSA (about 35% of sales) and FEMSA Comerico which is divided to Proximity division (approximately 35% of sales) Health division (about 15%) and Fuel division (more than 5%). Other business unit accounts for the rest.

Geographic Reach

Headquartered in Nuevo Le n Mexico FEMSA operates in Argentina Brazil Colombia Costa Rica Guatemala Mexico Nicaragua Panama and Ecuador. Subsidiary Coca-Cola FEMSA operates in Argentina Brazil Central America Colombia Mexico and Venezuela.

Sales and Marketing

FEMSA relies extensively on advertising sales promotions and retailer support programs to target the particular preferences of its consumers. It advertises in all major communications media. Its principal channels are small retailers on-premise accounts such as restaurants and bars supermarkets and third-party distributors.

Financial Performance

FEMSA's consolidated total revenues decreased 3% to Ps. 493 million in 2020 compared to Ps. 506.7 billion in 2019. Coca-Cola FEMSA's total revenues decreased 6% to Ps. 183.6 billion mainly as a result of unfavorable price-mix effects in connection with the COVID-19 pandemic.

The company's net income was Ps. 3.8 million an 87% decrease from the previous year reflecting lower income from operations; higher taxes and other non-operating expenses reflecting the extraordinary tax payment of Ps. 8.8 billion agreed with the Mexican tax authority during the second quarter; impairments including for certain assets at Coca-Cola FEMSA and the closure of its Specialty's Cafe and Bakery operation also during the second quarter; higher interest expenses and a negative impact due to FEMSA's participation in Heineken's results. These were partially offset by a non-cash foreign exchange gain related to FEMSA's US dollar-denominated cash position as impacted by the depreciation of the Mexican peso.

The company's cash at the end of 2020 totaled Ps. 107.6 million. Operating activities generated Ps. 53.2 million while investing activities used Ps. 31.4 million mainly for the acquisition of Synergy and other businesses. Financing activities provided another Ps. 19.6 million.

Strategy

FEMSA understands the importance of connecting with its end consumers by interpreting their needs and ultimately delivering the right products to them for the right occasions and the optimal value proposition. The company strives to achieve this by developing brand value expanding its significant distribution capabilities and improving the efficiency of its operations while aiming to reach its full potential. FEMSA continues to improve its information gathering and processing systems in order to better know and understand what consumers want and need and it is improving its production and distribution by more efficiently leveraging its asset base.

Mergers and Acquisitions

In 2020 FEMSA agreed to acquire two independent specialized distribution businesses in the US: Southeastern Paper Group based in Spartanburg South Carolina and Southwest Paper Company (dba "SWPlus") based in Wichita Kansas. These acquisitions fit well with FEMSA's strategy of creating a national distribution platform building on FEMSA's capabilities and the foundation formed by the merger of WAXIE Sanitary Supply and North American Corporation earlier in the year.

HISTORY

FEMSA's 2005 purchase of Panamerican Beverages (Panamco) through its Coca-Cola subsidiary gave the company access to markets in Brazil Colombia Costa Rica Guatemala Nicaragua Panama and Venezuela.

EXECUTIVES

Executive Chairman of the Board of Directors, Jose Fernandez Carbajal
Director, Javier Gerardo Astaburuaga Sanjines
Independent Director, Ricardo Guajardo Touche
Director, Francisco Javier Fernandez Carbajal
Director, Jose Fernando Calderon Rojas
Director, Alberto Bailleres Gonzalez
Senior Vice President - Administration and Corporate Control, Gerardo Estrada Attolini
Independent Director, Michael Larson
Chief Executive Officer, Director, Miguel Eduardo Padilla Silva
Director, Paulina Garza Laguera Gonda de Marroquin
Independent Director, Robert Denham
Director, Barbara Garza Laguera Gonda
Independent Director, Alfonso Gonzalez Migoya
Chief Executive Officer of FEMSA Comercio, Daniel Alberto Rodriguez Cofre
General Counsel, Secretary of the Board of Directors, Carlos Eduardo Aldrete Ancira
Chief Executive Officer of Coca Cola FEMSA, John Anthony Santa Maria Otazua
Independent Director, Alfonso De Angoitia Noriega
Director, Mariana Garza Laguera Gonda
Independent Director, Ricardo Ernesto Saldivar Escajadillo
Chief Executive Officer of Strategic Businesses of FEMSA, Director, Alfonso Garza Garza
Director, Bertha Gonzalez
Senior Vice President - Corporate Affairs, Roberto Cifrian
Independent Director, Victor Tiburcio Celorio
Chief Corporate Officer, Francisco Camacho Beltran

Senior Vice President of Human Resources, Raymundo Yutani Vela
Auditors: Mancera, S.C. (member of Ernst & Young Global)

LOCATIONS

HQ: Fomento Economico Mexicano, S.A.B. de C.V. General Anaya No. 601 Pte., Colonia Bella Vista, Monterrey, Nuevo Leon NL 64410
Phone: (52) 818 328 6000   **Fax:** (52) 818 328 6080
Web: www.femsa.com

2014

Geography mil (pesos)		%
Mexico and Central America	186,736	71
South America	69,172	26
Venezuela	8,835	3
Consolidation adjustments	(1294)	-
Total	**263,449**	**100**

PRODUCTS/OPERATIONS

2014

Business Unit mil (pesos)		%
Coca-Cola FEMSA	147,298	53
FEMSA Comercio	109,624	40
Other	20,069	7
Consolidation Adjustments	(13542)	-
Total	**263,449**	**100**

COMPETITORS

Alpek S.A.B. de C.V.
Arca Continental S.A.B. de C.V.
Brenntag Holding GmbH
COCA-COLA EUROPACIFIC PARTNERS PLC
Companhia Brasileira de Distribuicao
EDP - ENERGIAS DE PORTUGAL S.A.
FONTERRA CO-OPERATIVE GROUP LIMITED
Falabella S.A.
Louis Dreyfus Holding B.V.
MAPFRE SA
Metal rgica Gerdau S/A
SONAE - SGPS S.A.
STEINHOFF INTERNATIONAL HOLDINGS LTD
WH Group Limited

HISTORICAL FINANCIALS

Company Type: Public

Income Statement   FYE: December 31

	REVENUE ($ mil.)	NET INCOME ($ mil.)	NET PROFIT MARGIN	EMPLOYEES
12/20	24,810	(97)	—	320,618
12/19	26,782	1,094	4.1%	314,656
12/18	23,888	1,219	5.1%	297,073
12/17	23,373	2,152	9.2%	295,097
12/16	19,307	1,021	5.3%	266,144
Annual Growth	6.5%	—		4.8%

2020 Year-End Financials

Debt ratio: 1.3%	No. of shares (mil.): —
Return on equity: (-0.7%)	Dividends
Cash ($ mil.): 5,416	Yield: 1.8%
Current ratio: 1.70	Payout: 2,755.6%
Long-term debt ($ mil.): 9,052	Market value ($ mil.): —

	STOCK PRICE ($) FY Close	P/E High/Low		PER SHARE ($) Earnings	Dividends	Book Value
12/20	75.77	90	56	0.05	1.43	0.67
12/19	94.51	98	85	0.05	1.48	0.74
12/18	86.05	80	68	0.06	1.39	0.73
12/17	93.90	44	37	0.11	1.29	0.71
12/16	76.21	84	70	0.05	1.17	0.57
Annual Growth	(0.1%)	—	—	0.5%	5.2%	4.0%

Fonterra Co-Operative Group Ltd

Green lush and overflowing with cows New Zealand makes more milk than its citizens can drink. Fonterra Co-operative Group sells the excess and value-added dairy products to more than 130 markets around the world (China is its largest single market). The co-op is the world's largest dairy exporter providing industrial dairy ingredients as well as fluid milk yogurt butter and spreads cheese and ice cream for consumers. Its well-known brands include Anchor Anmum Anlene NZMP and Farm Source. Fonterra operates more than 30 manufacturing sites across New Zealand which process some 16 billion liters of milk annually. The co-op is owned by its 10000 farmer shareholders.

Operations
Fonterra's reportable segments are Asia Pacific AMENA and Greater China.

AMENA represents the ingredients foodservice and FMCG businesses in Africa Middle East Europe North Asia and Americas (including Latin America). The segment accounts for nearly 40% of the company's revenue.

Asia Pacific represents the ingredients foodservice and FMCG businesses in New Zealand South East Asia and Australia (including export to the Pacific Islands) and Sri Lanka and Indian sub-continent and Fonterra Farm Source stores. The segment accounts for about 35% of the company's revenue.

Greater China represents the ingredients foodservice and FMCG businesses in Greater China and the Falcon China Farms joint venture. The segment accounts for about 25% of the company's revenue.

Geographic Reach
Based in New Zealand Fonterra operations in US Australia Brazil China Indonesia Japan Malaysia Philippines Sri Lanka Thailand Valenzuela Vietnam the Netherlands and the UAE.

Financial Performance
Fonterra's revenue has been trending up since fiscal 2016 (ended July) and experienced a slight decrease in 2019 but overall it has an 18% five-year increase since 2016 to 2020. Net income had been growing strongly until fiscal 2017 when it fell slightly; it plummeted into the red in fiscal 2019 but became profitable in 2020

In fiscal 2020 the company reported revenue of NZ$20.2 billion up by NZ$1.1 billion or 5% from the prior year mainly due to improved Ingredients pricing and the product mix we sold. Its Greater China Foodservice business also contributed an additional $166 million in revenue despite the disruption of Covid-19.

Net income dramatically rose that year from a loss of NZ$562 million in fiscal 2019 to a profit of NZ$686 million. The results were impacted by the increase in earnings before interest and taxes.

Cash at the end of fiscal 2020 was NZ$780 million an increase of NZ$264 million from the prior year. Cash from operations contributed NZ$1.5 billion to the coffers while investing activities contributed another NZ$336 million and financing activities used another NZ$1.5 billion for repayment of borrowings.

Strategy
Fonterra has determined that its operating segments are Asia Pacific AMENA Greater China and oCOO. As a result of the Group's matrix structure the company's reportable segments are Asia Pacific AMENA and Greater China inclusive of their respective attribution of oCOO. This presentation provides a full end-to-end view of performance for each of the customer facing regional business units.

In July 2020 the new operating model formed the basis for the company's operating segments. Under the new operating model the business is managed as a matrix form of organization whereby regional business unit CEOs and the COO have overlapping responsibility for the performance of operating segments. Information about the performance of oCOO is reported to the FMT both separately and attributed to each of the regional business units.

In September 2019 Fonterra announced a new strategy and operating model. The Fonterra's new operating model is based around the three regional business units supported by a shared infrastructure (the office of the COO ? oCOO) that includes New Zealand milk collection and processing operations and assets a central portfolio management function Group IT and Innovation functions.

Since July 2019 the progress of the strategy review includes completion of the sales processes relating to the company's investments in Goodminton AG (Goodminton) and DMV Fonterra Excipients GmbH & Co. KG (DFE Pharma) and the sale of Dennington manufacturing site. The company's holdings of Beingmate Baby & Child Food Co. Ltd. (Beingmate) shares continue to be held for trading with an active sales process in place. During the year the company reduced its holdings in Beingmate from 18.82% down to 9.11% on 31 July 2020. The company expects to sell its remaining investment within 12 months of balance date.

The strategic reviews of the China Farms and Brazil consumer and foodservice businesses have advanced such that the businesses meet the requirements to be classified as held for sale on 31 July 2020. Both the China Farms and Brazil consumer and foodservice businesses are considered to be discontinued operations. Challenges with the operational performance of the Falcon China Farms JV led to the reassessment of the carrying value of the investment.

EXECUTIVES

Chief Operating Officer - Global Operations, Robert Spurway
Managing Director - Co-operative Affairs, Mike Cronin
Chief Operating Officer - Global Consumer and Foodservice, Judith Swales
Independent Director, Holly Kramer
Chief Executive Officer - Greater China, Teh-Han Chow
Independent Director, Scott St. John
Independent Director, Bruce Hassall
Independent Director, Clinton Dines
Chief Financial Officer, Marc Rivers
Vice President - Commercial, Paul Washer
Director, Ashley Waugh
Chief Executive Officer, Miles Hurrell
Director, Nicola Shadbolt
Chief Operating Officer - NZMP, Kelvin Wickham
Auditors: KPMG

LOCATIONS

HQ: Fonterra Co-Operative Group Ltd
Private Bag 92032, Auckland 1142
Phone: (64) 9 374 9000   **Fax:** (64) 9 374 9001
Web: www.fonterra.com

2018 Sales

	% of total
China	20
Other Asia	28
Latin America	11
New Zealand	10
Australia	9
US	4
Europe	3
Rest of World	15
Total	**100**

PRODUCTS/OPERATIONS

2018 Sales

	% of total
Ingredients	69
Consumer and Food Service	30
China Farms	1
Total	**100**

COMPETITORS

BEL
BEL BRANDS USA INC.
BRAIME GROUP PLC
BRITISH RED CROSS SOCIETY
Clariant AG
DEVRO PLC
FOREMOST FARMS USA COOPERATIVE
GALAXY NUTRITIONAL FOODS INC.
HEWLETT WILLIAM AND FLORA FOUNDATION (INC)
HONG KONG AND CHINA GAS COMPANY LIMITED THE
Holcim AG
ILG LLC
SAPUTO CHEESE USA INC.
SHELL FOUNDATION
SSP GROUP PLC
THE AUTOMOBILE ASSOCIATION LIMITED
THE LEUKEMIA & LYMPHOMA SOCIETY INC
TRUTH INITIATIVE FOUNDATION
UNITED STATES GOLF ASSOCIATION INC.
WH Group Limited

HISTORICAL FINANCIALS

Company Type: Public

Income Statement   FYE: July 31

	REVENUE ($ mil.)	NET INCOME ($ mil.)	NET PROFIT MARGIN	EMPLOYEES
07/20	13,511	456	3.4%	0
07/19	13,291	(368)	—	0
07/18	13,934	(150)	—	0
07/17	14,402	549	3.8%	21,400
07/16	12,237	576	4.7%	21,300
Annual Growth	2.5%	(5.6%)	—	—

2020 Year-End Financials

Debt ratio: 22.5%	No. of shares (mil.): 1,612
Return on equity: 10.9%	Dividends
Cash ($ mil.): 524	Yield: —
Current ratio: 1.43	Payout: —
Long-term debt ($ mil.): 3,515	Market value ($ mil.): —

Fortescue Metals Group Ltd

Fortescue Metals Group is one of the world's largest producers of iron ore. Fortescue's wholly owned and integrated operations in the Pilbara include the Chichester Solomon and Western mining hubs. Its mining infrastructure is connected to the five berth Herb Elliott Port and Judith Street Harbour towage facility in Port Hedland via the fastest heavy haul railway in the world. Fortescue has a well-established presence in South America. In Ecuador it has concessions prospective for copper in exploration phase covering 135000 hectares (ha) and in Argentina the company currently hold 323000 ha of tenements prospective for copper-gold.

Operations

Fortescue Metals has discovered and developed significant iron ore deposits and constructed some of the largest mines in the world.

The Chichester Hub which includes the Cloudbreak and Christmas Creek mines is located in the Chichester Ranges and produces more than 100 million tonnes per annum from Ore Processing Facilities (OPFs).

The Solomon Hub in the Hamersley Ranges is located 60 km north of Tom Price and 120 km to the west of its Chichester Hub. It comprises the Firetail Kings Valley and Queens Valley mines which together have a production capacity of 75 million tonnes per annum.

Fortescue Metals is developing the Western Hub which includes significant amounts of high iron content bedded iron ore and is now home to the Eliwana mine. Located 140 km to the west of Solomon the Eliwana mine spans over 50 km. The operation includes 143 km of rail linking to the Hamersley rail line and a 30 mtpa dry OPF.

Fortescue Metals wholly owns its purpose-designed rail and port facilities constructed to deliver iron ore from its mines to Port Hedland for shipment to its customers.

Geographic Reach

Based in Australia Fortescue Metals' primary market is China which accounts for about 90% of the company's total sales.

Sales and Marketing

Fortescue products are sold to a global customer base with the majority of tonnes sold to long-term customers in China. The company established its wholly owned Chinese sales entity FMG Trading Shanghai a portside sales capability to supply its products directly to Chinese steel mills from regional ports. This capability is now well established and has allowed the company to enhance its service to small and medium-sized customers through direct supply in Renminbi complementing its existing contractual seaborne arrangements.

Financial Performance

The company's revenue for fiscal 2021 increased to $22.3 billion compared from the prior year with $12.8 billion.

Profit for fiscal 2021 increased to $10.3 billion compared from the prior year with $4.7 billion.

Cash held by the company at the end of fiscal 2021 increased to $6.9 billion. Cash provided by operations was $12.6 billion while cash used for investing and financing activities were $3.6 billion and $6.9 billion respectively. Main uses of cash were payments for property plant and equipment and dividends paid.

Strategy

During the year the company continued to deliver on its integrated operations and marketing strategy while increasing capacity within its supply chain and delivering consistent and predictable operational performance to achieve record sales volumes. Importantly the company have remained a low cost producer of seaborne iron ore. Strategic initiatives delivered in FY21 include:

The Eliwana mine and rail project transitioned to the operations team in January 2021 with the focus in the second half of the financial year on commissioning and ramp up to full production.

The Eliwana project is a high grade low strip ratio operation with dry processing which con-

tributes to its low cost structure Commissioning of the WHIMS plant at Christmas Creek occurred through December 2020. WHIMS delivers benefits in yield and grade with the plant transitioning to full capacity in the second half of FY21.

The Queens Valley development at Solomon commenced mining through FY21 providing feed to existing OPFs.

Ongoing business improvement processes focused on industry benchmarking and engaging its people to drive productivity improvements across the supply chain through data-driven informed decision making.

Company Background

Fortescue Metals was formed in 2003 after its majority shareholder The Metal Group purchased Allied Mining & Processing.

EXECUTIVES

Chairman, Andrew Forrest
Lead Non-Executive Independent Deputy Chairman of the Board, Mark Barnaba
Non-Executive Director, Ya-Qin Zhang
Director Operations, Fernando Pereira
Director Projects, Derek Brown
Director Australia – Eastern States, Felicity Underhill
Director - Projects Fortescue Future Industries, Gordon Cowe, $438,381 total compensation
Chief Operating Officer - Iron Ore, Dino Otranto
Chief Financial Officer, Ian Wells, $766,800 total compensation
Non-Executive Director, Penny Bingham-Hall
Non-Executive Director, Sebastian Coe
Non-Executive Director, Cao Zhiqiang
Joint Company Secretary, Cameron Wilson
Director Fortescue People, Linda O'Farrell
Director of Sales and Marketing, Danny Goeman
Director - Aboriginal Engagement, Community, Environment and Government, Warren Fish
Director Corporate Development, Legal and Strategy, Peter Huston
Director Sustainability and Corporate Affairs and Joint Company Secretary, Alison Terry
Director Health and Safety, Robert Watson
Director Community, Environment and Government, Tim Langmead
Chief Executive Officer, Managing Director, Executive Director, Elizabeth Gaines, $1,472,747 total compensation
Non-Executive Director, Jean Baderschneider
Non-Executive Director, Jennifer Morris
Chief Executive Officer - Fortescue Future Industries, Julie Shuttleworth, $751,886 total compensation
Auditors: PricewaterhouseCoopers

LOCATIONS

HQ: Fortescue Metals Group Ltd
  Level 2, 87 Adelaide Terrace, East Perth, Western Australia 6004
Phone: (61) 8 6218 8888   **Fax:** (61) 8 6218 8880
Web: www.fmgl.com.au

2015 Sales

	% of total
China	94
Others	6
Total	**100**

PRODUCTS/OPERATIONS

2015 Sales

	% of total
Sales of iron ore	97
Sales of joint venture ore	1
Other revenue	2
Total	**100**

COMPETITORS

Adastra Labs Holdings Ltd	Ternium Mexico S.A. de C.V.
Alderon Iron Ore Corp	VEDANTA LIMITED
Anyang Iron & Steel Group Co.Ltd	WARRIOR MET COAL INC.
CLOUD PEAK ENERGY INC.	Western Magnesium Corporation
KAZ MINERALS LIMITED	Zijin Mining Group Company Limited
Teck Resources Limited	

HISTORICAL FINANCIALS

Company Type: Public

Income Statement   FYE: June 30

	REVENUE ($ mil.)	NET INCOME ($ mil.)	NET PROFIT MARGIN	EMPLOYEES
06/20	12,820	4,735	36.9%	0
06/19	9,965	3,187	32.0%	0
06/18	6,887	879	12.8%	0
06/17	8,447	2,093	24.8%	0
06/16	7,083	984	13.9%	3,890
Annual Growth	16.0%	48.1%	—	—

2020 Year-End Financials

Debt ratio: 18.1%	No. of shares (mil.): —
Return on equity: 39.6%	Dividends
Cash ($ mil.): 4,855	Yield: 10.4%
Current ratio: 2.25	Payout: 78.5%
Long-term debt ($ mil.): 4,193	Market value ($ mil.): —

	STOCK PRICE ($) FY Close	P/E High/Low		PER SHARE ($) Earnings	Dividends	Book Value
06/20	19.21	14	6	1.53	2.01	4.30
06/19	12.70	12	5	1.03	1.39	3.44
06/18	6.53	34	23	0.28	0.52	3.12
06/17	8.03	17	8	0.67	0.44	3.12
06/16	5.28	17	6	0.32	0.06	2.70
Annual Growth	38.1%	—	—	48.4%	142.0%	12.4%

Fortum OYJ

Fortum generates energy or electric power across Europe. The company has a total of more than 50000 MW generation capacity in areas such as Finland Sweden Russia Germany the UK and Netherlands. Further the company produces power such as hydropower nuclear power combined heat and power condensing power wind power and solar power. The company also has significant operations in a growth area Russia including 15.7 MW of power generation capacity in 2020. (Russia accounted for about less than 5% of Fortum's total revenues that year). The Finnish government owns over 50% of Fortum.

Operations

Fortum operates through four reporting segments: Generation; City Solutions; Russia; Uniper; and Consumer Solutions.

Generation is responsible for Nordic power production. The segment comprises nuclear hydro wind and thermal power production as well as power portfolio optimization trading industrial intelligence and global nuclear services. It generates roughly 5% of revenue. City Solutions (less than 5%) is responsible for developing sustainable solutions for urban areas into a growing business for Fortum. The segment comprises heating cooling waste-to-energy biomass and other circular economy solutions as well as solar power production. The Russia segment consists of power and heat generation and sales in Russia. It generates less than 5% of revenue.

Consumer Solutions (less than 5%) is responsible for the electricity and gas retail businesses in the Nordics and Poland including the customer service invoicing and debt collection businesses. The Uniper segment accounts for majority of the company's revenue of about 90%. The company has a majority ownership in this subsidiary that operates in more than 40 countries providing energy and related services.

Geographic Reach

Finland-based company it has operations in more than 40 countries through its about 20000 professionals. Some of these countries include Finland Sweden Russia Poland Lithuania Latvia Norway Great Britain Estonia and India.

Its largest geographic sales are Western central Europe accounting for about 40% of the company's revenue. Followed by Germany (25%) the UK (20%) and Nordic (10%).

Sales and Marketing

Fortum have 2.4 million customers across different brands. The company is one of the world's largest producers carbon dioxide-free electricity in Europe.

Financial Performance

Fortum's performance for the span of five years have continued to grow year-by-year with 2020 having a significant increase among the other years during the period.

Fortum's sales in 2020 increased by 800% to ?49 billion compared to ?5.4 billion in the prior year.

Net profit for 2020 also increased by ?348 million to ?1.9 billion compared to ?1.5 billion.

Cash held by the company amounted to ?1.9 billion in 2020. Cash provided by operations and financing activities were ?2.5 billion and ?505 million respectively. Cash used for investing activities was ?2.1 million primarily for acquisition of shares.

Strategy

The company has updated its strategies to align better with Europe's ambition and goals of carbon neutrality by 205 as stated in The Paris Agreement. Fortum focuses on its four strategic priorities namely: to transform its own operations to carbon neutral; strengthen and grow in CO2-free power generation; to leverage a strong position in gas to enable the energy transition and to partner with industrial and infrastructure customers.

Company Background

The Loviisa power plant was the first nuclear power plant in Finland. The power plant has two units: unit 1 started operating in February 1977 and unit 2 in November 1980. The units are VVER-440 type pressurized water reactors.

HISTORY

The 1998 betrothal of two Finnish state-controlled businesses created the country's largest enterprise and even the European Union extended its blessing. Called Fortum the new company combined the oil gas and chemical businesses of Neste with electric utility Imatran Voima Oy (IVO).

IVO was founded in 1932 when it built its first hydroelectric power plant (100 MW). The utility began expanding rapidly in the 1960s when it built a giant coal-fired plant (then the largest in the Nordic region) and extended its transmission lines to the Soviet Union and Sweden. It built Finland's first nuclear reactor in 1977 at Lovissa.

The utility introduced district heating services in 1982 and began developing combined heat and power plants in the 1980s. The company began acquiring stakes in power projects around the world in the late 1980s and by the early 1990s it was involved in power projects in the Czech Re-

public Germany Poland and Russia as well as in Asia.

The Nordic energy industry was deregulated in the mid-1990s. IVO which had already acquired several small Finnish utilities bought Sweden's Gullspangs Kraft in 1997 picking up 5000 MW of generating capacity.

Neste was created in 1948 as Finland's state-controlled oil and gas enterprise. Since Finland imported all of its oil products WWII left the country with shortages and forced a rationing policy. Neste's job was to develop storage facilities for fuel oil; however a major fire in 1949 prompted the company to look beyond storage.

Department of Industry director Uolevi Raade pushed for a national refinery and the Finnish parliament approved the plan in 1954. Raade became president of Neste in 1955 and the refinery opened two years later. A second refinery opened in 1967. Lacking a stable natural gas source Neste began taking gas deliveries from the Soviet Union in 1971.

Neste entered the petrochemicals arena in 1972 when it began producing ethylene polyethylene and polyvinylchloride. In the early 1980s the company added service stations to its operations buying three Finnish petroleum marketers. Continuing to buy oil abroad Neste had nearly 20 tankers in its fleet by the mid-1980s.

In 1994 Neste and Russia's Gazprom set up Gasum a joint venture responsible for natural gas production and transportation. Partially privatized in 1995 Neste reorganized and cut its workforce by a third. By the end of 1996 the Finnish government held an 83% stake in Neste.

After the 1998 merger Fortum sold 50% of its stake in Gasum (reducing its stake to 25%) in 1999 to comply with merger conditions. It also sold Neste Chemicals to private equity fund Industri Kapital.

In 2000 Fortum acquired Stora Enso's power plants in Sweden and Finland. It also grabbed a 49% stake in Ishavskraft a Norwegian electricity sales company and acquired German utility group Wesertal. The next year Fortum acquired Estonian power company Saue Thermo and sold its shares in Hungarian power generator Budapesti Er ¶m and Latvian gas company Latvijas Gaze.

In 2001 the company also acquired full ownership of Birka Energi the Swedish utility that serves Stockholm. In 2002 the company divested its oil and gas assets in Oman.

In 2003 Fortum sold its Norwegian oil and gas business (Fortum Petroleum) to Eni.

In 2005 Fortum acquired a 60% interest in Suomijos Energija a Lithuania-based company providing heat generation through natural gas and biofuel firing from Finnish firm Kotkan Energia. The transaction increased Fortum's holding in Suomijos to 70% and expanded its municipal and industrial heating operations. Fortum renamed the company Fortum Heat Lietuva.

Also in 2005 the company spun off its oil and gas operations as Neste Oil Oy.

In 2007 the company launched a project to build up to eight 2-3 MW wind power plants in the Rosa Finnmark area of Sweden.

In 2008 the company acquired Siberia based Russian Territorial Generating Company 10 (TGC 10) which has significant power generation assets. By 2009 some 92% of Fortum's power generation in EU countries came from non-carbon emission power sources (renewable and nuclear power plants).

As part of its wind energy push in 2008 Fortum and Finland's National Forest Enterprise (Mets ¤hallitus) signed a deal to reserve state-owned Pitk ¤matala and Maakrunni sea areas off-shore of the municipalities of Kemi Simo and Ii for the development of large scale wind power farms.

In 2009 the two partners also agreed to develop wind farms onshore in Northern Finland in the Kuolavaara-Keulakkop ¤ ¤ area located in the Kittil ¤ and Sodankyl ¤ municipalities.

Also on the renewables front in 2010 the company acquired a 40% stake in the Blaiken wind power project with the remaining 60% held by the Swedish energy company Skelleftea Kraft. The Blaiken Vind joint venture will be a wind farm to be constructed in the Blaiken region in northern Sweden with a maximum of 100 wind turbines and a capacity of 250 MW.

Auditors: Deloitte Oy

LOCATIONS

HQ: Fortum OYJ
   Keilaniementie 1, Espoo FI-00048
Phone: (358) 10 452 9151   **Fax:** (358) 10 45 24447
Web: www.fortum.com

2014 Sales

	% of total
Nordic	68
Russia	22
Poland	5
Estonia	1
Others	4
Total	**100**

PRODUCTS/OPERATIONS

2014 Sales

	% of total
Power and Technology	40
Heat Electricity Sales and Solutions	25
Russia	20
Distribution	14
Other	1
Netting of Nord Pool transactions	-
Eliminations	-
Total	**100**

2014 Sales

	% of total
Power Sales (excluding indirect tax)	64
Heat Sales	16
Network transmissions	15
Others	5
Total	**100**

COMPETITORS

ABB Ltd
CGG
GKN LIMITED
GREENERGY INTERNATIONAL LIMITED
IBERDROLA SOCIEDAD ANONIMA
INTERNATIONAL POWER LTD.
SSAB AB
SSE PLC
Svenska Cellulosa AB SCA
VEOLIA ENVIRONNEMENT
Vattenfall AB

HISTORICAL FINANCIALS

Company Type: Public

Income Statement   FYE: December 31

	REVENUE ($ mil.)	NET INCOME ($ mil.)	NET PROFIT MARGIN	EMPLOYEES
12/20	60,155	2,237	3.7%	19,933
12/19	6,115	1,663	27.2%	8,191
12/18	6,003	965	16.1%	8,286
12/17	5,418	1,038	19.2%	8,785
12/16	3,834	523	13.7%	8,108
Annual Growth	**99.0%**	**43.8%**	**—**	**25.2%**

2020 Year-End Financials

Debt ratio: 20.7%
Return on equity: 14.0%
Cash ($ mil.): 2,832
Current ratio: 1.08
Long-term debt ($ mil.): 9,685

No. of shares (mil.): 888
Dividends
 Yield: 5.0%
 Payout: 10.7%
Market value ($ mil.): 4,184

	STOCK PRICE ($) FY Close	P/E High/Low		PER SHARE ($) Earnings	Dividends	Book Value
12/20	4.71	3	1	2.52	0.24	17.90
12/19	5.09	3	2	1.88	0.25	16.41
12/18	4.17	5	4	1.09	0.25	15.27
12/17	3.91	4	3	1.17	0.26	17.61
12/16	2.95	6	4	0.59	0.23	16.00
Annual Growth	12.4%	—	—	43.6%	0.9%	2.8%

Fosun International Ltd

Auditors: Ernst & Young

LOCATIONS

HQ: Fosun International Ltd
 Room 808, ICBC Tower, 3 Garden Road, Central,
Phone: (852) 2509 3228   **Fax:** (852) 2509 9028
Web: www.fosun.com

HISTORICAL FINANCIALS

Company Type: Public

Income Statement   FYE: December 31

	REVENUE ($ mil.)	NET INCOME ($ mil.)	NET PROFIT MARGIN	EMPLOYEES
12/19	20,548	2,127	10.4%	71,000
12/18	15,898	1,949	12.3%	70,000
12/17	13,526	2,022	15.0%	63,000
12/16	10,651	1,478	13.9%	53,000
12/15	12,132	1,237	10.2%	55,800
Annual Growth	14.1%	14.5%		6.2%

2019 Year-End Financials

Debt ratio: 4.1%
Return on equity: 12.8%
Cash ($ mil.): 13,458
Current ratio: 1.04
Long-term debt ($ mil.): 18,043

No. of shares (mil.): —
Dividends
 Yield: —
 Payout: 23.1%
Market value ($ mil.): —

Fresenius Medical Care AG & Co KGaA

Fresenius Medical Care is one of the largest dialysis providers in the world. Its staff treats about 346555 patients at more than 4090 dialysis clinics worldwide. In addition to performing dialysis Fresenius Medical Care is a leading manufacturer of dialysis machines peritoneal dialysis cyclers dialyzers and other supplies that are sold to hospitals and clinics through internal sales efforts and independent distributors. It also offers dialysis support services including laboratory testing and care coordination programs. Fresenius SE owns more than 30% of Fresenius Medical Care. North America generates approximately 70% of the company's revenues.

Operations

Health care services account for a majority (nearly 80%) of annual revenue. The company provides hemodialysis treatments through its global network of more than 4090 dialysis clinics as well as on an as-needed basis for contracted hospitals. Related offerings include laboratory diagnostic and medication administration services as well as the provision of equipment and support for home dialysis patients. Care coordination offerings include value and risk based arrangements; pharmacy services; vascular cardiovascular and endovascular specialty services as well as ambulatory surgery center services; physician nephrology and cardiology services and ambulant treatment services.

Health care products accounting for about 20% of sales include hemodialysis machines dialyzers peritoneal dialysis cyclers hemodialysis concentrates bloodlines and water treatment systems. It also makes renal pharmaceuticals apherisis (blood cleansing) products liver support therapies and acute cardiopulmonary products.

Geographic Reach

With a majority of its operations in the US (North America accounts for approximately 70% of sales) Fresenius Medical Care is increasing its presence in other regions including EMEA Asia-Pacific and Latin America. The company has dialysis clinic operations in about 50 countries while its dialysis products segment serves customers in around 150 countries.

Fresenius Medical Care's corporate headquarters is in Bad Homburg Germany. The North America operations are based in Waltham Massachusetts while the Asia-Pacific headquarters is located in Hong Kong and the Latin America headquarters is in Rio de Janeiro.

Sales and Marketing

In the US Fresenius Medical Care's core health care segment relies generally with third party payors such as Medicare Medicaid or commercial insurers. Outside the US the reimbursement arrangement is usually made through national or local government programs with reimbursement rates established by statute or regulation.

The company markets its products and services for individuals with renal diseases of which around 3.7 million patients worldwide regularly undergo dialysis treatment.

Financial Performance

Note: Growth rates may differ after conversion to US Dollars.

Revenue for fiscal 2020 increased by 5% to ?17.9 billion compared from the prior year with ?17.5 billion.

Net income for fiscal 2020 decreased to ?1.436 billion compared from the prior year with ?1.439 billion.

Cash held by the company at the end of fiscal 2020 increased to ?1.1 billion. Cash provided by operations was ?4.2 billion while cash used for investing and financing activities were ?1.3 billion and ?2.7 billion respectively. Main uses of cash were purchases of property plant and equipment and capitalized development costs; and repayments of long-term debt.

Strategy

The company's research and development strategy contributes to its strategy 2025 which aims to provide health care for chronically and critically ill patients across the renal care continuum in critical settings and by acquiring and developing complementary assets. It is globally orientated enabling it to respond even better to the worldwide rise in demand for high-quality yet cost-efficient treatment and therapy methods.

Fresenius' aim is to continuously improve its patients' quality of life and the outcomes of their treatment as well as to ensure its growth in the medium to long term. To this end the company are not only working on new products that are close to market launch but also on an extensive portfolio of innovation projects. These focus on technologies in its core business as well as related areas of strategic interest.

Company Background

Fresenius Medical Care was formed in 1996 by the merger of Fresenius AG's dialysis systems division with chemical maker W. R. Grace's National Medical Care (NMC) dialysis services division. Fresenius traces its roots back to the 1462 founding of Hirsch Pharmacy in Frankfurt (acquired by the Fresenius family in the 18th century) and its 1966 entry into the dialysis equipment market. NMC was founded in 1968 by Constantine Hampers who opened his first dialysis clinic in Boston in 1971.

In 1998 Fresenius Medical Care expanded its clinics through the purchase of NEOMEDICA and expanded its laboratory services by buying Spectra Laboratories. Subsequent acquisitions expanded international operations.

In 2005 the company transformed its structure from a corporation to a share-limited partnership; the restructuring included a name change from Fresenius Medical Care AG to Fresenius Medical Care AG & Co. KGaA.

The company acquired US rival Renal Care Group which had 460 locations in 2006. Later acquisitions added dialysis medications and dialysis filter cartridges.

In 2017 Fresenius Medical Care acquired day-hospital operator Cura Group to further expand in Australia's dialysis market.

HISTORY

Fresenius Medical Care was formed in 1996 by the merger of Fresenius AG's dialysis systems division with National Medical Care (NMC). While Fresenius traces its roots back to the 1462 founding of Hirsch Pharmacy in Frankfurt (the Fresenius family gained control of the company in the 18th century) and its 1966 entry into the dialysis equipment market NMC was founded in 1968 by Constantine Hampers who recognized that for-profit companies could provide dialysis services more cheaply than not-for-profit hospitals. He opened his first clinic in Boston (it grew to some 600 clinics) and took the company public in 1971. In 1984 he sold the company to chemical maker W. R. Grace which was on a diversification binge but attempted to buy it back after 10 contentious years.

The birth of Fresenius Medical was also mired in legal muck. NMC was under investigation for fraudulent Medicare billing and illegal kickbacks and its manufacturing operations were restricted by court order. Fresenius Medical put an end to the fraud but the ongoing investigation took its toll on its bottom line.

In 1997 a US federal court lifted the manufacturing injunction against NMC. That year Fresenius Medical grew its US clinic practices with the purchase of NEOMEDICA and expanded its laboratory services by buying Spectra Laboratories. The next year it sold its diagnostic services and home care divisions to concentrate on its core dialysis operations. In 1998 it also partnered with Kaiser Permanente a leading not-for-profit HMO to run dialysis clinics and provide other services to patients. Growth continued the next year with key acquisitions in such regions as western Europe South Korea and the US.

Fresenius Medical was finally able to put its NMC woes behind it in 2000 when it settled the Medicare fraud suit for some $425 million. Undaunted the firm also acquired the non-US operations of rival DaVita (formerly Total Renal Care). The next year it bought the perfusion services business of Edwards Lifesciences.

In 2005 the company transformed its structure from a corporation to a share-limited partnership; the restructuring included the formation of the company's general partner Fresenius Medical Care Management AG and a name change from Fresenius Medical Care AG to Fresenius Medical Care AG & Co. KGaA.

In a larger than usual transaction the company also acquired US rival Renal Care Group which had 460 locations in 2006. The deal was valued at $3.5 billion and made Fresenius Medical Care the top US dialysis center operator (despite the required divestiture of some 100 centers to clear the deal). Fresenius Medical Care also later sold the former RCG laboratory operations.

Also in 2006 the company purchased the 50% stake in venture Renaissance Health Care that it didn't already own and the 20% stake in Optimal Renal Care (a former venture with health care provider Kaiser Permanente) and merged Optimal Renal Care into Renaissance Health Care; the combined entity was renamed KidneyTel.

Fresenius Medical Care acquired its first dialysis medication the PhosLo brand calcium acetate and related assets from Nabi Biopharmaceuticals in 2006. The following year it acquired privately held Renal Solutions which makes filter cartridges that can be used in home dialysis a growing field in the hemodialysis market.

In 2007 the company sealed its position in the Asian dialysis market with the acquisition of a majority stake in Taiwan-based Jiate Excelsior.

In 2008 it entered drug distribution agreement with pharma companies Luitpold and Galenica to expand its therapeutic offerings.

To further cement its position in Asia in 2010 the company agreed to purchase Asia Renal Care from Bumrungrad International to expand its operations in Taiwan Singapore and other Asia/Pacific countries. It also established operations in countries including Japan Korea and Russia that year.

Also in 2010 it expanded its home care offerings by purchasing the peritoneal (abdominal) dialysis operation of Gambro and the assets of home therapy device development firm Xcorporeal.

Fresenius Medical Care continued its growth efforts in 2011 when it acquired Dutch firm Euromedic International's dialysis business International Dialysis Centers (IDC) for some ?485 million ($647 million). The purchase gave Fresenius about 70 clinics in Central and Eastern Europe.

In 2017 Fresenius Medical Care acquired day-hospital operator Cura Group to further expand in Australia's dialysis market.

EXECUTIVES

Honorary Chairman, Ben Lipps
Chairman of the Supervisory Board, Dieter Schenk, $132,171 total compensation
Chairman of the Management Board, Chief Executive Officer, Rice Powell, $2,015,609 total compensation
Independent Member of the Supervisory Board, Pascale Witz, $87,734 total compensation
Independent Vice Chairman of the Supervisory Board, Rolf Classon, $87,734 total compensation
Member of the Management Board, Chief Executive Officer for the North America Segment, William Valle, $1,556,428 total compensation
Independent Member of the Supervisory Board, William Johnston, $44,436 total compensation
Member of the Management Board, Chief Executive Officer for Europe, Middle East and Africa (EMEA) Segment, Katarzyna Mazur-Hofsaess, $1,036,859 total compensation

Member of the Management Board, Chief Executive Officer for the Asia-Pacific Segment, Harry de Wit, $837,463 total compensation
Independent Member of the Supervisory Board, Gregor Zuend, $87,734 total compensation
Independent Member of the Supervisory Board, Dorothea Wenzel, $87,734 total compensation
Chief Financial Officer, Member of the Management Board, Helen Giza, $974,191 total compensation
Member of the Management Board, Chief Executive Officer for Global Manufacturing and Quality & Supply, Kent Wanzek, $902,409 total compensation
Member of the Management Board, Global Chief Medical Officer, Frank Maddux, $917,221 total compensation
Member of the Management Board, Chief Executive Officer for Research and Development, Olaf Schermeier, $826,069 total compensation
Auditors: KPMG AG Wirtschaftsprüfungsgesellschaft

LOCATIONS

HQ: Fresenius Medical Care AG & Co KGaA
Else-Kroener-Strasse 1, Bad Homburg 61346
Phone: (49) 6172 608 2522   **Fax:** (49) 6172 609 2301
Web: www.fmc-ag.com

2011 Sales

	% of total
North America	
Dialysis care	57
Dialysis products	6
International	
Dialysis products	19
Dialysis care	17
Total	**100**

PRODUCTS/OPERATIONS

2011 Payer Breakdown

	% of total
Medicare ESRD program	46
Private/alternative payers	43
Medicaid & other government sources	6
Hospitals	5
Total	**100**

Selected Acquisitions

COMPETITORS

AMERISOURCEBERGEN CORPORATION	Fresenius SE & Co. KGaA
CHINDEX INTERNATIONAL INC.	OWENS & MINOR INC.
DAVITA INC.	PATTERSON COMPANIES INC.
FRESENIUS MEDICAL CARE HOLDINGS INC.	ROTECH HEALTHCARE INC.
	TRIVIDIA HEALTH INC.

HISTORICAL FINANCIALS

Company Type: Public

Income Statement   FYE: December 31

	REVENUE ($ mil.)	NET INCOME ($ mil.)	NET PROFIT MARGIN	EMPLOYEES
12/20	21,918	1,429	6.5%	125,364
12/19	19,622	1,346	6.9%	120,659
12/18	18,949	2,269	12.0%	112,658
12/17	21,318	1,534	7.2%	114,000
12/16	17,910	1,243	6.9%	109,319
Annual Growth	5.2%	3.5%	—	3.5%

2020 Year-End Financials

Debt ratio: 47.9%	No. of shares (mil.): 292
Return on equity: 10.0%	Dividends
Cash ($ mil.): 1,327	Yield: 1.2%
Current ratio: 1.18	Payout: 10.2%
Long-term debt ($ mil.): 13,111	Market value ($ mil.): 12,172

	STOCK PRICE ($) FY Close	P/E High/Low		PER SHARE ($) Earnings	Dividends	Book Value
12/20	41.56	12	8	4.86	0.50	47.00
12/19	36.83	11	8	4.45	0.45	45.00
12/18	32.39	8	5	7.39	0.43	43.88
12/17	52.55	13	11	4.99	0.41	38.41
12/16	42.21	12	9	4.06	0.31	35.30
Annual Growth	(0.4%)	—	—	4.6%	12.3%	7.4%

Fresenius SE & Co KGaA

Fresenius offers a wide range of dialysis and infusion products and services through its four core business segments which operate as legally independent entities: Fresenius Medical Care Fresenius Kabi Fresenius Helios and Fresenius Vamed. The company's Medical Care division specializes in treating chronic kidney failure in almost 4000 dialysis clinics worldwide. Fresenius Kabi provides nutrition infusion and IV therapies and related equipment. Fresenius Helios operates private hospitals in Germany while Fresenius Vamed offers facility management project development and other services to hospitals and health facilities. Fresenius has operations in more than 100 countries and the Europe is its biggest market.

Operations

Of its four segments Medical Care is Fresenius' largest at around half the company's annual sales. Helios brings in around a quarter Kabi a fifth and Vamed is the remainder or so.

Medical Care serves almost 350000 patients via a network of upwards of around 4100 clinics. Its production sites found on every continent provide dialysis products (machines dialyzers and disposables).

Fresenius Helios runs some 135 hospitals (including about 90 acute-care facilities and seven maximum-care hospitals) with more than 35000 beds in Germany.

Fresenius Kabi produces IV drips and other infusion and nutrition devices.

Fresemius Vamed provides project development planning technical and operation management and turnkey construction services to hospitals and other health care facilities around the world.

Geographic Reach

Headquartered in Bad Homburg near Frankfurt in Germany. Europe is Fresenius' largest market at nearly 45% of total sales. North America follows with over 40% while the Asia/Pacific region (about 10%) Latin America (5%) and Africa account for the remainder.

The company's 90 or so production sites are located in the US China Japan Germany and Sweden. The company also has production facilities in other European countries and in Latin America and South Africa.

Sales and Marketing

Fresenius provides products and services for dialysis hospitals and outpatient medical care. In addition Fresenius focuses on hospital operations. It also manages projects and provides services for hospitals and other health care facilities worldwide. More than 311000 employees have dedicated themselves to the service of health in over 100 countries worldwide.

Financial Performance

Note: Growth rates may differ after conversion to US Dollars.

The company's revenue increased by 2% to ?36.3 billion compared to ?35.4 billion in the prior year. The rise was due to the increase of every business segment of the company except Fresenius Vamed. Sales also increase in most geographic locations expect in Asia and Africa.

Fresenius' net income decreased by 9% to ?1.7 million. An impairment of goodwill and brand names at Fresenius Medical Care Latin America has a negative impact. The impairment was due to the macroeconomic downturn in several countries in the region and the resulting increase in risk premiums In addition the change in the valuation of the biosimilars contingent purchase liabilities which was due to the higher prospect of success of individual projects also has a negative impact.

Fresenius' cash ending the year 2020 at ?1.8 billion a ?183 million increase. Cash provided by operations was ?6.5 billion while cash used for investing and financing activities were ?3.3 billion and ?2.1 billion respectively

Strategy

Fresenius invests in and manages a diversified portfolio of healthcare businesses that create value. With their four business segments they focus on a defined number of health care areas. The company continuously develop those business areas and strive to assume leading positions in the respective healthcare areas. Fresenius has a defined strategic priorities to pursue its goal to strengthen the position of the company as a leading global provider of products and therapies for critically and chronically ill patients: Profit from megatrends: gearing businesses towards the megatrends health and demographics; Create value: long-term value creation by allocating capital to profitable growth areas; Act responsibly: commitment to responsible management and ethical business principles; and Collaborate: fostering intragroup cooperation to leverage synergies.

Mergers and Acquisitions

In late 2020 Fresenius Helios announced the acquisition of Eugin Group one of the leading international fertility groups. With the acquisition of Eugin Group Fresenius Helios becomes a leading player in this dynamic growing market and establishes a strong basis for further expansion. Fresenius Helios acquires Eugin at a valuation of ?430 million including approximately ?80 million.

In 2020 Fresenius Helios announced the acquisition of three hospitals and four connected medical care centers in the cities of Duisburg and Krefeld from the Malteser humanitarian aid group. The facilities have a total of 870 beds and sales in 2019 were about ?160 million. The two Malteser Hospitals in Duisburg cover specialty areas including general surgery; internal medicine; ear nose and throat medicine; oral and maxillofacial surgery and geriatrics. Special expertise in hematological oncology is offered. At the Malteser Hospital in Krefeld a comprehensive range of medical services includes oral and maxillo- facial surgery general surgery and internal medicine as the main specialty areas.

Also in 2020 Fresenius Helios acquired CliÂ´nica de la Mujer in BogotaÂ´ further expanding the company's presence in Colombia's private hospital market. The hospital puts a special focus on gynecology pediatrics and obstetrics while also offering a broad range of other medical specialties and services. It has approximately 80 beds and 5 operating rooms and generated sales of about ?20 million in 2019.

In mid-2020 Fresenius acquires Malteser Hospital (MKHB) in the western German city of Bonn.

MKHB offers a wide range of medical services with specialties in general surgery pulmonology and oncology including palliative care. With certified centers for prostate intestinal and lung cancers it will complement the existing Fresenius Helios hospital in the neighboring city of Siegburg which specializes in cardiovascular medicine and oncology.

Company Background

Fresenius can trace its lineage all the way back to an apothecary founded in 1462 in Frankfurt. A few centuries later in the 1870s the business was bought by the Fresenius family and in 1912 Eduard Fresenius began making medicines based on purified water his speciality. WWII — and Eduard's death in 1946 — almost destroyed the company which was saved by his 26-year-old daughter Else. She and her new husband Hans Kroner rebuilt the company and turned it into a global infusions solutions company including developing its own dialysis machines in the 1970s. Over the coming decades the company expanded by acquisitions notable National Medical Care in 1996 which became Fresenius Medical Care today the company's biggest business. Else's charitable foundation Else Kroner-Fresenius-Stiftung is Germany's largest charitable foundation.

HISTORY

Fresenius was founded as the Hirsch Pharmacy in 1462. The Fresenius family took over its ownership in the 18th century and converted it into a pharmaceutical manufacturing entity in 1912.

Fresenius entered the dialysis equipment market in 1966. The company formed its Fresenius Medical Care unit in 1996 when it merged its dialysis systems division with National Medical Care (NMC).

In 1999 Fresenius formed its Fresenius Kabi division by combining its infusion pharmaceutical operations with the former infusion solution business of drugmaker Pharmacia & Upjohn which it acquired the previous year.

The company conducted a number of expansion efforts within the Kabi division in the following decade including the 2007 purchase of IV drug manufacturing firms Labesfal (Portugal) and Filaxis (Argentina) as well as German medical device maker Clinico. Also that year the company bought the artificial colloid product business of Kyorin to build up a presence in the Tokyo market.

It then purchased Indian oncology drug manufacturer Dabur Pharma in 2008. Also that year the unit expanded its reach in the US market for injectable drugs by acquiring US generics maker APP Pharmaceuticals for $3.7 billion plus debt.

Following the acquisition of German private clinic operator Helios Kliniken Fresenius refreshed its acute care operations by separating its hospital division (Fresenius ProServe) into two business segments Fresenius Helios and Fresenius Vamed in 2008.

EXECUTIVES

Chairman and CEO, Stephan Sturm, $1,253,346 total compensation

CEO, Fresenius Medical Care and Director, Rice Powell, $2,015,609 total compensation

Deputy Chairman, Supervisory Board, Grit Genster

CEO, Fresenius Helios, Francesco De Meo, $717,825 total compensation

Chief Financial Officer and Director, Rachel Empey, $802,141 total compensation

Legal, Compliance, Insurance, Human Resources and Labor Relations Director, Sebastian Biedenkopf, $56,970 total compensation

Auditors: KPMG AG

LOCATIONS

HQ: Fresenius SE & Co KGaA
Else-Kroener-Strasse 1, Bad Homburg D-61352
Phone: (49) 6172 608 0   **Fax:** (49) 6172 608 2488
Web: www.fresenius.com

2017 Sales

	% of total
North America	45
Europe	41
Asia Pacific	9
Latin America & other regions	4
Africa	1
Total	**100**

PRODUCTS/OPERATIONS

2017 Sales

	% of total
Fresenius Medical Care	52
Fresenius Kabi	19
Fresenius Helios	26
Fresenius Vamed	3
Corporate/Other (-)	
Total	**100**

Selected Services

Fresenius Medical Care
  Dialysis facility operation
  Disease management
  Disposable dialysis supplies
  Hemodialysis equipment
  Peritoneal dialysis equipment
Fresenius Kabi
  Blood volume replacement
  Enteral nutrition
  Infusion and IV devices
  Infusion therapies
  IV generic drugs
  Parenteral nutrition
  Tranfusion products
Fresenius Helios
  HELIOS Kliniken Group (61 private hospitals Germany)
Fresenius Vamed
  Construction management
  Facility planning
  Maintenance services
  Operational management
  Project development
  Staff recruitment and training

COMPETITORS

ABIOMED INC.
AMERISOURCEBERGEN CORPORATION
DAVITA INC.
ESCALON MEDICAL CORP.
Fresenius Medical Care AG & Co. KGaA
HOLOGIC INC.
MASIMO CORPORATION
NATUS MEDICAL INCORPORATED
OLYMPUS CORPORATION
PHILIPS IMAGE GUIDED THERAPY CORPORATION
SONIC HEALTHCARE LIMITED
TENET HEALTHCARE CORPORATION
VARIAN MEDICAL SYSTEMS INC.

HISTORICAL FINANCIALS

Company Type: Public

Income Statement — FYE: December 31

	REVENUE ($ mil.)	NET INCOME ($ mil.)	NET PROFIT MARGIN	EMPLOYEES
12/20	44,522	2,094	4.7%	311,269
12/19	39,756	2,114	5.3%	294,134
12/18	38,398	2,321	6.0%	276,750
12/17	40,620	2,174	5.4%	273,249
12/16	31,117	1,647	5.3%	228,968
Annual Growth	**9.4%**	**6.2%**	**—**	**8.0%**

2020 Year-End Financials

Debt ratio: 36.3%
Return on equity: 10.0%
Cash ($ mil.): 2,254
Current ratio: 1.19
Long-term debt ($ mil.): 20,644

No. of shares (mil.): 557
Dividends
  Yield: 1.4%
  Payout: 4.6%
Market value ($ mil.): 6,495

	STOCK PRICE ($) FY Close	P/E High/Low		PER SHARE ($) Earnings	Dividends	Book Value
12/20	11.65	5	3	3.76	0.17	37.31
12/19	13.96	4	3	3.79	0.15	33.80
12/18	12.15	6	3	4.16	0.15	31.73
12/17	19.43	7	6	3.90	0.12	29.93
12/16	19.48	7	5	2.99	0.09	24.44
Annual Growth	(12.1%)	—	—	5.9%	16.2%	11.2%

FUJIFILM Holdings Corp

Fujifilm's main businesses over 85% of revenue together are document operations and healthcare and materials. The document business sells printers and office products and provides manage prints services. The Healthcare & Material Solutions business's products include diagnostic instruments such as X-ray and ultrasound machines as well as pharmaceuticals. The company's imaging unit which makes photographic films and papers digital cameras and photofinishing equipment is its smallest. Customers overseas account for over 55% sales. Founded in 1934 the company's first product was film for motion pictures.

Operations

Fujifilm's document solutions business generates about 45% of revenue. Besides printers and office equipment the segment has a commercial printer business that provides high-speed digital printing systems and printing workflow tools.

The Healthcare & Materials segment about 45% of revenue has businesses in medical systems pharmaceuticals bio CDMO regenerative medicine and life sciences as well as display materials industrial products electronic materials and fine chemicals.

The Imaging Solutions business about 15% of revenue makes photographic equipment as the Instax instant camera digital cameras and optical devices such as lenses.

As of March 2020 the company has over 315 consolidated subsidiaries.

Geographic Reach

The company is headquartered in Tokyo Japan.

Financial Performance

In FY2019 FUJIFILM recorded 2.3 trillion in consolidated revenue a 5% decrease compared to the previous year. This is caused by factors such as a sales decrease in the photo imaging business optical device and electronic imaging business and document business although sales increased in the medical systems business bio CDMO business regenerative medicine business and electronic materials business.

Net income attributable to FUJIFILM Holdings was 125 billion a 10% decrease from the previous year.

The company's cash for FY 2019 was 396.1 billion. Operating activities generated 255.7 billion while investing activities used 244.9 billion mainly for acquisitions of businesses. Financing activities used another 250.9 billion mainly for equity transactions.

Strategy

The company promotes its growth strategy by consistently anticipating the future and centering on a variety of technologies such as optics chemicals and electronics.

Mergers and Acquisitions

l

HISTORY

In 1934 Fuji Photo Film Co. was established through a government plan to build a domestic photographic film manufacturing industry in Japan. The new company inherited the split-off photographic film operations of Dainippon Celluloid Company Limited.

In 2006 Fuji Photo Film Co. Ltd. has been transformed into a holding company and renamed as Fujifilm Holdings Corp.

EXECUTIVES

Vice President, Chairman of Subsidiary, Director, Kouichi Tamai
Independent Director, Takashi Shimada
SVP, Takatoshi Ishikawa
Chairman of the Board, Chairman of the Board of Directors, Chairman of Subsidiary, Representative Director, Kenji Sukeno
Chief Financial Officer, Executive Officer, Director of Business Planning, Director, Masayuki Higuchi
Independent Director, Makiko Eda
SVP, Teiichi Goto
SVP, Takashi Iwasaki
Corporate VP, Junji Okada
Auditors: KPMG AZSA LLC

LOCATIONS

HQ: FUJIFILM Holdings Corp
9-7-3 Akasaka, Minato-ku, Tokyo 107-0052
Phone: (81) 3 6271 1111
Web: www.fujifilmholdings.com

2018 Sales

	% of total
Japan	41
Asia	27
Americas	19
Europe	13
Total	100

PRODUCTS/OPERATIONS

2018 Sales

	% of total
Document Solutions	43
Healthcare & Material Solutions	41
Imaging Solutions	16
Total	100

2018 Sales

	% of total
Sales	86
Rentals	14
Total	100

Selected Products

Document
  Color/Monochrome digital multifunction devices
  DocuWorks docyument handlingn software
  On-demand publishing systems
  Computer publishing systems
Imaging
  Color photo printing paper and chemicals
  Digital cameras and accessories
  Instant films
  Digital minilabs/dry minilabs
  Motion picture films
  Photo lab equipment
  Photographic films
Healthcare and Material Solutions
  Digital mammography systems
  Synapse medical-use picture archiving and communications systems
  X-ray films
  Digital endoscopes
  Low-molecular pharmaceuticals functional cosmetics

COMPETITORS

3D SYSTEMS CORPORATION
ALFRESA HOLDINGS CORPORATION
ASTEELFLASH GROUP
ELECTROCOMPONENTS PUBLIC LIMITED COMPANY
HAKUHODO DY HOLDINGS INCORPORATED
JFE HOLDINGS INC.
KONICA MINOLTA INC.
MEDIPAL HOLDINGS CORPORATION
MITSUBISHI CHEMICAL HOLDINGS CORPORATION
NORITSU KOKI CO. LTD.
OJI HOLDINGS CORPORATION
RICOH COMPANYLTD.
SOMPO HOLDINGS INC.
SONY GROUP CORPORATION
TELEDYNE E2V LIMITED
TOYO SEIKAN GROUP HOLDINGSLTD.

HISTORICAL FINANCIALS

Company Type: Public

Income Statement				FYE: March 31
	REVENUE ($ mil.)	NET INCOME ($ mil.)	NET PROFIT MARGIN	EMPLOYEES
03/21	19,801	1,636	8.3%	83,006
03/20	21,327	1,151	5.4%	83,987
03/19	21,955	1,247	5.7%	82,841
03/18	22,915	1,324	5.8%	88,392
03/17	20,769	1,176	5.7%	88,690
Annual Growth	(1.2%)	8.6%	—	(1.6%)

2021 Year-End Financials

Debt ratio: 0.1%
Return on equity: 8.7%
Cash ($ mil.): 3,565
Current ratio: 2.10
Long-term debt ($ mil.): 3,967

No. of shares (mil.): 399
Dividends
  Yield: 0.7%
  Payout: 10.6%
Market value ($ mil.): 23,868

	STOCK PRICE ($) FY Close	P/E High/Low		PER SHARE ($) Earnings	Dividends	Book Value
03/21	59.70	0	0	4.08	0.45	49.80
03/20	50.02	0	0	2.81	0.80	45.02
03/19	45.55	0	0	2.94	0.70	44.94
03/18	40.11	0	0	3.03	0.68	45.51
03/17	39.16	0	0	2.64	0.62	41.75
Annual Growth	11.1%	—	—	11.5%	(7.9%)	4.5%

Fujitsu Ltd

Auditors: Ernst & Young ShinNihon LLC

LOCATIONS

HQ: Fujitsu Ltd
Shiodome City Center, 1-5-2 Higashi-Shinbashi, Minato-ku, Tokyo 105-7123
Phone: (81) 3 6252 2220
Web: www.fujitsu.com

HISTORICAL FINANCIALS

Company Type: Public

Income Statement				FYE: March 31
	REVENUE ($ mil.)	**NET INCOME** ($ mil.)	**NET PROFIT MARGIN**	**EMPLOYEES**
03/21	32,420	1,830	5.6%	138,698
03/20	35,539	1,474	4.1%	141,947
03/19	35,689	944	2.6%	145,845
03/18	38,595	1,594	4.1%	156,471
03/17	40,334	791	2.0%	171,753
Annual Growth	(5.3%)	23.3%	—	(5.2%)

2021 Year-End Financials

Debt ratio: 0.0%
Return on equity: 15.0%
Cash ($ mil.): 4,351
Current ratio: 1.45
Long-term debt ($ mil.): 342

No. of shares (mil.): 199
Dividends
  Yield: 1.2%
  Payout: 3.9%
Market value ($ mil.): 5,811

	STOCK PRICE ($) FY Close	**P/E** High/Low		**PER SHARE ($)** Earnings	Dividends	Book Value
03/21	29.20	0	0	9.15	0.38	65.81
03/20	17.81	0	0	7.28	0.29	57.09
03/19	14.43	0	0	4.63	0.23	50.43
03/18	30.37	0	0	7.77	0.19	49.76
03/17	30.97	0	0	3.83	0.15	38.44
Annual Growth	(1.5%)	—	—	24.3%	26.9%	14.4%

Fukui Bank Ltd.

Fukui Bank provides banking and other financial services in the Fukui prefecture of Japan. The regional bank serves both retail and commercial customers through nearly 100 branches and nine subsidiaries. Individuals regional businesses and public agencies use Fukui Bank for general banking financial leasing and real estate services among others. The bank was established in 1899.

EXECUTIVES

Independent Director, Nana Yoshikawa
Executive Officer, Manager of Business Planning Group, Koichi Makino
Managing Executive Officer, Director, Hiroaki Nakajima
Managing Executive Officer, Director, Masahiro Hayashi
Independent Director, Kazue Nomura
President, Representative Executive Officer, Director, Tadaaki Ito
Executive Officer, Manager of Risk Supervision Group, Masato Kobayashi
Managing Executive Officer, Director, Masahiro Asakura
Director, Hideo Hata
Managing Executive Officer, Senior Manager of Store of Main Store Area, Director of Main Store Sales, Director, Tetsuo Inoue
Independent Director, Naoyuki Nomura
Auditors: KPMG AZSA LLC

LOCATIONS

HQ: Fukui Bank Ltd.
  1-1-1 Junka, Fukui 910-8660
Phone: (81) 776 24 2030
Web: www.fukuibank.co.jp

COMPETITORS

HIROSHIMA BANK LTD.   THE AOMORI BANKLTD. THE

HISTORICAL FINANCIALS

Company Type: Public

Income Statement				FYE: March 31
	ASSETS ($ mil.)	**NET INCOME** ($ mil.)	**INCOME AS % OF ASSETS**	**EMPLOYEES**
03/21	31,730	23	0.1%	1,981
03/20	27,185	19	0.1%	2,012
03/19	25,307	28	0.1%	2,043
03/18	25,174	36	0.1%	2,062
03/17	23,251	37	0.2%	2,051
Annual Growth	8.1%	(11.4%)		(0.9%)

2021 Year-End Financials

Return on assets: 0.0%
Return on equity: 1.9%
Long-term debt ($ mil.): —
No. of shares (mil.): 24
Sales ($ mil): 384

Dividends
  Yield: —
  Payout: —
Market value ($ mil.): —

Future Land Development Holdings Ltd

Auditors: PricewaterhouseCoopers

LOCATIONS

HQ: Future Land Development Holdings Ltd
  11/F, Seazen Holdings Tower B, No. 6, Lane 388, Zhongjiang Road, Shanghai
Phone:
Web: www.seazengroup.com.cn

HISTORICAL FINANCIALS

Company Type: Public

Income Statement				FYE: December 31
	REVENUE ($ mil.)	**NET INCOME** ($ mil.)	**NET PROFIT MARGIN**	**EMPLOYEES**
12/20	22,341	1,556	7.0%	32,127
12/19	12,481	1,122	9.0%	30,908
12/18	7,964	982	12.3%	22,903
12/17	6,272	583	9.3%	12,887
12/16	4,065	199	4.9%	7,322
Annual Growth	53.1%	67.2%	—	44.7%

2020 Year-End Financials

Debt ratio: 2.9%
Return on equity: 33.4%
Cash ($ mil.): 9,015
Current ratio: 1.10
Long-term debt ($ mil.): 11,225

No. of shares (mil.): —
Dividends
  Yield: —
  Payout: 24.8%
Market value ($ mil.): —

Galp Energia, SGPS, SA

Portugal's primary oil and gas group Galp Energia (formerly Petr leos de Portugal) produces transports refines distributes and sells crude oil natural gas and oil products. It operates mainly in Portugal and Spain but also has operations in a half-dozen former Portuguese colonies. Although Galp Energia is primarily a refining and marketing company with more than 1450 gas stations it is seeking to expand its exploration and production efforts. The company has significant exploration and production activities in Angola Brazil and Portugal and holds gas and power infrastructure assets in Portugal. Italian energy giant Eni and Portuguese investment firm Amorim Energia each own 33% of the company.

EXECUTIVES

Non-Executive Vice Chairman of the Board, Lead Independent Director, Miguel Athayde Marques, $116,219 total compensation
Non-Executive Chairman of the Board, Paula Fernanda Ramos Amorim
Non-Executive Director, Marta Claudia Ramos Amorim Barroca de Oliveira, $47,855 total compensation
Executive Director, Chief Operating Officer - Corporate, Carlos Manuel Costa Pina, $478,550 total compensation
Non-Executive Director, Diogo Mendonca Rodrigues Tavares, $95,710 total compensation
Non-Executive Director, Rui Paulo da Costa Cunha e Silva Goncalves, $95,710 total compensation
Non-Executive Director, Jorge Manuel Seabra de Freitas, $95,710 total compensation
Non-Executive Independent Director, Luis Manuel Pego Todo Bom, $102,546 total compensation
Non-Executive Director, Francisco Vahia de Castro Teixeira Rego, $47,855 total compensation
Executive Director, Chief Operating Officer - Midstream and Refining, Jose Carlos Da Silva Costa, $478,550 total compensation
Non-Executive Independent Director, Adolfo Nunes, $101,862 total compensation
Non-Executive Director, Carlos Pinto, $95,710 total compensation
Non-Executive Independent Director, Cristina Fonseca, $54,691 total compensation
Executive Director, Chief Operating Officer - Commercial, Sofia Tenreiro, $478,550 total compensation
Chief Financial Officer, Executive Director, Filipe Quintin Silva, $478,550 total compensation
Executive Director, Chief Operating Officer - Renewables and New Business, Susana Quintana-Plaza, $478,550 total compensation
Executive Director, Chief Operating Officer - Upstream, Thore Ernst Kristiansen, $558,308 total compensation
Non-Executive Independent Director, Edmar De Almeida, $95,710 total compensation
Chief Executive Officer, Vice Chairman of the Board of Director, Andy Brown
Auditors: Ernst & Young Audit & Associados - SROC, S.A.

LOCATIONS

HQ: Galp Energia, SGPS, SA
  Rua Tomas da Fonseca, Torre A, Lisbon 1600-209
Phone: (351) 217 242 500   **Fax:** (351) 217 242 965
Web: www.galp.com

PRODUCTS/OPERATIONS

2013 Sales

	% of total
Refining & marketing	83
Gas & power	17
Total	**100**

Selected Subsidiaries

Galp Power (electricity generation and sales)
Galpgeste (management and operation of service stations)
GDP Gá;s de Portugal
Petróleos de Portugal (Petrogal; exploration and production refining transport distribution and sales of oil products)
Sacor Maritima (marine transport)
Sopor (51% distribution and sale of oil products)
Transgá;s Armazenagem (natural gas underground storage)

COMPETITORS

BP P.L.C. COMPANY	KUNLUN ENERGY
CAMAC INTERNATIONAL CORPORATION	LIMITED
	LUKOIL PAO
CLEAN TECH ASSETS LIMITED	Queiroz Galvao S/A
	REPSOL SA.
EDP - ENERGIAS DE PORTUGAL S.A.	ROYAL DUTCH SHELL plc
	Winstar Resources Ltd
HELLENIC PETROLEUM S.A. HOLDING	

HISTORICAL FINANCIALS

Company Type: Public

Income Statement				FYE: December 31
	REVENUE ($ mil.)	NET INCOME ($ mil.)	NET PROFIT MARGIN	EMPLOYEES
12/20	14,197	(676)		6,114
12/19	19,017	436	2.3%	6,386
12/18	19,837	848	4.3%	6,360
12/17	18,352	736	4.0%	6,389
12/16	13,980	189	1.4%	6,475
Annual Growth	0.4%	—	—	(1.4%)

2020 Year-End Financials

Debt ratio: 36.7%	No. of shares (mil.): 829
Return on equity: (-14.5%)	Dividends
Cash ($ mil.): 2,059	Yield: 7.3%
Current ratio: 1.93	Payout: —
Long-term debt ($ mil.): 3,933	Market value ($ mil.): 4,354

	STOCK PRICE ($)	P/E	PER SHARE ($)		
	FY Close	High/Low	Earnings	Dividends	Book Value
12/20	5.25	— —	(0.81)	0.38	4.68
12/19	8.36	18 15	0.53	0.37	5.98
12/18	7.76	12 8	1.02	0.34	6.33
12/17	9.17	13 10	0.89	0.30	6.68
12/16	7.51	34 22	0.23	0.24	6.34
Annual Growth	(8.6%)	— —	—	12.5%	(7.3%)

Gazprom Neft PJSC

One of Russia's largest integrated oil companies and its third-largest refiner Gazprom Neft explores for produces refines and markets petroleum products. Its retail operations include more than 1800 gas stations. The company with proved reserves of 2.8 billion barrels of oil equivalent controls refineries in Moscow Yaroslav Serbia and Omsk that produce more than 45.7 million tonnes of petroleum products per year. It refines about 80% of the oil it produces a high ratio for Russia. Gazprom Neft also shares ownership of major natural gas project SeverEnergia with NOVATEK the country's largest independent gas producer. State-owned gas giant Gazprom controls Gazprom Neft.

Operations

Gazprom Neft operates through two segments: Downstream and Upstream.

The Downstream segment processes crude oil into refined products. It also trades and transports crude oil and refined products. The segment brings in about two-thirds of the group's total revenue.

The Upstream segment explores develops produces and sells crude oil and natural gas. It also provides oil fields services. The segment brings in about one-third of total sales.

Geographic Reach

Gazprom Neft operates in Russia and in other nations in Europe the Middle East South America and Africa. The company exports to more than 50 countries around the world. Russia accounts for more than half of total revenue.

Its key refining facilities are located near Omsk Moscow and Yaroslavl and Serbia.

Financial Performance

Note: Growth rates may differ after conversion to US dollars.

With the steep decline in oil prices that hit the markets worldwide Gazprom Neft's revenue fell in 2015 and 2016; revenue has been recovering in the years since. Net income has been growing as well hitting record levels in 2017 and 2018.

In 2018 revenue increased 29% to 2.5 trillion RUB thanks largely to recovering oil prices and to production growth at certain fields. Hydrocarbon production grew 7% that year and oil product sales grew 4%. Aviation fuel sales alone rose 10% due both to an increase in air traffic and to the company's expanded geographic coverage in that sector.

Net income rose 49% to 376.7 billion RUB in 2018. While revenue has been rising the company is also implementing measures (such as utilizing new technologies) to operate more efficiently which has boosted its bottom line.

The company ended 2018 with 247.6 billion RUB in net cash some 150 billion RUB more than it had at the end of 2017. Operating activities provided 537.5 billion RUB in cash while investing activities used 335 billion RUB and financing activities used another 56.5 billion RUB.

Strategy

Gazprom Neft has worked to become a global company over the past decade by expanding production and selling products around the world. It became Russia's third-largest oil producer in 2017.

Strategies to build business include expanding corporate sales partnering with the largest consumers of petroleum products growing its portfolio of gas stations and digitizing business processes. The company is actively developing the first major domestic offshore project — the Prirazlomnoye field in Russia's Arctic shelf — and has production projects in other nations including Venezuela and Iraq.

Volume of conventional reserves has declined which means that oil companies will need to increasingly concentrate on unconventional and complex segments (offshore shale) where reserves are more difficult to recover. As a result Gazprom Neft is heavily invested in technological projects that involve 3D modeling artificial intelligence big data and cloud technologies.

Because the company has a number of foreign projects and is exploring additional geographies it runs the risk of encountering political challenges. There is also the risk of having a competitive disadvantage in new markets. Gazprom Neft carefully assesses these risks when expanding.

HISTORY

In the aftermath of the fall of the Soviet Union in the early 1990s Sibneft was formed in 1995 as part of Russia's privatization of state industries. Sibneft included western Siberian oil producer Noyabrskneftegas and the Omsk oil refinery. The Russian government was to retain a 51% stake for three years while limiting foreign ownership to 15%. Finance Oil Company (FNK) controlled by business oligarch Boris Berezovsky the man reportedly behind Sibneft's formation gained a controlling stake in Sibneft. The new integrated oil company's prize asset was the Omsk refinery. Built in the mid-1980s it was Russia's largest and most modern refinery.

In 1997 Sibneft became the first Russian company to issue a Eurobond. Despite an economic crisis in 1998 Sibneft continued to service all of its financial obligations. That year Sibneft made plans to merge with rival oil company Yukos (controlled by oligarch Mikhail Khodorkovsky) but falling oil prices led the two firms to scuttle the proposed union.

Also in 1998 Sibneft published a corporate governance charter compiled by leading European experts to bring the company in line with international practices. This move was followed up with the appointment of three non-executives to the company's board of nine directors. A year later Sibneft became the first major Russian oil company to publish its financial accounts (audited by Arthur Andersen) according to US generally accepted accounting principles. In 1999 Sibneft also formed alliances with two Western oil services firms US-based Schlumberger and Canadian-based BJ Services to enhance its extraction of oil and gas.

During the 1999 Russian Duma elections reclusive oligarch Roman Abramovich (who had acquired a 12% stake in Sibneft in 1996) claimed to control Sibneft whereas Berezovsky (also elected to the Duma) was said to have only a background role in Sibneft.

The company announced plans in 2000 to invest $52 million to modernize the Omsk refinery upgrading its capacity to produce lead-free gasoline. That year Sibneft also agreed to acquire majority stakes in two refined products retailers in the Urals region which together controlled 132 service stations and 20 storage sites.

Sibneft lost out in its bid to gain control of Onako another former state-owned oil company that was privatized in 2000. Sibneft had teamed up with two other oil companies Yukos and Stroitransgaz (a unit of Russian gas giant Gazprom) to bid for Onako but lost out to rival Tyumen Oil Co. (TNK). However Sibneft which had gained control of a 40% stake in Onako's main oil producing subsidiary Orenburgneft reportedly made an arrangement with TNK to swap its Orenburgneft shares for a minority stake in Onako. Also in 2000 Sibneft and other Russian oil companies were investigated by Russian authorities after allegations of tax evasion.

In 2001 the company announced plans to search for oil in the Chukotka autonomous district. (Abramovich is the governor of Chukotka). This unexplored area has a similar geological structure to Alaska's oil-rich North Slope. Later that year Sibneft acquired a 36% stake in a Moscow refinery from oil giant LUKOIL allowing the company to supply markets in European Russia.

In 2002 Sibneft opened its first gas station in Moscow.

Gazprom Neft (as Sibneft) was once controlled by UK-residing Chelsea soccer club-owning Russian oligarch Roman Abramovich through investment company Millhouse Capital. In 2005 Gazprom bought its majority stake in Sibneft from Millhouse Capital for $11 billion. The company changed its name to Gazprom Neft the next year and ENI acquired 20% of Gazprom Neft in 2007 following the bankruptcy of Yukos. Gazprom had the option to buy ENI's stake within two years and exercised that right in 2009 paying just more than $4 billion to ENI. Gazprom now directly owns or indirectly controls through subsidiaries about 95% of Gazprom Neft.

EXECUTIVES

Non-Executive Director, Mikhail Sereda
Non-Executive Director, Valery Serdyukov
Secretary to the Board of Directors, Viktoriya Nenadyshina
Non-Executive Director, Vitaly Markelov
Non-Executive Director, Famil Sadygov
Deputy Chief Executive Officer for Federal Government Relations, Member of the Management Board, Pavel Kolobkov
Non-Executive Director, Sergei Kuznets
Non-Executive Director, Alexander Medvedev
Deputy Chief Executive Officer for International Business, Member of the Management Board, Pavel Oderov
Member of the Management Board, Deputy Chief Executive Officer for Economics and Finance, Alexei Yankevich
Non-Executive Director, Gennady Sukhov
Member of the Management Board, Deputy Chief Executive Officer for Corporate Communications, Alexander Dybal
Executive Director, General Director (Chief Executive Officer), Chairman of the Management Board, Dyukov Valerevich
Deputy Chairman of the Management Board, Deputy Chief Executive Officer for Logistics, Processing and Sales (Downstream), Anatoly Cherner
Member of the Management Board, Deputy Chief Executive Officer for Administration Affairs, Kirill Kravchenko
Deputy Chief Executive Officer for Exploration and Production, Deputy Chairman of the Management Board, Vadim Yakovlev
Non-Executive Director, Kirill Seleznev
Deputy Chief Executive Officer for Legal and Corporate Affairs, Member of the Management Board, Elena Ilyukhina
Non-Executive Director, Vladimir Alisov
Non-Executive Director, Elena Mikhailova
Non-Executive Director, Sergey Menshikov
Deputy Chief Executive Officer for Security, Member of the Management Board, Igor Antonov
Non-Executive Chairman of the Board, Aleksey Miller
Auditors: Limited Liability Company & Accounting Consultants (FBK)

LOCATIONS

HQ: Gazprom Neft PJSC
3-5 Pochtamtskaya St., St. Petersburg 190000
Phone: (7) 812 363 31 52   **Fax:** (7) 812 363 31 51
Web: www.gazprom-neft.ru

2018 Sales

	% of total
Russian Federation	51
Commonwealth of Independent States	1
Export & international operations	44
Total	**100**

PRODUCTS/OPERATIONS

2018 Sales

	% of total
Petroleum products	67
Crude oil	29
Gas	1
Other	3
Total	**100**

2018 Sales by Segment

	% of total
Downstream	33
Upstream	67
Total	**100**

COMPETITORS

AEGEAN MARINE PETROLEUM S.A.
AFREN PLC
Athabasca Oil Corporation
CNOOC LIMITED
ENI SPA
LUKOIL PAO
MITSUI & CO. LTD.
MOTIVA ENTERPRISES LLC
NK ROSNEFT PAO
WORLD FUEL SERVICES CORPORATION

HISTORICAL FINANCIALS

Company Type: Public

Income Statement				FYE: December 31
	REVENUE ($ mil.)	NET INCOME ($ mil.)	NET PROFIT MARGIN	EMPLOYEES
12/20	26,731	1,573	5.9%	82,960
12/19	39,933	6,430	16.1%	78,800
12/18	35,716	5,404	15.1%	66,500
12/17	32,136	4,380	13.6%	67,882
12/16	25,241	3,269	13.0%	0
Annual Growth	1.4%	(16.7%)	—	—

2020 Year-End Financials

Debt ratio: 0.2%
Return on equity: 5.6%
Cash ($ mil.): 3,168
Current ratio: 0.97
Long-term debt ($ mil.): 9,872
No. of shares (mil.): —
Dividends
　Yield: 7.8%
　Payout: 562.9%
Market value ($ mil.): —

	STOCK PRICE ($) FY Close	P/E High/Low		PER SHARE ($) Earnings	Dividends	Book Value
12/20	22.00	1	1	0.33	1.73	5.91
12/19	34.30	0	0	1.36	3.72	7.01
12/18	25.38	0	0	1.15	2.05	5.60
12/17	20.88	0	0	0.93	2.00	5.69
12/16	17.52	0	0	0.69	0.06	4.71
Annual Growth	5.9%		—	(16.7%)	136.1%	5.8%

GD Power Development Co, Ltd.

EXECUTIVES

Deputy General Manager, Meijian Luo
General Manager, Director, Shuchen Feng
Deputy General Manager, Chief Engineer, Qi Xu
Chief Accounting Officer, Hongyuan Jiang
Auditors: RSM China Certified Public Accountants

LOCATIONS

HQ: GD Power Development Co, Ltd.
No. 19, Anyuan, Anhui Beili, Chaoyang District, Beijing 100101
Phone: (86) 10 58682200   **Fax:** (86) 10 64829900
Web: www.600795.com.cn

HISTORICAL FINANCIALS

Company Type: Public

Income Statement				FYE: December 31
	REVENUE ($ mil.)	NET INCOME ($ mil.)	NET PROFIT MARGIN	EMPLOYEES
12/20	17,800	402	2.3%	0
12/19	16,757	268	1.6%	0
12/18	9,521	199	2.1%	0
12/17	9,194	341	3.7%	0
12/16	8,412	680	8.1%	0
Annual Growth	20.6%	(12.3%)		

2020 Year-End Financials

Debt ratio: 7.8%
Return on equity: 4.9%
Cash ($ mil.): 1,441
Current ratio: 0.37
Long-term debt ($ mil.): 18,464
No. of shares (mil.): —
Dividends
　Yield: —
　Payout: —
Market value ($ mil.): —

Geely Automobile Holdings Ltd

Geely Automobile is one of the top 10 automobile makers in China. It manufactures cars that are exported to more than 40 countries and makes automotive parts for use throughout China. Geely's nine manufacturing plants produce about two dozen sedan models sold under the brands GLEagle Emgrand and Englon. Its economy-model cars are sold from about 1000 dealerships located across China; the export market accounts for about 25% of sales. It also owns two European car brands Swedish car and truck company Volvo and the London Electric Vehicle Company (the maker of the black cabs that can be seen roving the city's streets). It sells over 1.2 million cars a year its most popular models being the Geely Boyue New Emgrand New Vision Emgrand GS and Vision SUV.

EXECUTIVES

Non-Executive Independent Director, Jie Gao
Executive Chairman of the Board, Shu Fu Li, $50,254 total compensation
Chief Executive Officer, Executive Director, Sheng Yue Gui, $552,515 total compensation
VP, HR Management and Training, Mei Wei
Executive Vice Chairman of the Board, Dong Hui Li
Executive Director, Cong Hui An
Non-Executive Independent Director, Yin Shan Lam
Auditors: Grant Thornton Hong Kong Limited

LOCATIONS

HQ: Geely Automobile Holdings Ltd
Room 2301, 23rd Floor, Great Eagle Centre, 23 Harbour Road, Wan Chai,
Phone: (852) 2598 3333   **Fax:** (852) 2598 3399
Web: www.geelyauto.com.hk

PRODUCTS/OPERATIONS

Selected Subsidiaries
Centurion Industries Limited
DSI Holdings Pty Limited
Jinan Geely Automobile Parts and Components
   Company Limited
Linkstate Overseas Limited
Luckview Group Limited
Value Century Group Limited
Zhejiang Geely Gearbox Limited

COMPETITORS

AIRWALK INTERNATIONAL LLC
AMERICAN HONDA MOTOR CO. INC.
BRP Inc
Bayerische Motoren Werke AG
CAPITACOMMERCIAL TRUST
CONCEPT AUTOMOTIVE SERVICES LIMITED
DE BEERS S.A.
Dongfeng Motor Group Company Limited
Exceed Company Ltd.
FLYING BRANDS LIMITED
MAZDA MOTOR OF AMERICA INC.
MERCEDES-BENZ USA LLC
OU YUAN DA TRADING CO. LIMITED
PENNSYLVANIA AUTO DEALERS' EXCHANGE INC.
SAPPI LTD
SMITH ELECTRIC VEHICLES CORP.
TOYOTA MOTOR CORPORATION AUSTRALIA
   LIMITED
VEHICLE DISTRIBUTORS AUSTRALIA PTY LTD

HISTORICAL FINANCIALS
Company Type: Public

Income Statement				FYE: December 31
	REVENUE ($ mil.)	NET INCOME ($ mil.)	NET PROFIT MARGIN	EMPLOYEES
12/19	13,997	1,176	8.4%	43,000
12/18	15,497	1,825	11.8%	52,400
12/17	14,254	1,634	11.5%	41,600
12/16	7,736	736	9.5%	35,100
12/15	4,640	348	7.5%	18,700
Annual Growth	31.8%	35.6%	—	23.1%

2019 Year-End Financials
Debt ratio: 0.5%
Return on equity: 16.4%
Cash ($ mil.): 2,770
Current ratio: 1.03
Long-term debt ($ mil.): 596
No. of shares (mil.): —
Dividends
  Yield: 2.2%
  Payout: 28.0%
Market value ($ mil.): —

Gemdale Corp

EXECUTIVES

Chairman of the Board, Ke Ling
Independent Director, Yebi Hu
Director, Sheng Luo
President, Director, Juncan Huang
Director, Xuemei Bian
Vice President, Yibin Hao
Senior Vice President, Changchun Chen
Senior Vice President, Secretary of the Board, Director, Jiajun Xu
Independent Director, Tianguang Wang
Independent Director, Jin Chen
Finance Director, Senior Vice President, Director, Chuanjun Wei
Vice President, Xiaofeng Zhang
Vice President, Kan Yang

Director, Juyi Sun
Senior Vice President, Director, Bi'an Chen
Senior Vice President, Jiarong Yan
Director, Shengde Lin
Vice President, Nan Wang
Independent Director, Zhiwei Lu
Independent Director, Feng Gu
Senior Vice President, Weiyang Qiu
Auditors: Deloitte Touche Tohmatsu Certified Public Accountant LLP

LOCATIONS

HQ: Gemdale Corp
  Gemdale Commercial Building, Fuqiang Road, Futian District, Shenzhen, Guangdong Province 518048
Phone: (86) 755 82039509   **Fax:** (86) 755 82039900
Web: www.gemdale.com

HISTORICAL FINANCIALS
Company Type: Public

Income Statement				FYE: December 31
	REVENUE ($ mil.)	NET INCOME ($ mil.)	NET PROFIT MARGIN	EMPLOYEES
12/20	12,840	1,589	12.4%	0
12/19	9,114	1,447	15.9%	0
12/18	7,370	1,177	16.0%	0
12/17	5,787	1,051	18.2%	0
12/16	7,993	907	11.4%	0
Annual Growth	12.6%	15.1%	—	—

2020 Year-End Financials
Debt ratio: 4.1%
Return on equity: 18.5%
Cash ($ mil.): 8,286
Current ratio: 1.41
Long-term debt ($ mil.): 10,159
No. of shares (mil.): —
Dividends
  Yield: —
  Payout: —
Market value ($ mil.): —

GlaxoSmithKline Plc

GlaxoSmithKline (GSK) is a science-led global healthcare company. GSK's bestsellers include respiratory HIV immune-inflammation oncology and anti-virals as well as central nervous system cardiovascular and urogenital metabolic anti-bacterials and dermatology products. Its major products include Advair/Seretide its stalwart asthma medication; Relvar/Breo Ellipta a chronic obstructive pulmonary disease treatment; and two HIV medications Triumeq and Tivicay. In the consumer healthcare business GSK racks up big sales from its Sensodyne toothpaste brand joint-pain relief medicine Voltaren and fever relief medicine Panadol. Based in the UK GSK has customers across the globe. The US accounts for nearly 45% of the company's turnover.

Operations
GSK operates through three primary segments: Pharmaceuticals Consumer Healthcare and Vaccines. Pharmaceuticals is the largest by far pulling approximately half of revenue.

The Pharmaceuticals division has a broad portfolio of innovative and established medicines in respiratory HIV immuno-inflammation and oncology. Asthma medication Advair has been GSK's primary money spinner for many years although it faces intensifying competition from biosimilars and generics. HIV drugs Trimueq and Tivicay are GSK's next biggest while other respiratory drugs include Relvar/Breo Ellipta Ventolin and Flixotide.

The division's R&D activity focuses on immunology human genetics and advanced technologies.

GSK's Consumer Healthcare segment generates about 30% of sales and produces products in the oral health wellness nutrition and skin health categories. Its major brands include Advil Voltaren Centrum Caltrate and Otrivin.

The Vaccines segment develops produces and distributes around 2 million vaccines daily on the market in more than 160 countries. Meningitis vaccines Bexsero and Menveo are its biggest earner followed by flu vaccine Fluarix and Shingles vaccine Shingrix. Sales of vaccines account for around 20% of GSK's annual sales.

Geographic Reach
Headquartered in London GSK's Vaccines business has over 10 manufacturing sites across nine countries. It has presence in more than 160 countries.

The US is GSK's largest market at nearly 45% of sales. Europe generates about a quarter.

Sales and Marketing
GSK sells its products through a small number of wholesalers in addition to hospitals pharmacies physicians and other groups. Sales to the three largest wholesalers amounted to nearly 80% of the sales of the US Pharmaceuticals and Vaccines business.

Financial Performance
Note: Growth rates may differ after conversion to US dollars.

The company's revenue for fiscal 2020 increased to 34.1 billion compared from the prior year with 33.8 billion.

Profit for fiscal 2020 increased to 6.4 billion compared from the prior year with 5.3 billion.

Cash held by the company at the end of fiscal 2020 increased to 5.3 billion. Cash provided by operations and investing activities were 8.4 billion and 2.2 billion respectively. Cash used for financing activities was 10.1 billion mainly for dividends paid to shareholders.

Strategy
The company's priorities of Innovation Performance and Trust are underpinned by its ambition to build a more purpose and performance driven culture aligned to its values ? patient focus transparency respect and integrity ? and expectations ? courage accountability development and teamwork.

Innovation is critical to how we improve health and create financial value. In 2020 Total R&D expenditure was 5.1 billion which was 15.0% of turnover and an increase of 12% (AER and CER) from the previous year. On an Adjusted basis R&D expenditure was 4.6 billion (13.5% of turnover) 6% higher at AER 7% higher at CER than in 2019. On a pro-forma basis Adjusted R&D expenditure grew 6% CER compared with 2019.

In Pharmaceuticals and Vaccines the company focus on science related to the immune system human genetics and advanced technology. In Consumer Healthcare GSK leverage its scientific expertise and deep consumer insights to create healthcare products that meet consumer demands. As a research-based healthcare company the company rely on intellectual property protection to help ensure a reasonable return on its investments so the company can continue to research and develop new and innovative medicines.

HISTORY

Englishman Joseph Nathan started an import-export business in New Zealand in 1873. He obtained the rights to a process for drying milk and began making powdered milk in New Zealand selling it as baby food Glaxo.

Nathan's son Alec dispatched to London to oversee baby food sales in Britain increased Glaxo's name recognition by publishing the Glaxo Baby Book a guide to child care. After WWI the company began distribution in India and South America.

In the 1920s Glaxo launched vitamin D-fortified formulations. It entered the pharmaceutical business with its 1927 introduction of Ostelin a liquid vitamin D concentrate and continued to grow globally in the 1930s introducing Ostermilk (vitamin-fortified milk).

Glaxo began making penicillin and anesthetics during WWII; it went public in 1947. A steep drop in antibiotic prices in the mid-1950s led Glaxo to diversify; it bought veterinary medical instrument and drug distribution firms.

In the 1970s the British Monopolies Commission quashed both a hostile takeover attempt by Beecham and a proposed merger with retailer and drugmaker Boots. Glaxo launched US operations in 1978.

Glaxo shed nondrug operations in the 1980s to concentrate on pharmaceuticals. A 1981 marketing blitz launched antiulcer drug Zantac (to vie with SmithKline's Tagamet) in the US where Glaxo's sales had been small. The company boosted outreach by contracting to use Hoffmann-La Roche's sales staff. The Zantac sales assault gave Glaxo leadership in US antiulcer drug sales.

Under CEO Sir Richard Sykes Glaxo in 1995 made a surprise bid for UK rival Wellcome. Founded in 1880 by Americans Silas Burroughs and Henry Wellcome to sell McKesson-Robbins' products outside the US Burroughs Wellcome and Co. began making its own products two years later. By the 1990s the company which fostered Nobel Prize-winning researchers led the world in antiviral medicines. Its primary drug products were Zovirax (launched 1981) and Retrovir (1987).

Though an earlier bid by Glaxo had been rejected Sykes won the takeover with backing from Wellcome Trust Wellcome's largest shareholder.

In 1997 the company formed a new genetics division buying Spectra Biomedical and its gene variation technology. That year the company pulled diabetes drug Romozin (Rezulin in the US) from the UK market over concerns that it caused liver damage.

Glaxo in 1998 ended its joint venture with Warner-Lambert (begun 1993) selling its former partner the Canadian and US marketing rights to acid blocker Zantac 75.

In 1999 Glaxo trimmed its product line pulling hepatitis treatment Wellferon because of slow sales and selling the US rights to several anesthesia products. It also cut some 3400 jobs (half from the UK). Also that year Glaxo threatened to leave the UK after the National Health Service opted not to cover antiflu inhalant Relenza claiming the drug is not cost-effective.

The FDA in 2000 approved Glaxo's Lotronex for irritable bowel syndrome but several hospitalizations linked to the drug prompted the FDA to ask the company to withdraw it from the US market. Later that year Glaxo completed its merger with former UK rival SmithKline Beecham to create GlaxoSmithKline (GSK).

In 2015 GSK bought Novartis' Vaccines and Consumer Health business and sold its cancer drugs business to the same company.

EXECUTIVES

Chief Executive Officer & Executive Director, Emma Walmsley, $1,537,789 total compensation
President, Global Affairs, Phil Thomson
Independent Non-Executive Director, Lynn Elsenhans
President, Vaccines & Global Health, Roger Connor

Senior Vice President and General Counsel, James Ford
Independent Non-Executive Director, Urs Rohner
Independent Non-Executive Director, Jesse Goodman
Independent Non-Executive Director, Vivienne Cox
Independent Non-Executive Director, Charles Bancroft
Independent Non-Executive Director, Anne Beal
Independent Non-Executive Director, Harry Dietz
Chief Scientific Officer - Designate, Tony Wood
Senior Vice President, Human Resources, Diana Conrad
Chief Strategy Officer, David Redfern
Chief Executive Officer, GSK Consumer Healthcare, Brian McNamara
Chief Executive Officer of ViiV Healthcare, Deborah Waterhouse
Chief Commercial Officer, Luke Miels
Independent Non-Executive Director, Laurie Glimcher
President - Pharmaceutical Supply Chain, Regis Simard
Chief Scientific Officer and President, R&D, Hal Barron, $1,786,000 total compensation
Chief Financial Officer & Executive Director, Iain Mackay, $1,117,110 total compensation
Senior Vice President, Global Communications and CEO Office, Sally Jackson
Non-Executive Chairman, Jonathan Symonds
Auditors: Deloitte LLP

LOCATIONS

HQ: GlaxoSmithKline Plc
980 Great West Road, Brentford, Middlesex TW8 9GS
Phone: (44) 20 8047 5000   **Fax:** (44) 20 8047 7807
Web: www.gsk.com

2017 Sales

	% of total
US	37
International	36
Europe	27
Total	**100**

PRODUCTS/OPERATIONS

2017 Sales

	% of total
Pharmaceuticals	57
Consumer healthcare	26
Vaccines	17
Total	**100**

Selected Products

Pharmaceuticals
  Respiratory
    Beconase (allergies)
    Becotide/Beclovent (asthma and chronic obstructive pulmonary disease)
    Flixonase/Flonase (allergies)
    Flixotide/Flovent (asthma and chronic obstructive pulmonary disease)
    Seretide/Advair (asthma and chronic obstructive pulmonary disease)
    Serevent (asthma and chronic obstructive pulmonary disease)
    Ventolin (asthma and chronic obstructive pulmonary disease)
    Veramyst/Avamys (rhinitis)
  Cardiovascular and urogenital
    Arixtra (deep vein thrombosis and pulmonary embolism)
    Avodart (prostatic hyperplasia)
    Benlysta (systemic lupus erychematosus with HGS)
    Coreg CR (heart failure and hypertension)
    Fraxiparine (deep vein thrombosis and pulmonary embolism)
    Levitra (erectile dysfunction with Bayer)
    Lovaza (coronary heart disease)
    Vesicare (overactive bladder)
    Volibris (pulmonary hypertension)
  Central nervous system disorders

Horizant (post-herpetic neuralgia or restless leg syndrome)
Imigran/Imitrex (migraines)
Lamictal (epilepsy and bipolar disorder)
Potiga/Trobalt (epilepsy and partial seizures)
Requip (Parkinson's disease)
Seroxat/Paxil (depression)
Treximet (migraine)
Wellbutrin SR (depression)
ViiV Healthcare (HIV with Pfizer)
Combivir/Biovir (reverse transcriptase inhibitor for HIV/AIDS)
Epivir/3TC (reverse transcriptase inhibitor for HIV/AIDS)
Epizicom/Kivexa (combination of Epivir and Ziagen for HIV/AIDS)
Lexiva/Telzir (protease inhibitor for HIV/AIDS)
Selzentry (HIV)
Trizivir (three reverse transcriptase inhibitors for HIV/AIDS)
Antibacterials
Amoxil and Augmentin (antibiotics non-US only)
Dermatology
Bactroban (skin infections)
Duac (acne vulgaris)
Zovirax (herpes infections shingles chicken pox and cold sores)
Antivirals
Relenza (influenza)
Hepsera (hepatitis B)
Valtrex/Zelitrex (shingles and genital herpes)
Zeffix/Septavir/Heptodin/Epivir HBV (hepatitis B)
Vaccines
Cervarix (human papilloma virus)
Fluarix (influenza)
FluLaval (influenza)
Infanrix/Pediarix (diphtheria tetanus pertussis polio and hepatitis B)
Rotarix (rotavirus)
Synflorix (pneumonia)
Twinrix (hepatitis A and hepatitis B)
Metabolic
Avandia Avandamet (type 2 diabetes)
Boniva/Bonviva (osteoporosis with Roche)
Consumer products
Over-the-counter medicines
Abreva (cold sores)
alli (weight loss)
Breathe Right (nasal strips)
Citrucel (laxative)
Commit (smoking-cessation)
Contac (respiratory product)
Nicabate/NicoDerm/NiQuitin CQ (smoking-cessation)
Nicorette (smoking-cessation)
Panadol (analgesic)
Tums (antacid)
Oral care
Aquafresh (toothpaste and toothbrushes)
Corega (denture care)
Dr Best (toothbrushes)
Macleans (toothpaste)
Odol (toothpaste)
Polident (denture cleaner)
Poli-Grip (denture adhesive)
Sensodyne (toothpaste)
Nutritional health care
Horlicks (milk-based malted food and chocolate drinks)
Lucozade (glucose energy drink)
Ribena (line of juice drinks rich in vitamin C)

COMPETITORS

ALLERGAN LIMITED	ELI LILLY AND COMPANY
BRISTOL-MYERS SQUIBB COMPANY	GILEAD SCIENCES INC.
Boehringer Ingelheim International GmbH	MERCK KG auf Aktien
	Novartis AG
CIPLA LIMITED	Roche Holding AG
EISAI CO. LTD.	SANOFI

HISTORICAL FINANCIALS

Company Type: Public

Income Statement
FYE: December 31

	REVENUE ($ mil.)	NET INCOME ($ mil.)	NET PROFIT MARGIN	EMPLOYEES
12/20	46,535	7,845	16.9%	94,066
12/19	44,574	6,134	13.8%	99,437
12/18	39,351	4,625	11.8%	95,490
12/17	40,771	2,069	5.1%	98,462
12/16	34,307	1,121	3.3%	99,300
Annual Growth	7.9%	62.6%	—	(1.3%)

2020 Year-End Financials

Debt ratio: 44.1%	No. of shares (mil.): —
Return on equity: 44.1%	Dividends
Cash ($ mil.): 8,586	Yield: 5.4%
Current ratio: 0.91	Payout: 138.0%
Long-term debt ($ mil.): 30,757	Market value ($ mil.): —

	STOCK PRICE ($) FY Close	P/E High/Low	PER SHARE ($) Earnings	Dividends	Book Value
12/20	36.80	43 30	1.56	2.02	3.96
12/19	46.99	51 41	1.22	2.01	3.02
12/18	38.21	57 44	0.93	2.11	1.12
12/17	35.47	150 111	0.42	2.16	(0.02)
12/16	38.51	227 175	0.23	2.37	0.28
Annual Growth	(1.1%)	—	61.5%	(3.9%)	93.6%

Glencore PLC

One of the world's largest energy metals and agricultural products companies Glencore is active at every stage of commodity supply chain. With presence in approximately 35 countries and a diversified portfolio of upwards of 90 commodities its operations span some 150 sites and facilities from crude oil production and coal mining to custom metallurgical products biofuels and storage and handling of grains. Customers include the automotive steel power generation oil and food processing industries. Glencore was founded in 1974.

IPO

Operations

The company produce metals and minerals which accounts for some 55% of revenue ? such as copper cobalt zinc nickel and ferroalloys - and also market aluminum/alumina and iron ore from third parties. In Energy products which are about 45% of total revenue Glencore is a major producer and marketer of coal with mines in Australia Africa and South America ? while its oil business is one of the leading marketers of crude oil refined products and natural gas.

Glencore is organized and operates on a worldwide basis in two core business segments ? Marketing activities and Industrial activities.

Marketing activities which generates around 75% of company's revenue use their scale and capabilities to extract additional margin throughout their business model and provide a high quality service to their customers and a reliable supply of quality product.

Industrial activities which generates the remaining 25% of total revenue provide a consistent source of volumes for their marketing operations which are supplemented by third party production.

Geographic Reach

Glencore headquartered in Switzerland has operations approximately in 35 countries has 150-plus sites and more than 40 offices around the world.

Asia is the largest market which generates more than 40% followed by Europe which generates approximately 30%. Americas generates almost 20% and Oceania and Africa generates the remainder.

Sales and Marketing

Glencore markets to a broad base of industrial consumers in sectors such as automotive steel semi-fabricators power generation and oil.

Financial Performance

The company's revenue for 2020 was $142.3 million a 34% decrease from the previous year's revenue of $215.1 million. The decrease was primarily due to a drastic drop in the company's sale of commodities.

In 2020 the company had a loss of $3.9 billion a 162% increase from the previous year's net loss of $1.5 billion.

The company's cash at the end of 2020 was $1.5 billion. Operating activities generated $2.7 billion while investing activities used $2.7 billion mainly for purchase of property plant and equipment. Financing activities used another $320 million primarily for repayment of capital market notes.

Strategy

The company's strategy is to sustainably grow total shareholder returns while maintaining a strong investment grade rating and acting as a responsible operator.

The company will prioritize investment in metals that support the decarbonization of energy usage as well as help meet demand for metals needed in everyday life. The company will also reduce its coal production in line with its various climate action commitments and the electrification and decarbonization of energy systems.

Company Background

EXECUTIVES

Independent Non-Executive Director, Gill Marcus
Senior Independent Director, Martin Gilbert
Chairman, Kalidas Madhavpeddi
Chief Executive Officer and Director, Gary Nagle
Independent Non-Executive Director, Cynthia Carroll
Non-Executive Director, Peter Coates
Independent Non-executive Director, Patrice Merrin
Auditors: Deloitte LLP

LOCATIONS

HQ: Glencore PLC
Baarermattstrasse 3, P.O. Box 1363, Baar CH-6341
Phone: (41) 41 709 2000   **Fax:** (41) 41 709 3000
Web: www.glencore.com

2018 Sales

	% of total
Asia	43
Europe	35
The Americas	17
Oceania	3
Africa	2
Total	**100**

PRODUCTS/OPERATIONS

2018 Sales

	% of total
Energy products	63
Metals and minerals	37
Corporate and other	-
Total	**100**

Selected Operations

Agricultural Products
  Barley
  Corn
  Meals
  Rice
  Sugar
  Wheat
Energy Products
  Coal
  Oil
Metals and Minerals
  Copper
  Ferroalloys
  Lead
  Nickel
  Zinc
Viterra ($6.2 billion; Canada; grain merchant)

COMPETITORS

Borealis AG	ORICA LIMITED
FERROGLOBE PLC	RUBIS
K+S AG	RUSAL AO
KOPPERS HOLDINGS INC.	TERNIUM S.A.
MECHEL PAO	TRICORN GROUP PLC
NATURGY ENERGY GROUP SA.	TransAlta Corporation
	VALLOUREC
NLMK PAO	VENATOR MATERIALS PLC

HISTORICAL FINANCIALS

Company Type: Public

Income Statement
FYE: December 31

	REVENUE ($ mil.)	NET INCOME ($ mil.)	NET PROFIT MARGIN	EMPLOYEES
12/20	142,338	(1,903)	—	145,000
12/19	215,111	(404)	—	160,000
12/18	219,754	3,408	1.6%	158,000
12/17	205,476	5,777	2.8%	145,977
12/16	152,948	1,379	0.9%	154,832
Annual Growth	(1.8%)	—	—	(1.6%)

2020 Year-End Financials

Debt ratio: 31.7%	No. of shares (mil.): —
Return on equity: (-4.8%)	Dividends
Cash ($ mil.): 1,498	Yield: 2.7%
Current ratio: 1.10	Payout: —
Long-term debt ($ mil.): 29,227	Market value ($ mil.): —

	STOCK PRICE ($) FY Close	P/E High/Low	PER SHARE ($) Earnings	Dividends	Book Value
12/20	6.27	— —	(0.14)	0.17	2.85
12/19	6.18	— —	(0.03)	0.34	3.05
12/18	7.24	49 29	0.24	0.34	3.31
12/17	10.41	25 17	0.40	0.18	3.49
12/16	6.74	76 20	0.10	0.00	3.11
Annual Growth	(1.8%)	—	—	—	(2.2%)

Gold Corp Holdings

Auditors: Caroline Spencer

LOCATIONS

HQ: Gold Corp Holdings
Perth Mint Buildings, 310 Hay Street, East Perth, Western Australia 6004
Phone: (61) 8 9421 7222   **Fax:** (61) 8 9221 2258
Web: www.perthmint.com

HISTORICAL FINANCIALS
Company Type: Public

Income Statement   FYE: June 30

	REVENUE ($ mil.)	NET INCOME ($ mil.)	NET PROFIT MARGIN	EMPLOYEES
06/19	12,660	5	0.0%	397
06/18	13,921	4	0.0%	413
06/17	6,226	13	0.2%	454
06/16	6,701	21	0.3%	441
06/15	5,076	10	0.2%	410
Annual Growth	25.7%	(15.3%)	—	(0.8%)

2019 Year-End Financials
Debt ratio: 65.5%
Return on equity: 6.2%
Cash ($ mil.): 86
Current ratio: 1.02
Long-term debt ($ mil.): —

No. of shares (mil.): 31
Dividends
 Yield: —
 Payout: —
Market value ($ mil.): —

Great Eastern Holdings Ltd (Singapore)

Great Eastern Holdings Limited holds quite a few insurance companies in the far east and they all want to be great. The company through its subsidiaries has operations in Singapore and Malaysia where it is the largest and oldest insurer as well as in Brunei Indonesia China (via joint venture) and Vietnam. It offers asset management investment holding management services life insurance (through Great Eastern Life Assurance) and other financial services. Great Eastern Holdings' 20000 dedicated agents sell its products; representatives at major banks also offer its wares. The company which was incorporated in 1908 is owned by Oversea-Chinese Banking Corp.

EXECUTIVES

Group Company Secretary, General Counsel, Pakshong Wong
Chief Executive Officer - Malaysia, Yaw Hui Koh
Group Chief Internal Auditor, Jeffrey Lowe
Non-Executive Director, Pik Kuen Wong
Managing Director - Group Marketing, Chan Colin
Managing Director - Digital for Business, Kwok Leong Cheong
Non-Executive Director, Ka Cheung Ip
Independent Non-Executive Director, Nam Yew Thean
Non-Executive Chairman of the Board, Beng Seng Koh
Independent Non-Executive Director, Lian Ee Teoh
Managing Director - General and Group Insurance, Jimmy Tong
Group Chief Executive Officer, Hock Seng Khor, $797,469 total compensation
Independent Non-Executive Director, Fook Sun Lee
Chief Executive Officer - Indonesia, Clement Lien
Independent Non-Executive Director, Tit Koon Soon
Group Chief Financial Officer, Yew Chye Tan
Group Chief Investment Officer, Ai Ning Wee
Managing Director - Group Information Technology, Gary Teh
Managing Director - Group Human Capital, James Lee

Managing Director - Group Operations, Patrick Kok
Independent Non-Executive Director, Khai Fatt Lee
Independent Non-Executive Director, Song Keng Law
Non-Executive and Non-independent Director, Joo Yeow Wee
Non-Executive Independent Director, Chee Peng Ng
Auditors: PricewaterhouseCoopers LLP

LOCATIONS

HQ: Great Eastern Holdings Ltd (Singapore)
 1 Pickering Street, #16-01 Great Eastern Centre, 048659
Phone: (65) 6248 2000   **Fax:** (65) 6438 3889
Web: www.greateasternlife.com

COMPETITORS

Hannover R   ck SE
Hyundai Marine & Fire Insurance Co. Ltd.
MUTUAL OF OMAHA INSURANCE COMPANY
Noah Holdings Limited
SANLAM LTD
Swiss Life Deutschland Vertriebsholding GmbH
TOKIO MARINE HOLDINGS INC.
W   stenrot & W   rttembergische AG

HISTORICAL FINANCIALS
Company Type: Public

Income Statement   FYE: December 31

	ASSETS ($ mil.)	NET INCOME ($ mil.)	INCOME AS % OF ASSETS	EMPLOYEES
12/20	80,899	726	0.9%	4,726
12/19	71,729	746	1.0%	4,595
12/18	62,452	543	0.9%	4,255
12/17	63,298	865	1.4%	4,779
12/16	49,220	407	0.8%	4,614
Annual Growth	13.2%	15.5%	—	0.6%

2020 Year-End Financials
Return on assets: 0.9%
Return on equity: 10.6%
Long-term debt ($ mil.): —
No. of shares (mil.): 473
Sales ($ mil): 16,242

Dividends
 Yield: 0.0%
 Payout: 54.7%
Market value ($ mil.): 13,054

	STOCK PRICE ($) FY Close	P/E High/Low	Earnings	Dividends	Book Value
12/20	27.58	14 14	1.54	0.84	14.96
12/19	41.15	— —	1.58	0.82	13.52
12/18	41.15	26 26	1.15	0.26	11.54
12/17	33.04	— —	1.83	0.67	11.93
12/16	33.04	— —	0.87	0.73	9.63
Annual Growth	(4.4%)	— —	15.4%	3.6%	11.6%

Great Wall Motor Co Ltd

Great Wall Motor (GWM) is a Chinese automaker that produces a variety of products that cover three categories: SUV passenger car and pickup. The company has nearly 10 vehicle production facilities and a production capacity of almost 2 million units per year. China accounts for nearly 95% of sales but GWM has exported vehicles to regions including Australia Chile Russia Saudi Arabia South Africa and other overseas

countries. GWM owns four brands which are HAVAL WEY ORA and GWM Pickup. The company also offer adter-sales services which include a complete supportive system on technology and parts center and over 500 service outlets present in around 60 countries globally. GWM produced its first car in 1993.

EXECUTIVES

Chairman of the Board, Executive Director, Jianjun Wei
Non-Executive Director, Ping He
Independent Non-Executive Director, Wanjun Li
Independent Non-Executive Director, Zhijie Wu
Deputy General Manager, Guoqing Zhao
Independent Non-Executive Director, Ying Yue
Auditors: Deloitte Touche Tohmatsu Certified Public Accountants LLP

LOCATIONS

HQ: Great Wall Motor Co Ltd
 No. 2266 Chao Yang Road South, Baoding, Hebei Province 071000
Phone: (86) 312 2197813   **Fax:** (86) 312 2197812
Web: www.gwm.com.cn

COMPETITORS

AB Volvo	HONDA MOTOR CO. LTD.
ACCURIDE CORPORATION	MACK TRUCKS INC.
DAIHATSU MOTOR CO. LTD.	NAVISTAR INTERNATIONAL CORPORATION
DAIMLER TRUCKS NORTH AMERICA LLC	NISSAN MOTOR CO.LTD.
	VOLKSWAGEN AG

HISTORICAL FINANCIALS
Company Type: Public

Income Statement   FYE: December 31

	REVENUE ($ mil.)	NET INCOME ($ mil.)	NET PROFIT MARGIN	EMPLOYEES
12/20	15,795	819	5.2%	0
12/19	13,826	646	4.7%	0
12/18	14,426	757	5.2%	0
12/17	15,546	772	5.0%	0
12/16	14,201	1,519	10.7%	0
Annual Growth	2.7%	(14.3%)	—	—

2020 Year-End Financials
Debt ratio: 1.8%
Return on equity: 9.5%
Cash ($ mil.): 2,230
Current ratio: 1.22
Long-term debt ($ mil.): 1,647

No. of shares (mil.): —
Dividends
 Yield: 0.9%
 Payout: —
Market value ($ mil.): —

Great-West Lifeco Inc

Holding company Great-West Lifeco majority-owned by Power Financial is one of Canada's largest insurance organizations. Through subsidiaries (including Great-West Life Assurance in Canada) the company offers a range of individual and group life and health insurance retirement savings and investment products reinsurance and services to financial institutions. Great-West Life Assurance's two major subsidiaries Canada Life and London Life Insurance provide individual insurance and wealth-management products in Canada Germany Ireland and the UK. Great-West Lifeco also has retirement and asset management operations in the US.

Operations

In the US Great-West Life & Annuity (GWL&A) provides retirement savings plans to employers. Great-West Lifeco's companies also provide reinsurance to niche markets in the US and Europe. Great-West Lifeco has approximately $2 trillion in assets under administration.

The company divides its business geographically: it offers financial services and asset management in the US its largest market individual and group insurance and wealth management services in Canada and insurance and annuities along with reinsurance in Europe.

Financial Performance

For the twelve months ended December 31 2020 net earnings attributable to common shareholders (net earnings) were C$2.9 billion compared to C$2.4 billion for the previous year primarily reflecting the net positive impact from a number of strategic initiatives undertaken during the year.

Cash held by the company at the end of fiscal 2020 increased to C$7.9 billion. Cash provided by operations and financing activities were C$9.6 billion and C$2.0 billion respectively. Cash used for investing activities was C$8.2 billion mainly for investment in bonds.

Strategy

In 2021 Individual Customer will continue to advance on strategies to position for growth. The company will further establish the value propositions for advisors in all channels providing them with strategies and tools for helping customers focus on achieving long-term financial security regardless of life stage and market fluctuations. This commitment to advice is beneficial to strong customer retention as well as helping advisors attract new customers to the company. A key distribution strategy will be to maximize the use of common tools processes and support while tailoring support to specific segments of advisors where appropriate.

The company will continue to competitively develop price and market its comprehensive range of individual insurance and individual wealth management products while maintaining its focus on sales and service support to customers and advisors in all channels. The company will also continue to monitor and respond to the impacts of long-term interest rates and fee income compression.

EXECUTIVES

Independent Director, Marcel Coutu
President and Group Head, Strategy, Investments, Reinsurance and Corporate Development, Arshil Jamal, $540,556 total compensation
Independent Director, T. Timothy Ryan
Executive Vice-President and Chief Financial Officer of Lifeco and Canada Life, Garry MacNicholas, $530,531 total compensation
President, Chief Executive Officer, Director, Paul Mahon, $977,401 total compensation
Independent Director, Gregory Tretiak
Senior Vice-President and Chief Internal Auditor of Lifeco and Canada Life, Nancy Russell
Executive Vice-President, Chief Human Resources Officer of Lifeco and Canada Life, Grace Palombo
Executive Vice-President and Chief Risk Officer of Lifeco and Canada Life, Graham Bird, $482,182 total compensation
Executive Vice-President, Chief Actuary of Lifeco and Canada Life, Dervla Tomlin
Executive Vice-President and Global Chief Information Officer, Philip Armstrong, $296,075 total compensation
Independent Director, Gary Doer
Independent Director, Susan McArthur
Independent Director, Siim Vanaselja

Executive Vice-President and Global Chief Investment Officer, Lifeco, Great-West, London Life and Canada Life, Raman Srivastava, $456,956 total compensation
Independent Director, Elizabeth Lempres
Independent Director, Michael Amend
Independent Director, David Fuller
Independent Director, Deborah Barrett
Independent Director, Paula Madoff
Senior Vice-President and Chief Compliance Officer of Lifeco and Canada Life, Anne Sonnen
President and Chief Operating Officer, Canada, Jeffrey Macoun, $502,822 total compensation
Independent Director, Claude Genereux
Senior Vice-President, Corporate Secretary and Chief Governance Officer of Lifeco and Canada Life, Jeremy Trickett
Executive Vice-President and General Counsel of Lifeco and Canada Life, Sharon Geraghty, $419,120 total compensation
Independent Director, Heather Conway
Independent Director, Robin Bienfait
Independent Chairman of the Board, R. Jeffrey Orr
Independent Director, Paul Desmarais
Independent Director, Andre Desmarais
Independent Director, Brian Walsh
President and Chief Operating Officer, Europe of Lifeco and Canada Life, David Harney
Auditors: Deloitte LLP

LOCATIONS

HQ: Great-West Lifeco Inc
100 Osborne Street North, Winnipeg, Manitoba R3C 1V3
Phone: 204 946-1190 **Fax:** 204 946-4139
Web: www.greatwestlifeco.com

2012 Sales

	$ mil.	% of total
US		
Asset management	23	40
Financial services	6	10
Canada		
Wealth management	9	16
Group insurance	7	12
Individual insurance	3	7
Europe		
Insurance & annuities	5	8
Reinsurance	4	7
Total	**59**	**100**

PRODUCTS/OPERATIONS

Selected Subsidiaries & Affiliates
The Great-West Life Assurance Company
  Canada Life Financial Corporation
  The Canada Life Assurance Company
  Canada Life Capital Corporation Inc.
  The Canada Life Group (U.K.) Limited
  Canada Life International Re Limited
  Canada Life Irish Holding Company Limited
  Crown Life Insurance Company
  Laketon Investment Management Ltd.
  London Insurance Group
  London Life Insurance Company
  London Reinsurance Group Inc.
GWL&A Financial Inc. (US)
  Great-West Life & Annuity Insurance Company
  Advised Assets Group LLC
  FASCore LLC

COMPETITORS

ALLIANZ INSURANCE PLC
CINCINNATI FINANCIAL CORPORATION
Corporation Financire Power
EMPLOYERS HOLDINGS INC.
FBL FINANCIAL GROUP INC.
FUKOKU MUTUAL LIFE INSURANCE COMPANY
GREAT-WEST LIFE & ANNUITY INSURANCE COMPANY
LINCOLN NATIONAL CORPORATION
NATIONWIDE FINANCIAL SERVICES INC.

NEW YORK LIFE INSURANCE COMPANY
PRINCIPAL FINANCIAL GROUP INC.
PRUDENTIAL FINANCIAL INC.
Sun Life Financial Inc.
THE PENN MUTUAL LIFE INSURANCE COMPANY
The Canada Life Assurance Company
VOYA FINANCIAL INC.
WESTERN & SOUTHERN FINANCIAL GROUP INC.

HISTORICAL FINANCIALS
Company Type: Public

Income Statement
FYE: December 31

	ASSETS ($ mil.)	NET INCOME ($ mil.)	INCOME AS % OF ASSETS	EMPLOYEES
12/21	495,027	2,561	0.5%	28,000
12/20	471,620	2,415	0.5%	24,500
12/19	346,468	1,913	0.6%	24,000
12/18	314,064	2,272	0.7%	24,200
12/17	334,899	1,817	0.5%	23,300
Annual Growth	**10.3%**	**9.0%**	**—**	**4.7%**

2021 Year-End Financials

Return on assets: 0.5%	Dividends
Return on equity: 12.7%	Yield: 0.0%
Long-term debt ($ mil.): —	Payout: 55.2%
No. of shares (mil.): 930	Market value ($ mil.): 27,940
Sales ($ mil): 50,576	

	STOCK PRICE ($) FY Close	P/E High/Low		PER SHARE ($) Earnings	Dividends	Book Value
12/21	30.02	9	7	2.64	1.46	22.96
12/20	23.00	9	5	2.49	1.38	20.34
12/19	25.66	11	8	1.91	1.27	18.78
12/18	20.60	9	6	2.20	1.14	18.23
12/17	27.89	14	12	1.73	1.17	18.23
Annual Growth	**1.9%**	**—**	**—**	**11.1%**	**5.6%**	**5.9%**

Gree Electric Appliances Inc Of Zhuhai

Gree Electric Appliances finds it agreeable to keep things cool. The world's #1 maker of household air conditioners manufactures and distributes about a dozen different types of air conditioners — from small window units to large commercial systems. Gree Electric Appliances has manufacturing facilities in China Brazil and Pakistan capable of producing 10 million air conditioning units per year. The firm has been expanding its manufacturing facilities for several years and continues to explore new areas. Its appliances are sold in more than 180 countries. Company president Mingszhu Dong regularly makes Fortune magazine's list of the 50 most powerful women in business. Gree Group owns Gree Electric Appliances.

Operations

Gree Electric Appliances is an international air conditioning enterprise with integrated R&D manufacturing marketing and service. It has three brands — GREE TOSOT and KINGHOME — with a wide product range which includes residential air conditioners central air conditioners air source water heaters smart phones home appliances refrigerators etc.

Geographic Reach

The company has about 10 production bases around the world seven in China (Zhuhai Chongqing Hefei Zhengzhou Wuhan Shijiazhuang and Wuhu) as well as in Brazil and Pakistan.

Sales and Marketing

The company uses e-commerce to sell its products.

Financial Performance

In fiscal 2015 Gree Electric Appliances' net sales decreased by RMB 40 billion due to lower sales from household appliance manufacturing. Sale of air conditioners saw a decrease of about RMB 35 billion.

Net income dropped by RMB 1.6 billion due to decreased sales and lower income from investments.

In fiscal 2015 net cash provided by the operating activities increased by 31% due to a change in refund of tax and levies.

Strategy

Gree Electric Appliances' is focused on increasing its investment in R&D sustaining innovation in products and improving product quality and competitiveness.

Mergers and Acquisitions

In 2016 Gree Electric Appliances suspended its planned acquisition of electric vehicle maker Zhuhai Yinlong New Energy Co. Zhuhai Yinlong's shareholders declined to sell the company. The acquisition would have established Gree Electric's entry into the electric vehicle market.

EXECUTIVES

Chairman of the Board, President, Mingzhu Dong
Director, Shuzhan Guo
Independent Director, Qiusheng Zhang
Director, Jundu Zhang
Independent Director, Ziwen Xing
Vice President, Pei Zhuang
Director, Wei Zhang
Independent Director, Shuwei Liu
Independent Director, Xiaohua Wang
Vice President, Chief Engineer, Jianming Tan
Vice President, Secretary of the Board, Xiaobo Deng
Vice President, Lizhi Shu
Auditors: China Audit Asia Pacific Certified Public Accountants Co., Ltd.

LOCATIONS

HQ: Gree Electric Appliances Inc Of Zhuhai
Jinji West Road, Qianshan, Zhuhai, Guangdong Province 519070
Phone: (86) 756 8669232 **Fax:** (86) 756 8622581
Web: www.gree.com.cn

2015 Sales

	% of total
Domestic	85
Overseas	15
Total	**100**

PRODUCTS/OPERATIONS

2015 Sales

	% of total
Household appliance manufacturing	90
Other businesses	10
Total	**100**

2015 Sales

	% of total
Air conditioners	85
Home appliances	2
Others	3
Other businesses	10
Total	**100**

COMPETITORS

AAON INC.	GOODMAN GLOBAL INC.
BRISTOL COMPRESSORS INTERNATIONAL LLC	LENNOX INTERNATIONAL INC.
DAIKIN INDUSTRIES LTD.	TECOGEN INC.
Danfoss A/S	TECUMSEH PRODUCTS COMPANY LLC
FRANKLIN ELECTRIC CO. INC.	

HISTORICAL FINANCIALS

Company Type: Public

Income Statement   FYE: December 31

	REVENUE ($ mil.)	NET INCOME ($ mil.)	NET PROFIT MARGIN	EMPLOYEES
12/20	26,068	3,390	13.0%	0
12/19	28,816	3,549	12.3%	0
12/18	29,080	3,809	13.1%	0
12/17	23,053	3,442	14.9%	0
12/16	15,857	2,220	14.0%	0
Annual Growth	13.2%	11.2%	—	—

2020 Year-End Financials

Debt ratio: 1.2%	No. of shares (mil.): —
Return on equity: 19.6%	Dividends
Cash ($ mil.): 20,857	Yield: —
Current ratio: 1.35	Payout: —
Long-term debt ($ mil.): 284	Market value ($ mil.): —

Grupo Bimbo SAB de CV (Mexico)

Grupo Bimbo is the world's largest and leading baking company and an important playersnack in Mexico. Offering more than 13000-plus products under some 100-plus umbrella brands Grupo Bimbo produces bread cookies and tortillas under the T a Rosa Bimbo Wonder and Marinela brands. Not content with dominating the Latin American bread markets the company also owns major operations in the US including Bimbo Bakeries USA. Majority of its sales were generated in North America.

Operations

Grupo Bimbo makes snacks which include sliced bread buns & rolls pastries cakes cookies english muffins and tortillas though its 1700 sales centers. These products are sold under over 100 brand names including Bimbo Marinela Sara Lee Ricolina and more.

Geographic Reach

Mexico-based Grupo Bimbo operates facilities in about 35 countries North America generate about 55% of company's revenue followed by Europe with about 30% and both Latin America and EAA brings about 10% of revenue.

Sales and Marketing

Grupo Bimbo spent $12.6 million $11 million and $11.5 million in advertising and promotional expense for years 2020 2019 and 2018 respectively. Its largest customer accounts for about 15% of its net sales.

Financial Performance

Net sales rose 13% from Mex$291.9 billion in 2019 to Mex$331.1 billion in 2020 primarily due to favorable price mix strong volume performance across all regions and FX rate benefit.

In 2020 the company had a net profit of Mex$16.7 billion a 38% increase from the previous year's net income of Mex$12.1 billion.

The company's cash at the end of 2020 was Mex$9.3 billion. Operating activities generated Mex$43.9 billion while investing activities used Mex$16.7 billion mainly for purchase of property plant and equipment. Financing activities used another Mex$4.2 billion primarily for repayments of loans.

Strategy

Nourishing a Better World is centered on three priority areas where Grupo Bimbo has a significant level of impact or capacity to drive positive change socially economically and environmentally.

"Baked for you" is about developing products in such a way that the health and lifestyle of consumers improves.

"Baked for life" focuses on the company's efforts towards the community and its associates that makes it what it is.

"Baked for nature" is the company's ambition that its products give back to the planet more than what the company takes from it the company wants to feed in a restorative and regenerative way. Grupo Bimbo seeks to strengthen its sustainability position and its performance for the year 2030.

Mergers and Acquisitions

Grupo Bimbo would strengthen its US operations and add bakeries in several other countries with its proposed $650 million acquisition of East Balt Bakeries. One Equity Partners East Balt's owner agreed to the deal which is to close in 2017. East Balt based in Chicago has 21 bakeries in the US Europe the Middle East and Africa. Among its customers are McDonalds Wendy's and Kentucky Fried Chicken.

Bimbo completed its acquisition of Canada Bread which stocks the company a range of well-known brands in the country. It also provides Bimbo with expertise in frozen products an area the company has targeted for growth. Besides Canada the acquisition expands Bimbo's exposure in Europe through Canada Bread's UK operations. In 2015 the Canadian operation bought Saputo Bakery which makes snack cakes under brand names that include Vachon Joe Louis Passion Flakie and May West.

In South America Bimbo bought Supan the leading bread company in Ecuador. Supan operates plants in Guayaquil and Quito to produce brands such as Dulzones Pansol and Rey-pan.

HISTORY

Starting with 10 trucks and bread in cellophane wrappers in 1945 Lorenzo Servitje and associates including Jaime Jorba began deliveries of their Bimbo-brand breads around Mexico City.

Two years later distribution spread to three other cities. Steady growth for Grupo Industrial Bimbo followed during the 1950s and 1960s with new plants opening in Guadalajara and Monterrey. In 1962 Jorba left the company returned to Spain and created Bimbo España. In 1964 when Continental Bakeries introduced Wonder Bread to Mexico Bimbo countered with a similarly positioned bread line using the licensed US Sunbeam brand.

By 1972 the company was firmly established as the bread-market leader in Mexico when it began making corn tortillas. The next year the company founded Frexport its jam and jelly unit.

The company went public in 1980 but remained firmly under the control of the Servitje family. A major leap in the company's vision for itself came when it created a bun for McDonald's. Bimbo won the exclusive contract to supply buns to Mexico's McDonald's in 1985. In 1986 Bimbo acquired rival Continental Bakeries' Wonder Bread brand in Mexico thus securing a virtual monopoly on the Mexican packaged-bread market. Future growth would come from international expansion.

During the 1990s Bimbo began a steady stream of acquisitions and construction of plants in Guatemala (1990) Chile (1992) Venezuela (1993) and Peru (1998). Daniel Servitje Montull was named CEO of Bimbo in 1997.

The company began doing contract work in the mid-1990s for German confectioner Park Lane leading up to its 1998 purchase of Park Lane; it also established a factory in the Czech Republic. However the company's boldest move was its 1998 purchase of Mrs. Baird's the largest family-owned US bakery based in Fort Worth Texas. The company formed Bimbo Bakeries USA to control the Mrs. Baird's business and move closer to its US competition. In 1999 it acquired the Four-S bakery business in California. Four-S came with the popular local Weber brand of bread.

In 1999 the company shortened its name to Grupo Bimbo. That year it was awarded the exclusive contract to supply buns to McDonald's in Colombia Peru and Venezuela.

During 2000 Grupo Bimbo completed the spin-off of its flour mills and processed jellies units with the agreement that they would continue supplying Grupo Bimbo. Roberto Servitje Ach tegui grandson of founder Lorenzo Servitje left the company that year to run a new company Grupo Altex. In 2001 Bimbo bought Plus Vita a fresh bread and baked goods business from Bunge Alimentos (a subsidiary of agribusiness giant Bunge Limited). In 2001 Grupo Bimbo purchased a bread baking operation in Costa Rica from tortilla-giant and rival Gruma.

Grupo Bimbo purchased five western US Orowheat production facilities in 2002 from George Weston. The acquisition gave the company access to some well-known consumer brands including Thomas' English Muffins Entenmann's and Boboli. That year it also closed its Mrs. Baird's bakery facility in Dallas.

As part of its strategy to concentrate on its consumer businesses in 2003 Bimbo sold its 42% stake in packaging business Novacel to French aluminum company Pechiney (now a part of Rio Tinto Alcan) for $38 million. It also closed its Dallas Orowheat bakery that year. Bimbo along with a consortium of other companies took over Argentinean bakery business Compañ a de Alimentos de Fargo in 2003. Bimbo's stake in Fargo is 30%.

In 2004 the company bought three Mexican confectionery companies: Joyco de Mexico Alimentos Duval and Lolimen. Bimbo expanded into frozen bakery-product manufacturing that yearas well when it formed a joint venture with Rich Products to produce frozen and partially baked goods under the Fripan brand name.

The number of Bimbo's acquisitions continued to increase during 2005 as the company bought Colombian bread maker Lalo Chilean pastry manufacturer Lagos el Sur Mexican pastry manufacturer Pasteler as El Globo and Mexican confectioner La Corona. It purchased two Uruguayan bakery companies in 2006 for about $7 million: Walter M. Doldan y Cia and Los Sorchantes.

Marking its entry into China in 2006 the company purchased the Chinese unit of Spanish baker Panrico SA.

EXECUTIVES

President of Bimbo, Miguel Angel Espinoza Ramirez
Director, Mauricio Jorba Servitje
Independent Director, Arturo Manuel Fernandez Perez
Independent Director, Ricardo Guajardo Touche
Independent Director, Edmundo Miguel Vallejo Venegas
Independent Director, Ignacio Perez Lizaur
Director, Jaime Chico Pardo
Independent Director, Maria Luisa Jorda Castro
Director, Luis Jorba Servitje
Director, Nicolas Mariscal Servitje
Global Vice President - Administration and Finance, Diego Gaxiola Cuevas
Executive Vice President of Grupo Bimbo, Gabino Miguel Gomez Carbajal
Global Vice President - Transformation, Raul Ignacio Obregon Servitje
President of BBU, Alfred Penny
Director, Jorge Pedro Jaime Sendra Mata
Chairman and CEO, Daniel Javier Servitje Montull
Director, Jose Ignacio Mariscal Torroella
Director, Javier de Pedro Espinola
Director, Maria Isabel Mata Torrallardona
Director, Andres Servitje
Director, Estibalitz Servitje
Independent Director, Rogelio Rebolledo Rojas
Global Vice President - People, Juan Muldoon Barrena
Independent Director, Jaime Antonio El Koury
Auditors: Mancera, S.C. (Ernst & Young Global)

LOCATIONS

HQ: Grupo Bimbo SAB de CV (Mexico)
Prolongacion Paseo de la Reforma 1000, Colonia Pena Blanca Santa Fe, Delegacion Alvaro Obregon, Mexico City 01210
Phone: (52) 55 5268 6600   **Fax:** (525) 55 5268 6697
Web: www.grupobimbo.com

2014 Plants

	No.
US & Canada	85
Latin America	32
Mexico	39
Europe	10
Asia	1
Total	**167**

2014 Sales

	% of total
US & Canada	47
Mexico	38
Other countries	15
Total	**100**

PRODUCTS/OPERATIONS

Selected Brands
Asia
  Bimbo
Latin America
  Mexico
  Barcel
  Bimbo
  Clever
  Coronado
  Del Hogar
  El Globo
  La Corona
  Lonchibon
  Marinela
  Milpa Real
  Ricolino
  Suandy
  Tí;a Rosa
  Vero
  Other countries
  Bimbo Centroamé;rica
  Breddy
  Coronado Centroamé;rica
  Ideal
  La Mejor
  Lido
  Marinela
  Monarca
  Pix
  Schmidt
  Tulipan
Europe
  Bimbo

Eagle
US
  Arnold
  Bimbo USA
  Boboli
  Brownberry
  Earthgrains
  Entenmann's
  Francisco
  Frenchbakery
  Heiner's
  Holsum
  Home Maid Bread
  Marinela USA
  Master
  Mickey
  Mrs. Baird's
  Old Country
  Old Home
  Orowea
  Rainbo
  Sara Lee
  Stroehmann
  Taystee
  Thomas'
  Tia Rosa USA

COMPETITORS

BAKKAVOR GROUP PLC
BIG HEART PET BRANDS INC.
DANONE
Fresh Del Monte Produce Inc.
GENERAL MILLS INC.
GOLDEN ENTERPRISES INC.
GREENCORE GROUP PUBLIC LIMITED COMPANY
George Weston Limited
Grupo Lala S.A.B. de C.V.
KERRY GROUP PUBLIC LIMITED COMPANY
Koninklijke Ahold Delhaize N.V.
McCain Foods Limited

HISTORICAL FINANCIALS

Company Type: Public

Income Statement

	REVENUE ($ mil.)	NET INCOME ($ mil.)	NET PROFIT MARGIN	EMPLOYEES
				FYE: December 31
12/20	16,661	458	2.8%	148,746
12/19	15,429	333	2.2%	148,638
12/18	14,659	295	2.0%	138,432
12/17	13,579	234	1.7%	138,171
12/16	12,185	285	2.3%	130,913
Annual Growth	**8.1%**	**12.6%**	**—**	**3.2%**

2020 Year-End Financials

Debt ratio: 1.3%	No. of shares (mil.): —
Return on equity: 11.5%	Dividends
Cash ($ mil.): 466	Yield: —
Current ratio: 0.83	Payout: —
Long-term debt ($ mil.): 4,259	Market value ($ mil.): —

Grupo Financiero Banorte S.A. BDE C V

Auditors: Galaz, Yamazaki, Ruiz Urquiza, S.C. (member of Deloitte & Touche Tohmatsu)

LOCATIONS

HQ: Grupo Financiero Banorte S.A. BDE C V
Avenida Prolongacion Reforma 1230, 14 piso, Col. Cruz Manca Santa Fe, Delegacion Cuajimalpa, Mexico City 05349
Phone: (52) 55 1670 2256
Web: www.banorte.com

HISTORICAL FINANCIALS
Company Type: Public

Income Statement   FYE: December 31

	ASSETS ($ mil.)	NET INCOME ($ mil.)	INCOME AS % OF ASSETS	EMPLOYEES
12/20	89,984	1,535	1.7%	29,920
12/19	83,511	1,930	2.3%	0
12/18	82,407	1,625	2.0%	30,548
12/17	68,737	1,213	1.8%	29,915
12/16	61,287	933	1.5%	27,929
Annual Growth	10.1%	13.3%	—	1.7%

2020 Year-End Financials
Return on assets: 1.8%
Return on equity: 14.6%
Long-term debt ($ mil.): —
No. of shares (mil.): —
Sales ($ mil): 10,281

Dividends
  Yield: 0.0%
  Payout: —
Market value ($ mil.): —

	STOCK PRICE ($) FY Close	P/E High/Low		PER SHARE ($) Earnings	Dividends	Book Value
12/20	27.78	3	1	0.53	0.00	3.93
12/19	27.88	3	2	0.67	1.42	3.57
12/18	24.50	3	2	0.56	0.82	3.06
12/17	27.36	—	—	0.44	0.00	2.69
12/16	24.86	—	—	0.34	0.00	2.47
Annual Growth	2.8%	—	—	12.2%	—	12.3%

Grupo Financiero Citibanamex SA de CV

One of the largest financial services groups in Mexico (along with rival Bancomer) Grupo Financiero Banamex offers personal and corporate banking through such services as deposit accounts mortgages consumer loans mutual funds and credit cards. Flagship subsidiary Banco Nacional de Mexico (aka Banamex) operates more than 1500 branches and some 5000 ATMs. The company's Accival (or Acciones y Valores) subsidiary is among Mexico's top securities brokerage houses. Grupo Financiero Banamex also offers insurance (Seguros Banamex) and pension services (Afore Banamex). In one of the largest-ever US-Mexico corporate mergers Citigroup bought Banamex in 2001.

LOCATIONS
HQ: Grupo Financiero Citibanamex SA de CV
  Avenida Isabel la Catolica 44, Col. Centro, Mexico City
Phone:
Web: www.banamex.com

PRODUCTS/OPERATIONS

Selected Subsidiaries
Acciones 7 Valores de Mé;xico S.A. de C.V. (dba Accival)
Afore Banamex (pension fund manager)
Arrendadora Banamex S.A. de C.V
Fomento Cultural Banamex (cultural programs and art collection)
Seguros Banamex (medical services life insurance car insurance)

COMPETITORS
BANCO BBVA ARGENTINA S.A.

Banco Santander-Chile
CREDIT INDUSTRIEL ET COMMERCIAL
Grupo Financiero BBVA Mexico S.A. de C.V.
Grupo Financiero Banorte S.A.B. de C.V.
Grupo Financiero Santander Mexico S.A.B. de C.V.
Invex Controladora S.A.B. de C.V.
Ixe Grupo Financiero S.A.B. de C.V.
Slovensk sporitelna a.s.

HISTORICAL FINANCIALS
Company Type: Public

Income Statement   FYE: December 31

	ASSETS ($ mil.)	NET INCOME ($ mil.)	INCOME AS % OF ASSETS	EMPLOYEES
12/20	78,057	716	0.9%	0
12/19	74,858	1,544	2.1%	0
12/18	71,600	1,413	2.0%	0
12/17	66,456	1,235	1.9%	0
12/16	61,010	804	1.3%	0
Annual Growth	6.4%	(2.8%)	—	—

2020 Year-End Financials
Return on assets: 0.9%
Return on equity: 7.1%
Long-term debt ($ mil.): —
No. of shares (mil.): —
Sales ($ mil): 9,620

Dividends
  Yield: —
  Payout: —
Market value ($ mil.): —

Gunma Bank Ltd (The)

Gunma Bank hopes that you have more than just a yen for its services. Through more than 140 branches The Gunma Bank provides banking services in the Gunma prefecture and surrounding areas of Japan through some 150 branches. The Gunma Bank also operates a subsidiary in Hong Kong and a branch in New York City. As the company's name might imply the Gunma prefecture (known for its industry and agriculture-based economy) accounts for more than 80% of deposits. Besides deposits Gunma Bank's services include loans to companies individuals and the government securities insurance and exchange. The Gunma Bank was founded in 1932.

EXECUTIVES
Vice President, Director, Nobuyuki Horie
Chairman of the Board, Representative Director, Kazuo Saito
Managing Director, Yukio Yuasa
President, Representative Director, Akihiko Fukai
Independent Director, Jun Kondo
Managing Director, Satoshi Inoue
Managing Director, Hiroyuki Irisawa
Independent Director, Kuniko Nishikawa
Independent Director, Kazuhito Ohsugi
Auditors: Ernst & Young ShinNihon LLC

LOCATIONS
HQ: Gunma Bank Ltd (The)
  194 Motosoja-machi, Maebashi, Gunma 371-8611
Phone: (81) 27 252 1111
Web: www.gunmabank.co.jp

COMPETITORS
HACHIJUNI BANK LTD.   SHIGA BANK LTD. THE
  THE

HISTORICAL FINANCIALS
Company Type: Public

Income Statement   FYE: March 31

	ASSETS ($ mil.)	NET INCOME ($ mil.)	INCOME AS % OF ASSETS	EMPLOYEES
03/21	95,875	121	0.1%	4,694
03/20	77,538	205	0.3%	4,730
03/19	73,504	210	0.3%	4,743
03/18	75,383	267	0.4%	4,737
03/17	71,432	235	0.3%	4,724
Annual Growth	7.6%	(15.2%)	—	(0.2%)

2021 Year-End Financials
Return on assets: 0.1%
Return on equity: 2.6%
Long-term debt ($ mil.): —
No. of shares (mil.): 420
Sales ($ mil): 1,296

Dividends
  Yield: —
  Payout: —
Market value ($ mil.): —

Hachijuni Bank, Ltd. (Japan)

Auditors: Deloitte Touche Tohmatsu LLC

LOCATIONS
HQ: Hachijuni Bank, Ltd. (Japan)
  178-8 Aza Okada, Oaza Nakagosho, Nagano 380-8682
Phone: (81) 26 227 1182
Web: www.82bank.co.jp

HISTORICAL FINANCIALS
Company Type: Public

Income Statement   FYE: March 31

	ASSETS ($ mil.)	NET INCOME ($ mil.)	INCOME AS % OF ASSETS	EMPLOYEES
03/21	109,827	202	0.2%	5,029
03/20	96,458	203	0.2%	5,101
03/19	94,375	203	0.2%	5,301
03/18	87,666	243	0.3%	5,484
03/17	77,847	235	0.3%	5,449
Annual Growth	9.0%	(3.7%)	—	(2.0%)

2021 Year-End Financials
Return on assets: 0.2%
Return on equity: 2.7%
Long-term debt ($ mil.): —
No. of shares (mil.): 489
Sales ($ mil): 1,390

Dividends
  Yield: —
  Payout: 30.6%
Market value ($ mil.): —

Haci Omer Sabanci Holding AS

Haci —mer Sabanci is one of Turkey's largest industrial and financial conglomerates with interests in the energy banking retail building materials and other industries. Its primary holding is a stake in Turkish banking firm Akbank which provides commercial banking retail banking and private banking as well as international banking. Other holdings include stakes in domestic energy company Enerjisa and supermarket operator Carrefoursa a joint venture with Carrefour. Sabanci's portfolio spans about 15 countries and markets its products in Europe the Middle East North Africa Asia and the Americas. It also has multinational partnerships including Bridgestone and Philip Morris. The wealthy Sabanci family is the major shareholder group of Sabanci Holding.

EXECUTIVES

Non-Executive Vice Chairman of the Board, Erol Sabanci
President of Finance, Accounting and Investor Relations, Levent Demirag
Non-Executive Member of the Board of Directors, Serra Sabanci
Secretary General, Goekhan Eyiguen
President of the Finance Group, Haluk Dincer
President of the Building and Materials Group, Tamer Saka
President of the Energy Group, Kivanc Zaimler
Auditors: PwC Bagimsiz Denetim ve Serbest Muhasebeci Mali Musavirlik A.S.

LOCATIONS

HQ: Haci Omer Sabanci Holding AS
Sabanci Center 4, Levent, Istanbul 34330
Phone: (90) 212 385 80 80   **Fax:** (90) 212 385 88 88
Web: www.sabanci.com

PRODUCTS/OPERATIONS

2016 sales

	% of total
Domestic sales	88
Foreign sales	12
Total	**100**

2016 sales

	% of total
Turkey	92
EU Countries	8
Total	**100**

2016 sales

	% of total
Financial instutions	27
Manufacturing	18
Public sector	17
Individual	15
Wholesale and retail trade	9
Other	14
Total	**100**

Selected Investments

Cement
  Akçansa
  Çimsa
Energy
  Enerjisa
Financial services
  Akbank
  Aksigorta
Retail
  Carrefoursa
  Teknosa
Industrial
  Brisa
  Kordsa Global
  Temsa
  Sasa
  Yunsa
Other
  Bimsa
  Philip Morrissa
  Philsa
  Tursa

COMPETITORS

ARCADIS N.V.
Brederode
CIMB GROUP HOLDINGS BERHAD
DRAGADOS SOCIEDAD ANONIMA
Dalian Wanda Group Co. Ltd.
EIFFAGE
FOMENTO DE CONSTRUCCIONES Y CONTRATAS SA
HANOVER ACCEPTANCES LIMITED
HOCHTIEF AG
KOC HOLDING ANONIM SIRKETI
KUKA AG
MACQUARIE GROUP LIMITED
OM RESIDUAL UK LIMITED
SEQUANA

HISTORICAL FINANCIALS
Company Type: Public

Income Statement   FYE: December 31

	ASSETS ($ mil.)	NET INCOME ($ mil.)	INCOME AS % OF ASSETS	EMPLOYEES
12/19	68,286	635	0.9%	62,051
12/18	70,249	723	1.0%	64,294
12/17	93,633	920	1.0%	63,152
12/16	87,371	753	0.9%	62,312
12/15	90,896	765	0.8%	63,281
Annual Growth	**(6.9%)**	**(4.6%)**	**—**	**(0.5%)**

2019 Year-End Financials

Return on assets: 0.9%
Return on equity: 12.0%
Long-term debt ($ mil.): —
No. of shares (mil.): —
Sales ($ mil): 10,240
Dividends
  Yield: —
  Payout: 264.6%
Market value ($ mil.): —

	STOCK PRICE ($) FY Close	P/E High/Low	Earnings	Dividends	Book Value
12/19	0.00	— —	0.00	0.01	0.03
12/18	0.00	— —	0.00	0.01	0.03
12/17	0.72	40 23	0.00	0.02	0.03
Annual Growth (5.6%)		**— —**	**(8.9%)**	**(14.0%)**	

Haier Smart Home Co Ltd

Auditors: Shandong Huide CPA Co., Ltd.

LOCATIONS

HQ: Haier Smart Home Co Ltd
Haier Industrial Park, Laoshan District, Qingdao, Shandong Province 266101
Phone: (86) 532 88931670   **Fax:** (86) 532 88931689
Web: www.haier.net/cn/

HISTORICAL FINANCIALS
Company Type: Public

Income Statement   FYE: December 31

	REVENUE ($ mil.)	NET INCOME ($ mil.)	NET PROFIT MARGIN	EMPLOYEES
12/20	32,066	1,357	4.2%	0
12/19	28,852	1,179	4.1%	0
12/18	26,651	1,081	4.1%	0
12/17	24,472	1,064	4.3%	0
12/16	17,146	725	4.2%	0
Annual Growth	**16.9%**	**17.0%**	**—**	**—**

2020 Year-End Financials

Debt ratio: 2.5%
Return on equity: 15.4%
Cash ($ mil.): 7,103
Current ratio: 1.04
Long-term debt ($ mil.): 2,833
No. of shares (mil.): —
Dividends
  Yield: —
  Payout: —
Market value ($ mil.): —

Hang Seng Bank Ltd.

Auditors: PricewaterhouseCoopers

LOCATIONS

HQ: Hang Seng Bank Ltd.
83 Des Voeux Road Central,
Phone: (852) 2198 1111   **Fax:** (852) 2868 4047
Web: www.hangseng.com

HISTORICAL FINANCIALS
Company Type: Public

Income Statement   FYE: December 31

	ASSETS ($ mil.)	NET INCOME ($ mil.)	INCOME AS % OF ASSETS	EMPLOYEES
12/20	226,987	2,152	0.9%	9,563
12/19	215,363	3,190	1.5%	10,331
12/18	200,622	3,091	1.5%	10,298
12/17	189,171	2,561	1.4%	9,980
12/16	177,604	2,090	1.2%	9,708
Annual Growth	**6.3%**	**0.7%**	**—**	**(0.4%)**

2020 Year-End Financials

Return on assets: 0.9%
Return on equity: 9.2%
Long-term debt ($ mil.): —
No. of shares (mil.): 1,911
Sales ($ mil): 8,335
Dividends
  Yield: 4.6%
  Payout: 74.5%
Market value ($ mil.): 33,075

	STOCK PRICE ($) FY Close	P/E High/Low	Earnings	Dividends	Book Value
12/20	17.30	3 2	1.08	0.80	12.35
12/19	20.62	2 2	1.64	0.92	12.01
12/18	22.38	2 2	1.59	0.81	10.82
12/17	24.75	2 2	1.32	0.74	10.18
12/16	18.55	2 2	1.07	1.07	9.49
Annual Growth (1.7%)		**— —**	**0.2%**	**(7.0%)**	**6.8%**

Hannover Rueckversicherung SE

Established in 1966 the Hannover Re Group today has a network of more than 170 subsidiaries branches and representative offices worldwide. The group's German business is written by the subsidiary E+S R ck. Hannover Re with gross premium of more than ?24 billion is the third-largest reinsurer in the world. It transacts all lines of property & casualty and life & health reinsurance and is present on all continents with more than 3000 staff. Fifty percent of Hannover's is owned by Talanx AG.

Operations

The company operates through two operating segments: Property & casualty reinsurance and Life & health reinsurance.

Property & casualty reinsurance offers reinsurance services and risk solutions. Within the Hannover Re Group these companies are Property & Casualty subsidiaries: Hannover ReTakaful Bahrain Hannover Re (Bermuda) Bermuda Hannover Re (Ireland) Ireland Hannover Re Africa South Africa.

Life & health reinsurance segment offers risk solutions financial solutions and reinsurance services.

Geographic Reach

Property & Casualty operates in around 20 locations worldwide. Life & Health segment is headquartered at Hannover Germany and operates in around 25 locations worldwide.

Financial Performance

Net income for fiscal 2020 decreased by 31% to ?883.1 million compared from the prior year with ?1.3 billion.

Cash held by the company at the end of fiscal 2020 increased to ?1.3 billion. Cash provided by operations was ?3.2 billion while cash used for investing and financing activities were ?2.2 billion and ?726.0 million respectively. Main uses of cash were for purchases of fixed-income securities and dividends payment.

Strategy

The company's strategic initiatives are: customer excellence; innovation and digital strategy; Asia-Pacific growth; and talent management.

The customer excellence strategic initiative seeks leadership in customer-centricity and aims to broaden its client relationships by raising them to a strategic level. With the Asia-Pacific growth initiative the company are teaming up with its customers to create joint opportunities in the world's fastest growing economic region. In the framework of innovation & digital strategy Hannover RE focus on digital partnerships as well as on its role in assisting clients in their digital transformation. And all these efforts would be futile without the talent management initiative ? hiring and retaining engaged and high-performing employees are absolutely crucial for the company's future.

HISTORY

Hannover Re was founded in 1966 as the Aktiengesellschaft f r Transport und R ckversicherung (ATR) by the Feuerschadenverband Rheinisch-Westfaelischer Zechen (FSV) a mutual insurer specializing in fire damage in the town of Bochum. Within five years ATR had expanded into international reinsurance markets. In 1970 FSV merged with another mutual HDI Haftpflichtverband der Deutschen Industrie which owned reinsurer Eisen und Stahl R ckversicherungs-AG. ATR's headquarters relocated to Hannover and six years later it was renamed Hannover R ckversicherungs-Gesellschaft.

Jointly managed by HDI Hannover Re and Eisen und Stahl operated separately until 1996: Hannover Re targeted international markets while Eisen und Stahl operated mostly within Germany.

Hannover Re maintained its foreign focus throughout the 1970s and 80s expanding in Europe and South Africa and making its first forays into the US. In 1990 the firm acquired US life insurer Reassurance Company of Hannover.

Hannover Re went public in 1994 selling 25% of its stock. Also that year the firm formed an Australian subsidiary. The next year Hannover Re acquired Eisen und Stahl (renamed E+S Ruck 1996) which then assumed total control of the company's domestic business.

In 1998 Hannover Re became the first reinsurer to securitize life insurance business (reinsurers often securitize non-life policies to protect against natural catastrophe risks) through an agreement with Interpolis an Irish reinsurance subsidiary of the Netherlands' Rabobank. Also that year the firm expanded its financial reinsurance business reorganizing the Irish consortium it formed with another subsidiary of HDI into Hannover Re Advanced Solutions.

As various natural disasters offset earnings in Hannover Re's property & casualty division in 1998 and 1999 its life and health segment boomed. To facilitate further growth the firm restructured these operations into a new subsidiary Hannover Life Re. Also in 1999 the firm acquired the Clarendon Insurance Group of New York. In 2001 Hannover Re joined Inreon an online reinsurance trading exchange set up by rivals Munich Re and Swiss Re. Also in 2001 the company established a Bermuda-based subsidiary focused on catastrophe business. The following year Hannover Re split its stock in order to stimulate demand and become a more widely held company.

Like many other insurers the company was hit hard by the attacks of September 11 2001 falling stock markets and in 2005 damages in the Gulf of Mexico caused by hurricanes Katrina and Rita.

Late in 2006 China loosened its regulation of a number of industries and insurance was one of them — Hannover Re was one of the first to gain permission to enter the Chinese market for life and health reinsurance.

At about the same time the company announced plans to cut down on its noncore business operations. The first move in this direction was the sale of its US-based Praetorian Group subsidiary to QBE's US-based subsidiary for a sum in excess of $800 million. Hannover Re used the proceeds to shore up its property/casualty and life/health reinsurance businesses.

EXECUTIVES

Member of the Supervisory Board, Erhard Schipporeit, $34 total compensation

Member of the Executive Board, Michael Pickel, $781,290 total compensation

Deputy Chairman of the Board, Member of the Supervisory Board, Herbert Haas, $51,273 total compensation

Member of the Executive Board, Silke Sehm, $490,286 total compensation

Independent Member of the Supervisory Board, Michael Ollmann, $34,182 total compensation

Member of the Executive Board, Klaus Miller, $743,006 total compensation

Independent Member of the Supervisory Board, Andrea Pollak, $34,182 total compensation

Member of the Executive Board, Sven Althoff, $721,129 total compensation

Chairman of the Management Board, Chief Executive Officer, Jean-Jacques Henchoz, $1,262,689 total compensation

Independent Member of the Supervisory Board, Ursula Lipowsky, $34,182 total compensation

Independent Chairman of the Supervisory Board, Torsten Leue, $113,940 total compensation

Member of the Supervisory Board, Employee Representative, Frauke Heitmueller, $34,182 total compensation

Member of the Executive Board, Claude Chevre, $890,217 total compensation

Auditors: PricewaterhouseCoopers GmbH Wirtschaftpruefungsgesellschaft

LOCATIONS

HQ: Hannover Rueckversicherung SE
Karl-Wiechert-Allee 50, Hannover D-30625
Phone: (49) 511 5604 0   **Fax:** (49) 511 5604 1188
Web: www.hannover-re.com

2013 Premiums Written

	% of total
Europe	
Germany	9
UK	19
France	4
Other countries	12
North America	
US	24
Other countries	5
Asia	12
Australia	6
Africa	3
Other regions	6
Total	**100**

COMPETITORS

ANTHEM INC.	PRINCIPAL FINANCIAL
Allianz SE	GROUP INC.
ERGO Group AG	SCOR SE
GENERAL RE CORPORATION	Swiss Re AG
Generali Deutschland	Tower Group
AG	International Ltd
Hyundai Marine & Fire	UNUM GROUP
Insurance Co. Ltd.	

HISTORICAL FINANCIALS

Company Type: Public

Income Statement

FYE: December 31

	ASSETS ($ mil.)	NET INCOME ($ mil.)	INCOME AS % OF ASSETS	EMPLOYEES
12/20	87,677	1,083	1.2%	3,218
12/19	80,116	1,441	1.8%	3,083
12/18	73,874	1,213	1.6%	3,317
12/17	73,359	1,149	1.6%	3,251
12/16	67,078	1,236	1.8%	2,893
Annual Growth	6.9%	(3.2%)	—	2.7%

2020 Year-End Financials

Return on assets: 1.2%	Dividends
Return on equity: 8.1%	Yield: 2.7%
Long-term debt ($ mil.): —	Payout: 102.8%
No. of shares (mil.): 120	Market value ($ mil.): 9,587
Sales ($ mil): 28,281	

	STOCK PRICE ($) FY Close	P/E High/Low		Earnings	Dividends	Book Value
12/20	79.50	16	9	8.98	2.19	111.89
12/19	97.75	9	6	11.96	2.15	98.02
12/18	67.66	8	7	10.07	2.19	83.34
12/17	62.92	9	7	9.53	8.26	84.77
12/16	54.20	6	5	10.25	6.86	78.77
Annual Growth	10.1%	—	—	(3.2%)	(24.8%)	9.2%

Hanwa Co Ltd (Japan)

Auditors: KPMG AZSA LLC

LOCATIONS

HQ: Hanwa Co Ltd (Japan)
1-13-1 Tsukiji, Chuo-ku, Tokyo 104-8429
Phone: (81) 3 3544 2202   **Fax:** (81) 3 3544 2351
Web: www.hanwa.co.jp

HISTORICAL FINANCIALS
Company Type: Public

Income Statement				FYE: March 31
	REVENUE ($ mil.)	NET INCOME ($ mil.)	NET PROFIT MARGIN	EMPLOYEES
03/21	15,764	177	1.1%	5,696
03/20	17,572	(125)	—	5,455
03/19	18,733	125	0.7%	4,733
03/18	16,867	163	1.0%	4,211
03/17	13,541	146	1.1%	3,774
Annual Growth	3.9%	4.9%	—	10.8%

2021 Year-End Financials
Debt ratio: 0.3%
Return on equity: 11.1%
Cash ($ mil.): 459
Current ratio: 1.62
Long-term debt ($ mil.): 2,023
No. of shares (mil.): 40
Dividends
  Yield: —
  Payout: —
Market value ($ mil.): —

Hapag-Lloyd Aktiengesellschaft

Hapag-Lloyd is Germany's largest container liner shipping company and is one of the world's leading container liner shipping companies in terms of global market coverage. The shipping company operates a fleet in over 235 vessels and a shipping capacity of approximately 1.7 million TEU as well as 1.6 million containers with a capacity of 2.7 million TEU. The Line's routes link around 130 countries throughout Europe Asia the Americas and Africa. The company traces its historical roots back to 1847 when the founding companies ? Hamburg-Amerikanische Packetfahrt-Actien-Gesellschaft (Hapag) and North German Lloyd ? put their first ships to sea carrying general cargo and passengers to New York. Majority of its sales were generated in Latin America.

Operations
The company is managed as a single global business unit with one sphere of activity.

Hapag-Lloyd's fleet offers a total transport capacity of around 1.7 million standard containers as well as a container fleet of 1.6 million TEU — including one of the world's largest and state-of-the-art reefer fleets. The company successfully converted its vessel fleet to operate using low-sulphur fuel which reduces sulphur dioxide emissions by more than 70%.

The company generates its revenue solely through its activities as a container liner shipping company. The revenue comprises income from transporting and handling containers and from related services and commissions all of which are generated globally.

Geographic Reach
Headquartered in Hamburg UK Hapag-Lloyd's has Seven geographical segment; Atlantic generates over 15% Transpacific about 20% Far East approximately 15% Middle East with about 10% Intra-Asia less than 5% Latin America over 20% EMA (Europe - Mediterranean - Africa) approximately 5% and the rest of its total revenue under Revenue not assigned to trades around 10% in the year 2020.

Sales and Marketing
The company serves approximately 30400 customers through some 395 sales offices in about 130 countries and offers its customers worldwide access to a network of some 120 liner services.

Financial Performance
The company's revenue increased by ?164 million to ?12.8 billion in 2020 from ?.6 billion in 2019. This was primarily due to a increase in average freight rates of 4.0% compared with the previous year. Adjusted for exchange rate movements revenue would have risen by approximately ?0.4 billion or 3.3%. However a 1.6% decrease in the average transport volume compared with the previous year softened the impact of the increased freight rate on overall revenue.

Profit for 2020 increased to ?935.4 million from ?373.4 million in 2019.

Cash held by the company at the end of 2020 increased to ?681.3 million. Cash provided by operations was ?2.9 billion while investing and financing activities used ?477.6 million and ?2.2 billion respectively. Main cash uses were payments made for the redemption of financial debt and payments made for investments in property plant and equipment and intangible assets.

Strategy
In 2018 Hapag-Lloyd developed and presented its medium-term strategy based on these premises. Successful implementation of the strategy should safeguard the future and provide the foundations for further organic growth. The three core objectives of Strategy 2023 are: Become number one for quality; Remain a global player; and Profitability throughout the entire economic cycle.

Hapag-Lloyd is aiming for a global market share (excl. Intra-Asia) of around 10%. As of 31 December 2020 the market share (excl. Intra-Asia) was approximately 11% (previous year: 10%). Hapag-Lloyd plans to grow with the market and thereby retain its market share. In addition Hapag-Lloyd wants to increase its presence in attractive growth markets and in the area of special cargo in particular. This includes the transportation of reefer containers which HapagLloyd sees today as an area of strength.

As part of Strategy 2023 Hapag-Lloyd is pursuing profitability throughout the entire economic cycle. This is reflected in a suitable return on invested capital (ROIC) one that at least matches the company's weighted average cost of capital. The company is also aiming to strengthen its balance sheet.

Mergers and Acquisitions
In mid-2021 Hapag-Lloyd successfully closed the acquisition of the Dutch container shipping company Nile Dutch Investments B.V. (NileDutch) one the leading providers of container services from and to West Africa headquartered in Rotterdam. The acquisition of NileDutch strengthens the company's position in West Africa and will be an excellent addition to its existing activities on the continent. Terms were not disclosed.

EXECUTIVES

Chairman of the Supervisory Board, Michael Behrendt, $205,093 total compensation
Chairman of the Executive Board, Chief Executive Officer, Rolf Habben Jansen, $854,554 total compensation
Member of the Supervisory Board, Felix Albrecht, $68,364 total compensation
Chief Personnel and Global Procurement Officer, Member of the Executive Board, Joachim Schlotfeldt, $512,732 total compensation
Member of the Supervisory Board, Turqi Alnowaiser, $68,364 total compensation
Member of the Supervisory Board, Oscar Eduardo Hasbun Martinez, $88,303 total compensation
Chief Financial Officer, Member of the Executive Board, Mark Frese, $752,007 total compensation
Chief Operating Officer, Member of the Executive Board, Maximilian Rothkopf, $512,732 total compensation
Auditors: KPMG AG Wirtschaftspruefungsgesellschaft

LOCATIONS
HQ: Hapag-Lloyd Aktiengesellschaft
  Ballindamm 25, Hamburg D-20095
Phone: (49) 40 3001 2529   **Fax:** (49) 40 3353 60
Web: www.hapag-lloyd.com

COMPETITORS

AMERICAN COMMERCIAL LINES INC.
CAESARSTONE LTD
CAI INTERNATIONAL INC.
CMA CGM ASIA PACIFIC LIMITED
HMM Company Limited.
HOMESERVE PLC
Hamburg S damerikanische Dampfschifffahrts-Ges
KIRBY CORPORATION
PREMIER LOGISTICS INC.
TOUAX SCA - SGTR - CITE - SGT - CMTE - TAF - SLM TOUAGE INVE
U.S. SHIPPING CORP
UNITED MARITIME GROUP LLC

HISTORICAL FINANCIALS
Company Type: Public

Income Statement				FYE: December 31
	REVENUE ($ mil.)	NET INCOME ($ mil.)	NET PROFIT MARGIN	EMPLOYEES
12/20	15,675	1,137	7.3%	13,117
12/19	14,155	406	2.9%	12,996
12/18	13,187	42	0.3%	12,765
12/17	11,955	32	0.3%	12,567
12/16	8,166	(102)	—	9,413
Annual Growth	17.7%	—	—	8.6%

2020 Year-End Financials
Debt ratio: 30.2%
Return on equity: 13.8%
Cash ($ mil.): 836
Current ratio: 0.67
Long-term debt ($ mil.): 3,964
No. of shares (mil.): 175
Dividends
  Yield: 0.0%
  Payout: 9.6%
Market value ($ mil.): 10,329

	STOCK PRICE ($) FY Close	P/E High/Low		PER SHARE ($)		
				Earnings	Dividends	Book Value
12/20	58.77	21	5	6.47	0.63	46.83
12/19	32.50	19	6	2.31	0.05	42.20
12/18	13.14	103	63	0.24	0.29	40.71
12/17	18.25	101	97	0.23	0.00	41.23
Annual Growth	47.7%	—	-130.8%	—	3.2%	

HDFC Bank Ltd

Auditors: KPMG Assurance and Consulting Services LLP

LOCATIONS
HQ: HDFC Bank Ltd
  HDFC Bank House, Senapati Bapat Marg, Lower Parel, Mumbai 400 013
Phone: (91) 22 6652 1000   **Fax:** (91) 22 2496 0737
Web: www.hdfcbank.com

HISTORICAL FINANCIALS
Company Type: Public

Income Statement   FYE: March 31

	ASSETS ($ mil.)	NET INCOME ($ mil.)	INCOME AS % OF ASSETS	EMPLOYEES
03/21	245,736	4,455	1.8%	120,093
03/20	211,318	3,445	1.6%	116,971
03/19	191,923	3,180	1.7%	98,061
03/18	174,718	2,743	1.6%	88,253
03/17	139,811	2,166	1.5%	84,325
Annual Growth 15.1%		19.7%	—	9.2%

2021 Year-End Financials

Return on assets: 1.9%	Dividends
Return on equity: 16.0%	Yield: 0.0%
Long-term debt ($ mil.): —	Payout: 11.0%
No. of shares (mil.): —	Market value ($ mil.): —
Sales ($ mil): 20,896	

	STOCK PRICE ($) FY Close	P/E High/Low		PER SHARE ($) Earnings	Dividends	Book Value
03/21	77.69	1	1	0.81	0.09	5.35
03/20	38.46	3	1	0.63	0.41	4.57
03/19	115.91	3	2	0.59	0.27	4.33
03/18	98.77	3	2	0.52	0.24	3.48
03/17	75.22	3	2	0.42	0.20	3.09
Annual Growth 0.8%		—	—	17.7%	(18.5%)	14.8%

Hebei Iron & Steel Co Ltd

Hesteel (formerly the Hebei Iron and Steel or the HBIS Group) has a steely presence in China as its second largest (and longest established) iron & steel company producing around 45 million metric tons annually. The company is #4 in the world by steel output behind ArcelorMittal Baosteel and Nippon Steel. It smelts processes and distributes some 200-different iron and steel products. Products include plates rods wires and profiles primarily serving the automobile manufacturing and construction industries. Almost all its sales come from the domestic Chinese market.

Operations
Hesteel reports four business segments.

Iron & Steel is the core business segment producing around 200 products almost everything except seamless tube. The company's cold-rolled sheet ultra-strength rebar heavy plate steel pipe and special steel bars are the dominant products. This segment also has its own regional marketing and R&D divisions catering to customers globally.

Hesteel's Overseas business manages four steel companies and two mines spreading across three continents.

The Non-Steel sector is a budding segment within the company that aims to focus on the expansion of Hesteel's activities from mining resources to modern logistics equipment manufacturing steel trade processing resource utilization technology medical health and even providing social services.

Centered on integration of production and finance Hesteel's Finance segment is geared towards efficient capital operations and providing leases securities and supply chain financial services like factoring.

Geographic Reach
Though majority of Hesteel's iron and steel products serves the domestic Chinese market the company claims that its products are present in more than 100 countries. Additionally the company has direct ownership or shares in approximately 70 companies including the US the UK Australia South Africa Canada Singapore Switzerland and Hong Kong. A clear majority of the company's sales (more than 70%) is concentrated in North China region.

Sales and Marketing
Hesteel's leading products include coils (hot & cold rolled pickling and galvanized) heavy plates rebars wire rods sections and strips serving a wide range of industries including construction manufacturing shipping and energy. More than 70% of the company's sales comprised of specialized products sold to automakers including BMW Mercedes-Benz Volkswagen and Toyota as well as producers of appliances.

Strategy
Hesteel's domestic sales has been boosted by the Belt and Road Initiative a development strategy adopted by the Chinese government to build road and maritime infrastructure. However with increasing global competition and a continued weak demand in the industry due to oversupply Hesteel is trying to expand its steel business globally by boosting the number of international assets and global marketing service platforms.

The company acquired the Smederevo mill in Serbia back in 2016 to increase its presence in Europe's high-end manufacturing business which saw significant production and profitability increases the following year. In 2017 Hesteel acquired Palabora Mining the largest copper producer in South Africa. A few years earlier the company's 51% stake in Switzerland-based Duferco the world's largest steel products marketing service provider indicated its desire to boost global steel sales. Hesteel also claims to be investing in mineral resources financial services modern logistics steel trading and social services including setting up of specialized subsidiaries like HBIS Energy HBIS Chemical and HBIS New Material. However almost all its revenue continues to come from iron & steel sales in North China.

Though an excess supply of steel products in the Chinese market dampened demand for 2017 Hesteel aims to produce 2% more steel for 2018 (some 27 million tons). Stronger demand from the construction of the new city of Xiongan infrastructure projects in the Beijing-Tianjin-Hebei region plus the continued construction of the Belts & Roads projects has resulted in a slightly improved forecast. One indication is the company's incremental raising of domestic steel prices three times between August 2017 and September 2018.

However domestic output restrictions may lower output while stringent environmental standards may raise production costs. For instance Hesteel is looking to set up new plants away from its home province of Hebei as tight regulations over steel producers in the area are expected to be maintained in the near future due to smog pollution.

Mergers and Acquisitions
Hesteel acquired 98 properties of Serbia's steel mill Zelezara Smederevo in July 2016 for a total of €46 million with an aim to increases its global sales of steel products with a special eye on Europe's high-end manufacturing business.

In 2017 the company along with other investors also acquired Palabora Copper a South African copper mining company. It operates a mine with an annual capacity of 45000 tons and a smelter comples in Limpopo.

Company Background

EXECUTIVES
Independent Director, Li Ma
Independent Director, Dongzhang Gao
Vice Chairman of the Board, General Manager, Bin Xu
Director, Huaming Zhu
Director, Litang Geng
Deputy General Manager, Maoguang Li
Deputy General Manager, Guosheng Jia
Director, Jianju Deng
Director, Xin Tian
Staff Elected Director, Yueming Hu
General Manager, Lanyu Wang
Independent Director, Yuzhu Zhang
Secretary of the Board, Buhai Li
Chief Accounting Officer, Director, Guangshen Chang
Independent Director, Daqiang Cang
Auditors: Zhongxing Caiguanghua CPA Office Co., Ltd.

LOCATIONS
HQ: Hebei Iron & Steel Co Ltd
No. 40, Yuhua West Road, Qiaoxi District, Shijiazhuang, Hebei Province 050000
Phone: (86) 311 66770709   **Fax:** (86) 311 66778711
Web: www.hebgtgf.com

COMPETITORS
BLUESCOPE STEEL LIMITED
CARPENTER TECHNOLOGY CORPORATION
COMMERCIAL METALS COMPANY
Companhia Siderurgica Nacional
NIPPON STEEL CORPORATION
STEEL AUTHORITY OF INDIA LIMITED
STEEL DYNAMICS INC.

HISTORICAL FINANCIALS
Company Type: Public

Income Statement   FYE: December 31

	REVENUE ($ mil.)	NET INCOME ($ mil.)	NET PROFIT MARGIN	EMPLOYEES
12/20	16,460	259	1.6%	0
12/19	17,460	367	2.1%	0
12/18	17,585	527	3.0%	0
12/17	16,747	279	1.7%	0
12/16	10,735	224	2.1%	0
Annual Growth 11.3%		3.8%	—	—

2020 Year-End Financials

Debt ratio: 6.2%	No. of shares (mil.): —
Return on equity: 2.9%	Dividends
Cash ($ mil.): 4,345	Yield: —
Current ratio: 0.46	Payout: —
Long-term debt ($ mil.): 4,018	Market value ($ mil.): —

HeidelbergCement AG

HeidelbergCement believes in concrete results. One of the world's largest building materials companies HeidelbergCement sells cement concrete sand and gravel. It is No.1 worldwide in aggregates production and ready-mixed concrete and No. 2 in cement. Together the three product categories account for about 85% of sales. (Aggregates are the main component in concrete and asphalt but are also used as base courses in the construction of infrastructure such as roads.) HeidelbergCement also offers services such as worldwide trading in cement and coal by sea. The company has around 600 mining sites and over 3000 plants worldwide. All total it has some 2700 locations across five continents.

Operations

HeidelbergCement extracts raw materials produces building materials conducts marketing and distributes materials to customers. Specific activities include geological exploration of raw material deposits purchasing or leasing the land where the deposits are located obtaining mining concessions and environmental certifications constructing manufacturing facilities in cooperation with external service providers extracting raw materials and facilities maintenance.

The company sold nearly 126 million metric tons of cement some 308 million metric tons of aggregates roughly 50 million cubic meters of ready-mixed concrete and about 11 million metric tons of asphalt. It operates about 135 cement plants (plus 20 as part of joint ventures) around 600 quarries and aggregate pits and over 1460 ready-mixed concrete production sites worldwide.

Cement contributes more than 40% to total sales ready-mixed concrete-asphalt some 25% and aggregates about 20%. Other service-based joint ventures account for the remainder.

Geographic Reach

Headquartered in Germany HeidelbergCement has operations in more than 50 countries.The company is divided into five geographic regions: Western and Southern Europe (more than 25% of total sales) North America (slightly less than 25%) Asia/Pacific (about 20%) Northern and Eastern Europe-Central Asia (about 15%) and Africa-Eastern Mediterranean Basin (about 10%). Trading subsidiary HTC accounts for the remaining revenue. HCT supplies customers in about 90 countries from about 45 supplier countries. The majority of deliveries go to Africa Asia and North America. Key supplier countries include Saudi Arabia Turkey Vietnam and Indonesia.The US is the company's largest market by country at around 20% of sales. Other major markets include the UK Germany Australia and France.

Sales and Marketing

HeidelbergCement's products are used for the construction of houses traffic routes infrastructure and commercial and industrial facilities.

Financial Performance

Note: Growth rates may differ after conversion to US Dollars.

The company's revenue has been rising in the last five years with an overall growth of 40% between 2015 and 2019.

Group revenue rose by 4% in comparison with the previous year to ?18.9 billion (previous year: ?18.1 billion). Excluding consolidation and exchange rate effects Group revenue grew by 2%. Changes to the scope of consolidation of ?71 million and exchange rate effects of ?326 million had a positive impact on revenue.

The company's profit for the year ended 2019 was ?1.1 billion a 5% decrease compared to the previous year.

The company's cash for the year ended 2019 totaled ?3.5 billion. Operating activities generated ?2.7 billion while investing activities used ?905.8 million mainly for capital expenditures. Financing activities used another ?873.4 million mainly for repayment of bonds loans and lease liabilities.

Strategy

HeidelbergCement's target is to increase the value of the group in the long term through sustainable and result-oriented growth. Earning the cost of capital is the necessary prerequisite to guarantee the company's permanent entrepreneurial ability to act and invest continuously in innovation and growth as well as in the development of its personnel and the company.

The four pillars of our business strategy are as follows:

Operational excellence and digitalization. A key objective is to make sure that the productivity enhancement in input factors such as working time capital and energy at least offsets inflation-related cost increases;

Sustainability. The sustainability strategy has six action areas: Driving profitability and innovation; Achieving excellence in occupational health and safety; Reducing the company's ecological footprint; Enabling the circular economy; Being a good neighbor; and ensuring compliance and creating transparency;

Profitable growth and vertical integration. The creation development and maintenance of vertically integrated market positions in the cement aggregates ready-mixed concrete and asphalt business lines is the core of the growth strategy of HeidelbergCement. The company's goal are strong positions in markets with long-term potential. It strives to avoid markets with unjustifiable high political economic or compliance risks and to retain key market positions regardless of economic cycles; and

Financial performance. The company aims to achieve a balance between short-term profitability and long-term value creation. Investment decisions are taken based on their market strategic financial and technical attractiveness.

Mergers and Acquisitions

To strengthen its market position in Bangladesh HeidelbergCement completed the purchase of a 100% shareholding in both Emirates Cement Bangladesh Limited and Emirates Power Company Limited Munshiganj in late 2019. The purchase price of ?19.7 million was paid in cash

In 2019 HeidelbergCement finalized the acquisition of the aggregates and ready-mixed concrete activities of Cemex in central France. By purchasing 100% of the shares in Cemex Betons Centre et Ouest S.A.S. Rungis as well as production sites and distribution facilities for aggregates HeidelbergCement has acquired 28 ready-mixed concrete plants and seven aggregates quarries and has strengthened its vertically integrated market position in central France. The purchase price of ?28.0 million was paid in cash.

Company Background

HeidelbergCement traces its roots back to 1872 when Johann Philipp Schifferdecker a wealthy brewer went to Heidelberg Germany where his son was studying chemistry. Once there he bought a bankrupt cement plant located on the Neckar River near Heidelberg.

HISTORY

HeidelbergCement AG's history began in 1872 when Johann Philipp Schifferdecker a wealthy brewer went to Heidelberg Germany where his son was studying chemistry. Once there he bought a bankrupt cement plant located on the Neckar River near Heidelberg in 1873. Schifferdecker named the firm Portland-Cement-Werk Heidelberg Schifferdecker & Sohne OHG.

The company's first year of operation 1875 ended in a loss. The raw materials used to make its cement contained too much magnesium. To correct the problem Schifferdecker leased a new limestone mine to obtain higher-quality raw materials. Transport presented a problem and in 1883 Schifferdecker built a railroad to transport limestone to the plant. With these problems solved the company built a second plant in 1888 the year that Schifferdecker died. The company went public the next year and Schifferdecker's heirs renamed the firm Portland-Cementwerk Heidelberg vormals Schifferdecker & Sohne.

A fire destroyed the company's plant in 1895 but the Schifferdeckers used the disaster as an opportunity to modernize the plant. The construction boom sparked at the turn of the century increased cement sales and the enterprise continued to expand. In 1901 the company merged with its rival Mannheimer Portland-Cement-Fabrik AG to create Portland-Cementwerke Heidelberg und Mannheim AG.

Heidelberg-Mannheimer's plans for expansion died in WWI. From 1916 to 1923 the German government took control of the entire German cement industry. During that time the company merged with Stuttgarter Immobilien- und Bau-Geschaft AG to create Portland-Cementwerke Heidelberg-Mannheim-Stuttgart AG.

After the war peace did not bring prosperity to Germany. Hyperinflation made German cement 765 times more expensive than it had been in 1914. By 1926 the German economy had recovered and one year later the company converted its plants to electrical operations. The good times did not last long however. As the Great Depression strangled the German economy the company's cement shipments dropped by two-thirds from 1927 levels.

Just before WWII the company renamed itself Portland-Zementwerke Heidelberg AG. During the war the German cement industry was highly regulated by the German government. The destructive WWII years all but assured the renewed growth of the German cement industry and Portland-Zementwerke Heidelberg grew steadily during the 1940s and 1950s. Annual shipments of 6 million tons were reached by 1965.

Peter Schumacher took over the company in 1971 and transformed it into an international enterprise with the 1977 acquisition of Pennsylvania-based Lehigh Portland Cement Company. That year the company adopted the name Heidelberger Zement AG. (Schumacher who led the company for 25 years died in 2002.)

During the 1980s Heidelberger Zement bought Atlas Cement Company and founded Addiment Inc. in Georgia to market its building chemicals. The company also boosted its operations in Italy and France. It expanded into Eastern Europe in the early 1990s and by 1997 had broadened its geographic reach to include acquisitions in countries such as China and Turkey.

Heidelberger Zement purchased Scancem a Scandinavian cement operation in 1999 to open up new markets in Africa the Baltic States and the UK. It also bolstered its building materials segment by increasing its stake in maxit Group a Germany-based leader in the dry mortar business. In 2001 the company acquired majority stakes in regional cement makers Indocement Tunggal Prakarsa (Indonesia) Cesla (Russia) and Kryvyi Rih (Ukraine).

In 2003 the company moved its entire Heidelberg Building Materials Europe division under the maxit Group unit.

Spohn Group run by long-time HeidelbergCement board members the Merckle family acquired a majority stake in 2005.

In 2007 HeidelbergCement acquired UK's Hanson one of the largest producers of aggregates in the world. The ?9 billion ($12 billion) acquisition helped position HeidelbergCement as a global integrated supplier of building materials and strengthened its materials base for aggregates.

Adolf Merckle committed suicide in 2009. His family later sold a large stake in HeidelbergCement.

EXECUTIVES

Independent Member of the Supervisory Board, Marion Weissenberger-Eibl, $86,594 total compensation

Member of the Managing Board, Jon Morrish, $930,894 total compensation

Member of the Managing Board, Kevin Gluskie, $914,942 total compensation

Member of the Managing Board, Hakan Gurdal, $757,704 total compensation

Independent Member of the Supervisory Board, Margret Suckale, $86,594 total compensation

Independent Chairman of the Supervisory Board, Fritz-Juergen Heckmann, $216,487 total compensation

Deputy Chairman of the Managing Board, Chief Financial Officer, Lorenz Naeger, $1,166,751 total compensation

Independent Member of the Supervisory Board, Employee Representative, Barbara Breuninger, $86,594 total compensation

Member of the Managing Board, Ernest Jelito, $757,704 total compensation

Independent Member of the Supervisory Board, Luka Mucic, $86,594 total compensation

Member of the Supervisory Board, Employee Representative, Ines Ploss, $86,594 total compensation

Member of the Supervisory Board, Employee Representative, Peter Riedel, $86,594 total compensation

Member of the Management Board, Chris Ward, $796,444 total compensation

Member of the Supervisory Board, Employee Representative, Birgit Jochens, $86,594 total compensation

Chairman of the Managing Board, Dominik von Achten, $1,535,919 total compensation

Independent Member of the Supervisory Board, Tobias Merckle, $86,594 total compensation

Independent Member of the Supervisory Board, Ludwig Merckle, $86,594 total compensation

Independent Deputy Chairman of the Supervisory Board, Employee Representative, Heinz Schmitt, $129,892 total compensation

Independent Member of the Supervisory Board, Employee Representative, Werner Schraeder, $86,594 total compensation

Auditors: PricewaterhouseCoopers GmbH Wirtschaftpruefungsgesellschaft

LOCATIONS

HQ: HeidelbergCement AG
Berliner Strasse 6, Heidelberg 69120
Phone: (49) 6221 481 13227   **Fax:** (49) 6221 481 13217
Web: www.heidelbergcement.com

2015 sales

	% of total
Western and Northern Europe	30
North America	27
Asia-Pacific	20
Eastern Europe-Central Asia	8
Africa-Mediterranean Basin	7
Group Services	8
Total	**100**

PRODUCTS/OPERATIONS

2015 sales

	% of total
Cement	40
Aggregates	20
Ready-mixed concrete-asphalt	27
Service-joint ventures other	13
Total	**100**

Selected Products

Cement

Binders for geotechnology environmental technology and road construction
Decorative concrete
Fast-hardening cement
Masonry cement
Specialty cements for hydraulic engineering sewage works construction soil injection and masonry repair and waste dump sealing
Concrete
Light heavy and aerated concrete building blocks
Pavers
Prefab ceilings walls cellar units and sewage works units
Building Materials
Building chemicals
Dry mortar
Environmental technology
Expanded clay
Limestone and lime products
Sand-lime bricks
Special gypsums
Aggregates
Other
Plaster
Self-compacting concrete
Steel-fiber concrete

COMPETITORS

Bilfinger SE	SEKISUI CHEMICAL CO.
Dyckerhoff GmbH	LTD.
HOLCIM (US) INC.	TAIHEIYO CEMENT
Holcim AG	CORPORATION
Outokumpu Oyj	TITAN AMERICA LLC

HISTORICAL FINANCIALS

Company Type: Public

Income Statement   FYE: December 31

	REVENUE ($ mil.)	NET INCOME ($ mil.)	NET PROFIT MARGIN	EMPLOYEES
12/20	21,556	(2,625)	—	53,122
12/19	21,264	1,224	5.8%	55,047
12/18	20,787	1,308	6.3%	57,939
12/17	20,755	1,100	5.3%	59,054
12/16	15,973	745	4.7%	60,424
Annual Growth	**7.8%**	—	—	**(3.2%)**

2020 Year-End Financials

Debt ratio: 37.3%
Return on equity: (-14.1%)
Cash ($ mil.): 3,506
Current ratio: 1.24
Long-term debt ($ mil.): 10,696

No. of shares (mil.): 198
Dividends
  Yield: 0.5%
  Payout: —
Market value ($ mil.): 2,962

	STOCK PRICE ($) FY Close	P/E High/Low		PER SHARE ($) Earnings	Dividends	Book Value
12/20	14.93	—	—	(13.23)	0.09	82.09
12/19	14.47	4	2	6.18	0.30	96.12
12/18	12.22	4	2	6.60	0.29	89.06
12/17	21.58	5	4	5.54	0.25	87.95
12/16	18.62	5	3	3.86	0.18	85.64
Annual Growth	**(5.4%)**	—	—	—	**(16.0%)**	**(1.1%)**

Heineken Holding NV (Netherlands)

Auditors: Deloitte Accountants B.V.

LOCATIONS

HQ: Heineken Holding NV (Netherlands)
Tweede Weteringplantsoen 5, Amsterdam 1017 ZD
Phone: (31) 20 622 11 52   **Fax:** (31) 20 625 22 13
Web: www.heinekenholding.com

HISTORICAL FINANCIALS

Company Type: Public

Income Statement   FYE: December 31

	REVENUE ($ mil.)	NET INCOME ($ mil.)	NET PROFIT MARGIN	EMPLOYEES
12/20	24,196	(125)	—	84,394
12/19	26,911	1,220	4.5%	85,853
12/18	25,733	1,100	4.3%	85,610
12/17	26,238	1,171	4.5%	80,425
12/16	21,953	822	3.7%	73,525
Annual Growth	**2.5%**	—	—	**3.5%**

2020 Year-End Financials

Debt ratio: 49.6%
Return on equity: (-1.3%)
Cash ($ mil.): 4,909
Current ratio: 0.83
Long-term debt ($ mil.): 16,789

No. of shares (mil.): 288
Dividends
  Yield: 1.5%
  Payout: —
Market value ($ mil.): —

Heineken NV (Netherlands)

Auditors: Deloitte Accountants B.V.

LOCATIONS

HQ: Heineken NV (Netherlands)
Tweede Weteringplantsoen 5, Amsterdam 1017 ZD
Phone: (31) 20 523 92 39   **Fax:** (31) 20 626 35 03
Web: www.theheinekencompany.com

HISTORICAL FINANCIALS

Company Type: Public

Income Statement   FYE: December 31

	REVENUE ($ mil.)	NET INCOME ($ mil.)	NET PROFIT MARGIN	EMPLOYEES
12/20	24,196	(250)	—	84,394
12/19	26,911	2,431	9.0%	85,853
12/18	25,733	2,179	8.5%	85,610
12/17	26,238	2,319	8.8%	80,425
12/16	21,953	1,626	7.4%	73,525
Annual Growth	**2.5%**	—	—	**3.5%**

2020 Year-End Financials

Debt ratio: 49.6%
Return on equity: (-1.3%)
Cash ($ mil.): 4,909
Current ratio: 0.83
Long-term debt ($ mil.): 16,789

No. of shares (mil.): 575
Dividends
  Yield: 1.3%
  Payout: —
Market value ($ mil.): 32,148

	STOCK PRICE ($) FY Close	P/E High/Low		PER SHARE ($) Earnings	Dividends	Book Value
12/20	55.84	—	—	(0.44)	0.74	28.55
12/19	53.43	15	11	4.23	0.75	31.51
12/18	43.97	16	13	3.82	0.72	28.84
12/17	52.12	16	12	4.06	0.66	28.01
12/16	37.41	17	13	2.85	0.59	24.54
Annual Growth	**10.5%**	—	—	—	**5.9%**	**3.9%**

Hengli Petrochemical Co Ltd

Auditors: Dalian Hualian Certified Public Accountants Co., Ltd.

LOCATIONS

HQ: Hengli Petrochemical Co Ltd
No. 1, Zhoushuizi Square, Ganjingzi District, Dalian, Liaoning Province 116033
Phone: (86) 411 86641861   **Fax:** (86) 411 86641645
Web: www.dlrpm.com

HISTORICAL FINANCIALS

Company Type: Public

Income Statement				FYE: December 31
	REVENUE ($ mil.)	NET INCOME ($ mil.)	NET PROFIT MARGIN	EMPLOYEES
12/20	23,297	2,058	8.8%	0
12/19	14,483	1,440	9.9%	0
12/18	8,732	483	5.5%	0
12/17	3,425	264	7.7%	0
12/16	2,770	169	6.1%	0
Annual Growth	70.3%	86.6%	—	—

2020 Year-End Financials

Debt ratio: 8.6%	No. of shares (mil.): —
Return on equity: 32.2%	Dividends
Cash ($ mil.): 2,396	Yield: —
Current ratio: 0.61	Payout: —
Long-term debt ($ mil.): 8,393	Market value ($ mil.): —

Hengyi Petrochemical Co Ltd

EXECUTIVES

Secretary of the Board, Xingang Zheng
Vice President, Director, Zhong Wu
Vice President, Donghua Zhao
Vice Chairman of the Board, Xianshui Fang
Chairman of the Board, President, Yibo Qiu
Executive Vice President, Songlin Wang
Director, Defeng Ni
Vice President, Liancai Chen
Independent Director, Liuyong Yang
Independent Director, Baizhang Yang
Independent Director, Sanlian Chen
Vice President, Jianchang Lou
Auditors: Tianjian Guanghua (Beijing) Certified Public Accountants Co., Ltd.

LOCATIONS

HQ: Hengyi Petrochemical Co Ltd
20/F., Youzheng Building, No. 59, Garden Road, Zhengzhou, Henan Province 450003
Phone: (86) 371 67422266   **Fax:** (86) 371 69356196

HISTORICAL FINANCIALS

Company Type: Public

Income Statement				FYE: December 31
	REVENUE ($ mil.)	NET INCOME ($ mil.)	NET PROFIT MARGIN	EMPLOYEES
12/20	13,215	469	3.6%	0
12/19	11,442	460	4.0%	0
12/18	12,350	285	2.3%	0
12/17	9,878	249	2.5%	0
12/16	4,668	119	2.6%	0
Annual Growth	29.7%	40.8%	—	—

2020 Year-End Financials

Debt ratio: 8.4%	No. of shares (mil.): —
Return on equity: 12.9%	Dividends
Cash ($ mil.): 1,541	Yield: —
Current ratio: 0.71	Payout: —
Long-term debt ($ mil.): 3,078	Market value ($ mil.): —

Henkel AG & Co KGAA

Home and hearth are at the heart of Henkel. The company makes branded products for laundry and homecare (Persil All Pril) cosmetics and toiletries (Schwarzkopf Dial Syoss) and many adhesives (Loctite Pritt UniBond). Henkel's business is centered in Europe with a growing presence in developing economies such as Asia Africa the Middle East and Latin America. Henkel owns subsidiaries in about 80 countries including Henkel North American Consumer Goods in the US with offices located nearly everywhere. Started in 1876 the company is owned by descendants of the founding Henkel family.

Operations

Henkel divides its business into three units. Adhesive technologies accounts for more than 45% of sales which includes industrial adhesives as well as those for consumers craftsmen and building. Laundry & Home Care accounts for about one-third of sales; and Beauty Care accounts for about 20%.

Geographic Reach

Laundry & Homecare and Beauty Care products are primarily sold in Europe and North America as well as certain developing regions. The company's adhesive products have a worldwide presence. Emerging markets (Eastern Europe Africa/Middle East Latin America and Asia excluding Japan) generate more than 40% of Henkel's sales. Henkel's business in Europe and North America is highly mature so it relies on its emerging markets for organic growth.

Henkel has around 185 manufacturing facilities that dot around 55 countries. Its largest plants are located in D sseldorf Germany (its headquarters) and in Bowling Green Kentucky US and make detergents and household cleaning products as well as adhesives. The company's cosmetics and toiletries are produced at about 10 plants. Henkel's regional centers are located in Mexico Brazil Austria UAE China and US (Connecticut).

Sales and Marketing

Each of Henkel's three units claims a large share of their market through established brands. In Beauty Care 90% of sales are driven by the business unit's top-10 brands; in Laundry and Homecare around 65%; and in Adhesive Technologies more than 80%.

Henkel's customer base of around 130000 industry and retail clients is managed primarily by its own sales teams. Henkel's retail customers service the needs of private users craftsmen and smaller industrial customers.

Financial Performance

Note: Growth rates may differ after conversion to US Dollars.

Henkel's last five years have been characterized by consistent revenue and profit growth although it slipped back in both regards in 2018.

In fiscal 2018 the company's sales fell by less than 1% to ?19.9 billion as a fall in the Laundry and Home Care segment was partially offset by marginal gains in the Adhesive and Beauty segments. The fall in the Laundry and Home Care segment was largely a result of unfavorable exchange rate movements while on a like-for-like basis sales grew 2% thanks to pricing increases.

Geographically Henkel's emerging markets grew strongly overall particularly Africa and the Middle East Eastern Europe and Latin America while sales in Asia fell below prior year. Sales in North America fell due to delivery difficulties and intense competition while sales in Europe were flat.

Net income fell 8% in 2018 to ?2.3 billion adversely affected by the 2017 US Tax Cuts and Jobs Act which pushed up the effective tax rate from 15% to nearly 24%. Income before tax was more or less the same in 2017 and 2018.

Henkel's cash position weakened slightly during 2018 falling ?470 million to ?919 million by year-end. It generated ?2.5 billion from operations while Henkel's investing activities used a similar amount. Financing activities absorbed ?412 million.

Strategy

Henkel maintains a robust investment program. In 2018 its capital expenditure amounted to ?853 million which mainly went towards increasing production capacity new products and improving business processes. More specifically its 2018 projects included supply chain optimizations and enhancing IT system architecture; acquiring new technologies; expanding detergent capsule production capacity at its Salt Lake City and Bowling Green facilities; building a new adhesive factory in Spain and a new adhesives and metal pretreatment factory in India. Henkel spreads its investments evenly across its three business units and from a geographic standpoint focuses its investment program on Western Europe Eastern Europe and North America.

Mergers and Acquisitions

Henkel is an acquisitive firm buying up companies to build out its presence in certain markets and boost its product portfolio. Henkel made three acquisitions in 2018. In early 2018 it acquired Uni n Tecnico Comercial based in Lima Peru strengthening Henkel's presence in the maintenance repair and overhaul adhesives market in Latin America. Later in 2018 Henkel acquired Canada-based JemPak Corporation strengthening the existing Laundry & Home Care portfolio in North America. Towards the end of the year Henkel acquired Chile-based Aislantes Nacionales strengthening its presence in the Chilean tile adhesives and building materials market.

In 2017 Henkel made acquisitions in its adhesive technologies and beauty care businesses including Darex Packaging in the US and Sonderhoff in Germany. Professional hair care in the US has been a particular focus of the company with the late 2017 purchases of Zotos International for about $485 million and Nattura for an undisclosed amount. (In 2014 it picked up three US-based professional hair care product companies - Sexy Hair Alterna and Kenra.)

Company Background

In 1876 Fritz Henkel and his two partners founded Henkel & Cie in Aachen Germany. The company launched a laundry detergent based on sodium silicate which they named "Universal-Washmittel". Henkel's first branded product was launched in 1878. In 1913 Henkel founded a subsidiary in Switzerland. Fritz passed in 1930 and was succeeded by his capable sons Fritz Jr. and Hugo. Henkel became a limited company in 1975 and in 1985 it went public. Major product launches have included Persil (1907) and the Pritt stick (1969); it acquired Loctite in 1997. The company was renamed Henkel AG & Co in 2008.

HISTORY

In 1876 Fritz Henkel a chemical plant worker started Henkel & Cie in Aachen Germany to make a universal detergent. He moved the business to D sseldorf in 1878 and launched Henkel's Bleaching Soda one of Germany's first brand-name products. In the 1880s the company began making water glass an ingredient of its detergent which differs from soap in the way it emulsifies dirt. Henkel debuted Persil a detergent that eliminated the need for rubbing or bleaching clothes in 1907. Persil became a leading detergent in Germany.

Henkel set up an Austrian subsidiary in 1913. In response to a postwar adhesives shortage the company started making glue for its own packaging and soon became Europe's leading glue maker. Henkel began making cleansers with newly developed phosphates in the late 1920s.

When Fritz died in 1930 Henkel stock was divided among his three children. In the 1930s the company sponsored a whaling fleet that provided fats for its products and by 1939 the firm had 16 plants in Europe.

During WWII Henkel lost most of its foreign plants and made unbranded soap in Germany. After the war the company retooled its plants branched out into personal care products and competed with Unilever Procter & Gamble and Colgate-Palmolive for control of the German detergent market. (By 1968 Henkel dominated with close to a 50% share.)

In 1960 Henkel bought its first US company Standard Chemicals (renamed Henkel Corp. in 1971). Konrad Henkel who took over in 1961 modernized the company's image by making changes in management structure and marketing techniques. Henkel patented a substitute for environmentally harmful phosphates acquired 15% of Clorox in 1974 and bought General Mills' chemical business in 1977.

Henkel owned at the time by 66 family members went public with nonvoting shares in 1985. It bought US companies Nopco (specialty chemicals) and Parker Chemical (metal surface pretreatment) in 1987 and Emery the #1 US oleochemicals maker in 1989.

Henkel reorganized its product lines in 1991 by selling several noncore businesses. That year Henkel formed a partnership with Ecolab (of which it owned 24% — later expanded to 50%); acquired interests in Hungary Poland Russia and Slovenia; and introduced Persil in Spain and Portugal. In 1994 Henkel expanded into China and bought 25% of a Brazilian detergent maker.

The company's 1995 acquisition of Hans Schwarzkopf GmbH made Henkel the #1 hair-coloring manufacturer in Germany. The company bought Novamax Technologies a US-based maker of metal-surface treatments in 1996. The next year Henkel paid $1.3 billion for US adhesive giant Loctite its biggest purchase to date. In 1998 it bought Ohio-based adhesive maker Manco to combine its

US and Canadian consumer adhesive businesses (parts of Loctite and LePage respectively) under Manco. Henkel pushed into the US toiletries market in 1998 by paying $93 million for DEP and creating a new subsidiary Schwarzkopf & DEP Inc.

In 1999 Henkel created chemicals unit Cognis to focus primarily on palm kernel- and coconut oil-based products. To strengthen Cognis Henkel bought Laboratoires Serobiologiques a French producer of ingredients for the cosmetic and food industries and divested specialty-paper chemicals operations. Henkel also formed a joint venture with soap maker Dial (Dial/Henkel LLC); the joint venture later bought the Custom Cleaner home dry cleaning business from Creative Products Resource.

Henkel picked up Yamahatsu Sangyo a Japanese maker of hair colorants in 2000. The company sold its Substral unit (fertilizer and plant care) to Scotts Company (now Scotts Miracle-Gro). In 2001 Henkel bought TOTAL's metal-treatment chemicals business. In addition the company sold its Cognis specialty chemicals unit to private equity funds Schroeder Ventures and Goldman Sachs Capital Partners for about $2.2 billion. Also in 2001 Henkel said it would cut 2500-3000 jobs (about 5% of its workforce) over the next two years.

In 2003 Henkel purchased a majority stake in La Luz S.A. a Central American manufacturer and marketer of detergents and household cleaners. (Henkel entered the Latin American detergents market via Mexico in 2000.)

Henkel strengthened its adhesives business in Russia and North Central and Eastern Europe when it acquired Makroflex from YIT Construction Ltd. in July 2003. Makroflex located in Finland and Estonia developed and made old sealants and insulation materials for the construction industry.

In 2004 Henkel acquired Alberto-Culver's Indola European professional hair care business which had logged about $55 million in recent annual sales. That year Henkel and US bleach giant Clorox agreed to a deal (in the form of an asset swap) that dissolved Henkel's nearly 30% stake in Clorox. The $2.8 billion transaction involved Henkel's purchase of Clorox's 20% stake in Henkel Iberica a joint venture between the two in Portugal and Spain. Henkel also bought Clorox's stake in a pesticide company as part of the transaction and added Combat insecticides and Soft Scrub bathroom cleaner to its brand portfolio.

Henkel acquired Advanced Research Laboratories in 2004 and folded the company into its existing Schwarzkopf & Dep subsidiary based in California. The deal boosted the company's share of the US hairstyling market. Henkel bought US-based Dial Corporation (Dial soap Purex laundry products Renuzit air fresheners) in 2004 for $2.9 billion in cash.

Also in 2004 Henkel bought 70% of Coventry's Chemtek an independent firm that specializes in formulating and manufacturing liquid cleaners. The balance of the share is owned by Charteredbrands of Edinburgh.

To strengthen its foothold in the electronics market in China Henkel in late 2005 bought a majority stake in Huawei Electronics Co. Ltd. a maker of epoxy molding compounds for semiconductors.

EXECUTIVES

EVP, HR and Infrastructure Services, Sylvie Nicol, $610,640 total compensation

EVP, Adhesive Technologies, Jan-Dirk Auris, $839,630 total compensation

EVP, Laundry and Home Care, Bruno Piacenza, $854,554 total compensation

Chairman of the Management Board, Carsten Knobel, $839,630 total compensation

Independent Member of the Supervisory Board, Barbara Kux, $79,758 total compensation

Member of the Supervisory Board, Employee Representative, Martina Seiler, $79,758 total compensation

Member of the Supervisory Board, Employee Representative, Edgar Topsch, $79,758 total compensation

Independent Member of the Supervisory Board, Timotheus Hoettges, $79,758 total compensation

Member of the Management Board, Executive Vice President Beauty Care, Jens-Martin Schwaerzler, $854,554 total compensation

Member of the Supervisory Board, Benedikt-Richard Freiherr von Herman, $79,758 total compensation

Member of the Supervisory Board, Employee Representative, Dirk Thiede, $79,758 total compensation

Member of the Supervisory Board, Philipp Scholz, $79,758 total compensation

Director, Michael Baumscheiper, $4,358 total compensation

Chairwoman of the Supervisory Board, Simone Bagel-Trah, $159,516 total compensation

Member of the Supervisory Board, Employee Representative, Michael Vassiliadis, $79,758 total compensation

Independent Member of the Supervisory Board, Michael Kaschke, $79,758 total compensation

Executive Vice President - Finance(CFO), Purchasing, Integrated Business Solutions. Member of the Management Board, Marco Swoboda, $854,554 total compensation

Vice Chairman of the Supervisory Board, Employee Representative, Birgit Helten-Kindlein, $119,637 total compensation

Member of the Supervisory Board, Employee Representative, Andrea Pichottka, $79,758 total compensation

Member of the Supervisory Board, Employee Representative, Jutta Bernicke, $79,758 total compensation

Auditors: KPMG AG

LOCATIONS

HQ: Henkel AG & Co KGAA
Henkelstrasse 67, Duesseldorf D-40191
Phone: (49) 211 797 0   **Fax:** (49) 211 798 4040
Web: www.henkel.com

2018 Sales

	% of total
Western Europe	31
North America	25
Asia Pacific	17
Eastern Europe	14
Africa/Middle East	6
Latin America	6
Corporate	1
Total	**100**

PRODUCTS/OPERATIONS

2018 Sales

	% of total
Adhesive Technologies	50
Industrial Business	38
Consumers Craftsmen and Building	9
Laundry & Home Care	32
Beauty Care	20
Corporate	1
Total	**100**

Selected Brands

Adhesives technologies
  Ariasana
  Ceresit
  LePage
  Loctite

Metylan
Pattex
Ponal
Pritt
Rubson
Sellotape
Sista
Solvite
Tangit
Technomelt
Teroson
UniBond
Cosmetics and toiletries
Aok
Barnängen
Clynol viton
Denivit
Diadermine
Dial
Dry Idea
Fa
La Toja
Licor del Polo
Neutromed
Right Guard
Schwarzkopf
Smooth 'N Shine
Syoss
Theramed
Tone
Vademecum
Laundry and homecare
Bref
Dixan
Mir
Persil
Perwoll
Pril
Pur
Purex
Soft Scrub
Somat
Spee
Vernel

COMPETITORS

Akzo Nobel N.V.
Beiersdorf AG
DIVERSEY INC.
GOJO INDUSTRIES INC.
H.B. FULLER COMPANY
MACDERMID INCORPORATED

OIL-DRI CORPORATION OF
  AMERICA
RECKITT BENCKISER
  GROUP PLC
S. C. JOHNSON & SON
  INC.

HISTORICAL FINANCIALS
Company Type: Public

Income Statement				FYE: December 31
	REVENUE ($ mil.)	NET INCOME ($ mil.)	NET PROFIT MARGIN	EMPLOYEES
12/20	23,625	1,728	7.3%	52,950
12/19	22,583	2,340	10.4%	52,450
12/18	22,788	2,646	11.6%	53,000
12/17	24,009	3,019	12.6%	53,700
12/16	19,759	2,167	11.0%	51,350
Annual Growth	4.6%	(5.5%)	—	0.8%

2020 Year-End Financials
Debt ratio: 12.5%
Return on equity: 7.7%
Cash ($ mil.): 2,119
Current ratio: 1.12
Long-term debt ($ mil.): 2,044

No. of shares (mil.): 259
Dividends
  Yield: 1.3%
  Payout: 9.1%
Market value ($ mil.): 6,281

	STOCK PRICE ($) FY Close	P/E High/Low		PER SHARE ($) Earnings	Dividends	Book Value
12/20	24.18	8	5	3.96	0.33	83.98
12/19	23.57	21	4	5.38	0.36	80.05
12/18	98.36	23	18	6.08	0.40	75.01
12/17	120.16	23	20	6.94	0.35	71.87
12/16	105.00	24	17	4.98	0.28	61.15
Annual Growth	(30.7%)	—	—	(5.6%)	4.6%	8.3%

Hennes & Mauritz AB

Auditors: Ernst & Young AB

LOCATIONS

HQ: Hennes & Mauritz AB
  Master Samuelsgatan 46A, Stockholm SE-106 38
Phone: (46) 8 796 55 00   **Fax:** (46) 8 24 80 78
Web: www.hm.com

HISTORICAL FINANCIALS
Company Type: Public

Income Statement				FYE: November 30
	REVENUE ($ mil.)	NET INCOME ($ mil.)	NET PROFIT MARGIN	EMPLOYEES
11/20	22,126	147	0.7%	0
11/19	24,365	1,407	5.8%	126,376
11/18	23,165	1,393	6.0%	123,283
11/17	23,877	1,932	8.1%	123,178
11/16	21,007	2,036	9.7%	114,586
Annual Growth	1.3%	(48.2%)	—	—

2020 Year-End Financials
Debt ratio: 5.4%
Return on equity: 2.2%
Cash ($ mil.): 1,956
Current ratio: 1.16
Long-term debt ($ mil.): 6,967

No. of shares (mil.): —
Dividends
  Yield: —
  Payout: —
Market value ($ mil.): —

	STOCK PRICE ($) FY Close	P/E High/Low		PER SHARE ($) Earnings	Dividends	Book Value
11/20	4.18	7	3	0.09	0.00	(0.00)
11/19	3.81	1	0	0.85	0.20	3.61
11/18	3.63	1	0	0.84	0.22	3.89
11/17	4.64	1	0	1.17	0.23	4.31
11/16	5.77	1	0	1.23	0.24	4.04
Annual Growth	(7.7%)	—	—	(48.2%)	—	—

Hino Motors, Ltd.

Hino Motors introduced Japan's first truck in 1918 long before Godzilla was throwing vehicles all over Tokyo. These days the company not only manufactures medium- and heavy-duty diesel trucks but it also makes buses special-purpose vehicles and industrial diesel engines. Hino Motors dominates Japan's domestic truck market beating out such competitors as Mitsubishi Motors and Isuzu Motors and manufactures 150000 Hino-brand trucks and buses each year. Toyota Motor owns more than 50% of the company.
  Geographic Reach
Auditors: PricewaterhouseCoopers Aarata LLC

LOCATIONS

HQ: Hino Motors, Ltd.
  3-1-1 Hinodai, Hino, Tokyo 191-8660
Phone: (81) 42 586 5111   **Fax:** 248 699-9310
Web: www.hino.co.jp

2016 Sales

	% of total
Japan	66
Asia	21
Other	13
Total	**100**

PRODUCTS/OPERATIONS

2016 Sales

	% of total
Trucks and buses	53
Total	20
Service parts	6
Other	21
Total	**100**

Selected Overseas Subsidiaries and Affiliates
Hino Motor Sales Australia Pty. Ltd.
Hino Motor Sales U.S.A. Inc.
Hino Motors (Malaysia) Sdn. Bhd.
Hino Motors Sales (Thailand) Ltd.
Hinopak Motors Ltd. (Pakistan)
Shenyang Shenfei Hino Automobile Manufacturing Co.
  Ltd. (China)

COMPETITORS

MAZDA MOTOR CORPORATION
MITSUBISHI MOTORS CORPORATION
NISSAN DIESEL (THAILAND) COMPANY LIMITED
NISSAN MOTOR CO.LTD.
SUZUKI MOTOR CORPORATION
TOYOTA MOTOR CORPORATION
TOYOTA MOTOR CORPORATION AUSTRALIA
  LIMITED

HISTORICAL FINANCIALS
Company Type: Public

Income Statement				FYE: March 31
	REVENUE ($ mil.)	NET INCOME ($ mil.)	NET PROFIT MARGIN	EMPLOYEES
03/21	13,533	(67)	—	41,890
03/20	16,725	289	1.7%	44,188
03/19	17,891	495	2.8%	45,442
03/18	17,308	483	2.8%	44,629
03/17	15,059	441	2.9%	42,775
Annual Growth	(2.6%)	—	—	(0.5%)

2021 Year-End Financials
Debt ratio: 0.1%
Return on equity: (-1.3%)
Cash ($ mil.): 507
Current ratio: 1.16
Long-term debt ($ mil.): 128

No. of shares (mil.): 574
Dividends
  Yield: 0.0%
  Payout: —
Market value ($ mil.): 5,311

	STOCK PRICE ($) FY Close	P/E High/Low		PER SHARE ($) Earnings	Dividends	Book Value
03/21	9.25	—	—	(0.12)	0.11	8.72
03/20	5.30	0	0	0.51	0.18	8.70
03/19	8.35	0	0	0.86	0.26	8.54
03/18	13.90	0	0	0.84	0.26	8.24
03/17	11.16	0	0	0.77	0.00	7.25
Annual Growth	(4.6%)	—	—	—	—	4.7%

Hirogin Holdings Inc

Few banks have deeper roots in the Hiroshima Prefecture than the Hiroshima Bank. Established in 1878 the bank serves Japan's Chugoku and Shikoku regions through more than 175 offices and 830 ATMs. Hiroshima organizes its business approach into three distinct areas: financial inter-mediation risk management assistance and infor-mation provision. It offers the traditional array of financial services including investment and private banking products real estate appraisal banking software venture capital support and assistance with corporate restructuring.

EXECUTIVES

Chairman of the Board, Chairman of Subsidiary, Representative Director, Koji Ikeda
President, Preseident of Subsidiary, Representative Director, Toshio Heya
Independent Director, Satoshi Miura
Independent Director, Kaori Maeda
Managing Executive Officer, President of Subsidiary, Director, Fumitsugu Kariyada
Senior Managing Executive Officer, Director, Akira Ogi
Independent Director, Yoshinori Takahashi
Director, Hitoshi Katayama
Auditors: KPMG AZSA LLC

LOCATIONS

HQ: Hirogin Holdings Inc
1-1-7 Nishikaniya, Minami-ku, Hiroshima 732-0804
Phone: (81) 82 247 5151
Web: www.hirogin.co.jp

COMPETITORS

AOZORA BANK LTD. THE   MIZUHO BANK LTD.
JUROKU BANKLTD. THE   NANTO BANKLTD. THE

HISTORICAL FINANCIALS

Company Type: Public

Income Statement   FYE: March 31

	ASSETS ($ mil.)	NET INCOME ($ mil.)	INCOME AS % OF ASSETS	EMPLOYEES
03/20	86,951	223	0.3%	4,729
03/19	80,841	230	0.3%	4,767
03/18	85,247	243	0.3%	4,792
03/17	79,362	279	0.4%	4,520
03/16	73,028	279	0.4%	4,517
Annual Growth	4.5%	(5.4%)	—	1.2%

2020 Year-End Financials

Return on assets: 0.2%	Dividends
Return on equity: 4.9%	Yield: —
Long-term debt ($ mil.): —	Payout: 28.8%
No. of shares (mil.): 312	Market value ($ mil.): —
Sales ($ mil): 1,171	

Hitachi, Ltd.

Auditors: Ernst & Young ShinNihon LLC

LOCATIONS

HQ: Hitachi, Ltd.
1-6-6 Marunouchi, Chiyoda-ku, Tokyo 100-8280
Phone: (81) 3 3258 1111   **Fax:** 650 244-7037
Web: www.hitachi.co.jp

HISTORICAL FINANCIALS

Company Type: Public

Income Statement   FYE: March 31

	REVENUE ($ mil.)	NET INCOME ($ mil.)	NET PROFIT MARGIN	EMPLOYEES
03/21	78,837	4,530	5.7%	350,864
03/20	80,766	806	1.0%	301,056
03/19	85,608	2,009	2.3%	295,941
03/18	88,227	3,418	3.9%	307,275
03/17	81,947	2,068	2.5%	309,887
Annual Growth	(1.0%)	21.7%	—	3.2%

2021 Year-End Financials

Debt ratio: 0.1%	No. of shares (mil.): 966
Return on equity: 15.0%	Dividends
Cash ($ mil.): 9,174	Yield: 2.0%
Current ratio: 1.29	Payout: 38.2%
Long-term debt ($ mil.): 12,528	Market value ($ mil.): 89,383

	STOCK PRICE ($) FY Close	P/E High/Low		PER SHARE ($) Earnings	Dividends	Book Value
03/21	92.45	0	0	4.68	1.88	32.93
03/20	57.45	1	1	0.83	1.74	30.13
03/19	64.87	0	0	2.08	1.45	30.51
03/18	73.09	0	0	3.54	1.32	31.97
03/17	54.33	0	0	2.14	1.08	27.48
Annual Growth	14.2%	—	—	21.6%	14.9%	4.6%

Hochtief AG

HOCHTIEF is an engineering-led global infrastructure group with leading positions across its core activities of construction services and concessions/public-private partnerships (PPP) focused on Australia North America and Europe. The US subsidiaries Turner E.E. Cruz Clark Builders and Flatiron provide building and infrastructure construction. CIMIC based in Australia provides engineering and construction services for the infrastructure and mining industries. The group also operates in such European countries as the Austria Czech Republic Poland Russia and the UK. HOCHTIEF has 20% stake in Abertis a leading international toll road operator that operates a total of over 8300 kilometers of toll road in more than 15 countries particularly France Spain North America Brazil Chile and Mexico. About 95% of its revenue comes from outside Germany.

Operations
HOCHTIEF operates through HOCHTIEF Americas HOCHTIEF Asia Pacific HOCHTIEF Europe and Abertis.

HOCHTIEF Americas encompasses the construction management and construction activities of operational units in the USA and Canada. The segment generates some 65% of total revenue.

HOCHTIEF Asia Pacific (about 30%) pools the construction activities contract mining and services in the Asia-Pacific region.

HOCHTIEF Europe (around 5% of total revenue) brings together the core business in Europe as well as selected other regions and designs develops builds operates and manages real estate and infrastructure.

Abertis Investment comprises the investment in Spanish toll road operator Abertis Infraestructuras S.A.

Overall construction management/services account for about 75% of revenue and Construction/PPP for the remaining some 25%.

Geographic Reach
Based in Germany HOCHTIEF generates about 60% of revenue in US and more than 20% in Australia.

Financial Performance
The ?23 billion (2019: ?25.9 billion) sales figure comprises performance obligations recognized under the percentage of completion method in the mainstream construction business construction management and contract mining plus products and services provided to construction joint ventures and other related services.

In 2020 the company had a net income of ?582.1 million a 323% improvement from the previous year's net loss of ?261.3 million.

The company's cash at the end of 2020 was ?5 billion. Operating activities generated ?707.3 million while financing activities used ?632.1 million primarily for debt repayment. Investing activities provided another ?647.7 million.

Strategy
The HOCHTIEF vision looks to the future: "HOCHTIEF is building the world of tomorrow." Its business activities are based on a common corporate culture with shared values. The company's values are represented by five guiding principles: integrity accountability innovation delivery and sustainability?all underpinned by the precondition of safety. These principles apply to all employees at HOCHTIEF as well as to all work areas both operational and strategic. Its integrated approach to projects fosters a culture of collaboration among its group companies to the benefit of its stakeholders.

HOCHTIEF's strategy is to further strengthen its position in its core markets and to pursue market growth opportunities while sustaining cash-backed profitability and a rigorous risk management approach. Its businesses are flexible allowing its management to quickly adapt to varying market conditions. Active and disciplined capital allocation is a high priority for the company. It continues to focus on attractive shareholder remuneration as well as investing in strategic growth opportunities to create sustainable value for all stakeholders.

Key elements of its strategy aimed at achieving its objectives are as follows: Focus on activities and geographies with strong competitive positions; Focus on sustainable and cash-backed profitability; Continuous focus on risk management; Diversification and optimization of the financing instruments; Active and disciplined capital allocation a key priority for management; Accelerating innovation by making use of digital developments; and Further enhancing its attractiveness as an employer.

HISTORY

Brothers Philipp and Balthasar Helfmann mill and farm workers from Kelsterbach Germany started construction company Fa. Gebr. Helfmann Bauunternehmer in Frankfurt am Main in 1875. The firm primarily built houses until 1878 when it was contracted to build the university at Giessen.

In 1884 the company was made a general partnership. Projects of this era included Frankfurt's Hotel Continental and Wiesbaden's Hotel Kaiserhof. When Balthasar died in 1896 Philipp converted the business to a joint stock company and renamed it Actien-Gesellschaft f r Hoch- und Tiefbauten. Three years later with new capital for expansion the company won its first contract abroad — construction of a pneumatic conveyer-equipped granary in the harbor at Genoa (its first reinforced-concrete project).

Philipp Helfmann died in 1899 but the company continued operating. The battlefields of WWI took away most of the workforce and construction slowed to a near halt. But in the years following the war the company grew. In 1921 German industrialist Hugo Stinnes began buying stakes in the company and was its major shareholder by 1923. The company decided in 1922 to relocate to Essen closer to the Stinnes Group's operations and in 1923 it was renamed HOCHTIEF Aktiengesellschaft f r Hoch- und Tiefbauten vorm. Gebr. Helfmann.

Stinnes died in 1924 and two years later his empire collapsed. But German banks helped keep HOCHTIEF alive and operating as an independent company. That year Rheinisch-Westf lische-Elektrizit ¤tswerke AG (RWE) the electric utility that Stinnes helped create became the main shareholder in HOCHTIEF with a 31% stake.

Many of RWE's facilities were damaged during WWII including its Essen headquarters and the RWE staff used the HOCHTIEF building until 1961. Postwar reconstruction kept the company active including Germany's first nuclear reactor built by HOCHTIEF and commissioned in 1966. After the war RWE began increasing its stake in HOCHTIEF until it became the majority shareholder (56%) in 1989.

As a division of the RWE Group HOCHTIEF began acquiring former state-owned companies throughout Germany. By 1996 it had added financing and operation of major projects to its services. That year it led a consortium to build and operate an international airport in Athens. In 1997 it teamed with Ireland's Aer Rianta to build new terminals and manage the airport in D sseldorf Germany. The next year HOCHTIEF won a bid to build and operate Berlin's new airport but a rival's allegations of bidding irregularities led to a raid by prosecutors on HOCHTIEF's headquarters. Charges were dismissed but the company was disqualified from the project.

The company sought to expand internationally with an agreement to take a 49% stake in the US holdings of its main rival Philipp Holzmann (1997). But when these plans failed and HOCHTIEF was blocked by regulators from increasing its 20% stake in the competitor (held since 1981) it lost interest and relinquished its shares.

HOCHTIEF like many of its competitors expanded abroad in 1999 by helping engineer Canadian firm Armbro's takeover of rival BFC (and then grabbing a 49% share in the merged firm now Aecon Group) and by acquiring US construction giant Turner. The company suffered a $75 million operating loss in 2000 because of a slowdown in the German construction industry and expenses related to acquisitions.

It secured a contract to build a rail tunnel under the River Thames in London in 2001. Also that year it merged its building and civil units into HOCHTIEF Construction and made plans to join former rival IVG Immobilien to bid on building Berlin's new airport Berlin-Brandenburg. HOCHTIEF reorganized in 2001 to reflect its increasingly international operations.

By 2002 Philipp Holzmann was in insolvency and HOCHTIEF initially made plans to bid on its former rival's technical services group HSG. However after reviewing the unit's prospectus HOCHTIEF withdrew from the bidding.

Longtime shareholder and German energy giant RWE sold its 56% stake in HOCHTIEF in 2004 to European and US institutional investors. It was the largest such transaction involving a German stock.

HOCHTIEF subsidiary Leighton and joint venture partner Downer EDI won a ?100 million contract to build a four-lane highway in New Zealand in 2006. The project is expected to be finished in 2010.

In 2007 the company acquired the energy contracting business of Vattenfall Europe adding to its existing service portfolio of energy contracting and management operations. Also that year HOCHTIEF acquired Flatiron Construction from Royal BAM Group. That deal provided the group with entry into infrastructure PPP markets in the US and Canada.

EXECUTIVES

Independent Member of the Supervisory Board, Angel Manuel Garcia Altozano, $148,122 total compensation

Independent Member of the Supervisory Board, Francisco Garcia Sanz, $74,061 total compensation

Labor Director, Member of the Executive Board, Nikolaus Graf von Matuschka, $462,598 total compensation

Chairman of the Executive Board, Chief Executive Officer, Marcelino Verdes, $1,481,227 total compensation

Independent Member of the Supervisory Board, Christine Wolff, $111,092 total compensation

Chairman of the Supervisory Board, Pedro Jose Lopez Jimenez, $222,184 total compensation

Member of the Supervisory Board, Employee Representative, Carsten Burckhardt, $111,092 total compensation

Member of the Supervisory Board, Employee Representative, Nikolaos Paraskevopoulos, $111,092 total compensation

Member of the Supervisory Board, Employee Representative, Klaus Stuemper, $111,092 total compensation

Deputy Chairman of the Supervisory Board, Employee Representative, Matthias Maurer, $148,122 total compensation

Independent Member of the Supervisory Board, Beate Bell, $111,092 total compensation

Independent Member of the Supervisory Board, Patricia Geibel-Conrad, $111,092 total compensation

Chief Financial Officer, Member of the Executive Board, Peter-Wilhelm Sassenfeld, $793,026 total compensation

Member of the Supervisory Board, Employee representative, Nicole Simons, $111,092 total compensation

Member of the Supervisory Board, Employee Representative, Arno Gellweiler, $111,092 total compensation

Member of the Supervisory Board, Employee Representative, Christoph Breimann, $74,061 total compensation

Member of the Supervisory Board, Employee Representative, Sabine Roth, $111,092 total compensation

Member of the Supervisory Board, Jose del Valle Perez, $111,092 total compensation

Member of the Supervisory Board, Luis Miguelsanz, $111,092 total compensation

Chief Operating Officer, Member of the Executive Board, Jose Legorburo, $396,513 total compensation

Auditors: KPMG AG Wirtschaftspruefungsgesellschaft

LOCATIONS

HQ: Hochtief AG
Alfredstrasse 236, Essen 45133
Phone: (49) 201 824 0   **Fax:** (49) 201 824 2777
Web: www.hochtief.com

2013 Sales

	% of total
Australia	47
Americas	32
Asia	10
Germany	8
Rest of Europe	3
Total	**100**

PRODUCTS/OPERATIONS

2013 Sales

	% of totoal
HOCHTIEF Asia Pacific	57
HOCHTIEF Americas	32
HOCHTIEF Europe	11
Total	**100**

Selected Subsidiaries and Associates

Airport
  HOCHTIEF AirPort Capital Verwaltungs GmbH & Co. KG
  HOCHTIEF AirPort GmbH
Construction Services Americas
  Flatiron Construction Corp. (US)
  HOCHTIEF Americas GmbH
  HOCHTIEF do Brasil S.A. (92%)
  The Turner Corporation (US)
Construction Services Asia Pacific
  HOCHTIEF Asia Pacific GmbH
Construction Services Europe
  DURST-BAU GmbH (Austria)
  HOCHTIEF Construction AG
Development
  Deutsche Bau-und Siedlungs-Gesellschaft mbH
  HOCHTIEF Aurestis Beteiligungsgesellschaft mbH

COMPETITORS

ARCADIS N.V.
Bilfinger SE
China Railway Engineering Group Co. Ltd.
China Railway Group Limited
DRAGADOS SOCIEDAD ANONIMA
FERROVIAL SA
FUELCELL ENERGY INC.
GEE CONSTRUCTION LTD
HELIX ENERGY SOLUTIONS GROUP INC.
LAGAN CONSTRUCTION LIMITED
STRABAG SE
Skanska AB
VIANINI LAVORI SPA
Vale Canada Limited
VolkerWessels Nederland B.V.

HISTORICAL FINANCIALS

Company Type: Public

Income Statement				FYE: December 31
	REVENUE ($ mil.)	NET INCOME ($ mil.)	NET PROFIT MARGIN	EMPLOYEES
12/20	28,208	524	1.9%	46,644
12/19	29,029	(231)	—	53,282
12/18	27,327	619	2.3%	55,777
12/17	27,064	504	1.9%	53,890
12/16	20,922	338	1.6%	46,039
Annual Growth	7.8%	11.6%	—	0.3%

2020 Year-End Financials

Debt ratio: 35.6%	No. of shares (mil.): 68
Return on equity: 43.8%	Dividends
Cash ($ mil.) 6,074	Yield: —
Current ratio: 1.09	Payout: 63.8%
Long-term debt ($ mil.): 4,793	Market value ($ mil.): —

Hokkoku Financial Holdings Inc

Hokkoku Bank knows that not all of the gold in its hometown is in the bank vault. The regional bank is headquartered in Kanazawa (which translates to 'marsh of gold') a city noted for its production of gold leaf. It serves the Ishikawa Fukui and Toyama prefectures (in the Hokuriku region) through 100-plus branches. It also has offices in Osaka Nagoya and Tokyo as well as overseas in Shanghai and Singapore. Besides traditional deposit banking Hokkoku Bank subsidiaries are engaged in leasing credit cards debt collection business restructuring funding revitalization and credit guarantee. With total assets of $37 billion in fiscal

2013 the bank was founded in 1943 when three banks merged.
Auditors: Ernst & Young ShinNihon LLC

LOCATIONS

HQ: Hokkoku Financial Holdings Inc
2-12-6 Hirooka, Kanazawa, Ishikawa 920-8670
Phone: (81) 76 263 1111
Web: www.hokkokubank.co.jp

PRODUCTS/OPERATIONS

Selected Subsidiaries
The Hokkoku General Leasing Co. Ltd.
The Hokkoku Credit Service Co. Ltd.
The Hokkoku Credit Guarantee Co. Ltd.
The Hokkoku Management Ltd.
The Hokkoku Servicer Ltd.

COMPETITORS

BANK OF THE RYUKYUS LIMITED

NISHI-NIPPON CITYBANKLTD.

HISTORICAL FINANCIALS

Company Type: Public

Income Statement				FYE: March 31
	ASSETS ($ mil.)	NET INCOME ($ mil.)	INCOME AS % OF ASSETS	EMPLOYEES
03/20	46,957	67	0.1%	2,278
03/19	45,413	77	0.2%	2,309
03/18	44,948	95	0.2%	2,338
03/17	38,641	97	0.3%	2,327
03/16	34,765	85	0.2%	2,348
Annual Growth	7.8%	(5.7%)	—	(0.8%)

2020 Year-End Financials

Return on assets: 0.1%	Dividends
Return on equity: 2.9%	Yield: —
Long-term debt ($ mil.): —	Payout: —
No. of shares (mil.): 28	Market value ($ mil.): —
Sales ($ mil): 688	

Hokuhoku Financial Group Inc

Short on cash and passing through the Hokuriku or Hokkaido districts of Japan? You might want to check in with this group. The Hokuhoku Financial Group's core business is banking primarily through its chief subsidiaries: The Hokuriku Bank and The Hokkaido Bank. Through both banks' approximately 325 branches the financial services group targets the Toyama Ishikawa and Fukui Prefectures. In addition to banking Hokuhoku Financial Group provides credit cards leasing services venture capital and financing products. Hokuriku Bank (founded in 1877) merged with Hokkaido Bank in 2004 to form Hokuhoku Financial Group which today operates in the Hokuriku and Hokkaido district and Tokyo Osaka and Nagoya.

EXECUTIVES

President, President of Subsidiary, Representative Director, Eishin Ihori
Chairman of Subsidiary, Director, Hidenori Mugino

Independent Director, Nobuya Suzuki
Vice President, President of Subsidiary, Representative Director, Yuji Kanema
Independent Director, Masaaki Manabe
Director, Masahiko Kobayashi
Director, Hirokuni Kitagawa
Director, Hiroshi Nakazawa
Director, Yoshimasa Takada
Director, Akira Sakai
Independent Director, Kaoru Funamoto
Auditors: Deloitte Touche Tohmatsu LLC

LOCATIONS

HQ: Hokuhoku Financial Group Inc
1-2-26 Tsutsumicho-dori, Toyama 930-8637
Phone: (81) 76 423 7331
Web: www.hokuhoku-fg.co.jp

PRODUCTS/OPERATIONS

Selected Subsidiaries and Affiliated Companies
Hokugin Lease Co. Ltd.
Hokugin Software Co. Ltd.
Hokuriku Capital Co. Ltd.
Hokuriku Card Co. Ltd.
Hokuriku Hosho Services Co. Ltd.
Nihonkai Services Co. Ltd.
The Hokkaido Bank Ltd.
  Dogin Business Service Ltd.
  Dogin Card Co. Ltd.
The Hokuriku Bank Ltd.
  Hokugin Business Services Co. Ltd.
  Hokugin Corporate Co. Ltd.
  Hokugin Office Services Co. Ltd.
  Hokugin Real Estate Services Co. Ltd.
  Hokugin Shisankanri Co. Ltd.
  Hokuriku International Cayman Limited

COMPETITORS

E. SUN FINANCIAL HOLDING COMPANY LTD.
Hana Financial Group Inc.
JAPAN POST HOLDINGS CO.LTD.
MIZUHO FINANCIAL GROUP INC.
MS&AD INSURANCE GROUP HOLDINGS INC.
SINOPAC FINANCIAL HOLDINGS COMPANY LIMITED

HISTORICAL FINANCIALS

Company Type: Public

Income Statement				FYE: March 31
	ASSETS ($ mil.)	NET INCOME ($ mil.)	INCOME AS % OF ASSETS	EMPLOYEES
03/20	125,700	186	0.1%	7,983
03/19	119,067	219	0.2%	8,412
03/18	122,390	199	0.2%	8,751
03/17	111,168	251	0.2%	8,808
03/16	103,567	256	0.2%	8,755
Annual Growth	5.0%	(7.7%)	—	(2.3%)

2020 Year-End Financials

Return on assets: 0.1%	Dividends
Return on equity: 3.3%	Yield: —
Long-term debt ($ mil.): —	Payout: 28.1%
No. of shares (mil.): 131	Market value ($ mil.): —
Sales ($ mil): 1,683	

Holcim Ltd (New)

Holcim formerly known as LafargeHolcim is a global leader in innovative and sustainable building solutions. Holcim is the company behind some of the world's most trusted brands in the building sector including ACC Aggregate Industries Ambuja Cement Disensa Firestone Building Products Geocycle Holcim and Lafarge. Each year the Swiss company produces around 445 million tons of building materials in the form of cement aggregates asphalt and ready-mix concrete products. It has a global presence managed through its offices scattered around approximately 70 countries. Holcim generates majority of its revenue from Europe.

Operations
Holcim operates four business segments: Cement Ready- Mix Concrete Aggregates and Solutions & Products.

The Cement segment produces typical masonry products to high-performance offerings tailored for specialized uses. It sells roughly 190.4 million tons of it to individuals buying bags of cement to businesses embarking on major construction projects.

The Ready-Mix segment delivers concrete in various forms all of them ready for individuals and businesses to deploy for its specific projects. Holcim delivers around 42.3 million cubic meters annually.

The Aggregates segment provides the raw materials for concrete masonry and asphalt. It also produces base materials for roads buildings and landfills including recycled aggregates (such as crushed concrete and asphalt left over from deconstruction activities). Holcim delivers about 256.3 million tonnes of aggregates each year.

The fourth segment Solutions & Products works closely with customers to define and deliver solutions tailored to customers' requirements.

All told the company has around 2260 plants including more than 1300 ready-mix concrete some 655 aggregates and nearly 270 cement and grinding plants.

Geographic Reach
Switzerland-headquartered Holcim has a large asset presence in around 70 countries and boasts a market presence in just about every developed region on the globe.

Holcim's sales are well-balanced across the world's major regions. The company generates around 30% of its total sales from Europe; the Asia/Pacific regions accounts for nearly 25% North America brings in about 25% of total sales; and Latin America Middle East and Africa together pull in the remaining more than 20% of Lafarge's total sales.

Sales and Marketing
Holcim's customers span major multinationals to small-scale businesses and individual customers. Its customers include manufacturers of prefabricated products concrete and asphalt producers construction and public work contractors.

Financial Performance
Note: Growth rates may differ after conversion to US Dollars.

The company's net sales for 2020 was CHF23.1 million a 13% decrease from the previous year.

In the same period the company had a net income of CHF1.9 million a 24% decrease from the previous year.

Strategy
Holcim has a new strategy aptly named Strategy 2022 ? "Building for Growth" which aims to drive profitable growth and simplify the business to deliver resilient returns and attractive value to stakeholders. It has four value drivers: Growth; Simplification & Performance; Financial Strength; and Vision & People.

Advancing its "Building for Growth" strategy the company completed eight bolt-on acquisitions in 2020 in the US UK Canada Australia and Switzerland. It anticipates further bolt-ons in 2021 accelerated by the development of its Solutions & Products segment.

Mergers and Acquisitions
In 2021 Holcim has reached an agreement to acquire Heinrich Teufel GmbH & Co.KG a regional

player in aggregates and ready-mix concrete in southern Germany. The acquisition of Heinrich Teufel will strengthen Holcim's footprint in southern Germany in aggregates and ready-mixed concrete.

In mid-2021 Holcim's HERACLES Group has signed an agreement with HALYPS Domika Ylika SA of Heidelberg Cement to acquire the aggregates business and two ready-mix concrete plants in Athens Greece. The acquisition will strengthen HERACLES Group's position to support Athens thriving metropolitan area and key infrastructure projects with sustainable building solutions. This is LafargeHolcim's fifth bolt-on acquisition in 2021 a key driver of the company's growth strategy.

In early 2021 Holcim announces that its Holcim Participations (US) Inc. subsidiary has successfully completed the acquisition of Tennessee-based Firestone Building Products following all regulatory approvals. The transaction closed earlier than expected due to smooth collaboration with Bridgestone and all 1900 employees will be joining LafargeHolcim. With its leading roofing systems Firestone Building Products makes the company a partner of choice from rooftop to foundation. This truly is a milestone for LafargeHolcim as it becomes the global leader in innovative and sustainable building solutions.

Also in early 2021 Holcim announces the acquisition of Edile Commerciale and the signing of Cemex Rhone Alpes both suppliers of ready-mix concrete and aggregates ideally located in two of Europe's largest metropolitan areas Milan Italy and Lyon France. With 35 ready-mix concrete plants these operations strengthen LafargeHolcim's position in two of the most dynamic and attractive areas in Europe with strong demographic trends and key infrastructure projects. These two bolt-on acquisitions add to eight similar transactions carried out by LafargeHolcim in 2020 as a key driver of its growth strategy.

HISTORY

Cement company Aargauische Portlandcementfabrik Holderbank-Wildegg was founded near Zurich in 1912. Two years later Ernst Schmidheiny bought a stake in the company. His son and namesake later expanded the company beyond Switzerland then grouped its interests under holding company "Holderbank" Financi re Glaris Ltd. in 1930. By WWII Holderbank had operations in Belgium Egypt Greece Lebanon and South Africa.

After the war Holderbank expanded into the Americas. It purchased Canada-based St. Lawrence Cement in 1953 and was listed on the Zurich stock exchange in 1958.

In 1970 the company swapped some assets with rival Swiss Cement-Industrie-Gesellschaft in a deal that increased Holderbank's presence in Costa Rica Lebanon Mexico and West Germany. The company also converted several of its minority stakes into majority shareholdings. Thomas Schmidheiny became chairman of Holderbank's executive committee in 1978 and chairman of the board in 1984 upon his father's (Ernst's brother Max) retirement.

During a late-1980s market slump Holderbank bought stakes in several US cement companies. It became the #1 US cement maker by purchasing Ideal Basic Industries in 1986. As the decade closed Holderbank consolidated in Europe and in 1990 placed many of its US operations under holding company Holnam.

Holderbank then pushed into Central and Eastern Europe where it gained production capacity in Hungary among other countries. The company bought a 51% stake in Morocco-based Les Ciments de l'Oriental (CIOR) in 1993. Geographic diversity helped Holderbank weather depressed periods in regional markets such as in Mexico

where profits dropped 83% from 1994 to 1995 during an economic crisis there.

The company picked up major acquisitions in Malaysia the Philippines Sri Lanka and Thailand during a crippled economic period in Asia in the late 1990s. It also added capacity in the booming US market. Holderbank sought to invest in India in 1999 but the fragmented market there prevented it from finding a sizable company. Meanwhile Holderbank continued searching for investments in China to expand its presence there. The following year the company became the majority shareholder of Indonesian cement company PT Semen Cibinong (now PT Holcim Indonesia). Its joint bid (with Portugal's Secil) for CIMPOR the largest Portuguese cement manufacturer got stuck in regulatory issues however.

Holderbank changed its name to Holcim Ltd. in 2001. The name is derived from "Holderbank" (where it was founded) and "ciment" (French for cement). In 2002 Holcim's Thai subsidiary Siam City Cement acquired a controlling stake in TPI Polene beating out rival CEMEX for the deal. Holcim acquired Spain-based Cementos de Hispania and disposed of Eternit AG business in 2003.

That year when operations in Europe and North America showed little growth the company looked toward emerging markets in Africa Asia and Latin America. Holcim tightened its hold on Holcim Apasco in Mexico by increasing its stake in the company from 69% to 93% in 2004; it later took full ownership.

In 2005 Holcim acquired UK-based construction products provider Aggregate Industries. The deal gave the group more than 140 quarries in the UK and US. It followed that up the following year with the purchases of aggregates producer Foster Yeoman in the UK and ready-mix concrete maker Meyer Material in the US.

In 2007 Holcim acquired control of Ambuja Cements in India; took a majority stake in the Croatian Plovanija Kamen cement plant and stone quarry; and bought building materials supplier Jurong Cement in Singapore.

The company acquired Tarmac Iberia from Anglo American for some ?148 million ($228 million) in 2008. The deal added about 50 ready-mixed concrete plants in Spain.

EXECUTIVES

Chairman, Beat Hess
Chief Sustainability and Innovation Officer, Magali Anderson
Region Head Latin America, Oliver Osswald
Region Head Asia Pacific, Martin Kriegner
Chief Executive Officer, Jan Jenisch, $1,810,097 total compensation
Chief Financial Officer, Geraldine Picaud
Region Head North America, Rene Thibault
Head HR, Feliciano González Mu oz
Region Head EMEA, Miljan Gutovic
Auditors: Deloitte AG

LOCATIONS

HQ: Holcim Ltd (New)
Zurcherstrasse 156, Rapperswil-Jona CH-8645
Phone: (41) 58 858 58 58   **Fax:** (41) 58 858 87 19
Web: www.lafargeholcim.com

2018 sales

	%
Asia Pacific	27
Europe	28
Latin America	10
Middle East & Africa	11
North America	21
Corporate/Eliminations	2
Total	**100**

PRODUCTS/OPERATIONS

2018 sales

	%
Cement	60
Aggregates	14
Ready-mix concrete	18
Products and Solutions	8
Total	**100**

COMPETITORS

Alpiq Holding SA	SSAB AB
Cemex S.A.B. de C.V.	Schindler Holding AG
Clariant AG	Swiss Re AG
DEXUS PROPERTY	Votorantim Cimentos
SERVICES PTY LIMITED	S/A
HeidelbergCement AG	Weatherford
ICAHN ENTERPRISES L.P.	International Ltd.
Outokumpu Oyj	Zurich Insurance Group
PEAK INVESTMENTS LLC	AG
SEQUANA	

HISTORICAL FINANCIALS

Company Type: Public

Income Statement				FYE: December 31
	REVENUE ($ mil.)	NET INCOME ($ mil.)	NET PROFIT MARGIN	EMPLOYEES
12/20	26,275	1,926	7.3%	67,409
12/19	27,642	2,323	8.4%	72,452
12/18	27,920	1,526	5.5%	77,055
12/17	26,772	(1,716)	—	81,960
12/16	26,430	1,759	6.7%	90,903
Annual Growth	(0.1%)	2.3%	—	(7.2%)

2020 Year-End Financials

Debt ratio: 26.4%	No. of shares (mil.): 611
Return on equity: 6.1%	Dividends
Cash ($ mil.): 5,892	Yield: 0.2%
Current ratio: 1.33	Payout: 72.9%
Long-term debt ($ mil.): 14,099	Market value ($ mil.): 6,631

	STOCK PRICE ($) FY Close	P/E High/Low		PER SHARE ($) Earnings	Dividends	Book Value
12/20	10.84	4	2	3.11	2.27	48.39
12/19	11.06	3	2	3.81	2.07	48.15
12/18	8.16	5	3	2.56	0.00	45.91
12/17	11.21	—	—	(2.85)	0.00	47.68
12/16	10.52	4	2	2.91	0.00	49.99
Annual Growth	0.8%	—	—	1.7%	—	(0.8%)

Hon Hai Precision Industry Co Ltd

Hon Hai Precision Industry Co. also known by its trade name Foxconn is the world's largest contract electronics manufacturer. It makes mobile phones computers servers and TVs. Other products include components such as connectors game consoles and Netcom. It covers the four major product areas of consumer electronics cloud network products computer terminal products components and others. The global company's customers include Apple Cisco Dell and Amazon. Chairman Terry Gou founded Hon Hai in 1974 to make plastic switches for TVs. Over 30% of the company's total sales is generated from the US and Ireland each.

Operations

The company offers consumer and smart products for personal use including smart phones feature phones wearable devices etc. as well as smart entertainment systems and equipment in home life including televisions game consoles set-top boxes speakers and more. Its related cloud network equipment required for enterprises and general consumers are used in network communications and cloud space including routers servers edge computing data centers satellite communications and other related equipment. It also offers computer terminal product field which includes desktop computers notebook computers tablet computers business machines printers etc. covering the 3C product categories. In addition it also offers components and other product areas including connectors precision optical components and lenses electronic components semiconductor products automotive electronic parts tools/mold fixtures and mechanical equipment.

Geographic Reach

Taipei-based Hon Hai has facilities in China Mexico Brazil the Czech Republic Hungary Slovakia Vietnam India and the US.

The US and Ireland each supplies over 30% of Hon Hai's revenue China account for about 10% and others generate the remaining sales.

Sales and Marketing

Hon Hai's biggest customer Customer E accounts for approximately 55% of total revenue.

Financial Performance

The company's revenue for 2020 totaled NT$5.4 trillion a NT$15.2 billion increase from the previous year's revenue. The increase is primarily due to a higher sales volume of total reported segment revenue.

In 2020 the company had a net profit of NT$145.5 billion an 11% increase from the previous year's net profit of NT$163.9 billion.

The company's cash at the end of 2020 was NT$1.2 trillion. Operating activities generated NT$377.6 billion while financing activities used NT$12.2 billion mainly for payments of cash dividends as well as interest. Investing activities provided another NT$34.6 billion.

Strategy

Hon Hai pursues continued excellence in operational management and cost control and provides a "One-Stop Shop" solution for global leading brands. Its commitment is to maintain the high quality of service and related added-value services enable computing communication consumer electronics (3C) to enrich lives of the world population. In order to provide its customers with more timely services the company has actively established related manufacturing bases design centers service centers in Europe the Americas and Asia to satisfy its clients' global design manufacturing and assembly needs.

The company has formulated transformation and upgrade plans beginning the long-term transformation from brawn-intensive to brain-intensive. The company will take this opportunity to upgrade its level of industry improve profits and commit to the development of three main areas of electric vehicles digital health and robotics; and also emphasize the three main core technologies of AI semiconductors and 5th/6th generation mobile communication technologies. The company's development and implementation of the "3+3" new industry technology fields have also are also an advanced deployment of technologies and products for 3-5 years in advance; among them the company has initiated the MIH Alliance in the field of electric vehicles and will cooperate and strive with more than 1500 member companies at home and abroad to become the android platform of the electric vehicle industry.

The group's long-term strategy is to form strategic partnerships to formulate a comprehensive vertically integrated supply chain leveraging its core expertise and advantages.

Company Background

Hon Hai Precision Industry Co. Ltd. or also knew to their business as Foxconn Technology Group or better known as Foxconn is a Taiwanese multinational electronics contract manufacturer headquartered in Tucheng New Taipei City Taiwan. It was founded in 1974 as Hon Hai Plastics Corporation by Terry Gou and later renamed as Hon Hai Precision Industry Co. Ltd. in 1982.

EXECUTIVES

Director, Fang-Ming Lu
Chief Financial Officer, Head of Finance, De-Cai Huang
Independent Director, Kuo-Chuan Kung
Director, Yee-ru Liu
General Manager-Business Group, Cheng-Yang Wang
Director, Sung-Ching Lu
Independent Director, Tei-Wei Kuo
General Manager-Business Group, Chih-Siung Chiang
Vice Chairman of the Board, Jay Lee
General Manager-Business Group, Cheng-Qing Chu
General Manager-Business Group, Chung-Cheng Lin
Chairman and CEO, Young-way Liu
Auditors: PricewaterhouseCoopers Taiwan

LOCATIONS

HQ: Hon Hai Precision Industry Co Ltd
No. 66, Zhongshan Road, Tucheng Industrial Zone, Tucheng District, New Taipei
Phone: (886) 2 2268 3466
Web: www.foxconn.com

PRODUCTS/OPERATIONS

2017 Sales

	% of total
Ireland	30
US	29
China	9
Singapore	8
Japan	3
Taiwan	2
Others	19
Total	**100**

Selected Products

Cable assemblies
CD-ROMs
Connectors
E-book readers
Enclosures
Flat-panel displays
Game consoles
Handsets
Keyboards
LCD (liquid-crystal display) TVs
Mobile phones
Motherboards
Personal computers
Servers
Smartphones
Switches
Tablets
Thermal products

COMPETITORS

BENCHMARK ELECTRONICS INC.
Compal Electronics Inc.
FLEX LTD.
SANMINA CORPORATION
SIGMATRON INTERNATIONAL INC.
SKYWORKS SOLUTIONS INC.
MERCURY SYSTEMS INC.
PLEXUS CORP.
Quanta Computer Inc.
Samsung Electronics Co. Ltd.
TTM TECHNOLOGIES INC.

HISTORICAL FINANCIALS

Company Type: Public

Income Statement — FYE: December 31

	REVENUE ($ mil.)	NET INCOME ($ mil.)	NET PROFIT MARGIN	EMPLOYEES
12/20	190,662	3,622	1.9%	0
12/19	178,459	3,851	2.2%	0
12/18	173,086	4,219	2.4%	0
12/17	158,732	4,678	2.9%	0
12/16	134,728	4,595	3.4%	0
Annual Growth	**9.1%**	**(5.8%)**	**—**	**—**

2020 Year-End Financials

Debt ratio: 0.7%
Return on equity: 8.0%
Cash ($ mil.): 43,868
Current ratio: 1.51
Long-term debt ($ mil.): 8,301
No. of shares (mil.): —
Dividends
 Yield: 3.1%
 Payout: 83.1%
Market value ($ mil.): —

	STOCK PRICE ($) FY Close	P/E High/Low		PER SHARE ($) Earnings	Dividends	Book Value
12/20	6.63	1	1	0.26	0.21	3.33
12/19	6.12	1	1	0.28	0.18	2.99
12/18	4.75	1	1	0.26	0.00	2.86
12/17	6.20	1	1	0.27	0.00	2.11
12/16	5.05	1	1	0.26	0.00	1.92
Annual Growth	**7.0%**	**—**	**—**	**(0.4%)**	**—**	**14.7%**

Honda Motor Co Ltd

Established in 1948 Honda Motor Company is one of the world's largest automaker with about 430 domestic and overseas affiliated companies. The company's global car models include the Accord CR-V Civic Fit and its new Clarity Fuel Cell model. Honda's line of motorcycles includes everything from scooters to superbikes. The company's power products division makes commercial and residential machinery (lawn mowers snow blowers and tillers); portable generators; an outboard motors. Its Honda Aero subsidiary also manufactures jet and turboprop engines. More than half of Honda's sales comes from North America.

Operations

Four reporting segments comprise Honda Motor's operations: the Automobile business Financial Services business Motorcycle business and Life Creation and other businesses.

Automobile business generates more than 65% of total sales. It offers vehicles that use gasoline engines of three four or six-cylinder configurations diesel engines gasoline-electric hybrid systems and gasoline-electric plug-in hybrid systems.

Financial Services generates nearly 20% of total sales. It offers retail lending leasing to customers and other financial services such as wholesale financing to dealers through finance subsidiaries.

Motorcycle Business generates about 15% of total sales. Honda produces a wide range of motorcycles with engine displacement ranging from the 50cc class to the 1800cc class. Honda's motorcycle lineup uses internal combustion engine of air- or water-cooled and in single two four or six-cylinder configurations. Honda also has electric vehicles in its lineup. Honda's motorcycle lineup consists of sports business and commuter models.

Life Creation and Other Businesses generates more than 1% of total sales. Honda manufactured a variety of power products including general purpose engines generators water pumps lawn mowers riding mowers robotic mowers brush cutters tillers snow blowers outboard marine engines walking assist devices and portable battery inverter power sources.

Geographic Reach

Headquartered in Tokyo Honda's major geographic areas are concentrated in North America (the US Canada and Mexico); Asia (Thailand Indonesia China India and Vietnam); Japan; and Europe (the UK Germany Italy Belgium France) as well as Brazil and Australia.

The Financial Services business provides financing and leasing through its subsidiaries in Japan the US Canada the UK Germany Brazil and Thailand.

North America generates roughly 55% of net sales while Asia brings in about 25% of sales. Japan accounts about 15% and Europe and other regions generates less than 10% of sales combined.

Sales and Marketing

Most of Honda's products are distributed under the Honda trademarks in Japan and/or in overseas markets. In Japan Honda produces and sells motorcycles automobiles and power products through its domestic sales subsidiaries and independent retail dealers. It also sells spare parts and provides after-sales services through retail dealers directly or via its overseas operations independent distributors and licensees.

Financial Performance

The company's sales revenue has grown in the past years but experienced a decline in the last two years. Profit has fluctuated in the same five-year period.

Honda's consolidated sales revenue for the fiscal year 2021 decreased by 1.8 trillion or 11.8% to 13.2 trillion from the fiscal year ended March 31 2020 due mainly to decreased sales revenue in all business operations.

Profit for the year increased by 201.6 billion or 44.3% to 657.4 billion from the previous fiscal year.

Consolidated cash and cash equivalents in 2021 (ended March) increased by 85.7 billion from 2020 (ended March) to 2.8 trillion. Net cash provided by operating activities amounted to 1.1 trillion of cash inflows while net cash used in investing activities amounted to 796.9 billion and net cash used in financing activities amounted to 284 billion.

Strategy

Honda engages in business operations through alliances and joint ventures with other companies in expectation of synergy effects and increased efficiency or to meet the requirements of the countries in which business development is being undertaken.

As Honda advances its mid- and long-term initiatives toward further electrification more widespread use and evolution of driver-assistive technologies and further provision of mobility services the utilization of alliances and other forms of partnership are gaining importance.

Trends in the negotiations regarding trade agreements particularly those related to the United States could have adverse effects on Honda's business and operating results. Honda will continue to monitor the status of negotiations and take action in consideration of the impact on Honda. The United States-Mexico-Canada Agreement (USMCA) took effect in July 2020. The revision of various rules such as the rules of country of origin for automobiles sold within the regions covered in USMCA may adversely affect Honda's business in North America.

HISTORY

Soichiro Honda spent six years as an apprentice at Tokyo service station Art Shokai before opening his own branch of the repair shop in Hamamatsu in 1928. He also raced cars and in 1931 received a patent for metal spokes that replaced wood in wheels.

Honda started a piston ring company in 1937. During WWII the company produced metal propellers for Japanese bombers. When bombs and an earthquake destroyed most of his factory Honda sold it to Toyota in 1945.

In 1946 Honda began motorizing bicycles with war-surplus engines. When this proved popular Honda began making engines. The company was renamed Honda Motor Co. in 1948 and began producing motorcycles. Soichiro Honda hired Takeo Fujisawa in 1949 to manage the company so Honda could focus on engineering. Honda's innovative overhead valve design made its early 1950s Dream model a runaway success. In 1952 the smaller Cub sold through bicycle dealers accounted for 70% of Japan's motorcycle production.

Funded by a 1954 public offering and Mitsubishi Bank Honda expanded capacity and began exporting. American Honda Motor Company was formed in Los Angeles in 1959 accompanied by the slogan "You meet the nicest people on a Honda" in a campaign crafted to counter the stereotypical biker image. Honda added overseas factories in the 1960s and began producing lightweight trucks sports cars and minicars.

The company began selling its tiny 600 model in the US in 1970 but it was the Civic introduced in 1973 that first scored with the US car market. Three years later Honda introduced the Accord which featured an innovative frame adaptable for many models. In 1982 Accord production started at the company's Ohio plant.

Auditors: KPMG AZSA LLC

LOCATIONS

HQ: Honda Motor Co Ltd
1-1, Minami-Aoyama 2-chome, Minato-ku, Tokyo 107-8556
Phone: (81) 3 5412 1134
Web: www.honda.co.jp

2017 Sales

	% of total
North America	56
Asia	19
Japan	14
Europe	5
Other regions	6
Total	**100**

PRODUCTS/OPERATIONS

2017 Sales

	% of total
Automobiles	72
Financial Services	13
Motorcycles	12
Power products & other businesses	3
Total	**100**

Selected Acura Models

ILX sedan
TLX sedan
RLX sedan
RDX SUV
MDX SUV
NSX Supercar

Selected Honda Car and Truck ModelsPassenger cars

Gold Wing
CB1100
CBR1000RR

CB1000R
VFR800F
Rebel
CB250R/CB300R
CB125R
CRF1000L Africa Twin
X-ADV
CRF250 Rally
PCX
SuperCub
Monkey

Selected ATVs

Utility ATVs
TRX250X ATV sport
TRX90X sport
FourTrax Rincon
FourTrax Foreman Rubicon 4x4
FourTrax Rancher
FourTrax Recon
Pioner SxS
Forza scooter
PCX150 scooter
Ruckus scooter
Metropolitan scooter

Selected Power Products

Lawn mowers
Miimo robotic lawnmower
Marine motors
Portable generators
LiB-AID E500 portable power source
Pumps
Snowblowers
Tillers

COMPETITORS

Bayerische Motoren Werke AG
GENERAL MOTORS COMPANY
HONDA DEVELOPMENT & MANUFACTURING OF AMERICA LLC
ISUZU MOTORS LIMITED
PEUGEOT SA
SUZUKI MOTOR CORPORATION
TATA MOTORS LIMITED
TOYOTA MOTOR NORTH AMERICA INC.
YAMAHA MOTOR CO. LTD.

HISTORICAL FINANCIALS

Company Type: Public

Income Statement / FYE: March 31

	REVENUE ($ mil.)	NET INCOME ($ mil.)	NET PROFIT MARGIN	EMPLOYEES
03/21	118,948	5,937	5.0%	211,374
03/20	137,549	4,198	3.1%	218,674
03/19	143,471	5,511	3.8%	219,722
03/18	144,661	9,976	6.9%	215,638
03/17	125,208	5,514	4.4%	211,915
Annual Growth	(1.3%)	1.9%	—	(0.1%)

2021 Year-End Financials

Debt ratio: 0.3%	No. of shares (mil.): 1,726
Return on equity: 7.6%	Dividends
Cash ($ mil.): 24,908	Yield: 2.5%
Current ratio: 1.33	Payout: 33.4%
Long-term debt ($ mil.): 42,586	Market value ($ mil.): 52,145

	STOCK PRICE ($) FY Close	P/E High/Low		PER SHARE ($) Earnings	Dividends	Book Value
03/21	30.20	0	0	3.44	0.78	47.51
03/20	22.46	0	0	2.40	1.04	42.75
03/19	27.17	0	0	3.12	0.99	42.43
03/18	34.73	0	0	5.56	0.91	42.01
03/17	30.26	0	0	3.06	0.84	36.20
Annual Growth	(0.0%)	—	—	3.0%	(1.7%)	7.0%

Hong Leong Bank Berhad

One of Malaysia's largest banks Hong Leong Bank operates about 200 branches in its home country. It offers loans deposits credit cards investments and insurance to retail customers. The bank's offerings for corporate and commercial clients include loans trade financing economic research and debt capital markets services. Hong Leong Bank also provides Syariah-compliant banking services and Takaful (insurance) to Islamic customers. Its Singapore branch focuses on private banking investment banking Islamic banking treasury and asset management. The bank also has an office in Hong Kong. Started in 1905 as Kwong Lee Mortgage and Remittance Hong Leong Bank is a subsidiary of Hong Leong Group.

EXECUTIVES

Group Managing Director and CEO, Domenic Fuda, $2,720,985 total compensation
Chief Executive Officer - HLISB, Enick Jasani Bin Abdullah
Managing Director & Chief Executive, HLB Singapore Branch, Wee Lee Ng
Chief Financial Officer, Malkit Maan
Managing Director & Chief Executive Officer - HLBCAM, Yih Min Teoh
Independent Non-Executive Director, Chye Neo Chong, $3,877 total compensation
Independent Non-Executive Director, Souk Huan Lau, $9,208 total compensation
Non-Independent Executive Director, Kong Khoon Tan, $1,054,733 total compensation
Independent Non-Executive Director, Md Hamzah Bin Md Kassim, $8,238 total compensation
Non-Independent Non-Executive Director, Nicholas Lough, $8,238 total compensation
Independent Non-Executive Director, Kwee Bee Chok, $7,996 total compensation
Non-Independent Non-Executive Chairman of the Board, Leng Chan Quek
Non-Independent Non-Executive Director, Leng Hai Kwek
Managing Director - Business and Corporate Banking, Kuan Tuck Yow
Managing Director & Chief Executive - HLB Hong Kong Branch, Luk Kai Man
Managing Director & General Director - HLBVN, a wholly-owned subsidiary, Duc Hung Duong
Managing Director - China Operations, Ho Wai Choong
Managing Director - Personal Financial Services, Wan King Sik
Managing Director - Global Markets, Kwok Wai Hor
Auditors: PricewaterhouseCoopers PLT

LOCATIONS

HQ: Hong Leong Bank Berhad
Level 30, Menara Hong Leong, No. 6, Jalan Damanlela, Bukit Damansara, Kuala Lumpur 50490
Phone: (60) 3 2080 9888   **Fax:** (60) 3 2080 9801
Web: www.hlb.com.my

COMPETITORS

BANK OF EAST ASIA LIMITED THE
CHONG HING BANK LIMITED

PUBLIC FINANCIAL HOLDINGS LIMITED

HISTORICAL FINANCIALS
Company Type: Public

Income Statement
FYE: June 30

	ASSETS ($ mil.)	NET INCOME ($ mil.)	INCOME AS % OF ASSETS	EMPLOYEES
06/20	51,637	582	1.1%	8,090
06/19	50,153	644	1.3%	7,958
06/18	50,238	653	1.3%	8,045
06/17	45,556	499	1.1%	8,212
06/16	47,604	477	1.0%	0
Annual Growth	2.1%	5.1%	—	—

2020 Year-End Financials

Return on assets: 1.1%
Return on equity: 9.4%
Long-term debt ($ mil.): —
No. of shares (mil.): 2,086
Sales ($ mil): 2,062

Dividends
Yield: —
Payout: 29.5%
Market value ($ mil.): —

Hongkong & Shanghai Banking Corp Ltd

Auditors: PricewaterhouseCoopers

LOCATIONS

HQ: Hongkong & Shanghai Banking Corp Ltd
HSBC Main Building, 1 Queen's Road Central,
Phone: (852) 2822 1111   **Fax:** (852) 2810 1112
Web: www.hsbc.com.hk

HISTORICAL FINANCIALS
Company Type: Public

Income Statement
FYE: December 31

	REVENUE ($ mil.)	NET INCOME ($ mil.)	NET PROFIT MARGIN	EMPLOYEES
12/19	45,691	13,381	29.3%	0
12/18	39,830	13,152	33.0%	0
12/17	36,787	11,327	30.8%	0
12/16	32,847	10,141	30.9%	0
12/15	33,732	11,551	34.2%	67,552
Annual Growth	7.9%	3.7%	—	—

2019 Year-End Financials

Debt ratio: —
Return on equity: 13.3%
Cash ($ mil.): 28,751
Current ratio: —
Long-term debt ($ mil.): —

No. of shares (mil.): —
Dividends
Yield: —
Payout: —
Market value ($ mil.): —

HSBC Bank Canada

Boasting around $70 billion in assets HSBC Bank Canada is one of the largest foreign-owned banks in Canada. Through more than 150 bank branches across the country it provides a range of commercial and retail financial services including deposit accounts loans and mortgages import and export financing equipment leasing and investment capital financing. Through subsidiaries the bank also offers brokerage services insurance mutual funds merchant banking trust services and portfolio management and investment counseling. HSBC Bank Canada is controlled by one of the largest banks on the planet UK-based financial services heavyweight HSBC Holdings.

Operations
HSBC Bank Canada operates three business segments: Retail banking and Wealth management which offers banking services to 800000 retail and high-net-worth clients; Commercial Banking which serves small and mid-sized businesses and multinational companies; and Global Banking and Markets which consists of its markets capital financing and investment banking divisions.

The bank made 68% of its total revenue from interest income during 2015 with 80% of that being loan interest. Another 30% came from fee income with about half of that coming from credit facilities and funds under management fees and the rest coming from various service fees involving account services credit card corporate finance remittance brokerage commissions insurance and trustee fees among others.

Geographic Reach
The Vancouver-based bank operates branches across Canada.

Financial Performance
Note: Growth rates may differ after conversion to US dollars. This analysis uses financials from the company's annual report.

HSBC Bank Canada's annual revenues and profits have been in decline in recent years mostly as it's struggled to grow its loan business and as interest margins have been shrinking in the low-interest environment.

The bank's revenue slipped 9% to C$2.5 billion ($1.8 billion) during 2015 with all three segments reporting lower revenue due to the tough Canadian economy and the sharp decline in oil prices.

Revenue declines low interest margins and higher loan loss provisions stemming from more non-performing energy loans in 2015 caused HSBC Bank Canada's net income to fall more than 30% to C$447 million ($322.4 million). The bank's operating cash levels climbed sharply to C$3.65 billion ($2.63 billion) for the year (operations used C$546 million in 2014) despite the drop in earnings mostly thanks to favorable working capital changes related to changes in operating liabilities.

Strategy
HSBC Canada continued to follow its four strategic initiatives in early 2016 which included: leveraging its distinct geographic network which connects developed and fast-growing regions; connecting its clients to global growth opportunities; continuing to leverage its wide variety of financial products to benefit from global trends; and boost collaboration with other global businesses to better serve international clients.

Company Background
In 2012 as part of parent HSBC's restructuring efforts to create a leaner group HSBC Bank Canada announced plans to wind down the Consumer Finance segment which provided products including mortgages loans specialty insurance and credit cards through subsidiary HSBC Financial. The closure followed the 2011 sale of the full-service investment advisory business of HSBC Securities (Canada) to National Bank of Canada. Both divestitures reflected the group's strategy to focus on commercial banking retail banking and wealth management.

Auditors: PricewaterCoopers LLP

LOCATIONS

HQ: HSBC Bank Canada
 300-885 West Georgia Street, Vancouver, British
 Columbia V6C 3E9
Phone: 604 685-1000   **Fax:** 604 641-3098
Web: www.hsbc.ca

PRODUCTS/OPERATIONS

2015 sales

	%
Interest income	66
Fee income	25
Net trading income	5
Gains less losses from financial investments	2
Other operating income	2
Total	**100**

Selected Products

Banking
Chequing accounts
Credit cards
eSwitch
Foreign currency accounts
Savings accounts
Tax-Free Savings Accounts (TFSA)
Travel insurance

Selected Subsidiaries

Household Trust Company
HSBC Capital (Canada) Inc.
HSBC Financial Corporation Limited
HSBC Global Asset Management (Canada) Limited
HSBC Investment Funds (Canada) Inc.
HSBC Loan Corporation (Canada)
HSBC Mortgage Corporation (Canada)
HSBC Securities (Canada) Inc.
HSBC South Point Investments (Barbados) LLP
HSBC Trust Company (Canada)

COMPETITORS

AKBANK TURK ANONIM SIRKETI
BOKF MERGER CORPORATION NUMBER SIXTEEN
Banco Bradesco S/A
Bank of Communications Co. Ltd.
FINANCIAL INSTITUTIONS INC.
M&T BANK CORPORATION
MUFG AMERICAS HOLDINGS CORPORATION
SHINSEI BANK LIMITED
Shinhan Financial Group Co. Ltd.
TCF FINANCIAL CORPORATION
The Bank of Nova Scotia
WEBSTER FINANCIAL CORPORATION
Woori Finance Holdings Co. Ltd.

HISTORICAL FINANCIALS

Company Type: Public

Income Statement				FYE: December 31
	ASSETS ($ mil.)	NET INCOME ($ mil.)	INCOME AS % OF ASSETS	EMPLOYEES
12/20	92,163	204	0.2%	5,499
12/19	81,839	426	0.5%	5,688
12/18	75,934	500	0.7%	5,779
12/17	76,880	502	0.7%	5,681
12/16	70,238	360	0.5%	5,870
Annual Growth	7.0%	(13.3%)	—	(1.6%)

2020 Year-End Financials

Return on assets: 0.2%
Return on equity: 3.9%
Long-term debt ($ mil.): —
No. of shares (mil.): 548
Sales ($ mil): 2,502

Dividends
 Yield: —
 Payout: 66.8%
Market value ($ mil.): —

	STOCK PRICE ($) FY Close	P/E High/Low	PER SHARE ($) Earnings	Dividends	Book Value
12/20	0.00	— —	0.38	0.25	9.85
Annual Growth	—		—	—	—

HSBC Bank Plc (United Kingdom)

EXECUTIVES

Non-Executive Independent Deputy Chairman of the Board, John Trueman
Non-Executive Independent Director, Eric Strutz
Non-Executive Independent Director, Andrew Wright
Chairman of the Board, Stephen O'Connor
Non-Executive Independent Director, Yukiko Omura
Chief Finance Officer, Executive Director, Jacques Fleurant
Company Secretary, Philip Jockelson
Auditors: PricewaterhouseCoopers LLP

LOCATIONS

HQ: HSBC Bank Plc (United Kingdom)
 8 Canada Square, London E14 5HQ
Phone: (44) 20 7991 8888
Web: www.hsbc.co.uk

HISTORICAL FINANCIALS

Company Type: Public

Income Statement				FYE: December 31
	ASSETS ($ mil.)	NET INCOME ($ mil.)	INCOME AS % OF ASSETS	EMPLOYEES
12/19	840,525	(1,337)	—	17,754
12/18	772,386	1,922	0.2%	30,437
12/17	1,106,036	2,443	0.2%	45,342
12/16	1,004,814	(260)	—	55,346
12/15	1,078,768	2,877	0.3%	67,290
Annual Growth	(6.0%)	—	—	(28.3%)

2019 Year-End Financials

Return on assets: (-0.1%)
Return on equity: (-4.0%)
Long-term debt ($ mil.): —
No. of shares (mil.): 796
Sales ($ mil): 19,368

Dividends
 Yield: —
 Payout: —
Market value ($ mil.): —

HSBC Holdings Plc

HSBC is one of the largest banking and financial services organizations in the. Alongside its home markets of Hong Kong and the UK HSBC has subsidiaries throughout Europe the wider Asia/Pacific region the Middle East Africa and the Americas. All told the company serves more than 40 million customers in about 65 countries. Its activities include wealth and personal banking commercial banking and global banking and markets. HSBC was founded by the Scot Sir Thomas Sutherland in Hong Kong then a British colony in 1865 as was incorporated in the UK in 1991. Asian markets account for the majority of its sales.

Operations
HSBC operates three core business segments: Wealth and Personal Banking (about 45% of sales) Global Banking and Markets (some 30%) and Commercial Banking (around 25%).

The Wealth and Personal Banking (WPB) provides a full range of retail banking and wealth products to its customers from personal banking to ultra-high net worth individuals. Typically customer offerings include retail banking products such as current and savings accounts mortgages and personal loans credit cards debit cards and local and international payment services. It also provides wealth management services including insurance and investment products global asset management services investment management and Private Wealth Solutions for customers with more sophisticated and international requirements.

The Global Banking and Markets (GBM) provides tailored financial solutions to major government corporate and institutional clients and private investors worldwide. The client-focused business lines deliver a full range of banking capabilities including financing advisory and transaction services a markets business that provides services in credit rates foreign exchange equities money markets and securities services and principal investment activities.

The Commercial Banking (CMB) offers a broad range of products and services to serve the needs of its commercial customers including small and medium-sized enterprises mid-market enterprises and corporates. These include credit and lending international trade and receivables finance treasury management and liquidity solutions (payments and cash management and commercial cards) commercial insurance and investments. CMB also offers customers access to products and services offered by other global businesses such as Global Banking and Markets which include foreign exchange products raising capital on debt and equity markets and advisory services.

Overall roughly 45% of sales were generated from its net interest income while net fee income accounts for about 20% The net insurance premium income as well as net income from financial instruments account for around 15% each.

Geographic Reach
London-based HSBC operates in around 65 countries. It generates over 45% its revenue from the Asia/Pacific region (including Hong Kong) and over 30% from Europe (including the UK). North America brings in around 10% of sales Latin America around 5% and the Middle East and North Africa around 5% as well.

Sales and Marketing
HSBC serves more than 40 million customers ranging from individuals to large corporations and everything in between.

Financial Performance
Reported revenue down 10% to $50.4 billion primarily due to the progressive impact of lower interest rates across its global businesses in part offset by higher revenue in Global Markets.

Profit for fiscal 2020 decreased to $4.3 billion compared with $9.3 billion in the prior year.

Cash held by the company at the end of fiscal 2020 increased to $6.2 billion. Cash provided by operations was $5.2 billion while investing and financing activities used $3.4 billion and $1.6 billion respectively. Main cash uses were proceeds from the sale and maturity of financial investments and debt securities repaid.

Strategy
In February 2020 HSBC outlined its plan to upgrade the return profile of its risk-weighted assets ('RWAs') reduce its cost base and streamline the organization. Despite the significant headwinds posed by the impact of the Covid-19 outbreak the company has made good progress in implementing its plan.

HSBC has aligned its strategy accordingly. The company intends to increase its focus on areas where HSBC is strongest. HSBC aims to increase and accelerate its investments in technology to enhance the capabilities it provides to customers and improve efficiency to drive down its cost base. The company also intends to continue the transformation of its underperforming businesses. As part of its climate ambitions the company has set out its plans to capture the opportunities presented by the transition to a low-carbon economy.

Mergers and Acquisitions

In 2021 HSBC Insurance (Asia-Pacific) Holdings Ltd an indirect wholly-owned subsidiary of HSBC Holdings plc (HSBC) has entered into an agreement to acquire 100% of the issued share capital of AXA Insurance Pte Limited (AXA Singapore) for US$575m. The proposed acquisition which is subject to regulatory approval is a key step in achieving HSBC's stated ambition of becoming a leading wealth manager in Asia by expanding its insurance and wealth franchise in Singapore a strategically important scale market for HSBC and a major hub for its ASEAN wealth business. AXA Singapore is currently the 8th largest life insurer in Singapore by annualized new premiums 5th largest property and casualty (P&C) insurer and a leading group health player.

In 2020 HSBC Insurance (Asia) Limited an indirect wholly-owned subsidiary of HSBC Holdings plc has entered into an agreement to acquire the remaining 50% equity interest in HSBC Life Insurance Company Limited its life insurance joint venture in China from The National Trust Limited. The transaction will be structured as a transfer of equity interest and is subject to regulatory approvals including from the China Banking and Insurance Regulatory Commission. Terms were not disclosed.

Company Background

In Asia HSBC sold its private banking operations in Japan to Credit Suisse in 2012. It also shut down its retail banking operations in Japan though it continues to offer corporate banking there. HSBC sold its US credit card portfolio worth some $30 billion to Capital One in 2012 and sold 195 US bank branches mainly in upstate New York to First Niagara Financial Group for 613 million ($1 billion).

HISTORY

Scotsman Thomas Sutherland and other businessmen in 1865 opened the doors to Hongkong & Shanghai Bank financing and promoting British imperial trade in opium silk and tea in East Asia. It soon established a London office and created an international branch network emphasizing China and East Asia. It claims to have been the first bank in Thailand (1888).

War repeatedly disrupted but never demolished the bank's operations. During WWII the headquarters were temporarily moved to London. (They moved back on a permanent basis in 1991.) The bank's chief prewar manager Sir Vandeleur Grayborn died in a Japanese POW camp. After the Communists took power in China in 1949 the bank gradually withdrew; by 1955 only its Shanghai office remained and it was later closed. The bank played a key role in Hong Kong's postwar growth by financing industrialists who fled there from China.

In the late 1950s Hongkong & Shanghai Bank's acquisitions included the British Bank of the Middle East (founded 1889; now The Saudi British Bank) and Mercantile Bank (with offices in India and Southeast Asia). In 1965 the company bought 62% of Hang Seng Hong Kong's #2 bank. It also added new subsidiaries including Wayfoong (mortgage and small-business finance 1960) and Wardley (investment banking Hong Kong 1972).

In the late 1970s and into the 1980s China began opening to foreign business. The bank added operations in North America to capitalize on business between China and the US and Canada. Acquisitions included Marine Midland Bank (US 1980) Hongkong Bank of Canada (1981) 51% of treasury securities dealer Carroll McEntee & McGinley (US 1983) most of the assets and liabilities of the Bank of British Columbia (1986) and Lloyds Bank Canada (1990).

Following the 1984 agreement to return Hong Kong to China Hongkong & Shanghai Bank began beefing up in the UK buying London securities dealer James Capel & Co. (1986) and the UK's #3 bank Midland plc (1992). In 1993 the company formed London-based HSBC Holdings and divested assets most notably its interest in Hong Kong-based Cathay Pacific Airways.

HSBC then began expanding in Asia again particularly in Malaysia where its Hongkong Bank Malaysia became the country's first locally incorporated foreign bank. The company returned to China with offices in Beijing and Guangzhou. It also added new European branches.

Latin American banks acquired in 1997 were among the non-Asian operations that cushioned HSBC from the worst of 1998's economic crises. Nonetheless The Hong Kong Monetary Authority took a stake in the bank to shore up the stock exchange and foil short-sellers.

In 1999 China's government made HSBC a loan for mainland expansion. That year the company was foiled in its attempt to buy South Korea's government-owned Seoulbank but did buy the late Edmond Safra's Republic New York Corporation and his international bank holding company Safra Republic Holdings (it negotiated a $450 million discount on the $10 billion deal after a Japanese probe of Republic's securities division caused delays).

The company unveiled several online initiatives in 2000 including Internet ventures with CK Hutchison Holdings and Merrill Lynch and bought CCF (then called Cr dit Commercial de France now HSBC France). However HSBC's plans to buy a controlling stake in Bangkok Metropolitan Bank fell through before the year's end.

In 2001 HSBC agreed to pick up Barclays Bank's fund management operations in Greece. Later in response to the slowing economy it froze the salaries of 14000 employees. Argentina's 2001 peso devaluation cost the company half a billion dollars in currency conversion losses alone. Total charges pertaining to Argentina equaled more than $1 billion that year.

HSBC expanded its consumer finance operations with the purchase of US-based Household International (now HSBC Finance) in 2003.

The next year HSBC acquired The Bank of Bermuda as well as Marks and Spencer Financial Services (aka M&S Money) one of the UK's leading credit card issuers. It bought US credit card company Metris the following year.

HSBC's Latin American operations at this point were primarily in Argentina Brazil and Mexico. The company expanded its presence in Central America and the Caribbean with the 2006 purchase of Panama-based Banistmo a banking group with offices in the Bahamas Colombia Costa Rica El Salvador Honduras and Nicaragua.

HSBC sold its regional banking operations in France to Banque Populaire in 2008. The deal included eight banks with around 400 branches. Also that year the company canceled its proposed $6 billion acquisition of Lone Star's 51% stake in Korea Exchange Bank a deal that had been held up for months by an investigation by the South Korean government. HSBC cited weakened asset values in the global financial markets for the cancellation.

Beset by mortgage defaults the group closed its Decision One US-based wholesale subprime lending unit in 2007. In 2009 it shuttered its North American consumer lending business placing related portfolios (excluding credit cards) in run-off.

To further reduce its exposure to consumer credit it sold a $4 billion car loan portfolio and servicing platform to an affiliate of Santander USA.

The company acquired a majority stake in Indonesian lender Bank Ekonomi in 2009 doubling its presence in the nation.

In 2010 HSBC sold HSBC Insurance Brokers to Marsh & McLennan in a 135 million ($218 million) cash-and-stock deal. As part of the transaction the companies entered into a strategic partnership under which Marsh markets insurance and risk management services to HSBC's corporate and private clients ahead of other providers.

In late 2011 the Financial Services Authority (the UK regulator of financial services providers) fined HSBC 10.3 million after it was found that salespeople at its NHFA Limited subsidiary had sold inappropriate and unsuitable five-year bonds to nearly 3000 elderly customers. HSBC which had alerted the FSA once it was made aware of the issue closed NHFA to new business that year.

EXECUTIVES

Group Head, Internal Audit, Jonathan Calvert-Davies
President and CEO, HSBC USA and Americas, Michael Roberts
Co-CEO, Global Banking and Markets, Georges Elhedery
Independent Non-Executive Director, Dame Carolyn Fairbairn
Non-Executive Independent Director, Rachel Duan
Group Company Secretary and Chief Governance Officer, Aileen Taylor
Independent Non-Executive Group Chairman of the Board, Mark Tucker
CEO, Wealth and Personal Banking, Nuno Matos
Group Chief Legal Officer, Bob Hoyt
Group Head of Compliance, Kirsty Everett
Independent Non-Executive Director, Eileen Murray
Independent Non-Executive Director, James Forese
Independent Non-Executive Director, Steven Guggenheimer
Independent Non-Executive Director, Yun Lien Lee
Chief Executive Officer, HSBC Bank plc and HSBC Europe, Colin Bell
Independent Non-Executive Director, Jackson Tai
Senior Independent Non-Executive Director, David Nish
Group Chief Risk and Compliance Officer, Pam Kaur
Group Chief Executive, Noel Quinn, $1,623,721 total compensation
Independent Non-Executive Director, Pauline van der Meer Mohr
Independent Non-Executive Director, Jose Antonio Meade Kuribrena
Director, HSBC Global Banking and Markets, Peter Wong
Auditors: PricewaterhouseCoopers LLP

LOCATIONS

HQ: HSBC Holdings Plc
8 Canada Square, London E14 5HQ
Phone: (44) 20 7991 8888   **Fax:** (44) 20 7992 4880
Web: www.hsbc.com

2018 income

	% of total
Asia	49
Europe	30
North America	11
Latin America	5
MENA	5
Total	**100**

PRODUCTS/OPERATIONS

2018 Sales by Segment

	% of total
Retail banking & wealth management	40
Global banking & markets	29
Commercial banking	28
Global private banking	3
Total	**100**

Selected Subsidiaries

Hang Seng Bank Limited (62% Hong Kong)
The Hong Kong and Shanghai Banking Corporation Limited
HSBC Asset Finance (UK) Ltd.
HSBC Bank Argentina S.A. (99.9%)
HSBC Bank A.S. (Turkey)
HSBC Bank Australia Limited
HSBC Bank Bermuda Limited
HSBC Bank Brasil S.A. - Banco Mùltiplo
HSBC Bank Canada
HSBC Bank (China) Company Limited
HSBC Bank Egypt S.A.E. (95%)
HSBC Bank International Limited (Jersey)
HSBC Bank Malaysia Berhad
HSBC Bank Malta p.l.c. (70%)
HSBC Bank Middle East Limited
HSBC Bank (Panama) S.A.
HSBC Bank plc
HSBC Bank USA N.A.
HSBC Finance Corporation (US)
HSBC France
HSBC Mexico S.A. Institución de Banca Mùltiplo Grupo Financiero HSBC (99.9%)
HSBC Private Banking Holdings (Suisse) S.A. (Switzerland)
HSBC Securities (USA) Inc.
HSBC Trinkaus & Burkhardt AG (80% Germany)
Marks and Spencer Retail Financial Services Holdings Limited

COMPETITORS

AEGON N.V.
AVIVA PLC
Ageas
BARCLAYS PLC
CLOSE BROTHERS GROUP PLC
ING Groep N.V.
LENLYN HOLDINGS LIMITED
NOMURA HOLDINGS INC.
OM RESIDUAL UK LIMITED
RSA INSURANCE GROUP LIMITED
Royal Bank of Canada
SCHRODERS PLC
STANDARD CHARTERED PLC

HISTORICAL FINANCIALS

Company Type: Public

Income Statement				FYE: December 31
	ASSETS ($ mil.)	NET INCOME ($ mil.)	INCOME AS % OF ASSETS	EMPLOYEES
12/20	2,984,164	5,139	0.2%	226,059
12/19	2,715,152	7,293	0.3%	235,351
12/18	2,558,124	13,637	0.5%	235,217
12/17	2,521,771	10,798	0.4%	228,687
12/16	2,374,986	2,479	0.1%	241,000
Annual Growth	**5.9%**	**20.0%**	**—**	**(1.6%)**

2020 Year-End Financials

Return on assets: 0.1%
Return on equity: 2.6%
Long-term debt ($ mil.): —
No. of shares (mil.): —
Sales ($ mil): 82,026
Dividends
Yield: 5.7%
Payout: 786.8%
Market value ($ mil.): —

	STOCK PRICE ($) FY Close	P/E High/Low	PER SHARE ($) Earnings	Dividends	Book Value
12/20	25.91	207 95	0.19	1.50	9.64
12/19	39.09	149 118	0.30	2.55	9.06
12/18	41.11	88 61	0.63	2.55	9.30
12/17	51.64	108 83	0.48	2.55	9.51
12/16	40.18	614 418	0.07	2.55	8.83
Annual Growth	**(10.4%)**	**—**	**28.4%**	**(12.5%)**	**2.2%**

Huadian Power International Corp., Ltd.

Huadian Power International is one of the largest comprehensive energy companies in the People's Republic of China. The company constructs and operates power plants and oversees other businesses related to power generation. Huadian Power owns or has stakes in about 60 power plants and power plant companies with a total net installed capacity of about 55615 MW. The company owns the entire interests in a dozen plants in Shandong Province including Zouxian Power Plant Shiliquan Power Plant and Laicheng Power Plant. Huadian Power which was founded in 1994 is around 45% owned by China Huadian Corporation Limited.

Operations

The company is primarily engaged in the construction and operation of power plants including large-scale efficient coal- or gas-fired generating units and various renewable energy projects. It had a total of some 60 controlled power plants which have commenced operations involving a total of around 56615 MW controlled installed capacity with a total of some 43235 MW attributable to coal-fired generating units about 6875 MW attributable to gas-fired generating units and approximately 6505 MW attributable to renewable energy generating units such as hydropower wind power and solar power generating units.

Sales of electricity accounts for some 80% of total sales coal has about 15% and heat with around 5%.f

Geographic Reach

The company is headquartered in Shandong Province China.

Sales and Marketing

The company's largest customer accounts for about 30% of total sales while its top five customers generate nearly 60%.

Financial Performance

In 2019 the company's turnover amounted to approximately RMB91.8 billion representing an increase of approximately 5% over 2018.

In 2019 the company's operating profit amounted to approximately RMB 8.2 billion representing an increase of approximately 31% over 2018 mainly due to the year-on-year decrease in coal prices.

Cash held by the company in 2019 decreased to RMB 6.5 billion compared to RMB 6.6 billion in the prior year. Cash provided by operations was RMB 15.5 billion while cash used for investing and financing activities were RMB 15.2 billion and RMB 553.5 million respectively. Main uses for cash were payment of purchase of property plant and equipment construction in progress investment properties and intangible assets.

Strategy

In 2020 the company will focus on the following four aspects:

Enhancing the control of operations and comprehensively improving quality and efficiency. Continuing to improve the level of leanness in marketing and fuel management strengthening policy analysis implementing strategies according to each factory's situation identifying superior themes and striving for favorable priority power generation plans and base quantity of electricity. Accelerating the construction of supporting mechanisms for trading in the electricity market participating in market competition in a coordinated manner of quantity and price and striving to seize the opportunity in the reform of the electricity market. Study-

ing and establishing risk management and control mechanism for electricity market transactions and preventing market risks and compliance risks. Strengthening the management of the whole process of fuel procurement and performing well the coal market analysis and procurement strategy research.

Strengthening strategic leadership and promoting high-quality development. Enhancing energy and power policy analysis and planning research scientifically analyzing development trends and vigorously promoting project construction. Further reinforcing investment plans and capital management combining project progress and actual needs improving the efficiency of capital use and protecting the needs of project development and infrastructure projects.

Consolidating the safety foundation and strengthening environmental protection. Strictly implementing production safety responsibilities at all levels focusing on key investigations and management timely detecting hidden problems and earnestly carrying out rectification work.

Promoting standardized operations and strictly controlling regulatory risks. Further standardizing the procedures of "general meetings the Board and the Supervisory Committee" of the Company in accordance with the latest requirements of regulatory agencies. Further opening channels for information acquisition and properly managing risks.

EXECUTIVES

Chairman of the Board, Huande Ding
Independent Director, Yuesheng Wang
General Manager, Director, Xiaoqian Luo
Deputy General Manager, Guoquan Peng
General Counsel, Deputy General Manager, Acting Secretary of the Board, Bin Chen
Chief Financial Officer, Director, Rong Feng
Vice Chairman of the Board, Shoumin Ni
Director, Xiaobo Wang
Independent Director, Xingchun Li
Director, Xingyu Peng
Director, Pengyun Li
Chief Engineer, Jingshang Song
Director, Zhiqiang Zhang
Independent Director, Zhenping Feng
Auditors: Deloitte Touche Tohmatsu Certified Public Accountants LLP

LOCATIONS

HQ: Huadian Power International Corp., Ltd.
No. 2 Xuanwumennei Street, Xicheng District, Beijing 100032
Phone: (86) 10 8356 7888   **Fax:** (86) 10 8356 7963
Web: www.hdpi.com.cn

PRODUCTS/OPERATIONS

2013 Sales

	% of total
PRC power Segment	88
Singapore Segment	11
All other Segment	1
Total	**100**

2013 Sales

	% of total
Sales of power & heat	97
Port service	1
Transportation service	1
Others	1
Total	**100**

COMPETITORS

CHINA POWER INTERNATIONAL DEVELOPMENT LIMITED

HOKKAIDO ELECTRIC POWER COMPANY
  INCORPORATED
Huaneng Power International Inc.
IDACORP INC.
INTERGEN SERVICES INC.
INTERNATIONAL POWER LTD.
Korea Electric Power Corporation
PPC S.A.
TUCSON ELECTRIC POWER COMPANY

HISTORICAL FINANCIALS
Company Type: Public

Income Statement				FYE: December 31
	REVENUE ($ mil.)	NET INCOME ($ mil.)	NET PROFIT MARGIN	EMPLOYEES
12/20	13,874	639	4.6%	0
12/19	13,459	489	3.6%	0
12/18	12,846	246	1.9%	0
12/17	12,141	66	0.5%	0
12/16	9,122	481	5.3%	0
Annual Growth	11.1%	7.3%		

2020 Year-End Financials
Debt ratio: 6.9%
Return on equity: 6.2%
Cash ($ mil.): 1,021
Current ratio: 0.42
Long-term debt ($ mil.): 11,451

No. of shares (mil.): —
Dividends
  Yield: 0.0%
  Payout: —
Market value ($ mil.): —

	STOCK PRICE ($) FY Close	P/E High/Low	PER SHARE ($) Earnings	Dividends	Book Value
12/20	0.00	32 24	0.05	0.55	(0.00)
12/19	14.25	49 49	0.04	0.22	(0.00)
Annual Growth	—	— —	4.9%	25.0%	—

Huaneng Power International Inc

Huaneng Power International is one of China's largest independent power producers. Its nearly 50 power plants in about 20 provinces have a capacity of more than 66700 MW; nearly all of the company's power is produced from coal. Huaneng Power International which is always expanding also owns Singapore's electricity retailer Tuas Power. Huaneng Power International sells power to local utilities primarily in China's coastal provinces. Huaneng International Power Development Corporation a subsidiary of the China Huaneng Group owns 36% of Huaneng Power International; China Huaneng Group 16%. Huaneng Power International was formed in 1994.

EXECUTIVES

Director, Jian Huang
Independent Director, Qing Xia
Independent Director, Haifeng Xu
Deputy General Manager, Ranxing Liu
Director, Dabin Mi
Deputy General Manager, Secretary of the Board, Chaoquan Huang
Independent Director, Xianzhi Zhang
Deputy General Manager, Jianmin Li
Director, Chong Lin
Deputy General Manager, Senrong Wu
Independent Director, Mengzhou Xu

General Manager, Director, Ping Zhao
Chairman of the Board, Keyu Zhao
Director, Heng Cheng
Chief Accounting Officer, Lixin Huang
Independent Director, Jizhen Liu
Deputy General Manager, Shuping Chen
Director, Kui Wang
Director, Haifeng Li
Director, Yu Teng
Chief Economist, Qiyang Fu
Chief Engineer, Wei Liu
Director, Fei Lu
Auditors: KPMG Huazhen LLP

LOCATIONS
HQ: Huaneng Power International Inc
  Huaneng Building, 6 Fuxingmennei Street, Xicheng District, Beijing 100031
Phone: (86) 10 6322 6999   **Fax:** (86) 10 6322 6888
Web: www.hpi.com.cn

2013 Sales	% of total
PRC power	89
Singapore	11
Total	**100**

COMPETITORS
Datang International Power Generation Co. Ltd.
Huadian Power International Corporation Limited
INTERGEN SERVICES INC.
KANSAI ELECTRIC POWER COMPANY
  INCORPORATED THE
Korea Electric Power Corporation
TAIWAN POWER COMPANY

HISTORICAL FINANCIALS
Company Type: Public

Income Statement				FYE: December 31
	REVENUE ($ mil.)	NET INCOME ($ mil.)	NET PROFIT MARGIN	EMPLOYEES
12/20	25,907	697	2.7%	0
12/19	24,932	242	1.0%	0
12/18	24,695	209	0.8%	57,960
12/17	23,428	275	1.2%	53,962
12/16	16,390	1,269	7.7%	42,210
Annual Growth	12.1%	(13.9%)		—

2020 Year-End Financials
Debt ratio: 8.1%
Return on equity: 4.1%
Cash ($ mil.): 2,120
Current ratio: 0.43
Long-term debt ($ mil.): 20,253

No. of shares (mil.): —
Dividends
  Yield: 4.7%
  Payout: 2,420.1%
Market value ($ mil.): —

	STOCK PRICE ($) FY Close	P/E High/Low	PER SHARE ($) Earnings	Dividends	Book Value
12/20	14.41	124 71	0.03	0.68	(0.00)
12/19	20.09	435305	0.01	0.52	(0.00)
12/18	25.01	437298	0.01	2.02	(0.00)
12/17	25.00	303227	0.02	1.56	(0.00)
12/16	26.04	61 38	0.08	2.47	(0.00)
Annual Growth	(13.8%)	—	(24.2%)	(27.7%)	—

Huayu Automotive Systems Company Ltd

EXECUTIVES

Independent Director, Ruiqing Shao
Vice Chairman of the Board, Xiaoqiu Wang
General Manager, Director, Haitao Zhang
Chairman of the Board, Hong Chen
Secretary of the Board, Qiwei Mao
Staff Elected Director, Lixin Zhong
Director, Weijiong Zhang
Independent Director, Jun Zhang
Director, Rong'en Zhu
Independent Director, Yande Yin
Auditors: Deloitte Touche Tohmatsu CPA Ltd.

LOCATIONS
HQ: Huayu Automotive Systems Company Ltd
  No. 489, Weihai Road, Shanghai 200041
Phone: (86) 21 22011701   **Fax:** (86) 21 22011790

HISTORICAL FINANCIALS
Company Type: Public

Income Statement				FYE: December 31
	REVENUE ($ mil.)	NET INCOME ($ mil.)	NET PROFIT MARGIN	EMPLOYEES
12/20	20,423	826	4.0%	0
12/19	20,698	928	4.5%	0
12/18	22,850	1,167	5.1%	0
12/17	21,588	1,007	4.7%	0
12/16	17,899	874	4.9%	0
Annual Growth	3.4%	(1.4%)		—

2020 Year-End Financials
Debt ratio: 1.2%
Return on equity: 10.5%
Cash ($ mil.): 5,542
Current ratio: 1.11
Long-term debt ($ mil.): 416

No. of shares (mil.): —
Dividends
  Yield: —
  Payout: —
Market value ($ mil.): —

Hunan Valin Steel Co Ltd

EXECUTIVES

Independent Director, Bingchun Guan
Director, Xianghong Yang
Chief Financial Officer, Director, Ji Xiao
Deputy General Manager, Chief Engineer, Yingqi Zhou
Chairman of the Board, General Manager, Zhiqiang Cao
Independent Director, Junwu Zhao
Independent Director, Ling Xie
Director, Zuo Yi
Independent Director, Jianping Zhang
Director, Xueyan Wang
Auditors: KPMG Huazhen

LOCATIONS

HQ: Hunan Valin Steel Co Ltd
20th Floor Valin Plaza, Main Building, Valin Park, No. 222, Xiangfu West Road, Changsha, Hunan Province 410014
Phone: (86) 731 89952818   **Fax:** (86) 731 82245196
Web: www.valin.cn

HISTORICAL FINANCIALS

Company Type: Public

Income Statement				FYE: December 31
	REVENUE ($ mil.)	NET INCOME ($ mil.)	NET PROFIT MARGIN	EMPLOYEES
12/20	17,817	977	5.5%	0
12/19	15,423	631	4.1%	0
12/18	13,283	985	7.4%	0
12/17	11,779	633	5.4%	0
12/16	7,193	(151)	—	0
Annual Growth	25.5%	—	—	—

2020 Year-End Financials

Debt ratio: 2.8%
Return on equity: 20.6%
Cash ($ mil.): 1,152
Current ratio: 0.86
Long-term debt ($ mil.): 942

No. of shares (mil.): —
Dividends
  Yield: —
  Payout: —
  Market value ($ mil.): —

Hyakugo Bank Ltd. (Japan)

Serving its primary business base in the Mie Prefecture Hyakugo Bank is a Japanese regional bank offering traditional banking services such as electronic corporate and consumer banking as well as international and securities offerings. Hyakugo Bank serves its products through more than 100 branches and 26 sub-branches and also owns foreign offices in Singapore and Shanghai. Listed subsidiaries include Hyakugo Business Service Company Hyakugo Staff Service Company and Hyakugo Property Research Company. The bank goes all the way back to 1878 when it was established as The 105th National Chartered Bank.

EXECUTIVES

Senior Managing Executive Officer, Manager of Secretary Office, Representative Director, Masakazu Sugiura
President, Representative Director, Toshiyasu Ito
Independent Director, Nagahisa Kobayashi
Independent Director, Hisashi Kawakita
Independent Director, Ichiro Wakasa
Managing Executive Officer, Director, Kei Yamazaki
Independent Director, Keiko Nishioka
Managing Executive Officer, Chief Director of Fund Management, Director, Satoru Fujiwara
Auditors: KPMG AZSA LLC

LOCATIONS

HQ: Hyakugo Bank Ltd. (Japan)
21-27 Iwata, Tsu, Mie 514-8666
Phone: (81) 59 227 2151
Web: www.hyakugo.co.jp

COMPETITORS

AUSTRALIA AND NEW ZEALAND BANKING GROUP LIMITED
IYO BANK LTD. THE
NANTO BANKLTD. THE

HISTORICAL FINANCIALS

Company Type: Public

Income Statement				FYE: March 31
	ASSETS ($ mil.)	NET INCOME ($ mil.)	INCOME AS % OF ASSETS	EMPLOYEES
03/21	67,309	117	0.2%	4,185
03/20	59,303	105	0.2%	4,194
03/19	56,574	97	0.2%	4,238
03/18	54,072	110	0.2%	4,231
03/17	49,525	80	0.2%	4,229
Annual Growth	8.0%	9.7%	—	(0.3%)

2021 Year-End Financials

Return on assets: 0.1%
Return on equity: 3.5%
Long-term debt ($ mil.): —
No. of shares (mil.): 254
Sales ($ mil): 845

Dividends
  Yield: —
  Payout: 19.6%
  Market value ($ mil.): —

Hyakujushi Bank, Ltd.

Businesses and individuals who say "Hi" to Hyakujushi Bank might find themselves saying " Hai " (yes) to the institution's banking and financial services offerings. One of Japan's regional banks Hyakujushi Bank serves the Kagawa prefecture and about 10 other nearby prefectures through some 120 banking offices and a network of about 300 ATMs. (Most of the bank's loans originate outside its home base.) Hyakujushi Bank also has operations in Tokyo and Osaka. Hyakujushi Bank offers a variety of traditional banking services including deposit banking and lending.

EXECUTIVES

Independent Director, Tomoko Fujimoto
Independent Director, Yasuko Yamada
Executive Officer, Kazushi Kozuchi
President, Representative Director, Yujiro Ayada
Director, Toshiya Yoritomi
Managing Executive Officer, Director, Akihiko Fujimura
Chief Compliance Officer, Vice President, Representative Director, Ryohei Kagawa
Independent Director, Junichi Ito
Managing Executive Officer, Director, Hideaki Kanemoto
Managing Executive Officer, Director, Masakazu Toyoshima
Managing Executive Officer, Director, Kazuhisa Anata
Senior Managing Executive Officer, Representative Director, Kiichiro Ohyama
Director, Kazuhiro Kumihashi
Managing Executive Officer, Director, Hiroyuki Kurokawa
Independent Director, Michiyo Ihara
Independent Director, Nobuyuki Souda
Auditors: Ernst & Young ShinNihon LLC

LOCATIONS

HQ: Hyakujushi Bank, Ltd.
5-1 Kamei-cho, Takamatsu, Kagawa 760-8574
Phone: (81) 87 831 0114
Web: www.114bank.co.jp

COMPETITORS

HANG SENG BANK LIMITED
NISHI-NIPPON
  CITYBANKLTD.

HISTORICAL FINANCIALS

Company Type: Public

Income Statement				FYE: March 31
	ASSETS ($ mil.)	NET INCOME ($ mil.)	INCOME AS % OF ASSETS	EMPLOYEES
03/21	48,549	23	0.0%	2,891
03/20	45,637	71	0.2%	2,978
03/19	44,206	50	0.1%	3,050
03/18	44,987	96	0.2%	3,164
03/17	44,063	86	0.2%	3,216
Annual Growth	2.5%	(28.0%)	—	(2.6%)

2021 Year-End Financials

Return on assets: 0.0%
Return on equity: 0.9%
Long-term debt ($ mil.): —
No. of shares (mil.): 29
Sales ($ mil): 623

Dividends
  Yield: —
  Payout: 80.5%
  Market value ($ mil.): —

Hyundai Motor Co., Ltd.

South Korea's leading carmaker Hyundai Motor produces compact and luxury cars SUVs minivans trucks buses and other commercial vehicles. Its cars are sold in 200 countries and produces more than 3.7 million units. Hyundai generates more than one-third of its sales in South Korea but its vehicles are also popular in emerging markets such as China and India. The company operates a dozen manufacturing plants in Brazil China the Czech Republic India Russia Turkey and the US.

Operations

The company has vehicle segment finance segment and others segment. The vehicle segment is engaged in the manufacturing and sale of motor vehicles. The finance segment operates vehicle financing credit card processing and other financing activities. Others segment includes the R&D train manufacturing and other activities.

Geographic Reach

Headquartered in Seoul South Korea. Hyundai's geographic areas are in Asia (excluding South Korea) North America and Europe. South Korea generates about 40% of total sales while North America brings in more than a third of total sales Europe gives about 15% of total sales and Asia and other countries generates about 10% of total sales combined. Hyundai have manufacturing plants in India Indonesia the Czech Republic Russia Turkey Singapore and Brazil.

Financial Performance

The company's sales in 2020 decreased to ?104.0 trillion compared to ?105.7 trillion in the prior year.

Profit in 2020 ?1.9 trillion compared with ?3.2 trillion.

Cash held by the company at the end of 2020 increased to ?9.9 trillion. Cash provided by financing activities was ?11.4 trillion while cash used for operations and investing activities ?409.8 billion and ?9.3 trillion.

Strategy

Hyundai Motor has updated its 2025 Strategy to reflect a rapidly accelerating digital transformation and energy shift in the automobile industry and customer needs and wants that have made the issue of ESG governance increasingly important. In addition to its already-existing smart mobility devices and services the company is developing medium- to long-term strategies involving the growth of its new "H2 Solutions" fuel cell-based hydrogen enterprise.

The company is committed to seeking balanced growth and enhancing its operating abilities by instituting strategies to enhance its competitiveness and add to its leadership in the field of electrification within the finished vehicle business; building a foundation for its mobility services business; and enhancing its leadership in the hydrogen ecosystem. It is also committed to becoming an early leader in the fuel cell-based hydrogen market that will help it achieve its vision of becoming smart mobility solutions provider.

Hyundai Motor will expand global sales of high-margin models from Genesis as well as various SUV models while reducing production costs by paring down fixed costs and expanding the application of common modular components. Hyundai Motor will also continuously strengthen its digital-based innovation efforts throughout the entire value chain. In order to elevate quality competitiveness ? the fundamental capability of any automaker.

To secure future business competitiveness and leadership in the competitive global electrified mobility market Hyundai Motor will drastically strengthen its electrified vehicle lineup. As part of this transition the company successfully launched in April 2021 its first dedicated EV the IONIQ 5 which is equipped with a dedicated EV platform the E-GMP (Electric Global Modular Platform). The company are also striving constantly to provide new value to our customers by offering specialized EV-based service packages.

HISTORY

Hyundai Motor Company was established in 1967 and it initially began manufacturing cars and light trucks through a technology collaboration with Ford's UK operations. By the early 1970s Hyundai was ready to build cars under its own nameplate. The company debuted the subcompact Hyundai Pony in 1974 at Italy's annual Turin Motor Show.

The Pony was an instant domestic success and soon propelled Hyundai to the top spot among South Korea's carmakers. During the mid-1970s the company began exporting the Pony to El Salvador and Guatemala.

By the 1980s Hyundai was ready to shift into high gear and begin high-volume production in anticipation of penetrating more overseas markets. The company began exporting to Canada in 1983.

Hyundai introduced the Hyundai Excel in 1985. That year the company established its US subsidiary Hyundai Motor America. By 1986 Hyundai was exporting Excels for sale in the US. Sales of the Excel soared the next year so Hyundai decided to build a factory in Bromont Quebec.

But by the time the factory was finished in 1989 consumers were tiring of the aging compact car and the quality problems that came with it. Hyundai closed the plant after just four years of operation.

The company introduced its first sports car the Scoupe in 1990. The following year it developed the first Hyundai-designed engine called the Alpha.

Two years later the carmaker unveiled its second-generation proprietary engine the Beta.

By 1998 Hyundai was beginning to feel the pinch of the Asian economic crisis as domestic demand dropped drastically. However the decrease in Korean demand was largely offset by exports. That year Hyundai took a controlling stake in Korean competitor Kia Motors.

In hopes of increasing its share of the Asian automotive market Daimler AG took a 10% stake in Hyundai in 2000 (sold 2004). The deal included the establishment of a joint venture to manufacture commercial vehicles as well as an agreement among Hyundai Daimler and Mitsubishi Motors to develop small cars for the global market.

In 2001 Hyundai decreased its stake in Kia Motors to about 46%.

The following year Daimler announced it would exercise its option to take a 50% stake in Hyundai's heavy truck business.

In 2004 Hyundai CEO Kim Dong-Jin was indicted in South Korea on charges that he violated campaign finance laws and engaged in managerial negligence. The charges stemmed from a general crackdown on campaign finance violations during which more than a dozen members of South Korea's parliament were either indicted or detained. Later in 2004 Kim was convicted of the charges against him and sentenced to a suspended two-year prison term.

To increase its presence in the US Hyundai completed construction of a new manufacturing plant Hyundai Motor Manufacturing Alabama in 2005. The plant's annual production was about 300000 cars.

In 2006 Hyundai's legal woes persisted when two executives were arrested as part of a Korean bribery investigation. The pair were accused of creating a slush fund that was allegedly used to fund a lobbyist who sought favors for Hyundai from the South Korean government. Officials were also investigating whether the slush fund was created at the behest of Hyundai chairman Chung Mong-Koo.

Chung then was indicted and arrested on charges that he embezzled Hyundai company cash to finance bribes for Korean government officials in exchange for corporate favors. After two months of incarceration Chung was released from jail on $1 million bail.

He was convicted early in 2007. Under Korean law Chung faced a potential life sentence but received only a three-year prison term as the judge in the case said Chung contributed hugely to the development of the Korean economy. During his trial Chung admitted some wrongdoing when he said "I admit to my guilt to some extent." However Chung appealed the conviction. Three other Hyundai officials were also convicted but they received suspended sentences. Chung's son Kia Motors boss Chung Eui-Sun also was under investigation but prosecutors did not indict him.

Later in 2007 Chung's three-year prison sentence was suspended by an appeals court with a three-judge panel citing his importance to Korea's economy. The appellate judges however required the Hyundai executive to maintain a clean record for five years to avoid prison and to fulfill a promise he made to donate $1.1 billion of his personal assets to society.

EXECUTIVES

Co-President, Co-Chief Executive Officer, Director, Eon Tae Ha

Co-President, Jeong Guk Park

Co-President, Chief Operating Officer, Jose Munoz

Non-Executive Independent Director, Chi Won Yoon

Non-Executive Independent Director, Sang Seung Lee

Auditors: KPMG Samjong Accounting Corp.

LOCATIONS

HQ: Hyundai Motor Co., Ltd.
 12, Heolleung-ro Seocho-gu, Seoul 06797
Phone: (82) 2 3464 1114   **Fax:** (82) 2 3463 3484
Web: www.hyundai-motor.com

2018 Sales

	% of total
South Korea	16
Overseas	84
Total	**100**

PRODUCTS/OPERATIONS

Selected Models

Commercial vehicles
  Aero (large city bus)
  Aero Town (medium bus)
  County (small bus)
  e-Mighty (light commercial truck)
  Super Aero City (bus)
  Universe (large coach bus)
Passenger cars
  Accent (compact coupe)
  Atos Prime (subcompact)
  Avante XD
  Azera (sedan)
  Elantra (sedan)
  Entourage (minivan)
  Equus/Centennial (premium sedan)
  Genesis (premium coupe)
  Getz (compact sedan)
  Santa Fe (SUV)
  Sonata (sedan)
  Tiburon (coupe)
  Tucson (SUV)
  Trajet (SUV)
  Veracruz (SUV)

COMPETITORS

ALLISON TRANSMISSION HOLDINGS INC.
APTIV PLC
Continental AG
DANA INCORPORATED
FCA US LLC
KIA CORPORATION
MANN+HUMMEL FILTRATION TECHNOLOGY
 INTERMEDIATE HOLDINGS
Mercedes-Benz Group AG
Rheinmetall AG
SUBARU CORPORATION
TOYOTA BOSHOKU CORPORATION
VOLKSWAGEN AG

HISTORICAL FINANCIALS

Company Type: Public

Income Statement				FYE: December 31
	REVENUE ($ mil.)	NET INCOME ($ mil.)	NET PROFIT MARGIN	EMPLOYEES
12/20	95,557	1,308	1.4%	0
12/19	91,585	2,580	2.8%	0
12/18	86,836	1,352	1.6%	0
12/17	90,399	3,782	4.2%	68,590
12/16	77,952	4,500	5.8%	67,517
Annual Growth	5.2%	(26.6%)	—	—

2020 Year-End Financials

Debt ratio: 0.0%   No. of shares (mil.): 200
Return on equity: 2.0%   Dividends
Cash ($ mil.): 9,061   Yield: 3.8%
Current ratio: 1.41   Payout: 73.3%
Long-term debt ($ mil.): 56,528   Market value ($ mil.): —

IA Financial Corp Inc

Industrial Alliance Insurance and Financial Services (iA Financial Group) is one of the largest insurance and wealth management groups in Canada with operations in the United States. The company sells life health and disability insurance as well as retirement savings plans and annuities to individuals and employers across the country. To a much lesser extent it offers life insurance products in parts of the US. The group manages mutual funds through its IA Clarington unit and it brokers securities and funds through Investia FundEX Investments and iA Securities. iA Financial Group also sells auto and homeowners insurance. Its products are distributed by more than 25000 representatives.

EXECUTIVES

Independent Director, Mario Albert
Executive Vice President - Group Benefits and Retirement Solutions, Eric Jobin
Executive Vice-President, Corporate Development, Lilia Sham
President, Industrial Alliance Auto, Home Insurance and Prysm General Insurance, François Blais
President and Chief Executive Officer, Denis Ricard, $708,498 total compensation
Executive Vice President - Corporate Strategy, Chief Growth Officer, Michael Stickney, $464,289 total compensation
Executive Vice President - Client and Employee Experience, Jean-Francois Boulet
Independent Chairman of the Board, Jacques Martin
Executive Vice-President, Chief Actuary and CFO, Jacques Potvin, $343,808 total compensation
Independent Director, Marc Poulin
Executive Vice President - Information Technology and Investment Operations, Pierre Miron
Independent Director, Nicolas Darveau - Garneau
Independent Director, Benoit Daignault
Independent Director, Monique Mercier
Executive Vice President - Wealth Management, Sean O'Brien
Executive Vice President, Chief Investment Officer, Alain Bergeron, $420,624 total compensation
Independent Director, Ginette Maillee
Auditors: Deloitte LLP

LOCATIONS

HQ: IA Financial Corp Inc
1080, Grande Allee West, P.O. 1907 Station Terminus, Quebec City, Quebec G1K 7M3
Phone: 418 684-5000   **Fax:** 418 684-5185
Web: www.ia.ca

PRODUCTS/OPERATIONS

2017 Sales by Segment

	% of total
Individual Insurance	36
Individual Wealth Management	30
Group Savings and Retirement	16
Group Insurance	15
Other	3
Total	**100**

Selected Subsidiaries

FundEX Investments Inc. (mutual fund broker)
IA American Life Insurance Company (US)
IA Clarington Investments Inc. (mutual fund management and promotion)
Investia Financial Services Inc. (mutual fund broker)

Solicour Inc. (financial services brokerage)
The Excellence Life Insurance Company (life and health insurance)

COMPETITORS

CINCINNATI FINANCIAL CORPORATION
CMFG LIFE INSURANCE COMPANY
CNO FINANCIAL GROUP INC.
METLIFE INC.
MS&AD INSURANCE GROUP HOLDINGS INC.
PACIFIC LIFE INSURANCE COMPANY
PRINCIPAL FINANCIAL GROUP INC.
SYMETRA FINANCIAL CORPORATION
UNITED OF OMAHA LIFE INSURANCE COMPANY
VOYA SERVICES COMPANY
WESTERN & SOUTHERN FINANCIAL GROUP INC.

HISTORICAL FINANCIALS

Company Type: Public

Income Statement

	ASSETS ($ mil.)	NET INCOME ($ mil.)	INCOME AS % OF ASSETS	EMPLOYEES
12/21	74,321	668	0.9%	0
12/20	67,909	497	0.7%	0
12/19	56,173	544	1.0%	6,800
12/18	46,659	465	1.0%	0
12/17	49,381	423	0.9%	6,115
Annual Growth	**10.8%**	**12.1%**	**—**	**—**

FYE: December 31

2021 Year-End Financials

Return on assets: 0.9%
Return on equity: 12.3%
Long-term debt ($ mil.): —
No. of shares (mil.): 107
Sales ($ mil): 12,158
Dividends
Yield: 0.0%
Payout: 27.0%
Market value ($ mil.): 6,116

	STOCK PRICE ($) FY Close	P/E High/Low		Earnings	Dividends	Book Value
12/21	56.86	8	5	6.05	1.63	52.89
12/20	46.16	10	5	4.48	1.52	47.78
12/19	32.01	5	5	4.91	1.36	44.01
12/18	31.50	8	5	4.10	1.17	38.67
12/17	47.22	10	9	3.84	1.14	38.38
Annual Growth	**4.8%**	**—**	**—**	**12.0%**	**9.4%**	**8.3%**

Iberdrola SA

Auditors: KPMG Auditores, S.L.

LOCATIONS

HQ: Iberdrola SA
Plaza Euskadi 5, Bilbao 48009
Phone: (34) 944 151 411   **Fax:** (34) 944 663 194
Web: www.iberdrola.com

HISTORICAL FINANCIALS

Company Type: Public

Income Statement

	REVENUE ($ mil.)	NET INCOME ($ mil.)	NET PROFIT MARGIN	EMPLOYEES
12/20	40,678	4,431	10.9%	35,637
12/19	40,911	3,824	9.3%	34,306
12/18	40,168	3,451	8.6%	34,078
12/17	37,476	3,361	9.0%	28,750
12/16	30,848	2,856	9.3%	28,389
Annual Growth	**7.2%**	**11.6%**	**—**	**5.8%**

FYE: December 31

2020 Year-End Financials

Debt ratio: 38.1%
Return on equity: 9.8%
Cash ($ mil.): 4,205
Current ratio: 0.83
Long-term debt ($ mil.): 37,228
No. of shares (mil.): —
Dividends
Yield: 2.5%
Payout: 235.6%
Market value ($ mil.): —

	STOCK PRICE ($) FY Close	P/E High/Low	Earnings	Dividends	Book Value
12/20	57.50	105 70	0.67	1.45	6.94
12/19	41.31	82 59	0.59	1.23	6.65
12/18	32.09	69 56	0.53	1.22	6.86
12/17	30.94	80 63	0.53	1.20	7.03
12/16	26.23	66 54	0.44	0.91	6.18
Annual Growth	**21.7%**	**—**	**10.9%**	**12.2%**	**2.9%**

ICICI Bank Ltd (India)

ICICI Bank is a large private sector bank in India offering a diversified portfolio of financial products and services to retail SME and corporate customers and boasts around 15.7 trillion rupees in assets. The bank has approximately 5265 branches nationwide. Its Retail SME and rural banking group offers deposit credit and other financial products and services to individuals households and small businesses across India through its digital channels and extensive branch network spanning urban and rural areas while Wholesale Banking offers financial solutions to large and medium-sized companies and their business and channel partners and to financial and government/public sector entities. Its International Banking unit deals with the bank's foreign operations and international trade finance-related service. Almost all of its sales were generated domestically.

Operations

ICICI operates in segments including: Retail Banking (around 30% of sales) Treasury (over 25%) Life Insurance (nearly 20%) Wholesale Banking (some 15%) and General Insurance (some 5%). Other banking and others account for the rest.

Retail banking includes exposures of the Bank which satisfy the four criteria of orientation product granularity and low value of individual exposures for retail exposures laid down in Basel Committee on Banking Supervision document "International Convergence of Capital Measurement and Capital Standards: A Revised Framework". This segment also includes income from credit cards debit cards third party product distribution and the associated costs.

Treasury includes the entire investment and derivative portfolio of the Bank and ICICI Strategic Investments Fund. Life insurance represents results of ICICI Prudential Life Insurance Company Limited.

Wholesale banking includes all advances to trusts partnership firms companies and statutory bodies by the bank which are not included under Retail banking.

General insurance represents results of ICICI Lombard General Insurance Company Limited.

Other banking includes leasing operations and other items not attributable to any particular business segment of the bank.

Overall interest income generated some 55% of sales. Other income accounts for the rest.

Geographic Reach

Mumbai-based ICICI generates almost all of its total revenue in its home country. The bank has an international presence through its ICICI Bank UK and ICICI Bank Canada subsidiaries in the UK and Canada respectively. It also has branches in the US China Singapore Hong Kong Dubai Sri Lanka Bahrain and South Africa.

Sales and Marketing

ICICI's customers can execute their trade finance and foreign exchange transactions through the Trade Online and FXOnline.

Financial Performance

The company's revenue for fiscal 2021 increased to ?1.81 trillion compared with ?1.76 trillion in the prior year.

Profit for fiscal 2021 increased to ?161.9 billion compared to ?79.3 billion in the prior year.

Cash held by the company at the end of fiscal 2021 increased to ?1.3 trillion. Cash provided by operations was `1.2 trillion while investing and financing activities used ?534.9 billion and ?488.8 billion respectively. Main cash used were repayment of short-term and long-term borrowings and purchase of held-to-maturity securities.

Strategy

The retail business continued to be a key driver of growth in fiscal 2021 as the company pursued a strategy of building a diversified and granular loan portfolio. The focus in the retail business was on understanding and fulfilling customer needs to be underpinned by personalized banking simple banking fair banking and strong risk management.

During fiscal 2021 with challenges posed by the Covid-19 pandemic the company responded quickly to enable customers to meet their financial requirements safely. About 97% of the company's branches were functional with reduced working hours during the months of lockdown in April-May 2020.

The company focuses on creating holistic value propositions for its customers by having a 360-degree customer centric approach and capturing opportunities across customer ecosystems leveraging internal synergies building partnerships and decongesting processes. Cross-functional teams have been created to tap into key customer and market segments enabling 360-degree coverage of customers and increasing wallet share. The company has also delayered its organizational structure and empowered teams at the local level to create flexibility and agility in capturing business opportunities. This improves the ability of the Bank to connect with customers and respond to their needs.

EXECUTIVES

Managing Director and Chief Executive Officer, Executive Director, Sandeep Bakhshi

Executive Director, Sandeep Batra, $299,335 total compensation

Non-Executive Independent Director, Radhakrishnan Nair

Non-Executive Independent Director, B. Sriram

Company Secretary, Ranganath Athreya, $214,999 total compensation

Additional Independent Director, Vibha Rishi

Interim Chairman, Chandra Chaturvedi

Auditors: KPMG Assurance and Consulting Services LLP

LOCATIONS

HQ: ICICI Bank Ltd (India)
ICICI Bank Towers, Bandra-Kurla Complex, Mumbai 400051
Phone: (91) 22 33667777   **Fax:** (91) 22 26531122
Web: www.icicibank.com

PRODUCTS/OPERATIONS

2015 Sales by Segment

	% of total
Treasury	39
Wholesale Banking	30
Retail Banking	30
Other Banking	1
Total	**100**

COMPETITORS

AXIS BANK LIMITED
BARCLAYS BANK PLC
Banco Bradesco S/A
Bank of Communications Co. Ltd.
CHINA MINSHENG BANKING CORP. LTD.
China Construction Bank Corporation
HDFC BANK LIMITED
HYDROGEN GROUP PLC
IMPELLAM GROUP PLC
Industrial And Commercial Bank Of China Limited
KORN FERRY
MITSUBISHI UFJ FINANCIAL GROUP INC.
NATIONAL AUSTRALIA BANK LIMITED
PARITY GROUP PUBLIC LIMITED COMPANY
QATAR NATIONAL BANK (Q.P.S.C.)
ROBERT WALTERS PLC
STANDARD BANK GROUP LTD
STATE BANK OF INDIA
Shanghai Pudong Development Bank Co.Ltd.
YORKSHIRE BANK PUBLIC LIMITED COMPANY

HISTORICAL FINANCIALS

Company Type: Public

Income Statement				FYE: March 31
	ASSETS ($ mil.)	NET INCOME ($ mil.)	INCOME AS % OF ASSETS	EMPLOYEES
03/21	215,098	2,512	1.2%	130,170
03/20	182,339	1,266	0.7%	131,232
03/19	179,030	614	0.3%	117,340
03/18	172,804	1,185	0.7%	112,360
03/17	152,046	1,571	1.0%	107,971
Annual Growth	9.1%	12.5%	—	4.8%

2021 Year-End Financials

Return on assets: 1.2%
Return on equity: 13.1%
Long-term debt ($ mil.): —
No. of shares (mil.): —
Sales ($ mil): 22,050

Dividends
Yield: 0.0%
Payout: —
Market value ($ mil.): —

	STOCK PRICE ($) FY Close	P/E High/Low		PER SHARE ($) Earnings	Dividends	Book Value
03/21	16.03	1	0	0.37	0.00	3.11
03/20	8.50	1	0	0.19	0.07	2.51
03/19	11.46	2	1	0.09	0.04	2.56
03/18	8.85	1	1	0.18	0.07	2.65
03/17	8.60	1	0	0.27	0.14	2.77
Annual Growth	16.8%	—	—	8.1%	—	2.9%

Idemitsu Kosan Co Ltd

Idemitsu Kosan is a Japanese petrochemical corporation founded in 1911. At its refineries in Japan (processing some 969000 barrels per day) Idemitsu Kosan produces petroleum products such as gasoline and other fuels kerosene and lubricants. It markets its fuel products through a network of approximately 6300 service stations. Idemitsu Kosan sells heavy oil and jet fuels to in-

dustries and kerosene and liquefied petroleum gas to the residential sector. The company also has interests in oil exploration and production as well as coal and uranium. Majority of the company's revenue is generated in Japan.

Operations

Idemitsu Kosan has five reportable segments: petroleum basic chemicals functional materials power and renewable energy and resources.

Its petroleum business accounts for nearly 80% of the company's total revenue includes fuel oil and petrochemical products. It has a crude oil processing capacity of 945000 barrels per day and manages some 20 ships.

Basic chemicals products and functional materials bring in more than 5% each. Basic chemicals include production sales and others of olefin/aroma products. It has an ethylene production capacity of 1 million tons per year and BTX production capacity of 2.5 million tons per year. Functional materials include lubricants performance chemicals electronic materials high functional asphalt and agricultural biotechnology products business it has.

Geographic Reach

Idemitsu Kosan has offices in Africa Asia (East South East and South West) Australia Europe (including Russia) the Middle East and North and South America. Headquartered in Japan (the company's largest market representing about 75% of the total sales) the company generates more than 15% of sales in Asia and Oceania approximately 5% in North America other countries account for the remaining.

Financial Performance

The company's revenue for fiscal 2021 decreased to 4.6 billion compared from the prior year with 6.0 billion.

Net income for fiscal 2021 was 34.9 billion compared from the prior year with a net loss of 22.9 billion.

Cash held by the company at the end of fiscal 2021 increased to 131.0 billion. Cash provided by operations was 170.5 billion while cash used for investing and financing activities were 109.9 billion and 56.2 billion respectively. Main uses of cash were purchases of tangible fixed assets and repayments of long-term debt.

Company Background

Pooling their LPG resources and expertise in 2006 Idemitsu Kosan merged its LPG operations with those of Mitsubishi to form Astomos Energy.

EXECUTIVES

President, Executive President, Chief Executive Officer, Representative Director, Shunichi Kito

Executive Vice President, Vice President, Representative Director, Takashi Matsushita

Executive Vice President, Vice President, Representative Director, Susumu Nibuya

Chief Financial Officer, Managing Executive Officer, Director, Noriaki Sakai

Managing Executive Officer, Director, Atsuhiko Hirano

Non-Executive Director, Masakazu Idemitsu

Independent Director, Yumiko Noda

Independent Director, Maki Kado

Independent Director, Mitsunobu Koshiba

Independent Director, Kazunari Kubohara

Independent Director, Takeo Kikkawa

Auditors: Deloitte Touche Tohmatsu LLC

LOCATIONS

HQ: Idemitsu Kosan Co Ltd
3-1-1 Marunouchi, Chiyoda-ku, Tokyo 100-8321
Phone: (81) 3 3213 3150
Web: www.idss.co.jp

2016 Sales

	% of total
Japan	75
Asia and Oceania	16
North America	6
Europe	2
Other	1
Total	**100**

PRODUCTS/OPERATIONS

2016 Sales

	% of total
Petroleum products	77
Petrochemical products	15
Resources	6
Others	2
Total	**100**

Products & Services

Agri-Bio
Electronic Materials
Lubricants
Packing Materials Logistics Plastics
Petrochemicals
Petroleum Transportation
Refinery & Plant
Renewable Energy
Research & Development
Resource Development
SUBSIDIARIES
AltaGas Idemitsu Joint Venture Limited Partnership
Apolloretailing Co.Ltd.
Astomos Energy Corp.
Formosa Idemitsu Petrochemicals Corporation
Idemitsu Apollo Corporation
Idemitsu Australia Resources Pty Ltd
Idemitsu Canada Corporation
Idemitsu Canada Resoucves Ltd.
Idemitsu Credit Co. Ltd.
Idemitsu Engineering Co. Ltd.
Idemitsu Insurance Service Co.Ltd.
Idemitsu International (Asia) Pte.Ltd.
Idemitsu Oita Geothermal Co.Ltd.
Idemitsu Petroleum Norge AS
Idemitsu Petroleum UK Ltd.
Idemitsu Retail Marketing Co. Ltd.
Idemitsu SM (Malaysia) Sdn.Bhd.
Idemitsu Tanker Co. Ltd.
Idemitsu Unitech Co. Ltd.
Nghi Son Refinery and Petrochemical LLC
Prime Polymer Co. Ltd.
PS Japan Corp.
SDS Biotech K.K.

COMPETITORS

AMPOL LIMITED
BHARAT PETROLEUM CORPORATION LIMITED
CALUMET SPECIALTY PRODUCTS PARTNERS L.P.
COSMO OIL CO. LTD.
CVR ENERGY INC.
GLENCORE PLC
Imperial Oil Limited
KINDER MORGAN INC
MANGALORE REFINERY AND PETROCHEMICALS
 LIMITED
NGL ENERGY PARTNERS LP
OIL REFINERIES LTD
PHILLIPS 66
REPSOL SA.
RS ENERGY K.K.
SASOL LTD
Suncor Energy Inc
TURKIYE PETROL RAFINERILERI ANONIM SIRKETI

Iida Group Holdings Co., Ltd.

Auditors: Ernst & Young ShinNihon LLC

LOCATIONS

HQ: Iida Group Holdings Co., Ltd.
 1-2-11 Nishikubo, Musashino, Tokyo 180-0013
Phone: (81) 422 60 8888
Web: www.ighd.co.jp

HISTORICAL FINANCIALS

Company Type: Public

Income Statement   FYE: March 31

	REVENUE ($ mil.)	NET INCOME ($ mil.)	NET PROFIT MARGIN	EMPLOYEES
03/21	13,151	752	5.7%	10,134
03/20	12,915	495	3.8%	9,693
03/19	12,145	591	4.9%	8,561
03/18	12,575	654	5.2%	7,736
03/17	11,023	686	6.2%	7,041
Annual Growth	**4.5%**	**2.3%**	**—**	**9.5%**

2021 Year-End Financials

Debt ratio: 0.2%
Return on equity: 10.0%
Cash ($ mil.): 4,972
Current ratio: 2.88
Long-term debt ($ mil.): 1,808

No. of shares (mil.): 288
Dividends
  Yield: —
  Payout: —
Market value ($ mil.): —

Imperial Brands PLC

Auditors: Ernst & Young LLP

LOCATIONS

HQ: Imperial Brands PLC
 121 Winterstoke Road, Bristol BS3 2LL
Phone: (44) 117 963 6636
Web: www.imperialbrandsplc.com

HISTORICAL FINANCIALS

Company Type: Public

Income Statement   FYE: March 31

	REVENUE ($ mil.)	NET INCOME ($ mil.)	NET PROFIT MARGIN	EMPLOYEES
03/21	41,152	315	0.8%	19,075
03/20	55,696	(211)	—	18,273
03/19	39,958	735	1.8%	13,398
03/18	35,133	1,528	4.4%	12,657
03/17	28,534	788	2.8%	12,655
Annual Growth	**9.6%**	**(20.5%)**	**—**	**10.8%**

2021 Year-End Financials

Debt ratio: 0.2%
Return on equity: 3.0%
Cash ($ mil.): 1,186
Current ratio: 1.03
Long-term debt ($ mil.): 6,660

No. of shares (mil.): 297
Dividends
  Yield: —
  Payout: —
Market value ($ mil.): —

Imperial Oil Ltd

Imperial Oil Canada's fifth-largest oil integrated company behind Canadian Natural Resources holds sway over a vast empire of oil and gas resources. Imperial is one of Canada's top natural gas producers a leading refiner and marketer of petroleum products and a major supplier of petrochemicals. It sells petroleum products including gasoline heating oil and diesel fuel under the Esso name and other brand names. The company reported proved reserves in 2019 of about 3.5 billion barrels of oil-equivalent including nearly 40 million barrels of liquids about 580 billion cu. ft. of natural gas approximately 415 million barrels of synthetic oil and roughly 3 billion barrels of bitumen. Exxon Mobil owns about 70% of Imperial.

Operations

Imperial has three main segments: Downstream Upstream and Chemical.

Downstream operations (almost 70%) consist of the transportation and refining of crude oil blending of refined products and the distribution and marketing of those products. Its Upstream operations (almost 30%) include the exploration for and production of crude oil natural gas synthetic oil and bitumen. The company's Chemical operations consist of the manufacturing and marketing of various petrochemicals such as ethylene benzene aromatic and aliphatic solvents plasticizer intermediates and polyethylene resin.

In addition to its conventional upstream operations Imperial owns 25% of Syncrude Canada which operates the world's largest oil sands development with synthetic oil and bitumen/heavy oil end products.

The Downstream segment owns and operates three refineries. The Strathcona and Sarnia refineries process Canadian crude oil and the Nanticoke refinery processes a combination of Canadian and foreign crude oil. The Strathcona refinery op-

HISTORICAL FINANCIALS

Company Type: Public

Income Statement   FYE: September 30

	REVENUE ($ mil.)	NET INCOME ($ mil.)	NET PROFIT MARGIN	EMPLOYEES
09/20	41,773	1,917	4.6%	32,500
09/19	38,895	1,243	3.2%	32,700
09/18	39,809	1,784	4.5%	33,300
09/17	40,504	1,886	4.7%	33,800
09/16	35,803	817	2.3%	33,900
Annual Growth	**3.9%**	**23.8%**	**—**	**(1.0%)**

2020 Year-End Financials

Debt ratio: 46.2%
Return on equity: 30.4%
Cash ($ mil.): 2,085
Current ratio: 0.78
Long-term debt ($ mil.): 13,098

No. of shares (mil.): 946
Dividends
  Yield: 13.2%
  Payout: 115.5%
Market value ($ mil.): 16,751

	STOCK PRICE ($) FY Close	P/E High/Low		PER SHARE ($) Earnings	Dividends	Book Value
09/20	17.70	17	10	2.03	2.35	6.60
09/19	22.60	32	21	1.30	2.45	6.39
09/18	34.71	30	21	1.87	2.30	7.89
09/17	43.27	37	29	1.97	2.14	7.97
09/16	51.47	162	76	0.86	1.39	7.18
Annual Growth	**(23.4%)**	**—**	**—**	**24.1%**	**14.1%**	**(2.1%)**

erates lubricating oil production facilities. The company maintains a nationwide distribution system to handle bulk and packaged petroleum products moving from refineries to market by pipeline tanker rail and road transport It also owns and operates natural gas liquids and products pipelines in Alberta Manitoba and Ontario and has interests in the capital stock of one crude oil and two products pipeline companies.

Geographic Reach

Most of the company's production comes from fields in Alberta and the Northwest Territories. The company operates its business in Canada.

Sales and Marketing

The company sells gasoline to motorists at more than 2300 primarily Esso-branded gas stations across Canada.

It markets almost 500 petroleum products throughout Canada to all types of customers. It also serves the Canadian agriculture residential heating and small commercial markets and sells petroleum products to large industrial and commercial accounts as well as to other refiners and marketers.

Financial Performance

Net income in 2019 was C$2.2 billion compared to net income of C$2.3 million in 2018. The 2019 results include a favorable impact largely non-cash of C$662 million associated with the Alberta corporate income tax rate decrease. In June 2019 the Alberta government enacted a 4% decrease in the provincial tax rate from 12% to 8% by 2022.

Cash held by the company at the end of 2019 increased by C$730 million to C$1.7 billion. Cash provided by operations was C$4.4 billion while cash used for investing and financing activities were C$1.7 billion and C$2.0 billion respectively. Cash usage was primarily for additions to property plant and equipment and common shares purchased.

Strategy

Imperial's Upstream business strategies guide the company's exploration development production research and gas marketing activities. These strategies include maximizing asset reliability accelerating development and application of high impact technologies maximizing value by capturing new business opportunities and managing the existing portfolio as well as pursuing sustainable improvements in organizational efficiency and effectiveness. These strategies are underpinned by a relentless focus on operations integrity commitment to innovative technologies disciplined approach to investing and cost management development of employees and investment in the communities within which the company operates.

Imperial's Downstream business strategies competitively position the company across a range of market conditions. These strategies include targeting industry leading performance in reliability safety and operations integrity as well as maximizing value from advanced technologies capitalizing on integration across Imperial's businesses selectively investing for resilient and advantaged returns operating efficiently and effectively and providing quality valued and differentiated products and services to customers.

HISTORY

London Ontario boomed from the discovery of oil in the 1860s and 1870s but when the market for Canadian kerosene became saturated in 1880 16 refiners banded together to form the Imperial Oil Company.

The company refined sulfurous Canadian oil nicknamed "skunk oil" for its powerful smell. Imperial faced tough competition from America's Standard Oil which marketed kerosene made from lighter less-odorous Pennsylvania crude. Guided by American expatriate Jacob Englehart Imperial built a better refinery and hired a chemist to develop a process to clean sulfur from the crude.

By the mid-1890s Imperial had expanded from coast to Canadian coast. Cash-starved from its expansion the company turned to old nemesis Standard Oil which bought a controlling interest in Imperial in 1898. That interest is today held by Exxon Mobil.

After the turn of the century Imperial began producing gasoline to serve the new automobiles. The horseless carriages were spooking the workhorses at the warehouse where fuel was sold so an Imperial manager in Vancouver opened the first Canadian service station in 1907. The company marketed its gas under the Esso banner borrowed from Standard Oil.

An Imperial crew discovered oil in 1920 at Norman Wells in the remote Northwest Territories. In 1924 a subsidiary sparked a new boom with a gas well discovery in the Turner Valley area northeast of Edmonton. But soon Imperial's luck ran as dry as the holes it was drilling; it came away empty from the next 133 consecutive wells. That string ended in 1947 when it struck oil in Alberta at the Leduc No. 1. To get the oil to market Imperial invested in the Interprovincial Pipe Line from Alberta to Superior Wisconsin.

The company began research in 1964 to extract bitumen from the oil sands in Cold Lake Alberta. During the 1970s oil crisis Imperial continued to search for oil in northern Canada. It found crude on land near the Beaufort Sea (1970) and in its icy waters (1972). The company formed its Esso Resources Canadian Ltd. subsidiary in 1978 to oversee natural resources production.

In 1989 Texaco (acquired by Chevron in 2001) still reeling from a court battle with Pennzoil sold Texaco Canada to Imperial. To diminish debt and comply with regulators Imperial agreed to sell some of Texaco Canada's refining and marketing assets in Atlantic Canada its interests in Interhome Energy and oil and gas properties in western Canada.

Imperial reorganized in 1992 centralizing several units and in 1993 closed its refinery at Port Moody British Columbia. It sold most of its fertilizer business in 1994 disposed of 339 unprofitable gas stations in 1995 and the next year closed down Canada's northernmost oil refinery at Norman Wells.

In 1997 Imperial announced an ambitious program to expand Syncrude's oil sands bitumen upgrading plant. In 1998 Exxon agreed to buy Mobil which had substantial Canadian oil assets. In 1999 Canada preapproved the potential merger of Imperial Oil and Mobil Canada. Later that year Exxon completed its purchase of Mobil to form Exxon Mobil.

Expanding its exploration and production assets in 2007 Imperial and ExxonMobil Canada acquired exploration rights for a development parcel in the Beaufort Sea and in 2008 in the Horn River area of northeastern British Columbia.

EXECUTIVES

Independent Director, David Cornhill
Vice President - Imperial Oil downstream and manager, western Canada fuels, Jonathan Wetmore
Vice President, General Counsel, Corporate Secretary, Ian Laing
Senior Vice President - Finance and Administration, Controller, Daniel Lyons, $514,076 total compensation
Chairman of the Board, President, Chief Executive Officer, Bradley Corson, $743,351 total compensation
Senior Vice President - Upstream, Simon Younger, $393,123 total compensation
Treasurer, Kitty Lee
Vice President - Commercial and Corporate Development, Sherri Evers
Independent Director, Jack Mintz
Independent Director, Krystyna Hoeg
Assistant controller, Bruce Jolly, $331,502 total compensation
Independent Director, David Sutherland
Independent Director, Miranda Hubbs
Vice President of Human Resources, Kristi Desjardins
Auditors: PricewaterhouseCoopers LLP

LOCATIONS

HQ: Imperial Oil Ltd
505 Quarry Park Boulevard S.E., Calgary, Alberta T2C 5N1
Phone: 587 476-3740   **Fax:** 587 476-1166
Web: www.imperialoil.ca

PRODUCTS/OPERATIONS

2016 Sales

	% of total
Downstream	74
Upstream	22
Chemical	4
Total	**100**

COMPETITORS

DELEK US ENERGY INC.
ENEOS HOLDINGS INC.
EXXON MOBIL CORPORATION
GENESIS ENERGY L.P.
HELLENIC PETROLEUM S.A. HOLDING
IDEMITSU KOSAN CO.LTD.
MARATHON OIL CORPORATION
ROYAL DUTCH SHELL plc
SURGUTNEFTEGAZ PAO
WESTERN REFINING INC.

HISTORICAL FINANCIALS

Company Type: Public

Income Statement				FYE: December 31
	REVENUE ($ mil.)	NET INCOME ($ mil.)	NET PROFIT MARGIN	EMPLOYEES
12/20	17,583	(1,458)	—	5,800
12/19	26,187	1,689	6.5%	6,000
12/18	25,774	1,699	6.6%	5,700
12/17	23,471	390	1.7%	5,400
12/16	20,297	1,606	7.9%	5,600
Annual Growth	(3.5%)	—	—	0.9%

2020 Year-End Financials

Debt ratio: 10.7%
Return on equity: (-8.1%)
Cash ($ mil.): 605
Current ratio: 1.34
Long-term debt ($ mil.): 3,893

No. of shares (mil.): 734
Dividends
  Yield: 3.4%
  Payout: —
Market value ($ mil.): 13,969

	STOCK PRICE ($) FY Close	P/E High/Low		PER SHARE ($) Earnings	Dividends	Book Value
12/20	19.03	—	—	(1.99)	0.66	22.92
12/19	26.47	11	8	2.21	0.64	25.06
12/18	25.32	11	8	2.10	0.56	22.98
12/17	31.19	65	49	0.46	0.50	23.45
12/16	34.76	14	11	1.89	0.44	21.90
Annual Growth	(14.0%)	—	—	—	11.0%	1.1%

Industria De Diseno Textil (Inditex) SA

Industria de Diseño Textil (Inditex) is one of the world's largest fashion retailers. Inditex sells on a global scale with nearly 6830 shops under eight different banners: Zara Oysho Massimo Dutti Pull&Bear Bershka Stradivarius Zara Home and Uterq e. The firm's constant contact between the stores and online teams answer the popular trends by feeding back to designers on what are the customers' preferences. Amancio Ortega Gaona one of the world's wealthiest men founded Zara in 1975 and later created Inditex as a holding company. The company's largest market is Europe excluding Spain.

Operations

Inditex's eight brands – Zara Oysho Massimo Dutti Pull&Bear Bershka Stradivarius Zara Home and Uterq e – have brick-and-mortar and online stores.

Zara is Inditex's primary brand and include Zara Home. It brings in nearly 70% of the company's revenue. It has incorporated new product categories through launches including The Female Gaze -its first lingerie collection- that offers an empowering perspective of the notion of intimacy; The Essential Collection timeless pieces of high-end jewellery; and the nostalgic collection Archive which retrieves and reinterprets pieces from collections created in previous years and brings them into the present. Other notable collections are ZARA WO(MAN) which unifies styles in search of perfect minimal wardrobe staples for women and men as well as various capsule collaborations such as those created by the Pantone Color Institute or with The Josef and Anni Albers Foundation members of the Bauhaus School.

Bershka is Inditex's second-biggest earner bringing in almost 10% of revenue. It targets a younger demographic at a lower price point. It has three main lines: Bershka BSK and Man.

Its other brands Massimo Dutti (upscale fashion) Oysho (lingerie and undergarments) Pull&Bear (teenagers and adults who have grown up with the brand) Uterque (high-end women's fashion) and Stradivarius account for more than 20% of revenue combined.

Geographic Reach

Inditex is based in Spain. It owns or manages stores and franchises around the world divided to its eight major brands; Zara (about 2025 stores) Bershka (some 1005) Stradivarius (around) Pull & Bear (about 875) Massimo Dutti (over 675) Oysho (approximately 600) Zara Home (some 535) and Uterque (around 85).

In Spain and Europe its stores are almost all owned stores while in the Americas and the Rest of the World it has a larger concentration of franchises. Europe (excluding Spain) is host to over 45% of Inditex's total store count while Spain accounts for around 20%. The Asia and other also has about 20% and the Americas hosts the remainder.

By revenue Europe (excl. Spain) generates around 50% of sales Spain brings in around 15% the Americas for roughly 15% and the Asia and rest of the world accounts for nearly 20%.

Much of Inditex's manufacturing is located close to Spain (such as in Portugal Morocco Turkey and Spain itself) giving it an advantage over rivals.

Sales and Marketing

The company carries out twice-weekly stock distributions to all its stores worldwide.

Financial Performance

Inditex generated a strong operating performance. In FY2020 net sales reached ?20.4 billion (?28.3 billion in FY2019). Sales in constant currencies decreased 25%. Despite the disruption caused by the lockdowns and restrictions the strength of the business model is reflected in the high sales productivity. Trading hours were down 26% versus 2019.

In 2020 the company had a net income of ?1.4 billion a 70% decrease from the previous year's net income of ?4.7 billion.

The company's cash at the end of 2020 was ?7.4 billion Operating activities generated ?3.9 billion while financing activities used ?2.8 billion primarily for lease payments fixed charge. Investment activities provided another ?2.5 billion.

Strategy

Beyond the important role played by its team's approach to the company's performance 2020 was crucial to the company's transformation strategy. The model it has been putting in place over a number of years centered on its unique model which fully integrates stores and the world of online shopping truly proved its merit. For Inditex 2020 - a year in which all of its stores were either closed at one time or had to operate under trading hour or capacity restrictions - can be summed up both by the admirable attitude displayed by all of its professionals and the tremendous responsiveness of its integrated platform. In rising to the COVID challenge the company's unique business model ? characterized by its global flexible digitally integrated and sustainable platform ? has been strengthened positioning us well to tackle future challenges.

HISTORY

Holding company Industria de Diseño Textil (Inditex) got its start as Confecciones Goa in 1963 making women's lingerie and housecoats in La Coruña Spain.

Founder Amancio Ortega learned the rag trade as a boy when at age 13 he made deliveries for a shirtmaker. Managing a tailor shop when he was a young man Ortega spied an expensive negligee for sale and he thought he could make copies and sell them for half the price. From there he made nightshirts and pajamas before he opened the first Zara store in La Coruña in 1975 where Ortega began expanding his offerings for women.

Ortega formed Inditex as a holding company for his growing operations in 1985. Inditex ran nearly 100 Zara stores before venturing out of the country to Portugal in 1988. New York City and Paris stores opened in 1989.

The company created the Pull & Bear clothing chain in 1991. About that time Inditex purchased a 65% stake in the Massimo Dutti group. (Inditex owns it all now.) The group continued to open stores around the globe: Mexico in 1992 Greece in 1993 Belgium and Sweden in 1994 Malta and Cyprus in 1996 and Israel and Norway in 1997.

In 1998 Inditex opened the Berksha chain to lure young females. The company further expanded that year into Argentina Japan Lebanon the UK and Venezuela.

Inditex then acquired 90% of Stradivarius a young women's chain with about 80 stores mostly in Spain. Meanwhile that year Inditex moved into nine more countries: Bahrain Brazil Canada Chile Germany the Netherlands Poland Saudi Arabia and Uruguay.

In 2000 the company announced it would open 150 new stores in the next two years including perhaps 40 in the US. Later in the year however the company said it would hold off on US expansion to concentrate on European growth. To fuel the growth of its Zara chain Inditex floated 26% of the company in a public offering in May 2001.

Over the course of 2001 Inditex entered six new markets: the Czech Republic Iceland Ireland Jordan Luxembourg and Puerto Rico.

In 2003 the first Zara Home stores opened and Inditex entered new markets in Malaysia Russia Slovakia and Slovenia. The following year the group surpassed the 2000 store count and entered Estonia Hungary Latvia Lithuania Morocco Panama and Romania.

Early in 2005 Inditex stopped selling fur items in all of its stores worldwide. In June Pablo Isla Ivarez de Tejera succeeded Jose Mar a Castellano R os as chief executive of the Spanish fashion giant. Castellano remained a non-executive vice chairman of the company until September when he resigned unexpectedly following a disagreement with Inditex's chairman Amancio Ortega over his failed bid for Fenosa a Spanish utility company. Castellano's departure ended a 31-year partnership between the two men.

Overall Inditex opened about 450 stores in 2005 and in the process became Europe's largest apparel retailer ahead of Sweden's H&M Hennes & Mauritz.

In February 2006 the first Zara store opened its doors in Shanghai the first Inditex shop in China.

In 2007 80% of new stores opened were located outside of Spain. Overall the group added 560 stores in some 50 countries. Also in 2007 the group's Kiddy's Class business segment combined operations with Zara Childrenswear. In October Zara Home launched an online shopping site. The online portal is a first for Inditex which has focused on the international expansion of its fashion chains.

In 2009 Inditex signed a joint venture with the Tata Group to open stores in India beginning in 2010. Also in 2009 the firm opened its first stores in Syria.

General Counsel, Secretary of the Board, Antonio Abril Abadin

Non-Executive Proprietary Director, Representative of Pontegadea Inversiones S.L., Flora Perez Marcote, $114,794 total compensation

Executive Chairman of the Board, Pablo Isla Alvarez De Tejera, $3,730,816 total compensation

Deputy Chairman, Non-Executive Proprietary Director, Jose Arnau Sierra, $114,794 total compensation

Group CEO, Carlos Crespo Gonzalez, $1,721,915 total compensation

Non-Executive Independent Director, Anne Lange, $114,794 total compensation

Auditors: DELOITTE, S.L.

LOCATIONS

HQ: Industria De Diseno Textil (Inditex) SA
Avda. de la Diputacion s/n, Edificio INDITEX, La Coruna, Arteixo 15142
Phone: (34) 98 118 5400
Web: www.inditex.es

2010 Sales

	% of total
Europe	
Spain	32
Other countries	46
America	10
Asia & other regions	12
Total	**100**

2010 Stores

	No.
Europe	
Spain	1,916
Other countries	2,006
Americas	390
Asia & other regions	595
Total	**4,907**

PRODUCTS/OPERATIONS

2015 Stores

	No.
Zara	2,162
Bershka	1,044
Pull & Bear	936
Stradivarius	950
Massimo Dutti	740
Oysho	607
Zara Home	502
Uterqüe	72
Total	**7,013**

2015 Sales

	% of total
Zara	65
Bershka	9
Massimo Dutti	7
Pull & Bear	7
Stradivarius	6
Zara Home	3
Oysho	2
Uterqüe	1
Total	**100**

COMPETITORS

ABERCROMBIE & FITCH CO.	Hummel A/S
BRODER BROS. CO.	LEVI STRAUSS & CO.
GIORGIO ARMANI CORPORATION	PRADA USA CORP.
	THE GAP INC
	Tengelmann
H & M Hennes & Mauritz AB	YGM TRADING LIMITED

HISTORICAL FINANCIALS

Company Type: Public

Income Statement   FYE: January 31

	REVENUE ($ mil.)	NET INCOME ($ mil.)	NET PROFIT MARGIN	EMPLOYEES
01/21	24,746	1,341	5.4%	144,116
01/20	31,222	4,016	12.9%	176,611
01/19	30,036	3,956	13.2%	174,386
01/18	31,553	4,194	13.3%	171,839
01/17	25,053	3,392	13.5%	162,450
Annual Growth	(0.3%)	(20.7%)	—	(2.9%)

2021 Year-End Financials

Debt ratio: 0.0%
Return on equity: 7.4%
Cash ($ mil.): 8,973
Current ratio: 1.73
Long-term debt ($ mil.): 3

No. of shares (mil.): —
Dividends
Yield: 0.0%
Payout: 35.0%
Market value ($ mil.): —

	STOCK PRICE ($) FY Close	P/E High/Low	PER SHARE ($) Earnings	Dividends	Book Value
01/21	14.85	55 33	0.43	0.15	5.65
01/20	16.82	15 11	1.29	0.35	5.29
01/19	14.00	16 11	1.27	0.31	5.41
01/18	17.88	21 16	1.35	0.27	5.40
01/17	16.54	18 14	1.09	0.24	4.39
Annual Growth	(2.7%)	—	—(20.7%)	(11.0%)	6.5%

Industrial and Commercial Bank of China Ltd

Boasting assets of roughly RMB$33 trillion Industrial and Commercial Bank of China (ICBC) provides corporate retail and investment banking as well as asset management pensions financial leasing insurance and other financial services to 8.6 million corporate customers and 680 million personal customers across China through 430 overseas institutions in about nearly 50 countries and regions. ICBC provides its products and services to corporations government agencies financial institutions individual customers and other transactions. Industrial and Commercial Bank of China was founded on 1984. ICBC generates more than 90% of its operating income from mainland China.

Operations

Industrial and Commercial Bank of China (ICBC) operates three business segments. Corporate banking?which brings in roughly 50% of the bank's total operating income?provides traditional banking products loans trade financing deposit-taking activities corporate wealth management services custody activities and various other financial services to corporations government agencies and financial institutions. Its personal banking division makes up about 40% of the bank's operating income and provides deposit loan products as well as private banking services card business personal wealth management services and various types of personal intermediary services to individuals. Its treasury operations?which provide about 10% of total revenues?manage the bank's money market foreign exchange and investment securities.

In addition to these divisions the bank also provides wealth management asset custody and pension services and has a precious metals franchise treasury and asset securitization businesses.

Altogether the bank makes around 80% of its operating income from net interest (mostly from loans and advances followed by investment interest) while around 20% comes from net fee and commission income.

Geographic Reach

Industrial and Commercial Bank of China (ICBC) is based in Beijing and generates more than 90% of its operating income from China while the remainder comes from about 50 other countries and regions.

ICBC has subsidiaries and approximately 430 branches overseas. It has operations in Asia Pacific Americas Europe and Middle East.

Sales and Marketing

Industrial and Commercial Bank of China (ICBC) offers its services through its e-banking network the internet telephone and self-service banking centers. It has about 15800 outlets more than 25165 self-service banks about 79670 intelligent devices and about 73060 ATMs as well as roughly 430 overseas branches in about 50 countries and regions.

ICBC also caters to institutional customers in the fields of medical care education labor union religion public resources land and resources housing and construction.

The number of ICBC Mobile customers reached 416 million while ICBC Mall ICBC e Life and ICBC Link reached 161 million 91 million and 177 million users respectively.

Financial Performance

Note: Growth rates may differ after conversion to US dollars.

ICBC's operating income consistently grew over the last five years recording a 25% growth between 2016 and 2020. Net profit followed the same trend posting about 14% growth.

Operating income amounted to RMB800.1 billion representing an increase of 3.1% of which net interest income grew by 2.3% to RMB646.8 billion; non-interest income was RMB153.3 billion up by 6.6%.

Its net profit stood at RMB317.7 billion an increase of 1.4% over the previous year.

ICBC's cash stores gained RMB$375.6 billion in 2020 to end the year at RMB$1.8 trillion. Operations provided RMB$1.6 trillion. Investments used RMB$1.1 trillion mostly for financial investments and financing activities used another RMB$46.9 billion primarily for repayment of debt securities.

Strategy

The bank explored the new growth model of corporate deposits and accelerated the pilot promotion of innovative products to meet the customized financial needs of corporate customers. New technologies such as big data and visualization were innovated and adopted to build a fund transfer map and promote the research and implementation of closed-loop management of corporate deposit funds.

The bank strengthened the application and promotion of advantageous platforms and continued to consolidate its leading advantages in the field of corporate payment. It promoted its global cash management platform and deepened its global business by virtue of the bank's international strategy to build a global cash management business system.

In terms of personal banking the bank promoted the online service of "ICBC e-Wallet" and provided customers with financial services such as settlement wealth management and financing in cooperation with JD and Vanke. It also improved the intelligent services of offline outlets to boost their intelligent transformation.

Moreover the bank continued to deepen the No.1 Personal Bank Strategy its consolidated personal customer base strengthened FinTech empowerment and further enhanced its market competitiveness. At the end of 2020 personal financial assets totaled RMB16.0 trillion. Adhering to "customer-centric" the strategy strives to achieve the overall improvement of personal banking business in terms of market competitiveness value contribution risk control and customer satisfaction and leads the market on a comprehensive sustainable and high quality basis.

Mergers and Acquisitions

Company Background

Industrial and Commercial Bank of China (ICBC) was established in 1984 and went public in 2006. The bank ventured into the US broker-dealer business in 2010 when it acquired the Prime Dealer Services unit of Fortis Securities from BNP Paribas.

EXECUTIVES

Independent Non-Executive Director, Zuliu Hu
Non-Executive Director, Weidong Feng
Non-Executive Director, Liqun Cao
President, Executive Vice Chairman of the Board, Lin Liao
Non-Executive Director, Yongzhen Lu
Deputy Head of the Bank, Wenwu Zhang
Deputy Head of the Bank, Shouben Xu
Executive Director, Jingwu Wang
Executive Director, Deputy Head of the Bank, Guoyu Zheng
Non-Executive Director, Yang Dong
Chairman of the Board, Executive Director, Siqing Chen
Secretary of the Board, Xueqing Guan
Auditors: KPMG

LOCATIONS

HQ: Industrial and Commercial Bank of China Ltd
55 Fuxingmennei Avenue, Xicheng District, Beijing 100140
Phone: (86) 10 66106114   **Fax:** (86) 10 66107571
Web: www.icbc.com.cn

2018 Sales

	% of total
Mainland China	92
Overseas and other	8
Total	**100**

PRODUCTS/OPERATIONS

2018 Sales

	% of total
Interest	85
Non-interest	
Fees and commissions	15
Other	-
Total	**100**

2018 Sales by Segment

	% of total
Corporate banking	48
Personal banking	38
Treasury operations	13
Other	1
Total	**100**

Selected Services

Corporate banking services
Corporate Deposits and Loans
Institutional Banking
Investment Banking
Small and medium-sized enterprise business
Settlement and cash management
International settlement and trade finance
E-finance
ICBC Mobile
ICBC Mall
ICBC Link
Financing product line
Payment product line
Investment and wealth management product line
Personal banking services
Personal Finance
E-banking
Bank Card
Precious Metals
Private Banking
Global Market
Financial Asset Services
Wealth Management business
Asset Custody services
Pension services
Precious metal
Agency Treasury business
Asset securitization business
Agency sales
Treasury operations
Money Market activities
Investment
Financing
Channel and Development and Service Enhancement
Service enhancement
Consumer protection

COMPETITORS

AKBANK TURK ANONIM SIRKETI
AL RAJHI BANKING AND INVESTMENT
  CORPORATION
Agricultural Bank of China Limited
Banco Bradesco S/A
CITIZENS FINANCIAL GROUP INC.
China Construction Bank Corporation
China Merchants Bank Co. Ltd.
HDFC BANK LIMITED
ICICI BANK LIMITED
ITAU UNIBANCO HOLDING SA
NATIONAL AUSTRALIA BANK LIMITED
QATAR NATIONAL BANK (Q.P.S.C.)
The Bank of Nova Scotia

HISTORICAL FINANCIALS

Company Type: Public

Income Statement

FYE: December 31

	ASSETS ($ mil.)	NET INCOME ($ mil.)	INCOME AS % OF ASSETS	EMPLOYEES
12/20	5,098,439	48,301	0.9%	439,787
12/19	4,327,168	44,871	1.0%	445,106
12/18	4,027,096	43,277	1.1%	449,296
12/17	4,008,806	43,957	1.1%	453,048
12/16	3,475,954	40,070	1.2%	461,749
Annual Growth	10.1%	4.8%	—	(1.2%)

2020 Year-End Financials

Return on assets: 0.9%
Return on equity: 11.3%
Long-term debt ($ mil.): —
No. of shares (mil.): —
Sales ($ mil): 201,208

Dividends
Yield: 4.8%
Payout: 508.0%
Market value ($ mil.): —

	STOCK PRICE ($) FY Close	P/E High/Low	PER SHARE ($) Earnings	Dividends	Book Value
12/20	12.81	19 12	0.13	0.62	1.24
12/19	15.37	18 14	0.12	0.61	1.08
12/18	14.16	21 16	0.12	0.61	0.95
12/17	16.11	21 16	0.12	0.59	0.92
12/16	11.84	16 12	0.11	0.56	0.80
Annual Growth	2.0%	— —	4.4%	2.3%	11.8%

Infineon Technologies AG

Infineon Technologies is a world leader in semiconductor solutions. It makes semiconductors microcontrollers sensors switches and other devices that manage power energy security and other functions in cars phone appliances and machinery. The company's products are No. 1 in their markets for automotive industrial power control power & sensor systems and connected secure systems applications. Automotive is Infineon's biggest market accounting for about 45% of sales. Customers include Bosch Bombardier Brother and Osram. Geographically Greater China accounts for over 35% of the Germany-based company's sales.

Operations

The company operates in four segments: Automotive (around 40% of sales) Power & Sensor Systems (some 30%) Industrial Power Control (over 15%) and Connected Secure Systems (roughly 10%).

The Automotive segment is responsible for the semiconductor business for automotive electronics and for activities with memory products. The Power & Sensor Systems segment addresses more consumer-oriented applications and power supplies in general. In addition activities in the area of radio frequency and sensor-based applications (including the recording of sensor data and interaction with machines and devices) fall within the sphere of responsibility of the Power & Sensor Systems segment. The Industrial Power Control segment concentrates on power semiconductors primarily used in industrial applications and renewable energy. Activities relating to traditional and new security applications microcontrollers for non-automotive electronic applications and connectivity solutions are bundled in the Connected Secure Systems segment.

Geographic Reach

Headquartered in Germany Greater China is Infineon's largest single country market accounting for over 35% of revenue. Customers in other parts of the Asia-Pacific region were around 15% of Infineon's sales. The Europe Middle East and Africa market made up some 15%% of sales with the Americas and Germany coming in at over 10% each. It also generated about 10% in Japan. It operates manufacturing sites in eight countries in Asia and three countries in Europe.

Sales and Marketing

Customers include Bosch Hyundai US Government Printing Office Samsung Siemens and Tesla Motors.

Financial Performance

The company's revenue for fiscal 2020 increased by 7% to ?8.6 billion compared from the prior year with $8.0 billion.

Net income for fiscal 2020 decreased to ?368 million compared from the prior year with ?870 million.

Cash held by the company at the end of fiscal 2020 increased to ?1.9 billion. Cash provided by operations and financing activities were ?1.8 billion and ?6.3 billion respectively. Cash used for investing activities was ?7.2 billion mainly for acquisitions of businesses.

Strategy

Infineon want to continue to develop grow and to create value for its customers and its shareholders as well as for the company employees and for society. In the past few years the company's strategy has been guided by global megatrends which will continue to shape the world in the future: demographic and social change climate change and scarce resources urbanization and digital transformation. From these megatrends the company derive its focus on the following growth areas: energy efficiency mobility security and the IoT & big data. In these markets Infineon orient ourselves to structural drivers; areas which are expected to see disproportionate growth in the long term as a result of these trends or which have major innovation potential. The coronavirus has not altered the underlying assumptions. Partially it is acting as a catalyst that will speed up changes in society and in the economy.

Mergers and Acquisitions

In early 2020 Infineon Technologies AG announced the closing of the acquisition of Cypress Semiconductor Corporation. The San Jose-based company has become part of Infineon effective as of the closing. The addition of Cypress lets Infineon further strengthen its focus on structural growth drivers and on a broader range of applications. This will accelerate the company's path of profitable growth. Cypress adds a differentiated portfolio of microcontrollers connectivity components software ecosystems and high-performance memories. The company acquired Cypress for US$23.85 per share in cash corresponding to an enterprise value of ?9.0 billion.

HISTORY

Infineon Technologies was formed in 1999 from German industrial and electronics giant Siemens' semiconductor operations. Siemens which was founded in 1847 began its semiconductor R&D program in 1952 — just five years after scientists at Bell Laboratories invented the transistor. During the 1960s Siemens' semiconductor operations developed chips for consumer electronics. By the early 1970s the company's facilities included chip factories in Malaysia and the Philippines. In 1985 Siemens released one of the first chipsets to comply with the ISDN communications standard. Five years later it released the first chipset for the Global System for Mobile Communications (GSM) cell phone standard.

Siemens in 1998 became one of the top 10 semiconductor companies by sales despite falling DRAM prices that contributed to a loss for the year. In 1999 Siemens formed OSRAM Opto Semiconductor an optoelectronics joint venture with its own subsidiary OSRAM. (Infineon subsequently sold its stake in the joint venture back to Siemens and exited the optoelectronics business.) Also in 1999 Siemens organized its semiconductor operations into a subsidiary Infineon Technologies. Ulrich Schumacher who had headed the semiconductor business became Infineon's chairman and CEO. That year Infineon's alliance with IBM was converted into a joint venture ALTIS Semiconductor.

In 2011 Infineon sold its wireless unit to Intel for about $1.4 billion in cash. Intel is looking to expand its offerings in the wireless market by purchasing what amounts to a complete portfolio of wireless chips while Infineon wants to improve its results by concentrating on its core automotive industrial and security chip segments. The company had hoped to get around $2 billion for the wireless unit which makes up around 30% of Infineon's total sales but continues to lag behind wireless sector leaders QUALCOMM Texas Instruments and Broadcom.

EXECUTIVES

Chief Marketing Officer, Member of the Management Board, Helmut Gassel, $896,350 total compensation

Member of the Management Board, Chief Operations Officer, Jochen Hanebeck, $896,350 total compensation

Independent Chairman of the Supervisory Board, Wolfgang Eder, $107,562 total compensation

Deputy Chairman of the Supervisory Board, Johann Dechant, $107,562 total compensation

Member of the Supervisory Board, Employee Representative, Melanie Riedl, $107,562 total compensation

Independent Member of the Supervisory Board, Margret Suckale, $107,562 total compensation

Independent Member of the Supervisory Board, Friedrich Eichiner, $107,562 total compensation

Independent Member of the Supervisory Board, Xiaoqun Clever, $107,562 total compensation

Independent Member of the Supervisory Board, Ulrich Spiesshofer, $107,562 total compensation

Chief Financial Officer, Member of the Management Board, Sven Schneider, $985,985 total compensation

Chief Digital Transformation Officer, Constanze Hufenbecher, $414,222 total compensation

Chairman of the Management Board, Chief Executive Officer, Reinhard Ploss, $1,481,966 total compensation

Auditors: KPMG AG

LOCATIONS

HQ: Infineon Technologies AG
Am Campeon 1-15, Neubiberg D-85579
Phone: (49) 89 234 0   **Fax:** (49) 89 234 9552987
Web: www.infineon.com

2018 sales

	% of total
Germany	15
Greater China	34
Europe Middle East Africa	17
Americas	12
Asia-Pacific	15
Japan	7
Total	**100**

PRODUCTS/OPERATIONS

2018 sales

	% of total
Automotive	43
Power Management & Multi-market	31
Industrial Power Control	17
Digital Security Solutions	9
Other Operating Segments	
Total	**100**

COMPETITORS

ALPS ALPINE CO. LTD.
APC TECHNOLOGY GROUP PLC
CML MICROSYSTEMS PLC
LATTICE SEMICONDUCTOR CORPORATION
LG Display Co. Ltd.
MAXIM INTEGRATED PRODUCTS INC.
NIDEC CORPORATION
NITTO DENKO CORPORATION
RENESAS ELECTRONICS AMERICA INC.
RENESAS ELECTRONICS CORPORATION
SEMTECH CORPORATION
SL INDUSTRIES INC.
STMicroelectronics SA
Siemens AG
TDK CORPORATION

HISTORICAL FINANCIALS
Company Type: Public

Income Statement				FYE: September 30
	REVENUE ($ mil.)	NET INCOME ($ mil.)	NET PROFIT MARGIN	EMPLOYEES
09/21	12,802	1,353	10.6%	50,288
09/20	10,030	430	4.3%	46,665
09/19	8,758	949	10.8%	41,418
09/18	8,801	1,245	14.1%	40,098
09/17	8,344	933	11.2%	37,479
Annual Growth	11.3%	9.7%	—	7.6%

2021 Year-End Financials

Debt ratio: 32.6%	No. of shares (mil.): 1,301
Return on equity: 10.8%	Dividends
Cash ($ mil.): 2,024	Yield: 0.4%
Current ratio: 1.86	Payout: 17.1%
Long-term debt ($ mil.): 6,657	Market value ($ mil.): 53,539

	STOCK PRICE ($) FY Close	P/E High/Low		PER SHARE ($) Earnings	Dividends	Book Value
09/21	41.14	51	31	1.01	0.18	10.14
09/20	28.24	111	46	0.30	0.20	9.20
09/19	18.01	31	20	0.82	0.21	7.57
09/18	22.72	31	23	1.10	0.27	6.61
09/17	25.22	36	26	0.83	0.24	5.89
Annual Growth	13.0%	—	—	5.0%	(7.1%)	14.5%

Infosys Ltd.

Infosys Technologies is a leading provider of consulting technology outsourcing and next-generation digital services enabling clients around the world to create and execute strategies for their digital transformation. The company also provides digital marketing artificial intelligence automation analytics engineering services and Internet of Things services among others. Its subsidiary Infosys BPM provides business process outsourcing services. Infosys makes almost all of its sales overseas with North America accounting for around 60% of the total. Key industries served by the company are financial services insurance manufacturing telecom retail and consumer goods.

Operations

The company's business segment are enterprises primarily in Financial Services and Insurance (over 30% of sales) enterprises in Retail (some 15%) enterprises in Communication (about 15%) enterprises in the Energy Utilities Resources and Services (over 10%) enterprises in Manufacturing (roughly 10%) enterprises in Hi-Tech (nearly 10%) enterprises in Life Sciences and Healthcare (over 5%) Consumer Packaged Goods and Logistics Telecom OEM and Media and all other segments. The Financial Services reportable segments has been aggregated to include the Financial Services operating segment and Finacle operating segment because of the similarity of the economic characteristics. All other segments represent the operating segments of businesses in India Japan China Infosys Public Services & other enterprises in Public Services.

About 95% of sales were generated from software services. Overall Core business account for over half of its sale while the other roughly half accounts from its Digital business.

Geographic Reach

The company headquartered in Bengaluru India currently has presence in about 35 locations across more than 50 countries. Sales from North American markets account for around 60% followed by Europe with about 25% India with less than 5% and the rest of the world accounts for the remaining sales.

Sales and Marketing

The company organized its sales and marketing functions into teams across more than 50 countries around the world focusing on delivering digital solutions for specific industries and geographies. It serves industries such as Aerospace & Defense Agriculture Automotive Communication Services Consumer Packaged Goods Education and Engineering Procurement & Construction among others.

Financial Performance

The company's revenue increased 6% from $12.8 billion in 2020 to $13.6 billion in 2021. This was mainly due to higher sales volume in both of the company's segments.

In 2021 the company had a net income of $2.6 billion a 12% increase from the previous year's net income of $2.3 billion.

The company's cash for the year ended 2021 was $3.4 billion. Operating activities generated $4.1 billion while financing activities used $1.1 billion mainly for quoted debt securities. Investing activities provided another $3.3 billion.

Strategy

Infosys seeks to acquire or make strategic investments in complementary businesses new and emerging technologies services or products or enter into strategic partnerships or alliances with third parties in order to enhance its business.

The company has made and may in the future make strategic investments in early-stage technology start-up companies in order to gain experience in or exploit niche technologies.

Mergers and Acquisitions

Infosys in 2021 announced a strategic collaboration with Spirit AeroSystems a leading aero structures manufacturer. Spirit has chosen Infosys as its lead technology integration partner to help drive and set up the end-to-end applications and infrastructure integration of a few of Bombardier's former aerostructures and aftermarket services assets which have been recently acquired by Spirit. Terms were not disclosed.

In late 2020 Infosys has completed the acquisition of Blue Acorn iCi an Adobe Platinum partner in the US and a leader in digital customer experience commerce and analytics for an undisclosed amount. This acquisition further strengthens Infosys' end-to-end customer experience offerings and demonstrates its continued commitment to help clients navigate their digital transformation journey. Blue Acorn iCi brings to Infosys significant cross-technology capabilities through the convergence of customer experience digital commerce analytics and experience driven commerce services.

Also in late 2020 Infosys has completed the acquisition of Kaleidoscope Innovation a full-spectrum product design development and insights firm innovating across medical consumer and industrial markets bolstering capabilities in the design of smart products. This acquisition demonstrates Infosys' commitment to innovate for its clients and make meaningful impact on human lives through a combination of cutting-edge technologies. This collaboration further aims to revolutionize patient care treatment diagnostics and consumer health across the world. Terms were not disclosed.

In 2020 Infosys has completed the acquisition of GuideVision one of the largest ServiceNow Elite Partners in Europe and an award winning enterprise service management consultancy specialised in offering strategic advisory consulting implementations training and support on the ServiceNow platform. Through this acquisition Infosys further enhances its digital capabilities strengthens Infosys Cobalt portfolio of cloud services and reaffirms commitment to the growing ServiceNow ecosystem. Terms were not disclosed.

In early 2020 Infosys as completed the acquisition of Simplus one of the fastest growing Salesforce Platinum Partners in the USA and Australia. Through this acquisition Infosys further elevates its position as an end-to-end Salesforce enterprise cloud solutions and services provider offering clients unparalleled capabilities for cloud-first digital transformation. Terms were not disclosed.

HISTORY

After receiving a master's degree in electrical engineering from one of India's highly regarded Institutes of Technology (Kanpur) in the 1960s Narayana Murthy left for France and a job developing software for the air traffic control system at Paris' Charles de Gaulle airport.

During college Murthy had developed the belief that communism was the answer to his country's problems with poverty and corruption a stance that was fortified during his time spent with Paris leftists in the 1970s. But while hitchhiking back to India in 1974 Murthy's Marxist sympathies eroded quickly after he was jailed in Hungary for allegedly disclosing state secrets while talking with Austrian tourists on a train. Murthy became a socialist at heart but capitalist in practice setting out on a mission to create wealth rather than redistribute it.

That mission officially began in 1981 when Murthy convinced six fellow software engineers to start their own company. Infosys was founded that year with $250 in capital (mostly borrowed from their wives) and no idea of what it would sell.

From the beginning Murthy looked for business outside India where he was able to sell customizable inexpensive software to multinational corporations such as Reebok and Nordstrom. But a lack of reputation and government regulations made business difficult for Infosys during the 1980s — it took nine months just to get the company's first telephone line and three years to import new computers. Infosys opened its first US office in 1987.

Many of the government regulations that had kept India's economy stagnant were lifted when reform swept the country in 1991. But this also opened the door for companies such as IBM (which had been asked to leave in 1977) and Dig-

ital Equipment (later acquired by Compaq) to enter India and lure away its best engineers. While no Indian company had ever done this before Murthy initiated a stock option plan and other perks to retain his employees. Infosys went public in 1993. Morgan Stanley swooped in to salvage the undersubscribed IPO in a move that would later reap millions when Infosys' stock began to soar.

EXECUTIVES

Executive Vice President, Group Head - Human Resource and Infosys Leadership Institute, Krishnamurthy Shankar
Non-Executive Non-Independent Chairman of the Board, Nandan Nilekani, $411 total compensation
Executive Vice President, Head - US Operations and Global Head – Education, Training and Assessment, Srikantan Moorthy
President, Mohit Joshi
Independent Director, Michael Gibbs
Chief Financial Officer, Nilanjan Roy, $730,823 total compensation
Independent Director, Uri Levine
Additional Independent Director, Bobby Parikh
Additional Independent Director, Chitra Nayak
Chief Compliance Officer, Group General Counsel, Inderpreet Sawhney
Chief Executive Officer, Managing Director, Whole Time Director, Salil Parekh, $766,379 total compensation
Chief Operating Officer, U. B. Pravin Rao, $568,386 total compensation
Auditors: Deloitte Haskins & Sells LLP

LOCATIONS

HQ: Infosys Ltd.
Electronics City, Hosur Road, Bangalore, Karnataka 560 100
Phone: (91) 80 2852 0261   **Fax:** (91) 80 2852 0362
Web: www.infosys.com

2019 Sales

	% of total
North America	61
Europe	24
India	2
Rest of the World	13
Total	**100**

PRODUCTS/OPERATIONS

2019 Sales

	% of total
Software services	95
Software products	5
Total	**100**

2019 Sales by Market

	% of total
Financial services & insurance	32
Retail	16
Communication	13
Manufacturing	10
Life Sciences	6
All Other Segments	3
Total	**100**

Selected Services

Business process management
Custom application development
Engineering
Information technology consulting
Infrastructure management
Maintenance and production support
Management consulting
Operations and business process consulting
Package evaluation and implementation
Software re-engineering
Systems integration
Testing

COMPETITORS

ACCENTURE PUBLIC LIMITED COMPANY
ATOS SYNTEL INC.
CAPGEMINI
CGI Inc
COGNIZANT TECHNOLOGY SOLUTIONS CORPORATION
COMPUTACENTER PLC
DATASITE GLOBAL CORPORATION
FORESCOUT TECHNOLOGIES INC.
SOFTCAT PLC
SOPRA STERIA GROUP
STARTEK INC.
Software AG

HISTORICAL FINANCIALS

Company Type: Public

Income Statement   FYE: March 31

	REVENUE ($ mil.)	NET INCOME ($ mil.)	NET PROFIT MARGIN	EMPLOYEES
03/21	13,561	2,613	19.3%	259,619
03/20	12,780	2,331	18.2%	242,371
03/19	11,799	2,199	18.6%	228,123
03/18	10,939	2,486	22.7%	204,107
03/17	10,208	2,140	21.0%	200,364
Annual Growth	7.4%	5.1%	—	6.7%

2021 Year-End Financials

Debt ratio: —
Return on equity: 27.3%
Cash ($ mil.): 3,380
Current ratio: 2.55
Long-term debt ($ mil.): —

No. of shares (mil.): —
Dividends
Yield: 1.2%
Payout: 41.4%
Market value ($ mil.): —

	STOCK PRICE ($) FY Close	P/E High/Low	PER SHARE ($) Earnings	Dividends	Book Value
03/21	18.72	31 12	0.61	0.24	2.46
03/20	8.21	22 13	0.55	0.30	2.04
03/19	10.93	41 18	0.51	0.96	2.17
03/18	17.85	34 26	0.55	0.19	2.29
03/17	15.80	43 29	0.47	0.17	2.33
Annual Growth	4.3%	—	6.7%	8.9%	1.4%

ING Groep NV

ING Groep with its tagline "do your thing" offers banking services and activities for small and medium enterprises (SMEs) and mid-corporate clients. The group serves an estimate of about 40 million individual customers. Some of the group's services include payments savings insurance investments and lending products. ING made improvements and developments in its end-to-end digitalization in its operation as a result of the growing demand for digital and platform services. The group generates majority of its revenues from the Netherlands Belgium and Luxembourg. ING has its presence in more than 40 countries.

Operations

ING operates through six primary banking segments: Wholesale Banking (around 30%) Retail Netherlands (roughly 25%) Retail Other (about 20%) Retail Belgium (nearly 15%) Retail Germany (some 10%) and Corporate Line Banking.

ING's retail banking services countries are in the Market Leaders category (Netherlands Belgium and Germany). Most of its income is generated from the retail and private banking activities in these countries. Some of the products include savings accounts business lending mortgages and other consumer lending in the Netherlands.

The group's wholesale banking offer products such as lending debt capital markets working capital solutions export finance daily banking solutions treasury and risk solutions as well as corporate finance.

Geographic Reach

ING operates in more than 40 countries in Europe North America Latin America Australia and the Asia region. Its revenue base is diversified with the Netherlands its largest single market accounting for more than 30% of its total underlying banking income followed by Belgium (more than 15%) and Germany (nearly 15%). Other important countries are Australia Austria Czech Republic France Germany Italy and Spain.

ING is headquartered in the Netherlands.

Sales and Marketing

ING serves approximately 40 million clients ranging from large companies to multinational corporations and financial institutions.

Financial Performance

ING's performance for the span of five years has continued to fluctuate.

The group's revenue decreased by ?669 million to ?17.6 billion compared to 2019's revenue of ?18.3 billion. The decrease was mainly due to the decrease in all its segments.

Net income decreased by ?495 million to ?13.6 billion compared to the prior year's net income of ?14.1 billion.

ING's cash held in 2020 at the end of the year amounted to ?111.5 billion. The bank's operations generated ?101.2 billion. Investing activities and financing activities used ?8.5 billion and ?34.7 billion respectively. Main cash uses were for payment of securities at amortized cost and repayment of debt securities.

Strategy

ING's strategy revolves around its data-driven digital and mobile-first approach. With the effects of the global pandemic the urgency to implement end-to-end digitalization was increased. This was to meet the growing demand for mobile banking as well as enhancing operational excellence.

The company's "Think Forward" strategy aims to empower its customers through earning primary relationship mastering data and being innovative through providing service to the changing customer needs. The group also incorporated banking to their platform for customers to be able to connect to the products and services of others in the banking sector. ING is building digital channels such as its OneApp which is used by customers in the Netherlands Belgium and Germany.

Company Background

Prior to the economic meltdown ING took aim at becoming a financial services player in all four corners of the world and made acquisitions accordingly. Along with much of the insurance industry it shifted its base from traditional life insurance products to investment-backed products which favor companies that can sell through banks. ING utilized its owns banks to distribute such products. The company also targeted expansion in growing economies such as South Korea Turkey and Thailand to meet anticipated consumer demand for new banking and retirement options. In more mature markets like North America and Europe the company had the aging population in its sights and placed retirement planning and pensions as sources of future growth.

HISTORY

ING Groep's roots go back to 1845 when its earliest predecessor the Netherlands Insurance Co. was founded. The firm began expanding geographically; in 1903 it added life insurance. In 1963 it

merged with the century-old Nationale Life Insurance Bank to form Nationale-Nederland (NN). Over the next three decades the company grew primarily through acquisitions in Europe North America and Australia. In 1986 NN became the first European life insurance company to be licensed in Japan.

Another predecessor the Rijkspostspaarbank was founded in 1881 to provide Dutch citizens with simple post office savings accounts. In 1918 the Postcheque-en Girondienst (giro) system was established to allow people to use vouchers drawn on their savings accounts to pay bills. This system became the main method of settling accounts (instead of bank checking accounts).

Rijkspostspaarbank and Postcheque merged in 1986 to become Postbank. Postbank merged in 1989 with the Nederlandse Middenstandsbank (founded 1927) to become NMB Postbank. The vast amounts of cash tied up in the post office savings and giro systems fueled NMB's business.

In 1991 as the European economic union became a reality and barriers between banking and insurance began to fall NN merged with NMB Postbank to form Internationale Nederland Groep (ING). ING began cutting costs shedding redundant offices and unprofitable operations in both its segments. In the US where insurance and banking were legally divided the company "debanked" itself in order to keep its more lucrative insurance operations (but retained the right to provide banking services to those operations).

ING sought to increase its investment banking and finance operations in the 1990s. In 1995 it took over UK-based Barings Bank (personal banker to the Queen of England) after Nicholas Leeson a trader in Barings' Singapore office lost huge sums of money in derivatives trading. The acquisition gave the firm a higher profile but cost more than anticipated and left it embroiled in lingering legal actions.

In 1996 ING bought Poland's Bank Slaski (the company had first entered Poland in 1994). The next year it expanded its securities business by acquiring investment bank Furman Selz doubled its US life insurance operations by purchasing Equitable of Iowa and listed on the NYSE. In 1998 ING's acquisition strategy again involved Europe and North America: It bought Belgium's Banque Bruxelles Lambert and Canadian life insurer Guardian Insurance Co. (from Guardian Royal Exchange now part of AXA UK).

ING turned eastward in 1999 kicking off asset management operations in India and buying a minority stake in South Korea's HC&B (formerly Housing & Commercial Bank). In 2000 the company bulked up its North American operations with the purchase of 40% of Savia SA a Mexican insurance concern. It also bought US firm ReliaStar Financial in a $6 billion deal and Charterhouse Securities from CCF (then called Credit Commercial de France).

In 2004 ING realigned its management structure dividing the company's operations into six business lines: Insurance Americas Insurance Europe Insurance Asia-Pacific Wholesale Banking Retail Banking and ING Direct. ING boosted its North American insurance operations with the acquisition of Allianz's Canadian property and casualty operations.

The company struggled with investment banking arm ING Barings. The unit was reorganized and streamlined for cost-savings purposes but ultimately was put on the block. Its Asian equities operations were sold to Macquarie Bank in 2004. Barings Private Equity Partners unit was sold to its management. The Barings investment management operations were sold as well.

The company struggled with investment banking arm ING Barings. The unit was reorganized and streamlined for cost-savings purposes but ul-

timately was put on the block. Its Asian equities operations were sold to Macquarie Bank in 2004. Barings Private Equity Partners unit was sold to its management. The Barings investment management operations were sold to MassMutual in 2005 while Northern Trust bought up its fund administration trust and custody operations.

ING sold most of ING BHF-Bank to Sal. Oppenheim during 2004. The next year ING turned over its US life reinsurance operations to Scottish Re and sold subsidiary Life Insurance Company of Georgia to Jackson National Life.

During 2005 ING acquired a 20% stake in the Bank of Beijing as part of a strategic alliance. In 2006 the company sold off its UK brokerage business Williams de Bro to The Evolution Group.

In 2008 the company acquired CitiStreet a leading US administrator of defined-contribution retirement savings pension health and other plans; it paid about $900 million for the firm.

After the global financial crisis hit in 2008 ING accepted a ?10 billion (more than $13 billion) bailout loan from the Dutch government. The bailout was intended to shore up the company's capital position and reassure wary investors. Strategic measures to further offset losses and repay debt were enacted in 2009 including layoffs and asset sales. CEO Michael Tilmant stepped down and was replaced by former chairman Jan Hommen. By the end of 2009 job cuts totaled about 10% of its workforce. The company also outlined plans to split the company in half by separating its insurance and banking operations.

Prior to the bailout ING has already been working to simplify and streamline its operations through a "Back to Basics" strategy. Restructuring measures under the strategy include the refocusing of ING's banking operations on (mostly Central) Europe and the reduction of the company's US financial product offerings.

In early 2009 the company sold its ING Canada property/casualty business which was then renamed Intact Financial. ING sold its life insurance joint venture stake in Australia and New Zealand to partner ANZ and offloaded its noncore annuity and mortgage businesses in Chile to life insurer Corp Group Vida Chile in late 2009. The company also sold its Taiwanese life insurance business to Fubon Financial Holding in a deal worth ?447 million ($600 million) in mid-2009. ING gained a 5% stake in Fubon through the deal which it sold the following year for another ?395 million ($522 million).

In early 2010 ING completed sales of the company's Swiss Private Banking unit to Julius Baer for $506 million and its Asian Private Banking unit (operating in Hong Kong the Philippines and Singapore) to OCBC Bank for nearly $1.5 billion. In addition the company sold its North American reinsurance operations to RGA and most of its US insurance brokerage operations to Lightyear Capital in early 2010. ING has also agreed to sell its stake in one of its Chinese life insurance ventures (Pacific Antai with China Pacific Insurance) to China Construction Bank.

In 2011 ING sold its Asian and European real estate investment management (REIM) operations as well as select US REIM assets for about $940 million to broker CBRE Group (formerly CB Richard Ellis Group). The firm sold its remaining US REIM assets to Lightyear Capital for some $100 million. Also that year the firm agreed to sell its Australian investment management business to UBS for an undisclosed sum.

Farther south in 2011 the company sold its Latin American insurance operations to Columbian insurer GrupoSura for $3.7 billion. The sale included insurance savings and investment management operations in Chile Colombia Mexico

Uruguay and Peru. It also sold ING Car Least to BMW.

In 2016 the group exited the insurance business to focus on the European banking market.

EXECUTIVES

Independent Member of the Supervisory Board, Hendrica Verhagen
Independent Member of the Supervisory Board, H. Hulst
Independent Member of the Supervisory Board, H. Naus
Independent Member of the Supervisory Board, J. Colombas
Chief Operations Officer, Chief Transformation Officer, Marnix Van Stiphout
Independent Vice Chairman of the Supervisory Board, A. Rees
Independent Chairman of the Supervisory Board, Hans Wijers
Auditors: KPMG Accountants N.V.

LOCATIONS

HQ: ING Groep NV
Bijlmerdreef 106, Amsterdam 1102 CT
Phone: (31) 20 564 7705
Web: www.ing.com

2018 sales

	%
Netherlands	32
Belgium	17
Germany	14
Other Challengers	10
Growth Markets	13
Wholesale Banking Rest of the World	13
Other	1
Total	**100**

PRODUCTS/OPERATIONS

2018 Sales

	% of total
Net interest income	76
Net fee and commission income	15
Valuation results & net trading income	6
Investment income	1
Share of results from associates and joint ventures	1
Other	1
Total	**100**

2018 sales

	%
Retail Banking	67
Wholesale Banking	32
Corporate Line Banking	1
Total	**100**

COMPETITORS

AON GLOBAL LIMITED	NATWEST GROUP PLC
AVIVA PLC	PRUDENTIAL PUBLIC
Ageas	LIMITED COMPANY
Airbus SE	Randstad N.V.
COMMONWEALTH BANK OF	Redefine
International	
AUSTRALIA	P.L.C.
Credit Suisse Group AG	STANDARD CHARTERED
PLC	
DEUTSCHE BANK AG	Sampo Oyj
Dexia	Victoria Retail Group
HSBC HOLDINGS PLC	B.V.
Koninklijke Vopak N.V.	Wolters Kluwer N.V.
MMC VENTURES LIMITED	

HISTORICAL FINANCIALS

Company Type: Public

Income Statement

FYE: December 31

	ASSETS ($ mil.)	NET INCOME ($ mil.)	INCOME AS % OF ASSETS	EMPLOYEES
12/20	1,146,154	2,761	0.2%	55,901
12/19	997,600	4,382	0.4%	53,431
12/18	1,013,043	5,452	0.5%	52,233
12/17	1,011,602	6,549	0.6%	51,504
12/16	889,281	5,253	0.6%	51,943
Annual Growth	**6.5%**	**(14.9%)**	**—**	**1.9%**

2020 Year-End Financials

Return on assets: 0.2%	Dividends
Return on equity: 4.3%	Yield: 0.0%
Long-term debt ($ mil.): —	Payout: 20.6%
No. of shares (mil.): —	Market value ($ mil.): —
Sales ($ mil): 28,605	

	STOCK PRICE ($) FY Close	P/E High/Low		PER SHARE ($) Earnings	Dividends	Book Value
12/20	9.44	24	9	0.71	0.15	16.24
12/19	12.05	14	9	1.12	0.62	14.70
12/18	10.66	16	9	1.40	0.64	14.44
12/17	18.46	14	11	1.69	0.65	14.94
12/16	14.10	11	7	1.35	0.56	12.87
Annual Growth	**(9.5%)**	**—**		**(14.8%)**	**(28.5%)**	**6.0%**

Inner Mongolia Yili Industrial Group Co., Ltd.

Auditors: Da Hua Certified Public Accountants (Special General Partnership)

LOCATIONS

HQ: Inner Mongolia Yili Industrial Group Co., Ltd.
No. 1, Jinshan Road, Jinshan Development Zone,
Hohhot, Inner Mongolia Autonomous Region 010110
Phone: (86) 471 3350092   **Fax:** (86) 471 3601621
Web: www.yili.com

HISTORICAL FINANCIALS

Company Type: Public

Income Statement

FYE: December 31

	REVENUE ($ mil.)	NET INCOME ($ mil.)	NET PROFIT MARGIN	EMPLOYEES
12/20	14,813	1,082	7.3%	0
12/19	12,966	996	7.7%	0
12/18	11,565	936	8.1%	0
12/17	10,458	922	8.8%	0
12/16	8,728	815	9.3%	54,983
Annual Growth	**14.1%**	**7.3%**	**—**	**—**

2020 Year-End Financials

Debt ratio: 1.9%	No. of shares (mil.): —
Return on equity: 24.9%	Dividends
Cash ($ mil.): 1,788	Yield: —
Current ratio: 0.82	Payout: —
Long-term debt ($ mil.): 210	Market value ($ mil.): —

innogy SE

Auditors: PricewaterhouseCoopers GmbH Wirtschaftpruefungsgesellschaft

LOCATIONS

HQ: innogy SE
Opernplatz 1, Essen 45128
Phone: (49) 201 12 02
Web: www.innogy.com

HISTORICAL FINANCIALS

Company Type: Public

Income Statement

FYE: December 31

	REVENUE ($ mil.)	NET INCOME ($ mil.)	NET PROFIT MARGIN	EMPLOYEES
12/19	37,651	433	1.2%	34,523
12/18	40,153	(747)	—	42,904
12/17	49,291	932	1.9%	42,393
Annual Growth	**(12.6%)**	**(31.8%)**	**—**	**(9.8%)**

2019 Year-End Financials

Debt ratio: —	No. of shares (mil.): 555
Return on equity: 5.0%	Dividends
Cash ($ mil.): 637	Yield: —
Current ratio: 1.16	Payout: —
Long-term debt ($ mil.): —	Market value ($ mil.): —

	STOCK PRICE ($) FY Close	P/E High/Low	PER SHARE ($) Earnings	Dividends	Book Value
12/19	0.00	—	0.79	0.00	15.01
12/18	0.00	—	(1.35)	0.00	16.28
Annual Growth	**—**	**—**	**—**	**—**	**(4.0%)**

Intact Financial Corp

Intact Financial is active in Canada's and US' property/casualty marketplaces providing automobile property and liability insurance to both individual and small to midsized commercial clients. In Canada Intact provides repair and restoration services through its subsidiary On Side Restoration a leading restoration company restoring damaged homes and businesses. Outside of North America the company provides personal commercial and specialty insurance solutions across the UK Ireland Europe and the Middle East through the RSA brands. Intact also provides affinity insurance solutions through the Johnson Affinity Groups. Intact Financial generates of its revenue in Canada. Intact Financial began in 1809 as The Halifax Fire Insurance Association.

IPO

Operations

Personal property business accounts for about 20% of direct premiums written while commercial insurance accounts for nearly 45%. Personal auto coverage alone contributes more than 35% of all direct premiums written.

The company has two reportable segments: Canada which accounts for more than 80% of sales and US with nearly 15%.

In Canada Intact distributes insurance under the Intact Insurance brand through a wide network of brokers including its whollyowned subsidiary BrokerLink and directly to consumers through belairdirect. Frank Cowan Company a leading managing general agent distributes public entity insurance programs including risk and claims management services in Canada.

In the U.S. Intact Insurance Specialty Solutions provides a range of specialty insurance products and services through independent agencies regional and national brokers wholesalers and managing general agencies. Products are underwritten by the insurance company subsidiaries of Intact Insurance Group USA LLC.

Geographic Reach

Based in Toronto Canada Intact Financial operates across Canada and the US.

Sales and Marketing

The company distributes its products through independent agencies brokers wholesalers subsidiaries and managing general agencies.

Financial Performance

Company revenue for fiscal 2020 increased to C$12.1 billion compared from the prior year with $11.1 billion. The increase was primarily due to the C$ 1 billion increase on the company's domestic revenues.

Net income for fiscal 2020 increased to C$182 million compared from the prior year with C$165 million.

Cash held by the company at the end of fiscal 2020 decreased to C$917 million. Cash provided by operations and financing activities were C$2.4 billion and C$79 million respectively. Cash used for investing activities was C$2.4 billion mainly for proceeds from sale of investments.

Strategy

The Intact Data Lab is focused on data and information strategy the exploitation of enterprise data and research and development on new data sources. It will enhance its abilities to use data in risk and pricing but also enhance its sales and services abilities in the long term.

AI and machine learning have transformational potential for the insurance industry the economy and consumers. The company's strategic partnerships with academia (such as Montreal's IVADO Laval University and the Vector Institute) and the creation of the Intact Data Lab position the company to harness the potential of these emerging technologies now and into the future.

The company also constantly seeks to develop innovative and competitive products. Intact Financial launched the Intact Lab its center for digital excellence in 2015 to accelerate its digital innovation and expand its customer experiences by exploring advanced technology solutions in the service of its various lines of business in addition to partnering with user experience and digital analytics specialists project managers front-end developers research and development teams and other digital specialists from across the organization.

Mergers and Acquisitions

In 2021 Intact Financial announced that together with Tryg A/S (Tryg) it has completed the acquisition of RSA Insurance Group plc. (RSA) for cash consideration of approximately 7.2 billion ($12.5 billion). With the Acquisition Intact is taking a significant step to accelerate its strategy and drive significant value creation. Pursuant to the Acquisition Intact retains RSA's Canadian U.K. and International entities Tryg retains RSA's Swedish and Norwegian businesses and Intact and Tryg co-own RSA's Danish business.

Company Background

As ING Canada the company went public in 2004 and used a portion of the proceeds from the IPO to acquire the Canadian operations of Allianz Group. After the IPO Dutch insurance giant ING Groep held 70% of the company. It sold its holdings in 2008 to help offset losses elsewhere. Half of its holdings were sold to the public while the other half went to institutional investors. Following the separation the company changed its name to Intact Financial in 2009.

EXECUTIVES

Independent Director, Carolyn Wilkins
Independent Director, Janet De Silva
President, US and Specialty Solutions, Timothy Miller, $711,537 total compensation
Chief Executive Officer, Director, Charles Brindamour, $940,437 total compensation
President - Canadian Operations, Louis Gagnon, $559,340 total compensation
Independent Director, Timothy Penner
Chief Financial Officer, Senior Vice President, Louis Marcotte, $372,893 total compensation
Chief Operating Officer, Executive Vice President, Mathieu Lamy, $372,893 total compensation
Independent Director, Frederick Singer
Senior Vice President - Direct Distribution, Chief Marketing Officer, Anne Fortin
Senior Vice President, Chief Risk and Actuarial Officer, Benoit Morissette
Independent Director, Robert Leary
Senior Vice President - Claims, Patrick Barbeau
Senior Vice President, Managing Director of Intact Investment Management Inc, Werner Muehlemann
Senior Vice President - Commercial Lines, Intact Insurance, Darren Godfrey
Independent Director, Sylvie Paquette
Senior Vice President - Corporate and Legal Services, Secretary, Frederic Cotnoir
Independent Director, Jane Kinney
Independent Director, William Young
Senior Vice President - Personal Lines, Isabelle Girard
Independent Director, Stuart Russell
Independent Chairman of the Board, Claude Dussault
Executive Vice President of Intact Insurance Company, Debbie Coull-Cicchini
Senior Vice President and Chief Underwriting Officer, Specialty Solutions, North America, Peter Weightman
Auditors: Ernst & Young LLP

LOCATIONS

HQ: Intact Financial Corp
700 University Avenue, Toronto, Ontario M5G 0A1
Phone: 514 985-7111   **Fax:** 514 842-6958
Web: www.intactfc.com

2015 Premiums

	% of total
Ontario	41
Quebec	27
Alberta	18
British Columbia	6
Rest of Canada	8
Total	**100**

PRODUCTS/OPERATIONS

2015 Premiums

	% of total
Personal auto	45
Commercial property & casualty	23
Personal property	23
Commercial auto	9
Total	**100**

COMPETITORS

ALLEGHANY CORPORATION
ALLIANZ INSURANCE PLC
AMERICAN FINANCIAL GROUP INC.
AMERICAN INTERNATIONAL GROUP INC.
Argo Group International Holdings Ltd.
Aspen Insurance Holdings Limited

CNO FINANCIAL GROUP INC.
DST SYSTEMS INC.
FACTORY MUTUAL INSURANCE COMPANY
MARKEL CORPORATION
Picc Property And Casualty Company Limited
SOMPO HOLDINGS INC.
THE HARTFORD FINANCIAL SERVICES GROUP INC.
VERISK ANALYTICS INC.
ZENITH NATIONAL INSURANCE CORP.

HISTORICAL FINANCIALS

Company Type: Public

Income Statement

FYE: December 31

	ASSETS ($ mil.)	NET INCOME ($ mil.)	INCOME AS % OF ASSETS	EMPLOYEES
12/21	52,093	1,622	3.1%	26,000
12/20	27,582	849	3.1%	0
12/19	24,798	579	2.3%	0
12/18	20,899	519	2.5%	14,000
12/17	22,277	631	2.8%	0
Annual Growth	**23.7%**	**26.6%**	**—**	**—**

2021 Year-End Financials

Return on assets: 4.0%	Dividends
Return on equity: 16.3%	Yield: 0.0%
Long-term debt ($ mil.): —	Payout: 27.4%
No. of shares (mil.): 176	Market value ($ mil.): 22,903
Sales ($ mil.): 13,502	

	STOCK PRICE ($) FY Close	P/E High/Low		PER SHARE ($) Earnings	Dividends	Book Value
12/21	130.07	11	9	9.74	2.67	69.89
12/20	118.84	17	12	5.65	2.61	52.63
12/19	107.42	21	15	3.90	2.33	46.97
12/18	71.89	17	14	3.52	2.06	41.20
12/17	83.39	15	13	4.59	2.04	42.77
Annual Growth	**11.8%**	**—**	**—**	**20.7%**	**6.9%**	**13.1%**

Inter RAO UES PJSC

Auditors: Ernst & Young LLC (member of Ernst & Young Global Limited)

LOCATIONS

HQ: Inter RAO UES PJSC
Bolshaya Pirogovskaya Street, Building 27-2, Moscow 119435
Phone: (7) 495 664 88 40   **Fax:** (7) 495 664 88 41
Web: www.interrao.ru

HISTORICAL FINANCIALS

Company Type: Public

Income Statement

FYE: December 31

	REVENUE ($ mil.)	NET INCOME ($ mil.)	NET PROFIT MARGIN	EMPLOYEES
12/19	16,583	1,311	7.9%	0
12/18	13,811	1,015	7.4%	0
12/17	15,862	931	5.9%	0
12/16	14,178	992	7.0%	48,945
12/15	10,905	307	2.8%	50,797
Annual Growth	**11.0%**	**43.7%**	**—**	**—**

2019 Year-End Financials

Debt ratio: 0.0%	No. of shares (mil.): —
Return on equity: 15.7%	Dividends
Cash ($ mil.): 1,541	Yield: —
Current ratio: 2.99	Payout: 1,580.4%
Long-term debt ($ mil.): 7	Market value ($ mil.): —

Intesa Sanpaolo S.P.A.

The Intensa Sanpaolo group is one of the leading banking groups in Europe offering services to business sectors such as retail corporate and wealth management. The group caters about 13.5 million customers through 43000 branches domestically. The company has about 1000 branches internationally including subsidiary banks under its commercial banking in regions such as Central and Eastern Europe the middle East and North Africa. The group has six main business units; Bianca deo Territori IMI Corporate & Investment Banking; International Subsidiary Banks; Private Banking; Asset Management; Insurance; and the UBI Group. The group was founded in January 2007 from the merger of Banca Intesa and Sanpaolo IMI.

Operations

The group has six main business units; Bianca deo Territori IMI Corporate & Investment Banking; International Subsidiary Banks; Private Banking; Asset Management; Insurance; and the UBI Group.

The Banca del Territori account for more than 40% of the company's revenue. The IMI Corporate & Investment Banking which accounts for more than 30% of the company's revenue is responsible for corporate and transaction banking investment banking and public finance and capital markets in Italy and internationally.

The International Subsidiary Banks Division (10%) manages the group's activities in foreign markets through commercial banking subsidiaries and associates which are focuses in retail banking. The Private Banking segment (more than 10%) serves the top customer segment which is comprised of private and high net worth individuals.

The Asset management division (less than 10%) develops the best asset management solutions for the group's customers. The Insurance division includes the following businesses: Intesa Sanpaolo Vita Intesa Sanpaolo Life Fideuran Vita Intesa Sanpaolo Assicura and Intesa Sanpaolo RBM Salute.

Geographic Reach

The group caters about 13.5 million customers through 43000 branches domestically. It has about 1000 branches internationally including subsidiary banks under its commercial banking in regions such as Central and Eastern Europe the middle East and North Africa.

Italy accounts for about 80% of the company's operations with Europe accounting for more than 15%.

Sales and Marketing

Intensa Sanpaolo offers services to business sectors such as retail corporate and wealth management.

Financial Performance

Intesa's performance for the span of five years have slowly grown with the recent years seeing an upward trend.

For 2020 Intesa Sanpaolo's operating income grew 4.2% to ?19 billion as compared to 2019's operating income of about ?18.1 billion.

Net income increased by about 1% to ?7.7 billion in 2020 as compared to the prior year's net income of about ?7 billion.

Intesa Sanpaolo's cash position for 2020 amounted to ?9.8 billion. The bank's operations used ?2.1 billion. The group's investing activities used ?375 billion while its financing activities provided ?152 million.

Strategy

Intesa Sanpaolo's strategy is geared towards solid and sustainable value creation for all stakeholders with whom the Bank has relations. It is aiming at a sharp increase in profitability and efficiency while preserving a low risk profile deriving from solid revenue creation continuous cost management and dynamic credit and risk management with efficient use of capital and liquidity. Significant excess capital and high growth / high value businesses with a European scale allow Intesa Sanpaolo ample strategic flexibility.

Company Background

Intesa Sanpaolo is the result of the 2007 megamerger between Banca Intesa and Sanpaolo IMI. After the merger the company reshuffled its assets and sold off some branches in order to comply with antitrust orders and raise capital.

HISTORY

In Italy charity begins at home and often heads to the financial institutions. In 1563 Turin citizens founded Compagnia di San Paolo a foundation that provided education and dowries to orphaned girls and aid to impoverished nobility. In 1579 the organization began a pawn shop the Monte di Pieta or Mountain of Mercy (founded in 1519 and reopened by the Compagnia). The foundation grew over the next 200 years fattened by bequests and inheritances from wealthy Piedmontese families.

The French Republican government in Piedmonte gradually took control of the foundation's operations and closed it in 1802. The Monte di Pieta was reopened in 1804 and under the French influence became more bank-like. In 1848 the charitable and financial operations were formally divided.

Industrialization came slowly to Italy after its unification in the 1860s (the country remained largely agricultural until after WWII) and the organization survived a banking crisis from 1887 to 1894 by operating conservatively. It contributed to the WWI effort by purchasing government bonds. In 1928 the foundation separated Monte di Pieta's credit and pawn operations and adopted the name Istituto di San Paolo di Torino - Beneficenza e Credito (San Paolo).

Specialized institutions were founded in the 1920s to finance utilities and transportation; one of them La Centrale Societa per il Finanziamento di Imprese Elettriche e Telefoniche was formed in 1925 to help finance Italy's energy and telecommunications industries. In 1965 this entity enlarged its focus and changed its name to La Centrale Finanziaria Generale a forerunner of Banca Intesa.

La Centrale's interests in energy were transferred to ENEL the state holding company in 1985 leaving it with banking finance and insurance holdings. That year the bank merged with Nuovo Banco Ambrosiano formerly Banco Ambrosiano.

Banco Ambrosiano was founded in 1896 by Guiseppi Tovino whose good works and sturdy faith made him a saint (he was beatified in 1998). Betraying his legacy in 1981 chairman Roberto Calvi was found hanging under the Blackfriars Bridge in London. Calvi called "God's Banker" for his connections to the Vatican left behind a tangle of debt phony holding companies and fraud that implicated the Catholic Church brought down an archbishop and involved a secretive Masonic lodge. Banco Ambrosiano was taken over by a group of creditor banks and its name was changed to Nuovo Banco Ambrosiano.

In 1989 Nuovo Banco Ambrosiano merged with its subsidiary Banco Cattolica del Veneto and became known as Banco Ambroveneto. It bought La Cassa di Risparmio delle Provincie Lombarde (Cariplo) Italy's biggest savings bank in 1997; they merged to form Banca Intesa the following year. Cariplo was founded by the Austro-Hungarian government in 1823 when the region was still recovering from Napoleon's depredations. Count Giovanni Pietro Porro wanted to allow artisans and day laborers to set aside money and the company remained true to that mission throughout Italy's unification and two world wars.

Italy began its race toward privatization in 1990 to counter the growing interest of foreign banks in the Italian market and help the nation meet the criteria for joining the European Union. In 1992 San Paolo was one of the first banks to sell a 20% stake in itself (it sold another 20% in 1997). The bank bought several regional and national banks over the next few years and in 1998 merged with investment bank Istituto Mobiliare Italiano or IMI (founded 1931) to form Sanpaolo IMI.

Banca Intesa was the product of a combination of the staid Cassa di Risparmio delle Provincie Lombarde (Cariplo) and the somewhat more colorful Banco Ambroveneto whose history helped inspire the plot of The Godfather Part III . It took over Banca Commerciale Italiana (BCI or Comit) in 2000 creating one of Italy's largest banks. Banca Intesa integrated BCI to form IntesaBci the following year and then in late 2002 rebranded as Banca Intesa.

Banca Intesa and Sanpaolo IMI merged in 2007. After the deal antitrust authorities ordred the company to sell some 200 branches to France-based Credit Agricole. In late 2008 the Italian banking group sold 36 branches to Veneto Banca for ?274 million ($401 million).

A good portion of its branches were acquired in 2007 when Intesa Sanpaolo increased its stake in Banca CR Firenze to some 60% in preparation for taking over the bank outright. Banca CR Firenze added about 550 locations in Tuscany and surrounding regions to Intesa Sanpaolo's network.

The next year the bank upped its stake in Cassa dei Risparmi di Forli e della Romagna to about 70% increasing its influence in northern Italy. During more reshuffling of assets Intesa Sanpaolo sold a 30% stake in Cassa di Risparmio di Fano to Credito Valtellinese in 2009.

EXECUTIVES

Independent Director, Milena Motta, $271,178 total compensation

Chief Risk Officer, Davide Alfonsi

CEO, Fideuram - Intesa Sanpaolo Private Banking, Tommaso Corcos

Chief Institutional Affairs and External Communication, Stefano Lucchini

Independent Director, Alberto Pisani, $345,239 total compensation

Non-Executive Director, Franco Ceruti, $125,334 total compensation

Chief Audit Officer, Claudio Testa

Head of Insurance Division, Nicola Fioravanti

Head of Domestic Commercial Banking, Stefano Barrese

Non-Executive Chairman of the Board, Gian Maria Gros-Pietro, $934,312 total compensation

Independent Director, Maria Cristina Zoppo, $271,178 total compensation

Independent Director, Rosella Locatelli, $193,699 total compensation

Chief Operating Officer, Paola Angeletti

Head of the Asset Management Division, Saverio Perissinotto

Independent Director, Roberto Franchini, $176,607 total compensation

Chief IT, Digital and Innovation Officer, Massimo Proverbio

Head of the International Subsidiary Banks Division, Marco Rottigni

Chief Cost Management Officer, Alfonso Guido

Chief Financial Officer, Stefano Del Punta

Non-Executive Director, Bruno Picca, $113,940 total compensation

Chief Executive Officer, Managing Director, General Manager, Carlo Messina, $2,985,243 total compensation
Chief Governance officer, Paolo Grandi
Chief Lending Officer, Raffaello Ruggieri
Chief Compliance Officer, Piero Franco Maria Boccassino
Chief of IMI Corporate and Investment Banking Division, Mauro Micillo
Independent Director, Livia Pomodoro, $193,699 total compensation
Independent Deputy Chairperson of the Board, Paolo Colombo, $364,609 total compensation
Independent Director, Maria Mazzarella, $125,334 total compensation
Auditors: KPMG S.p.A.

LOCATIONS

HQ: Intesa Sanpaolo S.P.A.
Piazza San Carlo, 156, Torino 10121
Phone: (39) 011 555 1
Web: www.group.intesasanpaolo.com

2018 Sales

	% of total
Italy	80
Europe	16
Rest of the world	4
Total	**100**

PRODUCTS/OPERATIONS

2018 Sales

	% of total
Net interest income	41
Net fee and commission income	44
Profits on tradings	6
Income from insurance business	9
Total	**100**

2018 sales

	%
Banca del Territori	50
Corporate and Investment Banking	20
International Subsidiary Banking	10
Private Banking	10
Asset Management	4
Insurance	6
Total	**100**

Selected Subsidiaries

Banca CR Firenze
Banca dell'Adriatico
Banca di Credito Sardo
Banca di Trento e Bolzano
Banca Fideuram
Banca IMI
Banca Intesa
Banca Intesa Beograd
Banca Monte Parma
Banca Prossima
Banco di Napoli
Bank of Alexandria
Banka Koper
Cassa dei Risparmi di Forlì e della Romagna
Cassa di Risparmio del Friuli Venezia Giulia
Cassa di Risparmio del Veneto
Cassa di Risparmio della Provincia di Viterbo (CARIVIT)
Cassa di Risparmio di Civitavecchia
Cassa di Risparmio di Pistoia e della Lucchesia
Cassa di Risparmio di Rieti (CARIRI)
Cassa di Risparmio di Venezia
Cassa di Risparmio in Bologna
Casse di Risparmio dell'Umbria
CIB Bank
Epsilon Associati SGR
Equiter
Eurizon A.I. SGR
Eurizon Capital
IMI Fondi Chiusi SGR
IMI Investimenti
Infogroup

COMPETITORS

BANCA NAZIONALE DEL LAVORO SPA IN FORMA CONTRATTA BNL SPA
BANCO BILBAO VIZCAYA ARGENTARIA SOCIEDAD ANONIMA
BANCO POPULAR ESPA 'OL SA (EXTINGUIDA)
BPER BANCA SPA
Co ¶peratieve Rabobank U.A.
DZ BANK AG Deutsche
Nordea Bank AB
Skandinaviska Enskilda Banken AB
UniCredit Bank AG

HISTORICAL FINANCIALS

Company Type: Public

Income Statement   FYE: December 31

	ASSETS ($ mil.)	NET INCOME ($ mil.)	INCOME AS % OF ASSETS	EMPLOYEES
12/20	1,230,498	4,021	0.3%	105,615
12/19	916,291	4,695	0.5%	59,998
12/18	902,094	4,638	0.5%	92,117
12/17	955,240	8,770	0.9%	1
12/16	765,620	3,284	0.4%	89,126
Annual Growth	**12.6%**	**5.2%**	**—**	**4.3%**

2020 Year-End Financials

Return on assets: 0.3%
Return on equity: 5.3%
Long-term debt ($ mil.): —
No. of shares (mil.): —
Sales ($ mil): 44,543
Dividends
Yield: 0.0%
Payout: 20.0%
Market value ($ mil.): —

	STOCK PRICE ($) FY Close	P/E High/Low	PER SHARE ($) Earnings	Dividends	Book Value
12/20	14.15	106 54	0.22	0.04	4.17
12/19	15.73	67 51	0.27	0.96	3.59
12/18	13.42	91 52	0.27	1.03	3.54
12/17	19.96	49 35	0.53	0.93	4.25
12/16	15.23	108 56	0.19	0.63	3.26
Annual Growth	**(1.8%)**	**— —**	**3.8%**	**(48.6%)**	**6.4%**

Investec Ltd

Auditors: Ernst & Young Inc.

LOCATIONS

HQ: Investec Ltd
100 Grayston Drive, Sandown, Sandton 2196
Phone: (27) 11 286 7000   **Fax:** (27) 11 286 7777
Web: www.investec.com

HISTORICAL FINANCIALS

Company Type: Public

Income Statement   FYE: March 31

	ASSETS ($ mil.)	NET INCOME ($ mil.)	INCOME AS % OF ASSETS	EMPLOYEES
03/20	32,143	542	1.7%	5,784
03/19	45,516	424	0.9%	5,284
03/18	80,962	710	0.9%	0
03/17	66,835	552	0.8%	9,716
03/16	65,280	530	0.8%	8,966
Annual Growth	**(16.2%)**	**0.6%**	**—**	**(10.4%)**

2020 Year-End Financials

Return on assets: 1.5%
Return on equity: 21.9%
Long-term debt ($ mil.): —
No. of shares (mil.): 267
Sales ($ mil): 2,456
Dividends
Yield: —
Payout: —
Market value ($ mil.): —

Investec plc

Investec plc is one half of a dual-listed financial services firm providing private banking asset management brokerage and investment banking primarily to wealthy clients and financial institutions. (Partner Investec Limited is based in South Africa.) Investec plc delivers solutions for its clients in three core areas: Asset Management Wealth and Investment and Specialist Banking. It makes half of its operating income through its various Specialty Banking services and the rest comes from its Asset Management and Wealth & Investment services. Investec plc's top markets are in the UK Europe and Australia.

Operations

Investec plc operates three business segments: Specialist Banking Asset Management and Wealth & Investment.

Specialist Banking generates about 40% of the company's overall revenue. It manages principal investments which provide capital to entrepreneurs and existing commercial enterprises and via property investment and property fund management. It also offers corporate and institutional banking activities such as treasury and trading services specialized lending (including funds & debt) and institutional research. This segment also makes available private banking services like foreign exchange lending deposits and investments. Specialist Banking serves entrepreneurs business of all sizes institutions private equity managers and high net worth investors.

Asset Management makes money for its clients by allocating their investment funds to various financial instruments including physical property equities bonds and the like. It hosts nearly 200 investment professionals operates through five geographically-defined departments all supported by the company's global operations platform. It accounts for roughly 35% of revenue.

Wealth & Investment tends to the investment needs of charities pension schemes and private individuals. It's Investec Wealth & Investment subsidiary manages services for UK clients while other units (such as Investec Bank Switzerland Investec Wealth & Investment Ireland and Investec Capital Asia Limited) cares for non-UK customers. In general the segment provides investments and savings vehicles pensions and retirement schemes and financial planning.

Broadly speaking Investec plc generates 60% of total revenue from fee and commission income about 20% from interest income and the rest from trading and other income sources. Investec plc manages some 95 billion in assets.

Geographic Reach

London-based Investec plc has a scattered worldwide presence. In Europe it has a well-established brand and operations particularly in the UK Switzerland the Republic of Ireland and Guernsey. It also conducts business via offices in Canada Hong Kong Singapore Australia and India.

Financial Performance

Investec plc interest income rose about 3% in FY2017 (ended 31 March 2017) to 563 million and fee income jumped nearly 15% to 932 million. Investment income was 60 million and trading income rose about 40% to $130 million. In total the firm earned 1.7 billion. Operating income for the year rose 18% to 1.2 billion.

Earnings for FY2017 were 160 million up more than 30% compared to the prior year. Investec plc continued to lower its impairment charges by managing down the quality-challenged assets contained in its legacy UK loan portfolio.

Cash at the end of the year was 3.7 billion up 257 million from the prior year. Operating activities contributed 375 million while investing and financing activities combined used about 125 million.

Strategy

Following the 2015 divestitures businesses Investec Bank (Australia) Ltd Kensington Group plc (UK) and Start Mortgage Holdings Ltd (Republic of Ireland) the firm's operations and financial results stabilized. In 2017 it appears poised to pursue growth opportunities. It brought on board additional personnel in part to help build out its suite of UK private offerings. It spent money to improve its IT infrastructure and even funded upgrades to its UK office space.

Although former businesses were shed in years past some leftover financial headwinds still require attention. The company continues to actively manage down the UK legacy portfolio in which are held a number of asset experiencing credit quality issues. Since the peak in 2012 when it held some 200 million of legacy impairments Investec plc has steadily reduced such assets to a 2017 mark of some 50 million. The lower amount reduces overall risk to the company and lowers the amount of loan loss allowance is must put aside in anticipation of loan defaults.

One of its strengths is its international reach which allows clients to invest deposit obtain financing and move money between countries where its customers live work and holiday. Operating from its UK base it can assist customers located in countries linked to past and present British ties including Australia Republic of Ireland Canada and into South Africa where its corporate affiliate calls home.

Investec plc must be doing something right as the amount of funds under management grew nearly 20% in 2017 to 97 billion. Customer deposits ticked up 2% to 11 billion.

According to reports Investec entered talks in 2019 to sell its private client stockbroking business in Ireland for up to $68 million to either Brewin Dolphin Holdings Allied Irish Banks or Rathbone Brothers.

Company Background

With its beginnings as a South African leasing company Investec expanded into the UK in 2002. In 2010 it acquired UK asset manager Rensburg Sheppards (now Investec Wealth & Investment) boosting its funds under management by about half.

EXECUTIVES

Group Chief Executive Officer, Executive Director, Fani Titi
Group Chief Finance Officer, Group Finance Director, Executive Director, Nishlan Samujh
Independent Non-Executive Director, Henrietta Baldock
Independent Non-Executive Director, Philisiwe Sibiya
Group Chief Operating Officer, Executive Director, James Whelan
Executive Director, Richard Wainwright
Independent Non-Executive Director, Jasandra Nyker
Independent Non-Executive Director, Nicky Newton-king
Independent Non-Executive Director, Brian Stevenson
Auditors: Ernst & Young LLP

LOCATIONS

HQ: Investec plc
  30 Gresham Street, London EC2V 7QP
Phone: (44) 20 7597 4000   **Fax:** (44) 20 7597 4491
Web: www.investec.com

PRODUCTS/OPERATIONS

FY2017 Operating Income

	% of total
Net Interest income	20
Fee and commission income	65
Trading income	10
Investment income	4
Others	1
Total	**100**

FY2017 Operating Income

	% of total
Speciality Banking	52
Wealth & Investment	22
Asset Management	26
Total	**100**

Selected Segments

Asset Management
Wealth & Investment
Specialist Banking

COMPETITORS

BANCO DE SABADELL SA
Bank of Communications Co. Ltd.
COMMUNITY BANK SYSTEM INC.
Canaccord Genuity Group Inc
FIRSTRAND LTD
Fiera Capital Corporation
ITAU UNIBANCO HOLDING SA

SANTANDER UK GROUP HOLDINGS PLC
STANDARD BANK GROUP LTD
Shin Kong Financial Holding Co. Ltd.
Shinhan Financial Group Co. Ltd.
TP ICAP FINANCE PLC

HISTORICAL FINANCIALS

Company Type: Public

Income Statement				FYE: March 31
	ASSETS ($ mil.)	NET INCOME ($ mil.)	INCOME AS % OF ASSETS	EMPLOYEES
03/20	30,791	797	2.6%	0
03/19	29,653	247	0.8%	0
03/18	28,963	190	0.7%	0
03/17	23,456	199	0.9%	9,716
03/16	26,998	176	0.7%	8,966
Annual Growth	3.3%	45.8%	—	—

2020 Year-End Financials

Return on assets: 2.7%
Return on equity: 27.6%
Long-term debt ($ mil.): —
No. of shares (mil.): 664
Sales ($ mil): 1,666
Dividends
  Yield: 0.0%
  Payout: —
Market value ($ mil.): 3,021

	STOCK PRICE ($) FY Close	P/E High/Low	PER SHARE ($) Earnings	Dividends	Book Value
03/20	4.55	— —	(0.00)	0.54	4.44
03/19	12.65	— —	(0.00)	0.00	4.51
Annual Growth	(64.1%)	— —	—	—	(0.4%)

Israel Discount Bank Ltd.

Who doesn't love a discount? Israel Discount Bank the third-largest bank in Israel has about 150 locations across the country. The bank offers standard consumer services like deposits loans and credit cards in addition to private banking international trade and commercial banking activities. Israel Discount Bank oversees four subsidiaries — Discount Mortgage Bank Mercantile Discount Bank (which has about 75 branches) Israel Discount Bank of New York and IDB (Swiss) Bank Ltd. It also owns a 26% stake in First International Bank of Israel the country's fifth-largest bank. In 2015 IDB sold Uruguay-based subsidiary Discount Bank Latin America to Bank of Nova Scotia in a deal worth $65 million.

Company Background

In 2010 Israel Discount Bank announced it was selling off Tachlit Investment House its portfolio management subsidiary that has about $3 billion in assets under management.

EXECUTIVES

Executive Vice President, The Internal Auditor, Nir Abel
Senior Executive Vice President, Head of the Retail Banking Division, Yafit Gheriani
Senior Executive Vice President, Chief Risk Officer and Head of Risk Management Division, Avraham Levy
Independent Director, Miriyam Katz
External and Independent Director, Shalom Hochman
Director, Reuven Adler
Executive Vice President, Head of the Financial Markets Division, Asaf Pasterna
Independent Director, Iris Avner
Chairman of the Board of Directors, Shaul Kobrinsky
External and Independent Director, Baruch Lederman
External and Independent Director, Aharon Abramovich
Director, Yodfat Harel Buchris
Executive Vice President, Head of Operations and Properties Division, Assaf Eldar
Executive Vice President, Chief Legal Counsel and Head of the Legal Counsel Division, Hagit Hamdani Meirovitz
Senior Executive Vice President, Chief Accountant and Head of the Accounting Division, Joseph Beressi
Independent Director, Yaacov Lifshitz
Senior Executive Vice President, Head of the Group Management and Regulation Division, Esther Deutsch
Director, Ben-Zion Zilberfarb
Executive Vice President, Head of the Planning, Strategy and Finance Division, Barak Nardi
Senior Executive Vice President, Head of the Corporate Division, Yuval Gavish, $296,835 total compensation
President, Chief Executive Officer, Uri Levin
Auditors: Ziv Haft

LOCATIONS

HQ: Israel Discount Bank Ltd.
  23 Yehuda Halevi Street, Tel-Aviv 65136
Phone: (972) 3 514 5555   **Fax:** (972) 3 514 5346
Web: www.discountbank.co.il

HSBC HOLDINGS PLC
HSBC NORTH AMERICA HOLDINGS INC.
INTER-AMERICAN DEVELOPMENT BANK (INC)
INTERNATIONAL MONETARY FUND
Luen Thai Co
SINOPAC FINANCIAL HOLDINGS COMPANY LIMITED
THE WORLD BANK GROUP

HISTORICAL FINANCIALS

Company Type: Public

Income Statement

FYE: December 31

	ASSETS ($ mil.)	NET INCOME ($ mil.)	INCOME AS % OF ASSETS	EMPLOYEES
12/19	75,199	492	0.7%	9,472
12/18	63,744	401	0.6%	9,407
12/17	63,728	362	0.6%	9,374
12/16	57,168	235	0.4%	9,401
12/15	52,477	191	0.4%	9,710
Annual Growth	9.4%	26.6%	—	(0.6%)

2019 Year-End Financials

Return on assets: 0.6%	Dividends
Return on equity: 9.5%	Yield: 0.0%
Long-term debt ($ mil.): —	Payout: 98.2%
No. of shares (mil.): 116	Market value ($ mil.): 5,471
Sales ($ mil): 3,281	

	STOCK PRICE ($) FY Close	P/E High/Low	PER SHARE ($) Earnings	Dividends	Book Value
12/19	47.00	32 23	0.42	0.41	46.44
12/18	30.23	28 20	0.34	0.18	39.27
12/17	29.97	27 22	0.31	0.00	38.59
12/16	19.03	22 19	0.22	0.00	33.37
12/15	16.50	26 21	0.18	0.00	32.24
Annual Growth	29.9%	— —	23.5%	—	9.6%

Isuzu Motors, Ltd. (Japan)

Isuzu Motors was the first company in Japan to successfully develop a diesel engine. It consistently provided the innovative products and services with a focus on developing and manufacturing commercial vehicles (CVs) light commercial vehicles (LCVs) and diesel engines. It offers an array of products from light-duty pickup trucks to heavy-duty tractors. Its industrial engine can be found in construction machinery commercial boats and vessels generators and other products. The company also offer after-sales service. Major customers include Tri Petch Isuzu Sales Co. Ltd General Motors Corporations. Its vehicles sales accounts for about 70% of its revenue majority of which came of its Japan market.

Operations

The company compose a single business segment primarily engaged in the manufacture and sale of vehicle (around 70% of the revenue) its components (more than 5%) and industrial engine (less than 5%).

The company's major product lineup includes light- to heavy- duty truck known with its exceptional fuel efficiency reliability durability and advanced environmental performance. Its offers a range of powertrain options not only diesel engines but also CNG and hybrid models to meet the full range of customer needs and applications its buses meanwhile earned customer's trust by delivering outstanding comfort and safety.

Geographic Reach

Headquartered in Tokyo Japan is the company's largest market representing more around 40% of total sales. Other major market includes Thailand generating nearly 19%. Other countries produces the remaining over 40%.

Sales and Marketing

Isuze supplies and sells its products in the form of vehicles and vehicle components through a network of distributors in Europe Middle East Africa Asia Oceania & Pacific Ocean North America Central America & the Caribbean and South America. Some of its customers Tri Petch Isuzu Sales Co. Ltd as well as General Motors Corporation and its affiliates.

Financial Performance

Net sales for the year ended 2020 totaled 2.1 trillion a 3% dip from the previous year.

Profit attributable to the company fell 28% to 81.2 billion.

The company's cash for the year ended 2020 totaled 304 billion. Operating activities generated 123.7 billion while investing activities used 92.7 billion mainly for capital expenditures. Financing activities used another 25.2 billion mainly for repayments on long-term debts.

Strategy

Isuzu Motors Limited continues to work on expanding sales by taking advantage of the global network facilities it built under the previous Midterm Business Plan which enables it to more quickly deliver vehicles that accommodate changes in customers' operating conditions and modes of use.

HISTORY

After collaborating on car and truck production for 21 years Tokyo Ishikawajima Shipbuilding and Engineering and Tokyo Gas and Electric Industrial formed Tokyo Motors Inc. in 1937. The partners began producing the A truck (1918) and the A9 car (1922) under licenses from Wolseley (UK).

Tokyo Motors made its first truck under the Isuzu nameplate in 1938. It spun off Hino Heavy Industries in 1942. By 1943 the company was selling trucks powered by its own diesel engines mostly to the Japanese military.

By 1948 the company was Japan's premier maker of diesel engines. It was renamed Isuzu (Japanese for "50 bells") in 1949. With generous public- and private-sector financing and truck orders from the US Army during the Korean War Isuzu survived and refined its engine- and truck-making prowess. A pact with the Rootes Group (UK) enabled Isuzu to enter automaking. Beginning in 1953 Isuzu built Rootes' Hillman Minx in Japan.

Despite its strong reputation as a truck builder Isuzu suffered financially and by the late 1960s its bankers were shopping the company around to more stable competitors. GM after witnessing rapid Japanese progress in US and Asian auto markets bought about 34% of Isuzu in 1971. During the 1970s Isuzu launched the popular Gemini car and gained rapid entry to the US through GM exporting such vehicles as the Chevy Luv truck and the Buick Opel.

As exports to GM waned Isuzu set up its own dealer network in the US in 1981. That year GM CEO Roger Smith told a stunned Isuzu chairman Toshio Okamoto that Isuzu lacked the global scale GM was seeking. Smith asked Okamoto for help in buying a piece of Honda. After Honda declined and GM settled for 5% of Suzuki Isuzu extended its GM ties building the Geo Storm and establishing joint production facilities in the UK and Australia.

Despite a high-profile advertising campaign featuring Joe Isuzu the company suffered in the 1980s in its efforts to gain any kind of significant share of the US passenger car market. Post-1985 yen appreciation hurt exports. Subaru-Isuzu Automotive a joint venture with Fuji Heavy Industries initiated production of Rodeos in Lafayette Indiana in 1989.

After Isuzu lost nearly $500 million in 1991 and 1992 it called on GM for help. GM responded by sending Donald Sullivan a strategic business planning expert to become Isuzu's #2 operations executive.

Isuzu signed a joint venture with Jiangxi Automobile Factory and ITOCHU in 1993 to build light-duty trucks in China. In 1994 Nissan and Isuzu agreed to cross-supply vehicles.

Isuzu weathered a public relations storm in 1996 when Consumer Reports magazine claimed that the top-selling Trooper sport utility vehicle was prone to tip over at relatively low speeds. Isuzu dismissed the report as unscientific and the National Highway Traffic Safety Administration sided with the automaker. In 1997 the company sued the magazine for defamation. (Isuzu lost the case in 2000.) Also in 1997 Isuzu agreed to develop GM's diesel engines and began constructing a plant in Poland to supply engines to GM's Germany-based subsidiary Opel AG.

The next year GM and Isuzu announced a joint venture to make diesel engines in the US. Also in 1998 Isuzu announced restructuring plans that included cutting 4000 jobs and reducing the number of its domestic marketing subsidiaries. In 1999 the plant in Poland opened and GM boosted its stake in Isuzu to 49%. Isuzu also agreed to form a joint venture with Toyota to manufacture buses.

Amid mounting losses and pressure from GM Isuzu announced a management shake-up in 2001 that included naming GM chairman John Smith Jr. as special advisor and installing Randall Schwarz (GM truck group) as VP. Days later Isuzu announced its "Isuzu V plan" its sweeping cost-savings scheme that included job cuts and the closure of one factory.

The Isuzu V plan was revised in 2002 when the company announced GM would write off its entire stake while infusing Isuzu with about $84 million. Near the close of 2002 Isuzu agreed to sell its 49% stake in carmaking joint venture Subaru-Isuzu Automotive Inc. to Fuji Heavy Industries (FHI). When the deal was completed in January 2003 FHI renamed the company Subaru of Indiana Automotive Inc.

Isuzu had some rocky going in the early part of the 21st century. The company asked its creditor banks to forgive 100 billion yen (about $750 million) in debt in exchange for stakes in the company. As part of the plan GM wrote off its entire stake in Isuzu and reinfused the ailing carmaker with $84 million. The deal resulted in a recapitalized Isuzu and reduced GM's stake to 8%. Early in 2006 GM sold its 8% stake in Isuzu to entities including Mitsubishi Corporation ITOCHU Corporation and Mizuho Corporate Bank.

As 2006 wound near its close Toyota Motor picked up a 6% stake in Isuzu Motors from Mitsubishi and ITOCHU. The two companies agreed to cooperate on engine technologies with Isuzu focusing on small diesel engines and diesel emission controls and Toyota concentrating on environmental improvements to gasoline engines and alternative fuels.

EXECUTIVES

Vice President, Chief Director of Technology, Director, Takahashi Shinichi

President, Representative Director, Masanori Katayama

Managing Executive Officer, Director, Koichi Seto

Managing Executive Officer, Director, Shun Fujimori

Managing Executive Officer, President of Isuzu Motors International, Shigeji Sugimoto

Independent Director, Mitsuyoshi Shibata

Senior Managing Executive Officer, Director, Shinsuke Minami

Managing Executive Officer, Kazuya Igeta

Managing Executive Officer, Chairman of Subsidiary, Director, Tetsuya Ikemoto

Managing Executive Officer, Tetsuya Aiba

Independent Director, Kozuru Nakayama

Independent Director, Tetsuhiko Shindo

Independent Director, Kimie Sakuragi

Independent Director, Kanji Kawamura

Auditors: Ernst & Young ShinNihon LLC

LOCATIONS

HQ: Isuzu Motors, Ltd. (Japan)
6-26-1 Minami-Oi, Shinagawa-ku, Tokyo 140-8722
Phone: (81) 3 5471 1169
Web: www.isuzu.co.jp

2016 Sales

	% of total
Japan	36
Thailand	18
Other	46
Total	**100**

PRODUCTS/OPERATIONS

2016 Sales

	% of total
Vehicles	72
Engines & components	5
Parts of overseas production	4
Other	19
Total	**0**

Selected Vehicles and Brands

Buses
  Erga heavy-duty bus
  Erga Mio medium-duty bus
Commercial vehicles
  C&E Series heavy-duty trucks & tractors
  F Series medium-duty trucks
  N Series light-duty trucks
Diesel engines
  Automotive
  Industrial
  Marine
Pickup trucks & SUVs
  D-MAX
  MU-7 (Thailand)
  Panther (Indonesia)

Selected Subsidiaries and Affiliates

Anadolu Isuzu Otomotiv Sanayi Ve Ticaret AS (Turkey)
DMAX Ltd. (US)
Isuzu Australia Limited
Isuzu Motors Europe N.V. (Belgium)
Isuzu (China) Holding Co. Ltd.
Isuzu Commercial Truck of America Inc.
Isuzu Commercial Truck of Canada Inc.
Isuzu Motors America LLC
Isuzu Motors Asia Ltd. (Singapore)
Isuzu Motors Co. (Thailand) Ltd.
Isuzu Motors Germany GmbH
Isuzu Motors Polska Sp. zo. o. (Poland)
Isuzu Philippines Corporation
Isuzu Truck (UK) Ltd.
P.T. Isuzu Astra Motor Indonesia
Qingling Motors Co. Ltd. (China)

COMPETITORS

FORD MOTOR COMPANY LIMITED	RENAULT
HONDA MOTOR CO. LTD.	SUBARU CORPORATION
MITSUBISHI MOTORS	SUZUKI MOTOR CORPORATION

CORPORATION   Scania AB
PEUGEOT SA

HISTORICAL FINANCIALS

Company Type: Public

Income Statement

	REVENUE ($ mil.)	NET INCOME ($ mil.)	NET PROFIT MARGIN	EMPLOYEES
03/21	17,233	385	2.2%	46,407
03/20	19,161	748	3.9%	46,925
03/19	19,406	1,024	5.3%	47,255
03/18	19,497	995	5.1%	44,532
03/17	17,469	839	4.8%	42,610
Annual Growth	**(0.3%)**	**(17.7%)**	**—**	**2.2%**

FYE: March 31

2021 Year-End Financials

Debt ratio: 0.1%
Return on equity: 4.3%
Cash ($ mil.): 3,655
Current ratio: 1.90
Long-term debt ($ mil.): 2,196
No. of shares (mil.): 738
Dividends
  Yield: 2.5%
  Payout: —
Market value ($ mil.): 7,983

	STOCK PRICE ($) FY Close	P/E High/Low		PER SHARE ($) Earnings	Dividends	Book Value
03/21	10.81	0	0	0.52	0.27	12.50
03/20	6.46	0	0	1.01	0.35	11.89
03/19	13.14	0	0	1.36	0.32	11.37
03/18	15.44	0	0	1.26	0.30	10.98
03/17	13.23	0	0	1.07	0.30	9.28
Annual Growth	**(4.9%)**	**—**		**(16.3%)**	**(2.1%)**	**7.7%**

Itau CorpBanca

As Chile's oldest operating bank CORPBANCA has been processing procuring and protecting pesos since 1871. Through its network of more than 120 branches (which operate under the Corp-Banca and Banco Condell banners) across Chile the bank offers the conventional range of commercial and retail banking services. It also owns and operates 500-plus ATMs in Chile. CorpBanca also has a New York branch. It additionally offers mutual fund management financial advisory and insurance brokerage services. Key subsidiaries include Corredores de Seguros an insurance provider and Corredores de Bolsa a securities brokerage. Itau Unibanco acquired CORPBANCA in April 2016.

EXECUTIVES

Independent Director, Pedro Samhan Escandar
Corporate Director - Treasury, Pedro Silva Yrarrazaval
Director, Rogerio Carvalho Braga
Independent Director, Gustavo Arriagada Morales
Director, Fernando Aguad Dagach
Chairman of the Board, Jorge Andres Saieh Guzman
Vice Chairman of the Board, Ricardo Villela Marino
Corporate Director - People Management and Performance, Marcela Jimenez Pardo
Director, Jorge Selume Zaror
Corporate Director - Digital Business Development, Jorge Novis Neto
Corporate Director - Marketing and Products, Luciana Hildebrandi Marchione
Independent Director, Fernando Concha Ureta

Chief Risk Officer, Mauricio Baeza Letelier
General Counsel, Cristian Toro Canas
Corporate Director - Retail Banking, Julian Acuna Moreno
Chief Executive Officer, Director, Gabriel Amado de Moura
Director, Milton Maluhy Filho
Independent Director, Bernard Pasquier
Corporate Director - Wholesale Banking, Christian Tauber Dominguez
General Manager, New York Branch, Joaquin Walbaum
Chief Compliance Officer, Cristobal Soto
Chief Audit Officer, Emerson Vergara
Director, Matias Granata
Corporate Director - Information Technology, Eduardo Neves
Chief Executive Officer - Itau Corpbanca Colombia, Baruc Saez
Auditors: PricewaterhouseCoopers Consultores Auditores SpA

LOCATIONS

HQ: Itau CorpBanca
Rosario Norte 660, Santiago, Las Condes
Phone: (56) 2 660 2240   **Fax:** (56) 2 660 2206
Web: www.itau.cl

PRODUCTS/OPERATIONS

Selected Subsidiaries
Corp Legal S.A.
CorpBanca Administradores General de Fondos S.A.
CorpBanca Agencia de Valores S.A.
CorpBanca Asesoríʒas Financieras S.A.
CorpBanca Corredores de Seguros S.A.
CorpBanka Corredores de Bolsa S.A.
SMU Corp S.A.

COMPETITORS

DnB ASA
FIRST CITIZENS BANCORPORATION INC.
INVESTORSBANCORP INC.
SINOPAC FINANCIAL HOLDINGS COMPANY LIMITED
STANDARD BANCSHARES INC

HISTORICAL FINANCIALS

Company Type: Public

Income Statement

	ASSETS ($ mil.)	NET INCOME ($ mil.)	INCOME AS % OF ASSETS	EMPLOYEES
12/20	49,924	(1,137)	—	8,364
12/19	45,602	154	0.3%	8,987
12/18	42,251	246	0.6%	9,179
12/17	45,581	110	0.2%	9,492
12/16	43,355	21	0.0%	9,607
Annual Growth	**3.6%**	**—**	**—**	**(3.4%)**

FYE: December 31

2020 Year-End Financials

Return on assets: (-2.3%)
Return on equity: (-29.0%)
Long-term debt ($ mil.): —
No. of shares (mil.): —
Sales ($ mil): 1,951
Dividends
  Yield: 6.2%
  Payout: —
Market value ($ mil.): —

	STOCK PRICE ($) FY Close	P/E High/Low		PER SHARE ($) Earnings	Dividends	Book Value
12/20	4.95	—	—	(0.00)	0.31	0.01
12/19	8.61	63	34	0.00	0.15	0.01
12/18	13.60	45	36	0.00	0.09	0.01
12/17	13.44	120	87	0.00	0.00	0.01
12/16	12.44	414	328	0.00	0.56	0.01
Annual Growth	**(20.6%)**	**—**	**—**		**(13.7%)**	**(9.1%)**

Itau Unibanco Holding S.A.

Ita Unibanco is the largest private bank in Brazil the largest financial institution in Latin America and one of the largest in the world by market cap. It offers financial products and services for different sectors of the economy and leaders in several segments in which it operates whether in solutions for individuals micro small and medium-sized companies and very small companies. It provides investment banking securities brokerage and insurance services. Besides its network of more than 4335 branches and site branches and around 195 digital branches the firm boasts operations in Brazil Latin America and in about 20 countries. Banco Ita merged with Unibanco in 2009 to become Ita Unibanco.

Operations

The company has three business segments. These are Retail Banking (nearly 65% of the total sales) Wholesale Banking (about 30%) and Activities with the Market and Corporation (roughly 10%).

Retail Banking consists of business with retail customers account holders and non-account holders individuals and legal entities high income clients (Ita Uniclass and Personnalite) and the companies segment (microenterprises and small companies). It includes financing and credit offers made outside the branch network in addition to credit cards and payroll loans.

Wholesale banking consists of products and services offered to middle-market companies high net worth clients (Private Banking) and the operation of Latin American units and Ita BBA which is the unit responsible for business with large companies and investment banking operations.

Overall the company provides mortgage loans consortia brokerage private pension products and insurance just to name a few. It has partnerships with Itaucard Hipercard Credicard and ConnectCar.

In addition net interest income and non-interest income generated equally half of the company's sales.

Geographic Reach

Headquartered in S o Paulo Brazil it has its presence in Latin America's and with operations in nearly 20 countries.

Sales and Marketing

Wholesale Banking looks after customers with high financial net worth (private banking) through units in Latin America banking for middle-market and large companies and corporations through the activities of Ita BBA the unit responsible for corporate clients and in its role as an investment bank.

Retail Banking offers its services to account holders and non-account holders.

Financial Performance

The company's revenue for fiscal 2020 decreased by 1% to R$117.9 billion compared from the prior year with R$119.6 billion.

Profit for fiscal 2020 decreased by 46% to R$15.1 billion compared from the prior year with R$27.8 billion.

Strategy

Ita Unibanco's compensation and benefit strategies vary according to the area of activity and market parameters. The company's fixed and variable compensation policy is in line with market practices and its compensation strategy varies according to the unit in which each employee works. The company periodically verifies these parameters by: commissioning salary surveys conducted by specialized consultants; and participating in specialized compensation and benefit forums.

Auditors: PricewaterhouseCoopers Auditores Independentes

LOCATIONS

HQ: Itau Unibanco Holding S.A.
Praca Alfredo Egydio de Souza Aranha, n 100, Sao Paulo 04344-902
Phone: (55) 11 5019 1267
Web: www.itau.com.br

PRODUCTS/OPERATIONS

2015 Sales

	% of total
Interest and similar income	73
Banking service fees	15
Income related to insurance and private pension	11
Other income	1
Total	**100**

COMPETITORS

BANK VTB PAO
BPCE
Banco Bradesco S/A
Banco Santander Brasil S/A
Banco do Brasil S/A
CAIXABANK SA
CHINA MINSHENG BANKING CORP. LTD.
CREDIT INDUSTRIEL ET COMMERCIAL
China Construction Bank Corporation
DnB ASA
METROPOLITAN BANK HOLDING CORP.

NATIONAL AUSTRALIA BANK LIMITED
NATIONAL BANK HOLDINGS CORPORATION
SANTANDER UK GROUP HOLDINGS PLC
SBERBANK PAO
SMITH & WILLIAMSON HOLDINGS LIMITED
The Bank of Nova Scotia
W.H. IRELAND GROUP PLC
Woori Finance Holdings Co. Ltd.

HISTORICAL FINANCIALS

Company Type: Public

Income Statement
FYE: December 31

	ASSETS ($ mil.)	NET INCOME ($ mil.)	INCOME AS % OF ASSETS	EMPLOYEES
12/20	388,799	3,638	0.9%	56,444
12/19	407,363	6,745	1.7%	94,881
12/18	400,090	6,417	1.6%	100,300
12/17	433,165	7,215	1.7%	99,332
12/16	415,782	7,147	1.7%	94,779
Annual Growth	(1.7%)	(15.5%)	—	(12.2%)

2020 Year-End Financials

Return on assets: 1.0%
Return on equity: 13.4%
Long-term debt ($ mil.): —
No. of shares (mil.): —
Sales ($ mil): 28,287

Dividends
Yield: 4.4%
Payout: 72.6%
Market value ($ mil.): —

	STOCK PRICE ($) FY Close	P/E High/Low		PER SHARE ($) Earnings	Dividends	Book Value
12/20	6.09	4	2	0.37	0.22	5.55
12/19	9.15	4	3	0.69	0.64	6.87
12/18	9.14	5	3	0.66	0.55	7.11
12/17	13.00	6	4	0.73	0.25	8.21
12/16	10.28	5	3	0.73	0.24	7.49
Annual Growth	(12.3%)	—	—	(15.4%)	(1.8%)	(7.2%)

ITOCHU Corp (Japan)

Itochu Enex is totally immersed in Japan's oil and gas markets. The company operates some 45 subsidiaries. The home life segment supplies liquefied petroleum gas (LPG) to some 1.5 million homes and businesses throughout Japan. The company's car life and industrial materials divisions operate full service gas stations and sells gasoline kerosene and oil to service stations. The group is engaged in the sale of LPG gasoline Kerosene diesel oil fuel oil asphalt electricity automobiles and other goods.

Operations

The group operates four reportable segments: Car-Life (some 60% of sales) Industrial Business (approximately 20%) Home-Life and Power & Utility (each accounts for some 10%).

The Car-Life division is engaged in sales and services involving LPG kerosene diesel oil electricity automobiles car rental and automotive products as well as in import/export of petroleum products and terminal tank rental.

The Industrial Business division is engaged in sales and service involving gasoline kerosene diesel oil fuel oil LPG high grade urea solution AdBlue GTL fuel corporate fleet refuelling cards asphalt and marine fuels as well as in the fly ash recycling business and slop recovery and recycling business.

The Home-Life division is engaged in sales and services involving LPG kerosene town gas industrial gas electricity household equipment smart energy equipment remodelling residential lithium-ion electricity storage systems pressure resistance inspection for gas containers and welding materials.

The Power Utility division is engaged in the sale of electricity (coal-fired natural gas-fired wind hydro and photovoltaic power) and steam as well as in providing district heating services comprehensive energy services electricity/heat supply services electric power supply/demand management services and asset management business.

Geographic Reach

The company is headquartered in Japan.

Sales and Marketing

The home-life division serves some 1.5 million customers throughout Japan corporate users and some 2700 distributors. The car-life division serves approximately 1700 affiliated car-life stations. The industrial business division serves some 3500 corporate users domestic road construction companies sea shippers and public agencies. The power and utility division serves corporations individuals electricity retailers office buildings and commercial facilities.

Financial Performance

The company's revenue in 2020 decreased to 897.4 billion due to a decrease of 81.6 billion in the company's Car-Life segment.

Net income for 2020 increased to 19.3 billion compared to 17.9 billion in the prior year.

Cash held by the company at the end of 2020 increased to 19.2 billion from 18.7 billion in 2018. Cash provided by operations was 28.1 billion while cash used for investing and financing activities were 1.4 billion and 26.2 billion respectively. Main uses of cash were payments for purchases of property plant and equipment and investment property.

Strategy

The company is implementing the two-year medium-term business plan "Moving 2020 Horizons" part of the growth strategy the company initiated based on the theme of "Moving". The strategies focus on: deepening connections utilizing new tools and expanding abroad.

Using all of its resources the company is working to create new businesses including the development of environment-related businesses. In 2019 Itochu Enex focuses on expanding sales of GTL fuel and the use of this fuel has begun at New Yokohama City Hall and a major construction company.

EXECUTIVES

Independent Director, Motoyo Yamane
Managing Executive Officer, Director, Fumio Shimizu
President, Chief Executive Officer, Representative Director, Kenji Okada
Independent Director, Ichiro Saeki
Chief Compliance Officer, Senior Managing Executive Officer, Director, Kyosuke Wakamatsu
Director, Hisato Ohkubo
Executive Officer, Manager of Home Life, Tatsuro Utsumi
Chief Financial Officer, Chief Information Officer, Managing Executive Officer, Manager of Corporate, Director, Atsushi Katsu
Independent Director, Hiroshi Endo
Auditors: Deloitte Touche Tohmatsu LLC

LOCATIONS

HQ: ITOCHU Corp (Japan)
3-1-3 Umeda, Kita-ku, Osaka 530-8448
Phone: (81) 6 7638 2121   **Fax:** 212 818-8293
Web: www.itochu.co.jp

PRODUCTS/OPERATIONS

2014 Sales

	% of total
Energy Trade	25
Car-Life	59
Total	13
Power and Utility	3
Other	-
Total	**100**

COMPETITORS

COMPANHIA BRASILEIRA DE PETROLEO IPIRANGA	RS ENERGY K.K.
NGL TM LLC	SAN-AI OIL CO.LTD.
PETROLEUM TRADERS CORPORATION	SUN COAST RESOURCES INC.
	TAUBER OIL COMPANY

HISTORICAL FINANCIALS

Company Type: Public

Income Statement			FYE: March 31
	REVENUE ($ mil.)	NET INCOME ($ mil.)	NET PROFIT MARGIN	EMPLOYEES
---	---	---	---	---
03/21	93,589	3,625	3.9%	171,829
03/20	101,178	4,618	4.6%	174,713
03/19	104,750	4,519	4.3%	158,517
03/18	51,890	3,770	7.3%	132,062
03/17	43,275	3,150	7.3%	124,469
Annual Growth	**21.3%**	**3.6%**	**—**	**8.4%**

2021 Year-End Financials

Debt ratio: 0.2%	No. of shares (mil.): 1,487
Return on equity: 12.7%	Dividends
Cash ($ mil.): 4,913	Yield: 2.5%
Current ratio: 1.20	Payout: 63.8%
Long-term debt ($ mil.): 22,082	Market value ($ mil.): 97,166

	STOCK PRICE ($) FY Close	P/E High/Low		PER SHARE ($) Earnings	Dividends	Book Value
03/21	65.33	0	0	2.44	1.63	20.14
03/20	40.92	0	0	3.09	1.63	18.49
03/19	36.14	0	0	2.93	1.35	17.40
03/18	39.19	0	0	2.43	1.13	16.19
03/17	28.41	0	0	2.00	0.97	13.69
Annual Growth	**23.1%**	**—**		**5.1%**	**13.9%**	**10.1%**

Iyo Bank, Ltd. (Japan)

With 15-plus branches and about a dozen subsidiaries The Iyo Bank targets customers across the four prefectures of Shikoku and the seven prefectures surrounding the Seto Inland Sea. The institution which has grown to become Japan's #1 regional bank offers retail products including deposits leasing services trusts and pension products and mergers and acquisitions support services. The Iyo Bank also operates a securities brokerage business arm. Its Corporate Consulting Division helps companies galvanize their operations and capital. Established in 1941 the bank owns and operates branch offices in Hong Kong Shanghai and New York. It boasts alliances with banks in China Thailand Indonesia and India.

EXECUTIVES

Chairman of the Board, Iwao Otsuka
Vice President, Group Chief Operating Officer, Representative Director, Kenji Takata
Director, Tetsuo Takeuchi
Managing Director, Group Chief Strategy Officer, Director of General Planning, Manager of Related Business Office in General Planning Unit, Hiroshi Nagata
Independent Director, Kaname Saeki
President, Group Chief Executive Officer, Representative Director, Kenji Miyoshi
Managing Director, Group Chief Risk Officer, Kensei Yamamoto
Managing Director, Group Chief Credit Officer, Director of Ship Finance, Masamichi Ito
Independent Director, Junko Miyoshi
Independent Director, Keiji Joko
Managing Director, Group Chief Business Officer, Chief Director of Sales, Director of Direct Sales, Hirohisa Senba
Independent Director, Yuichi Ohashi
Independent Director, Yoriko Noma
Auditors: KPMG AZSA LLC

LOCATIONS

HQ: Iyo Bank, Ltd. (Japan)
1 Minami-Horibatacho, Matsuyama, Ehime 790-8514
Phone: (81) 89 941 1141
Web: www.iyobank.co.jp

Selected Branch Locations

Head Offic
Aichi
Fukuoka
Hiroshima
Hyogo
Kagawa
Kochi
Oita
Okayama
Osaka
Tokushima
Tokyo
Yamaguchi

PRODUCTS/OPERATIONS

Selected Subsidiaries

Computer Services Inc. Iyogin
Iyogin Business Service Co. Ltd.
Iyogin Capital Co. Ltd.
Iyogin guarantee Ltd.
Iyogin Leasing Co. Ltd.
Iyogin Securities Co. Ltd.
Ltd. Iyo silver Regional Center for Economic Research
Ltd. Iyogin Dee Sea card

COMPETITORS

CHUGOKU BANKLIMITED THE	JUROKU BANKLTD. THE
	SHIZUOKA BANK LTD. THE

HISTORICAL FINANCIALS

Company Type: Public

Income Statement			FYE: March 31
	ASSETS ($ mil.)	NET INCOME ($ mil.)	INCOME AS % OF ASSETS	EMPLOYEES
---	---	---	---	---
03/20	71,815	174	0.2%	4,485
03/19	64,704	167	0.3%	4,558
03/18	66,831	222	0.3%	4,589
03/17	61,260	194	0.3%	4,575
03/16	57,972	217	0.4%	4,511
Annual Growth	**5.5%**	**(5.4%)**	**—**	**(0.1%)**

2020 Year-End Financials

Return on assets: 0.2%	Dividends
Return on equity: 2.9%	Yield: —
Long-term debt ($ mil.): —	Payout: 23.4%
No. of shares (mil.): 316	Market value ($ mil.): —
Sales ($ mil.): 1,165	

J Sainsbury PLC

J Sainsbury is one of the UK's largest food retailer Sainsbury's operates about 600 supermarkets roughly 815 convenience stores throughout the UK and an e-commerce offering. In addition to groceries Sainsbury's sells apparel (under the Tu brand) homeware and cookware (Sainsbury's Home and Habitat) and consumer electronics. Its Argos brand sells consumer goods through stand-alone stores in Sainsbury's supermarkets and online. The company also offers consumer banking through Sainsbury's Bank which provides banking and insurance products to its some 1.8 million customers.

Operations

J Sainsbury operates around 2150 supermarkets convenience stores and Argos stores in the UK and Ireland as well as its online business. The business are organized into three operating segments; Retail ? Food; Retail ? General Merchandising and Clothing; and Financial Services. The company's retailing business generates almost all of the company's total revenue. Financial services include Sainsbury's Bank plc and Argos Financial Services entities and provides its customers with affordable ways to manage its finances and reward them for their loyalty through Nectar. Argus operates in about 735 stores nearly 600 Sainsbury's in supermarkets and roughly 815 Sainsbury's in convenient stores.

Geographic Reach

Based in London Sainsbury trades predominantly in the UK and the Republic of Ireland.

Sales and Marketing

Two thirds of the UK population have shopped with Sainsbury. It has some 7.4 million downloads of the Nectar app who benefit from the UK's leading loyalty programme. In the company's Financial Services business it has some 1.8 million active Sainsbury's Bank customers and around 2.2 million Argos Financial Services customers.

Financial Performance

In fiscal 2021 (ended March) Sainsbury's revenue increased to 29.04 billion compared from 28.99 billion in the prior year.

Net loss for fiscal 2021 was 261 million compared to a profit of 255 million.

Cash held by the company at the end of fiscal 2021 increased to 1.5 billion. Cash provided by operations was 2.3 billion while investing and financing activities used 553 million and 1.3 billion respectively. Main cash uses were purchase of property plant and equipment; and repayment of short-term borrowings.

Strategy

Sainsbury is raising its ambitions and speeding up the pace of change simplifying its operations and accelerating its cost savings programmes so the company can invest more in food quality choice innovation and consistently lower prices for its customers. Sainsbury's portfolio brands are supporting its core food business delivering for customers and shareholders in their own right. And the company will pursue partnerships or outsource where faster and where they will make a big impact for its customers.

The company is reducing complexity aiming to reduce its retail operating costs to sales ratio by at least 200 basis points and is focused on robust profit delivery and consistent dependable cash flow. By delivering for its customers Sainsbury will drive stronger financial outcomes.

Mergers and Acquisitions

In the same year it paid around 60 million to bring its long-running loyalty program Nectar into direct ownership. The scheme had been operated by the UK arm of Aimia Inc.

In February 2016 Sainsbury's acquired Home Retail Group for 1.3 billion (around $1.9 billion). Home Retail Group's Argos business is a leading consumer products retailer in the UK. The combined company makes Sainsbury's one of the UK largest food and non-food retailers with over 90000 products 2000 stores.

HISTORY

Newlyweds John James and Mary Ann Sainsbury established a small dairy shop in their London home in 1869. Customers flocked to the clean and efficient store a far cry from most cluttered and dirty London shops. They opened a second store in 1876. By 1914 115 stores had been opened and the couple's sons had entered the business.

During WWI the company's stores established grocery departments to meet demand for preserved products such as meat and jams which were sold under the Sainsbury's label.

Mary Ann died in 1927 and John James the next year. Son John Benjamin wholly devoted to the family business took charge. (He is reported to have said on his deathbed "Keep the stores well lit.") In the 1930s he engineered the company's first acquisition the Thoroughgood stores.

Sales dropped by 50% during WWII and some shops were destroyed by German bombing. Under third-generation leader Alan John Sainsbury the company opened its first self-service store in 1950 in Croydon. The 75000-sq.-ft. store opened in 1955 in Lewisham was considered to be the largest supermarket in Europe.

J Sainsbury went public in 1973. It established a joint venture with British Home Stores in 1975

forming the Savacentre hypermarkets (the company bought out its partner in 1989).

Sainsbury partnered with Grand Bazaar Innovation Bon Marche of Belgium in 1979 to establish Homebase a do-it-yourself chain. (It bought the remaining 25% in 1996 and then sold the company in 2001 retaining only 18%.)

By 1983 most of Sainsbury's 229 stores were clustered in the south of England. A mature market and stiff competition forced the company to look elsewhere — both overseas and close to home. It began buying out US-based Shaw's Supermarkets in New England and in 1984 opened its first Scottish hypermarket. By 1987 the grocer owned 100% of Shaw's which had 60 stores in Massachusetts Maine and New Hampshire.

In 1991 Sainsbury came under competitive pressure from Tesco and the Argyll Group (later renamed Safeway plc) which also began building superstores. It responded with an expansion drive of its own including opening its first Scottish supermarket (in Glasgow) the next year.

In 1994 the company purchased a $325 million stake in Maryland-based Giant Food. Sainsbury bought home improvement retailer Texas Homecare from UK leisure concern Ladbroke in 1995 and integrated it into its Homebase unit. The following year it bought 12 supermarkets in Connecticut from Dutch retailer Ahold Delhaize (the purchase lowered its profits for the year) and entered Northern Ireland.

A year later the company opened Sainsbury's Bank. Royal Ahold bought Giant Food including Sainsbury's 20% stake in 1998. David Sainsbury — a great-grandson of the founders — retired as chairman in 1998 to pursue politics marking the first time a Sainsbury had not headed up the company in its more-than-a-century history.

As a cost-cutting effort in 1999 Sainsbury cut 2200 jobs more than half in management. It also launched its convenience store concept called Sainsbury's Local. Also that year Sainsbury bought the 53-store Star Markets chain of Massachusetts merging it into its Shaw's operations. In March 2000 Sir Peter Davis took over as CEO of Sainsbury's Supermarkets replacing David Bremner.

In 2001 Sainsbury acquired 19 Grand Union stores in the US (17 of which were converted to the Shaw's banner) and opened 25 new stores in the UK. The company also exited the Egyptian market and sold its home-and-garden chain Homebase to private equity firm Permira.

In 2002 Shaw's Supermarkets bought control of 18 stores in New England from bankrupt discounter Ames.

In November 2003 Sainsbury reached a 2 million out-of-court settlement with designer Jeff Banks over termination of his contract to revamp its clothing line in a bid to emulate rival ASDA's success with its George line of apparel.

In January 2004 the grocery chain acquired Swan Infrastructure (an Accenture affiliate) the company that ran its information technology systems for about $1 billion. The move brought the grocers information technology operations which were outsourced in 2000 back in-house.

In February 2004 Sainsbury acquired 54 Bells convenience stores. (Bells Stores was founded in 1968 by Les Bell and was owned by the Bell family until its acquisition.) Justin King (formerly of Marks & Spencer) joined Sainsbury as its CEO in March 2004 succeeding Sir Peter Davis who became chairman of the board. In April Sainsbury sold JS USA Holdings which operated 203 Shaw's and Star Markets stores in New England to US grocery chain Albertson's in a deal worth about $2.4 billion. The retailer also disposed of JS Developments its property development operation in fiscal 2004. Davis stepped down as chairman of Sainsbury on July 1 2004 one year ahead of schedule and fol-

lowing a prolonged dispute with investors that culminated in a fight over his compensation.

Philip Hampton (former finance director of Lloyds TSB (now Lloyds Banking Group) BT Group and BG Group) joined Sainsbury as its new chairman on July 19 2004. Hampton's appointment and experience with mergers and acquisitions fueled speculation that the struggling grocery chain may become a takeover target. In August Sainsbury acquired Jacksons Stores Ltd. and its wholly owned subsidiary Jacksons Stores 2002 Ltd. for about 100 million. In September Sainsbury agreed to pay ex-chairman Davis 2.6 million despite shareholder protests in July that forced the grocery retailer to withdraw a similar offer. At that time Lord Levene of Portsoken and Keith Butler-Wheelhouse both nonexecutive directors of the company and members of the remuneration committee resigned from the board.

In October 2004 Sainsbury said it was writing off 140 million against information technology systems and an another 120 million linked to ineffective supply-chain equipment as a result of a huge infrastructure investment program instituted by ex-chairman Davis that failed. In November the company acquired JB Beaumont a convenience store chain with six stores in the East Midlands. In 2005 the grocery chain acquired the five-store SL Shaw chain in southeastern England. Sainsbury renamed the shops Sainsbury's Local. The acquisitions pushed Sainsbury's convenience store count to nearly 300 outlets throughout the UK giving the company a 2% share of the convenience market.

The company sold 5% of its majority stake in Sainsbury's Bank in February 2007 to its joint venture partner HBOS for about 21 million ($40 million). As a result the bank became a 50-50 joint venture between the two firms. Also in 2007 the company shutdown its online entertainment division Sainsbury's Entertain You which offered books CDs DVDs videos computer games and a DVD rental service citing stiff competition in the online arena. The company removed hydrogenated fats from its branded products in 2007.

In mid-2008 Qatar Holding-backed real estate investment group Delta Two increased its stake in Sainsbury to about 25% fueling speculation that it may attempt to take over the British grocer. (In 2007 Delta Two made a bid to buy the remainder of the company but withdrew the offering in November amid turmoil in the credit markets.) Delta Two was the second suitor to leave the grocery chain at the altar. The company and key shareholders from the founding Sainsbury family rebuffed a group of private equity investors led by CVC Capital earlier in the year.

In mid-2009 the grocery chain launched online sales of some 8000 nonfood items such as kitchenware and furniture. It also extended its online home grocery delivery service to an additional 200 stores. The company welcomed David Tyler formerly chairman of Logica as its new chairman in November 2009. Tyler succeeded Sir Philip Hampton.

In November 2010 the company launched Sainsbury's Entertainment a digital download service that provides customers with access to more than 150000 books DVDs Blu-rays CDs and games to purchase online.

EXECUTIVES

Company Secretary and Corporate Services Director, Tim Fallowfield

Senior Non-Executive Independent Director, Dame Rice

Group HR Director, Angie Risley

Non-Executive Independent Director, Brian Cassin

Non-Executive Independent Director, Jo Harlow
Chairman, Martin Scicluna
Non-Executive Independent Director, Keith Weed
Non-Executive Independent Director, Tanuj Kapilashrami
Non-Executive Independent Director, Adrian Hennah
Chief Executive Officer, Sainsbury's Bank, Jim Brown
Chief Executive Officer and Director, Simon Roberts, $871,347 total compensation
Chief Financial Officer and Director, Kevin O'Byrne, $850,631 total compensation
Chief Information Officer, Phil Jordan
Food Commercial Director, Rhian Bartlett
Chief Marketing Officer, Mark Given
Auditors: Ernst & Young LLP

LOCATIONS

HQ: J Sainsbury PLC
33 Holborn, London EC1N 2HT
Phone:
Web: www.about.sainsburys.co.uk

PRODUCTS/OPERATIONS

2019 sales

	%
Retailing	9
Financial services	2
Total	**100**

2019 Stores

	No.
Sainsbury's Supermarkets	608
Convenience stores	820
Argos	
Standalone	594
In Sainsbury's	281
In Homebase	8
Habitat	16
Total	**2,327**

PRODUCTS

Summer
Fruit & veg
Meat & fish
Dairy eggs & chilled
Bakery
Frozen
Food cupboard
Drinks
Health & beauty
Baby
Household
Pet
Home
Cook event
Electronics

COMPETITORS

C&S WHOLESALE GROCERS INC.
CO-OPERATIVE GROUP LIMITED
COLES GROUP LIMITED
KINGFISHER PLC
Koninklijke Ahold Delhaize N.V.
Loblaw Companies Limited
MARKS AND SPENCER GROUP P.L.C.
SUPERVALU INC.
TARGET CORPORATION
WOOLWORTHS GROUP LIMITED

HISTORICAL FINANCIALS

Company Type: Public

Income Statement				FYE: March 6
	REVENUE ($ mil.)	NET INCOME ($ mil.)	NET PROFIT MARGIN	EMPLOYEES
03/21	40,138	(386)	—	180,000
03/20	37,734	197	0.5%	171,400
03/19	37,921	286	0.8%	179,900
03/18	39,329	427	1.1%	186,900
03/17	31,840	457	1.4%	181,900
Annual Growth	6.0%	—	—	(0.3%)

2021 Year-End Financials

Debt ratio: 5.5%
Return on equity: (-3.9%)
Cash ($ mil.): 2,040
Current ratio: 0.60
Long-term debt ($ mil.): 1,033

No. of shares (mil.): —
Dividends
  Yield: 0.0%
  Payout: —
Market value ($ mil.): —

	STOCK PRICE ($) FY Close	P/E High/Low		PER SHARE ($) Earnings	Dividends	Book Value
03/21	12.80	—	—	(0.18)	0.57	4.12
03/20	11.11	215	161	0.08	0.54	4.58
03/19	11.69	196	128	0.12	0.48	5.01
03/18	13.66	119	94	0.18	0.49	4.67
03/17	13.24	81	60	0.20	0.49	3.81
Annual Growth	(0.8%)	—	—	—	3.9%	2.0%

Japan Post Bank Co Ltd

Auditors: KPMG AZSA LLC

LOCATIONS

HQ: Japan Post Bank Co Ltd
2-3-1 Otemachi, Chiyoda-ku, Tokyo 100-8793
Phone: (81) 3 3477 0111
Web: www.jp-bank.japanpost.jp

HISTORICAL FINANCIALS

Company Type: Public

Income Statement				FYE: March 31
	REVENUE ($ mil.)	NET INCOME ($ mil.)	NET PROFIT MARGIN	EMPLOYEES
03/21	17,581	2,529	14.4%	16,054
03/20	16,577	2,518	15.2%	16,383
03/19	16,663	2,403	14.4%	17,006
03/18	19,257	3,322	17.3%	17,635
03/17	16,111	2,792	17.3%	12,965
Annual Growth	2.2%	(2.4%)	—	5.5%

2021 Year-End Financials

Debt ratio: —
Return on equity: 2.7%
Cash ($ mil.): 598,937
Current ratio: —
Long-term debt ($ mil.): —

No. of shares (mil.): —
Dividends
  Yield: —
  Payout: —
Market value ($ mil.): —

Japan Post Holdings Co Ltd

Auditors: KPMG AZSA LLC

LOCATIONS

HQ: Japan Post Holdings Co Ltd
2-3-1 Otemachi, Chiyoda-Ku, Tokyo 100-8791
Phone: (81) 03 3477 0111
Web: www.japanpost.jp

HISTORICAL FINANCIALS

Company Type: Public

Income Statement				FYE: March 31
	REVENUE ($ mil.)	NET INCOME ($ mil.)	NET PROFIT MARGIN	EMPLOYEES
03/21	105,851	3,777	3.6%	390,775
03/20	110,089	4,456	4.0%	400,001
03/19	115,356	4,329	3.8%	407,488
03/18	121,675	4,337	3.6%	411,078
03/17	119,192	(259)	—	415,801
Annual Growth	(2.9%)	—	—	(1.5%)

2021 Year-End Financials

Debt ratio: —
Return on equity: 3.3%
Cash ($ mil.): 657,027
Current ratio: —
Long-term debt ($ mil.): —

No. of shares (mil.): —
Dividends
  Yield: —
  Payout: —
Market value ($ mil.): —

Japan Post Insurance Co Ltd

Auditors: KPMG AZSA LLC

LOCATIONS

HQ: Japan Post Insurance Co Ltd
2-3-1 Otemachi, Chiyoda-ku, Tokyo 100-8794
Phone: (81) 3 3477 2383
Web: www.jp-life.japanpost.jp

HISTORICAL FINANCIALS

Company Type: Public

Income Statement				FYE: March 31
	REVENUE ($ mil.)	NET INCOME ($ mil.)	NET PROFIT MARGIN	EMPLOYEES
03/21	60,649	1,500	2.5%	10,694
03/20	65,291	1,388	2.1%	10,802
03/19	70,167	1,087	1.6%	10,983
03/18	73,896	983	1.3%	11,009
03/17	76,015	792	1.0%	11,036
Annual Growth	(5.5%)	17.3%	—	(0.8%)

2021 Year-End Financials

Debt ratio: 0.0%
Return on equity: 6.9%
Cash ($ mil.): 49,892
Current ratio: —
Long-term debt ($ mil.): 2,709

No. of shares (mil.): 562
Dividends
  Yield: —
  Payout: —
Market value ($ mil.): —

Japan Tobacco Inc.

The company controls around 60% of Japan's cigarette market — one of the largest in the world — driven by its MEVIUS brand followed by Winston and Seven Stars among others. Japan Tobacco International handles JT's business outside Japan where it has operations in more than 70 countries and sales in more than 130. Japan Tobacco owns or has international rights to such brands as Winston Camel MEVIUS and LD. The company also has holdings in the fast-growing pharmaceutical and processed food businesses. JT gets nearly two-thirds of its revenue from international markets.

Operations

Japan Tobacco's international business JT International generates around 60% of Japan Tobacco's revenue. It sells cigarettes under brands including Winston Camel and Natural American Spirit; loose tobacco for rolling; snus under the brand Nordic Spirit and vapes under the Logic and Ploom brands.

In Japan JT is the market leader in tobacco products with a 60% market share. Its primary brands are MEVIUS Winston Seven Stars Natural American Spirit and Camel. Sales of tobacco products in Japan account for roughly 30% of JT's total sales.

Beyond tobacco the company is active in processed food and pharmaceuticals. TableMark Co. Ltd generates more than 5% of JT's sales and produces frozen and ambient processed food including frozen noodles frozen and cooked rice bread and seasoning. In the pharmaceutical business (about 5%) JT researches and develops treatments for metabolic diseases viral infections and autoimmune/inflammatory diseases. Subsidiary Torii Pharmaceutical Co handles its manufacturing sales and promotion in Japan.

Geographic Reach

Japan Tobacco's head office is in Tokyo. International subsidiary Japan Tobacco International (JTI) is headquartered in Geneva Switzerland. International markets include Europe Asia Africa Middle East and the Americas.

The company's cigarettes and other products are manufactured at more than 40 factories spanning all major continents. The International market generates nearly two-thirds of revenue and the remaining comes from Japan.

Sales and Marketing

Depending on the market JT sells its products through various channels such as supermarkets convenience stores street and train station kiosks and independent retailers.

The Megapolis Group in Russia is one of JTI's biggest customers representing more than 10% of its revenue in the international segment.

Financial Performance

Note: Growth rates may differ after conversion to US Dollars.

The Japan Tobacco Inc.'s performance over the span of five years have fluctuated with its performance being the highest in 2018 then decreased annually. Revenue decreased 83 billion or about 4% year-on-year to 2.1 trillion.

Cash held by the company by the end of 2020 was 538.8 billion. Cash provided by operations was 519.8 billion and Investing activities provided 297.4 billion while financing activities used 5.4 billion and respectively. Main use for cash was dividends paid to owners of the parent company

Strategy

The tobacco business has been focusing on sustainable profit growth consistently playing a pivotal role in JT Group's profit growth. Its role continues to be of paramount importance for the achievement of mid to high single-digit adjusted operating profit growth at constant currency which is its main target. In light of the evolving operating environment the company has been enhancing its focus on the sustainability of the profit growth generated by the tobacco business. Additionally in order to strengthen and speed up the decision-making process Japan Tobacco has streamlined the management structure as demonstrated by its Group CEO Masamichi Terabatake directly heading the tobacco business.

Company Background

Japan Tobacco is the result of the liberalization of the Japanese tobacco market in the mid-1980s. The government department that held a monopoly on the sale of tobacco products in Japan from 1898 was converted into a joint stock company and foreign companies were allowed to compete in the Japanese marketplace. The company changed significantly in the late 90s with the acquisition of R. J. Reynolds' non-US tobacco business which included the brands Camel Winston and others. Around that time it also entered the pharmaceutical and processed foods business.

HISTORY

In 1898 roughly 325 years after tobacco was introduced in Japan the nation's Ministry of Finance formed a bureau to monopolize its production to fund military and industrial expansion.

During WWII Japan's tobacco leaf imports from North and South America grew scarce and led to cigarette rationing. In 1949 the government began operating the tobacco production bureau as a business: the Japan Tobacco and Salt Public Corporation (in 1905 the bureau also became responsible for a salt monopoly).

The company launched Hope the first Japanese-made filter cigarette in 1957 and it became the world's best seller a decade later. In 1972 it began printing mild packaging "warnings": "Be careful not to smoke excessively for your health."

Japan Tobacco and Salt began selling Marlboro cigarettes licensed from Philip Morris in 1973. The Mild Seven brand (its current best-seller) went on sale in 1977; it became the world's #1 cigarette in 1981 but dropped to #2 (behind Marlboro) in 1993.

When its tobacco monopoly ended in 1985 the government established the firm as Japan Tobacco (a government-owned joint stock company). As competition from foreign imports increased the firm came up with new means of making yen. It formed Japan Tobacco International (cigarette exports mainly to the US and Southeast Asia) moved into agribusiness and real estate operations and in 1986 created JT Pharmaceutical. In 1987 cigarette import tariffs ended and importers lowered prices to match the company's; its sales and market share subsequently declined. During the late 1980s it introduced HALF TIME beverages and its first low-tar cigarettes (Mild Seven Lights is now the world's #1 light cigarette).

In 1992 Japan Tobacco bought its first overseas production facility Manchester Tobacco (closed in 2001). Former Ministry of Finance official Masaru Mizuno became CEO that year — and soon took up smoking. Also in 1992 the company and Agouron Pharmaceuticals agreed to jointly develop immune system drugs; in 1994 they added antiviral drugs. The government sold about 20% of the firm's stock to the public in 1994 and 13% in 1996. The firm began operating Burger King restaurants in Japan in 1996. Japan Tobacco bought Pillsbury Japan in 1998.

Japan Tobacco in 1999 paid nearly $8 billion for R.J. Reynolds International the international tobacco unit of what was then RJR Nabisco. The company then renamed the unit which has operations in 70 countries worldwide JT International. It also bought the food products division of Asahi Chemical Torii Pharmaceutical from Asahi Breweries and the Unimat vending machine company.

Slowing sales prompted Japan Tobacco to announce in 2000 that it would reduce its workforce by 6100 by 2005. Company exec Katsuhiko Honda became CEO that year (Mizuno remained as chairman) and said he'd push the government to sell its stake. Honda retired in 2006. In February 2001 the company announced plans to sell parts of its

OTC drugs and health care businesses to Nichiiko Pharmaceutical to concentrate on prescription drugs. It also intends to sell all 25 of its Burger King outlets. In May Mizuno stepped down as chairman and was replaced by Takashi Ogawa.

In December 2001 Japan's Ministry of Finance recommended that it cut its holdings in the company from 66% to 50%; it would also allow the company to sell additional shares which could further dilute the government's stake to as little as 33%. In 2002 Japan Tobacco completed the sale of its 25 Burger King outlets and its OTC drug business.

In January 2004 the company unveiled six new brands: Mild Seven One Menthol Box Bitter Valley Fuji Renaissance Fuji Renaissance 100's Hi-Lite Menthol and BB Slugger. An added brand Hope Menthol currently being tested in the marketplace also will see expanded availability. Japan Tobacco's Canadian subsidiary filed for bankruptcy protection in August 2004 following a billion-dollar smuggling claim by the Canadian government. Canada said that the company owed $1.4 billion in Canadian back taxes for allegedly smuggling cigarettes in 1998 and 1999.

Japan Tobacco in 2005 ended its agreement with Philip Morris to make and sell Marlboro cigarettes. The company closed 13 of its 25 manufacturing plants and six of its 30 sales branches by early 2006 as part of an effort to increase profits. These reductions slashed as many as 4000 jobs from company payrolls as demand for cigarettes partly depressed by higher taxes continues to decline. Japan Tobacco is also using its own line of premium smokes to fill the gap left in the product line by the absence of Marlboro cigarettes. The company's deal with Philip Morris to sell Marlboro lapsed in 2005.

In April 2007 JT acquired Britain's Gallaher Group for about $15 billion. The purchase which added Silk Cut and Benson & Hedges cigarette brands to its products portfolio was the largest foreign acquisition by a Japanese company.

In January 2008 the company acquired a majority stake in Katokichi Co. for about $900 million. It then sold a 49% stake in the business to Nissin Foods forming a joint venture. In April JT entered the seasonings business acquiring a controlling stake in Fuji Foods.

At the end of 2008 Japan Tobacco placed Hans Group its Australia-based chilled foods venture and its subsidiaries into administration under the care of KordaMetha.

In 2009 Japan Tobacco acquired the UK's Tribac Leaf and Brazil-based leaf suppliers Kannenberg & Cia and Kannenberg Barker Hail & Cotton Tabacos.

EXECUTIVES

Independent Director, Masato Kitera
Independent Director, Main Koda
Chairman of the Board, Yasutake Tango
Vice President, Representative Director, Naohiro Minami
Vice President, Representative Director, Kiyohide Hirowatari
President, Chief Executive Officer, Chief Director of Tobacco Business, Chairman of Subsidiary, Representative Director, Masamichi Terabatake
Independent Director, Yukiko Nagashima
Senior Managing Executive Officer, Director, Kazuhito Yamashita
Vice Chairman of the Board, Mutsuo Iwai
Auditors: Deloitte Touche Tohmatsu LLC

LOCATIONS

HQ: Japan Tobacco Inc.
4-1-1 Toranomon, Minato-ku, Tokyo 105-6927
Phone: (81) 3 6636 2914 **Fax:** 201 871-1417
Web: www.jti.co.jp

PRODUCTS/OPERATIONS

2018 Sales

	% of total
International tobacco	59
Japanese domestic tobacco	28
Processed food	7
Pharmaceutical	6
Total	**100**

COMPETITORS

ALTRIA GROUP INC.	PHILIP MORRIS
BRITISH AMERICAN	INTERNATIONAL INC.
TOBACCO P.L.C.	PYXUS INTERNATIONAL
IMPERIAL BRANDS PLC	INC.
LORILLARD TOBACCO	REYNOLDS AMERICAN INC.
COMPANY LLC	UNIVERSAL CORPORATION

HISTORICAL FINANCIALS

Company Type: Public

Income Statement				FYE: December 31
	REVENUE ($ mil.)	NET INCOME ($ mil.)	NET PROFIT MARGIN	EMPLOYEES
12/20	20,302	3,010	14.8%	64,981
12/19	20,039	3,207	16.0%	69,091
12/18	20,150	3,507	17.4%	70,586
12/17	19,016	3,487	18.3%	64,707
12/16	18,324	3,605	19.7%	52,571
Annual Growth	2.6%	(4.4%)	—	5.4%

2020 Year-End Financials

Debt ratio: 0.1%
Return on equity: 11.9%
Cash ($ mil.): 5,227
Current ratio: 1.51
Long-term debt ($ mil.): 7,930
No. of shares (mil.): 1,774
Dividends
Yield: 6.9%
Payout: 43.4%
Market value ($ mil.): 18,080

	STOCK PRICE ($) FY Close	P/E High/Low		PER SHARE ($) Earnings	Dividends	Book Value
12/20	10.19	0	0	1.70	0.71	13.80
12/19	11.12	0	0	1.80	0.70	13.83
12/18	11.75	0	0	1.96	0.67	13.35
12/17	16.07	0	0	1.95	0.61	13.70
12/16	16.34	0	0	2.01	0.53	11.73
Annual Growth	(11.1%)	—	—	(4.2%)	7.4%	4.1%

Jardine Cycle & Carriage Ltd

Jardine Cycle & Carriage is a driving force in Singapore. The company known as JC&C distributes and retails a range of vehicles including Toyota Honda Kia Peugeot Daihatsu BMW and Mercedes-Benz cars and commercial vehicles in southeast Asia. In addition to subsidiaries operating under the Cycle & Carriage banner in Singapore and Malaysia JC&C owns more than 50% of diversified Indonesian auto group Astra International and about 44% of Indonesian vehicle retailer Tunas Ridean. It also has auto stakes in Vietnam and Myanmar. Founded in 1899 JC&C is majority owned by sister companies Jardine Strategic Holdings and Jardine Matheson Holdings.

EXECUTIVES

Non-Independent Non-Executive Director, Anthony Nightingale
Non-Executive Chairman of the Board, Benjamin Keswick
Non-Executive Independent Director, Yen Yen Tan
Non-Executive and Independent Director, Swee Kim Phan
Group Managing Director, Executive Director, Benjamin Briks, $461,082 total compensation
Group Finance Director, Executive Director, Stephen Gore, $444,408 total compensation
Managing Director - Business Development, Kim Teck Cheah, $382,785 total compensation
Lead Non-Executive Independent Director, Vimala Menon
Non-Executive and Independent Director, Marty Natalegawa
Non-Executive and Independent Director, Hwee Hua Lim
Group General Counsel, Director of Legal and Corporate Affairs and Company Secretary, Eng Heong Tan, $371,185 total compensation
Non-Executive and Independent Director, Pak Kuan Kok
Auditors: PricewaterhouseCoopers LLP

LOCATIONS

HQ: Jardine Cycle & Carriage Ltd
239 Alexandra Road, 159930
Phone: (65) 6473 3122 **Fax:** (65) 6475 7088
Web: www.jcclgroup.com

PRODUCTS/OPERATIONS

2015 Sales

	% of total
Sale of goods	72
Rendering of services	21
Financial services	7
Total	**100**

2015 Sales

	% of total
Indonesia	87
Others	13
Total	**100**

2015 Sales

	% of total
Astra	87
Direct motor interest	13
Total	**100**

Selected Operations

Astra International (50.1% Indonesia conglomerate with auto finance industrial agriculture infrastructure logistics and technology holdings)
Cycle & Carriage Automobile Myanmar (60% vehicle repair)
Cycle & Carriage Bintang (59% Malaysia vehicle retail and distribution)
Singapore Motors (retail and distribution)
Truong Hai Auto Corporation (32% Vietnam)
Tunas Ridean (44% Indonesia vehicle retailer)

COMPETITORS

INCHCAPE PLC
LISTERS GROUP LIMITED
MERCEDES-BENZ USA LLC
PT. ASTRA INTERNATIONAL TBK
RAC GROUP LIMITED
S. JENNINGS GROUP LIMITED
Shanghai Automotive Industry Corporation (Group)
VEHICLE DISTRIBUTORS AUSTRALIA PTY LTD
VOLKSWAGEN FINANCIAL SERVICES AG

HISTORICAL FINANCIALS

Company Type: Public

Income Statement				FYE: December 31
	REVENUE ($ mil.)	NET INCOME ($ mil.)	NET PROFIT MARGIN	EMPLOYEES
12/20	13,234	540	4.1%	240,000
12/19	18,591	881	4.7%	250,000
12/18	18,991	419	2.2%	250,000
12/17	17,701	811	4.6%	250,000
12/16	15,764	701	4.5%	240,000
Annual Growth	(4.3%)	(6.3%)	—	0.0%

2020 Year-End Financials

Debt ratio: 25.9%
Return on equity: 7.7%
Cash ($ mil.): 3,497
Current ratio: 1.26
Long-term debt ($ mil.): 2,965
No. of shares (mil.): 395
Dividends
Yield: 0.0%
Payout: 108.6%
Market value ($ mil.): 11,681

	STOCK PRICE ($) FY Close	P/E High/Low		PER SHARE ($) Earnings	Dividends	Book Value
12/20	29.56	33	19	1.37	1.49	17.65
12/19	44.16	24	20	2.23	1.65	17.36
12/18	48.51	59	46	1.06	1.63	15.55
12/17	57.68	34	28	2.05	1.39	16.26
12/16	56.70	37	26	1.78	1.29	14.56
Annual Growth	(15.0%)	—	—	(6.3%)	3.7%	4.9%

Jardine Matheson Holdings Ltd.

Jardine Matheson Holdings (JMH) which governs the many interests of its affiliate Jardine Strategic Holdings oversees a portfolio of market-leading businesses and supports their long-term development. It was founded in China in 1832. Comprised with a broad portfolio of market-leading businesses which represent a combination of cash generating activities and long-term property assets that are closely aligned to the increasingly prosperous consumers of the region. JMH's subsidiaries include Jardine Pacific and Jardine Motors Group Jardine Cycle & Carriage Asian supermarket operator Dairy Farm and Hongkong Land which owns prime real estate in Hong Kong. Other businesses include financial services hotels (Mandarin Oriental) construction mining and transport services. Members of the Keswick family descendants of the co-founder William Jardine control JMH and Jardine Strategic through a complex ownership structure.

Operations

Jardine Matheson operates it business into seven reportable segment Astra Dairy Farm Jardine Motors Jardine Pacific Hongkong Land Mandarin Oriental and Jardine Cycle & Carriage.

Astra generates the higher revenue with more than 35% of sales it offers automotive financial services heavy equipment mining construction and energy agribusiness infrastructure and logistics IT and Property. With about 240 subsidiaries associated companies and other entities.

Dairy Farm segment accounts for around 30% of sales operates under well-known brands across five divisions being food (including Grocery Retail and Convenience Stores) health and beauty home furnishings restaurants and other retailing.

Jardine Motors with some 15% of sales is currently comprised of asian automotive businesses including Zung Fu Motors Group in the Chinese mainland Cycle & Carriage in Singapore Malaysia and Myanmar and Tunas Ridean in Indonesia.

Jardine Pacific (engineering and construction aviation and transport services restaurants and IT.) and Hongkong Land (property investment management and development with offices in Hong Kong Singapore Beijing Jakarta and other major asian cities) both accounts for about 5% of sales. Jardine Cycle & Carriage (Singapore-listed investment holding company) and Mandarin Oriental (hotel investment with about 35 hotels and seven residences in about 25 countries and territories) accounts for the rest.

Overall Retail and restaurant products and Motor vehicles account for about 35% of sales each followed by Engineering heavy equipment construction and mining with roughly 15% as well as Property Financial services Hotels Others which account for the rest.

Geographic Reach

With its headquarters in Bermuda Jardine Matheson also operates in more than 10 Asian countries and territories. They operate mainly in Greater China and Southeast Asia. Greater China and Southeast Asia generates around 35% and about 55% of sales respectively. UK and other regions accounts for the rest.

Sales and Marketing

Jardine Matheson Holdings Limited provides a wide range of businesses including motor vehicles and related operations property investment and development food retailing health and beauty home furnishings engineering and construction transport services restaurants luxury hotels financial services heavy equipment mining energy and agribusiness. Jardine Matheson distributes its businesses by their subsidiaries and affiliate companies. For fiscal 2020 and 2019 the company spend $4.4 billion and $4.5 billion respectively in selling and marketing.

Financial Performance

The company's revenue of $32.6 billion in 2020 was 20% below the prior year. Astra recorded an overall decrease in sales of 29% from 2019 with lower sales in the majority of its businesses particularly Automotive due to lower sales volumes in its car sales operations.

In 2020 the company had a net loss of $394 million a 105% decrease from the previous year's net income of $3.2 billion.

The company's cash at the end of 2020 was $9.2 billion. Operating activities generated $5.3 billion while investing activities used $1.1 billion mainly for additions to investment properties. Financing activities used another $2.3 billion mainly for repayment of borrowings.

Strategy

Jardines continues to have a strong presence in and a key focus on two of the fastest growing consumer markets in the world: China and Southeast Asia. The Chinese mainland is an increasingly important market for the group.

The company will build on it proven track record of actively managing its portfolio to be in the more attractive markets of Asia and in businesses where the company can achieve market leading positions in order to sustain growth and create long-term sustainable value.

Company Background

Jardine Matheson & Co (JM & Co) was founded in Canton in July 1832 by Scots William Jardine and James Matheson. Jardine Matheson sent its first private shipments of tea to England in 1834. Following years after that JM & Co completed the move of its main office to Hong Kong and opened its office in Shanghai. More offices were subsequently opened in Canton Amoy and Foochow.

In the 1860s JM & Co's trading activities were enhanced by the expansion of its shipping banking and insurance interests. They moved its main office from East Point to Central Hong Kong in 1864.

JM & Co constructed the first railway line in China from Shanghai to Woosung in 1876.

By the 1910s the heart of the business was in Shanghai and from 1912 onwards the city was regarded as the Firm's headquarters. The Firm began to expand into new products and services to meet the needs of the growing industrialization of China.

EXECUTIVES

Executive Chairman of the Board, Benjamin Keswick
Executive Director, David Hsu
Group Managing Director, Executive Director, John Witt
Group General Counsel, Executive Director, Jeremy Parr
Non-Executive Director, Stuart Gulliver
Finance Director, Executive Director, Graham Baker
Auditors: PricewaterhouseCoopers LLP

LOCATIONS

HQ: Jardine Matheson Holdings Ltd.
48th Floor, Jardine House, G.P.O. Box 70,
Phone: (852) 2843 8288   **Fax:** (441) 292 4072
Web: www.jardines.com

2016 sales

	$ mil.	% of total
Southeast Asia	21,612	58
Greater China	12,495	34
UK	2,665	7
Other regions	279	1
Total	**37,051**	**100**

PRODUCTS/OPERATIONS

2016 Revenues

	$ mil.	% of total
Astra (automotive financial services agribusiness heavy equipment & other)	13,610	37
Dairy Farm	11,201	30
Jardine Motors Group	5,197	14
Jardine Pacific	2,356	6
Jardine Cycle & Carriage	2,154	6
Hongkong Land	1,994	5
Mandarin Oriental	597	2
Adjustment	(58)	-
Total	**37,051**	**100**

2016 Revenues

	$ mil.	% of total
Motor vehicles	13,610	37
Retail and restaurants	11,201	30
Engineering construction and mining contracting	5,197	14
Property	1,989	5
Insurance broking and financial services	1,357	4
Hotels	596	2
Others	3,013	8
Total	**37,051**	**100**

Selected Major Subsidiaries and Affiliates

Astra International (automobile distribution and manufacturing financial and IT services heavy machinery)
Cycle & Carriage Ltd (69% motor trading Singapore)
Dairy Farm International Holdings Ltd (78%; supermarkets hypermarkets health and beauty and home furnishings stores convenience stores and restaurants)
Honkong Land Holdings Ltd (50% real estate)
Jardine Lloyd Thompson plc (32% insurance and brokerage UK)
Jardine Motors Group Holdings Ltd. (auto distribution sales and service; China Hong Kong Macao and the UK)

Jardine Pacific Holdings Ltd. (transport services engineering and construction restaurants and IT services)
Jardine Strategic Holdings Ltd. (81% holding company)
Mandarin Oriental International Ltd. (74% hotels)

COMPETITORS

ANDREWS SYKES GROUP PLC	JOHN SWIRE & SONS LIMITED
Brenntag Holding GmbH	KOC HOLDING ANONIM SIRKETI
CAPITALAND GROUP PTE. LTD.	MITSUI FUDOSAN CO. LTD.
CK Hutchison Holdings Limited	NEW WORLD DEVELOPMENT COMPANY LIMITED
CLS HOLDINGS PLC	RSA INSURANCE GROUP LIMITED
GGL GROUP NUMBER TWO LIMITED	

HISTORICAL FINANCIALS
Company Type: Public

Income Statement
FYE: December 31

	REVENUE ($ mil.)	NET INCOME ($ mil.)	NET PROFIT MARGIN	EMPLOYEES
12/20	32,647	(394)	—	403,000
12/19	40,922	2,838	6.9%	464,000
12/18	42,527	1,732	4.1%	469,000
12/17	39,456	3,785	9.6%	443,700
12/16	37,051	2,503	6.8%	0
Annual Growth	(3.1%)	—	—	—

2020 Year-End Financials

Debt ratio: 16.7%   No. of shares (mil.): 724
Return on equity: (-1.3%)   Dividends
Cash ($ mil.): 9,203   Yield: 2.8%
Current ratio: 1.34   Payout: —
Long-term debt ($ mil.): 9,822   Market value ($ mil.): 40,703

	STOCK PRICE ($) FY Close	P/E High/Low		PER SHARE ($) Earnings	Dividends	Book Value
12/20	56.22	—	—	(1.07)	1.62	40.59
12/19	55.25	9	7	7.56	1.62	41.41
12/18	69.05	15	12	4.59	1.52	35.74
12/17	60.74	7	6	10.04	1.42	83.07
12/16	55.47	9	7	6.68	1.35	70.78
Annual Growth (13.0%)	0.3%	—	—	—	4.6%	

JBS SA

Auditors: Grant Thornton Auditores Independentes

LOCATIONS

HQ: JBS SA
Avenida Marginal Direita do Tiete, 500, Vila Jaguara,
Sao Paulo 05118-100
Phone: (55) 11 3144 4000   **Fax:** (55) 11 3144 4279
Web: www.jbs.com.br

HISTORICAL FINANCIALS
Company Type: Public

Income Statement
FYE: December 31

	REVENUE ($ mil.)	NET INCOME ($ mil.)	NET PROFIT MARGIN	EMPLOYEES
12/20	52,026	885	1.7%	250,000
12/19	50,880	1,509	3.0%	242,000
12/18	46,811	6	0.0%	230,000
12/17	49,255	161	0.3%	235,000
12/16	52,349	115	0.2%	237,061
Annual Growth	(0.2%)	66.4%	—	1.3%

2020 Year-End Financials

Debt ratio: 7.7%
Return on equity: 13.1%
Cash ($ mil.): 3,789
Current ratio: 1.48
Long-term debt ($ mil.): 11,811

No. of shares (mil.): —
Dividends
  Yield: 1.7%
  Payout: 55.3%
Market value ($ mil.): —

	STOCK PRICE ($) FY Close	P/E High/Low		PER SHARE ($) Earnings	Dividends	Book Value
12/20	9.16	7	4	0.33	0.16	2.96
12/19	12.93	7	3	0.57	0.00	2.77
12/18	5.93	636423		0.00	0.02	2.48
12/17	5.91	40	19	0.06	0.02	2.57
12/16	7.00	58	37	0.04	0.24	2.56
Annual Growth	7.0%	—	—	66.8%	(9.4%)	3.7%

JD.com, Inc.

Auditors: Deloitte Touche Tohmatsu Certified Public Accountants LLP

LOCATIONS

HQ: JD.com, Inc.
  20th Floor, Building A, No. 18 Kechuang 11 Street, Daxing District, Beijing 101111
Phone: (86) 10 8911 8888
Web: www.jd.com

HISTORICAL FINANCIALS

Company Type: Public

Income Statement   FYE: December 31

	REVENUE ($ mil.)	NET INCOME ($ mil.)	NET PROFIT MARGIN	EMPLOYEES
12/20	114,032	7,554	6.6%	314,906
12/19	82,907	1,751	2.1%	227,730
12/18	67,170	(362)	—	178,927
12/17	55,679	(23)	—	157,831
12/16	37,459	(548)	—	120,622
Annual Growth	32.1%	—	—	27.1%

2020 Year-End Financials

Debt ratio: 0.5%
Return on equity: 36.5%
Cash ($ mil.): 13,840
Current ratio: 1.35
Long-term debt ($ mil.): 1,915

No. of shares (mil.): —
Dividends
  Yield: —
  Payout: —
Market value ($ mil.): —

	STOCK PRICE ($) FY Close	P/E High/Low		PER SHARE ($) Earnings	Dividends	Book Value
12/20	87.90	6	2	2.42	0.00	9.24
12/19	35.23	9	5	0.59	0.00	4.02
12/18	20.93	—	—	(0.13)	0.00	3.00
12/17	41.42	—	—	(0.01)	0.00	2.80
12/16	25.44	—	—	(0.20)	0.00	1.72
Annual Growth	36.3%	—	—	—	—	52.3%

Jeronimo Martins S.G.P.S. SA

Jer "nimo Martins (JM) is a major Portuguese retailer with more than 4500 stores dispersed across Portugal Poland and Colombia. In Portugal its Pingo Doce chain is a leading supermarket with more than 455 stores while Recheio is a major player in the Cash & Carry sector. With more than 3000 stores Biedronka is Poland's biggest food retailer while in Colombia JM operates a network of more than 615 Ara-branded neighborhood stores. JM's specialized retail division consists of Hebe drugstores in Poland as well as Jeronymo coffee shops and Hussel confectioners in Portugal. JM generate about 70% of its sales from Poland.

Operations

The Biedronka business in Poland accounts for more than 65% of Jer "nimo Martins' total sales. Pingo Doce generates nearly 25% Recheio 5% and Ara business in Colombia generate the rest.

Geographic Reach

Jer "nimo Martins is headquartered in Portugal and its main operations are in Portugal Poland and Colombia. It supplies its store based from more than 15 distribution centers. JM generate about 70% of its revenue from Poland followed by Portugal which brings up more than 25% and the rest comes from Colombia.

Sales and Marketing

Jer "nimo Martins' serves more than five million customers while the Hebe drugstore has more than 3.7 million members.

The company's advertising costs for the years 2019 and 2018 were ?110 million and ?111 million respectively.

Financial Performance

Note: Growth rates may differ after conversion to US Dollars.

Jer "nimo Martins has achieved continuous revenue growth for the last five years with a recorded 36% increase from 2015 to 2019. Net income was fluctuating for the last five years recording its highest in 2016 and its lowest in 2015.

Revenue in 2019 was ?18.6 billion 8% less more than ?17.3 billion in the previous year. This resulted from an increase in revenue among all the company's segments.

Net income was ?390 million ?43 million less than in the previous year.

Cash and cash equivalents at the end of the year were ?929.3 million 70% higher compared to ?546 million the previous year. Cash provided by operating activities was ?1.5 billion. Investing activities used ?567 million primarily for acquisition of tangible and intangible assets while financing activities used ?549.5 million primarily for payment of leases and dividends.

Strategy

Jer "nimo Martins adopts continuous and sustainable value creation and growth.

The company's strategic vision is based on promoting profitable and sustainable growth through guiding principles of leadership responsibility and independence. Within this context when doing business the company has two core focuses: consumer whose characteristics needs and preferences require a progressive adjustment and reinforcement of the value proposition as well as a continuous and significant contribution towards the wellbeing of the communities surrounding the stores; and employee providing him or her with skills instruments and working conditions to be able to simultaneously be the agent for promoting profitable growth through satisfied consumers and also a decisive point of contact in the company for the surrounding communities.

EXECUTIVES

Chairman of the Board, Chief Executive Officer, Chairman of the Managing Committee, Pedro Manuel de Castro Soares dos Santos
Non-Executive Independent Director, Clara Christina Streit
Non-Executive Independent Director, Francisco Manuel Seixas da Costa
Non-Executive Independent Director, Antonio Pedro de Carvalho Viana-Baptista
Non-Executive Independent Director, Elizabeth Bastoni
Non-Executive Independent Director, Maria Angela Cuellar
Non-Executive Director, Jose Manuel Soares dos Santos
Non-Executive Director, Artur Kirsten
Non-Executive Independent Director, Sergio Tavares Rebelo
Non-Executive Director, Andrzej Szlezak

LOCATIONS

HQ: Jeronimo Martins S.G.P.S. SA
  Rua Actor Antonio Silva, n.o7, Lisboa 1649-033
Phone: (351) 21 753 20 00   **Fax:** (351) 21 752 61 74
Web: www.jeronimomartins.com

PRODUCTS/OPERATIONS

2017 Sales

	% of total
Poland Retail	68
Portugal Retail	25
Portugal Cash & Carry	6
Adjustments (2)	
Total	**100**

COMPETITORS

AEON CO. LTD.
ANDREWS SYKES GROUP PLC
BRITVIC PLC
COHORT PLC
FRASERS GROUP PLC
GoEasy Ltd
K+S AG

NATURGY ENERGY GROUP SA.
Ontex Group
Organizaci n Soriana S.A.B. de C.V.
SMITHS NEWS PLC
THE RESTAURANT GROUP PLC

HISTORICAL FINANCIALS

Company Type: Public

Income Statement   FYE: December 31

	REVENUE ($ mil.)	NET INCOME ($ mil.)	NET PROFIT MARGIN	EMPLOYEES
12/20	23,678	383	1.6%	0
12/19	20,926	437	2.1%	115,428
12/18	19,853	459	2.3%	108,560
12/17	19,511	461	2.4%	104,203
12/16	15,438	626	4.1%	96,233
Annual Growth	11.3%	(11.6%)	—	—

2020 Year-End Financials

Debt ratio: 6.8%
Return on equity: 15.6%
Cash ($ mil.): 1,278
Current ratio: 0.51
Long-term debt ($ mil.): 446

No. of shares (mil.): —
Dividends
  Yield: 2.3%
  Payout: 139.5%
Market value ($ mil.): —

	STOCK PRICE ($) FY Close	P/E High/Low		PER SHARE ($) Earnings	Dividends	Book Value
12/20	34.03	82	66	0.61	0.81	(0.00)
12/19	33.16	57	38	0.70	0.73	3.53
12/18	23.02	63	37	0.73	1.45	3.24
12/17	38.75	69	60	0.74	1.46	3.41
12/16	31.15	38	26	1.00	0.56	2.92
Annual Growth	2.2%	—	—	(11.6%)	9.6%	—

JFE Holdings Inc

JFE Holdings has an iron will unmatched in Japan and much of the rest of the world. JFE Holdings operates as a streamlined group headquarters responsible for strategic planning risk management accountability and corporate communications for all the subsidiaries and affiliates. JFE Holdings' steel business unit JFE Steel accounts for more than 60% of total sales and manufactures steel products such as bars pipes steel frames tubes and stainless steel for the automotive construction and petroleum industries.

Operations

The company organized under JFE Holdings executed commercial activities through three operating companies JFE Steel Corporation JFE Engineering Corporation and JFE Shoji Corporation.

The steel business produced and sold various steel products processed steel products and raw materials and provided transportation and other related businesses such as facility maintenance and construction.

The engineering business handled engineering for energy urban environment steel structures and industrial machines recycling and electricity retailing.

The trading business purchased processed and distributed steel products raw materials for steel production nonferrous metal products and food etc.

Geographic Reach

While most of its steel production facilities are in Japan JFE's reach is global and it has offices in about 20 other countries. Its corporate headquarters Is located in Tokyo.

Financial Performance

The company's revenue for fiscal 2020 decreased to 3.2 trillion yen compared from the prior year with 3.7 trillion yen.

Loss for fiscal 2020 increased to 213.5 billion yen compared from the prior year with 4.9 billion yen.

Cash held by the company at the end of fiscal 2020 increased to 86.7 billion yen. Cash provided by operations and financing activities were 261.1 billion yen and 103.9 billion yen respectively. Cash used for investing activities was 358.4 billion yen mainly for Purchase of property plant and equipment intangible assets and investment property.

Strategy

The JFE Group is confronted with a range of structural changes in the business environment such as dramatic fluctuations in markets in Japan and overseas generational change including the retirement of veteran engineers and the aging of equipment. The company have identified Group-wide digital transformation (DX) as an important strategy to enable JFE to respond flexibly and swiftly to increasingly challenging changes in the business environment. This includes the use of data and digital technology to transform products services and business models as well as the transformation of organizations processes corporate culture and the nature of business operations themselves.

JFE Steel's DX strategy pivots on technological innovation and the use of data resources through the proactive introduction of technologies such as the IoT AI and data science (DS). Compared to steel mills overseas JFE Steel has accumulated a large amount of know-how and data over many years. These abundant data resources are the source of value creation. By actively utilizing these resources through the latest DS and AI technologies JFE aim to achieve innovative productivity enhancements quality improvements and stable operations to further enhance its competitive strength.

EXECUTIVES

President, Chief Executive Officer, Representative Director, Koji Kakigi
President of Subsidiary, Director, Hajime Oshita
Independent Director, Yoshiko Ando
President of Subsidiary, Director, Toshinori Kobayashi
President of Subsidiary, Representative Director, Yoshihisa Kitano
Chief Financial Officer, Executive Vice President, Representative Director, Masashi Terahata
Independent Director, Nobumasa Kemori
Auditors: Ernst & Young ShinNihon LLC

LOCATIONS

HQ: JFE Holdings Inc
2-2-3 Uchisaiwai-cho, Chiyoda-ku, Tokyo 100-0011
Phone: (81) 3 3597 4321
Web: www.jfe-holdings.co.jp

PRODUCTS/OPERATIONS

2015 Sales

	% of total
Steel	53
Engineering	38
Trading	9
Adjustment	-
Total	**100**

Selected Products

Electrical Steel
Energy
Environment
Iron Powders
Pipes and Tubes
Plates
Shapes
Sheets
Slag
Stainless
Steel Bars and Wire Rods
Steel Structure
Titanium

COMPETITORS

Andritz AG
ENEOS HOLDINGS INC.
FAST RETAILING CO. LTD.
FURUKAWA CO. LTD.
GRAPHITE CAPITAL MANAGEMENT LLP
HAKUHODO DY HOLDINGS INCORPORATED
Hyundai Steel Company
ITT INC.
MITSUBISHI CHEMICAL HOLDINGS CORPORATION
NIPPON STEEL NISSHIN CO. LTD.
NIPPON STEEL TRADING CORPORATION
OJI HOLDINGS CORPORATION
Outokumpu Oyj
SOMPO HOLDINGS INC.
SSAB AB
TERNIUM S.A.
THE FIDELITY GLOBAL GROUP LTD
TOYO SEIKAN GROUP HOLDINGSLTD.
TUBOS REUNIDOS SA
VALLOUREC

HISTORICAL FINANCIALS

Company Type: Public

Income Statement				FYE: March 31
	REVENUE ($ mil.)	NET INCOME ($ mil.)	NET PROFIT MARGIN	EMPLOYEES
03/21	29,146	(197)	—	64,371
03/20	34,359	(1,821)	—	64,009
03/19	34,978	1,476	4.2%	62,083
03/18	34,642	1,362	3.9%	61,234
03/17	29,595	607	2.1%	60,439
Annual Growth	(0.4%)	—	—	1.6%

2021 Year-End Financials

Debt ratio: 0.3%
Return on equity: (-1.3%)
Cash ($ mil.): 1,286
Current ratio: 1.66
Long-term debt ($ mil.): 13,810
No. of shares (mil.): 576
Dividends
  Yield: —
  Payout: —
Market value ($ mil.): —

Jiangsu Zhongnan Construction Group Co., Ltd.

Auditors: Zonzun Accounting Office Ltd.

LOCATIONS

HQ: Jiangsu Zhongnan Construction Group Co., Ltd.
No. 4, Gongxing Road, Ganjingzi District, Dalian, Liaoning Province 116031
Phone: (86) 411 86672112   **Fax:** (86) 411 86678899
Web: www.dljn.com

HISTORICAL FINANCIALS

Company Type: Public

Income Statement				FYE: December 31
	REVENUE ($ mil.)	NET INCOME ($ mil.)	NET PROFIT MARGIN	EMPLOYEES
12/20	12,018	1,082	9.0%	0
12/19	10,323	598	5.8%	0
12/18	5,831	318	5.5%	0
12/17	4,694	92	2.0%	0
12/16	4,959	58	1.2%	0
Annual Growth	24.8%	107.2%	—	—

2020 Year-End Financials

Debt ratio: 3.4%
Return on equity: 28.1%
Cash ($ mil.): 5,024
Current ratio: 1.18
Long-term debt ($ mil.): 8,643
No. of shares (mil.): —
Dividends
  Yield: —
  Payout: —
Market value ($ mil.): —

Jiangxi Copper Co., Ltd.

Auditors: Deloitte Touche Tohmatsu Certified Public Accountants LLP

LOCATIONS

HQ: Jiangxi Copper Co., Ltd.
7666 Changdong Avenue, High and New Technology Development Zone, Nanchang, Jiangxi Province 330096
Phone: (86) 791 82710117   **Fax:** (86) 791 82710114
Web: www.jxcc.com

HISTORICAL FINANCIALS

Company Type: Public

Income Statement

FYE: December 31

	REVENUE ($ mil.)	NET INCOME ($ mil.)	NET PROFIT MARGIN	EMPLOYEES
12/20	48,708	354	0.7%	0
12/19	34,543	354	1.0%	0
12/18	31,299	355	1.1%	0
12/17	31,509	246	0.8%	0
12/16	29,133	113	0.4%	0
Annual Growth	13.7%	33.0%	—	—

2020 Year-End Financials

Debt ratio: 5.3%
Return on equity: 4.1%
Cash ($ mil.): 3,826
Current ratio: 1.39
Long-term debt ($ mil.): 2,228

No. of shares (mil.): —
Dividends
  Yield: 0.0%
  Payout: —
Market value ($ mil.): —

	STOCK PRICE ($) FY Close	P/E High/Low	PER SHARE ($) Earnings	Dividends	Book Value
12/20	61.50	100 60	0.10	0.53	(0.00)
12/19	54.07	77 66	0.10	1.01	(0.00)
12/18	47.46	91 60	0.10	1.03	(0.00)
12/17	63.98	162 127	0.07	0.80	(0.00)
12/16	57.59	278 153	0.03	0.51	(0.00)
Annual Growth	1.7%	— —	32.6%	0.8%	

Jinke Property Group Co., Ltd.

EXECUTIVES

Vice President, Secretary of the Board, Qiang Zhang
Co-President, Licheng Luo
Director, Jing Liu
Chairman of the Board, Da Zhou
Vice President, Mingfu Fang
Staff Elected Director, Gang Chen
Vice Chairman of the Board, Staff Elected Director, Hongfei Wang
Independent Director, Yuntong Hu
Co-President, Wei Wang
Co-President, Director, Chengjun Yang
Vice President, Ke Song
Director, Liu Yang
Independent Director, Wen Wang
Vice President, Zhongqiang Huang
Independent Director, Ning Zhu
Auditors: Pan-China (Chongqing) Certified Public Accountants

LOCATIONS

HQ: Jinke Property Group Co., Ltd.
  5th Floor, Block C, No. 68, Tianwangxing Building, Xingguan Avenue, Gaoxin Yuan, Chongqing 401120
Phone: (86) 23 89072387   **Fax:** (86) 23 89072387

HISTORICAL FINANCIALS

Company Type: Public

Income Statement

FYE: December 31

	REVENUE ($ mil.)	NET INCOME ($ mil.)	NET PROFIT MARGIN	EMPLOYEES
12/20	13,409	1,074	8.0%	0
12/19	9,740	815	8.4%	0
12/18	5,994	564	9.4%	0
12/17	5,341	308	5.8%	0
12/16	4,642	200	4.3%	0
Annual Growth	30.4%	52.1%	—	—

2020 Year-End Financials

Debt ratio: 3.2%
Return on equity: 21.8%
Cash ($ mil.): 6,649
Current ratio: 1.38
Long-term debt ($ mil.): 9,871

No. of shares (mil.): —
Dividends
  Yield: —
  Payout: —
Market value ($ mil.): —

Johnson Controls International plc

Auditors: PricewaterhouseCoopers LLP

LOCATIONS

HQ: Johnson Controls International plc
  One Albert Quay, Cork T12 X8N6
Phone: (353) 21 423 5000
Web: www.johnsoncontrols.com

HISTORICAL FINANCIALS

Company Type: Public

Income Statement

FYE: September 30

	REVENUE ($ mil.)	NET INCOME ($ mil.)	NET PROFIT MARGIN	EMPLOYEES
09/21	23,668	1,637	6.9%	101,000
09/20	22,317	631	2.8%	97,000
09/19	23,968	5,674	23.7%	104,000
09/18	31,400	2,162	6.9%	122,000
09/17	30,172	1,611	5.3%	121,000
Annual Growth	(5.9%)	0.4%	—	(4.4%)

2021 Year-End Financials

Debt ratio: 18.4%
Return on equity: 9.3%
Cash ($ mil.): 1,336
Current ratio: 1.10
Long-term debt ($ mil.): 7,506

No. of shares (mil.): 708
Dividends
  Yield: 1.5%
  Payout: 42.9%
Market value ($ mil.): —

Johnson Matthey Plc (United Kingdom)

Founded in 1817 Johnson Matthey is a global leader in science that enables a cleaner and healthier world. It makes catalysts and licenses process designs and technologies that help customers in the chemicals and energy industries turn a wide range of feedstock into many of products that are essentials for modern life. Johnson Matthey supplies customers with pgms and are also a key supplier to other parts of John Matthey. Its key customers are chemical manufacturing companies oil and gas companies and other industrial customers and pgm-using industries. Its largest geographic sales is in the UK.

Operations

Johnson Matthey operates through four segments: Efficient Natural Resources Clean Air New Markets and Health.

Efficient Natural Resources generates more than 60% of total revenue provides products and processing services for the efficient use and transformation of critical natural resources including oil gas biomass and platinum group metals.

Clean air (about 35%) provides catalysts for cars other light duty vehicles trucks buses and non-road equipment.

New Markets segment (less than 5% of total revenue) includes battery systems for a range of application fuel cell technologies and battery materials for automotive applications. The segment also develops products found in devices used in medical procedures and advanced catalysts for pharmaceutical and agricultural chemicals markets.

Health segment develops and manufactures active pharmaceutical ingredients (APIs) for a variety of treatment and new drugs.

Geographic Reach

London-based Johnson Matthey operates some 45 major manufacturing sites in more than 30 countries. Europe accounted around 45% of its revenue of which more than 20% was contributed by the UK. The Asia (including China and Hong Kong) accounted for roughly 20% and US about 15%.

Sales and Marketing

The company serve industries such as automotive chemicals pharmaceutical and medical oil and gas food and beverage and other industries.

Johnson Matthey has one customer in the Clean Air segment which represents more than 10% of the company's total revenue.

Financial Performance

Company's revenue for fiscal 2020 decreased by 5% to 3.9 billion compared from the prior year with 4.2 billion.

Profit for fiscal 2020 decreased to 238 million compared from the prior year with 305 million.

Cash held by the company at the end of fiscal 2020 increased to 545 million. Cash provided by operation was 769 million while cash used for investing and financing activities were 291 million and 202 million respectively. Main uses of cash were purchases of property plant and equipment and repayment of intangible assets.

Strategy

The company have continued to plan and invest for the future despite the pandemic and Johnson Matthey are laying the groundwork to deliver on its three key strategic objectives: invest in growth areas targeted at climate change and circularity; manage its established businesses to support growth; and promote a fast paced efficient business and high performance culture.

HISTORY

Percival Johnson set up an assayer's shop in London in 1817. Using chemical and physical tests he determined the amount of gold in a given bar and guaranteed his results by offering to buy the bars he assayed. Johnson then set up a gold refinery in the early 1830s and developed a method for extracting platinum group metals. As part of that process he produced vitreous colors for pottery and glass refined nickel and silver nitrate for medical use and later for photographic uses.

George Matthey joined the company in 1838 and championed the platinum business securing a steady supply of platinum from Russia. The company thrived on business generated by gold rushes in California (1849) and Australia (1851). It built a silver refinery to melt down European coinage and extract component metals and in 1870 it bought a company that produced magnesium antimony vanadium and aluminum. In 1891 the company became Johnson Matthey & Co. Limited. Around the turn of the century it bought rolling mills and began forming metals into sheet tube and wire to better serve jewelers.

During WWI Johnson Matthey & Co. provided platinum catalysts and magnesium powder for explosives and in WWII the company was appointed the government's agent for controlling platinum stocks. Johnson Matthey & Co. expanded its international operations rapidly during the post-war boom adding holdings in Australia India North America and South Africa. It established subsidiaries in France and the Netherlands (1956) Italy (1959) Sweden (1960) Belgium (1961) and Austria (1962). The company also began conducting research on automotive catalytic converters to reduce pollution. It formed Johnson Matthey Bankers (JMB) to carry out its banking and trading activities.

A foray into the US jewelry business led to big losses in 1980 and the company pressed JMB to make higher-risk loans. JMB's contribution to profits went from less than 25% in 1981 (the year the company took its present name) to more than 60% in 1983. The bank ended up with so many bad loans that the Bank of England had to arrange a bailout in 1984. Gene Anderson who became CEO in 1985 cut 3000 jobs and reduced the number of divisions from 78 to 4. Profits rebounded but Anderson resigned in 1989 after failing to persuade the board to diversify away from platinum.

During the 1990s the company invested heavily in its electronics division which had been doing well since the 1989 acquisition of Cominco Electronic Materials (ultra-pure metals for microchips). By 1995 the division was responsible for about a third of Johnson Matthey's profits. In 1998 it bought Cookson Group's 50% share of its ceramics joint venture.

In 1998 Johnson Matthey shifted its focus to three core businesses: catalysts colors and coatings and precious metals. The next year it sold its electronic materials business Johnson Matthey Electronics to US-based AlliedSignal (now Honeywell International) and began looking for takeover opportunities in its core markets. In 2001 the company acquired pharmaceuticals manufacturers Meconic (now Macfarlan Smith; it's the UK's only maker of medical opiates — cocaine and heroin) and Pharm-Eco then used these acquisitions as the basis for a fourth division: Pharmaceutical Materials (now a part of its Fine Chemicals and Catalysts Division).

In 2002 the company acquired Cascade Biochem Limited to strengthen its Pharmaceutical Materials division and metal catalyst company Synetix. CEO Chris Clark retired in 2003. He was succeeded by Neil Carson former executive director of the precious metals and catalysts operations.

Following the sale of its Pigments & Dispersions unit to Rockwood Pigments in 2004 Johnson Matthey restructured its Colours and Coatings division by closing several of its manufacturing sites and transferring some operations to its Precious Metal Products division. The moves created what became the Ceramics division the 2007 sale of which was the last in the dismantling of the Colours and Coatings division.

At the beginning of 2008 the company acquired the Argillon Group which manufactured catalysts and advanced ceramic materials from Ceramics Luxembourg (owned by KKR). Later that year

Johnson Matthey sold the acquired ceramic insulators alumina business for about $40 million.

In 2010 a Johnson Matthey subsidiary formed a joint venture with Aoxing Pharmaceutical to manufacture ingredients for narcotics and neurological drugs for the Chinese market. That same year Johnson Matthey acquired Intercat a supplier of fluid catalytic cracking services for the petroleum refining industry for $56 million. It became part of Johnson Matthey's Process Technologies division's Ammonia Methanol Oil and Gas unit.

EXECUTIVES

Non-Executive Independent Chairman of the Board, Patrick Thomas, $481,753 total compensation
Non-Executive Independent Director, Jane Griffiths, $87,472 total compensation
Non-Executive Independent Director, Xiaozhi Liu, $87,472 total compensation
Non-Executive Independent Director, Douglas Webb, $105,750 total compensation
Chief Financial Officer, Executive Director, Stephen Oxley
Non-Executive Independent Director, Rita Forst
Non-Executive Independent Director, Christopher Mottershead, $109,667 total compensation
Senior Non-Executive Independent Director, John O'Higgins, $103,139 total compensation
Auditors: PricewaterhouseCoopers LLP

LOCATIONS

HQ: Johnson Matthey Plc (United Kingdom)
5th Floor, 25 Farringdon Street, London EC4A 4AB
Phone: (44) 20 7269 8400   **Fax:** (44) 20 7269 8433
Web: www.matthey.com

2015 Sales

	%
Europe	
UK	24
Germany	12
Rest of Europe	11
USA	25
Rest of North America	2
China (including Hong Kong)	11
Rest of Asia	10
Rest of World	5
Total	**100**

PRODUCTS/OPERATIONS

2015 Sales

	% of total
Precious Metals	56
Emission Control Technologies	33
Process Technologies	6
Fine Chemicals	4
New Businesses	1
Total	**100**

Businesses
Emission Control Technologies Division
Emission Control Technologies website
Stationary Emissions Control website
Process Technologies Division
Process Technologies website
Chemical Catalysts website
Johnson Matthey Formox website
Johnson Matthey Davy Technologies website
Tracerco website
Precious Metal Products Division
Services Businesses
Precious Metals Management
Global Precious Metal Refining website
Scavenging Technologies
PGM Database
Johnson Matthey & Brandenberger website
Manufacturing Businesses
Noble Metals website
Medical Device Components website
Metal Joining website
USA Jewellery Products

Advanced Glass Technologies website
Silver and Coating Technologies website
Chemical Products website
Piezoproducts website
Fine Chemicals Division
API Manufacturing
Johnson Matthey Macfarlan Smith website
Johnson Matthey Pharmaceutical Materials - USA website
Johnson Matthey Pharma Services website

COMPETITORS

DONGKUK STEEL MILL COMPANY LIMITED
HANDY & HARMAN LTD.
MATERION CORPORATION
MORGAN ADVANCED MATERIALS PLC
Solvay
Umicore
W. R. GRACE & CO.
Zijin Mining Group Company Limited

HISTORICAL FINANCIALS
Company Type: Public

Income Statement				FYE: March 31
	REVENUE ($ mil.)	NET INCOME ($ mil.)	NET PROFIT MARGIN	EMPLOYEES
03/21	21,576	282	1.3%	14,582
03/20	18,008	315	1.7%	15,352
03/19	14,075	541	3.8%	14,795
03/18	19,844	418	2.1%	14,130
03/17	15,020	481	3.2%	12,306
Annual Growth	9.5%	(12.5%)	—	4.3%

2021 Year-End Financials

Debt ratio: 23.3%	No. of shares (mil.): 193
Return on equity: 7.4%	Dividends
Cash ($ mil.): 799	Yield: 1.5%
Current ratio: 1.35	Payout: 97.0%
Long-term debt ($ mil.): 1,719	Market value ($ mil.): 16,429

	STOCK PRICE ($) FY Close	P/E High/Low		PER SHARE ($) Earnings	Dividends	Book Value
03/21	84.89	87	43	1.46	1.32	19.10
03/20	43.71	66	33	1.63	2.11	18.03
03/19	84.00	47	32	2.81	2.07	17.67
03/18	85.60	65	50	2.18	2.17	17.27
03/17	78.10	44	33	2.51	6.72	14.43
Annual Growth	2.1%	—	—	(12.6%)	(33.5%)	7.3%

JSC VTB Bank

Auditors: Ernst & Young LLC

LOCATIONS

HQ: JSC VTB Bank
11a Degtyarnyy Pereulok, Saint-Petersburg 191144
Phone:
Web: www.vtb.com

HISTORICAL FINANCIALS
Company Type: Public

Income Statement				FYE: December 31
	REVENUE ($ mil.)	NET INCOME ($ mil.)	NET PROFIT MARGIN	EMPLOYEES
12/20	16,584	1,077	6.5%	79,217
12/19	22,305	3,245	14.6%	82,300
12/18	17,321	2,571	14.8%	0
12/17	21,724	2,080	9.6%	0
12/16	20,546	854	4.2%	94,966
Annual Growth	(5.2%)	6.0%	—	(4.4%)

2020 Year-End Financials

Debt ratio: —
Return on equity: 4.7%
Cash ($ mil.): 18,270
Current ratio: —
Long-term debt ($ mil.): —
No. of shares (mil.): —
Dividends
  Yield: —
  Payout: 31,055.4%
Market value ($ mil.): —

Juroku Financial Group Inc

The Juroku Bank is industriously working to serve its customers in the prefectures of Gifu and Aichi both part of the industrial region of Chubu. The regional bank has about 150 offices in its primary service areas as well as offices in Osaka and Tokyo and overseas offices in Hong Kong and Shanghai. In addition to traditional deposit banking products and services The Juroku Bank and its subsidiaries do business in such areas as credit cards credit guarantees investments and leasing. The bank joined with five other regional banks to form the Tokai-Kinki PFI Financial Network which is intended to help its member strengthen their abilities related to private finance initiatives.

Auditors: Deloitte Touche Tohmatsu LLC

LOCATIONS

HQ: Juroku Financial Group Inc
8-26 Kanda-machi, Gifu 500-8516
Phone: (81) 58 265 2111
Web: www.juroku.co.jp

COMPETITORS

AOZORA BANK LTD. THE
CHUKYO BANK LIMITED.
KAGOSHIMA BANK LTD.
  THE

HISTORICAL FINANCIALS

Company Type: Public

Income Statement				FYE: March 31
	ASSETS ($ mil.)	NET INCOME ($ mil.)	INCOME AS % OF ASSETS	EMPLOYEES
03/21	65,372	132	0.2%	3,624
03/20	59,626	118	0.2%	3,741
03/19	57,512	96	0.2%	3,911
03/18	57,413	93	0.2%	4,184
03/17	54,006	89	0.2%	4,319
Annual Growth	4.9%	10.3%	—	(4.3%)

2021 Year-End Financials

Return on assets: 0.2%
Return on equity: 3.9%
Long-term debt ($ mil.): —
No. of shares (mil.): 37
Sales ($ mil): 1,005
Dividends
  Yield: —
  Payout: 22.8%
Market value ($ mil.): —

Jyske Bank A/S

Jyske Bank is a leading independent Danish bank offering a variety of financial services to private customers and small and medium-sized businesses. The shareholder-owned bank operates a decentralized network of around 110 domestic branches that operate separately under a guiding set of policies and goals. Securities and currency transactions asset management investment services and leasing are among Jyske Bank's primary offerings. The bank was established in 1967 as the result of a merger of four Danish banks. It has international branch operations in Switzerland Gibraltar Germany France and the Netherlands.

EXECUTIVES

Member of the Supervisory Board, Jens Borup
Managing Director and Chief Executive Officer; Member of the Executive Board, Anders Dam, $1,543,578 total compensation
Member of the Supervisory Board, Employee Representative, Marianne Lillevang
Managing Director, Member of the Executive Board, Niels Jakobsen, $1,207,353 total compensation
Deputy Chairman of the Supervisory Board, Philip Baruch
Member of the Supervisory Board, Keld Norup
Member of the Supervisory Board, Employee Representative, Christina Munk
Managing Director, Member of the Executive Board, Per Skovhus, $1,253,202 total compensation
Independent Member of the Supervisory Board, Rina Asmussen
Managing Director, Member of the Executive Board, Peter Schleidt, $1,237,919 total compensation
Independent Chairman of the Supervisory Board, Kurt Bligaard Pedersen
Member of the Supervisory Board, Employee Representative, Johnny Christensen
Independent Member of the Supervisory Board, Anker Laden-Andersen
Independent Member of the Supervisory Board, Per Schnack
Independent Member of the Supervisory Board, Bente Overgaard
Auditors: Deloitte Statsautoriseret Revisionsaktieselskab

LOCATIONS

HQ: Jyske Bank A/S
Vestergade 8-16, Silkeborg DK-8600
Phone: (45) 89 89 89 89   **Fax:** (45) 89 89 19 99
Web: www.jyskebank.dk

COMPETITORS

BANCA PROFILO SPA
Cesk sporitelna a.s.
Danske Bank A/S
FARMERS CAPITAL BANK CORPORATION
Royal Bank of Canada
Skandinaviska Enskilda Banken AB

HISTORICAL FINANCIALS

Company Type: Public

Income Statement				FYE: December 31
	ASSETS ($ mil.)	NET INCOME ($ mil.)	INCOME AS % OF ASSETS	EMPLOYEES
12/19	97,643	343	0.4%	3,593
12/18	92,009	363	0.4%	3,698
12/17	96,196	491	0.5%	3,932
12/16	83,329	439	0.5%	3,981
12/15	79,313	361	0.5%	4,021
Annual Growth	5.3%	(1.3%)	—	(2.8%)

2019 Year-End Financials

Return on assets: 0.3%
Return on equity: 6.5%
Long-term debt ($ mil.): —
No. of shares (mil.): 74
Sales ($ mil): 2,042
Dividends
  Yield: —
  Payout: —
Market value ($ mil.): —

Kajima Corp. (Japan)

Kajima Corporation conduct construction engineering real estate development and other business globally. The company provides planning development design engineering capabilities and provide communities and customers around the world with urban and architectural spaces and infrastructure and built in highest standard. Kajima has a presence in more than 50 countries in Africa Asia and the Middle East.

Operations
Kajima Corporation generated 47% of its total revenue from its building construction business in FY2020 (ended March 31) with its Civil Engineering business making up another 14%. Its domestic subsidiary and affiliate companies made up 19% of total revenues while its overseas subsidiaries and affiliates made up 23%. The remainder of revenues came from its real estate development business.

The company's Kajima USA subsidiary runs the North American arm of the business.

Geographic Reach
Kajima Headquarters was based in Japan. Its offices in Japan are located in the cities of Hokkaido Tohoku Kanto Yokohama Hokuriku Chubu Kansai Shikoku Chugoku and Kyushu. Its international offices are in Taiwan Singapore Indonesia Vietnam and Myanmar.

Sales and Marketing
Kajima overseas operation division is responsible for promoting cooperation among overseas subsidiaries in USA Europe Asia Oceania and elsewhere through regular communication which office and spread Kajima Japan's various technologies and expertise.

Financial Performance
In 2020 the company had a net revenue of 1.9 trillion a 5% decrease from the previous year. In the same year the company had a net income of 98.5 million also a 5% decrease compared to the previous year.

The company's cash at the end of 2020 was 301 billion. Operating activities generated 153.1 billion while investing and financing activities used 65.4 billion and 39.1 billion respectively.

Strategy
The company's strategy consists of: improving productivity and creating an attractive work environment; enhancing efforts in promising markets and fields; ensuring proper execution in upstream and downstream businesses anddiversifying revenue sources; increasing profitability in the real estate development business; enhancing efforts to address social issues including the environment energy and disaster prevention and mitigation; and strategically promoting R&D and establishing a suitable business platform for group management.

Company Background
Founded in 1840 Kajima has had an illustrious and venerable history. It began earthquake remediation work in the early 1920s and built railroads and the first Western-style buildings in Japan.

EXECUTIVES

President, Executive President, Representative Director, Hiromasa Amano
Senior Managing Executive Officer, Chief Director of General Affairs Administration, Director, Takeshi Katsumi
Independent Director, Koji Furukawa
Independent Director, Masahiro Sakane
Senior Managing Executive Officer, Chief Director of Finance, Director, Ken Uchida
Independent Director, Kiyomi Saito
Independent Director, Yoichi Suzuki
Chairman of the Board, Representative Director, Yoshikazu Oshimi
Executive Vice President, Chief Director of Sales, Director, Hiroshi Ishikawa
Executive Vice President, Chief Director of Civil Engineering Management, Representative Director, Masayasu Kayano
Executive Vice President, Chief Director of Overseas Business, Representative Director, Keisuke Koshijima
Director, Nobuyuki Hiraizumi
Auditors: Deloitte Touche Tohmatsu LLC

LOCATIONS

HQ: Kajima Corp. (Japan)
1-3-1 Motoakasaka, Minato-ku, Tokyo 107-8388
Phone: (81) 3 5544 1111
Web: www.kajima.co.jp

2013 Sales

	% of total
Asia	
Japan	85
Other countries	7
North America	6
Europe	1
Other regions	-
Total	**0**

PRODUCTS/OPERATIONS

2013 Sales

	% of total
Construction	88
Real Estate & others	12
Total	**100**

2013 Sales

	% of total
Building construction	50
Civil Engineering	18
Real estate development and others	4
Others	28
Total	**100**

Selected Subsidiaries

Act Technical Support Inc. (sales and services)
Azuma Kanko Kaihatsu Co. Ltd. (hotels and leisure)
Chung-Lu Construction Co. Ltd. (Taiwan)
East Real Estate Co. Ltd.
Green Materials Recycle Corporation (sales and services)
Hawaiian Dredging Construction Company Inc. (US)
Ilya Corporation (design and consulting)
Kajima Kress Co. Ltd. (procurement and construction)
Kajima Real Estate Investment Advisors Inc.
Kajima Tatemono Sogo Kanri Co. Ltd. (real estate development and management)
Public Relations Officer Corporation (sales and services)
Shinrinkohen Golf Club Co. Ltd.
Taiko Trading Co. Ltd. (procurement and construction)
Yaesu Book Center Co. Ltd. (culture)

COMPETITORS

AECOM	LAING O'ROURKE PLC.
ALLENBUILD LIMITED	LENDLEASE CORPORATION
BECHTEL GROUP INC.	LIMITED
CHIYODA CORPORATION	OBAYASHI CORPORATION
FLUOR CORPORATION	PRIME PEOPLE PLC
HELIX ENERGY SOLUTIONS	SHEPHERD BUILDING
GROUP INC.	GROUP LIMITED
HOCHTIEF AG	SHIMIZU CORPORATION
HYDER CONSULTING GROUP	STRABAG SE
HOLDINGS LIMITED	TAISEI CORPORATION
INSTALLED BUILDING	TAKENAKA CORPORATION
PRODUCTS INC.	

HISTORICAL FINANCIALS

Company Type: Public

Income Statement

FYE: March 31

	REVENUE ($ mil.)	NET INCOME ($ mil.)	NET PROFIT MARGIN	EMPLOYEES
03/21	17,224	889	5.2%	22,364
03/20	18,523	951	5.1%	22,114
03/19	17,827	991	5.6%	21,616
03/18	17,239	1,193	6.9%	20,893
03/17	16,294	937	5.8%	19,561
Annual Growth	**1.4%**	**(1.3%)**	**—**	**3.4%**

2021 Year-End Financials

Debt ratio: 0.1%
Return on equity: 11.8%
Cash ($ mil.): 2,778
Current ratio: 1.28
Long-term debt ($ mil.): 1,477

No. of shares (mil.): 506
Dividends
Yield: 3.3%
Payout: —
Market value ($ mil.): 7,227

	STOCK PRICE ($) FY Close	P/E High/Low		PER SHARE ($) Earnings	Dividends	Book Value
03/21	14.28	0	0	1.74	0.47	15.61
03/20	10.76	0	0	1.85	0.47	14.20
03/19	14.89	0	0	1.91	0.47	13.08
03/18	92.28	0	0	2.30	0.43	12.06
03/17	65.35	0	0	1.81	0.30	9.44
Annual Growth	**(31.6%)**	**—**	**—**	**(0.9%)**	**12.4%**	**13.4%**

Kansai Electric Power Co., Inc. (Kansai Denryoku K. K.) (Japan)

The Kansai Electric Power Company (KEPCO) provides electricity to customers in Japan's Kansai region. The company produced about 98.2 billion kilowatts per hour with a capacity of about 30.6 GW in its power generating facilities. The company provides services through its roughly 170 facilities. KEPCO's power sources are composed of Liquefied Natural Gas (LNG) coal general hydroelectric renewable energy nuclear and pumped storage. Additionally Kansai Electric Power Company Inc is engaged in comprehensive real estate services such as leasing condominium sales property management leisure etc.) with home security for individuals and call-center and staffing services for businesses.

Operations

Kansai Electric Power operates through four reportable segments: electrical power (about 70% of revenue) gas and other energies (about 20%) IT/Communication (about 10%) and life/business support (roughly 5%).

The company's power plant portfolio includes more than 150 hydroelectric plants 10 thermal power facilities three renewable energy plants and three nuclear plants. It has more than 132660 km of overhead distribution lines and about 18 800 km. of transmission lines.

Geographic Reach

Osaka-based Kansai Electric Power Company supplies areas covering Chugoku Hokuriku Shikoku and Chubu.

Financial Performance

Note: Growth rates may differ after conversion to US Dollars.

The company's revenue decreased by 2% to 3.6 trillion in 2020 compared to 3.7 trillion in 2019 primarily due to the decrease of revenue in operating segments.

Net income attributable to the owners of the parent increased by 15 billion to 130 billion compared to 115 billion in the prior year.

Cash held by the company at the end of the year amounted to 255 billion. Operating activities contributed 463.4 billion to the coffers. Investing activities used 577.3 billion while financing activities provided 97.3 billion. Main cash uses were for the purchase of property plant and equipment as well as payments for investments and advances.

Strategy

Kansai Electric Power Company's strategy is centered around its business improvement plans. These include compliance through the reform of its corporate culture new business management structure and shifting to a company with a nominating committee and the review of the mechanism governing order placement procedures. The company also aims to restructure the governance system for its Nuclear Power Division through strengthening checks and support of the segment and creating an open organization.

Company Background

The company was established in 1951.

KEPCO has a longstanding relationship with Australia's North West Shelf liquefied natural gas (LNG) joint venture. One of the venture's first customers in 1989 the company in 2009 signed a new deal guaranteeing the Japanese utility some 3.3 million metric tons a year in LNG supply.

EXECUTIVES

Vice President, Representative Executive Officer, Chief Director of Regional Energy, Takao Matsumura
President, Representative Executive Officer, Director, Takashi Morimoto
Independent Director, Kyoji Shimamoto
Vice President, Representative Executive Officer, Director, Nozomi Mori
Director, Yasuji Shimamoto
Independent Director, Atsuko Kaga
Independent Director, Kazuko Takamatsu
Independent Director, Fumio Naito
Independent Director, Shigeo Sasaki
Independent Director, Hiroshi Tomono
Chairman of the Board, Independent Director, Sadayuki Sakakibara
Vice President, Representative Executive Officer, Director, Toyokazu Misono
Independent Director, Tetsuya Kobayashi
Vice President, Representative Executive Officer, Director, Koji Inada
Independent Director, Takamune Okihara
Auditors: Deloitte Touche Tohmatsu LLC

LOCATIONS

HQ: Kansai Electric Power Co., Inc. (Kansai Denryoku K. K.) (Japan)
3-6-16 Nakanoshima, Kita-ku, Osaka 530-8270
Phone: (81) 50 7105 9084
Web: www.kepco.co.jp

PRODUCTS/OPERATIONS

2016 Sales

	% of total
Electric power	86
IT/Communications	5
Other	9
Total	**100**

Selected Subsidiaries

Kanden Energy Solution Co. Inc
SAKAI LNG Corp
ECHIZEN ENELINE CO. INC
Osaka Bioenergy Co. Ltd
K-Opticom Corp
Kanden System Solutions Co. Inc
Kanden Realty & Development Co. Ltd.
Clearpass Co. Ltd
KANDEN AMENIX Corp
Kanden Community Co. Ltd
Kanden CS Forum Inc.
Kanden Oce Work Co. Inc
Kanden Power-Tech Corp
Kanden Business Support Corp.
San Roque Power Corporation
LNG EBISU Shipping Corporation
KPIC Netherlands B.V.

COMPETITORS

BERKSHIRE HATHAWAY ENERGY COMPANY
CENTERPOINT ENERGY INC.
CMS ENERGY CORPORATION
Capital Power Corporation
DYNEGY INC.
EXELON CORPORATION
EnBW Energie Baden-W rttemberg AG
HOKKAIDO ELECTRIC POWER COMPANY
 INCORPORATED
KYUSHU ELECTRIC POWER COMPANY
 INCORPORATED
Korea Electric Power Corporation
OSAKA GAS CO. LTD.
SNAM SPA
TC Energy Corporation
TUCSON ELECTRIC POWER COMPANY
Uniper SE
VISTRA CORP.
Vattenfall AB
WEC ENERGY GROUP INC.

HISTORICAL FINANCIALS

Company Type: Public

Income Statement

FYE: March 31

	REVENUE ($ mil.)	NET INCOME ($ mil.)	NET PROFIT MARGIN	EMPLOYEES
03/21	27,928	984	3.5%	44,179
03/20	29,334	1,197	4.1%	44,251
03/19	29,867	1,039	3.5%	45,699
03/18	29,510	1,430	4.8%	45,916
03/17	26,933	1,259	4.7%	45,836
Annual Growth	0.9%	(6.0%)	—	(0.9%)

2021 Year-End Financials

Debt ratio: 0.5%
Return on equity: 6.6%
Cash ($ mil.): 2,251
Current ratio: 0.57
Long-term debt ($ mil.): 31,109
No. of shares (mil.): 893
Dividends
 Yield: 4.5%
 Payout: —
Market value ($ mil.): —

Kao Corp

Kao (pronounced "cow") is one of Japan's leading makers of personal care laundry and cleaning products. Its brand names include Attack (a top laundry detergent in Japan) Biore (skin care) Laurier (sanitary napkins) Merries (disposable diapers) and PureOra (toothpaste). The company also manufactures Healthya brand beverages (green tea and water) cooking oils and fatty chemicals printer and copier toner products and plastics used in products such as athletic shoe soles. Kao which generates nearly two-thirds of sales from Japan is well-diversified with all five of its business segments contributing more than 15% of revenue.

Financial Performance

Note: Growth rates may differ after conversion of USD.

Kao has seen its sales flat to slightly up over the past few years with overall revenue up about 2% since 2015. Net income has shown stronger growth up about 45% during that same time.

In 2018 the company reported revenue of 1.5 trillion yen (about $13.6 billion) up 1% from the prior year. The cosmetics skin and hair care and fabric and home care businesses grew that year offsetting flat sales in chemicals and a decline in human health care.

Net income jumped 5% that year to 153.7 billion yen as compared to 2017 boosted primarily by the slight revenue increase and lower income taxes.

Cash at the end of 2018 was 266 billion yen a decrease of 70.9 billion yen from the prior year. Cash from operations contributed 195.6 billion yen to the coffers while investing activities used 157.9 billion yen mainly for capital expenditures and business combinations. Financing activities used another 108.6 billion yen for dividends to stockholders and purchase of treasury shares.

Strategy

Building a robust pipeline of innovative products and product enhancements is a key element of Kao's strategy. It invests some 4% of total sales in research & development to drive growth during a time when consumer attitudes and behaviors are rapidly changing. In late 2018 the company announced five new key technologies that will underpin new products in the coming years including fine fiber (a superfine membrane that will smooth the skin and improve the look of cosmetics) as well as RNA monitoring (non-invasive analytical method for monitoring RNA expression on the skin) Created Color (hair science) Bio IOS (a sustainable detergent base made from palm oil) and Package RecyCreation (eco-friendly upcycling).

Kao is also focused on brand building a key element of improving the cosmetics business (which has been struggling in recent years) among others. It has selected 11 global brands and 8 regional brands for investment.

In addition the company grows via acquisition and in mid-2018 strengthened its professional-use products business with the purchase of US-based Washing Systems LLC.

HISTORY

Tomiro Nagase founded the Kao Soap Company in 1887; shortly afterward he began selling bars under the motto "A Clean Nation Prospers." Kao's longtime rivalry with Procter & Gamble (P&G) was foreshadowed when it adopted a moon trademark in 1890 strikingly similar to the one chosen by P&G eight years earlier.

Kao moved into detergents in the 1940s. In the 1960s the company struck upon an idea that would vertically integrate it and set it apart from other consumer products manufacturers: It set up a network of wholesale distributors ("hansha") who sell only Kao products. The hansha system improved distribution time and cut costs by eliminating middlemen.

Yoshio Maruta one of several chemical engineers to run Kao took over as president in 1971.

Maruta presented himself as more Buddhist scholar than corporate honcho; during his 19 years at the top he gave the company a wider vision through his emphasis on creativity and his insistence on an active learning environment. To encourage sharing of ideas the company used open conference rooms for meetings and anyone interested could attend and participate in any meeting.

Under Maruta Kao launched a string of successful products in new areas in the 1980s. In 1982 the company introduced its Sofina cosmetics line emphasizing the line's scientific basis in a break from traditional beauty products marketing. The next year its Super Merries diapers (with a new design that reduced diaper rash) trounced P&G's Pampers in Japan. Its popular Attack laundry detergent (the first concentrated laundry soap) led the market within six months of its 1987 debut.

Seeking a way to enter the US market Kao bought the Andrew Jergens skin care company — based in Cincinnati as is P&G — in 1988. (It also purchased a chemical company to supply the materials to make Jergens' products.) P&G and Unilever braced themselves for the new competition but Kao didn't deliver releasing products like fizzy bath tablets that didn't sell well in a nation of shower-takers. In 1989 it bought a 75% interest in Goldwell a German maker of hair care and beauty products sold through hair stylists. (By 1994 Kao owned all of Goldwell which is now called Kao Professional Salon Services.)

In the mid-1980s Kao built a name for itself in the floppy disk market and became the top producer of 3.5-in. floppy disks in North America by 1990. However competition crowded the field and drove the price of disks down. In 1997 the company stopped production of floppy disks in the US.

Chemical engineer Takuya Goto took over as president that year. Kao looked to other Asian markets and the US for potential consumers and found a willing audience in the US for its Biore face strips. In 1998 Kao purchased Bausch & Lomb's skin care business gaining the Curel and Soft Sense lotion brands.

In 2000 Kao established a joint venture with Novartis to make baby foods and over-the-counter drugs such as stomach medicines and other pain relief drugs. In 2001 Kao lost out on its offer for Clairol to P&G. Also in 2001 it formed a joint venture with Archer Daniels Midland to produce an anti-obesity diacylglycerol oil (used in margarine cooking oil salad dressing and mayonnaise) and in 2002 began marketing it in the US under the brand name Enova. That year Kao dissolved its OTC-medicine-manufacturing joint venture with Novartis and renamed its Sofina cosmetics brand Prestige Cosmetics. Additionally in 2002 Kao acquired John Frieda Professional Hair Care through Andrew Jergens. (Andrew Jergens became Kao Brands in 2004.)

In 2004 Goto became chairman and Motoki Ozaki was promoted from president of the Global Fabric and Home Care division to president and CEO. The same year Kao broke off talks to purchase Kanebo.

In 2008 the company sold its fatty amine business to Akzo Nobel Surface Chemistry a unit of Akzo Nobel.

EXECUTIVES

Chairman of the Board, Michitaka Sawada
Independent Director, Nobuhide Hayashi
Independent Director, Sonosuke Kadonaga
Senior Managing Executive Officer, Executive President of Subsidiary, Representative Director, Toshiaki Takeuchi
Senior Managing Executive Officer, Representative Director, Tomoharu Matsuda

Executive President, Chief Executive Officer, Representative Director, Yoshihiro Hasebe
Independent Director, Chiaki Mukai
Independent Director, Osamu Shinobe
Auditors: Deloitte Touche Tohmatsu LLC

LOCATIONS

HQ: Kao Corp
  1-14-10 Nihonbashi-Kayabacho, Chuo-ku, Tokyo 103-8210
Phone: (81) 3 3660 7111
Web: www.kao.com

PRODUCTS/OPERATIONS

2018 Sales

	% of total
Fabric & home care	23
Skin care & hair care	23
Chemical	18
Cosmetics	18
Human health care	18
Total	**100**

Selected Brand Names

Attack (laundry detergent)
Bioré; (skin care)
Bub (shower gel)
Curel (skin care)
Essential (hair care)
Jergens (skin care)
Laurier (sanitary napkins)
Magiclean (household cleaner)
Merries (disposable diapers)
Primavista (makeup)
PureOra (toothpaste)
Quickle Wiper (household wipers)

COMPETITORS

BEIERSDORF INC.
CHURCH & DWIGHT CO. INC.
COLGATE-PALMOLIVE COMPANY
CR BRANDS INC.
ECOLAB INC.
EDGEWELL PERSONAL CARE COMPANY
HINDUSTAN UNILEVER LIMITED
INTERNATIONAL FLAVORS & FRAGRANCES INC.
LION CORPORATION
RECKITT BENCKISER GROUP PLC
REVLON INC.
THE CLOROX COMPANY
THE DIAL CORPORATION
THE ESTEE LAUDER COMPANIES INC
THE SUN PRODUCTS CORPORATION

HISTORICAL FINANCIALS

Company Type: Public

Income Statement				FYE: December 31
	REVENUE ($ mil.)	NET INCOME ($ mil.)	NET PROFIT MARGIN	EMPLOYEES
12/20	13,408	1,223	9.1%	45,378
12/19	13,836	1,365	9.9%	45,796
12/18	13,713	1,397	10.2%	46,306
12/17	13,237	1,306	9.9%	46,898
12/16	12,462	1,082	8.7%	46,520
Annual Growth	**1.8%**	**3.1%**	**—**	**(0.6%)**

2020 Year-End Financials

Debt ratio: 0.0%
Return on equity: 14.1%
Cash ($ mil.): 3,185
Current ratio: 1.83
Long-term debt ($ mil.): 943
No. of shares (mil.): 481
Dividends
  Yield: 1.6%
  Payout: 10.2%
Market value ($ mil.): 7,438

	STOCK PRICE ($)	P/E		PER SHARE ($)		
	FY Close	High/Low		Earnings	Dividends	Book Value
12/20	15.44	0	0	2.54	0.25	18.60
12/19	16.58	0	0	2.82	0.23	16.40
12/18	14.90	0	0	2.86	0.11	15.34
Annual Growth	**1.8%**	**—**	**—**	**(2.9%)**	**23.5%**	**4.9%**

Kasikornbank Public Co Ltd

Thais take their money — and their investing needs — straight to the KASIKORNBANK (known as KBank). One of Thailand's largest commercial banks KBank operates some 1050 domestic branches. It offers banking and financial services through offices in the Cayman Islands greater China Hong Kong Japan and the US. Its services include retail and commercial banking asset management consumer lending trade finance factoring and securities handling as well as hire purchase and leasing businesses. The bank which was established in 1945 and listed on the Thai stock exchange in 1976 boasted total assets of Baht 2.3 million total deposits of Baht 1.6 million and total loans of Baht 1.5 million in 2013.

EXECUTIVES

Director, Abhijai Chandrasen
Senior Executive Vice President, Capital Markets Business Division Head, Thiti Tantikulanan
Senior Executive Vice President, Corporate Secretariat Division Head, Company Secretary, Adit Laixuthai
Senior Executive Vice President, Finance and Control Division Head and Chief Financial Officer, Chongrak Rattanapian
Senior Executive Vice President, Strategy and Analytics Division Head, Wirawat Panthawangkun
President, Director, Pipatpong Poshyanonda
Vice Chairperson of the Board, Sujitpan Lamsam
President, Director, Pipit Aneaknithi
Senior Executive Vice President, Private Banking Group Head, Jirawat Supornpaibul
President, Director, Krit Jitjang
Chief Executive Officer, Executive Director, Kattiya Indaravijaya
Executive Vice President, Audit Division Head, Internal Audit Head, Surasak Dudsdeemaytha
Independent Director, Kalin Sarasin
Independent Director, Piyasvasti Amranand
President, Director, Patchara Samalapa
Independent Director, Saravoot Yoovidhya
Independent Director, Wiboon Khusakul
Independent Director, Suphajee Suthumpun
First Senior Vice President, Phaisarn Vorasetsiri
Independent Director, Nalinee Paiboon
First Senior Vice President, Karin Boonlertvanich
First Senior Vice President, Natcha Argasreog
Independent Chairman of the Board, Khobkarn Watanarangkun
First Senior Vice President, Wasana Surakit
Director, Sara Lamsam
Independent Director, Chanin Donavanik
Auditors: KPMG Phoomchai Audit Ltd.

LOCATIONS

HQ: Kasikornbank Public Co Ltd
  1 Soi Rat Burana 27/1, Rat Burana Road, Rat Burana Sub-District, Rat Burana District, Bangkok 10140
Phone: (66) 2 222 0000   **Fax:** (66) 2 470 1144
Web: www.kasikornbank.com

PRODUCTS/OPERATIONS

2013 Sales

	% of total
Interest income	53
Fees & service income	14
Other income	33
Total	**100**

Selected Companies

Kasikorn asset management co. ltd
Kasikorn factory & equipment co. ltd.
Kasikorn leasing co. ltd.
Kasikorn research center co. ltd.
Kasikorn securities pcl

COMPETITORS

AKBANK TURK ANONIM SIRKETI
Agricultural Bank of China Limited
BANCO DE SABADELL SA
BANK OF AYUDHYA PUBLIC COMPANY LIMITED
BANK OF INDIA
China Merchants Bank Co. Ltd.
HANG SENG BANK LIMITED
HSBC USA INC.
Industrial And Commercial Bank Of China Limited
Shinhan Financial Group Co. Ltd.
TURKIYE IS BANKASI ANONIM SIRKETI
UNITED OVERSEAS BANK LIMITED
Woori Finance Holdings Co. Ltd.

HISTORICAL FINANCIALS

Company Type: Public

Income Statement				FYE: December 31
	ASSETS ($ mil.)	NET INCOME ($ mil.)	INCOME AS % OF ASSETS	EMPLOYEES
12/20	122,212	984	0.8%	0
12/19	110,578	1,300	1.2%	0
12/18	97,531	1,188	1.2%	0
12/17	89,042	1,054	1.2%	0
12/16	79,504	1,122	1.4%	21,029
Annual Growth	**11.3%**	**(3.2%)**	**—**	**—**

2020 Year-End Financials

Return on assets: 0.8%
Return on equity: 6.9%
Long-term debt ($ mil.): —
No. of shares (mil.): —
Sales ($ mil): 8,641
Dividends
  Yield: 3.3%
  Payout: —
Market value ($ mil.): —

	STOCK PRICE ($)	P/E		PER SHARE ($)		
	FY Close	High/Low		Earnings	Dividends	Book Value
12/20	15.02	2	1	0.41	0.50	6.14
12/19	20.05	2	1	0.54	0.40	5.70
12/18	22.69	2	1	0.50	0.40	4.86
12/17	29.58	2	2	0.44	0.39	4.47
12/16	19.70	1	1	0.47	0.36	3.76
Annual Growth	**(6.6%)**	**—**	**—**	**(3.0%)**	**8.9%**	**13.1%**

Kawasaki Heavy Industries Ltd

Auditors: KPMG AZSA LLC

LOCATIONS

HQ: Kawasaki Heavy Industries Ltd
Kobe Crystal Tower, 1-1-3 Higashi-Kawasakicho,
Chuo-ku, Kobe, Hyogo 650-8680
Phone: (81) 78 371 9551   **Fax:** (81) 78 371 9568
Web: www.khi.co.jp

HISTORICAL FINANCIALS

Company Type: Public

Income Statement				FYE: March 31
	REVENUE ($ mil.)	NET INCOME ($ mil.)	NET PROFIT MARGIN	EMPLOYEES
03/21	13,443	(174)	—	36,691
03/20	15,120	171	1.1%	36,332
03/19	14,400	247	1.7%	35,691
03/18	14,825	272	1.8%	35,805
03/17	13,584	234	1.7%	35,127
Annual Growth	(0.3%)	—	—	1.1%

2021 Year-End Financials

Debt ratio: 0.2%   No. of shares (mil.): 167
Return on equity: (-4.2%)   Dividends
Cash ($ mil.): 1,144   Yield: —
Current ratio: 1.40   Payout: —
Long-term debt ($ mil.): 3,514   Market value ($ mil.): —

KB Financial Group, Inc.

KB Financial Group holding company for Kookmin Bank provides commercial and consumer banking services in South Korea. It offers asset management and life insurance through alliances with Netherlands-based ING Groep. The bank's lending activities mainly entail residential mortgages home equity loans consumer loans and corporate loans. Kookmin Bank has more than 1200 branches in its home country where it claims some 26 million customers or about half of the population of South Korea. The bank provides corporate services such as foreign exchange and securities trading from offices at home and abroad in New York London Hong Kong Tokyo and Auckland New Zealand.

EXECUTIVES

Non-Executive Independent Director, Myeong Hui Choi
Non-Executive Independent Director, Gu Hwan Jung
Non-Executive Independent Director, Seok Ho Sunwoo
Chairman of the Board, Chief Executive Officer, Jong Gyu Yoon
Non-Executive Independent Director, Gyu Taek Oh
Non-Executive Independent Director, Stuart B Solomon
Non-Executive Independent Director, Gyeong Ho Kim
Auditors: Samil PricewaterhouseCoopers

LOCATIONS

HQ: KB Financial Group, Inc.
26, Gukjegeumyung-ro 8-gil,, Yeongdeungpo-gu,
Seoul 07331
Phone: (82) 2 2073 7807   **Fax:** (82) 2 2073 2848
Web: www.kbfng.com

PRODUCTS/OPERATIONS

Selected Subsidiaries

KB Asset Management Co. Ltd. (80%)
KB Credit Information Co. Ltd. (99.7%)
KB Data Systems Co. Ltd. (99.99%)
KB Futures Co. Ltd. (99.98%)
KB Investment Co. Ltd. (99.99%)
KB Real Estate Trust Co. Ltd. (99.99%)
Kookmin Bank
Kookmin Bank Hong Kong Ltd.
Kookmin Bank International Ltd.

COMPETITORS

ALLEGHENY VALLEY BANCORP INC.
BANK HAPOALIM LTD.
CIMB GROUP HOLDINGS BERHAD
CITIBANK NATIONAL ASSOCIATION
FIRST CITIZENS BANCORPORATION INC.
ISRAEL DISCOUNT BANK OF NEW YORK
LONE STAR NATIONAL BANCSHARES—TEXAS INC.
NORTHERN STAR FINANCIAL INC
SOUTH STATE CORPORATION

HISTORICAL FINANCIALS

Company Type: Public

Income Statement				FYE: December 31
	ASSETS ($ mil.)	NET INCOME ($ mil.)	INCOME AS % OF ASSETS	EMPLOYEES
12/20	561,110	3,174	0.6%	154
12/19	449,100	2,868	0.6%	153
12/18	430,166	2,745	0.6%	185
12/17	409,700	3,106	0.8%	164
12/16	312,707	1,784	0.6%	159
Annual Growth	15.7%	15.5%	—	(0.8%)

2020 Year-End Financials

Return on assets: 0.6%   Dividends
Return on equity: 8.5%   Yield: 4.5%
Long-term debt ($ mil.): —   Payout: 24.1%
No. of shares (mil.): 389   Market value ($ mil.): 15,430
Sales ($ mil): 31,577

	STOCK PRICE ($) FY Close	P/E High/Low		PER SHARE ($) Earnings	Dividends	Book Value
12/20	39.60	0	0	7.99	1.79	100.23
12/19	41.37	0	0	7.27	1.68	85.65
12/18	41.98	0	0	6.88	1.79	80.93
12/17	58.51	0	0	7.74	1.17	79.95
12/16	35.29	0	0	4.63	0.81	64.76
Annual Growth	2.9%	—	—	14.6%	22.0%	11.5%

KBC Group NV

Auditors: PwC Bedrijfsrevisoren BV

LOCATIONS

HQ: KBC Group NV
Havenlaan 2, Brussels 1080
Phone: (32) 2 429 49 16   **Fax:** (32) 2 429 44 16
Web: www.kbc.com

HISTORICAL FINANCIALS

Company Type: Public

Income Statement				FYE: December 31
	ASSETS ($ mil.)	NET INCOME ($ mil.)	INCOME AS % OF ASSETS	EMPLOYEES
12/20	393,644	1,767	0.4%	40,863
12/19	326,427	2,794	0.9%	37,854
12/18	325,015	2,943	0.9%	38,368
12/17	350,446	3,086	0.9%	38,459
12/16	290,579	2,562	0.9%	36,315
Annual Growth	7.9%	(8.9%)	—	3.0%

2020 Year-End Financials

Return on assets: 0.4%   Dividends
Return on equity: 6.8%   Yield: 0.9%
Long-term debt ($ mil.): —   Payout: 13.1%
No. of shares (mil.): 416   Market value ($ mil.): 14,538
Sales ($ mil): 11,974

	STOCK PRICE ($) FY Close	P/E High/Low		PER SHARE ($) Earnings	Dividends	Book Value
12/20	34.89	13	7	4.10	0.34	63.41
12/19	37.55	7	5	6.57	1.27	54.91
12/18	31.96	8	5	6.85	1.13	54.03
12/17	42.76	7	6	7.23	1.07	53.85
12/16	30.99	6	4	6.00	0.33	43.81
Annual Growth	3.0%	—	—	(9.1%)	0.7%	9.7%

KDDI Corp

Auditors: PricewaterhouseCoopers Kyoto

LOCATIONS

HQ: KDDI Corp
3-10-10 Iidabashi, Chiyoda-ku, Tokyo 102-8460
Phone: (81) 3 3347 0077
Web: www.kddi.com

HISTORICAL FINANCIALS

Company Type: Public

Income Statement				FYE: March 31
	REVENUE ($ mil.)	NET INCOME ($ mil.)	NET PROFIT MARGIN	EMPLOYEES
03/21	47,980	5,883	12.3%	82,560
03/20	48,247	5,893	12.2%	83,308
03/19	45,874	5,577	12.2%	78,337
03/18	47,482	5,391	11.4%	73,508
03/17	42,468	4,889	11.5%	69,234
Annual Growth	3.1%	4.7%	—	4.5%

2021 Year-End Financials

Debt ratio: 0.1%   No. of shares (mil.): —
Return on equity: 14.2%   Dividends
Cash ($ mil.): 7,313   Yield: 3.6%
Current ratio: 1.94   Payout: 21.0%
Long-term debt ($ mil.): 10,401   Market value ($ mil.): —

	STOCK PRICE ($) FY Close	P/E High/Low		PER SHARE ($) Earnings	Dividends	Book Value
03/21	15.49	0	0	2.56	0.57	18.86
03/20	14.60	0	0	2.54	0.51	17.53
03/19	10.72	0	0	2.34	0.43	16.04
03/18	12.81	0	0	2.22	0.43	14.76
03/17	13.16	0	0	1.98	0.34	12.93
Annual Growth	4.2%	—	—	6.6%	13.6%	9.9%

Keiyo Bank, Ltd. (The) (Japan)

Keiyo Bank aims to be chief in Chiba. Founded in 1943 the regional bank operates mainly in the urban areas in and surrounding Chiba Prefecture Japan. Among its commercial banking services are ATM consumer loans and foreign currency deposits. Keiyo operates via some 262 locations including a Tokyo branch and 114 in Chiba proper. Japan Trustee Services Bank claims a 5.37% stake in the bank alongside Nipponkoa Insurance (4.33%) and The Chiba Bank (4.19%).

EXECUTIVES

President, Representative Director, Toshiyuki Kumagai

Independent Director, Katsusada Akiyama

Independent Director, Tomoko Tobe

Independent Director, Yasushi Saito

Managing Executive Officer, Director, Tatsushi Ichikawa

Vice President, Representative Director, Kiyoshi Hashimoto

Independent Director, Hiroshi Uchimura

Managing Executive Officer, Director, Seiji Sato

Senior Managing Executive Officer, Director, Satoru Akiyama

Managing Executive Officer, Director, Kazuo Fujisaki

Auditors: Ernst & Young ShinNihon LLC

LOCATIONS

HQ: Keiyo Bank, Ltd. (The) (Japan)
5-45 Chibaminato, Chuo-ku, Chiba 260-0026
Phone: (81) 43 222 2121
Web: www.keiyobank.co.jp

COMPETITORS

AICHI BANKLTD. THE	UNITED OVERSEAS BANK
BANK OF AYUDHYA PUBLIC	LIMITED
COMPANY LIMITED	

HISTORICAL FINANCIALS

Company Type: Public

Income Statement				FYE: March 31
	ASSETS ($ mil.)	NET INCOME ($ mil.)	INCOME AS % OF ASSETS	EMPLOYEES
03/21	50,151	66	0.1%	3,062
03/20	46,013	51	0.1%	3,071
03/19	44,204	95	0.2%	3,055
03/18	45,104	114	0.3%	3,108
03/17	41,128	104	0.3%	3,130
Annual Growth	5.1%	(10.5%)	—	(0.5%)

2021 Year-End Financials

Return on assets: 0.1%	Dividends
Return on equity: 2.5%	Yield: —
Long-term debt ($ mil.): —	Payout: 33.7%
No. of shares (mil.): 130	Market value ($ mil.): —
Sales ($ mil): 569	

Kering SA

Kering (pronounced "caring") has transformed itself from a conglomerate to the world's third-largest luxury group (behind LVMH and Richemont). The Paris-based company's stable of global luxury brands includes Italian high end label Gucci as well as Alexander McQueen Balenciaga Bottega Veneta and Saint Laurent. Kering also owns German athletic shoemaker PUMA. More than a third of Kering's sales are generated from Asia-Pacific. Fran Şois Pinault founded the firm in 1963 as Pinault Group which eventually became Pinault-Printemps-Redoute (PPR) and later Kering.

Operations

Kering's top three brands by revenue include Gucci (more than 60% of the company's revenue) Saint Lauren (nearly 15%) and Bottega Veneta (more than 5%). Other houses account for the remainder.

In terms of product category leather goods account for about 60% of Kering's revenue. Other major categories include shoes (more than 15%) ready-to-wear (about 15%) and watches and jewelry (about 5%).

By distribution channel more than 60% of the company's sales are generated in wholesale sales and other revenue including royalties Retail channel account for the remaining 40%.

Geographic Reach

Paris-based Kering rings up about 35% of its sales in Asia-Pacific. Western Europe and North America are also important markets for the luxury goods maker representing more than 30% and about 20% of sales respectively. Japan accounts for about 10% of sales and the rest comes EMEA and South America.

Kering operates about 1400 direct operated stores of which more than 320 are in Western Europe 220 are in Japan and about 230 are in North America. More than 600 direct operated stores are located in emerging markets.

Sales and Marketing

ering's distribution channel is split into six sales formats: Mono brand stores specialty stores department stores outlets e-commerce and airport stores.

The company's retail channel operates a directly operated store network and its wholesale channel includes department stores independent high-end multi-brand stores and franchise stores.

Financial Performance

Note: Growth rates may differ after conversion to US Dollars.

In 2019 Kering reported revenue of ?15.9 billion up 16% from ?13.7 billion in 2018. The company attributes the increase to organic growth at Gucci where sales reached ?9.6 billion up 16% from the prior year and at Saint Laurent which increased its revenue by 18% to ?2 billion.

Net income from continuing operations rose to ?3.2 billion in 2018 up from ?2.8 billion in 2018 mainly due to higher revenue and a decrease in costs and expenses and a rise in income tax expense that year.

Cash at the end of 2019 was ?1.8 billion. Cash from operations was ?2.5 billion while investing activities used ?1.2 billion. Financing activities used ?1.5 billion. Kering's main cash uses in 2019 were purchases of property plant and equipment dividends paid to owners of the parent company and repayment of lease liabilities.

Strategy

Kering operates through a two-tiered strategy consisting of promoting organic growth and enhancing synergies through integration.

Its organic growth is centered on providing an improved in-store client experience which enables it to create and sustain lasting connections. With this in mind in 2019 Kering completed the roll-out of a dedicated application designed with Apple. It also internalized its Couture & Leather brands' e-commerce activities in 2020. With this move the group aims to oversee the whole value chain so as to provide clients with truly exceptional experience across all channels and touchpoints aligning the e-commerce side with the standards of excellence seen in its boutiques.

Kering strives to create value for its Houses and is geared to unlocking their creative potential. In order to enrich its brands' offerings the group draws on cross-business expertise. Kering is also constantly improving and adapting its operating model to ensure its structures are always more up-to-date and flexible. The group has launched an ambitious transformation project focusing on its information systems supply chain and logistics.

Company Background

Sixteen-year-old Fran Şois Pinault left school in 1952 to join the family timber business. He took over the firm when his father died in 1963; that year the company was renamed Pinault Group. Pinault diversified the company into wood importing and retailing eventually building a flourishing enterprise. In 1973 Pinault began to show his talent for the art of the deal. Sensing the demand for timber was peaking he sold 80% of the business buying it back two years later at an 85% discount.

Pinault began to diversify outside the timber industry in the 1990s. It acquired a series of companies including Au Printemps (owner of Printemps stores and 54% of catalog company Redoute) in 1992. The firm then became the Pinault-Printemps Group. In 1993 the group reorganized into four divisions: retail business-to-business financial services and international trade and eventually renamed itself Pinault-Printemps-Redoute (PPR).

In 2005 Fran Şois-Henri Pinault the son of the company's founder joined the company as its new CEO. During his 10 years at the helm Weinberg oversaw the transformation of the company from a business-to-business concern to a focused luxury retail group. To underscore the company's transformation begun in 2005 in 2013 PPR became Kering.

HISTORY

Sixteen-year-old Fran Şois Pinault left school in 1952 to join the family timber business. He took over the firm when his father died in 1963; that year the company was renamed Pinault Group. Pinault diversified the company into wood importing and retailing eventually building a flourishing enterprise. In 1973 Pinault began to show his talent for the art of the deal. Sensing the demand for timber was peaking he sold 80% of the business buying it back two years later at an 85% discount.

During the 1970s Pinault bought struggling timber businesses and turned them around. (He was helped in part by a policy of the French government that subsidized purchases of failing companies in order to preserve jobs.) Pinault purchased bankrupt wood panel manufacturer Isoroy in 1986 for a token fee. In 1987 he bought ailing paper company Chapelle Darblay selling it three years later at a 40% profit. By 1988 when it filed to go public on the Paris exchange Pinault Group was a vertically integrated timber manufacturing trading and distribution company.

Pinault began to diversify outside the timber industry in the 1990s. It acquired electrical equipment distributor CFAO (Compagnie Fran Şaise de l'Afrique Occidentale) in 1990 the Conforama furniture chain in 1991 and Au Printemps (owner of Printemps stores and 54% of catalog company Redoute) in 1992. The firm then became the Pinault-Printemps Group. The purchase of Au Printemps left the company heavily in debt and it sold some of its noncore assets during the early 1990s.

In 1993 the group reorganized into four divisions: retail business-to-business financial services and international trade. That year Pinault-Printemps bought a majority stake in Groupelec and merged it with electrical equipment subsidiary CDME forming Rexel. In 1994 the company completed its acquisition of Redoute. After renaming itself Pinault-Printemps-Redoute (PPR) it bought a majority stake in French book and music retailer Fnac (buying the rest in 1995). In 1995 Rexel head Serge Weinberg took over the company after CEO Pierre Blayau ran afoul of Pinault over strategy. PPR added West African pharmaceuticals distributor SCOA in 1996. While Rexel gobbled up 11 companies in Europe and the US that year PPR launched a new chain of women's lingerie stores called Orcanta and started its own venture capital fund.

PPR acquired Becob France's #3 building materials distributor in 1997. Expanding globally Redcats (Redoute's new name) launched the Vertbaudet (children's wear) and Cyrillus (sportswear) catalogs in the UK that year.

In 1998 PPR bought a majority stake in Guilbert the European leader in office supplies and furniture and a 44% stake in Brylane (renamed Redcats USA in 2004) the US's #4 mail-order company. PPR also opened a new store format in France called Made in Sport (sporting goods). In addition it began offering phone cards through subsidiary Kertel.

PPR bought the remainder of Brylane in 1999 and also launched a new division to oversee the online efforts of its various businesses. Later that year PPR sparked a string of legal battles between it and LVMH when it purchased 42% of luxury goods maker Gucci. (The move thwarted LVMH's efforts to take over Gucci by diluting LVMH's stake in the firm.) In early 2000 PPR bought France's largest computer retailer Surcouf.

In March 2001 a Dutch court granted a request by LVMH and ordered an investigation into the legality of the alliance of PPR and Gucci. In a deal to end years of litigation PPR purchased LVMH's stake in Gucci for $806.5 million in October 2001 increasing its ownership to 53.2%.

The company sold Yves Saint Laurent's haute couture division to French dressmaking company SLPB Prestige Services in March 2002. Guilbert's mail-order business was sold to US office supplies retailer Staples in October of that year for $815 million. (The rest of Guilbert was later sold to Office Depot in May 2003.) In June 2003 PPR's timber wholesale business Pinault Bois & Materiaux was sold to the UK's Wolseley plc. In December PPR sold 14.5% of Finaref and Finaref Nordic to Agricole. Also in 2003 PPR increased its stake in Gucci to 67.58%.

To fund its transformation the company sold Guilbert and Pinault Bois & Materiaux (lumber and building supplies) to shore up its balance sheet and fund its offer for the rest of Gucci in 2004. In November PPR finalized a deal to sell its controlling stake in electrical equipment distributor Rexel to Ray Acquisition SCA a consortium made up of three investment firms.

In March 2005 Fran Şois-Henri Pinault the son of the company's founder joined the company as its new CEO succeeding Serge Weinberg. During his 10 years at the helm Weinberg oversaw the transformation of the company from a business-to-business concern to a focused luxury retail group. At the annual general meeting in May shareholders approved the offical name change to PPR from Pinault-Printemps-Redoute.

In August 2006 as part of its strategy to focus on its luxury business PPR sold its Paris-based department store chain Printemps to Italy's La Rinascente for about $1.3 billion. The divestiture included all of the chain's 17 stores. In September PPR's Redcats Group acquired The Sportman's Guide a catalog and online marketer for about $265 million. In July 2008 Redcats Group's US division completed the sale of its Missy Group apparel line which included the Chadwick's of Boston metrostyle and Closeout Catalog Outlets brands to the US private equity fund Monomoy Capital Partners for about $24 million.

To secure a foothold in the international premium footwear market PPR increased its nearly 30% stake in PUMA in July 2007 to more than 60%. The deal valued at more than $7 billion placed the German athletic shoemaker in PPR's brand portfolio alongside its luxury holdings.

In a bid to increase its presence in the luxury watch business PPR in 2008 acquired a 23% stake in the Swiss watchmaking company Sowind Group the maker of high-end Girard-Perregaux and Jean-Richard watches.

In December 2009 PPR sold a majority stake in its indirect subsidiary CFAO to the public. The ?806 million ($1.2 billion) in proceeds from the offering of the African car distributor went to Discodis a wholly-owned subsidiary of PPR. In addition to auto distribution CFAO's other business units include: Eurapharma a distributor of pharmaceuticals; CFAO Technologies; and CFAO Industries & Trading. The shares trade on Euronext Paris.

The company sold its Conforama chain of household furniture and appliance stores to South Africa's Steinhoff International Holdings (SIH) in early 2011.The deal valued at ?1.2 billion (about $1.6 billion) allowed PPR to devote more attention to its core Gucci and PUMA units. In June PPR made US youth brand Volcom Inc. a wholly-owned subsidiary via a tender offer for the California company's shares in a deal valued at $608 million.

To underscore the company's transformation begun in 2005 in June 2013 PPR became Kering. The name change reaffirms the Group's international scope while acknowledging its origins in the Brittany region of France. (In Breton ker means "home" and "place to live in.")

EXECUTIVES

Director, Jean-Pierre Denis, $145,663 total compensation

Group Managing Director, Member of the Executive Committee, Non-Independent Director, Jean-Francois Palus, $1,367,287 total compensation

Director - Employee Representative, Claire Lacaze, $95,869 total compensation

Independent Director, Yseulys Costes, $131,894 total compensation

President and Chief Executive Officer of Gucci, Member of the Executive Committee, Marco Bizzarri

Chief Sustainability Officer and Head of International Institutional Affairs, Member of the Executive Committee, Marie-Claire Daveu

Independent Director, Daniela Riccardi, $81,924 total compensation

Chief Communications & Image Officer, Member of the Executive Committee, Valerie Duport

Lead Independent Director, Sophie L'Helias, $145,663 total compensation

President and Chief Executive Officer of Kering Eyewear, Member of the Executive Committee, Roberto Vedovotto

Vice Chairwoman of the Board - Representative of Financiere Pinault, Heloise Temple-Boyer

Chief People Officer, Member of the Executive Committee, Beatrice Lazat

Chief Financial Officer, Member of the Executive Committee, Jean-Marc Duplaix

Chief Executive Officer of Bottega Veneta, Member of the Executive Committee, Bartolomeo Rongone

Independent Director, Emma Watson

Director representing employees, Concetta Battaglia

Independent Director, Jean Liu

Non-Independent Chairman of the Board, Chief Executive Officer, Member of the Executive Committee, Francoishenri Pinault, $1,093,829 total compensation

Independent Director, Tidjane Thiam

President - Kering North and South-East Asia Pacific, Thierry Marty

President and Chief Executive Officer of Yves Saint Laurent, Member of the Executive Committee, Francesca Bellettini

Chief Client & Digital Officer, Member of the Executive Committee, Gregory Boutte

Auditors: Deloitte & Associés

LOCATIONS

HQ: Kering SA
40 Rue de Sevres, Paris 75007
Phone: (33) 1 45 64 61 00   **Fax:** (33) 1 45 64 60 00
Web: www.kering.com

2015 Sales

	% of total
Western Europe	31
Asia/Pacific	26
North America	23
Japan	10
Other countries	10
Total	**100**

PRODUCTS/OPERATIONS

2015 Sales

	% of total
Luxury	68
Sports & Lifestyle	32
Total	**100**

Selected Brands

Luxury
  Alexander McQueen
  Balenciaga
  Bottega Veneta
  Boucheron
  Brioni
  Christopher Kane
  Girard-Perregaux
  Gucci
  JeanRichard
  Sergio Rossi
  Stella McCartney
  Yves Saint Laurent
Sport & lifestyle
  Electric
  Puma
  Volcom

Selected Operations

Luxury Goods
  Gucci Group N.V. (99.39% leather goods and apparel)
  PUMA (athletic footwear)
  Sowind Group (50.1% watches)
Retail
  Fnac (electronics books music; Belgium Brazil France Italy Monaco Portugal Spain Switzerland and Taiwan)
  Volcom Inc. (US young men's and women's apparel)

COMPETITORS

Bertelsmann SE & Co. KGaA	LEVI STRAUSS & CO.
DESTINATION XL GROUP INC.	RALLYE
	Signet Jewelers Limited
Koninklijke Ahold Delhaize N.V.	TAILORED BRANDS INC.
LAGARDERE SA	TARKETT
	V.F. CORPORATION

HISTORICAL FINANCIALS

Company Type: Public

Income Statement

FYE: December 31

	REVENUE ($ mil.)	NET INCOME ($ mil.)	NET PROFIT MARGIN	EMPLOYEES
12/20	16,077	2,639	16.4%	38,553
12/19	17,833	2,592	14.5%	38,068
12/18	15,649	4,254	27.2%	34,795
12/17	18,553	2,140	11.5%	44,055
12/16	13,077	858	6.6%	40,052
Annual Growth	5.3%	32.4%	—	(0.9%)

2020 Year-End Financials

Debt ratio: 26.8%
Return on equity: 19.4%
Cash ($ mil.): 4,225
Current ratio: 1.34
Long-term debt ($ mil.): 4,682

No. of shares (mil.): 124
Dividends
 Yield: 1.2%
 Payout: 4.6%
Market value ($ mil.): 9,051

	STOCK PRICE ($) FY Close	P/E High/Low		PER SHARE ($) Earnings	Dividends	Book Value
12/20	72.45	4	2	21.11	0.89	116.13
12/19	65.36	4	2	20.66	5.84	92.31
12/18	46.76	2	1	33.77	5.38	90.14
12/17	47.07	3	2	16.99	0.55	113.42
12/16	22.35	4	2	6.82	0.42	94.23
Annual Growth	34.2%	—	—	32.6%	20.7%	5.4%

Kesko OYJ

Kesko is a Finish trading sector in forerunner and operates in the grocery trade building and technical trade and the car trade. The company operates in 1800 chain stores in Finland Estonia Latvia Lithuania Norway Sweden and Poland. Its largest division Grocery Trade operates some 1200 "K" food stores of a variety of formats. Kesko's building and technical trade division operates another 500 stores and includes Onninen a wholesaler of building materials to contractors industry infrastructure building and retailers; and K-Rauta Byggmakker K-Senukai and OMA which serve professionals and consumers. It also offers sporting goods through Intersport Budget Sport. Keska's third division Car Trade sells cars and trucks from the Volkswagen Group as K-Caara.

Operations

Kesko operates in three divisions: Grocery trade Building and technical trade and Car trade.

The Grocery Trade (nearly 55% of revenue) the second biggest trade operator in Finland. Nearly 1000 independent retailers and 1200K-food Stores in Finland with 1.2 million daily customers and 470 stores offer online services. The K-food store chains are K-Citymarket K-Supermarket K-Market and Neste K service stations.

Building and Technical Trade division generates nearly 40% of revenue and operates in seven countries such as Finland Sweden Norway Estonia Latvia Lithuania and Poland with a total of some 500 stores. The division's chains are Onninen which serves technical professionals and K-Rauta Byggmakker Carlsen Fritz ,e and K-Bygg which serve bothprofessional builders and consumers. The division also comprises leisure trade and the chains Intersport and Budget Sport.

In Car trade division (less than 10% of revenue) Kesko imports and sells Volkswagen Audi SEAT CUPRAPorsche and Bentley passenger cars and Volkswagen Commercial Vehicles and MAN trucks in Finland and SEAT in the Baltics. Kesko's retail company K-Caara and independent dealers sell new and used vehicles and offer servicing and after-sales services at some 70 outlets across Finland.

Geographic Reach

Finland-based Kesko operates in more than 1800 stores in Finland Sweden Norway Estonia Latvia and Poland.

Sales and Marketing

Kesko markets its products and services through online sales and digital services with the store network and enable a seamless customer experience in all channels.

Financial Performance

Note: Growth rates may differ after conversion to US Dollars.

The company's consolidated net sales amounted to ?10.7 billion a ?51.1 million decrease from the previous year.

In 2020 the company had a net income of ?527.6 million a 31% increase from the previous year's net income of ?403.3 million.

The company's cash at the end of 2020 was ?154.5 million. Operating activities generated ?1.2 billion while investing activities used ?413.7 million. Financing activities used another ?707.5 million.

Strategy

Kesko manages its portfolio of companies to achieve growth and profitability and raise cash for investing. In 2018 it acquired two foodservice wholesalers two building and home improvement companies and an online retailer; on the flipside it disposed its K-maatalous agricultural business the Asko and Sotka furniture businesses the Yamarin boat business and a Yamaha distribution operation.

In its building and technical trade business Kesko is granting its countries of operation greater autonomy rolling out digital services and targeting growth in the B2B trade through acquisitions.

Mergers and Acquisitions

In late 2020 Kesko acquired Reider Flokkmanns Eftf AS (Flokkmann) which part of the Norwegian Byggmakker chain and the store property Arn Eiendom AS.

In 2020 Kesko acquired Carlsen Fritz ,e Handel AS in Norway. The acquisition strengthens Kesko's position in the Oslo fjord region where the Carlsen Fritz ,e Handel network of 25 stores complements Kesko's existing Byggmakker store network.

In early 2020 Kesko acquired the Swedish Mark & Infra i Sverige AB (MIAB) a company specializing in the sales of water and sewage products. The acquisition strengthens Onninen's technical wholesale offering to Infra customers in Sweden.

HISTORY

Kesko sprung from four Finnish wholesalers and retailers (Kauppiaitten Oy Keski-Suomen Tukkukauppa Oy Maakauppiaitten Oy and Savo-Karjalan Tukkuliike) in 1940. To centralize their purchasing and business needs the foursome merged. Kesko was up and running early the next year with some 5800 retail members. In 1947 the company formed a retail group and Kesko's signature K-emblem made its debut.

In the 1950s Kesko's K-emblem appeared on about 3700 member stores and the company expanded into the agricultural and construction supplies industry.

The company listed on the Helsinki Stock Exchange in 1960. That decade Kesko added fresh foods to its general stores which later helped it evolve into a grocery retailer. Self-service became the norm in the mid 1960s permanently changing the Finnish retailing landscape. A centralized distribution center was established near Helsinki and Kesko began selling its industrial operations.

In the 1970s Kesko developed its first supermarket and started selling home products specialty merchandise (opening sporting goods retailer Kesport) and hardware items.

Investments (and divestments) were Kesko's game in the 1980s; it bought new offices a new warehouse site and a few large retail units. The company continued to sell most of its industrial operations which had grown to include a flourmill match and bicycle factories and a rye crisp business. Kesko kept its most profitable unit — a coffee roastery (Viking Coffee). That decade Kesko introduced its first private-label food brand (Pirkka).

Kesko's sales slumped in the early 1990s in response to recessions in Finland and the world . By 1994 though all was well again. The company began expanding into Sweden and then Russia opening stores under a variety of formats. In 1996 Kesko acquired Kaukomarkkinat Oy (commercial trading house) sold metal distributor Keskometalli Oy and tried acquiring Finnish supermarket chain Tuko. But Finland's European Commission stopped the deal from going through to protect the country's smaller merchants. The following year Kesko bought information technology firm Academica Oy.

The 1990s also saw Kesko acquiring Anttila Oy a department store operator. In 1999 the company appointed Matti Honkala as its new CEO (the former was Eero Utter). The company controlled 50% of the Finnish market.

In 2000 Kesko announced it would open four hypermarkets in Latvia by 2004. In early 2001 Kesko turned its foods unit and home and specialty goods group into wholly owned subsidiaries; it plans to do the same to the hardware and builders' supplies unit and the agriculture and machinery segment later in 2001. Also that year it acquired 17 Saastumarket stores in Estonia opened two more and announced plans to build at least 10 more.

In 2004 Matti Halmesm ¤ki replaced the retiring Matti Honkala as CEO.

In July 2005 Rautakesko acquired the Stroymaster DIY chain in Russia and converted them to the K-rauta banner in August 2006.

In January 2006 Konekesko sold its warehouse technology (forklifts and warehouse racks) business in Finland to BT Industries of Sweden for a gain of about ?2.6 million. In December Kesko Food sold its 50% stake in Rimi Baltic AB to ICA Baltic AB for ?190 million.

In March 2008 Kesko sold its interest in T ¤hti Optikko Group an optical goods chain. In April the company sold its export/import firm Kauko-Telko to Aspo. Kauko-Telko (formerly Kaukomarkkinat) traded in home electronics technical products optical items sporting goods and watches.

EXECUTIVES

Chairman of the Board, Esa Kiiskinen
President - Car Trade Division, Member of the Group Management Board, Matti Virtanen
Chief Financial Officer, Executive Vice President, Member of the Group Management Board, Jukka Erlund
Director, Toni Pokela
Executive Vice President, Human Resources, Corporate Responsibility and Regional Relations, Member of the Group Management Board, Matti Mettala
President - Building and Technical Trade Division, Deputy to President and Chief Executive Officer, Member of the Group Management Board, Jorma Rauhala, $504,870 total compensation

Chairman of the Group Management Board, President, Chief Executive Officer, Mikko Helander, $1,086,993 total compensation
President - Grocery Trade Division, Member of the Group Management Board, Ari Akseli
Director, Matti Naumanen
Independent Deputy Chairman of the Board, Peter Fagernas
Director, Piia Karhu
Independent Director, Jannica Fagerholm
Independent Director, Matti Kyytsonen
Executive Vice President, Chief Digital Officer, Member of the Group Management Board, Anni Ronkainen
Executive Vice President - Communications, Brand and Stakeholder Relations, Member of the Group Management Board, Karoliina Partanen
Auditors: Deloitte Oy

LOCATIONS

HQ: Kesko OYJ
P.O.Box 1, Kesko FI-00016
Phone: (358) 10 5311   **Fax:** (358) 9 174 398
Web: www.kesko.fi

2018 Sales

	% of total
Finland	80
Other Nordic countries	9
Baltic countries	8
Others	3
Total	**100**

PRODUCTS/OPERATIONS

2018 Sales

	% of total
Grocery trade	52
Building and technical trade	39
Car trade	9
Total	**100**

Selected Kesko Divisions

Anttila (department stores home and specialty goods)
Kesko Agro Ltd. (agriculture and machinery)
Kesko Food Ltd. (groceries)
Rautakesko Ltd. (building supplies interior decoration and hardware)
VV-Auto (auto dealerships)

COMPETITORS

Acer Incorporated
Axel Johnson AB
CONCORD RESOURCES LIMITED
FNAC DARTY PARTICIPATIONS ET SERVICES
Franz Haniel & Cie. GmbH
GRAHAM PACKAGING COMPANY L.P.
KINGFISHER PLC
MARKET AMERICA INC.
Suomen Osuuskauppojen Keskuskunta
TRUE VALUE COMPANY L.L.C.
Victoria Retail Group B.V.

HISTORICAL FINANCIALS

Company Type: Public

Income Statement   FYE: December 31

	REVENUE ($ mil.)	NET INCOME ($ mil.)	NET PROFIT MARGIN	EMPLOYEES
12/20	13,094	531	4.1%	17,650
12/19	12,036	380	3.2%	25,168
12/18	11,890	183	1.5%	23,458
12/17	12,797	309	2.4%	24,983
12/16	10,749	104	1.0%	27,656
Annual Growth	**5.1%**	**50.3%**	**—**	**(10.6%)**

2020 Year-End Financials

Debt ratio: 15.5%   No. of shares (mil.): 396
Return on equity: 20.5%   Dividends
Cash ($ mil.): 189   Yield: —
Current ratio: 0.97   Payout: 68.8%
Long-term debt ($ mil.): 537   Market value ($ mil.): —

Kingfisher PLC

Kingfisher is an eye-catching home improvement company. The firm operates more than 1350 B&Q Screwfix Castorama and Brico Dep´t stores in seven European countries plus Turkey and Russia. The UK is the company's home market and where the majority of the group's stores are located. Customers visit Kingfisher in-store and online to buy an array of home improvement products under the categories outdoor & garden home & bedroom building & hardware and kitchen & bathroom. Kingfisher operates the Ko §tas joint venture in Turkey. It generates about 45% of sales in the UK and Ireland.

Operations

Kingfisher operates under retail banners including B&Q Castorama Brico Dep´t Screwfix TradePoint and Ko §tas. The company offers home improvement products and services to consumers and trade professionals.

In the UK Kingfisher's biggest market the company offers around 40000 home improvement and garden products at B&Q. Screwfix which has more than 11000 items in stock serves a professional customer base via mail-order and in store with trade tools plumbing electrical products and products for fixing and improving bathrooms and kitchens. In France and Poland Castorama-branded stores stock nearly 50000 products; and Brico Dep´t addresses similar markets at a lower price.

Geographic Reach

Kingfisher operates more than 1350 stores in total. It has more than 980 in the UK and Ireland almost 220 in France some 80 in Poland approximately 35 in Romania about 30 in Spain roughly 20 in Russia and about five in Portugal.

Overall Kingfisher generates about 45% of revenue in the UK and Ireland more than 35% in France and about 15% in Poland.

Sales and Marketing

Kingfisher reaches customers via several different touchpoints. Its physical locations are its primary channel but it also offers online delivery and for professional customers mail-order. In the UK B&Q is aimed at DIYers while Screwfix serves wholesalers tradesmen and DIY experts.

Financial Performance

Note: Growth rates may differ after conversion to US Dollars.

Revenue for 2020 totaled 11.5 billion a 1% dip from the previous year.

The company had a profit of 8 million for the year ended 2020 a 96% decrease compared to the previous year.

The company's cash for the year ended 2020 was 195 million. Operating activities generated 897 million while investing activities used 138 million mainly for capital expenditures. Financing activities used another 757 million primarily for lease rental payments.

Strategy

Kingfisher's clear intent is to become a more digital and service orientated company using its strong store assets as a platform. The company will continue to develop its own exclusive brands

as a differentiator cater for diverse local customer needs and each retail banner will have its own positioning and plan. The company will 'power' these banners as a group. This is Kingfisher's new strategic direction 'Powered by Kingfisher'. The company will rebalance local and group responsibilities with the overall aim of enabling its retail banners to have flexibility and agility to address specific needs in local markets. The company's key strategic priorities under 'Powered by Kingfisher' are as follows:

Focus and fix' in 2020 (including managing the impact of Covid-19 on the business); Move to a balanced simpler local-group operating model with an agile culture; Grow e-commerce sales; Build a mobile-first service orientated customer experience; Differentiate and grow through own exclusive brands (OEB); Test new store concepts and adapt its store footprint; Source and buy better reduce its costs and its inventory; and Lead the industry in Responsible Business practices.

Mergers and Acquisitions

In late 2020 Kingfisher plc has acquired NeedHelp one of Europe's leading home improvement services marketplaces for a total cash consideration of ?10 million. NeedHelp is an innovative B2B2C online platform that connects customers who need home improvement help either in-store or online with vetted professional tradespeople and other skilled experts. As part of the transaction Guillaume de Kergariou the founder of NeedHelp has reinvested proceeds from the sale in a 20% interest in the business resulting in Kingfisher owning 80%.

Company Background

Kingfisher traces its lineage back to the international expansion efforts of US retailer Woolworth which set up shop in Liverpool in 1909. The company grew quickly and went public in 1931 with Woolworth retaining a majority stake. Activity kicked up a notch in 1980 following which it acquired do-it-yourself chain B&Q was bought out by private equity acquired electronics retailer Comet renamed F.W. Woolworth stores as Woolworths acquired Superdrug and two further drugstore chains. At the end of the 1980s the company changed its name to Kingfisher. In the next few decades further acquisitions followed including several businesses (such as Castorama) in France as did spin-offs and divestitures such as Woolworth's and Superdrug in 2001.

HISTORY

The beginning of Kingfisher is directly tied to the former US Woolworth chain (now Foot Locker). With the success of F.W. Woolworth general merchandise stores in the US founder Frank Woolworth expanded overseas first to Canada then in 1909 to Liverpool England. By 1914 Woolworth's UK subsidiaries had 31 stores.

Growing quickly the company went public in 1931 with its US parent retaining a 53% stake. The company spent most of the postwar years rebuilding bombed stores and had 762 stores by 1950.

The company opened its first Woolco Department Store modeled after the US Woolco stores of its parent in 1967. However other retailers had cut into sales and by 1968 it lost its place as Britain's leading retailer to Marks and Spencer. In 1973 it opened Shoppers World a catalog showroom. It made its first takeover in 1980 buying B&Q a chain of 40 do-it-yourself stores.

An investment group acquired Woolworth in 1982 using the vehicle Paternoster Stores. (The US parent sold its stake in Woolworth.) The company renamed Woolworth Holdings closed unprofitable Woolworth stores and sold its Shoppers World stores in 1983 and its Ireland Woolworth stores in 1984. It also acquired Comet a UK home electronics chain and continued to expand B&Q.

Two years later all of its F.W. Woolworth stores were renamed Woolworths and food and clothing lines were abandoned. Also in 1986 the company sold its Woolco stores and bought record and tape distributor Record Merchandisers (later renamed Entertainment UK). The next year Woolworth Holdings acquired Superdrug a chain of 297 discount drugstores. Adding to its Superdrug chain in 1988 the company acquired and integrated two UK pharmacy chains: 110-store Tip Top Drugstores and 145-store Share Drug.

To reflect its growing diversity of businesses the company was renamed Kingfisher in 1989. Also that year it bought drug retailer Medicare with 86 stores. Expanding further into electronics in 1993 Kingfisher acquired Darty with 130 stores. Adding music retail to music distribution that year the firm founded Music and Video Club (MVC).

In 1998 Kingfisher increased its presence in France by taking control of electronics chain BUT. It also merged its B&Q chain with the do-it-yourself stores of France's Castorama in 1998 and gained a 55% stake in the new group (though as part of the deal Kingfisher received only 50% of the group's voting rights).

Following the lead of rival Dixons in 1999 Kingfisher launched its own free Internet access service in France called Libertysurf. Soon thereafter Libertysurf acquired 70% of Objectif Net and its website Nomade.fr. Kingfisher's planned purchase of food retailer ASDA Group collapsed in June 1999 after being outbid by Wal-Mart Stores.

Kingfisher sold its 35% stake in Libertysurf to Italian ISP Tiscali in 2001 and it sold its Superdrug chain to Kruidvat a Dutch health and beauty group. Kingfisher demerged Woolworths Group the same year in a public offering. With Woolies went electronic entertainment companies EUK MVC VCI and Streets Online. Also in 2001 Kingfisher bought 25% plus one share of the unlisted ordinary voting shares of Germany's Hornbach Holding a family-owned group that owns 80% of one of Germany's leading DIY chains Hornbach-Baumarkt.

In 2002 Kingfisher acquired the remainder of Castorama and bought 17.4% of Hornbach's listed non-voting preference shares (which with the 2001 purchase represents a 21.2% stake in Hornbach). Kingfisher additionally bought 5.5% of the ordinary shares of Hornbach-Baumarkt.

CEO Geoffrey Mulcahy stepped down in 2002 and was replaced by Gerry Murphy formerly CEO for Carlton (now ITV plc) in 2003. Kingfisher sold its 20 retail parks for $1.1 billion to a consortium that includes real estate firms Pillar Property and Capital & Regional Properties the same year. Also in 2003 Kingfisher sold ProMarkt with about 190 stores in Germany to its former owners Michael and Matthias Wegert.

To focus on DIY Kingfisher floated its electrical businesses as a new company Kesa Electricals in 2003. Kesa Electricals includes Darty France's leading electrical retailer with more than 180 stores and Comet with some 260 stores in the UK. Kingfisher sold two home-improvement chains that year. Reno-Dep´t which operates about 20 home-improvement stores in Canada was sold to RONA. NOMI with about 40 stores in Poland was acquired by Enterprise Investors.

And in 2003 Kingfisher sold Dubois Materiaux a French building materials dealer to Saint-Gobain Building Distribution.

In June 2005 the company acquired its biggest competitor in Asia OBI Asia which added about a dozen stores in China and its first outlet in South Korea. The next year Kingfisher entered its 11th market Russia with its first Castorama store there. In May Sir Francis Mackay retired as chairman of

the company and was succeeded by Peter Jackson.

Kingfisher named Ian Cheshire as its new chief executive in 2008 succeeding Gerry Murphy who resigned in late 2007. Cheshire joined B&Q in 1998. Also in 2008 Kingfisher sold its Italian Castorama business to France's Groupe ADEO for $871 million. In addition the company sold its Castorama business in Spain in search of higher returns elsewhere in Europe. The retailer also closed its unprofitable Trade Depot format in the UK.

Daniel Bernard took over the chairman's seat from Jackson in 2009.

EXECUTIVES

Non-Executive Independent Director, Jeff Carr, $98,441 total compensation
Non-Executive Independent Director, Claudia Arney, $98,441 total compensation
Non-Executive Independent Director, Sophie Gasperment, $75,278 total compensation
CEO Screwfix, John Mewett
Chief Offer and Sourcing Officer, Henri Solere
Chief People Officer, Kate Seljeflot
Senior Independent Non-Executive Director, Catherine Bradley, $20,975 total compensation
Chairman, Andy Cosslett, $579,067 total compensation
Chief Executive Officer, Executive Director, Thierry Garnier, $960,866 total compensation
Chief Financial Officer, Executive Director, Bernard Bot, $678,538 total compensation
Auditors: Deloitte LLP

LOCATIONS

HQ: Kingfisher PLC
3 Sheldon Square, Paddington, London W2 6PX
Phone: (44) 20 7372 8008   **Fax:** (44) 20 7644 1001
Web: www.kingfisher.com

2019 Sales

	% of total
UK & Ireland	43
France	37
Poland	12
Others	8
Total	**100**

2019 Stores

	No.of Stores
UK & Ireland	923
France	224
Poland	76
Spain	29
Romania	38
Spain	28
Russia	20
Germany	19
Portugal	3
Total	**1,331**

COMPETITORS

DAIWA HOUSE INDUSTRY CO. LTD.
DEBENHAMS PLC
INSTALLED BUILDING PRODUCTS INC.
J SAINSBURY PLC
KAJIMA CORPORATION

LLANMOOR DEVELOPMENT CO. LIMITED
TAKENAKA CORPORATION
Victoria Retail Group B.V.
WESTON HOMES PLC

HISTORICAL FINANCIALS

Company Type: Public

Income Statement

				FYE: January 31
	REVENUE ($ mil.)	NET INCOME ($ mil.)	NET PROFIT MARGIN	EMPLOYEES
01/21	16,924	811	4.8%	78,000
01/20	15,110	10	0.1%	78,000
01/19	15,345	286	1.9%	79,000
01/18	16,496	686	4.2%	78,000
01/17	13,983	759	5.4%	77,000
Annual Growth	**4.9%**	**1.7%**	**—**	**0.3%**

2021 Year-End Financials

Debt ratio: 1.1%
Return on equity: 9.5%
Cash ($ mil.): 1,565
Current ratio: 1.24
Long-term debt ($ mil.): 2

No. of shares (mil.): 2,111
Dividends
  Yield: 0.0%
  Payout: 29.5%
Market value ($ mil.): 15,938

	STOCK PRICE ($) FY Close	P/E High/Low		PER SHARE ($)		
				Earnings	Dividends	Book Value
01/21	7.55	31	12	0.38	0.11	4.27
01/20	5.34	1753	1232	0.01	0.24	3.61
01/19	5.97	95	52	0.13	0.25	4.14
01/18	10.05	48	37	0.31	0.24	4.42
01/17	8.66	35	28	0.34	0.25	3.77
Annual Growth	**(3.4%)**	**—**	**—**	**3.3%**	**(18.1%)**	**3.2%**

Kirin Holdings Co Ltd

Kirin Holdings Company Ltd has established itself as one of the prominent beer brands in Japan and overseas and continuing to expand and acquiring the leading beer brand in Asia and Oceania. In addition to its domestic Kirin-branded beers the company owns brewers that serve overseas markets such as Australia's Lion and Philippines-based San Miguel Brewery. The beer brewer also makes well-known brands including Kirin Ichiban Kirin Hyoketsu Kirin Gogo-no-Kocha and more. The alcoholic fruit drink chu-hi and owns Japanese wine producer Mercian Corporation. Beyond beverages Kirin Holdings three business domains such as health and sciences and food and beverages and pharmaceutical.

Operations

The company has four segments: Japanese beer and spirits (about 35%) Japan non-alcoholic beverages (about 15%) Oceania Adult Beverages (some 15%) and pharmaceuticals (more than 15%).

For Japanese beer and spirits the company is called Kirin Brewery which manufactures and sales of alcoholic brewery. In Japan non-alcoholic beverages it is known as Kirin Beverage Company. On the other hand Lion Pty Limited is carrying out an integrated beverage strategy in Oceania.

For pharmaceuticals the company has Kyowa Kirin Group. It is carrying out independent research from a unique perspective and development using advanced technology in the pharmaceuticals business and provides high-quality products globally.

In reference to others the company has Mercian Corporation (wine) Myanmar Brewery (beer) Coca-Cola Beverages (soft drinks) and Kyowa Hakko Bio (manufacture pharmaceuticals raw material various amino acids and health foods). In addition manages share acquisition for investment in the Beer Business of San Miguel.

Geographic Reach

Tokyo Based Kirin Holdings has established local operations in Australia China the Philippines Myanmar Singapore the Germany the US and Vietnam. In the US it owns soft-drink bottler Coca-Cola Bottling Company of Northern New England and bourbon maker Four Roses Distillery in Kentucky.

Sales and Marketing

Kirin's marketing campaign includes TV commercial online advertising and in-store contact points with the aim of enlisting 100000 members for the Kirin Home Tap services and reinvigorating business in the beer category.

Financial Performance

The company's revenue for fiscal 2020 decreased by 5% to 1.8 trillion compared from 1.9 trillion in fiscal 2019. Revenue declined in 2020 as the COVID-19 pandemic deeply impacted the performances of many of its businesses.

Profit attributable to the owners of the company increased by 12.3 billion to 71.9 billion compared to 59.6 billion in 2019.

Cash held by the company at the end of fiscal 2020 decreased to 161.7 billion. Cash provided by operations and investing activities were 164.8 billion and 116.0 billion respectively. Financing activities used 52.5 billion.

Strategy

The company's financial strategy aims to maximize corporate value by using the operating cash flow generated by the growth of existing businesses for stable dividends and disciplined growth investments as well as by considering flexibly allocating the cash to additional shareholder returns.

Key initiatives implement three specific strategies as the first stage of KV2027: Profit growth of existing businesses; Food: Further strengthen profitability; Pharmaceuticals: Achieve outstanding growth; Establish and foster new businesses bridging Pharmaceuticals and Food & Beverages; and Strengthen organizational capabilities for innovation.

Company Background

Kirin Brewery Co. Ltd. was established on February 23 1907 taking over the business of The Japan Brewery Co. Ltd. which had started marketing Kirin Beer in 1888.

Kirin Ichiban Shibori which first hit the market in 1990 went on to become one of the most popular beers in Japan. Kirin Brewery's soft-drink business division was spun off to become Kirin Beverage Co. Ltd. in 1991.

In 2007 celebrating its 100th anniversary Kirin Brewery changed its trade name to Kirin Holdings Co. Ltd. established as a pure holding company for the Kirin Group.

HISTORY

American William Copeland went to Yokohama Japan in 1864 and five years later established the Spring Valley Brewery the first in Japan to provide beer for foreign nationals. Lacking funds to continue the brewery Copeland closed it in 1884. The next year a group of foreign and Japanese businessmen reopened it as Japan Brewery. The business created the Kirin label in 1888 and was soon profitable.

The operation was run primarily by Americans and Europeans at first but by 1907 Japanese workers had filled the ranks and adopted the Kirin Brewery Company name. Sales plummeted during WWII when the government limited brewing output. After the war the US occupation forces inadvertently assisted Kirin when they split Dai Nippon Brewery (Kirin's main competitor) into two companies (Asahi and Sapporo Breweries) while leaving Kirin intact. The company became Japan's leading brewer during the 1950s.

During the 1970s Kirin introduced several soft drinks and in 1972 branched into hard liquor through a joint venture with Seagram (Kirin-Seagram).

The firm bought several Coca-Cola bottling operations in New England and Japan in the 1980s. Kirin also entered the pharmaceuticals business in part through a joint venture with US-based Amgen. In 1988 the brewer signed an agreement with Molson to produce Kirin beer for the North American market. In 1989 Kirin bought Napa Valley's Raymond Vineyards.

In 1991 Kirin formed a partnership to market Tropicana drinks in Japan. It also entered an alliance with Sankyo (Japan's #2 drug company) in 1991 to market Kirin's medication for anemia which it had developed with Amgen.

Chairman Hideyo Motoyama resigned in 1993 after four company executives were arrested for allegedly paying a group of racketeers who had threatened to disrupt Kirin's annual meeting. Joint venture Kirin-Amgen won the rights to make thrombopoietin (TPO) a blood platelet growth stimulator in 1995.

Yasuhiro Satoh became president of Kirin in 1996. The brewer moved into China that year through an agreement with China Resources (Shenyang) Snowflake Brewery. To brew its beers in the US the company formed Kirin Brewery of America also in 1996.

In response to losing market share to Asahi Kirin cut its workforce in 1998 and introduced Tanrei a cheaper low-malt beer that quickly captured half its market. Building on its presence in China Kirin bought 46% of brewer Lion Nathan (based in Australia and New Zealand) for $742.5 million that year. It became a licensed brewer of Anheuser-Busch in 1999.

Like other Japanese brewers Kirin struggled against dwindling demand for its most expensive brews in 2000. Koichiro Aramaki was named president of the company the following year and began to expand and diversify Kirin's operations to overcome slow growth domestically. In 2002 the company bought 15% of Philippine food and drink giant San Miguel for about $530 million. It also boosted ties with beverage giant Pernod Ricard by purchasing 32% of SIFA a French food services firm for an estimated $155 million. In 2002 Kirin also formed Flower Season Ltd. a joint venture with Dole Food Company to sell flowers to Japanese retailers. Also in 2002 Kirin launched its new Pure Blue brand of "shochu" distilled liquor.

In 2006 Aramaki stepped down as president (he remained chairman) and turned the reins over to former managing director Kazuyasu Kato. The following year Kirin reorganized as a holding company.

The company added to its international dairy holdings with its 2007 acquisition of Australian milk and cheese producer National Foods. The following year National Foods acquired Australian dairy company Australian Co-operative Foods Limited (dba Dairy Farmers) for about $763 million. With some 2000 members Dairy Farmers is one of the biggest dairy product makers in Australia. These acquisitions made Kirin a top player in the Oceania dairy sector which is part of the company's larger strategy to focus and grow in the Asian and Oceania markets.

In 2009 Kirin acquired a 100% interest in San Miguel Brewery of the Philippines. Following Kirin's successful tender offer to acquire the remainder of Lion Nathan's shares later that year Lion Nathan and National Foods were consolidated under Kirin's Australian holding company which was renamed Lion Nathan National Foods.

Early in 2010 company veteran Senji Miyake was named president and CEO of the Japanese brewer (among other top management changes). Miyake joined Kirin Brewery Company in 1970. In December Kirin made Mercian Corp. a wholly owned subsidiary following a scandal at Mercian's fish feedstuffs division.

EXECUTIVES

Independent Director, Noriko Shiono
Independent Director, George Olcott
Independent Director, Roderick Eddington
Independent Director, Chieko Matsuda
Independent Director, Masakatsu Mori
Executive Vice President, Hiroshi Ogawa
President, Chief Executive Officer and Director, Yoshinori Isozaki
Vice President, Representative Director, Keisuke Nishimura
Managing Executive Officer, Director, Toshiya Miyoshi
Managing Executive Officer, Director, Noriaki Kobayashi
Managing Executive Officer, Director, Noriya Yokota
Independent Director, Hiroyuki Yanagi
Independent Director, Kaoru Kato
Auditors: KPMG AZSA LLC

LOCATIONS

HQ: Kirin Holdings Co Ltd
NAKANO CENTRAL PARK SOUTH, 4-10-2 Nakano, Nakano-ku, Tokyo 164-0001
Phone: (81) 3 6837 7015
Web: www.kirinholdings.co.jp

2013 Sales

	% of total
Japan	65
Asia/Oceania	22
Others	13
Total	**100**

PRODUCTS/OPERATIONS

2013 sales

	% of total
Japan integrated beverages	45
Overseas integrated beverages	35
Pharmaceuticals and bio-chemicals	17
Others	3
Total	**100**

COMPETITORS

AEON CO. LTD.
ANHEUSER-BUSCH COMPANIES LLC
ASSOCIATED BRITISH FOODS PLC
CANDOVER INVESTMENTS PLC
COCA - COLA HELLENIC BOTTLING COMPANY S.A.
DANONE
DENTSU GROUP INC.
DIAGEO PLC
J.FRONT RETAILING CO.LTD.
LION PTY LTD
MOLSON COORS BEVERAGE COMPANY
SAPPORO HOLDINGS LIMITED
SOFTBANK GROUP CORP.
SUNTORY HOLDINGS LIMITED
TPG CAPITAL MANAGEMENT L.P.
UNITED BISCUITS TOPCO LIMITED

HISTORICAL FINANCIALS

Company Type: Public

Income Statement
FYE: December 31

	REVENUE ($ mil.)	NET INCOME ($ mil.)	NET PROFIT MARGIN	EMPLOYEES
12/20	17,944	697	3.9%	36,214
12/19	17,880	549	3.1%	35,717
12/18	17,555	1,493	8.5%	36,376
12/17	16,563	2,151	13.0%	37,874
12/16	17,741	1,010	5.7%	46,439
Annual Growth	0.3%	(8.8%)	—	(6.0%)

2020 Year-End Financials

Debt ratio: 0.2%
Return on equity: 8.2%
Cash ($ mil.): 1,568
Current ratio: 1.18
Long-term debt ($ mil.): 3,818

No. of shares (mil.): 834
Dividends
  Yield: 2.5%
  Payout: 76.2%
Market value ($ mil.): 19,849

	STOCK PRICE ($) FY Close	P/E High/Low		PER SHARE ($) Earnings	Dividends	Book Value
12/20	23.80	0	0	0.83	0.61	9.76
12/19	21.82	0	0	0.63	0.54	9.61
12/18	20.78	0	0	1.67	0.45	9.49
12/17	25.26	0	0	2.36	0.36	9.33
12/16	16.29	0	0	1.11	0.32	6.38
Annual Growth	9.9%	—	—	(6.9%)	17.5%	11.2%

KLM Royal Dutch Airlines

The legendary Flying Dutchman sails on alone but Koninklijke Luchtvaart Maatschappij (KLM Royal Dutch Airlines) is part of Air France-KLM one of Europe's largest airline company. KLM Royal Dutch Airlines and Air France operate from their own hubs in Amsterdam and Paris as independent carriers but coordinate their businesses. It flies to more than 170 destinations and operates almost 215 planes The airline's two other Netherlands-based subsidiaries Transavia and Martinair offer budget charter and scheduled flights. KLM Royal Dutch Airlines also offers engineering services. KLM Royal Dutch Airlines and Air France are members of the SkyTeam alliance which also includes carriers such as Delta Alitalia and Korean Air Lines. The company's largest market is Europe and North Africa region.

Operations
KLM Royal Dutch Airlines has four Business segment: Network Maintenance Leisure and Other.

Network segment includes passenger and cargo activities. Passenger's main activity is the transportation of passengers on scheduled flights that have the company's airline code. Cargo activities relate to the transportation of freight on flights under the company's code and the sale of cargo capacity to third parties. The segment generates more than 75% of the company's total sales.

Maintenance segment which accounts for almost 15% of total sales includes engine services component services and airframe maintenance provided to other airlines and clients around the world.

The Leisure segment covers primarily the provision of charter flights and (low-cost) scheduled flights operated by transavia.com and produces about 10% of total sales.

The company's Other segment which brings in the remaining sales covers primarily catering and

handling services to third-party airlines and clients around the world.

Geographic Reach
KLM Royal Dutch Airlines' head office is located in Netherlands. The company offers services all over the world via a vast network of more than 90 European cities and approximately 70 intercontinental destinations. Its largest revenue generating region is Europe and North Africa which accounts for more than 40% of total. Americas Polynesia region is the second largest with over 25% of total. The remaining revenues are from Asia and New Caledonia (more than 15% of total revenue) Africa Middle East (around 10%) and Caribbean and Indian Ocean (almost 5%).

Sales and Marketing
KLM offers direct services to key economic centres all over the world. The company is also a partner in the SkyTeam Alliance which offers passengers even more possibilities. KLM already a social media leader in the airline industry also gives its customers even more options. It added support for LINE a popular social media platform in Japan and introduced Family Updates which allows KLM to send flight information to a WhatsApp group chat for family and friends. In addition KLM and Air France have a common frequent flyer program "Flying Blue" a program which allows members to acquire "miles" as it fly on KLM Air France or with other partner companies. The miles entitle members to a variety of benefits such as free flights with the two companies.

Financial Performance
Note: Growth rates may differ after conversion to US Dollars.

KLM revenues came in at ?11.1 billion 2% above last year's ?10.9 billion. Traffic (revenue passenger kilometers) increased by 2% and cargo traffic decreased by 4%. The capacity was 2% higher than last year. Unit revenue remained stable (less than 1% at constant exchange rates). Yield decreased to less than 1% while the load factor increased to 90%.

Net income for 2019 was ?449 million compared to ?566 million for 2018. Total expenses amounted to ?9.1 billion an increase of ?363 million compared to 2018. Overall fuel cost also increased by ?190 million compared to 2018.

Cash and cash equivalents at the end of the period were ?696 million a ?178 million decrease from the year prior. Operating activities generated ?1.9 billion in 2019 while investing activities used ?1.3 billion mainly for purchase of aircraft. Financing activities used another ?671 million mostly for long-term debt repayments and lease debt payments.

Strategy
KLM translates its overall strategy and long-term goals into a Flight Plan. This comprises five pillars: Customer & Product Network & Fleet Operations People & Organization and Innovation & Sustainability. For each of these pillars the actions and achievements are described including a case study which tells the story behind one of KLM's achievements.

KLM substantially upgrades the quality of its product and services year after year in 2019 KLM strengthened the fundamentals of its product by more digital and personalized services working more closely with operational departments and partners as well as changing the way it handles disruptions. Throughout the customer journey services are aligned with customer expectations making the company a whole more customer-centric.

KLM improved the performance of its network by more quickly replacing underperforming destinations working closely with Transavia and strengthening its global alliances. KLM also took delivery of more sustainable aircraft.

The operational goal for 2019 was to ensure a stable network performance while preparing the operation for sustainable growth. Ongoing investments in integral-decision making and Artificial Intelligence (AI) have made KLM's operations more agile and robust. Safety both operational and occupational improved.

KLM celebrated the future of its staff with responsible salary increases leadership development a focus on diversity and inclusion and support for career planning. With talent being scarce and KLM's growth ambitions tangible the wok has begun to create a sustainable workforce that can flourish for years.

Innovation and sustainability have become powerful forces shaping the future of KLM the industry and the world. In 2019 KLM and its partners took pioneering steps in Artificial Intelligence (AI) sustainable aviation fuel production and radical plane design whose impact will be felt for decades to come.

HISTORY

Flight lieutenant Albert Plesman founded Koninklijke Luchtvaart Maatschappij voor Nederland en Kolonien (Royal Airline Company for the Netherlands and Colonies) in The Hague in 1919. Queen Wilhelmina granted the honorary title of koninklijke (or royal) and Dutch businessmen financed the venture. Early passengers — who flew in an open cockpit with the pilot — were issued leather jackets goggles gloves and parachutes.

Under Plesman's leadership KLM established service between Amsterdam and Brussels Copenhagen London and Paris in the early 1920s. The airline initiated the longest air route in the world from Amsterdam to Indonesia in 1928 and extended its European network in the years before WWII. Hitler's occupation of Holland shut down KLM's European operations in 1940; the Germans imprisoned Plesman from 1940 to 1942 and bombed or confiscated two-thirds of KLM's planes.

After the war Plesman quickly re-established commercial service using 47 US military surplus airplanes and in 1946 KLM became the first continental European airline to offer scheduled service from Europe to the US. Plesman died in 1953 and KLM began trading on the NYSE in 1957.

KLM established NLM Dutch Airlines in 1966 (renamed Cityhopper in 1976) to provide commuter flights within the Netherlands. The airline addressed overcapacity problems in the 1970s by converting the rear portions of its 747s to cargo space.

Air France acquired KLM and formed the Air France-KLM holding company in 2004. By 2005 their freight businesses had been brought together as Air France-KLM Cargo.

EXECUTIVES

Member of the Supervisory Board, Irene Asscher-Vonk
Chairman of the Supervisory Board, Hans Smits
President, Chief Executive Officer, Member of the Board of Managing Directors, Pieter Elbers
Chief Financial Officer, Member of the Board of Managing Directors, Erik Swelheim
Member of the Supervisory Board, Remmert Laan
Member of the Board of Managing Directors, Erik Varwijk
Member of the Supervisory Board, Philippe Calavia
Member of the Supervisory Board, Annemieke Roobeek
Member of the Supervisory Board, Henri Guillaume
Member of the Supervisory Board, Jean Peyrelevade

HQ: KLM Royal Dutch Airlines
Amsterdamseweg 55, Amstelveen 1182 GP
Phone: (31) 20 649 91 23 **Fax:** (31) 20 649 23 24
Web: www.klm.com

COMPETITORS

AIR FRANCE - KLM
AIRBUS
ALASKA AIR GROUP INC.
ANA HOLDINGS INC.
DELTA AIR LINES INC.
Deutsche Lufthansa AG
EASYJET PLC
Embraer S/A
GENERAL DYNAMICS CORPORATION
INTERNATIONAL CONSOLIDATED AIRLINES GROUP
 SA
JAPAN AIRLINES CO.LTD.
KAMAN CORPORATION
Korean Airlines Co. Ltd.
LATECOERE
SINGAPORE AIRLINES LIMITED
TEXTRON INC.
UNITED AIRLINES HOLDINGS INC.
UNITED AIRLINES INC.
WIZZ AIR HOLDINGS PLC

HISTORICAL FINANCIALS

Company Type: Public

Income Statement   FYE: December 31

	REVENUE ($ mil.)	NET INCOME ($ mil.)	NET PROFIT MARGIN	EMPLOYEES
12/19	12,434	503	4.0%	30,716
12/18	12,545	655	5.2%	29,642
12/17	12,395	(843)	—	29,375
12/16	10,347	545	5.3%	28,741
12/15	10,788	57	0.5%	29,824
Annual Growth	3.6%	71.8%	—	0.7%

2019 Year-End Financials

Debt ratio: 22.8%
Return on equity: 34.9%
Cash ($ mil.): 782
Current ratio: 0.55
Long-term debt ($ mil.): 2,397

No. of shares (mil.): 46
Dividends
 Yield: 0.0%
 Payout: 3.5%
Market value ($ mil.): 482

	STOCK PRICE ($) FY Close	P/E High	P/E Low	PER SHARE ($) Earnings	PER SHARE ($) Dividends	PER SHARE ($) Book Value
12/19	10.30	2	1	10.74	0.38	37.39
12/18	10.10	1	1	13.99	0.00	24.59
12/17	12.00	—	—	(18.03)	0.36	23.71
12/16	5.46	1	0	11.65	0.00	22.26
12/15	1.50	3	1	1.24	0.00	9.12
Annual Growth	61.9%	—	—	71.5%	—	42.3%

Kobe Steel Ltd

A diversified manufacturer Kobe Steel's portfolio includes aluminum copper titanium welding products and industrial machinery like compressors and rolling mill. The company also provides wholesale power supply operating two power plants in Kobe. Its real estate division rents manages and sells properties. The company was founded when major pre-war conglomerate Suzuki Shoten enters heavy industry field in 1905.

Operations

All operations at Kobe Steel are divided under steel & aluminum construction machinery ad-

vanced materials machinery engineering electric power welding and other businesses.

Steel & Aluminum is the leading product of Kobe (about 40% revenue) while Advanced Materials (about 15%). Products range from steel castings and forgings to aluminum and copper sheets. Welding products and services adds nearly 5% more to the annual revenue.

Kobelco's Construction machinery segment alone makes up about 20% of annual sales by selling hydraulic excavators crawler and wheel cranes. More than 20% of combined revenue comes from Machinery Engineering and Electric Power segments mostly catering to the energy and ironmaking fields.

Lastly Kobelco engages in real estate construction sales brokering remodeling; leasing building management; condominium management; special alloys and other new materials (target materials etc.); material analysis and testing; high-pressure gas cylinder manufacturing; superconducting products; general trading company. These businesses account for less than 5% of the total revenue.

Geographic Reach

Japan-based Kobelco has more than 10 branch and sales offices (including head offices) five works facilities two R&D laboratories and five plants domestically. It has also operations overseas in China Germany Thailand and the US.

Sales and Marketing

Kobe Steel sells to automobile trains and shipbuilding industries as well as to energy industry and other industrial customers.

Financial Performance

Note: Growth rates may differ after conversion to US Dollars.

The company's net sales for 2020 totaled 1.7 trillion a 9% decrease from the previous year's net sales of 1.9 trillion. In the same year the company had a net income of 23.2 billion a 134% improvement from the previous year's net loss of 68 billion.

The company's operating activities generated 194.8 billion. Financing activities provided another 118.4 billion while investing activities used 141.9 billion.

Strategy

In mid-2020 Kobe Steel Ltd. together with its wholly-owned US subsidiary Midrex Technologies Inc. has reached a non-binding agreement with Vale S.A. the world's largest iron ore producer and Mitsui & Co. Ltd. a global trading and investment company with a diversified business portfolio to collaborate in providing low CO_2 iron metallics and ironmaking solutions to the world's steel industry.

Kobe Steel has also obtained further subsidiaries. For example it turned its Chinese affiliate Wuxi Compressor Co. Ltd. into a subsidiary after acquiring additional shares in the company in early 2020.

As it operates new subsidiaries Kobe Steel has also decided to close select locations such as its closure of Kobe Steel Asia Pte. Ltd. in Singapore in early 2020. Kobe Steel moved KSA's business to Kobelco South East Asia Ltd. (KSEA) and integrate sales support for steel products and technical services at one location to make operations more efficient.

Company Background

In 1905 general partnership trading company Suzuki Shoten acquired a steel business in Wakinohama Kobe called Kobayashi Seikosho operated by Seiichiro Kobayashi and changed its name to Kobe Seikosho. Then in 1911 Suzuki Shoten spun off the company to establish Kobe Steel Works Ltd. with a capital of ¥1.4 million of Wakinohamacho Kobe. This was the beginning of the company that is today known as Kobelco.

EXECUTIVES

Chairman of the Board of Directors, Independent Director, Takao Kitabata
Executive Vice President, Manager of Steel & Aluminum Business, Makoto Mizuguchi
President, Chief Executive Officer, Representative Director, Mitsugu Yamaguchi
Executive Vice President, Representative Director, Koichiro Shibata
Executive Vice President, Representative Director, Fusaki Koshiishi
Executive Vice President, Manager of Engineering Business, Kazuto Morisaki
Director, Yasushi Tsushima
Independent Director, Yumiko Ito
Executive Officer, Ryosaku Kadowaki
Executive Officer, Chief Director of Rotating Machine in Compressor Business Unit, Director of CS Engineering in Main Rotating Machine Unit in Compressor Business Unit, Yoshinori Kurioka
Executive Officer, Director, Yoshihiko Katsukawa
Executive Officer, Seiji Hirata
Executive Officer, Manager of Electric Power Business, Jiro Kitagawa
Executive Officer, Manager of Kakogawa Steel Works in Steel and Aluminum Business Division, Shuji Kitayama
Executive Officer, Manager of Wire Rod Steel Unit, Manager of Thick Plate Unit, Kazuhiko Kimoto
Executive Officer, Manager of Machinery Business, Masamichi Takeuchi
Executive Officer, Kazuaki Kawahara
Director, Hiroshi Ishikawa
Executive Officer, Manager of Raw Material Business, Shoji Miyazaki
Executive Officer, Director, Hajime Nagara
Executive Officer, Chief Director of Project Engineering, Masahiro Motoyuki
Executive Officer, Hiroaki Matsubara
Executive Officer, Chief Director Technology Development, Yuichiro Goto
Independent Director, Yoshiiku Miyata
Executive Officer, Manager of Welding Business, Akira Yamamoto
Executive Officer, Shoji Nakamura
Independent Director, Masaaki Kono
Independent Director, Hiroyuki Bamba
Executive Officer, Director of Safety and Environment, Daisuke Ogura
Executive Officer, Director of General Affairs & CSR, Keitaro Nakamori
Executive Officer, Takeharu Kato
Executive Officer, Yasushi Okano
Independent Director, Kunio Miura
Auditors: KPMG AZSA LLC

LOCATIONS

HQ: Kobe Steel Ltd
2-2-4 Wakinohama-Kaigandori, Chuo-ku, Kobe, Hyogo 651-8585
Phone: (81) 78 261 5194 **Fax:** (81) 78 261 4123
Web: www.kobelco.co.jp

PRODUCTS/OPERATIONS

2017 Sales

	% of total
Materials Businesses	
Iron & Steel	37
Aluminum & Copper	18
Welding	4
Machinery Business	
Construction Machinery	19
Machinery	8
Engineering	6
Electric Power Business	
Electric Power	4
Other Businesses	4
Total	**100**

Selected Products

Aluminum and Copper
　Aluminum plate
　Copper sheet and strip
Construction Machinery
　Crawler cranes
　Environmental Recycling Machinery
　Hydraulic excavators
　Mini hydraulic excavators
　Wheel cranes
Electric Power
　Kobe Power Plant
Engineering
　Advanced Urban Transit System
　Iron Unit Field
Iron and Steel
　Steel bars
　Steel castings and forgings
　Steel plates
　Steel powder
　Steel sheets
　Titanium
　Wire rod and bars
Machinery
　Standard compressors
　Rotating machinery
　Tire and rubber machinery
　Plastic processing machinery
　Advance Technology Equipment
　Rolling Mill
　Ultra High Pressure Equipment
　Energy & Chemical Field
Welding
　Electrodes
　Flux-cored wires
　Metallic flux-cored wire
　Solid wires
　Welding fluxes

COMPETITORS

ArcelorMittal	NIPPON STEEL
CARPENTER TECHNOLOGY	CORPORATION
CORPORATION	NUCOR CORPORATION
CLEVELAND-CLIFFS STEEL	OKAYA & CO. LTD.
HOLDING CORPORATION	RELIANCE STEEL &
Gerdau S/A	ALUMINUM CO.
HANWA CO.LTD.	STEEL DYNAMICS INC.
MAANSHAN IRON & STEEL	UNITED STATES STEEL
COMPANY LIMITED	CORPORATION

HISTORICAL FINANCIALS

Company Type: Public

Income Statement   FYE: March 31

	REVENUE ($ mil.)	NET INCOME ($ mil.)	NET PROFIT MARGIN	EMPLOYEES
03/21	15,403	209	1.4%	46,428
03/20	17,225	(626)	—	47,807
03/19	17,805	324	1.8%	45,404
03/18	17,715	595	3.4%	44,083
03/17	15,167	(206)	—	43,513
Annual Growth	0.4%	—		1.6%

2021 Year-End Financials

Debt ratio: 0.3%	No. of shares (mil.): 364
Return on equity: 3.4%	Dividends
Cash ($ mil.): 2,369	Yield: —
Current ratio: 1.42	Payout: —
Long-term debt ($ mil.): 7,815	Market value ($ mil.): —

Koc Holdings AS

Led by its energy businesses Ko § Holding is Turkey's dominant industrial conglomerate. The company operates through its 100000 employees and a distribution network composed of about 840 bank branches and 11000 dealers and after-sales service points. Through these the company serves more than 12 million customers. The company's Tofas unit an alliance with Fiat is Turkey's champion carmaker; Ko §'s joint venture with Ford Motor sells imported Ford models. Other businesses include consumer goods such as large household appliances (Ar §elik teaming up with LG Electronics) and energy (distribution of liquefied petroleum gas). Subsidiaries engage in food production construction international trading and hospitality and tourism. The Ko § family one of the wealthiest in Turkey controls the company.

Operations

Ko § Holding is organized under five core business segments: Energy Automotive Consumer durables Finance and Other.

The Energy segment that generates more than 36% of total revenue offers petroleum products the Koc Group companies operating in the energy sector Turkey's demand for petroleum fuel products. T PRAS controls 40% ownership in the fuel distribution company Opet Petrolc l k.

Automotive generates about 30% of total revenue offers automotive retailing and car rentals commercial vehicles buses passenger cars and trucks.

Consumer durables generates about 15% of total revenue offers white goods and appliances. The Koc Group is the leader in white goods sector in Turkey with roughly 40% market share.

The company's finance segment generates about 15% of total revenue. Portfolio management brokerage services leasing and factoring are included in the banking sector.

Other business lines that generates more than 5% of total revenue offers tourism Food production IT support centralized purchasing services and marina operations.

Geographic Reach

Koc Holding A.S. is headquartered in Nakkastepe Turkey. It operates in more than 150 countries with more than 60 production facilities worldwide some in Australia Egypt China Spain France and Russia. Roughly 70% of total revenues is generated domestically and the rest comes from sales abroad.

Sales and Marketing

Ko § serves more than 12 million customers for the year 2020 through about 12000 dealers and aftersales service points.

Financial Performance

In a span of five years Koc's performance have grown year-by year with 2020 as its highest performing year.

In 2020 the company's consolidated revenues increased by 20% to ?183.7 billion as compared to 2019's revenue of about ?153.5 billion.

The company recorded a net profit of about ?9.3 billion in 2020 as compared to the prior year's net profit of about ?4.4 billion.

Cash held by the company at the end of 2020 was at ?84.6 billion. Operating activities provided about ?20.2 billion. Investing activities provided ?12.8 billion while financing activities used another ?10.8 billion. Main cash uses were for repayment of borrowings.

Strategy

KoC's innovation strategy includes: Building a culture of innovation and creating the right working environment to enhance its innovation capacity; Cultivating corporate entrepreneurship across the company and supporting employees' entrepreneurial spirit and efforts; Extending innovative endeavors not only across product and service development activities but in all business units and operations; Increasing partnership with external stakeholders an important source of innovation and managing these collaborations more effectively; and Managing innovative operations via clear processes to ensure sustainability.

In order to implement its innovation strategy Ko § Holding has been conducting the Ko § Innovation Program since 2014. As part of this program innovation management infrastructures are built up at Ko § Group companies in line with the self-developed Ko § Innovation Management Model.

HISTORY

In 1917 16-year-old Vehbi Ko § and his father opened a small grocery store in Ankara Turkey. With the fall of the Ottoman Empire after WWI Turkey's capital was moved to Ankara which was then only a village. The Ko §s recognized an opportunity and expanded into construction and building supplies winning a contract to repair the roof of the Turkish parliament building. By age 26 Ko § was a millionaire.

Ford Motor made Ko § its Turkish agent in 1928. In 1931 Mobil Oil and Ko § entered an exclusive agreement to search for oil in Turkey. The company incorporated in 1938 as Ko § Ticaret Corporation the first Turkish joint stock company with an employee stock-ownership program.

Despite Turkey's neutrality in WWII the fighting disrupted Ko §'s business. The nation became isolationist after the war and restricted foreign concerns to selling through local agents; Ko § benefited by importing foreign products.

General Electric and Ko § entered a joint venture in 1946 to build Turkey's first lightbulb factory. In 1955 Ko § set up Ar §elik the first Turkish producer of refrigerators washing machines and water heaters; T rk Demir D ¶k m the first Turkish producer of radiators and later auto castings; and Turkay the country's first private producer of matches. In 1959 Ko § constructed Turkey's first truck assembly plant (Otosan).

Other firsts followed in the 1960s as the company leveraged its size and government influence to attract more ventures. These included a tire factory (with Uniroyal) a cable factory (with Siemens) production of electric motors and compressors (with GE) and the production of Anadol the first car to be made entirely in Turkey (by Otosan under license from Ford). In 1974 Ko § expanded into retailing with the purchase of Migros Turkey's largest chain of supermarkets.

The Turkish military imposed martial law in 1980 and restricted foreign exchange payments forcing Ko § to limit its operations. In 1986 a year after foreign companies were allowed to export products directly to Turkey Ko § and American Express started Ko §-Amerikan Bank (which Ko § bought out and renamed Ko §bank in 1992). In the late 1980s Vehbi's only son Rahmi took over the company's leadership. Vehbi Ko § died in 1996.

Auto sales fell sharply in 1996 as buyers awaited the country's entry into the European Union's customs union. In an effort to offset market risks Ko § forged a number of alliances in 1997. It participated in a British-Canadian-Turkish consortium that was building a large power plant in central Turkey.

Reflecting a greater willingness to open the company to foreign investors Ko § announced plans to offer $250 million in shares in a public offering in 1998 but it soon canceled the offering because of market volatility. A year later the company completed an auto plant in Samarkand Uzbekistan to build Otoyol-Iveco buses and trucks.

Ko § entered into a joint venture — Ko § Finansal Hizmetler — with Unicredito Italiano in 2002 in an effort to further consolidate its financial holdings.

Significant company moves in 2008 included selling its Otomotiv Lastikleri Tevzi (Oltas) to Germany's Continental AG. Oltas had distributed Continental tires and related products since 2003. The company's interest in supermarkets dwindled to less than 50% with the sale of its stake in Migros. Its sway however in the IT data processing business of Ko §Net Haberlesme Teknolojileri ve Iletisim Hizmetleri A.S. increased to almost 100%. The company picked up military aero and marine tech simulator Kaletron an arm of Kale Group too.

In 2009 the global recession curtailed industrial output and demand and hurt the company's revenues. However its diversified portfolio and cost saving measures enabled it to post a modest improvement in net income.

EXECUTIVES

Non-Executive Independent Director, Jacques Nasser
Non-Executive Director, Caroline Koc
Chief Legal and Compliance Officer, Kenan Yilmaz
President of Energy Group, Yagiz Eyuboglu
Corporate Communications and External Affairs Director, Oya Unlu Kizil
President of Consumer Durables Group, Fatih Ebiclioglu
Non-Executive Independent Director, Emily Rafferty
Human Resources Director, Ozgur Akkol
Non-Executive Chairman of the Board, Omer Koc
Chief Financial Officer, Ahmet Ashaboglu
President of Tourism, Food and Retailing Group, Ibrahim Hasimoglu
President of Audit Group, Ali Uzun
Non-Executive Director, Semahat Arsel
President of Automotive Group, Ismail Cimen
Non-Executive Vice Chairman of the Board, Ali Koc
Non-Executive Independent Director, Cem Kozlu
Honorary Chairman of the Board of Directors, Rahmi Koc
Chief Executive Officer, Member of the Board of Directors, Levent Cakiroglu
Non-Executive Independent Director, Anne Lauvergeon
Director of Public Affairs, Ufuk Ciplak
Non-Executive Director, Ipek Kirac
Auditors: PwC Bagimsiz Denetim ve Serbest Muhasebeci Mali Müsavirlik A.S.

LOCATIONS

HQ: Koc Holdings AS
Nakkastepe, Azizbey Sokak No. 1, Istanbul, Kuzguncuk 34674
Phone: (90) 216 531 0000   **Fax:** (90) 216 531 0099
Web: www.koc.com.tr

2016 Sales

	% of total
Domestic	74
Foreign	26
Total	**100**

PRODUCTS/OPERATIONS

2016 Sales

	% of total
Energy	42
Automotive	26
Finance	15
Consumer durables	11
Other	6
Total	**100**

Core Businesses

Automotive
Construction and mining
Durable goods
Food/Beverage/Tobacco

Energy
Financial services
Information technology
International trade
Marinas
New business development
Tourism and services

COMPETITORS

ACCIONA SA	ITOCHU CORPORATION
AGGREKO LIMITED	MAHINDRA AND MAHINDRA
ASHTEAD GROUP PUBLIC	LIMITED
LIMITED COMPANY	MANUTAN INTERNATIONAL
Adolf W rth GmbH &	MARUBENI CORPORATION
Co. KG	Outokumpu Oyj
COMPUTACENTER PLC	WH Group Limited
E.ON SE	thyssenkrupp AG
ENDESA SA	

HISTORICAL FINANCIALS

Company Type: Public

Income Statement				FYE: December 31
	REVENUE ($ mil.)	NET INCOME ($ mil.)	NET PROFIT MARGIN	EMPLOYEES
12/20	24,720	1,247	5.0%	0
12/19	25,798	737	2.9%	92,990
12/18	27,074	1,046	3.9%	92,631
12/17	26,140	1,297	5.0%	94,111
12/16	20,103	980	4.9%	95,456
Annual Growth	**5.3%**	**6.2%**	**—**	**—**

2020 Year-End Financials

Debt ratio: 3.8%
Return on equity: 22.3%
Cash ($ mil.): 14,706
Current ratio: 0.82
Long-term debt ($ mil.): 14,807

No. of shares (mil.): —
Dividends
  Yield: 0.8%
  Payout: —
Market value ($ mil.): —

	STOCK PRICE ($) FY Close	P/E High/Low		PER SHARE ($) Earnings	Dividends	Book Value
12/20	13.50	4	2	0.49	0.12	(0.00)
12/19	17.05	10	7	0.29	0.26	0.02
12/18	13.20	8	5	0.41	0.32	0.02
12/17	24.43	13	9	0.51	0.32	0.03
12/16	19.42	16	11	0.39	0.31	0.03
Annual Growth	**(8.7%)**	**—**	**—**	**6.2%**	**(21.6%)**	

Komatsu Ltd

Auditors: KPMG AZSA LLC

LOCATIONS

HQ: Komatsu Ltd
2-3-6 Akasaka, Minato-ku, Tokyo 107-8414
Phone: (81) 3 5561 2604   **Fax:** 847 437-5814
Web: home.komatsu/en/

HISTORICAL FINANCIALS

Company Type: Public

Income Statement				FYE: March 31
	REVENUE ($ mil.)	NET INCOME ($ mil.)	NET PROFIT MARGIN	EMPLOYEES
03/21	19,774	959	4.9%	65,620
03/20	22,522	1,417	6.3%	68,879
03/19	24,608	2,316	9.4%	68,674
03/18	23,553	1,849	7.9%	65,017
03/17	16,125	1,014	6.3%	50,614
Annual Growth	**5.2%**	**(1.4%)**	**—**	**6.7%**

2021 Year-End Financials

Debt ratio: 0.2%
Return on equity: 5.7%
Cash ($ mil.): 2,195
Current ratio: 2.00
Long-term debt ($ mil.): 4,881

No. of shares (mil.): 945
Dividends
  Yield: 1.7%
  Payout: 50.7%
Market value ($ mil.): 29,530

	STOCK PRICE ($) FY Close	P/E High/Low		PER SHARE ($) Earnings	Dividends	Book Value
03/21	31.23	0	0	1.02	0.54	18.26
03/20	16.41	0	0	1.50	1.05	17.27
03/19	23.30	0	0	2.45	0.89	17.36
03/18	33.65	0	0	1.96	0.62	16.61
03/17	26.18	0	0	1.07	0.53	14.95
Annual Growth	**4.5%**	**—**	**—**	**(1.4%)**	**0.5%**	**5.1%**

Komercni Banka AS (Czech Republic)

EXECUTIVES

Vice Chairman of the Supervisory Board, Giovanni Soma
Independent Member of the Supervisory Board, Petr Dvorak
Member of the Executive Board, Senior Executive Director - Retail Banking, Miroslav Hirsl
Chairman of the Supervisory Board, Jean-Luc Parer
Member of the Executive Board, Senior Executive Director, Chief Digital Officer (CDO), Margus Simson
Member of the Supervisory Board, Employee Representative, Sylva Kynychova
Member of the Supervisory Board, Employee Representative, Ondrej Kudrna
Member of the Supervisory Board, Cecile Camilli
Member of the Supervisory Board, Employee Representative, Vojtech Smajer
Independent Member of the Supervisory Board, Petra Wandelova
Member of the Executive Board, Senior Executive Director, Corporate and Investment Banking (CIB), David Formanek
Member of the Executive Board, Senior Executive Director, Chief Risk Officer (CRO), Didier Colin
Chairman of the Executive Board, Chief Executive Officer, Jan Juchelka
Member of the Supervisory Board, Maylis Coupet
Auditors: Deloitte Audit s.r.o.

LOCATIONS

HQ: Komercni Banka AS (Czech Republic)
Na Prikope 33/969, Prague 1 114 07
Phone: (420) 485 262 800   **Fax:** (420) 224 243 020
Web: www.kb.cz

HISTORICAL FINANCIALS

Company Type: Public

Income Statement				FYE: December 31
	ASSETS ($ mil.)	NET INCOME ($ mil.)	INCOME AS % OF ASSETS	EMPLOYEES
12/19	47,607	658	1.4%	8,351
12/18	47,183	660	1.4%	8,454
12/17	47,049	699	1.5%	8,696
12/16	36,059	534	1.5%	8,615
12/15	35,939	514	1.4%	8,575
Annual Growth	**7.3%**	**6.4%**	**—**	**(0.7%)**

2019 Year-End Financials

Return on assets: 1.3%
Return on equity: 14.5%
Long-term debt ($ mil.): —
No. of shares (mil.): 188
Sales ($ mil): 2,358

Dividends
Yield: —
Payout: —
Market value ($ mil.): —

Kommunalbanken A/S (Norway)

Auditors: Ernst & Young AS

LOCATIONS

HQ: Kommunalbanken A/S (Norway)
  Haakon VIIs gate 5b, Oslo 0161
Phone: (47) 2150 2000
Web: www.kbn.org

HISTORICAL FINANCIALS

Company Type: Public

Income Statement				FYE: December 31
	ASSETS ($ mil.)	NET INCOME ($ mil.)	INCOME AS % OF ASSETS	EMPLOYEES
12/20	58,476	128	0.2%	0
12/19	52,431	140	0.3%	85
12/18	52,730	166	0.3%	82
12/17	50,352	170	0.3%	80
12/16	48,620	77	0.2%	72
Annual Growth	4.7%	13.3%	—	—

2020 Year-End Financials

Return on assets: 0.2%
Return on equity: 6.2%
Long-term debt ($ mil.): —
No. of shares (mil.): 3
Sales ($ mil): 683

Dividends
Yield: —
Payout: —
Market value ($ mil.): —

KommuneKredit (Denmark)

LOCATIONS

HQ: KommuneKredit (Denmark)
  Kultorvet 16, Copenhagen K DK-1175
Phone: (45) 33 11 15 12   **Fax:** (45) 33 91 15 21
Web: www.kommunekredit.dk

HISTORICAL FINANCIALS

Company Type: Public

Income Statement				FYE: December 31
	ASSETS ($ mil.)	NET INCOME ($ mil.)	INCOME AS % OF ASSETS	EMPLOYEES
12/19	35,606	67	0.2%	76
12/18	34,753	64	0.2%	70
12/17	35,836	78	0.2%	70
12/16	31,805	70	0.2%	66
12/15	31,118	15	0.0%	62
Annual Growth	3.4%	45.1%	—	5.2%

Kone OYJ

Auditors: PricewaterhouseCoopers Oy

LOCATIONS

HQ: Kone OYJ
  Keilasatama 3, P.O. Box 7, Espoo FIN-02150
Phone: (358) 9 204 751   **Fax:** (358) 9 204 75 4309
Web: www.kone.com

HISTORICAL FINANCIALS

Company Type: Public

Income Statement				FYE: December 31
	REVENUE ($ mil.)	NET INCOME ($ mil.)	NET PROFIT MARGIN	EMPLOYEES
12/20	12,197	1,152	9.5%	61,380
12/19	11,207	1,045	9.3%	59,825
12/18	10,387	962	9.3%	57,359
12/17	10,719	1,160	10.8%	55,075
12/16	9,275	1,080	11.7%	52,104
Annual Growth	7.1%	1.6%	—	4.2%

2020 Year-End Financials

Debt ratio: 7.0%
Return on equity: 29.5%
Cash ($ mil.): 561
Current ratio: 1.25
Long-term debt ($ mil.): 299

No. of shares (mil.): 518
Dividends
  Yield: 2.3%
  Payout: 48.1%
Market value ($ mil.): 21,054

	STOCK PRICE ($) FY Close	P/E High/Low	PER SHARE ($) Earnings	Dividends	Book Value
12/20	40.64	26 15	2.22	0.95	7.52
12/19	32.63	18 13	2.02	0.93	6.88
12/18	23.88	17 14	1.87	1.02	6.80
12/17	26.78	15 13	2.25	0.93	6.74
12/16	22.35	13 10	2.10	0.75	5.72
Annual Growth	16.1%	— —	1.4%	6.1%	7.1%

Koninklijke Ahold Delhaize NV

Koninklijke Ahold Delhaize is one of Europe's is a family of great local brands serving millions of customers in the United States Europe and Indonesia with around 7135 stores. Formed in 2016 from the merger of Royal Ahold and Delhaize Group the company operates as Giant Food Stop & Shop Food Lion and other banners in the US. Other interests include meal kit delivery service Peapod in the US Gall & Gall liquor stores in the Netherlands and joint ventures in Portugal and Indonesia. Ahold Delhaize owns about 18 retail brands. Most of the company's sales were generated from the US accounting to around 60% of total sales.

HISTORY

Albert Heijn and his wife took over his father's grocery store in Ootzaan Netherlands in 1887. By the end of WWI the company had 50 Albert Heijn grocery stores in Holland and at WWII's end it had almost 250 stores. In 1948 the company went public.

It opened its first self-service store in 1952 and its first supermarket in 1955. Growing into the #1 grocer in the Netherlands Albert Heijn opened liquor and cosmetic stores in 1973. (It changed its name to Ahold that year to better reflect its range of businesses.) Ahold expanded outside the Netherlands in 1976 when it founded supermarket chain Cadadia in Spain (sold 1985).

Ahold entered the US in 1977 by purchasing BI-LO and furthered its expansion in 1981 by adding Pennsylvania-based Giant Food Stores. In 1987 in honor of its 100th anniversary Ahold was granted the title Koninklijke (Dutch for "royal"). In 1988 it bought a majority stake in Dutch food wholesaler Schuitema.

The company added New York-based TOPS Markets in 1991. That year Royal Ahold founded food retailer and distributor Euronova (now called Ahold Czech Republic) and in 1992 it acquired 49% of Portuguese food retailer Jer nimo Martins Retail. In 1993 Cees van der Hoeven was promoted to chief executive and Royal Ahold was listed on the NYSE.

Other acquisitions included New England grocery giant The Stop & Shop Companies in 1996. That year saw the beginning of several Asian joint ventures that gave Royal Ahold stores in Singapore Malaysia and Thailand. It also formed a joint venture in 1998 with Argentina's Velox Retail Holdings (owner of about 90% of supermarket operators DISCO and Santa Isabel) and Royal Ahold added Maryland-based grocer Giant Food Inc. (unrelated to Royal Ahold's Giant Food Stores).

Royal Ahold's moves in 1999 included the acquisition of several Spanish supermarket chains (with a total of about 200 stores) the purchase of Dutch institutional food wholesaler Gastronoom and the acquisition of 50% of Sweden's top food seller ICA AB. In Central America it acquired half of La Fragua an operator of supermarkets and discount stores. However North American expansion plans hit a snag when Royal Ahold backed out of a deal to buy Pathmark Stores.

In 2000 Royal Ahold acquired Spanish food retailer Kampio+ #2 and #4 foodservice distributors U.S. Foodservice and PYA/Monarch US convenience store chains Sugar Creek and Golden Gallon and all of the voting stock of Brazilian retailer Bompre §o. In June the firm bought a 51% stake in online grocer Peapod. Royal Ahold took over food retailer Superdiplo which runs more than 300 stores in Spain (including the Canary Islands) in late 2000.

In March 2001 Royal Ahold began buying the remaining outstanding shares of Bompre §o with the intention of delisting the company from the Brazilian Luxembourg and New York stock exchanges (which it did in late December). Chicago-based Peapod became a wholly owned Royal Ahold subsidiary in 2001. The retailer also expanded its bricks-and-mortar US presence in 2001 by purchasing Alliant Exchange parent of Alliant Foodservice which distributes food to more than 100000 customers and Bruno's Supermarkets which operates more than 180 stores in the Southeast. In December Ahold also agreed to buy the 32-store G. Barbosa supermarket chain which would add to its holdings in Brazil.

Royal Ahold reported its first net loss in nearly 30 years in the second quarter of 2002. In August 2002 Royal Ahold assumed full control of Disco Ahold International Holdings its former joint venture company with Velox Retail Holdings. Soon after the company increased its ownership stake in Chilean grocery chain Santa Isabel from 70% to 97% in a tender offer. In October the company integrated its Polish Czech and Slovak operations under the umbrella of Ahold Central Europe (ACE). ACE will manage more than 400 Albert supermarkets and Hypernova hypermarkets in Central Europe. In late 2002 subsidiary U.S. Foodservice agreed to buy Allen Foods a major independent foodservice distributor in the Central Plains region.

In February 2003 CEO Cees van der Hoeven and CFO Michiel Meurs resigned following an announcement that the grocery giant would restate its financial results by at least $500 million because of accounting irregularities at U.S. Foodservice. (van der Hoeven is facing charges by Dutch prosecutors in connection with the scandal at U.S. Foodservice.) Chairman Henny de Ruiter became acting CEO of the company and Dudley Eustace a British national who serves as a director of several Dutch companies was named interim CFO in March. In May 2003 IKEA veteran Anders Moberg became acting CEO; de Ruiter remained chairman. Soon after Ahold said it would restate earnings downward by $880 million (much more than the original $500 million projection) because of the accounting scandal at U.S. Foodservice. Further accounting investigations uncovered about $29 million in irregularities at the company's TOPS Markets US subsidiary.

In May Ahold completed the sale of its De Tuinen natural product stores to NBTY's British subsidiary Holland & Barrett Europe. In June it sold its Jamin chain of candy stores to Jamin management. The Santa Isabel chain in Chile was sold in July to Cencosud for about $95 million far less than the $150 million originally discussed. Adding to its woes in July the public prosecutor in Amsterdam launched a criminal investigation into possible falsification of accounts by the company. Soon after Ahold completed the sale of 22 stores in Indonesia to PT Hero Supermarket as well as its Malaysian retail business. In September the board of directors of Royal Ahold approved the appointment of Moberg and Ry¶pp¶nen as CEO and CFO respectively. Later in the month the global grocer sold its operations in Paraguay (Supermercados Stock S.A.) to A.J. Vierci for about $4 million.

In October 2003 Royal Ahold published its long-awaited 2002 results revealing a $1.27 billion loss which the retailer attributed to special charges related to overstated profits at U.S. Foodservice. That month the company completed the sale of its 138-store Golden Gallon convenience chain to The Pantry for about $187 million and de Ruiter resigned and was succeeded by Karel Vuursteen previously a board member. In November Royal Ahold sold two hypermarkets in Poland to Carrefour Poland as part of its overall strategy to restructure its retail portfolio. In December the Peruvian operations of its Santa Isabel chain were sold to Grupo Interbank and other investors led by Nexus Group.

In March 2004 Royal Ahold sold its 118-store Bompre §o chain in Brazil to Wal-Mart Stores and its credit card business (Hipercard) there to Unibanco S.A. for a combined price of about $500 million. Also in March the Dutch chain sold its stake in CRC Ahold operating in Thailand to its partner the Central Food Retail Co. completing the company's withdrawal from Asia. At a shareholders meeting in March Ahold placed the blame for the accounting scandal which nearly bankrupted the company in 2003 squarely on the shoulders of Jim Miller the former CEO of U.S. Foodservice. (Later Miller and Ahold agreed in late 2007 to settle litigation related to the matter with Miller paying Ahold $8 million.) In August Karel Vuursteen resigned as chairman of the supervisory board for personal reasons as was succeeded by Rene Dahan. In September Ahold reached a settlement with the Dutch public prosecutor in which the company agreed to pay ?8 million. In return the Dutch prosecutor agreed not to undertake proceedings against Royal Ahold. In October the company reached a settlement with the US Securities and Exchange Commission that imposed no fines

on Royal Ahold due in part to its "extensive co-operation" with the investigation. The company also finalized a deal to increase its stake in its Scandinavian retail joint venture ICA AB. It paid its ?811 million for a 20% stake in the partnership sold by Canica. In December Ahold completed the sale of its retail activities in Spain and the Canary Islands (nearly 600 stores) to the Permira Funds.

In January 2005 the grocery giant sold its BI-LO and Bruno's chains in the southeastern US to an affiliate of Lone Star Funds for some $660 million. In February the Dutch retailer completed the sale of a dozen Hypernova hypermarkets in Poland to rival Carrefour followed by the sale of a single large hypermarket to a local Polish firm two months later. Also in April Royal Ahold completed its exit from Brazil with the sale of 32 G. Barbosa hypermarkets there to ACON Investments a US-based investment firm. In May the company announced completion of the sale of its 50% stake in Spanish winery Bodegas Williams & Humbert (formerly known as Luis Paez) to its joint venture partner Jose Medina y Cia SA for an undisclosed sum. In June Ahold completed the sale of its chain of 198 Wilson Farms and Sugarcreek convenience stores part of its TOPS Markets subsidiary in the US to WFI Acquisition for an undisclosed sum. In September Ahold sold its Deli XL foodservice operation in Belgium and the Netherlands to a subsidiary of South Africa-based The Bidvest Group for about ?140 million.

CFO Hannu Ry¶pp¶nen resigned at the end of August 2005 to join Stora Enso an integrated paper packaging and forest products company. In October Royal Ahold completed the acquisition of 56 stores in the Czech Republic from Julius Meinl a.s. In November the company settled a US class action lawsuit by paying $1.1 billion to shareholders who purchased stock between July 3 1999 and February 23 2003; just before the 2003 accounting scandal broke. Concurrently the company reached an agreement to settle litigation with the Dutch Shareholders' Association.

The grocery chain also sold 13 large Hypernova hypermarkets in Poland to Carrefour and a local operator in early 2005. The company also moved its corporate headquarters from Zaandam to Amsterdam later in the year.

In 2006 the company sold three shopping centers in Poland and the Czech Republic for about ?108 million. In April Jose Alvarez was named president and CEO of the combined Stop & Shop/Giant-Landover organization succeeding Marc Smith who retired. In September Royal Ahold was reported to be in talks with its Belgian counterpart Delhaize regarding a possible merger. However negotiations were later suspended. In November the Dutch grocer completed the acquisition of 27 Konmar stores in the Netherlands from Laurus B.V. for about $130 million.

More than three years after teetering on the brink of bankruptcy as a result of one of Europe's largest financial scandals a Dutch court found former CEO Cees van der Hoeven and former CFO Michael Meurs guilty of fraud. Van der Hoeven and Meurs were accused of improperly booking sales from four subsidiaries in Scandinavia Argentina and Brazil. Both men were fined and given suspended sentences. Former executive board member Jan Andreae who headed Ahold's European operations was sentenced to four months in jail suspended for two years and fined.

CEO Anders Moberg left the company in July 2007. Also in July U.S. Foodservice was finally sold to a consortium of Clayton Dubilier & Rice and Kohlberg Kravis Roberts & Co. for about $7.1 billion. In November John Rishton Ahold's CFO who had been serving as interim chief executive since Moberg's departure was named to the post permanently. In December Royal Ahold sold its

underperforming TOPS Markets chain to Morgan Stanley Private Equity for about $310 million.

In June 2008 the company completed sold its 73% stake in Schuitema N.V. to private equity firm CVC Capital Partners in return for cash and the transfer of 50-plus Schuitema stores to Ahold.

In 2009 Royal Ahold's Albert/Hypernova business in the Czech Republic and Slovakia closed 23 underperforming stores and downsized a dozen hypermarkets. It also finished converting its Hypernova stores to the Albert brand in the Czech Republic.

In February 2010 Ahold acquired 25 Ukrop's Super Market stores inventory equipment and leases in a $140 million transaction. The Ukrop's chain became part of Ahold USA's Giant-Carlisle division.

In March 2013 the company sold its 60% stake in the Sweden's largest food retailer ICA AB to Sweden's Hakon Invest for SEK 21.2 billion ($3.3 billion) in cash to better stick to its strategy of focusing on businesses it controls.

EXECUTIVES

Global Chief Information Officer, Member of the Executive Committee, Ben Wishart
Chairman of the Management Board, President, Chief Executive Officer, Member of the Executive Committee, Interim Chief Human Resources Officer, Frans Muller, $1,256,491 total compensation
Independent Vice Chairman of the Supervisory Board, Bill McEwan
Chief Executive Officer of Ahold Delhaize USA, Member Management Board and Executive Committee, Kevin Holt, $1,087,743 total compensation
Chief Executive Officer, Europe and Indonesia, Member of the Management Board and Executive Committee, Wouter Kolk, $818,657 total compensation
Chief Legal Officer, Member Executive Committee, Jan de Groot
Independent Member of the Supervisory Board, Katie Doyle
Independent Chairman of the Supervisory Board, Peter Agnefjaell
Independent Member of the Supervisory Board, Helen Weir
Independent Member of the Supervisory Board, Frank van Zanten
Chief Digital Officer, Member Executive Committee, Farhan Siddiqi
Auditors: PricewaterhouseCoopers Accountants N.V.

LOCATIONS

HQ: Koninklijke Ahold Delhaize NV
Provincialeweg 11, Zaandam 1506 MA
Phone: (31) 88 659 5100
Web: www.aholddelhaize.com

2018 sales

	%
US	60
Netherlands	23
Belgium	8
Central and Southeastern Europe	9
Total	**100**

PRODUCTS/OPERATIONS

2018 sales

	%
Owned store sales	86
Franchise and affiliate store sales	9
Online sales	5
Wholesale sales	-
Other	-
Total	**100**

Selected Operations

Retail
 Europe
  Albert (supermarkets Czech Republic and Slovakia)
  Albert Heijn (supermarkets convenience stores)
  Alfa-Beta (supermarkets)
  Delhaize (supermarkets)
  Etos (drugstores online shopping)
  Gall & Gall (liquor stores)
  MAXI (supermarkets)
  Mega Image (supermarkets)
  Shop & Go (convenience stores)
 US
  Food Lion (supermarkets)
  Giant-Carlisle (supermarkets & superstores)
  Giant-Landover (supermarkets)
  Stop & Go (convenience stores)
  Stop & Shop (supermarkets)

COMPETITORS

CASINO GUICHARD-PERRACHON
Hudson's Bay Company ULC
J SAINSBURY PLC
KERING
LAURA ASHLEY HOLDINGS PLC
RALLYE
THE GREAT ATLANTIC & PACIFIC TEA COMPANY
 INC.
Victoria Retail Group B.V.

HISTORICAL FINANCIALS

Company Type: Public

Income Statement — FYE: January 3

	REVENUE ($ mil.)	NET INCOME ($ mil.)	NET PROFIT MARGIN	EMPLOYEES
01/21*	90,686	1,695	1.9%	414,000
12/19	73,853	1,968	2.7%	380,000
12/18	71,599	2,044	2.9%	372,000
12/17	75,389	2,178	2.9%	369,000
01/17	52,472	876	1.7%	370,000
Annual Growth	14.7%	17.9%	—	2.8%

*Fiscal year change

2021 Year-End Financials

Debt ratio: 14.8%
Return on equity: 10.3%
Cash ($ mil.): 3,558
Current ratio: 0.70
Long-term debt ($ mil.): 4,687

No. of shares (mil.): 1,047
Dividends
 Yield: 0.0%
 Payout: 59.9%
Market value ($ mil.): 29,553

	STOCK PRICE ($) FY Close	P/E High/Low		PER SHARE ($) Earnings	Dividends	Book Value
01/21*	28.23	24	17	1.58	0.95	14.41
12/19	25.30	17	14	1.77	0.91	14.43
12/18	25.15	17	13	1.73	0.60	14.95
12/17	22.01	17	12	1.71	0.57	14.81
01/17	20.99	29	24	0.86	0.00	13.51
Annual Growth	7.7%	—	—	16.5%	—	1.6%

*Fiscal year change

Koninklijke Philips NV

Auditors: Ernst & Young Accountants LLP

LOCATIONS

HQ: Koninklijke Philips NV
 Breitner Center, Amstelplein 2, Amsterdam 1096 BC
Phone: (31) 20 59 77 232
Web: www.philips.com

HISTORICAL FINANCIALS

Company Type: Public

Income Statement — FYE: December 31

	REVENUE ($ mil.)	NET INCOME ($ mil.)	NET PROFIT MARGIN	EMPLOYEES
12/20	23,975	1,456	6.1%	81,592
12/19	21,873	1,310	6.0%	80,495
12/18	20,752	1,248	6.0%	77,400
12/17	21,313	1,986	9.3%	115,392
12/16	25,886	1,528	5.9%	113,678
Annual Growth	(1.9%)	(1.2%)	—	(8.0%)

2020 Year-End Financials

Debt ratio: 30.7%
Return on equity: 9.6%
Cash ($ mil.): 3,959
Current ratio: 1.45
Long-term debt ($ mil.): 7,001

No. of shares (mil.): 905
Dividends
 Yield: 0.0%
 Payout: 65.8%
Market value ($ mil.): 49,031

	STOCK PRICE ($) FY Close	P/E High/Low		PER SHARE ($) Earnings	Dividends	Book Value
12/20	54.17	43	27	1.58	1.04	16.09
12/19	48.80	39	25	1.44	0.82	15.87
12/18	35.11	38	29	1.33	0.80	15.14
12/17	37.80	24	18	2.10	0.84	15.53
12/16	30.57	19	14	1.65	0.71	14.42
Annual Growth	15.4%	—	—	(1.0%)	10.0%	2.8%

Korea Electric Power Corp

Auditors: Ernst & Young Han Young

LOCATIONS

HQ: Korea Electric Power Corp
 55, Jeollyeok-ro, Naju-si, Jeollanam-do 58322
Phone: (82) 61 345 4299   **Fax:** 201 613-40093
Web: www.kepco.co.kr

HISTORICAL FINANCIALS

Company Type: Public

Income Statement — FYE: December 31

	REVENUE ($ mil.)	NET INCOME ($ mil.)	NET PROFIT MARGIN	EMPLOYEES
12/20	53,224	1,829	3.4%	48,519
12/19	50,725	(2,031)	—	22,973
12/18	54,379	(1,179)	—	22,595
12/17	55,656	1,218	2.2%	22,196
12/16	50,101	5,867	11.7%	21,560
Annual Growth	1.5%	(25.3%)	—	22.5%

2020 Year-End Financials

Debt ratio: 0.0%
Return on equity: 2.9%
Cash ($ mil.): 1,864
Current ratio: 0.79
Long-term debt ($ mil.): 54,546

No. of shares (mil.): 641
Dividends
 Yield: —
 Payout: —
Market value ($ mil.): 7,877

	STOCK PRICE ($) FY Close	P/E High/Low		PER SHARE ($) Earnings	Dividends	Book Value
12/20	12.27	0	0	2.85	0.00	99.18
12/19	11.83	—	—	(3.16)	0.00	91.06
12/18	14.75	—	—	(1.84)	0.37	97.45
12/17	17.71	0	0	1.90	0.92	104.74
12/16	18.48	0	0	9.14	1.31	93.00
Annual Growth	(9.7%)	—	—	(25.3%)	—	1.6%

Krung Thai Bank Public Co. Ltd.

One of Thailand's largest financial institutions Krung Thai Bank provides banking and financial services to consumers and corporate clients throughout the country. It offers deposit accounts credit and debit cards loans mortgages and leasing as well as life insurance commercial insurance wealth management and access to investments such as securities and mutual funds. In addition to approximately 1160 domestic locations Krung Thai Bank also operates a fleet of some 90 mobile vans that provide on-the-go banking services in remote areas and at tourist destinations and festival sites. Founded in 1966 Krung Thai Bank listed on the Stock Exchange of Thailand in 1989.

EXECUTIVES

Director, Kulaya Tantitemit
Executive Chairman of the Board, Krisada Chinavicharana
First Executive Vice President - Head of Retail Shared Services Group, Chanchai Sinsuparatn
Independent Director, Kittipong Kittayarak
Independent Director, Tienchai Rubporn
Independent Director, Nitima Thepvanangkul
Senior Executive Vice President - Head of Corporate Banking Group 1, Ekachai Techawiriyakul
First Executive Vice President - Head of Government & State Enterprise Relations Group, Kittipat Peantham
Senior Executive Vice President – Head of Financial Management Group, Saranya Vejakul
Chairman of the Executive Board, Vice Chairman of the Board, Krairit Euchukanonchai
Executive Director, Poonnis Sakuntanaga
Senior Executive Vice President - Head of Business Center Group, Weerapong Suppasedsak
Senior Executive Vice President - Head of Human Resources and Corporate Governance Group, Suppawat Wadhanapatee
Independent Director, Vichai Assarasakorn
Senior Executive Vice President - Head of Operation Group, Santi Parivisutt
Independent Director, Thanwa Laohasiriwong
Senior Executive Vice President - Head of Risk Management Group, Poonpat Sripleng
First Executive Vice President, Pativate Santavanond
Senior Executive Vice President - Head of Digital Solutions Group, Praralee Ratanaprasartporn
Senior Executive Vice President - Head of Global Markets Group, Rawin Boonyanusasna
Senior Executive Vice President - Head of Global Transaction Banking Group, Tawatchai Cheevanon

Senior Executive Vice President - Head of
Corporate Banking Group 2, Suratun Kongton
First Executive Vice President, Kosol Chamchuen
First Executive Vice President - Head of Retail
Strategy Product & Segmentation Group, Pichit
Jongsaliswang
President, Executive Director, Payong Srivanich
Auditors: EY Office Limited

LOCATIONS

HQ: Krung Thai Bank Public Co. Ltd.
35 Sukhumvit Road, Klongtoey Nua, Wattana,
Bangkok 10110
Phone: (66) 2 255 2222   Fax: (66) 2 255 9391
Web: www.ktb.co.th

COMPETITORS

BANK OF THE PHILIPPINE   METROPOLITAN BANK &
ISLANDS   TRUST COMPANY
EHIME BANK LTD. THE

HISTORICAL FINANCIALS

Company Type: Public

Income Statement   FYE: December 31

	ASSETS ($ mil.)	NET INCOME ($ mil.)	INCOME AS % OF ASSETS	EMPLOYEES
12/20	111,156	558	0.5%	0
12/19	101,122	983	1.0%	0
12/18	84,675	880	1.0%	0
12/17	87,610	688	0.8%	0
12/16	75,134	901	1.2%	0
Annual Growth	10.3%	(11.3%)	—	—

2020 Year-End Financials

Return on assets: 0.5%   Dividends
Return on equity: 4.9%   Yield: 0.0%
Long-term debt ($ mil.): —   Payout: —
No. of shares (mil.): —   Market value ($ mil.): —
Sales ($ mil): 5,140

	STOCK PRICE ($) FY Close	P/E High/Low		PER SHARE ($) Earnings	Dividends	Book Value
12/20	7.77	9	5	0.04	0.40	0.82
12/19	10.74	6	5	0.07	0.38	0.81
12/18	12.01	6	5	0.06	0.29	0.68
12/17	11.87	8	7	0.05	0.43	0.63
12/16	9.89	5	4	0.06	0.33	0.55
Annual Growth	(5.9%)			(11.2%)	5.0%	10.7%

KT Corp (Korea)

Auditors: Samil PricewaterhouseCoopers

LOCATIONS

HQ: KT Corp (Korea)
KT Gwanghwamun Building East, 33, Jong-ro 3-Gil,
Seol, Jongno-gu 03155
Phone: (82) 31 727 0114   Fax: (82) 31 727 0949
Web: www.kt.co.kr

HISTORICAL FINANCIALS

Company Type: Public

Income Statement   FYE: December 31

	REVENUE ($ mil.)	NET INCOME ($ mil.)	NET PROFIT MARGIN	EMPLOYEES
12/20	22,457	644	2.9%	22,720
12/19	21,564	562	2.6%	23,372
12/18	21,042	617	2.9%	23,835
12/17	21,937	447	2.0%	23,817
12/16	18,931	591	3.1%	23,575
Annual Growth	4.4%	2.1%	—	(0.9%)

2020 Year-End Financials

Debt ratio: 0.0%   No. of shares (mil.): 241
Return on equity: 5.0%   Dividends
Cash ($ mil.): 2,420   Yield: 4.0%
Current ratio: 1.21   Payout: 18.9%
Long-term debt ($ mil.): 5,419 Market value ($ mil.): 2,663

	STOCK PRICE ($) FY Close	P/E High/Low		PER SHARE ($) Earnings	Dividends	Book Value
12/20	11.01	0	0	2.63	0.44	53.23
12/19	11.60	0	0	2.29	0.47	48.11
12/18	14.22	0	0	2.52	0.47	48.31
12/17	15.61	0	0	1.82	0.37	44.72
12/16	14.09	0	0	2.42	0.21	38.88
Annual Growth	(6.0%)			2.1%	20.8%	8.2%

Kubota Corp. (Japan)

Kubota has been the hand that turns the earth's
soil for over a century. The diversified enterprise
is Japan's maker of tractors and farm equipment
from rice trans planters to combine harvesters. It
also leads in producing iron ductile pipe for water
supply systems as well as PVC pipe and the engines for its agricultural and industrial movers.
The company has also entered into building environmental control plants and pumps. International
sales subsidiaries dot the globe. Kubota generates
around half of its sales in Asia. Its largest segment
Farm and industrial machinery accounts for
around 80% of sales.

Operations

Kubota operates in the three segments: farm
and industrial machinery water and environment
and other.

Farm and industrial machinery segment accounts for more than 80% of the company's total
sales. It includes production of agricultural machinery and agricultural-related products such as
tractors and combine harvesters pumps construction machinery inclusive of skid steer loaders and
wheel loaders and engines.

The water and environment systems segment
produces pipe systems water treatment facilities
and plants for incinerating melting crushing and
recycling wastes. It generates over 15% of total
sales.

Geographic Reach

Based in Osaka Kubota manufactures its products not only in Japan but also in overseas countries like the Africa Asia Europe Latin and North
America and Oceania. Asia is the company's
largest market generating around 50% of net sales.
Other major markets include North America
(around 35%) and Europe (more than 10%).

Financial Performance

In 2019 the revenue of Kubota has increased
by 69.7 billion [4%] from the prior year to 1.9 trillion. Domestic revenue increased by 48.0 billion
[8%] from the prior year to 625.4 billion due to
revenue in Water & Environment whose businesses are mainly related to public works projects
increased mainly due to significantly increased
sales of environment-related products and strong
sales of ductile iron pipes.

Profit for the year increased by 8.9 billion [6.0%]
from the prior year to 159.1 billion.

Strategy

Based on its corporate philosophy the company
sets a long-term goal of building "Global Major
Brand (GMB)" or in other terms a brand that can
make the greatest social contribution as a result
of being trusted by the largest number of customers. The company aims to establish the GMB
Kubota make the greatest contribution to success
of the Sustainable Development Goals (SDGs) promoted by the United Nations and achieve sustainable development over the long term. To these
ends the company will team up and work together
with various players across its business domains
encompassing the areas of food water and the environment and provide society with total solutions
created through those synergies.

Moreover to achieve the above objectives the
company will engage in three initiatives — a more
flexible and proactive task setting development of
open and innovative technologies and business
schemes creation and provision of total solutions
through the promotion of DX by utilizing new IT.
In addition the company will draw up its GMB
2030 long-term vision looking ten years ahead at
the year 2030 and will also formulate its Mid-term
Plan for making that vision a reality.

Company Background

Kubota Corporation was founded in 1890 as a
casting manufacturer. The company developed the
cultivator in 1947 and a tractor in 1960. It stated
manufacturing mini-excavators in 1974. In 2011
it became the first company in the world to acquire
the US CARB certificate. It established its manufacturing company in France in 2014 and water
treatment facilities in Myanmar in 2015.

HISTORY

The son of a poor farmer and coppersmith Gon-
shiro Oode left home in 1885 at age 14 and moved
to Osaka to find work. He began as an apprentice
at the Kuro Casting Shop where he learned about
metal casting. He saved his money and in 1890
opened Oode Casting.

Oode's shop grew rapidly thanks to the industrialization of the Japanese economy and the expansion of the iron and steel industries. One of
Oode's customers Toshiro Kubota took a liking to
the hardworking young man and in 1897 Kubota
adopted him. Oode changed his own name to Kubota and also changed the name of his company to
Kubota Iron Works.

Kubota made a number of technological breakthroughs in the early 1900s including a new
method of producing cast-iron pipe (developed in
1900). The company became the first to make the
pipe in Japan and it continued to grow as the country modernized its infrastructure.

Kubota began making steam engines machine
tools and agricultural engines in 1917 and it also
began exporting products to countries in Southeast Asia. In 1930 Kubota restructured and incorporated. It continued to add product lines including
agricultural and industrial motors.

Although WWII brought massive destruction to
Japan the peacetime that followed created plenty
of work for Kubota's farm equipment and pipe operations as the country rebuilt. By 1960 the com-

pany was Japan's largest maker of farm equipment ductile iron pipe and cement roofing materials. That year Kubota introduced the first small agricultural tractor in Japan.

EXECUTIVES

Independent Director, Kumi Arakane
Independent Director, Koichi Ina
Independent Director, Yutaro Shintaku
Senior Managing Executive Officer, Chief Director of Machinery Business, Manager of Innovation Center, Director, Dai Watanabe
Executive Vice President, Chief Director of Planning, Chief Director of Global ICT, Representative Director, Masato Yoshikawa
Independent Director, Yuzuru Matsuda
President, Representative Director, Yuichi Kitao
Chairman of the Board, Representative Director, Masatoshi Kimata
Auditors: Deloitte Touche Tohmatsu LLC

LOCATIONS

HQ: Kubota Corp. (Japan)
1-2-47 Shikitsuhigashi, Naniwa-Ku, Osaka 556-8601
Phone: (81) 6 6648 2115
Web: www.kubota.co.jp

2015 Sales

	% of total
Asia	
Japan	42
Other Asian countries	19
North America	24
Europe	12
Other regions	3
Total	**100**

PRODUCTS/OPERATIONS

2015 Sales

	% of total
Farm & industrial machinery	76
Water & environment systems	21
Other	3
Total	**100**

Selected Products

Farm & industrial machinery
  Construction machinery (mini-excavators wheel loaders)
  Engines (industrial applications)
  Farm equipment (tractors combine harvesters rice transplanters power tillers reaper binders)
Other
  Construction
  Services & other businesses
Social infrastructure
  Air conditioning equipment
  Electronic-equipped machinery
  Industrial castings
  Steel pipes
  Vending machines
Water & environment systems
  Ductile iron pipes
  Environmental control plants (water & sewage treatment plants submerged membrane systems biogas production systems pulverizing facilities irrigation systems)
  Plastic pipes & fittings
  Pumps
  Valves

COMPETITORS

ALAMO GROUP INC.
Buhler Industries Inc
D rr AG
HeidelbergCement AG
ISEKI & CO. LTD.
METALCRAFT OF MAYVILLE INC.
OXBO INTERNATIONAL CORPORATION
Outokumpu Oyj
Posco Co. Ltd.
WAHL CLIPPER CORPORATION

HISTORICAL FINANCIALS

Company Type: Public

Income Statement   FYE: December 31

	REVENUE ($ mil.)	NET INCOME ($ mil.)	NET PROFIT MARGIN	EMPLOYEES
12/20	17,980	1,246	6.9%	44,304
12/19	17,684	1,372	7.8%	43,907
12/18	16,825	1,260	7.5%	43,206
12/17	15,566	1,212	7.8%	42,441
12/16	13,646	1,132	8.3%	41,571
Annual Growth	**7.1%**	**2.4%**	**—**	**1.6%**

2020 Year-End Financials

Debt ratio: 0.2%
Return on equity: 8.7%
Cash ($ mil.): 1,771
Current ratio: 1.60
Long-term debt ($ mil.): 4,932

No. of shares (mil.): 1,208
Dividends
  Yield: 1.5%
  Payout: —
Market value ($ mil.): 133,321

	STOCK PRICE ($) FY Close	P/E High/Low		PER SHARE ($) Earnings	Dividends	Book Value
12/20	110.34	1	1	1.03	1.66	11.85
12/19	79.00	1	1	1.12	1.62	10.89
12/18	70.45	1	1	1.02	1.52	9.89
12/17	98.68	1	1	0.98	1.37	9.37
12/16	71.10	1	1	0.91	1.18	8.26
Annual Growth	**11.6%**	**—**	**—**	**3.0%**	**8.9%**	**9.5%**

Kuehne & Nagel International AG

Pass it on — Kuehne + Nagel International is one of the world's top freight forwarding and logistics groups. Kuehne + Nagel (pronounced "KOO-nuh and NAH-gel") provides sea freight and airfreight forwarding arranges the transportation of goods by road and rail and offers customs brokerage services. The company's contract logistics unit offers warehousing and distribution services and it manages more than 7 million sq. meters of warehouse space. Overall Kuehne + Nagel operates from about 900 locations in more than 100 countries worldwide. Executive chairman Klaus-Michael Kuehne grandson of the company's co-founder owns a controlling stake in Kuehne + Nagel.

HISTORY

Kuehne + Nagel (also K hne + Nagel) was founded in 1890 in Bremen Germany by shipping veterans August Kuehne and Friedrich Nagel. The forwarding and commissioning agency's initial contracts were for glassware and cotton. Kuehne + Nagel convinced Hamburg sugar refiners to use its services to transport sugar by rail to the ice-free port of Bremen when the refiners' major export route the Weser River was frozen. By 1902 Kuehne + Nagel had an office in Hamburg. Nagel died in 1907.

Rebuilding after WWI Kuehne + Nagel acquired the Weber & Freund import company in the early 1920s and expanded into Austria Czechoslovakia Switzerland and the Balkans. In 1932 when August Kuehne died sons Alfred and Werner became sole owners of Kuehne + Nagel. (Werner left the company in 1951.)

Kuehne + Nagel's headquarters in Bremen was destroyed in WWII. As postwar German trade recovered Kuehne + Nagel grew rapidly opening a subsidiary in Canada in 1953 and setting up branches across Germany including Frankfurt (1949) Bonn and Hanover (1950) Wuppertal (1961) and Nuremberg (1963).

After the European Economic Community was founded Kuehne + Nagel established a network of forwarding agents and subsidiaries across Europe including offices in Antwerp Belgium and Rotterdam the Netherlands in 1954 and offices in Basel and Zurich Switzerland in 1963. Kuehne + Nagel took control of Greek forwarder Proodos in 1963 and set up an Italian subsidiary a year later.

Alfred Kuehne died in 1981. Heavy losses resulting from the expansion of the shipping fleet of Kuehne + Nagel prompted it to sell half of the company to British conglomerate Lonrho (renamed Lonmin in 1999). Alfred's son Klaus-Michael Kuehne and Lonrho's Roland "Tiny" Rowland were appointed as joint chief executives.

In 1985 Kuehne + Nagel began expanding its transportation warehousing and distribution network by acquiring stakes in leading freight companies including Domenichelli (Italy) Hollis Transportation (UK) and Van Vliet (the Netherlands). The Kuehne family expanded Kuehne + Nagel's presence in Switzerland (seen as a pan-European center) during the 1970s and 1980s and in 1992 Kuehne + Nagel moved its global headquarters to Schindellegi near Zurich.

In the early 1990s after German reunification and the fall of the Soviet Union Kuehne + Nagel acquired former East German state-owned forwarder VEB Deutrans. It also signed deals with local freight-forwarding operators in Russia and across Eastern Europe.

In 1992 Klaus-Michael Kuehne bought out Lonrho's stake and later sold a 33% stake to German conglomerate VIAG (later part of E.ON) which sold it back to Kuehne + Nagel in 1999. In 1994 Kuehne + Nagel went public.

To expand its rail network the company in 1997 acquired a 51% stake in Swiss rail forwarder Ferroviasped a major player in freight services for national railroads in Denmark France Spain and Switzerland.

To stay competitive in a rapidly consolidating industry Kuehne + Nagel formed an alliance in 1999 with French freight forwarder GEFCO a subsidiary of Peugeot S.A. A year later Kuehne + Nagel formed an alliance with Singapore-based SembCorp Logistics which later acquired a 20% stake in Kuehne + Nagel. In return Kuehne + Nagel bought 5% of SembCorp Logistics.

In 2000 Kuehne + Nagel also made plans to expand operations in the US. The company followed through the next year when it bought Connecticut-based USCO Logistics for $300 million. USCO Logistics was renamed Kuehne + Nagel Logistics in 2004.

Also in 2004 Kuehne + Nagel and SembCorp Logistics terminated their alliance in order to proceed independently.

EXECUTIVES

Member of the Management Board, Executive Vice President - Road Logistics, Stefan Paul
Member of the Management Board, Chief Financial Officer, Markus Blanka-Graff
Non-Executive Member of the Board of Directors, Martin Wittig
Member of the Management Board, Executive Vice President - Contract Logistics, Gianfranco Sgro
Non-Executive Member of the Board of Directors, Hauke Stars

Member of the Management Board, Chief Human Resource Officer, Lothar Harings
Chairman of the Management Board, Chief Executive Officer, Detlef Trefzger, $1,107,353 total compensation
Member of the Management Board, Chief Information Officer, Martin Kolbe
Honorary Chairman of the Board of Directors, Klaus-Michael Kuehne
Non-Executive Vice Chairman of the Board, Karl Gernandt
Non-Executive Chairman of the Board, Joerg Wolle
Non-Executive Member of the Board of Directors, Renato Fassbind
Member of the Management Board, Executive Vice President - Sea Logistics, Horst Schacht
Non-Executive Member of the Board of Directors, David Kamenetzky
Member of the Management Board, Executive Vice President - Airfreight, Yngve Ruud
Auditors: Ernst & Young Ltd

LOCATIONS

HQ: Kuehne & Nagel International AG
Kuehne & Nagel House, P.O. Box 67, Schindellegi CH-8834
Phone: (41) 44 786 95 11   Fax: (41) 44 786 95 95
Web: www.kuehne-nagel.com

COMPETITORS

Holcim AG	Swiss Life Holding AG
PHAROL - SGPS S.A.	Zurich Insurance Group
Rieter Holding AG	AG

HISTORICAL FINANCIALS

Company Type: Public

Income Statement   FYE: December 31

	REVENUE ($ mil.)	NET INCOME ($ mil.)	NET PROFIT MARGIN	EMPLOYEES
12/20	23,142	894	3.9%	78,249
12/19	21,820	825	3.8%	83,161
12/18	21,117	782	3.7%	81,900
12/17	19,051	755	4.0%	75,876
12/16	16,234	707	4.4%	70,038
Annual Growth	9.3%	6.1%	—	2.8%

2020 Year-End Financials

Debt ratio: 4.6%
Return on equity: 33.2%
Cash ($ mil.): 1,926
Current ratio: 1.14
Long-term debt ($ mil.): 454
No. of shares (mil.): 119
Dividends
  Yield: 1.1%
  Payout: 7.1%
Market value ($ mil.): 5,440

	STOCK PRICE ($) FY Close	P/E High/Low		PER SHARE ($) Earnings	Dividends	Book Value
12/20	45.49	7	4	7.46	0.52	22.85
12/19	33.95	5	4	6.89	0.72	20.00
12/18	25.46	6	4	6.53	0.71	19.68
12/17	35.50	6	4	6.30	0.69	(0.00)
12/16	26.55	5	4	5.87	0.58	17.75
Annual Growth	14.4%	—	—	6.2%	(2.9%)	6.5%

Kunlun Energy Co., Ltd.

KunLun Energy Company's mission is to find and deliver crude oil and natural gas for its customers. It specializes in the production and exploration for crude oil and natural gas in Asia South America and the Middle East. KunLun a subsidiary of PetroChina Company works with its parent and other oil companies through production-sharing contracts to find develop and produce oil and gas. In 2013 it boasted a volume of some 24 billion cubic meters in natural gas transmission. KunLun has about 10 oil exploration and production projects in Azerbaijan China Indonesia Kazakhstan Oman Peru and Thailand. KunLun changed its name in 2010 from CNPC Hong Kong to KunLun Energy.

EXECUTIVES

Company Secretary, Mao Xie
Chief Financial Officer, Executive Director, Yong Miao
Executive Director, Yuanhong Zhou
Independent Non-Executive Director, Yok Sing Tsang
Chief Executive Officer, Executive Director, Zhijia Qian
Executive Chairman of the Board, Bin Fu
Auditors: KPMG

LOCATIONS

HQ: Kunlun Energy Co., Ltd.
39/F., 118 Connaught Road West,
Phone: (852) 2522 2282   Fax: (852) 2868 1741
Web: www.kunlun.com.hk

PRODUCTS/OPERATIONS

2016 Sales

	% of total
Natural Gas Distribution	
Natural Gas Sales	78
Natural Gas Pipeline	17
LNG Terminal	2
LNG Processing	1
Exploration & Production	2
Total	100

Selected Subsidiaries & Owned Oil Field Projects

Projects
Azerbaijan K&K Project (25% owned)Indonesia Bengara-II Project (70% owned)Kazakhstan Aktobe Project (15% owned)Liaohe Leng Jiapu Cooperation Project (70% owned)Oman Block 5 Project (25% owned)Peru Talara Project (50% owned)Thailand Sukhothai Project (96%)
Subsidiaires
Binhai New Energy Co. Ltd.Cangzhou Gas Limited Company PetroChinaChina City Natural Gas Investment Group Co. Ltd.China Natural Gas Co. Ltd.CNPC Shennan Oil Technology Development Co. LtdGreen Ever Company LimitedHuagang Gas Group Company LimitedJilin Jig

COMPETITORS

CNOOC LIMITED	TAUBER OIL COMPANY
KUWAIT PETROLEUM	Tidal Energy Marketing
CORPORATION S.A.K	Inc
MOTIVA ENTERPRISES LLC	
SINGAPORE PETROLEUM	
COMPANY LIMITED	

HISTORICAL FINANCIALS

Company Type: Public

Income Statement   FYE: December 31

	REVENUE ($ mil.)	NET INCOME ($ mil.)	NET PROFIT MARGIN	EMPLOYEES
12/19	16,284	797	4.9%	38,557
12/18	15,333	673	4.4%	42,278
12/17	13,631	731	5.4%	41,835
12/16	10,559	84	0.8%	37,281
12/15	5,372	17	0.3%	19,696
Annual Growth	31.9%	159.2%	—	18.3%

2019 Year-End Financials

Debt ratio: 3.3%
Return on equity: 11.9%
Cash ($ mil.): 2,678
Current ratio: 0.75
Long-term debt ($ mil.): 3,697
No. of shares (mil.): —
Dividends
  Yield: —
  Payout: 40.6%
Market value ($ mil.): —

Kweichow Moutai Co., Ltd.

Kweichow Moutai's liquor will really put some hair on your chest. The company makes Moutai (sometimes known as Maotai in the West) the national liquor of China. Moutai is a type of baijiu a 100 proof distilled spirit made of wheat and sorghum. Kweichow Moutai produces about 20000 tons of Moutai every year — the most expensive being an 80-year-old bottle that sells for hundreds of dollars. Moutai is exported to 100 countries including the US. The distillery is located in Moutai Town in Kweichow Province in southwestern China. Moutai has been made in China for thousands of years but the state-owned Kweichow Moutai company was formed in 1951.

Financial Performance
The company is targeting one billion yuan ($165 million) in sales in 2014 and has set the figure to 5 to 10 billion yuan ($826 million to $1.65 billion) in three to five years.

Strategy
Kweichow Moutai is pursuing the high-end of the market with the formation in 2014 of Kweichow Moutai Custom-Made Marketing Limited which customizes maotai orders for individuals businesses celebrities and other groups. Bottles sell for as much as CNY100000 ($16500).

EXECUTIVES

Acting General Manager, Director, Jingren Li
Deputy General Manager, Xiaowei Wang
Deputy General Manager, Zhengqiang Zhong
Independent Director, Jingzhong Zhang
Independent Director, Dingbo Xu
Independent Director, Jinhai Lu
Deputy General Manager, Huabin Tu
Chairman of the Board, Xiongjun Ding
Chief Financial Officer, Deputy General Manager, Yan Jiang
Auditors: BDO China Shu Lun Pan Certified Public Accountants

LOCATIONS

HQ: Kweichow Moutai Co., Ltd.
Maotai Town, Renhuai, Guizhou Province 564501
Phone: (86) 852 2386002   Fax: (86) 852 2386005
Web: www.moutaichina.com

PRODUCTS/OPERATIONS

Selected Products
Elite General
Great China
Kweichow Moutai liquor (Feitian)
Kweichow Moutai liquor (Five-Star)
Kweichow Moutai liquor (New Feitian)
Kweichow Moutai liquor (New Five-Star)
Moutai Prince
Moutai Ying Bin Chiew
Han jiang
Ren

COMPETITORS

CASTLE BRANDS INC.	THE GLENMORANGIE
DIAGEO PLC	COMPANY LIMITED
MGP INGREDIENTS INC.	

HISTORICAL FINANCIALS

Company Type: Public

Income Statement · FYE: December 31

	REVENUE ($ mil.)	NET INCOME ($ mil.)	NET PROFIT MARGIN	EMPLOYEES
12/20	14,983	7,139	47.7%	0
12/19	12,769	5,921	46.4%	0
12/18	11,223	5,118	45.6%	0
12/17	9,383	4,161	44.3%	0
12/16	5,782	2,407	41.6%	0
Annual Growth	26.9%	31.2%	—	—

2020 Year-End Financials

Debt ratio: —
Return on equity: 31.3%
Cash ($ mil.): 5,518
Current ratio: 4.06
Long-term debt ($ mil.): —

No. of shares (mil.): —
Dividends
 Yield: —
 Payout: —
Market value ($ mil.): —

Kyocera Corp

Auditors: PricewaterhouseCoopers Kyoto

LOCATIONS

HQ: Kyocera Corp
 6 Takeda Tobadono-cho, Fushimi-ku, Kyoto 612-8501
Phone: (81) 75 604 3500 **Fax:** (81) 75 604 3501
Web: www.kyocera.co.jp

HISTORICAL FINANCIALS

Company Type: Public

Income Statement · FYE: March 31

	REVENUE ($ mil.)	NET INCOME ($ mil.)	NET PROFIT MARGIN	EMPLOYEES
03/21	13,790	814	5.9%	78,490
03/20	14,731	992	6.7%	75,505
03/19	14,661	931	6.4%	76,863
03/18	14,851	770	5.2%	75,940
03/17	12,725	928	7.3%	70,153
Annual Growth	2.0%	(3.2%)	—	2.8%

2021 Year-End Financials

Debt ratio: 0.0%
Return on equity: 3.5%
Cash ($ mil.): 3,492
Current ratio: 2.84
Long-term debt ($ mil.): 522

No. of shares (mil.): 362
Dividends
 Yield: 2.0%
 Payout: —
Market value ($ mil.): 23,225

	STOCK PRICE ($) FY Close	P/E High/Low		PER SHARE ($) Earnings	Dividends	Book Value
03/21	64.08	0	0	2.25	1.32	64.57
03/20	58.63	0	0	2.74	1.48	61.82
03/19	58.91	0	0	2.57	1.09	56.56
03/18	56.74	0	0	2.09	1.14	59.83
03/17	56.13	0	0	2.53	0.93	56.78
Annual Growth	3.4%	—	—	(2.9%)	9.2%	3.3%

Kyushu Electric Power Co Inc

Kyushu Electric Power generates transmits and distributes electricity on Japan's southernmost island. The company serves customers in the Kyushu region providing nuclear thermal and hydroelectric power generation. The company's other operations include telecommunications information system development business and data center business. It also sells wholesale electricity and has international power production and consulting operations primarily in Asia. Kyushu Electric was established in 1951. The power transmission and distribution business of Kyushu Electric Power was spun off as Kyushu Electric Power Transmission and Distribution Co. Inc. in 2020 to enhance the neutrality of the power transmission and distribution network.

Operations

Kyushu Electric's segments are Domestic Electric power (some 85% of sales) Other Energy Service (about 10%) Information and Communication Technology (ICT) Service (some 5%) and Other

The Domestic Electric Power segment is engaged in the business of power generation and retail electricity in Japan and electricity transmission and distribution in Kyushu region.

The Other Energy Service segment is engaged in the business that provides a stable supply of electric power such as construction and maintenance of electricity-related facilities selling gas and LNG a renewable energy business and overseas business.

The ICT Service segment is engaged in the data communication business optical broadband business construction and maintenance of telecommunications facilities information system development business and data center business.

Other segment is engaged in the real estate business nursing home business and other business.

Overall about 90% of sales were generated from electric operations.

Geographic Reach

Headquartered in Fukuoka Japan Kyushu Electric has around 55 offices across Japan.

Financial Performance

In terms of income as of March 31 for 2020 consolidated operating revenues decreased 0.2% from the previous fiscal year to 2.01 trillion despite an increase in sales in the ICT service business. Factors include a decrease in retail electricity sales and in electricity sales to other suppliers as well as an increase in renewable energy-related subsidies.

As a result of the foregoing factors net income attributable to owners of the parent declined by 31.3 billion over the previous fiscal year to 400 million.

Cash held by the company at the end of fiscal 2020 decreased to 205.5 billion compared to 245.3 billion in the prior. Cash provided by operation and financing activities were 226.9 billion and 158.0 billion respectively. Cash used for investing activities was 424.6 billion mainly for capital expenditures including nuclear fuel.

Strategy

In recent years there have been growing expectations toward efforts to bring about a sustainable society on a global scale. These include efforts to achieve the United Nations' sustainable development goals (SDGs) for the international community and ESG investment that evaluates companies' consideration of factors such as the environment. The company recognizes the importance of meeting these expectations.

That is why its group strategy and ESG initiatives are inseparable. To name an example its management vision includes a business performance target of contributing to the reduction of Kyushu's CO_2 emissions by 70%. This is consistent with Japan's plan to combat global warming (a 26% reduction from 2013 levels in 2030) under the Paris Agreement. We have set three strategies for achieving its vision: Strategy I tied to E (Environment) Strategy II tied to S (Society) and Strategy III tied to G (Governance). Its entire management vision is linked to ESG.

In Strategy I the company will contribute to a sustainable low-carbon society by improving our ratio of non-fossil fuel power sources Environment through the use of renewable and nuclear energy and by promoting electricity usage in many fields. Strategy II will contribute to the resolution of various issues affecting communities and wider society by creating markets through new businesses and services. Strategy III will strengthen the business foundations that support the growth of the Kyuden Group.

Mergers and Acquisitions

In 2019 Kyushu Electric Power Co. Inc. participates in the management of EGCO which is one of the largest Independent Power Producers in Thailand by acquiring indirect interest in the Electricity Generating Public Company Limited. With this participation its equity ownership in overseas electricity generation project is approximately 2300MW which approaches its target in its midterm management policy to expand equity ownership of 5000MW by 2030. Terms were not disclosed.

EXECUTIVES

Executive Vice President, Chief Senior Director of Business Solution, Representative Director, Ichiro Fujii
Executive President, Chief Executive Officer, Representative Director, Kazuhiro Ikebe
Managing Executive Officer, President of Subsidiaries, Director, Yoshio Ogura
Managing Executive Officer, Chief Senior Director of Energy Services Business, President of Subsidiary, Director, Yasuji Akiyama
Managing Executive Officer, Chief Senior Director of Energy Service Business, Director, Junichi Fujimoto
Director, Yasuaki Endo
Non-Executive Independent Director, Kazutaka Koga
Chairman of the Board, Representative Director, Michiaki Uriu
Executive Vice President, Representative Director, Makoto Toyoma
Managing Executive Officer, Chief Director of Nuclear Power Generation, Director, Naoyuki Toyoshima
Managing Executive Officer, Deputy Chief Senior Director of Energy Service Business, Chief Director of Sales, Director, Yoshifumi Kuriyama
Non-Executive Independent Director, Hiroko Tani

Non-Executive Independent Director, Sakie
 Fukushima
Non-Executive Independent Director, Kazuko
 Fujita
Non-Executive Independent Director, Junji Tsuda
Auditors: Deloitte Touche Tohmatsu LLC

LOCATIONS

HQ: Kyushu Electric Power Co Inc
 2-1-82 Watanabe-dori, Chuo-ku, Fukuoka 810-8720
Phone: (81) 92 761 3031
Web: www.kyuden.co.jp

PRODUCTS/OPERATIONS

2016 Sales

	% of total
Electric power	92
IT and Telecommunication	4
Energy related Business	3
Others	1
Total	**100**

COMPETITORS

ASSYSTEM
EnBW Energie Baden-Württemberg AG
FUELCELL ENERGY INC.
HOKKAIDO ELECTRIC POWER COMPANY
 INCORPORATED
Huadian Power International Corporation Limited
Hydro One Inc
IDACORP INC.
KANSAI ELECTRIC POWER COMPANY
 INCORPORATED THE
Korea Electric Power Corporation
NATURGY ENERGY GROUP SA.
TUCSON ELECTRIC POWER COMPANY
YASKAWA ELECTRIC CORPORATION

HISTORICAL FINANCIALS

Company Type: Public

Income Statement   FYE: March 31

	REVENUE ($ mil.)	NET INCOME ($ mil.)	NET PROFIT MARGIN	EMPLOYEES
03/21	19,253	290	1.5%	21,273
03/20	18,544	(3)	—	21,180
03/19	18,214	279	1.5%	21,103
03/18	18,461	816	4.4%	20,968
03/17	16,345	708	4.3%	20,889
Annual Growth	**4.2%**	**(20.0%)**	**—**	**0.5%**

2021 Year-End Financials

Debt ratio: 0.6%
Return on equity: 5.0%
Cash ($ mil.): 2,114
Current ratio: 0.60
Long-term debt ($ mil.): 26,597
No. of shares (mil.): 473
Dividends
 Yield: 0.0%
 Payout: 56.8%
Market value ($ mil.): 4,194

	STOCK PRICE ($) FY Close	P/E High/Low		Earnings	PER SHARE ($) Dividends	Book Value
03/21	8.85	0	0	0.51	0.29	12.46
03/20	8.46	—	—	(0.06)	0.32	11.87
03/19	12.13	0	0	0.43	0.23	12.18
03/18	11.65	0	0	1.36	0.24	12.50
03/17	10.69	0	0	1.43	0.04	10.40
Annual Growth	**(4.6%)**	—	—	**(22.5%)**	**67.9%**	**4.6%**

L'Air Liquide S.A. (France)

Auditors: ERNST & YOUNG et Autres

LOCATIONS

HQ: L'Air Liquide S.A. (France)
 75, quai d'Orsay, Paris, Cedex 07 75007
Phone: (33) 1 40 62 55 55
Web: www.airliquide.com

HISTORICAL FINANCIALS

Company Type: Public

Income Statement   FYE: December 31

	REVENUE ($ mil.)	NET INCOME ($ mil.)	NET PROFIT MARGIN	EMPLOYEES
12/20	25,406	2,988	11.8%	64,445
12/19	24,836	2,516	10.1%	67,200
12/18	24,277	2,420	10.0%	66,000
12/17	24,659	2,636	10.7%	65,200
12/16	19,331	1,947	10.1%	66,700
Annual Growth	**7.1%**	**11.3%**	**—**	**(0.9%)**

2020 Year-End Financials

Debt ratio: 36.2%
Return on equity: 12.9%
Cash ($ mil.): 2,198
Current ratio: 0.87
Long-term debt ($ mil.): 12,543
No. of shares (mil.): 472
Dividends
 Yield: 1.7%
 Payout: 10.5%
Market value ($ mil.): 15,529

	STOCK PRICE ($) FY Close	P/E High/Low		Earnings	PER SHARE ($) Dividends	Book Value
12/20	32.89	7	5	6.31	0.58	48.20
12/19	28.05	6	5	5.31	0.54	44.94
12/18	24.67	6	5	5.13	0.56	43.26
12/17	25.16	6	5	5.60	0.53	41.67
12/16	22.24	5	4	4.45	0.88	37.68
Annual Growth	**10.3%**	—	—	**9.1%**	**(9.6%)**	**6.4%**

L'Oreal S.A. (France)

Auditors: Deloitte & Associés

LOCATIONS

HQ: L'Oreal S.A. (France)
 14, rue Royale, Paris 75008
Phone: (33) 1 47 56 70 00   **Fax:** (33) 1 47 56 86 42
Web: www.loreal.com

HISTORICAL FINANCIALS

Company Type: Public

Income Statement   FYE: December 31

	REVENUE ($ mil.)	NET INCOME ($ mil.)	NET PROFIT MARGIN	EMPLOYEES
12/20	34,354	4,373	12.7%	85,392
12/19	33,541	4,210	12.6%	87,974
12/18	30,848	4,460	14.5%	85,000
12/17	31,196	4,293	13.8%	82,578
12/16	27,280	3,279	12.0%	89,331
Annual Growth	**5.9%**	**7.5%**		**(1.1%)**

2020 Year-End Financials

Debt ratio: 2.4%
Return on equity: 12.1%
Cash ($ mil.): 7,861
Long-term debt ($ mil.): 10
No. of shares (mil.): 559
Dividends
 Yield: 1.1%
 Payout: 12.2%
Market value ($ mil.): 42,634

	STOCK PRICE ($) FY Close	P/E High/Low		Earnings	PER SHARE ($) Dividends	Book Value
12/20	76.15	12	8	7.78	0.87	63.56
12/19	58.87	9	7	7.48	0.86	59.18
12/18	45.66	7	6	7.92	0.86	55.11
12/17	44.28	7	6	7.62	0.79	53.15
12/16	36.41	7	6	5.81	0.67	46.19
Annual Growth	**20.3%**	—	—	**7.6%**	**6.8%**	**8.3%**

Larsen & Toubro Ltd

Auditors: M/S Deloitte Haskins & Sells LLP

LOCATIONS

HQ: Larsen & Toubro Ltd
 L&T House, Ballard Estate, Mumbai 400 001
Phone: (91) 22 6752 5656   **Fax:** (91) 22 6752 5893
Web: www.larsentoubro.com

HISTORICAL FINANCIALS

Company Type: Public

Income Statement   FYE: March 31

	REVENUE ($ mil.)	NET INCOME ($ mil.)	NET PROFIT MARGIN	EMPLOYEES
03/21	18,584	1,583	8.5%	40,527
03/20	19,256	1,264	6.6%	45,467
03/19	20,378	1,286	6.3%	44,761
03/18	18,423	1,132	6.1%	42,924
03/17	17,179	931	5.4%	41,466
Annual Growth	**2.0%**	**14.2%**	**—**	**(0.6%)**

2021 Year-End Financials

Debt ratio: 0.5%
Return on equity: 16.2%
Cash ($ mil.): 2,219
Current ratio: 1.42
Long-term debt ($ mil.): 11,223
No. of shares (mil.): 1,404
Dividends
 Yield: —
 Payout: 21.8%
Market value ($ mil.): —

Laurentian Bank of Canada

Laurentian Bank of Canada is a financial institution that operates mainly across Canada. The bank caters for the needs of retail clients via its branch network based in Quebec. The bank stands out for its expertise among small and medium-sized enterprises and real estate developers owing to specialized teams across Canada. Its subsidiary B2B Bank one of the major Canadian leaders in providing banking products and services investment accounts through financial advisors and brokers. Laurentian Banks Securities offers integrated brokerage services to clientele of institutional and retail investors. The banks line of business are Retail Services Business Services B2B Bank Laurentian Bank Securities and Capital Markets and more.

EXECUTIVES

Independent Director, David Morris
Independent Chairman of the Board, Michael Mueller
Independent Director, David Mowat
President, Chief Executive Officer, Director, Rania Llewellyn, $1,992 total compensation
Chief Human Resource Officer, Executive Vice President, Sebastien Belair
Senior Vice President - Digital Banking, Adam Swinemar
Executive Vice President, Chief Information Technology Officer, Beel Yaqub
Independent Director, Sonia Baxendale
Executive Vice President, Chief Risk Officer, William Mason, $282,493 total compensation
Executive Vice President - Operations, Yves Denomme
Executive Vice President, Head of Personal Banking, Karine Abgrall-Teslyk
Independent Director, Nicholas Zelenczuk
Independent Director, Andrea Bolger
Executive Vice President - Capital Markets, President, Chief Executive Officer, Laurentian Bank Securities Inc., Kelsey Gunderson
Independent Director, Michelle Savoy
Independent Director, Michael Boychuk
Independent Director, Susan Wolburgh Jenah
Auditors: Ernst & Young LLP

LOCATIONS

HQ: Laurentian Bank of Canada
1360 Rene-Levesque Blvd West, Suite 600, Montreal, Quebec H3G 0E5
Phone:
Web: www.lbcfg.ca

2013 Loans

	% of total
Qué;bec	60
Ontario	29
Rest of Canada	11
Total	**100**

PRODUCTS/OPERATIONS

2016 Revenue

	% of total
Interest income:	
loans	71
securities	2
Other including derivatives	4
Other income:	
Fees and commissions on loans and deposits	10
Income from brokerage operations	5
Income from sales of mutual funds	3
Income from investment accounts	2
Insurance income net	1
Income from treasury and financial market operations	1
Other	1
Total	**100**

2016 Loans

	% of total
Residential mortgage	71
Personal	29
Total	**100**

Selected Subsidiaries

B2B Bank
Laurentian Bank Securities Inc.
Laurentian Trust of Canada Inc.
LBC Financial Services Inc.
LBC Investment Management Inc.
LBC Trust
V.R. Holding Insurance Holding Company Ltd.

COMPETITORS

B2B Bank
BANCO ESPA 'OL DE CREDITO SA (EXTINGUIDA)
BANK BPH S A
Banco Bradesco S/A
CITY HOLDING COMPANY
COMMERCE BANCSHARES INC.
FINANCIAL INSTITUTIONS INC.
FIRST BUSINESS FINANCIAL SERVICES INC.
Jyske Bank A/S
LYONS NATIONAL BANK
M&T BANK CORPORATION
MUFG AMERICAS HOLDINGS CORPORATION
NIBDAN LIMITED
Slovensk sporitelna a.s.
TD BANK NATIONAL ASSOCIATION
WSFS FINANCIAL CORPORATION

HISTORICAL FINANCIALS

Company Type: Public

Income Statement   FYE: October 31

	ASSETS ($ mil.)	NET INCOME ($ mil.)	INCOME AS % OF ASSETS	EMPLOYEES
10/21	36,491	46	0.1%	2,871
10/20	33,202	85	0.3%	3,048
10/19	33,672	131	0.4%	3,256
10/18	34,952	171	0.5%	3,642
10/17	36,338	160	0.4%	3,732
Annual Growth	**0.1%**	**(26.8%)**	**—**	**(6.3%)**

2021 Year-End Financials

Return on assets: 0.1%	Dividends
Return on equity: 2.1%	Yield: 0.0%
Long-term debt ($ mil.): —	Payout: 155.3%
No. of shares (mil.): 43	Market value ($ mil.): 1,478
Sales ($ mil): 1,265	

	STOCK PRICE ($) FY Close	P/E High/Low		Earnings	PER SHARE ($) Dividends	Book Value
10/21	33.92	36	21	0.83	1.30	49.05
10/20	19.82	15	8	1.78	1.61	45.40
10/19	34.32	9	7	2.86	1.99	45.73
10/18	31.86	9	6	3.88	1.93	45.18
10/17	46.83	9	7	4.20	1.91	46.55
Annual Growth	**(7.7%)**	**—**	**—**	**(33.3%)**	**(9.3%)**	**1.3%**

Legal & General Group PLC (United Kingdom)

Legal & General Group (L&G) is one of the UK's largest financial services companies. The London-based company operates across four broad business areas of retirement investment management capital investment and insurance through its subsidiaries and associates in the UK the US and other countries around the world. With approximately 1.3 trillion assets under management L&G's pensions business offers annuity contracts longevity insurance contracts lifetime mortgages retirement interest only mortgages and life time care plan. The UK's top life insurer operates in the US as Banner Life Insurance Company and William Penn Life Insurance Company of New York.

Operations

L&G divides its operations into four business segments namely Legal & General Retirement (LGR) Legal & General Investment Management (LGIM) Legal & General Insurance (LGI) and Legal & General Capital (LGC).

LGIM generates more than 40% of L&G's revenue and offers a range of pooled index funds fixed income funds and defined benefit pension scheme de-risking.

LGR accounting for approximately 30% of the company's revenue serves institutional and retail clients. It provides annuities defined benefit pension scheme buy-ins and buyouts lifetime mortgages and longevity insurance.

LGC and LGI bring in about 30% of revenue combined. LGC makes capital investments in housing urban regeneration clean energy and SME finance (including venture capital). LGI offers life insurance in the UK and US.

All in L&G has more than 1.3 trillion in assets under management making it the largest investment manager in the UK.

Geographic Reach

Based in the UK L&G operates throughout North America Asia Pacific Europe and some other countries worldwide.

Sales and Marketing

L&G serves more than 8 million individual customers. It mainly distributes its insurance products in the UK and the US through direct distribution channels existing broker and agency channels.

Financial Performance

The company's revenue for fiscal 2020 decreased to 50.2 billion compared from the prior year with 66.8 billion.

Profit for fiscal 2020 decreased to 1.6 billion compared from the prior year with 1.8 billion.

Cash held by the company at the end of fiscal 2020 increased to 18.0 billion. Cash provided by operations was 4.3 billion while cash used for investing activities and financing activities were 457 million and 29 million respectively. Main uses of cash were net disposal of operations and dividend distributions to ordinary equity holders during the year.

Strategy

Six long-term global growth drivers shape its world and its markets. L&G's respond to these drivers through its strategic priorities:

Ageing demographics: the company aim to build a truly global asset management business entering new markets and expanding its existing operations.

Globalization of asset markets: L&G aim to build a truly global asset management business entering new markets and expanding its existing operations.

Investing in the real economy: By investing capital over the long term the company aim to become leaders in direct investments whilst benefitting society through socially responsible investments.

Welfare reforms: the company want to help people take responsibility for their own financial security through insurance pensions and savings.

Technological innovation: Technology and innovative solutions improve customers' lives and increase efficiency. The company aim to be market leaders in the digital provision of insurance and other financial solutions.

Addressing climate change: L&G are able to support the fight against climate catastrophe through the positioning of its own investments L&G's influence as one of the world's largest asset managers and managing its own operational footprint.

HISTORY

The Legal in Legal & General's name comes from its founding mission — to provide life insurance to members of the legal profession. The company was started in 1836 by six lawyers as the Legal & General Life Assurance Society; its first customer solicitor Thomas Smith ill-manneredly died four years later after paying less than 200 pounds on a 1000-pound policy.

Throughout that century and into the next the company made loans to individuals and corporations; it also moved into real estate. After struggling under claims during WWI and the 1918 flu pandemic it moved into fire and accident coverage in 1920. It opened membership to nonlawyers in 1929. The company took over the UK operations of the US firm Metropolitan Life (MetLife) in 1933.

In 1934 Legal & General bought Gresham Life Assurance and Gresham Fire and Accident to gain a presence in Australia. During WWII the company was hit hard by German air attacks both physically (it had to relocate away from London for a time) and at the bottom line.

The postwar years were a time of expansion as the company moved into South Africa and also broadened its operations at home. In 1949 it moved into marine insurance and in 1956 inaugurated life insurance in Australia.

The company began expanding its product offerings in the 1970s with managed pension funds and retail unit trusts. It established a direct sales force for life and pensions in 1977. The company also formed alliances with several European insurance companies and sold its Gresham life subsidiary. In 1979 it formed Legal & General Group Limited as a holding company for its now-separate insurance international and investment management operations.

In 1981 Legal & General bought US auto insurer GEICO's two-thirds interest in Government Employees Life Insurance Company changing the subsidiary's name to Banner Life. Three years later it bought the Dutch operations of Unilife Assurance and created a subsidiary in the Netherlands. Despite all this activity however the company's performance during the 1980s was poor and it brought in David Prosser (who became CEO in 1991) to goose its asset management operations.

In 1989 the company bought William Penn Life Insurance from Continental Corp. and opened its first real estate agency — just in time for the real estate market crash. Legal & General and other mortgage guarantee insurers were also squeezed by the resulting increase in mortgage default rates as homebuyers were caught between high interest rates and high unemployment.

The company formed a joint venture with Woolwich Building Society to provide Woolwich customers with insurance products in 1995. The next year it followed the insurance industry trend by establishing a bank of its own.

With each succeeding merger of its rivals Legal & General became the target of rumors about its own fate. The company has remained adamantly independent with Prosser claiming that Legal & General could instead benefit by picking up business left behind by the new entities.

In 1998 the British insurance industry was stung by scandalous revelations regarding improper pension sales in the late 1980s and early 1990s. Legal & General set aside about $1 billion to compensate victims; it also sold its Australian operations. In 1999 banking company National Westminster and Legal & General talked takeover but the deal fell through. (NatWest was eventually bought by Royal Bank of Scotland.)

In 2001 Legal & General announced a deal with UK-based Barclays to provide the bank's customers with life insurance and pension products. In 2002 Legal & General extended its marketing agreement with UK financial services company Alliance & Leicester.

The company then discontinued its health insurance offerings and reduced its venture capital investment operations. In 2005 the company sold its Gresham Insurance subsidiary to Barclays Bank.

EXECUTIVES

Independent Non-Executive Director, Henrietta Baldock
Group Chief Executive Officer, Executive Director, Nigel Wilson, $1,249,213 total compensation
Non-Executive Independent Chairman of the Board, John Kingman
Group HR Director, Emma Hardaker-Jones
Group Chief Internal Auditor, Stephen Licence
Independent Non-Executive Director, Ric Lewis
Chief Executive Officer, Legal & General Retirement, Retail – elect, Andrew Kail
Non-Executive Independent Director, Nilufer Von Bismarck
Independent Non-Executive Director, George Lewis
Non-Executive Independent Director, Laura Wade-Gery
Group Corporate Affairs Director, John Godfrey
Group Chief Risk Officer, Simon Gadd
Chief Executive Officer, Legal & General Insurance, Bernie Hickman
Chief Executive Officer - Legal & General Retirement, Retail, Chris Knight
Chief Executive Officer - Legal & General Retirement, Institutional, Laura Mason
Auditors: KPMG LLP

LOCATIONS

HQ: Legal & General Group PLC (United Kingdom) One Coleman Street, London EC2R 5AA
Phone: (44) 20 3124 2000   **Fax:** (44) 20 3124 2500
Web: www.legalandgeneralgroup.com

PRODUCTS/OPERATIONS

2018 operating profit

	%
LGR (Retirement)	
LGR Retail	44
LGR Institutional	16
LGIM (Investment Management)	16
LGI (Insurance)	12
LGC (Capital)	12
Total	**100**

Selected Subsidiaries

Banner Life Insurance Company Inc - long-term business; US
First British American Reinsurance Company II - reinsurance; US
First British Bermudan Reinsurance Company II Limited - reinsurance; Bermuda
First British Vermont Reinsurance Company II - reinsurance; US
First British Vermont Reinsurance Company - reinsurance; US
Legal & General (France) SA - long-term business
Legal & General (Portfolio Management Services) Limited - institutional fund management
Legal & General (Unit Trust Managers) Limited - unit trust management
Legal & General Assurance (Pensions Management) Limited - long-term business
Legal & General Assurance Society Limited - long-term and general insurance
Legal & General Bank (France) SA - financial services
Legal & General Finance PLC1 - treasury operations
Legal & General Insurance Limited - general insurance
Legal & General International (Ireland) Limited - long-term business
Legal & General Investment Management America Inc - institutional fund management
Legal & General Investment Management Limited - institutional fund management
Legal & General Nederland Levensverzekering Maatschappij NV - long-term business; Netherlands
Legal & General Partnership Services Limited - provision of services
Legal & General Pensions Limited - reinsurance
Legal & General Property Limited - property management

Legal & General Resources Limited1 - provision of services
Legal & General Risques Divers (France) SA - insurance company
LGV Capital Limited - private equity
Nationwide Life Limited - long-term business
Suffolk Life Annuities Limited - long-term business
Suffolk Life Pensions Limited - long-term business
William Penn Life Insurance Company of New York Inc - long-term business; US

COMPETITORS

ABRDN PLC
ALDERMORE GROUP PLC
AMERICAN FINANCIAL GROUP INC.
CNO FINANCIAL GROUP INC.
INVESTEC PLC
ITAU UNIBANCO HOLDING SA
NIPPON LIFE INSURANCE COMPANY
SUFFOLK LIFE GROUP LIMITED
Shinhan Financial Group Co. Ltd.
THE HARTFORD FINANCIAL SERVICES GROUP INC.
VIRGIN MONEY HOLDINGS (UK) PLC

HISTORICAL FINANCIALS

Company Type: Public

Income Statement

FYE: December 31

	ASSETS ($ mil.)	NET INCOME ($ mil.)	INCOME AS % OF ASSETS	EMPLOYEES
12/20	778,655	2,193	0.3%	10,046
12/19	740,316	2,421	0.3%	8,542
12/18	628,826	2,332	0.4%	7,981
12/17	683,282	2,554	0.4%	7,629
12/16	575,526	1,547	0.3%	8,939
Annual Growth	7.9%	9.1%	—	3.0%

2020 Year-End Financials

Return on assets: 0.2%
Return on equity: 16.5%
Long-term debt ($ mil.): —
No. of shares (mil.): —
Sales ($ mil): 68,550
Dividends
Yield: 5.6%
Payout: 325.4%
Market value ($ mil.): —

	STOCK PRICE ($) FY Close	P/E High/Low	PER SHARE ($) Earnings	Dividends	Book Value
12/20	18.42	81 35	0.35	1.05	2.30
12/19	20.29	68 46	0.41	0.99	2.08
12/18	14.81	60 47	0.39	0.98	1.85
12/17	18.63	59 49	0.43	0.95	1.78
12/16	15.08	79 48	0.26	0.80	1.44
Annual Growth	5.1%	— —	7.7%	6.9%	12.4%

Lenovo Group Ltd

Lenovo Group tops the worldwide PC market ahead of HP Inc. and Dell Technologies and it operates competitive phone and server businesses. Through a series of acquisitions the Hong Kong-based company is focused on a bold vision to deliver smarter technology for all we are developing world-changing technologies that create a more inclusive trustworthy and sustainable digital society. Lenovo has resurrected the Motorola brand in smartphones. Besides ThinkPad-branded commercial PCs Lenovo turns out tablets and software. Its sales are evenly sourced from the major world markets of China Asia Pacific America and Europe-Middle East-Africa (EMEA).

Operations

Lenovo operates in two reportable segments: Intelligent Devices Group and Data Center Group.

Lenovo's Intelligent Devices Group includes the company's biggest business the PC and Smart Devices unit which accounts for about 80% of the company's revenue. It continues to lead the sector with record PC market share of nearly 25% continuing to extend its leadership as the #1 PC company in the world and with sustained industry-beating profitability. Intelligent Devices Group also includes the Mobile business which accounts for some 10% of revenue.

The Data Center Business Group about 10% of revenue offers servers storage networking software and services.

Geographic Reach

Lenovo's logistics teams work closely with logistics partners to ship products responsibly. Lighter and smaller products more compact and reusable packaging materials bulk shipping alternatives and regional distribution facilities allow for lighter loads load consolidation and full truckload shipments. The company sold less than 10% of its goods and services to its five largest customers. T he company spent $796 million in 2020 and $708 million in 2019 on advertising and promotional expenses.

Sales and Marketing

Lenovo rebranded itself under the tag line "Never Stand Still" marking its expansion in size and scope. The rebranding rollout included the company's first conference Lenovo Tech World held in Beijing where it brought users and developers together and touted new products.

Financial Performance

After sales dipped in 2016 and 2017 it rebounded back the next two years. Profits also bounced back in 2019 and 2020 after a loss in 2018.

In 2020 (ended March) revenue fell by about 1% to $50.7 billion almost the same as the record revenue in 2019. The unprecedented outbreak of COVID-19 and the subsequent factory shutdowns had a material impact on the Group's revenue which dropped 9.7 percent year-on-year in the last quarter of the fiscal year.

Profit jumped by 22% to $804.5 million in fiscal 2020 brought about by lesser cost of sales.

Lenovo had $3.6 billion in cash and equivalents in 2020 compared to $2.7 billion from the year before. In 2020 operations generated $2.2 billion investing activities used $957 million and financing activities used another $238 million.

Strategy

Lenovo continues to execute its strategy to be the leader and enabler of Intelligent Transformation. The company has the vision of bringing smarter technology to all ? through Smart Infrastructure Smart Verticals and Smart IoT. This "3S" strategy in parallel with its customer-centric positioning has led to a higher Software and Services attach rate. The Software and Services business is considered a strong long-term growth catalyst for profitable growth.

Smart infrastructure provides the computing storage and networking power to support smart devices. The company launched its next-generation data center solutions in SDI and expects it to remain a future growth catalyst. These new solutions which include collaboration with several partners based on the ThinkAgile platform have grown revenue at a double-digits rate during the fiscal year under review.

The company will continue to invest in Smart IoT consisting of a network of many touchpoints for the connected world we live in. Specifically the Lenovo's investments will accelerate in the area of edge computing cloud big data and AI in vertical industries to deepen its strategic transformation and further accentuate its core competencies. These investments aim to strengthen the company's capability as a competitive end-to-end solution provider in the era of Intelligent Transformation.

Mergers and Acquisitions

In the last two years Lenovo has made acquisitions to beef up its hardware offerings and support expansion in select markets. In 2014 it paid more than $5 billion to acquire two new major product lines. First it bought IBM's low-end x86 server business for $2.3 billion.

Also in 2014 Lenovo spent some $2.9 billion for Motorola Mobility from Google. As part of the deal Lenovo owns the brands Moto X Moto G and the DROID Ultra series while Google retained the patent portfolio.

Company Background

Liu Chuanzhi an engineer at the Chinese Academy of Sciences who wrote industry research reports established Legend Group Holdings Co. in 1984 in Beijing. Backed by a modest investment from the academy Liu who went on to become something of an entrepreneurial hero in China and 10 other engineers were given a green light to form a retail business. They first bought and sold items ranging from TVs to roller skates but later focused on distributing computer products and eventually moved into manufacturing PCs for AST Research. Legend introduced its first proprietary product a Chinese character system for PCs in 1985.

In 1988 the company formed Legend Holdings Limited which was originally a Hong Kong-based PC distributor. The following year the parent company began designing and manufacturing motherboards and added systems integration services to its offerings. In 1990 China reduced import tariffs a move that opened the trade door for companies such as IBM and Compaq. That year Legend Group Holdings began making its own brand of PCs.

In the 2000s Lenovo bought computer and mobile phone operations from US companies and became the top PC maker.

HISTORY

Liu Chuanzhi an engineer at the Chinese Academy of Sciences who wrote industry research reports established Legend Group Holdings Co. in 1984 in Beijing. Backed by a modest investment from the academy Liu who went on to become something of an entrepreneurial hero in China and 10 other engineers were given a green light to form a retail business. They first bought and sold items ranging from TVs to roller skates but later focused on distributing computer products and eventually moved into manufacturing PCs for AST Research. Legend introduced its first proprietary product a Chinese character system for PCs in 1985.

In 1988 the company formed Legend Holdings Limited which was originally a Hong Kong-based PC distributor. The following year the parent company began designing and manufacturing motherboards and added systems integration services to its offerings. In 1990 China reduced import tariffs a move that opened the trade door for companies such as IBM and Compaq. That year Legend Group Holdings began making its own brand of PCs.

Legend Holdings went public in 1994 and the following year began absorbing operations from its parent company which retained approximately 60% ownership in the subsidiary. By 1996 it was tied with IBM for PC market share in China; it became the country's top brand the following year.

In 1998 parent company Legend Group Holdings transferred Beijing Legend Group to its Hong Kong-based subsidiary. The following year Microsoft looking to extend its operating system dominance into China teamed up with Legend Holdings to create set-top boxes. In 2000 the company partnered with Pacific Century CyberWorks to provide broadband Internet services. The following year Legend spun off its distribution business Digital China as a separate public company. In 2001 Yang Yuanqing was named CEO of the company.

In 2002 Legend Holdings changed its English company name to Legend Group Limited. The company launched a corporate brand Lenovo the following year and in 2004 it officially adopted Lenovo as its English name. It also sold its non-telecom IT services business to AsiaInfo Holdings renamed AsiaInfo-Linkage in 2004.

Lenovo acquired IBM's worldwide PC operations for approximately $1.75 billion in 2005. IBM executive Stephen Ward was named CEO of Lenovo at the time of the merger but he was replaced by William Amelio before year's end. Amelio headed Dell's Asia/Pacific operations before joining Lenovo. In 2006 Lenovo launched a unit called Lenovo Services.

In 2007 Lenovo stopped using the IBM PC brand to which it still held the rights and began offering only Lenovo-branded machines. The following year it sponsored and supported the Olympic Summer Games in Beijing providing more than 30000 pieces of equipment and 600 engineers.

Looking to focus on its core PC operations Lenovo sold its mobile phone business Lenovo Mobile Communications to Hony Capital in 2008. Hony the private equity arm of Legend Holdings paid $100 million for the unit.

A year later Lenovo bought back the mobile communications business for about $200 million in cash and stock. The company cited the growth of the mobile Internet market and the increasing convergence between the PC and wireless handset sectors for the about-face in product strategy. Lenovo's move came as Dell introduced a mobile phone for the Chinese market.

Citing a flagging economy Lenovo announced a restructuring plan in 2009 that included a workforce reduction of 11% executive pay cuts and the consolidation of its China and the Asia/Pacific units. The company also initiated a management shakeup including its chairman taking over as CEO. The change may in part have reflected a strategy shift for Lenovo. With corporate spending flagging particularly in the US the company planned to focus on China and other emerging markets with an emphasis on consumers.

EXECUTIVES

Executive Chairman of the Board, Chief Executive Officer, Yuanqing Yang, $1,301,000 total compensation
Senior Vice President, President of Lenovo Capital, Zhiqiang He
Executive Vice President and Chief Financial Officer, Wai Ming Wong
Executive Vice President and President - China Geography, Jun Liu
Senior Vice President, Chief Strategy Officer, and Chief Marketing Officer, Gina Qiao
Senior Vice President and Chief Technology Officer, Yong Rui
Senior Vice President, Human Resources, Lan Gao
Non-Executive Director, Linghuan Zhao
Senior Vice President and President, North America Intelligent Devices Group, Matthew Zielinski
Executive Vice President and President, Data Center Group, Kirk Skaugen

Senior Vice President and Chief Legal Officer, Laura Quatela
Auditors: PricewaterhouseCoopers

LOCATIONS

HQ: Lenovo Group Ltd
23rd Floor, Lincoln House, Taikoo Place, 979 King's Road, Quarry Bay,
Phone: (852) 2590 0228   **Fax:** (852) 2516 5384
Web: www.lenovo.com

2018 Sales

	$ mil.	% of total
Americas (AG)	16,413	31
Europe Middle east & Africa (EMEA)	12,502	28
China	12,357	25
Asia Pacific (AP)	9,764	16
Total	**51,037**	**100**

PRODUCTS/OPERATIONS

2019 Sales

	% of total
Personal Computers & Smart Devices	75
Mobile Business	13
Data Center Group	12
Total	**100**

Product Categories

Laptops
Desktops & All-in-Ones
Smartphones
Tablet PCs
Network Storage
Workstations
Accessories & Upgrades

COMPETITORS

Acer Incorporated
BIGBEN INTERACTIVE
CDW CORPORATION
COMPUTACENTER PLC
DELL INC.
FLEX LTD.

KINGSTON TECHNOLOGY COMPANY INC.
NORTHAMBER PLC
SPEED COMMERCE INC.
TECH DATA CORPORATION

HISTORICAL FINANCIALS

Company Type: Public

Income Statement

FYE: March 31

	REVENUE ($ mil.)	NET INCOME ($ mil.)	NET PROFIT MARGIN	EMPLOYEES
03/21	60,742	1,178	1.9%	71,500
03/20	50,716	665	1.3%	63,000
03/19	51,037	596	1.2%	57,000
03/18	45,349	(189)	—	54,000
03/17	43,034	535	1.2%	52,000
Annual Growth	**9.0%**	**21.8%**	—	**8.3%**

2021 Year-End Financials

Debt ratio: 10.5%
Return on equity: 45.1%
Cash ($ mil.): 3,068
Current ratio: 0.85
Long-term debt ($ mil.): 3,299

No. of shares (mil.): —
Dividends
Yield: 2.4%
Payout: 768.7%
Market value ($ mil.): —

	STOCK PRICE ($) FY Close	P/E High/Low	PER SHARE ($) Earnings	Dividends	Book Value
03/21	28.58	300107	0.09	0.68	0.23
03/20	10.71	341171	0.05	0.68	0.20
03/19	17.99	370182	0.05	0.64	0.22
03/18	10.25	— —	(0.02)	0.64	0.28
03/17	13.13	346234	0.05	0.64	0.27
Annual Growth	**21.5%**	— —	**16.4%**	**1.6%**	**(3.8%)**

Leonardo SpA

Italy's largest engineering and aerospace/defense group Leonardo (formerly Leonardo-Finmeccanica) makes helicopters military aircraft defense systems satellites and much more. The company's US-based DRS Technologies provides infrared technology persistent surveillance battle management satellite networks communications infrastructures and other technologies. Other operations make sensors defensive aids tracking targeting navigation simulation avionics logistics automation and other products. It works closely with the Italian British Polish and American militaries its biggest customers; the Italian government owns around 30% of Leonardo. About 85% of its revenue comes from outside of Italy.

Operations

Leonardo operates through Defense Electronics & Security (about 45%) Helicopters (some 30%) and Aeronautics (nearly 25%) Space and Other Activities (around 5%).

Defense Electronics & Security composed of two divisions: Electronics Division and Cyber Security Division. Electronic Division designs and develops airborne land and naval applications from advanced components to fully integrated ISRC4I ISTAR solutions; combat and mission management systems tactical unmanned systems radar communications electronic warfare optronics infrared search and track artillery underwater systems air and maritime traffic management automation systems and space payloads and equipment. Cyber Security Division designs develops and produces a competitive solutions and services for cybersecurity and homeland security critical infrastructure protection transportation.

Helicopters segment designs develops produces customer supports and markets an extensive range of helicopters from the 1.8 tons single-engine to the 16 tons three-engine.

Aeronautics designs develops produces logistics support for trainers combat and tactical transport aircraft multi-role and regional turboprop aircraft and unmanned systems.

Space designs and develops integrated satellite systems management of satellite communication networks and development of geo-information and Earth observation applications: Leonardo provides a full offer which includes sensors payloads advanced robotics systems solutions and services.

Leonardo participates in a number of joint ventures particularly with Thales (Telespazio Group and Thales Alenia Space Group) to develop satellite services and systems; and with Airbus (GIE ATP and MBDA Group) for the development of regional turboprop aircraft and missiles.

Geographic Reach

Based in Rome Leonardo has direct operations in Italy the UK Poland and the US. Outside those companies Leonardo operates through a network of subsidiaries joint ventures and strategic collaborations reaching customers in more than 150 countries.

Leonardo's most prominent sources of revenue are North America (nearly 30%) Italy (around 15%) the UK (about 10%) and Europe (excl. Italy and UK) nearly 25%. All other countries account for the remaining above 20%.

Sales and Marketing

Leonardo's main customers are national governments or public institutions.

Financial Performance

Note: Growth rates may differ after conversion to US Dollars.

In 2019 Leonardo's sales grew 13% to ?13.8 billion which was mainly attributable to an increase in sales from the Defence Electronics & Security and Aeronautics Divisions.

Net income climbed 61% to ?822 million due largely to higher revenue and lower non-recurring charges and restructuring costs.

Leonardo's cash on hand decreased by ?87 million during 2019 ending the year at ?2.0 billion. The company's operations generated ?645 million partially offset by ?466 million used in investing and ?262 million used in financing activities. Leonardo's main cash uses in 2019 were for investments in property plant and equipment and intangible assets and for bond redemption.

Strategy

The aim of the management of technological and product research in Leonardo is to ensure constant ongoing equilibrium between technological enhancement projects whose objectives are to develop technologies competencies and products with a medium- to long-term impact on one hand and to improve existing products on the other. In order to seize the best opportunities also on the basis of different TRLs (Technology Readiness Levels) Leonardo's technological strategy is to involve various other players in an Open Innovation scenario such as the major national and international universities and research centers and innovative start-ups and SMEs as well as to collaborate with other industrial players within the scope of financed projects.

In 2019 Leonardo invested about 11% of its revenues in R&D involving about 9000 highly qualified human resources (engineering graduates mostly in aeronautics aerospace electronics mechanics IT and telecommunications physics in addition to specialist technicians). These resources belong to its engineering departments and divisional facilities responsible for both technological and product innovation allocated to the following areas of competence: Technology Office Management Engineering Management System Engineering Aeronautic Engineering Mechanical Engineering Electronics Engineering Software Engineering and Verification and Validation Engineering.

The Group also takes part in regional domestic and European Research and Innovation projects and funding programs. The regional and domestic initiatives include the Italian Technology Clusters (Leonardo holds the chairmanship of the "National Aerospace Technology Cluster") and the Regional Technology Districts.

Mergers and Acquisitions

In 2020 Leonardo acquired Kopter Group AG (Kopter) from Lynwood (Schweiz). The purchase price on a cash and debt free basis consists of a $185 million fixed component plus an earn-out mechanism linked to certain milestones over the life of the programme starting from 2022. The acquisition of Kopter allows Leonardo to further strengthen its worldwide leadership and position in the rotorcraft sector in line with the Industrial Plan's objectives for the reinforcement of the core businesses.

EXECUTIVES

New Business Development and Country Support Director, Enrico Peruzzi
Customer Support, Services and Training Director, Zaira Burlo
Chief Procurement & Supply Chain Officer, Giacinto Carullo
Italian Institutional Affairs Director, Filippo Grasso
Chief Commercial Officer and Chief Executive Officer of Leonardo International, Pasquale Di Bartolomeo
Non-Executive Independent Director, Maurizio Pinnaro
Communication Director, Stefano Amoroso

Managing Director - Electronic Division, Chairman and Managing Director of Leonardo MW Ltd, Norman Bone
Chief Executive Officer, Executive Director, Alessandro Profumo
Chief People, Organization and Transformation Officer, Simonetta Iarlori
Chief Financial Officer, Alessandra Genco
Non-Executive Independent Director, Paola Giannetakis
Non-Executive Independent Director, Ferruccio Resta
Non-Executive Independent Director, Patrizia Giangualano
Chief Security Officer, Andrea Salpietro
Coordinator - Space Activities and Chief Executive Officer - Telespazio, Luigi Pasquali
Managing Director - Helicopters Division, Gian Cutillo
Chief Strategic Equity Officer, Giovanni Soccodato
Non-Executive Director, Elena Comparato
Chief Executive Officer - Leonardo DRS, William Lynn
Non-Executive Independent Director, Dario Frigerio
Non-Executive Independent Director, Marina Rubini
General Manager, Lucio Valerio Cioffi
Chief Audit Executive, Marco Di Capua
Manufacturing and Program Management Optimization Director, Fabio Barsotti
Chief Risk Officer, Salvatore Lampone
Senior Vice President, Unmanned Systems, Laurent Sissmann
Group General Counsel, Andrea Parrella
Managing Director - Aerostructures Division, Giancarlo Schisano
Managing Director - Cyber Security Division, Tommaso Profeta
Non-Executive Chairman of the Board, Luciano Carta
Non-Executive Independent Director, Federica Guidi
Non-Executive Independent Director, Pierfrancesco Barletta
Non-Executive Independent Director, Carmine America
Auditors: KPMG S.p.A.

LOCATIONS

HQ: Leonardo SpA
  Piazza Monte Grappa 4, Rome
Phone: (39) 06 324 731   **Fax:** (39) 06 320 8621
Web: www.leonardocompany.com

2018 Sales

	% of total
Europe	
Italy	15
UK	11
Rest of Europe	25
North America	8
Rest of the world	21
Total	**100**

PRODUCTS/OPERATIONS

2018 Sales

	% of total
Defense & Security Electronics	46
Helicopters	29
Aeronautics	22
Other activities	3
Space	-
Eliminations	-
Total	**100**

Selected Products

Defense electronics
  Air traffic management
  Avionics
  Command and control systems
  Communications equipment
  Electronic systems
  Radar
  Simulators
  Unmanned aerial vehicles
Helicopters
  A109 Light Utility Helicopter
  A109 Power
  A119 Koala
  A129
  AW139
  BA609
  EH 101
  Grand Light Utility Helicopter
  NH90
  Super Lynx 300
Aeronautics
  Control surfaces
  Fuselage components
  Horizontal stabilizers
  Mechanical parts
  Winglet
Transportation
  Chopper and inverter drives
  Converters
  DC AC and multi-voltage locomotives
  DC and AC motors
  Electric multiple units
  High-speed trains
  Light and heavy metropolitan railways
  Trambuses
  Trolley buses
Defense systems
  Airborne and naval weaponry
  Armored vehicles
  Main battle tanks
  Missile systems
  Naval systems
  Weapons systems
Energy
  Boilers
  Cogeneration plants
  Combined cycle generators
  Geothermal generators
  Hydrogenerators
  Nuclear power plants
  Steam and gas turbines
  Turbogas generators
Space
  Modules
  Satellites

Selected Operations

Alenia Aermacchi
Alenia Aeronautica (aerospace)
SELEX Sistemi Integrati SpA (formerly Alenia Marconi Systems)
Ansaldo Energia (energy)
AgustaWestland (helicopters)
DRS Technologies (military data systems)
MBDA (25% with EADS and BAE SYSTEMS)

COMPETITORS

AEROVIRONMENT INC.
EXELIS INC.
KAMAN CORPORATION
KAWASAKI HEAVY INDUSTRIES LTD.
KRATOS DEFENSE & SECURITY SOLUTIONS INC.
L3HARRIS TECHNOLOGIES INC.
LATECOERE
MERCURY SYSTEMS INC.
TEXTRON INC.
THE BOEING COMPANY

HISTORICAL FINANCIALS

Company Type: Public

Income Statement

FYE: December 31

	REVENUE ($ mil.)	NET INCOME ($ mil.)	NET PROFIT MARGIN	EMPLOYEES
12/19	15,476	921	6.0%	49,530
12/18	14,017	582	4.2%	46,462
12/17	13,818	326	2.4%	45,134
12/16	12,672	533	4.2%	45,631
12/15	14,154	530	3.7%	47,156
Annual Growth	**2.3%**	**14.8%**	**—**	**1.2%**

2019 Year-End Financials

Debt ratio: 20.9%
Return on equity: 16.7%
Cash ($ mil.): 2,202
Current ratio: 0.94
Long-term debt ($ mil.): 4,463
No. of shares (mil.): 578
Dividends
  Yield: 0.0%
  Payout: 3.1%
Market value ($ mil.): 3,353

	STOCK PRICE ($) FY Close	P/E High	P/E Low	PER SHARE ($) Earnings	PER SHARE ($) Dividends	PER SHARE ($) Book Value
12/19	5.80	5	3	1.60	0.05	10.34
12/18	4.33	7	5	1.02	0.05	8.96
12/17	5.97	20	12	0.57	0.05	9.32
12/16	7.01	8	5	0.93	0.00	8.01
12/15	6.91	8	4	0.99	0.00	8.07
Annual Growth	**(4.3%)**	**—**	**—**	**12.9%**	**—**	**6.4%**

Lewis (John) Partnership Plc (United Kingdom)

Diversified retailer John Lewis Partnership (JLP) is Britain's greatest purveyor of the middle-class lifestyle. JLP operates two major upmarket retail businesses: John Lewis the department store chain that provides homeware clothing and electronics; and Waitrose one of the UK's largest supermarket chains. The company's department stores number is more than 40 while it runs 335 Waitrose branches. John Lewis operates an e-commerce site while Waitrose partners carry out home delivery. John Lewis Partnership is owned by its 80000 staff or partners.

Operations

The company's Waitrose business operates some 335 branches Waitrose also operates Waitrose farm which supplies its own shops with milk flour cox cider apple juice and sparkling wine among others. Sales from Waitrose constitute about 65% of total group revenue.

JLP's more than 40 department stores stock a wide range of home and garden products for essentially all conceivable purposes; clothing for men women and children including own-brand and designer goods; and electricals from personal items like tablets and wearable tech via television and audio to large electrical appliances like coffee machines fridges and washing machines. The company's department store activities account for more than 35% of revenue.

About 65% of sales were generated from groceries about 15% generated from EHT and over 10% came from home and fashion each.

Geographic Reach

London-based JLP operates mainly within the UK where it has more than 40 department stores and 335 Waitrose stores.

Sales and Marketing

The company follows a multichannel approach to selling its products; these include shops and online shops.

Financial Performance

Note: Growth rates may differ after conversion to US Dollars.

In fiscal 2020 revenue slid almost 2% coming in at 10.2 billion as sales from Waitrose and John Lewis fell.

The company increased its profits by 40% to 108.4 million. The increase in profit was due to lower cost of sale and an exceptional item of 107.4 million.

Net cash and cash equivalents at the end of the year was 598.3 million. Net cash generated from operating activities was 514.2 million while cash used in investing and financing activities were 209.8 million and 422.9 million respectively. Main cash uses were for purchases of property plant and equipment intangible assets and payment of debts.

Strategy

In October 2020 the company unveiled its five-year self-funding Partnership Plan. It positions Waitrose and John Lewis as the go-to brands for customers who want quality value and sustainability and was the result of seven months' work where it listened to feedback from more than 10000 customers over 100 suppliers and local community groups and 12000 Partners who submitted more than 650 ideas.

The nature of the Partnership model allows it to invest with a longer-term perspective than a conventional business even in challenging times and amidst a very uncertain economic outlook. With this in mind its five-year plan is self-funding and takes into account uncertain trading. The Partnership Plan sees its business continuing to adapt rapidly to changing shopping habits getting closer to customers online and in-store. It will also expand in new areas where it believes its values can be a force for good.

The Plan aims to see the John Lewis Partnership reach 400m profit by year 5; Expansion of digital virtual and delivery services to get closer to customers; Inspirational new services and partnerships to rebalance business beyond retail; Pledge to recruit young people coming out of the care system; and Major commitments on cutting waste and net zero carbon.

Company Background

Founded in 1864 by John Lewis JLP became a partnership in 1929 when Lewis' son Spedan created a trust to own the company. All of the company's 85500 employees (called partners) are beneficiaries of the trust and as such receive unique perks as well as a share of the profits. A system of committees and councils made up of partners vote to determine the company's direction — and trustees. The Leckford Farm which supplies Waitrose supermarkets is also available for partners to use as a retreat.

EXECUTIVES

Chairman, Sharon White
Operations Director, Bérang re Michel
Executive Director - Operations, Andrew Murphy
Executive Director - People, Nikki Humphrey
Deputy Chairman, Rita Clifton
Auditors: KPMG LLP

LOCATIONS

HQ: Lewis (John) Partnership Plc (United Kingdom)
  171 Victoria Street, London SW1E 5NN
Phone: (44) 207 828 1000
Web: www.johnlewispartnership.co.uk

PRODUCTS/OPERATIONS

2013 Stores

	No.
Waitrose supermarkets	255
Waitrose convenience	35
John Lewis department stores	30
John Lewis at home	9
Total	**329**

2013 Sales

	% of total
Waitrose	64
John Lewis	36
Total	**100**

Selected Subsidiaries

Greenbee (travel leisure and financial services)
Herbert Parkinson Limited (weaving and making up)
JLP Holdings BV (investment holding company Holland)
JLP Insurance Limited (insurance Guernsey)
JPL Scottish Limited Partnership (investment holding undertaking)
JPL Scottish Partnership (investment holding undertaking)
JLP Victoria Limited (investment holding company)
John Lewis Properties plc (property holding company)
Waitrose Limited (food retailing)
Waitrose (Guernsey) Limited (food retailing Guernsey)
Waitrose (Jersey) Limited (food retailing Jersey)

COMPETITORS

BLEACH GROUP INC.
CASEY'S GENERAL STORES INC.
CECONOMY AG
CHRISTIE GROUP PLC
CO-OPERATIVE GROUP LIMITED
E.H.BOOTH & CO.LIMITED
GROCERY OUTLET INC.
HEART OF ENGLAND CO-OPERATIVE SOCIETY LIMITED
INNERWORKINGS INC.
J SAINSBURY PLC
MARTIN MCCOLL LIMITED
NEXT FIFTEEN COMMUNICATIONS GROUP PLC
NEXT PLC
OCADO GROUP PLC
PENNSYLVANIA REAL ESTATE INVESTMENT TRUST
SPROUTS FARMERS MARKET INC.
SUPERDRY PLC
TESCO PLC
VIAD CORP
WAKEFERN FOOD CORP.

HISTORICAL FINANCIALS

Company Type: Public

Income Statement				FYE: January 25
	REVENUE ($ mil.)	NET INCOME ($ mil.)	NET PROFIT MARGIN	EMPLOYEES
01/20	20,286	216	1.1%	80,800
01/19	20,616	154	0.7%	83,900
01/18	20,391	148	0.7%	85,500
01/17	20,036	706	3.5%	86,700
01/16	19,481	446	2.3%	91,500
Annual Growth	1.0%	(16.5%)	—	(3.1%)

2020 Year-End Financials

Debt ratio: 19.7%	No. of shares (mil.): 0
Return on equity: 4.2%	Dividends
Cash ($ mil.): 1,195	Yield: —
Current ratio: 1.00	Payout: —
Long-term debt ($ mil.): 1,437	Market value ($ mil.): —

Lewis (John) Plc (United Kingdom)

Auditors: KPMG LLP

LOCATIONS

HQ: Lewis (John) Plc (United Kingdom)
  171 Victoria Street, London SW1E 5NN
Phone:
Web: www.johnlewispartnership.co.uk

HISTORICAL FINANCIALS

Company Type: Public

Income Statement				FYE: January 25
	REVENUE ($ mil.)	NET INCOME ($ mil.)	NET PROFIT MARGIN	EMPLOYEES
01/20	20,286	215	1.1%	80,800
01/19	20,616	151	0.7%	83,900
01/18	20,391	143	0.7%	85,500
01/17	20,036	705	3.5%	86,700
01/16	19,481	444	2.3%	91,500
Annual Growth	1.0%	(16.6%)	—	(3.1%)

2020 Year-End Financials

Debt ratio: 72.4%	No. of shares (mil.): 6
Return on equity: 4.1%	Dividends
Cash ($ mil.): 1,195	Yield: —
Current ratio: 1.00	Payout: —
Long-term debt ($ mil.): 5,431	Market value ($ mil.): —

LG Display Co Ltd

LG Display manufactures TFT-LCD and OLED technology-based display panels in a broad range of sizes and specifications primarily for use in IT products (comprising notebook computers desktop monitors and tablet computers) televisions and mobile devices including smartphones and it is one of the world's leading suppliers of large-sized OLED television panels. It also manufactures display panels for industrial and other applications including entertainment systems automotive displays portable navigation devices and medical diagnostic equipment. LG Electronics is LG Display's biggest shareholder as well as one of its biggest customers. Most of LG Display's sales are made to China.

Operations

LG Display sells through three product categories. The company's biggest product IT products accounts for over 40% of revenue. The mobile and other applications product category supplies more than some 30% of revenue and television provides nearly 30% of revenue.

Geographic Reach

Headquartered in Korea LG Display gets about 70% of revenue from sales to customers in China. Customers in other Asian countries comprise of approximately 10% of revenue and in Korea accounts for about 5% of revenue. The remaining revenues are from customers in the US (about 10%) Europe (more than 5%) and Poland (almost 5%).

Sales and Marketing

LG Display sells through direct sales to end-brand customers and their system integrators and overseas subsidiaries. The company also sells through its affiliated trading company LG International and its subsidiaries.

Sales to LG Electronics account for around 20% of revenue while LG Display's 10 biggest customers supply a significant majority of its sales.

Advertising expenses for the year ended in 2020 and 2019 were 114 billion Korean Won and 193 billion Korean Won respectively.

Financial Performance

The company increased by 3% from ?23.5 trillion in 2019 to ?24.2 trillion (US$22.3 billion) in 2020. The increase in revenue resulted from increases in revenue derived from sales of panels for IT products and mobile and other applications which were in turn mainly due to increases in the number of panels sold for IT products and the average selling price of mobile and other applications offset in part by a decrease in revenue derived from sales of panels for televisions.

In 2020 the company had a net loss of ?70.6 billion a ?2.8 trillion improvement from the previous year.

The company's cash at the end of 2020 was ?2.4 trillion. Operating activities generated ?2.3 trillion while investing activities used ?2.3 trillion mainly for acquisition of property plant and equipment. Financing activities provided another ?931 billion.

Strategy

In connection with its strategy to further enhance the diversity and capacity of its display panel production the company anticipates that it will continue to incur significant capital expenditures for the construction of new production facilities and the maintenance and enhancement of existing production facilities particularly in connection with its continued investments in OLED technology. LG's significant recent and pending capital expenditures include:

In response to and in anticipation of growing demand in the China market in July 2017 the company announced their plan to establish a joint venture with the government of Guangzhou to construct a new fabrication facility to manufacture next generation large-sized OLED panels which was established under the name of LG Display High-Tech (China) Co. Ltd. in July 2018. LG currently holds a 70% ownership interest in the joint venture and the government of Guangzhou holds the remaining 30% ownership interest. The company has invested approximately ?6.0 trillion in capital expenditures for the joint venture and commenced mass production of large-sized OLED panels at such fabrication facility in July 2020.

Company Background

LG Display was formed in 1999 when LG Electronics and Philips merged their LCD businesses. Philips no longer owns any part of LG Display.

EXECUTIVES

Vice President, Hyeong Seok Choi
Director, Yeong Su Gwon
Chief Financial Officer, Managing Director, Director, Dong Hui Seo
President, Chief Executive Officer, Director, Ho Yeong Jung
Managing Director, Hyeon Cheol Choi
Managing Director, Jong Wu Kim
Managing Director, Yeong Geun Choi
Managing Director, Tae Seung Kim
Non-Executive Independent Director, Geun Tae Han
Non-Executive Independent Director, Seong Sik Hwang
Auditors: KPMG Samjong Accounting Corp.

LOCATIONS

HQ: LG Display Co Ltd
LG Twin Towers, 128 Yeoui-daero, Yeongdeungpo-gu, Seoul 07336
Phone: (82) 2 3777 1010   **Fax:** (82) 2 3777 0793
Web: www.lgdisplay.com

2017 Sales

	% of total
Asia/Pacific	
China	65
Other countries	8
Korea	7
Europe	9
Americas	10
Poland	1
Total	**100**

PRODUCTS/OPERATIONS

2017 Sales

	% of total
Televisions	42
Desktop monitors	16
Tablet products	9
Notebook computers	8
Mobile and others	25
Total	**100**

Products Selected

TV Display
Commercial Display
Monitor Display
Notebook Display
Mobile Display
Auto Display
IPS
AIT
Transparent flexible display
3D
OLED Light

COMPETITORS

ADVANCED ENERGY INDUSTRIES INC.	PULSE ELECTRONICS CORPORATION
ALPS ALPINE CO. LTD.	SOLID STATE PLC
APC TECHNOLOGY GROUP PLC	SONIM INC.
CONTROL4 CORPORATION	Samsung Electronics Co. Ltd.
INVENTEC CORPORATION	
NITTO DENKO CORPORATION	Silicom Ltd.
PHOTRONICS INC.	TDK CORPORATION
PLANAR SYSTEMS INC.	VICOR CORPORATION
	ZYTRONIC PLC

HISTORICAL FINANCIALS

Company Type: Public

Income Statement   FYE: December 31

	REVENUE ($ mil.)	NET INCOME ($ mil.)	NET PROFIT MARGIN	EMPLOYEES
12/20	22,263	(82)	—	63,360
12/19	20,331	(2,450)	—	60,429
12/18	21,828	(185)	—	30,438
12/17	26,066	1,690	6.5%	33,335
12/16	22,061	754	3.4%	32,118
Annual Growth	0.2%	—	—	18.5%

2020 Year-End Financials

Debt ratio: 0.0%	No. of shares (mil.): 357
Return on equity: (-0.7%)	Dividends
Cash ($ mil.): 3,948	Yield: —
Current ratio: 1.01	Payout: —
Long-term debt ($ mil.): 10,078	Market value ($ mil.): 3,020

	STOCK PRICE ($) FY Close	P/E High/Low		PER SHARE ($) Earnings	Dividends	Book Value
12/20	8.44	— —		(0.23)	0.00	29.28
12/19	6.94	— —		(6.85)	0.00	27.45
12/18	8.19	— —		(0.52)	0.23	35.04
12/17	13.76	0 0		4.73	0.23	37.68
12/16	12.85	0 0		2.11	0.21	30.14
Annual Growth	(10.0%)	— —		—	—	(0.7%)

LG Electronics Inc

LG Electronics is a world-class company with innovative technologies in the fields of electronics and home appliances making products found in the kitchen in the media room and on the go. A leader in consumer electronics mobile communications and home appliances LGE operates in some 130 business sites worldwide that design and make flat panel TVs audio and video products mobile handsets air conditioners washing machines refrigerators and more. About a third of LG Electronics is owned by South Korea's LG Corp. Majority of its sales were generated from outside its home country Korea.

Operations

The company operates in six operating segments: Home Appliance & Air Solutions (H&A) Home entertainment (HE) Innotek Vehicle components solutions (VS) Business solutions (BS) Mobile communications (MC) and Other.

Home Appliances & Air Solutions with some 35% of revenue manufactures and sells refrigerators washing machines vacuum cleaners and residential and commercial air conditioners. Home Entertainment segment which accounts for around 20% of revenue manufactures and sells TVs monitors and digital media products.

Innotek (some 15%) operates LED optics solutions substrate materials and automotive components businesses. Vehicle Solutions segment (about 10%) designs and manufactures automobile parts. Business Solutions segment (nearly 10%) manufactures and sells information display solar panels and others. Mobile Communication segment (about 10%) manufactures and sells mobile communications equipment.

Overall sales of goods account for over 95% of sales.

Geographic Reach

LG Electronics is based in Seoul South Korea. Approximately 35% of sales were generated in Korea followed by North America with some 25% Europe with around 15% and Asia with some 10%. Other major markets are South America Middle East & Africa and China.

Financial Performance

The company's revenue for fiscal 2020 increased to ?9.6 trillion compared to ?8.3 trillion in the prior year.

Profit for fiscal 2020 increased to ?236.1 billion compared with ?102.3 million in the prior year.

Cash held by the company at the end of fiscal 2020 increased to ?5.9 trillion. Cash provided by operations was ?4.6 trillion while investing and financing activities used ?2.3 trillion and ?993.9 billion respectively. Main cash uses were acquisitions and repayments of borrowings.

Mergers and Acquisitions

In 2021 LG Electronics' (LG) has approved the acquisition of Cybellum a leading vehicle cybersecurity risk assessment solution provider based in

Tel Aviv. The deal allows LG to assume an approximate 64 percent stake in the tech company valued at USD 140 million a strategic move that will enhance LG's cybersecurity capabilities and accelerate its efforts to become an Innovation Partner for Future Mobility.

In early 2021 LG Electronics (LG) and Alphonso announced a significant investment by LG in Alphonso to bring together the two TV industry leaders' technologies and innovations to LG's smart TV lineup. With this investment of nearly USD 80 million LG will become Alphonso's largest investor with a controlling stake of more than 50 percent. LG has made understanding customer tastes and consumer trends one of its highest priorities as part of its digital transformation strategy to deliver better customized services. LG plans to utilize Alphonso software and services ? including Alphonso's data analytics media planning and activation and Video AI capabilities ? with its broad range of home entertainment products.

EXECUTIVES

President of Vehicle Component Solutions Company, Jin Yong Kim
Co-President, Sun Hwang Gwon
Co-Chief Executive Officer, Chief Financial Officer, Vice President, Director, Du Yong Bae
Vice President, Seung Geol Song
Vice President, Yeon Mo Lee
Vice President, Gyeong Ho Kim
Auditors: Samil Accounting Corporation (A Member Firm of PircewaterhouseCoopers)

LOCATIONS

HQ: LG Electronics Inc
LG Twin Towers, 128 Yeouido-dong, Yeongdeungpo-gu, Seoul 07336
Phone: (82) 2 3777 1114   **Fax:** (82) 2 3777 3428
Web: www.lge.com

2017 Sales

	% of total
Korea	33
North America	275
Asia	11
Europe	10
South America	7
Middle East & Africa	5
China	4
Other	3
Total	**100**

PRODUCTS/OPERATIONS

2017 Sales

	% of total
Home Appliance & Air Solution	31
Home Entertainment	30
Mobile communications	19
Innotek	11
Vehicle components	6
Other	3
Total	**100**

Selected Major Products & Services

Home Entertainment (LCD TVs plasma TVs audio video & optical storage)
Mobile Communication (mobile handsets mobile accessory)
Home Appliance & Air Solution (washing machines refrigerators cooking appliances vacuum cleaners built-in appliances air conditioners and air purifiers)
Business Solutions (monitors commercial displays car infotainment security business)
Vehicle Component Solutions (in-vehicle infotainment HVAC and Motor Vehicle Engineering)

COMPETITORS

CLEARONE INC.
COMMSCOPE HOLDING COMPANY INC.
MEDIATEK INC.
MONOLITHIC POWER SYSTEMS INC.
NXP Semiconductors N.V.
QUALCOMM INCORPORATED
Quanta Computer Inc.
RUCKUS WIRELESS INC.
STARHUB LTD.
Samsung Electronics Co. Ltd.
VIASAT INC.
VOXX INTERNATIONAL CORPORATION

HISTORICAL FINANCIALS

Company Type: Public

Income Statement

	REVENUE ($ mil.)	NET INCOME ($ mil.)	NET PROFIT MARGIN	EMPLOYEES
12/19	53,962	27	0.1%	0
12/18	55,020	1,112	2.0%	37,698
12/17	57,589	1,618	2.8%	37,653
12/16	46,086	63	0.1%	37,909
12/15	48,029	105	0.2%	37,902
Annual Growth	**3.0%**	**(28.8%)**	**—**	**—**

FYE: December 31

2019 Year-End Financials

Debt ratio: 0.0%
Return on equity: 0.2%
Cash ($ mil.): 4,194
Current ratio: 1.12
Long-term debt ($ mil.): 7,659
No. of shares (mil.): 162
Dividends
  Yield: —
  Payout: 443.7%
Market value ($ mil.): —

Linde plc

Linde Inc. (formerly Praxair Inc.) a wholly-owned subsidiary of Linde plc since 2018 is a leading industrial gas company in North and South America and one of the largest worldwide. Linde produces sells and distributes atmospheric process and specialty gases. Its products services and technologies are offered to a wide variety of industries including aerospace chemicals food and beverage electronics energy healthcare manufacturing primary metals and many others.

Operations

Linde's business segments are gas supply and management; industrial services; and oil and gas services.

Gas supply and management offers cylinders and liquid containers; bulk and microbulk delivery; pipeline; on-site production; mobile nitrogen pumping service; and small on-site production.

Through Linde Services Inc. Industrial services provides nitrogen pumping and integrity testing to ensure optimal efficiency in your operation. Its services are extensive and include cleaning purging drying emergency oxygenation aeration displacing leak detection hydro-testing and inspection for piping and storage tanks.

Oil and gas provides services in enhanced oil recovery energized fluid fracking and well injection services.

Geographic Reach

Based in Danbury Connecticut Linde has regional sales offices in Arizona Connecticut Georgia Illinois New York and Texas.

Sales and Marketing

Linde serves a wide range of industries which consists of aerospace & aircraft automotive & transportation equipment chemicals electronics energy food & beverage healthcare metals production & mining oil & gas as well as welding & metal fabrication among others.

Financial Performance

In fiscal 2016 sales fell 2% to $10.5 billion due mostly to unfavorable currency effects and lower cost pass-through. These factors aside it recorded 2% organic growth due to higher prices in North and South America new project start-ups and acquisitions in Europe.

Net income fell 3% to $1.5 billion due mostly to lower net revenue and tighter margins. The company incurred a $96 million expense relating to cost reductions and a $4 million pension settlement.

Cash from operations was up 3% to $2.8 billion due to lower working capital requirements and favorable changes in other long-term assets and liabilities partially offset by lower net income.

Mergers and AcquisitionsPraxair and bitter German rival Linde originally proposed to merge in 2016 for a $80 billion deal. As of August 2018 the deal is yet to go through. This is because the merger will form the world's largest gas company and easily surpassing French rival Air Liquide in annual sales. There seems to be lingering antitrust concerns as the US federal Trade Commission demanded more asset sales than the companies originally proposed. As a result Praxair and Linde?which used to be the same company more than a century ago before falling out?remain under "a constructive dialogue".

In 2016 the company acquired Norway-based Yara International a leading carbon dioxide supplier for $363 million. The acquisition expends its presence in end-markets such as food and drinks.

Also in 2016 Praxair acquired five industrial and medical gas companies with combined annual sales of more than $40 million. Of the five three — The Welding center Welder Services and A&B Electric Motors — are in the US; one — Geneva Industrial Gases — is in Panama; and the fifth Ossigas is in Italy. The companies add to Praxair's geographic density.

Company Background

Praxair and Linde both go back to the origins of the industrial gas industry in the 19th century.

Karl von Linde a professor of mechanical engineering at the College of Technology in Munich Germany in the late 1800s created the cryogenic air liquefier. Von Linde built his first oxygen-production plant in 1902 and a nitrogen plant in 1904 and in the first decade of the 20th century he built a number of air-separation plants throughout Europe.

By 1907 von Linde founded Linde Air Products in Cleveland as the US subsidiary of his German company. Linde Air Products joined rival Union Carbide in 1911 in experimenting with the production of acetylene; it became a unit of Union Carbide in 1917 during World War I.

In the 1990s the gases business spun out of Union Carbide and became Praxair.

HISTORY

The origins of Praxair date to the work of Karl von Linde a professor of mechanical engineering at the College of Technology in Munich Germany in the late 1800s. In 1895 he created the cryogenic air liquefier. Von Linde built his first oxygen-production plant in 1902 and a nitrogen plant in 1904 and in the first decade of the 20th century he built a number of air-separation plants throughout Europe.

By 1907 von Linde had moved to the US and founded Linde Air Products in Cleveland to extract oxygen from air. Linde Air Products joined rival Union Carbide in 1911 in experimenting with the production of acetylene; it became a unit of Union Carbide in 1917. America's war effort and economic expansion in the 1920s spurred the development of new uses for industrial gases. Union

Carbide's Linde unit also contributed to the development of the atomic bomb in the 1940s when its scientists perfected a process for refining uranium.

As Union Carbide expanded worldwide over the next two decades Linde became America's #1 producer of industrial gases. In the 1960s Linde expanded into oxygen-fired furnaces for steel production and the use of nitrogen in refrigerators. By the early 1980s Linde accounted for 11% of Union Carbide's annual sales.

The disastrous 1984 chemical accident at Union Carbide's plant in Bhopal India coupled with heavy debt and falling sales forced Union Carbide to reorganize. In 1992 Linde was spun off as Praxair. William Lichtenberger former president of Union Carbide headed the new company and pushed global expansion. Two years later Praxair set up China's first helium transfill plants for medical magnetic resonance imaging. In 1995 the company began operations in India and Peru.

In 1996 Praxair Surface Technologies bought Miller Thermal (thermal spray coatings) and Maxima Air Separation Center (industrial and specialty gases Israel). Also that year the company picked up $60 million when it sold the Linde name and trademark to Linde a German engineering and industrial gas company. Praxair purchased and then spun off Chicago Bridge & Iron. The company kept only its Liquid Carbonic division the world's leading supplier of carbon dioxide for processing. The move opened up a new market in carbonated beverages for Praxair.

In 1997 and 1998 Praxair constructed plants and to control its own delivery systems acquired 20 packaged-gases distributors in the US and one in Germany. The company also formed a joint venture in China to produce high-purity nitrogen and other specialty gases for electronics and then teamed up with rival L'Air Liquide in a production joint venture.

Praxair supplied an argon-based protection system for the Shroud of Turin's public display in Italy in 1998. It also installed the industry's first small on-site hydrogen-generating system at an Indiana powdered-metals plant. In 1999 the company formed a global alliance with German pharmaceutical and chemicals company Merck KGaA to provide gases and chemicals to the semiconductor industry. The same year Praxair acquired Materials Research Corporation a maker of thin-film deposition materials for semiconductors and the TAFA Group which makes thermal-spray equipment and related products.

In 2001 Praxair underwent a restructuring that included layoffs in its surface technologies unit (hurt by the decline in jet orders) and Brazilian operations. The next year the company started work on a new plant to serve Singapore's high-tech industry. Praxair boosted its health care segment with the acquisition of Alpine Medicine.

In 2004 Praxair Healthcare Services bought Home Care Supply for $245 million. With Home Care Supply joining the company's existing operations the combined Healthcare Services unit grew its sales to $750 million worldwide slightly more than 10% of Praxair's total annual sales. The home care market became more important for Praxair as the company saw high growth potential in it (and high margins) and wanted to be able to compete with rivals L'Air Liquide and Air Products and Chemicals.

The company bought some of L'Air Liquide's German assets for about $650 million later that year. Due to antitrust requirements the French company needed to dispose of the businesses after buying much of Messer Group earlier in the year. The acquisition put Praxair's European sales over $1 billion annually.

In 2006 Praxair sold the aviation repair business of the Surface Technologies unit to Gridiron Capital and Skyview Capital. The firms created a new company called PAS Technologies to house operations that serve both the commercial and military sectors with the repair of aviation engine and airframe parts and the application of protective coatings to those parts. Also that year Praxair's distribution unit acquired Medical Gas of Illinois and Withrow Oxygen Service of California.

Praxair expanded its presence in the Middle East in 2010 by acquiring a 49% stake in the ROC Group's operations in Kuwait United Arab Emirates and Qatar.

In 2011 Praxair sold its US homecare business to Apria Healthcare. The former Praxair segment provided home respiratory services home medical equipment and nutrition therapies through a network of more than 80 branches across the country. The transaction allowed Praxair to focus on expanding its institutional healthcare business worldwide although it maintains some of its homecare units outside of the US.

In 2011 the company spent $294 million on acquisitions primarily for industrial and specialty packaged gas distributors in the US. It also invested in a joint venture in the Middle East and gained a larger ownership stake in its Scandinavian joint venture (Yara Praxair).

That year Praxair also agreed to develop and market a new process technology with Midrex Technologies (a subsidiary of Kobe Steel) to produce direct reduced iron (DRI) using a variety of fuels including coke oven gas. The company hopes to find new markets for the production of DRI which is usually made from a gas produced from natural gas or coal.

Subsidiary Praxair Distribution also expanded in 2011 acquiring Houston-based National Alloy and Equipment which supplies technical support to makers of high-pressure control packages and drilling risers for oil and energy companies and American Gas Group one of the largest independent specialty gas producers in North America.

Building on its presence in Russia Praxair agreed to acquire the industrial and packaged gases operations of Russian tire company SIBUR - Russian Tyres in 2012. With four major projects in Russia having a total production capacity of more than 3500 tons of gases per day under its belt the company hopes to become the leading industrial gas manufacturer throughout southern Russia.

In 2012 it signed a 15-year agreement with Honeywell Resins & Chemicals to buy carbon dioxide for Praxair's new plant at the Honeywell site.

That year the company's Shanghai-based Praxair China unit started up a new air separation plant in Nanjing for Meishan Iron and Steel Co. a subsidiary of giant steel manufacturer Baosteel Group.

In 2012 Praxair Canada acquired Canadian Cylinder & Gases Inc. an independent distributor of industrial and specialty gases and welding equipment. It also acquired five Airgas branch locations in western Canada including Calgary Red Deer and Edmonton Alberta and Regina and Saskatoon Saskatchewan. This acquisition supports its growth strategy in western Canada to better serve existing customers and home oxygen clients in Alberta and Saskatchewan.

In 2012 Praxair Distribution acquired Harlingen Texas-based Acetylene Oxygen Company a distributor of Praxair industrial gases. Praxair Distribution also acquired Welders Industrial Supply LLC an independent distributor of industrial and specialty gases welding equipment supplies and related services to customers in the greater Houston area.

In 2013 company opened its first air separation plant in Bahrain to produce liquid nitrogen oxygen and argon to supply a diverse group of customers in the regional merchant market including hospitals metal fabricators and aluminum manufacturers. That year Praxair China signed a new contract to expand supply with its existing customer Jinlong Copper Co Ltd. the largest copper smelting joint venture in China.

In 2013 Praxair India Private Limited signed a long-term contract with its existing customer JSW Steel Ltd. to expand the supply of gaseous oxygen nitrogen and argon to JSW's steel mill located in Tornagallu in Karnataka.

Auditors: PricewaterhouseCoopers LLP

LOCATIONS

HQ: Linde plc
  The Priestley Centre, 10 Priestley Road, Surrey
  Research Park, Guildford, Surrey 06810-6268
Phone: (44) 1483 242200
Web: www.linde.com

2016 Sales

	% of total
North America	53
Asia	15
South America	13
Europe	13
Surface technologies	6
Total	**100**

PRODUCTS/OPERATIONS

2016 Sales by End Market

	% of total
Manufacturing	21
Metals	16
Chemicals	14
Food & Beverage	12
Healthcare	11
Electronics	7
Energy	5
Aerospace	1
Other	13
Total	**100**

2016 Sales by Distribution Method

	% of total
Merchant(delivered liquids)	38
On-site (includes noncryogenics)	28
Packaged gases (cylinders)	31
Other	3
Total	**100**

COMPETITORS

AIR PRODUCTS AND CHEMICALS INC.
AIR WATER INC.
AIRGAS INC.
AMERICAN AIR LIQUIDE INC.
CITY ENERGY PTE. LTD.
Chicago Bridge & Iron Company N.V.
L'AIR LIQUIDE SOCIETE ANONYME POUR L'ETUDE
  ET L'EXPLOITATION DES
NATIONAL WELDERS SUPPLY COMPANY INC.
WORTHINGTON INDUSTRIES INC.
White Martins Gases Industriais Ltda

HISTORICAL FINANCIALS

Company Type: Public

Income Statement				FYE: December 31
	REVENUE ($ mil.)	NET INCOME ($ mil.)	NET PROFIT MARGIN	EMPLOYEES
12/20	27,243	2,501	9.2%	74,207
12/19	28,228	2,285	8.1%	79,886
12/18	14,900	4,381	29.4%	80,820
12/17	11,437	1,247	10.9%	26,461
12/16	10,534	1,500	14.2%	26,498
Annual Growth	26.8%	13.6%	—	29.4%

2020 Year-End Financials

Debt ratio: 18.3%
Return on equity: 5.1%
Cash ($ mil.): 3,754
Current ratio: 0.80
Long-term debt ($ mil.): 12,152
No. of shares (mil.): 523
Dividends
Yield: 1.4%
Payout: 81.7%
Market value ($ mil.): —

LIXIL Corp

When opportunity knocks in Japan it's probably knocking on a LIXIL door. The company is a leading supplier of housing and building materials in Japan. Through approximately 270 subsidiaries and affiliates it makes products that improve how people live from shower toilets to baths kitchen systems windows doors building exteriors and interior furnishings. Combined with its housing and building-related services it meets the demand for better homes in markets worldwide. LIXIL Group works with distributors and has sales offices throughout Japan. Other operations include a real estate brokerage franchise and ground inspections and improvement. Its Water Technology business segment accounts for nearly half of the company's sales. Japan market accounts for nearly 80% of sales.

Operations

The company's products and services are categorized in five business segments: Water Technology (nearly 50% of sales) Housing Technology (more than 30%) Distribution & Retail Business (above 10%) Building Technology (more than 5%)and the Housing & Services Business (less than 5%).

Lixil Water Technology makes attractive and purposefully designed products for bathrooms and kitchens through powerful global brands such as INAX GROHE and American Standard as well as product brands such as RICHELLE and SPAGE.

Lixil Housing Technology's brands include TOSTEM INTERIO EXSIOR SUPER WALL and Kawashima SelkonTextiles produce a range of housing-related products from window sashes to entrance doors exterior building materials interior furnishing materials and fabrics helping to make better homes a reality.

Building Technology segment manufactures products and offers services to support the construction of buildings that are environmentally conscious and which provide better spaces to live work study and play. Major products are curtain walls building window sashes and store facades.

Distribution and Retail Business provides consumers with a unique array of housing- and lifestyle-related products materials and services through its Super VIVA Home and VIVA Home stores in Japan.

Housing and services business offers comprehensive housing and lifestyle support to customers in Japan throughout all stages of their lives.

Geographic Reach

The company's head office is located in Tokyo Japan. LIXIL has almost more than 95 manufacturing and sales sites worldwide. More than 40 are in Japan over 30 in Asia Pacific above 10 in the Americas. The rest are in Europe and Africa. LIXIL also operates over 130 showrooms in over 25 countries with more than 100 of these in Japan.

Japan is the company's largest market representing more than 75% of total sales. International market accounts for the remaining less than 23%.

Sales and Marketing

The company sells directly to customers such as dealers sales agencies construction companies architectural firms developers wholesalers volume retailers and general consumers.

Financial Performance

Note: Growth rates may differ after conversion to US Dollars.

Due to strong first-half performance revenue increased by 0.1% year on year to 1.7 trillion despite the decline in demand following the consumption tax hike in Japan and the impact of foreign currency translation.

Lixil's profit for the year increased by 64.7 billion year on year to 12.5 billion due to the increase in core earnings and decrease in loss associated with Permasteelisa.

The company's cash for the year ended 2020 totaled 95.9 billion. Operating activities generated 157.7 billion while investing and financing activities used 41.3 billion and 153.3 billion respectively.

Strategy

Lixil will harness strategic marketing to increase its touch points with consumers and influencers such as contractors designers and builders. In addition through the promotion of services such as "LIXIL PATTO Reform" the company will create new demand for home renovation in Japan by providing solutions to challenges holding back market growth.

Company Background

LIXIL was founded in 2011 through the merger of five of Japan's most successful building materials and housing companies?TOSTEM INAX Shin Nikkei Sunwave and TOEX. From the early 20th Century the founding fathers of their legacy companies ushered in an era of innovation and laid down the principles that would make LIXIL one of the most respected names in the Japanese building and housing industry.

EXECUTIVES

Independent Director, Shiho Konno
Independent Director, Mariko Watabiki
Independent Director, Tamio Uchibori
Independent Director, Daisuke Hamaguchi
Independent Director, Yuji Nishiura
Chairman of the Board of Directors, Independent Director, Masatoshi Matsuzaki
Independent Director, Teruo Suzuki
Senior Managing Executive Officer, Chief People Officer, Director, Hwa Jin Song Montesano
Senior Managing Executive Officer, Chief Digital Officer, Yugo Kanazawa
President, CEO and Director, Kinya Seto
Chief Financial Officer, Executive Vice President, Representative Executive Officer, President of Subsidiary, Director, Sachio Matsumoto
Auditors: Deloitte Touche Tohmatsu LLC

LOCATIONS

HQ: LIXIL Corp
 2-1-1 Ojima, Koto-ku, Tokyo 136-8535
Phone: (81) 3 3638 8111
Web: www.lixil.com

2018 Sales

	% of total
Japan	76
EMEA	9
Americas	8
Asia/Pacific	7
Total	**100**

PRODUCTS/OPERATIONS

2018 Sales

	% of total
LIXIL Water Technology (LWT)	42
LIXIL Housing Technology (LHT)	32
Distribution & Retail Business (D&R)	10
LIXIL Kitchen Technology (LKT)	7
LIXIL Building Technology (LBT)	6
Housing & Services Business (H&S)	3
Total	**100**

Selected Subsidiaries

Kawashima Selkon Textiles (fabric manufacturer)
LIXIL Group Finance (financial services)
LIXIL Housing Research Institute (homebuilding franchise chain)
LIXIL Realty (real estate services)
LIXIL Viva (operates Viva Home and Super Viva Home retail chains)
LIXIL ENERGY Co. Ltd.
LIXIL Building Materials Manufacturing Corporation

Selected Brands

Global
 INAX
 GROHE
 American Standard
 TOSTEM
 LIXIL
Global Specialty
 Kawashima Selkon
 Cobra
 DXV
 Jaxson
 SATO
Japan
 RICHELLE
 SPAGE
 INTERIO
 EXSIOR
 SUPER WALL
 AHAHI TOTEM

COMPETITORS

COMPAGNIE DE SAINT-GOBAIN	JELD-WEN INC.
FORTUNE BRANDS HOME & SECURITY INC.	KAWNEER COMPANY INC. LightInTheBox Holding Co. Ltd.
GRIFFON CORPORATION	MANUTAN INTERNATIONAL
HORMANN LLC	OVERHEAD DOOR CORPORATION
HUTTIG BUILDING PRODUCTS INC.	PGT INNOVATIONS INC.
INTERFACE INC.	RYTEC CORPORATION
JELD-WEN HOLDING INC.	TITON HOLDINGS PLC

HISTORICAL FINANCIALS

Company Type: Public

Income Statement

FYE: March 31

	REVENUE ($ mil.)	NET INCOME ($ mil.)	NET PROFIT MARGIN	EMPLOYEES
03/21	12,447	298	2.4%	59,169
03/20	15,609	115	0.7%	73,426
03/19	16,548	(471)	—	76,182
03/18	15,678	514	3.3%	74,895
03/17	15,978	380	2.4%	72,603
Annual Growth	**(6.1%)**	**(5.9%)**	**—**	**(5.0%)**

2021 Year-End Financials

Debt ratio: 0.2%
Return on equity: 6.2%
Cash ($ mil.): 1,003
Current ratio: 1.09
Long-term debt ($ mil.): 3,313
No. of shares (mil.): 290
Dividends
Yield: 2.3%
Payout: 193.0%
Market value ($ mil.): 16,334

	STOCK PRICE ($) FY Close	P/E High/Low		PER SHARE ($) Earnings	Dividends	Book Value
03/21	56.28	1	0	0.98	1.32	17.19
03/20	24.45	1	0	0.37	1.94	15.95
03/19	27.72	—	—	(1.63)	1.58	16.61
03/18	44.25	0	0	1.61	1.76	20.05
03/17	50.91	0	0	1.20	1.07	17.01
Annual Growth	**2.5%**			**(4.9%)**	**5.4%**	**0.3%**

Lloyds Bank plc

Auditors: PricewaterhouseCoopers LLP

LOCATIONS

HQ: Lloyds Bank plc
25 Gresham Street, London EC2V 7HN
Phone:
Web: www.lloydsbankinggroup.com

HISTORICAL FINANCIALS
Company Type: Public

Income Statement | | | | FYE: December 31

	REVENUE ($ mil.)	NET INCOME ($ mil.)	NET PROFIT MARGIN	EMPLOYEES
12/20	25,369	1,965	7.7%	67,630
12/19	28,409	2,895	10.2%	70,083
12/18	27,659	6,014	21.7%	71,786
12/17	29,532	5,590	18.9%	73,438
12/16	25,709	1,355	5.3%	77,726
Annual Growth	(0.3%)	9.7%	—	(3.4%)

2020 Year-End Financials

Debt ratio: — | No. of shares (mil.): 1,574
Return on equity: 3.6% | Dividends
Cash ($ mil.): 68,492 | Yield: —
Current ratio: — | Payout: —
Long-term debt ($ mil.): — | Market value ($ mil.): —

	STOCK PRICE ($) FY Close	P/E High/Low		Earnings	Dividends	Book Value
12/20	1.96	288	104	0.02	0.06	0.96
12/19	3.31	101	72	0.04	0.16	0.91
12/18	2.56	69	46	0.07	0.16	0.90
12/17	3.75	91	77	0.06	0.18	0.92
12/16	3.10	154	101	0.03	0.20	0.83
Annual Growth	(10.8%)	—		(13.7%)	(27.5%)	3.7%

Lloyds Banking Group Plc

Auditors: PricewaterhouseCoopers LLP

LOCATIONS

HQ: Lloyds Banking Group Plc
25 Gresham Street, 5th Floor, London EC2V 7HN
Phone: (44) 20 7626 1500
Web: www.lloydsbankinggroup.com

HISTORICAL FINANCIALS
Company Type: Public

Income Statement | | | | FYE: December 31

	ASSETS ($ mil.)	NET INCOME ($ mil.)	INCOME AS % OF ASSETS	EMPLOYEES
12/20	1,189,028	1,798	0.2%	61,576
12/19	1,101,207	3,862	0.4%	63,069
12/18	1,018,342	5,492	0.5%	64,928
12/17	1,096,907	4,669	0.4%	67,905
12/16	1,006,000	2,537	0.3%	70,433
Annual Growth	4.3%	(8.2%)	—	(3.3%)

2020 Year-End Financials

Return on assets: 0.1% | Dividends
Return on equity: 2.7% | Yield: 2.8%
Long-term debt ($ mil.): — | Payout: 47.5%
No. of shares (mil.): — | Market value ($ mil.): —
Sales ($ mil): 46,225

Loblaw Companies Ltd

Auditors: KPMG LLP

LOCATIONS

HQ: Loblaw Companies Ltd
1 President's Choice Circle, Brampton, Ontario L6Y 5S5
Phone: 416 965-5209   **Fax:** 416 922-4394
Web: www.loblaw.ca

HISTORICAL FINANCIALS
Company Type: Public

Income Statement | | | | FYE: January 2

	REVENUE ($ mil.)	NET INCOME ($ mil.)	NET PROFIT MARGIN	EMPLOYEES
01/21*	41,378	869	2.1%	220,000
12/19	36,687	825	2.3%	194,000
12/18	34,717	569	1.6%	197,000
12/17	37,253	1,198	3.2%	198,000
12/16	34,419	734	2.1%	195,000
Annual Growth	4.7%	4.3%	—	3.1%

*Fiscal year change

2021 Year-End Financials

Debt ratio: 19.8% | No. of shares (mil.): 346
Return on equity: 9.8% | Dividends
Cash ($ mil.): 1,309 | Yield: 0.0%
Current ratio: 1.32 | Payout: 41.8%
Long-term debt ($ mil.): 5,062 | Market value ($ mil.): 17,151

	STOCK PRICE ($) FY Close	P/E High/Low		Earnings	Dividends	Book Value
01/21*	49.47	19	15	2.40	1.00	24.88
12/19	51.00	20	16	2.21	0.95	23.83
12/18	44.75	26	19	1.48	0.86	24.24
12/17	54.34	16	14	2.99	0.85	26.87
12/16	52.79	23	19	1.76	0.76	24.07
Annual Growth	(1.6%)	—	—	8.1%	7.1%	0.8%

*Fiscal year change

Longfor Group Holdings Ltd

Auditors: Deloitte Touche Tohmatsu

LOCATIONS

HQ: Longfor Group Holdings Ltd
18/F., CSC Fortune International Center, No. 5 An'ding Road, Chaoyang District, Beijing
Phone:
Web: www.longfor.com

HISTORICAL FINANCIALS
Company Type: Public

Income Statement | | | | FYE: December 31

	REVENUE ($ mil.)	NET INCOME ($ mil.)	NET PROFIT MARGIN	EMPLOYEES
12/19	21,704	2,635	12.1%	26,316
12/18	16,835	2,360	14.0%	27,010
12/17	11,075	1,936	17.5%	19,903
12/16	7,891	1,318	16.7%	17,172
12/15	7,301	1,383	19.0%	15,633
Annual Growth	31.3%	17.5%	—	13.9%

2019 Year-End Financials

Debt ratio: 3.2% | No. of shares (mil.): —
Return on equity: 20.8% | Dividends
Cash ($ mil.): 8,735 | Yield: 0.0%
Current ratio: 1.48 | Payout: 407.3%
Long-term debt ($ mil.): 18,980 | Market value ($ mil.): —

	STOCK PRICE ($) FY Close	P/E High/Low		Earnings	Dividends	Book Value
12/19	47.00	15	9	0.44	1.80	2.29
12/18	29.18	11	8	0.40	0.82	2.00
12/17	25.59	13	6	0.33	0.93	1.84
12/16	12.65	11	8	0.23	0.00	1.52
12/15	15.65	—	—	0.24	0.00	1.45
Annual Growth	31.6%	—	—	17.0%	—	12.0%

LVMH Moet Hennessy Louis Vuitton

A family-run group LVMH Mo«t Hennessy Louis Vuitton strives to ensure the long-term development of each of its Houses in keeping with their identity their heritage and their expertise. LVMH makes wines and spirits (Dom Perignon Mo«t & Chandon Veuve Clicquot and Hennessy) perfumes (Christian Dior Guerlain and Givenchy) cosmetics (Make Up For Ever Fresh and Benefit) fashion and leather goods (Marc Jacobs Givenchy Kenzo and Louis Vuitton) and watches and jewelry (TAG Heuer Bulgari). LVMH's selective retail division includes Sephora cosmetics stores Le Bon Marche Paris department stores and DFS Group (duty-free shops). LVMH is owned by holding company Christian Dior and Bernard Arnault the richest man in France. Majority of its sales were generated in Asia.

Operations

The group's brands and trade names are organized into six business groups. Four business groups ? Wines and Spirits over 45% of sales) Fashion and Leather Goods (around 10%) Perfumes and Cosmetics (more than 10%) and Watches and Jewelry (over 5%) ? comprise brands dealing with the same category of products that use similar production and distribution processes. The Selective Retailing business group (about 25%) comprises the Group's own-label retailing activities. The Other and holding companies business group comprises brands and businesses that are not associated with any of the above-mentioned business groups.

Geographic Reach

Headquartered in Paris France The company has nearly 5005 stores in Europe Asia the US and other regions. Around 40% of sales were generated from Asia of which over 5% were generated from Japan; followed by the European countries with about 25% (about 10% from France); the US with roughly 25%; and other regions with the remaining.

Sales and Marketing

Revenue mainly comprises retail sales within the group's store network (including e-commerce websites) and wholesale sales through agents and distributors. Direct sales to customers are mostly made through retail stores in Fashion and Leather Goods and Selective Retailing as well as certain Watches and Jewelry and Perfumes and Cosmetics brands. Wholesale sales mainly concern the Wines and Spirits businesses as well as certain Perfumes and Cosmetics and Watches and Jewelry brands.

Financial Performance

The company's revenue for fiscal 2020 decreased to ?44.7 billion compared from the prior year with ?53.7 billion.

Profit for fiscal 2020 increased to ?8.0 billion compared from the prior year with ?11.3 billion.

Cash held by the company at the end of fiscal 2020 increased to ?19.8 billion. Cash provided by operations and financing activities were ?10.9 billion and ?7.4 billion respectively. Cash used for investing activities was ?2.9 billion mainly for operating investments.

Strategy

Louis Vuitton continued to be driven by its exceptional momentum and creativity with the art of innovating in all its businesses and offering its customers a unique experience. During this unprecedented period Louis Vuitton was able to very quickly transform and boost its customer relationships with a high-quality and highly effective digital service strategy. Numerous innovations were unveiled throughout the year: in leather goods the contemporary yet timeless Pont 9 leather model; the summery colorful Escale collection; the Since 1854 Jacquard canvas inspired by the Maison's heritage; and the iconic Capucines bag reinterpreted by six major contemporary artists.

Mergers and Acquisitions

In early 2021 LVMH Mo «t Hennessy Louis Vuitton SE has completed the acquisition of US-based Tiffany & Co. the global luxury jeweler. The acquisition of this iconic US jeweler will deeply transform LVMH's Watches & Jewelry division and complement LVMH's 75 distinguished Maisons. Terms were not disclosed.

HISTORY

Woodworker Louis Vuitton started his Paris career packing dresses for French Empress Eugenie. He later designed new types of luggage and in 1854 he opened a store to sell his designs. In 1896 Vuitton introduced the LV monogram fabric that the company still uses. By 1900 Louis Vuitton had stores in the US and England and by WWI Louis' son Georges had the world's largest retail store for travel goods.

Henry Racamier a former steel executive who had married into the Vuitton family took charge in 1977 repositioning the company's goods from esoteric status symbols to designer must-haves. Sales soared from $20 million to nearly $2.5 billion within a decade. Concerned about being a takeover target Racamier merged Louis Vuitton in 1987 with Mo «t Hennessy (which made wines spirits and fragrances) and adopted the name LVMH Mo «t Hennessy Louis Vuitton.

Mo «t Hennessy had been formed through the 1971 merger of Mo «t et Chandon (the world's #1 champagne maker) and the Hennessy Cognac company (founded by Irish mercenary Richard Hennessy in 1765). Mo «t Hennessy acquired rights to Christian Dior fragrances in 1971.

Racamier tried to reverse the merger when disagreements with chairman Alain Chevalier arose. Racamier invited outside investor Bernard Arnault to increase his interest in the company. Arnault gained control of 43% of LVMH and became chairman in 1989. Chevalier stepped down but Racamier fought for control for another 18 months and then set up Orcofi a partner of cosmetics rival L'Oreal.

LVMH increased its fashion holdings with the purchases of the Givenchy Couture Group (1988) Christian Lacroix (1993) and Kenzo (1993). The company also acquired 55% of French media firm Desfosses International (1993) Celine fashions (1996) the Chateau d'Yquem winery (1996) and duty-free retailer DFS Group (1996). Next LVMH bought perfume chains Sephora (1997) and Marie-Jeanne Godard (1998). In 1998 LVMH integrated the Paris department store Le Bon Marche which was controlled by Arnault.

LVMH accumulated a 34% stake in Italian luxury goods maker Gucci in early 1999 and planned to buy all of it. Fellow French conglomerate Pinault-Printemps-Redoute (PPR) later thwarted LVMH by purchasing 42% of Gucci.

Through its LV Capital unit in 1999 LVMH began acquiring stakes in a host of luxury companies including a joint venture with fashion company Prada to buy 51% of design house Fendi (LVMH bought Prada's 25.5% stake for $265 million in November 2001). It has since upped its Fendi stake to about 70%. LVMH later added the Ebel Chaumet and TAG Heuer brands to its new watch division.

In early 2000 LVMH bought Miami Cruiseline Services which operates duty-free shops on cruise ships auction house L'Etude Tajan and 67% of Italian fashion house Emilio Pucci. The company later purchased 35% of French video game retailer Micromania and 51% of department store Samaritaine. In late 2000 LVMH acquired Gabrielle Studio which owns all Donna Karan licenses. In 2001 the company bought Donna Karan International.

LVMH bought in 2001 the Newton and MountAdam vineyards for about $45 million. It then began marketing De Beers diamond jewelry in a 50-50 joint venture with the diamond powerhouse. In March LVMH prompted the investigation of a Dutch court into the PPR-Gucci alliance. The company sold its stake in Gucci to PPR for $806.5 million in October.

In October 2002 LVMH ceased trading on the Brussels and Nasdaq exchanges to concentrate on its Euronext investors. In October 2003 the company sold Canard-Duchene to the Alain Thienot Group. LVMH shed several of the less productive of its 50 brands in 2003 including auction house Phillips de Pury & Luxemborg and fashion brand Michael Kors.

LVMH opened its biggest store — a four-story emporium on New York's Fifth Avenue — in February 2004. A few months later the company added whisky-maker Glenmorangie PLC to its subsidiary roster. LVMH also made its debut in the South African market in October 2004 opening its first sub-Saharan boutique in Johannesburg. Also during the year Bliss spas was sold off.

In early 2004 LVMH won a landmark lawsuit against Morgan Stanley alleging that the firm had used biased research in misstatements about the financial health of LVMH that caused damage to the company's image. The presiding Parisian court ordered Morgan Stanley to pay 100 million euros (about $38 million) in damages. Morgan Stanley appealed the ruling later that year.

In late 2005 LVMH opened its largest store to date on the Champs-Elysees in Paris and the De Beers brand was introduced in the US with stores in New York and Los Angeles. Also that year LVMH was the winning bidder for whisky maker

Glenmorangie PLC for which it paid 300 million. On the sell side LVMH divested fashion design house Christian Lacroix SNC.

In May 2007 LVMH acquired a 55% stake in Chinese distillery Wenjun for an undisclosed amount. (Jiannanchun the distillery's previous owner retained a 45% stake in Wenjun.) In December 2007 the luxury goods firm acquired the French newspaper Les Echos from publisher Pearson. LVMH controls Les Echos' rival the financial daily La Tribune but has agreed to sell it. Group Les Echos deal includes the newspaper Web site business magazine Enjeux and other financial information services.

In late 2008 Sephora SA acquired a 45% stake in the Russian perfume and cosmetics chain Ile de Beaute. (The agreement which gave Sephora the option to become a majority shareholder allowed LVMH to up its share to 65% in mid-2011.) The firm acquired the luxury yacht-maker Royal Van Lent.

In August 2009 LVMH acquired 50% stakes in two French wine makers: privately-held Cheval Blanc; and La Tour du Pin owner of the Chateau Quinault l'Enclose estate.

In early 2010 LVMH acquired a 40% stake in Dondup an Italian apparel and denim brand for more than $43 million (or 30 million euros). Its plans are to expand Dondup's business internationally. Later in 2010 the company purchased a 70% stake in the Brazilian fragrance and cosmetics retailer Sack's. The acquisition estimated to be worth R$250 million is a move on LVMH's part to expand its Sephora beauty chain in Brazil one of the fastest-growing beauty markets in the world.

Adding to its vast portfolio of luxury brands in February 2011 LVMH acquired Ole Henriksen a leading luxury botanical skincare company founded and owned by its namesake. Later that same week LVMH bought a 70% stake in Nude Brands skin care as the company continues to acquire niche brands. The four-year-old line - described as "biocompatible luxury skin care" - was founded by Bryan Meehan and Ali Hewson wife of U2 front man Bono. In March LVMH fired Dior star designer John Galliano amid charges of anti-Semitism. In September LVMH completed its tender offer from Rome-based Bulgari acquiring about 98% of the shares.

EXECUTIVES

Director representing the employees, Dominique Aumont

Chairman and CEO of Christian Dior Couture, Member of the Executive Committee, Pietro Beccari

Chairman and CEO of Louis Vuitton, Member of the Executive Committee, Michael Burke

Chairman and CEO of LVMH Fashion Group, Member of the Executive Committee, Sidney Toledano

Group Managing Director, Member of the Executive Committee, Director, Antonio Belloni, $3,144,796 total compensation

Chairman and Chief Executive Officer, Member of the Executive Committee, Bernard Arnault, $1,080,828 total compensation

Chief Financial Officer, Member of the Executive Committee, Jean-Jacques Guiony

Group Director of Human Resources and Synergies, Member of the Executive Committee, Chantal Gaemperle

Development and Acquisitions, Member of the Executive Committee, Director, Nicolas Bazire

Independent Director, Iris Knobloch

Chief Executive and Chairman - Selective Retailing Division, Member of the Executive Committee, Christopher de Lapuente

Chief Executive Officer of Moet Hennessy Wines and Spirits Division, Member of the Executive Committee, Philippe Schaus
Chief Strategy Officer, Member of the Executive Committee, Jean-Baptiste Voisin
Independent Director, Sophie Chassat
Director representing the employees, Marie Veronique Belloeil-Melkin
Auditors: ERNST & YOUNG Audit

LOCATIONS

HQ: LVMH Moet Hennessy Louis Vuitton
22 avenue Montaigne, Paris 75008
Phone: (33) 1 44 13 22 22   Fax: (33) 1 44 13 21 19
Web: www.lvmh.com

2018 Stores

	No.
Europe	
France	514
Other countries	1,153
Asia	
Japan	422
Other countries	1,289
US	783
Other regions	431
Total	**4,592**

2018 Sales

	% of total
Europe	
France	10
Other countries	19
Asia	
Japan	7
Other countries	29
US	24
Other regions	11
Total	**100**

PRODUCTS/OPERATIONS

2018 Sales

	% of total
Fashion & leather goods	39
Selective retailing	28
Wines & spirits	11
Perfumes & cosmetics	13
Watches & jewelry	9
Total	**100**

Selected Brands and Operations

Fashion and leather goods
  Berluti
  Celine
  Donna Karan
  Emilio Pucci
  Fendi
  Gabrielle Studio (Donna Karan label)
  Givenchy
  Kenzo
  Loewe
  Loro Piana
  Louis Vuitton
  Marc Jacobs
  Thomas Pink
Retailing
  DFS Group
  La Samaritaine
  Le Bon Marché;
  Miami Cruiseline Services (duty-free shops)
  Sephora
Fragrances and cosmetics
  Aqua di Parma
  BeneFit
  Bliss
  Fresh
  Guerlain
  Kenzo Parfums
  Make Up For Ever
  Marc Jacobs Fragrances
  Nude skin care
  Ole Henriksen
  Parfums Christian Dior
  Parfums Givenchy
Spirits and wines

10 Cane
Belvedere
Canard-Duchêne
Chandon Estates
Château d'Yquem
Dom Pé;rignon
Hennessy
Krug
Mercier
Moët & Chandon
MountAdam
Newton
Ruinart
Veuve Clicquot
Watches and jewelry
  Bulgari
  Chaumet
  De Beers
  Ebel
  Fred
  Omas
  TAG Heuer
  Zenith
Media (Desfosses International Group)
  Investir
  La Tribune
  Les Echos
  Radio Classique
Other
  Royal van Lent (luxury yachts)

COMPETITORS

CHANEL	LUXOTTICA GROUP SPA
DEBENHAMS PLC	MULBERRY GROUP PLC
HERMES INTERNATIONAL	NEIMAN MARCUS GROUP
KERING	INC
Kering Holland N.V.	Signet Jewelers
Koninklijke Ahold	Limited
Delhaize N.V.	TIFFANY & CO.
LAURA ASHLEY HOLDINGS	
PLC	

HISTORICAL FINANCIALS

Company Type: Public

Income Statement				FYE: December 31
	REVENUE ($ mil.)	NET INCOME ($ mil.)	NET PROFIT MARGIN	EMPLOYEES
12/20	54,748	5,770	10.5%	150,479
12/19	60,290	8,051	13.4%	163,309
12/18	53,651	7,276	13.6%	156,088
12/17	51,106	6,148	12.0%	145,247
12/16	39,704	4,203	10.6%	134,476
Annual Growth	8.4%	8.2%	—	2.9%

2020 Year-End Financials

Debt ratio: 27.9%
Return on equity: 12.6%
Cash ($ mil.): 24,500
Current ratio: 1.58
Long-term debt ($ mil.): 17,261

No. of shares (mil.): 503
Dividends
  Yield: 0.8%
  Payout: 9.9%
Market value ($ mil.): 62,851

	STOCK PRICE ($) FY Close	P/E High/Low		PER SHARE ($) Earnings	Dividends	Book Value
12/20	124.73	13	7	11.44	1.07	91.12
12/19	93.27	7	4	15.98	1.38	81.56
12/18	58.46	6	4	14.44	1.29	73.54
12/17	58.70	6	4	12.20	1.01	68.79
12/16	38.00	5	4	8.33	0.76	55.51
Annual Growth	34.6%	—	—	8.2%	9.1%	13.2%

LyondellBasell Industries NV

Auditors: PricewaterhouseCoopers LLP

LOCATIONS

HQ: LyondellBasell Industries NV
  4th Floor, One Vine Street, London W1J0AH
Phone: (44) 207 220 2600
Web: www.lyb.com

HISTORICAL FINANCIALS

Company Type: Public

Income Statement				FYE: December 31
	REVENUE ($ mil.)	NET INCOME ($ mil.)	NET PROFIT MARGIN	EMPLOYEES
12/20	27,753	1,427	5.1%	19,200
12/19	34,727	3,397	9.8%	19,100
12/18	39,004	4,690	12.0%	19,450
12/17	34,484	4,879	14.1%	13,400
12/16	29,183	3,836	13.1%	13,000
Annual Growth	(1.2%)	(21.9%)	—	10.2%

2020 Year-End Financials

Debt ratio: 45.0%
Return on equity: 17.5%
Cash ($ mil.): 1,763
Current ratio: 2.11
Long-term debt ($ mil.): 15,286

No. of shares (mil.): 334
Dividends
  Yield: 4.5%
  Payout: 118.3%
Market value ($ mil.): —

M&G plc

Auditors: KPMG LLP

LOCATIONS

HQ: M&G plc
  10 Fenchurch Avenue, London EC3M 5AG
Phone: (44) 207 626 4588
Web: www.mandgprudential.com

HISTORICAL FINANCIALS

Company Type: Public

Income Statement				FYE: December 31
	REVENUE ($ mil.)	NET INCOME ($ mil.)	NET PROFIT MARGIN	EMPLOYEES
12/20	20,765	1,553	7.5%	6,683
12/19	42,428	1,479	3.5%	5,680
12/18	2,759	1,029		6,447
12/17	37,651	1,450	3.9%	6,823
12/16	40,084	1,394	3.5%	6,246
Annual Growth	(15.2%)	2.7%	—	1.7%

2020 Year-End Financials

Debt ratio: —
Return on equity: 21.2%
Cash ($ mil.): 9,247
Current ratio: —
Long-term debt ($ mil.): —

No. of shares (mil.): —
Dividends
  Yield: —
  Payout: 41.4%
Market value ($ mil.): —

Maanshan Iron & Steel Co., Ltd.

Maanshan Iron & Steel (or Masteel) is among China's largest steel producers. The company specializes in steel plates section steel wire rods and train wheels. The company turns out some 18 million tons of pig iron over 19.8 million tons of crude steel and about 18.7 million tons of steel products annually about 95% of which is sold domestically (China). Its H-beam products become the number one in comprehensive competitiveness at home the Special Steel Company a production base for premium special steel and wire rod and the Changjiang Steel a production base for important premium construction materials. Masteel's plate and structural products are used by the automotive and construction industries primarily; it also makes wheels for locomotives. Magang (Group) Holding Company controls the company.

Operations

The group divides the operation services into two operating segments which are determined based on the internal organization structure management requirements and internal reporting system: the production and sale of iron and steel products and related by-products; and Financial service under Masteel Finance.

The main production processes include iron making steel making steel rolling etc. Major products of the company are steel which can be roughly divided into three types i.e. plates long products and wheels and axles.

Plates include hot and cold-rolled thin plates galvanized plates and coilcoating plates. Hot-rolled thin plates are mostly used in the construction automobile bridge-building machinery businesses and petroleum transportation while cold-rolled thin plates are used in high-grade light industries home electrical appliances and medium and high-grade production of automobile parts.

Long products include section steel and wire rod. H beams is mostly used in construction steel structures machinery manufacturing and the construction of petroleum drilling platforms and railways.

Wheels and axles include train wheels axles and rings which are widely used in railway transport port machinery petrochemical industries aerospace industry and so forth.

About 90% of sales were generated through its steel products. Almost all of its sales comes from principal operating income.

Geographic Reach

Headquartered in Anhui Province China about 95% of sales were generated in its home country where nearly 35% of were generated in Anhui.

Sales and Marketing

The amount of total sales to the top five customers was RMB5.946 billion accounting for about 10% of the annual sales.

Financial Performance

Revenue for the year 2019 was RMB 78.3 billion a 5% decline compared to the previous year.

In 2019 Net profit totaled RMB 1.1 billion an 81% decrease from the previous year. This was primarily due to a lower sales volume for the year coupled with a higher cost of sales.

The company's cash for the year ended 2019 was RMB 2.7 billion. Operating activities generated RMB 91.6 million while investing activities used RMB 3.4 billion mainly for capital expenditures. Financing activities generated another RMB 137.6 million.

Strategy

Against a complex and fast-changing domestic and international environment the company shall maintain strategic focus treat national development and industry changes from a comprehensive dialectical and long-term perspective unswervingly implement the new development philosophy and the overall development strategy of China Baowu and pursue high quality development.

The company will follow the general idea for a "better stronger and bigger" high-quality growth focus on three types of products of "wheels and axles steel plates premium long products" and highlight the development of rail transit (wheels and axles) automobile plates home electrical appliances plates H beams and premium special steel.

The company will implement a strategy of "premium product + scale" making wheels and axles become the number one in comprehensive competitiveness at home and abroad.

The company will adhere to the purpose and requirements of the "four principles for intelligent production" advance big data AI IoT block chain and similar technologies and apply them in intelligent equipment intelligent plant and intelligent operation to improve the level of intelligent manufacturing.

The company will also vigorously promote new processes new technologies new equipment and new standards in terms of ultra-low emission energy saving and environmental protection enhance green development integrate into the high-quality steel ecosystem.

EXECUTIVES

Chairman of the Board, Yi Ding
General Manager, Executive Director, Tianbao Ren
Director, Qiangmin Wang
General Manager, Director, Wenyang Zhang
Independent Director, Shaofang Zhu
Deputy General Manager, Ming Fu
Independent Director, Xianzhu Wang
Secretary of the Board, Hongyun He
Deputy General Manager, Maohan Zhang
Deputy General Manager, Zhanhong Mao
Auditors: Ernst & Young Hua Ming LLP

LOCATIONS

HQ: Maanshan Iron & Steel Co., Ltd.
No. 8 Jiu Hua Xi Road, Maanshan City, Anhui Province 243003
Phone: (86) 555 2888158   **Fax:** (86) 555 2887284
Web: www.magang.com.cn

2015 Sales

	% of total
China	
Anhui	36
Jiangsu	13
Shanghai	12
Shanghai	12
Zhejiang	5
Guangdong	3
Other domestic regions	11
Overseas & Hong Kong	8
Total	**100**

PRODUCTS/OPERATIONS

2015 Operating income

	% of total
Steel products	95
Steel billets and pig iron	2
Coke by-products	1
Others	2
Total	**100**

2015 Sales

	% of total
Principal operating income	98
Other operating income	2
Total	**100**

Selected Products

Special Steel
Steel Section
Strip and Plate
Train Wheel
Wire Rod

COMPETITORS

CALIFORNIA STEEL INDUSTRIES INC.
Chongqing Iron & Steel Company Limited
KEYSTONE CONSOLIDATED INDUSTRIES INC.
KOBE STEEL LTD.
NLMK PAO
SEVERSTAL PAO
STEEL AUTHORITY OF INDIA LIMITED
STEEL DYNAMICS INC.
TIMKENSTEEL CORPORATION
USS-UPI LLC

HISTORICAL FINANCIALS

Company Type: Public

Income Statement

	REVENUE ($ mil.)	NET INCOME ($ mil.)	NET PROFIT MARGIN	EMPLOYEES
12/20	12,478	303	2.4%	0
12/19	11,247	162	1.4%	0
12/18	11,914	864	7.3%	0
12/17	11,252	634	5.6%	0
12/16	6,951	176	2.5%	0
Annual Growth	15.7%	14.4%	—	—

FYE: December 31

2020 Year-End Financials

Debt ratio: 3.5%	No. of shares (mil.): —
Return on equity: 7.1%	Dividends
Cash ($ mil.): 817	Yield: —
Current ratio: 0.87	Payout: —
Long-term debt ($ mil.): 540	Market value ($ mil.): —

Macquarie Group Ltd

Boasting assets under management of around A$245.7 billion the holding company for Macquarie Bank and other subsidiaries operates an investment banking practice that provides asset management and finance banking advisory lending wealth management and risk and capital services across debt equity and commodities for institutional corporate government and retail clients. Founded in 1969 Macquarie Group has offices in about 30 countries. Domestic activities account for some 30% of the company's revenue.

Operations

Macquarie is divided into four Operating Groups which are supported by four Central Service Groups: Risk Management Group Legal and Governance Financial Management Group and Corporate Operations Group.

The Operating Groups are split between annuity-style businesses and markets-facing businesses.

Annuity-style businesses is divided into two division — Macquarie Asset Management (MAM) is a leading specialist global asset manager and Banking and Financial Services (BFS) which serves the Australian market through personal banking wealth management and business banking.

Marketing facing businesses include Commodities and Global Markets and Macquarie Capital. CGM provides clients with an integrated end-to-end offering across global markets including equities fixed income foreign exchange commodities and technology media and telecoms. Macquarie Capital has global capability in advisory and capital raising services investing alongside partners and clients across the capital structure providing clients with specialist expertise advice and flexible capital solutions across a range of sectors.

Geographic Reach

Adelaide SA Australia-based Macquarie Group generates some 40% of its total external customer revenue domestically in Australia. The Americas accounts for more than 35% and the Europe Middle East and Africa (EMEA) with nearly 25%. Less than 10% comes from the Asia Pacific region. Macquarie and its subsidiaries have offices in more than 30 countries in the Americas EMEA Asia Australia and New Zealand regions.

Sales and Marketing

Macquarie's customers include governmental institutional corporate retail and counterparties around the world providing a diversified range of products and services. It has established leading market positions as a global specialist in a wide range of sectors including resources and commodities renewables conventional energy financial institutions infrastructure and real estate and have a deep knowledge of Asia-Pacific financial markets.

Financial Performance

Note: Growth rates may differ after conversion to US dollars. This analysis uses financials from the company's annual report.

The company in fiscal year 2020 had a net operating income of $12.8 million a 4% increase from the previous year's net operating income of $742 million.

In fiscal year 2020 the company had a net income of $4 billion a 22% decrease from the previous year's net income of $5.1 billion.

The company's cash at the end of fiscal year 2020 was $33.5 billion. Operating activities generated $2.8 billion. Investing and financing activities generated another $2.9 billion and $1.9 billion respectively.

Strategy

Consistent with the principles of What We Stand For Macquarie's business strategy is focused on the medium-term with the following key aspects: Risk management approach; Strong balance sheet; Business mix; Diversification; Proven expertise; Adjacencies; as well as pursuit of growth opportunities.

Mergers and Acquisitions

In 2021 Macquarie Capital Principal Finance (Macquarie Capital) announced the majority acquisition of Wavenet Group Holdings Limited (Wavenet) a multi-award-winning provider of telecoms and technology solutions ? serving thousands of small and medium-sized businesses and enterprises across the United Kingdom (UK). The new partnership with Macquarie Capital will boost this growth potential by providing both expertise and flexible growth capital. This will enable more investment in the people at Wavenet and provide a renewed focus on strategic acquisitions.

Also in 2021 Macquarie Asset Management (MAM) the asset management division of Macquarie Group announced the completion of its acquisition of Waddell & Reed Financial Inc. one of the oldest asset and wealth management companies in the US. This combination along with its enhanced partnership with LPL unlocks substantial value for Waddell & Reed advisors and their clients.

Company Background

Macquarie's predecessor organization Hill Samuel Australia launched in 1969 as a subsidiary of UK merchant bank Hill Samuel & Co. with three staff members. Macquarie Bank listed on the Australian Securities Exchange in 1996 and was established as non-operating holding company Macquarie Group in 2007.

HISTORY

Macquarie has made a slew of acquisitions in its past. It acquired several North America-based financial services companies including investment bank Fox-Pitt Kelton Cochran Caronia Waller. In 2010 Macquarie expanded upon its individual and institutional asset management business when it acquired US-based Delaware Investments. It also bought the Canadian investment dealing business of Blackmont Capital and rebranded it as Macquarie Private Wealth.

Two more US acquisitions were designed to enhance Macquarie Capital's advisory business. In 2010 Macquarie bought US-based specialist Presidio Partners which performs real estate advisory and capital raising advisory services. Macquarie also bought Los Angeles-based investment bank Regal Capital Advisors a specialist in strategic and financial advice for the gaming lodging and leisure industries.

Overseas Macquarie acquired the cash equities sales and research business of German private bank Sal. Oppenheim Jr. & Cie. in 2010. The acquisition broadened Macquarie's European business bolstering its presence in several key markets. Macquarie is looking to buy trading and investment banking businesses in Europe.

The company has also used acquisitions to bolster its position in the energy and other non-traditional banking markets.

In 2009 it acquired Canadian boutique investment bank Tristone Capital which served the oil and gas industry. Macquarie also acquired the downstream natural gas trading operations of Constellation Energy. The company then combined that business with its Macquarie Cook Energy business to form Macquarie Energy a larger North American wholesale gas company.

In 2010 Macquarie Energy acquired the wholesale electric marketing and trading portfolio of Integrys Energy Services in a deal that more than doubled Macquarie Energy's customer base and strengthened its position in key North American power markets. Also that year subsidiary Macquarie Aerospace agreed to purchase a portfolio of 53 aircraft from AIG unit International Lease Finance Corporation.

EXECUTIVES

Chief Financial Officer and Executive Chairman - Macquarie Group, Asia, Alex Harvey, $551,691 total compensation

Group Co-Heads of Macquarie Capital, Michael Silverton, $518,329 total compensation

Co-Head of Macquarie Capital, Daniel Wong, $3,343,918 total compensation

Non-Executive Independent Director, Jillian Broadbent

Assistant Company Secretary, Simone Kovacic

Non-Executive Independent Director, Rebecca McGrath

Independent Non-Executive Chairman of the Board, Peter Warne

Head of Commodity Markets and Finance, Nicholas O'Kane, $584,173 total compensation

Chief Operating Officer, Head - Corporate Operations Group, Nicole Sorbara, $551,691 total compensation

Group Head of Macquarie Asset Management (MAM), Martin Stanley, $508,267 total compensation

Chief Executive Officer, Managing Director, Director, Shemara Wikramanayake, $586,685 total compensation

Deputy Managing Director, Head - Banking and Financial Services Group, Greg Ward, $551,691 total compensation

Non-Executive Independent Director, Michael Roche

Head of Macquarie Capital Principal Finance, Florian Herold, $517,229 total compensation

Chief Risk Officer, Head of RMG, Patrick Upfold, $551,691 total compensation

Chief Executive Officer and Managing Director of Macquarie Bank, Mary Reemst, $551,691 total compensation

Auditors: PricewaterhouseCoopers

LOCATIONS

HQ: Macquarie Group Ltd
50 Martin Place, Sydney, New South Wales 2000
Phone: (61) 2 8232 3333
Web: www.macquarie.com

2018 Sales

	% of total
Australia	38
Europe Middle East and Africa	29
Americas	25
Asia/Pacific	8
Total	**100**

PRODUCTS/OPERATIONS

2018 Sales

	% of total
Lending	39
Financial markets	25
Asset & wealth management	18
Capital Markets	18
Total	**100**

2018 Sales

	% of total
Interest and similar income	38
Fee and commission income	36
Net trading income	15
Other operating income and charges	9
Others	2
Total	**100**

Selected Services

Bank Accounts
Transaction accounts
Savings account
Cash management accounts
Term deposits
Saving calculator
Credit Cards
Flexible Rewards
Qantas Rewards
Hilton Honors
Balance Transfer
Home Loans
Basic home loan
Offset home loan
Home loan calculators
Vehicle Loans
Car loans
Motorcycle loans
Recreational vehicle loans
Investments
Online trading
Managed funds
Specialists investments
International Money Transfers
Macquarie Wrap
Private Bank
Financial Advice

COMPETITORS

APAX PARTNERS HOLDINGS LTD	INVESTEC PLC
CLOSE BROTHERS GROUP PLC	JEFFERIES FINANCIAL GROUP INC.
COWEN INC.	NOMURA HOLDINGS INC.
Canaccord Genuity Group Inc	NUMIS CORPORATION PLC
EATON VANCE CORP.	OM RESIDUAL UK LIMITED
Fiera Capital Corporation	OPPENHEIMERFUNDS INC.
GGL GROUP NUMBER TWO LIMITED	ROTHSCHILD & CO
	SAVILLS PLC

Company Type: Public

Income Statement				FYE: March 31
	ASSETS ($ mil.)	NET INCOME ($ mil.)	INCOME AS % OF ASSETS	EMPLOYEES
03/21	187,002	2,295	1.2%	16,459
03/20	156,194	1,667	1.1%	15,849
03/19	144,076	2,114	1.5%	15,700
03/18	147,250	1,967	1.3%	14,469
03/17	139,887	1,695	1.2%	13,500
Annual Growth	7.5%	7.9%	—	5.1%

2021 Year-End Financials

Return on assets: 1.2%	Dividends
Return on equity: 13.9%	Yield: 1.9%
Long-term debt ($ mil.): —	Payout: 39.2%
No. of shares (mil.): 346	Market value ($ mil.): 40,500
Sales ($ mil): 11,470	

	STOCK PRICE ($) FY Close	P/E High/Low		PER SHARE ($) Earnings	Dividends	Book Value
03/21	116.82	14	8	6.28	2.22	48.41
03/20	52.95	12	6	4.67	4.19	37.83
03/19	92.21	10	8	6.16	3.68	38.88
03/18	80.26	11	8	5.72	3.75	39.03
03/17	69.14	11	7	4.93	3.17	37.08
Annual Growth	14.0%	—	—	6.2%	(8.5%)	6.9%

Magna International Inc

Through its various subsidiaries and divisions Magna International makes just about everything needed to put together a motor vehicle. Besides being one of the world's largest automotive suppliers Magna also considers itself a technology company delivering mobility solutions. The company makes body exteriors and chassis powertrain active driver assistance electronics mechatronics seating systems roofing and lighting systems and mirrors. Operations in North America and Europe represent nearly 95% of total revenues.

Operations

The company based in Ontario Canada operates segments based on four global product-oriented operating segments: Body Exteriors & Structures (accounts for over 40% of the company's total sales) Power & Vision (nearly 30%) Complete Vehicles (more than 15%) and Seating Systems (around 15%).

The company's operating results are primarily dependent on the levels of North American European Chinese car and light truck production by the customers. While Magna International supply systems and components to every major original equipment manufacturer it do not supply systems and components for every vehicle nor is the value of the content consistent from one vehicle to the next.

Geographic Reach

Based on Ontario Canada Magna boasts over 345 manufacturing facilities and roughly 95 product development engineering and sales centers in more than 25 countries Its operations in North America generates about 50% of its total sales around 45% were produced in Europe Asia pacific

accounts for some 5% and the rest of the world for the remaining.

Sales and Marketing

A significant majority of Magna International's sales are to six customers: General Motors (generates around 15% of sales) BMW (around 15%) Ford (nearly 15%) Fiat Chrysler (roughly 15%) Daimler (more than 10%) and Volkswagen (some 10%). Other customer accounts for the remaining nearly 25% of its sales.

Financial Performance

Total sales decreased 3% to $39.4 billion in 2019 compared to $40.8 billion in 2018. The Company's sales in 2019 were negatively impacted by among other factors the weakening of a number of currencies against the U.S. dollar the divestiture of their Fluid Pressure & Controls ["FP&C"] business in the first quarter of 2019 and the impact of the labour strike at GM.

Net income attributable to Magna International Inc. decreased $531 million to $1.8 billion for 2019 compared to $2.3 billion for 2018 as a result of a decrease in income from operations before income taxes of $728 million partially offset by a loss attributable to non-controlling interests of $133 million in 2019 compared to income attributable to non-controlling interests of $36 million in 2018 and a decrease in income taxes of $28 million.

Cash held by the company at the end of 2019 increased by $590 million to $1.4 billion compared to $802 million in the prior year. Cash provided by operations was $4.0 billion while cash used for investing and financing activities were $434 million and $2.9 billion respectively

Strategy

Magna's capital strategy is to maintain a strong balance sheet ample liquidity and high investment-grade credit ratings. In December 31 2019 the company has over $4 billion of available liquidity between cash and credit lines. This strategy allows the company to invest prudently for growth through organic opportunities innovation spending and acquisitions that fit their strategy as well as to return capital to shareholders. It also leaves them well-positioned in times of economic downturn.

Aligned with Magna's customer product and geographic strategy their innovation approach focuses on three key trends:

Driver Assistance: Creating solutions that improve safety and provide a more comfortable driving experience. The company's technologies give drivers active guidance with a 360° view of their environment with the ability to detect various objects and predict their dynamic behavior around the vehicle and on its path.

Electrification: Developing powertrain innovations that are both modular and scalable ? serving as building blocks to provide competitive solutions to automakers facing electric/hybrid powertrain proliferation.

Smart Mobility: Accommodating a variety of new mobility use cases like enhancing the occupant experience by making seats more flexible and reconfigurable.

Mergers and Acquisitions

In 2019 Magna has completed the acquisition of VIZA Geca SL a Spain-based supplier of seat structures and related systems. The transaction was made to further enhance Magna's capabilities in future-ready seating solutions that enable added functionality which starts with the streat structure itself. The terms of this acquisition were not disclosed.

Company Background

Magna International has historically expanded its product lines through acquisitions of other auto parts manufacturers. In early 2011 Magna Seating acquired Germany-based Vogelsitze GmbH which made seats for buses and passenger trains. In 2012 Magna obtained Verwaltungs GmbH a maker of

automotive vacuum engine and transmission pumps with two facilities in Germany and one in each of China and Bulgaria. Also in 2012 to strengthen its automotive pump operations Magna purchased the remaining 50% interest it didn't already own of STT Technologies which made transmission and engine related pumps for the North American market.

HISTORY

Magna International is rooted in a tool and die shop founded by Frank Stronach and friend Tony Czapka in Ontario Canada in 1957. Austrian-born Stronach immigrated to Canada in 1954. By the end of 1957 the business called Multimatic had 10 employees. Multimatic delved into car parts when it landed a contract in 1960 to make sun visor brackets for a General Motors division in Canada.

To go public Multimatic underwent a reverse merger in 1969 with Magna Electronics a publicly traded maker of components for aerospace defense and industrial markets. (Stronach retained control of the company.) Annual sales reached $10 million that year. The company expanded its automotive operations during the early 1970s by adding more stamped and electronic components. Magna was renamed Magna International in 1973.

With sales increasing steadily among its auto parts businesses Magna sold its aerospace and defense business (now part of Heroux-Devtek) in 1981. The new Magna consisted of five distinct automotive divisions that made seat tracks door latches electronic components and other auto parts. During the 1980s the company expanded by adding factories and product lines. It also capitalized on car makers' penchant for outsourcing labor and bypassing unions. By 1987 when sales reached $1 billion the company was producing systems for every area of the automobile. Stronach didn't spend all his time on cars however; he owned race horses and restaurants. He had opened restaurants tried various publishing ventures (which failed) and even made an unsuccessful run for a Canadian parliament seat in 1988.

Aggressive expansion during the 1980s eventually caught up with the company and in 1989 Magna began to restructure selling assets to pay off its debt. The company also was bailed out in part by two of its principal customers — General Motors and Chrysler. Having recovered somewhat Magna began acquiring small auto parts companies in Europe in 1992.

Magna expanded its European presence with the purchase of Austria-based Steyr-Daimler-Puch in 1998 adding about $1 billion in annual sales. The deal steered Magna into the auto assembly business. Stronach also added Santa Anita Park to his holdings that year. In late 1999 the company's racetrack interests were spun off as Magna Entertainment with Magna retaining a 78% stake. Stronach's horse Red Bullet won the 2000 Preakness. Later that year Magna sold its 50% stake in Webasto Sunroofs to privately-owned German auto parts maker Webasto.

Early in 2001 Stronach's daughter Belinda was named vice chairman and CEO. The company then prepared to spin off Magna Steyr and Intier (now Magna's interiors and seating divisions) as public companies; Intier was spun off later in 2001.

Magna acquired rival automotive mirror maker Donnelly in 2002 in a stock-and-debt deal worth $320 million. The company divested its stake in Magna Entertainment in 2003.

Belinda Stronach stepped down as president CEO and director in order to make a bid for the leadership of Canada's new Conservative Party. Her father assumed the role of interim president in early 2004. Ms. Stronach's bid for the leadership of the Conservative Party was not successful. Mr.

Stronach ran the company until 2005 when Magna adopted a co-CEO management structure with Donald Walker and Siegfried Wolf at the helm.

Magna and Daimler announced in 2004 that Magna would buy Daimler's drivetrain manufacturing subsidiary New Venture Gear for about $435 million. After approval by the European Commission New Venture Gear was acquired by a newly created joint venture called New Process Gear with Magna holding an 80% interest; Daimler held 20% until 2007 when Magna bought out its stake.

Russian conglomerate Basic Element led by Russian aluminum magnate Oleg Deripaska spent about $1.5 billion to purchase 20% of Magna in 2007. The transaction gave Magna entry to the Russian market but late in 2008 Deripaska's bank BNP Paribas made a margin call that forced the businessman to give up his shares. In 2008 Magna International acquired Technoplast a Russia-based manufacturer of plastic automotive interior and exterior parts which bolstered its capacity in Eastern Europe and Russia.

On the heels of the General Motors bankruptcy filing in 2009 the German government selected Magna International as a partner for Adam Opel and agreed to provide about ?1.5 billion (around $2 billion) in bridge loans while GM and Magna finalized the contract. A trusteeship for Opel was arranged to keep European operations separate from the Chapter 11 proceedings of GM.

Magna teamed up with Russian banking firm Sberbank to purchase a 55% interest in Opel and its UK-based Vauxhall unit. While GM initially agreed to the sale in September 2009 it backed out in November. The GM board decided to restructure Opel and its European operations instead because business conditions were improving and the Opel brand was important to its global strategy. In Europe the decision was met with demands by the German government that its ?1.5 billion in bridge loans be returned as well as protests and planned work stoppages by the German labor union.

The GM bankruptcy was brought on by the economic crisis of 2008 and 2009. Magna responded by implementing cost cutting measures which included reducing its headcount by approximately 11500 representing a 14% cutback between 2007 and 2009. It also sold off some of its non-core assets.

Founder and chairman Frank Stronach stepped down in 2010 citing the trend toward more regulatory limitations on company management as one of the reasons. He gave up his controlling share in the company and with it his voting control. The company purchased and cancelled all of its Class B shares held by the Stronach Group and issued Class A Common shares. This capital transaction ended the company's dual class stock structure. The former premier of Ontario Mike Harris took Stronach's place. Co-CEO Siegfried ("Sigi") Wolf also resigned which made co-CEO Donald Walker the sole CEO of Magna International as of mid-2011.

In early 2011 Magna Seating acquired Germany-based Vogelsitze GmbH which made seats for buses and passenger trains. In 2012 Magna obtained Verwaltungs GmbH a maker of automotive vacuum engine and transmission pumps with two facilities in Germany and one in each of China and Bulgaria.

EXECUTIVES

Independent Director, Kurt Lauk
Independent Director, Peter Bowie
Chief Executive Officer, Director, Seetarama Kotagiri, $325,000 total compensation
Independent Director, Cynthia Niekamp
Independent Director, Indira Samarasekera
Independent Director, Mary Chan
Independent Director, William Ruh
Independent Director, Robert MacLellan
Independent Director, Lisa Westlake
Executive Vice President, Chief Sales & Marketing Officer, Eric Wilds
Executive Vice President - Technology and Investments, Boris Shulkin
Chief Operating Officer, Executive Vice President, Tommy Skudutis, $325,000 total compensation
Chief Financial Officer, Executive Vice President, Vincent Galifi, $325,000 total compensation
President - Magna Steyr, Magna Europe, Guenther Apfalter, $245,000 total compensation
Independent Director, V. Peter Harder
Chief Human Resource Officer, Executive Vice President, Aaron Mccarthy
Auditors: Deloitte LLP

LOCATIONS

HQ: Magna International Inc
337 Magna Drive, Aurora, Ontario L4G 7K1
Phone: 905 726-2462   **Fax:** 905 726-7164
Web: www.magna.com

2017 Sales

	$ mil.	% of total
North America	20,905	53
Europe	15,177	39
Asia	2,791	7
Rest of World	584	1
Corporate & Other	(511)	-
Total	**38,946**	**100**

PRODUCTS/OPERATIONS

2017 Sales

	$ mil.	% of total
Body systems and chassis systems	9,744	25
Powertrain systems	6,773	17
Exterior systems	5,325	14
Seating systems	5,203	13
Tooling engineering & other	3,397	9
Complete vehicle assembly	2,944	8
Vision & electronic systems	2,891	7
Closure systems	2,669	7
Total	**38,946**	**100**

2017 Sales

	$ mil.	% of total
General Motors	6,854	18
Ford Motor Company	6,085	16
Fiat / Chrysler Group	5,502	14
Daimler AG	4,719	12
BMW	3,231	11
Volkswagen	4,025	10
Other	7,557	19
Total	**38,946**	**100**

Selected Operations Products and Services Body systems

Chassis systems
Seating
Powertrain
Electronics
Mechatronics
D-Optic headlights
Clearview mirrors
Vehicle engineering and manufacturing
Hybrid dual clutch transmission
Liteflex modular process
48 volt edrive
Driver monitoring systems
MAX4 Autonomous Drive Platform

COMPETITORS

AGGREKO LIMITED	Hyundai Motor Company
ALLISON TRANSMISSION HOLDINGS INC.	KOC HOLDING ANONIM SIRKETI
APTIV PLC	Rheinmetall AG
DANA INCORPORATED	TOYOTA BOSHOKU CORPORATION
FAURECIA	
GKN LIMITED	VALEO

HISTORICAL FINANCIALS

Company Type: Public

Income Statement

FYE: December 31

	REVENUE ($ mil.)	NET INCOME ($ mil.)	NET PROFIT MARGIN	EMPLOYEES
12/20	32,647	757	2.3%	158,000
12/19	39,431	1,765	4.5%	0
12/18	40,827	2,296	5.6%	0
12/17	38,946	2,206	5.7%	0
12/16	36,445	2,031	5.6%	155,450
Annual Growth	**(2.7%)**	**(21.9%)**	**—**	**0.4%**

2020 Year-End Financials

Debt ratio: 14.3%
Return on equity: 6.8%
Cash ($ mil.): 3,268
Current ratio: 1.37
Long-term debt ($ mil.): 3,973
No. of shares (mil.): 300
Dividends
Yield: 2.2%
Payout: 108.1%
Market value ($ mil.): 21,277

	STOCK PRICE ($) FY Close	P/E High/Low		PER SHARE ($) Earnings	Dividends	Book Value
12/20	70.80	29	10	2.52	1.60	37.83
12/19	54.84	10	8	5.59	1.46	35.72
12/18	45.45	10	7	6.61	1.32	32.69
12/17	56.67	10	7	5.90	1.10	31.35
12/16	43.40	9	6	5.16	1.00	25.55
Annual Growth	**13.0%**	**—**	**—**	**(16.4%)**	**12.5%**	**10.3%**

Magnit PJSC

Auditors: Ernst & Young LLC

LOCATIONS

HQ: Magnit PJSC
15/5, Solnechnaya Street, Krasnodar 350072
Phone: (7) 861 210 98 10
Web: www.magnit-info.ru

HISTORICAL FINANCIALS

Company Type: Public

Income Statement

FYE: December 31

	REVENUE ($ mil.)	NET INCOME ($ mil.)	NET PROFIT MARGIN	EMPLOYEES
12/20	20,771	441	2.1%	316,001
12/19	21,991	153	0.7%	308,432
12/18	17,748	485	2.7%	295,882
12/17	19,593	609	3.1%	0
12/16	16,033	811	5.1%	0
Annual Growth	**6.7%**	**(14.1%)**	**—**	**—**

2020 Year-End Financials

Debt ratio: 0.2%
Return on equity: 17.7%
Cash ($ mil.): 597
Current ratio: 0.94
Long-term debt ($ mil.): 1,974
No. of shares (mil.): 97
Dividends
Yield: —
Payout: 72.9%
Market value ($ mil.): —

Malayan Banking Berhad

Malayan Banking Berhad (better known as Maybank) is Malaysia's largest financial services group.

Boasting assets of RM640 billion ($145 billion) the firm and its subsidiaries provide deposit services mortgages credit cards and other loan products to businesses and individuals through some 400 branches in Malaysia nearly 430 branches in Indonesia over 20 branches in Singapore and 30-plus branches across Southeast Asia. The firm also offers investment banking asset management online banking brokerage insurance unit trusts and other investments and corporate finance services through 2400 offices in 20 countries. Amanah Raya a trust company controlled by the Malaysian government owns over 45% of Maybank.

Operations

Maybank also in 2014 ranked as South East Asia's fourth-largest bank the largest Islamic financing bank in Malaysia and the third-largest Islamic financing bank globally by assets. As Malaysia's largest bank it controlled an 18.4% market share of the loans advances and financing market in Malaysia as well as a 27.6% share of the savings deposit market and 21.1% share of the checking account market.

The bank categorizes its financial services under three key business pillars. Its Community Financial Services (which generated 35% of the company's net operating income or NOI in 2014) includes consumer banking SME and business banking services. The Global Banking pillar includes corporate banking (12% of NOI) investment banking (7%) global markets (8%) transaction banking and asset management. The Insurance & Takaful (8% of NOI) pillar offers insurance and Islamic services and also consists of Maybank's international business operations (28% NOI). Islamic financial services are also offered across all of its business units. Broadly speaking Maybank generates about half of its operating income from net interest income (mostly from loans and advances including from Islamic Banking Scheme operations). Around 20% of its operating income comes from net earned insurance premiums. The company had 46000 employees at the end of 2014.

Geographic Reach

Maybank's home markets are in Malaysia Singapore and Indonesia; which contributed nearly 89% of the group's profit before tax (PBT) in fiscal 2014. About 60% of its loans and 71% of its PBT were originated in Malaysia alone during the fiscal year. Singapore made up about 14% of its PBT. Outside of these markets Maybank operates in 20 countries (including 10 ASEAN countries) in major financial centers such as Hong Kong Shanghai London New York and Bahrain. It also has associates in Pakistan (MCB Bank's 1242 branches) and Vietnam (An Binh Bank's 145 branches).

Sales and Marketing

The firm serves more than 22 million individuals organizations and businesses (including those of Muslim faith).

Financial Performance

Note: Growth rates may differ after conversion to US dollars. This analysis uses financials from the company's annual report.

Maybank's revenues and profits have risen more than 30% since 2011 thanks largely to strong loan business growth.

The company's revenue rose by 7% to RM35.7 billion ($10.2 billion) in 2014 mostly thanks to higher interest income as its loan advances and financing assets grew by 13% driven by a 47.5% jump in international loan growth and buoyed by better-than-industry loan growth in Malaysia and Singapore. Its financial investment portfolio assets also grew 8% during the year which boosted interest income further.

Higher revenue in 2014 drove Maybank's net income up 3% to a record RM6.7 billion ($1.91 billion) for the year. The company's operating cash levels fell by 39% to RM5.27 billion ($1.5 billion)

despite higher earnings due to unfavorable working capital changes mostly related to financial assets purchased under resale agreements and because it used more cash toward loans advances and financing.

Strategy

Maybank's strategic objectives over the past five years (2010 through 2015) have included: being Malaysia's no. 1 retail financial services provider in 2015; be the leading ASEAN Wholesale bank expanding into the Middle East China and India; be Malaysia's leading Insurance and Takaful provider and an emerging regional player in the field as well; become a "truly regional organization" with around 40% of pre-tax profit coming from international operations by 2015; and becoming a global leader in Islamic Finance.

Some of Maybank's fastest growing businesses include Islamic financing and Takaful (insurance) services that adhere to Islamic law which prohibits the collection of interest but allows profit-sharing and the sale and buy-back of homes (instead of the origination of mortgages). Serving Muslim individuals organizations and businesses the company is opening branches at home and abroad that offer such services. Indeed Islamic Financing grew by 25% during 2014 which increased its proportion of total Malaysia loans to 43.8% at the end of 2014 (from 38.9% at the end of 2013). The growth also solidified Maybank as the largest Islamic bank in Malaysia and the third-largest globally by assets.

Maybank also continues to expand its global reach beyond its home markets. During 2014 it opened its first branch in Myanmar and its third branch in Kunming China. That year it also launched its Etiqa Insurance and Private Wealth businesses in Singapore.

Company Background

Maybank has made several acquisitions in the past to boost its international presence. In 2011 the company acquired 100% of Singapore brokerage Kim Eng Holdings. The addition boosted Maybank's international profile and expanded its distribution capabilities.

In 2008 the bank completed its acquisition of the 250-branch Bank Internasional Indonesia (BII). The deal had stalled when banking regulator Bank Negara Malaysia prohibited the transaction but that decision was reversed and the acquisition was ultimately allowed. Also in 2008 the bank acquired minority stakes in Pakistan's MCB Bank and Vietnam's An Binh Bank (ABBank) as well as Kookmin Bank's minority stake in PT Bank Internasional Indonesia.

EXECUTIVES

Non-Executive Independent Director, Shirley Goh
Group Chief Executive Officer - Community Financial Services, John Chong Eng Chuan
Non-Executive Non-Independent Chairman of the Board, Zamzamzairani Bin Mohd Isa
Member of the Shariah Supervisory Board, Marjan Muhammad
Chairman of the Shariah Supervisory Board, Harussani Bin Zakaria
Member of the Shariah Supervisory Board, Mohamed Fairooz Abdul Khir
Chief Financial Officer, Khalijah Binti Ismail
Group Chief Audit Executive, Nazlee Abdul Hamid
Independent Director, Zulkiflee Abbas bin Abdul Hamid
Group Chief Human Capital Officer, Nora Abd Manaf
Group Chief Executive Officer - Global Banking, Muzaffar Hisham
Group Chief Executive Officer - Islamic Banking, Mohamed Rafique Merican bin Mohd Wahiduddin Merican

Group Chief Executive Officer, Insurance & Takaful, Kamaludin Ahmad
Group President, Chief Executive Officer, Non-Independent Executive Director, Abdul Farid Alias, $656,802 total compensation
President Director - Maybank Indonesia, Taswin Zakaria
Group Chief Operations Officer, Kah Cho Hon
Group Chief Strategy Officer and Chief Executive Officer- International, Seong Yew Foong
Country Chief Executive Officer & Chief Executive Officer, Maybank Singapore, Hin Hock Lee
Independent Non-Executive Director, Hasnita Binti Dato' Hashim
Non-Executive Independent Director, Idris bin Kechot
Group General Counsel, Group Company Secretary, Marzimin Bin Wan Muhammad
Senior Independent Non-Executive Director, R. Karunakaran
Member of the Shariah Supervisory Board, Mohd Kamal Bin Mokhtar
Group Chief Technology Officer, Mohd Suhail Abdullah
Group Chief Risk Officer, Gilbert Kohnke
Independent Non-Executive Director, Fauziah Binti Hisham
Independent Non-Executive Director, Che Zakiah Binti Che Din
Member of the Shariah Supervisory Board, Nik Abdul Rahim Nik Abdul Ghani
Member of the Shariah Supervisory Board, Akhtarzaite Binti Abdul Aziz
Member of the Shariah Supervisory Board, Azrul Iskandar Mirza
Chairman of the Shariah Supervisory Board, Aznan Hasan
Independent Non-Executive Director, Shariffuddin bin Khalid
Independent Non-Executive Director, Anthony Elam
Joint Company Secretary, Fariz bin Abdul Aziz
Non-Independent Non-Executive Director, Kee Check Cheng
Independent Non-Executive Director, Edwin Gerungan
Auditors: Ernst & Young PLT

LOCATIONS

HQ: Malayan Banking Berhad
14th Floor, Menara Maybank, 100, Jalan Tun Perak, Kuala Lumpur 50050
Phone: (60) 3 2070 8833   **Fax:** (60) 3 2031 0071
Web: www.maybank.com

PRODUCTS/OPERATIONS

2013 Sales

	% of total
Interest income	65
Income from islamic banking scheme operations	11
Non-interest income	24
Total	**100**

Selected Subsidiaries

BinaFikir Sdn. Bhd.
Etiqa Insurance Berhad
Etiqa Life International (L) Ltd.
Etiqa Takaful Berhad
Maybank (PNG) Limited2
Maybank Ageas Holding Berhad (formerly known as Maybank Fortis Holdings Berhad)
Maybank Allied Credit & Leasing Sdn. Bhd.
Maybank International (L) Ltd.
Maybank Investment Bank Berhad
Maybank Islamic Berhad
Maybank Philippines Incorporated1
Maysec Sdn. Bhd.
PT Bank Internasional Indonesia TBK1
PT Bank Maybank Syariah Indonesia1
PT BII Finance Centre1
PT Wahana Ottomitra Multiartha TBK1

COMPETITORS

AKBANK TURK ANONIM	Shinhan Financial
SIRKETI	Group Co. Ltd.
BANK OF INDIA	TURKIYE IS BANKASI
BANK VTB PAO	ANONIM SIRKETI
CANARA BANK	UNITED OVERSEAS BANK
China Construction	LIMITED
Bank Corporation	YAPI VE KREDI BANKASI
FIRSTRAND LTD	ANONIM SIRKETI
PT. BANK CENTRAL ASIA	
TBK	

HISTORICAL FINANCIALS

Company Type: Public

Income Statement FYE: December 31

	ASSETS ($ mil.)	NET INCOME ($ mil.)	INCOME AS % OF ASSETS	EMPLOYEES
12/20	212,808	1,609	0.8%	42,000
12/19	203,956	2,003	1.0%	43,000
12/18	195,251	1,963	1.0%	43,000
12/17	188,535	1,852	1.0%	43,000
12/16	164,056	1,503	0.9%	43,976
Annual Growth	6.7%	1.7%	—	(1.1%)

2020 Year-End Financials

Return on assets: 0.7%	Dividends
Return on equity: 7.7%	Yield: 5.0%
Long-term debt ($ mil.): —	Payout: 160.0%
No. of shares (mil.): —	Market value ($ mil.): —
Sales ($ mil): 10,543	

	STOCK PRICE ($) FY Close	P/E High/Low		PER SHARE ($) Earnings	Dividends	Book Value
12/20	4.29	11	6	0.14	0.22	1.87
12/19	4.15	7	5	0.18	0.24	1.77
12/18	4.66	7	5	0.18	0.24	1.65
12/17	4.70	7	6	0.18	0.24	1.67
12/16	3.56	6	5	0.15	0.21	1.50
Annual Growth	4.8%	—	—	(1.3%)	1.3%	5.6%

Manulife Financial Corp

Manulife Financial Corporation is a leading international financial services group that helps people make their decisions easier and lives better. It operates as Manulife across its offices in Canada Asia and Europe and primarily as John Hancock in the US. Manulife provides financial advice insurance as well as wealth and asset management solutions for individuals groups and institutions. At the end of 2020 it had more than 118000 agents and thousands of distribution partners serving over 30 million customers. It has almost C$1.3 trillion in assets under management and administration. About 75% of Manulife's total sales comes from Asia and US.

Operations

Its segments are composed of its geographic locations in Asia Canada and US. Other segments are: Global Wealth and Asset Management (more than 5%) which provides fee-based wealth solutions to retail retirement and institutional customers and Corporate & other which comprised of investment performance on assets backing capital net of amounts allocated to operating segments; financing costs; costs incurred by the corporate office related to shareholder activities; Property and Casualty Reinsurance business; and run-off reinsurance business lines.

Geographic Reach

Headquartered in Ontario Canada Manulife operates in the Americas (Canada and the US) Europe and the Asia region (Japan Hong Kong Macau Singapore mainland China Vietnam Indonesia the Philippines Malaysia and Cambodia and have recently started operations in Myanmar).

The company's segment sales in Asia generates around 40% sales in the US bring in some 35% of Manulife's annual revenue and Canada accounts for some 25%.

Sales and Marketing

Manulife distributes its insurance products through agents brokers banks and financial planners. It also markets products directly to customers. The group has over 115000 contracted agents and more than 100 bank partnerships in Asia.

The company's pension contracts mutual fund offerings annuities and banking products are distributed through affiliated insurance agents and brokers securities brokerage firms financial planners pension plan sponsors and consultants and banks.

Financial Performance

Note: Growth rates may differ after conversion to US Dollars.

The company's revenue for fiscal 2020 decreased to C$78.9 billion compared from the prior year with C$79.6 million.

The decrease was due to higher premiums ceded to reinsurers. Net income for fiscal 2020 increased by C$0.3 billion to C$5.9 billion compared from the prior year with C$5.6 billion.

Cash held by the company at the end of fiscal 2020 increased to C$25.6 billion. Cash provided by operations and financing activities were C$20.0 billion and C$663 million respectively. Cash used by investing activities was C$14.1 billion mainly for purchases and mortgage advances.

Strategy

Manulife has five strategic priorities it set out at the start of its transformation. These five strategic priorities being: Portfolio Optimization; Expense Efficiency; Accelerate Growth; Digital Customer Leader' and High Performing Team.

Portfolio Optimization ? Manulife is continually optimizing its portfolio and has already surpassed its original target to release $5 billion of capital by 2022 delivering $5.9 billion of cumulative capital benefits through 2020. In 2020 the company broadened the portfolio optimization priority to include all of its global in-force insurance and annuity management.

Expense Efficiency ? Manulife is focused on driving efficient growth targeting a less than 50% expense efficiency ratio and has already delivered on its original target of $1 billion in expense efficiencies.

Accelerate Growth ? The company's growth ambition seeks to generate two-thirds of core earnings from its high potential businesses.

Digital Customer Leader ? In line with the company's mission to become the most digital customer-centric global company in its industry Manulife aims to improve Net Promoter Score by 30 points.

High Performing Team ? Manulife is committed to enabling a high performing team and achieving top quartile employee engagement.

Company Background

Manulife acquired US financial services giant John Hancock in a $10 billion deal in 2004 bringing Manulife into the top ranks of US and global life insurers. Manulife subsequently rebranded its US financial products with the more-recognizable John Hancock name and logo. Manulife also consolidated John Hancock's Canadian subsidiary Maritime Life Assurance Company into its flagship subsidiary The Manufacturers Life Insurance Company.

EXECUTIVES

Independent Director, John Palmer
President and Chief Executive Officer, John Hancock, Marianne Harrison, $737,601 total compensation
Independent Director, Nicole Arnaboldi
Global Head, Inforce Management, Naveed Irshad
Independent Director, Donald Lindsay
Independent Director, Andrea Rosen
Independent Director, Tsun-Yan Hsieh
Independent Director, Claude Prieur
Chief Actuary, Steven Finch
Chief Executive Officer, President, and Director, Roy Gori, $1,181,989 total compensation
Chief Human Resource Officer, Pamela Kimmet
President and Chief Executive Officer, Manulife Canada, Michael Doughty
Chief Risk Officer, Rahim Badrudin Hassanali Hirji
General Counsel, James Gallagher
Independent Director, Julie Dickson
Independent Director, Guy Bainbridge
Independent Director, Leagh Turner
President and Chief Executive Officer, Manulife Asia, Anil Wadhwani, $687,261 total compensation
Independent Director, Joseph Caron
Independent Director, Susan Dabarno
Chief Financial Officer, Philip Witherington, $676,429 total compensation
Chief Distribution Officer, Asia, Pankaj Banerjee
Director, May Tan
Chief Investment Officer, Scott Hartz, $697,883 total compensation
President and Chief Executive Officer, Global Wealth and Asset Management, Paul Lorentz
Auditors: Ernst & Young LLP

LOCATIONS

HQ: Manulife Financial Corp
200 Bloor Street East, Toronto, Ontario M4W 1E5
Phone: 416 926 3000 **Fax:** 416 926-5657
Web: www.manulife.com

2017 Sales

	% of total
US	41
Asia	37
Canada	21
Other	1
Total	**100**

PRODUCTS/OPERATIONS

2017 Sales

	% of total
Premiums	
Life & health	44
Annuities & pensions	8
Net investment income	27
Other	21
Total	**100**

COMPETITORS

AIA Group Limited
ALLIANZ INSURANCE PLC
ASSURANT INC.
Banco Bradesco S/A
Bank of Communications Co. Ltd.
DONEGAL GROUP INC.
FRANKLIN RESOURCES INC.
HCI GROUP INC.
OPPENHEIMER HOLDINGS INC.
Power Corporation of Canada
REINSURANCE GROUP OF AMERICA INCORPORATED
TOWERGATE PARTNERSHIPCO LIMITED
The Bank of Nova Scotia

HISTORICAL FINANCIALS

Company Type: Public

Income Statement				FYE: December 31
	ASSETS ($ mil.)	NET INCOME ($ mil.)	INCOME AS % OF ASSETS	EMPLOYEES
12/21	720,486	5,578	0.8%	0
12/20	691,419	4,611	0.7%	0
12/19	621,361	4,301	0.7%	35,000
12/18	550,946	3,524	0.6%	34,000
12/17	581,938	1,678	0.3%	34,300
Annual Growth	5.5%	35.0%	—	—

2021 Year-End Financials

Return on assets: 0.7%
Return on equity: 13.0%
Long-term debt ($ mil.): —
No. of shares (mil.): 1,943
Sales ($ mil): 48,538

Dividends
Yield: 4.9%
Payout: 43.8%
Market value ($ mil.): 37,053

	STOCK PRICE ($) FY Close	P/E High/Low		PER SHARE ($)		
				Earnings	Dividends	Book Value
12/21	19.07	6	5	2.78	0.93	23.10
12/20	17.82	7	3	2.30	1.13	20.77
12/19	20.29	7	5	2.13	0.75	19.27
12/18	14.19	9	6	1.71	0.71	17.16
12/17	20.86	22	18	0.78	0.65	16.60
Annual Growth	(2.2%)	—	—	37.3%	9.3%	8.6%

Mapfre SA

Auditors: KPMG Auditores S.L.

LOCATIONS

HQ: Mapfre SA
Carretera de Pozuelo 52, Madrid, Majadahonda
Phone: (34) 91 581 1100   **Fax:** (34) 91 581 1143
Web: www.mapfre.com

HISTORICAL FINANCIALS

Company Type: Public

Income Statement				FYE: December 31
	ASSETS ($ mil.)	NET INCOME ($ mil.)	INCOME AS % OF ASSETS	EMPLOYEES
12/20	84,870	646	0.8%	33,730
12/19	81,411	684	0.8%	34,324
12/18	77,061	605	0.8%	35,390
12/17	80,999	839	1.0%	36,271
12/16	71,675	818	1.1%	37,020
Annual Growth	4.3%	(5.7%)	—	(2.3%)

2020 Year-End Financials

Return on assets: 0.7%
Return on equity: 6.0%
Long-term debt ($ mil.): —
No. of shares (mil.): —
Sales ($ mil): 23,155

Dividends
Yield: 0.0%
Payout: 113.3%
Market value ($ mil.): —

	STOCK PRICE ($) FY Close	P/E High/Low		PER SHARE ($)		
				Earnings	Dividends	Book Value
12/20	4.00	26	18	0.21	0.24	3.44
12/19	5.50	32	25	0.22	0.23	3.26
12/18	5.42	42	32	0.19	0.24	3.00
12/17	5.89	38	26	0.28	0.25	3.35
12/16	5.23	117	15	0.26	0.20	3.13
Annual Growth	(6.5%)	—	—	(5.7%)	4.9%	2.4%

Marfrig Global Foods SA

Marfrig Global Foods is the world leader in production of hamburgers and one of the largest companies in the world when it comes to bovine-based protein in terms of capacity. It also supplies lamb pork poultry and fish as well as frozen vegetables sheep and sauces. Marfrig has more than 30 processing plants and other facilities in Brazil and more than 10 other countries around the world. The company which serves restaurant and supermarket chains and foodservice companies processes approximately 222 million tons of hamburger per year and some 209 million tons of other meat products annually. Pioneer in production of vegetable protein foodstuffs generates most of its sales in North America.

Operations

Marfrig's business dealings are divided between two platforms: North America (about 70%) and South America (nearly 30%). Together the company has the capacity to slaughter approximately 30100 head of cattle each day producing 222000 tons of hamburger per year and 209000 tons of other processed meats.

Both divisions featured diversified production embracing meat processing and industrialization. Its farm produce operations are also divided between the two regions. A joint venture it operates with the US corporation Archer Daniels Midland Company (ADM) one of the biggest suppliers of food ingredients in the world resulted in creation of PlantPlus! and establishes its company as responsible for the production and distribution of products via installations at V ̄rzea Grande (Mato Grosso) in Brazil and via National Beef in the US.

The company commands its own logistics National Carriers. Using a fleet of more than 1200 trucks the company offers transport and cattle-related logistical services for clients all over North America. In South America Marfrig dedicates its operations to the slaughtering and de-boning of bovine protein and the production of industrialized and processed food products such as hamburger canned meats beef jerky sauces ready-made meals and many others.

Geographic Reach

Headquartered in Brazil Marfrig's products are available in some 100 countries.

It has more than 30 different facilities in Brazil and more than 10 other countries in the Americas the Asia-Pacific region the Middle East and Europe.

Generates about 70% of the company's revenue in North America the company also has approximately 10 distribution centers spread in more than four continents.

Sales and Marketing

The company disseminates more information about its brands on television and through digital platforms. It also brought in Marfrig Ambassadors a total of approximately20 celebrities ? among them famous chefs and singers ? releasing more than 100 videos and 300 posts during the year and reaching some 80 million people. In addition it recorded commercials for TV with singer Michel Tel and with chef Salt Bae which were aired during major soccer games and on Brazilian news shows. Altogether over 100 million Brazilians saw the company's brands presented in this way during the year. In addition to its sales offices spread worldwide Marfrig products and brand names are made available through retailers wholesalers and food services.

More than 85% of sales made to the internal market go directly to premium clients.

Financial Performance

The company's net revenue for 2020 was R$67.5 billion an increase of 35% explained by the increased volume of exports in the face of a 31% depreciation of the Brazilian Real against the US dollar in addition to a 25% rise in operational revenue from the South American region and by a 6.5% increase from North America.

Strategy

The company has over the past two years or more refocused on the basics: effective purchasing good processing and more sales. It maintains as lodestars higher productivity and lower fixed costs. The strategy also includes diversification with investments in the area of hamburger meat and processed products; the company also focuses on innovation as seen in the launching of the new Viva! brand which uses meat cuts from cattle raised at low-carbon installations.

EXECUTIVES

Member of the Executive Board, Director, Rodrigo Filho
Chief Executive Officer, Member of the Executive Board, Miguel Gularte
Chief Legal Officer, Member of the Executive Board, Heraldo Geres
Chief Financial Officer, Member of the Executive Board, Tang David
Independent Director, Herculano Anibal Alves
Director, Alain Emile Henry Martinet
Chairman of the Board, Marcos Antonio Molina dos Santos
Director, Marcia Aparecida Pascoal Marcal dos Santos
Independent Director, Antonio dos Santos Maciel
Independent Director, Roberto Faldini
Independent Director, Roberto Silva Waack

LOCATIONS

HQ: Marfrig Global Foods SA
Avenida Queiroz Filho 1.560, Bloco 5, Sala 306, Vila Hamburguesa, Sao Paulo 04551-065
Phone: (55) 11 3792 8994   **Fax:** (55) 11 3792 8611
Web: www.marfrig.com.br

2017 Sales

	% of total
Brazil	23
Other countries	77
Total	**100**

PRODUCTS/OPERATIONS

2017 Sales

	% of total
Marfrig Beef	52
Keystone	48
Total	**100**

COMPETITORS

A. Moksel GmbH
BAKKAVOR GROUP PLC
CRANSWICK PLC
EBRO FOODS SA
Henan Shuanghui Investment & Development Co.Ltd.
Jbs S/A
Maple Leaf Foods Inc
SEABOARD CORPORATION
SMITHFIELD FOODS INC.
TYSON FOODS INC.
VISCOFAN SA
WH Group Limited

HISTORICAL FINANCIALS

Company Type: Public

Income Statement

FYE: December 31

	REVENUE ($ mil.)	NET INCOME ($ mil.)	NET PROFIT MARGIN	EMPLOYEES
12/19	12,130	54	0.4%	32,222
12/18	7,656	359	4.7%	30,167
12/17	5,607	(145)	—	32,846
12/16	5,940	(208)	—	29,203
12/15	4,769	(147)	—	30,276
Annual Growth	26.3%	—	—	1.6%

2019 Year-End Financials

Debt ratio: 17.7%
Return on equity: 33.7%
Cash ($ mil.): 441
Current ratio: 1.36
Long-term debt ($ mil.): 4,415
No. of shares (mil.): 701
Dividends
  Yield: —
  Payout: —
Market value ($ mil.): 1,717

	STOCK PRICE ($) FY Close	P/E High/Low		PER SHARE ($) Earnings	Dividends	Book Value
12/19	2.45	9	4	0.09	0.00	0.22
12/18	1.42	1	1	0.58	0.00	0.28
12/17	2.18	—	—	(0.25)	0.00	1.16
12/16	1.98	—	—	(0.40)	0.00	0.53
12/15	1.56	—	—	(0.28)	0.00	0.31
Annual Growth	11.9%	—	—	—	—	(8.4%)

Marks & Spencer Group PLC

Fashion and food are the bread and butter of stalwart British retail chain Marks and Spencer (M&S). The company is a British Value money retailer that is focused on its own label business including food clothing & home in the U.K. and Internationally. In addition the company sells high-quality great value products in over 1500 stores in the UK and another in some 60 countries and 45 websites globally. The company has around 300 owned stores and over 400 franchise food stores. M&S is the UK's #1 retailer of womenswear lingerie and menswear; its private label brands include Autograph Classic and per una. M&S Foods sells exclusively own-brand upmarket groceries and owns 50% of online grocer Ocado's UK retail business and is its sole supplier. M&S has been in business for more than 135 years.

Operations

Marks and Spencer Group plc operates a family of parallel business each trading value for many ranges.

M&S Food sells sustainably sourced fresh convenient products of outstanding quality through five main categories: protein deli and dairy; produce; ambient and in-store bakery; meals dessert and frozen; hospitality and 'Food on the Move'.

The company also sells stylish own-brand clothing and homeware through our principal product departments: Womenswear Menswear Lingerie Kidswear and Home.

Through M&S Bank (operated by HSBC) the company provides a range of financial services including credit cards current account and savings insurance and mortgages. M&S Energy is a competitive fully renewable energy source provider (operated by Octopus).

Lastly M&S operates an active Property Development team to maximize the value of our property assets through investment and development opportunities.

Geographic Reach

Marks and Spencer Group plc headquarters is based in U.K. The company exports Food and Clothing & Home around the world in select target markets across Europe the Middle East and Asia. Customers purchase products through a network of mainly partner-led or owned businesses in territories with growth potential or through online-only channels in growing markets such as Australia and the United States.

Sales and Marketing

Marks and Spencer Group plc markets its products through its website.

Financial Performance

Note: Growth rates may differ after conversion to US Dollars.

In fiscal 2020 (ended March 30) M&S's sales fell 2% to 10.2 billion largely as a result of lower UK Clothing & Home sales. It is estimated that the Covid-19 impacted group revenue by 83.5 million in March 2020.

Profit declined 40% from 45.3 million in 2019 to 27.4 million in 2020. The decline was mainly due to the drop in revenue largely affected by the Covid-19 pandemic.

M&S's cash levels are low and a threat to the company's liquidity. In fiscal 2020 the company's cash balance fell 49.5 million to 164.1 million. M&S's operations generated 973.1 million while its investing activities used 765.7 million and its financing used 156.9 million. Its main cash uses in fiscal 2020 were capital expenditures dividends purchase of investments in associates and joint ventures and redemption of notes.

Strategy

The aim of Marks & Spencer's transformation is to restore the company to sustainable profitable growth. However in the new landscape?where the way it works and how customers shop may never be the same again?M&S is learning from the crisis to ensure that it is changed for good.

M&S will accelerate aspects of the transformation to increase its relevance in a new-consumer environment. M&S moved to 'trusted value' in Clothing & Home and option count reduction and supplier concentration brought forward. The reduction in range and shift towards fast moving product at great value necessitated by the crisis resulting in a permanent reduction of 20% in autumn/winter store option count. The role of sourcing offices will be increased so that sampling ordering and quality issues are dealt with offshore. M&S is also developing a faster "near-sourcing" supply chain to enable a test and re-order of seasonal fashion lines particularly for the online business.

M&S is also establishing a store estate for the new world with the replacement of ageing stores already under way and shift in relationships with property providers to go faster. In addition M&S is turbocharging growth to become an online winner in Clothing & Home and Food. The sharp growth of online grocery during the crisis is evidence of this as is the strengthening performance of its online Clothing & Home.

HISTORY

Fleeing anti-Semitic persecution in Russian Poland 19-year-old Michael Marks immigrated to England in 1882. Eventually settling in Leeds Marks eked out a meager existence as a traveling peddler until he opened a small stall at the town market in 1884. Because he spoke little English Marks laid out all of his merchandise and hung a sign that read "Don't Ask the Price It's a Penny"

unaware at the time that self-service would eventually become the retailing standard. His methods were so successful that he had penny bazaars in five cities by 1890.

Finding himself unable to run the growing operation alone Marks established an equal partnership with Englishman Tom Spencer a cashier for a local distributor forming Marks and Spencer in 1894. By the turn of the century the company had 36 branches. Following the deaths of Spencer (1905) and Marks (1907) management of the company did not return to family hands until 1916 when Marks' 28-year-old son Simon became chairman.

Marks and Spencer broke with time-honored British retailing tradition in 1924 by eliminating wholesalers and establishing direct links with manufacturers. In 1926 the firm went public and two years later it launched its now famous St Michael brand. The company turned its attention to pruning unprofitable departments to concentrate on goods that had a rapid turnover. In 1931 the Marks & Spencer stores (M&S) introduced a food department that sold produce and canned goods.

The company sustained severe losses during WWII when bombing damaged approximately half of its stores. Marks and Spencer rebuilt and in 1964 Simon's brother-in-law Israel Sieff became chairman. The company expanded to North America a decade later by buying three Canadian chains: Peoples (general merchandise sold 1992) D'Allaird's (women's clothing sold 1996) and Walker's (clothing shops converted to M&S). Sieff's son Marcus Sieff became chairman in 1972. It opened its first store in Paris in 1975.

Derek Rayner replaced Marcus Sieff as chairman in 1984 becoming the first chairman hired from outside the Marks family since 1916. Under Rayner Marks and Spencer moved into financial services by launching a charge card in 1985. The company purchased US-based Kings Super Markets and Brooks Brothers (upscale clothing stores) in 1988. Rayner retired in 1991 and CEO Richard Greenbury became chairman. During the 1990s M&S opened new stores in Germany Hong Kong Hungary Spain and Turkey.

In 1997 it paid Littlewoods $323 million for 19 UK stores which it converted to M&S. Greenbury facing criticism that the company was too slow to expand and embrace new ideas was succeeded in 1999 as CEO by handpicked heir Peter Salsbury. That year continued poor sales led Marks and Spencer to cut 700 jobs close its 38 M&S stores in Canada and part ways with its clothing supplier of 30 years William Baird. In early 2000 Marks and Spencer dodged a takeover attempt by investor Philip Green. Chairman Luc Vandevelde took over as CEO in September when Salsbury resigned.

In spring 2001 Marks and Spencer announced a recovery plan to salvage its struggling M&S chain by selling off many of its global operations including its profitable US businesses (Brooks Brothers and Kings Super Markets). Unhappy with the company's direction and its departure from older values Marks and Spencer board members Sir David Sieff (the last remaining founder member) Sir Ralph Robins and Sir Michael Perry left the board in July 2001. Marks and Spencer sold Brooks Brothers to Retail Brand Alliance for $225 million (a loss from the $750 million the company paid for it in 1988) in November 2001 and nearly managed to sell its Kings Super Markets business to New York supermarket operator D'Agostino in July 2002 but the deal fell through later in the year due to a lack of financing.

Also in July 2002 Vandevelde — who is credited with masterminding the M&S turnaround — announced he would give up his role as CEO and hand the reins to managing director Roger

Holmes. Vandevelde became the company's part-time chairman in January 2003.

In May 2004 both Vandevelde and Holmes left M&S. Stuart Rose formerly head of Arcadia was named CEO; non-executive board member Paul Myners was named interim chairman of the company. Prior to the shift in management billionaire entrepreneur Philip Green (who owns Arcadia and Bhs in the UK) confirmed that he would mount a takeover bid for the retail group. Ultimately Green's final proposal (the third he made for the retailer in a five week period) was rejected by the M&S board in July 2004. In October M&S bought the Per Una brand from designer George Davies for about 126 million and moved its head office from the old Baker Street location to Waterside House by the Grand Union Canal in London. In November Rose ousted more than a handful of company executives including Maurice Helfgott Mark McKeon Laurel Powers-Freeling Jean Tomlin Jack Paterson and 20-year veteran Alison Reed who stepped down as CFO in April 2005.

M&S relaunched its Home catalogue in early 2005. In February of that year the company announced the sale of its former Baker Street headquarters Michael House to real estate company London & Regional Properties for 115 million. M&S which is in a profit squeeze said it plans to used the proceeds for "general corporate purposes." In August M&S sold its Lifestore in Gateshead to Active Asset Investment Management for 43 million. In December M&S won a ruling by the European Court of Justice that resulted in the company receiving a 30 million tax windfall from the Treasury.

In April 2006 M&S completed the sale of its 26-store Kings Super Markets chain in the US for about $61.5 million. Lord Burns a former chairman of Abbey National took up the post of chairman in July 2006 after joining Marks and Spencer as deputy chairman in 2005. Burns succeeded interim chairman Paul Myners.

In 2007 M&S opened three stores in Taiwan. (Marks & Spencer Taiwan is 60%-owned by the British retailer and 40% by President Chain Store.) The following year M&S opened its first store on the mainland in Shanghai.

In June 2008 Lord Burns stepped down as chairman of the company and was succeeded by CEO Stuart Rose who became executive chairman. David Michels was appointed deputy chairman as well. Rose stepped down as CEO in May 2010 to make way for Marc Bolland thus decoupling the roles of chairman and chief executive at the firm.

EXECUTIVES

Chief Executive, Executive Director, Steve Rowe, $1,089,807 total compensation
International Director, Paul Friston
Chairman, Audit, Andy Halford, $92,777 total compensation
Independent Non-Executive Director, Justin King, $92,777 total compensation
Group General Counsel, Company Secretary, Nick Folland
Independent Non-Executive Director, Sapna Sood, $78,403 total compensation
Independent Non-Executive Director, Tamara Ingram, $78,403 total compensation
Chief Financial Officer, Executive Director, Eoin Tonge, $638,987 total compensation
Independent Non-Executive Director, Evelyn Bourke, $15,680 total compensation
Independent Non-Executive Director, Fiona Dawson
Clothing & Home Managing Director, Richard Price
Retail Director, Sacha Berendji

Non-Executive Chairman of the Board, Archie Norman, $92,777 total compensation
Chief Operating Officer, Stuart Machin
Auditors: Deloitte LLP

LOCATIONS

HQ: Marks & Spencer Group PLC
 Waterside House, 35 North Wharf Road, London W2 1NW
Phone: (44) 20 7935 4422
Web: www.marksandspencer.com

2018 Sales

	% of total
UK	91
International	9
Total	**100**

PRODUCTS/OPERATIONS

2018 Sales

	% of total
UK	
Food	57
Clothing and Home	34
International	9
Total	**100**

COMPETITORS

COSTCO WHOLESALE CORPORATION
DAIEI INC. THE
DUNNES STORES UNLIMITED COMPANY
HARVEY NICHOLS GROUP LIMITED
POUNDLAND LIMITED
THE GREAT ATLANTIC & PACIFIC TEA COMPANY INC.
Victoria Retail Group B.V.
WILKO LIMITED
WM MORRISON SUPERMARKETS LIMITED

HISTORICAL FINANCIALS

Company Type: Public

Income Statement

FYE: April 3

	REVENUE ($ mil.)	NET INCOME ($ mil.)	NET PROFIT MARGIN	EMPLOYEES
04/21*	12,661	(273)	—	69,846
03/20	12,438	28	0.2%	75,505
03/19	13,594	43	0.3%	78,597
03/18	15,033	36	0.2%	80,787
04/17	13,261	146	1.1%	84,939
Annual Growth	**(1.2%)**	—	—	**(4.8%)**

*Fiscal year change

2021 Year-End Financials

Debt ratio: 30.5%	No. of shares (mil.): 1,956
Return on equity: (-6.5%)	Dividends
Cash ($ mil.): 932	Yield: —
Current ratio: 0.69	Payout: —
Long-term debt ($ mil.): 2,037	Market value ($ mil.): 8,198

	STOCK PRICE ($) FY Close	P/E High/Low		PER SHARE ($) Earnings	Dividends	Book Value
04/21*	4.19	—	—	(0.14)	0.00	1.61
03/20	2.43	540	166	0.01	0.42	2.32
03/19	7.26	394	302	0.03	0.45	2.16
03/18	7.59	699	462	0.02	0.50	2.56
04/17	8.43	158	99	0.09	0.51	2.43
Annual Growth	**(16.0%)**	—	—	—	—	**(9.7%)**

*Fiscal year change

Marubeni Corp.

One of Japan's largest sogo shosha (general trading companies) Marubeni conducts a broad range of import/export activities across numerous sectors. These include lifestyle ICT & real estate business forest products food agri business chemicals power business energy metals & mineral resources plant aerospace & ship finance & leasing business construction auto & industrial machinery. Its footprint spans around 135 branches in about 60 countries including twelve in Japan nearly 30 overseas branches and about 30 operated by overseas subsidiaries. The Marubeni traces the origins of its business to the linen cloth business started by its founder Chubei Itoh in 1858.

Operations
Marubeni consists of six business group: Transportation & Industrial Machinery Financial Business Group (roughly 5% of sales); Food Agriculture and Chemical Group (about 70%); Consumer Product Group (more than 10%); Power Business & Infrastructure Group (less than 5%); Energy & Metals Group (more than 10%); and CDIO. Under these business groups it has about 15 business divisions.

The Transportation & Industrial Machinery Financial Business Group consists of Construction Industrial Machinery & Mobility Division Aerospace and Ship Division and Finance & Leasing Business Division. The Construction Industrial Machinery & Mobility Division includes Sales services and financing of construction and mining equipment. The Aerospace & Ship Division is involved in aircraft & engine parts trading business and fund establishment and development investment. The Finance & Leasing Business Division includes Auto finance business aircraft and aircraft engine leasing business comprehensive leasing business leasing of various commercial vehicles and freight railcars private equity investment and asset management.

The Food Agriculture & Chemicals Group includes divisions such as Food Chemicals and Agri Business. The Food Division includes grain products such as corn soybeans wheat rapeseed etc.; feed ingredients including soybean meal rapeseed meal fish meal etc.; compound feed and fresh and processed meat among others. The Chemical Division includes basic petrochemical products and plastic derivatives salt and chlor-alkali products and life science-related products such as functional ingredients for foods functional feed additives oleochemicals and personal care ingredients. Its Agri Business Division crop protection products fertilizers seeds and proprietary products.

The Consumer Product Group makes up ICT & Real Estate Business Division Lifestyle Division and Forest Products Division. The ICT & Real Estate Business Division provides a wide range of high-added-value services and solutions in operating domains related to consumers' everyday lives including ICT real estate logistics and insurance The Lifestyle Division is OEM/ODM manufacturing of products such as apparel and footwear. The Forest Products Division's products include wood chips and biomass fuel pulp and waste water paper paperboard and hygiene products as well as building & construction materials and wood products.

The Power Business & Infrastructure Group includes Power Business Division Infrastructure Project Division.

The Energy and Metals Group consists of Energy Division and Metals & Mineral Resources Division. The Energy Division is involved in exploration development and production of oil and gas. The Metals & Mineral Resources Division develops iron ore coal and copper mines smelting and refining of aluminum and magnesium trading of iron ore coal ferroalloy ferrous raw materials and cement-related materials.

The CDIO includes Next Generation Business Development which includes Chinese children education business inbound tourism business next-generation retail business and smart city and smart infrastructure business among others.

Geographic Reach

Headquartered in Tokyo Marubeni has roughly 135 branches and offices spread across about 60 countries and regions. It has a dozen branches in Japan and nearly 60 overseas branches in addition to nearly 30 offices run by about 30 overseas corporate subsidiaries.

Financial Performance

The company's revenue for fiscal 2021 decreased by 495.2 billion yen to 6.3 trillion yen compared from 6.8 trillion yen in the prior year.

Profit for fiscal 2021 was 233.1 billion yen compared from the prior year with a loss of 190.2 billion yen.

Cash held by the company at the end of fiscal 2021 increased to 745.9 billion yen. Cash provided by operations was 397.1 billion yen while cash used for investing and financing activities were 116.3 billion yen and 68.5 billion yen respectively. Main cash uses were purchase of investments in associates and joint ventures and other investments and repayments of long-term bonds and borrowings.

Strategy

To build Marubeni's global competitiveness via the development of individual employees the company are expanding its HR development programs. These consist mainly of on-the-job training supplemented by off-the-job training.

On-the-job training includes assigning hands-on experience and recommending junior employees for overseas assignments to build professionalism early in their careers. The Marubeni Group training curriculum that supports off-the job training has been revamped since the fiscal year ended March 31 2017. Established to help realize the Marubeni Group's HR strategy the Marubeni Global Academy (MGA) is being upgraded. The company plan to roll out its HR development programs at the global and group levels to continue building human capital across the Marubeni Group.

Mergers and Acquisitions

In 2021 Marubeni acquired 100% of the shares of Solton Co. Ltd. a company that operates an industrial connector distribution business in Japan. With the acquisition of Solton Marubeni will strengthen product coverage optimize logistics and contribute to the development of the electronic component industry.

In mid-2021 Marubeni acquired Euroma Holding B.V. a major European spices and seasonings manufacturer with the intention to become 100% shareholder. Marubeni utilize its network of food and agriculture to support Euroma's business expansion in Europe and work to expand sales in the US and Asia.

Also in 2021 Marubeni acquired 100% of the shares of Remacan Industries Inc. a company that operates a conveyor belt distribution business in Ontario Canada through Marubeni's subsidiary Belterra Corporation. Belterra's strategy is to expand its business to Eastern Canada and the acquisition of Rematech is integral to achieving this strategy.

In the latter part of 3rd quarter of 2020 Marubeni Corporation announces that the company acquired 25% of the shares of Mexico-based APP Coatzacoalcos Villahermosa S.A.P.I. De C.V. which is a concessionaire to execute a project for improvement and 7.5-year maintenance of 135km

roads between Coatzacoalcos in Veracruz State and Villahermosa in Tabasco State located in southern Mexico under a Public Private Partnership from Hycsa group a local Mexican construction company. Marubeni considers PPP projects in the field of transport and infrastructure to be one of its core strategies and has been expanding its footprint in the market. Terms were not disclosed.

In mid-2020 Daio Paper Corporation and Marubeni Corporation agreed to jointly acquire indirectly all shares of Santher - F brica de Papel Santa Therezinha S.A. through a joint investment company established in Brazil called H&PC BRAZIL PARTICIPA •ES S.A in which Daio and Marubeni hold 51.0% and 49.0% stake respectively. Marubeni seeks to enhance Santher's corporate value by integrating Marubeni's existing functions resources and networks as a general trading house and through Santher's business contribute to the realization of a hygienic environment and safe and comfortable lifestyles. Terms were not disclosed.

In early 2020 Marubeni Corporation has executed a Share Purchase Agreement with I Squared Capital to acquire Chenya Energy Co. Ltd a solar power developer and operator in Taiwan. Chenya will become a wholly owned subsidiary of Marubeni upon the conclusion of this transaction. By acquiring Chenya and Chenya's solar power generation assets including one of the world's largest floating solar power plants Marubeni will gain expertise in the floating solar power business and continue to enhance its renewable energy development capabilities. Terms were not disclosed.

HISTORY

Marubeni's origins are closely linked to those of another leading Japanese trading company. ITOCHU founder Chubei Itoh set up Marubeni Shoten K. K. in 1858 as an outlet in Osaka for his textile trading business (originally C. Itoh & Co.). The symbol for the store was a circle (maru) drawn around the Japanese word for red (beni). As C. Itoh's global operations expanded the Marubeni store served as headquarters.

Marubeni was split off from C. Itoh in 1921 to trade textiles although it soon expanded its operations to include industrial and consumer goods. To mobilize for WWII the Japanese government reunited Marubeni and C. Itoh in 1941 merging them with another trading company Kishimoto into a new entity Sanko Kabushiki Kaisha. In 1944 Sanko Daido Boeki and Kureha Spinning were ordered to consolidate into a larger entity to be called the Daiken Co. but the war ended before all operations were fully integrated.

Spun off from Daiken in 1949 Marubeni began trading internationally. It opened a New York office in 1951 and diversified into food metals and machinery. During the Korean War Marubeni benefited from the UN's use of Japan as a supply base.

In 1955 Marubeni merged with Iida & Company and changed its name to Marubeni-Iida. It received a government concession to supply silicon steel and iron sheets critical to the growing Japanese auto and appliance industries. The company expanded into engineering — building factories aircraft and a nuclear reactor for the Japan Atomic Energy Research Institute — and into petrochemicals fertilizers and rubber products.

Marubeni-Iida was behind the Fuyo keiretsu formed in the early 1960s. Fuyo (another word for Mt. Fuji) is a powerful assemblage of some 150 companies including Canon Hitachi and Nissan that form joint ventures and develop think tanks.

The firm became Marubeni Corp. in 1972 and a year later it bought Nanyo Bussan another trading company. In 1973 Marubeni's image was tar-

nished by allegations that it had hoarded rice for sale on the Japanese black market.

In the 1990s Marubeni won several major construction contracts. Among them Marubeni formed a venture in 1998 with John Laing and Turkey's Alarko Alsim to rebuild three airports in Uzbekistan.

Marubeni had begun offering Internet access in 1995 and two years later it launched an Internet-based long-distance telephone service. In 1999 the trading house formed two ventures with US firm Global Crossing one to start operating Pacific Crossing One (the Japan-US cable) and another to lay a cable network in Japan.

That year Marubeni tied up with fellow trading company ITOCHU to integrate their steel processing subsidiaries in China to try to keep their Chinese businesses afloat. In 2000 ITOCHU and Marubeni formed an online steel trading joint venture with US-based e-commerce company MetalSite. The two companies also integrated their entire steel divisions in 2001 forming the Marubeni-Itochu Steel joint venture among the largest steel companies in Japan.

Taking responsibility for the sharp downturn in Marubeni's financial performance chairman Iwao Toriumi announced in 2001 that he would step down. The company launched a major restructuring effort the next year that was designed to give more autonomy to the managers of individual business units.

In 2005 Marubeni launched a large power and water project in Abu Dhabi.

In 2007 Marubeni entered into the finance leasing industry in the US launching subsidiary CoActiv Capital Partners.

In 2008 Marubeni acquired US-based The PIC Group Inc. an independent global provider of services and programs focused on power generation and other industrial facilities and services. In 2009 it acquired 49% of Invenergy Thermal Financing LLC which owns three natural-gas fired power plants (with 1014 MW of generating capcity) in the US.

In 2009 the company completed the Laffan Refinery in Qatar which began commercial operations that year. It also signed a $2 billion deal to build the Shuweihat S2 Independent Water and Power Producer project in the United Arab Emirates.

EXECUTIVES

Independent Director, Takashi Hatchoji
Independent Director, Masato Kitera
Chairman of the Board, Fumiya Kokubu
President, Chief Executive Officer, Representative Director, Masumi Kakinoki
Executive Vice President, Chief Executive Officer of Food, Agribusiness & Chemicals Group, Representative Director, Akira Terakawa
Independent Director, Takao Kitabata
Senior Managing Executive Officer, Chief Administrative Officer, Chief Information Officer, Chief Compliance Officer, Mutsumi Ishizuki
Senior Managing Executive Officer, President of Subsidiary, Nobuhiro Yabe
Senior Managing Executive Officer, Chief Executive Officer of Social Industry & Financial Group, Hajime Kawamura
Managing Executive Officer, President of Subsidiary, Shinichi Kobayashi
Managing Executive Officer, Chief Executive Officer of Energy & Metal Group, Akihiko Sagara
Vice Chairman, Ichiro Takahara
Managing Executive Officer, Chief Digital Innovation Officer, Chief Strategy Officer, Representative Director, Kenichiro Oikawa
Executive Officer, President of Chiba Office, Soji Sakai

Independent Director, Yuri Okina
Independent Director, Kyohei Takahashi
Chief Financial Officer, Managing Executive Officer, Chief Sustainable Development Officer, Representative Director, Takayuki Furuya
Managing Executive Officer, Chief Executive Officer of Life Industrial Group, Jun Hirasawa
Independent Director, Shigeki Ishizuka
Auditors: Ernst & Young ShinNihon LLC

LOCATIONS

HQ: Marubeni Corp.
  1-4-2, Otemachi, Chiyoda-ku, Tokyo 100-0004
Phone: (81) 3 3282 2111
Web: www.marubeni.co.jp

2016 Sales

	% of total
Japan	53
US	33
Singapore	4
Other countries	10
Total	**100**

PRODUCTS/OPERATIONS

2019 Sales

	% of total
Food	54
Chemical & Forest Products	22
Energy & Metals	11
Consumer Products	5
Transportation & Industrial Machinery	5
Power projects & Plant	3
Total	**100**

2019 Sales

	% of total
Goods	97
Commission on service & trading margins	3
Total	**100**

COMPETITORS

CORE-MARK HOLDING COMPANY INC.
ENERPAC TOOL GROUP CORP.
GEA Group AG
GOODWIN PLC
ITOCHU CORPORATION
J.W. FILSHILL LIMITED
MAHINDRA AND MAHINDRA LIMITED
MITSUBISHI CORPORATION
MITSUI & CO. LTD.
Mets oliitto Osuuskunta
PERFORMANCE FOOD GROUP COMPANY
Restricted Data - Order Investigation 653708586
SEALASKA CORPORATION
SOJITZ CORPORATION
SPARTANNASH COMPANY
SUMITOMO CORPORATION
TOYOTA TSUSHO CORPORATION

HISTORICAL FINANCIALS

Company Type: Public

Income Statement
FYE: March 31

	REVENUE ($ mil.)	NET INCOME ($ mil.)	NET PROFIT MARGIN	EMPLOYEES
03/21	57,190	2,035	3.6%	53,059
03/20	62,898	(1,818)	—	53,395
03/19	66,832	2,084	3.1%	50,540
03/18	71,010	1,989	2.8%	49,125
03/17	63,760	1,389	2.2%	47,938
Annual Growth	**(2.7%)**	**10.0%**	**—**	**2.6%**

2021 Year-End Financials

Debt ratio: 0.3%	No. of shares (mil.): 1,736
Return on equity: 13.5%	Dividends
Cash ($ mil.): 6,736	Yield: 3.1%
Current ratio: 1.26	Payout: 219.6%
Long-term debt ($ mil.): 16,350	Market value ($ mil.): 145,997

STOCK PRICE ($) FY Close	P/E High/Low		PER SHARE ($) Earnings	Dividends	Book Value
03/21	84.07	1	0	1.15	2.65	9.46
03/20	49.17	—	—	(1.07)	3.17	8.04
03/19	70.47	1	1	1.18	3.21	10.29
03/18	72.85	1	1	1.12	2.45	9.61
03/17	61.41	1	0	0.79	1.82	8.68
Annual Growth	**8.2%**	—	—	**9.9%**	**9.9%**	**2.2%**

Mashreqbank

Auditors: PricewaterhouseCoopers

LOCATIONS

HQ: Mashreqbank
  P.O. Box 1250, Dubai
Phone: (971) 4 2223333   **Fax:** (971) 4 2226061
Web: www.mashreqbank.com

HISTORICAL FINANCIALS

Company Type: Public

Income Statement
FYE: December 31

	ASSETS ($ mil.)	NET INCOME ($ mil.)	INCOME AS % OF ASSETS	EMPLOYEES
12/20	43,164	(347)	—	0
12/19	43,412	562	1.3%	0
12/18	38,102	560	1.5%	0
12/17	34,088	558	1.6%	0
12/16	33,435	524	1.6%	0
Annual Growth	**6.6%**	—	—	—

2020 Year-End Financials

Return on assets: (-0.8%)	Dividends
Return on equity: (-6.2%)	Yield: —
Long-term debt ($ mil.): —	Payout: —
No. of shares (mil.): 177	Market value ($ mil.): —
Sales ($ mil): 2,424	

Mazda Motor Corp. (Japan)

Mazda Zoom-Zooms along with the top automakers in Japan. Known for its "Zoom-Zoom" slogan Mazda sells about 1.5 million passenger cars and pickup trucks in about130 countries annually. The company has manufacturing operations in Japan China Thailand Mexico Vietnam Malaysia and Russia. Its lineup consists of the Mazda 2 3 6 and the MX-5 (passenger vehicles) the CX-3 -4 -5 -8 -30 -9 (crossover SUVs) and the BT-50 (pickup truck). The company produces the majority of its vehicles at home in Japan although North America is its largest market. Ford holds approximately 3.5% stake in the company. Mazda was founded in 1920.

Operations

Mazda has been introducing products featuring Skyactiv Technology and Kodo?Soul of Motion design which provide both driving pleasure and out-

standing environmental and safety performance. The launch of the all-new Mazda3 in 2019 marked the roll-out of its first new-generation product. The company's major product line includes MAZDA CX-3 CX-30 CX-4 CX-5 CX-8 CX-9 MAZDA 2 MAZDA 3 MAZDA 6 MAZDA MX-5 and MAZDA BT-50.

Passenger vehicles account for some 50% of Mazda's sales and crossover vehicles the other about 50%.

Geographic Reach

Based in Hiroshima Japan North America is Mazda's biggest market at more than 25% of total sales. China accounts for over 15% Europe more than 15% and Japan under 15%. Australia the wider Asia/Pacific region and other markets account for the remaining revenue. Nearly 65% of Mazda's vehicles are produced in Japan.

Mazda has major production sites in Japan Mexico Thailand and China. The Company conducts sales in more than 130 countries and regions around the world.

Sales and Marketing

Mazda has around 220 sales companies in Japan and some 140 internationally.

Strategy

Mazda's long-term plan the catchily titled "Sustainable Zoom-Zoom 2030" is to produce cars that will develop a bond between driver and company. It will do this by increasing sustainability safety and driving pleasure. With fuel economy at or near the top of many consumers' priorities Mazda developed an engine technology that can reliably combust a leaner fuel/air mixture called SKYACTIV-X and runs 20% more efficiently in real-world driving conditions. To improve safety the company continues to tweak its driving positions and visibility and will roll out semi-autonomous driving technology by 2025. Lastly to provide an emotionally enriching driving experience the company will design its cars with the "horse and rider as one" philosophy in mind.

HISTORY

Ingiro Matsuda founded cork producer Toyo Cork Kogyo in Hiroshima in 1920. The company changed its name to Toyo Kogyo in 1927 and began making machine tools. Impressed by Ford trucks used in 1923 earthquake-relief efforts Matsuda had the company make a three-wheel motorcycle/truck hybrid in 1931.

During the 1930s the company supplied products to the Sumitomo industrial conglomerate. The Sumitomo Bank became a major shareholder of Toyo Kogyo.

The second Sino-Japanese War forced Toyo Kogyo to make rifles and cut back on its truck production. Although the company built a prototype passenger car in 1940 the outbreak of WWII refocused it on weapons. The August 1945 bombing of Hiroshima killed more than 400 Toyo Kogyo workers but the company persevered producing 10 trucks that December. By 1949 it was turning out 800 per month.

The company launched the first Mazda a two-seat minicar in 1960. The next year Toyo Kogyo licensed AUDI's new rotary engine technology. After releasing a string of models the company became Japan's #3 automaker in 1964. Toyo Kogyo introduced the first Mazda powered by a rotary engine Cosmo/110S in 1967 followed by the Familia in 1968.

The company grew rapidly and began exporting to the US in 1970. However recession high gas prices and concern over the inefficiency of rotary engines halted growth in the mid-1970s. Sumitomo Bank bailed out Toyo Kogyo. The company shifted emphasis back to piston engines but managed to launch the rotary engine RX-7 in 1978.

Ford's need for small-car expertise and Sumitomo's desire for a large partner for its client led to Ford's purchase of 25% of Toyo Kogyo in 1979. The company's early 1980s GLC/323 and 626 models were sold as Fords in Asia Latin America and the Middle East.

Toyo Kogyo changed its name to Mazda Motor Corporation in 1984. ("Mazda" is loosely derived from Matsuda's name but the carmaker has never discouraged an association with the Zoroastrian god of light Ahura Mazda.) The company opened a US plant in 1985 but a strong yen expensive increases in production capacity and a growing number of models led to increased overhead soaring debt and shrinking margins. By 1988 Mazda had begun to focus on sporty niche cars launching the hot-selling Miata in 1989.

The company faced more problems with the early 1990s recession. In 1992 Mazda introduced a new 626 model. That year Mazda also sold half its interest in its Flat Rock Michigan plant to Ford. As the yen development costs and prices for its cars in the US all rose sales in the US fell. In 1993 Mazda reorganized subsidiary Mazda of America by cutting staff.

Ford sank $481 million into Mazda in 1996 increasing its stake to 33%. That year the Ford-appointed former EVP of Mazda Henry Wallace became Mazda's president making history as the first non-Japanese to head a major Japanese corporation. In 1997 Wallace resigned to become CFO of Ford's European operations and former Ford executive James Miller replaced him. That year Mazda consolidated four US operations into Mazda North American Operations.

Restructuring continued in 1998 as Mazda consolidated some European operations and closed a plant in Thailand. In 1999 Mazda sold its credit division to Ford and its Naldec auto parts unit to Ford's Visteon unit. It announced plans to sell its stake in South Korean carmaker Kia Motors. Later in the year another American Ford's Mark Fields took over as president.

In 2000 Mazda recalled 30000 of that year's MPV minivans to fix a powertrain control module and asked owners of all 2000 MPVs to bring in their vehicles for front-bumper reinforcement. Mazda also announced plans to close about 40% of its North American dealership outlets over the next three years. The following year Mazda completed a program to assume direct control over distribution in some European markets including France Italy Spain and the UK.

In 2007 Mazda opened a new vehicle assembly plant in Nanjing China and also began building its passenger vehicle plant in Thailand. To strengthen its sales in Japan the company introduced the Mazda Advantage Loan in 2007 in cooperation with PRIMUS Financial Services. Mazda acquired a 40% stake in PRIMUS in March 2008 to strengthen its auto financing business.

Ford's 33% stake in the company was reduced to about 13% in 2008 after the cash-starved company sold off approximately 20% of its holdings. A consortium of Hiroshima Bank Panasonic (both Mazda business partners) and Mazda itself paid a combined sum of about $540 million to bring control of the company back to Japan.

EXECUTIVES

Independent Director, Kiyoshi Sato
Independent Director, Masato Sugimori
Senior Managing Executive Officer, Director, Masahiro Moro
Senior Managing Executive Officer, Director, Akira Koga
Executive Vice President, Chief Operating Officer, Representative Director, Kiyoshi Fujiwara

Chairman of the Board, Representative Director, Kiyotaka Shobuda
Independent Director, Ichiro Sakai
President, Chief Executive Officer, Representative Director, Akira Marumoto
Senior Managing Executive Officer, Director, Mitsuru Ono
Director, Masatoshi Maruyama
Senior Managing Executive Officer, Director, Yasuhiro Aoyama
Director, Nobuhiko Watabe
Independent Director, Michiko Ogawa
Independent Director, Hiroko Shibasaki
Independent Director, Akira Kitamura
Auditors: KPMG AZSA LLC

LOCATIONS

HQ: Mazda Motor Corp. (Japan)
3-1 Shinchi, Fuchu-cho, Aki-gun, Hiroshima 730-8670
Phone: (81) 82 282 1111
Web: www.mazda.co.jp

2017 Sales

	% of total
Japan	18
North America	34
Europe	20
Other regions	28
Total	**100**

PRODUCTS/OPERATIONS

Selected Models
BT-50 (pickup)
CX-3 (crossover SUV)
CX-4 (crossover SUV)
CX-5 (crossover SUV)
CX-8 (crossover SUV)
CX-9 (crossover SUV)
Mazda 2 (Demio)
Mazda 3 (Axela hatchback sedan)
Mazda 6 (sport sedan)
Mazda 8 (MPV)
MX-5 (roadster)

Selected Subsidiaries and Affiliates
Mazda Australia Pty. Ltd.
Mazda Motor Logistics Europe NV (Belgium)
Mazda Motor of America Inc.

COMPETITORS

AUDI AG	PEUGEOT SA
FCA US LLC	RENAULT
FORD MOTOR COMPANY	SUBARU CORPORATION
ISUZU MOTORS LIMITED	SUZUKI MOTOR
KIA CORPORATION	CORPORATION

HISTORICAL FINANCIALS
Company Type: Public

Income Statement
FYE: March 31

	REVENUE ($ mil.)	NET INCOME ($ mil.)	NET PROFIT MARGIN	EMPLOYEES
03/21	26,029	(285)	—	49,786
03/20	31,600	111	0.4%	50,479
03/19	32,188	573	1.8%	49,998
03/18	32,716	1,055	3.2%	49,755
03/17	28,749	838	2.9%	42,849
Annual Growth	**(2.5%)**	**—**	**—**	**3.8%**

2021 Year-End Financials
Debt ratio: 0.2%
Return on equity: (-2.6%)
Cash ($ mil.): 5,338
Current ratio: 1.84
Long-term debt ($ mil.): 6,510
No. of shares (mil.): 629
Dividends
 Yield: 2.2%
 Payout: —
Market value ($ mil.): 2,576

	STOCK PRICE ($) FY Close	P/E High/Low		PER SHARE ($) Earnings	Dividends	Book Value
03/21	4.09	—	—	(0.45)	0.09	16.95
03/20	2.66	0	0	0.18	0.16	17.19
03/19	5.56	0	0	0.91	0.16	17.48
03/18	6.68	0	0	1.72	0.17	17.84
03/17	7.18	0	0	1.40	0.14	15.55
Annual Growth	**(13.1%)**	—	—	**—**	**(9.6%)**	**2.2%**

mBank SA

Auditors: Ernst & Young Audyt Polska spolka z ograniczona odpowiedzialnoscia sp. k.

LOCATIONS

HQ: mBank SA
ul. Senatorska 18, Warsaw 00-950
Phone: (48) 22 829 00 00   **Fax:** (48) 22 829 00 33
Web: www.brebank.com.pl

HISTORICAL FINANCIALS
Company Type: Public

Income Statement
FYE: December 31

	ASSETS ($ mil.)	NET INCOME ($ mil.)	INCOME AS % OF ASSETS	EMPLOYEES
12/19	41,836	266	0.6%	9,352
12/18	38,830	350	0.9%	8,823
12/17	37,735	313	0.8%	8,556
12/16	31,974	291	0.9%	8,401
12/15	31,558	332	1.1%	8,587
Annual Growth	**7.3%**	**(5.4%)**	**—**	**2.2%**

2019 Year-End Financials
Return on assets: 0.6%
Return on equity: 6.4%
Long-term debt ($ mil.): —
No. of shares (mil.): 42
Sales ($ mil): 1,992
Dividends
 Yield: —
 Payout: —
Market value ($ mil.): —

McKesson Europe AG

McKesson Europe (formerly Celesio) is a global leader in healthcare supply chain management solutions retail pharmacy community oncology and specialty care. Its largest wholesale markets are France Germany and the UK. In addition to around 100 distribution centers serving more than 56000 pharmacies McKesson Europe operates approximately 1850 own pharmacies and manage more than 300 pharmacies in six European countries. The company which was founded by Fraz Ludwig Gehe in 1835 and has a presence in about 15 European countries generates about 40% of sales in the UK.

Operations

McKesson Europe operates through two divisions: Pharmaceutical Distribution and Retail Pharmacy.

The Pharmaceutical Distribution business accounts for more than 75% of sales delivers pharmaceutical and other healthcare-related products to pharmacies across Europe. This business functions as a vital link connecting manufacturers to retail pharmacies by supplying medicines and other products sold in pharmacies. Pharmaceutical and other healthcare-related products are stored at regional wholesale branches using technology-enabled management systems.

Brings in about 25% of sales Retail Pharmacy business includes outpatient dispensing and homecare arrangements by providing traditional prescription pharmaceuticals non-prescription products and medical services.

Geographic Reach
Headquartered in Stuttgart Germany McKesson Europe generates about 40% of sales in the UK. France provides nearly 35% of sales while other countries represent the remaining. The Lloyds Pharmacy brand operates in Belgium Ireland Italy and the UK.

Sales and Marketing
McKesson Europe serves patients and consumers in European countries directly through its own pharmacies and franchise pharmacies. The company partners with pharmaceutical manufacturers providers pharmacies governments and other healthcare organizations to help provide the right medicines medical products and healthcare services to the right patients. In addition it also partners with independent pharmacies under its franchise program.

Financial Performance
McKesson Europe's revenue came to ?17.1 billion in fiscal 2020 up 4% from the fiscal 2019 amount of ?16.4 billion. The positive development was mainly caused by growth in Pharmaceutical Distribution UK Pharmaceutical Distribution France and Pharmaceutical Distribution Austria.

Net loss for fiscal 2020 was ?243.3 million compared from the prior year with ?54.6 million.

Cash held by the company at the end of fiscal 2020 increased to ?977.0 million. Cash provided by operations and financing activities were ?312.6 million and ?29.2 million respectively. Cash used for investing activities was ?194.4 million mainly for capital expenditures.

Strategy
McKesson Europe strategy is to focus on European core markets that offer the right mix of economic growth potential competitive landscape and customer type coupled with an ability to scale and leverage its operations to generate maximum efficiencies. Following this strategy the company closed further acquisitions in fiscal year 2020 to extend its European footprint within countries in which it already operate.

Due to an ongoing strategic review McKesson Europe has implemented several restructuring programs to enhance the profitability of its business. These programs include reorganization and consolidation of its business operations and related headcount reductions as well as further closures of retail pharmacies.

EXECUTIVES

Member of the Supervisory Board, Jack Stephens
Member of the Supervisory Board, Employee Representative, Susan Naumann, $20,581 total compensation
Deputy Chairman of the Supervisory Board, W.M. Rehder, $20,581 total compensation
Member of the Supervisory Board, Lori Schechter
Member of the Supervisory Board, Pauline Lindwall, $20,581 total compensation
Member of the Supervisory Board, Employee Representative, Joerg Lauenroth-Mago, $20,581 total compensation
Member of the Management Board, Legal Affairs and Compliance, Tilo Koester, $111,113 total compensation
Auditors: Deloitte GmbH

LOCATIONS

HQ: McKesson Europe AG
Stockholmer Platz 1, Stuttgart 70137
Phone: (49) 711 5001 00   **Fax:** (49) 711 5001 12 60
Web: www.mckesson.eu

2013 Sales

	% of total
France	30
UK	22
Germany	21
Brazil	9
Other	18
Total	**100**

PRODUCTS/OPERATIONS

2013 Sales

	% of total
Pharmacy solutions	84
Customer solutions	16
Total	**100**

Selected Subsidiaries
Pharmacy Solutions (wholesale distribution division)
  AAH Pharmaceuticals Ltd. (UK)
  AFM S.p.A. (Italy)
  Cahill May Roberts Group Ltd (Ireland)
  GEHE Pharma Handel GmbH (Germany)
  GEHE Pharma Praha spol. S r.o. (Czech Republic)
  Herba Chemosan Apotheker AG (Austria)
  Kemofarmacija d.d. (Slovenia Romania and Croatia)
  Laboratoria Flandria NV (Belgian)
  Norsk Medisinaldepot AS (Norway)
  OCP Repartition (France)
  OCP Portugal Produtos Farmacêuticos SA (Portugal)
  Panpharma Participacoes S.A. (54% Brazil)
  Pharma Belgium SA
  Rudolf Spiegel GmbH (Germany)
  Tjellesen Max Jenne A/S (Denmark)
Patient and Consumer Solutions (retail pharmacies division)
  Admenta Italia S.p.A.
  Apotheke DocMorris (retail franchise)
  Brocacef (45% Netherlands)
  DocMorris Kooperationen GmbH (mail order)
  Lé;ká;rny Lloyds s.r.o. (Czech Republic)
  Lloyds Pharmacy Limited (UK)
  Lloydspharma SA (Belgium)
  Unicare Pharmacy Limited (Ireland)
  Vitusapotek AS (Norway)

COMPETITORS

CARDINAL HEALTH INC.
China National Pharmacertical Group Corporation
HIKMA PHARMACEUTICALS PUBLIC LIMITED COMPANY
MAWDSLEY-BROOKS & COMPANY LIMITED
MEDIPAL HOLDINGS CORPORATION
Mediq B.V.
SUZUKEN CO. LTD.
Shenzhen Haiwang Xingchen Health Pharmacy Chain Co. Lt
TEVA PHARMACEUTICAL INDUSTRIES LIMITED
THE HARVARD DRUG GROUP L L C
TOHO HOLDINGS CO.LTD.
WALGREENS BOOTS ALLIANCE INC.

HISTORICAL FINANCIALS

Company Type: Public

Income Statement				FYE: March 31
	REVENUE ($ mil.)	NET INCOME ($ mil.)	NET PROFIT MARGIN	EMPLOYEES
03/20	18,752	(272)	—	31,912
03/19	23,782	(66)	—	32,946
03/18	25,998	(368)	—	34,338
03/17	22,055	(1,033)	—	35,716
03/16	24,388	447	1.8%	23,404
Annual Growth	(6.4%)	—	—	8.1%

2020 Year-End Financials

Debt ratio: 13.1%   No. of shares (mil.): 203
Return on equity: (-13.3%)   Dividends
Cash ($ mil.): 1,070   Yield: —
Current ratio: 1.16   Payout: —
Long-term debt ($ mil.): 581   Market value ($ mil.): —

Mediobanca Banca Di Credito Finanziario SpA

There's not much room for mediocrity at Mediobanca. A leading Italian investment bank the firm offers underwriting M&A support wholesale banking and financial advisory to corporate clients worldwide. It also offers retail banking private banking factoring credit management and leasing services. Despite being known as a top investment bank nearly 50% of Mediobanca's revenue comes from its Retail and Consumer Banking businesses which include Compass Futuro Compass RE Creditech and CheBanca! About 40% of its revenue comes from its Corporate and Investment Banking division. Mediobanca's international offices are in Frankfurt Istanbul London Madrid Mexico City New York and Paris.

Operations
Mediobanca operates four divisions. The bank's Retail and Consumer Banking (RCB) business (which made up 48% of its total revenue during fiscal 2015 ended June 30 2015) counts its consumer credit and retail banking business which includes Compass Futuro Compass RE Creditech and CheBanca!

Mediobanca's Corporate and Investment Banking (CIB) division (37% of revenue) consists of the Wholesale Banking (WSB) unit which includes lending structured finance and investment banking; as well as the Private Banking (PB) unit which counts Compagnie Monegasque de Banque Spafid and Prudentia and 50% of Banca Esperia pro rata. The Principal Investing (PI) division (12% of revenue) mostly counts the bank's 13% equity stake in Assicurazioni Generali. The Corporate division (3% of revenue) houses other businesses including the leasing business.

Broadly speaking about 75% of Mediobanca's revenue came from interest and similar income (about three-fourths of which came from retail loans) in FY2015 while about 15% came from fee and commission income. Around 47% of its ?30 billion loan book was tied to RCB loans while about 44% was tied to CIB loans.

Geographic Reach
Mediobanca generates most of its business in Italy though it operates international branches and subsidiary offices in Frankfurt Istanbul London Madrid Mexico City New York and Paris. About 80% of its banking revenue came from Italy during FY2015 while 20% came from other parts of Europe. Around 55% of its wholesale banking revenue came from Italy that year while 24% came from the UK and another 16% was split between Germany France and Spain.

Sales and Marketing
About 48% of Mediobanca's revenue came from consumer finance and retail clients in FY2015 while 31% came from wholesale banking clients and 12% came from principal investing clients.

Financial Performance

Note: Growth rates may differ after conversion to US dollars. This analysis uses financials from the company's annual report.

Mediobanca's annual revenues and profits have been growing over the past few years with revenue growing more than 25% since fiscal 2013 (ended June). The bank's revenue jumped 12% to ?2.05 billion ($2.27 billion) during FY2015 while net profit rose 27% to ?590 million ($654.57 million).

Strategy

Mediobanca plans to continue building its capital-light fee-generating businesses to boost its overall profitability. Indeed during FY2015 the bank generated 47% of its before-tax profit from its Corporate and Investment Banking (CIB) division despite it making up 37% of its revenue. By comparison Mediobanca's interest-focused Retail and Consumer Banking (RCB) division generated nearly half of the group's revenue but only 17% of its profit.

Mergers and Acquisitions

In August 2015 Mediobanca agreed to buy a 51% majority interest in London-based credit asset manager and advisory firm Cairn Capital Group. The move would continue to build on Mediobanca's international Alternative Asset Management business which involves strategic partnerships with asset managers with strong track records "high quality" management teams and scalable platforms.

HISTORY

In 1946 the three Italian "banks of national interest" Banca Commerciale Italiana (Comit) Credito Italiano (now Unicredito Italiano) and Banco di Roma (now part of Banca di Roma) founded Mediobanca to offer medium-term credit a market they were barred from.

Enrico Cuccia was with Comit at the time Mediobanca was formed and moved over to head the new institution. In 1955 he created the shareholder structure that later caused a twin uproar in Italian banking and politics: Although the state owned well more than half of the bank's shares a group of wealthy shareholders who together owned less than 10% of the bank wielded the power.

Over the next several decades Cuccia and Mediobanca operated on the behalf of these powerful shareholders and their family businesses devising deals on terms that other companies could not get. Mediobanca also created a web of crossholdings in other banks which made money for the bank by selling its funds and other services.

In the 1960s and 1970s the bank was at the center of a number of deals not all of which were stellar successes. The bank engineered a merger between Pirelli and Dunlop which fizzled and also pushed the merger of chemical companies Montecatini and Edison into Montedison which took a beating in the marketplace.

In 1982 Cuccia ostensibly retired taking the title of honorary chairman. However his influence never waned and the 1980s brought a war for the soul of Italian business. In 1985 Romano Prodi head of IRI the state-run organization (liquidated in 2000) that owned nearly 60% of the bank planned to privatize the bank. Instead the noble wing came up with its own privatization plan: The private shareholders requested that the state bring its stake in Mediobanca to below 50% by selling some of its shares to the Mediobanca cabal. In 1988 the privatization went through but as part of the pact it was stipulated that the new shareholders would share decision-making powers with the Ala Nobile.

If the 1980s were wild the 1990s were out of control. Italy's banking industry hampered by red tape and old alliances was left behind the rest of Europe. Many of Italy's banks became stock companies when banking laws changed and many merged to compete in the European Union. Many of those deals threatened Mediobanca's hegemony so it tried to block them. The bank nixed Unicredito's 1998 bid for Comit (which instead merged with Banca Intesa) as well as Sanpaolo IMI's 1999 offer for Banca di Roma.

In 2000 the bank still keeping a grip on the wheels of finance orchestrated investment firm Compart's buyout of Montedison (the merged entity took the Montedison name). That year the company launched an online private banking joint venture with Banca Mediolanum.

Also in 2000 its 46-year relationship with Lazard ended when the international investment banker announced plans to sell back to Mediobanca its 4% stake in the company along with its nearly 5% stake in Assicurazioni Generali.

After Cuccia's death in 2000 successor Vincenzo Maranghi battled such controlling shareholders as the Agnelli and Pirelli families and Deutsche Bank over the bank's future. These shareholders wanted to bring Mediobanca into the modern world by possibly merging it with another top Italian bank or even separating its investment management operations from its investment banking which generates a large majority of Mediobanca's profits.

However in a bid to stick to the old ways Maranghi arranged for backing (in exchange for a small stake in Mediobanca) from Swiss Life. Maranghi was blamed in part for the bank's decline: He forced out some of the investment banking division's top talent in the late 1990s and eventually resigned in 2003

Despite efforts to become more open some of the mystery surrounding Mediobanca remains. The shareholder dispute erupted after the death of Cuccia (whose body was subsequently robbed from its grave and later found).

Maranghi's replacement Gabriele Galateri di Genola had his work cut out for him repairing cracks in Mediobanca's image but he saw profits rise considerably. Under his watch the group has made its first foray into operations abroad opening an office in Paris. By 2004 the company posted improved financial results for a second consecutive year including a 20% increase in investment banking fees.

Galateri di Genola resigned from Mediobanca in 2007 after he lost the support of the supervisory board. He was succeeded by Alberto Nagel the company's general manager.

EXECUTIVES

Non-Executive Chairman of the Board, Renato Pagliaro, $1,990,294 total compensation
Chief Executive Officer, Executive Director, Alberto Nagel, $1,990,294 total compensation
Non-Executive Independent Director, Elisabetta Magistretti, $221,143 total compensation
Non-Executive Independent Deputy Chairman of the Board, Maurizia Comneno, $226,672 total compensation
Executive Director, Group General Manager, Francesco Vinci, $1,658,579 total compensation
Non-Executive Independent Director, Maurizio Costa, $116,100 total compensation
Non-Executive Independent Director, Valerie Hortefeux, $210,086 total compensation
Non-Executive Independent Director, Maurizio Carfagna, $259,844 total compensation
Secretary of the Board of Directors, Massimo Bertolini
Head of Group Investor Relations & Strategic Corporate Development, Jessica Spina
Non-Executive Independent Director, Gabriele Villa, $243,258 total compensation

Non-Executive Independent Director, Angela Gamba, $176,915 total compensation
Non-Executive Independent Director, Alberto Lupoi, $158,375 total compensation
Non-Executive Independent Director, Virginie Banet
Non-Executive Independent Director, Laura Cioli
Non-Executive Independent Director, Vittorio Campori, $176,915 total compensation
Auditors: PricewaterhouseCoopers S.p.A.

LOCATIONS

HQ: Mediobanca Banca Di Credito Finanziario SpA
Piazzetta Enrico Cuccia 1, Milan 20121
Phone: (39) 02 8829 1   **Fax:** (39) 02 882 9367
Web: www.mediobanca.com

PRODUCTS/OPERATIONS

2015 Sales

	% of total
Retail and consumer banking	50
Corporate and private banking	32
Principal investing	15
Corporate center	3
Total	**100**

COMPETITORS

BANKINTER SOCIEDAD ANONIMA	SYNOVUS FINANCIAL CORP.
Bayerische Landesbank	Skandinaviska Enskilda Banken AB
COMMONWEALTH BANK OF AUSTRALIA	Svenska Handelsbanken AB
SANTANDER HOLDINGS USA INC.	UBS AG
SUNTRUST BANKS INC.	UniCredit Bank AG

HISTORICAL FINANCIALS

Company Type: Public

Income Statement

	ASSETS ($ mil.)	NET INCOME ($ mil.)	INCOME AS % OF ASSETS	EMPLOYEES
				FYE: June 30
06/21	98,244	960	1.0%	4,754
06/20	88,392	672	0.8%	4,746
06/19	74,989	439	0.6%	986
06/18	84,244	1,006	1.2%	4,717
06/17	80,338	855	1.1%	4,798
Annual Growth	5.2%	2.9%	—	(0.2%)

2021 Year-End Financials

Return on assets: 1.0%	Dividends
Return on equity: 7.7%	Yield: 0.0%
Long-term debt ($ mil.): —	Payout: 70.9%
No. of shares (mil.): 862	Market value ($ mil.): 10,029
Sales ($ mil.): 3,771	

	STOCK PRICE ($) FY Close	P/E High/Low		PER SHARE ($) Earnings	Dividends	Book Value
06/21	11.63	13	8	1.11	0.79	15.31
06/20	7.13	17	6	0.77	0.34	12.67
06/19	10.23	25	18	0.50	0.35	6.79
06/18	9.23	12	9	1.17	0.28	12.92
06/17	9.27	12	6	0.99	0.20	12.11
Annual Growth	5.8%	—	—	2.8%	40.8%	6.0%

Medipal Holdings Corp

Medipal is one of the largest distribution networking groups. Its primary business is the wholesale distribution of prescription and OTC pharmaceuticals medical supplies cosmetics and personal sundries. In addition to supplying some 240000 Japanese pharmacies and retail stores Medipal distributes to hospitals and provides information technology support to its customers through its numerous subsidiaries and affiliates including Mediceo Everlth Atol and PharField. Its MP Agro subsidiary distributes animal health products.

Operations

Medipal operates through three primary segments: Prescription Pharmaceutical Wholesale (accounting for more than 65% of net sales); Cosmetics Daily Necessities and OTC Pharmaceutical Wholesale (accounting for more than 30% of net sales); and Animal Health Products and Food Processing Raw Materials Wholesale (roughly 5% of net sales).

The Prescription Pharmaceutical Wholesale Business procures prescription pharmaceuticals and also healthcare products related to diagnostics testing treatment and administration including medical equipment and medical materials and clinical diagnostic reagents for use from the presymptomatic stage.

Cosmetics Daily Necessities and OTC Pharmaceutical Wholesale operating through Paltac sells a range of products to drug stores supermarkets convenience stores and other retail establishments.

Animal Health Products and Food Processing Raw Materials Wholesale business sells animal health products to animal hospitals and livestock and fishery businesses; through the newly established Medipal Foods Corporation (2016) it distributes raw materials for processing food to food manufacturers.

Geographic Reach

Medipal operates throughout Japan. Its corporate headquarters is located in Tokyo Japan.

Sales to outside customers in Japan were more than 90% of net sales.

Sales and Marketing

Medipal supplies to about 240000 customers in hospitals clinics pharmacies drugstores convenience stores animal hospitals livestock and fishery businesses and manufacturers of processed foods all across the nation coming from about 5000 suppliers.

Financial Performance

The company's revenue for fiscal 2021 decreased to 3.2 trillion compared with 3.3 trillion. In the Prescription Pharmaceutical Wholesale Business sales decreased 1.4% year-on-year in challenging market conditions caused by the NHI (National Health Insurance) drug price reduction implemented on April 1 2020 and fewer visits to medical doctors and surgeries due to the COVID-19 pandemic. In the Cosmetics Daily Necessities and OTC Pharmaceutical Wholesale Business sales decreased 1.3% year-on-year. In the Animal Health Products and Food Processing Raw Materials Wholesale Business sales increased 1.1% year-on-year.

Profit for fiscal 2021 decreased by 37% to 23.9 billion compared with 38.0 billion in the prior year primarily due to Medipal recorded a gain on sales of investment securities in extraordinary income and extra retirement payments in extraordinary losses.

Cash held by the company at the end of fiscal 2021 increased to 240.0 billion. Cash provided by operations was 34.4 billion while cash used for investing and financing activities were 2.9 billion and 16.0 billion respectively. Main cash uses were purchase of property plant and equipment; and cash dividends paid.

Strategy

The current medium-term vision is "2022 MEDIPAL Medium-Term Vision: Change the Oroshi Future ? Innovation for the Future." Medipal's three growth strategies are to innovate existing businesses expand new businesses and establish business partnerships.

DX (digital transformation) using ICT is a major theme in the medical and healthcare sector. DX progress in the medical field will likely reduce wastefulness in medical care improve the operating efficiency of medical institutions and enhance patient convenience.

Company Background

Medipal was formed when Mediceo Holdings took over household products distributor Paltac in 2005. Paltac brought with it a distribution network and logistical prowess which allowed the new firm to move further into the OTC and non-drugs business. Previously Mediceo Holdings become Japan's largest drug wholesaler in 2004 when it was formed through the merger of three smaller drug wholesalers (Kuraya Pharmaceuticals Sanseido and Tokyo Iyakuhin).

EXECUTIVES

Executive Officer, Deputy Chief Director of System, Kazuki Kakutani
President, Chief Executive Officer, Chairman of Subsidiary, Representative Director, Shuichi Watanabe
President of Subsidiary, Director, Takuro Hasegawa
Vice President, President of Subsidiary, Director, Yasuhiro Chofuku
Senior Executive Officer, Deputy Chief Director of Business Development, President of Subsidiary, Hideaki Takemura
Senior Executive Officer, Kikuo Miki
Senior Managing Director, Chief Director of Business Development, Director of Business Investment in Main Business Development Unit, Toshihide Yoda
Chief Director of System, President of Subsidiary, Director, Shinjiro Watanabe
Independent Director, Toshio Asano
Independent Director, Mitsuko Kagami
Independent Director, Kuniko Shoji
Director, Koichi Mimura
Managing Director, Chief Director of Administration, Yuji Sakon
President of subsidiary, Director, Seiichi Kasutani
Independent Director, Hiroshi Iwamoto
Auditors: KPMG AZSA LLC

LOCATIONS

HQ: Medipal Holdings Corp
2-7-15 Yaesu, Chuo-ku, Tokyo 104-8461
Phone: (81) 3 3517 5800
Web: www.medipal.co.jp

PRODUCTS/OPERATIONS

2017 Net Sales

	% of total
Prescription Pharmaceutical Wholesale	68
Cosmetics Daily Necessities and OTC Pharmaceutical Wholesale	30
Animal Health Products Raw Materials Wholesale	2
Total	**100**

Selected Divisions and Brands

Atol Co. Ltd.
Everlth Co. Ltd.
Mediceo Corporation
M.I.C. (Medical Information College) Inc.
MM Corporation
MP Agro Co. Ltd.
Paltac Corporation
Trim Co. Ltd.

COMPETITORS

AEON CO. LTD.
AMERISOURCEBERGEN CORPORATION
China National Pharmacertical Group Corporation
DKSH Holding AG
FAST RETAILING CO. LTD.
GRIFOLS SA
KIKKOMAN CORPORATION
MALLINCKRODT PUBLIC LIMITED COMPANY
MITSUBISHI CHEMICAL HOLDINGS CORPORATION
PERRIGO COMPANY PUBLIC LIMITED COMPANY
PHIBRO ANIMAL HEALTH CORPORATION
SEVEN & I HOLDINGS CO. LTD.
SOMPO HOLDINGS INC.
STERIS LIMITED
SUZUKEN CO. LTD.
TOYO SEIKAN GROUP HOLDINGSLTD.

HISTORICAL FINANCIALS

Company Type: Public

Income Statement
FYE: March 31

	REVENUE ($ mil.)	NET INCOME ($ mil.)	NET PROFIT MARGIN	EMPLOYEES
03/21	29,001	216	0.7%	20,588
03/20	29,968	349	1.2%	21,393
03/19	28,732	310	1.1%	21,731
03/18	29,630	327	1.1%	22,068
03/17	27,404	259	0.9%	20,984
Annual Growth	**1.4%**	**(4.5%)**	**—**	**(0.5%)**

2021 Year-End Financials

Debt ratio: 0.0%
Return on equity: 4.6%
Cash ($ mil.): 2,011
Current ratio: 1.23
Long-term debt ($ mil.): 273
No. of shares (mil.): 209
Dividends
Yield: 1.9%
Payout: 39.3%
Market value ($ mil.): —

Medtronic PLC

Auditors: PricewaterhouseCoopers LLP

LOCATIONS

HQ: Medtronic PLC
20 On Hatch, Lower Hatch Street, Dublin 2
Phone: (353) 1 438 1700
Web: www.medtronic.com

HISTORICAL FINANCIALS

Company Type: Public

Income Statement
FYE: April 30

	REVENUE ($ mil.)	NET INCOME ($ mil.)	NET PROFIT MARGIN	EMPLOYEES
04/21	30,117	3,606	12.0%	90,000
04/20	28,913	4,789	16.6%	90,000
04/19	30,557	4,631	15.2%	90,000
04/18	29,953	3,104	10.4%	86,000
04/17	29,710	4,028	13.6%	91,000
Annual Growth	**0.3%**	**(2.7%)**	**—**	**(0.3%)**

2021 Year-End Financials

Debt ratio: 28.3%
Return on equity: 6.9%
Cash ($ mil.): 3,593
Current ratio: 2.65
Long-term debt ($ mil.): 26,378
No. of shares (mil.): 1,345
Dividends
Yield: 1.7%
Payout: 108.9%
Market value ($ mil.): —

Meiji Yasuda Life Insurance Co.

Meiji Yasuda Life Insurance one of Japan's largest life insurers offers individual life and annuities group life and pensions and investment products. It also has some general insurance health care and investment and financial services operations. Meiji Yasuda provides its products to a range of customers including individuals small businesses and corporations. The company has about 116 trillion of life insurance policies in force and more than 6.4 million policy holders. While most of its operations are in Japan Meiji Yasuda also operates in Asia Europe and North America.

Operations

Meiji Yasuda's operating segments include Insurance businesses that provide accident insurance products for corporate customers; Asset management businesses that provide investment advisory services as well as building and real estate management; Outsourcing service businesses that provide policy maintenance and system development; and Health research and wellness promotion businesses including operation of nursing care facilities.

Geographic Reach

Meiji Yasuda is headquartered in Tokyo. It also has more than 95 regional offices more than 20 marketing centers and more than 1000 agency locations. The group has international affiliate locations in nine global cities: Beijing Frankfurt Hong Kong Honolulu London Los Angeles New York Shanghai and Warsaw.

Sales and Marketing

Meiji Yasuda sells its products through an internal sales force of nearly 32450 personnel. It makes some sales to banks and other financial institutions through general agents.

Financial Performance

Note: Growth rates may differ after conversion to US Dollars.

Meiji Yasuda's revenue increased only 2% to 4.2 trillion in fiscal 2019 (ended March) from 4.1 trillion the year prior as insurance premiums and investment and dividend income increased.

Net income that year was 230.9 billion a 13% decrease from 265.9 billion the year prior mainly due to an increase in expenses.

The company ended fiscal 2019 with 1.3 trillion in net cash 627.3 billion more than it had at the end of fiscal 2018. Operating activities provided 743.4 billion in cash and financing activities provided 101.8 billion while investment activities used 217.8 billion for purchase of securities and extended loans.

Strategy

Meiji Yasuda has been implementing the My Innovation 2020 a three-year program that encompasses a Medium-Term Business Plan and the Corporate Vision Realization Project. These two components are both designed to facilitate business innovation driving its transformative and creative initiatives aimed at realizing its corporate philosophy the "Meiji Yasuda Philosophy."

The company has also identified the Twelve Reforms that will drive its growth strategy and operating base reinforcement strategy effectively focusing its management resources and capital on these reforms. The Twelve Reforms encompass growth strategy initiatives to facilitate business innovation in the domestic life insurance business and the oversees insurance business as well as the domestic affiliate business along with its operating base

reinforcement strategy aimed at securing a more robust foundation for future growth.

For its Domestic Life Insurance Business Meiji Yasuda launched the "Wellness for All Project" on a full-scale in 2020. In conjunction with this move the company released "Best Style Health Cash Back" in 2019 aimed at providing customers with ongoing assistance to their health improvement efforts.

Meiji Yasuda has also expanded the lineup of paperless enrollment procedures duly named "Meister Mobile" in 2019. These procedures now also allow corporate customers to apply for enrollment in new policies. It has also upgraded the "MY Hoken Page" which is a website dedicated to policyholder services expanding the scope of procedures that can be performed via this website.

Mergers and Acquisitions
Company Background

Tracing its roots back to 1881 Meiji Yasuda in its current incarnation was formed through the merger of Meiji Life Insurance and Yasuda Mutual Life in 2004. Prior to their merger Meiji Life and Yasuda Mutual Life were part of the Mitsubishi Group and Mizuho Financial Group respectively.

In the US the company acquired StanCorp Financial Group (parent of Standard Insurance) for $5 billion in 2016. That company became Meiji Yasuda's primary US unit.

Auditors: KPMG AZSA LLC

LOCATIONS

HQ: Meiji Yasuda Life Insurance Co.
2-1-1 Marunouchi, Chiyoda-ku, Tokyo 100-0005
Phone: (81) 3 3283 8293   **Fax:** (81) 3 3215 8123
Web: www.meijiyasuda.co.jp

PRODUCTS/OPERATIONS

Selected Subsidiaries
Meiji Yasuda America Incorporated
Meiji Yasuda Asia Limited
Meiji Yasuda Europe Limited
Pacific Guardian Life Insurance Company Limited (California)
Pacific Guardian Life Insurance Company Limited (Hawaii)
StanCorp Financial Group Inc

COMPETITORS

AIA Group Limited
CNO FINANCIAL GROUP INC.
GIBRALTAR LIFE INSURANCE CO. LTD. THE
MS&AD INSURANCE GROUP HOLDINGS INC.
NIPPON LIFE INSURANCE COMPANY
PRUDENTIAL FINANCIAL INC.
SOMPO HOLDINGS INC.
STANCORP FINANCIAL GROUP INC.
Sun Life Financial Inc.
T&D HOLDINGS INC.

HISTORICAL FINANCIALS
Company Type: Public

Income Statement				FYE: March 31
	REVENUE ($ mil.)	NET INCOME ($ mil.)	NET PROFIT MARGIN	EMPLOYEES
03/19	35,810	2,073	5.8%	42,950
03/18	36,930	2,495	6.8%	42,261
03/17	33,261	2,001	6.0%	41,872
03/16	38,082	1,906	5.0%	41,045
03/15	37,631	2,212	5.9%	40,793
Annual Growth	(1.2%)	(1.6%)	—	1.3%

2019 Year-End Financials

Debt ratio: 0.0%	No. of shares (mil.): —
Return on equity: 5.6%	Dividends
Cash ($ mil.): 13,739	Yield: —
Current ratio: 0.86	Payout: —
Long-term debt ($ mil.): —	Market value ($ mil.): —

Meituan

Auditors: PricewaterhouseCoopers

LOCATIONS

HQ: Meituan
Block B&C, Hengjiweiye Building, No.4 Wang Jing
East Road, Chaoyang District, Beijing 100102
Phone: (86) 10 5737 6600
Web: www.about.meituan.com

HISTORICAL FINANCIALS
Company Type: Public

Income Statement				FYE: December 31
	REVENUE ($ mil.)	NET INCOME ($ mil.)	NET PROFIT MARGIN	EMPLOYEES
12/19	14,016	321	2.3%	54,580
12/18	9,483	(16,788)	—	58,390
12/17	5,213	(2,906)	—	0
Annual Growth	64.0%	—	—	—

2019 Year-End Financials

Debt ratio: 0.4%	No. of shares (mil.): —
Return on equity: 2.5%	Dividends
Cash ($ mil.): 1,925	Yield: —
Current ratio: 2.24	Payout: —
Long-term debt ($ mil.): 67	Market value ($ mil.): —

	STOCK PRICE ($) FY Close	P/E High/Low	Earnings	PER SHARE ($) Dividends	Book Value
12/19	0.00	— —	0.05	0.00	2.28
12/18	0.00	— —	(6.16)	0.00	2.20
Annual Growth	—	— —	—	—	1.9%

Mercedes-Benz AG

Daimler is one of the leading global suppliers of premium and luxury cars and one of the world's largest manufacturer of commercial vehicles. It also offers financing leasing fleet management investments insurance brokerage as well as innovative mobility services. As of January 1 2020 the operational business activities of the Group have been managed in the business divisions Mercedes-Benz Cars Mercedes-Benz Vans Daimler Trucks & Buses and Daimler Mobility. Daimler sells its vehicles worldwide but North Europe represents more than 40% of its net sales.

Operations

As of January 1 2020 the operational business activities of the Group have been managed in the business divisions Mercedes-Benz Cars Mercedes-Benz Vans Daimler Trucks & Buses and Daimler Mobility.

For the purposes of external reporting the segments Mercedes-Benz Cars and MercedesBenz

Vans have been combined into the reportable segment Mercedes-Benz Cars & Vans which generates over 60% of revenue. It is focused on production preparations for the new S-Class and the successor models of the compact vehicles as well as the preparations for the launch of the new C-Class.

Daimler Trucks & Buses (over 20%) aims to offer only new vehicles that are CO2- neutral in driving operation ("tank-to-wheel") in the triad markets of Europe Japan and North America by 2039. We intend to offer series-produced trucks and buses with battery-electric drive systems in the main sales regions Europe the United States and Japan by 2022.

Daimler Mobility (over 15%) offers financing leasing fleet management investments credit card and insurance brokerage as well as innovative mobility services.

Geographic Reach

Based in Stuttgart Germany Daimler is active in nearly all the countries of the world. The Group has production facilities in Europe North and South America Asia and Africa. The global networking of research and development activities as well as of production and sales locations gives Daimler advantages in the international competitive field and also offers additional growth opportunities.

Europe is its biggest market with more than 40% of sales followed by North America with nearly 30% and the Asia/Pacific with over 25% of sales.

Sales and Marketing

Daimler's digital mobility solutions offers maximum flexibility. Carsharing allows customer to rent cars per minute. SHARE NOW is one of the world's largest car-sharing services with over 20000 vehicles in over 30 cities. FREE NOW is a Ride-Hailing and an optimal supplement for all who want to be chauffeured by taxi through a foreign city. The company's offer reaches up to the Micro-Mobility solution of an E-Scooter. Daimler's multimodal platform REACH NOW they bundle mobility solutions with the local public transport of cities.

Financial Performance

Note: Growth rates may differ after conversion to US Dollars.

The company's revenue has been increasing in the past years but experienced a decline in the most recent fiscal year. Net income has fluctuated over the last five years.

The Daimler Group's revenue of ?154.3 billion in 2020 was significantly below the prior-year figure (2019: ?172.7 billion). This is primarily due to the major impact of the covid-19 pandemic in the automotive segments.

Net profit of ?4.0 billion is significantly above the prior-year figure (2019: ?2.7 billion).

Daimler's cash on hand grew ?4.2 billion during 2020 ending the year at ?23 billion. The company's operations generated ?22.3 billion while its financial used ?10.7 billion and investing activities used ?6.4 billion.

Strategy

Sustainability means harmonizing economic ecological and social objectives. Daimler is committed to the United Nations' Sustainable Development Goals and to the Paris Agreement on climate change. For Daimler sustainability means permanently creating value for all stakeholders: customers employees investors business partners and society as a whole. For us sustainability is not an isolated area where it takes action but an integral part of its corporate strategy. In line with this approach it works to achieve CO2-neutral mobility by 2039 reduce its resource consumption despite growth implement measures that increase safety on the road continue to utilize data responsibly and assume responsibility for upholding human rights along the entire value chain.

Daimler's "Ambition 2039" strategy for Mercedes-Benz Cars demonstrates its commitment to climate protection. Its goal here is to become CO2-neutral by 2039. More specifically this means it plans to achieve CO2-neutral production at its own car plants from 2022 have plug-in hybrids and all-electric drive systems account for more than 50% of its portfolio by 2030 and offer a CO2-neutral new car fleet to its customers within less than three product life cycles. An example of this is the new Factory 56 at the Sindelfingen plant. This facility whose first series-production model is the new S-Class consumes less energy than previous vehicle assembly operations for comparable model series and has a CO2-neutral footprint. Among other things this is made possible by the facility's energy concept which includes a photovoltaic system a direct-current network and energy storage devices made of reused vehicle batteries. A holistic view of the CO2-reduction issue also needs to take the recycling of raw materials into account. After all it also wants to drive forward the implementation of its climate neutrality objective at its suppliers and partners.

Daimler is also developing completely new business models for Daimler Trucks when it comes to autonomous driving. In doing so it is pursuing its dual strategy by working together with two strong partners in order to offer customers the best possible integrated fully automated SAE Level 4 solutions. To this end Torc Robotics became part of the Autonomous Technology Group at Daimler Trucks in September 2019. With Torc it is focusing on the development of its own SAE Level 4 solution for operations between two logistics centers (hub-to-hub operations).

Mergers and Acquisitions

In early 2020 Mercedes-Benz AG and Zhejiang Geely Holding Group announced the establishment of a 50-50 joint venture for the smart brand. Its goals here are to further develop smart into a leading supplier of intelligent premium electric vehicles and extend the smart portfolio into the fast-growing B-segment. The new generation of smart vehicles will be designed in the Mercedes-Benz Design network developed in the Geely engineering network and manufactured at a new electric-vehicle plant in China. Global sales of the first model of the next-generation smart an electric SUV are scheduled to begin in 2022. All of the sales marketing and aftersales activities for Europe of the next smart generation will be managed by smart Europe GmbH which is based in the Stuttgart area.

HISTORY

Daimler-Benz was formed by the merger of two German motor companies — Daimler and Benz — in 1926. Daimler-Benz bought Auto Union (Audi) in 1958 (sold to Volkswagen in 1966). The company's Mercedes cars gained international fame and sales expanded worldwide in the 1970s.

Daimler-Benz diversified in the 1980s buying aerospace heavy truck (Freightliner) and consumer and industrial electrical companies. Although diversification continued sales slowed. Losses at its aerospace unit forced Daimler-Benz into the red in 1995. Also that year the company and ABB Asea Brown Boveri (now ABB) formed joint venture Adtranz the #1 train maker in the world and J rgen Schrempp became chairman of the management board (CEO).

In 1998 Daimler-Benz acquired Chrysler and introduced a subcompact car the smart in Europe. The newly formed DaimlerChrysler rolled both companies' financial services units into Daimler-Chrysler Interservices (DEBIS) in 1999.

EXECUTIVES

Chairman of the Management Board, Chairman of Mercedes-Benz Cars & Vans, Chief Executive Officer, Ola Kaellenius, $1,612,259 total compensation

Member of the Board of Management of Daimler AG. Mercedes-Benz Cars Marketing & Sales, Britta Seeger, $805,559 total compensation

Member of the Board of Management of Daimler AG. Integrity and Legal Affairs, Renata Jungo Brüngger, $805,559 total compensation

Member of the Board of Management of Daimler AG. Human Resources and Director of Labor Relations, Wilfried Porth, $805,559 total compensation

Member of the Board of Management of Daimler AG and Chairman of the Board of Management of Daimler Truck AG, Martin Daum, $805,559 total compensation

Member of the Board of Management of Daimler AG. Group Research and Mercedes-Benz Cars Chief Operating Officer, Markus Schäfer, $805,559 total compensation

Member of the Divisional Board of Management of Mercedes-Benz Cars, Production and Supply Chain, Jörg Burzer

Member of the Board of Management of Daimler AG. Finance & Controlling/Daimler Mobility, Harald Wilhelm, $823,790 total compensation

Auditors: KPMG AG, Wirtschaftsprüfungsgesellschaft

LOCATIONS

HQ: Mercedes-Benz AG
Mercedesstrasse 120, Stuttgart 70372
Phone: (49) 711 17 97875   **Fax:** (49) 711 17 94075
Web: www.daimler.com

2018 Sales

	% of total
Europe	36
North America (NAFTA)	25
Asia	23
Other markets	6
Other revenue	10
Total	**100**

PRODUCTS/OPERATIONS

2018 Sales

	% of Sales
Mercedes-Benz Cars	53
Daimler Trucks	22
Daimler Financial Services	14
Mercedes-Benz Vans	8
Daimler Buses	2
Total	**100**

Selected Divisions and Brands

Mercedes-Benz Cars
  Mercedes-AMG
  Mercedes-Maybach
  Mercedes me
  smart
  EQ
Daimler Trucks
  Freightliner
  FUSO
  Mercedez-Benz
  Western Star
  BharatBenz
Mercedes-Benz Vans
  Mercedez-Benz
  Freightliner
Daimler Buses
  Mercedes-Benz
  Setra
  BharatBenz
Daimler Financial Services
  Mercedes-Benz Bank
  Daimler Truck Financial
  moovel
  Car2Go
  mytaxi

COMPETITORS

AB Volvo
APTIV PLC
Continental AG
DANA INCORPORATED
Dongfeng Motor Group Company Limited
HELLA GmbH & Co. KGaA
Hyundai Motor Company
MAHINDRA AND MAHINDRA LIMITED
MANN+HUMMEL FILTRATION TECHNOLOGY
 INTERMEDIATE HOLDINGS
MERCEDES-BENZ USA LLC
MERITOR INC.
MOTORCAR PARTS OF AMERICA INC.
TATA MOTORS LIMITED
TOYOTA BOSHOKU CORPORATION
VOLKSWAGEN AG
WABCO HOLDINGS INC.
ZF Friedrichshafen AG

HISTORICAL FINANCIALS

Company Type: Public

Income Statement   FYE: December 31

	REVENUE ($ mil.)	NET INCOME ($ mil.)	NET PROFIT MARGIN	EMPLOYEES
12/20	189,381	4,451	2.4%	288,481
12/19	193,952	2,668	1.4%	298,655
12/18	191,662	8,301	4.3%	298,683
12/17	196,991	12,616	6.4%	289,321
12/16	161,825	9,002	5.6%	282,488
Annual Growth	4.0%	(16.1%)	—	0.5%

2020 Year-End Financials

Debt ratio: 47.6%
Return on equity: 5.9%
Cash ($ mil.): 28,286
Current ratio: 1.15
Long-term debt ($ mil.): 88,455

No. of shares (mil.): 1,069
Dividends
Yield: 0.9%
Payout: 4.1%
Market value ($ mil.): 18,744

	STOCK PRICE ($) FY Close	P/E High/Low		PER SHARE ($) Earnings	Dividends	Book Value
12/20	17.52	5	2	4.16	0.16	69.62
12/19	13.58	7	5	2.49	0.62	64.38
12/18	13.11	13	2	7.76	0.81	69.22
12/17	84.64	9	7	11.80	0.70	71.74
Annual Growth	(40.8%) (0.7%)	—		—	(22.9%)	(31.1%)

Merck KGaA (Germany)

Science and technology firm Merck KGaA develops manufactures and sells biotech pharmaceutical life science and specialty chemical products for global consumption. The company manufactures and sells prescription drugs including treatments for multiple sclerosis cancers growth disorders infertility and cardiovascular and metabolic diseases. It also produces laboratory research tools including chemicals antibodies and cells and bioprocessing systems. Merck's specialty chemicals include liquid crystals semiconductor materials and coatings. It holds the global rights to the Merck name and brand. The only exceptions are Canada and the US. In these countries it operates as EMD Serono in the biopharmaceutical business as MilliporeSigma in the life science business and as EMD Performance Materials in the high-tech materials business.

Operations

Merck operates through three divisions: Life Science Healthcare and Performance Materials.

Merck's Life Sciences segment also accounting for about 45% of sales makes tools equipment and chemicals used in pharmaceutical biotech and academic laboratories. Its product portfolio numbers some 300000 and includes ultrapure reagents testing kits lab water systems antibodies and cells gene-editing technologies and bioprocessing systems. The division includes the Sigma-Aldrich subsidiary and operates as MilliporeSigma in the US and Canada.

The Healthcare segment accounts for about 40% of sales discovers develops manufactures and markets innovative pharmaceutical and biological prescription drugs to treat cancer multiple sclerosis (MS) infertility growth disorders and certain cardiovascular and metabolic diseases. Healthcare operates in four franchises: Neurology and Immunology Oncology Fertility and General Medicine & Endocrinology. Its R&D pipeline positions with a clear focus on becoming a global specialty innovator in oncology immuno-oncology neurology and immunology.

The Performance Materials segment bringing in 20% of sales deals in high-tech chemicals for use in consumer electronics semiconductors automotive displays lighting pigments coatings and cosmetics. It includes the Display Solutions Semiconductor Solutions and Surface Solutions business units. The unit operates as EMD Performance Materials in the US and Canada.

Geographic Reach

Merck is headquartered in Germany with operations spread across around 65 countries. The Asia-Pacific region is the company's single largest region accounting for about a 35% of sales closely followed by Europe (30% of sales) and North America (more than 25%). The remainder of sales comes from the Latin America (about 5%) and Middle East and Africa (less than 5%) regions.

Financial Performance

Note: Growth rates may differ after conversion to US Dollars.

In fiscal 2020 the Group generated net sales of ?17.5 billion representing a year-on-year increase of ?1.4 villion or 9%. This positive development was attributable to organic sales growth in the Life Science and Healthcare business sectors as well as acquisition-related sales growth in the Performance Materials business sector.

Net income rose 51% to ?2 billion in 2020.

The company ended 2020 with ?1.4 billion in cash up ?574 billion from 2019. Operating activities contributed ?3.5 billion while investing activities used ?1.3 billion. Financing activities used another ?1.5 billion via bond payments.

Strategy

Over the past years the company has grown significantly through a series of strategic moves that have enabled it to develop into a vibrant science and technology company. It has systematically and continuously strengthened and focused its portfolio of innovative science and technology throughout its business sectors.

In Healthcare the company focuses on development and commercialization of innovative specialty medicines. To do so the company actively managed its portfolio and acquired Serono SA in 2007. Today the company is focusing its R&D efforts on oncology immuno-oncology neurology and immunology.

Within Life Science the company solidified its position as one of the industry leaders following the acquisition of Millipore Corporation in 2010 and Sigma-Aldrich Corporation in 2015.

Performance Materials is currently undergoing a major transformation by repositioning its overall business toward the highly attractive electronic

materials market. With the acquisitions of Versum Materials Inc. and Intermolecular Inc. both in 2019 the company achieved a leading position in this market with a focus on Semiconductor Solutions.

With its Group strategy it wants to become the vibrant science and technology company. By 2022 the company aims to have strong innovative science- and technology-focused business sectors with leadership positions in its areas.

Mergers and Acquisitions

In late 2020 Merck acquired all of the shares in AmpTec GmbH (AmpTec) Hamburg one of the leading contract development and manufacturing organizations for mRNA (messenger ribonucleic acid). The deal strengthens Merck's capabilities to develop and manufacture mRNA. The acquisition adds to Merck's lipid manufacturing expertise and creates an integrated offering across the entire mRNA value chain. The company will be integrated into the Process Solutions business unit which is part of the Life Science business sector. The preliminary purchase price comprised a payment of ?7 million and milestone payments of up to ?18 million for the achievement of technological development targets and sales- and profit-based targets.

In 2020 Merck completed the acquisition of all of the shares in Resolution Spectra Systems S.A.S. a leading provider of systems for real-time analysis and monitoring of bioprocesses. The acquisition strengthens Merck's bioprocessing product portfolio within the Life Science business sector. The purchase price comprised a fixed compensation of ?4 million and future sales-based milestone payments of up to ?4 million.

Company Background

Merck KGaA was founded in 1668 as a pharmacy and is the oldest pharmaceuticals business in the world.

The German firm is ancestor to US drug giant Merck & Co. but the American firm broke away during WWI. Subsequently the company's current North American operations can't use the Merck name; they instead operate under the name EMD. Legal tussles over use of the name flare up sporadically as globalization brings the two into shared markets.

Merck launched an initiative in 2007 to transition from a classic pharmaceuticals and chemicals company to a science and technology company. The most significant move was the 2015 acquisition of Sigma-Aldrich a research equipment maker for $17 billion. Other major acquisitions include AZ Electronic Materials a supplier of high-tech materials for the electronics industry for $2.5 billion in 2014.

The firm sold its Biosimilars (generic biotech drugs) unit in 2017 to Fresenius for ?156 million plus ?497 in potential milestone payments.

HISTORY

In 1668 apothecary Friedrich Jacob Merck bought the Engel-Apotheke (Angel Pharmacy) in Darmstadt establishing the family's presence in the drug business. Some 150 years later descendant Emanuel Merck inherited the company; an experienced chemist Merck transformed it into a drugmaker by 1827 producing morphine codeine cocaine and other bulk pharmaceuticals. By the time Merck died in 1854 the company had sales around the world.

Two years later the company headed to the US. By the turn of the century Merck had a production facility in New Jersey run by Emanuel's grandson George. When the US joined WWI George turned over Merck's control of the US subsidiary (Merck & Co.) to the Alien Property Custodian which sold the stock after the war. Merck lost its other overseas subsidiaries after WWI.

WWII left Merck struggling for supplies and labor and its factories were decimated by Allied air raids. After the war the military government allowed the firm to make drugs then pesticides food preservatives reagents and laboratory chemicals. Merck struggled along until the Wirthschaftswunder (economic miracle) in 1948 that turned around the German economy.

The war had lingering effects that cost the firm during the later half of the 20th century. Although Merck rebuilt its presence around the world product development (particularly its ventures into biotechnology in the 1980s) was hampered by an exodus of talent to other countries and by certain protectionist policies of the German government.

Despite a sluggish economy and Germany's health care system reforms Merck began an acquisition spree in 1990 that continued for several years. The firm diversified its pharmaceuticals and chemicals operations but drove itself into debt. In 1995 Merck offered a quarter of its stock to the public to pay its debt and continue its spree.

Some of its purchases in the late 1990s helped it establish itself in the cancer treatment niche; these buys included Lexigen Pharmaceuticals (1998). The next year the Merck family had to inject money into the company again to pay off debt from the acquisitions.

In 2004 the company sold its laboratory supplies distribution subsidiary VWR International to Clayton Dubilier & Rice for $1.65 billion. VWR has since been sold to Madison Dearborn Partners.

In 2006 Merck made a failed $18 billion bid for Schering which was instead acquired by Bayer.

That failed purchase was made up for through the $13 billion acquisition of Swiss biotech firm Serono (later Merck Serono) in 2007. The purchase made Merck the largest biotech company in Europe adding biological operations focused on reproductive health neurology metabolism and other areas. Following the acquisition Merck combined Serono with its Merck Ethicals Division to form a new prescription pharmaceuticals division named Merck Serono. The Ethicals Division contributed cancer cardiovascular and other therapies including marketing rights for ImClone's cancer drug Erbitux outside of the US and Canada.

In support of its status among the biggest players in the biotech field Merck offloaded its generics unit which had accounted for nearly 30% of the company's overall sales that same year in order to pay down its debt from the Serono acquisition. Merck sold the unit to Mylan for a robust price of about $6.7 billion. Along with paying down debt Merck used the money to fund additional acquisitions targeting the over-the-counter medicine and chemical industries.

Merck moved to gain a tighter foothold in the Chinese chemical market in 2009 when it purchased pigment manufacturer Suzhou Taizhu Technology Development for $40 million. That same year the company increased its bioscience holdings in India by acquiring Bangalore Genei Private an India-based company that specialized in making and selling genomics and proteomics research products from the Sanmar Group.

Despite making some broad strokes at expansion the company was hit by a decline in demand for its chemicals (including pigments) in 2009 and was forced to initiate some cutbacks in the division's manufacturing operations early in the year primarily due to economic conditions and an ensuing lower demand for liquid crystals.

Merck launched a transformation initiative in 2007 to transition from a classic pharmaceuticals and chemicals company to a science and technology company. The most significant move was the 2015 acquisition of Sigma-Aldrich a pharmaceutical equipment maker for $17 billion. The acquisition positioned Merck as a leader in the life sci-

ence industry. Other major acquisitions include AZ Electronic Materials a supplier of high-tech materials for the electronics industry for $2.5 billion in 2014.

Merck backed up its completed transformation with a complete re-branding in 2015 which included a re-naming of the separate division names such as Merck Serono and Merck Millipore in all geographies (bar the US and Canada) and bringing them under one Merck umbrella. The move is partly intended to boost awareness of the difference between the rival companies.

EXECUTIVES

Chief Executive Officer - Performance Materials, Member of the Executive Board, Kai Beckmann, $1,253,346 total compensation
Member of the Supervisory Board, Juergen Glaser, $53,552 total compensation
Member of the Executive Board, Chief Financial Officer, Marcus Kuhnert, $1,139,406 total compensation
Member of the Supervisory Board, Christian Raabe, $53,552 total compensation
Independent Member of the Supervisory Board, Helene von Roeder, $53,552 total compensation
Vice Chairman of the Supervisory Board, Sascha Held, $80,328 total compensation
Independent Member of the Supervisory Board, Simon Thelen, $53,552 total compensation
Independent Member of the Supervisory Board, Renate Koehler, $53,552 total compensation
Member of the Supervisory Board, Anne Lange, $53,552 total compensation
Independent Member of the Supervisory Board, Peter Merck, $53,552 total compensation
Independent Member of the Supervisory Board, Daniel Thelen, $53,552 total compensation
Independent Chairman of the Supervisory Board, Wolfgang Buechele, $107,104 total compensation
Chairman of the Management Board, Chief Executive Officer, Belen Garijo, $1,367,287 total compensation
Auditors: KPMG AG Wirtschaftsprüfungsgesellscha

LOCATIONS

HQ: Merck KGaA (Germany)
Frankfurter Strasse 250, Darmstadt D-64293
Phone: (49) 6151 72 0   **Fax:** (49) 6151 72 5577
Web: www.emdgroup.com

2015 Sales

	% of total
Asia-Pacific	33
Europe	32
North America	21
Latin America	10
Middle East & Africa	4
Total	**100**

PRODUCTS/OPERATIONS

2015 Sales

	% of total
Healthcare	54
Life Sciences	26
Performance Materials	20
Total	**100**

Selected Pharmaceutical Products

Merck Serono
  Concor (antihypertensive)
  Erbitux (colorectal and neck cancer)
  Euthyrox (hypothyroid treatment)
  Glucophage (diabetes)
  Gonal-f (fertility)
  Pergoveris (fertility)
  Rebif (relapsing multiple sclerosis)
  Saizen (growth hormone deficiency)
  Serostim (HIV-associated wasting)
Consumer health care

BION and MULTIBION (probiotic multivitamin)
Cebion (vitamins and minerals)
Fembion Metfolin (multivitamins for women)
Flexagil Kytta and Seven Seas (natural joint pain remedies and supplements)
Kidabion (children's vitamins)
Nasivin (cold remedy)
Seven seas (diet supplement)
Sangobion (anemia remedy)

COMPETITORS

ASTRAZENECA PLC	SANOFI
BIOVERATIV INC.	SUMITOMO DAINIPPON
BRISTOL-MYERS SQUIBB	PHARMA CO. LTD.
COMPANY	Solvay
BTG LIMITED	TAKEDA PHARMACEUTICAL
Bausch Health	COMPANY LIMITED
Companies Inc	TEVA PHARMACEUTICAL
EMD MILLIPORE	INDUSTRIES LIMITED
CORPORATION	
MALLINCKRODT PUBLIC	
LIMITED COMPANY	

HISTORICAL FINANCIALS

Company Type: Public

Income Statement

FYE: December 31

	REVENUE ($ mil.)	NET INCOME ($ mil.)	NET PROFIT MARGIN	EMPLOYEES
12/20	21,519	2,438	11.3%	58,096
12/19	18,134	1,482	8.2%	57,071
12/18	16,990	3,863	22.7%	51,749
12/17	18,373	3,116	17.0%	52,880
12/16	15,863	1,720	10.8%	50,439
Annual Growth	**7.9%**	**9.1%**	**—**	**3.6%**

2020 Year-End Financials

Debt ratio: 31.7%	No. of shares (mil.): 129
Return on equity: 11.3%	Dividends
Cash ($ mil.): 1,662	Yield: 0.5%
Current ratio: 1.01	Payout: 3.8%
Long-term debt ($ mil.): 11,610	Market value ($ mil.): 4,442

	STOCK PRICE ($) FY Close	P/E High/Low		PER SHARE ($) Earnings	Dividends	Book Value
12/20	34.37	8	4	5.61	0.19	160.92
12/19	23.70	8	6	3.41	0.19	155.20
12/18	20.76	3	2	8.89	0.20	152.41
12/17	21.50	8	4	7.17	1.50	129.89
Annual Growth	**16.9%**			**—**	**(6.0%)(40.0%)**	**5.5%**

Metallurgical Corp China Ltd

EXECUTIVES

Independent Non-Executive Director, Li Liu
President, Executive Director, Mengxing Zhang
Chief Accounting Officer, Vice President, Hongying Zou
Independent Non-Executive Director, Jichang Zhou
Vice President, Fuming Liu
Vice President, Yang Qu
Vice President, Jianzhong Zeng
Staff Elected Director, Aizhong Yan
Secretary of the Board, Gang Zeng
Vice President, Guangxia Zhu
Independent Non-Executive Director, Jianing Wu
Vice President, Xiaohu Bai
Auditors: PricewaterhouseCoopers Zhong Tian CPAs Limited Company

LOCATIONS

HQ: Metallurgical Corp China Ltd
MCC Tower, 28 Shuguang Xili, Chaoyang District,
Beijing 100028
Phone: (86) 10 59868666   **Fax:** (86) 10 59868999
Web: www.mccchina.com

HISTORICAL FINANCIALS

Company Type: Public

Income Statement   FYE: December 31

	REVENUE ($ mil.)	NET INCOME ($ mil.)	NET PROFIT MARGIN	EMPLOYEES
12/20	61,177	1,202	2.0%	0
12/19	48,667	948	1.9%	0
12/18	42,093	926	2.2%	0
12/17	37,495	931	2.5%	0
12/16	31,618	774	2.4%	0
Annual Growth	17.9%	11.6%	—	—

2020 Year-End Financials

Debt ratio: 2.0%
Return on equity: 8.0%
Cash ($ mil.): 8,118
Current ratio: 1.17
Long-term debt ($ mil.): 4,039

No. of shares (mil.): —
Dividends
Yield: 0.0%
Payout: —
Market value ($ mil.): —

	STOCK PRICE ($) FY Close	P/E High/Low		PER SHARE ($) Earnings	Dividends	Book Value
12/20	0.00	15	10	0.05	0.17	(0.00)
12/19	4.58	20	17	0.04	0.16	(0.00)
12/18	5.00	27	19	0.04	0.16	(0.00)
12/17	6.88	27	27	0.04	0.14	(0.00)
Annual Growth	—	—	—	5.2%	4.6%	—

Metro AG (New)

Auditors: KPMG AG
Wirtschaftspruefungsgesellschaft

LOCATIONS

HQ: Metro AG (New)
Metro-Strase 1, Duesseldorf 40235
Phone: (49) 211 6886 0
Web: www.metroag.de/en

HISTORICAL FINANCIALS

Company Type: Public

Income Statement   FYE: September 30

	REVENUE ($ mil.)	NET INCOME ($ mil.)	NET PROFIT MARGIN	EMPLOYEES
09/20	30,011	538	1.8%	97,639
09/19	29,542	(137)		101,654
09/18	34,141	398	1.2%	152,426
09/17	35,329	383	1.1%	155,082
Annual Growth	(5.3%)	11.9%	—	(14.3%)

2020 Year-End Financials

Debt ratio: —
Return on equity: 19.2%
Cash ($ mil.): 1,785
Current ratio: 0.87
Long-term debt ($ mil.): —

No. of shares (mil.): 360
Dividends
Yield: —
Payout: —
Market value ($ mil.): —

	STOCK PRICE ($) FY Close	P/E High/Low	PER SHARE ($) Earnings	Dividends	Book Value
09/20	0.00	—	1.49	0.00	6.67
Annual Growth	—	—	—	—	—

Metro Inc

METRO is a food and pharmacy leader in Quebec and Ontario. As a retailer franchisor distributor and manufacturer the corporation operates or services a network of about 955 food stores under several banners including Metro Metro Plus Super C Food Basics Adonis and Premi¨re Moisson as well as nearly 650 drugstores primarily under the Jean Coutu Brunet Metro Pharmacy and Food Basics Pharmacy banners. METRO was founded in 1947 when a few independent grocery retailers decided to form a buying group that would enable them to offer its customers products at prices comparable to those of major food chains.

Operations

The reportable operating segment comprises the food operations segment and the pharmaceutical operations segment. The corporation has aggregated these two business segments due to the similar nature of their goods and services and similar economic characteristics: operations are carried on primarily in Quebec and Ontario.

It operates about 955 food stores including some 340 supermarkets around 235 discount stores about 355 neighborhood stores and about 25 specialized stores as well as about 650 drugstores.

Geographic Reach

Headquartered in Montreal Quebec it has over 1215 stores in Quebec around 355 in Ontario and nearly 30 in New Brunswick.

Sales and Marketing

The company sells its products through their stores. It offers two loyalty programs. The first program for which the corporation acts as an agent belongs to a third party and its cost is recorded as a reduction in sales at the time of sale to the customer. The second program belongs to the corporation. At the time of a sale to the customer part of it is recorded as deferred revenue equal to the fair value of the program's issued points.

Financial Performance

The company sells its products through their stores. It offers two loyalty programs. The first program for which the corporation acts as an agent belongs to a third party and its cost is recorded as a reduction in sales at the time of sale to the customer. The second program belongs to the corporation. At the time of a sale to the customer part of it is recorded as deferred revenue equal to the fair value of the program's issued points.

Strategy

The four pillars of its business strategy are: customer focus best team operational excellence and financial discipline.

The company online grocery service websites and various mobile applications are part of the company's overall digital strategy which aims to position METRO as the retailer that offers the food experience most suited to the needs and behaviors of consumers.

EXECUTIVES

Vice President - Real Estate and Engineering, Martin Allaire
President, Chief Executive Officer, Non-Independent Director, Eric La Fleche, $801,375 total compensation
Executive Vice President, Quebec Division Head and eCommerce, Marc Giroux, $402,055 total compensation
Senior Vice President - National Procurement and Corporate Brands, Serge Boulanger, $285,331 total compensation
Independent Director, Maryse Bertrand
Chief Financial Officer, Executive Vice President, Treasurer, Francois Thibault, $425,049 total compensation
Independent Director, Russell Goodman
Vice President - Human Resources, Genevieve Bich
Independent Director, Stephanie Coyles
Independent Director, Christian Haub
Independent Director, Marc Guay
Independent Director, Christine Magee
Non-Independent Director, Francois Coutu
Non-Independent Director, Michel Coutu
Independent Chairman of the Board, Pierre Boivin
Independent Director, Brian McManus
Auditors: Ernst & Young LLP

LOCATIONS

HQ: Metro Inc
11011 Maurice-Duplessis Blvd., Montreal, Quebec H1C 1V6
Phone: 514 643-1000   **Fax:** 514 643-1215
Web: www.metro.ca

2015 Stores

	No.
Qué;bec	508
Ontario	336
Total	**844**

PRODUCTS/OPERATIONS

2015 Stores

	No.
Food	
Supermarkets	343
Discount stores	213
Partners	34
Drug	254
Total	**844**

Selected Retail Banners

Brunet (pharmacy)
Clini Plus (pharmacy)
Drug Basics (pharmacy)
Food Basics (discount supermarkets)
METRO (supermarkets)
METRO PLUS (supermarkets)
Super C (discount supermarkets)
The Pharmacy (pharmacy)

COMPETITORS

A.F.BLAKEMORE AND SON LIMITED
ASSOCIATED GROCERS INC.
CECONOMY AG
CORE-MARK HOLDING COMPANY INC.
DEARBORN WHOLESALE GROCERS L.P.
DIERBERGS MARKETS INC.
J.W. FILSHILL LIMITED
MARTIN MCCOLL LIMITED
METCASH LIMITED
Organizaci n Soriana S.A.B. de C.V.

PALMER & HARVEY MCLANE LIMITED
PITTSBURG WHOLESALE GROCERS INC.
PURITY WHOLESALE GROCERS INC.
SPARTANNASH COMPANY
SUPERVALU INC.
Shoppers Drug Mart Corporation
Sobeys Inc
TOPCO ASSOCIATES LLC

HISTORICAL FINANCIALS
Company Type: Public

Income Statement
FYE: September 25

	REVENUE ($ mil.)	NET INCOME ($ mil.)	NET PROFIT MARGIN	EMPLOYEES
09/21	14,387	647	4.5%	90,000
09/20	13,457	594	4.4%	90,000
09/19	12,650	536	4.2%	90,000
09/18	11,052	1,318	11.9%	90,000
09/17	10,599	476	4.5%	65,000
Annual Growth	7.9%	8.0%	—	8.5%

2021 Year-End Financials
Debt ratio: 15.2%
Return on equity: 13.1%
Cash ($ mil.): 350
Current ratio: 1.12
Long-term debt ($ mil.): 1,824
No. of shares (mil.): 242
Dividends
Yield: 0.0%
Payout: 29.2%
Market value ($ mil.): 11,567

	STOCK PRICE ($) FY Close	P/E High/Low	PER SHARE ($) Earnings	Dividends	Book Value
09/21	47.61	16 13	2.62	0.77	20.73
09/20	47.55	15 12	2.35	0.65	18.35
09/19	43.52	16 11	2.10	0.59	17.70
09/18	31.26	5 4	5.50	0.54	16.96
09/17	33.06	15 12	2.07	0.50	10.31
Annual Growth	9.5%	— —	6.1%	11.0%	19.1%

Metropolitan Bank & Trust Co. (Philippines)

Don't let the name fool you — Metrobank is a global operation. The Metropolitan Bank and Trust Company provides a full range of banking services to individual and commercial clients through a network of more than 1950 ATMs in the Philippines; more than 860 domestic branches; and 31 overseas branches subsidiaries and representative offices in Asia Europe and the US. Its services include deposits savings loans credit investment assistance life insurance trade finance money transfer and remittance and Internet banking. Its subsidiaries and affiliate companies can be found throughout Asia as well as several major cities in the US. George Ty established the Metrobank in 1962 in Manila.Shareholders approved a merger with Renasant Bank in mid-2017.

EXECUTIVES

Non-Executive Chairman of the Board, Arthur Ty
Executive Vice President, President of Metrobank Foundation, Inc., Aniceto Sobrepena
Executive Vice President - Head of Products, Channels and Overseas Banking Group, Richard Benedict So
President, Executive Director, Fabian Dee
Non-Executive Director, Alfred Ty
Senior Executive Vice President, Executive Director, Vicente Cuna
Senior Executive Vice President, Head of Financial Market Sector, Treasurer, Fernand Antonio Tansingco
Independent Director, Angelica Lavares
Senior Executive Vice President, Head of Financial and Control Sector, Joshua Naing
Independent Director, Jesli Lapus

Senior Vice President and Head of Treasury Group, Angelica Reyes
Independent Director, Philip Soliven
Senior Vice President, Head - Cards and Personal Credit, Ramon Jaime Del Rosario
Executive Vice President, Regular Executive Committee Member, Corazon Ma. Therese Nepomuceno
Senior Vice President, Head of Customer Engagement Group, David Holmes
Non-Executive Vice Chairman of the Board, Francisco Sebastian
Senior Vice President and Head - Special Accounts Management Group, Pocholo Dela Pena
Senior Vice President, Head of Markets Sales, Rommel Enrico Dionisio
Senior Vice President and Head of Trust Banking Group, Leandro Santillan
First Vice President, Head of Operations Control Group, Ely Roy Lindo
Senior Vice President, Head of Commercial Banking Group, Ferlou Evangelista
Independent Director, Francisco Del Rosario
Non-Executive Director, Solomon Cua
Independent Director, Edgar Chua
First Vice President and Head of Internal Audit Group, Leo Fragante
Senior Vice President and Head of Corporate Banking Group, Antonio Ocampo
Senior Vice President and Head of Information Technology Group, Bernardino Ramos
Executive Vice President, Head of Institutional Banking Sector, Mary Mylene Caparas
Executive Vice President, Head of Operations Group, Paul Robert Murga
Senior Vice President and Head of General Services, Christine Carandang
Senior Vice President, Head of RBS, Anthony Paul Yap
Senior Vice President, Head, Controllership Group, Renato De Borja
Senior Vice President - Head of Branch Banking Group, Lita Tan
Senior Vice President, Head, Consumer Lending Group, Anna Therese Cuenco
Senior Vice President, Chief Marketing Officer, Head of the Analytics, Brand, Communications & Marketing-Technology, Hierbert Dimagiba
Auditors: SyCip Gorres Velayo & Co.

LOCATIONS
HQ: Metropolitan Bank & Trust Co. (Philippines)
Metrobank Plaza, Sen. Gil Puyat Avenue, Urdaneta Village, Makati City, Metro Manila 1200
Phone: (63) 2 898 8805
Web: www.metrobank.com.ph

COMPETITORS
Bank of Shanghai Co. Ltd.
HANG SENG BANK LIMITED
NATIONAL BANK OF KUWAIT S.A.K.P.

HISTORICAL FINANCIALS
Company Type: Public

Income Statement
FYE: December 31

	ASSETS ($ mil.)	NET INCOME ($ mil.)	INCOME AS % OF ASSETS	EMPLOYEES
12/19	48,400	554	1.1%	13,150
12/18	42,721	419	1.0%	12,851
12/17	41,760	365	0.9%	12,133
12/16	37,889	365	1.0%	0
12/15	37,581	397	1.1%	0
Annual Growth	6.5%	8.7%	—	—

2019 Year-End Financials
Return on assets: 1.2%
Return on equity: 9.4%
Long-term debt ($ mil.): —
No. of shares (mil.): —
Sales ($ mil): 2,885
Dividends
Yield: —
Payout: —
Market value ($ mil.): —

Mitsubishi Chemical Holdings Corp

Established in 2005 Mitsubishi Chemical Holdings Corporation (MCHC) is among the largest chemical manufacturers in Japan with over 660 major subsidiaries and affiliates around the world. Its businesses are Mitsubishi Chemical which makes chemicals plastics and textiles; Mitsubishi Tanabe Pharma which makes pharmaceutical products for central nervous system diabetes and kidney; Life Sciences Institute which offers health and medical ICT solutions next generation healthcare and drug discovery; and Nippon Sanso Holdings produces industrial gases. Headquartered in Tokyo MCHC generates about 65% of sales in Japan.

Operations
MCHC has four business segments: Performance Products Chemicals Industrial Gases and Health Care.

The Performance Products segment generates around 30% of the company's revenue. It is further divided into two units: functional products which consists of ICT electronics & displays high performance films environment and living solutions and advanced moldings and composites; and performance chemicals which consists of advanced polymers high performance chemicals and new energy.

The Chemicals segment generates about 25% of the revenue. It produces methyl methacrylate petrochemicals and carbon products.

The Industrial Gases segment generates more than 20% of the company's revenue. It consists of industrial gases and industrial gas-related equipment and facilities.

The Health Care segment which generates over 10% of the company's sales consists of two divisions ethical pharmaceuticals and life science. Life science provides clinical testing diagnostic reagents capsules and pharmaceutical processing equipment and active pharmaceutical ingredients and intermediates.

Geographic Reach
Headquartered in Tokyo MCHC generates about 65% of its revenue from Japan while the rest come from other countries. It has about 660 subsidiaries and affiliates globally primarily in Japan (more than 160) the Asia/Pacific region (excluding Japan) and Europe.

Sales and Marketing
MCHC sells products globally to various industries including petrochemicals carbon products steels chemicals electronics and pharmaceuticals.

Financial Performance
Note: Growth rates may differ after conversion to US Dollars.

In fiscal 2021 (ended March) the company's sales decreased 9% to 3.3 trillion due to decreases in sales in the all its business segments as a result of the global COVID-19 pandemic.

Net income fell 74% to 22.7 billion from 86.6 billion from the prior year.

Mitsubishi Chemical Holdings' cash on hand increased by 120.4 million during fiscal 2021 ending the year at 349.6 billion. The company's operations generated 467.1 billion while investing activities used 217 billion and financing used 142.8 billion. Mitsubishi Chemical Holdings' main cash uses in 2019 were for capital expenditures purchases and acquisitions.

Strategy
Considering social and technological trends and backcasting from its social vision and corporate approach for the year 2050 Mitsubishi Chemical Holdings Corporation has clearly defined the vision and the goals of the Group for 2030 to formulate KAITEKI Vision 30 (KV30). KV30 serves as a foundation for the company's medium to long-term basic management strategy.

The MCHC Group aims to realize its own sustainable growth while creating a society where all of today's social issues have been resolved by 2050 through providing solutions to social issues. The vision for 2030 in KV30 is not a final goal but just a waypoint for reforms that it will pursue with a long-term perspective to realize the society it envisions for 2050.

Three perspectives leading to the vision include: business portfolio transformation; thorough sustainability management; and human capital systems and framework reforms.

In addition in order to realize digital transformation the company leverages both digital technology and a "digital way of thinking" to solve problems relevant to its business. It exploits machine learning text mining and optimization techniques to improve plant stability optimize energy usage and improve product quality. It continuously introduces these capabilities to the operating groups of MCHC.

Mergers and Acquisitions
In 2020 Mitsubishi Chemical acquired Pennsylvania-based Gelest through Mitsubishi Chemical America. Gelest is a manufacturer and developer of silicon chemicals methacrylates and metal-organic compounds. This purchase will enable MCC to broaden its customer solutions by combining its advanced technologies business resources and customer network with Gelest's capabilities.

EXECUTIVES
Independent Director, Tatsumi Yamada
Director, Hiroshi Katayama
Director, Yoshimitsu Kobayashi
Managing Executive Officer, Representative Executive Officer, Yoshihiro Ikegawa
Chief Financial Officer, Managing Executive Officer, Director, Hidefumi Date
Independent Director, Takayuki Hashimoto
Group Chief Compliance Officer, Managing Executive Officer, Director, Ken Fujiwara
Managing Executive Officer, Larry Meixner
Director, Glen Fredrikson
Independent Director, Chikatomo Hodo
Independent Director, Kiyomi Kikuchi
Director, Shigeru Kobayashi
Independent Director, Takako Masai
President and Chief Executive Officer, Jean-Marc Gilson
Auditors: Ernst & Young ShinNihon LLC

LOCATIONS
HQ: Mitsubishi Chemical Holdings Corp
1-1-1 Marunouchi, Chiyoda-ku, Tokyo 100-8251
Phone: (81) 3 6748 7115
Web: www.mitsubishichem-hd.co.jp

2018 Sales

	% of total
Japan	70
Other countries	30
Total	**100**

PRODUCTS/OPERATIONS

2018 Sales

	% of total
Performance Products	31
Chemicals	32
Industrial Gases	17
Health Care	15
Other	5
Total	**100**

COMPETITORS
ALFRESA HOLDINGS CORPORATION
Andritz AG
CRODA INTERNATIONAL PUBLIC LIMITED COMPANY
DUPONT DE NEMOURS INC.
ENEOS HOLDINGS INC.
FUJIFILM HOLDINGS CORPORATION
FURUKAWA CO. LTD.
GOODWIN PLC
JFE HOLDINGS INC.
KANEKA CORPORATION
LUXFER HOLDINGS PLC
MEDIPAL HOLDINGS CORPORATION
MITSUI CHEMICALSINC.
NISSAN CHEMICAL CORPORATION
OJI HOLDINGS CORPORATION
SEKISUI CHEMICAL CO. LTD.
SOMPO HOLDINGS INC.
TOYO SEIKAN GROUP HOLDINGSLTD.
TUBOS REUNIDOS SA
UNIVAR SOLUTIONS INC.

HISTORICAL FINANCIALS
Company Type: Public

Income Statement
FYE: March 31

	REVENUE ($ mil.)	NET INCOME ($ mil.)	NET PROFIT MARGIN	EMPLOYEES
03/21	29,420	(68)	—	75,638
03/20	32,984	498	1.5%	76,362
03/19	35,428	1,530	4.3%	79,578
03/18	35,074	1,994	5.7%	76,658
03/17	30,195	1,397	4.6%	76,169
Annual Growth	(0.6%)	—	—	(0.2%)

2021 Year-End Financials
Debt ratio: 0.4%
Return on equity: (-0.6%)
Cash ($ mil.): 3,030
Current ratio: 1.20
Long-term debt ($ mil.): 15,317
No. of shares (mil.): 1,423
Dividends
Yield: 2.9%
Payout: —
Market value ($ mil.): 54,246

	STOCK PRICE ($) FY Close	P/E High/Low		PER SHARE ($) Earnings	Dividends	Book Value
03/21	38.11	—	—	(0.05)	1.13	7.84
03/20	32.31	1	1	0.32	1.84	7.57
03/19	35.24	0	0	0.99	1.67	8.74
03/18	49.26	0	0	1.28	1.28	8.41
03/17	39.20	0	0	0.95	0.73	6.78
Annual Growth	(0.7%)	—	—	—	11.8%	3.7%

Mitsubishi Corp

In Japanese mitsubishi means "three diamonds" and Mitsubishi Corporation is one of Japan's crown jewels. It is one of the world's top integrated business enterprises with operations across many industries including retail and consumer products energy metals machinery and chemicals. Beyond its core businesses Mitsubishi also invests in diverse businesses like natural resources development new energy and technology-related businesses. With approximately 125 offices plus a network of more than 1700 group companies Mitsubishi is present in about 75 countries.

Operations
Mitsubishi has ten reporting segments that run the gamut from apparel to water infrastructure.

Mineral Resources generates about 40% of revenue. It engages in investing and developing mineral resources such as metallurgical coal copper iron ore and aluminium.

Natural Gases generates about 15% of revenue. It engages in natural gas/oil exploration production and development business and the liquefied natural gas (LNG) business.

Food Industry gives in roughly 10% of revenue. It engages in sales trading business development and other operations across a wide range of business areas related to food.

Other segments like Power Solution and Industrial Infrastructure gives in about 10% while Urban Development Industrial Materials Consumer Industry Automotive Mobility and Petroleum & Chemicals generate more than 20% of revenue combined.

Geographic Reach
Tokyo-based Mitsubishi has roughly 175 offices in Japan and in about 75 other countries. Its natural gases segment operates in North America South East Asia Australia Russia and other region.

Financial Performance
The company's revenue has been volatile in the past five years. Despite this revenues had a 113% growth between 2016 and 2020.

Revenues was 14.8 trillion a decrease of 1.3 billion or 8% year over year. This was mainly due to a decrease in transaction volumes in the Petrochemicals business.

Net income decreased to 535.4 billion in 2020 compared with 590.7 billion in 2019.

Cash and cash equivalents at the end of 2020 totaled 1.3 trillion. Operating activities provided 849.7 billion while investing activities used 500.7 billion. Financing activities used another 156.6 billion mainly for repayments of long-term debts.

Strategy
Mitsubishi Corporation has conceived its latest management plan entitled "Midterm Corporate Strategy 2021: Achieving Growth Through Business Management Model." It will take effect from fiscal year 2019.

The new strategy will lay the groundwork for MC's sustainable growth over the next three years recognizing how worldwide economic and geopolitical trends are putting pressure on enterprises to evolve its business models. Such trends include the US administration's America-First agenda China' One-Belt One-Road policy and the so-called "Fourth Industrial Revolution" the hallmarks of which are advancing digital technologies and the evolution of platform businesses.

Mergers and Acquisitions
In late 2019 Mitsubishi Corporation (MC) and Chubu Electric Power Co. Inc. (Chubu) were selected as the preferred buyers in a bid for the Netherland-based Energy Company Eneco an integrated energy company that is actively engaged in renewable power generation projects for 4.1 billion Euros. This acquisition will help Mitsubishi to accelerate its own renewable developments in Europe and around the world.

Company Background
Mitsubishi Corporation was founded and went public as Mitsubishi Shoji in 1954. In 1968 it took on the first large-scale international project in Brunei to develop LNG assets followed by iron-ore and metallurgical coal projects in Australia and Canada and salt field business in Mexico.

In 1971 the company made "Mitsubishi Corporation" its official English name. In 1989 it was listed on the London Stock Exchange.

HISTORY

Yataro Iwasaki's close ties to the Japanese government (along with subsidies and monopoly rights) ensured the success of his shipping and trading company Mitsubishi. Founded in 1870 Mitsubishi diversified into mining (1873) banking (1885) and shipbuilding (1887); it began to withdraw from shipping in the 1880s. During the next decade it invested in Japanese railroads and property.

In 1918 the Mitsubishi zaibatsu (conglomerate) spun off its central management arm Mitsubishi Trading (the forerunner of Mitsubishi Corporation). By WWII the group was a huge amalgam of divisions and public companies. During the war it made warplanes ships explosives and beer.

The zaibatsu were dissolved by US occupation forces and Mitsubishi was split into 139 entities. After the occupation the Japanese government encouraged many of the former business groups to reunite around the old zaibatsu banks. In 1954 Mitsubishi Trading became the leader of the Mitsubishi Group and established Mitsubishi International (US) which became a leading exporter of US goods.

The 1964 merger of three Mitsubishi companies created Mitsubishi Heavy Industries a top Japanese maker of ships aircraft plants and heavy machinery. Mitsubishi Kasei separated from Asahi Glass and Mitsubishi Rayon by a US fiat became Japan's #1 chemical concern. Mitsubishi Electric emerged as one of the country's leading electrical equipment and electronics manufacturers. In 1971 Chrysler invested in Mitsubishi Motors which began making cars for the US automaker. That year Mitsubishi Trading was renamed Mitsubishi Corporation.

Through the 1980s Japan seemed economically invincible. Then its "bubble economy" burst. The group fell behind in electronics and autos in the US consumer demand dried up at home and Mitsubishi Bank was left with a heavy burden of bad loans. Group members which traditionally provided materials supplies and sales outlets for each other began loosening old keiretsu ties during Japan's recession of the 1990s.

In 1993 Chrysler sold its stock in Mitsubishi Motors and two years later the companies severed production ties. This loss and declining demand in the US for Mitsubishi cars hurt auto sales.

Mitsubishi Bank merged with Bank of Tokyo in 1996 to form the biggest bank in the world The Bank of Tokyo-Mitsubishi (BTM). In 1997 several Mitsubishi companies admitted paying off a corporate racketeer setting off a wave of executive resignations.

By 1999 BTM had tumbled from the top spot and was unable to keep the money freely flowing to fellow Mitsubishi members.

Hit hard by the Asian economic crisis all the struggling Mitsubishi companies had to look outside of the keiretsu for help. In 1999 Mitsubishi Motors found a foreign partner Volvo for its truck making operations. Mitsubishi Oil merged with an outsider Nippon Oil to form Nippon Mitsubishi Oil (later renamed Nippon Oil). In 2000 Daimler-Chrysler (now Chrysler and Daimler) acquired a controlling stake in Mitsubishi Motors for $2.1 billion.

Executives at Mitsubishi Motors were charged in 2001 after they allegedly kept the lid on thousands of reported defects in Mitsubishi cars instead of issuing recalls. Stung by this and the after-effects of scandals from the previous decade Mitsubishi unveiled a new corporate philosophy as part of a strategy to revive the group's reputation.

In 2003 Mitsubishi disbanded its information technology and electronics business unit. The unit's operations were divided between the new business and machinery groups. In 2004 the company formed an alliance with GE Yokogawa Medical Systems (GEYMS) to provide GEYMS with help in developing its presence in the Japanese diagnostic imaging market.

In 2004 the company formed a food distribution joint venture with five Japanese food wholesalers comprising national wholesaler Meidi-ya and four regional companies. The joint venture called Alliance Network became one of Japan's largest food wholesalers. Mitsubishi had a 51% stake in Alliance Network. Later in 2004 Mitsubishi acquired the food beverage additive and pharmaceutical active and excipient businesses of Ashland Distribution.

In 2006 Mitsubishi bolstered its automotive operations when it acquired shares in Isuzu from General Motors; Mitsubishi ended up with a 10% stake in Isuzu. Mitsubishi and Isuzu soon after formed a European joint venture to market light-duty trucks throughout the continent. Later that year Mitsubishi bought the Avon Automotive subsidiary of Avon Rubber in a deal worth $120 million.

The following year Mitsubishi bought majority control of Nosan Corporation a manufacturer of livestock feed. In late 2007 the company acquired the majority interest in Kentucky Fried Chicken Japan.

On the medical health care front Mitsubishi shifted the focus of certain of its subsidiaries to providing services to hospitals and nursing care facilities. It established the Trinity Healthcare Fund in 2007 to provide management support for the restructuring of hospitals and other medical institutions. Other Mitsubishi subsidiaries focused on medical services include ProCure which is a medical equipment wholesale distributor and Apprecia which provides hospital construction consulting services.

During 2007 the group began investing in energy-related assets as part of this strategy. It acquired nearly 40% of Encore Energy Pte. which in turn owns 51% of Medco Energy an Indonesian oil and gas concern. The deal was valued at about $350 million and gave Mitsubishi a 20% stake in Medco. Mitsubishi was already working with Medco on an Indonesian gas plant and the two companies plan to pursue further international energy partnerships.

In 2009 it entered the solar energy business buying 34% of a subsidiary of Spanish renewable energy firm Acciona SA

Mitsubishi in 2010 it merged subsidiaries Mitsubishi Corporation Unimetals and Mitsubishi Shoji Light Metal Sales Corporation. The resulting company was named Mitsubishi Corporation Unimetals and remained a subsidiary of Mitsubishi. The merger was made to concentrate the company's management expertise in the non-ferrous metals industry.

EXECUTIVES

EVP, Corporate Functional Officer and CFO, Kazuyuki Masu

EVP, Corporate Functional Officer, Global Strategy and Chief Compliance Officer, Emergency Crisis Management, Yasuteru Hirai

EVP and Group CEO, Urban Development Group, Mitsumasa Icho

EVP and President, Americas, Hidenori Takaoka

Independent Director, Tsuneyoshi Tatsuoka

Independent Director, Akitaka Saiki

Independent Director, Akihiko Nishiyama

EVP, Corporate Functional Officer, Business Development and GM, Kansai, Yutaka Kashiwagi

Independent Director, Shunichi Miyanaga

Chairman, Ken Kobayashi

Independent Director, Sakie Akiyama

EVP and Group CEO, Automotive and Mobility Group, Iwao Toide

President, Chief Executive Officer, Takehiko Kakiuchi

EVP, Corporate Functional Officer, CDO and CAO, Corporate Communications, Corporate Sustainability, Akira Murakoshi

Auditors: Deloitte Touche Tohmatsu LLC

LOCATIONS

HQ: Mitsubishi Corp
2-3-1 Marunouchi, Chiyoda-ku, Tokyo 100-8086
Phone: (81) 3 3210 2121
Web: www.mitsubishicorp.com

2018 Sales

	% of total
Japan	54
Singapore	13
US	12
Other countries	21
Total	**100**

PRODUCTS/OPERATIONS

2018 Sales

	% of total
Living Essentials	31
Energy	24
Metals	24
Chemicals	13
Machinery	7
Global Environmental & Infrastructure Business	1
Total	**100**

Selected Products and Services

Metals
  Bullion and metals futures
  Fabricated steel structures
  Metallurgical and thermal coal
  Nonferrous metal products
  Nonferrous metals
  Nuclear fuel and components
  Precious metals
  Raw materials for steel
  Semifinished products
  Steel materials
  Specialty steel
Living Essentials
  Apparel
  Canned foods
  Ceramic materials
  Cigarettes
  Coffee beans coffee and beverages
  Confections and snacks
  Contract food services
  Dairy foods and processed foods
  Fabrics
  Feedstuffs
  Fresh and frozen foods
  Grains and agricultural products
  Marine products
  Meat and livestock
  Mineral water
  Oils and fats
  Photosensitized materials
  Pulp paper and packaging materials
  Soft drinks
  Sweeteners
  Textile raw materials
  Textiles for industrial use
  Tires
  Wood wood products and construction materials
Machinery
  Automobiles
  Commercial aviation
  Defense systems and equipment
  Electronics products
  Industrial agricultural construction and other general machinery
  Plant and machinery for power generation electricity oil/gas/chemicals steel/cement and environmental protection

Project development and construction
Satellite communications
Ships
Space systems
Transportation systems
Energy
  Carbon materials and products
  Crude oil
  LNG
  LPG
  Orimulsion
  Petroleum products
Chemicals
  Fertilizers
  Fine and specialty chemicals
  Inorganic chemicals
  Petrochemicals
  Plastics

COMPETITORS

ASHLAND LLC	MARUBENI CORPORATION
ECO ANIMAL HEALTH GROUP PLC	MITSUBISHI CHEMICAL CORPORATION
FORMOSA PLASTICS CORPORATION	MITSUBISHI MOTORS CORPORATION
HELM AG	MITSUI & CO. LTD.
ITOCHU CORPORATION	REMINGTON OUTDOOR COMPANY INC
KOC HOLDING ANONIM SIRKETI	SUMITOMO CORPORATION

HISTORICAL FINANCIALS

Company Type: Public

Income Statement   FYE: March 31

	REVENUE ($ mil.)	NET INCOME ($ mil.)	NET PROFIT MARGIN	EMPLOYEES
03/21	116,365	1,558	1.3%	106,902
03/20	136,155	4,931	3.6%	110,006
03/19	145,414	5,334	3.7%	104,168
03/18	71,264	5,275	7.4%	98,146
03/17	57,472	3,937	6.9%	99,123
Annual Growth	19.3%	(20.7%)	—	1.9%

2021 Year-End Financials

Debt ratio: 0.2%
Return on equity: 3.1%
Cash ($ mil.): 11,901
Current ratio: 1.32
Long-term debt ($ mil.): 39,573
No. of shares (mil.): 1,479
Dividends
  Yield: 4.2%
  Payout: 114.9%
Market value ($ mil.): —

Mitsubishi Electric Corp

Auditors: KPMG AZSA LLC

LOCATIONS

HQ: Mitsubishi Electric Corp
2-7-3 Marunouchi, Chiyoda-ku, Tokyo 100-8310
Phone: (81) 3 3218 2272
Web: www.mitsubishielectric.co.jp

HISTORICAL FINANCIALS

Company Type: Public

Income Statement   FYE: March 31

	REVENUE ($ mil.)	NET INCOME ($ mil.)	NET PROFIT MARGIN	EMPLOYEES
03/21	37,854	1,744	4.6%	145,653
03/20	41,110	2,043	5.0%	146,518
03/19	40,814	2,046	5.0%	145,817
03/18	41,730	2,560	6.1%	142,340
03/17	37,910	1,882	5.0%	138,700
Annual Growth	(0.0%)	(1.9%)	—	1.2%

2021 Year-End Financials

Debt ratio: 0.0%
Return on equity: 7.4%
Cash ($ mil.): 6,930
Current ratio: 1.89
Long-term debt ($ mil.): 869
No. of shares (mil.): 2,146
Dividends
  Yield: 2.1%
  Payout: 78.6%
Market value ($ mil.): 65,734

	STOCK PRICE ($) FY Close	P/E High	P/E Low	PER SHARE ($) Earnings	PER SHARE ($) Dividends	PER SHARE ($) Book Value
03/21	30.62	0	0	0.81	0.67	11.59
03/20	24.65	0	0	0.95	0.74	10.43
03/19	25.73	0	0	0.95	0.72	10.09
03/18	32.41	0	0	1.19	0.60	9.91
03/17	28.81	0	0	0.88	0.49	8.50
Annual Growth	1.5%	—	—	(1.9%)	8.2%	8.1%

Mitsubishi Heavy Industries Ltd

Mitsubishi Heavy Industries (MHI) builds and supplies everything from nuclear power plants and aircraft to engines ships and air conditioners and serves various industries and customers around the world. MHI operates through four main industry segments: Energy Systems Plants & Infrastructure Logistics Thermal & Drive Systems and Aircraft Defense & Space. The company's core market is Japan where it earns about 55% of its revenue but also does business in other parts of Asia the US Europe Central and South America Africa and the Middle East.

Operations

MHI operates through four reportable segments: Energy Systems (around 40% of sales); Logistics Thermal & Drive Systems (about 25%); Aircraft Defense & Space (about 20%); and Plants & Infrastructure Systems (more than 15%).

Energy systems include thermal power systems (Gas turbine combined cycle [GTCC] and Steam power) nuclear power generation system (Lightwater reactors Nuclear fuel cycle & Advanced solutions) wind power generators engines for aircrafts compressors environmental plants marine machinery. Its Logistics Thermal & Drive Systems offers material handling equipment turbochargers engines air-conditioning & refrigeration systems automotive thermal systems. The Aircraft Defense & Space provides commercial aircraft defense aircraft missile systems naval ships special vehicles maritime systems (torpedoes) space systems. Lastly the Plants & Infrastructure Systems offers metals machinery commercial ships engineering environmental systems mechatronics systems machine tools.

Geographic Reach

The company is based in Tokyo Japan and has over 400 worldwide locations. Japan accounts for about 55% of its total revenue and the US represents some 15%.

Sales and Marketing

Major external customer from which revenue accounts for 10% or more of the revenue recorded in the consolidated statement of profit or loss was Ministry of Defense. Its revenue mainly belonged to the reporting segment of Aircraft Defense & Space and the amount of revenue was 400723 million.

Financial Performance

MHI's revenue for fiscal 2020 increased to 4.0 trillion compared from the prior year with 3.7 trillion.

Loss for fiscal 2020 was 32.7 billion compared from the prior year with a profit of 49.4 billion.

Cash held by the company at the end of fiscal 2020 decreased to 281.6 billion. Cash provided by operations was 452.6 billion while cash used for investing and financing activities were 239.6 billion and 204.5 billion respectively. Main uses of cash were purchases of property plant and equipment and intangible assets; and repayment of liabilities under factoring agreements.

Mergers and Acquisitions

In mid-2020 MHI acquired Canada-based Bombardier Inc.'s Canadair Regional Jet (CRJ) Program for a cash consideration of approximately $550 million. Bombardier's CRJ Program includes the maintenance support refurbishment marketing and sales activities for the CRJ Series aircraft along with the type certificates. MHI now owns CRJ's related services and support network mainly located in Mirabel Quebec and Toronto Ontario in Canada Bridgeport West Virginia and Tucson Arizona in the United States.

EXECUTIVES

Independent Director, Hiroo Unoura
Independent Director, Noriko Morikawa
Independent Director, Masako Ii
Chairman of the Board, Shunichi Miyanaga
Managing Executive Officer, Chief Executive Officer of Domain, Manager of Logistics, Cold & Drive System Domain, Chairman of Subsidiary, Takashi Mikogami
Chief Technology Officer, Managing Executive Officer, Eisaku Ito
Director, Setsuo Tokunaga
Managing Executive Officer, Masahiko Mishima
President, Chief Executive Officer, Representative Director, Seiji Izumisawa
Director, Koji Ohkura
Managing Executive Officer, President of Subsidiary, Yoshihiro Shiraiwa
Managing Executive Officer, Chief Strategy Officer, CEO of Domain, Manager of Energy Domain, Representative Director, Hitoshi Kaguchi
Chief Financial Officer, Managing Executive Officer, Representative Director, Hisato Kozawa
Independent Director, Nobuyuki Hirano
Auditors: KPMG AZSA LLC

LOCATIONS

HQ: Mitsubishi Heavy Industries Ltd
3-2-3 Marunouchi, Chiyoda-ku, Tokyo 100-8332
Phone: (81) 3 6275 6200
Web: www.mhi.co.jp

2018 Sales

	% of total
Asia	
Japan	46
Other countries	17
USA	15
Europe	11
Central and South America	4
Middle East	3
Africa	2
Other regions	2
Total	**100**

PRODUCTS/OPERATIONS

2018 Sales

	% of total
Industry & Infrastructure	45
Power Systems	35
Aircraft Defense & Space	17
Others	3
Total	**100**

Selected Products

Aerospace
  Aeroengines
  Civil aircraft
  Defense aircraft
  Guided weapon systems
  Laser radar surveillance system
  Launch vehicles
  Rocket engines
  Space stations
General Machinery & Special Vehicles
  Agricultural machinery
  Construction machinery
  Forklift trucks
  Medium- and small-sized engines
  Tractors
  Turbochargers
Machinery & Steel Structures
  Air brakes
  Automated people movers
  Chemical plants
  CO2 recovery plants
  Crane and material handling systems
  Flue gas desulphurization plants
  Injection molding machines
  Monorails
  Production robots
  Rail transit systems
  Sludge treatment systems
  Testing equipment
Power Systems
  Boilers
  Desalination plants
  Fans and blowers
  Diesel engines
  Gas turbines
  Hydraulic equipment (actuators generators motors pumps and water pressure systems)
  Instrumentation and control systems
  Lithium-ion secondary batteries
  Solid oxide fuel cells
  Steam turbines
  Thin-film photovoltaic module
  Wind turbines
Shipbuilding & Ocean Development
  Cargo ships
  Floating facilities
  Marine engines
  Marine machinery
  Passenger ships
  Pure car carriers
  Special-purpose ships
  Tankers
Others
  Air conditioning and refrigeration systems
  Automotive thermal systems
  Centrifugal chillers
  Machine tools

COMPETITORS

ATS Automation Tooling Systems Inc
BROADWIND INC.
GENERAL DYNAMICS CORPORATION
HIROTEC AMERICA INC.
HONEYWELL INTERNATIONAL INC.
HYDRATIGHT LIMITED
IHI CORPORATION
ITT INC.
JSC POWER MACHINES
MEGGITT PLC
MITSUBISHI POWER AMERICAS INC.
MOOG INC.
Ovivo Inc
PARKER-HANNIFIN CORPORATION
PMFG INC.
SIA ENGINEERING COMPANY LIMITED
SUMITOMO HEAVY INDUSTRIES LTD.
SUZLON ENERGY LIMITED
TANFIELD GROUP PLC
TRIUMPH GROUP INC.
WESTERN FILTER A DIVISION OF DONALDSON COMPANY INC
WOODWARD INC.

HISTORICAL FINANCIALS

Company Type: Public

Income Statement

FYE: March 31

	REVENUE ($ mil.)	NET INCOME ($ mil.)	NET PROFIT MARGIN	EMPLOYEES
03/21	33,415	367	1.1%	90,322
03/20	37,230	802	2.2%	93,075
03/19	36,826	915	2.5%	93,173
03/18	38,713	663	1.7%	95,927
03/17	35,007	784	2.2%	99,340
Annual Growth	(1.2%)	(17.3%)	—	(2.4%)

2021 Year-End Financials

Debt ratio: 0.1%
Return on equity: 3.1%
Cash ($ mil.): 2,216
Current ratio: 1.05
Long-term debt ($ mil.): 7,142
No. of shares (mil.): 336
Dividends
  Yield: —
  Payout: 62.0%
Market value ($ mil.): —

Mitsubishi Materials Corp.

With operations in copper cement and aluminum Mitsubishi Materials makes a material difference with its end products. The company offers a wide range of products for next-generation vehicles IoT and AI. It also include electronic devices heat dissipating insulators for power modules materials for terminal connectors as well as heat reflective coatings for windshields. Mitsubishi Materials' business cover a wide range of industries which includes infrastructures transportation energy and consumer electronics.

Operations

Mitsubishi Materials operates through six segments: Metals (about 50% of total revenue) Metalworking Solutions Cement Aluminum Advanced Products Environment & Energy Business and Other Businesses.

Metals includes copper smelting (copper gold and silver) and copper alloy products.

Metalworking Solutions operates businesses globally for cemented carbide products such as cutting tools and sintered products used for automotive parts in addition to other products.

Cement includes cement and related products ready-mixed concrete and aggregate.

Aluminum consist of aluminum cans rolled aluminum products and processed aluminum products.

Advanced Products includes copper and fabricated products electronic components and materials fabricated copper products and many more.

Environment & Energy Business offers recycle of home appliance products consult of natural resources exploration civil engineering washing of incineration fly ash and operation of hydroelectric and geothermal power stations.

Geographic Reach

Mitsubishi Materials operates in 30 countries worldwide including in Europe (Germany the UK Spain and France) Asia (Indonesia South Korea Malaysia Singapore China Taiwan Hong Kong and Thailand) and in Australia Canada Brazil.

Japan accounts for about 65% of Mitsubishi Materials' total revenue.

Financial Performance

Note: Growth rates may differ after conversion to US Dollars.

Company's revenue for fiscal 2021 decreased to 1.49 trillion compared from the prior year with 1.52 trillion.

Net income for fiscal 2021 was 24.4 billion compared from the prior year with a net loss of 72.9 billion.

Cash held by the company at the end of fiscal 2021 increased to 147.5 billion. Cash provided by operations and financing activities were 78.4 billion and 41.5 billion respectively. Cash used for investing activities was 101.8 billion.

Strategy

The company-wide policy of the FY2023 Strategy is "Optimization of business portfolio" "Comprehensive efforts to increase business competitiveness" and "Creation of new products and businesses" which is the same as that of FY 2020 Strategy.

Comprehensive efforts to increase business competitiveness involves polishing core technologies and knowledge that can be provided to the market and acquiring things that the company lack or that need supplementation via M&A and collaboration.

EXECUTIVES

Independent Director, Koji Igarashi
Chairman of the Board, Akira Takeuchi
Executive President, Chief Executive Officer, Director, Naoki Ono
Executive Vice President, Representative Executive Officer, President of High Performance Products Company, Yasunobu Suzuki
Managing Executive Officer, Corporate Strategy Committee Member and GM, Governance Division, Environment & Energy Business, Makoto Shibata
Managing Executive Officer, Shinichi Nakamura
Managing Executive Officer, Corporate Strategy Committee Member, GM, HR & General Affairs Division and GM, HR Department Affiliated Corporations, Yoshikazu Yasui
Executive Officer, VP, Metals Company and GM, Metallurgy Division, Tetsuro Sakai
Chief Financial Officer, Managing Executive Officer, Director of Business Planning, Director, Nobuhiro Takayanagi
Executive Officer and GM, Environment & Energy Business Unit, Shogo Yamaguchi
Independent Director, Tatsuo Wakabayashi
Independent Director, Mariko Tokuno
Independent Director, Hiroshi Sato
Independent Director, Hiroshi Watanabe
Independent Director, Hikaru Sugi
Auditors: KPMG AZSA LLC

LOCATIONS

HQ: Mitsubishi Materials Corp.
3-2-3 Marunouchi, Chiyoda-ku, Tokyo 100-8117
Phone: (81) 3 5252 5226
Web: www.mmc.co.jp

2016 Sales

	% of total
Asia	25
Japan	64
US	8
Europe	2
Others	1
Total	**100**

PRODUCTS/OPERATIONS

2016 Sales

	% of total
Metals	48
Cement	14
Aluminum	11
Advanced materials & tools	9
Electronic materials & components	4
Other	14
Total	**100**

COMPETITORS

CHINO MINES COMPANY
HANWA CO.LTD.
Hbis Company Limited
IMERYS
JX NIPPON MINING &
  METALS CORPORATION
KAISER ALUMINUM
  CORPORATION
MATERION CORPORATION

MINERALS TECHNOLOGIES
  INC.
PARK-OHIO HOLDINGS
  CORP.
SHOWA DENKO K.K.
TEIJIN LIMITED
TITANIUM METALS
  CORPORATION
UFP TECHNOLOGIES INC.

HISTORICAL FINANCIALS

Company Type: Public

Income Statement				FYE: March 31
	REVENUE ($ mil.)	NET INCOME ($ mil.)	NET PROFIT MARGIN	EMPLOYEES
03/21	13,412	220	1.6%	31,565
03/20	13,966	(671)	—	34,260
03/19	15,016	11	0.1%	34,079
03/18	15,063	325	2.2%	32,069
03/17	11,663	253	2.2%	29,811
Annual Growth	3.6%	(3.4%)	—	1.4%

2021 Year-End Financials

Debt ratio: 0.2%
Return on equity: 4.6%
Cash ($ mil.): 1,382
Current ratio: 1.21
Long-term debt ($ mil.): 3,556

No. of shares (mil.): 130
Dividends
  Yield: —
  Payout: —
Market value ($ mil.): —

Mitsubishi Motors Corp. (Japan)

Mitsubishi Motors is a small fish in the big pond of global car manufacturing. The company sells about a million cars per year (far below rival Toyota) worldwide. The six models of cars trucks minivans and SUVs are made at its plants in Asia Europe and the US. Mitsubishi products include the Lancer Pajero Triton Mirage and Outlander vehicles. It also offers an electric minicar under its i-MiEV model. Mitsubishi Corporation and Mitsubishi Heavy Industries together own about a 30% stake in Mitsubishi Motors which traces its roots to Heavy Industries' 1917 "Mitsubishi Model A" project. About 70% of sales come from outside of Japan.

Operations

The company develops plug-in hybrids and other electric vehicles through its research and development facilities and through joint ventures with other auto makers.

Mitsubishi already has an electric minicar the i-MiEV on the market in Japan and Europe. Minicars are a popular vehicle class in the Japanese and European markets and are gaining popularity in other parts of the world. While it sells in Japan under its own brand the MiEV is sold in Europe through an agreement with French car maker Peugeot S.A. which buys and resells MiEV under a different brand.

Geographic Reach

Mitsubishi's largest market is ASEAN representing more than 20% of net sales. Other major markets include Japan (30%) Europe (more than 10%) North America (more than 10%) Oceania (more than 10%) and other countries (about 15%).

Financial Performance

The company's revenue for fiscal 2020 decreased to 1.5 trillion compared from the prior year with 2.3 trillion.

Loss for fiscal 2020 was 298.3 billion compared from the prior year with a profit of 3.8 billion.

Cash held by the company at the end of fiscal 2020 decreased to 399.6 billion. Cash provided by operations and financing activities were 18.8 billion and 9.6 billion respectively. Cash used for investing activities was 105.7 billion mainly for purchase of property plant and equipment

Strategy

In fiscal 2021 Mitsubishi will continue making a steady effort to implement its medium-term business plan "Small but Beautiful" to further strengthen its management base. The company expect a series of measures it put in place in fiscal 2020 to lower fixed costs to bear fruit throughout fiscal 2021. At the same time Mitsubishi need to make investments for growth such as advertising expenses for the launch of new vehicles as well as expenses for new product development. In fiscal 2021 the company expect the full year's impact of its cost-cutting efforts to cover these forward-looking investments. As a result Mitsubishi intend to keep overall fixed costs at the same level as in fiscal 2020.

In terms of regional strategies the company will steadily implement necessary measures in countries where the operating environment remains severe. At the same time Mitsubishi will seize opportunities in countries where the business environment is improving.

Company Background

Mitsubishi Motors Corporation was created in 1970 when Mitsubishi Heavy Industries spun off its motor vehicle division. Mitsubishi Heavy Industries was created in 1934 by the merger of Mitsubishi Aircraft and Mitsubishi Shipbuilding (which had been making cars since 1917).

EXECUTIVES

Independent Director, Joji Tagawa
Chairman of the Board, Independent Director, Tomofumi Hiraku
Chief Executive Officer, Takao Kato
Independent Director, Kiyoshi Sono
Independent Director, Takahiko Ikushima
Independent Director, Yoshihiko Nakamura
Director, Kozo Shiraji
Vice President, Chief Financial Officer, Representative Executive Officer, Koji Ikeya
Independent Director, Main Koda
Independent Director, Ken Kobayashi
Independent Director, Shunichi Miyanaga
Independent Director, Kenichiro Sasae
Independent Director, Yaeko Takeoka
Independent Director, Hideyuki Sakamoto
Auditors: Ernst & Young ShinNihon LLC

LOCATIONS

HQ: Mitsubishi Motors Corp. (Japan)
  3-1-21 Shibaura, Minato-ku, Tokyo 108-8410
Phone: (81) 3 3456 1111
Web: www.mitsubishi-motors.com

2015 Sales

	% of total
Europe	24
Japan	20
Asia	19
North America	13
Oceania	10
Other regions	14
Total	**100**

PRODUCTS/OPERATIONS

2015

	%
Automobiles	99
Financial services	1
Total	**100**

Selected Models

Challenger
Colt
Diamante
Eclipse
Eclipse Spyder
Endeavor
Galant
i MiEV
Lancer
Lancer Evolution
Mirage
Outlander
Raider

COMPETITORS

Bayerische Motoren
  Werke AG
GENERAL MOTORS COMPANY
GROUP LOTUS LIMITED
ISUZU MOTORS LIMITED
KIA CORPORATION
MAHINDRA AND MAHINDRA
  LIMITED
MITSUBISHI CORPORATION
NISSAN MOTOR CO.LTD.

PEUGEOT SA
SUBARU CORPORATION
SUZUKI MOTOR
  CORPORATION
TATA MOTORS LIMITED
TOYOTA BOSHOKU
  CORPORATION
TOYOTA TSUSHO
  CORPORATION
YAMAHA MOTOR CO. LTD.

HISTORICAL FINANCIALS

Company Type: Public

Income Statement				FYE: March 31
	REVENUE ($ mil.)	NET INCOME ($ mil.)	NET PROFIT MARGIN	EMPLOYEES
03/21	13,145	(2,820)	—	36,525
03/20	20,914	(237)	—	39,729
03/19	22,706	1,199	5.3%	39,996
03/18	20,646	1,013	4.9%	37,629
03/17	17,052	(1,775)	—	33,496
Annual Growth	(6.3%)	—	—	2.2%

2021 Year-End Financials

Debt ratio: 0.2%
Return on equity: (-48.7%)
Cash ($ mil.): 4,115
Current ratio: 1.41
Long-term debt ($ mil.): 3,142

No. of shares (mil.): 1,488
Dividends
  Yield: —
  Payout: —
Market value ($ mil.): —

Mitsubishi Shokuhin Co., Ltd.

Mitsubishi Shokuhin is a leading wholesale food distributor in Japan. It supplies retailers throughout the country with a wide assortment of products including processed foods seasonings and sauces chilled and frozen foods confectionery and canned goods. In addition the company distributes both alcoholic and non-alcoholic beverages. Trading company Mitsubishi Corporation owns just more than 50% of Mitsubishi Shokuhin. Formerly named Ryoshoku the company adopted the Mitsubishi Shokuhin moniker in 2011. It also began absorbing three of its food wholesaling operations – San-Esu Food Service Network and Meidi-ya. The integration is expected to be completed in 2012.

EXECUTIVES

Chief Financial Officer, Managing Executive
  Officer, Director, Kazuaki Yamana
Director, Wataru Kato
President, Executive President, Chief Executive
  Officer, Chief Sustainability Officer,
  Representative Director, Yutaka Kyoya
Independent Director, Nobuyuki Teshima
Chief Health Officer, Managing Executive Officer,
  Director, Yasuo Yamamoto
Independent Director, Tamaki Kakizaki
Chief Compliance Officer, Managing Executive
  Officer, Chief Director of Business Planning,
  Director, Koichi Enomoto
Independent Director, Masahiro Yoshikawa
Managing Executive Officer, Director, Koji
  Tamura
Auditors: Deloitte Touche Tohmatsu LLC

LOCATIONS

HQ: Mitsubishi Shokuhin Co., Ltd.
  1-1-1 Koishikawa, Bunkyo-ku, Tokyo 112-8778
Phone: (81) 3 4553 5111
Web: www.mitsubishi-shokuhin.com

PRODUCTS/OPERATIONS

2016 sales

	% of total
Frozen and chilled foods business	39
Processed food business	32
Alcoholic beverages business	18
Confectioneries business	11
Total	**100**

COMPETITORS

COLAVITA USA L.L.C.	MONOGRAM FOOD
JETRO CASH AND CARRY	SOLUTIONS LLC
ENTERPRISES LLC	OMAHA STEAKS
JFC INTERNATIONAL INC.	INTERNATIONAL INC.
KDN HOLDINGS INC.	SUPERIOR FOODS INC.
KOKUBU GROUP CORP.	UNITED NATURAL FOODS
MARKETFARE FOODS LLC	INC.

HISTORICAL FINANCIALS

Company Type: Public

Income Statement				FYE: March 31
	REVENUE ($ mil.)	NET INCOME ($ mil.)	NET PROFIT MARGIN	EMPLOYEES
03/21	23,279	100	0.4%	6,441
03/20	24,455	105	0.4%	6,429
03/19	23,661	108	0.5%	6,427
03/18	23,669	101	0.4%	6,474
03/17	21,568	110	0.5%	6,407
Annual Growth	1.9%	(2.5%)	—	0.1%

2021 Year-End Financials

Debt ratio: 0.0%
Return on equity: 5.8%
Cash ($ mil.): 3
Current ratio: 1.16
Long-term debt ($ mil.): —
No. of shares (mil.): 57
Dividends
  Yield: —
  Payout: —
Market value ($ mil.): —

Mitsubishi UFJ Financial Group Inc

Mitsubishi UFJ Financial Group (MUFG) is a banking group in Japan with total assets of 331.75 trillion. The group is comprised of MUFG Bank Mitsubishi UFJ Trust and Banking Mitsubishi UFJ Morgan Stanley Securities (through Mitsubishi UFJ Securities Holdings) Mitsubishi UFJ NICOS and other subsidiaries and affiliates. The group provides commercial banking trust banking securities credit cards consumer finance asset management leasing and other fields of financial services. In Japan the company operates approximately 600 business locations and the group had the largest overseas network among Japanese banks consisting of approximately 2100 business locations in more than 50 countries including MUFG Union Bank in the United States Krungsri in Thailand and Bank Danamon in Indonesia. Other holdings include investment bank Mitsubishi UFJ Securities and California-based MUFG Union Bank. Domestic operations accounts for more than a third of total revenue.

Operations

Mitsubishi UFJ Financial Group (MUFG) operates an integrated business group system concentrated on six main business areas.

Retail & Commercial Banking (more than 35%) which integrates the Japanese retail and commercial banking businesses of MUFG Bank Mitsubishi UFJ Trust and Banking Mitsubishi UFJ Securities Holdings and Mitsubishi UFJ NICOS. This business group offers retail and small and medium-sized enterprise customers in Japan an extensive array of commercial banking trust banking and securities products and services.

Global Commercial Banking (20%) which provides financial products and services including loans deposits fund transfers investments asset management services for local retail small and medium-sized enterprise and corporate customers globally through partner banks (including MUFG Union Bank in the US and among others).

Japanese Corporate & Investment Banking (almost 15%) covering the Japanese corporate businesses (including transaction banking investment banking trust banking and securities businesses) of MUFG Bank Mitsubishi UFJ Trust and Banking and Mitsubishi UFJ Securities Holdings. This business group offers large Japanese corporations advanced financial solutions.

Global Markets (approximately 15%) which covers customer business and treasury operations of MUFG Bank Mitsubishi UFJ Trust and Banking and Mitsubishi UFJ Securities Holdings. The customer business includes sales and trading in fixed income instruments currencies equities and other investment products.

Global Corporate & Investment Banking (about 10%) including the corporate investment and transaction banking businesses of MUFG Bank and Mitsubishi UFJ Securities Holdings.

Asset Management & Investor Services Business Group (more than 5%) covers the asset management and asset administration businesses of Mitsubishi UFJ Trust and Banking and MUFG Bank.

MUFG has a diversified revenue stream. Nearly 45% of its total revenue comes from loan interest (including fees); about 30% comes from fees and commissions. More than 15% comes from interest income on investments trading account assets and deposits in other banks. Investment security gains and equity earnings (if applicable) make up the remainder.

Geographic Reach

Mitsubishi UFJ Financial Group (MUFG) operates in the US Japan and more than 50 countries such as Europe and Asia/Oceania including MUFG Union Bank in the United States Krungsri in Thailand and Bank Danamon in Indonesia.

About 65% of its revenue came from Japan followed by the United States with approximately 30%.

Sales and Marketing

Mitsubishi UFJ Financial Group (MUFG) mainly markets its products through sales agents. The company also offers direct banking channels and internet banking services for corporate customers and to enhance productivity through migration to digital channels for the housing loan business and expanded use of robotics and artificial intelligence and primarily targets small- and medium-sized enterprise owners.

Financial Performance

Note: Growth rates may differ after conversion to US dollars.

Mitsubishi UFJ Financial Group (MUFG) revenues in the last five years fallen by 28% with its lowest at 1.9 trillion in 2017 before settling at 3.4 trillion in 2019. Net income followed a similar pattern as it has risen and fallen in the same period with 1.2 trillion in 2017 at its peak and 202.7 billion in 2017 at its lowest.

MUFG recognizes revenue from net interest income trust fees and commissions net trading profit and net other operating profit which together amounted to 4.1 trillion in 2020 up from 3.6 trillion.

The company's net income fell by 57% to 306 billion in 2020. General and administrative expenses for the year increased 154.7 billion to 2.8 trillion due to increase in expenses for overseas operations because of the expansion of business and expenses for regulatory compliance purposes.

The holding company added 3.9 trillion to its cash stores in 2020 to 78.6 trillion. Operations used 1.4 trillion mostly on reductions in trading account liabilities excluding foreign exchange contracts. The company used another 18.1 trillion for investments mostly for loans funds sold and receivables as well as the acquisition of Bank Danamon and FSI. Financing activities provided 23.8 trillion primarily from net increases in deposits call money funds purchased and payables under repurchase agreements and securities lending transactions.

Strategy

MUFG is implementing "Eleven Transformation Initiatives" ? specific strategic initiatives designed to enable the company to cope with adverse changes in the domestic or overseas business environment and to achieve sustainable growth. Each initiative constitutes a pillar involving business operations that have large growth potential allows MUFG to expand its group capabilities to the fullest extent and is expected to grow as a core business or a foundation for such.

The company took strategic steps towards building a business platform in South East Asia through the expansion of Krungsri's business in Thailand and strategic investments in Security Bank in the Philippines and Bank Danamon in Indonesia. The Bank enhances the enterprise value of each of MUFG Union Bank in the United States and other major local commercial banking subsidiaries.

The bank will implement core strategies based on enhanced management policy due to the impact of the COVID-19 pandemic. These core strategies include digitalization of the domestic retail business restructuring of the global strategy implementation of further operational foundation and process reforms and creation of a work environment and operational infrastructure that reflect and support the diverse values of employees and work style reforms.

In relation with its implementation of these core strategies MUFG invested $706 million in Grab to jointly develop next generation bespoke financial services in Southeast Asia to boost financial inclusion in the region.

Mergers and Acquisitions

In August 2019 Mitsubishi UFJ Trust and Banking completed its acquisition of 100% of the shares in each of nine subsidiaries of Colonial First State Group Limited which collectively represent the global asset management business known as Colonial First State Global Asset Management or CFSGAM from Australian financial group Commonwealth Bank of Australia and its wholly-owned subsidiary Colonial First State Group Limited. As a result of the acquisition the nine subsidiaries became our consolidated subsidiaries. In September 2019 CFSGAM was rebranded as First Sentier Investors. The price was approximately AU$4.2 billion or 312 billion in cash.

In November 2019 MUFG Bank completed its acquisition from DVB Bank SE in Germany of DVB Bank's aviation finance lending portfolio employees and related operating infrastructure based on an agreement entered into among the two banks and BOT Lease Co. Ltd

Company Background

MUFG was formed in the 2005 merger of Mitsubishi Tokyo Financial Group and UFJ Holdings.

HISTORY

Mitsubishi Bank emerged from the exchange office of the original Mitsubishi zaibatsu (industrial group) in 1885. It evolved into a full-service bank by 1895 and became independent in 1919 though its primary customers were Mitsubishi group companies. The bank survived WWII but a US fiat dismantled the zaibatsu after the war. Mitsubishi Bank reopened as Chiyoda Bank in 1948. After reopening offices in London and New York the bank readopted the Mitsubishi name.

In the 1950s Mitsubishi Bank became the lead lender for the reconstituted Mitsubishi group (keiretsu). In the 1960s it followed its Mitsubishi partners overseas helping finance Japan's growing international trade. In 1972 it acquired the Bank of California and began doing more business outside the group.

Japan's overinflated real estate market of the 1980s devastated many of the country's banks including Nippon Trust Bank of which Mitsubishi owned 5%. Japan's Ministry of Finance (MoF) urged Mitsubishi to bail Nippon out; as a reward for raising its stake in Nippon to 69% and assuming a mountain of unrecoverable loans the MoF allowed Mitsubishi to begin issuing debt before other Japanese banks. In 1995 Mitsubishi Bank and Bank of Tokyo agreed to merge.

Bank of Tokyo (BOT) was established in 1880 as the Yokohama Specie Bank; the Iwasaki family founders of the Mitsubishi group served on its board. With links to the Imperial family the bank was heavily influenced by government policy. With Japan isolated after the Sino-Japanese War its international operations suffered greatly even before WWII. Completely dismantled after WWII the bank was re-established in 1946 as the Bank of Tokyo a commercial city bank bereft of its foreign exchange business. During the 1950s the government restored it as a foreign exchange specialist but regulations limited its domestic business.

BOT evolved into an investment bank in the 1970s; its reputation as the leading foreign exchange bank brought in international clients and successful derivatives trading and overseas banking. By the time BOT and Mitsubishi Bank agreed to merge BOT had 363 foreign offices (only 37 in Japan) with more foreign than Japanese employees.

The two banks merged in 1996 to form The Bank of Tokyo-Mitsubishi (BTM); Mitsubishi was the surviving entity. Their California banks merged to create Union Bank of California (UnionBanCal). The next year BTM reorganized its operations but had problems assimilating its disparate corporate cultures.

In 1998 Japanese banking regulators doled out nearly $240 billion to the industry to prop up failing banks and to strengthen healthier ones. Also that year BTM was fined for bribing MoF officials with entertainment gifts and posted a huge loss after writing off $8.4 billion in bad debt. Losses continued in 1999 and the bank responded by reorganizing operationally cutting jobs and offices and selling stock in UnionBanCal.

In 2000 BTM announced plans to form a financial group with Mitsubishi Trust Bank and Nippon Trust Bank. The following year the three banks unified and formed Mitsubishi Tokyo Financial Group. Before rolling into Mitsubishi Tokyo Financial Group BTM paid back the money showered upon it by the Japanese government in 1998.

In 2004 MTFG introduced a new organizational structure that focused on its three core markets — retail corporate and trust asset businesses. The company planned to unify business within each division and to improve decision-making companywide. The group also introduced a new executive officer system with the idea of separating company oversight and business execution. A mechanism for credit risk control was also added.

It was all to change in 2005 however. During this time Mitsubishi Tokyo Financial Group merged with UFJ Holdings emerging (at that time) as the world's largest bank by assets. As a result of the merger the group was renamed Mitsubishi UFJ Financial Group (MUFG).

As with most of its peers MUFG was not immune to the global credit crisis that began in 2007. Its NICOS consumer lending subsidiary had a disappointing year due to the credit crunch. The unit sold its installment credit car loan and car leasing businesses to JACCS in 2008. In 2009 MUFG announced plans to close 50 branches and cut nearly 1000 jobs as a part of a long-term restructuring plan. In addition the bank shut down some 200 ATMs and relocated another 1000 employees.

In 2008 the group bought the rest of UnionBanCal and Mitsubishi UFJ NICOS it didn't already own and acquired a stake in bulge-bracket firm Morgan Stanley. MUFG also bought a 10% stake in UK-based Aberdeen Asset Management that year. (It later upped its interest to around 17%.)

EXECUTIVES

Independent Director, Keiko Honda
Independent Director, Hirofumi Nomoto
Independent Director, Mariko Fujii
Director, Ritsuo Ogura
Vice Chairman of the Executive Board, Representative Executive Officer, President & Chief Executive Officer of Subsidiaries, Director, Saburo Araki, $235,808 total compensation
Executive Chairman of the Board, Director, Kanetsugu Mike, $386,725 total compensation
Senior Managing Executive Officer, Chief Director of Corporate Banking Business, Naomi Hayashi
President, Representative Executive Officer, Group CEO, Director, Hironori Kamezawa, $613,101 total compensation
Senior Managing Executive Officer, Chief Director of Market Business, Shigeru Yoshifuji
Senior Managing Executive Officer, Chief Director of Contract Property Business, Masamichi Yasuda
Vice Chairman of the Executive Board, Representative Executive Officer, Director, Junichi Hanzawa
Independent Director, Kaoru Kato
Vice Chairman of the Executive Board, Representative Executive Officer, President of Subsidiary, Director, Iwao Nagashima, $330,131 total compensation
Independent Director, Koichi Tsuji

Director, Kenichi Miyanaga
Independent Director, Satoko Kuwabara
Auditors: Deloitte Touche Tohmatsu LLC

LOCATIONS

HQ: Mitsubishi UFJ Financial Group Inc
7-1 Marunouchi 2-chome, Chiyoda-ku, Tokyo 100-8330
Phone: (81) 3 3240 8111   **Fax:** (81) 3 3240 7073
Web: www.mufg.jp

2018 Sales

	% of total
Japan	41
US	26
Europe	10
Asia/Oceania	15
Other regions	8
Total	**100**

PRODUCTS/OPERATIONS

2018 Sales

	% of total
Interest	
Loans including fees	44
Deposits in other banks	2
Investment securities	
Interest	4
Dividends	3
Trading account assets	8
Other	2
Noninterest	
Fees & commissions	28
Foreign exchange gains	-
Trading accounts profits	-
Investment securities gains	6
Equity in earnings of equity method investees	4
Gains in sales of loans	-
Other	1
Total	**100**

2018 Sales

	% of total
Retail & Commercial Banking Business Group	41
Japanese Corporate & Investment Banking Business Group	13
Global Corporate & Investment Banking Business Group	9
Global Commercial Banking Business Group	16
Asset Management & Investor Services Business Group	5
Global Markets Business Group	15
Total	**100**

COMPETITORS

BANK OF CHINA LIMITED
COMMONWEALTH BANK OF AUSTRALIA
Credit Suisse Group AG
DAIWA SECURITIES GROUP INC.
DEUTSCHE BANK AG
MS&AD INSURANCE GROUP HOLDINGS INC.
NOMURA HOLDINGS INC.
PERMIRA ADVISERS LLP
RESONA HOLDINGS INC.
SUMITOMO MITSUI FINANCIAL GROUP INC.

HISTORICAL FINANCIALS

Company Type: Public

Income Statement				FYE: March 31
	ASSETS ($ mil.)	NET INCOME ($ mil.)	INCOME AS % OF ASSETS	EMPLOYEES
03/21	3,195,538	10,090	0.3%	163,500
03/20	3,056,220	2,818	0.1%	168,400
03/19	2,756,168	6,489	0.2%	144,700
03/18	2,830,578	11,566	0.4%	144,000
03/17	2,658,025	1,812	0.1%	143,400
Annual Growth	4.7%	53.6%	—	3.3%

2021 Year-End Financials

Return on assets: 0.3%
Return on equity: 7.2%
Long-term debt ($ mil.): —
No. of shares (mil.): —
Sales ($ mil): 39,637
Dividends
Yield: 4.3%
Payout: 28.5%
Market value ($ mil.): —

STOCK PRICE ($)		P/E		PER SHARE ($)		
	FY Close	High/Low		Earnings	Dividends	Book Value
03/21	5.38	0	0	0.78	0.24	11.01
03/20	3.66	0	0	0.22	0.22	10.77
03/19	4.95	0	0	0.49	0.19	10.62
03/18	6.64	0	0	0.87	0.17	10.71
03/17	6.34	0	0	0.13	0.17	9.31
Annual Growth	(4.0%)	—	—	56.2%	9.1%	4.3%

Mitsui & Co., Ltd.

Auditors: Deloitte Touche Tohmatsu LLC

LOCATIONS

HQ: Mitsui & Co., Ltd.
1-2-1 Otemachi, Chiyoda-ku, Tokyo 100-8631
Phone: (81) 3 3285 1111   **Fax:** (81) 3 3285 9819
Web: www.mitsui.com/jp/ja/

HISTORICAL FINANCIALS

Company Type: Public

Income Statement   FYE: March 31

	REVENUE ($ mil.)	NET INCOME ($ mil.)	NET PROFIT MARGIN	EMPLOYEES
03/21	72,343	3,029	4.2%	54,230
03/20	63,427	3,606	5.7%	56,384
03/19	62,825	3,740	6.0%	54,347
03/18	46,071	3,940	8.6%	54,288
03/17	39,031	2,738	7.0%	52,304
Annual Growth	16.7%	2.6%	—	0.9%

2021 Year-End Financials

Debt ratio: 0.3%
Return on equity: 8.0%
Cash ($ mil.): 9,601
Current ratio: 1.56
Long-term debt ($ mil.): 32,965

No. of shares (mil.): 1,672
Dividends
Yield: 3.5%
Payout: 803.5%
Market value ($ mil.): 704,901

STOCK PRICE ($)		P/E		PER SHARE ($)		
	FY Close	High/Low		Earnings	Dividends	Book Value
03/21	421.49	2	1	1.80	15.11	24.68
03/20	274.34	2	1	2.08	14.78	20.60
03/19	311.09	2	1	2.15	14.52	22.15
03/18	346.53	2	1	2.24	11.38	21.54
03/17	291.47	2	1	1.53	10.50	18.92
Annual Growth	9.7%	—	—	4.1%	9.5%	6.9%

Mitsui Fudosan Co Ltd

Mitsui Fudosan the real estate arm of Mitsui & Co. builds sells leases and manages a variety of luxury real estate including office buildings residential subdivisions and condominiums. Its leasing portfolio is comprised of approximately 5300 tenants in office and retail facilities. The company also owns hotels and engages in real estate brokerage services. Mitsui Fudosan is developing luxury and lifestyle properties to match Japan's rising incomes and high street tastes. Besides Japan where it generates most of its sales the company also operates offices in China Hong Kong Singapore the UK and the US.

Operations

Mitsui Fudosan operates three main lines of business: Leasing Property Sales and Management. Leasing and Property Sales each generate nearly 30% of group revenue and Management accounts for another more than 20%.

The Leasing segment manages the leasing of office and retail space. Its portfolio is concentrated in central Tokyo and rents space to approximately 5300 companies.

The Property Sales business sells condominiums and detached homes to individuals and income-generating properties to institutional investors (including Mitsui Fudosan subsidiaries). In a typical year the segment sells more than 3700 condominiums to individuals and it has the land and intention of building approximately 28000 units over the next several years.

The Management segment provides stable earnings growth for the company by overseeing car parks condominium buildings offices and retail facilitates. It also offers brokerage and asset management services through its Mitsui Rehouse subsidiary and REITs.

Mitsui Fudosan operates other businesses as well including a logistics service focused in and around Tokyo a hotel & resort business with properties throughout Japan and global endeavors in North America & Europe (office buildings & hotels) and China & Asia (retail & condominiums).

Geographic Reach

Mitsui Fudosan is a global company with a significant presence in its home country of Japan. More than 80% of its asset base is in Japan and much of that in Tokyo and the remaining nearly 20% is scattered throughout USA Europe China and other Asia locales.

Its corporate office is located in Tokyo Japan.

Sales and Marketing

The company has about 5300 number of tenant companies in offices and retail facilities.

Financial Performance

Note: Financial results are denoted in Japanese currency the Yen (). Growth rates may differ after conversion to US dollars.

Note: Financial results are denoted in Japanese currency the Yen ().

As for Mitsui Fudosan's consolidated business results for the period revenue from operations was 1.9 trillion a decrease of 107.3 billion or 5% compared to the full year forecast of 2.0 trillion.

Profit attributable to owners of parent was 183.9 billion a decrease of 8.0 billion or 4% compared to the full year forecast of 192.0 billion.

Cash held by the company at the end of 2019 increased to 179.5 billion. Cash provided by operations and financing activities were 87.1 billion and 467.8 billion respectively. Cash used for investing activities was 532.8 billion.

Strategy

The focus will be on new strategic areas like aerospace mobility and food in addition to life science to promote industry-creation distinctive to Nihonbashi. The company will support both the hard and soft aspects of industry growth by generating an original Nihonbashi business and culture and facilitating co-creation by providing spaces and creating opportunities.

Going forward the company will continue striving to formulate financial strategy that is in tune with the real estate business cycles maintain financial soundness through its debt/equity ratio and maintain its credit rating as well as ensuring that any interest-bearing debt procured is diverse and long-term.

Company Background

Mitsui Company Japan's first holding company was founded in 1909 and in 1914 its real estate section was established to manage land and buildings owned by the Mitsui family.

EXECUTIVES

Independent Director, Eriko Kawai
Chairman of the Board, Representative Director, Hiromichi Iwasa
Independent Director, Tsunehiro Nakayama
Executive Vice President, Director, Yasuo Onozawa
Independent Director, Shinichiro Ito
President, Chief Executive Officer, Executive President, Representative Director, Masanobu Komoda
Executive Vice President, Representative Director, Yoshikazu Kitahara
Executive Vice President, Chief Director of House & Life Cooperation, Chairman of Subsidiary, Director, Kiyotaka Fujibayashi
Senior Managing Executive Officer, Yoshihiro Hirokawa
Group Executive Officer, Yosuke Seko
Senior Managing Executive Officer, Chief Director of Overseas Business, Director, Takashi Yamamoto
Senior Managing Executive Officer, Takayuki Miki
Senior Managing Executive Officer, Chief Director of DX, Director, Wataru Hamamoto
Senior Managing Executive Officer, Director, Takashi Ueda
Independent Director, Masafumi Nogimori
Auditors: KPMG AZSA LLC

LOCATIONS

HQ: Mitsui Fudosan Co Ltd
2-1-1 Nihonbashi-Muromachi, Chuo-ku, Tokyo 103-0022
Phone: (81) 3 3246 3055
Web: www.mitsuifudosan.co.jp

PRODUCTS/OPERATIONS

FY2016 Sales

	% of total
Leasing	31
Property Sales	29
Management	20
Mitsui Home	14
Other	6
Total	**100**

Selected Group Companies

Housing
 Daiichi Engei Co. Ltd.
 MITSUI Designtec Co. Ltd.
 Mitsui Fudosan Housing Lease Co. Ltd.
 Mitsui Fudosan Realty Co. Ltd.
 Mitsui Fudosan Reform Co. Ltd.
 Mitsui Fudosan Residential Co. Ltd.
 Mitsui Fudosan Residential Service Chugoku Co. Ltd.
 Mitsui Fudosan Residential Service Co. Ltd.
 Mitsui Fudosan Residential Service Hokkaido Co. Ltd.
 Mitsui Fudosan Residential Service Kansai Co. Ltd.
 Mitsui Fudosan Residential Service Kyusyu Co. Ltd.
 Mitsui Fudosan Residential Service Tohoku Co. Ltd.
 Mitsui Home Co. Ltd.
 Mitsui Home Estate Co. Ltd.
Office Buildings
 First Facilities West Co. Ltd.
 Mitsui Fudosan Building Management Co. Ltd.
 Mitsui Fudosan Facilities Co. Ltd.
 NBF Office Management Co. Ltd.
 Nippon Building Fund Management Ltd.
Retail Properties
 Frontier REIT SC Management Co. Ltd.
 Mitsui Fudosan Frontier REIT Management Inc.
 Mitsui Fudosan Retail Management Co.Ltd.
Accommodation
 Celestine Hotel Co. Ltd.
 Mitsui Fudosan Accommodations Fund Management.
 Mitsui Fudosan Hotel Management Co. Ltd.
 Mitsui Fudosan Housing Lease Co. Ltd.

Real Estate Solutions
  Mitsui Fudosan Investment Advisors Inc.
Resort
  Kyusin Kaihatsu Inc.
  LaLaport Agency Co. Ltd.

COMPETITORS

ALEXANDER & BALDWIN INC.
Brookfield Asset Management Inc
CITY DEVELOPMENTS LIMITED
Cofinimmo
HEIWA REAL ESTATE CO.LTD.
LAND SECURITIES GROUP PLC
MAPELEY ESTATES LIMITED
MITSUBISHI ESTATE COMPANY LIMITED
MURRAY HILL PROPERTIES LLC
Redefine International P.L.C.
SILVER MERGER SUB 1 LLC
SUMITOMO REALTY & DEVELOPMENT CO. LTD.
SUN HUNG KAI PROPERTIES LIMITED
SmartCentres Real Estate Investment Trust
TOKYU LAND CORPORATION
TRITAX BIG BOX REIT PLC

HISTORICAL FINANCIALS

Company Type: Public

Income Statement				FYE: March 31
	REVENUE ($ mil.)	NET INCOME ($ mil.)	NET PROFIT MARGIN	EMPLOYEES
03/21	18,131	1,170	6.5%	38,230
03/20	17,555	1,694	9.7%	34,555
03/19	16,806	1,522	9.1%	32,327
03/18	16,490	1,467	8.9%	31,612
03/17	15,244	1,178	7.7%	30,691
Annual Growth	4.4%	(0.2%)	—	5.6%

2021 Year-End Financials

Debt ratio: 0.4%	No. of shares (mil.): 962
Return on equity: 5.2%	Dividends
Cash ($ mil.): 1,711	Yield: 0.0%
Current ratio: 2.45	Payout: 97.3%
Long-term debt ($ mil.): 28,542	Market value ($ mil.): 68,862

	STOCK PRICE ($) FY Close	P/E High/Low		Earnings	PER SHARE ($) Dividends	Book Value
03/21	71.57	1	0	1.21	1.18	24.00
03/20	46.68	0	0	1.73	1.28	22.86
03/19	75.63	0	0	1.55	1.14	21.55
03/18	63.00	0	0	1.48	1.02	21.02
03/17	53.85	—	—	1.19	0.88	17.97
Annual Growth	7.4%			0.4%	7.5%	7.5%

Miyazaki Bank, Ltd. (The)

Based in the Miyazaki Prefecture in Japan The Miyazaki Bank is a leading Japanese regional bank offering checking and saving accounts foreign currency deposits credit cards and other traditional banking products. Armed with eight subsidiaries and owning more than 90 branches Miyazaki Bank additionally offers fund management and investment advisement services. Key subsidiary Miyagin Lease Co. provides general leasing services to the bank's customers as well. Miyazaki was initially established in 1932 as the Hyuga Industrial Bank; it changed its name to Miyazaki Bank in 1962.

EXECUTIVES

Senior Managing Director, Representative Director, Nobuya Hirano
Director of Business Planning, Manager of Revenue Management Office, Director, Koji Sugita
Director of Home Office Sales, Director, Taizo Sekimoto
Director of Miyakonojo Sales, Director, Yuichi Umezaki
Managing Director, Norio Yano
Managing Director, Yasuo Yumiba
Senior Managing Director, Representative Director, Tetsuji Haraguchi
Auditors: Deloitte Touche Tohmatsu LLC

LOCATIONS

HQ: Miyazaki Bank, Ltd. (The)
  4-3-5 Tachibanadori-Higashi, Miyazaki 880-0805
Phone: (81) 985 27 3131
Web: www.miyagin.co.jp

COMPETITORS

MIE BANK LTD. THE   TOWA BANK. LTD. THE
MIZUHO BANK LTD.

HISTORICAL FINANCIALS

Company Type: Public

Income Statement				FYE: March 31
	ASSETS ($ mil.)	NET INCOME ($ mil.)	INCOME AS % OF ASSETS	EMPLOYEES
03/21	32,999	72	0.2%	1,928
03/20	30,631	65	0.2%	1,942
03/19	28,007	87	0.3%	2,000
03/18	27,937	82	0.3%	2,027
03/17	26,640	82	0.3%	2,014
Annual Growth	5.5%	(3.4%)	—	(1.1%)

2021 Year-End Financials

Return on assets: 0.2%	Dividends
Return on equity: 5.2%	Yield: —
Long-term debt ($ mil.): —	Payout: 21.6%
No. of shares (mil.): 17	Market value ($ mil.): —
Sales ($ mil): 493	

Mizrahi Tefahot Bank Ltd

Auditors: Brightman Almagor Zohar & Co.

LOCATIONS

HQ: Mizrahi Tefahot Bank Ltd
  7 Jabotinsky Street, P.O. Box 3450, Ramat Gan 5252007
Phone: (972) 3 7559000   **Fax:** (972) 3 7559210
Web: www.mizrahi-tefahot.co.il

HISTORICAL FINANCIALS

Company Type: Public

Income Statement				FYE: December 31
	ASSETS ($ mil.)	NET INCOME ($ mil.)	INCOME AS % OF ASSETS	EMPLOYEES
12/19	79,083	533	0.7%	6,433
12/18	68,727	321	0.5%	6,355
12/17	69,014	388	0.6%	6,271
12/16	60,000	329	0.5%	6,141
12/15	53,474	289	0.5%	5,864
Annual Growth	10.3%	16.4%	—	2.3%

2019 Year-End Financials

Return on assets: 0.6%	Dividends
Return on equity: 11.9%	Yield: —
Long-term debt ($ mil.): —	Payout: 30.5%
No. of shares (mil.): 234	Market value ($ mil.): —
Sales ($ mil): 2,800	

MMC Norilsk Nickel PJSC

Auditors: JSC KPMG

LOCATIONS

HQ: MMC Norilsk Nickel PJSC
  18 building 13, Stromynka Street, Moscow 107996
Phone: (7) 495 989 76 50   **Fax:** (7) 495 780 73 67
Web: www.nornik.ru

HISTORICAL FINANCIALS

Company Type: Public

Income Statement				FYE: December 31
	REVENUE ($ mil.)	NET INCOME ($ mil.)	NET PROFIT MARGIN	EMPLOYEES
12/20	15,545	3,385	21.8%	0
12/19	13,563	5,782	42.6%	0
12/18	11,670	3,085	26.4%	75,901
12/17	9,146	2,129	23.3%	78,950
12/16	8,259	2,536	30.7%	82,006
Annual Growth	17.1%	7.5%	—	—

2020 Year-End Financials

Debt ratio: 46.5%	No. of shares (mil.): 158
Return on equity: 86.0%	Dividends
Cash ($ mil.): 5,191	Yield: 4.7%
Current ratio: 1.58	Payout: 7.0%
Long-term debt ($ mil.): 9,622	Market value ($ mil.): 4,982

	STOCK PRICE ($) FY Close	P/E High/Low		Earnings	PER SHARE ($) Dividends	Book Value
12/20	31.48	2	1	21.40	1.49	25.46
12/19	30.49	1	1	36.50	3.58	24.10
12/18	18.84	1	1	19.50	2.13	20.37
12/17	18.91	2	1	13.50	1.11	27.34
12/16	16.92	1	1	16.10	1.11	24.15
Annual Growth	16.8%	—	—	7.4%	7.7%	1.3%

MOL Magyar Olaj es Gazipari Reszvenytar

The downstream operations of MOL Magyar Olaj-es G͂zipari Rt. (Hungarian Oil and Gas Company or MOL) have moved it up to become Hungary's biggest company and one of Central Europe's top refiners. MOL's refineries produce 98000 barrels of oil equivalent per day and it operates more than 1730 gas stations in Croatia the Czech Republic Hungary Italy Poland Romania Slovakia Slovenia and the Ukraine. Other activities include exploration and production in Hungary Russia and other areas of Central and Eastern Europe. In 2014 the company had proved and probable reserves of 553.2 million barrels of oil equivalent.

Operations

MOL's Downstream division turns crude oil into a range of refined products which are moved and marketed for domestic industrial and transport use. The products include gasoline diesel heating oil aviation fuel lubricants bitumen sulfur and liquefied petroleum gas (LPG). In addition it produces and sells petrochemicals worldwide and holds a leading position in the petrochemical sector in the Central Eastern Europe region.

Its FGSZ unit is currently the only company in Hungary that holds a natural gas transmission system operator's license. Aside from domestic natural gas transmission activity FGSZ also performs transit activities for Serbia Bosnia-Herzegovina as well as cross border deliveries towards Romania and Croatia and the Ukraine.

MOL's Upstream portfolio consists of oil and gas exploration and production assets in 13 countries with production activity in 8 countries.

Geographic Reach

MOL is an integrated independent international oil and gas company with operations in more than 40 countries. MOL's exploration and production activities are conducted in 13 countries. The Group operates four refineries and two petrochemicals plants under integrated supply chain management in Hungary Slovakia and Croatia. MOL also has a network of service stations in 11 countries across Central and South Eastern Europe.

Financial Performance

The company's revenues have been on a downward trend since 2012.

In 2014 net revenues decreased by 10% due to a drop in sales across the board — Gas Midstream revenues (down 40%); Upstream (down 15%); and Downstream (down 9%).

Gas Midstream's drop was a result of an enforced gas inventory sale due to regulatory changes in Croatia and a lack of revenues from storage following the sale of natural gas storage firm MMBF in 2013.

The Upstream decrease was due to lower oil prices the natural decline of matured assets and adverse regulatory changes. The combined effect of a regulated gas price reduction and doubled royalties in Croatia reached HUF 20 billion in 2014.

The Downstream division's clean carbon and storage results were 32% ahead of 2013. MOL's refinery margin as well as the integrated petrochemical margin widened which together with better retail performance supported the results. However these improvements could not outpace the drag of lower oil prices on revenues.

MOL's net loss increased by HUF 14 billion due to lower revenues and higher finance expenses (driven by the rise in foreign exchange losses due to weakening of the HUF against major currencies).

In 2014 net cash provided by the operating activities decreased by HUK 180 million due to change in other current assets trade payables and inventories.

Strategy

In addition to expanding its refining and marketing operations across Central Europe the company has restructured its exploration and production activities to focus on the development of oil fields in Russia. In line with the announced strategy CAPEX spending in 2014 was more focused on Upstream representing 61% of total Group CAPEX while Downstream was responsible for 35% of the spending.

The MOL sales and marketing strategy focuses on increasing sales in the CEE region where the company enjoys major advantages due to its central position in landlocked markets and its expert understanding of customer requirements. it is continuing to improve its logistics network in Romania.

In 2015 it acquired Eni's downstream assets (183 gas stations and a wholesale business) in Hungary.

Growing its upstream assets and international profile in 2014 MOL opened a regional office in Erbil Kurdistan Region of Iraq.

To raise cash the company sells non-core assets. In 2014 its sold its 49% stake BaiTex LLC (the holder of the hydrocarbon licenses in the Volga-Ural region Russia) to the Turkish Petroleum Corporation. It also sold its holdings in the Zapadno-Malobalykskoye field in 2013.

Mergers and Acquisitions

In 2015 MOL entered Norway by acquiring 100% ownership in Ithaca Petroleum Norge from Ithaca Petroleum Ltd. The deal fits well to MOL's E&P strategy which aims to further balance its country risk profile as well as to seek new accretive international exploration and development opportunities.

Further strengthening MOL's market share in Romania that year it bought ENI Romania including 42 service stations and in 2104 LUKOIL Czech Republic s.r.o. including 44 service stations.

Boosting its Upstream assets in 2013 MOL entered the North Sea region acquiring offshore assets from BASF Group member Wintershall.

HISTORY

The oil refining industry in Hungary dates to the 1880s when refineries were opened in Fiume (1882) and Budapest (1883). By 1913 Hungary had 28 plants.

Following Hungary's defeat in WWI the country's refining industry fell into decline as new national boundaries placed most of its former oil refineries and oil-producing regions outside its borders. By 1921 Hungary had only six operational refineries.

British and American investors set up the European Gas and Electric Company (EUROGASCO) in the US in 1931 to acquire oil and gas concessions in Central Europe and to build power plants. By 1937 EUROGASCO (controlled by Standard Oil of New Jersey) was producing oil. A year later Standard Oil set up the Hungarian-American Oil Industry Shareholding Co. (MAORT) to develop the fields and in 1940 MAORT's production was meeting all of Hungary's oil needs.

During WWII MAORT requisitioned all oil assets. The oil industry boomed as Hungary served as a major supplier for the German war machine. But by 1944 with German armies in retreat from the Eastern Front much of Hungary's oil machinery and plants were dismantled. The remaining plants suffered heavy bombing from Allied forces or had equipment confiscated by Russian and Romanian troops.

After the war the Hungarian Soviet Crude Oil Co. began rebuilding Hungary's oil industry and started drilling on the Great Hungarian Plain in 1946. MAORT also ramped up oil production in the Trans-Danubian fields. In 1949 following charges of sabotage against MAORT managers MAORT was nationalized and broken up into five national companies which re-merged in 1952 with Hungarian Soviet Oil Co. (successor to Hungarian Soviet Crude Oil Co.).

In 1957 all operations of the Hungarian crude oil industry were consolidated under Crude Oil Trust which took over the gas industry by 1960. That year the company was renamed National Crude Oil and Gas Trust (OKGT) and the focus of exploration soon shifted from Trans-Danubian fields to the Great Plain. By 1970 the Great Plain accounted for 67% of oil production and 96% of natural gas production.

Hungary began allowing foreign gasoline distributors to compete in domestic markets during the 1980s. Moving toward privatization the Hungarian government founded MOL in 1991 as the successor to OKGT which comprised nine oil and gas enterprises. In 1993 the socialist government sold 8% of MOL to the public. By 1998 the government had sold all but 25% of MOL.

During the 1990s the company also expanded in Central Europe. With Austria's OMV in 1994 it began building a 120-km pipeline linking Austria and Hungary which gave it access to natural gas from Western Europe for the first time. MOL also opened up service stations in neighboring countries beginning with one in Romania in 1996. By 2000 the company was operating about 80 stations in Romania 18 in Slovakia three in Ukraine and two in Slovenia in addition to its 330 stations in Hungary. MOL also acquired about 20% of chemical processor TVK in 1999 and upped the stake to nearly 33% by 2000. That year MOL also acquired 36% of Slovnaft Slovakia's only oil refiner and its major retailer.

In 2003 MOL concluded a long-term crude oil supply agreement with Russian oil giant YUKOS.

The company agreed in 2004 to sell its gas businesses to E.ON Ruhrgas for about $1 billion. (After much scrutiny by Hungarian and EU regulators the deal was completed in 2006.)

In 2005 MOL acquired the Romanian subsidiary of Royal Dutch Shell including the purchase of 59 Shell filling stations. Royal Dutch Shell also sold MOL its Romania-based lubricants aviation and commercial businesses.

In 2007 MOL acquired two refining and marketing companies — IES in Italy and Tifon in Croatia. Also that year MOL announced plans to merge with Austria's OMV though those plans were abandoned the next year due to regulatory concerns from the European Commission. In 2009 OMV sold its 21% stake in MOL to Russian oil company Surgutneftegas. Eyeing new areas of exploration that year MOL also acquired a 10% stake in Pearl Petroleum giving it access to gas-condensate fields in Iraq.

In 2011 the Hungarian government acquired Surgutneftegas' 21% stake in MOL for about EUR 1.9 billion (US$2.6 billion).

EXECUTIVES

Chairman of the Supervisory Board, Zoltan Aldott
Independent Vice Chairman of the Board of Directors, Sandor Csanyi, $74,601 total compensation
Chairman of the Board of Directors, Chairman of the Executive Board and Chief Executive Officer, Zsolt Hernadi, $59,681 total compensation

Group Chief Financial Officer and Member of the
Executive Board, Jozsef Simola
Group Chief Executive Officer and Member of the
Board of Directors, Member of the Executive
Board, Jozsef Molnar
Independent Deputy Chairman of the Supervisory
Board, Attila Chikan
Independent Member of the Supervisory Board,
Anett Pandurics
Independent Member of the Board of Directors,
Martin Roman
Independent Member of the Board of Directors,
Laszlo Parragh
Independent Member of the Board of Directors,
Zsigmond Jarai
Member of the Board of Directors, Anthony Radev
Independent Member of the Supervisory Board,
Vladimir Kestler
Member of the Executive Board, Executive Vice
President - Consumer Services, MOL Hungary
(COO), Peter Ratatics
Member of the Supervisory Board, Employees'
Representative, Piroska Bognar
Member of the Executive Board, Executive Vice
President - Downstream, Ferenc Horvath
Member of the Executive Board, Executive Vice
President, President of the Management Board
INA d.d., Sandor Fasimon
Member of the Supervisory Board, Employees'
Representative, Sandor Puskas
Member of the Supervisory Board, Employees'
Representative, Istvan Ordog
Independent Member of the Supervisory Board,
Ivan Miklos
Member of the Supervisory Board, Employees'
Representative, Andras Toth
Independent Member of the Board of Directors,
Janos Martonyi
Independent Member of the Supervisory Board,
Ilona David
Member of the Executive Board, Executive Vice
President - Exploration and Production, Berislav
Gaso
Member of the Executive Board, Member of the
Board of Directors, Executive Vice President -
Innovative Businesses and Services, Oszkar
Vilagi
Independent Member of the Supervisory Board,
Andras Lanczi
Member of the Supervisory Board, Employees'
Representative, Csaba Szabo
Independent member of the Board of Director,
Talal Al-Awfi
Group Downstream Executive Vice President,
Gabriel Szabo
Auditors: Ernst & Young Kft.

LOCATIONS

HQ: MOL Magyar Olaj es Gazipari Reszvenytar
Oktober huszonharmadika u. 18, Budapest H-1117
Phone: (36) 1 209 0000
Web: www.mol.hu

2014 Sales

Geographic %	
Hungary	28
Croatia	12
Italy	9
Austria	9
Slovakia	9
Czech Republic	7
Romania	6
Poland	4
Germany	3
Bosnia-Herzegovina	3
Serbia	2
Slovenia	2
Switzerland	2
United Kingdom	1
Rest of Europe	2
Rest of the World	3
Total	**100**

PRODUCTS/OPERATIONS

2014 Sales

	% of total
Downstream	82
Upstream	10
Midstream	4
Corporate and other	4
Total	**100**

COMPETITORS

COMPA IA ESPA OLA DE	LUKOIL PAO
PETROLEOS SAU	NK ROSNEFT PAO
COSMO OIL CO. LTD.	OMV Aktiengesellschaft
GAZPROM NEFT PAO	Petroleo Brasileiro S
HESS CORPORATION	A Petrobras
Imperial Oil Limited	

HISTORICAL FINANCIALS

Company Type: Public

Income Statement   FYE: December 31

	REVENUE ($ mil.)	NET INCOME ($ mil.)	NET PROFIT MARGIN	EMPLOYEES
12/20	13,510	(53)	—	24,948
12/19	17,885	758	4.2%	26,032
12/18	18,435	1,074	5.8%	25,970
12/17	15,970	1,186	7.4%	25,959
12/16	12,109	898	7.4%	24,986
Annual Growth	**2.8%**	—		**(0.0%)**

2020 Year-End Financials

Debt ratio: 0.0%   No. of shares (mil.): 625
Return on equity: (-0.7%) Dividends
Cash ($ mil.): 653   Yield: —
Current ratio: 0.94   Payout: —
Long-term debt ($ mil.): 2,765 Market value ($ mil.): 2,454

	STOCK PRICE ($) FY Close	P/E High/Low		PER SHARE ($) Earnings	Dividends	Book Value
12/20	3.92	—	—	(0.07)	0.00	11.92
12/19	5.05	0	0	1.07	0.22	11.50
12/18	5.35	0	0	1.54	0.22	9.58
12/17	5.40	0	0	1.69	0.15	9.13
12/16	35.57	0	0	1.22	0.12	6.73
Annual Growth	**(42.4%)**	—	—	—	—	**15.4%**

MS&AD Insurance Group Holdings

MS&AD Insurance Group is the holding company for several large Japanese insurance companies including Mitsui Sumitomo Insurance (MSI) Aioi Nissay Dowa Insurance (ADI) Mitsui Direct General MSI Aioi Life and MSI Primary Life. Together the insurance companies offer property/casualty (e.g. auto personal fire marine) and life insurance as well as asset management (mutual funds financial consulting) and risk management services. MS&AD Insurance's about 155 subsidiaries which serve individuals and businesses in Japan also offer products and services to customers in about 50 countries in Europe Asia and the Americas.

Operations

MS&AD has five primary operating divisions: domestic non-life (property/casualty) insurance domestic life insurance international business financial services and risk-related services. Each of its non-life firms underwrites policies in the fire and allied marine personal accident automobile and other arenas. The life insurers underwrite individual policies individual annuity insurance group insurance and other products.

Geographic Reach

Japan-based MS&AD operates in about 50 countries in the Asia/Pacific region in Europe and in the Americas.

Financial Performance

In 2020 the company had a net income of 12.5 billion a 94% decrease from the previous year's net income of 201.7 billion.

The company's cash at the end of 2020 was 2.2 trillion. Operating activities generated 668 billion while investing activities used 210.1 billion mainly for purchases of securities. Financing activities provided another $65.3 billion mainly for repayment of borrowings.

Strategy

The MS&AD Insurance Group is on the verge of creating the world-leading insurance and financial services group that it has pursued since its founding through the story of value creation with customers shareholders and other stakeholders. As part of the medium-term management plan "Vision 2021" launched in fiscal 2018 the group set out "resilient and sustainable society" as the image of society it aims to achieve in 2030 and is charting sustainable growth by managing the group based on the creation of shared value (CSV).

The group steadily undertook initiatives geared toward returning the domestic non-life insurance business to profitability and moved forward in securing financial soundness. In addition it made progress with group business integration including the building of common platform systems for the domestic nonlife insurance business and it clarified the shape of group business integration as a result of reorganization by function in 2013.

The company made progress in reorganization by function while restoring profitability in the domestic non-life insurance business and putting in place a stable earnings foundation. It also realized improved capital efficiency and built a platform for growth by strengthening ERM and promoting sales of strategic equity holdings and investments in overseas businesses.

Company Background

Formed in 2008 as a holding company for the Mitsui Sumitomo operations MS&AD Insurance became the parent of a larger group of insurance companies through a three-way merger between Mitsui Sumitomo Aioi Insurance and Nissay Dowa General Insurance in 2010.

EXECUTIVES

Independent Director, Akira Arima
Vice Chairman of the Board, Vice Chairman of the Executive Board, President of Subsidiary, Representative Director, Yasuzo Kanasugi
Executive Officer, Director, Takaoki Endo
Senior Managing Executive Officer, Group Chief Risk Officer, Fumiaki Ohkawabata
Group Chief Financial Officer, Executive Vice President, Representative Director, Tetsuji Higuchi
President, Executive President, Group Chief Executive Officer, Chairman & Chairman of the Executive Board of Subsidiary, Representative Director, Noriyuki Hara
Independent Director, Junichi Tobimatsu
Independent Director, Mariko Bando
Executive Officer, Director, Masahito Fukuda
Independent Director, Rochelle Kopp
Chairman of the Board, Chairman of the Executive Board, Yasuyoshi Karasawa
Auditors: KPMG AZSA LLC

LOCATIONS

HQ: MS&AD Insurance Group Holdings
2-27-2 Shinkawa, Chuo-ku, Tokyo 104-0033
Phone: (81) 3-5117 0270
Web: www.ms-ad-hd.com

PRODUCTS/OPERATIONS

2018 Sales

	% of total
Underwriting income	89
Investment income	11
Total	**100**

Selected Products

Compulsory Automobile Liability
Fire and Allied Insurance
Life
Marine
Personal Accident
Voluntary Automobile

COMPETITORS

COMPUTERSHARE LIMITED
China Life Insurance Company Limited
Industrial Alliance Insurance and Financial Services In
METLIFE INC.
MITSUBISHI UFJ FINANCIAL GROUP INC.
MIZUHO FINANCIAL GROUP INC.
NIPPON LIFE INSURANCE COMPANY
PERMIRA ADVISERS LLP
PRINCIPAL FINANCIAL GROUP INC.
SUMITOMO LIFE INSURANCE COMPANY
SUMITOMO MITSUI FINANCIAL GROUP INC.
TOKIO MARINE HOLDINGS INC.
Zurich Insurance Group AG

HISTORICAL FINANCIALS

Company Type: Public

Income Statement				FYE: March 31
	REVENUE ($ mil.)	NET INCOME ($ mil.)	NET PROFIT MARGIN	EMPLOYEES
03/21	43,494	1,304	3.0%	50,116
03/20	42,602	1,317	3.1%	50,633
03/19	48,721	1,740	3.6%	50,609
03/18	47,601	1,450	3.0%	51,040
03/17	47,225	1,882	4.0%	50,791
Annual Growth	(2.0%)	(8.8%)	—	(0.3%)

2021 Year-End Financials

Debt ratio: —
Return on equity: 5.2%
Cash ($ mil.): 34,098
Current ratio: —
Long-term debt ($ mil.): —

No. of shares (mil.): 558
Dividends
 Yield: 4.8%
 Payout: 29.2%
Market value ($ mil.): 8,195

	STOCK PRICE ($) FY Close	P/E High/Low		PER SHARE ($) Earnings	Dividends	Book Value
03/21	14.68	0	0	2.31	0.71	49.92
03/20	13.81	0	0	2.29	0.67	39.71
03/19	15.24	0	0	2.97	0.61	42.56
03/18	15.61	0	0	2.45	0.64	46.76
03/17	15.92	0	0	3.14	0.48	40.90
Annual Growth	(2.0%)	—	—	(7.4%)	10.3%	5.1%

MTN Group Ltd (South Africa)

MTN Group offers cellular phone service in the mountains and the plains of Africa. The continent's largest wireless network operator has almost 200 million subscribers across Africa and the Middle East through a network of subsidiaries. MTN has operations in more than 20 countries and is the No. 1 or No. 2 operator in most of its markets. Eighty percent of its customers have prepaid no-contract plans. MTN earns the bulk of its sales from airtime and subscription fees but it generates about 20% of revenues from interconnect fees. The company partners with financial services companies to offer mobile banking services and money transfer services for clients without bank accounts.

Operations
MTN Group's biggest business is outgoing voice which brings in 61% of revenue. Data services account for about 20% of revenue and grew by 33% in 2014. Sales of phones and other devices generated 5% of revenue.

Geographic Reach
MTN has operations in most African countries including Benin Botswana Cameroon Ivory Coast Ghana Guinea Bissau Guinea Republic Liberia Nigeria Republic of Congo Rwanda South Africa Sudan South Sudan Swaziland Uganda Yemen and Zambia. It also provides service in Afghanistan Cyprus Iran and Syria. Nigeria accounted for 34% of the revenue in 2014.

Financial Performance
MTN Group rode a 12% increase in revenue in Nigeria to an overall revenue increase of 7% in 2014 from 2013. More customers in Nigeria used data with deeper smartphone penetration in the country and new products from MTN Group such as its 4.5G data plan. Overall 3G revenue jumped 33% with expanded 3G service and more smartphones. Higher revenue translated into a 20% rise in net income for 2014.

Strategy
MTN Group seeks to expand its information communications and telecom services to businesses and governments. The company partnered with EcoBank to provide more financial services via smartphone and it teamed up with Bharti Airtel for international money transfer services.

Mergers and Acquisitions
MTN made several purchases in 2014 to expand its reach and services.

It acquired a third of Africa Internet Holding a joint venture between Rocket Internet and Millicom International Cellular to develop internet businesses in Africa.

The company acquired controlling interest in Afrihost Proprietary Limited which will help push its SME strategy and its virtual market content and cloud offering.

EXECUTIVES

Lead Independent Non-Executive Director, Khotso Mokhele
Chief Digital and Fintech Officer, Yolanda Cuba
Chief Legal and Regulatory Officer, Lele Modise, $154,954 total compensation
Non-Executive Independent Director, Sindisiwe Mabaso-koyana
Group Chief Strategy and Transformation Officer, Chika Ekeji
Non-Executive Independent Director, Noluthando Gosa
Non-Executive Director, Azim Mikati

Group Chief Financial Officer, Tsholofelo Molefe
Group Chief Sustainability and Corporate Affairs, Nompilo Morafo
Group Chief Digital and Fintech Officer, Serigne Dioum
Independent Non-Executive Director, Paul Hanratty
Non-Executive Independent Director, Stanley Miller
Non-Executive Independent Director, Nkululeko Sowazi
Group Chief Regulatory and Corporate Affairs Officer, Felleng Sekha, $294,274 total compensation
Group President, CEO and Director, Ralph Mupita, $727,436 total compensation
Group Chief Operating Officer, Jens Schulte-Bockum, $586,324 total compensation
Chief Technology and Information Officer, Charles Molapisi
Vice President - SEAGHA, Ebenezer Asante, $614,705 total compensation
Chief Technology and Information Officer for Digital and Fintech, Hermann Tischendorf
Chief Technology Officer, Chief Information Officer, Mazen Mroue
Group Chief Human Resource Officer, Paul Norman, $373,016 total compensation
Non-Executive Independent Director, Nosipho Molope
Non-Executive Independent Director, Bajabulile Tshabalala
Chief Executive Officer, MTN Nigeria, Ferdinand Moolman, $499,968 total compensation
Group Chief M&A and Business Development Officer, Kholekile Ndamase
Group Vice President for Middle East and North Africa, Ismail Jaroudi, $707,624 total compensation
Vice President for West and Central Africa, Karl Toriola, $514,978 total compensation
Non-Executive Independent Director, Shaygan Kheradpir
Chairman, Mcebisi Jonas
Non-Executive Independent Director, Vincent Rague
Non-Executive Independent Director, Lamido Sanusi
Auditors: SizweNtsalubaGobodo Grant Thornton Inc.

LOCATIONS

HQ: MTN Group Ltd (South Africa)
 Innovation Centre, 216 - 14th Avenue, Fairland, Roodepoort, Gauteng 2195
Phone: (27) 11 912 3000   **Fax:** (27) 11 912 4093
Web: www.mtn.com

2014 Sales

	% of total
Nigeria	34
South Africa	24
Large opco cluster	20
Small opco cluster	14
Joint venture-Iran	7
Hyperinflation	1
Total	**100**

PRODUCTS/OPERATIONS

2014 Sales

	% of total
Outgoing voice	61
Data	19
Incoming voice	10
Devices	5
SMS	3
Other	1
Hyperinflation	1
Total	**100**

COMPETITORS

1&1 AG
America M vil S.A.B. de C.V.
BHARTI AIRTEL LIMITED
CHUNGHWA TELECOM CO. LTD.
HELLENIC TELECOMMUNICATIONS ORGANIZATION
 S.A.
HUGHES NETWORK SYSTEMS LLC
MTS PAO
Manitoba Telecom Services Inc
ROSTELEKOM PAO
SAUDI TELECOM COMPANY
SBA COMMUNICATIONS CORPORATION
TELUS Corporation

HISTORICAL FINANCIALS

Company Type: Public

Income Statement   FYE: December 31

	REVENUE ($ mil.)	NET INCOME ($ mil.)	NET PROFIT MARGIN	EMPLOYEES
12/20	12,223	1,160	9.5%	0
12/19	10,784	638	5.9%	19,288
12/18	9,358	606	6.5%	18,835
12/17	10,788	358	3.3%	15,901
12/16	10,770	(190)	—	15,980
Annual Growth	3.2%	—	—	—

2020 Year-End Financials

Debt ratio: 1.8%
Return on equity: 18.1%
Cash ($ mil.): 3,998
Current ratio: 1.01
Long-term debt ($ mil.): 5,346

No. of shares (mil.): 1,798
Dividends
 Yield: 5.4%
 Payout: 26.0%
Market value ($ mil.): 7,376

	STOCK PRICE ($) FY Close	P/E High/Low		PER SHARE ($) Earnings	Dividends	Book Value
12/20	4.10	1	0	0.64	0.22	3.90
12/19	5.91	2	1	0.35	0.25	3.32
12/18	6.10	2	1	0.33	0.36	3.28
12/17	10.87	4	4	0.20	0.41	4.19
12/16	9.05	—	—	(0.10)	0.63	4.15
Annual Growth	(18.0%)	—	—	—	(22.8%)	(1.5%)

Muenchener Rueckversicherungs-Gesellschaft AG (Germany)

M nchener R ckversicherungs-Gesellschaft Aktiengesellschaft (Munich Re) is one of the world's leading reinsurers and operates in life health and property-casualty business. Reinsurance coverage (insurance for insurers) includes fire life motor and liability policies on both a facultative (individual risk) and treaty (categorized risk) basis. The company also provides direct insurance including life health and property coverage through Germany-based ERGO and other subsidiaries and it provides asset management services through MEAG MUNICH ERGO. Through Munich Re America Munich Re enjoys greater access to the US market. Generates about 55% of the company's total gross pre-

miums written in Europe the company's ERGO operates in more than 30 countries.

Operations

Munich Re divides its business into five segments: Property-Casualty Reinsurance and Life and Health Reinsurance which both operate globally; and ERGO Life and Health Germany (life and health and property-casualty insurance in Germany and global travel insurance) ERGO Property-Casualty Germany and ERGO International.

Property-Casualty Reinsurance produces approximately 45% of total sales. Life and Health Reinsurance generates almost 25% of total sales. It focuses on traditional reinsurance solutions that concentrate on the transfer of mortality risk. It is also active in the market of living benefits products such as occupational disability long-term care and critical illness.

Overall Reinsurance activities account for about 70% of total sales while ERGO generates the rest. Munich Re also generates interest income on repurchase agreements on securities.

Geographic Reach

Headquartered in Munich Germany Europe is Munich Re's largest market accounting for almost 55% of the company's gross premiums written followed by North America that generates nearly 30% of gross premiums written. The remaining gross premiums written are from Asia and Australasia Africa Middle East and Latin America.

Sales and Marketing

Munich Re's ERGO serves approximately 35 million mostly retail customers. As a reinsurer the company also writes its business in direct collaboration with primary insurers and also via brokers.

Financial Performance

Note: Growth rates may differ after conversion to US Dollars.

The company's revenue for fiscal 2020 decreased to ?1.2 billion compared with ?2.7 billion.

Cash held by the company at the end of fiscal 2020 increased to ?5.6 billion. Cash provided by operations was ?7.2 billion while cash used for investing and financing activities were ?6.1 billion and ?323 million respectively. Main uses were acquisition sale and maturity of investments and dividend payments

Strategy

Digitalization is increasingly transforming the markets and the continuous changes in customer behavior are demanding greater flexibility in providing access coverage and solutions as well as in its underlying internal structures. Driving digital transformation therefore remains one of Munich Re's strategic priorities.

The company is continually adjusting its internal structures and processes to reduce complexity and costs while at the same time seizing the opportunities that digital transformation offers. Munich Re is attempting to automate as much as possible along the entire value chain and across all units.

Company Background

Munich Re dates back to 1880 where it gained an upper hand on an already mature reinsurance industry by taking an international approach to reinsurance. The company's guiding principles remain true to this day namely independence from primary insurers a broad spread of risks an efficient system of treaty management working in partnership with clients and innovative insurance concepts.

HISTORY

Investors Carl Thieme and Theodor Cramer-Klett founded Munich Re in 1880. Within a month Munich Re opened offices in Hamburg Berlin Vienna and St. Petersburg establishing treaties with German and Danish insurers. In 1888 Munich Re went public; two years later it opened an office in

London and helped finance the creation of Allianz which would soon come to dominate the German insurance industry. In 1892 the firm opened a branch in the US (it incurred severe losses from the 1906 San Francisco earthquake).

WWI interrupted Munich Re's UK and US operations. The company recovered after 1918 only to be hobbled again by the Great Depression. In 1933 Munich Re executive Kurt Schmitt became minister of economic affairs for the Nazis. Objecting to the evolving policies of National Socialism he left after a year returning to Munich Re where he became chief executive in 1938.

Hitler's ignition of WWII wasn't quite the boom Munich Re needed; its international business was again disrupted. After the war the Allies further limited overseas operations. Because of his involvement with the Nazi government Schmitt was replaced by Eberhard von Reininghaus in 1945. The division of Germany further hampered the company's recovery.

Jump-started by the Marshall Plan in 1950 the West German Wirtschaftswunder (economic miracle) kicked into high gear as the devastated country rebuilt. Relaxation of occupation-era trading limits also helped as the company rebuilt its foreign business. By 1969 Munich Re's sales topped DM 2 billion. Amid the global oil crisis and a rash of terrorist acts in Germany the firm reported its first-ever reinsurance loss in 1977.

German reunification in 1990 provided new markets for Munich Re but advantages from new business in the East were wiped out by claims arising from that year's harsh winter.

In 1992 an investigation by the German Federal Cartel Office prompted a realignment in the insurance business — Allianz ceded its controlling interests in three life insurers (Hamburg-Mannheimer Versicherungs Karlsruher Lebensversicherung and Berlinische Lebensversicherung) to Munich Re bringing it into direct insurance. Munich Re took over Deutsche Krankenversicherung (DKV) in 1996. Also that year Munich Re acquired American Re.

During the 1990s reinsurance sales dwindled as competition increased forcing lower premiums and alternatives to insurance and reinsurance became more common. Munich Re looked to direct insurance particularly individual property/casualty and life insurance to compensate. In 1997 it merged Hamburg-Mannheimer and DKV with another insurer Victoria AG to form ERGO Versicherungsgruppe. Within a year ERGO's insurance income accounted for half of all revenues.

Munich Re and ERGO launched asset management firm MEAG Munich ERGO AssetManagement in 1999. That year Munich Re experienced its worst year ever after natural disasters hit its reinsurance business hard. To recoup its losses the next year the firm expanded both its reinsurance and primary insurance operations into key markets in Europe North and South America and Asia. Also in 2000 Munich Re bought CNA Financial's life reinsurance operations. Together with Swiss Re the company launched Inreon an online reinsurance exchange in 2001.

As one of the companies hit hardest financially by the World Trade Center tragedy Munich Re paid out some $2 billion in claims. In 2003 Allianz and Munich Re terminated their cooperation agreement as their shareholdings in each other fell to under 15%. (The two companies gradually sold off nearly all of their ownership interests in following years.)

In 2004 Munich Re entered its first Asian market by forming a joint venture in China.

EXECUTIVES

Chairman of the Board of Management, Joachim Wenning, $2,649,118 total compensation
Member of the Management Board and Chairman of the Board Committee IT Investments, Thomas Blunck, $1,281,831 total compensation
Deputy Chairman, Supervisory Board, Anne Horstmann, $170,910 total compensation
Chief Financial Officer, Member of the Management Board, Christoph Jurecka, $1,709,108 total compensation
Chief Investment Officer, Member of the Management Board, Nicholas Gartside, $1,281,831 total compensation
Auditors: Ernst & Young GmbH Wirtschaftpruefungsgesellschaft

LOCATIONS

HQ: Muenchener Rueckversicherungs-Gesellschaft AG (Germany)
Koeniginstrasse 107, Munich 80802
Phone: (49) 89 3891 8202   **Fax:** (49) 89 3891 3599
Web: www.munichre.com

2017 Premiums

	% of total
Europe	53
North America	32
Asia & Australasia	9
Latin America	3
Africa Near & Middle East	3
Total	**100**

PRODUCTS/OPERATIONS

2017 Sales

	% of total
Reinsurance	
Property/casualty	35
Life and health	29
ERGO	
Life and health Germany	19
Property/casualty Germany	7
International	10
Total	**100**

Selected Brands

ERGO (primary insurance)
　Deutscher Automobil Schutz (D.A.S. auto insurance)
　Deutsche Krankenversicherung (DKV)
　ERV
ERGO Direkt (commercial customer consulting)
DKV (domestic health insurance)
Munich Health (international health insurance domestic and international health reinsurance)
Munich Re
Munich Re America
　American Modern Insurance (specialty property/casualty insurance life insurance reinsurance)
　Hartford Steam Boiler (HSB specialty property/casualty insurance and reinsurance)

COMPETITORS

AEGON N.V.	PRINCIPAL FINANCIAL
AFLAC INCORPORATED	GROUP INC.
ANTHEM INC.	SCOR SE
Allianz SE	Swiss Re AG
DELPHI FINANCIAL GROUP	Talanx AG
INC.	Zurich Insurance Group
ERGO Group AG	AG
Hyundai Marine & Fire	
Insurance Co. Ltd.	

HISTORICAL FINANCIALS

Company Type: Public

Income Statement

FYE: December 31

	ASSETS ($ mil.)	NET INCOME ($ mil.)	INCOME AS % OF ASSETS	EMPLOYEES
12/20	365,666	1,486	0.4%	39,642
12/19	322,854	3,058	0.9%	39,662
12/18	309,395	2,645	0.9%	41,410
12/17	318,535	449	0.1%	42,410
12/16	282,770	2,724	1.0%	43,428
Annual Growth	**6.6%**	**(14.1%)**	**—**	**(2.3%)**

2020 Year-End Financials

Return on assets: 0.4%	Dividends
Return on equity: 4.0%	Yield: 2.4%
Long-term debt (mil.): —	Payout: —
No. of shares (mil.): 140	Market value ($ mil.): 4,162
Sales ($ mil): 78,412	

	STOCK PRICE ($) FY Close	P/E High/Low		PER SHARE ($) Earnings	Dividends	Book Value
12/20	29.71	4	2	10.59	0.73	261.87
12/19	29.44	2	1	21.30	0.71	241.76
12/18	21.85	1	1	17.78	0.71	207.11
12/17	21.64	10	8	2.92	0.70	222.01
12/16	18.83	1	1	17.03	0.60	212.09
Annual Growth	**12.1%**	**—**		**(11.2%)**	**5.2%**	**5.4%**

Murata Manufacturing Co Ltd

Murata Manufacturing is one of the world's largest makers of passive electronic components primarily capacitors claiming large market share in several markets. The components many of which are made of the ceramic materials that have been a Murata specialty since its founding are used in electronic devices such as computers mobile phones automotive security & safety and medical equipment. Capacitors are its biggest product line accounting for more than a third of sales. With a presence in North America the Japan-based company also makes a wide variety of other components including filters antennas resistors power supplies and sensors. About 90% of Murata's sales are outside of Japan's borders.

Operations

The company has two operating segment: Components (nearly 70%) and Modules (more than 30%).

Components segment is composed of: Capacitors including products such as Multilayer ceramic capacitors Polymer aluminum electrolytic capacitors Silicon capacitors High temperature film capacitors for automotive etc.; Piezoelectric components products include SAW filters Ultrasonic sensors Resonators Piezoelectric sensors Ceramic filters etc.; and Other component products include Inductors (coils) EMI suppression filters Connectors MEMS sensors Thermistors Lithium-ion batteries etc.

Modules are essential compound components that wirelessly connect various devices. These are mounted on home appliances used in our daily lives such as smart phones tablet PCs digital cameras and air conditioners in-vehicle devices such as car navigation systems and in various settings

including enabling users to download and upload photos and music from the Internet and hands-free calling while driving.

Geographic Reach

Headquartered in Tokyo Japan Greater China is the company's largest market representing more than half of total sales. Other major markets include Asia generating over 15% United States above 10%. Japan and Europe account for nearly 10% each.

Financial Performance

The company's net sales for fiscal 2021 increased to 1.6 trillion compared from the prior year with 1.5 trillion.

Net income for fiscal 2021 increased to 237.0 billion compared from the prior year with 183.0 billion.

Cash held by the company at the end of fiscal 2021 increased to 407.7 billion. Cash provided by operations was 373.6 billion while cash used for investing and financing activities were 150.3 billion and 118.2 billion respectively.

Strategy

In order for Murata to continue to create value as an innovator in the drastically changing electronics industry it is necessary to capture the global trends of technology and changes in society and reflect them in business management. In order to create various innovations looking ahead to the future from a long-term perspective Murata uses a three-layer portfolio in its business management and focuses on four key fields with business opportunities to create value. The company's 3-layer portfolio are: creation of new business model; application-specific components business; and standard-products business

HISTORY

Akira Murata founded Murata Manufacturing Co. in 1944 to produce traditional ceramic tableware. However the company quickly moved into high-performance ceramics for electronics and expanded with new plants in Japan. (Its expansion of production capacity within Japan has remained consistent; since the 1960s Murata has opened at least three new domestic factories per decade.)

In 1963 the year it went public Murata also opened an office in New York. The company created MurataBourns a joint venture with Bourns in 1966 to make industrial potentiometers devices that control the amount of current that flows through a circuit.

Murata kept expanding overseas in the 1970s with new operations in Singapore (1972) the US (1973) Hong Kong (1973) Germany (1975) and Taiwan (1978).

In 1981 the company bought the Canadian subsidiary of Erie Technological Products (electromagnetic filters) following a year-long regulatory battle. That year Murata shuttered its MurataBourns joint venture.

Murata continued to expand in the 1980s with marketing trading and production offices in South Korea (1980) the UK (1982 and 1989) Brazil (1985 and 1986) Thailand (1988) Germany (1988) and the Netherlands (1989).

In 1991 Yasutaka Murata who had joined the company in 1973 succeeded his father Akira as president. Akira became chairman.

More Asian offices opened during the 1990s in Malaysia (1990 and 1993) and the Philippines (1998). Murata began a major push into China in the mid-1990s setting up operations in Beijing and Wuxi (1994) Shanghai (1995) and Suzhou (2001). Osamu Murata replaced his father as chairman in 1995. (Osamu retired as chairman in 2001; the post remained vacant until 2007.)

The company's profits surged in fiscal 2000 as a booming electronics market led to high demand for capacitors and other components; the next year though Murata warned of a sharp downturn in profits amid a steep slump in the worldwide electronics industry. The company took a big hit in the following years as the global chip industry went through its worst down period on record.

In 2004 Murata Electronics North America closed its plant in State College Pennsylvania. Some functions were relocated to the US subsidiary's plant in Smyrna Georgia. Later that year Murata Europe Management closed its capacitor taping operation in Plymouth UK shifting production to Japan and Singapore.

In 2005 Murata established a collaborative relationship with Nagano Japan Radio for switching power supplies agreeing to manufacture each other's products. The company also created a joint venture with Superwave Corporation called MTC Solutions to make multi-task communication modules for wireless authentication systems. In 2005 Wuxi Murata Electronics began construction on its third plant to make chip monolithic ceramic capacitors in China.

Akira Murata died in 2006 at the age of 84. He had served as the company's honorary chairman since 1995.

In 2006 the company acquired SyChip a US developer of radio-frequency (RF) semiconductors for digital music players Global Positioning System (GPS) products and PDAs for about $137 million.

Yasutaka Murata the first son of Akira Murata became chairman of the company his father founded in 2007. That year Murata also acquired the Power Electronics division of C&D Technologies for $85 million in cash. The division makes power supplies and converters.

EXECUTIVES

Independent Director, Takatoshi Yamamoto
Chairman of the Board, Representative Director, Tsuneo Murata
Independent Director, Naoko Munakata
Senior Executive Vice President and Director, Norio Nakajima
Senior Managing Executive Officer, Chief Director of Technology & Business Development, Director, Hiroshi Iwatsubo
Managing Executive Officer, Director of Business in Capacitor Business Unit, Director, Masahiro Ishitani
Managing Executive Officer, Senior Director of Administration Group, Director, Ryuji Miyamoto
Independent Director, Hiyoo Kambayashi
Independent Director, Yuko Yasuda
Independent Director, Takashi Shigematsu
Managing Executive Officer, Senior Director of Accounting, Finance & Planning Group, Director, Masanori Minamide
Auditors: Deloitte Touche Tohmatsu LLC

LOCATIONS

HQ: Murata Manufacturing Co Ltd
1-10-1 Higashikotari, Nagaokakyo, Kyoto 617-8555
Phone: (81) 75 955 6525   **Fax:** (81) 75 955 6526
Web: www.murata.com

2018 Sales

	% of total
Greater China	50
Asia and Others	17
The Americas	15
Japan	9
Europe	9
Total	**100**

PRODUCTS/OPERATIONS

2018 Sales

	% of total
Components	70
Modules	30
Others	
Total	**100**

Selected Products

Ceramic Capacitors
  Disc
  High-frequency power
  High-voltage
  Monolithic
  Trimmer
Microwave Components
  Chip dielectric and multilayer antennas
  Chip multilayer hybrid couplers
  Dielectric resonators
  Field-effect transistors (FETs)
  High-frequency coaxial connectors
  High-frequency microchip and monolithic ceramic capacitors
  Isolators/circulators
  Oscillators
  Radio-frequency (RF) diode switches
Piezoelectric Components
  Buzzers
  Diaphragms
  Ringers
  Speakers
Power Devices
  DC/DC converters
  High-voltage and switching power supplies
Sensors
  Electric potential
  Magnetic pattern recognition
  Non-contact potentiometers
  Piezoelectric vibrating gyroscopes
  Pyroelectric infrared sensors and modules
  Rotary
  Shock
  Ultrasonic
Thermistors and Resistors
  High-voltage resistors
  Resistor networks
  Thermistors
  Trimmer potentiometers
Other
  Chip coils
  Delay lines
  Electromagnetic interference (EMI) suppression filters
  Filters
  Flyback transformers
  High-voltage multipliers
  Resonators
  TV/LCD tuners

COMPETITORS

AMERICA II EUROPE LIMITED
APPLIED ENERGETICS INC.
CHECKPOINT SYSTEMS INC.
CYMER INC.
FUJI ELECTRIC CO. LTD.
IPG PHOTONICS CORPORATION
NOVANTA INC.
OLYMPUS CORPORATION
PLUG POWER INC.
POWERSECURE INTERNATIONAL INC.
PULSE ELECTRONICS CORPORATION
RENISHAW P L C
ROFIN-SINAR TECHNOLOGIES LLC
SOLAREDGE TECHNOLOGIES INC.
SOLON SE
STATIC CONTROL COMPONENTS INC.
TDK CORPORATION
VISHAY INTERTECHNOLOGY INC.
VOLEX PLC

HISTORICAL FINANCIALS

Company Type: Public

Income Statement

FYE: March 31

	REVENUE ($ mil.)	NET INCOME ($ mil.)	NET PROFIT MARGIN	EMPLOYEES
03/21	14,722	2,140	14.5%	75,184
03/20	14,132	1,685	11.9%	74,109
03/19	14,222	1,868	13.1%	77,571
03/18	12,919	1,375	10.6%	75,326
03/17	10,156	1,395	13.7%	59,985
Annual Growth	**9.7%**	**11.3%**	**—**	**5.8%**

2021 Year-End Financials

Debt ratio: 0.0%	No. of shares (mil.): 639
Return on equity: 13.1%	Dividends
Cash ($ mil.): 3,287	Yield: 1.2%
Current ratio: 3.72	Payout: 9.5%
Long-term debt ($ mil.): 6	Market value ($ mil.): 12,899

	STOCK PRICE ($) FY Close	P/E High/Low		PER SHARE ($) Earnings	Dividends	Book Value
03/21	20.16	0	0	2.44	0.25	27.11
03/20	12.56	0	0	2.64	0.43	24.39
03/19	37.65	0	0	2.92	0.20	22.64
03/18	34.60	0	0	2.15	0.19	21.44
03/17	35.64	0	0	2.19	0.51	18.99
Annual Growth	**(13.3%)**	**—**	**—**	**2.8%**	**(16.6%)**	**9.3%**

Musashino Bank, Ltd.

The Musashino Bank serves the Saitama region to the north of Tokyo in Japan. The bank and its 8 subsidiaries do business from about 90 offices throughout the area. Musashino Bank provides leasing and lending services in addition to its standard consumer and commercial banking services. The bank provides capital for new small and medium-sized businesses through its Musashino New Business Fund. Musashino Bank was founded in 1952.

EXECUTIVES

President, Representative Director, Kazumasa Nagahori
Managing Director, Ken Ohtomo
Independent Director, Ryuichi Mitsuoka
Independent Director, Yukimitsu Sanada
Chairman of the Board, Kikuo Kato
Managing Director, Susumu Kurosawa
Senior Managing Director, Representative Director, Toshihiko Shirai
Independent Director, Ayako Kobayashi
Auditors: Ernst & Young ShinNihon LLC

LOCATIONS

HQ: Musashino Bank, Ltd.
1-10-8 Sakuragi-cho, Omiya-ku, Saitama 330-0854
Phone: (81) 48 641 6111
Web: www.musashinobank.co.jp

COMPETITORS

JUROKU BANKLTD. THE
YAMANASHI CHUO BANK LTD. THE

HISTORICAL FINANCIALS

Company Type: Public

Income Statement

FYE: March 31

	ASSETS ($ mil.)	NET INCOME ($ mil.)	INCOME AS % OF ASSETS	EMPLOYEES
03/21	48,046	72	0.2%	2,869
03/20	43,058	74	0.2%	2,920
03/19	41,772	48	0.1%	3,003
03/18	42,949	102	0.2%	3,117
03/17	40,311	87	0.2%	3,206
Annual Growth	4.5%	(4.6%)	—	(2.7%)

2021 Year-End Financials

Return on assets: 0.1%
Return on equity: 3.3%
Long-term debt ($ mil.): —
No. of shares (mil.): 33
Sales ($ mil): 644

Dividends
Yield: —
Payout: 33.4%
Market value ($ mil.): —

Nanto Bank, Ltd.

The Nanto Bank primarily serves the Nara region of Japan. The bank operates from about 135 offices branches and other facilities located in the Hyogo Kyoto Mie Nara Osaka Tokyo and Wakayama areas of the country. Nanto Bank provides a selection of financial services including consumer banking credit card services securities leasing and lending. The bank traces its historical roots back to 1934. Major subsidiaries include Nanto Credit Guarantee Co. Nanto Lease co. Nanto Estate Co. Nanto Staff Service Co. and Nanto Investment Management Co.

Strategy

The Nanto Bank aims to increase its balance of loans deposits and assets by expanding its branch net work mainly through the establishment of new branches. In Osaka Prefecture identified as an important strategic area two new branches — the Eiwa branch and the Wakaeiwata branch — were built and opened in Higashiosaka City in September 2012. The company also opened in 2013 its Joto corporate business office and the Hokusetsu corporate business office with a plan to eventually developing these into branches.

EXECUTIVES

Executive Vice President, Representative Director, Satoshi Ishida
Independent Director, Shuhei Aoki
Independent Director, Hidetaka Matsusaka
Managing Executive Officer, Chief Director of Sales Promotion, Director, Ryuichiro Funaki
President, Representative Director, Takashi Hashimoto
Managing Executive Officer, Director, Tsuyoshi Sugiura
Managing Executive Officer, Director, Kazunobu Nishikawa
Managing Executive Officer, Director, Kazuya Yokotani
Independent Director, Matazaemon Kitamura
Auditors: KPMG AZSA LLC

LOCATIONS

HQ: Nanto Bank, Ltd.
   16 Hashimoto-cho, Nara 630-8677
Phone: (81) 742 22 1131
Web: www.nantobank.co.jp

COMPETITORS

MIE BANK LTD. THE   OITA BANKLTD. THE

HISTORICAL FINANCIALS

Company Type: Public

Income Statement

FYE: March 31

	ASSETS ($ mil.)	NET INCOME ($ mil.)	INCOME AS % OF ASSETS	EMPLOYEES
03/21	59,248	97	0.2%	3,482
03/20	52,242	29	0.1%	3,677
03/19	52,362	100	0.2%	3,771
03/18	54,700	123	0.2%	3,830
03/17	52,010	111	0.2%	3,790
Annual Growth	3.3%	(3.3%)	—	(2.1%)

2021 Year-End Financials

Return on assets: 0.1%
Return on equity: 3.9%
Long-term debt ($ mil.): —
No. of shares (mil.): 32
Sales ($ mil): 733

Dividends
Yield: —
Payout: 24.0%
Market value ($ mil.): —

National Australia Bank Ltd.

National Australia Bank (NAB) is Australia's largest business bank that serves approximately eight million customers. It provides banking wealth management and investment banking services in Australia as well as in New Zealand through its Bank of New Zealand (BNZ) subsidiary. NAB also offers financial and debt capital markets specialized capital custody and alternative investments for institutional clients. NAB funds some of the most important infrastructure in its communities ? including schools hospitals and roads.

Operations

NAB operates in five divisions: Business and Private Banking; Personal Banking; Corporate and Institutional Banking; New Zealand Banking; and Corporate Functions and Other.

Business and Private Banking focuses on NAB's priority small and medium (SME) customer segments. This division includes the leading NAB Business franchise specialised Agriculture Health Government Education and Community services along with Private Banking and JBWere as well as the micro and small business segments. This division accounts for almost 40% of revenue.

Personal Banking provides customers with products and services through proprietary networks in NAB as well as third party and mortgage brokers. Customers are served through the Personal Banking network to secure home loans or manage personal finances through deposit credit or personal loan facilities. The network also provides servicing support to individuals and business customers. The division accounts for about 30% of revenue.

Corporate and Institutional Banking provides a range of products and services including client coverage corporate finance markets asset servicing transactional banking and enterprise payments. The division services its customers in Australia and globally including branches in the US UK and Asia with specialised industry relationships and product teams. It includes Bank of New Zealand's

Markets Trading operations. The division accounts for about 15% of revenue.

New Zealand Banking provides banking and financial services across customer segments in New Zealand. It consists of Partnership Banking servicing consumer and SME segments; Corporate and Institutional Banking servicing Corporate Institutional Agribusiness and Property customers and includes Markets Sales operations in New Zealand. New Zealand Banking also includes the Wealth and Insurance franchises operating under the 'Bank of New Zealand' brand but excludes the Bank of New Zealand's Markets Trading operations. The division accounts for 15% of revenue.

Corporate Functions and Other business includes UBank and enabling units that support all businesses including Treasury Technology and Enterprise Operations Strategy and Innovation Support Units and Eliminations.

Geographic Reach

The company operates in more than 900 locations in Australia New Zealand and around the world.

Sales and Marketing

NAB served more than 8 million customers. Business and Private Banking serves small to medium businesses and investors; and also high net worth customers through Private Bank and JBWere.

NAB spent A$160 million on advertising and marketing expenses in 2021 compared to A$162 million in 2020.

Financial Performance

The company's revenue fell by about A$384 million to A$16.8 billion from A$17.2 billion from the prior year. Net interest income decreased by $74 million or 0.5%. Excluding large notable items of $49 million in the September 2020 full year net interest income decreased by $123 million or 0.9%. This includes an increase of $192 million due to movements in economic hedges offset in other operating income.

Net profit attributable to owners of NAB (statutory net profit) increased by $3805 million. Excluding the impact of discontinued operations statutory net profit increased by $2973 million or 85.0%.

The company's cash in 2021 decreased by about A$24.2 billion to A$37.9 billion from the prior year. Cash provided by operating activities was A$759 million while cash used by financing activities and investing activities were A$3.7 billion and $22 million respectively. Main uses of cash were for repayments of bonds and deposits with central banks and other regulatory authorities.

Strategy

The company's strategic focus aligns with major global trends with a particular focus on sustainability infrastructure (including renewables) and private capital.

Mergers and Acquisitions

In 2021 NAB completed the acquisition of 86 400 Holdings Ltd the holding company of Australian digital bank 86 400 ("86 400") for a total consideration of $261 million. Its strategy to grow UBank will be accelerated by the acquisition of 86 400. This brings together UBank's established business and 86 400's technology platform that will meet the changing needs of our customers. Together the companies will develop a leading digital bank that attracts and retains customers at scale and creates a new generation of simple fast and mobile banking solutions.

In the same year NAB also announced its proposed acquisition of Citigroup's Australian consumer business subject to regulatory approval. This planned transaction brings scale customers and deep expertise and supports NAB's strategic growth ambition for Personal banking.

EXECUTIVES

Non-Executive Independent Director, Kathryn Fagg, $203,120 total compensation
Non-Executive Independent Director, Simon Mckeon, $208,756 total compensation
Chief Operating Officer, Les Matheson, $584,307 total compensation
Assistant Company Secretary, Ricardo Vasquez
Managing Director and Chief Executive Officer of Bank of New Zealand, Dan Huggins
Non-Executive Independent Chairman of the Board, Philip Chronican, $576,923 total compensation
Group Chief Digital, Data and Analytics Officer, Angela Mentis, $1,084,851 total compensation
Group Executive - Legal and Commercial Services, Sharon Cook, $656,361 total compensation
Group Executive - Corporate and Institutional Banking, A. David Gall, $889,230 total compensation
Group Executive - Technology and Enterprise Operations, Patrick Wright, $1,142,188 total compensation
Group Company Secretary, Penny MacRae
Group Chief Risk Officer, Shaun Dooley, $784,317 total compensation
Group Executive - Personal Banking, Rachel Slade, $855,927 total compensation
Group Chief Financial Officer, Gary Lennon, $812,727 total compensation
Group Chief Executive Officer and Managing Director, Director, Ross McEwan, $1,863,784 total compensation
Auditors: Ernst & Young

LOCATIONS

HQ: National Australia Bank Ltd.
Level 28, 395 Bourke Street, Melbourne, Victoria 3000
Phone: (61) 3 8872 2461
Web: www.nab.com.au

PRODUCTS/OPERATIONS

2015 Cash Earnings

	% of total
Australian banking	69
NZ banking	10
UK banking	10
NAB Wealth	8
Corporate function and others	3
Total	**100**

Selected Subsidiaries

Calibre Asset Management
Great Western Bancorporation
nabCapital (formerly Institutional Markets & Services)
National Australia Group Europe Limited
   Clydesdale Bank PLC
   Yorkshire Bank Home Loans Limited
   Yorkshire Bank Investments Limited
   National Australia Group Europe Services Limited
National Australia Group (NZ) Limited
   Bank of New Zealand
   BNZ International Funding Limited
National Australia Trustees Limited
National Wealth Management Holdings Limited
MLC Limited
   National Wealth Management International Holdings Limited

COMPETITORS

AKBANK TURK ANONIM SIRKETI
Banco Bradesco S/A
COMMERCE BANCSHARES INC.
China Construction Bank Corporation
DBS GROUP HOLDINGS LTD
HDFC BANK LIMITED
ICICI BANK LIMITED
OPPENHEIMER HOLDINGS INC.

QATAR NATIONAL BANK (Q.P.S.C.)
SANTANDER UK GROUP HOLDINGS PLC
STANDARD BANK GROUP LTD
Shanghai Pudong Development Bank Co.Ltd.
The Bank of Nova Scotia
UMPQUA HOLDINGS CORPORATION
UNITED OVERSEAS BANK LIMITED

HISTORICAL FINANCIALS

Company Type: Public

Income Statement

FYE: September 30

	ASSETS ($ mil.)	NET INCOME ($ mil.)	INCOME AS % OF ASSETS	EMPLOYEES
09/21	666,210	4,578	0.7%	34,217
09/20	616,748	1,821	0.3%	34,841
09/19	572,359	3,241	0.6%	33,950
09/18	581,681	4,005	0.7%	33,747
09/17	617,904	4,142	0.7%	33,746
Annual Growth	1.9%	2.5%	—	0.3%

2021 Year-End Financials

Return on assets: 0.7%	Dividends
Return on equity: 10.2%	Yield: 3.1%
Long-term debt ($ mil.): —	Payout: 22.6%
No. of shares (mil.): —	Market value ($ mil.): —
Sales ($ mil): 15,196	

	STOCK PRICE ($) FY Close	P/E High/Low		PER SHARE ($) Earnings	Dividends	Book Value
09/21	9.94	5	3	1.33	0.32	13.79
09/20	6.45	13	6	0.57	0.37	13.28
09/19	10.07	6	4	1.11	0.63	13.06
09/18	10.08	6	5	1.40	0.68	13.94
09/17	12.40	7	5	1.48	0.76	15.03
Annual Growth	(5.4%) (2.1%)	—	—	(2.6%)	(19.5%)	

National Bank of Canada

The National Bank of Canada offers financial services to individuals businesses institutional clients and governments across Canada through Personal and Commercial Banking Wealth Management Financial Markets and US Specialty Finance and International segments. The Personal and Commercial segment meets the financial needs of close to 2.6 million individuals and over 140000 businesses across Canada. The bank also provides services such as treasury activities bank funding liquidity management and asset and liability management. Founded in 1856 The bank's assets have grown to more than $356 billion.

Operations

The National Bank of Canada operates through four business segments: Personal and Commercial Wealth Management Financial Markets and US Specialty Finance and International (USSF&I).

Personal and Commercial segment includes banking financing and investing services offered to individuals advisors and businesses as well as insurance operations. The segment accounts for more than 40% of the bank's total revenue.

Wealth Management segment comprises investment solutions trust services banking services lending services and other wealth management solutions offered through internal and third-party distribution networks. The segment accounts for nearly 25% of the total revenue.

Financial Markets segment provides corporate banking and investment banking and financial solutions for large and mid-size corporations public sector organizations and institutional investors. The segment accounts for nearly 25% of total revenue.

The USSF&I segment encompasses the specialty finance expertise provided by the Credigy subsidiary; the activities of the ABA Bank subsidiary which offers financial products and services to individuals and businesses in Cambodia; and the activities of targeted investments in certain emerging markets. It accounts for more than 10% of the total revenue.

Geographic Reach

The National Bank of Canada is headquartered in Montreal and has some 385 branches and about 925 banking machines across Canada.

Sales and Marketing

The bank serves small-and-medium sized enterprises (SMEs) corporations institutional clients and public sectors.

Financial Performance

The National Bank of Canada's financial performance for five years has continued to grow and increase year over year with 2021 as its highest performing year.

For 2021 the bank recorded a 13% increase or about C$1 billion to C$8.9 billion compared to C$7.9 billion. This increase was driven by revenue growth across all of the bank's business segments.

The bank's net income increased by about C$1.1 billion to C$3.2 billion compared to C$2.1 billion in the prior year a 53% year-over-year increase that was due to a significant decrease in provisions for credit losses on non-impaired loans as macroeconomic and credit conditions improved from fiscal 2020 and to a significant reduction in provisions for credit losses on impaired loans. Also contributing to the net income growth was the excellent performance turned in by all the Bank's business segments notably achieved through revenue growth.

Cash held by the bank at the end of the year amounted to C$33.9 billion. The bank's operating activities provided C$6.1 billion while investing activities provided another C$1.4 billion. Financing activities used C$1.7 billion mainly for dividends paid.

Mergers and Acquisitions

In 2021 the National Bank of Canada completed its acquisition of Flinks Technology Inc. a financial data aggregation and distribution company for C$73 million. The acquisition strategically positions the bank in a high-growth market to continue to enhance customer experiences and benefit from future technology-driven innovation. After its initial transaction the bank made another C$30 million investment in voting right preferred shares giving it an 85.9% equity interest in Flinks.

Company Background

The National Bank of Canada was founded in 1859.

EXECUTIVES

Independent Director, Patricia Curadeau-grou
President and Chief Executive Officer of the Bank, Non-Independent Director, Louis Vachon, $836,340 total compensation
Executive Vice President - Employee Experience, Brigitte Hebert
Independent Chairman of the Board, Jean Houde
Executive Vice President - Risk Management, William Bonnell
Chief Financial Officer, Executive Vice President - Finance, Ghislain Parent, $334,536 total compensation

Independent Director, Pierre Thabet
Independent Director, Maryse Bertrand
Independent Director, Pierre Boivin
Independent Director, Andree Savoie
Co-Head and Executive Vice President, Financial Markets, Denis Girouard, $334,536 total compensation
Independent Director, Rebecca McKillican
Executive Vice-President – Wealth Management and Co-President and Co-Chief Executive Officer - National Bank Financial, Martin Gagnon, $353,127 total compensation
Independent Director, Lino Saputo
Independent Director, Robert Pare
Executive Vice President - Personal Banking and Client Experience, Lucie Blanchet
Executive Vice President - Commercial Banking and Insurance, Stephane Achard
Independent Director, Manon Brouillette
Executive Vice-President – Operations, Nathalie Genereux
Independent Director, Yvon Charest
Executive Vice-President – Information Technology, Julie Levesque
Independent Director, Karen Kinsley
Independent Director, Pierre Blouin
Co-Head and Executive Vice-Presidents, Financial Markets, Laurent Ferreira, $334,536 total compensation
Auditors: Deloitte LLP

LOCATIONS

HQ: National Bank of Canada
600 De La Gauchetiere Street West, 4th Floor, Montreal, Quebec H3B 4L2
Phone: 514 394-6751   **Fax:** 514 394-8434
Web: www.nbc.ca

2016 sales

	% of total
Financial Markets	39
Personal and Commercial	38
Wealth Management	5
Other	18
Total	**100**

2016 sales

	% of total
Canada	89
United States	8
Other	3
Total	**100**

PRODUCTS/OPERATIONS

2016 Sales

	% of total
Interest	
Loans	50
Securities & other	8
Available-for-sale securities	4
Deposits with financial institutions	1
Noninterest	
Underwriting and advisory fees	5
Securities brokerage commissions	3
Mutual fund revenues	5
Trust service revenues	6
Credit fees	5
Card revenues	2
Deposit and payment service charges	3
Trading revenues (losses)	2
Gains (losses) on available-for-sale securities net	1
Insurance revenues net	1
Foreign exchange revenues other than trading	1
Other	3
Total	**100**

Selected Subsidiaries

Natbank (banking US)
NATCAN (75% portfolio management and investments)
National Bank Direct Brokerage (online brokerage)
National Bank Financial (investment banking)
National Bank General Insurance (home and auto coverage)
National Bank Insurance Firm (insurance brokerage)
National Bank Life Insurance Company
National Bank Securities (mutual funds)
National Bank Trust (trust services)

COMPETITORS

ASSOCIATED BANC-CORP
BANCO BBVA ARGENTINA S.A.
Banco Bradesco S/A
CITIZENS FINANCIAL GROUP INC.
COMMERCE BANCSHARES INC.
CONSUMERS BANCORP INC.
CROGHAN BANCSHARES INC.
CTBC Financial Holding Co. Ltd.
FIRST COMMONWEALTH FINANCIAL CORPORATION
FIRST HORIZON CORPORATION
FIRSTMERIT CORPORATION
FIRSTRUST SAVINGS BANK
HSBC Bank Canada
MUFG AMERICAS HOLDINGS CORPORATION
OPPENHEIMER HOLDINGS INC.
PRINCETON NATIONAL BANCORP INC.
QNB CORP.
Shinhan Financial Group Co. Ltd.
TCF FINANCIAL CORPORATION
TD BANK NATIONAL ASSOCIATION
THE PNC FINANCIAL SERVICES GROUP INC
The Bank of Nova Scotia
UMB FINANCIAL CORPORATION
WEBSTER FINANCIAL CORPORATION

HISTORICAL FINANCIALS

Company Type: Public

Income Statement

FYE: October 31

	ASSETS ($ mil.)	NET INCOME ($ mil.)	INCOME AS % OF ASSETS	EMPLOYEES
10/21	288,031	2,472	0.9%	26,920
10/20	249,297	1,445	0.6%	26,517
10/19	213,678	1,624	0.8%	25,487
10/18	199,893	1,553	0.8%	23,450
10/17	191,353	1,443	0.8%	21,635
Annual Growth	**10.8%**	**14.4%**	**—**	**5.6%**

2021 Year-End Financials

Return on assets: 0.8%
Return on equity: 17.3%
Long-term debt ($ mil.): —
No. of shares (mil.): 337
Sales ($ mil): 9,011

Dividends
Yield: 0.0%
Payout: 31.7%
Market value ($ mil.): 27,952

	STOCK PRICE ($) FY Close	P/E High/Low		PER SHARE ($) Earnings	Dividends	Book Value
10/21	82.72	10	6	7.25	2.30	45.17
10/20	47.63	10	5	4.28	2.13	36.65
10/19	51.65	8	6	4.81	2.00	33.57
10/18	45.69	8	7	4.52	1.88	31.77
10/17	48.66	9	7	4.19	1.75	29.23
Annual Growth	**14.2%**	**—**	**—**	**14.7%**	**7.1%**	**11.5%**

National Grid plc

National Grid PLC keeps the home fires burning and the lights shining brightly in UK and the US. The company owns and operates England and Wales' electricity infrastructure and operates Scotland's (Scotland's infrastructure is owned separately) which together span over 7210 kilometers of overhead lines. It also operates the UK's gas transmission infrastructure including some 7630 kilometers of pipeline. National Grid PLC's UK customers are mainly electricity generation and gas shipping companies. In the US subsidiary National Grid USA manages electricity generation & transmission assets and gas distribution networks in the New England region of the US reaching 20 million people. National Grid PLC also conducts liquefied natural gas (LNG) business in the UK and US. Majority of the company's sales were generated in the US.

Operations

National Grid PLC operates three principal businesses: US Regulated (about 65% of sales) UK Electricity Transmission (around 25%) and UK Gas Transmission (around 5%). It also operates National Grid Ventures and Other (some 5%).

The US Regulated includes gas distribution networks electricity distribution networks and high-voltage electricity transmission networks in New York and New England and electricity generation facilities in New York.

The UK Electricity Transmission includes high-voltage electricity transmission networks in England and Wales and independent Great Britain system operator.

The UK Gas Transmission involves high-pressure gas transmission networks in Great Britain and system operator in Great Britain.

The National Grid Ventures comprises all commercial operations in metering LNG at the Isle of Grain in the UK electricity interconnectors and new investments in Geronimo Energy LLC (Geronimo) and Emerald Energy Venture LLC (Emerald).

Geographic Reach

The primary serviced areas for London-headquartered National Grid PLC are England Wales Scotland and the New England region of the US. The company's US operations are in New York Massachusetts and Rhode Island. Its US power generation facilities are on Long Island NY.

National Grid PLC owns and operate Grain LNG an importation terminal and storage facility at the Isle of Grain in Kent.

About two-thirds of National Grid's revenue comes from US operations and the rest comes from the UK.

Sales and Marketing

National Grid PLC is regulated by Ofgem in the UK. Its client base includes residential customers industrial companies and commercial enterprises.

Financial Performance

National Grid's 2020 revenue was 14.5 billion 393 million less than the previous year. This resulted from a decrease in revenue of US Regulated and NGV and Other segments.

Net income fell 16% to 1.3 billion compared to the previous year which resulted from a decrease in earnings from continuing operations and negative earnings from discontinued operations.

Cash and cash equivalents at the end of the year were 73 million 179 million less than the previous year. Cash generated by operating activities was 4.7 billion. Investing activities used 3.2 billion primarily for purchases of property plant and equipment; financing activities used 1.6 billion primarily for repayment of loans.

Strategy

National Grid's strategy is to build own and operate large-scale long-life energy assets primarily in networks and renewables that deliver fair returns and high societal value. This strategy sets the bounds of National Grid's business and will ensure it is set up to play a leading role in the energy future. It will be delivered through four priorities: enable the energy transition for all deliver for customers efficiently grow organizational capability and empower colleagues for great performance.

For the company's digital transformation it is adopting a group-wide centralized hub model supported by regional delivery. The strategy for the transformation is formed centrally with regional autonomy. The company expanded a personalization platform to serve more than two million customers in Massachusetts and Rhode Island. Advanced data and analytics proactively identify eligible customers and present the next best offer to individuals increasing offer enrolment and reducing bad debt.

The company is supporting growth in distributed energy resources (DERs) in its US service territories where its US regulated business connected 314 MW of generation in the calendar year 2019. It also made investments in the grid to enable future growth including to increase distribution system capacity and to deploy advanced communications monitoring and control technologies essential to enhance DER integration.

Mergers and Acquisitions

In mid-2019 National Grid PLC completed the acquisition of Geronimo Energy a leading clean energy company based in Minneapolis MN for $100m. The acquisition is led by National Grid PLC's competitive business unit National Grid Ventures. Geronimo Energy has a strong track record of being farmer-friendly community-driven and customer focused which aligns with National Grid PLC's core value.

HISTORY

The National Grid Company was formed in 1990 as part of the privatization of the electricity industry in England and Wales. Until then the Central Electricity Generating Board (CEGB) a state monopoly responsible for power generation in England and Wales owned the national power grid (transmission system) and sold power to 12 area boards the regional authorities that distributed electricity to customers.

The Electricity Act of 1989 paved the way for competition; in 1990 the CEGB was split into The National Grid Company and three power-generating firms: National Power PowerGen and Nuclear Electric. The 12 area boards transferred their assets to 12 regional companies which jointly owned National Grid. The company keeping its monopoly status was charged to develop and operate an efficient coordinated and economical transmission system and to facilitate competition among power producers.

The company moved outside the UK when it invested in Citelec in 1993. An international consortium Citelec controlled Transener the surviving transmission system after Argentina privatized its electric utilities.

Also in 1993 National Grid set up Energis as a telecommunications firm to provide service to businesses. Piggybacking its fiber-optic lines on National Grid's transmission network Energis introduced national services in 1994 and by 1996 it had won several major customers including the BBC and Microsoft.

In 1995 National Grid went public as The National Grid Group. It also secured concessions to build transmission lines in Pakistan but in 1997 a new Pakistani government put the project on hold. That year it also upped its stake in Citelec from 15% to 41% which increased its control over the development of Argentina's transmission system. With partner CINergy Global it also acquired 80% of the Power Division of Zambia Consolidated Copper Mines in 1997 and it was chosen as a joint venture partner by India's Karnataka Electricity Board to build a transmission line in that state.

The company sold 26% of Energis in 1997; in 1998 it announced plans to sell the rest of Energis and launch a new company under the National Grid banner to set up telecom firms overseas. That year it laid plans to enter the US by agreeing to acquire New England Electric System (NEES). (The $3.2 billion purchase closed in 2000.)

In 1999 the company cut its stake in Energis to 46% and announced plans to shop for more US energy holdings. A deal was struck to purchase New York Utility Niagara Mohawk Holdings the following year. (The deal was completed in 2002.) Also in 2000 and 2001 the company continued to slim its stake in Energis (33%).

National Grid sold some noncore businesses in 2001 including UK metering company Datum Services and US energy marketer Allenergy and pulled out of the transmission project in India. It also agreed to manage the Alliance Regional Transmission Organization (RTO) in the US. In 2002 National Grid sold Niagara Mohawk's 50% interest in Canadian Niagara Power to Canadian utility Fortis.

The firm changed its name to National Grid Transco in 2002 upon completion of its acquisition of Lattice Group in a $21.5 billion deal.

In 2005 National Grid Transco sold four of its regional gas distribution networks; the North England network was acquired by a consortium that includes United Utilities and Cheung Kong Infrastructure; the South of England and Scotland networks were sold to Scottish and Southern Energy Borealis Infrastructure and Ontario Teachers' Pension Plan; and the Wales & West distribution network was purchased by a consortium managed by Macquarie Bank Limited. The company dropped Transco from its name in 2005.

National Grid dramatically boosted its North American assets in 2007 by acquiring gas distributor KeySpan for more than $7 billion. To comply with federal regulations connected to the KeySpan deal in 2008 National Grid sold its 2480-MW Ravenswood Generating Station in New York City to TransCanada for $2.9 billion.

In the second half of the decade to raise cash and narrow its operational focus the company jettisoned a number of noncore operations. National Grid sold its stakes in the alternative telecommunications network industry. The company also sold its telecom interests in Chile Argentina and Poland and wrote off its 33% stake in bankrupt UK telecommunications firm Energis which uses fiber-optic cable strung along National Grid's power lines. National Grid also sold former Lattice Group subsidiary 186k (fiber-optic networking) to Hutchison Whampoa and exited its telecom venture in Brazil. It also sold its electricity interconnector linking Australia to the island state of Tasmania.

In 2010 a National Grid and TenneT joint venture began laying the first section of a high-voltage cable that will link the power grids in the UK and the Netherlands bolstering power supply in both countries. The project will help the companies meet environmental goals by facilitating power flows from low-carbon generation plants.

With an eye on meeting ambitious European Union goals for carbon emission reductions in 2009 National Grid released a report that by 2020 half of the UK's heating needs could be provided by biogas (converted from sewage and injected into the national gas distribution system) compensating for a decline in North Sea gas supply. In 2010 the company had one renewable gas plant under development in the US and two in the UK.

The company reported a major jump in revenues and income in 2010 primarily driven by a rebounding economy (prompting increased demand for power and gas) and by improved rates in the US market. Revenues grew by 40% in 2011 and net income by 30% thanks to strong demand and higher prices in the UK and increased rates in the US.

In 2011 National Grid announced plans to save $200 million in a restructuring of its US operations including cutting 1200 jobs. Late in 2011 the company sold the Seneca-Upshur Petroleum subsidiary for approximately $152 million. The deal is a fur-

ther move to return to core business operations in gas and electricity distribution. That year it also agreed to sell its non-regulated metering business in the UK (Onstream) to Macquarie Bank for about $440 million.

EXECUTIVES

Non-Executive Independent Director, Earl Shipp
Non-Executive Independent Director, Jonathan Silver
Group General Counsel, Company Secretary, Justine Campbell
Non-Executive Director, Ian Livingston
Non-Executive Director, Tony Wood
Non-Executive Director, Martha Wyrsch
Non-Executive Director, Anne Robinson
Chairman, Paula Reynolds
Chief Financial Officer, Executive Director, Andy Agg, $814,671 total compensation
Non-Executive Independent Director, Liz Hewitt
Non-Executive Independent Director, Jonathan Dawson
Chief Executive Officer, Executive Director, John Pettigrew, $1,343,425 total compensation
Senior Non-Executive Independent Director, Therese Esperdy
Non-Executive Independent Director, Amanda Mesler
Auditors: Deloitte LLP

LOCATIONS

HQ: National Grid plc
1-3 Strand, London WC2N 5EH
Phone: (44) 20 7004 3000   **Fax:** (44) 20 7004 3004
Web: www.nationalgrid.com

PRODUCTS/OPERATIONS

2018 sales

	%
US Regulated	66
UK Electricity Transmission	22
UK Gas Transmission	6
National Grid Ventures	6
Total	**100**

COMPETITORS

ACCIONA SA	NATURGY ENERGY GROUP SA.
ASHTEAD GROUP PUBLIC LIMITED COMPANY	RED ELECTRICA CORPORACION SA
ENDESA SA	REXEL
ENERGIA GROUP NI HOLDINGS LIMITED	RWE AG
EXELON CORPORATION	SSE PLC
FIRSTENERGY CORP.	

HISTORICAL FINANCIALS

Company Type: Public

Income Statement				FYE: March 31
	REVENUE ($ mil.)	NET INCOME ($ mil.)	NET PROFIT MARGIN	EMPLOYEES
03/21	20,345	2,257	11.1%	23,683
03/20	17,962	1,561	8.7%	23,069
03/19	19,561	1,979	10.1%	22,576
03/18	21,429	4,988	23.3%	23,023
03/17	18,770	9,731	51.8%	22,132
Annual Growth	2.0%	(30.6%)	—	1.7%

2021 Year-End Financials

Debt ratio: 62.5%	No. of shares (mil.): —
Return on equity: 8.3%	Dividends
Cash ($ mil.): 216	Yield: 5.2%
Current ratio: 1.06	Payout: 528.4%
Long-term debt ($ mil.): 37,028	Market value ($ mil.): —

	STOCK PRICE ($)	P/E	PER SHARE ($)		
	FY Close	High/Low	Earnings	Dividends	Book Value
03/21	59.24	146 119	0.64	3.11	7.70
03/20	58.27	180 131	0.45	3.06	6.89
03/19	55.84	131 108	0.58	3.08	6.87
03/18	56.43	75 51	1.43	3.12	7.27
03/17	63.48	34 27	2.57	0.55	6.78
Annual Growth	(1.7%)	—	(29.5%)	54.0%	3.2%

National Westminster Bank Plc

National Westminster Bank (NatWest) is the main provider of shared services for the NatWest Group. This includes the provision of treasury services on behalf of the ring-fenced bank and NatWest Group. The bank operating segments include Retail Nanking which serves individuals customers in UK and Ulster Bank customers in Northern Ireland; Commercial Banking which serves start-up SME commercial and corporate customers in the UK; Private Banking which serves UK-connected high net worth individual and their business interest; and Central Item & Other which includes corporate functions treasury finance risk management compliance legal communications and human resources. National Westminster Bank is a wholly owned subsidiary of NatWest Holdings Limited.

Operations
NatWest's four business divisions are Retail Banking (which generates around 40% of revenue); Commercial Banking (around 40%); Private Banking (less than 8%); and Central Items & Other (about 20%).

The bank generates around 65% of its net revenue from interest. The rest arises from fees and commissions.

Geographic Reach
Headquartered in London NatWest generates the vast majority of its revenue in the UK. Outside the UK the company has subsidiaries in Ireland (Ulster Bank Ireland DAC) Coutts & Company (Great Britain) and Lombard North Central PLC (Great Britain).

Sales and Marketing
NatWest has wholesale customers including corporate banks and other financial institutions are grouped by industry sectors and geography as well as by products/assets class are managed on an individual basis.

Financial Performance
Note: Growth rates may differ after conversion to US Dollars.

The company's revenue for fiscal 2020 decreased to 10.3 billion compared from the prior year with 11.2 billion.

Profit for fiscal 2020 decreased to 602 million compared from the prior year with 1.3 billion.

Cash held by the company at the end of fiscal 2020 increased to 68 billion. Cash provided by operations investing and financing activities were 29.2 billion 4.1 billion and 817 million respectively.

Strategy
In December 2020 NatWest acquired a 3 billion portfolio of prime UK mortgages from Metro Bank plc. Growing its mortgage book is an important strategic priority as the company builds a bank that delivers sustainable returns for shareholders.

The addition of this loan book will supplement the strong organic growth that it continues to achieve.

At the start of 2020 NatWest Group launched its People Pledge ? a set of commitments made in response to what colleagues said meant most to them; helping colleagues develop skills supporting their wellbeing and creating an inclusive workplace helping customers thrive investing in teams and helping colleagues make a difference.

Auditors: Ernst & Young LLP

LOCATIONS
HQ: National Westminster Bank Plc
250 Bishopsgate, London EC2M 4AA
Phone: (44) 20 7085 5000
Web: www.natwest.com

PRODUCTS/OPERATIONS

2018 sales
	% of total
Interest income	61
Fees and commissions receivable	17
Other non-interest income	22
Total	**100**

2018 sales
	% of total
UK Personal & Business Banking	55
Commercial and Private Banking	33
Central Items & other	17
Total	**100**

Services
Personal Banking
Credit card
Insurance
Loans
Mortgages
Saving Account
Private Banking
Credit Cards
Current Accounts
Insurance
Loans
Mortgages
Business Banking
International business
Startup business

COMPETITORS
BPCE
Banco Bradesco S/A
CANARA BANK
CLYDESDALE BANK PLC
CREDIT INDUSTRIEL ET COMMERCIAL
China Construction Bank Corporation
DBRS Limited
Danske Bank A/S
FIRSTMERIT CORPORATION
FITCH GROUP INC.
HDFC BANK LIMITED
HSBC Bank Canada
ICE DATA SERVICES INC.
INVESTEC PLC
M&T BANK CORPORATION

NATIONAL AUSTRALIA BANK LIMITED
NATIONAL BANK HOLDINGS CORPORATION
PENTA CAPITAL PARTNERS LIMITED
SANTANDER UK GROUP HOLDINGS PLC
TD BANK NATIONAL ASSOCIATION
THE CO-OPERATIVE BANK P.L.C.
The Bank of Nova Scotia
ULSTER BANK LIMITED
YORKSHIRE BANK PUBLIC LIMITED COMPANY

HISTORICAL FINANCIALS
Company Type: Public

Income Statement
FYE: December 31

	ASSETS ($ mil.)	NET INCOME ($ mil.)	INCOME AS % OF ASSETS	EMPLOYEES
12/21	574,261	3,764	0.7%	0
12/20	519,412	518	0.1%	0
12/19	420,589	942	0.2%	51,700
12/18	395,716	3,343	0.8%	55,400
12/17	460,373	2,789	0.6%	14,400
Annual Growth	5.7%	7.8%	—	—

2021 Year-End Financials
Return on assets: 0.6%
Return on equity: 14.8%
Long-term debt ($ mil.): —
No. of shares (mil.): —
Sales ($ mil): 13,972

Dividends
Yield: —
Payout: —
Market value ($ mil.): —

Naturgy Energy Group SA

Auditors: Ernst & Young, S.L.

LOCATIONS
HQ: Naturgy Energy Group SA
Avenida San Luis 77, Madrid 28033
Phone: (34) 93 219 9199   **Fax:** (34) 93 402 5870
Web: www.naturgy.com

HISTORICAL FINANCIALS
Company Type: Public

Income Statement
FYE: December 31

	REVENUE ($ mil.)	NET INCOME ($ mil.)	NET PROFIT MARGIN	EMPLOYEES
12/20	18,832	(425)	—	9,580
12/19	25,862	1,573	6.1%	12,138
12/18	27,872	(3,231)	—	13,945
12/17	27,938	1,630	5.8%	15,374
12/16	24,479	1,422	5.8%	17,229
Annual Growth	(6.3%)	—	—	(13.6%)

2020 Year-End Financials
Debt ratio: 49.6%
Return on equity: (-3.7%)
Cash ($ mil.): 4,819
Current ratio: 1.40
Long-term debt ($ mil.): 16,741

No. of shares (mil.): 960
Dividends
Yield: 4.9%
Payout: —
Market value ($ mil.): 4,440

	STOCK PRICE ($)	P/E	PER SHARE ($)		
	FY Close	High/Low	Earnings	Dividends	Book Value
12/20	4.62	— —	(0.44)	0.23	10.25
12/19	4.97	4 3	1.61	0.21	12.21
12/18	5.09	— —	(3.24)	0.23	12.71
12/17	4.57	4 3	1.63	0.17	17.65
12/16	3.74	3 2	1.43	0.20	16.06
Annual Growth	5.4%	— —	—	3.3%	(10.6%)

NatWest Group PLC

The Royal Bank of Scotland (RBS) who changed its name to Natwest in 2020 is the largest business and commercial bank in the UK with a leading retail business. It is the biggest supporter of the business sector ? banking around 1 in 4 businesses across the UK and Ireland from start-ups to multinationals dating back to 1727. With total assets of nearly 799.5 million it offers retail banking which provides a comprehensive range of banking products and related financial services including current accounts mortgages personal unsecured lending and personal deposits.. Natwest's over 800 branches constitute the UK's second-largest branch network. Outside of Great Britain RBS operates as Ulster Bank in Ireland and Northern Ireland and has additional small operations in Europe the US and Asia. Majority of its sales were generated in the UK.

Operations

Natwest operates business segments including Retail Banking (about 40% of sales) Commercial Banking (around 35%) NatWest Markets (some 10%) Private Banking (over 5%) Ulster Bank (some 5%) RBS International (less than 5%) and Central items & other.

Retail Banking serves individuals and mass affluent customers in the UK and includes Ulster Bank customers in Northern Ireland. Commercial Banking serves start-up SME commercial and corporate customers in the UK. NatWest Markets helps NatWest Group's corporate and institutional customers manage their financial risks safely and achieve their short-term and long-term sustainable financial goals. Private Banking serves UK connected high net worth individuals and their business interests. Ulster Bank RoI serves individuals and businesses in the Republic of Ireland (RoI). RBS International (RBSI) serves retail commercial and corporate customers in the Channel Islands Isle of Man and Gibraltar and financial institution customers in those same locations in addition to the UK and Luxembourg. Central items & other includes corporate functions such as NatWest Group Treasury finance risk management compliance legal communications and human resources. Central functions manages NatWest Group capital resources and NatWest Groupwide regulatory projects and provides services to the reportable segments.

Overall net interest income accounts for around 70% of sales followed by net fees and commission with nearly 20% and income from trading activities with around 10%.

Geographic Reach

Natwest is based in Edinburgh Scotland and besides the UK rings up sales in and Europe the Asia/Pacific region and the US. The UK is by far its largest market at around 90% of sales.

Sales and Marketing

Natwest serves around 19 million customers including individuals high-net-worth individuals SMEs commercial enterprises corporates and financial institutions.

Financial Performance

The company's revenue for fiscal 2020 decreased by 16% to 1.1 billion compared with 1.3 billion in the prior year.

Cash held by the company at the end of fiscal 2020 increased to 139.2 billion. Cash provided by operating investing and financing activities were 29.1 billion 7.5 billion and 90 million respectively.

Strategy

NatWest Group will be a relationship bank for a digital world. The company's strategy is to deliver on its Purpose and drive sustainable returns to shareholders through its four strategic priorities.

The company invests around 1 billion each year to continuously improve its customers' experience by harnessing its internal expertise and partnering with some of the most innovative companies from around the world. NatWest has already created a strong culture of innovation with the development of customer propositions such as Mettle. The company has also partnered with Pollinate to produce the award-winning Tyl. And NatWest established a new relationship with BlackRock to support its investment management processing activity.

Company Background

The group was crippled by both the global financial crisis and its ambitious international expansion primarily its disastrous 2007 investment in Dutch bank ABN AMRO. In late 2008 the UK took a 60% stake in RBS but the bank still ended up reporting an annual loss of some 28 billion ($41 billion) — the largest loss in British corporate history. The government stepped in at least twice more to help RBS manage its debt and interest payments intervening with the contingency that RBS make significant efforts to get back on solid ground. The UK government is progressively selling off its stake in RBS. Standing at around 62% in 2019 the government expects to sell its entire stake in the company by 2024.

HISTORY

Royal Bank of Scotland was founded in 1727 but its roots go back to the Darien Company a merchant expedition that was established to set up a Scottish trading colony in Panama. The Darien expedition ended disastrously in 1699. In 1707 England voted to compensate Scottish creditors for the colony's failure (in part because England had promised support then reneged contributing to the collapse) and a small industry sprang up around paying creditors and loaning them money. In 1727 the Equivalent Company the combined entity of these organizations was granted a banking charter and became Royal Bank of Scotland.

In 1826 the Parliament voted to take away Scottish banks' right to issue banknotes for less than five pounds which would have required banks to use gold or silver. Few banks had such reserves and the move sparked an outcry. Novelist Sir Walter Scott's The Letters of Malachi Malagrowther which defended the Scottish one-pound note helped shoot down the proposal.

RBS expanded throughout Scotland over the next 50 years. It opened a London branch in 1874; it didn't establish a branch outside London until it bought Williams Deacon's Bank which had a branch network in North England. RBS continued to use the Williams Deacon's name as it did with Glyn Mills & Co. which it purchased in 1939.

In 1968 RBS took on its modern persona as a public company when it merged with National Commercial Bank. The company moved overseas during the 1970s establishing offices in Hong Kong and major US cities.

RBS spent the next 20 years trying to achieve another merger of the same scale as National Commercial. In 1981 the bank was wooed by Standard Chartered Bank and Hongkong and Shanghai Bank (now part of HSBC Holdings) but British regulators denied both suitors.

The bank moved into telephone operations in 1985 when it set up Direct Line for selling car insurance. In 1988 RBS bought New England bank Citizens Financial (but it plans to divest that business). In 1989 the company entered into an alliance with Banco Santander (now Santander Central Hispano) Spain's largest banking group. The alliance created a cross-pollination of ideas and strategies that boosted both banks' operations. The first fruit of the alliance came in 1991 with the launch of Interbank On-line Systems (IBOS) which connected several European banks and allowed for instantaneous money transfers.

In the 1990s RBS was linked with a variety of partners. It even made a bid for the much larger bank Barclays in a move regarded as cheeky but was rebuffed. In 1997 it announced a joint venture with Richard Branson's Virgin Group called Virgin Direct to offer personal banking. The company also bought Angel Trains Contract a rolling stock leasing company and established a transatlantic banking transfer system (similar to IBOS) with US bank CoreStates (now owned by First Union).

In 2000 RBS acquired NatWest after a prolonged takeover battle with rival Bank of Scotland (now part of HBOS plc). The bank sold Gartmore Investment Management its fund management unit to Nationwide Mutual Insurance Company. Royal Bank also sold the assets of NatWest's Equity Partners unit and launched NatWest Private Banking to target wealthy investors.

In 2004 RBS made several acquisitions to boost its US presence: It paid about $360 million for the credit card business of Connecticut-based People's Bank and bought payments processor Lynk Systems (now RBS Lynk) while Citizens Financial bought Cleveland-based bank Charter One Financial. Also that year Ulster Bank bought Ireland-based retail financial services provider First Active.

In 2007 RBS led the consortium that acquired the Dutch bank for ?71 billion in a deal that was called the largest ever in the banking industry. The buyers carved ABN AMRO into pieces; RBS took the global wholesale and international retail operations in Asia Eastern Europe and the Middle East. The ambitious takeover preceded the global economic crisis though and RBS was among the hardest hit financial groups.

The troubled company made several moves to try and raise capital. Early in 2008 the company announced a 12 billion rights issue. RBS also tried but failed to find a buyer for its insurance arm. However other assets were divested that year. The company sold rolling stock leasing firm Angel Trains to Babcock & Brown and others and it sold its joint venture Tesco Personal Finance back to supermarket giant Tesco. The efforts proved inadequate though. The government took a controlling stake in the group in 2008 the same year that RBS reported the largest corporate loss in British history.

Also as part of the government rescue RBS went through a management shakeup. Fred Goodwin the architect of the bank's international expansion was removed as CEO. He was replaced by Stephen Hester formerly the CEO of British Land Company. Johnny Cameron chairman of the group's global banking and markets segment (which lost the group's most money in 2008) was also ousted and chairman Tom McKillop retired early.

RBS also shuffled its corporate structure in 2009. It split its UK retail and commercial banking division into three segments (retail commercial and wealth) and made Ulster Bank its own segment. The group folded its operations support division into other arms and established a segment to manage the selling and runoff of noncore operations. RBS retained the Global Banking & Markets Global Transaction Services US Retail & Commercial and RBS Insurance (including Churchill Insurance) segments although several of their components were transferred to the noncore segment.

RBS has scaled back on the international growth that weakened the group during the economic fallout with the ultimate goal of reducing non-UK operations to less than a quarter of its assets. In 2009 the group sold its 4% stake in Bank of China for some 1.6 billion ($2.4 billion); it also sold most of its operations in Southeast Asia to Australia and New Zealand Banking Group for about $550 million. RBS divested units in Argentina Colombia Chile the United Arab Emirates Kazakhstan and Pakistan — all assets gained as part of its ABN AMRO transaction.

With the government having to step in at least twice to bail out the bank by 2011 RBC was forced to cut costs and sell non-core operations to refocus on its core banking business. In 2010 it sold more than 300 branches and offices to Banco Santander for some 1.65 billion ($2.6 billion). RBS sold its factoring and invoice financing unit to GE Capital and its payment services unit Global Merchant Services to Advent International and Bain Capital. It also sold its interest in RBS Sempra Commodities. In 2012 the company sold the international private banking business of Coutts to Royal Bank of Canada. Other divisions have been simply wound down and closed. RBS was ordered by the Federal Reserve in 2011 to improve its US operations or risk losing permission to do business in America. In October 2012 RBS sold a 30% stake in Direct Line Group part of its insurance group in an IPO valued at 2.6 billion ($4.2 billion).

EXECUTIVES

Non-Executive Independent Director, Lena Wilson, $230,860 total compensation
Group Chief Financial Officer, Executive Director, Katie Murray, $961,920 total compensation
Non-Executive Director, Yasmin Jetha, $164,167 total compensation
Chief Executive Officer - Private Banking, Peter Flavel
Head of Investor Relations, Alexander Holcroft
Chief Executive Officer - NatWest Markets, Robert Begbie
Chief Executive Officer - Commercial Banking, Paul Thwaite
Chief Communications Officer, Nigel Prideaux
Chief Audit Executive, Nicholas Crapp
Chief Transformation Officer, Jennifer Tippin
CEO, Retail Banking, David Lindberg
Chief Marketing Officer, Margaret Jobling
Non-Executive Independent Director, Mike Rogers, $218,035 total compensation
Non-Executive Independent Director, Frank Dangeard, $333,465 total compensation
Senior Non-Executive Independent Director, Mark Seligman, $242,403 total compensation
Chief Risk Officer, Bruce Fletcher
Chief Executive Officer - RBS International, Andrew McLaughlin
Group Chief of Staff, Rob Whittick
Non-Executive Chairman of the Board, Howard Davies, $956,658 total compensation
Chief Executive Officer, Executive Director, Alison Rose, $1,410,816 total compensation
Group Chief Administrative Officer, Simon McNamara
Non-Executive Independent Director, Morten Friis, $215,470 total compensation
Chief Human Resource Officer, Helen Cook
Auditors: Ernst & Young LLP

LOCATIONS

HQ: NatWest Group PLC
P.O. Box 1000, Gogarburn, Edinburgh EH12 1HQ
Phone: (44) 131 556 8555   **Fax:** (44) 131 626 3081
Web: www.natwestgroup.com

2018 Sales

	% of total
Net interest income	65
Net fees and commissions	18
Income from trading activities	10
Other operating income	7
Total	**100**

2018 Sales

	% of total
UK	92
Other countries	8
Total	**100**

PRODUCTS/OPERATIONS

2018 Sales by Segment

	% of total
Personal & Business Banking	
UK Personal & Business Banking	43
Ulster Bank	4
Commercial and Private Banking	
Commercial Banking	22
Private Banking	4
RBS International	4
NatWest Markets	17
Central items & other	2
Total	**100**

Selected Subsidiaries

Citizens Financial Group Inc. (banking US)
Coutts & Co (private banking)
Direct Line Insurance Group plc
National Westminster Bank Plc
The Royal Bank of Scotland plc
Ulster Bank Limited (Northern Ireland)

COMPETITORS

AEGON N.V.	Nordea Bank AB
Ageas	RSA INSURANCE GROUP
BARCLAYS PLC	LIMITED
CLOSE BROTHERS GROUP	STANDARD CHARTERED PLC
PLC	Sampo Oyj
DEUTSCHE BANK AG	TSB BANKING GROUP PLC
ING Groep N.V.	UniCredit Bank AG
LONDON STOCK EXCHANGE	VIRGIN MONEY UK PLC
GROUP PLC	WESTPAC BANKING
MAN GROUP LIMITED	CORPORATION
NOMURA HOLDINGS INC.	

HISTORICAL FINANCIALS

Company Type: Public

Income Statement   FYE: December 31

	ASSETS ($ mil.)	NET INCOME ($ mil.)	INCOME AS % OF ASSETS	EMPLOYEES
12/21	1,053,875	4,378	0.4%	58,735
12/20	1,091,072	(543)	—	59,900
12/19	954,817	4,621	0.5%	62,900
12/18	886,372	2,438	0.3%	65,400
12/17	996,884	1,547	0.2%	69,700
Annual Growth	**1.4%**	**29.7%**	**—**	**(4.2%)**

2021 Year-End Financials

Return on assets: 0.4%
Return on equity: 7.5%
Long-term debt ($ mil.): —
No. of shares (mil.): —
Sales ($ mil): 17,230
Dividends
Yield: 2.6%
Payout: 1,153.0%
Market value ($ mil.): —

	STOCK PRICE ($) FY Close	P/E High/Low		PER SHARE ($) Earnings	Dividends	Book Value
12/21	6.11	25	15	0.34	0.16	4.92
12/20	4.52	—	—	(0.08)	0.04	4.94
12/19	6.44	28	18	0.34	0.29	4.76
12/18	5.59	59	38	0.17	0.00	4.85
12/17	7.64	123	94	0.09	0.00	5.46
Annual Growth	**(5.4%)**	**—**	**—**	**41.5%**	**—**	**(2.6%)**

NEC Corp

Auditors: KPMG AZSA LLC

LOCATIONS

HQ: NEC Corp
5-7-1 Shiba, Minato-ku, Tokyo 108-8001
Phone: (81) 3 3454 1111
Web: www.nec.co.jp

HISTORICAL FINANCIALS

Company Type: Public

Income Statement   FYE: March 31

	REVENUE ($ mil.)	NET INCOME ($ mil.)	NET PROFIT MARGIN	EMPLOYEES
03/21	27,040	1,351	5.0%	114,714
03/20	28,514	920	3.2%	112,638
03/19	26,307	362	1.4%	110,595
03/18	26,787	431	1.6%	109,390
03/17	23,836	244	1.0%	107,729
Annual Growth	**3.2%**	**53.4%**	**—**	**1.6%**

2021 Year-End Financials

Debt ratio: 0.1%
Return on equity: 13.4%
Cash ($ mil.): 4,726
Current ratio: 1.55
Long-term debt ($ mil.): 4,414
No. of shares (mil.): 272
Dividends
Yield: —
Payout: 16.1%
Market value ($ mil.): —

Nedbank Group Ltd

Nedbank Group is one of the largest financial services group in Africa. The company offers a range of wholesale and retail banking services through its principal business clusters: Nedbank Corporate Nedbank Retail Nedbank Wealth Nedbank Business Banking and Nedbank Capital (investment banking and capital markets). Other services include property finance private banking credit card processing insurance and foreign exchange and securities trading. Nedbank has about 550 retail and commercial banking branches located primarily in South Africa's urban and suburban areas.
Auditors: Ernst & Young Inc.

LOCATIONS

HQ: Nedbank Group Ltd
Nedbank 135 Rivonia Campus, 135 Rivonia Road, Sandown, Sandton 2196
Phone: (27) 11 294 4444   **Fax:** (27) 11 294 6540
Web: www.nedbankgroup.co.za

COMPETITORS

AIFUL CORPORATION
AMMB HOLDINGS BERHAD
BARCLAYS BANK PLC
CLAYTON DUBILIER & RICE INC.
CREDIT SUISSE (UK) LIMITED
FORESIGHT GROUP LLP
HITACHI CAPITAL (UK) PLC
HONG LEONG FINANCE LIMITED
HSBC Private Bank (Suisse) SA
KLEINWORT BENSON (CHANNEL ISLANDS) LIMITED
LUMON EXCHANGE LTD
NIBC Bank N.V.
RELIANCE CAPITAL LIMITED
SOR OR KOR PUBLIC COMPANY LIMITED

HISTORICAL FINANCIALS
Company Type: Public

Income Statement
FYE: December 31

	ASSETS ($ mil.)	NET INCOME ($ mil.)	INCOME AS % OF ASSETS	EMPLOYEES
12/20	83,695	236	0.3%	0
12/19	81,411	854	1.0%	29,403
12/18	72,600	930	1.3%	30,877
12/17	79,872	943	1.2%	31,531
12/16	70,338	737	1.0%	32,401
Annual Growth	4.4%	(24.8%)	—	—

2020 Year-End Financials

Return on assets: 0.2%	Dividends
Return on equity: 3.9%	Yield: 7.3%
Long-term debt ($ mil.): —	Payout: 72.1%
No. of shares (mil.): 483	Market value ($ mil.): 4,273
Sales ($ mil): 6,460	

	STOCK PRICE ($) FY Close	P/E High/Low	PER SHARE ($) Earnings	Dividends	Book Value
12/20	8.83	2 1	0.48	0.65	12.53
12/19	15.40	1 1	1.75	0.76	12.96
12/18	19.32	1 1	1.89	0.77	12.21
12/17	20.68	1 1	1.93	0.77	13.80
12/16	17.20	1 1	1.51	0.61	11.53
Annual Growth	(15.3%)	— —	(24.8%)	1.3%	2.1%

Neste Oyj

Neste Oyj or Neste Corporation in English (formerly Neste Oil) is a Finnish oil refiner committed to a green energy strategy to lower carbon emissions. The state-controlled firm focuses on refining marketing and shipping oil products including gasoline biodiesel fuel and lubricants. Neste Oyj primarily sells its products domestically but also exports to customers in North America and Europe. It operates about 850 gas stations in Finland and almost 320 outside the country (in Estonia Latvia Lithuania Poland and northwestern Russia). The company has a biodiesel plant and a diesel production line. It has a crude oil refining capacity of 15 million tons per year and renewable diesel production capacity of 2.4 million tons per year.

Operations
Neste Oyj operates through four segments: Oil Products Renewable Products Oil Retail and Other.

Oil Products markets and sells gasoline diesel fuel light and heavy fuel oil aviation fuel base oils liquefied petroleum gas and related oil products and services to wholesale markets.

Renewable Products markets and wholesales NEXBTL renewable diesel based on the company's proprietary technology.

Oil Retail segment markets and sells petroleum products and associated services directly to end-users of which the most important are private motorists industry transport companies farmers and heating oil customers. The company has a network of over 1000 service stations in the Baltic Sea region.

Other consists of group administration shared service functions research and technology Neste Jacobs and Nynas AB.

Geographic Reach
Neste Oyj markets and sales fuels and oil products in Finland the St. Petersburg region in Northwest Russia Estonia Latvia and Lithuania.

It also owns and operates a total of eight rail-connected terminals in Finland Tallinn in Estonia and Riga in Latvia.

Sales and Marketing
Neste Oyj serves a range of markets including aviation marine municipalities resellers and retail chains wholesalers and blenders and base oils companies.

Financial Performance
The company's revenue has been restated due to divestiture of the crude oil vessel Tempera and Kilpilahden S ¤hk ¶nsiirto Oy. In 2014 the company's net revenue decreased by 14%

Net income fell by 89% in 2014 due to lower net revenues as a result of lower commodity prices (which dragged down trading activity by ?1.2 billion) and lower volumes of Oil Products sales.

Neste Oil's cash inflows decreased by 70%.

Strategy
Neste Oyj is seeking to become the world's top supplier of low-emission automotive fuels (sulfur-free diesel and other clean-burning fuels) as a way to give it a competitive edge in a crowded global refining market. As part of this push in 2015 the company signed an agreement with IBM for renewing the company's central enterprise resource planning system. Neste Oil plans to increase the capacity of its renewable diesel refineries to 2.6 million tons by the end of 2016.

To raise cash in 2015 the company agreed to sell crude oil vessel Tempera to Perenco. The sale follows the company's 2013 decision to divest its shipping operations.

Company Background
In 2008 Neste Oil announced plans to build a major renewable diesel plant in Rotterdam capable of producing 800000 metric tons a day. Construction on the facility began in 2009. Completed in 2011 the plant expanded the company's green diesel production capacity to 2 million tons per year.

To expand its base oil business the company completed a 400000 metric tons-per-year joint venture base oil plant in Bahrain in 2011.

At the end of 2010 Neste Oil merged its Oil Products and Renewable Fuels businesses to create Oil Products and Renewables to improve operational efficiency and create synergies between the two businesses. That year the company posted a jump in revenues and income as the global economy bounced make from a recession. The rebound triggered stronger demand for oil and gas and higher commodity prices.

The Finnish government owns 50.1% of the company which was founded shortly after WWII to ensure a steady oil supply for the country. Neste Oil was spun off by Fortum in 2005. In 2015 it changed its name to Neste Oyj (Neste Corporation).

EXECUTIVES

Senior Vice President, Innovation, Member of the Executive Committee, Lars Lindfors

Executive Vice President for Renewable Aviation, Member of the Executive Committee, Thorsten Lange

Executive Vice President, Renewable Road Transportation, Member of the Executive Committee, Carl Nyberg

Independent Director, Jean-Baptiste Renard

Independent Director, Martina Floel

Independent Chairman of the Board, Matti Kahkonen

General Counsel, Member of the Executive Committee, Christian Stahlberg

President and Chief Executive Officer, Chair of the Executive Committee, Peter Vanacker, $1,054,452 total compensation

Independent Vice Chairman of the Board, Marco Wiren

Senior Vice President - Sustainability, and Corporate Affairs, Member of the Executive Committee, Minna Aila

Executive Vice President, Marketing & Services, Member of the Executive Committee, Panu Kopra

Independent Director, Jari Rosendal

Independent Director, Johanna Soderstrom

Independent Director, Nick Elmslie

Senior Vice President, Human Resources, HSSEQ and Procurement; Member of the Executive Committee, Hannele Jakosuo-Jansson

Executive Vice President, Renewables Platform, Member of the Executive Committee, Matti Lehmus

Chief Financial Officer, Strategy and IT, Member of the Executive Committee, Jyrki Maki-Kala

Executive Vice President, Renewable Polymers and Chemicals, Member of the Executive Committee, Mercedes Alonso

Auditors: PricewaterhouseCoopers Oy

LOCATIONS
HQ: Neste Oyj
Keilaranta 21, P.O. Box 95, Espoo 00095
Phone: (358) 10 458 11   **Fax:** (358) 10 458 4442
Web: www.neste.com

2013 Sales

	% of total
Europe	
Nordic countries	
Finland	46
Other	17
Baltic Rim	12
Other countries	25
North & South America	18
Other regions	2
Total	**100**

PRODUCTS/OPERATIONS

2013 Sales

	% of total
Oil products	65
Oil retail	22
Renewable fuels	12
Others	1
Total	**100**

COMPETITORS

AMPOL LIMITED	RS ENERGY K.K.
HOLLYFRONTIER CORPORATION	STATE OIL LIMITED
	SURGUTNEFTEGAZ PAO
Husky Energy Inc	Suncor Energy Inc
Imperial Oil Limited	THAI OIL PUBLIC
REPSOL SA.	COMPANY LIMITED

HISTORICAL FINANCIALS
Company Type: Public

Income Statement
FYE: December 31

	REVENUE ($ mil.)	NET INCOME ($ mil.)	NET PROFIT MARGIN	EMPLOYEES
12/20	14,421	873	6.1%	4,825
12/19	17,784	2,007	11.3%	4,413
12/18	17,084	890	5.2%	5,413
12/17	15,843	1,092	6.9%	5,339
12/16	12,342	991	8.0%	5,001
Annual Growth	4.0%	(3.1%)	—	(0.9%)

2020 Year-End Financials

Debt ratio: 11.2%	No. of shares (mil.): 767
Return on equity: 11.9%	Dividends
Cash ($ mil.): 1,904	Yield: 1.5%
Current ratio: 2.17	Payout: 164.5%
Long-term debt ($ mil.): 933	Market value ($ mil.): 28,041

	STOCK PRICE ($)	P/E	PER SHARE ($)		
	FY Close	High/Low	Earnings	Dividends	Book Value
12/20	36.52	39 13	1.14	0.58	9.47
12/19	17.32	30 7	2.60	0.42	8.66
12/18	38.20	2871 2024	0.02	0.98	0.10
12/17	31.93	27 16	1.42	0.78	6.78
12/16	19.04	17 11	1.29	0.53	5.14
Annual Growth	17.7%	— —	(3.0%)	2.3%	16.5%

Nestle SA

Nestle one of the leading food and drinks company produces more than 2000 brands including the world's leading coffee brand Nescafe Haagen-Dazs ice cream Purina pet food DiGiorno pizza Kit-Kat chocolates and Perrier bottled water. Its brands produced at around 375 factories globally include global regional and local favorites. The Americas is Nestle's biggest market. The company traces its roots back in 1866.

HISTORY

Henri Nestle purchased a factory in Vevey Switzerland in 1843 that made products ranging from nut oils to rum. In 1867 he developed a powder made from cow's milk and wheat flour as a substitute for mother's milk. A year earlier Americans Charles and George Page had founded the Anglo-Swiss Condensed Milk Company in Cham Switzerland using Gail Borden's milk-canning technology.

In 1875 Nestle sold his eponymous company then doing business in 16 countries. When Anglo-Swiss launched a milk-based infant food in 1878 Nestle's new owners responded by introducing a condensed-milk product. In 1905 a year after Nestle began selling chocolate the companies ended their rivalry by merging under the Nestle name.

Hampered by limited milk supplies during WWI the company expanded into regions less affected by the war such as the US. In 1929 it acquired Cailler the first company to mass-produce chocolate bars and Swiss General inventor of milk chocolate.

An investment in a Brazilian condensed-milk factory during the 1920s paid an unexpected dividend when Brazilian coffee growers suggested the company develop a water-soluble "coffee cube." Released in 1938 Nescafe instant coffee quickly became popular.

Other new products included Nestle's Crunch bar (1938) Quik drink mix (1948) and Taster's Choice instant coffee (1966). Nestle expanded during the 1970s with acquisitions such as Beringer Brothers wines (sold in 1995) Stouffer's and Libby's.

Moving beyond foods in 1974 Nestle acquired a 49% stake in Gesparal a holding company that controls the French cosmetics company L'Oreal. It acquired pharmaceutical firm Alcon Laboratories three years later.

Helmut Maucher was named chairman and CEO in 1981. He began beefing up Nestle's global presence. Boycotters had long accused Nestle of harming children in developing countries through the unethical promotion of infant formula and Maucher acknowledged the ongoing boycott by meeting with the critics and setting up a commission to police adherence to World Health Organization guidelines.

Nestle bought Carnation in 1985. Maucher doubled the company's chocolate business in 1988 with the purchase of UK chocolate maker Rowntree (Kit Kat). Also in the 1980s Nestle acquired Buitoni pastas.

The company expanded in the 1990s with the purchases of Butterfinger and Baby Ruth candies Source Perrier water Alpo pet food and Ortega Mexican foods. Company veteran Peter Brabeck-Letmathe succeeded Maucher as CEO in 1997. He cleaned out Nestle's pantry by selling non-core businesses (Contadina tomato products Libby's canned meat products) but restocked with San Pellegrino (mineral water) and Dalgety's Spillers (pet food) in 1998.

By 1999 the company started rolling out its Nestle Pure Life bottled water. It also sold its Findus brand (fish vegetables) and its non-instant US coffee brands. That year Nestle merged its US novelty ice-cream unit with operations of Pillsbury's Häagen-Dazs to form Ice Cream Partners USA. In 2000 Nestle purchased snack maker PowerBar. In 2001 it bought Ralston Purina for $10.3 billion making it the world's largest pet food maker. To win FTC approval the companies agreed to sell Meow Mix and Alley Cat dry cat food brands to Hartz Mountain. In a deal that gives Nestle a 99-year license to use the Häagen-Dazs brand in the US the company agreed to pay $641 million to General Mills (which has bought Pillsbury from Britain's Diageo) for the other half of Ice Cream Partners.

In 2002 Nestle acquired German ice-cream maker Schoeller Holding Group as well as US food company Chef America maker of Hot Pockets and Lean Pockets. That same year Nestle also spun off eyecare subsidiary Alcon Laboratories but retained about 75% ownership of it. The company renamed its water unit from Perrier Vittel SA to Nestle Waters and bought Russian bottled water company Saint Springs. The company sold its savory flavor business Food Ingredients Specialties (FIS) to Swiss flavoring company Givaudan and its UK and Ireland ambient foods business to HM Capital Partners (then named Hicks Muse Tate & Furst). It also formed a joint venture with New Zealand dairy co-op Fonterra to produce and distribute dairy products in the Americas.

Nestle and Cadbury Schweppes (now Cadbury) made a joint $10.5 billion bid for The Hershey Company in 2002 but Hershey called the sale off later that year.

While Nestle already owned 30% of US ice cream powerhouse Dreyer's in 2002 it proposed a merger of its US ice cream businesses. After months of antitrust scrutiny the final deal gave Nestle 67% of Dreyer's.

Seeking to further strengthen its position in the worldwide ice cream market Nestle acquired the ice cream and related products of M¶venpick a Swiss food company 2003. The acquisition brought Nestle licensing agreements with companies in Egypt Finland Germany Norway Sweden and Saudi Arabia.

Other transactions in 2003 included the Nestle USA unit selling its Ortega brand Mexican food products to B&G Foods and the parent company selling Mont Blanc France's leading dessert brand to French investment firm Activa Capital. Also that year the company added to its bottled-water business by acquiring Hutchison Whampoa's Powwow which operates in Denmark France Germany Italy the Netherlands Portugal and the UK. In addition it acquired Clear Water a bottled-water home-and-office delivery company located in Russia.

In line with its strategy to concentrate on value-added products in 2004 Nestle sold its cocoa-processing facilities in Germany and the UK to Cargill. Also in 2004 the company acquired Finnish dairy company Valid's Valioj¤¤tel¶ ice cream business and increased its stake in Israeli bakery company Osem to 53%. In addition Nestle sold its German frozen food distributor Eastman that year and Nestle España bought Nestle Portugal for about $682 million. Nestle was ordered by the Brazilian government to sell its Chocolates Garoto in 2004 on the grounds that ownership of Garoto presented unfair market competition.

Later that same year CEO Peter Brabeck-Letmathe announced he was considering reducing the number of outside directorships that he held because of increased demands as the leader of Nestle. At the time Brabeck-Letmathe sat on the boards of Alcon Credit Suisse Dreyer's Grand Ice Cream L'Oreal Roche Holding and "Winterthur" Swiss Insurance Company. (He has since left the "Winterthur" board.) And that year in a tangle with a French union over retirement benefits Nestle threatened to sell Perrier or produce its popular water from another source. However the company reached a settlement with the union and the production of Perrier continued.

Long-time chairman Rainer Gut retired in 2005 and Brabeck-Letmathe replaced him.

In 2005 it became a 90% owner of Dreyer's Grand Ice Cream. The next year Nestle became the owner of more than 90% of Dreyer's as the result of an exercise of a Put Right whereby Nestle was required to purchase certain shareholders' Class A Callable Puttable Common Stock (or Class A shares). As a result of this "short form merger" Dreyer's ceased trading on the Nasdaq stock exchange.

In keeping with its strategy to concentrate on value-added products during 2006 Nestle sold its cocoa processing facilities in Germany and the UK to Cargill. Adding to its dominance in the European ice cream sector the company acquired Finnish dairy company Valid¤ Valioj¤¤tel¶'s ice cream business and Greece's Delta Ice cream which has operations in Bulgaria Greece Macedonia Montenegro Romania and Serbia. Later that year Nestle bought the Australian breakfast cereal snack and soup operations of Uncle Tobys from Burns Philp for $670 million. The cereal portion was integrated into Cereal Partners Worldwide. In another streamlining move the company agreed to sell its canned liquid milk businesses in Southeast Asia to Singapore-based Fraser and Neave.

Hedging its bets considering its food products (candy bars ice cream) are on the opposite end of the waistline wars Nestle acquired Jenny Craig for $600 million in 2006.

In 2007 the company purchased the medical-nutrition business of Novartis for ?1.88 billion ($2.5 billion). The business which has operations in 40 countries worldwide makes food for hospital patients. The purchase was seen as a move by Nestle to concentrate on higher-margin products. Brands in the acquisition included Boost and Resource nutritional supplements and Optifast dieting products. Nestle divested some operations in France and Spain in order to settle competitive concerns surrounding the deal voiced by the European Commission.

On the food front Nestle subsidiary Dreyer's purchased the Eskimo Pie and Chipwich brands from Canadian ice cream maker CoolBrands in 2007 for almost $19 million.

Nestle spooned out $5.5 billion in cash to purchase Gerber Products from Novartis in 2007. The deal made Nestle the world's largest baby food company.

Due to the increased workload as chairman Peter Brabeck-Letmathe stepped down as CEO in 2008; he remained in an active role as board chairman. Paul Bulcke former head of Zone Americas for Nestle replaced Brabeck-Letmathe as CEO.

The company it added to its "out of home food and beverage" operations (i.e. foodservice) in 2009 with the purchase of Tampa-based Vitality Food-service. Vitality provides commercial and non-commercial beverage services worldwide.

In August 2010 Nestle acquired Liverpool-based Vitaflo a maker of clinical nutrition products for people with metabolic disorders. Also in August it completed the sale of Alcon to Novartis. The pharmaceutical maker acquired Nestle's stake in Alcon in two steps beginning with the sale of a 25% stake for $11 billion in July 2008. Novartis exercised its option to buy Nestle's remaining percentage of Alcon for $28 billion in 2010.

In November 2011 Nestle acquired the Oscar stocks and sauces business from Paulig Group building Nestle Professional's presence in the culinary flavors sector. In late 2011 Nestle paid $2.1 billion for a 60% interest in China-based confectionery Hsu Fu Chi. The deal put Nestle at the helm of China's second-largest confectionery and the purchase ranked as one of the largest foreign takeovers of a Chinese company.

In 2012 Nestle made a historic $11.8 billion acquisition of Pfizer's nutrition business. The milestone deal enhanced Nestle's infant nutrition business in key segments and geographies.

In July 2014 Nestle acquired L'Oreal's 50% stake in Galderma a joint venture formed by the two companies in 1981. Going forward Galderma will operate as the pharmaceutical arm of Nestle Skin Health S.A. established in June 2014 as a fully-owned Nestle subsidiary.

EXECUTIVES

Executive Vice President and Chief Executive Officer, Zone Americas, Laurent Freixe
Chairman, Paul Bulcke, $638,857 total compensation
Senior Vice President, Corporate Governance, Compliance and Corporate Services, Secretary to the Board, David Frick
Executive Vice President and Chief Financial Officer, Francois-Xavier Roger
Executive Vice President and Head of Operations, Magdi Batato
Executive Vice President and Global Head Human Resources & Business Services, Beatrice Guillaume-Grabisch
Deputy Executive Vice President and Head of Group Strategy Business Development, Sanjay Bahadur
Member of the Executive Board, Executive Vice President, Chief Executive Officer - Zone Greater China, David Zhang
Executive Vice President and Head of Strategic Business Units and Marketing Sales, Patrice Bula
Executive Vice President and Chief Executive Officer, Zone Europe, Marco Settembri
Chief Executive Officer, Mark Schneider, $2,555,431 total compensation
Member of the Executive Board, Executive Vice President, Chief Executive Officer - Zone North America, Steve Presley
Executive Vice President and Chief Technology Officer, Stefan Palzer
Deputy Executive Vice President and Chief Executive Officer, Nestle Health Science, Gregory Behar
Executive Vice President and General Counsel, Corporate Governance and Compliance, Leanne Geale
Chairman and Chief Executive Officer, Nestlé Middle East and North Africa, Remy Ejel
Auditors: Ernst & Young Ltd

LOCATIONS

HQ: Nestle SA
Avenue Nestle 55, Vevey, Vaud CH-1800
Phone: (41) 21 924 2111   **Fax:** (41) 21 924 4800
Web: www.nestle.com

2018 sales

	% of total
Americas	45
EMENA	29
Zone Asia Oceania and Africa	26
Total	**100**

2018 Factories

	No.
Americas	159
EMENA	146
Asia Oceania & Africa	108
Total	**413**

PRODUCTS/OPERATIONS

2018 Product Sales

	% of total
Powdered & liquid beverages	24
Nutrition & health care	18
Milk products & ice cream	14
Prepared dishes & cooking aids	14
Pet care	13
Confectionery	9
Water	8
Total	**100**

Selected Products and Brands

Bouillons soups seasonings pasta and sauces
  Buitoni
  Maggi
  Thomy
  Winiary
Chilled Nestlé;
  Chiquitin
  La Laitière
  La Lechera
  LC1
  Molico
  Ski
  Sveltesse
  Svelty
  Yoco
Chocolate confectionery and biscuits
  Kit Kat
Coffee
  Bonka
  Loumidis
  Nescafé;
  Nespresso
  Ricoré; Ricoffy
  Taster's Choice
  Zoé;gas
Foodservice and professional products
  Chef
  Davigel
  Minor's
  Santa Rica
Frozen foods (prepared dishes pizzas)
  Buitoni
  California Pizza Kitchen (licensed)
  Delissio (Canada only)
  Hot Pockets
  Jack's Pizza
  Lean Cuisine
  Maggi
  Stouffer's
  Tombstone
Healthcare and nutrition
  Clinutren
  Modulen
  Nutren
  Peptamen
Ice cream
  Antica Gelateria del Corso
  Chipwich
  Dreyer's
  Drumstick/Extrême
  Edy's
  Eskimo Pie
  Häagen-Dazs
  Maxibon/Tandem

Mega
Mövenpick
Parar
Sin Parar/Sem
Infant food and nutrition
  Beba
  Cé;ré;lac
  Gerber
  Good Start
  Guigoz
  Lactogen
  Nan
  Neslac
  Nestlé;
  Nestogen
  Nestum
Other beverages
  Carnation
  Caro
  Libby's
  Milo
  Nescau
  Nesquik
  Nestea
Performance nutrition
  PowerBar
  Pria
Pet care
  Alpo
  Beneful
  Cat Chow
  Dog Chow
  Fancy Feast
  Felix
  Gourmet
  Pro Plan
  Purina Friskies
  Purina ONE
  Tidy Cats
Refrigerated products (cold meat products dough pasta pizzas sauces)
  Buitoni
  Herta
  Nestlé;
  Toll House
Shelf-stable products
  Bear Brand
  Carnation
  Coffee-Mate
  Gloria
  Klim
  La Lechera
  Milkmaid
  Moça
  Molico
  Nestlé; Omega
  Nido
  Ninho
  Svelty
Water
  Acqua Panna
  Al Manhal
  Arrowhead
  Contrex
  Deer Park
  Hé;par
  Ice Mountain
  Levissima
  Nestlé; Aquarel
  Nestlé; Pure Life
  Nestlé; Vera
  Ozarka
  Perrier
  Poland Spring
  Qué;zac
  S.Pellegrino
  San Bernardo
  Vittel
  Zephyrhills

Selected Subsidiaries Joint Ventures and Affiliates

Beverage Partners Worldwide (50% with The Coca-Cola Company US)
Cereal Partners Worldwide (50% with General Mills US)
Galderma and Laboratoires inné;ov (29% with L'Oreal cosmetic and nutritional supplement products)
Gerber Products Company (infant nutrition US)
Jenny Craig Inc. (weight-loss centers and foods US)
Uncle Tobys (soups breakfast cereal snacks Australia)

COMPETITORS

Anheuser-Busch InBev	GROUPE LACTALIS
BUNZL PUBLIC LIMITED	H & M Hennes & Mauritz
COMPANY	AB
Bakkavor Group ehf.	Huhtam oki Oyj
DANONE	MONDELEZ INTERNATIONAL
GENERAL MILLS INC.	INC.
GREEN & BLACK'S	Svenska Cellulosa AB
LIMITED	SCA

HISTORICAL FINANCIALS

Company Type: Public

Income Statement — FYE: December 31

	REVENUE ($ mil.)	NET INCOME ($ mil.)	NET PROFIT MARGIN	EMPLOYEES
12/20	96,148	13,888	14.4%	273,000
12/19	96,064	13,043	13.6%	291,000
12/18	93,269	10,302	11.0%	308,000
12/17	92,340	7,359	8.0%	323,000
12/16	88,206	8,380	9.5%	328,000
Annual Growth	2.2%	13.5%	—	(4.5%)

2020 Year-End Financials

Debt ratio: 34.0%	No. of shares (mil.): —
Return on equity: 24.9%	Dividends
Cash ($ mil.): 9,774	Yield: 2.3%
Current ratio: 0.86	Payout: 62.8%
Long-term debt ($ mil.): 28,554	Market value ($ mil.): —

	STOCK PRICE ($) FY Close	P/E High/Low	PER SHARE ($) Earnings	Dividends	Book Value
12/20	117.80	30 23	4.87	2.77	18.42
12/19	108.26	27 19	4.45	2.42	18.69
12/18	80.96	26 22	3.42	2.42	19.60
12/17	85.97	38 32	2.38	2.35	20.61
12/16	71.74	28 24	2.70	2.18	20.48
Annual Growth	13.2%	— —	15.9%	6.2%	(2.6%)

New China Life Insurance Co Ltd

Auditors: Ernst & Young Hua Ming LLP

LOCATIONS

HQ: New China Life Insurance Co Ltd
NCI Tower, A12 Jianguomenwai Avenue, Chaoyang
District, Beijing 100022
Phone: (86) 10 85213233   **Fax:** (86) 10 85213219
Web: www.newchinalife.com

HISTORICAL FINANCIALS

Company Type: Public

Income Statement — FYE: December 31

	REVENUE ($ mil.)	NET INCOME ($ mil.)	NET PROFIT MARGIN	EMPLOYEES
12/20	31,579	2,185	6.9%	0
12/19	25,087	2,092	8.3%	0
12/18	22,413	1,151	5.1%	0
12/17	16,585	827	5.0%	0
12/15	24,242	1,324	5.5%	52,474
Annual Growth	5.4%	10.5%	—	—

2020 Year-End Financials

Debt ratio: —	No. of shares (mil.): —
Return on equity: 15.3%	Dividends
Cash ($ mil.): 1,988	Yield: —
Current ratio: 0.06	Payout: —
Long-term debt ($ mil.): —	Market value ($ mil.): —

New Hope Liuhe Co Ltd

EXECUTIVES

Independent Director, Manli Cai
Chief Financial Officer, Vice President, Xingyao Chen
Chairman of the Board, Chang Liu
Independent Director, Feng Deng
Director, Hang Wang
Chief Investment Development Officer, Pusong Wang
Director, Yonghao Liu
Director, Jianxiong Li
Independent Director, Huanchun Chen
Vice President, Yuling Tao
Vice President, Chongxing Ji
Executive Chairman of the Board, President, Minggui Zhang
Chief Investment Officer, Secretary of the Board, Jia Lan
President Assistant, Liqiang Zhu
Auditors: Sichuan Huaxin (Group) CPA Firm

LOCATIONS

HQ: New Hope Liuhe Co Ltd
No. 376, Jinshi Road, Jinjiang Industrial Park,
Chengdu, Sichuan Province 610023
Phone: (86) 28 82000876   **Fax:** (86) 28 85950022
Web: www.newhopeagri.com

HISTORICAL FINANCIALS

Company Type: Public

Income Statement — FYE: December 31

	REVENUE ($ mil.)	NET INCOME ($ mil.)	NET PROFIT MARGIN	EMPLOYEES
12/20	16,792	755	4.5%	0
12/19	11,791	724	6.1%	0
12/18	10,040	247	2.5%	0
12/17	9,614	350	3.6%	0
12/16	8,767	355	4.1%	0
Annual Growth	17.6%	20.8%		

2020 Year-End Financials

Debt ratio: 5.3%	No. of shares (mil.): —
Return on equity: 14.9%	Dividends
Cash ($ mil.): 1,345	Yield: —
Current ratio: 0.91	Payout: —
Long-term debt ($ mil.): 3,931	Market value ($ mil.): —

Nidec Corp

Nidec claims to be the #1 comprehensive motor manufacturer for everything that spins and moves from the smallest motors to some of the largest. Based in Japan the company holds the largest global market share for the automotive motors such as electric power steering motors and brake motors. It is primarily engage in the development manufacturing and sales of small precision motors automotive motors home appliance motors commercial and industrial motors motors for machinery electronic and optical components and other related products. China is the company's largest markets with around 25% of sales. Other major markets include the US Japan Thailand and Germany. Nidec was founded in 1973 by Shigenobu Nagamori and three other engineers as Nippon Densan Corporation.

Operations

The company operates in eight segments: ACIM (around 30% of sales) SPMS (over 20%) AMEC (some 10%) Nidec Sankyo (about 10%) Nidec Techno Motor (some 5%) Nidec Mobility (approximately 5%) Nidec Shimpo (roughly 5%) and Other (about 15%).

The ACIM segment mainly conducts research and development of motors gears and control units for residential commercial home appliance and industrial uses with respect to vehicle driving motors encoders elevator components and systems for industrial automation.

In the SPMS segment research and development activities are currently conducted basic and applied research on precision small motors in general such as precision small DC motors and fan motors research and development for new products and research to provide technical support to other research bases.

The AMEC segment is engaged in R&D aimed at the mass production of new products and new models of various invehicle motors including those for driving electric vehicles (EVs) which will contribute to the realization of a decarbonized society and at the improvement of product quality.

The Nidec Sankyo segment develops stepping motors smartphone/game-related products motor drive unit products and system device-related products as part of its line-up of "karakuri-tronics" products integrating its "karakuri" or internal device mechanism technologies with the motor technologies and servo technologies developed through its business diversification.

The Nidec Techno Motor segment develops air conditioner and home appliance motors in Fukui Prefecture in Japan and industrial motors in Fukuoka Prefectures in Japan.

The Nidec Mobility segment has development and design functions in six countries based on its automotive body control business and power electronics business. In the Body Control Business it mainly develops body control modules door peripheral control units including power window switches and smart systems for motorcycles. In the Power Electronics Business it mainly develops electric power steering DC/DC converters for electric vehicles and in-vehicle chargers.

In the Nidec Shimpo segment it is developing products for reduction engines using integrated mechanical and electrical technologies in Japan China and Germany.

In the Others segment research and development activities are currently conducted on automotive products machinery electronic components and other small precision motors and others.

Among its products appliance commercial and industrial products account for over 35% of sales followed by small precision motors with nearly 30% automotive products with over 20% machinery with about 10% and electronic and optical components with nearly 5%.

Geographic Reach

Headquartered in Shiga Japan the company's largest single market is China which accounts for around 25% of sales. The sales from the US accounts for around 20% Japan with over 15% Thailand with about 10% Germany and Singapore with roughly 10% combined and the rest were generated from other countries.

Financial Performance

Consolidated net sales for fiscal 2021 from continuing operations increased 5% to 1.6 trillion for this fiscal year compared to the previous fiscal year recording the highest annual net sales by engaging in new demands one after another in the areas of home appliances IT game consoles and so on. In addition to the increase in sales by engaging in new demands as mentioned NIDEC executed manufacturing cost improvement and fixed cost rationalization through WPR4 project.

Profit attributable to owners of the parent increased 109% to 122.0 billion due to significant increase from continuing operations and decrease in net loss from discontinued operations related to the business transfer in the previous fiscal year.

Cash held by the company at the end of fiscal 2021 increased to 219.5 billion. Cash provided by operations was 219.2 billion while investing and financing activities used 100.6 billion and 136.2 billion respectively. Main cash uses were additions to property plant and equipment; and repayments of long term debt.

Strategy

NIDEC aims to ride five innovative waves. The five fields of "automotive electrification" "expansion of robot applications" "home appliances driven by brushless DC motors" "manpower-saving in agriculture & logistics" and "nextgeneration technologies arising from 5G communications" which are strongly demanded to solve the global issues such as carbon dioxide emissions road accidents and aging of population are promising growth markets. NIDEC will concentrate management resources in these fields. By combining M&As with the elemental technology NIDEC has accumulated NIDEC will control all five innovative waves and contribute to sustainable development of the world.

Mergers and Acquisitions

In early 2021 Nidec Corporation has completed the acquisitions of the shares of Japan-based Mitsubishi Heavy Industries Machine Tool Co. Ltd. a company that designs manufactures and sells machine tools cutting tools and related products from Mitsubishi Heavy Industries Ltd.; all the Mitsubishi Heavy Industries Group-owned shares of three overseas subsidiaries located in China India and the US that specialized in machine tool business; and the machine tool business run by overseas subsidiaries. The acquisition of machine tool business achieves a mutual complement with its existing businesses. Synergies are expected particularly in the machinery business element technology development manufacturing sales and other areas of its group's businesses. Terms were not disclosed.

In early 2020 Nidec Corporation has signed a definitive agreement with Austria-based Secop Austria GmbH (Secop) by which Nidec will acquire the Delta production line from Secop through the Company's sub-subsidiary Nidec Global Appliance Italy S.r.l. and its Austrian company. With this transaction Nidec and Secop aim to preserve as many jobs as possible at the site in F rstenfeld Austria. Terms were not disclosed.

HISTORY

A top engineer at tape deck manufacturer TEAC and machine tool maker Yamashina Siki in the early 1970s Shigenobu Nagamori had developed a reputation as a brilliant engineer but also as a young gun who was resistant to conformity and too indulged in personal challenges. Nagamori wasted no time in fulfilling his childhood dream of owning his own business. He lured away three engineers to start Nippon Densan Corporation (Nidec) out of his own home in 1973 when he was 29.

Nagamori knew he would have trouble selling his motors in Japan without an established reputation. (Most small businesses in Japan are founded with the acceptance that they will never grow beyond the role of subcontractor to one of the country's giant corporations.) But inspired by ancient Japanese traditions of self-determination and individualism Nagamori decided to bypass the modern power structure and pitch his products overseas in the US. He arrived unannounced at 3M with a suitcase full of tiny motors. Despite his nervous presentation 3M was impressed with the quality of Nidec motors and placed a small order.

In 1976 Nagamori established Nidec America Corporation to foster growing business in the US. The initial contract with 3M had ballooned into regular orders for thousands of motors which 3M used in its high-speed cassette duplicators.

Still unable to secure a business loan in Japan Nidec's staff took voluntary pay cuts to stay in business. (3M later offered a letter of credit on Nidec's behalf forcing Japanese banks to reconsider.) Nagamori struggled to retain employees who sought stability that only established companies such as NEC or Hitachi could provide. But Nagamori constantly improved his motors which opened doors into new markets (computer disk drives) and kept the business alive.

EXECUTIVES

Executive Officer, Senior Director of Sales in Precision Motor Business, Chairman, President, CEO of Subsidiaries, Kenji Ito
Independent Director, Osamu Shimizu
Independent Director, Takako Sakai
Independent Director, Takeshi Nakane
Director, Kazuya Murakami
Executive President, Chief Executive Officer, Chairman of Subsidiaries, Representative Director, Jun Seki
Vice Chairman of the Executive Board, Chief Sales Officer, Chairman of Subsidiary, Hiroshi Kobe
Chairman of the Board, Chairman of Subsidiaries, Representative Director, Shigenobu Nagamori
Managing Executive Officer, Deputy Chief Director of Small Precision Motor Business, Chairman of Subsidiaries, Kuniyasu Tampo
Executive Vice President, Chief Director of Small Precision Motor Business, Chairman of Subsidiaries, Toshihiko Miyabe
Director, Hiroyuki Ochiai
Senior Managing Executive Officer, Chief Director of Automotive Business, Director of 1st Automotive Business, Chairman of Subsidiary, Kazuya Hayafune
Senior Managing Executive Officer, Yoshihisa Kitao
Managing Executive Officer, Director of Second Automotive Business, Chairman of Subsidiaries, Hideki Nishimura
Independent Director, Teiichi Sato
Auditors: PricewaterhouseCoopers Kyoto

LOCATIONS

HQ: Nidec Corp
338 Kuzetonoshiro-cho, Minami-ku, Kyoto 601-8205
Phone: (81) 75 935 6200   **Fax:** (81) 75 935 6101
Web: www.nidec.com

2018 Sales

	% of total
China	23
Japan	20
US	17
Thailand	9
Germany	9
Singapore	3
Other countries	19
Total	**100**

PRODUCTS/OPERATIONS

2018 Sales

	% of total
Nidec Motor	23
Nidec Motor & Actuators	16
Nidec Corporation	11
Nidec Sankyo	8
Nidec (H.K.)	7
Nidec Electronics (Thailand)	6
Nidec Techno Motor	5
Nidec Singapore	2
Nidec Copal	2
All Others	20
Total	**100**

2018 Sales

	% of total
Appliance commercial and industrial products	35
Small precision motors	29
Automotive products	19
Machinery	12
Electronic and optical components	5
Other	-
Total	**0**

Selected Products

Mid-size DC motors
Pivot assemblies
Power supplies
Small high-precision AC motors
Small high-precision DC motors
Small high-precision fans

COMPETITORS

ALPS ALPINE CO. LTD.
APC TECHNOLOGY GROUP PLC
BARNES GROUP INC.
DELTA ELECTRONICS INC.
DEWHURST PLC
Doosan Corporation
D rr AG
ENERPAC TOOL GROUP CORP.
GENERAC HOLDINGS INC.
GKN LIMITED
Infineon Technologies AG
MOLEX LLC
NITTO DENKO CORPORATION
Nordex SE
Outokumpu Oyj
PULSE ELECTRONICS CORPORATION
REGAL REXNORD CORPORATION
RENESAS ELECTRONICS AMERICA INC.
SPECTRIS PLC
TOWER INTERNATIONAL INC.
ULTRALIFE CORPORATION
VICOR CORPORATION
ZAP

HISTORICAL FINANCIALS

Company Type: Public

Income Statement

	REVENUE ($ mil.)	NET INCOME ($ mil.)	NET PROFIT MARGIN	EMPLOYEES
FYE: March 31				
03/21	14,613	1,101	7.5%	136,186
03/20	14,139	553	3.9%	145,169
03/19	13,710	1,000	7.3%	137,791
03/18	14,013	1,237	8.8%	135,211
03/17	10,726	999	9.3%	132,766
Annual Growth	**8.0%**	**2.5%**	**—**	**0.6%**

2021 Year-End Financials

Debt ratio: 0.2%	No. of shares (mil.): 585
Return on equity: 11.9%	Dividends
Cash ($ mil.): 1,982	Yield: 0.6%
Current ratio: 1.63	Payout: —
Long-term debt ($ mil.): 3,837	Market value ($ mil.): 17,940

	STOCK PRICE ($) FY Close	P/E High/Low		PER SHARE ($) Earnings	Dividends	Book Value
03/21	30.62	0	0	1.88	0.21	16.90
03/20	26.34	0	0	0.94	0.25	14.93
03/19	31.88	0	0	1.70	0.11	15.30
03/18	38.54	0	0	2.09	0.11	14.85
03/17	23.92	0	0	1.68	0.18	12.78
Annual Growth	**6.4%**	**—**	**—**	**2.8%**	**4.2%**	**7.2%**

Nintendo Co., Ltd.

Nintendo wants everyone — from apprentice Marios to alpha Donkey Kongs — to play preferably on one of its Nintendo DS handheld devices or its Wii home video game console. The market-leading game company achieved its status in part by courting users that span generations and skill levels. Among the Big Three of the videogame console makers Nintendo's Wii (pronounced "we") is #1 battling with Microsoft's Xbox and Sony's PlayStation for the hearts and dollars of devoted gamers. Also leading in handheld consoles its DS device began in 2004 the most recent incarnation its no-glasses 3-D version launched in 2011 the 3DS. Wii successor Wii U featuring a controller with a touch screen is planned for 2012.

HISTORY

Nintendo Co. was founded in 1889 as the Marufuku Company to make and sell hanafuda Japanese game cards. In 1907 the company began producing Western playing cards. It became the Nintendo Playing Card Company in 1951 and began making theme cards under a licensing agreement with Disney in 1959.

During the 1950s and 1960s Hiroshi Yamauchi took the company public and diversified into new areas (including a "love hotel"). The company took its current name in 1963. Nintendo began making toys at the start of the 1970s and entered the budding field of video games toward the end of the decade by licensing Magnavox's Pong technology. Then it moved into arcade games. Nintendo established its US subsidiary Nintendo of America in 1980; its first hit was Donkey Kong ("silly monkey") and its next was Super Mario Bros. (named after Nintendo of America's warehouse landlord).

The company released Famicom a technologically advanced home video game system in Japan in 1983. With its high-quality sound and graphics Famicom was a smash selling 15.2 million consoles and more than 183 million game cartridges in Japan alone. Meanwhile in 1983 and 1984 the US home game market crashed sending pioneer Atari up in flames. Nintendo persevered successfully launching Famicom in the US in 1986 as the Nintendo Entertainment System (NES).

To prevent a barrage of independently produced low-quality software (which had contributed to Atari's demise) Nintendo established stringent licensing policies for its software developers. Licensees were required to have approval of every game design buy the blank cartridges from the company agree not to make the game for any of Nintendo's competitors and pay Nintendo royalties for the honor of developing a game.

As the market became saturated Nintendo sought new products releasing Game Boy in 1989 and the Super Family Computer game system (Super NES in the US) in 1991. The company broke with tradition in 1994 by making design alliances with companies like Silicon Graphics. After creating a 32-bit product in 1995 Nintendo launched the much-touted N64 game system in 1996. It also teamed with Microsoft and Nomura Research Institute on a satellite-delivered Internet system for Japan. Price wars between the top contenders continued in the US and Japan.

In 1998 Nintendo released Pokemon which involves trading and training virtual monsters (it had been popular in Japan since 1996) in the US. The company also launched the video game The Legend of Zelda: Ocarina of Time which sold 2.5 million units in about six weeks. Nintendo issued 50 new games for 1998 compared to Sony's 131.

Nintendo announced in 1999 that its next-generation game system Dolphin (later renamed GameCube) would use IBM's PowerPC microprocessor and Matsushita's (now Panasonic) DVD players.

The company bought a 3% stake in convenience store operator LAWSON in early 2000 in hopes of using its online operations to sell video games. Nintendo also teamed with advertising agency Dentsu to form ND Cube a joint company that develops game software for mobile phones and portable machines.

In September 2001 Nintendo launched its long-awaited GameCube console system (which retailed at $100 less than its console rivals Sony's PlayStation 2 and Microsoft's XBox); the system debuted in North America in November. In addition the company came out with Game Boy Advance its newest handheld model with a bigger screen and faster chip.

In April 2003 the company cut its royalty rates (charged to outside game developers) in an effort to enhance its video game titles portfolio. Later in the year Nintendo bought a stake (about 3%) in game developer and toy maker Bandai a move expected to solidify cooperation between the two companies in marketing game software.

As part of its concentration on games the company spun off its video game quality assurance division in 2009.

EXECUTIVES

Representative Director, Shigeru Miyamoto
Independent Director, Asa Shinkawa
Independent Director, Chris Meledandri
President, Representative Director, Shuntaro Furukawa
Senior Executive Officer, Chief Director of Technology Development, Director, Ko Shiota
Senior Executive Officer, Chief Director of Manufacturing, Hirokazu Shinshi
Independent Director, Masao Yamazaki
Senior Executive Officer, Chief Director of Sales, Chief Director of Operation, Director, Satoru Shibata
Independent Director, Katsuhiro Umeyama
Senior Managing Executive Officer, Chief Director of Planning & Production, Director, Shinya Takahashi
Director, Naoki Noguchi
Senior Executive Officer, President of Subsidiary, Satoshi Yamato
Auditors: PricewaterhouseCoopers Kyoto

LOCATIONS

HQ: Nintendo Co., Ltd.
11-1 Kamitoba Hokotate-cho, Minami-ku, Kyoto 601-8501
Phone: (81) 75 662 9600
Web: www.nintendo.co.jp

2012 Sales

	% of total
The Americas	
US	33
Other Americas	6
Europe	33
Japan	23
Other	5
Total	**100**

PRODUCTS/OPERATIONS

2012 Sales

	% of total
Handheld Hardware	36
Handheld Software	20
Home Console Software	18
Home Console Hardware	18
Other	8
Total	**100**

Selected Consoles

3DS
3DS XL
DS
DS Lite
DSi
DSi XL
Wii
Wii U

Selected Games

Donkey Kong Country Returns
Kid Icarus: Uprising
Kirby Tilt 'n' Tumble
The Legend of Zelda
Mario & Sonic at the London 2012 Olympic Games
Mario Kart
Mario Party
Metroid Prime
Poké;mon
Punch-Out!!
Sin and Punishment: Star Successor
Spider-Man
Super Mario Galaxy
Super Smash Bros. Brawl
Wii Fit Plus
Wii Play
Wii Sports Resort
Xenoblade Chronicles
Yoshi

Selected Subsidiaries

Nintendo Australia Pty. Ltd.
Nintendo Benelux B.V. (The Netherlands)
Nintendo Espóa S.A. (Spain)
Nintendo France S.A.R.L.
Nintendo of America Inc. (US)
Nintendo of Canada Ltd.
Nintendo of Europe GmbH (Germany)

COMPETITORS

ATARI SA
DEDRICKS' ORIGINAL GAME COMPANY INC.
ELECTRONIC ARTS INC.
EVERI GAMES HOLDING INC.
GAMEPLAY (GB) LIMITED
JAKKS PACIFIC INC.

Mad Catz Interactive Inc
PRESSMAN TOY CORPORATION
SEGA CORPORATION
WIZARDS OF THE COAST LLC

HISTORICAL FINANCIALS

Company Type: Public

Income Statement				FYE: March 31
	REVENUE ($ mil.)	NET INCOME ($ mil.)	NET PROFIT MARGIN	EMPLOYEES
03/21	15,885	4,338	27.3%	6,574
03/20	12,054	2,382	19.8%	6,200
03/19	10,840	1,751	16.2%	5,944
03/18	9,941	1,314	13.2%	6,030
03/17	4,374	917	21.0%	5,788
Annual Growth	**38.0%**	**47.5%**	**—**	**3.2%**

2021 Year-End Financials

Debt ratio: —
Return on equity: 28.1%
Cash ($ mil.): 10,703
Current ratio: 3.84
Long-term debt ($ mil.): —

No. of shares (mil.): 119
Dividends
Yield: 2.7%
Payout: —
Market value ($ mil.): 8,434

	STOCK PRICE ($) FY Close	P/E High/Low		PER SHARE ($) Earnings	Dividends	Book Value
03/21	70.80	0	0	36.42	1.92	142.11
03/20	48.28	0	0	20.00	1.05	119.15
03/19	35.87	0	0	14.59	0.74	106.86
03/18	55.51	0	0	10.95	0.64	103.41
03/17	29.02	0	0	7.64	0.18	93.13
Annual Growth	**25.0%**			**47.8%**	**81.7%**	**11.1%**

Nippon Express Holdings Inc

One of Japan's largest transportation companies Nippon Express moves all sorts of freight. The company's largest business motor transportation operates under brands including Arrow. Besides general freight transportation Nippon Express offers moving services and transportation of items such as cash and construction equipment. Nippon Express also provides warehousing services and air ocean and rail freight forwarding. The company operates from facilities throughout Japan which accounts for the vast majority of its sales and in more than 45 other countries around the world. Founded in 1937 Nippon Express also sells petroleum products and leases containers.

Operations

The company operates four segment reportable segments: Logistics Logistic Support Security Transportation and Heavy Haulage & Construction.

The Nippon Express' logistics segment has grown as transport modes have expanded from railways to automobiles ships and airplanes. It generates about 75% of total revenue.

Logistic Support segment generates some 20% of total revenue includes the sale e of distribution equipment wrapping and packaging materials vehicles petroleum liquefied petroleum (LP) gas etc. lease vehicle maintenance insurance agency mediation planning designing and management of real estate investigation and research logistics finance automobile driving instruction employee dispatching.

Security Transportation include security guard and motor cargo transportation. Heavy Haulage & Construction includes heavy haulage and construction. Each of which accounts to less than 5% of Nippon Express' revenue.

Geographic Reach

The company operates in Japan the Americas and Europe and stretching into the rapidly developing markets of East Asia South Asia and Oceania. It maintains a global presence with about 740 locations in nearly 320 cities spanning about 45 countries.

Financial Performance

The company's revenue posted grew over the past years but recorded a slight decline in 2020 and 2021. It's net income has fluctuated over the last five years.

Revenues in 2020 decreased by 1.1 billion or 0.1% year on year to 2.1 trillion. The main component of the decrease in revenues was a drop in 3.8 billion because of the COVID-19 pandemic.

The increase in profit before income taxes amounted to 84.8 billion with income taxes residents and enterprise taxes income taxes-deferred and profit attributable to owners of parent factoring in current net income attributable to non-controlling interests coming to 56.1 billion up 38.6 billion or 222.3% year-on-year.

Cash held by the company at the end of 2020 increased by 72.1 billion to 168.3 billion from 96.2 billion in the prior year. Cash provided by operation was 146.6 billion while cash used for financing activities was 23.5 million. Cash used for investing activities was 49.3 billion primarily for payment for purchase of property and equipment.

Strategy

The Nippon Express Group Business Plan 2023 ~"Dynamic Growth"~ which covers the period from fiscal 2019 to fiscal 2023 was formulated with the idea of answering the question of what the Nippon Express Group wanted to be as it approached the 100th anniversary of its founding in 2037. The plan also established the goal of being "a logistics company with a strong presence in the global market" as its long-term vision. The image for growth targets sales in fiscal 2037 of about 4.0 trillion and an overseas sales ratio of 50% equating to overseas sales of roughly 2.0 trillion.

The Nippon Express Group Business Plan 2023 ~"Dynamic Growth"~ includes: Defines a three-dimensional (Customer (Industry) Business and Area) approach as a growth strategy for its core business; Defines a realization of the high profitability to build the base of the company's growth strategy as a strategy to enhance domestic businesses in Japan; Defines M&A as an inorganic growth strategy to reinforce and expand its global management base; and Establishes ESG-oriented business management to realize sustainable development (e.g. global governance) and improve corporate value.

Auditors: Ernst & Young ShinNihon LLC

LOCATIONS

HQ: Nippon Express Holdings Inc
1-9-3 Higashi-Shimbashi, Minato-ku, Tokyo 105-8322
Phone: (81) 3 6251 1111   **Fax:** 212 758-2595
Web: www.nittsu.co.jp

PRODUCTS/OPERATIONS

2015 Sales

	% of total
Combined business	39
Goods sales	22
Air freight forwarding	11
Marine & harbor transportation	6
Others	22
Total	**100**

Selected Services

Air Freight
Fine Arts Transport
Heavy Haulage
Logistics Design & IT
Marine Transport
Moving Service

COMPETITORS

ARCBEST CORPORATION
BEAVEX INCORPORATED
COVENANT LOGISTICS GROUP INC.
Cosco Shipping Development Company Limited
Crrc Corporation Limited
DHL International GmbH
EXPEDITORS INTERNATIONAL OF WASHINGTON INC.
KINTETSU WORLD EXPRESS INC.
SAIA INC.
SANKYU INC.
TFI International Inc
TOUAX SCA - SGTR - CITE - SGT - CMTE - TAF - SLM TOUAGE INVE
UNITED PARCEL SERVICE INC.
VELOCITY EXPRESS LLC
WHISTL UK LIMITED
ZTO Express Co. Ltd.

HISTORICAL FINANCIALS

Company Type: Public

Income Statement				FYE: March 31
	REVENUE ($ mil.)	NET INCOME ($ mil.)	NET PROFIT MARGIN	EMPLOYEES
03/21	18,778	506	2.7%	87,041
03/20	19,164	160	0.8%	89,024
03/19	19,310	445	2.3%	88,835
03/18	18,790	61	0.3%	86,972
03/17	16,674	326	2.0%	87,765
Annual Growth	3.0%	11.7%	—	(0.2%)

2021 Year-End Financials

Debt ratio: 0.2%	No. of shares (mil.): 91
Return on equity: 10.0%	Dividends
Cash ($ mil.): 1,966	Yield: —
Current ratio: 1.50	Payout: —
Long-term debt ($ mil.): 3,013	Market value ($ mil.): —

Nippon Life Insurance Co. (Japan)

Nippon Life Insurance also known as Nissay is a top life insurer in Japan. The company which has some 14.48 million policyholders uses a door-to-door sales corps and a network of approximately 50000 sales representatives to peddle its traditional insurance products including individual and group life and annuity policies to Japanese consumers. In addition to its life insurance products the company administers pension plans and medical coverage plans and provides asset management services. Through its affiliates and subsidiaries the company also sells auto and other property/casualty insurance in Japan and it has some international life insurance operations as well as select real estate and financial service assets.

Operations

Nippon Life generates about 65% of its total revenue from insurance and reinsurance operations while investment income accounts for nearly 35%. The company is involved in underwriting insurance based on life insurance business licenses real estate investment securities lending and investment advisory among other financial services activities.

Nippon Life strives to offer services and develop products with primary emphasis on providing truly useful coverage for customers. The "Mirai no Katachi" product one of the company's life insurance products provides customers with lifelong support by allowing them to make up different combinations of insurance. Customers can flexibly combine approximately 15 types of insurance as needed and can be divided into four categories: death risk risk of serious diseases and nursing care medical risks and risk of requiring accumulated funds for old age and other risks. Other products include juvenile insurance education endowment insurance single-payment whole life insurance and single-payment endowment insurance among others.

Subsidiaries include Reliance Nippon Life Insurance Company Nippon Insurance Service NLI Insurance Agency Nissay Asset Management and Nissay Capital.

Geographic Reach

Japan-based Nippon Life has about 90 subsidiaries and affiliates and operates about 110 branch locations and about 1525 sales offices. It operates in Australia China India Indonesia Japan Thailand the UK and the US.

Sales and Marketing

Nippon Life primarily sells policies through its dedicated field sales force as well as through retail store locations call centers and online. It also sells through select insurance brokerages and via partnerships with financial services companies including banks.

Financial Performance

Note: Growth rates may differ after conversion to US Dollars.

The company's revenue for fiscal 2021 increased to 8.2 trillion compared with 8.1 trillion in the prior year.

Profit for fiscal 2021 increased to 475.6 billion compared with 281.4 billion in the prior year.

Cash held by the company at the end of fiscal 2021 increased to 2.3 trillion. Cash provided by operations and financing activities were 965.1 billion and 274.6 billion respectively. Investing activities used 1.2 trillion mainly for purchases of securities.

Strategy

The company's medium-term management priorities are: improve customer satisfaction and enhance the provision of information; address social issues through provision of products and services; provide universal services; provide insurance services suited to every region; contribute to shaping a sustainable society through asset management; build cooperative relationships and contribute to the development of communities and society; initiatives for climate change; recruitment development and retention of diverse human resources; promote diversity and inclusion; promote work style reforms and Health and Productivity Management; long-term stable business operation through the mutual company structure; proper distribution of economic value; strengthen corporate governance; integrate CSR issues into management; stakeholder engagement; strengthen the compliance system; management respectful of the human rights of all people; and upgrade the approach to ERM.

Company Background

Nippon Life was founded as Nippon Life Assurance in 1889. Nippon Life was the first Japanese life insurer to offer profit dividends to its policyholders.

HISTORY

Nippon Life known as Nissay was a product of the modernization that began after US Commodore Matthew Perry opened Japan's ports to foreigners in 1854. Industry and trade were Japan's first focus but financial infrastructure soon followed. The country's first insurer (Meiji Mutual) opened in 1881. In 1889 Osaka banker Sukesaburo Hirose founded Nippon Life as a stock company. It grew and opened branches in Tokyo (1890) and Kyushu (1895).

In the 20th century the company developed a direct sales force and began lending directly to businesses. Lending remained the backbone of its asset strategy through most of the century. The insurance market in Japan grew quickly until the late 1920s but had already slowed by the eve of the Depression.

After WWII the company reorganized as a mutual and began mobilizing an army of women to build its sales of installment-premium basic life policies. In 1962 the company began automating its systems and established operations in the US (1972) and the UK (1981).

As interest rates rose in the wake of oil price hikes in the 1970s the company began offering term life and annuities and slowly moved to diversify its asset holdings from mostly government bonds (whose yields declined as rates rose) to stocks. This movement accelerated in the 1980s as the businesses that traditionally borrowed from Nippon Life turned directly to capital markets to raise money through debt issues. Seeking to replace its shrinking lending business the company began investing in US real estate and businesses whose values rose in the mid-1980s. The company reached its zenith in 1987; it owned about 3% of all the stocks on the Tokyo Exchange held more real estate than Mitsubishi's real estate units and had bought 13% of US brokerage Shearson Lehman from American Express.

By the end of the year thanks to the US stock market crash the value of the Shearson investment had fallen 40%. But the company felt confident enough of its importance as the world's largest insurance company (by assets) to crow its intentions to strong-arm Japan's Ministry of Finance into letting it diversify into trust and securities operations.

Then its bubble burst. In 1989 real estate crashed and the stock market lost more than half its value. Japan's economy failed to improve and Nippon Life was left struggling with nonperforming loans and assets whose value had declined. The company suffered further from policy cancellations and from the Ministry of Finance's focus on buoying banks. In 1997 the ministry asked Nippon Life to convert its subordinated debt from Nippon Credit Bank (now Aozora Bank) to stock. That year Nippon Life formed an alliance with Marsh & McLennan's Putnam Investments subsidiary to help manage its assets; the relationship deepened in 1998 when they began developing investment trust products.

The next year Nippon Life faced a shareholder lawsuit over its involvement in the collapse of Nippon Credit Bank; the company claims the Ministry of Finance tricked it into bailing out the bank even though it was beyond rescue. In 2001 the company merged its Nissay General subsidiary with Dowa Fire & Marine creating nonlife insurer Nissay Dowa.

Auditors: Deloitte Touche Tohmatsu LLC

LOCATIONS

HQ: Nippon Life Insurance Co. (Japan)
3-5-12 Imabashi, Chuo-ku, Osaka 541-8501
Phone: (81) 6 6209 4500
Web: www.nissay.co.jp

PRODUCTS/OPERATIONS

2018 Sales

	% of total
Insurance & reinsurance	71
Investment income	26
Other	3
Total	**100**

Selected Products and Services

Products for Individuals
 Annuities
 Asset management
 Cancer Medical Insurance
 Dread Disease Insurance
 Endowment Insurance
 General Medical Insurance
 Limited Injury Insurance
 Non-life Insurance Products
 Nursing Care Insurance
 Physical Disability Insurance
 Products for Children
 Single-payment Products
 Term Life Insurance
 Term Life Insurance with Survival Benefits
 Whole Life Insurance
Products for Businesses
 Disability coverage
 Home buying preparation
 Medical coverage
Retirement coverage
Survivor coverage
Various life plans

COMPETITORS

ABRDN PLC
AEGON N.V.
AMERICAN INTERNATIONAL GROUP INC.
CNO FINANCIAL GROUP INC.
LEGAL & GENERAL GROUP PLC
MASSACHUSETTS MUTUAL LIFE INSURANCE
 COMPANY
METLIFE INC.
NEW YORK LIFE INSURANCE COMPANY
PRUDENTIAL FINANCIAL INC.
PRUDENTIAL PUBLIC LIMITED COMPANY
SUMITOMO LIFE INSURANCE COMPANY
THE HARTFORD FINANCIAL SERVICES GROUP INC.

HISTORICAL FINANCIALS

Company Type: Public

Income Statement   FYE: March 31

	ASSETS ($ mil.)	NET INCOME ($ mil.)	INCOME AS % OF ASSETS	EMPLOYEES
03/19	711,637	2,517	0.4%	0
03/18	700,581	2,297	0.3%	71,871
03/17	648,121	2,700	0.4%	70,651
03/16	628,761	3,592	0.6%	70,519
03/15	522,162	2,567	0.5%	70,783
Annual Growth	8.0%	(0.5%)	—	—

2019 Year-End Financials

Return on assets: 0.3%	Dividends
Return on equity: 4.1%	Yield: —
Long-term debt ($ mil.): —	Payout: —
No. of shares (mil.): —	Market value ($ mil.): —
Sales ($ mil): 74,446	

Nippon Steel Corp (New)

Nippon Steel (formerly Nippon Steel & Sumimoto Metal) the world's fifth-largest steelmaker after China Baowu Group ArcelorMittal HBIS Group and Shagang Group manufactures plates H-beams sheet piles pipe piles and rails as well as specialty processed and fabricated steel products. Nippon Steel's annual domestic crude steel output is approximately 54 million tons. The company's operations include steelmaking and fabrication engineering and construction chemicals and materials and system solutions. Though the company sells many products? from petrochemical to industrial machinery ? the clear majority of its revenue comes from its steel products. The company was founded in 1950 and is based in Tokyo Japan. The company generates around 65% of sales in Japan.

Operations

Nippon Steel operates in four segments: Steelmaking and Steel Fabrication (accounts for more than 85% of total revenue) Engineering and Construction Chemicals and Materials and System Solutions (accounts about 5% each).

Steelmaking and Steel Fabrication segment makes and markets steel products including pig iron and ingots steel bars plates sheets pipes tubes and specialty processed and fabricated steel items.

Engineering and Construction segment makes and markets industrial machinery and equipment and steel structures. It also offers construction work under contract waste processing and recycling services and supplies electricity civil engineering work pipe piling work building construction base-isolation vibration-control devices gas and heat.

Chemicals and Materials segment makes and sells coal-based chemical products petrochemicals and electronic materials. In addition the company also makes materials and components for semiconductors and electronic parts carbon fiber and composite products and products that utilize technologies for metal processing are part of this segment.

The System Solutions segment includes computer system engineering and consulting services; IT-enabled outsourcing; and other services.

Geographic Reach

Nippon Steel has operations across the world. Its main operations are in Japan (headquarters) but it also has overseas branches throughout the US Asia Middle East Africa North Central and South America.

In Japan it has six steelworks and three major research centers and laboratories located in Futtsu Amagasaki and Hasaki.

Sales and Marketing

Nippon Steel serves a diverse array of industries including automotive industrial construction recycling petrochemicals engineering transportation and consulting sectors among many others.

Financial Performance

Note: Growth rates may differ after conversion to US Dollars.

The company's revenue for fiscal 2020 decreased to 4.8 trillion compared with 5.9 trillion.

Loss for fiscal 2020 decreased to 32.4 billion compared with 431.5 billion.

The company's cash at the end of 2021 was 289.5 billion. Operating activities generated 494.3 billion while investing activities used 345.6 billion mainly for purchases of property plant and equipment and intangible assets. Financing activities used another 345.6 billion primarily for repayment of borrowings.

Strategy

The company's four pillars of medium-to-long-term management plans are rebuilding its domestic steel business and strengthening its company's management; promoting a global strategy to deepen and expand its overseas business; taking on the challenge of zero-carbon steel; and promoting digital transformation strategies.

Company Background

As Japan prepared for war the government in 1934 merged Yawata Works the country's largest steel producer and other Japanese steelmakers into one giant company ? Japan Iron & Steel.

As Japan lost the war Japan Iron & Steel was ordered to dissolve by the Allied forces. Two new companies? Yawata Iron & Steel and Fuji Iron & Steel?emerged from the dissolution.

With Western assistance the Japanese steel industry recovered from the war years in the 60s. Yawata and Fuji merged again in 1970 and became Nippon Steel the world's largest steelmaker.

The company diversified in the mid-1980s to wean itself from dependence on steel. It has remained a leading steel company since.

In 2012 Nippon acquired Sumitomo Metal Industries mating Japan's #1 and #3 steelmakers.

In 2019 the company shortened its name from Nippon Steel & Sumitomo Metal Corporation to Nippon Steel Corporation.

HISTORY

As Japan prepared for war the government in 1934 merged Yawata Works its largest steel producer and other Japanese steelmakers into one

giant company – Japan Iron & Steel. During post-war occupation Japan Iron & Steel was ordered to dissolve. Yawata Iron & Steel and Fuji Iron & Steel emerged from the dissolution and with Western assistance the Japanese steel industry recovered from the war years. In the late 1960s Fuji Steel bought Tokai Iron & Steel (1967) and Yawata Steel took over Yawata Steel Tube Company (1968).

Yawata and Fuji merged in 1970 and became Nippon Steel the world's largest steelmaker. In the 1970s the Japanese steel industry was criticized in the US; American competitors complained that Japan was "dumping" low-cost exports. Meanwhile Nippon Steel aggressively courted China.

The company diversified in the mid-1980s to wean itself from dependence on steel. It created a New Materials unit in 1984 retraining "redundant" steelworkers to make silicon wafers and forming an Electronics Division in 1986. Nippon Steel began joint ventures with IBM Japan (small computers and software) Hitachi (office workstations) and C. Itoh (information systems for small and midsized companies) in 1988 as increased steel demand for construction and cars in Japan's "bubble economy" took the company to new heights.

In an atmosphere of economic optimism the company spent more than four times the expected expense to build an amusement park capable of competing with Tokyo Disneyland. The company plowed ahead spending some $230 million on the park. Space World amusement park opened on the island of Kyushu in 1990. The company's bubble burst that year. (The theme park declared bankruptcy in May 2005 and was sold to Kamori Kanko later that year.)

In response Nippon Steel cut costs and intensified its diversification efforts by targeting electronics information and telecommunications new materials and chemicals markets. Seeking to remake its steel operations the company began a drastic phased restructuring in 1993 that included a step most Japanese companies try to avoid — cutting personnel. A semiconductor division was organized that year as part of the company's diversification strategy.

Upgrading its steel operations Nippon Steel and partner Mitsubishi in 1996 introduced the world's first mass-production method for making hot-rolled steel sheet directly from smelted stainless steel. Profits were hurt that year by a loss-making project in the information and communications segment and by a steep decline in computer memory-chip prices.

The company began operation of a Chinese steelmaking joint venture Guangzhou Pacific Tinplate in 1997. The next year its Singapore-based joint venture with Hitachi Ltd. began mass-producing computer memory chips in hopes of stemming semiconductor losses. But falling prices convinced Nippon Steel to get out of the memory chip business and in 1999 it sold its semiconductor subsidiary to South Korea's United Microelectronics.

That year the US imposed antidumping duties on the company's steel products. The next year Nippon Steel agreed to form a strategic alliance with South Korea-based Pohang Iron and Steel (POSCO) at that time the world's #1 steel maker. The deal called for the exploration of joint ventures shared research and joint procurement as well as increased equity stakes in each other (at 2%-3%). Also in 2000 Nippon Steel agreed to provide Sumitomo Metal Industries and Nisshin Steel Co. with stainless steel products.

Early in 2001 Nippon Steel formed a cooperative alliance — focused on automotive sheet products — with French steel giant Usinor (now a part of ArcelorMittal). At the end of the year Nippon Steel decided to form an alliance with Kobe Steel to

pare down costs and share in distribution and production facilities. In 2002 the company continued its series of comprehensive alliances by forming alliances with Japanese steelmaker Nippon Metal Industry to exchange its semi-finished stainless steel technologies and with POSCO to build environment-related businesses.

The company reported a loss of 51.69 billion ($430 million) for fiscal 2003 due to securities valuation losses and group restructuring charges. In 2004 Nippon Steel formed a joint venture with Baoshan Iron & Steel and Arcelor to manufacture high-grade automotive steel sheets.

Nippon Steel moved into the South American market in 2006 forming alliances with steelmaker Usiminas and iron miner CVRD. And the next year it created a JV with Baosteel and ArcelorMittal that produces automotive steel sheets.

The company joined up with Sumitomo Metal Industries in 2009 when the two companies agreed to form a joint venture that will combine their arc-welded stainless steel pipe and tube operations. Sumitomo will own 60% of the JV. The operations that make up the new company which will be called Sumikin & Nippon Steel Stainless Steel Pipe Co. achieved sales of more than $250 million in 2008.

EXECUTIVES

Vice President, Representative Director, Akio Migita

Vice President, Chief Director of Global Business Promotion, Representative Director, Takahiro Mori

Independent Director, Hiroshi Obayashi

Independent Director, Jiro Makino

Vice President, Chief Director of Technology Development, Representative Director, Shuhei Onoyama

Director, Shozo Furumoto

Vice President, Representative Director, Naoki Sato

Managing Director, Tadashi Imai

Director, Nobuhiro Miyoshi

Independent Director, Noriko Iki

Independent Director, Seiichiro Azuma

Chairman of the Board, Representative Director, Kosei Shindo

President and Director, Eiji Hashimoto

Independent Director, Hiroshi Yoshikawa

Independent Director, Tetsuro Tomita

Independent Director, Masato Kitera

Director, Masato Matsuno

Vice President, Chairman of the Board in Subsidiary, Representative Director, Shinichi Nakamura

Auditors: KPMG AZSA LLC

LOCATIONS

HQ: Nippon Steel Corp (New)
2-6-1 Marunouchi, Chiyoda-ku, Tokyo 100-8071
Phone: (81) 3 6867 4111
Web: www.nipponsteel.com

2016 Sales

	% of total
Japan	66
Rest of Asia	22
Other	12
Total	**100**

PRODUCTS/OPERATIONS

2018 Sales

	% of total
Steelmaking & Steel Fabrication	88
Engineering & Construction	5
Chemicals	3
Systems Solutions	3
New Materials	1
Total	**100**

Selected Products and Services

Steelmaking and Steel Fabrication
  Fabricated and processed steels
  Pig iron and ingots
  Pipes and tubes
  Plates and sheets
  Sections
  Specialty sheets
Engineering and Construction
  Building construction
  Civil engineering
  Marine construction
  Plant and machinery
  Technical cooperation
Chemicals
  Aluminum products
  Ammonium sulfate
  Cement
  Ceramic products
  Coal tar
  Coke
  Ferrite
  Metallic foils
  Slag products
System Solutions
  Communications services
  Computers and equipment
  Data processing
  Systems development and integration
Urban Development
  Condominiums
  Theme parks
New Materials
  Semiconductor bonding wire
  Silicon wafers
  Titanium products
  Transformers
Other operations
  Services
  Energy services
  Financial services
  Insurance services
  Transportation
  Loading and unloading
  Marine and land transportation
  Warehousing

Selected Subsidiaries and Affiliates

Subsidiaries
  Nippon Steel & Sumikin Coated Sheet Corporation
  Nippon Steel & Sumikin Metal Products Co. Ltd.
  Nippon Steel & Sumikin Stainless Steel Corporation
  Nippon Steel & Sumikin Welding Co. Ltd.
  Nippon Steel Australia Pty. Limited
  Nippon Steel Blast Furnace Slag Cement Co. Ltd.
  Nippon Steel Drum Co. Ltd. 1654
  Nippon Steel Logistics Co. Ltd.
  Nippon Steel Shipping Co. Ltd.
  Nippon Steel Transportation Co. Ltd.
  Nippon Steel U.S.A. Inc.
  Nittetsu Cement Co. Ltd.
  Nittetsu Elex Co. Ltd.
  Nittetsu Finance Co. Ltd.
  Nittetsu Steel Pipe Co. Ltd. 4832
  Nittetsu Tokai Steel Wire Co. Ltd.
  NS Preferred Capital Limited
  Osaka Steel Co. Ltd.
  Siam Nippon Steel Pipe Co. Ltd.
  The Siam United Steel (1995) Co. Ltd.
Affiliates
  Daiwa Can Company
  Geostr Corporation
  Godo Steel Ltd.
  Japan Casting & Forging Corporation
  Krosaki Harima Corporation
  Mitsui Mining Co. Ltd.
  Nichia Steel Works Ltd.
  Nippon Steel Trading Co. Ltd.
  Sanko Metal Industrial Co. Ltd.
  Sanyo Special Steel Co. Ltd.
  Sanyu Co. Ltd.
  Suzuki Metal Industry Co. Ltd.
  Taihei Kogyo Co. Ltd.
  Topy Industries Ltd.

COMPETITORS

A. FINKL & SONS CO.	JFE HOLDINGS INC.
ArcelorMittal	NUCOR CORPORATION
CHINA STEEL	OKAYA & CO. LTD.

CORPORATION	STEEL DYNAMICS INC.
GERDAU AMERISTEEL US INC.	STEEL TECHNOLOGIES LLC
Hbis Company Limited	TATA STEEL EUROPE LIMITED
Hyundai Steel Company	UNITED STATES STEEL
JAPAN STEEL WORKS LTD. THE	CORPORATION
	thyssenkrupp AG

HISTORICAL FINANCIALS
Company Type: Public

Income Statement   FYE: March 31

	REVENUE ($ mil.)	NET INCOME ($ mil.)	NET PROFIT MARGIN	EMPLOYEES
03/21	43,615	(292)	—	125,038
03/20	54,551	(3,975)	—	126,324
03/19	55,785	2,268	4.1%	125,960
03/18	53,383	1,836	3.4%	109,918
03/17	41,436	1,171	2.8%	108,029
Annual Growth	1.3%	—	—	3.7%

2021 Year-End Financials

Debt ratio: 0.2%
Return on equity: (-1.2%)
Cash ($ mil.): 3,246
Current ratio: 1.51
Long-term debt ($ mil.): 19,701

No. of shares (mil.): 921
Dividends
  Yield: 0.0%
  Payout: —
Market value ($ mil.): 15,950

	STOCK PRICE ($) FY Close	P/E High/Low		Earnings	PER SHARE ($) Dividends	Book Value
03/21	17.30	—	—	(0.32)	0.09	27.04
03/20	8.60	—	—	(4.32)	0.46	26.39
03/19	17.74	0	0	2.54	0.72	31.64
03/18	22.27	0	0	2.08	0.71	33.51
03/17	23.09	0	0	1.32	0.13	29.83
Annual Growth	(7.0%)	—	—	—	(9.4%)	(2.4%)

Nippon Steel Trading Corp

Nippon Steel Engineering is the steel-trading operation of Nippon Steel & Sumitomo Metal Japan's steelmaker. The company trades a range of products such as steel sheets flat products bar & wire rod and construction products which are distributed and manufactured in Asia Europe and North and Central America. Nippon Steel Engineering also imports steelmaking raw materials through investing in raw material mines that enable the company to procure such raw materials. About 20% of iron ore and coking coal used in the company's steelmaking operations is from these mines. Steel products account for 85% of company sales. More than 70% of the company's total revenue comes from Japan. Nippon Steel Engineering started as the engineering division of Nippon Steel in 1974.

Operations

Nippon Steel Engineering operates in four segments: Steel (85% of total revenue); Foodstuffs (over 5%); Textiles (about 5%); and Industrial Supply and Infrastructure (less than 5%).

The Steel segment is engaged in a full range of steelmaking activities from buying raw materials to the delivery of steel products to customers.

Foodstuffs offers imported meats (including beef pork and chicken) fishery products agricultural products and Other foodstuffs and processed foods.

Centering on OEM production for apparel makers Textiles is engaged in everything from materials development to product planning production and distribution.

Industrial Supply and Infrastructure invests in new businesses with growth potential such as industrial machinery infrastructure businesses and materials.

The company also has its non-steel segments namely Engineering and Construction Chemicals and Materials and System solutions.

Geographic Reach

Tokyo Japan-based Nippon Steel Engineering has more than 10 manufacturing bases which enables the company to produce more than 50 million tons of domestic crude steel per year. The company has overseas operations in ASEAN countries China India the Middle East North/Central America South America and Europe.

Japan accounts for more than 70% of total revenue followed by Asia with over 20%.

Financial Performance

Note: Growth rates may differ after conversion to US Dollars.

Nippon Engineering has generally grown its revenues in the last five years however had a slight decrease in performance from 2020 to 2021 slightly being higher than its 2018 performance.

The company's net sales dropped by 407 billion to 2.1 trillion in fiscal 2021 compared to 2.5 trillion in the prior year.

Net income declined by 5 billion to 15.9 billion in 2021 compared to 20.7 billion in the prior year.

The company held 55.9 billion at the end of 2021. Operating activities generated 47.3 billion. Investing activities and financing activities used 6.5 billion and 10 billion respectively. Main cash uses were for purchases of properties plants and equipment as well as repayment of long-term debts.

Strategy

Nippon Steel Engineering's strategy is made up of its medium- to long-term management plan. These plans include the goal of the company to rebuild the domestic steel business and strengthen the group's management through restructuring. The plan also includes the deepening and expansion of the company's overseas operation. The company intends to establish a global capacity of 100 million tons of crude steel production. In addition the company is also taking on the challenge of zero-carbon steel which is achieved through the provision of their technology and products to those that benefit from them. Lastly the company also aims to promote its digital transformation strategies through attentively collecting and analyzing the vast amounts of data generated at manufacturing and business sites to reduce costs and improve quality.

Company Background

In 2013 Nippon Steel Trading merged with Sumikin Bussan to form Nippon Steel & Sumikin Bussan Corporation.

EXECUTIVES

Managing Executive Officer, Director, Kazuhiro Koshikawa
President, Representative Director, Yasumitsu Saeki
Managing Executive Officer, Director, Shuichi Yoshida
Managing Executive Officer, Director, Kazumi Yoshimoto
Independent Director, Ryu Matsumoto
Executive Officer, Manager of Kyushu Office, Shinji Otsu

Executive Officer, Manager of Nagoya Office, Yasuhiro Nomura
Executive Officer, Tetsuya Okamoto
Senior Managing Executive Officer, Toshihiko Kunishi
Independent Director, Ryuko Inoue
Vice President, Director, Yutaka Takeuchi
Managing Executive Officer, Masanori Tochika
Independent Director, Yoshihiro Ogura
Managing Executive Officer, Director, Yasuyuki Tomioka
Independent Director, Keishiro Kinoshita
Auditors: Deloitte Touche Tohmatsu LLC

LOCATIONS

HQ: Nippon Steel Trading Corp
8-5-27 Akasaka, Minato-ku, Tokyo, smc 107-8527
Phone: (81) 3 5412 5098   **Fax:** 847 413-4030
Web: www.nst.nipponsteel.com

2016 Sales

	% of total
Japan	74
Asia	22
others	4
Total	**100**

COMPETITORS

CHINA STEEL CORPORATION
EDGEN GROUP INC.
HANWA CO.LTD.
MECHEL PAO
NOK CORPORATION
Russel Metals Inc
TERNIUM S.A.
TITANIUM METALS CORPORATION

HISTORICAL FINANCIALS

Company Type: Public

Income Statement   FYE: March 31

	REVENUE ($ mil.)	NET INCOME ($ mil.)	NET PROFIT MARGIN	EMPLOYEES
03/21	18,724	143	0.8%	9,028
03/20	22,848	190	0.8%	7,971
03/19	23,031	209	0.9%	7,914
03/18	19,421	204	1.1%	7,785
03/17	16,469	163	1.0%	8,273
Annual Growth	**3.3%**	**(3.1%)**	**—**	**2.2%**

2021 Year-End Financials

Debt ratio: 0.3%
Return on equity: 6.4%
Cash ($ mil.): 513
Current ratio: 1.71
Long-term debt ($ mil.): 1,489

No. of shares (mil.): 32
Dividends
  Yield: —
  Payout: —
Market value ($ mil.): —

Nippon Telegraph & Telephone Corp (Japan)

Auditors: KPMG AZSA LLC

LOCATIONS

HQ: Nippon Telegraph & Telephone Corp (Japan)
Otemachi First Square, East Tower, 1-5-1 Otemachi, Chiyoda-ku, Tokyo 100-8116
Phone: (81) 3 6838 5481   **Fax:** 212 661-1078
Web: www.ntt.co.jp

HISTORICAL FINANCIALS

Company Type: Public

Income Statement   FYE: March 31

	REVENUE ($ mil.)	NET INCOME ($ mil.)	NET PROFIT MARGIN	EMPLOYEES
03/21	107,870	8,274	7.7%	371,816
03/20	109,621	7,879	7.2%	370,826
03/19	107,273	7,716	7.2%	366,156
03/18	111,120	8,566	7.7%	363,014
03/17	101,881	7,156	7.0%	274,850
Annual Growth	**1.4%**	**3.7%**	**—**	**7.8%**

2021 Year-End Financials

Debt ratio: 0.3%
Return on equity: 11.0%
Cash ($ mil.): 8,450
Current ratio: 0.72
Long-term debt ($ mil.): 40,241

No. of shares (mil.): —
Dividends
  Yield: 3.5%
  Payout: —
Market value ($ mil.): —

	STOCK PRICE ($) FY Close	P/E High/Low		PER SHARE ($) Earnings	Dividends	Book Value
03/21	25.91	0	0	2.24	0.92	18.86
03/20	23.62	0	0	2.13	0.88	22.96
03/19	42.72	0	0	1.99	0.72	21.82
03/18	46.55	0	0	2.15	0.64	22.66
03/17	42.84	0	0	1.75	1.11	20.09
Annual Growth	**(11.8%)**	**—**	**—**	**6.4%**	**(4.4%)**	**(1.6%)**

Nippon Yusen Kabushiki Kaisha

Nippon Yusen Kabushiki Kaisha known as NYK Line is primarily engaged in liner & logistics (Liner Trade Air Cargo Transportation and Logistics) bulk shipping and Others (Real Estate and Other). The company is one of the world's largest marine transportation providers. The NYK Line fleet includes bulk carriers containerships tankers and a variety of specialized vessels including car carriers and liquefied natural gas (LNG) carriers. The company operates in more than 45 countries. The history of NYK has paralleled that of Japan a maritime nation ever since the company's founding in 1885.

Operations
NYK Line divides its operations into several segments. Liner and logistics headquarters is its largest contributing around 50% of the company's total sales (and includes liner trade some 10%) air cargo (over 5%) and logistics (nearly 35%) in 2020. Bulk shipping generated around 40% of the company's revenue. Its other operations accounted for the remainder of sales.

Geographic Reach
NYK Line has over 605 logistics locations around the world. Around 250 logistics and nearly 170 warehouses are located in South Asia and Oceania; nearly 85 logistics and around 40 warehouses in in East Asia; about 120 logistics and around 70 warehouses in Europe; almost 90 logistics and nearly 35 warehouses in Japan; and around 65 logistics and some 35 warehouses in the Americas.
NYK Line is headquartered in Tokyo Japan.

Financial Performance
The company's revenue for fiscal 2020 decreased to 1.6 trillion compared from the prior year with 1.7 trillion.

Profit for fiscal 2020 increased to 139.2 billion compared from the prior year with 31.1 billion.
Cash provided by operations was 159.3 billion while cash used for investing and financing activities were 16.9 billion and 125.5 billion respectively.

EXECUTIVES

Managing Executive Officer, Hitoshi Nagasawa
Chairman of the Board, Chairman of the Executive Board, Tadaaki Naito
Non-Executive Independent Director, Hiroko Kuniya
Non-Executive Independent Director, Yoshihiro Katayama
Chief Compliance Officer and Director, Yutaka Higurashi
Senior Managing Executive Officer, Chief Senior Director of Liner & Logistics Business, Representative Director, Hiroki Harada
Chief Financial Officer, Managing Executive Officer and Head-IR Group, Hiroshi Kubota
Non-Executive Independent Director, Eiichi Tanabe
Auditors: Deloitte Touche Tohmatsu LLC

LOCATIONS

HQ: Nippon Yusen Kabushiki Kaisha
2-3-2 Marunouchi, Chiyoda-ku, Tokyo 100-0005
Phone: (81) 3 3284 5151
Web: www.nyk.com

2015 Sales

	% of total
Japan	75
Asia	9
North America	8
Europe	7
Other area	1
Total	**100**

PRODUCTS/OPERATIONS

2015 Sales

	% of total
Bulk shipping	42
Liner trade	28
Logistics	20
Air cargo transport	4
Cruise	2
Real estate	0
Other	4
Total	**100**

List of Items

Bulk Shipping Business
  Car Transport
  Dry Bulk Transport
  Offshore Business
  Tanker Transport (LNG Transport)
  Tanker Transport (Petroleum Chemical and LPG Transport)
Global Logistics
  Air Cargo Transportation Business
  Liner Trade Business
  Logistics Business
  Terminal and Harbor Transport Business
Real Estate Business
Others
Worldwide Service Network

COMPETITORS

A.P. M ller - Mærsk A/S
BALTIC TRADING LIMITED
CMA CGM ASIA PACIFIC LIMITED
EAGLE BULK SHIPPING INC.
EURONAV MI II INC.
GATX CORPORATION
GULFMARK OFFSHORE INC.
MANITEX INTERNATIONAL INC.
MITSUI O.S.K. LINES LTD.

OVERSEAS SHIPHOLDING GROUP INC.
RZHD PAO
TOUAX SCA - SGTR - CITE - SGT - CMTE - TAF - SLM
TOUAGE INVE

HISTORICAL FINANCIALS
Company Type: Public

Income Statement				FYE: March 31
	REVENUE ($ mil.)	NET INCOME ($ mil.)	NET PROFIT MARGIN	EMPLOYEES
03/21	14,526	1,257	8.7%	46,044
03/20	15,369	286	1.9%	44,508
03/19	16,518	(401)	—	45,401
03/18	20,559	189	0.9%	47,191
03/17	17,207	(2,376)	—	44,352
Annual Growth	(4.1%)	—	—	0.9%

2021 Year-End Financials
Debt ratio: 0.3%
Return on equity: 25.5%
Cash ($ mil.): 969
Current ratio: 0.99
Long-term debt ($ mil.): 6,032

No. of shares (mil.): 169
Dividends
  Yield: 1.0%
  Payout: —
Market value ($ mil.): 1,195

	STOCK PRICE ($) FY Close	P/E High/Low		PER SHARE ($) Earnings	Dividends	Book Value
03/21	7.05	0	0	7.45	0.08	33.31
03/20	2.25	0	0	1.70	0.06	25.14
03/19	2.96	—	—	(2.38)	0.07	25.96
03/18	3.83	0	0	1.13	0.28	30.65
03/17	4.32	—	—	(14.06)	0.04	27.56
Annual Growth	13.0%	—	—	—	21.0%	4.9%

Nissan Motor Co., Ltd.

Nissan Motor is one of Japan's leading automakers. The company's models include the Maxima Sentra and Altima sedans and the all-electric LEAF. Its lineup also includes SUVs and crossovers (Rogue Pathfinder Murano) trucks (Frontier and Titan) sports cars (370Z and GT-R) as well as the Infiniti brand of upscale sedans. Renault holds a 43% stake in Nissan Motor and Nissan has a 15% stake in Renault as well as a 34% stake in Mitsubishi Motors; these connections constitute the Renault Nissan Mitsubishi Alliance a leading global auto partnership. Nissan also holds a 50% stake in Dongfeng Motor Company a joint venture between Nissan and China's Dongfeng Group.

Operations
Nissan continues its quest to optimize product development and deliver highly innovative technology. INFINITI the premium brand from Nissan Motor Co. Ltd. is renowned internationally for its world-first technologies and award-winning designs. INFINITI promises a driving experience with unparalleled appeal. Datsun is the third global brand of Nissan Motor Co. Ltd. alongside Nissan and INFINITI. Datsun represents 80 years of accumulated Japanese car-making expertise and is an important part of the company's heritage. Today it offers personal mobility to customers in India Indonesia Russia and South Africa.

Geographic Reach
Nissan headquartered in Kanagawa Japan manufactures in more than 20 countries sells and offer services products worldwide. The company operates over 5 production facilities in Japan along with about 10 R&D facilities.

It also has facilities spread across North America Europe Asia Oceania the Caribbean and Africa (nearly 5 production facilities).

Sales and Marketing
Nissan's products are sold through a global network of independent dealers. The company's Infiniti brand is marketed in the US Canada Europe Russia the Middle East China South Korea and about 15 other countries. The Datsun brand is focused on emerging markets including India Indonesia Russia and South Africa.

The company's marketing efforts include media advertising (including print TV web and social) as well as participation is motorsports.

Financial Performance
Strategy
In mid-2020 Nissan introduced the all-new Nissan Ariya an electric crossover SUV that lets customers travel farther while enjoying greater driving excitement confidence and comfort and connectivity.

With a 100% electric powertrain the Ariya promises powerful acceleration and smooth quiet operation. Drivers and passengers can relax and enjoy the ride thanks to autonomous driving technology concierge-level assistance seamless connectivity and a spacious lounge-like interior. With an estimated range of up to 610 kilometers the no-compromise Ariya is perfect for daily commutes and weekend road trips alike.

Earlier that year Nissan Motor Co. Ltd. unveiled a four-year plan to achieve sustainable growth financial stability and profitability by the end of fiscal-year 2023. The scalable plan involving cost-rationalization and business optimization will shift the company's strategy from its past focus on inflated expansion.

As part of the four-year plan Nissan will take decisive action to transform its business by streamlining unprofitable operations and surplus facilities alongside structural reforms. The company will also reduce fixed costs by rationalizing its production capacity global product range and expenses. Through disciplined management the company will prioritize and invest in business areas expected to deliver a solid recovery and sustainable growth.

Company Background
In 1911 US-trained Masujiro Hashimoto established Tokyo-based Kwaishinsha Motor Car Works to repair import and manufacture cars. Kwaishinsha made its first car sporting its DAT ("fast rabbit" in Japanese) logo in 1913. Renamed DAT Motors in 1925 the company consolidated with ailing Jitsuyo Motors in 1926. DAT introduced the son of DAT in 1931 — the Datsun minicar.

Tobata Casting (cast iron and auto parts) bought Datsun's production facilities in 1933. Tobata's Yoshisuke Aikawa believed there was a niche for small cars and the car operations were spun off as Nissan Motors that year.

During WWII the Japanese government limited Nissan's production to trucks and airplane engines; Nissan survived postwar occupation in part due to business with the US Army. The company went public in 1951 and signed a licensing agreement the next year with Austin Motor (UK) which put it back in the car business.

Nissan entered the US market in 1958 with the model 211 using the Datsun name; it established Nissan Motor Corporation in Los Angeles in 1960. In the 1970s Nissan expanded exports of fuel-efficient cars such as the Datsun B210.

The company's name change in the US from Datsun to Nissan during the 1980s confused customers and took six years to complete. It launched its high-end Infiniti line in the US in 1989.

HISTORY
In 1911 US-trained Masujiro Hashimoto established Tokyo-based Kwaishinsha Motor Car Works to repair import and manufacture cars. Kwaishinsha made its first car sporting its DAT ("fast rabbit" in Japanese) logo in 1913. Renamed DAT Motors in 1925 and suffering from a strong domestic preference for American cars the company consolidated with ailing Jitsuyo Motors in 1926. DAT introduced the son of DAT in 1931 — the Datsun minicar ("son" means "damage or loss" in Japanese hence the spelling change).

Tobata Casting (cast iron and auto parts) bought Datsun's production facilities in 1933. Tobata's Yoshisuke Aikawa believed there was a niche for small cars and the car operations were spun off as Nissan Motors that year.

During WWII the Japanese government limited Nissan's production to trucks and airplane engines; Nissan survived postwar occupation in part due to business with the US Army. The company went public in 1951 and signed a licensing agreement the next year with Austin Motor (UK) which put it back in the car business. A 40% import tax allowed Nissan to compete in Japan even though it had higher costs than those of foreign carmakers.

Nissan entered the US market in 1958 with the model 211 using the Datsun name; it established Nissan Motor Corporation in Los Angeles in 1960. Exports rose as factory automation led to higher quality and lower costs. In the 1970s Nissan expanded exports of fuel-efficient cars such as the Datsun B210. The company became the leading US car importer in 1975.

The company's name change in the US from Datsun to Nissan during the 1980s confused customers and took six years to complete. In 1986 Nissan became the first major Japanese carmaker to build its products in Europe. It launched its high-end Infiniti line in the US in 1989.

EXECUTIVES

EVP, Manufacturing and SCM Operations and Director, Hideyuki Sakamoto
President, Representative Executive Officer, Chief Executive Officer, Director, Makoto Uchida
Chairman, Yasushi Kimura
Auditors: Ernst & Young ShinNihon LLC

LOCATIONS

HQ: Nissan Motor Co., Ltd.
2 Takara-cho, Kanagawa-ku, Yokohama, Kanagawa 220-8623
Phone: (81) 45 523 5523
Web: www.nissan.co.jp

PRODUCTS/OPERATIONS

Selected Products
Forklifts
  Engine-powerd forklifts
  Electric-powered forklifts
  Warehouse products
  Order pickers
  Pallet stackers
  Pallet transporters
  Reach trucks
Infiniti
  Infiniti Q50
  Infiniti Q60
  Infiniti Q70
  Infiniti Q70L
  Infiniti QX30
  Infiniti QX50
  Infiniti QX60
  Infiniti QX70
  Infiniti QX80
Nissan
  370Z

370Z Roadster
Altima
Armada
Frontier
GT-R
Juke
Leaf EV
Maxima
Murano
NV200 Cargo
NV200 Taxi
NV Passenger
Pathfinder
Rogue
Rogue Sport
Sentra
Titan
Titan XD
Versa
Versa Note

COMPETITORS

FORD MOTOR COMPANY
HONDA MOTOR CO. LTD.
ISUZU MOTORS LIMITED
MAZDA MOTOR OF AMERICA
  INC.
MITSUBISHI MOTORS
  CORPORATION

PEUGEOT SA
SUBARU CORPORATION
SUBARU OF AMERICA INC.
SUZUKI MOTOR
  CORPORATION
VOLKSWAGEN AG

HISTORICAL FINANCIALS
Company Type: Public

Income Statement   FYE: March 31

	REVENUE ($ mil.)	NET INCOME ($ mil.)	NET PROFIT MARGIN	EMPLOYEES
03/21	71,010	(4,052)	—	148,559
03/20	91,007	(6,183)	—	155,811
03/19	104,513	2,881	2.8%	160,183
03/18	112,548	7,033	6.2%	160,893
03/17	104,824	5,934	5.7%	158,633
Annual Growth	(9.3%)	—	—	(1.6%)

2021 Year-End Financials

Debt ratio: 0.4%
Return on equity: (-11.2%)
Cash ($ mil.): 16,904
Current ratio: 1.54
Long-term debt ($ mil.): 38,115

No. of shares (mil.): —
Dividends
  Yield: —
  Payout: —
Market value ($ mil.): —

	STOCK PRICE ($) FY Close	P/E High/Low		PER SHARE ($) Earnings	Dividends	Book Value
03/21	11.28	—	—	(1.04)	0.00	8.50
03/20	6.70	—	—	(1.58)	0.71	8.93
03/19	16.42	0	0	0.74	0.99	11.42
03/18	20.68	0	0	1.80	0.96	12.10
03/17	19.26	0	0	1.48	0.82	10.38
Annual Growth	(12.5%)	—	—	—	—	(4.9%)

NN Group NV (Netherlands)

Auditors: KPMG Accountants N.V.

LOCATIONS

HQ: NN Group NV (Netherlands)
  Schenkkade 65, The Hauge 2595 AS
Phone: (31) 70 513 03 03
Web: www.nn-group.com

HISTORICAL FINANCIALS
Company Type: Public

Income Statement   FYE: December 31

	ASSETS ($ mil.)	NET INCOME ($ mil.)	INCOME AS % OF ASSETS	EMPLOYEES
12/20	323,682	2,336	0.7%	15,118
12/19	279,116	2,202	0.8%	15,194
12/18	256,805	1,279	0.5%	14,953
12/17	272,191	2,529	0.9%	14,971
12/16	177,921	1,255	0.7%	11,463
Annual Growth	16.1%	16.8%	—	7.2%

2020 Year-End Financials

Return on assets: 0.7%
Return on equity: 5.3%
Long-term debt ($ mil.): —
No. of shares (mil.): 310
Sales ($ mil): 24,788

Dividends
  Yield: 5.0%
  Payout: 15.7%
Market value ($ mil.): 6,693

	STOCK PRICE ($) FY Close	P/E High/Low		PER SHARE ($) Earnings	Dividends	Book Value
12/20	21.56	4	2	7.20	1.09	152.18
12/19	18.91	4	3	6.46	0.87	113.41
12/18	19.59	7	6	3.61	0.76	84.27
12/17	21.63	4	3	7.43	0.71	87.83
Annual Growth	(0.1%)	—	—	(0.8%)	11.3%	14.7%

Nokia Corp

Nokia is one of the world's leading makers of the telecommunications infrastructure of mobile phone networks. Once a leading mobile phone handset manufacturer its current businesses are Networks which provides a wide range of professional services Nokia Software which offers the cloud core software portfolio and Nokia Technologies its research and development and intellectual property rights unit. First incorporated in the Finnish city it's named after Nokia has operations and customers in approximately 120 countries. Finland's largest company Nokia redoubled its commitment to telecom infrastructure with its acquisition of the telecom-equipment maker Alcatel-Lucent. Nokia generates some 30% of its revenue in North America.

Operations

Nokia has three reportable segments for financial reporting purposes: Networks Nokia Software and Nokia Technologies. Segment-level information for Group Common and Other is also presented.

Nokia's networks span the globe so it follows that the networks segment generates about 80% of the company's revenue. Networks segment comprises Mobile Networks Global Services Fixed Networks and IP/Optical Networks operations.

The Nokia Software operating segment generates more than 10% of revenue offers the cloud core software portfolio in addition to software applications spanning customer experience management.

The Nokia Technologies operating segment generates more than 5% of revenue focuses on building innovation and R&D technologies used in virtual mobile devices used today.

Group Common and Other includes Alcatel-Lucent Submarine Networks and Radio Frequency Systems which generates about 5% of revenue. Overall almost 85% of sales were generated from

communication service providers and the rest came from enterprise licensees and others.

Geographic Reach

Finland-based Nokia generates roughly 30% of sales in North America Europe generates about 30% of sales Asia/Pacific region generates approximately 20% of sales while Middle East and Africa and Greater China both generates about 10% of sales and Latin America generates more than 5% of sales. It has key R&D and software development centers in many of the largest countries in those three regions as well including China the US Germany France India and the UK.

Sales and Marketing

Nokia's customers include communications service providers utility energy and transportation companies the public sector and other tech companies.

Financial Performance

Note: Growth rates may differ after conversion to US Dollars.

Nokia's revenue has fluctuated in the last five years failing to show consistent growth over the years. The acquisition of Alcatel-Lucent in 2016 added about ?11 billion to sales but the decline continued again in the years that followed before rebounding in 2019. Its profits have also seen a similar trend rising and falling in the last five years before recovering from a three-year consecutive net loss from the years 2016 to 2018.

Sales in 2019 were ?23.3 billion an increase of ?752 million or 3% compared to ?22.6 billion in 2018. The increase in sales was primarily due to an increase in Networks net sales and to a lesser extent Nokia Software net sales. This was partially offset by a decrease in Group Common and Other and Nokia Technologies net sales.

Profit in 2019 was ?14 million an increase of ?568 million compared to a loss of ?554 million in 2018. The change in profit attributable to equity holders of the parent was primarily due to the improvement in operating profit and to a lesser extent lower income tax expenses. This was partially offset by a net negative fluctuation in financial income and expenses.

Nokia's cash level decreased by ?351 million to ?5.9 billion. It generated ?390 million in cash from operations. Investing and financing activities used ?167 million and ?479 million respectively. Nokia's primary cash uses in 2019 were for purchase of property plant and equipment and repayment of long-term borrowings.

Strategy

Nokia's "Rebranding for growth" strategy sets the right direction for the company. Nokia has focused it to reflect the progress so far and to accelerate further execution. Nokia intends to become the leading trusted network equipment provider for end-to-end networks and the leader in customer intimacy. Over the long term it aims to differentiate with end-to-end solutions that allow it to offer its customers guaranteed mission-critical performance total cost of ownership savings time-to-market gains and higher reliability.

Nokia has various focus areas among which are implementing five end-to-end solutions such as 5G distributed cloud network slicing security and industrial automation. It is also investing in the architecture and 5G system-on-chip capabilities for its mobile radio network products and building technology leadership in its Optical Networks portfolio leveraging its PSE-3 chipset.

By the end of 2019 Nokia had won 62 commercial 5G deals and launched 18 commercial 5G networks with leading operators in particular in North America Korea Japan Australia and New Zealand Europe and Middle-East and Africa. It is also making progress with Mobile Networks radio design-to-cost reduction with significant annualized product cost and procurement savings.

Mergers and Acquisitions

In early 2020 Nokia acquired Elenion Technologies a U.S.-based company focusing on silicon photonics technology for an undisclosed amount. Elenion's technology expertise and unique design platform and services enable Nokia to expand its market footprint by addressing the critical and rapidly evolving optical connectivity requirements of 5G cloud and enterprise networking.

Company Background

Nokia has grown from its origins in 1865 as a papermill in Finland to one of the world's pre-eminent technology companies and whose fortunes have a tangible impact on the lives of the Finnish population. Nokia has found and nurtured success in several sectors over the years including cable paper products rubber boots and tires mobile devices and telecommunications infrastructure equipment. By 1998 Nokia was the world leader in mobile phones a position it enjoyed for more than a decade.

However its phones fell out of popularity in the smartphone era as the iOS and Android mobile operating systems vastly outperformed Nokia's Symbian software. A tie-up with Microsoft that saw Nokia's devices adopt Windows Phone 7 as their OS ultimately failed to save Nokia's device division as few people preferred Microsoft's OS either and Nokia sold the entire business to Microsoft.

The sale triggered a wholesale shift to telecoms equipment which Nokia took to the next level with the 2016 acquisition of Alcatel-Lucent.

HISTORY

Nokia got its start in 1865 when engineer Fredrik Idestam established a mill to manufacture pulp and paper on the Tammerkoski rapids of the Nokianvirta River in Finland. Although Nokia flourished within Finland the company was not well known to the rest of the world until it attempted to become a regional conglomerate in the early 1960s. French computer firm Machines Bull selected Nokia as its Finnish agent in 1962 and Nokia began researching radio transmission technology. In 1967 with the encouragement of Finland's government Nokia merged with Finnish Rubber Works (a maker of tires and rubber footwear formed in 1898) and Finnish Cable Works (a cable and electronics manufacturer formed in 1912) to form Nokia Corporation.

The company entered the phone business — after a series of deals that expanded its industrial holdings — when it acquired a 51% interest in the state-owned Finnish telecom company in 1981 and named it Telenokia.

Nokia caught the first wave of mobile phones riding the popularity of its handsets in the late 1990s and early 2000s. It however didn't move fast enough to compete against smartphones and it eventually sold the handset business to Microsoft.

EXECUTIVES

Chief Financial Officer, Marco Wiren
Chief Strategy and Technology Officer, Nishant Batra
Chair of the Board of Directors, Sari Baldauf
Vice Chair of the Board of Directors, Kari Stadigh
President, Network Infrastructure, Federico Guillen
President, Mobile Networks, Tommi Uitto
President, Cloud and Network Services, Raghav Sahgal
Chief Corporate Affairs Officer, Melissa Schoeb
Chief Customer Experience Officer, Ricky Corker
Chief Legal Officer, Nassib Abou-Khalil
President of Nokia Technologies, Jenni Lukander

President and Chief Executive Officer, Pekka Lundmark
Chief People Officer, Stephanie Werner-Dietz
Auditors: PricewaterhouseCoopers Oy

LOCATIONS

HQ: Nokia Corp
Karakaari 7, Espoo Fl-02610
Phone: (358) 10 44 88 000   **Fax:** (358) 10 44 81 002
Web: www.nokia.com

2017 Sales

	% of total
Europe	29
North America	28
Asia/Pacific	
Greater China	11
Other	18
Middle East & Africa	8
Latin America	6
Total	**100**

2017 Sales

	% of total
United States	26
China	9
Finland	8
India	6
France	6
United Kingdom	3
Japan	3
Germany	2
Italy	2
Saudi Arabia	2
Other	33
Total	**100**

PRODUCTS/OPERATIONS

2017 Sales

	% of total
Nokia Networks	
Ultra Broadband Networks	39
IP Networks and Applications	25
Global Services	25
Nokia Technologies	7
Group common and other	4
Total	**100**

Selected Products

Nokia Flexi Multiradio
  Telco Cloud
  NetAct
  IP routers
Switching systems
  Radio contollers
  Base stations
  transmission systems
  mapping systems and software

COMPETITORS

ALCATEL LUCENT
ASSA ABLOY AB
BLANCCO TECHNOLOGY GROUP PLC
FUJITSU LIMITED
HITACHI EUROPE LIMITED
Huawei Investment & Holding Co. Ltd.
ILIAD
INGENICO GROUP
NEXT FIFTEEN COMMUNICATIONS GROUP PLC
PENNANT INTERNATIONAL GROUP PLC
SIG PLC
UBER TECHNOLOGIES INC.
WESTERN DIGITAL CORPORATION

HISTORICAL FINANCIALS

Company Type: Public

Income Statement

FYE: December 31

	REVENUE ($ mil.)	NET INCOME ($ mil.)	NET PROFIT MARGIN	EMPLOYEES
12/20	26,818	(3,096)	—	92,039
12/19	26,177	7	0.0%	98,322
12/18	25,839	(389)	—	103,083
12/17	27,747	(1,790)	—	101,731
12/16	24,933	(808)	—	101,000
Annual Growth	**1.8%**	**—**	**—**	**(2.3%)**

2020 Year-End Financials

Debt ratio: 18.9%
Return on equity: (-18.1%)
Cash ($ mil.): 8,517
Current ratio: 1.55
Long-term debt ($ mil.): 6,154

No. of shares (mil.): —
Dividends
  Yield: 2.8%
  Payout: 73.8%
Market value ($ mil.): —

	STOCK PRICE ($) FY Close	P/E High/Low		Earnings	PER SHARE ($) Dividends	Book Value
12/20	3.91	—	—	(0.55)	0.11	2.72
12/19	3.71	—	—	(0.00)	0.11	3.07
12/18	5.82	—	—	(0.07)	0.22	3.13
12/17	4.66	—	—	(0.31)	0.20	3.47
12/16	4.81	—	—	(0.14)	0.27	3.71
Annual Growth	**(5.0%)**	**—**	**—**		**(20.0%)**	**(7.4%)**

Nomura Holdings Inc

Nomura Holdings is one of the leading financial services groups in Japan and provides services to individuals institutions corporates and governments through the company's three divisions ? Retail Wholesale and Investment Management. It also makes private equity and venture capital investments and oversees some 126.6 trillion of retail client assets. Subsidiary Nomura Asset Management is one of Japan's largest asset management companies in terms of assets under management in investment trusts. In addition Nomura Securities is the leading securities and investment banking company in Japan that provides individual investors and corporate clients with a broad range of services including investment advisory services and securities underwriting. Operates in more than 30 countries and regions Japan accounts for the majority of the company's revenue.

Operations

Nomura operates through three business divisions: Wholesale Retail and Investment Management.

The Wholesale Division generates approximately 50% of the company's revenue consists of two businesses Global Markets which is engaged in the trading sales and structuring of financial products and Investment Banking which is engaged in financing and advisory businesses.

In the company's Retail Division Nomura conducts business activities by delivering a wide range of financial products and high quality investment services mainly for individuals and corporations in Japan primarily through a network of nationwide branches of Nomura Securities. The segment brings in about 15% of the company's revenue.

Accounts for some 10% of the company's revenue Investment Management Division is responsible for the asset management business in a broad sense aims to increase added value by combining various types of expertise that have been accumulated within the group from traditional assets such as stocks and bonds to alternative assets such as non-listed equities.

The company's revenue streams are fairly diversified. About 25% of its total revenue came from commissions with another more than 20% coming from interest and dividends. Net gain on trading brings in nearly 20% while asset management and portfolio service fees provide about 15%. The remainder of its revenue came from fees from investment banking gain on investments in equity securities gain on private equity and debt investments and others.

Geographic Reach

Based in Tokyo Japan Nomura operates offices in countries and regions worldwide including Japan the US the UK Singapore and Hong Kong. Generates most of its revenue in Japan the Americas bring in nearly 15% Europe provides approximately 10% and Asia and Oceania represent the remainder.

Sales and Marketing

The company offers its variety of financial services to individuals corporations financial institutions governments and governmental agencies.

Financial Performance

Note: Growth rates may differ after conversion to US dollars.

Nomura Holdings' revenue for 2021 totaled 1.6 trillion a 17% decrease from the previous year's revenue of 2 trillion. This was mainly due to a lower sales in the company's interest and dividends.

In 2021 the company had a net income of 160.4 billion a 27% decrease from the previous year's net income of 219.4 billion.

The company's cash at the end of 2021 was 3.2 trillion. Operating activities provided $665.8 billion while investing activities used 139 billion. Financing activities used another $270 billion primarily for increase in short-term borrowings.

Strategy

Nomura has established a management vision for the year 2025 the 100th anniversary of its founding. In order to realize this management vision within the next five years Nomura will promote three core values: Business growth Trust from society and Employee satisfaction. By the fiscal year 2023 Nomura aims to expand existing businesses and improve productivity. At the same time the company will invest in and cultivate new business areas thereby expanding the company's strategic options. By the fiscal year 2025 Nomura aims to expand its core business domain which is not just in the public but also private space to make a leap to a "Next Stage of Growth."

HISTORY

Tokushichi Nomura started a currency exchange Nomura Shoten in Osaka in 1872 and began trading stock. His son Tokushichi II took over and in 1910 formed Nomura's first syndicate to underwrite part of a government bond issue. It established the Osaka Nomura Bank in 1918. The bond department became independent in 1925 and became Nomura Securities. The company opened a New York office in 1927 entering stock brokerage in 1938.

The firm rebuilt and expanded retail operations after WWII. It encouraged stock market investing by promoting "million ryo savings chests" — small boxes in which people saved cash (ryo was an old form of currency). When savings reached 5000 yen savers could buy into investment trusts. Nomura distributed more than a million chests in 10 years.

Nomura followed clients overseas in the 1960s helped underwrite a US issue of Sony stock and

opened a London office. It became Japan's leading securities firm after a 1965 stock market crash decimated rival Yamaichi Securities. The firm grew rapidly in the 1970s ushering investment capital in and out of Japan and competing with banks by issuing corporate debt securities.

As the Japanese economy soared in the 1980s the company opened Nomura Bank International in London (1986) and bought 20% of US mergers and acquisitions advisor Wasserstein Perella (1988 sold 2001).

Then the Japanese economic bubble burst. Nomura's stock toppled 70% from its 1987 peak and underwriting plummeted. In 1991 and 1992 amid revelations that Nomura and other brokerages had reimbursed favored clients' trading losses the firm was accused of manipulating stock in companies owned by Japanese racketeers. Nomura's chairman and president — both named Tabuchi — resigned admitting no wrongdoing.

The firm trimmed staff and offices and focused on its most efficient operations. From 1993 to 2000 it seesawed from red to black and back again.

Junichi Ujiie became president after the payoff scandal; he restructured operations to prepare for Japan's financial deregulation. Nomura invested in pub chain Inntrepreneur and William Hill a UK betting chain. It also created an entertainment lending unit to lend against future royalties or syndication fees and spun off a minority stake in its high-risk US real estate business which ceased lending altogether the next year.

In 1998 Nomura was dealt a double blow when Asian economies collapsed and Russia defaulted on its debts. Incurring substantial losses the firm refocused on its domestic market and reduced overseas operations. That year it teamed with Industrial Bank of Japan for derivatives sales in the UK and pension plan consulting in Japan.

In 1999 Nomura bailed out ailing property subsidiary Nomura Finance which had been crippled by the sinking Japanese real estate market. It also invested heavily in UK real estate and bought 40% of the Czech beer market with South African Breweries.

The next year the firm agreed to buy the business services arm of Welsh utilities firm Hyder; it also bought 114000 flats in Germany with local government authorities its first European deal outside the UK. Also in 2000 Nomura sold its assets in pachinko parlors and "love" hotels Japanese cultural traditions with less-than-sparkling reputations. British authorities that year fined Nomura traders in relation to charges of trying to rig Australia's stock market in 1996.

The company converted to a holding company structure in 2001 and months later made its debut on the NYSE. It made two big deals in the UK that year buying hotel chain Le Meridien and becoming the nation's largest pub owner via the purchase of some 1000 locations from Bass. The company also bought a stake in Thomas Weisel Partners to increase its participation in M&A action between US and Japanese firms. In 2002 the company decided to sell the network of more than 4100 pubs to a consortium of private investors for some $3 billion.

In 2007 Nomura acquired global agency brokerage Instinet. The deal allowed the company to begin offering electronic trading services.

In 2008 Japanese regulators chose a consortium led by Nomura to take control of troubled Ashikaga Bank from the government; Nomura's private equity arm took a stake of about 45% in Ashikaga. The deal marked Nomura's first foray into retail banking.

The global financial crisis heavily impacted Nomura which reported steep declines in 2008 and 2009. The company lost some 208 billion ($2 bil-

lion) in 2009 alone on trading and equity investments. The US subprime mortgage bust further hurt the group which lost money on mortgage-backed securities.

In response Nomura cut operating costs and fine-tuned its offerings. The following year the company boosted its global investment banking capabilities by acquiring parts of the fallen bulge-bracket firm Lehman Brothers including operations in Asia Europe and the Middle East as well as the India-based back office operations. (In its post-acquisition transition the company laid off some 11% of its UK workforce or about 1000 employees in its London office.) In an effort to boost its domestic asset management business Nomura bought NikkoCiti Trust and Banking from Citigroup in 2009. The company also exited the US residential mortgage-backed securities business entirely.

The Lehman Brothers acquisition helped boost Nomura's profile in European equities and fixed-income trading. Adding on to that purchase Nomura bought London-based Tricorn Partners — a move that further complements its UK corporate finance advisory business.

Nomura Asset Management also bought a 35% stake in LIC Mutual Fund Asset Management Company of India. The deal gave Nomura a larger foothold in the Indian market and strengthened its credentials as an international asset manager.

EXECUTIVES

Chairman of the Board, Chairman of Subsidiary, Koji Nagai

Chief Executive Officer and Director, Kentaro Okuda

Executive Officer, Satoshi Arai

Independent Director, Noriaki Shimazaki

Executive Officer, Manager of Future Co-creation Company, Hajime Ikeda

Independent Director, Laura Unger

Executive Officer, Chief Strategy Officer, Toru Ohtsuka

Executive Officer, Rikiya Nonomura

Chief Compliance Officer, Vice President, Representative Executive Officer, Director, Tomoyuki Teraguchi

Executive Officer, Etsuro Miwa

Chief Financial Officer, Executive Officer, Takumi Kitamura

Independent Director, Kazuhiko Ishimura

Chief Administrative Officer, Executive Officer, Chief Executive Officer of Subsidiary, Jonathan Lewis

Independent Director, Christopher Giancarlo

Independent Director, Patricia Mosser

Independent Director, Victor Chu

Independent Director, Takahisa Takahara

Independent Director, Mari Sono

Auditors: Ernst & Young ShinNihon LLC

LOCATIONS

HQ: Nomura Holdings Inc
13-1, Nihonbashi 1-chome, Chuo-Ku, Tokyo 103-8645
Phone: (81) 3 5255 1000
Web: www.nomuraholdings.com

2014 Sales

	% of total
Japan	69
Americas	13
Europe	13
Asia and Oceania	5
Total	**100**

PRODUCTS/OPERATIONS

2014 Sales

	% of total
Net gain on trading	28
Commissions	23
Interest and dividends	23
Asset management & portfolio service fees	11
Fees from investment banking	5
Gain on investments in equity securities	1
Other	9
Total	**100**

2014 Sales

	% of total
Wholesale	50
Retail	30
Asset Management	6
Others	14
Total	**100**

COMPETITORS

ABERDEEN ASSET MANAGEMENT PLC	NEX INTERNATIONAL LIMITED
ALLIANCEBERNSTEIN HOLDING L.P.	PERMIRA ADVISERS LLP
Credit Suisse Group AG	PINEBRIDGE INVESTMENTS LLC
DAIWA SECURITIES GROUP INC.	RESONA HOLDINGS INC.
HSBC HOLDINGS PLC	SOFTBANK GROUP CORP.
JAPAN POST HOLDINGS CO.LTD.	SUMITOMO MITSUI FINANCIAL GROUP INC.
MAN GROUP LIMITED	SUMITOMO MITSUI TRUST HOLDINGS INC.
MITSUBISHI UFJ FINANCIAL GROUP INC.	Street Capital Group Inc
MIZUHO FINANCIAL GROUP INC.	UBS AG

HISTORICAL FINANCIALS

Company Type: Public

Income Statement
FYE: March 31

	ASSETS ($ mil.)	NET INCOME ($ mil.)	INCOME AS % OF ASSETS	EMPLOYEES
03/21	383,984	1,382	0.4%	26,402
03/20	405,340	1,999	0.5%	26,629
03/19	369,947	(906)	—	27,864
03/18	382,263	2,065	0.5%	28,048
03/17	383,269	2,143	0.6%	28,186
Annual Growth	0.0%	(10.4%)	—	(1.6%)

2021 Year-End Financials

Return on assets: 0.3%
Return on equity: 5.7%
Long-term debt ($ mil.): —
No. of shares (mil.): —
Sales ($ mil): 6,261

Dividends
Yield: 4.4%
Payout: 27.5%
Market value ($ mil.): —

	STOCK PRICE ($) FY Close	P/E High/Low	PER SHARE ($) Earnings	Dividends	Book Value
03/21	5.36	0 0	0.44	0.24	7.95
03/20	4.27	0 0	0.61	0.16	8.04
03/19	3.59	— —	(0.27)	0.13	7.18
03/18	5.85	0 0	0.58	0.19	7.63
03/17	6.27	0 0	0.59	0.11	7.07
Annual Growth	(3.8%)	— —	(7.0%)	22.3%	3.0%

Nordea Bank ABp

Nordea Bank is one of the largest financial services groups in the Nordic and Baltic Sea regions.

Sweden is its home but Nordea also has a major presence in Denmark Finland Norway and Russia. The bank splits its operations into three main divisions: retail banking wholesale banking and wealth management. The bank also provides life and pension products. Originally founded in the 1820s Nordea Bank now boasts a network of about 700 branches and serves some 11 million customers including about 1 million corporate clients — a key customer segment for Nordea. About 55% of its lending activity is to corporations.

Operations

The bank operates through three main segments. Retail Banking generates roughly 55% of the bank's overall income and offers a wide range of traditional deposit and loan products for both household customers and corporate clients mostly in the Nordic markets and the Baltic countries.

Wholesale Banking brings in another 25% of total revenue and provides banking and other financial services to large Nordic and global corporate institutional and public companies. This division also serves financial sector clients with funds and equity products as well as consulting services within asset allocation and fund sales. Nordea Bank Russia offers a full range of bank services to corporate and private customers in Russia. Capital Markets unallocated includes the result in Capital Markets which is not allocated to the main business areas.

Roughly 15% of revenue comes from the Wealth Management division which provides investment savings and risk management products. It also manages customers' assets and gives financial advice to affluent and high net worth individuals and institutional investors.

Additionally Nordea offers financing and other services to clients in the Shipping Offshore & Oil Services industries. The bank also has a Life & Pensions business and an Asset Management division that is responsible for all actively-managed investment products.

Geographic Reach

Nordea Bank has an international network of branches subsidiaries and representative offices in almost 20 countries around the world with most of its operations in Denmark Finland Norway and Sweden. More than 30% of revenue comes from Denmark while Sweden generates another nearly 25%. Finland and Norway markets contribute more than 15% each. Other large markets include the Baltic countries and Russia.

Sales and Marketing

The bank serves private customers (from general retail to the highly-affluent) corporations financial institutions and other global institutional customers.

Nordea's mobile banking activity has been growing. In 2014 transaction volume from its mobile bank channels grew by 90% with the number of active mobile banking users growing by 1000 per day.

Financial Performance

Note: Growth rates may differ after conversion to US dollars.

Nordea's annual revenues have remained mostly stable for the past few years while profits have steadily been rising. Revenue in 2014 grew by 3% to ?10.22 billion ($12.42 billion) mostly thanks to higher commission income from investment and lending services from the bank's growing Wealth Management and Retail Banking divisions.

Higher revenue in 2014 pushed profit higher for a third straight year with net income rising by 7% to ?3.33 billion ($4.05 billion). Also helping the bank's bottom line net loan loss provisions declined by 26% as its loan portfolio gained credit strength.

Cash levels fell despite higher earnings in 2014 with operations using ?10.82 billion ($13.15 billion) primarily as deposit funding from credit institutions and the broader public declined over the year.

Strategy

Nordea Bank has continued to focus more on its four key markets in the Nordic and Baltic regions (including Denmark Finland Norway and Sweden). In mid-2014 to better concentrate resources on these key markets Nordea exited its banking life and financing businesses in Poland through the sale of its Nordea Bank Polska S.A. to PKO Bank Polski SA for ?694 million ($927 million).

As the industry moves from brick-and-mortar branch banking to digital banking Nordea has also been expanding its electronic offerings via its mobile tablet Netbank and Facebook platforms. Indeed during 2014 the bank reported that the number of mobile transactions grew by 90% reflecting the change in consumer tastes in the banking industry. In late 2014 the company announced that it would increase its IT investments by 30-35% over the coming years building new core banking and payment platforms to keep up with the digital banking trend.

Company Background

Sampo owns more than 20% of Nordea. The Swedish government held a nearly 20% stake in the bank but reduced that to 13% in 2011 as part of its plan to raise capital. It plans to sell more and possibly all of its Nordea stake over time.

Growth in European markets has been a focus for Nordea. In 2009 the company purchased a 75% stake in Russian bank JSB Orgresbank rebranding it as OJSC Nordea Bank. Nordea also bought the Polish life insurance operations of Finnish banking group Sampo doubling Nordea's customer base in Poland. However Nordea put the breaks on aggressive growth and completely halted branch expansion in Russia and the Baltic countries in light of the global financial crisis.

HISTORY

Nordea traces its roots to 1974 when two Swedish government-owned banks Postbanken and Sveriges Kreditbank merged to form the country's largest bank Post-och Kreditbanken (PKbanken) in order to compete with S-E-Banken and Svenska Handelsbanken.

PKbanken didn't hold on to the top spot long. By the early 1980s a recession and languid profits sank the company to third. However the firm did expand teaming with Norway's Christiana Bank og Kreditkasse to open joint offices in Hong Kong Houston London S o Paolo and Singapore.

As regulatory restrictions in Sweden eased the government spun off 15% of its interest in the company on the Stockholm Stock Exchange in 1984.

PKbanken pulled out of its deal in London with Christiana Bank in 1986 but it bought a stake in London-based English Trust Group to expand its merchant banking services. In 1988 PKbanken acquired government-owned Carnegie Fondkommission Sweden's largest brokerage and in 1989 purchased the state-controlled Swedish Investment Bank a provider of funding to small and midsized businesses.

A year later PKbanken acquired regional Swedish bank Nordbanken and assumed the smaller firm's name. Soon after the government axed the combined firm's top officers and installed new management. The purging didn't help as another recession and a real estate market crash hammered the company's bottom line. In 1992 the Swedish government intervened again acquiring all of the outstanding shares of Nordbanken that it did not already own. The company rebounded quickly after selling bad loans to the state and cutting staff by a fifth.

In 1994 the Swedish government transferred its ownership of Gota Bank to Nordbanken. The company resumed trading on the Stockholm Stock Exchange the following year.

Across the border in Finland rivals Union Bank of Finland and Kansallis-Osake-Pankki merged in 1995 to create Merita Bank the country's largest.

In 1997 Nordbanken and Merita Bank combined to form MeritaNordbanken but their parents Nordbanken Holdings and Merita Ab remained separate. In 2000 the company bought Danish bank Unidanmark. MeritaNordbanken's holding companies united and assumed the name Nordic Baltic Holding. Later the company changed its name to Nordea an amalgamation of "Nordic" and "idea."

In 2001 Nordea bought Christiania Bank og Kreditkasse and later that year attached the Nordea Bank name to its banking subsidiaries in Denmark Finland Norway and Sweden.

By 2003 the company composed primarily of the four national banking groups — Nordea Bank Denmark Nordea Bank Finland Nordea Bank Norway and Nordea Bank Sweden — decided to change its complex legal structure and create one European company under the Nordea Bank banner.

Nordea acquired Denmark's Fionia Bank in 2009 including the bank's staff and its 29 branches but excluding some 2000 troubled corporate customers. The Denmark government had taken control of the failing bank earlier in the year.

Auditors: PricewaterhouseCoopers Oy

LOCATIONS

HQ: Nordea Bank ABp
Smalandsgatan 17, Stockholm SE-105 71
Phone: (46) 8 614 78 00   **Fax:** (46) 8 614 87 70
Web: www.nordea.com

2014 Sales

	% of total
Denmark	31
Sweden	24
Finland	18
Norway	17
New European markets	4
Other	6
Total	**100**

PRODUCTS/OPERATIONS

2014 Sales

	% of total
Banking products	61
Capital markets products	19
Savings products and asset management	10
Life and pensions	5
Other	5
Total	**100**

2014 Sales

	% of total
Retail Banking	56
Wholesale Banking	24
Wealth Management	16
Group Corporate Centre	4
Total	**100**

2014 Sales

	% of total
Net Interest income	54
Net Fee abd commission income	28
Net results on items at fair value	14
Other Operating income	4
Total	**100**

COMPETITORS

COMMONWEALTH BANK OF AUSTRALIA	The Toronto-Dominion Bank
Danske Bank A/S	U.S. BANCORP
NATWEST GROUP PLC	

HISTORICAL FINANCIALS

Company Type: Public

Income Statement   FYE: December 31

	ASSETS ($ mil.)	NET INCOME ($ mil.)	INCOME AS % OF ASSETS	EMPLOYEES
12/20	677,660	2,746	0.4%	28,123
12/19	622,964	1,705	0.3%	29,300
12/18	631,469	3,515	0.6%	28,990
12/17	697,209	3,633	0.5%	30,399
12/16	650,063	3,976	0.6%	31,596
Annual Growth	1.0%	(8.8%)	—	(2.9%)

2020 Year-End Financials

Return on assets: 0.4%	Dividends
Return on equity: 6.8%	Yield: 0.1%
Long-term debt ($ mil.): —	Payout: 130.9%
No. of shares (mil.): —	Market value ($ mil.): —
Sales ($ mil): 14,020	

	STOCK PRICE ($) FY Close	P/E High/Low		Earnings	PER SHARE ($) Dividends	Book Value
12/20	8.16	18	10	0.68	0.88	10.22
12/19	8.12	25	16	0.43	0.52	8.73
12/18	8.39	0	0	87.03	0.79	9.30
Annual Growth	(1.4%)	—	—	(70.3%)	2.8%	2.4%

Norsk Hydro ASA

Like the aluminum products it mines manufactures and sells Norwegian industrial giant Norsk Hydro is both enduring and flexible. The company delivered some 2.8 million metric tons of sourced alumina in 2019. Its global operations include casthouse products building systems extruded and rolled products and automotive and transport products distributed worldwide. Norsk Hydro ranks among the world's largest aluminum producers along with Canada's Rio Tinto Alcan Russia's RUSAL and the US's Alcoa. It also owns and operates over 15 hydroelectric power stations in Norway. Majority of the company's sale were generated from the Europe.

Operations

The fully integrated aluminum company has operations across all the major aspects of the aluminum value chain from bauxite and alumina mining through aluminum smelting and production to sales and marketing. It is a global energy player purchasing and consuming substantial quantities of energy for its smelters rolling mills and alumina refinery operations. Norsk Hydro is also the largest publicly owned power producer in Norway stakes in some 25 hydroelectric power plants (approximately 2000 MW of installed capacity in 2019).

Norsk Hydro has six operating segments: Extruded Solutions Metal Markets Rolled Products Bauxite & Alumina Primary Metal and Energy.

Extruded Solutions (more than 40% of sales) delivers products within extrusion profiles building systems and precision tubing and is present in about 40 countries.

Metal Markets (over 25%) includes all sales and distribution activities relating to products from its primary metal plants and operational responsibility for the company's stand-alone remelters. It also includes metal sourcing and trading activities which provides operational risk management through LME hedging activities.

Rolled Products (more than 15%) consists of five European rolling mills which include the company's some 50% interest in the AluNorf rolling mill in Germany (and the Rheinwerk primary aluminum smelter in Neuss Germany).

Bauxite and Alumina (nearly 10%) includes bauxite mining activities comprised of the Paragominas mine and some 5% in Mineracao Rio de Norte (both located in Brazil) as well as over 90% of Brazilian alumina refinery Alunorte.

Primary Metal (some 5%) consists of aluminum production remelting and casting activities at company smelters and at the company's partly owned companies.

Energy (less than 5%) manages Hydro Norsk's captive hydropower production and external power sourcing arrangements to the aluminum business.

Geographic Reach

Based in Norway Norsk Hydro has primary metal production facilities in Europe Canada Australia Brazil and Qatar and remelting plants in a range of countries in Europe and the US. It has employees in around 40 countries.

Worldwide consumption amounted to approximately 28 million tons in 2019. Europe and North America each accounted for some 20% of world consumption.

The five largest producers in Western Europe supply about 70% of the European market. China is the largest single market representing around 35% of global consumption.

Overall the Europe generates around 55% of the company's total sales.

Sales and Marketing

To ensure a strong market orientation Norsk Hydro's sales function is organized centrally along business lines. The company is supported by sales offices in Europe Brazil the US and Singapore where it optimizes market contact and sales potential. The customers can contact the company through online contact forms which can be used anonymously. The products from Extruded Solutions are delivered to such sectors as construction automotive and heating ventilation and air conditioning.

Financial Performance

Revenues of the company in 2019 decreased by 3.6 billion NOK to 149.8 billion NOK primarily due to lower revenues on every operation.

Cash held by the company at the end of 2019 increased by 6.3 billion NOK to 12.3 billion NOK compared to the prior year with 6.0 million NOK. Cash provided by operations and financing activities were 12.6 billion NOK and 2.9 billion NOK respectively. Cash used by investing activities was 9.2 billion NOK primarily for purchases of property plant and equipment.

Strategy

Norsk Hydro's new strategic agenda is based on cost-competitive assets operational excellence strong market positions innovation and differentiation on sustainable processes and products. A clear capital allocation framework is established based on different strategic modes for each business area. The company also introduced a new capital allocation framework with strategic growth modes for the different parts of its value chain designed to increase returns and ensure that capital is allocated according to the following strategic objectives: more stable earnings profile; increased exposure in areas with a competitive advantage; larger customer base downstream; and sustainable value chain with lower environmental footprint to reduce risk.

Mergers and Acquisitions

In early 2019 Hydro has completed the acquisition of German powder coating company Metallbeschichtung Gerstungen GmbH (MBG) and welcomes around 100 new employees to Hydro. The acquisition strengthens Hydro's position in the building systems segment. It also supports Hydro's strategy of further integrating and expanding the DACH (Germany Austria and Switzerland) region's logistics center. Terms were not disclosed.

Also in early 2019 Hydro acquired the remaining 50 percent of Technal Middle East a company based in Bahrain delivering tailor-made aluminium building solutions in the Middle East. The acquisition strengthens Hydro Building Systems in Asia where the market growth is amongst the highest in the world. Financial terms were not disclosed.

HISTORY

Norwegian entrepreneurs Sam Eyde and Kristian Birkeland began Norsk Hydro-Elektrisk Kvaelstofaktieselskap (Norwegian Hydro-Electric Nitrogen Corp.) in 1905. The company used electricity generated from waterfalls to extract nitrogen from the air to produce fertilizer.

After WWII the Norwegian government seized German holdings in Norsk Hydro and took a 48% stake in the company. It grew to be the largest chemical firm in Scandinavia. In 1965 when Norway granted licenses for offshore petroleum exploration the company formed partnerships with foreign companies. These included Phillips Petroleum which spurred the North Sea boom in 1969 when its drilling rig Ocean Viking struck oil in the giant Ekofisk field and Elf Aquitaine which oversaw the Frigg discovery in 1971. The Norwegian state increased its share of Norsk Hydro to 51% in 1972.

The company also branched out with hydroelectric-powered aluminum processing at its Karmoy Works (1967) and with a fish-farming subsidiary Mowi (1969). During much of the 1970s it focused on oil and gas development which added to the treasury and helped finance growth often through acquisitions.

Norsk Hydro pushed into the European fertilizer market by buying Dutch company NSM in 1979; during the 1980s it acquired interests in fertilizer operations in France Sweden and the UK. In petrochemicals it expanded by buying two British PVC makers. Norsk Hydro-controlled Hydro Aluminum merged with ASV another Norwegian aluminum company in 1986 and the company consolidated its aluminum holdings two years later.

Hydro served as operator in the Oseberg field which began production in 1988 and grew rapidly to become a major source of oil and gas. In 1990 it bought 330 Danish gasoline stations from UNO-X; in 1992 it purchased Mobil Oil's Norwegian marketing and distribution system. Two years later Norsk Hydro merged its oil and marketing operations in Norway and Denmark with Texaco's.

A weak world economy and increased competition limited its revenues in 1992 and 1993. The company countered slumping sales by selling noncore subsidiaries including pharmaceutical unit Hydro Pharma (1992) and chocolate maker Freia Marabou (1993).

Norsk Hydro expanded further during the early 1990s acquiring fertilizer plants in Germany the UK and the US as well as W. R. Grace's ammonia plants in Trinidad and Tobago. The firm acquired Fisons' NPK fertilizer business in 1994. The company agreed to an asset swap with Petro-Canada in 1996 becoming a partner in oil and gas fields off the east coast of Canada. That year Norsk Hydro bought UNO-X's Swedish gas station operations.

The Norwegian government's stake in Norsk Hydro was reduced from 51% to about 45% in 1999 when the company and state-owned Statoil made a deal to take over Saga Petroleum Norway's leading independent oil producer to keep it out of foreign hands.

In light of major losses in 1999 by Hydro Agri the company made plans in 2000 to close several European nitrogen fertilizer operations. However it agreed to modernize and expand its Hydro Aluminum Sunndal facility to make it the largest aluminum plant in Europe. That year the company also sold Saga UK (North Sea assets) to Conoco and its fish-farming unit to Dutch company Nutreco.

In 2001 the company acquired a stake in Soquimich an industrial minerals company in Chile and majority control of Slovakian aluminum producer Slovalco.

The new decade brought with it a new focus; the company began to make aluminum its primary business lines. Toward that end Norsk Hydro bought VAW Aluminum from E.On AG for $2.8 billion in a deal that enabled it to expand its product base in Europe and the US especially to key customers in the automobile industry. It then sold its flexible packaging unit to Alcan for about $545 million in 2003. Furthering the same goal the company announced in 2003 and then followed through on a spinoff of its agrochemical unit the following year. The resultant company was Yara International.

Norsk Hydro sold its chemicals business to Ineos for $900 million in 2008.

In 2009 Svein Richard Brandtzæg took over as chief executive. He had been in charge of Hydro's Aluminum Products unit previously. Eivind Reiten resigned after eight years in charge of the company.

In 2011 Norsk Hydro acquired the Brazilian bauxite mining and alumina refining units of Vale SA for $5.7 billion making it a major bauxite and alumina miner.

The Vale purchase gave Norsk Hydro control of the world's third-largest bauxite mine and the world's biggest alumina refinery which have the capacity to supply the company with sufficient raw materials to operate without external suppliers for several decades. Norsk Hydro paid Vale about $1.1 billion in cash and a 22% stake in Norsk Hydro for the assets. The Norwegian government backed the deal and reduced its stake in Norsk Hydro by about 20%.

Although the Vale acquisition positioned Norsk Hydro for growth the aluminum markets have seen demand declining in 2011 and 30% of the aluminum producers losing money. Total demand growth declined to 7% in 2011 from a 19% increase in 2010. A drop in European demand has affected the market due primarily to uncertainty over eurozone debt. A weakening economy has Chinese producers starting to cut back on production and Hydro has stated that it would not restart its idled Sunndal smelter in Norway.

To raise cash in 2011 Norsk Hydro divested its 21% ownership stake in Norwegian power production company SKS Produksjon AS to Salten Kraftsamband AS for $187 million. The deal did not affect Hydro's other power grid holdings.

In 2012 it agreed to form an aluminum manufacturing joint venture with Orkla. The proposed joint venture which will retain the Sapa name (currently the aluminum products division of Orkla) will be equally owned by Norsk Hydro and Orkla and will combine their respective profiles building systems and tubing business to create the world's largest manufactured aluminum products provider.

EXECUTIVES

Independent Director, Employee Representative, Sten Martinsen

Executive Vice President-Legal & Compliance, Anne-Lene Midseim, $281,728 total compensation

EVP, Energy, Arvid Moss, $438,420 total compensation

Independent Director, Rune Bjerke

Independent Director, Employee Representative, Ellen Olstad

Independent Director, Liselott Kilaas

Executive Vice President - Hydro Aluminium Metal, Member of the Management Board, Eivind Kallevik, $398,371 total compensation

Independent Chairman of the Board, Dag Mejdell

Chief Financial Officer, Executive Vice President, Member of the Management Board, Pal Kildemo, $306,373 total compensation

Independent Deputy Chairman of the Board, Irene Rummelhoff

Independent Director, Marianne Wiinholt

Independent Director, Employee Representative, Arve Baade

Executive Vice President - People & Safety, Member of the Management Board, Hilde Vestheim Nordh, $254,107 total compensation

Executive Vice President - Hydro Rolling, Member of the Management Board, Einar Glomnes, $438,208 total compensation

EVP, Bauxite and Alumina, John Thuestad, $876,735 total compensation

Independent Director, Peter Kukielski

Head of Investor Relations, Line Haugetraa

Executive Vice President - Corporate Development, Member of the Management Board, Helena Nonka

President & Chief Executive Officer, Hilde Aasheim, $711,331 total compensation

Independent Director, Thomas Schulz

Auditors: KPMG AS

LOCATIONS

HQ: Norsk Hydro ASA
Drammensveien 260, Oslo N-0240
Phone: (47) 22 53 81 00   **Fax:** (47) 22 53 85 53
Web: www.hydro.com

2016 sales

	% of total
European Union	49
Non-European Union	7
Norway	4
Outside Europe	40
Total	**100**

PRODUCTS/OPERATIONS

2016 sales

	% of total
Bauxite & Alumina	15
Primary metal	7
Metal market	48
Rolled Products	27
Energy	3
Other and eliminations	-
Total	**100**

Selected Operations

Aluminum products
  Hydro aluminum automotive
  Hydro aluminum extrusion
  Hydro aluminum rolled products and wire rod
Aluminum metal
Energy
  Hydroelectric power stations

COMPETITORS

3A COMPOSITES USA INC.	Fortum Oyj
AIR PRODUCTS AND	Hydro Aluminium AS
CHEMICALS INC.	Nordural Grundartangi

COMPANHIA BRASILEIRA
DE ALUMINIO
COMPA IA ESPA OLA DE
PETROLEOS SAU

ehf.
OMV Aktiengesellschaft
SASOL LTD

HISTORICAL FINANCIALS
Company Type: Public

Income Statement — FYE: December 31

	REVENUE ($ mil.)	NET INCOME ($ mil.)	NET PROFIT MARGIN	EMPLOYEES
12/20	16,237	216	1.3%	34,240
12/19	17,069	(206)	—	36,310
12/18	18,449	490	2.7%	36,236
12/17	13,506	1,071	7.9%	34,625
12/16	9,639	742	7.7%	12,911
Annual Growth	13.9%	(26.5%)	—	27.6%

2020 Year-End Financials

Debt ratio: 1.8%
Return on equity: 2.3%
Cash ($ mil.): 2,070
Current ratio: 2.07
Long-term debt ($ mil.): 2,531

No. of shares (mil.): 2,049
Dividends
  Yield: 3.0%
  Payout: 138.9%
Market value ($ mil.): 9,385

	STOCK PRICE ($) FY Close	P/E High/Low		PER SHARE ($) Earnings	Dividends	Book Value
12/20	4.58	5	3	0.11	0.14	4.25
12/19	3.69	—	—	(0.10)	0.14	4.44
12/18	4.54	3	2	0.24	0.22	4.83
12/17	7.60	2	1	0.52	0.15	5.19
12/16	4.72	2	1	0.36	0.11	4.66
Annual Growth	(0.7%)	—		(26.6%)	5.2%	(2.2%)

North Pacific Bank Ltd

Sapporo Hokuyo Holdings supposes it has what customers need in the way of banking and financial services. The company was formed in 2001 to serve as the holding company for North Pacific Bank and The Sapporo Bank; together the regional banks have some 230 offices in Hokkaido as well as an office in Tokyo and two offices in China. North Pacific Bank which is the largest bank in Hokkaido accounts for most of the holding company's sales; the bank traces its roots to 1917. The company also has subsidiaries active in credit cards and leasing; bank subsidiaries engage in such activities as financing.
Auditors: KPMG AZSA LLC

LOCATIONS

HQ: North Pacific Bank Ltd
3-7 Odori-Nishi, Chuo-ku, Sapporo, Hokkaido 060-8661
Phone: (81) 11 261 1311
Web: www.hokuyobank.co.jp

COMPETITORS

Ageas
CANDOVER INVESTMENTS
  PLC
Clairvest Group Inc.
DEPFA BANK PUBLIC
  LIMITED COMPANY
EQUITY GROUP
  INVESTMENTS L.L.C.

IAP WORLDWIDE SERVICES
  INC.
ING Groep N.V.
KIYO HOLDINGSINC.
PRUDENTIAL PUBLIC
  LIMITED COMPANY

HISTORICAL FINANCIALS
Company Type: Public

Income Statement — FYE: March 31

	ASSETS ($ mil.)	NET INCOME ($ mil.)	INCOME AS % OF ASSETS	EMPLOYEES
03/21	107,096	85	0.1%	4,546
03/20	92,013	69	0.1%	4,722
03/19	88,129	127	0.1%	4,955
03/18	89,469	128	0.1%	5,112
03/17	81,334	149	0.2%	5,271
Annual Growth	7.1%	(13.1%)	—	(3.6%)

2021 Year-End Financials

Return on assets: 0.0%
Return on equity: 2.2%
Long-term debt ($ mil.): —
No. of shares (mil.): 389
Sales ($ mil.): 1,227

Dividends
  Yield: —
  Payout: 41.2%
Market value ($ mil.): —

Novartis AG Basel

Auditors: PricewaterhouseCoopers AG

LOCATIONS

HQ: Novartis AG Basel
Lichtstrasse 35, Basel CH-4056
Phone: (41) 61 324 1111   **Fax:** (41) 61 324 7826
Web: www.novartis.com

HISTORICAL FINANCIALS
Company Type: Public

Income Statement — FYE: December 31

	REVENUE ($ mil.)	NET INCOME ($ mil.)	NET PROFIT MARGIN	EMPLOYEES
12/21	52,877	24,021	45.4%	104,323
12/20	49,898	8,072	16.2%	105,794
12/19	48,677	11,732	24.1%	103,914
12/18	53,166	12,611	23.7%	125,161
12/17	50,135	7,703	15.4%	121,597
Annual Growth	1.3%	32.9%	—	(3.8%)

2021 Year-End Financials

Debt ratio: 22.1%
Return on equity: 38.6%
Cash ($ mil.): 12,407
Current ratio: 1.51
Long-term debt ($ mil.): 22,902

No. of shares (mil.): —
Dividends
  Yield: 2.3%
  Payout: 47.9%
Market value ($ mil.): —

	STOCK PRICE ($) FY Close	P/E High/Low		PER SHARE ($) Earnings	Dividends	Book Value
12/21	87.47	9	7	10.63	2.08	30.27
12/20	94.43	28	20	3.52	2.01	25.08
12/19	94.69	19	15	5.06	1.84	24.49
12/18	85.81	17	13	5.38	2.94	34.01
12/17	83.96	26	21	3.25	2.72	32.00
Annual Growth	1.0%	—	—	34.5%	(6.5%)	(1.4%)

Novo-Nordisk AS

Novo Nordisk is one of the world's leading producers of diabetes therapies including human insulin insulin analogues and injection devices. It makes modern insulin analogues Levemir and NovoLog (which mimic natural insulin regulation more closely than human insulin) Victoza for type 2 diabetes and Saxenda which treats obesity. The firm also has products in the areas of hemostasis management (blood clotting) human growth hormone and estrogen replacement therapy. The company has affiliates in some 80 countries and markets products in about 170 countries. The not-for-profit Novo Nordisk Foundation through its Novo A/S subsidiary controls the voting power in Novo Nordisk.

Operations

Novo Nordisk operates in two business segments: Diabetes and Obesity (which covers insulins oral anti-diabetic drugs and obesity therapies) and Biopharmaceuticals (which covers hemophilia care growth hormone therapy and hormone replacement therapy). Novo Nordisk is the world's leader in diabetes medicines with nearly half of the total insulin market in volume.

The Diabetes and Obesity segment accounts for about 85% of annual revenue primarily from diabetes treatments. Top product offerings include Levemir and Tresiba (long-acting insulin) NovoMix/NovoLog Mix (premix insulin) NovoRapid/NovoLog (fast-acting insulin) Victoza (type 2 diabetes and weight management) and Saxenda (obesity).

The remainder of sales comes from the Biopharmaceuticals segment which includes the NovoSeven (hemophilia) NovoEight (hemophilia) Norditropin (growth hormone deficiencies) and hormone replacement therapy offerings.

Geographic Reach

Headquartered in Denmark Novo Nordisk has some 15 production facilities and 10 research and development centers located in Algeria Brazil China Denmark France India Japan Russia UK and US.

Its primary markets are North America (about 50% of revenues) China Japan and major countries in Europe.

Financial Performance

Note: Growth rates may differ after conversion to US Dollars.

Novo Nordisk's revenue for the year ended 2020 was DKK 126.9 billion a 4% increase from the previous year. Sales growth was negatively impacted by COVID-19 driven by fewer patients initiating treatment. Novo Nordisk's 2020 sales and operating profit performance measured at constant exchange rates (CER) were within the ranges provided in October 2020.

For the year ended 2020 the company's net profit totaled DKK 42.1 billion an 8% growth from the previous year.

The company's cash for the year ended 2020 totaled DKK 12.2 billion. Operating activities generated DKK 52 billion while investing activities used DKK 22.4 billion mainly for purchases of intangible assets. Financing activities used another DKK 32.2 billion primarily for payment of dividends.

Strategy

Novo Nordisk has been focused on sustainability for many years ? but it is determined to continue to raise its game. In the past year the company launched a new social responsibility strategy Defeat Diabetes and initiated programs within renewable power and recycling as part of its Circular for Zero environmental strategy.

Above all 2020 underscored the need for strong corporate values and a shared sense of purpose. The company is fortunate that both are well-established across its organization empowering its employees to keep delivering for both patients and investors despite the unprecedented disruptions caused by COVID-19.

Mergers and Acquisitions

In late 2020 ? Novo Nordisk A/S completed the acquisition of Emisphere Technologies Inc. (Emisphere) a drug delivery company with proprietary technologies such as the Eligen SNAC technology that enable oral formulations of therapeutics. Novo Nordisk acquired all outstanding shares of Emisphere for about $1.35 billion. With these acquisitions Novo Nordisk eliminates its future royalty obligations to Emisphere and MHR and obtains full access to the Eligen SNAC technology platform thereby enabling Novo Nordisk to expand the portfolio of oral biologic pipeline assets across therapy areas.

In 2020 Novo Nordisk A/S agreed to acquire Corvidia Therapeutics Inc. a privately held clinical stage company focused on the research and development of transformative therapies for cardio-renal diseases. Novo Nordisk will acquire all outstanding shares of Corvidia Therapeutics for about $2.1 billion. The acquisition of Corvidia Therapeutics and its lead candidate ziltivekimab is aligned with Novo Nordisk's strategy to expand its presence across a range of cardiometabolic diseases that are closely linked to Novo Nordisk's core business within diabetes and obesity.

Company Background

Novo Nordisk was formed by the 1989 merger of Danish insulin producers Novo and Nordisk. The company traces its roots to the founding of two Danish insulin companies Nordisk Insulinlaboratorium and Novo Terapeutisk Laboratorium in 1923 and 1925 respectively.

HISTORY

Novo Nordisk was formed by the 1989 merger of Danish insulin producers Novo and Nordisk.

Soon after Canadian researchers first extracted insulin from the pancreases of cattle Danish researcher August Krogh (winner of the 1920 Nobel Prize in physiology) and physician Marie Krogh his wife teamed up with H. C. Hagedorn also a physician to found Nordisk Insulinlaboratorium. One of their lab workers was an inventor named Harald Pedersen and in 1923 Nordisk hired Pedersen's brother Thorvald to analyze chemicals. The relationship was unsuccessful however and the brothers left the company.

The Pedersens decided to produce insulin themselves and set up operations in their basement in 1924. Harald also designed a syringe that patients could use for their own insulin injections. Within a decade their firm Novo Terapeutisk Laboratorium was selling its product in 40 countries.

Meanwhile Nordisk introduced a slow-acting insulin in 1936. NPH insulin launched in the US in 1950 soon became the leading longer-acting insulin. Nordisk later became a major maker of human growth hormone.

During WWII Novo produced its first enzyme trypsin used to soften leather. It began producing penicillin in 1947 and during the 1950s developed Heparin a trypsin-based drug used to treat blood clots. The company unveiled more industrial enzymes in the 1960s.

In 1981 Novo began selling its insulin in the US through a joint venture with E. R. Squibb (now part of Bristol-Myers Squibb). The next year Novo was the first to produce human insulin (actually a modified form of pig insulin) and in 1983 Nordisk introduced the Nordisk Infuser a pump that constantly released small quantities of insulin. Two years later Novo debuted the NovoPen a refillable injector that looked like a fountain pen.

Novo was the world's #2 insulin maker (and the world's largest maker of industrial enzymes) when it merged with #3 Nordisk in 1989. By combining their research and market share they were better able to compete globally with then-#1 Eli Lilly. After the merger Novo Nordisk introduced the NovoLet the world's first prefilled disposable insulin syringe.

Novo Nordisk introduced drugs for depression (Seroxat 1992) epilepsy (Gabitril 1995) and hemophilia (NovoSeven 1995). The company entered a joint marketing alliance with Johnson & Johnson subsidiary LifeScan the world's #1 maker of blood glucose monitors in 1995. It also began working with Rhône-Poulenc Rorer on estrogen replacement therapies.

Eli Lilly raised a new challenge in 1996 with the FDA approval of Humalog (the US's first new insulin product in 14 years) which is absorbed faster giving users more flexibility in their injection schedule. (Novo Nordisk's own fast-acting insulin product NovoLog received FDA approval four years later.) A 1998 marketing pact with Schering-Plough signaled Novo Nordisk's desire to boost sales of its diabetes drugs in the US where Eli Lilly had historically dominated.

In 2000 Novo Nordisk split its health care and enzymes businesses; the split left Novo Nordisk with all the health care operations while a new company Novozymes was formed to carry out the enzyme business. It bought out the remaining shares in its Brazilian subsidiary Biobrás in 2001. In 2002 the company spun off its US-based biotechnology firm ZymoGenetics. It retained a one-third of the company until selling its shares to Bristol-Myers Squibb in 2010.

Further boosting its portfolio of diabetes and obesity intellectual property the company acquired two US biopharmaceutical research firms (Calibrium and MB2) for undisclosed amounts in 2015.

Auditors: Deloitte Statsautoriseret Revisionspartnerselskab

LOCATIONS

HQ: Novo-Nordisk AS
Novo Alle 1, Bagsvaerd DK-2880
Phone: (45) 4444 8888   **Fax:** (45) 4449 0555
Web: www.novonordisk.com

PRODUCTS/OPERATIONS

2016 Sales

	% of total
Diabetes and obesity care	
NovoRapid/Novolog	18
Levemir	15
Victoza	18
NovoMix/NovologMix	10
Human insulin	10
Other diabetes and obesity care (including Saxenda)	5
New-generation insulin	4
Biopharmaceuticals	
Haemophilia	9
Norditropin	8
Other products	3
Total	**100**

2016 sales

	% of total
USA	51
Europe	19
Region China	9
Pacific	8
other countries	13
Total	**100**

Selected Products

Diabetes products
  Human insulins
  Actrapid
  Insulatard
  Mixtard 30
  Glucagon-like Peptide-1
  Victoza
  Modern insulins
  Levemir
  NovoMix
  NovoRapid
  Oral antidiabetic agents
  NovoNorm
  PrandiMet
Biopharmaceuticals

NovoSeven (recombinant hemophilia therapy)
Norditropin (human growth hormone)
Hormone replacement therapy
Activelle
Estrofem
Novofem
Vagifem

COMPETITORS

ADARE PHARMACEUTICALS INC.	INCYTE CORPORATION
AMGEN INC.	IONIS PHARMACEUTICALS INC.
ASTRAZENECA PLC	MERCK & CO. INC.
BRISTOL-MYERS SQUIBB COMPANY	PFIZER INC.
Boehringer Ingelheim International GmbH	SANOFI
	TAKEDA PHARMACEUTICAL COMPANY LIMITED

HISTORICAL FINANCIALS

Company Type: Public

Income Statement

FYE: December 31

	REVENUE ($ mil.)	NET INCOME ($ mil.)	NET PROFIT MARGIN	EMPLOYEES
12/21	21,428	7,268	33.9%	48,478
12/20	20,939	6,950	33.2%	45,323
12/19	18,337	5,853	31.9%	43,258
12/18	17,150	5,924	34.5%	43,202
12/17	17,984	6,139	34.1%	42,076
Annual Growth	4.5%	4.3%	—	3.6%

2021 Year-End Financials

Debt ratio: 1.8%	No. of shares (mil.): —
Return on equity: 71.2%	Dividends
Cash ($ mil.): 1,631	Yield: 0.9%
Current ratio: 0.86	Payout: 36.1%
Long-term debt ($ mil.): 1,469	Market value ($ mil.): —

	STOCK PRICE ($) FY Close	P/E High/Low		PER SHARE ($) Earnings	Dividends	Book Value
12/21	112.00	6	3	3.16	1.05	4.66
12/20	69.85	4	3	2.97	0.93	4.52
12/19	57.88	4	3	2.46	0.87	3.68
12/18	46.07	3	3	2.44	0.91	3.24
12/17	53.67	4	2	2.48	0.88	3.28
Annual Growth	20.2%	—	—	6.2%	4.6%	9.2%

NTT Data Corp

Auditors: KPMG AZSA LLC

LOCATIONS

HQ: NTT Data Corp
3-3-3 Toyosu, Koto-ku, Tokyo 135-6033
Phone: (81) 3 5546 8119
Web: www.nttdata.com

HISTORICAL FINANCIALS

Company Type: Public

Income Statement

FYE: March 31

	REVENUE ($ mil.)	NET INCOME ($ mil.)	NET PROFIT MARGIN	EMPLOYEES
03/21	20,940	694	3.3%	143,081
03/20	20,882	692	3.3%	136,464
03/19	19,537	845	4.3%	126,953
03/18	19,938	547	2.7%	121,020
03/17	15,495	587	3.8%	114,658
Annual Growth	7.8%	4.3%	—	5.7%

2021 Year-End Financials

Debt ratio: 0.1%		No. of shares (mil.): 1,402	
Return on equity: 7.6%		Dividends	
Cash ($ mil.): 2,592		Yield: 0.0%	
Current ratio: 1.20		Payout: —	
Long-term debt ($ mil.): 4,273		Market value ($ mil.): 22,440	

	STOCK PRICE ($) FY Close	P/E High/Low		PER SHARE ($) Earnings	Dividends	Book Value
03/21	16.00	0	0	0.49	0.16	6.91
03/20	8.37	0	0	0.49	0.16	6.17
03/19	10.64	0	0	0.60	0.14	5.96
03/18	10.20	1	0	0.39	0.15	5.60
03/17	23.69	1	0	0.42	0.13	5.09
Annual Growth	(9.3%)	—	—	4.3%	5.2%	7.9%

Nutrien Ltd

Auditors: KPMG LLP

LOCATIONS

HQ: Nutrien Ltd
Suite 500, 122 - 1st Avenue South, Saskatoon,
Saskatchewan S7K 7G3
Phone: 306 933-8523   **Fax:** 306 933-8877
Web: www.nutrien.com

HISTORICAL FINANCIALS

Company Type: Public

Income Statement
FYE: December 31

	REVENUE ($ mil.)	NET INCOME ($ mil.)	NET PROFIT MARGIN	EMPLOYEES
12/20	20,908	459	2.2%	23,100
12/19	20,023	992	5.0%	22,300
12/18	19,636	3,573	18.2%	20,300
12/17	0	(0)	—	0
Annual Growth	—	—	—	—

2020 Year-End Financials

Debt ratio: 21.6%		No. of shares (mil.): 569	
Return on equity: 2.0%		Dividends	
Cash ($ mil.): 1,454		Yield: 3.7%	
Current ratio: 1.35		Payout: 124.1%	
Long-term debt ($ mil.): 10,047		Market value ($ mil.): 27,416	

	STOCK PRICE ($) FY Close	P/E High/Low		PER SHARE ($) Earnings	Dividends	Book Value
12/20	48.16	63	31	0.81	1.80	39.29
12/19	47.91	33	27	1.70	1.76	39.91
12/18	47.00	10	8	5.72	1.63	40.14
12/17	0.00	—	—	(0.00)	0.00	
(2,294.67)						
Annual Growth	—	—	—	—	—	

Obayashi Corp

Obayashi Corporation provide all types of buildings such as offices condominiums commercial facilities factories hospitals and schools that meet diverse needs including reduced environmental load and energy conservation comfort and convenience as well as seismic resistance and disaster readiness for securing business continuity. It builds infrastructure essential to people's lives such as tunnels bridges dams riverbanks railroads and expressways. Obayashi develop and own excellent leasing properties in prime locations primarily in metropolitan areas. In the urban redevelopment business it has experience in numerous projects as a project partner and specified agent. It promotes renewable energy PPP and agriculture business. Founded in 1892 by Yoshigoro Obayashi.

Operations

Obayashi operates four core business segments. Its Domestic Building Construction business (which generated 55% of net sales in fiscal 2020 ended March) builds offices condos commercial facilities factories hospitals and schools and designs for customers concerned with environmental harm energy conservation seismic resistance and disaster readiness. Its Domestic Civil Engineering business (16% of net sales) builds various types of infrastructure such as tunnels bridges dams riverbanks and more.

The company's Overseas Construction business (23% of net sales) builds infrastructure such as railroads bridges and expressway. Its Real Estate business (3% of net sales) works on redevelopment projects across Japan as a project partner or specified agent and sells properties for lease in favorable locations (mainly urban areas).

Geographic Reach

Obayashi Corporation is based in Japan. The company offices are internationally located in London Auckland Sydney Guam Taipei Jakarta Hanoi Phnom Penh Kuala Lumpur Bangkok Yangon Dhaka and Japan.

Sales and Marketing

Obayashi Corporation markets its products and services through its websites by its projects such as public facility such as government hospital educational and cultural. Office/ Industrial Facility; Logistic Research and Development Infrastructure; Telecommunications Dam Power Plant Railway Airport Amusement/Hospitality; Retail/Shopping Center Hotel Historical Building Structure Urban/Land Development Residence and Outsider Japan.

Financial Performance

Note: Growth rates may differ after conversion to US dollars. This analysis uses financials from the company's annual report.

The company's revenue for fiscal 2020 increased to 2.1 trillion from 2.0 trillion.

In 2020 net income decreased to 113.1 billion from the prior year's 113.2 billion.

Cash held by the company at the end of fiscal 2020 increased to 298.9 billion. Operating activities provided 237.6 billion while investing and financing activities used 47.3 billion and 49.4 billion respectively.

Strategy

In 2020 construction investment was steady in Obayashi's major markets. These included large-scale redevelopment of urban areas in Japan and building maintenance and repair of infrastructure.

The company's business strategy based on medium-term business plan includes:

Realize stable earnings by enhancing competitive advantages in growth markets and areas and providing integrated high-value-added services for buildings centered on leveraging the company's total capabilities and global network.

Improve productivity by building next-generation production systems utilizing IoT AI and robotics transforming business processes by basing then on BIM and developing labor-saving construction methods etc.

Eradicate serious accidents and quality and construction defects by implementing diverse education programs and rigorously managing safety and quality by ICT.

Secure production capacity by improving the working environment at construction sites developing multiskilled workers securing skilled workers and providing educational support etc.

Enhance earnings capacity and expand business domains by collaborating with local partners and sharing the company's technology in its overseas building construction business.

HISTORY

With the first wave of Japanese modernization in 1892 Yoshigoro Ohbayashi opened a small construction operation in Osaka. He won the bid for construction of the Abe Paper Mill. In 1898 he joined with partner Kamezo Shirasugi to lay the foundations for the Obayashi Corporation.

Obayashi's first big contract came in 1901 for the construction of buildings for Osaka's Fifth National Industry Fair. During the Russo-Japanese War the young corporation built 100 barracks in three weeks a feat that helped it win a contract to build Tokyo Station (completed 1914). Obayashi executives were invited to the US by the Fluor Company in the early 1920s to study advanced construction techniques. After a 1923 earthquake and firestorm leveled much of Tokyo Obayashi applied the technology it learned from Fluor to build quake-resistant fireproof buildings.

Like many Japanese companies Obayashi is quiet about its history in the years leading up to WWII and the rebuilding that followed. However the Korean War increased demand for company projects such as the Tokyo Station annex the Japan Broadcasting Corporation building and the first of 50 major dam projects.

In the 1960s Obayashi became the first Japanese construction firm to build an internal R&D facility. Its Technical Research Institute developed the OWS-Soletanche Diaphragm Wall Construction Method which it used on the New Osaka building in 1961 and has adapted to many other buildings since. In 1965 the company began its first major civil engineering project overseas doing its part in a 32-year-long excavation in Singapore that reclaimed about 3% of that country's land mass from the sea. Also that year Obayashi completed the first high-rise in Japan Yokohama's 21-story Hotel Empire.

Expo '70 in Osaka showcased Obayashi's air-membrane dome and roof lift-up method. During the 1970s the company played key roles in Japan's massive highway-building projects. In 1979 it was the first Japanese construction company to be awarded a public works contract in the US.

Obayashi completed thousands of projects during the 1980s. It helped build the Tsukuba Expo '85 and restored the Katsura Rikyu Detached Palace a national treasure.

In 1994 two former Obayashi executives were found guilty of giving a 10 million yen (about $100000) bribe to the mayor of Sendai two years earlier. The company was one of several major construction companies involved in the scandal.

In the 1990s Obayashi "mole" machines chewed through the earth to create the Tokyo Bay Aqualine tunnel. In 1996 the company developed anti-earthquake construction methods for structures built on soft ground (almost a fifth of buildings in Tokyo).

Obayashi was hard hit in 1998 and 1999 as financial crises created turmoil in Japan's construction industry. The company responded by reducing its workforce by about 5% taking advantage of economies of scale in materials purchasing and working with subcontractors to cut costs. Beefing up its project orders is another key strategy. New projects secured by Obayashi in 2000 included the Taiwan North-South High Speed Rail Project and a new head office for Japanese advertising giant Dentsu.

In 2002 the group completed the NHK Osaka Broadcasting Station and the renovation of Kobe Wing Stadium a site for part of the 2002 World Cup soccer finals. Obayashi and Kobe Steel won the contract to operate the stadium for 15 years.

Obayashi was caught in a building scandal in its home country in 2005 when it came to light that an outside architect had falsified documents regarding earthquake resistance for one of its projects a hotel. Obayashi said that the falsifications were too skillfully done to catch at the construction stage.

EXECUTIVES

Independent Director, Hiroyuki Kato
Independent Director, Naoki Izumiya
Independent Director, Yoko Kobayashi
Executive Vice President, Chief Director of Safety Quality Administration, Representative Director, Takehito Sato
Independent Director, Shinichi Koizumi
Executive Vice President, Chief Director of Total Sales, Director of Tokyo Main Office Construction Business, Manager of Tokyo Main Office, Director, Atsushi Sasagawa
President, Representative Director, Kenji Hasuwa
Executive Vice President, Chief Director of Yumeshima Development Promotion, Manager of Osaka Main Office, Director, Toshihiko Murata
Executive Vice President, Director, Yasuo Kotera
Independent Director, Masako Orii
Managing Executive Officer, Senior Director of Tokyo Main Office, Manager of Global Business Strategy Office, Director, Toshimi Sato
Chairman of the Board, Representative Director, Takeo Ohbayashi
Auditors: Ernst & Young ShinNihon LLC

LOCATIONS

HQ: Obayashi Corp
2-15-2 Konan, Minato-ku, Tokyo 108-8502
Phone: (81) 3 5769 1017   **Fax:** 650 589-8384
Web: www.obayashi.co.jp

2014 Sales

	% of total
Japan	81
Overseas	
North America	10
Asia	8
Others	1
Total	**100**

Obayashi has operations in Cambodia China Indonesia Japan Malaysia the Philippines Singapore Taiwan Thailand the UK the US and Vietnam.

PRODUCTS/OPERATIONS

2014 Sales

	% of total
Domestic Building Construction Business	56
Domestic Civil Engineering Business	20
Overseas Construction Business	18
Real Estate Business	3
Other Business	3
Total	**100**

Selected Subsidiaries and Affiliates

Atelier G&B Co. Ltd.
E.W. Howell Co. Inc. (US)
James E. Roberts-Obayashi Corporation (50% housing projects US)
Mutsuzawa Green Co. Ltd. (golf club and restaurant operations)
Naigai Technos Corporation
Obayashi Real Estate Corporation
Obayashi Road Corporation
OC Finance Corporation
OC Real Estate Management LLC (US)

SOMA Environment Service Corporation
Taiwan Obayashi Corporation
Thai Obayashi Corporation Limited (49%)

COMPETITORS

ARCADIS N.V.
BALFOUR BEATTY INFRASTRUCTURE INC.
BAM NUTTALL LIMITED
Bilfinger SE
CONTI ENTERPRISES INC.
COSTAIN GROUP PLC
EIFFAGE
ENGLISH CONSTRUCTION COMPANY INCORPORATED
FERROVIAL SA
GRIFFITH COMPANY
HASEKO CORPORATION
HILL & SMITH INFRASTRUCTURE PRODUCTS GROUP LIMITE
HOCHTIEF AG
KAJIMA CORPORATION
MORO CORPORATION
SKANSKA USA CIVIL INC.
STERLING CONSTRUCTION COMPANY INC.
STRABAG SE
TAISEI CORPORATION

HISTORICAL FINANCIALS

Company Type: Public

Income Statement

FYE: March 31

	REVENUE ($ mil.)	NET INCOME ($ mil.)	NET PROFIT MARGIN	EMPLOYEES
03/21	15,957	892	5.6%	19,058
03/20	19,097	1,041	5.5%	18,879
03/19	18,418	1,021	5.5%	18,832
03/18	17,899	872	4.9%	18,752
03/17	16,749	845	5.0%	18,525
Annual Growth	(1.2%)	1.4%	—	0.7%

2021 Year-End Financials

Debt ratio: 0.1%
Return on equity: 11.3%
Cash ($ mil.): 2,335
Current ratio: 1.28
Long-term debt ($ mil.): 1,841

No. of shares (mil.): 718
Dividends
  Yield: —
  Payout: —
Market value ($ mil.): —

Oberbank AG (Austria)

Border-hopping is painless for Oberbank the Central European regional bank that focuses on business banking and has designs on international expansion. Oberbank which has more than 130 locations has operations throughout Austria as well as in the Czech Republic Germany Hungary and Slovakia. The bank serves individual clients but caters to business particularly the industrial sector and small and midsized firms. Oberbank units are involved in such activities as investment leasing and real estate lending. A unit of Unicredit Bank Austria owns about one-third of Oberbank which has minority cross-ownership alliances with Bank für Kärnten und Steiermark (BKS) and Bank für Tirol and Vorarlberg (BTV).

EXECUTIVES

Member of the Supervisory Board, Employee Representative, Markus Rohrbacher
Member of the Management Board, Josef Weissl, $591,503 total compensation

Member of the Supervisory Board, Employee Representative, Alexandra Grabner
Chairman of the Management Board, Chief Executive Officer, Franz Gasselsberger, $950,912 total compensation
Independent First Vice Chairman of the Supervisory Board, Ludwig Andorfer, $22,533 total compensation
Independent Member of the Supervisory Board, Peter Mitterbauer, $20,280 total compensation
Independent Member of the Supervisory Board, Herbert Walterskirchen, $20,280 total compensation
Member of the Management Board, Florian Hagenauer, $499,116 total compensation
Independent Member of the Supervisory Board, Karl Samstag, $20,280 total compensation
Independent Chairman of the Supervisory Board, Herta Stockbauer, $27,040 total compensation
Independent Second Vice Chairman of the Supervisory Board, Gerhard Burtscher, $22,533 total compensation
Independent Member of the Supervisory Board, Wolfgang Eder, $20,280 total compensation
Member of the Supervisory Board, Employee Representative, Wolfgang Pischinger
Member of the Supervisory Board, Employee Representative, Stefan Prohaska
Independent Member of the Supervisory Board, Gregor Hofstaetter-Pobst
Member of the Supervisory Board, Employee Representative, Elfriede Hoechtel
Member of the Supervisory Board, Employee Representative, Herbert Skoff
Honorary President of the Supervisory Board, Hermann Bell, $10,081 total compensation
Independent Member of the Supervisory Board, Alfred Leu, $20,280 total compensation
Auditors: KPMG Austria GmbH

LOCATIONS

HQ: Oberbank AG (Austria)
Untere Donaulaende 28, Linz A-4020
Phone: (43) 732 78 02 0   **Fax:** (43) 732 78 58 10
Web: www.oberbank.com

COMPETITORS

ARAB BANK PLC   UniCredit Bank AG
BANK OF AYUDHYA PUBLIC COMPANY LIMITED

HISTORICAL FINANCIALS

Company Type: Public

Income Statement

FYE: December 31

	ASSETS ($ mil.)	NET INCOME ($ mil.)	INCOME AS % OF ASSETS	EMPLOYEES
12/19	35,923	338	0.9%	2,150
12/18	34,953	353	1.0%	2,101
12/17	32,779	314	1.0%	0
12/16	30,147	284	0.9%	2,049
12/15	28,707	261	0.9%	2,025
Annual Growth	5.8%	6.6%	—	1.5%

2019 Year-End Financials

Return on assets: 0.9%
Return on equity: 7.4%
Long-term debt ($ mil.): —
No. of shares (mil.): 32
Sales ($ mil): 1,128

Dividends
  Yield: —
  Payout: 18.7%
Market value ($ mil.): —

Ogaki Kyoritsu Bank, Ltd.

The Ogaki Kyoritsu Bank provides banking and other financial services in the Gifu prefecture in central Japan. The bank serves consumers and businesses from more than 140 domestic branch locations and from 3 international offices in Hong Kong Shanghai and New York. Services include banking credit cards credit guaranty and leasing. Ogaki Kyoritsu Bank was established in 1896.

EXECUTIVES

President, Representative Director, Toshiyuki Sakai

Auditors: KPMG AZSA LLC

LOCATIONS

HQ: Ogaki Kyoritsu Bank, Ltd.
  3-98 Kuruwa-machi, Ogaki, Gifu 503-0887
Phone: (81) 584 74 2111
Web: www.okb.co.jp

COMPETITORS

BANK OF EAST ASIA LIMITED THE
EHIME BANK LTD. THE
NISHI-NIPPON CITYBANKLTD.

HISTORICAL FINANCIALS

Company Type: Public

Income Statement				FYE: March 31
	ASSETS ($ mil.)	NET INCOME ($ mil.)	INCOME AS % OF ASSETS	EMPLOYEES
03/21	67,291	72	0.1%	4,285
03/20	55,118	50	0.1%	4,401
03/19	52,678	61	0.1%	4,484
03/18	54,190	91	0.2%	4,499
03/17	50,913	108	0.2%	4,457
Annual Growth	7.2%	(9.7%)	—	(1.0%)

2021 Year-End Financials

Return on assets: 0.1%
Return on equity: 2.6%
Long-term debt ($ mil.): —
No. of shares (mil.): 41
Sales ($ mil): 1,051

Dividends
Yield: —
Payout: 36.5%
Market value ($ mil.): —

Oita Bank Ltd (Japan)

Auditors: Deloitte Touche Tohmatsu LLC

LOCATIONS

HQ: Oita Bank Ltd (Japan)
  3-4-1 Funaimachi, Oita 870-0021
Phone: (81) 97 534 1111
Web: www.oitabank.co.jp

HISTORICAL FINANCIALS

Company Type: Public

Income Statement				FYE: March 31
	ASSETS ($ mil.)	NET INCOME ($ mil.)	INCOME AS % OF ASSETS	EMPLOYEES
03/21	34,442	32	0.1%	2,587
03/20	31,257	46	0.1%	2,656
03/19	30,049	52	0.2%	2,711
03/18	30,325	56	0.2%	2,786
03/17	28,719	67	0.2%	2,866
Annual Growth	4.6%	(16.6%)	—	(2.5%)

2021 Year-End Financials

Return on assets: 0.1%
Return on equity: 1.8%
Long-term debt ($ mil.): —
No. of shares (mil.): 15
Sales ($ mil): 521

Dividends
Yield: —
Payout: 35.0%
Market value ($ mil.): —

Oji Holdings Corp

One of Japan's top paper makers along with Nippon Paper Industries Co. Oji Holdings produces pulp and paper and converted paper products through nearly 190 subsidiaries and affiliates worldwide. Its business segments include: Industrial Materials Household and Consumer Products Functional Materials Forest Resources and Environment Marketing Printing and Communications Media and other businesses which focus on real estate engineering trading business and logistic. Products include container board and corrugated containers boxboard and folding cartons among others. Japan is responsible for more 70% of the sales. Customers include overseas and domestic companies in the retail and energy sectors. The company was founded in 1873.

Operations

The company has four operating segments. These being: Household and Industrial Materials accounting for nearly 40% Functional Faterials generates some 15% Forest Resource and Environment Marketing brings in more than 15% and Printing and Communications Media gets less than 20%.

Industrial Materials segment focuses on containerboard and corrugated containers boxboard and folding cartons. Household and Consumer Products segment centers on tissue toilet tissue and wet wipes. Functional Materials segment provides specialty paper thermal paper and film. Forest Resources and Environment Marketing segment concentrates on pulp energyplantation service and lumber processing. Printing and Communications Media segment makes newsprint printing and publication and communications paper.

Geographic Reach

Headquartered in Tokyo Japan is Oji Holdings' largest market accounting for 70%. Other sales are made in Asia which accounts for nearly 20% Oceania Europe and the Americas each contributes some 5%.

Sales and Marketing

It serves various industries such as energy retail film packaging and newsprint among others.

Financial Performance

Oji Holdings' net sales has been in the 1.4 billion to 1.6 billion range for the past five years recording a 5% increase from 2015 to 2019. Meanwhile the company's net income has achieved year-over-year growth after its decline in 2017. Net income increased by 358% from 2015 to 2019.

Net sales decreased from 1.6 billion in 2018 to 1.5 billion in 2019. Household and Industrial Materials remains to have the top net sales per business segment comprising 38.8% of the company's 2019 revenue. This was followed by the Printing and Communications Media segment (16.5%) Other (16.4%) Forest Resources and Environment Marketing Business (16.1%) and Functional Materials (12.2%).

Cash and cash equivalents at the end of the year were 82.4 billion similar to the previous year. Cash provided by operations was 124.5 billion. Investing activities used 64.8 billion primarily for payment for acquisition of property plant equipment and intangible assets. Financing activities on the other hand used 58.1 billion primarily for repayment of long-term loans payable.

Strategy

Oji Holdings' new corrugated container plant in Funabashi City Chiba Prefecture has started commercial production in July 2020 to meet the growth in demand for corrugated containers in the Kanto region. The Industrial Materials Company will enhance its competitive strength in the corrugated container business in the Kanto region by aggressively capturing new demand for corrugated containers and expanding its supply volume. At the same time as part of its initiatives to restructure manufacturing in response to structural changes in domestic demand we will shut down the manufacturing facilities at the Oji Materia Nayoro Mill and transfer other facilities to Oji Paper Tomakomai Mill and production facilities for newsprint at the Tomakomai Mill are now in the midst of modification for containerboard and kraft paper. To further reinforce earnings bases through the integration of material and converting a range of investments will be made for the optimization of the domestic business structure.

The Industrial Materials Company conducts business at 45 sites in nine countries in Southeast Asia India and Oceania. It has been focusing mainly on expanding converting sites to respond to growing packaging demand and now it will install new containerboard production facilities in Malaysia which is scheduled to start commercial operation in 2021. Through these efforts the company will further progress the development of overseas businesses by integrating material and converting.

HISTORY

Eiichi Shibusawa established Oji Paper in 1873 as Shoshi-Gaisha. Production began two years later at the company's mill in Oji. The company which was partially funded by the Mitsui Group was the first in Japan to use Western papermaking technology. During the 1890s the Mitsui Group granted the company additional funding to install the latest papermaking technology in Shoshi-Gaisha's facilities but the Group removed Shibusawa from the company's management team soon after. The company was renamed Oji Paper Manufacturing Company in 1893. Oji Paper enjoyed great success and expansion under the management of the Mitsui Group and during WWI as Japan's exports tripled the company's sales substantially increased.

In 1933 Oji Paper acquired Fuji Paper and Karafuto Industries and soon was producing about 80% of the country's paper needs. The company prospered through WWII despite significant shortages of raw materials. During the Allied occupation that followed the war the company was forced to split into three companies: Jujo Paper Honshu Paper and Tomakomai Paper. Tomakomai was renamed Oji Paper shortly after the split. Experiencing a shortage of imported pulp after the war the company propositioned US government officials to create a company that would import pulp from Alaska. In 1953 the Alaska Pulp Company was established and began supplying pulp to Oji Paper and its affiliates.

The company modernized its facilities during the 1960s which led to cutbacks in its workforce; the cutbacks were followed by strikes and lockouts during that period. The 1970s brought acquisitions that included Kita Nippon Paper and Nippon Pulp Industries. The company also built mills in New Zealand (1971) and Brazil (1972). Throughout the 1970s and 1980s Oji Paper enhanced its line of specialty and consumer paper products; it added its own line of disposable diapers in 1989. The company also increased its newsprint output that year when it purchased Toyo Pulp Company. Despite apparent decreases in demand for newsprint from the late 1980s the company continued to grow into the 1990s due to its higher reliance on other paper products.

The company's acquisitions of Kanzaki Paper (1993) and Honshu Paper (1996) reinforced its influence in international paper markets. In 1999 amid a recession in Japan the company began implementing major cutbacks on its operations that included reducing staff eliminating or stopping some of its paper machines and consolidating some of its divisions such as its self-adhesive products unit. The cutbacks proved successful and Oji Paper bounced back to profitability in 2000. To keep operating costs low the company is now expanding into Asia with new facilities planned or already open in China.

In 2002 Oji Paper continued to restructure and cut costs as Japan's slumping information technology and advertising business negatively affected its paper business and depressed sales of home appliances led to poor sales in its paperboard segment.

In mid-2006 Oji made an (ultimately unsuccessful) unsolicited $1.2 billion bid for rival Hokuetsu Paper Mills. The deal made a stir because it is highly unusual for Japanese firms to make unsolicited takeover bids. Oji's takeover attempt eventually inspired competitors Nippon Paper and Rengo to combine forces around cardboard manufacturing a segment that Oji had been leading.

In 2007 the company agreed to a partnership with Mitsubishi Paper Mills to combat increasing raw material costs and a shrinking domestic market. Mitsubishi plans to up its capacity at its mills to accommodate Oji orders while Oji has agreed to supply Mitsubishi paper with thermostatic recording paper from its Thailand subsidiary.

EXECUTIVES

Group Senior Managing Executive Officer, President of Resource Environment Business Company, President of Print Information Media Company, President of Subsidiary, Director, Fumio Shindo

Non-Executive Independent Director, Seiko Nagai
Non-Executive Independent Director, Toshihisa Takata

Group Managing Executive Officer, President of Functional Materials Company, President of Subsidiary, Director, Shigeki Aoki

Group Managing Executive Officer, Deputy Chief Director of Corporate Governance, President of Subsidiary, Director, Koichi Ishida

Group Senior Managing Executive Officer, Chief Director of Corporate Governance, President of Subsidiary, Director, Hiroyuki Isono

Non-Executive Independent Director, Michihiro Nara

Group Managing Executive Officer, Director, Kazuhiko Kamada

Group Senior Managing Executive Officer, President of Industrial Materials Company, President of Consumer Products Company, Chairman & President of Subsidiaries, Director, Yoshiki Koseki

President, Executive President, Group Chief Executive Officer, Representative Director, Masatoshi Kaku

Independent Director, Sachiko Ai

Chairman of the Board, Chairman of Board of Directors, Representative Director, Susumu Yajima

Auditors: Deloitte Touche Tohmatsu LLC

LOCATIONS

HQ: Oji Holdings Corp
4-7-5 Ginza, Chuo-ku, Tokyo 104-0061
Phone: (81) 3 3563 1111   **Fax:** (81) 3 3563 1135
Web: www.ojiholdings.co.jp

PRODUCTS/OPERATIONS

2016 Sales

	% of total
Household and industrial materials	42
Printing and communication media	21
Forest resource and environment marketing	19
Functional materials	15
Others	3
Total	**100**

COMPETITORS

AEON CO. LTD.	MITSUBISHI CHEMICAL
DOMTAR CORPORATION	HOLDINGS CORPORATION
DS SMITH PLC	Outokumpu Oyj
ENEOS HOLDINGS INC.	SOFTBANK GROUP CORP.
FUJIFILM HOLDINGS	SOMPO HOLDINGS INC.
CORPORATION	THE ALUMASC GROUP PLC
GEA Group AG	TOYO SEIKAN GROUP
HOKUETSU CORPORATION	HOLDINGSLTD.
JFE HOLDINGS INC.	UPM-Kymmene Oyj

HISTORICAL FINANCIALS

Company Type: Public

Income Statement				FYE: March 31
	REVENUE ($ mil.)	NET INCOME ($ mil.)	NET PROFIT MARGIN	EMPLOYEES
03/21	12,273	448	3.7%	36,034
03/20	13,888	535	3.9%	36,810
03/19	14,005	469	3.4%	36,309
03/18	13,993	341	2.4%	36,144
03/17	12,878	327	2.5%	38,389
Annual Growth	(1.2%)	8.2%	—	(1.6%)

2021 Year-End Financials

Debt ratio: 0.3%	No. of shares (mil.): 992
Return on equity: 6.8%	Dividends
Cash ($ mil.): 1,178	Yield: —
Current ratio: 1.51	Payout: 27.9%
Long-term debt ($ mil.): 4,675	Market value ($ mil.): —

Olam International Ltd.

Olam International is a leading global agribusiness serving more than 25000 customers across 60-plus countries. It farms processes and distributes food ingredients feed and fiber products and sources from a network of five million farmers. The company's top offering is food staples and packaged foods (rice sugar coffee cocoa and other

packaged foods); its stable of products also includes confectionery and beverage ingredients (cocoa and coffee) Industrial raw materials Infrastructure and Logistics (cotton and wood items) and edible nuts spices and beans. Asia Middle East and Australia is Olam's largest market accounting for approximately half of Olam's revenue.

Operations

Olam's has five business segments: Food Staples and Packaged Foods Confectionery and Beverage Ingredients Edible Nuts and Spices Industrial Raw Materials Infrastructure and Logistics and Commodity Financial Services.

Food Staples and Packaged Foods generate nearly 55% of revenue. Product includes of rice sugar and sweeteners grains and animal feed edible oils dairy and packaged foods. Confectionery and Beverage Ingredients gives in roughly 20% of revenue it offers cocoa and coffee based products.

Edible Nuts and Spices ring up about 15% of revenue product line includes cashew peanuts almonds hazelnuts pistachios walnuts. Olam is the leading supplier of edible nuts with 19500 hectares of plantation of almonds walnuts and pistachios.

Industrial Raw Materials Infrastructure and Logistics (accounts the remainder) offers cotton wood products rubber and fertilizer.

Commodity Financial Services offers risk management solutions market-making volatility and asset management and trade and structured finance.

Geographic Reach

Singapore-based Olam operates facilies comprising plants plantations warehouses and offices some are located in China India Indonesia Ethiopia Sudan Italy Georgia Germany Russia and South Africa. Asia Middle East and Australia generate roughly half of Olam's revenue followed by Europe which gives in roughly 20% Americas with more than 15% and Africa rings up about 15% of revenue.

Sales and Marketing

Olam serves more than 25000 customers. It includes food manufacturers retailers food service and e-commerce customers.

Financial Performance

Note: Growth rates may differ after conversion to US Dollar.

The company's revenue increased by 8% to S$33.0 billion in 2019 compared to the prior year with S$30.5 million. The increase was due to higher sales on the company's products in the food category.

Cash held by the company at the end of 2019 was S$3.0 billion compared to the previous year with S$2.4 billion. Cash provided by operations and financing activities were S$697.3 million and S$495.1 million respectively. Cash used for investing activities was S$562.7 million mainly for purchase of property plant and equipment.

Strategy

Capitalizing on key trends driven by consumers for healthier sustainable and natural products as well as ever advancing technologies for production and purchasing behavior the refreshed 2019 to 2024 Strategic Plan announced in early 2019 got off to a strong start. Deliverables are being met or even exceeded thanks to the focus and dedication of the Olam team.

The first strategic pathway of streamlining focusing and strengthening the portfolio saw the company reduce S$437.6 million of invested capital. S$1.1 billion was invested in strengthening the continuing businesses against the US$3.5 billion allocated for investment over the 6-year period.

The company's second pathway was to improve margins through capital and cost productivity. In this respect savings of some US$70 million were achieved and gearing is well within the net debt-to-equity target of 2.0 at 1.38 times. A significant element of these successes has been the focus on leveraging key enablers of operational excellence sustainability digitalization and leadership and talent. Innovative financing strategies demonstrate just one way of how Olam is embedding these enablers into the strategy with a second sustainability-linked loan and a world-first digital loan.

Mergers and Acquisitions

In late 2019 Olam acquired California-based Hughson Nut Inc. an almond processor and ingredient manufacturer and associated real estate assets from APB Partners LLC for $54 million. The acquisition will enable Olam to offer a fully integrated solution across the almond value chain from the US.

In early 2019 Olam submits binding offer to acquire Dangote Flour Mills Plc in Nigeria for $361 million. The proposed acquisition supports the strategy of the Grain and Animal Feed business one of Olam's prioritized platforms for growth to expand its wheat milling capacity in high-growth markets.

In early 2019 Olam acquired 85% share of Indonesia-based YTS Holdings Pte Limited. The largest cocoa processor in Indonesia for $90 million. The acquisition will help Olam to capitalize on Asia's trajectory to become the largest global consumer of cocoa powder.

EXECUTIVES

Group Chief Executive Officer, Co-Founder, Executive Director, Sunny Verghese
Non-Executive Independent Director, Joerg Wolle
Non-Executive Director, Kazuo Ito
Non-Executive Independent Chairman of the Board, Lim Ah Doo
Non-Executive Independent Director, Chee Keong Yap
Non-Executive Independent Director, Marie Elaine Teo
Non-Executive Independent Director, Ajai Puri
Non-Executive Director, Hamiyeh Nagi
Non-Executive Independent Director, Sanjiv Misra
Non-Executive Independent Director, Nihal Kaviratne
Auditors: Ernst & Young LLP

LOCATIONS

HQ: Olam International Ltd.
7 Straits View, Marina One East Tower, #20-01, 018936
Phone: (65) 6339 4100   **Fax:** (65) 6339 9755
Web: www.olamgroup.com

2018 Sales

	% of total
Asia & the Middle East	43
Africa	15
Europe	25
Americas	17
Total	**100**

PRODUCTS/OPERATIONS

2018 Sales

	% of total
Food staples & packaged foods	48
Edible nuts spices & beans	14
Confectionery & beverage ingredients	23
Industrial raw materials	15
Total	**100**

COMPETITORS

ARCHER-DANIELS-MIDLAND COMPANY
BASIC AMERICAN INC.
INGREDION INCORPORATED
SETTON'S INTERNATIONAL FOODS INC.
SHORELINE FRUIT LLC
VALLEY SUN PRODUCTS INC.
WILMAR INTERNATIONAL LIMITED

HISTORICAL FINANCIALS

Company Type: Public

Income Statement

	REVENUE ($ mil.)	NET INCOME ($ mil.)	NET PROFIT MARGIN	EMPLOYEES
				FYE: December 31
12/20	27,147	185	0.7%	81,600
12/19	24,567	419	1.7%	87,600
12/18	22,447	255	1.1%	74,500
12/17	19,821	434	2.2%	72,100
12/16	14,280	243	1.7%	69,772
Annual Growth	17.4%	(6.5%)	—	4.0%

2020 Year-End Financials

Debt ratio: 37.5%
Return on equity: 3.9%
Cash ($ mil.): 2,402
Current ratio: 1.38
Long-term debt ($ mil.): 5,130

No. of shares (mil.): —
Dividends
  Yield: 0.0%
  Payout: 2,519.8%
Market value ($ mil.): —

	STOCK PRICE ($) FY Close	P/E High/Low	PER SHARE ($) Earnings	Dividends	Book Value
12/20	23.00	477317	0.04	1.12	1.41
12/19	26.45	186161	0.12	0.05	1.50
12/18	23.76	385259	0.07	1.00	1.46
12/17	30.44	197152	0.13	0.87	1.55
12/16	27.64	252186	0.08	0.79	1.37
Annual Growth	(4.5%)	—	—(13.0%)	9.0%	0.8%

OMV AG (Austria)

Oil and chemicals group OMV is Austria's largest industrial company. A leading oil and gas company in Central and Eastern Europe it explores for natural gas and crude oil; refines crude oil; and imports transports and stores gas. In 2014 OMV reported proved reserves of 1.1 billion barrels of oil equivalent; it produced about 309000 barrels of oil equivalent per day and sold 13 billion cu. ft. of gas. The bulk of OMV's sales come from refining and marketing with the company operating three refineries. OMV is focusing on growing its exploration and production assets.

Operations

The company operates in three major segments. OMV Exploration and Production's core countries in Romania and Austria OMV is focusing on reducing the natural decline and on enhancing the recovery rates from mature fields. It is looking to find new growth areas within the Caspian Middle East and Africa regions.

OMV Gas and Power ensures the supply of natural gas to its customers via a 2000 km gas pipeline in Austria. Its natural gas network serving about 90% of Austria's natural gas demand draws gas supplies from Russia Norway and Germany as well as from domestic reserves. Austria's gas market now dominated by OMV is slated for full competition and OMV is among state-controlled companies set for full privatization.

The company operates a gas pipeline network in Austria and owns gas storage facilities with a capacity of 2.7 bcm (30 TWh).

OMV Solutions is the integrated shared service center for all of the OMV Group companies. Its portfolio spans IT financial services and human resources administration.

Geographic Reach

OMV gets the bulk of its oil and gas from Austria and Romania but it also has assets in Africa Nor-

way and the UK. The company operates refineries in Schwechat (Austria) Burghausen (Germany) and Petrobrazi (Romania).

Sales and Marketing

The company sells its product through industrial customers local distribution companies and wholesalers which focus on multi-country customers.

Financial Performance

OMV's revenues decreased by 15% in 2014 primarily due to decrease in gas and power sales due to the impairments of the Brazi power plant in Romania and the goodwill related to the Petrol Ofisi acquisition.

The company's net income declined by 69% in 2014 due to lower revenues and changes in interest expenses.

OMV's cash inflow decreased by 11% that year primarily due to lower net income and changes in working capital as a result of changes in short-term provisions.

Strategy

To raise cash in 2017 OMV agreed to Petrol Ofisi (gas station network) to Vitol for $1.45 billion.

In 2016 OMV sold its 49% minority stake in Gas Connect Austria to Allianz and Snam for $627.26 million.

Reorganizing to be more operationally efficient in 2015 OMV integrated the Gas and Power and Refining and Marketing business segments. In 2014 the company sold its 45% stake in the German Bayernoil refinery network. The remaining OMV refineries were integrated into crude and/or petrochemicals with the associated competitive advantages in its core markets.

Exploration and production is the growth driver of OMV. As part of OMV's strategy to build up a new exploration business in the region of Sub-Saharan Africa in 2014 the company signed an agreement with Tullow Oil an exploration-led company successful in finding and developing new resources in Africa. The first steps were taken with entries into offshore Madagascar Gabon and Namibia.

In 2013 the company announced plans to direct more than two-thirds of future investments towards exploration and production of oil and gas. It also plans to grow its integrated natural gas assets and restructure its downstream business by selling non-core refining and marketing assets.

Mergers and Acquisitions

As part of OMV's strategy of focusing on exploration and production in politically stable markets in 2013 the company acquired assets in Norway and the UK (West of Shetland area) from Statoil. It bought 19% in the producing Gullfaks field and 24% in the Gudrun field; both offshore oil and gas fields on the Norwegian Continental Shelf. In addition OMV took over 30% in Rosebank and 5.88% in Schiehallion both located west of the Shetland Islands and assets where OMV already holds a stake in.

HISTORY

Oil exploration began in Austria in the 1920s largely as joint ventures with foreign firms such as Shell and Socony-Vacuum. Full-scale production did not get underway until 1938 when the Anschluss (the absorption of Austria by Germany) paved the way for Germany to exploit Austria's natural resources to fuel its growing war machine. In the division of spoils following WWII Russia gained control of Austria's oil reserves.

The Russian-administered oil assets were transferred to the new Austrian government in 1955 which authorized the company –sterreichische Mineral ¶lverwaltung (–MG) in 1956 to control state oil assets. –MG state-controlled by the Austrian Mineral Oil Administration set about building a major refinery in 1960 and acquiring marketing companies Martha and –ROP in 1965.

In 1968 –MG became the first Western company to sign a natural gas supply contract with Russia. In 1974 the company commissioned the Trans-Austria Gas Pipeline which enabled the supply of natural gas to Italy. That year –MG changed its name to –MV Aktiengesellschaft (–MV became OMV in 1995 for international markets).

During the 1970s OMV expanded its crude supply arrangements tapping supplies from Iran Iraq Libya and other Middle Eastern countries. It moved into oil and gas exploration in the mid-1980s forming OMV Libya (acquiring 25% of Occidental's Libyan production) and OMV UK.

With Austria moving toward increasing privatization in 1987 about 15% of OMV's shares were sold to the public. The government sold another 10% two years later. In 1989 OMV acquired PCD Polymere. With the aim of merging state-owned oil and chemical activities OMV acquired Chemie Linz in 1990. The company also opened its first OMV-branded service station that year. In 1994 OMV reorganized itself as an integrated oil and gas group based in Central Europe with international exploration and production activities and with other operations in the chemical and petrochemical sectors.

In 1995 OMV acquired TOTAL-AUSTRIA expanding its service stations by 59. The company introduced OMV lubricants to the Greek market in 1996. It also expanded its OMV service station network in Hungary to 66 stations after acquiring 31 Q8 (Kuwait) sites. In 1997 the Stroh Company's retail network in Austria was merged into OMV.

Expanding its retail network even farther OMV acquired BP's retail network in the Czech Republic Slovakia and Hungary in 1998. It also sold its stake in Chemie Linz and acquired a 25% stake in major European polyolefin producer Borealis which in turn acquired PCD Polymere. In 1999 the company pushed its retail network into Bulgaria and Romania. That year OMV also acquired Australian company Cultus Petroleum.

OMV and Shell agreed to develop North Sea fields together in 2000. That year OMV also formed a joint venture with Italy's Edison International to explore in Vietnam and acquired more than 9% of Hungarian rival MOL. It upped that stake to 10% in 2001.

In 2002 OMV opened its first gas station in Serbia and Montenegro. It also increased its German gas station count from 79 to 151 with the purchase of 32 units from Royal Dutch Shell and 40 stations from Martin GmbH & Co.

In 2003 the company acquired Preussag Energie's exploration and production assets for $320 million. That year the company moved into Bosnia-Herzegovina opening nine gas stations.

During 2004 the company bought up 51% of Romania's Petrom making it the top oil and gas producer in Central Europe. As part of the deal OMV chose to divest itself of its quarter-chunk of Rompetrol.

In 2006 Russian energy giant Gazprom signed long-term contracts for gas deliveries with OMV.

In a major consolidation move in 2006 OMV agreed to buy Austrian power firm Verbund for $17 billion but the move was rebuffed by government regulators. The next year the company announced plans to merge with Hungary's energy powerhouse MOL but those plans were called off as well due to European Commission regulatory concerns in 2008.

After plans to merge with Hungary's MOL went south OMV the next year sold its 21% stake in it to Russian oil company Surgutneftegas for ?1.4 billion ($1.85 billion). Also in 2009 in keeping with its focus on retail markets in the Danube region

southeastern Europe and the Black Sea region OMV sold subsidiary OMV Italia; San Marco Petroli acquired the network of about 100 gas stations in the northern Italian region of Triveneto.

OMV has been disposing of some of its heating oil operations. In 2008 it unloaded Bayern GmbH and it plans to sell its OMV W ¤rme VertriebsgmbH by the end of 2010. At that point the sale of heating oil to private clients will be handled by partners but OMV will continue to service corporate customers.

Eyeing new areas of exploration that year OMV also acquired a 10% stake in Pearl Petroleum giving it access to gas-condensate fields in Iraq.

In 2010 the company boosted its share of Turkey-based oil products company Petrol Ofisi (renamed OMV Petrol Ofisi) from 42% to 96% by acquiring a 54% stake from Dogan Holding for about $1.4 billion. The deal gave OMV access to not only Turkey but the Caspian region and the Middle East.

The acquisition of full control (in 2010) of Petrol Ofisi Turkey's leading filling station and retail business with the only nationwide filling station network in the country (approximately 2300 stations) built a strategic bridge in the growth market of Turkey.

In a further push to grow in the Middle East in 2011 the company acquired two Tunisia-based exploration and production units from Pioneer Natural Resources for $866 million. It also boosted its footprint in Pakistan acquiring Petronas Carigali (Pakistan) Ltd. in 2011.

In 2012 the company sold its gas station subsidiary in Croatia. That year it boosted it E&P assets entering Abu Dhabi and acquiring natural gas assets in Norway.

EXECUTIVES

Chief Commercial Officer and Director, Elena Skvortsova, $353,215 total compensation
CFO and Director, Reinhard Florey, $797,583 total compensation
Deputy CEO, Exploration and Production and Director, Johann Pleininger, $854,554 total compensation
Auditors: Ernst & Young Wirtschaftsprüfungsgesellschaft m.b.H.

LOCATIONS

HQ: OMV AG (Austria)
Trabrennstrasse 6-8, Vienna 1020.
Phone: (43) 1 40440 0
Web: www.omv.com

2016 Sales

	% of total
Austria	25
Turkey	25
Romania	16
Germany	14
Rest of CEE	13
Rest of Europe	5
Rest of world	2
Total	**100**

PRODUCTS/OPERATIONS

2016 Sales

	% of total
D/S	95
U/S	5
Total	**100**

COMPETITORS

COMPA ÍA ESPA ÑOLA DE PETROLEOS SAU
China National Offshore Oil Corporation
DEVON ENERGY CORPORATION

GAZPROM PAO
LUKOIL PAO
MARATHON OIL CORPORATION
MOL Magyar Olaj- es G zipari Nyilv nosan
 M k ¶d
NK ROSNEFT PAO
NOBLE ENERGY INC.
SURGUTNEFTEGAZ PAO

HISTORICAL FINANCIALS

Company Type: Public

Income Statement				FYE: December 31
	REVENUE ($ mil.)	NET INCOME ($ mil.)	NET PROFIT MARGIN	EMPLOYEES
12/20	20,311	1,543	7.6%	25,291
12/19	26,341	1,884	7.2%	19,845
12/18	26,259	1,646	6.3%	20,231
12/17	24,241	521	2.2%	20,721
12/16	20,336	(425)	—	22,544
Annual Growth	(0.0%)	—		2.9%

2020 Year-End Financials

Debt ratio: 27.0% No. of shares (mil.): 326
Return on equity: 9.3% Dividends
Cash ($ mil.): 3,502   Yield: 3.7%
Current ratio: 1.14   Payout: 32.7%
Long-term debt ($ mil.): 11,412 Market value ($ mil.): 13,128

	STOCK PRICE ($) FY Close	P/E High/Low		PER SHARE ($) Earnings	Dividends	Book Value
12/20	40.15	16	5	4.73	1.49	51.57
12/19	55.70	12	9	5.76	1.42	44.69
12/18	44.32	15	10	5.04	1.27	41.73
12/17	63.37	49	30	1.59	1.05	41.18
12/16	35.46	—	—	(1.30)	0.76	35.30
Annual Growth	3.2%	—	—	—	18.2%	9.9%

Orange

For many in Europe and elsewhere the telecom landscape has an Orange glow. Orange is an operator of mobile and internet services in Europe and Africa and a global leader in corporate telecommunication services. The company serves more than 265 million customers in 25 countries. It is a leading European wireless operator and broadband service provider with about 210 million mobile customers and more than 20 million broadband subscribers. Orange's services for corporate clients are provided by its Orange Business Services unit which offers a wide range of managed business networking and data services.

Operations

The decisions regarding the allocation of resources and the performance assessment of the component parts of Orange (hereinafter referred to as "the Group") are made by the Chairman and Chief Executive Officer (main operational decision-maker) at operating segment level mainly consisting of the geographical establishments. The operating segments are: France (Enterprise excluded) with more than 40% of company's revenue; Spain with over 10% of revenue; Europe about 15% of revenue (Poland Belgium and Luxembourg and each Central European countries); Africa and Middle East with nearly 15% of revenue (in Senegal Orange Mali Orange Bissau Orange in Guinea and Orange in Sierra Leone) the C 'te d'Ivoire subgroup (including Orange C 'te d'Ivoire entities Orange in Burkina Faso and Orange in Liberia) and each of the other countries in Africa and Middle East); Enterprise with about 20% of revenue; International Carriers & Shared Services with nearly 5% (which contain certain resources mainly in the areas of networks information systems research and development and other shared Group activities as well as the Orange brand; and Orange Bank reportedly with no revenue.

Geographic Reach

Orange divides up its primary business — mobile and fixed-line telephony along with internet access services — by region with France comprising more than 40% of total operations. Spain Europe and Africa & the Middle East are its other two major regions with these services. The rest of the world makes up nearly a fifth of total revenues. The remaining business more than 15% of sales is largely the company's enterprise services operations.

Orange's retail network comprises more than 430 owned stores (including some 15 Megastores and over 120 Smart Stores) and over 200 exclusive partner stores (including nearly 25 G n rale de T l phone Smart Stores). Its retail operation accounts for more than 50% of sales.

Sales and Marketing

Orange serves over 265 million customers of which more than 210 million mobile customers and more than 20 million fixed broadband customers.

Advertising promotion sponsoring communication and brand marketing costs are recorded as expenses during the period in which they are incurred.

Financial Performance

Note: Growth rates may differ after conversion to US Dollars.

In fiscal 2019 the company grew its sales of two percent to ?42.2 billion from prior year despite the negative effects between the two periods of promotions on e-readers.

Consolidated net income rise up about 50% to ?3.2 billion in 2019 compared to ?2.2 billion from prior year. The increase was due to high sale in Telecom activities.

Orange's cash position up by ?847 million to ?6.5 billion at the end of 2019. Operating activities provided ?10.2 billion and financing activities also provided ?55 million while investing activities used ?9.4 billion.

Strategy

Orange's strategy is to accelerate its business in growth areas with a particular focus on mobile financial services (including Mobile Banking) B2B IT services and cyber security. Although building on the Group's strengths (digital expertise distribution strength capacity for innovation brand image and a strong presence in the MEA Region) the development of these new businesses requires substantial resources without any guarantee that the corresponding services will gain sufficient traction to generate a return on these investments.

The company has its new strategic plan named Engage 2025. With the Engage 2025 strategic plan Orange is staking its claim as an engaged and committed leader. The company's strength lies in reconciling business performance and a sustainable approach with customers employees stakeholders partners and society in general. With Engage 2025 Orange is capitalising on these strong choices and setting ambitious new targets for 2025 while making a responsible commitment to its employees customers and society at large. The company has 4 key ambitions for 2025: Reinvent its operator model; Accelerate in growth areas; Place data and AI at the heart of its innovation model; and Co-create a future-facing company.

In 2019 the company has two acquisitions. The SecureLink and SecureData for cyber security.

Mergers and Acquisitions

In early-2019 Orange acquired a 100% equity interest in SecureData a provider of cyber security solutions in the United Kingdom for 100 million euros. In mid-2019 the Group acquired 100% of SecureLink an independent cyber security operator in Europe for 377 million euros.

Company Background

Orange's history dates back to the foundation of the telegraph network in France. Much like BT Group in Britain which shares a similar timeline Orange in its present form is a result of the privatization of France's department for telecommunications. The department became an independent public entity in 1991 and was renamed France Télécom before being privatized six years later becoming a société anonyme (limited company) on 31 December 1996.

Over the next decade or so France Télécom grew organically and via acquisitions which included the purchase of Orange a British-founded mobile network sold by Vodafone as part of an anti-competition ruling. By the mid-00s France Télécom had become one of the world's largest telecoms companies and had built up significant operations outside France. It decided a new unifying brand identity was needed to replace the explicitly French "France Télecom" and with the use of mobile services on the sharp increase it settled on using Orange. Over the next decade the company brought its varied operations across the globe under the Orange brand and officially renamed itself Orange SA in 2013.

HISTORY

Shortly before he abdicated King Louis Philippe laid the groundwork for France's state-owned telegraphic service. Established in 1851 the operation became part of the French Post Office in the 1870s about the time Alexander Graham Bell invented the telephone. The French government licensed three private companies to provide telegraph service and during the 1880s they merged into the Societe Generale de Telephones (SGT). In 1883 the country's first exchange was initiated in Rheims. Four years later an international circuit was installed connecting Paris and Brussels. The government nationalized SGT in 1889.

By the turn of the century France had more than 60000 phone lines and in 1924 a standardized telephone was introduced. Long-distance service improved with underground cabling and phone exchanges in Paris and other leading cities became automated during the 1930s.

WWII proved a major setback to the French government's telephone operations Direction Generale des Telecommunications (DGT) because a large part of its equipment was destroyed or damaged. For the next two decades France lagged behind other nations in telephony infrastructure development. An exception to this technological stagnation was Centre National d'Etudes des Telecommunications (CNET) the research laboratory formed in 1944 that eventually became France Telecom's research arm.

In 1962 DGT was a key player in the first intercontinental television broadcast between the US and France via a Telstar satellite. The company began to catch up with its peers when it developed a digital phone system in the mid-1970s. In 1974 CNET was instrumental in the launch of France's first experimental communications satellite. In another technological advance DGT began replacing its paper directories with the innovative Minitel online terminals in 1980.

The French government created France Telecom in 1988. In 1993 France Telecom and Deutsche Telekom (DT) teamed up to form the Global One international telecommunications venture and Sprint joined the next year. Global One was formally launched in 1996. Also that year France Telecom began providing Internet access though Minitel still reigned as the country's top online service.

In 1997 the government sold about 20% of France Telecom to the public. With Europe's state telephone monopolies ending in 1998 France Telecom reorganized and brought prices in line with those of its competitors.

EXECUTIVES

Delegate Chief Executive Officer, Group Transformation and Chairman of Orange Business Services, Member of the Executive Committee, Gervais Pellissier, $683,643 total compensation

Chairman of the Board, Chief Executive Officer, Member of Executive Committee, Stephane Richard, $1,082,435 total compensation

Independent Director, Frederic Sanchez

Deputy Chief Executive Officer for Mobile Financial Services, Member of the Executive Committee, Paul De Leusse

Executive Director, Communications and Brand, Beatrice Mandine

Delegate Chief Executive Officer, Executive Director Finance, Performance and Europe, Member of the Executive Committee, Ramon Fernandez, $683,643 total compensation

Senior Executive Vice-President, Orange Business Services, Member of the Executive Committee, Helmut Reisinger

Senior Executive Vice-President, Group General Secretary and Secretary of the Board of Directors, Member of the Executive Committee, Nicolas Guerin

Deputy Chief Executive Director of Orange France, Member of the Executive Committee, Fabienne Dulac

Deputy Chief Executive Officer, Chief Technology and Innovation Officer, Member of the Executive Committee, Marie-noelle Jego-laveissiere

Senior Executive Vice-President of Wholesale and International Networks, Member of the Executive Committee, Jerome Barre

Head of Investor Relations, Patrice Lambert - de Diesbach

Independent Director, Anne-Gabrielle Heilbronner

Employee Representative on the Board of Directors, Laurence Dalboussiere

Representative Director, Claire Vernet-Garnier

Executive Director Group CSR, Diversity and Philanthropy, Elizabeth Tchoungui

Chief Executive Officer of Orange Middle East and Africa, Member of the Executive Committee, Alioune Ndiaye

Executive Director of Strategy and Cybersecurity Activities, Hugues Foulon

Auditors: Ernst & Young Audit

LOCATIONS

HQ: Orange
78 rue Olivier de Serres, Paris 75015
Phone: (33) 1 44 44 21 05
Web: www.orange.com

2017 sales

	% of total
France	42
Enterprise	17
Spain	13
Africa & Middle-East	12
Poland	6
Central European countries	4
International Carriers & Shared Services	4
Belgium & Luxembourg	2
Total	**100**

PRODUCTS/OPERATIONS

Selected Operations

Audience and advertising (Internet advertising business)
Content (partnerships with content providers and development of related technology platforms)
Enterprise communication services (communication services to companies)
Health (services to the health care industry)
Home communication services (residential communication services especially fixed-line broadband)
Personal communication services (communication services for individuals using mobile devices)

COMPETITORS

AT&T INC.
BOUYGUES
COMPUTACENTER PLC
FRONTIER COMMUNICATIONS CORPORATION
IOMART GROUP PLC
KCOM GROUP LIMITED
LEVEL 3 PARENT LLC
Proximus
TELEFONICA SA
Telia Company AB
XO HOLDINGS INC

HISTORICAL FINANCIALS

Company Type: Public

Income Statement				FYE: December 31
	REVENUE ($ mil.)	NET INCOME ($ mil.)	NET PROFIT MARGIN	EMPLOYEES
12/20	51,875	5,917	11.4%	142,150
12/19	47,432	3,375	7.1%	146,768
12/18	47,392	2,237	4.7%	150,711
12/17	49,271	2,284	4.6%	151,556
12/16	43,156	3,099	7.2%	141,257
Annual Growth	4.7%	17.6%	—	0.2%

2020 Year-End Financials

Debt ratio: —
Return on equity: 14.5%
Cash ($ mil.): 9,996
Current ratio: 0.89
Long-term debt ($ mil.): —

No. of shares (mil.): —
Dividends
Yield: 5.9%
Payout: 34.9%
Market value ($ mil.): —

	STOCK PRICE ($) FY Close	P/E High/Low		PER SHARE ($) Earnings	Dividends	Book Value
12/20	11.86	10	6	2.10	0.71	15.88
12/19	14.59	16	14	1.15	0.78	13.44
12/18	16.19	28	24	0.71	0.81	13.24
12/17	17.40	30	26	0.74	0.78	13.74
12/16	15.14	17	13	1.10	0.64	12.18
Annual Growth	(5.9%)	—	—	17.6%	2.6%	6.8%

Orix Corp

Established in 1964 ORIX is a financial services group which provides innovative products and services to its customers by constantly pursuing new businesses. ORIX has advanced into neighboring fields and at present has expanded into lending investment life insurance banking asset management automobile related real estate and environment and energy related. Going forward ORIX intends to utilize its strengths and expertise which generate new value to establish an independent ORIX business model that continues to evolve perpetually. ORIX expands its operations in approximately 30 countries and regions across the world.

Operations

ORIX operates 10 main business segments: Corporate Financial Services and Maintenance Leasing Real Estate PE Investment and Concession Environment and Energy Insurance Banking and Credit Aircraft and Ships ORIX USA ORIX Europe Asia and Australia.

Banking and Credit consists of banking and consumer finance. The segment generates about 25% of revenue.

Corporate Financial Services and Maintenance Leasing about 15% of total revenue involved in finance and fee business; leasing and rental of automobiles electronic measuring instruments and IT-related equipment; and Yayoi.

Asian and Australia about 10% consists of finance and investment with a focus on Asia and Australia.

Real Estate about 10% focuses on development rental of office building commercial facilities logistics centers and other properties; operations and businesses such hotels and aquariums in addition to asset management and development a brokerage of real estate and building maintenance.

ORIX USA about 10% consist of finance investments and asset management in the Americas.

PE Investment and Concession less than 5% of revenue consists of private equity investment and concession. Aircraft and Ships about 5% consists of aircraft leasing and management and ship-related finance and investment.

Environment and Energy about 5% consists of domestic and overseas renewable energy electric power retailing ESCO services sales of solar panels and electricity storage system and recycling and waste management.

Insurance segment consists of life insurance and generates more than 15% of total revenue.

ORIX Europe less than 5% consists of asset management with focus on Europe and the United States.

Geographic Reach

Based in Japan ORIX has more than 1660 corporate network and about 490 overseas corporate network.

Sales and Marketing

ORIX markets its products and services through its global expansion network in 30 countries. ORIX targets local needs and businesses.

Financial Performance

Note: Financial results are denoted in Japanese currency the Yen (). Growth rates may differ after conversion to US dollars.

Total revenues for fiscal 2021 increased 1% to 2.3 trillion compared to fiscal 2020 due to increases in life insurance premiums and related investment income and gains on investment securities and dividends despite decreases in services income and operating leases revenues.

In 2020 the company had 327.7 billion in net income down 7% compared to the previous year's net income of 302.7 billion.

The company's cash at the end of 2021 was 1.1 trillion. Operating activities provided another 587.7 trillion while investing activities used 874.0 trillion mainly for installment loans made to customers. Financing activities provided another 166.6 billion.

Strategy

Since the beginning of 2020 the spread of COVID-19 continued worldwide as did the various countermeasures and responses are undertaken by governments around the world including restrictions on the movement and gatherings of people. As a result the global economy has continued to experience a severe downturn due to demand and supply chain disruptions. In fiscal 2021 ORIX Group has experienced a deterioration in the business environments in which it operates and also declining profitability with the effects felt most strongly in the facility operation business in Real Estate Segment the concession business in PE Investment and Concession Segment and the aircraft leasing business in Aircraft and Ships Segment.

Mergers and Acquisitions

In 2021 ORIX Corporation Europe N.V. completed its acquisition of acquisition of Elawan Energy S.L. (Elawan) European subsidiary ORIX Corporation Europe N.V. successfully gained regulatory approvals to acquire 80% of Elawan's issued shares and becomes the majority shareholder in the business. Elawan develops and operates wind and solar power plants in 14 countries around the world with a focus on Europe and North and South America.

In 2020 ORIX Corporation Europe N.V. ("OCE") the company's wholly owned European subsidiary entered into an agreement to acquire a 70% equity stake in Gravis Capital Management Ltd ("Gravis"). Gravis is an independent asset management company headquartered in London; the U.K. Gravis currently acts as investment manager or advisor for six funds: three closed-ended listed funds and three open-ended funds with in excess of 2.9 billion pounds (approximately 400 billion yen) in assets under management.

EXECUTIVES

Senior Managing Executive Officer, President and CEO of Subsidiary, Director, Yoshiteru Suzuki
Group Managing Executive Officer, President of Subsidiaries, Toshinari Fukaya
Executive Officer, Chief Director of Legal & Compliance, Tomoko Kageura
Independent Director, Hiroshi Watanabe
Executive Officer, Deputy Chief Director of Business Investment, Seiichi Miyake
Group Executive Officer, President of Subsidiary, Nobuhisa Hosokawa
Managing Executive Officer, Chief Director of Environmental Energy, Hidetake Takahashi
Independent Director, Aiko Sekine
Executive Officer, Deputy Chief Director of Corporate Sales, Tetsuya Kodera
Executive Officer, Deputy Chief Director of Corporate Sales, Eiji Arita
Independent Director, Chikatomo Hodo
Executive Officer, Nobuki Watanabe
President, Group Chief Executive Officer, Representative Executive Officer, Director, Makoto Inoue
Group Executive Officer, Takaaki Nitanai
Independent Director, Sakie Akiyama
Independent Director, Michael Cusumano
Managing Executive Officer, Global General Counsel, Director, Stan Koyanagi
Executive Officer, Chief Director of Finance, Hitomaro Yano
Independent Director, Heizo Takenaka
Managing Executive Officer, Chief Director of Group Human Resource & General Affairs, Secretariat of The Board of Directors, Yasuaki Mikami
Senior Managing Executive Officer, Chief Director of Corporate Sales, Chairman of Subsidiaries, Director, Satoru Matsuzaki
Senior Managing Executive Officer, Chief Director of Business Investment, Director, Shuji Irie
Executive Officer, Chief Director of Investment & Loan Management, Yasuhiro Tsuboi
Group Executive Officer, Chairman of Subsidiary, Hiroko Yamashina
Executive Officer, Toyonori Takahashi
Group Executive Officer, President of Subsidiary, Yuji Kamiyauchi

Executive Officer, President of Subsidiary, Michio
Minato
Auditors: KPMG AZSA LLC

LOCATIONS

HQ: Orix Corp
World Trade Center Building, 2-4-1 Hamamatsu-cho,
Minato-ku, Tokyo 105-6135
Phone: (81) 3 3435 1274   **Fax:** (81) 3 3435 1276
Web: www.orix.co.jp

2018 Sales

	% of total
Japan	83
Americas	4
Others	13
Total	**100**

PRODUCTS/OPERATIONS

2018 Sales by Business Segment

	% of total
Corporate Financial Services	4
Maintenance Leasing	10
Real Estate	6
Investment and Operation	49
Retail	15
Overseas Business	16
Total	**100**

Selected Subsidiaries and Segments

ORIX Aircraft (aircraft leasing)
ORIX Asset Management & Loan Services Corporation
    (commercial mortgage servicing)
ORIX Auto (car rental and leasing)
ORIX Buffaloes Baseball Club (professional baseball
    team)
ORIX Life Insurance
ORIX Real Estate (real estate development and
    investment)
ORIX Real Estate Investment Advisors (asset
    management)
ORIX Rentec (rental operations)
ORIX Trust and Banking
ORIX USA
SUN Leasing Corporation (medical equipment leasing)

COMPETITORS

ATEL CAPITAL GROUP
AerCap Holdings N.V.
Agricultural Bank of China Limited
Bank of Communications Co. Ltd.
COMMERCE BANCSHARES INC.
F&C EQUITY PARTNERS PLC
FORD MOTOR CREDIT COMPANY LLC
H&E EQUIPMENT SERVICES INC.
HARSCO CORPORATION
HERC HOLDINGS INC.
INVESTEC PLC
Industrial And Commercial Bank Of China Limited
LINEDATA SERVICES
LIONTRUST ASSET MANAGEMENT PLC
ROBERT WALTERS PLC
SAVILLS PLC
TOKYO CENTURY CORPORATION
The Bank of Nova Scotia
Total Energy Services Ltd
UNITED RENTALS INC.
VP PLC

HISTORICAL FINANCIALS

Company Type: Public

Income Statement

FYE: March 31

	ASSETS ($ mil.)	NET INCOME ($ mil.)	INCOME AS % OF ASSETS	EMPLOYEES
03/21	122,493	1,737	1.4%	33,153
03/20	120,382	2,788	2.3%	31,233
03/19	109,937	2,923	2.7%	32,411
03/18	107,602	2,948	2.7%	31,890
03/17	100,458	2,443	2.4%	34,835
Annual Growth	**5.1%**	**(8.2%)**	**—**	**(1.2%)**

2021 Year-End Financials

Return on assets: 1.4%
Return on equity: 6.3%
Long-term debt ($ mil.): —
No. of shares (mil.): 1,217
Sales ($ mil): 20,551

Dividends
Yield: 4.2%
Payout: 243.8%
Market value ($ mil.): 103,218

	STOCK PRICE ($) FY Close	P/E High/Low		PER SHARE ($) Earnings	Dividends	Book Value
03/21	84.79	1	0	1.40	3.59	22.47
03/20	59.10	0	0	2.18	3.73	21.98
03/19	71.87	0	0	2.28	3.12	20.44
03/18	89.86	0	0	2.30	2.66	19.74
03/17	74.33	0	0	1.87	2.09	17.22
Annual Growth	**3.3%**	**—**	**—**	**(6.9%)**	**14.5%**	**6.9%**

Osaka Gas Co Ltd (Japan)

Osaka Gas keeps Osaka Hyogo Kyoto Shiga and
Wakayama cooking. A large Japanese gas supplier
the utility serves more than 9 million customers in
the Kansai region. The company imports a large
amount of its gas and has production operations
in Australia and Indonesia; it also owns liquefied
natural gas (LNG) terminals and tankers. Osaka
Gas has branched out into electricity: It generates
and markets power to wholesale and large retail
customers in Japan and abroad. It maintains a
pipeline of approximately 62400 km and a power
generation capacity of 2 megawatts in Japan. Other
operations include gas appliance sales pipeline installation real estate management and leasing.
Osaka Gas was established in 1897.

Operations

Osaka Gas operates through four reporting segments: Domestic Energy/Gas; Life & Business Solutions; Domestic Energy/Electricity; and International Energy.

Domestic Energy/Gas (more than 65% of revenues) manufactures supplies and sells city gas
and gas appliances conducts gas pipelines installations and sells LNG LPG and industrial gas.

Life and Business Solutions includes real estate
development and leasing IT services the marketing
of fine materials and carbon material products.
This segment represents 15% of the company's
total sales.

Domestic Energy/Electricity produces and sell
electricity and it accounts for about 15% of the
revenue.

Comprised the remaining revenue International
Energy Business includes overseas energy supply
LNG vessel chartering business and petroleum and
natural gas business development and investment.

Geographic Reach

The company's main natural gas reserves in Algeria Australia Brunei Canada China Egypt Indonesia Iran Iraq Kuwait Malaysia Nigeria Norway
Oman Papua New Guinea Qatar Russia Saudi Arabia Turkmenistan the UAE the US and Venezuela.

Headquartered in Osaka Japan has also office
in Tokyo and about 10 offices overseas located in
the Australia Indonesia the Philippines Singapore
Thailand UK and the US.

Sales and Marketing

Osaka Gas provides solutions that meets various
needs of more than 9 million customers for household factories and offices.

The company also serves residential commercial
and industrial customers.

Financial Performance

Osaka Gas has seen fluctuating revenue for the
last five years recording a 4% increase from 2016
to 2020. The same trend as revenue was seen in
the company's net income but with a recorded
50% decrease from 2016 to 2020.

Revenue was 1.4 trillion 3.2 billion less than in
the previous year. Domestic Energy/Gas contributed the highest revenue per segment comprising 70% of the company's 2020 revenue. This was
followed by Domestic Energy/Electricity (15%)
and Life and Business Solutions (12%).

Net income increased from 33.6 billion in 2019
to 41.8 billion in 2020.

Cash and cash equivalents at the end of the year
were 146.8 billion 31 billion more than in the previous year. Operating activities provided 182.9 billion to the coffers. Investing activities used 232.3
billion primarily for purchase of property plant and
equipment while financing activities provided 79.3
billion mostly from proceeds from issuance of
bonds.

Strategy

In 2020 Osaka Gas made significant progress
in its International Energy Business especially in
the US such as the commencement of commercial
operations of the Freeport LNG Project and the
Fairview natural gas-fired power plant as well as
the acquisition of all shares in Sabine Oil and Gas
Corporation a shale gas development company.

The company aims to maximize value for its
customers and to reach the goals under the current
Medium-term Management Plan as it develops
strategies for future growth while preventing the
spread of the coronavirus.

Mergers and Acquisitions

In late 2020 Osaka Gas has acquired issued
shares of Palette Cloud (Japan based) which provides Palette Kanri the property management system provided by Palette Cloud for rental housing
management companies. Palette Kanri is a cloud-
based tenant management system designed exclusively for the real estate industry. The two companies aim to make the most of their respective
strengths and produce a good synergy between
them to contribute to greater convenience in rental
collective housing and help continuous advancement in consumer and business life.

In late 2019 the company wholly-owned subsidiary Gas and Power Co Ltd has acquired all the
equity help by JGC Holdings Corporation of the issued shares of JGC Mirai Solar Co Ltd a photovoltaic power generation business operator based
in Oita City Oita Prefecture. As a result of the equity acquisition JGC Mirai will change its corporate
name to Daigas Oita Mirai Solar Co Ltd as wholly-
owned subsidiary of G& P.

In mid-2019 Osaka Gas entered into a definitive
agreement with Texas based Sabine Oil & Gas
Holding to acquire 100% of the outstanding shares
of its subsidiary Oil & Gas Corporation (Sabine).
Sabine holds acreage in East Texas located in Harrison Panola Rusk and Upshur counties among
others totaling 175000 net acres which is produc-

ing shale gas in the amount of 210 mmcfed with approximately 1200 wells at present showing a significant drilling inventory on the Haynesville and Cotton Valley formation. Through this acquisitions Osaka Gas has also gained operatorship of the upstream business along with Sabine's excellent management and operations capabilities.

Company Background
Osaka Gas was established in 1897.

EXECUTIVES

Independent Director, Kazutoshi Murao
Independent Director, Tatsuo Kijima
Chairman of the Board, Takehiro Honjo
Managing Executive Officer, Director, Fumitoshi Takeguchi
Executive Vice President, Director of Energy Solutions Business, Representative Director, Takayuki Tasaka
President, Executive President, Representative Director, Masataka Fujiwara
Executive Vice President, Chief Director of Business Planning, Representative Director, Takeshi Matsui
Managing Executive Officer, Director of Gas Production, Power Generation & Engineering Business, Kei Takeuchi
Managing Executive Officer, President of Subsidiary, Shigeru Chikamoto
Executive Vice President, Representative Director, Tadashi Miyagawa
Independent Director, Hideo Miyahara
Independent Director, Yumiko Sato
Auditors: KPMG AZSA LLC

LOCATIONS

HQ: Osaka Gas Co Ltd (Japan)
  4-1-2 Hiranomachi, Chuo-ku, Osaka 541-0046
Phone: (81) 6 6205 4537   **Fax:** 914 328-4430
Web: www.osakagas.co.jp

PRODUCTS/OPERATIONS

2015 Sales

	% of total
Gas	72
LPG Electricity and Other Energies	16
Life & Business Solutions	11
International Energies	1
Total	**100**

COMPETITORS

CHIYODA CORPORATION
Companhia de Gas de S o Paulo Comgas
EDF ENERGY LIMITED
HONG KONG AND CHINA GAS COMPANY LIMITED THE
ITALGAS RETI SPA
KINDER MORGAN ENERGY PARTNERS L.P.
ORIGIN ENERGY LIMITED
PHOENIX NATURAL GAS LIMITED
UGI CORPORATION

HISTORICAL FINANCIALS
Company Type: Public

Income Statement				FYE: March 31
	REVENUE ($ mil.)	NET INCOME ($ mil.)	NET PROFIT MARGIN	EMPLOYEES
03/21	12,319	730	5.9%	23,520
03/20	12,608	384	3.1%	23,265
03/19	12,387	303	2.4%	23,044
03/18	12,207	355	2.9%	22,858
03/17	10,588	548	5.2%	23,701
Annual Growth	3.9%	7.4%	—	(0.2%)

OSB Group plc

Auditors: Deloitte LLP

LOCATIONS

HQ: OSB Group plc
  OSB House, Quayside, Chatham Maritime, Chatham, Kent ME4 4QZ
Phone: (44) 1634 848944
Web: www.osb.co.uk

HISTORICAL FINANCIALS
Company Type: Public

Income Statement				FYE: December 31
	ASSETS ($ mil.)	NET INCOME ($ mil.)	INCOME AS % OF ASSETS	EMPLOYEES
12/20	30,916	267	0.9%	1,816
12/19	28,282	209	0.7%	1,279
12/18	13,355	179	1.3%	989
12/17	11,601	171	1.5%	813
12/16	8,095	148	1.8%	674
Annual Growth	39.8%	15.8%	—	28.1%

Otsuka Holdings Co., Ltd.

EXECUTIVES

President, Chief Executive Officer, Chairman of the Board of Subsidiary, Representative Director, Tatsuo Higuchi
President of Subsidiary, Director, Noriko Tojo
Chief Financial Officer, Director, Yuko Makino
Director, Sadanobu Tobe
Senior Managing Director, Yoshiro Matsuo
Executive Director, Shuichi Takagi
Independent Director, Mayo Mita
Chairman & President of Subsidiaries, Director, Masayuki Kobayashi
Executive Director, Makoto Inoue
Auditors: Deloitte Touche Tohmatsu LLC

LOCATIONS

HQ: Otsuka Holdings Co., Ltd.
  Shinagawa Grand Central Tower 12F, 2-16-4 Konan, Minato-ku, Tokyo 108-8241
Phone: (81) 3 6717 1410   **Fax:** 415 986-5361
Web: www.otsuka.com

Income Statement			FYE: December 31
	REVENUE ($ mil.)	NET INCOME ($ mil.)	NET PROFIT MARGIN	EMPLOYEES
12/20	13,804	1,437	10.4%	38,220
12/19	12,860	1,171	9.1%	37,837
12/18	11,748	750	6.4%	36,998
12/17	11,019	999	9.1%	37,184
12/16	10,221	791	7.7%	36,440
Annual Growth	7.8%	16.1%	—	1.2%

2020 Year-End Financials

Debt ratio: 0.0%
Return on equity: 8.1%
Cash ($ mil.): 3,428
Current ratio: 2.41
Long-term debt ($ mil.): 1,208

No. of shares (mil.): 542
Dividends
  Yield: 2.1%
  Payout: 18.1%
Market value ($ mil.): 11,622

	STOCK PRICE ($)	P/E		PER SHARE ($)		
	FY Close	High/Low		Earnings	Dividends	Book Value
12/20	21.43	0	0	2.64	0.47	33.14
12/19	22.28	0	0	2.13	0.46	30.00
12/18	20.22	0	0	1.38	0.46	28.61
12/17	21.92	0	0	1.84	0.44	29.41
12/16	21.92	0	0	1.46	0.42	26.99
Annual Growth	(0.6%)	—		16.0%	2.8%	5.3%

Oversea-Chinese Banking Corp. Ltd. (Singapore)

Singapore bank Oversea-Chinese Banking Corporation (OCBC Bank) operates roughly 480 branches and offices in about 20 countries including some 230 branches across over 60 cities in Indonesia through its Bank OCBC NISP subsidiary. The company offers traditional banking services for individuals and businesses as well as financial services such as brokerage and asset management. Private banking for high-net-worth families is offered through the Bank of Singapore while Great Eastern Holdings which provides life and property/casualty insurance is the largest insurance company in Singapore and Malaysia. OCBC Bank was founded in 1912 to serve the Chinese business community of Singapore and other parts of Asia but now serves the general public.

Geographic Reach
The bank's main operations are in its home country of Singapore which accounts more than 50% of business. Malaysia where it operates as OCBC Bank Malaysia and offers Islamic banking services through OCBC Al-Amin Bank accounts for about 20% of business. Indonesia and China each account for less than 10% of business.

In addition to its core markets OCBC also has a presence in Australia Brunei Dubai Hong Kong Japan The Philippines South Korea Taiwan Thailand the UK the US (in New York and Los Angeles) and Vietnam through branches and representative offices.

2021 Year-End Financials

Debt ratio: 0.3%
Return on equity: 7.7%
Cash ($ mil.): 1,509
Current ratio: 1.81
Long-term debt ($ mil.): 6,215

No. of shares (mil.): 415
Dividends
  Yield: —
  Payout: —
Market value ($ mil.): —

Financial Performance

OCBC's performance for the span of five years have fairly increased year by year from 2016 to 2019 and slightly decreased in 2020.

The company's revenue decreased by S\$732 million to S\$10.1 billion compared to S\$10.8 billion.

The company's net income for 2020 also decreased by S\$1.2 billion to S\$3.5 billion compared to the prior year's of S\$4.8 billion.

Cash held at the end of the year was \$22 billion. Operating activities provided \$15.6 billion to the coffers. Investing activities and financing activities used \$4.3 billion and \$7.5 billion respectively. Main cash uses were for purchases of life insurance fund investment securities and redemption of other debt issues.

Strategy

The company continues to build a resilient and diversified business in the regions wherein it operates namely North and Southeast Asia. Through its segments the company aims to help individuals and businesses across communities. For the company's Banking segment the company aims to support domestic economic activities and cross border trade. In addition the company also aims to capture the rising Asian wealth through the incorporation of their integrated model across private premier private and premier banking bancassurance securities brokerage and asset management. Lastly the company aims to deepen its insurance penetration in Singapore Malaysia and Indonesia.

EXECUTIVES

Non-Executive Non-Independent Director, Tih Shih Lee, \$102,221 total compensation

Non-Executive Independent Director, Ngiap Joo Tan, \$175,443 total compensation

Executive Vice President, Head - Group Brand and Communications, Ching Ching Koh

Non-Executive Non-Independent Director, Surjaudaja Pramukti, \$86,475 total compensation

Non-Executive Independent Director, Yen Yen Tan, \$104,396 total compensation

Group Chief Executive Officer, Pik Kuen Wong

Head of Consumer Financial Services - Singapore, Sunny Quek

Head of Global Treasury, Chin Kui Lai

Non-Executive Independent Director, Beng Seng Koh, \$134,844 total compensation

President Director, Chief Executive Officer - Bank OCBC NISP, Parwati Surjaudaja, \$79,021 total compensation

Non-Executive Non-Independent Chairman of the Board, Sang Kuang Ooi, \$1,181,705 total compensation

Chief Financial Officer, Executive Vice President, Siew Peng Tan

Group Chief Operating Officer, Khiang Tong Lim

Executive Vice President, Head of Global Investment Banking, Kok Kim Gan

Chief Executive Officer - OCBC Wing Hang Bank, Wu Beng Na

Chief Executive Officer - OCBC Bank Malaysia, Eng Bin Ong

Head of Group Human Resources, Poh Wah Ho

Head - Global Commercial Banking, Ti Liang Goh

Chief Executive Officer - Bank of Singapore, Bahren Shaari

Global Transaction Banking, Melvyn Low

Chief Executive Officer - OCBC Wing Hang Bank (China) Limited, Ke Wang

Head of Global Enterprise Banking - International, Chor Sen Tan

Regional General Manager, North East Asia, Wing Ming Tan

Head - Group Risk Management, Nyen Fui Choo

Non-Executive Independent Director, Kwee Fong Hon, \$102,221 total compensation

Executive Vice President, General Counsel and Head of Group Legal and Regulatory Compliance, Loretta Yuen

Company Secretary, Group Secretariat, Ban Aik Yeoh

Non-Executive Independent Director, Kim Chiu Chua, \$149,344 total compensation

Non-Executive Independent Director, Cheng Hoe Khoo

Executive Vice President, Head of Group Audit, Chin Yee Goh

Non-Executive Independent Director, Joo Yeow Wee, \$179,793 total compensation

Head - Global Corporate Banking, Elaine Lam

Auditors: PricewaterhouseCoopers LLP

LOCATIONS

HQ: Oversea-Chinese Banking Corp. Ltd. (Singapore)
63 Chulia Street, #10-00 OCBC Centre East, 049514
Phone: (65) 6363 3333   **Fax:** (65) 6534 3986
Web: www.ocbc.com

2012 Sales

	% of total
Singapore	63
Malaysia	20
Indonesia	7
China	7
Rest of Asia	2
Rest of world	1
Total	**100**

PRODUCTS/OPERATIONS

2012 Sales

	% of total
Interest	59
Noninterest	
Fees & commissions	12
Life insurance	7
General insurance	1
Rental income	1
Dividends	1
Other	19
Total	**100**

Selected Subsidiaries

Banking
  Bank of Singapore Limited
  OCBC Al-Amin Bank Berhad
  OCBC Bank (Malaysia) Berhad
  Singapore Island Bank Limited
Insurance
  Great Eastern Life Assurance (Malaysia) Berhad
  Overseas Assurance Corporation (Malaysia) Berhad
  The Great Eastern Life Assurance Company Limited
  The Overseas Assurance Corporation
Asset management
  Lion Global Investors Limited
  Great Eastern Holdings Limited
Stockbroker
  OCBC Securities Private Limited

COMPETITORS

AIA Group Limited
BANK OF AYUDHYA PUBLIC COMPANY LIMITED
BANK OF BARODA
BANK OF EAST ASIA LIMITED THE
BOC HONG KONG (HOLDINGS) LIMITED
Bank of Communications Co. Ltd.
CIMB GROUP HOLDINGS BERHAD
COMMONWEALTH BANK OF AUSTRALIA
HSBC HOLDINGS PLC
HSBC USA INC.
MALAYAN BANKING BERHAD
PT. BANK DANAMON INDONESIA TBK
QATAR NATIONAL BANK (Q.P.S.C.)
SINOPAC FINANCIAL HOLDINGS COMPANY LIMITED
STANDARD CHARTERED PLC
Shinhan Financial Group Co. Ltd.

HISTORICAL FINANCIALS

Company Type: Public

Income Statement

FYE: December 31

	ASSETS ($ mil.)	NET INCOME ($ mil.)	INCOME AS % OF ASSETS	EMPLOYEES
12/20	394,478	2,713	0.7%	30,538
12/19	365,454	3,619	1.0%	30,492
12/18	343,351	3,298	1.0%	29,706
12/17	340,545	3,103	0.9%	29,174
12/16	283,660	2,403	0.8%	29,792
Annual Growth	**8.6%**	**3.1%**	**—**	**0.6%**

2020 Year-End Financials

Return on assets: 0.7%
Return on equity: 7.3%
Long-term debt ($ mil.): —
No. of shares (mil.): —
Sales ($ mil): 25,814

Dividends
  Yield: 3.6%
  Payout: 97.5%
  Market value ($ mil.): —

	STOCK PRICE ($) FY Close	P/E High/Low	PER SHARE ($)		
			Earnings	Dividends	Book Value
12/20	15.28	22 15	0.61	0.56	8.39
12/19	16.20	16 14	0.83	0.62	7.96
12/18	16.62	19 14	0.78	0.50	7.28
12/17	18.65	19 14	0.73	0.47	6.97
12/16	12.27	16 12	0.57	0.44	6.12
Annual Growth	**5.6%**	**—**	**1.6%**	**6.3%**	**8.2%**

P.T. Astra International TBK

Auditors: Public Accountant Firm Tanudiredja, Wibisana, Rintis & Rekan (a member of the PricewaterhouseCoopers network of firms)

LOCATIONS

HQ: P.T. Astra International TBK
Menara Astra, Lantai 59, Jl. Jend. Sudirman Kav. 5-6, Jakarta 10220
Phone: (62) 21 5084 3888   **Fax:** (62) 21 6530 4957
Web: www.astra.co.id

HISTORICAL FINANCIALS

Company Type: Public

Income Statement

FYE: December 31

	REVENUE ($ mil.)	NET INCOME ($ mil.)	NET PROFIT MARGIN	EMPLOYEES
12/19	17,106	1,565	9.2%	226,105
12/18	16,627	1,506	9.1%	226,140
12/17	15,202	1,393	9.2%	218,463
12/16	13,472	1,127	8.4%	214,835
12/15	13,341	1,047	7.9%	221,046
Annual Growth	**6.4%**	**10.6%**	**—**	**0.6%**

2019 Year-End Financials

Debt ratio: 0.0%
Return on equity: 15.2%
Cash ($ mil.): 1,754
Current ratio: 1.29
Long-term debt ($ mil.): 3,646

No. of shares (mil.): —
Dividends
  Yield: 2.1%
  Payout: 39.9%
  Market value ($ mil.): —

Pan Pacific International Holdings Corp

	STOCK PRICE ($) FY Close	P/E High/Low		PER SHARE ($) Earnings	Dividends	Book Value
06/21	21.03	0	0	0.77	0.14	5.98
06/20	22.08	0	0	0.73	0.10	5.47
06/19	15.89	0	0	0.71	0.09	4.84
06/18	11.94	0	0	0.52	0.06	4.15
06/17	9.51	0	0	0.47	0.05	3.66
Annual Growth	22.0%	—	—	13.2%	27.7%	13.1%

EXECUTIVES

Chairman, President & Chief Executive Officer of Subsidiaries, Non-Executive Director, Takao Yasuda

President, Chief Executive Officer, President of Subsidiary, Representative Director, Naoki Yoshida

Director, Akio Ariga

Senior Managing Executive Officer, President of GMS Company, Director, Kenji Sekiguchi

Independent Director, Yukihiko Inoue

Independent Director, Yasunori Yoshimura

Independent Director, Tomiaki Fukuda

Senior Executive Officer, Kosuke Suzuki

Managing Executive Officer, Chief Administrative Officer, Director, Yuji Ishii

Independent Director, Jumpei Nishitani

Senior Executive Officer, Joint CMO, Tetsuji Maruyama

Executive Officer, Nobuharu Ohashi

Chief Marketing Officer (Global), Senior Managing Executive Officer, Vice President of Asia Company, Director, Kazuhiro Matsumoto

Managing Executive Officer, Chief Director of Business Strategy, Director of Management Council Secretariat, Director, Hideki Moriya

Senior Executive Officer, Joint CMO, Ken Sakakibara

Independent Director, Isao Kubo

Senior Managing Executive Officer, Chief Strategy Officer, Director, Seiji Shintani

Executive Officer, Director, Hitomi Ninomiya

Chief Financial Officer, Executive Officer, Director, Keita Shimizu

Auditors: UHY Tokyo & Co.

LOCATIONS

HQ: Pan Pacific International Holdings Corp
2-19-10 Aobadai, Meguro-ku, Tokyo 153-0042
Phone: (81) 3 5725 7532 **Fax:** (81) 3 5725 7322
Web: www.ppi-hd.co.jp

HISTORICAL FINANCIALS

Company Type: Public

Income Statement FYE: June 30

	REVENUE ($ mil.)	NET INCOME ($ mil.)	NET PROFIT MARGIN	EMPLOYEES
06/21	15,459	487	3.2%	55,689
06/20	15,611	466	3.0%	47,709
06/19	12,338	448	3.6%	48,351
06/18	8,509	329	3.9%	28,392
06/17	7,400	295	4.0%	25,500
Annual Growth	20.2%	13.3%	—	21.6%

2021 Year-End Financials

Debt ratio: 0.3%	No. of shares (mil.): 634
Return on equity: 13.5%	Dividends
Cash ($ mil.): 1,425	Yield: 0.6%
Current ratio: 1.40	Payout: 17.6%
Long-term debt ($ mil.): 4,302	Market value ($ mil.): 13,338

Panasonic Corp

Panasonic has been a prolific electronics manufacturers since 1918. Its offerings include automotive and industrial systems (including car infotainment products) and home appliances; the company also makes lighting products energy systems avionics systems and process automation machines and equipment. Panasonic sells its product to consumers (via retailers) as well as directly to original equipment manufacturers and other businesses. The company operates worldwide but generates nearly half its revenue from Japan.

Operations

Panasonic has five primary business segments: Appliances (around 35%) Life Solutions (around 20%) Connected Solutions (over 10%) Automotive (more than 15%) and Industrial Solutions (around 15%).

Panasonic's appliances include air conditioners TVs cameras and devices.

The company's life solutions offer office lighting fixtures LED floodlights for facilities home lighting fixtures energy system power-assisted bicycles and other products for elderly.

Connected Solutions handles aviation products for in-flight entertainment as well as factory process automation products logistics public services and entertainment technologies.

The Automotive business manufactures and sales of in-vehicle infotainment in-vehicle electronics automotive mirrors and motorized systems such as BMC (Battery Management Controller).

The Industrial segment covers electronic devices such as sensors resistors motors compressors industrial batteries and other custom devices.

Geographic Reach

Japan-based Panasonic sells its products and services in Asia the Americas India South Asia Middle East & Africa and Europe. The company is highly reliant on its home continent Japan which accounts for nearly half of total revenue.

Financial Performance

Note: Growth rates may differ after conversion to US dollars.

Panasonic's revenue and net income has been fluctuating for the last five years.

The company's consolidated sales for fiscal 2021 decreased by 11% to 6.7 trillion yen from a year ago. Domestic sales decreased due mainly to the impact of the spread of COVID-19 as well as the impact of deconsolidation in housing related businesses despite increased sales in products such as air purifiers. Overseas sales decreased due largely to the impact of the spread of COVID-19 despite increased sales in products such as mounting machines at Process Automation power storage systems for information- and communication-infrastructure as well as industrial-use motors.

Net profit for fiscal 2021 decreased to 165.1 billion yen compared from the prior year with 225.7 billion yen.

Cash held by the company at the end of fiscal 2021 increased to 1.5 trillion yen. Operating and investing activities provided 504.0 billion yen and 176.6 billion yen respectively. Financing activities used 177.7 billion yen mainly for dividends paid and repayment of long-term debt

Strategy

The company's key initiatives are: Investing for Growth; Enhancing competitiveness through co-creation; and Improving profitability.

As part of its Mid-term strategy that started in 2019 Panasonic has hitherto undertaken initiatives to enhance its management structure reform its business portfolio and improve profitability in automotive businesses with the overall objective of breaking away from a low-profitability structure.

Mergers and Acquisitions

In 2021 Panasonic completed the acquisition of Blue Yonder the leading end-to-end digital fulfillment platform provider. Panasonic has now purchased the remaining 80% of shares of Blue Yonder adding to the 20% which Panasonic acquired in July 2020. The investment values Blue Yonder at USD8.5 billion. The acquisition accelerates Panasonic's and Blue Yonder's shared vision for an Autonomous Supply Chain.

Company Background

Grade school dropout Konosuke Matsushita took $50 in 1918 and went into business making electric plugs (with his brother-in-law Toshio Iue founder of SANYO). His mission to help people by making high-quality low-priced conveniences while providing his employees with good working conditions earned him the sobriquet "god of business management." The company grew across the decades expanding into new regions (it opened its first manufacturing facility outside Japan — in Thailand — in 1961) and new products (washing machines TVs and refrigerators were launched in the 1950s). In 2008 it took the name Panasonic Corporation and consolidated all its brands under the Panasonic name.

HISTORY

Grade school dropout Konosuke Matsushita took $50 in 1918 and went into business making electric plugs (with his brother-in-law Toshio Iue founder of SANYO). His mission to help people by making high-quality low-priced conveniences while providing his employees with good working conditions earned him the sobriquet "god of business management." Matsushita Electric Industrial grew by developing inexpensive lamps batteries radios and motors in the 1920s and 1930s.

During WWII the Japanese government ordered the firm to build wood-laminate products for the military. Postwar occupation forces prevented Matsushita from working at his firm for four years. Thanks to unions' efforts he rejoined his namesake company shortly before it entered a joint venture with Dutch manufacturer Philips in 1952. The following year it moved into consumer goods making televisions refrigerators and washing machines and later expanding into high-performance audio products. Matsushita bought a majority stake in Victor Company of Japan (JVC originally established by RCA Victor) in 1954. Its 1959 New York subsidiary opening began Matsushita's drive overseas.

Sold under the National Panasonic and Technics names the firm's products were usually not cutting-edge but were attractively priced. Under Masaharu Matsushita the founder's son-in-law who became president in 1961 the company became Japan's largest home appliance maker introducing air conditioners microwave ovens stereo components and VCRs in the 1960s and 1970s. JVC developed the VHS format for VCRs which beat out Sony's Betamax format.

Matsushita built much of its sales growth on new industrial and commercial customers in the 1980s. The company expanded its semiconductor office and factory automation auto electronics audio-visual housing and air-conditioning product offerings that decade. Konosuke died in 1989.

EXECUTIVES

Senior Managing Executive Officer, Chief Director of Tokyo Olympic & Paralympic Promotion, Chief Director of Business Solution, Chief Director of Integrated Resort (IR) Business Promotion, Yoshiyuki Miyabe
Senior Managing Executive Officer, Masahisa Shibata
Independent Director, Michitaka Sawada
Executive Vice President, Chief Director of Corporate Strategy, President & CEO of US Company, Representative Director, Mototsugu Sato
President, CEO & Representative Director, Yuki Kusumi
Senior Managing Executive Officer, President & CEO of Industrial Solutions Company, Shinji Sakamoto
Managing Executive Officer, Chief Strategy Officer, Eiichi Katayama
Managing Executive Officer, President of Appliance Company, Masahiro Shinada
Chief Financial Officer, Senior Managing Executive Officer, Chairman, President & CEO of Subsidiaries, Director, Hirokazu Umeda
Executive Vice President, President & CEO of China & Northeast Asia Company, Chairman of Subsidiary, Representative Director, Tetsuro Homma
CEO, Panasonic Connected Solutions Company, Yasuyuki Higuchi
Independent Director, Kunio Noji
Chief Compliance Officer, Chief Risk Management Officer, General Counsel, Managing Executive Officer, Chief Director of Legal Affairs & Compliance, Director, Laurence W.Bates
Independent Director, Shinobu Matsui
Executive Officer, President of Subsidiary, Manish Sharma
Auditors: KPMG AZSA LLC

LOCATIONS

HQ: Panasonic Corp
1006 Oaza Kadoma, Kadoma, Osaka 571-8501
Phone: (81) 6 6908 1121
Web: www.panasonic.com/jp

2018 Sales

	% of total
Japan	47
Americas	17
China	12
Europe	10
Other Asia	14
Total	**100**

PRODUCTS/OPERATIONS

2018 Sales

	% of total
Automotive and industrial systems	32
Appliances	29
Eco solutions	18
Connected solutions	13
Other	8
Total	**100**

COMPETITORS

A. O. SMITH CORPORATION
EAST PENN MANUFACTURING CO.
LEHMAN HARDWARE AND APPLIANCES INC.

MICROLISE MIDCO LIMITED
MITSUBISHI ELECTRIC CORPORATION
NIDEC CORPORATION
PRESTOLITE WIRE LLC
ROBERT BOSCH LLC
Robert Bosch Gesellschaft mit beschr onkter Haftung
SAFRAN ELECTRICAL & POWER
SANYO ELECTRIC CO. LTD.
SVA (Group) Co. Ltd.
TOSHIBA CORPORATION
Uniform Industrial Corp.
VOXX INTERNATIONAL CORPORATION
Vacon Oy
WHIRLPOOL EMEA SPA

HISTORICAL FINANCIALS
Company Type: Public

Income Statement
FYE: March 31

	REVENUE ($ mil.)	NET INCOME ($ mil.)	NET PROFIT MARGIN	EMPLOYEES
03/21	60,499	1,490	2.5%	243,540
03/20	69,005	2,079	3.0%	259,385
03/19	72,263	2,565	3.6%	271,869
03/18	75,170	2,222	3.0%	274,143
03/17	65,682	1,335	2.0%	257,533
Annual Growth	(2.0%)	2.8%	—	(1.4%)

2021 Year-End Financials

Debt ratio: 0.1%
Return on equity: 7.1%
Cash ($ mil.): 14,389
Current ratio: 1.40
Long-term debt ($ mil.): 7,945

No. of shares (mil.): —
Dividends
  Yield: 1.8%
  Payout: 35.3%
Market value ($ mil.): —

	STOCK PRICE ($) FY Close	P/E High/Low		Earnings	PER SHARE ($) Dividends	Book Value
03/21	13.04	0	0	0.64	0.24	10.04
03/20	7.50	0	0	0.89	0.28	7.89
03/19	8.67	0	0	1.10	0.32	6.92
03/18	14.37	0	0	0.95	0.24	6.89
03/17	11.40	0	0	0.58	0.23	6.03
Annual Growth	3.4%	—	—	2.7%	0.9%	13.6%

PetroChina Co Ltd

If you want petroleum in China or elsewhere then PetroChina is your company. A subsidiary of state-owned China National Petroleum Corporation (CNPC) PetroChina produces two-thirds of China's oil and gas. The company has proved reserves of 10.8 billion barrels of oil and 69.3 trillion cu. ft. of natural gas. In China it owns more than 53400 kilometers of natural gas and refined products pipeline and operates 29 refineries and 13 chemical plants. PetroChina was created in 2000 as a separate company to initially manage the domestic operations — and in recent years some key international assets — of CNPC.

Strategy
PetroChina is taking advantage of the growing consumption of natural gas in China by expanding its transmission infrastructure. It is also expanding its oil reserves and refining operations through the purchase of international oil fields and refineries including several assets from its parent.

In 2015 the company agreed to sell 50% of Central Asia Natural Gas Pipeline Co. to Mansong Holdings Ltd a subsidiary of China Reform Holdings Corp. Ltd. for 15 billion to 15.5 billion yuan.

EXECUTIVES

Vice President, Xiao Ling
Vice President, Jigang Yang
Vice President, Luguang Li
Independent Non-Executive Director, Simon Henry
Non-Executive Director, Yongzhang Huang
Independent Non-Executive Director, Xiaoming Jiang
Independent Non-Executive Director, Jin-Yong Cai
Independent Non-Executive Director, Oi-sie Elsie Leung
Executive Director, Lixin Ren
Vice President, Longde Sun
Chairman of the Board, Houliang Dai
Non-Executive Director, Fangzheng Jiao
Non-Executive Director, Yuezhen Liu
Vice President, Jinghui Tian
Chief Financial Officer, Secretary of the Board, Shouping Chai
Vice Chairman, Non-Executive Director, Qijun Hou
President, Executive Director, Liangwei Duan
Independent Non-Executive Director, Tatsuhito Tokuchi
Auditors: KPMG Huazhen (Special General Partnership)

LOCATIONS

HQ: PetroChina Co Ltd
No. 9 Dongzhimen North Street, Dongcheng District, Beijing 100007
Phone: (86) 10 5998 6270   **Fax:** (86) 10 6209 9557
Web: www.petrochina.com.cn

2013 Sales

	% of total
Mainland China	67
Other countries	33
Total	**100**

PRODUCTS/OPERATIONS

2013 Sales

	% of total
Marketing	51
Refining & chemicals	23
Exploration & production	20
Natural gas & pipeline	6
Total	**100**

COMPETITORS

CNOOC LIMITED
Canadian Natural Resources Ltd
China National Offshore Oil Corporation
ESSAR ENERGY LIMITED
Equinor ASA
MARATHON OIL CORPORATION
NOBLE ENERGY INC.
NOVATEK PAO
OMV Aktiengesellschaft
REPSOL SA.
ROYAL DUTCH SHELL plc
Suncor Energy Inc

HISTORICAL FINANCIALS
Company Type: Public

Income Statement
FYE: December 31

	REVENUE ($ mil.)	NET INCOME ($ mil.)	NET PROFIT MARGIN	EMPLOYEES
12/20	295,682	2,905	1.0%	0
12/19	361,702	6,564	1.8%	0
12/18	342,176	7,645	2.2%	0
12/17	309,782	3,502	1.1%	0
12/16	232,846	1,137	0.5%	0
Annual Growth	6.2%	26.4%	—	—

2020 Year-End Financials

Debt ratio: 1.2%
Return on equity: 1.5%
Cash ($ mil.): 22,315
Current ratio: 0.80
Long-term debt ($ mil.): 24,485

No. of shares (mil.): —
Dividends
  Yield: 6.3%
  Payout: 13,032.9%
Market value ($ mil.): —

	STOCK PRICE ($) FY Close	P/E High/Low	PER SHARE ($) Earnings	Dividends	Book Value
12/20	30.72	569287	0.02	1.95	(0.00)
12/19	50.33	264184	0.04	2.17	(0.00)
12/18	61.55	285208	0.04	2.02	(0.00)
12/17	69.94	717521	0.02	1.42	(0.00)
12/16	73.70	19081281	0.01	0.56	(0.00)
Annual Growth	(19.6%)	—	27.6%	36.5%	—

Petroleo Brasileiro SA

The company operates and produces the majority of Brazil's oil and gas. Petrobras has proved oil and gas reserves and produced average daily production of more than 2 million barrels of oil equivalent. In Brazil it operates nearly 15 refineries and an extensive oil and gas pipeline network. Other units operate electricity (approximately 20 thermal power plants) petrochemicals and natural gas assets. Petrobras is controlled by the Brazilian government and generates majority of sales in its home country.

Operations

Petrobras operates through three business segments: Refining Transportation and Marketing Exploration and Production and Gas and Power.

The Refining Transporting and Marketing segment is Petrobras' most lucrative at over 50% of sales. The company operates the company's activities of refining logistics transport marketing and trading of crude oil and oil products in Brazil and abroad.

The Exploration and Production segment covers Petrobras' upstream activities including the exploration development and production of crude oil natural gas and natural gas liquids (NGLs) in Brazil and elsewhere. The segment represents nearly 40% of total revenue.

Gas and Power accounting for almost 10% of sales covers Petrobras' natural gas and electricity logistics and trading electricity generation at thermoelectric plants and its interest in natural gas transport companies in Brazil and abroad. It also includes a fertilizer business.

The company also generates sales from corporate and other businesses. It include Petrobras' distribution and biofuels activities.

Geographic Reach

Rio de Janeiro-based Petrobras does most of its business in Brazil but also explores for and produces oil in Argentina Bolivia Colombia Uruguay Netherlands. the UK the US and Singapore. In addition to its explorations activities the company also has support activities such as trade and financial in London Rotterdam Houston and Singapore.

Sales and Marketing

Petrobras distributes its oil products through a company-owned retail network wholesale channels and by supplying other fuel wholesalers and retailers.

Crude oil is primarily sold through long-term contracts and also in the spot market. The company's overseas portfolio includes approximately 60 clients such as refiners that process or have processed Brazilian oils regularly. The Natural gas is marketed to more than 20 clients most of which are distributors.

Financial Performance

Petrobras' performance for the past year has continued to decline with performance decreasing year by year.

The company's revenue decreased by about $22.9 billion as compared to last year's revenue of $75.5 billion.

The company's net income decreased significantly by about $6.5 billion to $1.1 billion as compared to the prior year's net income of $7.6 billion.

Petrobras' cash at the end of 2020 was $11.7 billion. Operating activities provided $28.8 billion while investing activities used $4.5 billion. Financing activities used another $19.2 billion.

Strategy

Petrobras' 2020-2025 Strategic Plan (the "Strategic Plan" or "2020-2025 Strategic Plan") consists of the continuous evaluation of the business environment and the implementation of the plan allowing adjustments to be made in a more efficient way. The Plan is focused on oil and natural gas exploration and production notably in the Brazilian pre-salt area which is one of the company's greatest strengths and sources of value creation. Digital transformation has gained strength as an important instrument for adding value to its business in a competitive environment.

HISTORY

"O petr leo e nosso!"

"The oil is ours!" proclaimed the Brazilian nationalists' slogan in 1953 and President Get lio Vargas approved a bill creating a state-run monopoly on petroleum discovery development refining and transport. The same year that PETR "LEO BRASILEIRO (PETROBRAS) was created a team led by American geologist Walter Link reported that the prospects of finding petroleum in Brazil were slim. The report outraged Brazilian nationalists who saw it as a ploy for foreign exploitation. PETROBRAS proved it could find oil but Brazil continued to import crude oil and petroleum products. By 1973 the company produced about 10% of the nation's needs.

When oil prices soared during the Arab embargo the government instead of encouraging exploration for domestic oil pushed PETROBRAS into a program to promote alcohol fuels. The company was forced to raise gasoline prices to make the more costly gasohol attractive to consumers. During the 1979 oil crunch the price of gasohol was fixed at 65% of gasoline. But during the oil glut of the mid-1980s PETROBRAS' cost of making gasohol was twice what it cost to buy gasoline — in other words PETROBRAS lost money.

PETROBRAS soon began overseas exploration. In 1980 it found an oil field in Iraq an important trading partner during the 1980s. The company also drilled in Angola and through a 1987 agreement with Texaco in the Gulf of Mexico.

In the mid-1980s PETROBRAS began production in the deepwater Campos basin off the coast of Rio de Janeiro state. Discoveries there in 1988 in the Marlim and Albacora fields more than tripled its oil reserves. It plunged deep into the thick Amazon jungle in 1986 to explore for oil and by 1990 Amazon wells were making a significant contribution to total production. That year to ease dependence on imports PETROBRAS launched a five-year $16.9 billion plan to boost crude oil production. It also began selling its mining and trading assets.

Before the invasion of Kuwait Brazil relied heavily on Iraq trading weapons for oil. After the invasion spawned increases in crude prices PETROBRAS raised pump prices but yielding to the government's anti-inflation program still did not raise them enough to cover costs. It lost $13 million a day.

The company sold 26% of Petrobras Distribuidora to the public in 1993 and privatized several of its petrochemical and fertilizer subsidiaries. A 1994 presidential order bent on stabilizing Brazil's 40%-per-month inflation cut the prices of oil products. In 1995 the government loosened its grip on the oil and gas industry and allowed foreign companies to enter the Brazilian market. In the wake of this reform PETROBRAS teamed up with a Japanese consortium to build Brazil's largest oil refinery.

In 1997 PETROBRAS appealed a $4 billion judgment from a 1992 shareholder lawsuit; the suit alleged PETROBRAS had undervalued shares during the privatization of the loss-making Petroquisa affiliate. (The appeal was granted in 1999.)

As part of an effort to boost oil production PETROBRAS also began to raise money abroad in 1999. The next year PETROBRAS and Spanish oil giant Repsol YPF agreed to swap oil and gas assets in Argentina and Brazil in a deal worth more than $1 billion.

In 2000 the company announced plans to change its corporate name to PETROBRAX but fierce political and popular reaction forced the company to abort this plan in 2001. In an even greater public relations disaster that year one of PETROBRAS' giant rigs sank off of Brazil and 10 workers were killed. In 2001 PETROBRAS announced that it was going to spend as much as $3 billion to buy an oil company in order to increase its production in the Gulf of Mexico.

In 2002 the company expressed an interest in buying Argentina's major oil company (YPF) from Spanish/Argentine energy giant Repsol YPF. That year PETROBRAS bought control (59%) of Argentine energy company Perez Companc in a deal valued at $1 billion. PETROBRAS also reported its first oil find in Argentina in 2002.

In 2006 the company acquired a 50% stake in a deepwater block in Equatorial Guinea from a private group of companies for an undisclosed sum.

The company also restructured the Brazilian petrochemical industry to make it more efficient. Its actions included the purchase of the petrochemical assets of the Ipiranga Group in 2007 and Suzano Petroqu mica a leader in Latin American polypropylene resin production in 2008.

In 2007 PETROBRAS announced a major offshore oil discovery in the Tupi. In 2008 it reported it had discovered a major natural gas field near the Tupi find.

In 2011 it was operating more than 130 production platforms. PETROBRAS has made a number of major offshore oil discoveries in offshore Brazil since 2000 including the Tupi field (found in 2007) and which has the potential to boost Brazil's oil reserves by 40%. In 2010 PETROBRAS announced another major discovery a 3.7 to 15 billion-barrels-of-oil-reserves find (offshore of Rio de Janeiro) that could double Brazil's known reserves.

Streamlining its Petrobras Argentina operations in 2011 the company acquired that unit's Brazilian petrochemicals business (Innova SA) for $332 million.

In 2012 it teamed up with GE Oil & Gas in a $1.1 billion deal through which the GE unit will supply 380 subsea wellhead systems to a number of PETROBRAS' oil and gas fields in offshore Brazil.

Brazil's government owns more than 55% of PETROBRAS.

EXECUTIVES

Independent Director, Nivio Ziviani
Independent Director, Joao Neto
Chairman of the Board, Eduardo Ferreira
Chief Institutional Relations and Sustainability Executive Officer, Roberto Ardenghy
Chief Digital Transformation and Innovation Executive Officer, Nicolas Simone
Chief Executive Officer, Joaquim Silva E Luna
Chief Trading & Logistics Officer, Cláudio Mastella
Chief Financial and Investor Relation Officer, Rodrigo Alves
Chief Governance & Compliance Officer, Salvador Dahan
Chief Production Development Officer, Joao Rittershaussen
Chief Exploration & Production Officer, Fernando Borges
Auditors: KPMG Auditores Independentes

LOCATIONS

HQ: Petroleo Brasileiro SA
Avenida Republica do Chile, 65, Rio de Janeiro 20031-912
Phone: (55) 21 3224 4477
Web: www.petrobras.com.br

2018 Sales

	% of total
Brazil	76
Other countries	24
Total	**100**

PRODUCTS/OPERATIONS

2018 Sales

	% of total
Refining transportation & marketing	44
Exploration & production	32
Distribution	17
Gas & Power	7
Biofuels	-
Total	**100**

Selected Subsidiaries

Downstream Participações S.A. (asset exchanges between Petrobras and Repsol-YPF)
Petrobras Argentina (59%; oil and gas Argentina)
Petrobras Comercializadora de Energia Ltda
Petrobras Distribuidora SA (BR; distribution and marketing of petroleum products fuel alcohol and natural gas)
Petrobras Gá;s SA (Gaspetro management of the Brazil-Bolivia pipeline and other natural gas assets)
Petrobras Internacional SA (Braspetro; overseas exploration and production marketing and services)
Petrobras International Finance Company - PIFCO (oil imports)
Petrobras Negócios Eletrônicos S.A.
Petrobras Quí;mica SA (Petroquisa petrochemicals)
Petrobras Transporte SA (Transpetro oil and gas transportation and storage)

COMPETITORS

CHEVRON CORPORATION
COMPA 'IA ESPA 'OLA DE PETROLEOS SAU
COSMO OIL CO. LTD.
ENI SPA
Equinor ASA
LUKOIL PAO
MARATHON OIL CORPORATION
MOL Magyar Olaj- es G zipari Nyilv nosan M k ¶d
ROYAL DUTCH SHELL plc
Suncor Energy Inc

HISTORICAL FINANCIALS

Company Type: Public

Income Statement
FYE: December 31

	REVENUE ($ mil.)	NET INCOME ($ mil.)	NET PROFIT MARGIN	EMPLOYEES
12/20	53,683	1,141	2.1%	49,050
12/19	76,589	10,151	13.3%	57,983
12/18	95,584	7,173	7.5%	63,361
12/17	88,827	(91)	—	0
12/16	81,405	(4,838)	—	68,829
Annual Growth	**(9.9%)**	**—**		**(8.1%)**

2020 Year-End Financials

Debt ratio: 31.3%
Return on equity: 1.7%
Cash ($ mil.): 11,711
Current ratio: 1.04
Long-term debt ($ mil.): 49,702

No. of shares (mil.): —
Dividends
Yield: 1.5%
Payout: 103.8%
Market value ($ mil.): —

	STOCK PRICE ($) FY Close	P/E High/Low	PER SHARE ($) Earnings	Dividends	Book Value
12/20	11.23	181 48	0.09	0.17	7.97
12/19	15.94	23 16	0.78	0.21	5.62
12/18	13.01	31 17	0.55	0.10	5.48
12/17	10.29	— —	(0.01)	0.00	6.12
12/16	10.11	— —	(0.37)	0.00	5.89
Annual Growth	**2.7%**	**— —**	**— —**		**7.9%**

Petroleos Mexicanos (Pemex) (Mexico)

Petr leos Mexicanos (PEMEX) is a state-owned oil company that fuels the nation's economy. It is the largest and most important company in Mexico and an international benchmark in the field of hydrocarbons. Its activities involve the entire production chain from exploration production industrial transformation logistics and marketing. PEMEX's P.M.I. Comercio Internacional subsidiary manages the company's trading operations outside the country. PEMEX generates approximately 1.7 million barrels of crude oil daily and about 4.8 million of cubic feet of natural gas. The company has over six refineries. Majority of its sales are generated domestically.

Operations

PEMEX's operations were conducted through eight business segments: Industrial Transformation (some 35% of sales) Exploration and Production (nearly 35%) Trading Companies (over 25%) Logistics (some 5%) Drilling and Services Ethylene Fertilizers and Corporate and Other Operating Subsidiary Companies.

Its industrial transformation segment is comprised of four principal activities: refining which converts crude oil into gasoline jet fuel diesel fuel oil asphalts and lubricants; gas and aromatics which processes wet natural gas to produce dry natural gas ethane liquefied petroleum gas (LPG) and other natural gas liquids along with aromatic derivatives chain products such as toluene benzene and xylene; ethylene and derivatives which produces distributes and markets ethane and propylene derivatives; and fertilizers which operated as an additional productive state-owned subsidiary.

Its exploration and production segment operates through the productive state-owned subsidiary

Pemex Exploration and Production and explores for and produces crude oil and natural gas primarily in the northeastern and southeastern regions of Mexico and offshore in the Gulf of Mexico.

The international trading segment provides it with international trading distribution risk management insurance and transportation services. This segment operates through P.M.I. Comercio Internacional S.A. de C.V. (which it refers to as PMI) P.M.I. Trading Designated Activity Company (formerly P.M.I. Trading Ltd. which it refers to as P.M.I. Trading DAC) P.M.I. Norteamerica S.A. de C.V. (which it refers to as PMI-NASA and together with PMI and P.M.I. Trading DAC it collectively refers to as the PMI Subsidiaries) and Mex Gas International S.L. (which together with the PMI Subsidiaries it collectively refers to as the Trading Companies).

Its logistics segment operates through the productive state-owned subsidiary Pemex Logistics and provides land maritime and pipeline transportation storage and distribution services to some of its subsidiaries and other companies including Tesoro Mexico Supply & Marketing S. de R.L. de C.V. (a subsidiary of Marathon Petroleum Corporation) local gas stations and distributors.

Geographic Reach

PEMEX's corporate headquarter is located in Mexico. About 55% of the company's revenue is generated domestically while it also has significant operations in the US with over 30% of sales as well as in Europe Canada Central and South America and others.

Sales and Marketing

PEMEX's primary business is the exploration and production of crude oil and natural gas as well as the production processing marketing and distribution of petroleum and petrochemical products.

The exploration and production segment earns revenues from domestic sales of crude oil and natural gas and from exporting crude oil through certain of the Trading Companies. Export sales are made through PMI CIM to over 20 major customers in various foreign markets. Approximately half of PEMEX's crude oil is sold to Pemex Industrial Transformation.

Industrial transformation segment earns revenues from sales of refined petroleum products and derivatives mainly to third parties within the domestic market. They sell a significant portion of the fuel oil it produces to the Comisi n Federal de Electricidad (Federal Eletricity Commission or "CFE") and a significant portion of jet fuel produced to the Aeropuertos y Servicios Auxiliares.

The trading companies which consist of PMI CIM PMI NASA PMI Trading and MGAS (the "Trading Companies") earn revenues from trading crude oil natural gas and petroleum and petrochemical products in international markets.

Financial Performance

Note: Growth rates may differ after conversion to US Dollars.

The company had a total revenue of $47.8 million in 2020 a 35% decrease from the previous year. This was primarily due to a lower sales volume across the company's business segments.

In 2020 the company had a net loss of $25.5 thousand.

The company's cash at the end of 2020 was $2 million. Operating activities generated $3.3 million while investing activities used $7.1 million mainly for acquisition of wells pipelines properties plant and equipment. Financing activities provided another $2.4 million.

Strategy

In advance of 2020 the company planned to invest in four new developments all of them in shallow water and continue with the development of the other 22 fields the company has been developing since 2019. During 2020 it incorporated the Teca Tlamatini Itta and Xolotl shallow water fields into its development plan bringing its total investment in new developments to 26 fields 22 in shallow water and four onshore fields. As of December 31 2020 the company had begun production in 13 of these 26 fields. These 13 fields had an average production of 77.8 thousand barrels per day of crude oil and 200.7 million cubic feet per day of natural gas in 2020.

The company's primary objectives for 2021 include: strengthening its financial condition; ensuring its sustainability by accelerating the incorporation of hydrocarbon reserves; and adapting and modernizing the company's production infrastructure.

It aims to meet these objectives through the following strategies: accelerating the incorporation of hydrocarbon reserves by prioritizing the company's exploration activities onshore in conventional shallow waters and in adjacent blocks; accelerating secondary and enhanced recovery processes to increase the recovery factor for hydrocarbon reserves in its mature fields; expediting the development of newly discovered fields; prioritizing and developing activities that improve the reclassification of possible and probable reserves into proved reserves; increasing its production of non-associated gas and enhancing the company's operations efficiency and optimizing our exploration and production costs.

HISTORY

Histories of precolonial Mexico recount the nation's first oil business: Natives along the Tampico coast gathered asphalt from naturally occurring deposits and traded with the Aztecs.

As the 20th century began Americans Edward Doheny and Charles Canfield struck oil near Tampico. Their success was eclipsed in 1910 by a nearby well drilled by British engineer Weetman Pearson leader of the firm that became Pearson PLC.

President Porfirio Daz had welcomed foreign ownership of Mexican resources but revolution ousted Daz and the 1917 Constitution proclaimed that natural resources belonged to the nation. Without enforcing legislation however foreign oil companies continued business as usual until a 1925 act limited their concessions. During a bitter labor dispute in 1938 President Lzaro Crdenas expropriated foreign oil holdings — the first nationalization of oil holdings by a non-Communist state. Subsequent legislation created Petrleos Mexicanos (PEMEX).

Without foreign capital and expertise the new state-owned company struggled and Mexico had to import petroleum in the early 1970s. But for many Mexicans PEMEX remained a symbol of national identity and economic independence. That faith was rewarded in 1972 when a major oil discovery made PEMEX one of the world's top oil producers again. Ample domestic oil supplies and high world prices during the Iranian upheaval in the late 1970s fueled a boom and a government borrowing spree in Mexico. Between 1982 and 1985 PEMEX contributed more than 50% of government revenues.

When oil prices collapsed in 1985 Mexico cut investment in exploration and production dropped. To decrease its reliance on oil Mexico began lowering trade barriers and encouraging manufacturing even allowing some foreign ownership of petrochemical processing.

Elected in 1988 President Carlos Salinas de Gortari began to reform PEMEX. Labor's grip on the company was loosened in 1989 when a union leader was arrested and jailed after a gun battle. In 1992 after a PEMEX pipeline explosion killed more than 200 people in Guadalajara four of its executives and several local officials were sent to prison amid public cries for company reform.

President Ernesto Zedillo appointed Adrin Lajous Vargas head of PEMEX in 1994. Under the professorial Lajous PEMEX began to adopt modern business practices (such as trimming its bloated payroll) look for more reserves and improve its refining capability. Lajous tried to sell some petrochemical assets in 1995 but had to modify the scheme the next year after massive public protests by the country's nationalists. Still PEMEX began selling off natural gas production distribution and storage networks to private companies.

Though oil prices were dropping in 1998 Mexico finally upped PEMEX's investment budget and PEMEX dramatically increased exploration and production. In spite of 2000's looming national election (elections traditionally had caused bureaucrats to keep a low profile to protect their jobs) Lajous again fanned the flames of the opposition: In 1998 he signed a major deal to sell Mexican crude to Exxon's Texas refinery and in 1999 a four-year-old PEMEX/Shell joint venture announced it would expand its US refinery.

In 1999 Lajous resigned and was replaced by Rogelio Montemayor a former governor. The next year Vicente Fox was elected as Mexico's new president the country's first non-Institutional Revolutionary Party (PRI) leader in seven decades. He announced plans to replace PEMEX's politician-staffed board with professionals — Montemayor was among the casualties — and modernize the company but he ruled out privatizing PEMEX as politically unfeasible.

Fox appointed Ral Muñoz formerly with Dupont Mexico in 2003 to lead PEMEX. Muñoz however was engulfed in a scandal involving the misuse of funds and forced to resign the following year. His replacement Luis Ramrez lasted until the next national election when incoming President Felipe Caldern appointed Jess Reyes.

Reyes was replaced by Juan Jose Surez Coppel in 2009.

In 2011 the company reported a major gas find in the Gulf of Mexico with estimated reserves of 400 to 600 billion cubic feet. The discovery is the tenth deepwater gas discovery PEMEX has made since 2004. However because of the persistence of low natural gas commodity prices the development of these fields is on hold while the company focuses on crude oil production (supported by high crude oil prices) mainly in southeast Mexico.

EXECUTIVES

Chief Executive Officer of Pemex Exploracion y Produccion, Juan Javier Hinojosa Puebla
Corporate Director of Administration and Services, Marco Antonio Murillo Soberanis
Chief Executive Officer of Pemex Logistica, Armando David Palacios Hernandez
Corporate Director of Planning, Coordination and Performance, Rudolfo Figueroa Alonso
Chief Executive Officer of Pemex Transformacion Industrial, Carlos Rafael Murrieta Cummings
Director of Legal Affairs, Jorge Eduardo Kim Villatoro
Chief Financial Officer, David Ruelas Rodriguez
Chief Executive Officer of Pemex Cogeneracion y Servicios, Eleazar Gomez Zapata
Corporate Director of Procurement and Supply, Miguel Angel Servin Diago
Director of Internal Audit, Luis Bartolini Esparza
Auditors: KPMG Cardenas Dosal, S.C.

LOCATIONS

HQ: Petroleos Mexicanos (Pemex) (Mexico)
Avenida Marina Nacional 329, Colonia Veronica Anzures, Mexico City 11300
Phone: (52) 55 1944 9700
Web: www.pemex.com

PRODUCTS/OPERATIONS

2016 Sales

	% of total
Domestic sales	62
Export sales:	
United States	21
Europe	6
Canada Central and South America	1
Other	9
Services income	1
Total	**0**

2016 Sales

	% of total
Trading Companies	35
Industrial Transformation	34
Exploration and Production	27
Logistics	3
Ethylene	1
Drilling and Service	-
Cogeneration and Services	-
Fertilizers	-
Corporate and other subsidiary companies	-
Total	**100**

Selected Subsidiaries

PEMEX Exploración y Producción (petroleum and natural gas exploration and production)
PEMEX Gas y Petroquímica Básica (natural gas liquids from natural gas and ethane processing)
PEMEX Petroquímica (petrochemical production)
PEMEX Refinación (refining and marketing)
P.M.I. Comercio Internacional (international trading)

COMPETITORS

ANADARKO PETROLEUM CORPORATION	LUKOIL PAO MARATHON OIL CORPORATION
COMPAIA ESPAOLA DE PETROLEOS SAU	NOBLE ENERGY INC.
ECOPETROL S A	OMV Aktiengesellschaft
ENI SPA	Petroleo Brasileiro S
GAZPROM NEFT PAO	A Petrobras

HISTORICAL FINANCIALS

Company Type: Public

Income Statement				FYE: December 31
	REVENUE ($ mil.)	NET INCOME ($ mil.)	NET PROFIT MARGIN	EMPLOYEES
12/20	47,997	(25,611)	—	120,936
12/19	74,101	(18,356)	—	122,646
12/18	85,491	(9,172)	—	124,818
12/17	70,914	(14,255)	—	124,660
12/16	52,173	(9,262)	—	126,940
Annual Growth	(2.1%)	—	—	(1.2%)

2020 Year-End Financials

Debt ratio: 5.8%	No. of shares (mil.): —
Return on equity: —	Dividends
Cash ($ mil.): 2,012	Yield: —
Current ratio: 0.43	Payout: —
Long-term debt ($ mil.): 93,996	Market value ($ mil.): —

Phoenix Group Holdings PLC

Apparently a Phoenix Group can hatch out of the right kind of Pearl. Formerly known as Pearl Group Phoenix Group operates through two primary companies: IGNIS Asset Management and Phoenix Life. Phoenix Life is made up of a handful of life insurance companies including Phoenix Life Ltd. London Life and NPI Ltd. However its companies don't sell new policies but instead maintain blocks of life insurance policies and pension products bought from other insurers (called closed life funds). It has more than 6 million such policies in force. Ignis Asset Management manages 67 billion of assets for customers within and outside of Phoenix Group.

Operations

Phoenix's operations include subsidiaries Phoenix Life Scottish Provident Scottish Mutual and Resolution Asset Management.

Mergers and Acquisitions

In 2018 Phoenix agreed to acquire Standard Life Aberdeen's insurance business for 3.2 billion. The deal is hoped to be mutually beneficial as Standard Life Aberdeen wants to be Phoenix's first-choice asset manager as Phoenix goes about accumulating insurance assets.

Company Background

In 2009 the company was acquired by Virgin Islands-based investment firm Liberty Acquisition Holdings. Following the acquisition — which valued Pearl Group at about 1.6 billion ($2.6 billion) — Liberty Acquisition a special purpose acquisition vehicle (or "blank check" company) changed its name to Pearl Group and began to inject up to 600 million ($987 million) into the new company with a focus on investing in additional financial service entities.

The company streamlined a bit in 2009 by merging its two asset management businesses Axial Investment management and Ignis into one company: Ignis Asset Management. It then began rebranding some products under the Phoenix Life name which paved the way for renaming the company Phoenix Group Holdings in 2010.

Internal mergers continued in 2011 when the company consolidated some of its life insurance businesses into Phoenix Life Ltd. Ultimately the company intends to have two primary life insurance companies under the Phoenix Life banner.

Auditors: Ernst & Young LLP

LOCATIONS

HQ: Phoenix Group Holdings PLC
Juxon House, 100 St Paul's Churchyard, London
EC4M 8BU
Phone:
Web: www.thephoenixgroup.com

PRODUCTS/OPERATIONS

2015 Sales

	% of total
Net investment income	91
Fees	8
Other	1
Total	**100**

COMPETITORS

ABRDN PLC	PRISM TECHNOLOGIES
AEGIS COMMUNICATIONS	GROUP INC.
GROUP LLC	RELX GROUP PLC
FAIR ISAAC CORPORATION	SERCO GROUP PLC

LEGAL & GENERAL GROUP PLC	STATE STREET CORPORATION
NEW YORK LIFE INSURANCE COMPANY	THE HARTFORD FINANCIAL SERVICES GROUP INC.

HISTORICAL FINANCIALS

Company Type: Public

Income Statement				FYE: December 31
	ASSETS ($ mil.)	NET INCOME ($ mil.)	INCOME AS % OF ASSETS	EMPLOYEES
12/19	320,470	112	0.0%	4,417
12/18	293,629	483	0.2%	4,088
12/17	112,705	(36)	—	1,249
12/16	105,790	(124)	—	1,301
12/15	95,606	297	0.3%	741
Annual Growth	35.3%	(21.7%)	—	56.3%

2019 Year-End Financials

Return on assets: 0.0%	Dividends
Return on equity: 1.5%	Yield: —
Long-term debt ($ mil.): —	Payout: 544.1%
No. of shares (mil.): 721	Market value ($ mil.): —
Sales ($ mil): 38,512	

Ping An Insurance (Group) Co of China Ltd.

Ping An Insurance is one of China's largest insurance companies. It specializes in life and health coverage but offers a variety of other products including auto insurance corporate property and casualty insurance engineering insurance cargo insurance liability insurance guarantee insurance credit insurance home contents insurance accident and health insurance as well as international reinsurance business. The company also provides stock trading equity investment funds and bonds property leasing and asset management services through Ping An Trust. Its Shenzhen Ping An Bank subsidiary offers retail banking and other consumer services such as credit card and mortgage lending. The group also includes Ping An Health Insurance.

Operations

Ping An Insurance operates through these primary segments: Life and Health Insurance Property & Casualty Insurance Banking Trust Securities Other Asset Management and Technology.

The largest segment Life and Health Insurance brings in approximately 55% of the group's total revenue. It offers life and health coverage to individual and corporate customers. Offerings include term whole-life endowment annuity investment-linked universal life health insurance subsidiaries and medical insurance.

Property & Casualty Insurance provides automobile non-automobile accident and health insurance. The segment brings in some 20% of total revenue.

The Banking segment provides loan and intermediary business with corporate and retail business customers. It also provides wealth management and credit card services to individuals. It accounts for about 20% of revenue.

The Other Asset Management segment provides finance leasing investment management and other asset management services. It brings in about 5% of revenue.

The Technology provides various financial and daily-life services through internet platforms such as financial transaction information service platform health care service platform reflecting performance summary of the technology business subsidiaries associates and jointly controlled entities. Its operating units include Lufax Holding OneConnect and Ping An HealthKonnect. The segment brings in less than 5% of revenue.

The smallest segments are Trust which operates through Ping An Trust and Ping An Capital; and Securities which provides brokerage trading investment banking and asset management services.

Geographic Reach

Ping is based in Shenzhen China and it operates mainly in China.

Ping An Life provides customers with life insurance products through its nationwide service network of more than 40 branches (including seven telemarketing centers) and over 3300 business outlets.

Ping An Bank has more than 100 branches (including the Hong Kong branch) and about 1100 business outlets. Ping An Property & Casualty distributes insurance products mainly through a network of roughly 45 branches and over 2760 central sub-branches sub-branches sales service outlets and business outlets across China.

Sales and Marketing

Ping An Insurance utilizes in-house sales representatives sales agents and insurance brokers as well as telemarketing online marketing and cross-selling.

The company has 223 million retail customers and more than 627million internet users.

Financial Performance

Note: Growth rates may differ after conversion to US Dollars.

During the COVID-19 epidemic Ping An Bank quickly resumed business by advancing online digital operations. In 2020 revenue grew by 11% year on year to RMB153.5 billion.

In 2020 the company had a net profit of RMB143.1 billion a 4% decrease from the previous year's net profit of RMB149.4 billion.

The company's cash at the end of 2020 was RMB424.7 billion. Operating activities generated RMB312.1 billion while investing activities used RMB447.1 billion primarily for purchases of investments. Financing activities provided another RMB260.6 billion.

Strategy

Ping An pursues customer development through its ecosystems. The company develops pan financial services pan healthcare and smart city ecosystems by leveraging its leading innovative technologies and extensive experience in financial services and healthcare. As of December 31 2020 Ping An's smart city business had served 151 cities across China. In healthcare Ping An Good Doctor's revenue of online healthcare services for 2020 grew strongly by 82% year on year. Benefiting from the "finance + ecosystem" transformation strategy the company acquires new and future users by expanding its ecosystems.

Ping An launched CN-ESG to establish ESG evaluation standards with Chinese characteristics. In 2020 Ping An built the AI-ESG smart management platform to enable responsible investments and launched the "Xinhua CN-ESG Evaluation System" together with China Economic Information Service to establish ESG evaluation standards with Chinese characteristics. As of December 31 2020 Ping An's responsible investments exceeded RMB1.03 trillion. Ping An has promoted industries healthcare and education in rural areas via the Ping An Rural Communities Support program for three years. The program has been implemented in 21 provinces and autonomous regions across China providing over RMB29834 million in poverty alleviation funds and benefiting an impoverished population of 730000. Ping An helped build or upgrade 1228 rural clinics trained 11843 village doctors and provided over 110000 people with free medical examinations. Ping An funded the upgrading of 1054 rural schools and the training of 14110 village teachers benefiting about 300000 students.

Company Background

Ping An Insurance was founded in 1988 as China's first joint-stock insurance company. It ventured beyond insurance in 1995 by establishing Ping An Securities.

EXECUTIVES

Non-Executive Director, Xiaoping Yang
Deputy General Manager, Guangheng Ji
Chairman of the Board, Executive Director, Mingzhe Ma
Chief Investment Executive Officer, Dexian Chen
Chief Investment Officer, Bin Deng
Co-Chief Executive Officer, Chief Financial Officer, Executive Deputy General Manager, Executive Director, Chief Actuary, Bo Yao
Deputy General Manager, Kexiang Chen
Chief Human Resource Officer, Deputy General Manager, Executive Director, Fangfang Cai
Non-Executive Director, Jiren Xie
Co-Chief Executive Officer, General Manager, Executive Director, Yonglin Xie
Co-Chief Executive Officer, Chief Operating Officer, Deputy General Manager, Executive Director, Xinying Chen
Deputy General Manager, Sulan Ye
Auditors: PricewaterhouseCoopers Zhong Tian LLP

LOCATIONS

HQ: Ping An Insurance (Group) Co of China Ltd.
47th, 48th, 109th, 110th, 111th and 112th Floors, Ping An Finance Center, No. 5033 Yitian Road, Futian District, Shenzhen, Guangdong Province 518033
Phone: (86) 400 8866 338   **Fax:** (86) 755 8243 1029
Web: www.pingan.cn

PRODUCTS/OPERATIONS

2018 Sales by Segment

	% of total
Life and Health Insurance	51
Property & Casualty Insurance	21
Banking	19
Other Asset Management	4
Fintech & Healthtech	3
Trust	1
Securities	1
Total	**100**

2018 Sales

	% of total
Net earned premiums	62
Interest revenue from banking operations	15
Interest revenue from non-banking operations	8
Fees & commission revenue from non-insurance operations	4
Investment income	3
Share of profits & losses of associates & jointly controlled entities	2
Reinsurance commission revenue	1
Other revenue & other gains	5
Total	**0**

Selected Subsidiaries and Affiliates

China Ping An Insurance Overseas (Holdings) Limited
  China Ping An Insurance (Hong Kong) Company Limited (75%)
  Ping An of China Asset Management (Hong Kong) Company Limited
China Ping An Trust & Investment Co. Ltd.
  Ping An Securities Co. Ltd.
Ping An Annuity Insurance Company of China Ltd.
Ping An Health Insurance Company of China Ltd.

Ping An Life Insurance Company of China Ltd.
Ping An Property & Casualty Insurance Company of China Ltd.
Shenzhen Ping An Bank Co. Ltd.

COMPETITORS

ADMIRAL GROUP PLC
AIA Group Limited
BESSO LIMITED
CHINA MINSHENG BANKING CORP. LTD.
CO-OPERATIVE INSURANCE SOCIETY LIMITED
HEALTHPLAN HOLDINGS INC.

MS&AD INSURANCE GROUP HOLDINGS INC.
PRINCIPAL FINANCIAL GROUP INC.
SCOR SE
USI INC.

HISTORICAL FINANCIALS

Company Type: Public

Income Statement				FYE: December 31
	ASSETS ($ mil.)	NET INCOME ($ mil.)	INCOME AS % OF ASSETS	EMPLOYEES
12/20	1,456,805	21,879	1.5%	0
12/19	1,181,755	21,471	1.8%	0
12/18	1,038,479	15,614	1.5%	376,900
12/17	997,793	13,690	1.4%	342,550
12/16	803,117	8,985	1.1%	318,588
Annual Growth	**16.1%**	**24.9%**	—	—

2020 Year-End Financials

Return on assets: 1.6%
Return on equity: 19.8%
Long-term debt ($ mil.): —
No. of shares (mil.): —
Sales ($ mil): 19,124

Dividends
  Yield: 2.0%
  Payout: 43.2%
  Market value ($ mil.): —

	STOCK PRICE ($) FY Close	P/E High/Low		PER SHARE ($) Earnings	Dividends	Book Value
12/20	24.50	3	2	1.23	0.50	(0.00)
12/19	23.80	3	2	1.20	0.45	(0.00)
12/18	17.39	4	3	0.87	0.48	4.43
12/17	20.89	5	2	0.77	0.25	3.98
12/16	9.96	3	2	0.50	0.13	3.02
Annual Growth	**25.2%**		—	**25.1%**	**40.8%**	—

Piraeus Financial Holdings SA

Greece is the word and Piraeus has most certainly heard. Piraeus Bank provides retail banking investment banking leasing and insurance services in the Mediterranean and in Central and Eastern Europe. Its network of branches across Greece numbers more than 1000 plus it has about 400 more in Albania (Tirana Bank) Romania Bulgaria Serbia the Ukraine and the US (New York's Marathon Bank). Piraeus Bank also provides its services through its electronic Winbank business which includes about 1900 ATMs Internet and phone banking. The company maintains a diverse loan portfolio with energy and transportation loans making up 30% of its portfolio. Piraeus Bank was founded in 1916 and under state control until 1991.

EXECUTIVES

Independent Non-Executive Director, Solomon Berahas
Non-Executive Director, Alexander Blades
Independent Non-Executive Director, Venetia Kontogouris
Independent Non-Executive Director, Enrico Cucchiani
Executive General Manager, Group Chief Treasurer - Piraeus Bank, Athanasios Arvanitis
Independent Non-Executive Vice Chairman of the Board, Karel De Boeck
Independent Non-Executive Director, David Hexter
Independent Non-Executive Director, Arne Berggren
Executive General Manager, Group Chief Financial Officer - Piraeus Bank, Theodore Gnardellis
Executive General Manager, Chief Corporate and Investment Banking - Piraeus Bank, Eleni Vrettou
Non-Executive Director, HFSF Representative, Periklis Dontas
Non-Executive Chairman of the Board, George Handjinicolaou
Chairman of the Group Executive Committee, Chief Executive Officer, Managing Director, Executive Director, Christos Megalou
Auditors: Deloitte Certified Public Accountants S.A.

LOCATIONS

HQ: Piraeus Financial Holdings SA
  4 Amerikis str., Athens 105 64
Phone: (30) 210 333 5000   **Fax:** (30) 210 333 5080
Web: www.piraeusbankgroup.com

Branch Locations

	No.
Greece	1,037
Romanis	140
Bulgaria	83
Albania	53
Serbia	42
Egypt	41
Ukraine	37
Cyprus	14
London	1
Frankfurt	1
Total	**1,449**

PRODUCTS/OPERATIONS

Selected Subsidiaries

ATEbank
ETBA Industrial Areas S.A.
Marathon Bank of New York (USA)
OJSC Piraeus Bank ICB (Ukraine)
Picar S.A.
Piraeus Asset Management Mutual Funds S.A.
Piraeus Bank AD Beograd (Serbia)
Piraeus Bank Bulgaria AD
Piraeus Bank (Cyprus) Ltd
Piraeus Bank Egypt SAE
Piraeus Capital Management
Piraeus Card Services
Piraeus Direct Services S.A.
Piraeus Insurance and Reinsurance Brokerage S.A.
Piraeus Insurance Agency S.A.
Piraeus Factoring S.A.
Piraeus Leaases SA
Piraeus Leasing Bulgaria
Piraeus Bank Romania S.A.
Piraeus Leasing Romania
Piraeus Private Equity
Piraeus Real Estate S.A.
Piraeus Securities S.A.
Piraeus Wealth Management
Tirana Bank S.A. (Albania)
Tirana Leasing (Albania)

COMPETITORS

BANCOLOMBIA S A	Islandsbanki hf.
BANK OF CYPRUS PUBLIC	LENLYN HOLDINGS
COMPANY LIMITED	LIMITED
CIMB GROUP HOLDINGS	MIZRAHI TEFAHOT BANK
BERHAD	LTD
HSBC HOLDINGS PLC	NORTHERN BANK LIMITED

HISTORICAL FINANCIALS

Company Type: Public

Income Statement
FYE: December 31

	ASSETS ($ mil.)	NET INCOME ($ mil.)	INCOME AS % OF ASSETS	EMPLOYEES
12/19	68,748	314	0.5%	12,613
12/18	70,864	(180)	—	15,000
12/17	80,815	(240)	—	18,581
12/16	86,055	(36)	—	18,995
12/15	95,336	(2,061)	—	20,719
Annual Growth	(7.8%)	—	—	(11.7%)

2019 Year-End Financials

Return on assets: 0.4%
Return on equity: 3.7%
Long-term debt ($ mil.): —
No. of shares (mil.): 436
Sales ($ mil): 3,028

Dividends
Yield: —
Payout: —
Market value ($ mil.): 2,837

	STOCK PRICE ($) FY Close	P/E High/Low	Earnings	PER SHARE ($) Dividends	Book Value
12/19	6.50	11 2	0.37	0.00	19.70
12/18	1.80	— —	(0.22)	0.00	19.40
12/17	7.33	— —	(0.29)	0.00	25.87
12/16	0.44	— —	(0.08)	0.00	23.38
12/15	0.61	— —	(18.57)	0.00	24.72
Annual Growth	80.8%			—	(5.5%)

PJSC Gazprom

Gazprom is one of the world's largest oil and gas companies in terms of reserves production and market capitalization. The company operates in more than 20 countries and its products are supplied to more than 100 markets around the world. Gazprom accounts for more than 50% of Russia's total gas processing volumes more than 10% of the country's oil and gas condensate production and nearly 15% of its total electricity generation. Gazprom expanded the geography of its operations and entered high-potential Asia Pacific market launched operations in Central Asia Africa and Latin America and is a player in the global LNG trade.

Operations

Gazprom is focused on geological exploration production transportation storage processing and sales of gas gas condensate and oil sales of gas as a vehicle fuel as well as generation and marketing of heat and electric power.

Its reportable segments are: Gas production (roughly 50% of total revenue) Refining (nearly 30% of total revenue) Crude oil & gas condensate (approximately 10% of total revenue) Electric & Heat generation (almost 10% of total revenue) and Gas transportation services (about 5% of total revenue).

The company owns the world's largest gas transmission network - the Unified Gas Supply System of Russia with the total length of around 175 thousand kilometers.

Geographic Reach

Russian-based Gazprom operates in more than 20 countries and its products are supplied to more than 100 markets around the world.

Sales and Marketing

Gazprom sells more than half of its gas to Russian consumers and exports gas to over 30 countries within and beyond the former Soviet Union.

Financial Performance

In 2020 Gazprom's net sales decreased by 17% to RUB 6.3 trillion primarily driven by lower net sales of gas to far abroad countries.

Its net income dropped by RUB 1.1 triillion to RUB 135.3 billion in 2020. The year-on-year decrease was mostly due to higher financial expenses following the revaluation of loans and borrowings in foreign currencies and lower operating profit.

In fiscal 2020 Gazprom held cash and cash equivalents of RUB 1.0 trillion. Operating activities provided RUB 1.9 trillion.

Strategy

The company's strategic goal is to strengthen its leading position among global energy companies by diversifying sales markets ensuring energy security and sustainable development improving operating efficiency and fulfilling its scientific and technical potential.

HISTORY

Following the breakup of the Soviet Union in the early 1990s one of the first priorities of the Russian government was to move some state monopolies toward a free-market economic system. A presidential decree in 1992 moved the company toward privatization by calling for the formation of a Russian joint-stock company to explore for and produce gas gas condensates and oil; provide for gas processing; operate gas wells; and build gas pipelines and storage facilities.

By 1993 the government had converted its natural gas monopoly Gazprom into a joint-stock company; the company had dated back to the 1940s and the USSR Ministry of the Gas Industry had kept all of its assets when it became a corporation in 1989.

The new Gazprom was 15%-owned by Gazprom workers and 28% by people living in Russia's gas-producing regions. The state retained about a 40% share (boosted to 51% in 2003). The company inherited all of the former Soviet republics' export contracts to Western and Central Europe.

Thanks to the power of Viktor Chernomyrdin (Gazprom's former Soviet boss and gas industry minister who became Russia's prime minister in 1992) the company was able to enjoy large tax breaks and maintain its role as a monopoly — even as other industries were being more deeply privatized. However the privatization of Gazprom was later attacked as being manipulated to profit the company's top management including Chernomyrdin. Top managers were rumored to have each received 1%-5% of shares — holdings potentially worth $1.2 billion-$10 billion each.

Needing to raise cash in 1996 Gazprom offered 1% of its stock to foreigners the first sale of stock to foreign investors. In 1997 Gazprom and Royal Dutch/Shell formally became partners. That year Gazprom began building its Blue Stream pipeline across the Black Sea to Turkey. Italian group Eni helped back the project and became a partner by 1999.

In 1998 Gazprom acquired a stake in Promstroibank Russia's fourth-largest financial institution. German energy powerhouse Ruhrgas acquired a 3% stake in Gazprom in 1998 which it increased to nearly 4% the next year. Also in 1999 Gazprom started building its Yamal-Europe pipeline which was to stretch to Germany for exports to Europe.

The next year an attempt by Gazprom to muscle into Hungary's chemicals sector by offering cheaper raw materials was blocked by Hungary's TVK and Borsodchem and their allies. Also in 2000 Gazprom became embroiled in a politically controversial issue when it called for the country's leading private media holding group Media-MOST to sell shares to the gas giant in order to settle millions of dollars of debt. Because Media-MOST held NTV television a major critic of Russian President Vladimir Putin the deal was alleged to have been directed by the Kremlin. A government probe into the deal was later ordered. (By 2002 Gazprom owned a significant stake in NTV which it sold that year so it could focus on its core energy businesses.)

The alignment of Gazprom's board changed in 2000 after the annual shareholder's meeting. For the first time in Gazprom's history company managers did not have a majority of seats. A new chairman Dmitri Medvedev second in command to Putin was elected to replace Chernomyrdin. In 2001 the board fired CEO Rem Vyakhirev and replaced him with Deputy Energy Minister Alexei Miller a Putin ally.

Gazprom had announced plans in 2004 to acquire Rosneft (effectively giving the Russian government control of Gazprom) though the deal was complicated by Rosneft's acquisition of the Yugansk assets acquired from YUKOS. In 2005 Gazprom abandoned plans to merge with Rosneft and acquired Sibneft in an effort to add significant oil operations to its business. Millhouse Capital a holding company controlled by Russian oligarch Roman Abramovich sold its majority stake in what was then a major exploration and production company called Sibneft (now Gazprom Neft) to Gazprom for a reported $13 billion. At the time Sibneft was Russia's fifth-largest oil company.

In 2006 Gazprom signed long-term contracts for gas deliveries with Austrian energy giant OMV. That year Royal Dutch/Shell agreed to give control of the $22 billion Sakhalin-2 project (run by Sakhalin Energy Investment) in Russia's Far East to Gazprom.

Former Gazprom chairman Dmitri Medvedev was elected president of Russia in 2008.

The company became embroiled in a pricing dispute with neighbor Ukraine in 2009 resulting in the disruption of gas supplies to Ukraine and because of its transnational pipelines to dozens of other countries in Europe.

Wanting to expand its Russian and international assets and diversify its profile in 2009 Gazprom acquired Italian energy titan ENI's 20% share in oil producer Gazprom Neft raising the Russian giant's direct ownership to 79%. ENI had acquired its stake in 2007 following the bankruptcy of YUKOS. Gazprom had the option to buy ENI's stake within two years and exercised that right in 2009 paying just more than $4 billion to ENI. Gazprom directly owns or indirectly controls through subsidiaries about 95% of Gazprom Neft.

In 2010 the company made its first entry into the US gas market when it began trading and marketing natural gas though Gazprom Marketing & Trading USA. It also signed a strategic partnership with Royal Dutch Shell to develop oil and gas assets in Russian Siberia and the Far East and process and market products in Russia and Europe.

To raise cash to pay down debt in 2010 the company sold its controlling stake in SeverEnergia (a natural gas project partly owned by ENI) to a joint venture owned by Gazprom Neft and OAO Novatek for $1.5 billion. To raise cash it sold 9% of its 19% stake in Novatek to Gazprombank for $2.8 billion.

In 2011 it installed 1.9 GW of combined heat and power generation units and deployed an offshore production platform at the Prirazlomnoye oil field in the Pechora Sea in the Arctic.

Expanding its energy footprint in 2011 Gazprom agreed to acquire power generation KES Holding (which owns four power companies) to create Russia's largest power company. KES Holding will hold 25% of the new joint venture.

To expand its gas supply in 2012 the company announced that it planned to spend 43 billion rubles (US $1.4 billion) that year to develop gas infrastructure projects (gas fields and pipelines) in the Sakhalin region of Eastern Russia. In 2011 Gazprom acquired TNK-BP's east Siberian Kovykta gas field for about $770 million. The purchase opens up the possibility of a major supply agreement with China.

EXECUTIVES

Deputy Chairwoman of the Management Committee, General Director (CEO) of Gazprom Export, Elena Burmistrova
Member of the Board of Directors, Independent Director, Viktor Martynov
Member of the Board of Directors, Non-Executive Director, Dmitry Patrushev
Member of the Board of Directors, Non-Executive Director, Denis Manturov
Member of the Management Committee, Head of Department (legal support), Sergey Kuznets
Deputy Chairman of the Management Committee, Head of Department (prospective development), Oleg Aksyutin
Member of the Management Committee, Head of Department (asset management and corporate relations), Elena Mikhailova
Member of the Board of Directors, Non-Executive Director, Alexander Novak
Member of the Board of Directors, Non-Executive Director, Andrei Akimov
Member of the Board of Directors, Non-Executive Director, Mikhail Sereda
Deputy Chairman of the Management Committee - General Director of the Corporate Security Service Branch, Sergey Khomyakov
Non-Executive Chairman of the Board, Viktor Zubkov
Member of the Management Committee, Head of Department (gas transportation and underground storage), Vyacheslav Mikhalenko
Member of the Management Committee, Head of Department (hydrocarbon exploration and production), Sergey Menshikov
Deputy Chairman of the Management Committee, Famil Sadygov
Member of the Management Committee, Head of Department (sales of hydrocarbons and refined products in the domestic market, power generation, expansion of gas supply and gas infrastructure), Gennady Sukhov
Member of the Board of Directors, Executive Director, Deputy Chairman of the Management Committee, Vitaly Markelov
Member of the Management Committee, Head of Department (government relations), Vladimir Markov
Chairman of the Management Committee, Deputy Chairman of the Board of Directors, Executive Director, Aleksey Miller
Deputy Chairman of the Management Committee, Mikhail Putin
Auditors: FBK, LLC

LOCATIONS

HQ: PJSC Gazprom
Nametkina St., 16, V-420, GSP-7, Moscow 117997
Phone: (7) 812 609 4129   **Fax:** (7) 812 609 4334
Web: www.gazprom.com

PRODUCTS/OPERATIONS

2014 Sales

	% of total
Distribution	53
Refining	29
Electric and heat energy generation and sales	7
Production of crude oil and gas condensate	4
Transport	3
Gas storage	0
Production of gas	0
All other segments	4
Total	**100**

COMPETITORS

AEGEAN MARINE PETROLEUM S.A.	Equinor ASA
AFREN PLC	LUKOIL PAO
BG GROUP LIMITED	MARATHON OIL CORPORATION
CNOOC LIMITED	MITSUI & CO. LTD.
CONOCOPHILLIPS	MOTIVA ENTERPRISES LLC
DEVON ENERGY CORPORATION	NK ROSNEFT PAO
ENI SPA	OMV Aktiengesellschaft
ENRON CREDITORS RECOVERY CORP.	SURGUTNEFTEGAZ PAO
	Wintershall Dea AG

HISTORICAL FINANCIALS

Company Type: Public

Income Statement   FYE: December 31

	REVENUE ($ mil.)	NET INCOME ($ mil.)	NET PROFIT MARGIN	EMPLOYEES
12/20	84,926	1,809	2.1%	467,000
12/19	122,671	19,327	15.8%	473,800
12/18	118,259	20,894	17.7%	466,100
12/17	112,945	12,355	10.9%	469,600
12/16	99,856	15,541	15.6%	467,400
Annual Growth	(4.0%)	(41.6%)	—	(0.0%)

2020 Year-End Financials

Debt ratio: 0.2%
Return on equity: 0.9%
Cash ($ mil.): 13,834
Current ratio: 1.44
Long-term debt ($ mil.): 56,334

No. of shares (mil.): —
Dividends
Yield: 7.3%
Payout: 3,103.9%
Market value ($ mil.): —

	STOCK PRICE ($) FY Close	P/E High/Low		PER SHARE ($) Earnings	Dividends	Book Value
12/20	5.60	1	1	0.08	0.41	8.05
12/19	8.22	0	0	0.86	0.50	9.58
12/18	4.42	0	0	0.95	0.24	8.62
12/17	4.41	0	0	0.56	1.64	9.09
12/16	5.09	0	0	0.69	1.51	8.19
Annual Growth (0.4%)	2.4%	—	—	(42.4%)	(27.7%)	

PJSC Lukoil

LUKOIL is one of the largest publicly traded vertically integrated oil and gas companies in the world accounting for some 2% of the world's oil production and around 1% of the proved hydrocarbon reserves globally. Present across the entire value chain Lukoil has significant exploration & production refining and marketing operations concentrated in Russia but spreading out to Europe Central Asia and the Middle East. In addition it engages in power generation including some solar in Russia Romania and Bulgaria. Lukoil gas filling stations serve customers in around 30 countries.

About 70% of Lukoil retail sales come from within Russia.

Operations

LUKOI generates approximately 40% of sales from crude oil followed by diesel fuel (about 20%) petrochemicals and gas (more than 20% combined) fuel oil and gasoline (some 5% each) jet fuel and other products account for the remaining. The company's proved hydrocarbon reserves include nearly 15.4 billion barrels of liquid hydrocarbons and some 28000 billion cubic feet of gas.

The company reports its activities under two core business segments.

Refining Marketing and Distribution is the core business of Lukoil. It includes refining petrochemical and gas processing marketing and trading of crude oil natural gas and refined products generation transportation and sales of electricity plus heat and related services.

Exploration and Production manages exploration development and production operations related to crude oil and gas. These activities are primarily located within Russia and internationally.

Geographic Reach

Based in Russia LUKOIL has significant operations in around 35 countries on four continents.

In Russia its major oil producing regions are Western Siberia Timan-Pechora Ural and Volga region. Internationally its upstream portfolio includes stakes in PSA's and other projects in Kazakhstan Azerbaijan Uzbekistan Romania Iraq Egypt Ghana Norway Cameroon Nigeria and Mexico.

Lukoil's refineries and petrochemical plants are concentrated in Russia with additional production in four European countries. Other than Russia power generation is concentrated in Italy.

Lukoil gas filling stations are in around 20 countries worldwide.

Sales and Marketing

LUKOIL serves customers across a diverse array of industries including oil and gas petrochemical power fuel marine aircraft and some other sectors. It sells the bulk of its petroleum products in the retail market via its well-diversified retail network of approximately 5005 filling stations worldwide.

Financial Performance

Revenue for 2020 was RUB 5.6 trillion down by 28% year-on-year. This was driven by weaker prices and lower volumes of hydrocarbon production as well as reduced output trading and retail sales volumes of petroleum products. The impact of these factors was partially offset by ruble devaluation.

In 2020 profit for the year attributable to PJSC LUKOIL shareholders was RUB 15 billion as compared to RUB 640 billion in 2019. In addition to the lower EBITDA profit was negatively affected by non-cash losses from asset impairment and FX differences.

Strategy

Despite the difficult market environment in the reporting year the company proceeded with the implementation of its long-term strategy. However some of the company's strategic goals became irrelevant in 2020 due to a drop in demand and deterioration in the market environment amid the COVID-19 pandemic.

The COVID-19 pandemic caused a significant imbalance between supply and demand in the global oil market. To normalize the situation OPEC+ countries agreed upon an unprecedented oil production cut followed by gradual increases. Due to the OPEC+ agreement LUKOIL cut its oil production in Russia and some of its international projects. In May 2020 LUKOIL cut its daily oil production in Russia by 19% as compared to average daily production in 2019. By the end of 2020 one third of this production cut has been recovered in accordance with the instructions of the Ministry of Energy of Russia. An important contributor to

LUKOIL's resilience amid production restrictions was diversified asset portfolio which allowed the Company to quickly adapt to the new conditions and manage production efficiently minimizing the impact on its financial performance. The production was reduced by shutting in the least profitable wells predominantly at mature fields in the key regions of operation with geological and process risks factored in. This sophisticated approach to the production cut allows the Company to quickly recover production.

Mergers and Acquisitions

In mid-2021 LUKOIL entered into an agreement to acquire the 50% operator interest in the Area 4 project in Mexico (hereinafter ? the Project) through the acquisition of the operator's holding company. The transaction value is approximately $435 million plus expenditures incurred in 2021 as of the transaction completion date. The new project is notable due to its considerable explored reserves and significant production potential. It naturally complements the company's existing portfolio of projects in the Gulf of Mexico.

Company Background

LUKOIL was formed from the combination of three major state-owned oil and gas exploration companies — Langepasneftegaz Uraineftegaz and Kogalymneftegaz — that traced their origins to the discovery of oil in western Siberia in 1964.

More than 25 years later after the Soviet Union broke up the oil and gas sector was one of the first industries marked for privatization.

In 1992 the government called for Langepasneftegaz Uraineftegaz and Kogalymneftegaz to merge and LUKOIL was created the next year. (The LUK of LUKOIL comes from the initials of the three companies.) Russian president Boris Yeltsin appointed Siberian oil veteran Vagit Alekperov as the company's first president. The Russian government also formed several other large integrated oil companies including Yukos Surgutneftegaz Sidanco and Sibneft.

LUKOIL went public on the fledgling Russian Trading System in 1994.

HISTORY

LUKOIL was formed from the combination of three major state-owned oil and gas exploration companies — Langepasneftegaz Uraineftegaz and Kogalymneftegaz — that traced their origins to the discovery of oil in western Siberia in 1964. More than 25 years later after the Soviet Union broke up the oil and gas sector was one of the first industries marked for privatization.

In 1992 the government called for Langepasneftegaz Uraineftegaz and Kogalymneftegaz to merge and LUKOIL was created the next year. (The LUK of LUKOIL comes from the initials of the three companies.) Russian president Boris Yeltsin appointed Siberian oil veteran Vagit Alekperov as the company's first president. The Russian government also formed several other large integrated oil companies including Yukos Surgutneftegaz Sidanco and Sibneft.

LUKOIL went public on the fledgling Russian Trading System in 1994. The next year the company absorbed nine other enterprises including oil exploration companies Astrakhanneft Kaliningradmorneftegaz and Permneft. That year LUKOIL became the first Russian oil company to set up an exploration and production trading arm. In 1996 LUKOIL acquired a 41% stake in Izvestia Russia's major independent newspaper.

Chevron and LUKOIL with seven other oil and gas companies and three governments agreed in 1996 to build a 1500-kilometer pipeline to link the Kazakhstan oil fields to world markets.

In 1997 LUKOIL became the first Russian corporation to sell bonds to international investors

and the government sold 15% of its stake in the company. That year LUKOIL's 50%-owned Nexus Fuels unit opened its first gas stations located in the parking lots of US grocery stores (the partnership dissolved and Nexus went bankrupt in 2000).

LUKOIL began a partnership with Conoco (later ConocoPhillips) in 1998 to develop oil and natural gas reserves in Russia's northern territories. LUKOIL also acquired 51% of Romania's Petrorel refinery. In 1999 it acquired control of refineries in Bulgaria and Ukraine and in a petrochemical firm in Saratov. It also acquired oil company KomiTEK in one of Russia's largest mergers.

The government sold a 9% stake in LUKOIL to a Cyprus-based unit Reforma Investments held in part by LUKOIL's "boss of bosses" Vagit Alekperov (gained at the bargain price of $200 million). Critics cited the sale as Yeltsin's bid to gain Alekperov's political support.

The company announced the first major oil find in the Russian part of the Caspian Sea in 2000 and formed a joint venture (Caspian Oil Company) with fellow Russian energy giants Gazprom and Yukos to exploit resources in the Caspian. The next year LUKOIL acquired more than 1300 gas stations on the East Coast of the US when it bought Getty Petroleum Marketing.

That year LUKOIL also acquired Bitech a Canadian oil exploration and production firm with operations in the Republic of Komi in the Russian Federation. In 2002 the company sold its oil service business a move that cut its overall workforce by some 20000 and resulted in savings of $500 million annually.

With an appetite for expansion the company upped its production with refinery acquisitions and invested heavily in new oil patches such as the Caspian Sea. In 2005 LUKOIL acquired Finland-based Oy Teboil AB and Suomen Petrooli Oy affiliated refined oil products companies for an undisclosed amount. LUKOIL also acquired Nelson Resources which had oil and gas interests in Western Kazakhstan for about $2 billion.

The next year the company acquired Marathon Oil's assets in Khanty-Mansiysk Autonomous Region — Yugra of Western Siberia — for $787 million. LUKOIL also acquired 376 European gas stations from ConocoPhillips in 2006.

In 2007 LUKOIL signed a strategic exploration and production agreement with Qatar Petroleum.

In 2008 the company diversified its operations further creating a power generation segment which encompasses its own generators at well sites and a number of generating units in Bulgaria Romania and Ukraine.

In 2008 it began to re-engage in Iraq where it had held oil concessions prior to the US-led invasion in 2003. It also acquired a retail network in Turkey in 2008 for $500 million.

EXECUTIVES

Member of the Management Board, Vice President - General Counsel, Ivan Maslyaev
Vice President for Human Resources Management and Social Policy, Member of the Management Board, Anatoly Moskalenko
Member of the Management Board, Senior Vice President for Overseas Oil and Gas Exploration and Production, Denis Rogachev
Independent Vice Chairman of the Board of Directors, Victor Blazheev
Member of the Management Board, First Executive Vice President, Vadim Vorobev
Independent Director, Sergey Shatalov
Independent Director, Pavel Teplukhin
Independent Director, Wolfgang Schussel
Non-Executive Director, Liubov Khoba
Member of the Management Board, Vice President for Finance, Pavel Zhdanov

Vice President for Exploration and Development, Member of the Management Board, Ilya Mandrik
Chairman of the Management Board, President, Chief Executive Officer, Executive Director, Vagit Alekperov
Member of the Management Board, First Vice President (Economics & Finance), Aleksandr Matytsyn
Chairman of the Board of Directors, Non-Executive Director, Ravil Maganov
Executive Director, Vice President of Strategic Development, Leonid Fedun
Vice President, Executive Director, Nikolay Nikolaev
Member of the Management Board, Chief Accountant, Vyacheslav Verkhov
First Vice President, Member of the Management Board, Azat Shamsuarov
Member of the Management Board, Senior Vice President - Supplies & Sales, Oleg Pashaev
Independent Director, Toby Gati
Independent Director, Roger Munnings
Member of the Management Board, Vice President - Economics and Planning, Gennady Fedotov
Member of the Management Board, Vice President - Chief of Staff, Evgeny Khavkin
Auditors: JSC KPMG

LOCATIONS

HQ: PJSC Lukoil
11 Sretensky Boulevard, Moscow 101000
Phone: (7) 495 627 4444   **Fax:** (7) 495 625 7016
Web: www.lukoil.com

2015 Sales

	% of total
Russia	30
Other countries	70
Total	**100**

PRODUCTS/OPERATIONS

2015 Sales

	% of total
Refining marketing and distribution	95
Exploration and production	4
Corporate and other	1
Total	**100**

2015 Sales

	% of total
Refined products	67
Crude oil	27
Gas & gas products	2
Petrochemicals	1
Sales of energy & related services	1
Other	2
Total	**100**

COMPETITORS

BP P.L.C.
DANA PETROLEUM LIMITED
ENDESA SA
ENI SPA
GAZPROM NEFT PAO
GREENERGY INTERNATIONAL LIMITED
HELLENIC PETROLEUM S.A. HOLDING
IBERDROLA SOCIEDAD ANONIMA
KCA DEUTAG DRILLING LIMITED
KOC HOLDING ANONIM SIRKETI
NK ROSNEFT PAO
OMV Aktiengesellschaft
REPSOL SA.
ROYAL DUTCH SHELL plc
SASOL LTD
SSAB AB
TECHNIP
TOTALENERGIES SE
VEOLIA ENVIRONNEMENT

HISTORICAL FINANCIALS

Company Type: Public

Income Statement

FYE: December 31

	REVENUE ($ mil.)	NET INCOME ($ mil.)	NET PROFIT MARGIN	EMPLOYEES
12/20	75,388	202	0.3%	100,800
12/19	125,990	10,286	8.2%	101,400
12/18	115,299	8,883	7.7%	0
12/17	102,686	7,244	7.1%	0
12/16	85,364	3,377	4.0%	0
Annual Growth	(3.1%)	(50.5%)	—	—

2020 Year-End Financials

Debt ratio: 0.1%
Return on equity: 0.3%
Cash ($ mil.): 4,596
Current ratio: 1.44
Long-term debt ($ mil.): 7,714

No. of shares (mil.): 652
Dividends
  Yield: 8.0%
  Payout: 1,727.6%
Market value ($ mil.): 44,605

	STOCK PRICE ($) FY Close	P/E High/Low		PER SHARE ($) Earnings	Dividends	Book Value
12/20	68.36	4	2	0.30	5.48	84.47
12/19	98.71	0	0	15.02	5.47	97.59
12/18	71.34	0	0	12.41	3.49	83.70
12/17	57.65	0	0	10.19	3.60	84.89
12/16	56.12	0	0	4.74	3.02	73.78
Annual Growth	5.1%	—	—	(49.8%)	16.0%	3.4%

PJSC Rosseti

Auditors: RSM RUS LTD

LOCATIONS

HQ: PJSC Rosseti
4 Belovezhskaya Street, Moscow 121353
Phone: (7) 495 363 2848   Fax: (7) 495 981 4121
Web: www.holding-mrsk.ru

HISTORICAL FINANCIALS

Company Type: Public

Income Statement

FYE: December 31

	REVENUE ($ mil.)	NET INCOME ($ mil.)	NET PROFIT MARGIN	EMPLOYEES
12/20	13,388	586	4.4%	0
12/19	16,544	1,233	7.5%	0
12/18	14,658	1,305	8.9%	0
12/17	16,403	1,769	10.8%	0
12/16	14,763	1,218	8.3%	0
Annual Growth	(2.4%)	(16.7%)	—	—

2020 Year-End Financials

Debt ratio: 0.2%
Return on equity: 3.6%
Cash ($ mil.): 881
Current ratio: 0.67
Long-term debt ($ mil.): 6,150

No. of shares (mil.): —
Dividends
  Yield: —
  Payout: 7,910.2%
Market value ($ mil.): —

Poly Developments and Holdings Group Co Ltd

EXECUTIVES

Director, Yi Xing
Director, Guanzhong Chen
Deputy General Manager, Yingchuan Liu
Deputy General Manager, Zhihua Pan
Independent Director, Fei Li
Deputy General Manager, Junfeng Kong
Independent Director, Deming Dai
Independent Director, Zhengfu Zhu
Secretary of the Board, Hai Huang
Chief Financial Officer, Dongli Zhou
Deputy General Manager, Wei Zhang
Chairman of the Board, Guangju Song
Director, Zaixin Hu
Director, Zigao Zhao
Deputy General Manager, Wensheng Liu
Deputy General Manager, Yanhua Zhang
General Manager, Director, Ping Liu
Auditors: Daxin Certified Public Accountants

LOCATIONS

HQ: Poly Developments and Holdings Group Co Ltd
29th - 33th Floor, South Tower, Poly International Building, No. 688, Yuejiang Zhonglu, Haizhu Distrct, Guangzhou, Guangdong Province 510308
Phone: (86) 20 89898833   Fax: (86) 20 89898666
Web: www.gzpoly.com

HISTORICAL FINANCIALS

Company Type: Public

Income Statement

FYE: December 31

	REVENUE ($ mil.)	NET INCOME ($ mil.)	NET PROFIT MARGIN	EMPLOYEES
12/20	37,186	4,426	11.9%	0
12/19	33,913	4,018	11.8%	0
12/18	28,285	2,748	9.7%	0
12/17	22,488	2,401	10.7%	0
12/16	22,288	1,788	8.0%	0
Annual Growth	13.7%	25.4%	—	—

2020 Year-End Financials

Debt ratio: 3.6%
Return on equity: 17.1%
Cash ($ mil.): 22,324
Current ratio: 1.51
Long-term debt ($ mil.): 35,507

No. of shares (mil.): —
Dividends
  Yield: —
  Payout: —
Market value ($ mil.): —

POSCO (South Korea)

POSCO posits itself firmly as global steel-maker selling more than 40 million tons of it annually. A steel producer in its home country to about 55 counties the company exports a wide range of steel products including hot rolled sheets plate wire rod cold rolled sheets galvanized sheets and stainless steel to 53 countries earning worldwide recognition for its superb technology and excellent quality. Beyond steel the company also engages in power generation materials trading and resource development activities. POSCO's Pohang and Gwangyang plants in Korea are the largest steel facilities in the world by production.

Operations

POSCO operates through four reportable operating segments ? a steel segment a trading segment a construction segment and a segment that contains operations of all other entities.

The steel segment (nearly 50% of revenue) includes production of steel products and sale of such products.

The trading segment (around 35% revenue) consists primarily of global trading activities and natural resources development activities of POSCO International. POSCO International exports and imports a wide range of steel products that are both obtained from and supplied to POSCO as well as between other suppliers and purchasers in Korea and overseas.

The construction segment (about 10% revenue) includes planning designing and construction of industrial plants civil engineering projects and commercial and residential buildings both in Korea and overseas.

The "others" segment (with over 5% revenue) includes power generation LNG logistics manufacturing of various industrial materials and network and system integration.

Geographic Reach

POSCO Steel is headquartered in Teheran-ro Gangnam-gu Seoul Republic of Korea. POSCO DAEWOO has some 35 local subsidiaries in South Korea and branches all around the world.

More than 65% of its revenue comes from Korea followed by China which accounts for more than 10%.

Sales and Marketing

POSCO's sales strategy has been to devote its production primarily to satisfy domestic demand while seeking export sales to utilize capacity to the fullest extent and to expand its international market presence.

POSCO's advertising expenses decreased by 23% or ?24 billion from ?107 billion in 2018 to ?83 billion in 2019 primarily reflecting its advertising activities in 2018 related to its sponsorship of the 2018 PyeongChang Olympic Games compared to no such advertising activities in 2019.

Financial Performance

Note: Growth rates may differ after conversion to US Dollars.

Company's revenue for fiscal 2020 decreased by 11% to ?57.5 trillion compared from the prior year with ?64.8 trillion.

Profit for fiscal 2020 decreased to ?1.7 trillion compared from the prior year with ?2 trillion.

Cash held by the company at the end of fiscal 2020 increased to ?4.8 trillion. Cash provided by operations was ?8.7 trillion while cash used for investing and financing activities were ?6.3 trillion and ?1.1 trillion respectively. Main uses of cash were acquisitions of short-term financial instruments; and repayment of borrowings.

Strategy

As part of POSCO's strategy to compete in this challenging landscape it will continue to invest in developing innovative products that offer the greatest potential returns and enhance the overall quality of their products as well as make additional investments in the development of new manufacturing technologies.

In part to prepare for the eventual maturation of the Korean steel market the company has made investments in the past decade to secure new growth engines by diversifying into new businesses related to its steel operations that it believes will offer greater potential returns such as participation in EPC projects in the steel sector and natural resources development as well as entering into new businesses not related to its steel operations such as power generation and alternative energy solutions LNG and agricultural trading and production of anode and cathode materials for rechargeable batteries as well as other comprehensive materials such as lithium. From time to time the company may selectively acquire or invest in companies to pursue such diversification strategy.

Company Background

POSCO traces its development very closely with that out its motherland South Korea. It was founded in April 1968 as the Pohang Iron and Steel Company. POSCO grew as South Korea grew hand-in-hand since the 1980s. In 1986 the CEO of POSCO also founded the Pohang University of Science & Technology (POSTECH University) the first research-oriented university in Korea. The company went private during the turn of the 21st Century. Today it is one of the world's most advanced integrated steel companies and one of the top five steelmakers by production.

HISTORY

After the Korean War South Korea the US and its allies wanted to rebuild South Korea's infrastructure as quickly as possible. Steel was given a high priority and before long about 15 companies were making various steel products. Quality was a problem though as the companies used dated production processes.

With the backing of South Korean president Chung Hee Park momentum for a large steel plant grew in the late 1960s. In 1967 the South Korean government and Korean International Steel Associates (KISA) — a consortium of seven Western steelmakers - signed an agreement that called for the completion of an integrated mill by 1972. Pohang Iron & Steel Co. (POSCO) the operating company was incorporated in 1968. Efforts to raise the necessary capital failed however and KISA was dissolved in 1969.

Undaunted the South Koreans turned to the Japanese who arranged loans covering most of the mill's costs and the early phases of planning and construction. The Japanese also transferred the technology needed to run such a plant. Slow and deliberate planning resulted in a plant far away from Seoul (part of a plan to locate industries throughout the country) and a design that lent itself to future expansion. The first stage including a blast furnace and two steel converters was completed in 1973. By the time the fourth stage of construction began in 1979 the Koreans had gained enough confidence to take over many of the tasks. When the last stage was completed in 1981 the plant had an annual capacity of 8.5 million tons.

To ensure steel of acceptable quality POSCO focused first on plain high-carbon steel for general construction rather than on specialized (and difficult to produce) varieties. The company gradually broadened its specialized offerings.

In 1985 POSCO began construction on a second integrated steel plant located in Kwangyang. That plant was also built in four stages; its annual production capacity when it was completed in 1992 was 11.4 million tons. By 1987 POSCO was exporting almost 3 million tons of steel a year and using its knowledge to assist in plant construction projects in other countries.

By the mid-1990s POSCO was exporting 6 million tons of steel annually. The South Korean government sold a 5% stake in POSCO to the public in 1998 and vowed to open up the primary steelmaking industry to competition. However facing a severe downturn in steel demand that year because of sluggishness in Asian and domestic markets the company canceled two projects in China and suspended two in Indonesia. In 1999 POSCO merged its two subsidiaries Pohang Coated Steel and Pohang Steel Industries to create Pohang Steel Co. That same year POSCO Machinery & Engineering POSEC-HAWAII and P.T. Posnesia Stainless Steel Industry were joined to form POSCO Machinery Co. The South Korean government continued selling off its 13% stake in 1999.

In 2000 POSCO sold its 51% stake in telecommunications company Shinsegi Telecom to SK Telecom in exchange for cash and a 6.5% stake in SK Telecom. It also formed a strategic alliance — exploration of joint ventures shared research and joint procurement — with Nippon Steel the world's #1 steelmaker. The deal also calls for each to take increased equity stakes (2% or 3%) in the other. After about 30 years of government control the

South Korean government sold its remaining shares of POSCO in 2001.

In June 2002 Chairman Yoo was indicted for influencing POSCO subsidiaries and contractors to buy inflated shares of Tiger Pools International (South Korea's sole sports lottery business) for Kim Hong-Gul the third son of South Korean President Kim Dae-Jung. That same year Pohang Iron & Steel Co. officially changed its company name to POSCO to try and strengthen brand recognition.

In 2003 Yoo resigned ahead of the company's shareholder meeting amid his possible involvement in illegal stock transactions.

The company invested in its Mexican operations in 2006 announcing a joint venture coil processing facility with Daewoo International to serve local carmakers. In 2010 POSCO acquired a majority stake in Daewoo International. Daewoo shareholders voted to put the company's depressed shares up for sale after the South Korean government gave its approval for the deal early in 2010.

EXECUTIVES

Managing Director, Jeong Su Kim
Managing Director, Gwang Mu Kim
Vice President, Su Hui Nam
Managing Director, Min Cheol Kim
Managing Director, Seung Gyu Yim
Chairman of the Board, Chief Executive Officer, Director, Jeong Wu Choi
Vice President, Chang Hwa Jung
Managing Director, Won Jun Yang
Managing Director, Dae Ryong Ha
Managing Director, Se Don Joo
Managing Director, Sun Gi Kim
Vice President, Ji Yong Kim
Vice President, Director, Hak Dong Kim
Vice President, Seong Wuk Lee
President, Chief Executive Officer, Director, Yin Hwa Jang
Vice President, Deok Rak Lee
Non-Executive Independent Director, Ju Hyeon Kim
Non-Executive Independent Director, Seung Hwa Jang
Vice President, Byeong Ok Yoo
Vice President, Director, Tak Jung
Non-Executive Independent Director, Mun Gi Jung
Non-Executive Independent Director, Seong Jin Kim
Managing Director, Bok Tae Kim
Vice President, Gyu Seok Oh
Vice President, Si Wu Lee
Managing Director, Yong Jun Choi
Vice President, Director, Jung Sun Jeon
Managing Director, Gi Su Kim
Non-Executive Independent Director, Hui Jae Park
Non-Executive Independent Director, Shin Bae Kim
Managing Director, Jae Yeol Lee
Managing Director, Gyo Seong Kim
Auditors: KPMG Samjong Accounting Corp.

LOCATIONS

HQ: POSCO (South Korea)
POSCO Center, 440 Teheran-ro, Seoul, Gangnam-gu 06194
Phone: (82) 2 3457 1386   **Fax:** (82) 2 3457 1997
Web: www.posco.co.kr

2017 Sales

	% of total
Domestic	65
China	11
Asia-other	13
Japan	4
North America	3
Others	4
Total	**100**

PRODUCTS/OPERATIONS

2017 Sales

	% of total
Steel	50
Trading	35
Construction	11
Others Segment	4
Total	**100**

COMPETITORS

ArcelorMittal
BONNEY FORGE
 CORPORATION
ITOCHU CORPORATION
Outokumpu Oyj

PSEG NUCLEAR LLC
SSAB AB
STANDARD STEEL LLC
WRIGHT TOOL COMPANY
thyssenkrupp AG

HISTORICAL FINANCIALS
Company Type: Public

Income Statement
FYE: December 31

	REVENUE ($ mil.)	NET INCOME ($ mil.)	NET PROFIT MARGIN	EMPLOYEES
12/20	52,802	1,452	2.8%	35,393
12/19	56,110	1,614	2.9%	35,261
12/18	58,281	1,516	2.6%	17,150
12/17	56,893	2,617	4.6%	17,055
12/16	44,186	1,134	2.6%	16,584
Annual Growth	4.6%	6.4%	—	20.9%

2020 Year-End Financials

Debt ratio: 0.0%	No. of shares (mil.): 76
Return on equity: 3.5%	Dividends
Cash ($ mil.): 4,368	Yield: 2.5%
Current ratio: 2.12	Payout: 8.5%
Long-term debt ($ mil.): 10,860	Market value ($ mil.): 4,737

	STOCK PRICE ($) FY Close	P/E High/Low		PER SHARE ($) Earnings	Dividends	Book Value
12/20	62.31	0	0	18.28	1.56	535.40
12/19	50.62	0	0	20.08	2.35	480.58
12/18	54.94	0	0	18.76	1.94	486.27
12/17	78.13	0	0	32.33	2.39	512.77
12/16	52.55	0	0	13.84	1.71	440.90
Annual Growth	4.4%	—	—	7.2%	(2.2%)	5.0%

Poste Italiane SpA

Auditors: PricewaterhouseCoopers SpA

LOCATIONS

HQ: Poste Italiane SpA
 Viale Europa 190, Rome 00144
Phone: (36) 06 59581   **Fax:** (36) 06 59589100
Web: www.poste.it

HISTORICAL FINANCIALS
Company Type: Public

Income Statement
FYE: December 31

	REVENUE ($ mil.)	NET INCOME ($ mil.)	NET PROFIT MARGIN	EMPLOYEES
12/19	12,683	1,506	11.9%	118,523
12/18	14,436	1,602	11.1%	122,665
12/17	13,313	825	6.2%	127,431
12/16	11,777	656	5.6%	132,502
Annual Growth	2.5%	31.9%	—	(3.6%)

Power Corp. of Canada

Incorporated in 1925 Power Corporation of Canada is an international management and holding company that focuses on financial services in North America Europe and Asia. The company's core holdings are leading insurance retirement wealth management and investment businesses including a portfolio of alternative asset investment platforms. Through its majority stake in Power Financial the company controls one of Canada's leading mutual fund firms (IGM Financial) one of its largest life insurers (Great-West Lifeco) and other insurance firms. Power generation is still in the mix as the company owns stakes in renewable energy companies. The US generates the largest sales with about 45% of the company's total sales.

Operations

Power Corporation is a diversified holding company that holds interests in financial services renewable energy asset management media and other businesses in North America Europe and Asia.

Most of its operations occur within its Power Financial subsidiary which itself owns controlling interests in Great-West Lifeco IGM Financial Wealthsimple and the Portag3 funds. Lifeco sells life insurance health insurance retirement and investment services asset management and reinsurance through its wholly-owned business including Canada Life Empower Retirement Putnam Investments and Irish Life. Lifeco accounts for about 95% of revenue.

IGM (accounts for some 5%) is a wealth and asset management company supporting financial advisors the clients it serve in Canada and institutional investors throughout North America Europe and Asia. Through its operating companies IGM provides a broad range of financial and investment planning services to help Canadians meet their financial goals. IGM serves the financial needs of Canadians through multiple distinct businesses including IG Wealth Management Mackenzie Investments and Investment Planning Counsel.

Power Corporation shares ownership of Pargesa Holding SA with Belgium-based Fr¯re family group. Through subsidiaries the partners invests large sums in well-known European companies such as LafargeHolcim (construction) Pernod Ricard (wines and spirits) and Adidas (sportswear).

The holding company also operates a Power Energy business through which it invests in companies that benefit from the global energy transition towards renewable sources. Power Corporation invests in companies that benefit from the global energy transformation and currently has invested in companies that develop own and operate solar and wind generating assets in North America.

Power Corporation's investment activities include investments in alternative asset managers and investment funds including Sagard Holdings and Power Sustainable.

Overall about 65% of the company's sales were accounted from premiums nearly 20% were generated from investments and fees and others generate of the remaining sales.

Geographic Reach

Power Corporation is headquartered in Montreal Quebec Canada. Its subsidiaries and holdings operate throughout North America Europe and Asia. The US generates the largest sales with about 45% of the company's total sales Canada accounts for more than 35% and Europe represents the remaining.

Sales and Marketing

In Canada through the Individual Customer and Group Customer business units Lifeco offers a broad portfolio of financial and benefit plan solutions for individuals families businesses and organizations including life disability and critical illness insurance products as well as wealth savings and income and other specialty products.

Financial Performance

Note: Financial results are denoted in the company's home currency the Canadian Dollar (CAD$).

The company's revenue for 2020 was $64.6 billion a 32% increase from the previous year's revenue of $48.8 billion.

Power Corporation's net earnings attributable to participating shareholders were $2 billion for the year ended December 31 2020 compared with $1.1 billion in 2019.

The company's cash at the end of 2020 was $1.2 billion. Operating activities generated $1.3 billion while investing activities used $1.3 billion mainly for dividends paid on participating shares. Financing activities used another $195 million primarily for purchase of investments.

Strategy

Power's value creation strategy is focused upon three levers.

The first lever is the pursuit of clearly articulated organic growth strategies at each of the company's public operating companies. Across the businesses that make up Great-West Lifeco IGM Financial and GBL the management teams are transforming its business models to meet the changing needs of its customers.

The second lever is the deployment of capital to add to growth inorganically such as via acquisition and the redeployment of capital from businesses not expected to meet its return aspirations. Power's public operating companies are continually reviewing opportunities to add to its competitive position and earnings potential through engaging in potential acquisition activity.

The third lever is the focus on actions it can take either at the Power level between Power and its operating companies or between its group companies. The recent collapse of Power's dual-holding-company structure the simultaneous share buybacks and the proposed simplification of Pargesa and GBL's structure all referred to above are examples of utilizing this third lever.

EXECUTIVES

Vice President, Hugo Breton
Independent Director, J. David Jackson
Vice President, Controller, Denis Le Vasseur
Vice President, Eoin O Hogain
Vice Chairman - Europe, Jocelyn Lefebvre
Independent Director, Pierre Beaudoin
President, Chief Executive Officer, Director, R. Jeffrey Orr, $3,561,881 total compensation

Deputy Chairman of the Board, Andre Desmarais, $277,160 total compensation
Vice President, General Counsel, Secretary, Stephane Lemay
Vice Chairman of the Management Board, Amaury de Seze, $1,042,637 total compensation
Vice Chairman of the Corporation, Michel Plessis-belair, $287,885 total compensation
Senior Vice President, Paul Desmarais
Vice President, Head - Corporate Finance, Richard Pan
Vice President, Luc Reny, $665,972 total compensation
Vice President, Mei Dong
Independent Director, Paula Madoff
Independent Director, Siim Vanaselja
Independent Director, Isabelle Marcoux
Chief Financial Officer, Executive Vice President, Gregory Tretiak, $559,340 total compensation
Independent Director, Marcel Coutu
Executive Vice President, Claude Genereux, $602,372 total compensation
Senior Vice President, Olivier Desmarais
Vice President, Yuhong Liu
Independent Director, Christian Noyer
Independent Director, Gary Doer
Vice President, Samuel Robinson
Senior Vice President, Paul Genest
Independent Director, T. Timothy Ryan
Vice President, Pierre Piche
Vice President, Arnaud Bellens
Vice President, Adam Vigna
Lead Independent Director, Anthony Graham
Auditors: Deloitte LLP

LOCATIONS

HQ: Power Corp. of Canada
751 Victoria Square, Montreal, Quebec H2Y 2J3
Phone: 514 286-7400   **Fax:** 514 286-7484
Web: www.powercorporation.com

2017 sales by geographic location

	% of total
Canada	42
US	19
Europe	39
Total	**100**

PRODUCTS/OPERATIONS

2017 sales

	% of total
Premium incomenet	66
Net investment income	16
Fees income	16
Other revenue	2
Total	**100**

2017 sales

	% of total
Lifeco	91
IGM	6
Corporate	-
Other	3
Total	**100**

Selected Investments

Communications
  Gesca Lté;e (newspaper publisher)
  Square Victoria Communications Group Inc.
  Square Victoria Digital Properties Inc.
Financial Services
  Great-West Lifeco Inc. (68%)
  The Canada Life Assurance Company
  Great-West Life & Annuity Insurance Company
  The Great-West Life Assurance Company
  London Life Insurance Company
  Putnam Investments LLC
  IGM Financial Inc. (57%)
  Investment Planning Counsel (91%)
  Investors Group
  Mackenzie Financial Corporation
  Power Financial Corporation (66%)

Victoria Square Ventures Inc.
Other
Pergesa Holding S.A. (Switzerland)
Eagle Creek Renewable Energy
Lumenpulse Group
Portage Ventures
Wealthsimple
Personal Capital

COMPETITORS

Aimia Inc	Investor AB
Banco do Brasil S/A	JEFFERIES FINANCIAL
Brookfield Asset	GROUP INC.
Management Inc	OPPENHEIMER HOLDINGS
COWEN INC.	INC.
EDWARD D. JONES & CO.	STONEX GROUP INC.
L.P.	Sun Life Financial
EVERCORE INC.	Inc.
Fiera Capital	TRADEWEB MARKETS LLC
Corporation	WADDELL & REED
Intact Corporation	FINANCIAL INC.
Financi ˜re	

HISTORICAL FINANCIALS

Company Type: Public

Income Statement FYE: December 31

	ASSETS ($ mil.)	NET INCOME ($ mil.)	INCOME AS % OF ASSETS	EMPLOYEES
12/20	494,093	40	0.0%	29,900
12/19	366,498	39	0.0%	30,600
12/18	332,139	38	0.0%	0
12/17	355,386	41	0.0%	30,484
12/16	313,806	38	0.0%	30,259
Annual Growth	12.0%	1.4%	—	(0.3%)

2020 Year-End Financials

Return on assets: 0.0%	Dividends
Return on equity: 0.2%	Yield: 0.0%
Long-term debt ($ mil.): —	Payout: 71.2%
No. of shares (mil.): 622	Market value ($ mil.): 14,306
Sales ($ mil): 50,882	

	STOCK PRICE ($) FY Close	P/E High/Low		PER SHARE ($) Earnings	Dividends	Book Value
12/20	22.99	9	4	2.42	1.72	28.02
12/19	25.71	10	7	1.94	1.23	28.83
12/18	17.96	9	6	2.03	1.10	26.62
12/17	25.55	10	8	2.20	1.13	28.06
12/16	22.40	10	9	1.72	0.98	24.82
Annual Growth	0.6%	—	—	8.9%	15.3%	3.1%

Prudential Plc

Prudential is a leading provider of life and health insurance products and asset management in Asia and Africa. It is focused on delivering profitable regular premium health and protection insurance products and fee-based earnings. In asset management Eastspring manages $247.8 billion across some 10 markets in Asia and provides focused investment solutions to third-party retail and institutional clients as well as to its internally sourced life funds. About 20 million of Prudential's customers are in Asia. Prudential plc was formed in 1848 to offer life insurance and loans to the professional people and is not affiliated with US insurance giant Prudential Financial.

Geographic Reach

Headquartered in London Prudential is focused on Asia and Africa. In Asia Prudential has opera-

tions in roughly 15 markets including Hong Kong Singapore Indonesia Malaysia China Thailand Vietnam Taiwan Philippines Cambodia Laos Myanmar and India.

Asia is Prudential's largest territory by revenue at some 65%.

Sales and Marketing

Prudential distributes products primarily through extensive distribution networks across digital agency and bancassurance channels. With a diverse customer base Prudential's five largest customers account for less than 30% of its annual sales.

Financial Performance

Note: Growth rates may differ after conversion to US Dollars.

The company's revenue totaled $56 billion a 40% decrease from the previous year's revenue of $93.7 billion. This was mainly due to a significantly higher outward reinsurance premiums for the year.

In 2020 the company had a profit of $2.1 billion a 12% increase from the previous year's profit of $1.9 billion.

The company's cash at the end of 2020 was $8 billion. Operating activities generated $2 billion while investing activities used $1.2 billion primarily for acquisition of business and intangibles. Financing activities generated another $212 million.

Strategy

Prudential's intention is to take full advantage of the long-term structural opportunities in Asia and Africa and to pursue a path for a fully independent Jackson. In January 2021 the board announced that it had decided to pursue the separation of Jackson from the group in the first half of 2021 through a demerger whereby shares in Jackson would be distributed to Prudential shareholders. The result of this separation will be two separately listed companies with distinct investment propositions which the group's board believes will lead to improved strategic outcomes for both businesses.

The Prudential Group will focus exclusively on its high-growth Asia and Africa businesses. The group will also accelerate its development of digitally enabled products and services to help prevent postpone and protect customers from threats to their health and wellbeing as well as supporting them to achieve their savings goals. Prudential's differentiated product and geographic portfolio is well positioned to meet the protection and savings needs of the growing populations in Asia and Africa where insurance penetration is currently low and demand for savings solutions is rapidly developing. In the United States Jackson remains a leading provider of variable annuities to retail investors. Following the proposed demerger of Jackson Prudential intends to take full advantage of the long-term structural opportunities in Asia and Africa. It seeks to operate with discipline in allocating capital for long-term returns and to deliver profitable and increasingly diversified growth.

Company Background

Knock knock. Who's there? It's the Man from the Pru — one of Prudential plc's famous army of door-to-door salesmen and financial advisors. Or at least that was the story for around 150 years before the Pru went all modern in 2001. With the acquisition of Jackson National it entered the US in 1986 and (re)entered life insurance in Asia at the turn of the millennium. In 2019 Prudential demerged its UK and Europe business M&G Prudential to focus on the US and Asia.

HISTORY

Actually prudence almost killed Prudential before it ever got started. Founded in 1848 as Prudential Mutual Assurance Investment and Loan Association the firm initially insured middle-class

customers. The Dickensian conditions of the working poor made them too risky for insurers. Unfortunately the company found few takers of the right sort and by 1852 Prudential was in peril.

Two events saved Prudential: The House of Commons pressed for insurance coverage for all classes and Prudential's own agents pushed for change. The company expanded into industrial insurance a modest coverage for the working poor. In 1864 to quell criticism of the insurance industry Prudential brought in independent auditors to confirm its soundness. This soon became a marketing tool and business took off. The Pru as it came to be known became the leading industrial insurer by the 1880s. It covered half the country's population by 1905. The firm's salesmen were known for making personal visits to customers (the "Man from the Pru" became a ubiquitous icon in the 1940s and was revived in 1997).

During the two world wars Prudential boosted its reputation by honoring the policies of war victims when it could have legally denied them. Between wars the company added fire and accident insurance in Europe.

The 1980s were volatile for insurance companies especially in the wake of Britain's financial deregulation in 1986. Therefore in 1982 under the direction of CEO Brian Corby the Pru reorganized product lines and in 1985 entered the real estate business. In 1986 it entered the US market by buying US-based Jackson National Life Insurance.

Prudential which had considered selling Mercantile and General Reinsurance in the early 1990s (purchased in 1969) sold the reinsurer back to Swiss Re in 1996. It also formed Prudential Bank and created an Asian emerging-market investment fund that year.

Insurance regulators reprimanded the company for mis-selling financial products in 1997. In 1998 Jackson National bought a California savings and loan enabling it to sell investment products in the US. Also that year the Pru sold its Australian and New Zealand businesses and Prudential Bank launched its pioneering Internet bank Egg Banking.

In 1999 Prudential bought investment manager M&G Group. The company then changed its name to Prudential plc and began talks with the Prudential Insurance Company of America to resolve confusion of their similar names as they expanded into new markets. Also in 1999 the Pru joined forces with the Bank of China to offer pension and asset management in Hong Kong.

The company announced plans in 2000 to sell a chunk of its institutional fund management business as well as its traditional balanced pension business to Deutsche Bank. That year the company spun off 20% of Egg (it sold the rest in 2007).

Entering the Japanese life insurance market Prudential bought Orico Life in 2001. Prudential's hopes of capturing the lucrative annuities market by acquiring American General were dashed that year as American General instead embraced American International Group leaving the Pru with a $600 million break-up fee. To consolidate operations the firm sold its general insurance business in 2001 to Swiss insurer Winterthur (a subsidiary of Credit Suisse).

In early 2006 Prudential rejected a takeover offer from larger rival Aviva valued at nearly $30 billion.

After helping oversee the shift in focus that brought the company growth in Asia and stability during the 2008 economic downturn CEO Mark Tucker stepped down at the end of September 2009. The company chose CFO Tidjane Thiam to replace him. Thiam a native of Ivory Coast became the first black CEO of a FTSE 100 company.

In early 2010 the company expanded its operations in Singapore by acquiring United Overseas Bank's life insurance unit for S$428 million ($307 million). Along with becoming owner of UOB Life Assurance Ltd. Prudential entered into an agreement through which UOB sells Prudential's life accident and health insurance policies for 12 years at the bank's more than 400 branches in Singapore Indonesia and Thailand giving Prudential a greater presence in those markets. In 2011 Prudential targeted the business of Singapore's class of "rising rich" individuals as an important area for growth.

Prudential made a splashy bid on AIG's Hong Kong-based American International Assurance (AIA) business in 2010. The $35.5 billion deal ($25 billion in cash $8.5 billion in securities and $2 billion in stock) would have made Prudential the largest life insurer in Hong Kong and allowed AIG to pay off a chunk of its debt to the US government. However Prudential's shareholders were not impressed and raised a ruckus over the deal. To appease them Prudential attempted to reduce its offer to $30 billion — which AIG coolly refused — and then simply withdrew its entire offer.

EXECUTIVES

Group Chief Digital Officer, Al-Noor Ramji
Independent Non-Executive Director, Alice Schroeder, $204,000 total compensation
Independent Non-Executive Director, David Law, $281,000 total compensation
Group Chief Financial Officer, Chief Operating Officer, Executive Director, Mark FitzPatrick, $980,000 total compensation
Group Human Resources Director and Chief Human Resources Officer for Prudential Corporation Asia, Jolene Chen
Non-Executive Independent Director, Jeremy Anderson, $252,000 total compensation
Chairman, Shriti Vadera, $97,000 total compensation
Chief Executive Officer - Jackson Holdings LLC, Laura Prieskorn
Non-Executive Director, Jeanette Wong
Non-Executive Director, Ming Lu
Non-Executive Director, Sock Koong Chua
Non-Executive Director, George Sartorel
Group Chief Executive, Executive Director, Michael Wells, $1,481,000 total compensation
Non-Executive Independent Director, Amy Yip, $165,000 total compensation
Senior Independent Non-Executive Director, Philip Remnant, $287,000 total compensation
Independent Non-Executive Director, Anthony Nightingale, $230,000 total compensation
Independent Non-Executive Director, Thomas Watjen, $242,000 total compensation
Group Chief Risk and Compliance Officer, Executive Director, James Turner, $950,000 total compensation
Auditors: KPMG LLP

LOCATIONS

HQ: Prudential Plc
13th Floor, One International Finance Centre, 1 Harbour View Street, Central,
Phone: (44) 22 7220 7588
Web: www.prudential.co.uk

2017 Sales

	% of total
US	39
UK and Europe	33
Asia	28
Other	
Total	**100**

COMPETITORS

AEGON N.V.
AMERICAN INTERNATIONAL GROUP INC.
AON GLOBAL LIMITED
Ageas
Allianz SE
HSBC HOLDINGS PLC
ING Groep N.V.
LEGAL & GENERAL GROUP PLC
NEW YORK LIFE INSURANCE COMPANY
RSA INSURANCE GROUP LIMITED
Sampo Oyj
THE HARTFORD FINANCIAL SERVICES GROUP INC.

HISTORICAL FINANCIALS

Company Type: Public

Income Statement

	ASSETS ($ mil.)	NET INCOME ($ mil.)	INCOME AS % OF ASSETS	EMPLOYEES
12/20	704,322	2,890	0.4%	17,256
12/19	599,817	1,034	0.2%	24,676
12/18	649,418	3,843	0.6%	28,206
12/17	667,161	3,226	0.5%	22,912
12/16	578,778	2,363	0.4%	22,498
Annual Growth	**5.0%**	**5.2%**	**—**	**(6.4%)**

FYE: December 31

2020 Year-End Financials

Return on assets: 0.4%
Return on equity: 10.4%
Long-term debt ($ mil.): —
No. of shares (mil.): —
Sales ($ mil): 77,092
Dividends
Yield: 16.3%
Payout: 0.6%
Market value ($ mil.): —

	STOCK PRICE ($) FY Close	P/E High/Low		PER SHARE ($) Earnings	Dividends	Book Value
12/20	36.93	1	0	111.36	5.83	10.92
12/19	38.09	2	1	40.01	6.47	9.89
12/18	35.37	43	29	1.49	1.28	8.49
12/17	50.78	56	45	1.26	1.27	8.40
12/16	39.79	54	36	0.92	1.23	6.99
Annual Growth	**(1.8%)**		**—**	**231.5%**	**47.5%**	**11.8%**

Prysmian SpA

In the energy and telecom sectors Prysmian's got connections. The Milan-based company makes sub-marine and underground power cables needed to transmit high-voltage electricity and high-speed broadband. Prysmian operates through two main divisions: Energy Cables & Systems produces industrial cables needed for cars trains and underground mining while its Telecom Cables & Systems division makes optical fiber and copper cables for video data and voice transmission. The company sells its products worldwide to such customers as Verizon Siemens and Orange. Prysmian has over 50 plants in 21 countries subsidiaries in 38 countries and seven R&D centers in Europe and North and South America.

EXECUTIVES

Chief Executive Officer, Executive Director, General Manager, Valerio Battista
Chief Financial Officer, Executive Director, Pier Facchini
Executive Director, Fabio Romeo
Projects EVP, Hakan Ozmen
Non-Executive Independent Chairman of the Board, Claudio De Conto

Group Chief Operating Officer, Executive Director, Massimo Battaini
Telecom EVP, Philippe Vanhille
Independent Non-Executive Director, Francesco Gori
Independent Non-Executive Director, Paolo Amato
Independent Non-Executive Director, Annalisa Stupenengo
Independent Non-Executive Director, Ines Kolmsee
Independent Non-Executive Director, Jaska De Bakker
Independent Non-Executive Director, Tarak Mehta
Energy EVP, Francesco Fanciulli
Auditors: EY S.p.A.

LOCATIONS

HQ: Prysmian SpA
Via Chiese 6, Milan 20126
Phone: (39) 02 6449 1
Web: www.prysmiangroup.com

2016 Sales

	% of total
Europe Middle East & Africa:	
Italy	18
Other EMEA	49
North America	14
Asia/Pacific	13
Latin America	6
Total	**100**

PRODUCTS/OPERATIONS

2016 sales

	% of total
Energy Products:	
E&I	40
Industries & NWC	18
Others	1
Oil & Gas	4
Energy projects	22
Telecom	15
Total	**100**

Selected Products & Solutions:
POWER GRIDS
HV&Submarine Transmission
Distribution
Offshore Wind Farms
Power From Shore
Asset Monitoring Systems
OIL & GAS
Exploration & Production
Pipelines & LNG
Refineries & Petrochemical
Services
TELECOMS
Optical Fibre
Telecom Networks
Multimedia & Enterprise Networks
CONSTRUCTION & INFRASTRUCTURE
Power & Control
Multimedia
Railways
TRANSPORTATION & MOBILITY
Elevator
Aerospace
Automotive
Trains & Trams
Marine
INDUSTRIES
Military & Defense
Mining
Crane
Nuclear Plants
Solar & Photovoltaics
Wind Turbines
Other Plants

COMPETITORS

ABB INSTALLATION PRODUCTS INC.
EDGEN GROUP INC.
Huber+Suhner AG

KELLY PIPE CO. LLC
KLOECKNER METALS CORPORATION
MATERION ADVANCED MATERIALS TECHNOLOGIES
 AND SERV
MEA REMAINCO L.L.C.
OKAYA & CO. LTD.
SUPERIOR ESSEX INC.
Taihan Cable & Solution Co. Ltd.

HISTORICAL FINANCIALS

Company Type: Public

Income Statement — FYE: December 31

	REVENUE ($ mil.)	NET INCOME ($ mil.)	NET PROFIT MARGIN	EMPLOYEES
12/19	13,022	327	2.5%	28,714
12/18	11,694	148	1.3%	29,159
12/17	9,636	272	2.8%	21,050
12/16	8,018	259	3.2%	20,493
12/15	8,083	233	2.9%	19,316
Annual Growth	12.7%	8.9%	—	10.4%

2019 Year-End Financials

Debt ratio: 33.2%
Return on equity: 12.5%
Cash ($ mil.): 1,201
Current ratio: 1.22
Long-term debt ($ mil.): 3,252
No. of shares (mil.): 263
Dividends
 Yield: 4.0%
 Payout: 12.4%
Market value ($ mil.): 3,227

	STOCK PRICE ($) FY Close	P/E High/Low		PER SHARE ($) Earnings	Dividends	Book Value
12/19	12.26	11	8	1.25	0.49	10.30
12/18	9.75	32	16	0.61	0.50	9.83
12/17	16.44	17	13	1.26	0.17	8.45
12/16	13.03	11	8	1.15	0.14	7.14
12/15	10.75	11	8	1.09	0.15	6.50
Annual Growth	3.3%	—	—	3.4%	35.1%	12.2%

PT Bank Negara (Indonesia)

Auditors: Purwantono, Sungkoro & Surja

LOCATIONS

HQ: PT Bank Negara (Indonesia)
 Gedung BNI, Jl. Jend. Sudirman Kav. 1, PO Box 1946,
 Jakarta 10220
Phone: (62) 21 251 1946   **Fax:** (62) 21 251 1214
Web: www.bni.co.id

HISTORICAL FINANCIALS

Company Type: Public

Income Statement — FYE: December 31

	ASSETS ($ mil.)	NET INCOME ($ mil.)	INCOME AS % OF ASSETS	EMPLOYEES
12/19	60,993	1,109	1.8%	27,211
12/18	56,203	1,043	1.9%	27,224
12/17	52,334	1,004	1.9%	27,803
12/16	44,865	843	1.9%	28,390
12/15	36,837	656	1.8%	0
Annual Growth	13.4%	14.0%	—	—

2019 Year-End Financials

Return on assets: 1.8%
Return on equity: 13.6%
Long-term debt ($ mil.): —
No. of shares (mil.): —
Sales ($ mil): 5,324
Dividends
 Yield: —
 Payout: —
Market value ($ mil.): —

PTT Public Co Ltd

Established on 1978 PTT is a fully integrated national petroleum and petrochemical company that operates through investment in subsidiaries joint ventures and associates (PTT Group) which are engaged in upstream and downstream petroleum coal electricity business and infrastructure business. Its Oil Business operates over 1300 gas stations. Gas Business covers supplying natural gas to both domestic and international industrial factories and petroleum service stations. PTT has a total refining capacity of about 355000 barrels per day or more than 25% of refining capacity in Thailand. PTT also has Petroleum Exploration and Production that focuses on exploration of natural gas condensate and crude oil (in Thailand and elsewhere).

Operations

PTT's core businesses are Petrochemical and Refining International Trading Oil and Retail Gas and Exploration & Production.

PTT invests comprehensively in the petrochemical and refining business (about 30% of revenue) through four PTT Group companies operating advanced high-efficiency oil refineries which command a combined 770000-barrel/day capacity. PTT plays its role in the supply of crude oil as well as the purchase of refined products from these refineries at equity volumes as a minimum for sale to its own customers.

International Trading Business (over 25%) operates fully-integrated international business to enhance national energy security in parallel with the expansion of the trading base to all regions of the world. The business unit covers procurement import export and international trade in several products including: crude oil condensate LPG petroleum and petrochemical products chemical solvents crude palm oil refined palm oil palm kernel shells and other commodities.

Oil and Retail Business (over 15%) engages in the oil and retail business together with related businesses striving to develop goods and services so as to deliver remarkable experiences to all consumers. Also it lends support to and nurtures SMEs engaging in the oil and retail businesses while promoting engagement in developing a good quality of life for society and communities.

PTT invest in petroleum exploration and production business (over 5%) through subsidiary company such as PTT Exploration and Production Public Company Limited or PTTEP which provides exploration and production of petroleum such as natural gas condensate and crude oil in Thailand and other countries such as Malaysia Myanmar Vietnam Indonesia United Arab Emirates Algeria Mozambique Australia Canada Mexico and Brazil.

The Gas Business Group (over 15%) engages in natural gas supply procurement pipeline transmission separation distribution and natural gas-related value-added businesses through PTT subsidiaries.

Geographic Reach

PTT's headquarter and main operation is located in Thailand. PTTEP also invested in nearly 40 projects in more than 10 countries around the globe including Canada Brazil Algeria Kenya Mozambique Oman and Australia.

Sales and Marketing

PTT conducts petroleum exploration and production businesses in both domestic and international. The target markets are both domestic and overseas where the company has invested. In 2020 the total sales ratio of natural gas to liquid was 78% : 22%. PTTEP sells its outputs from domestic and regional projects primarily to the Thai market through PTT the major buyer and processor of all products. PTT then turns the processed products to power sector petrochemical sector transportation sector industry sector and household sector.

The marketing of petroleum products varies with their characteristics and field location which results in differentiation of the market and sales price structures.

For its International Trading Business domestic markets feature main customers including refineries with demand for crude oil and condensate through the supply of domestic producers and import from overseas producers along with petrochemical plants needing feedstock from overseas producers import of gasoline for gasohol production import of LPG for the industrial transport and household sectors to cater to national demand for imports which reflect on the role of strengthening national energy security.

Financial Performance

Note: Growth rates may differ after conversion to US Dollars.

PTT Group recorded revenue of THB 1.6 trillion in 2020 decreasing by THB 604 billion or 27% from 2019 mainly from decline in almost all its products and services offset by utilities products.

PTT Group reported net income of THB 38 billion in 2020 decreasing by THB 55185 million or 59% from THB 93 billion in 2019.

PTT's cash held in 2020 is THB 332.0 billion. It generated THB 218.6 billion from its operations while investing activities used THB 188.6 billion and its financing activities generated THB8.1 billion.

Strategy

With dynamic innovation or technological progress resulting in disruptive technology that changes customers' needs and current business flows PTT values the determination of PTT Group's business strategic directions to accommodate changing directions of the economy society energy technology and consumers' behavior that align with global megatrends.

A new strategy of establishing a New S-Curve has therefore been devised to pursue opportunities and develop new business models to handle upcoming changes. A new set of vision direction and future business strategies has been mapped out by an annual Top Executive Thinking Session (TTS) and a Strategic Thinking Session (STS) among senior PTT Group executives. The resulting business strategies then translate into five-year business plans which are then integrated with risk management plans. In addition PTT holds a meeting of PTT Group executives every month to monitor all affiliates' performance and share ideas to modify short-term business plans and strategies to ensure planned performance outcomes.

As the Thai government has announced Thailand 4.0: a New Economic Model comprising three economic systems; Bio Economy Circular Economy and Green Economy (BCG Model) all of which emphasize on most effective resource consumption waste minimization towards zero waste and use of naturally based environmentally-friendly materials. The new economic model covers four targeted industries. One of them is the energy material and bio-chemical industry which relates to PTT Group's business operation. Besides Thailand has set a plastic waste management plan for the year 2018 - 2030 with the target to reuse and recycle 100% of plastic waste in 2027. Consequently PTT has brought this target as a driving force in reviewing its business strategy to find income from bio products that are naturally-based and environmentally-friendly. PTT has determined to apply the circular economy with its business operation to lower the use of natural resources reduce waste and limit greenhouse gas emissions.

Mergers and Acquisitions

In 2020 PTT's Board approved the purchase of about 4.655 million shares in GRP a wholly owned subsidiary of GPSC which accounted for 50% of the total shares by PTT Global Management (PTTGM) a PTT subsidiary. The deal was worth THB 693 million and was another step in promoting greater cooperation under the stakeholder-centric Powering Thailand's Transformation initiative and forming an operational network among PTT Group. This is in line with PTT Group's strategy in being the leader in the renewable energy or clean energy business. It also supported PTT Group's goal in reaching the renewable power generation capacity of 8000 MW by 2030. In addition the cooperation will synergize the forces of experienced and skilled personnel in renewable energy from PTT and GPSC which will increase efficiency and enhance the competitiveness which would ultimately lead to sustainable development of energy.

Company Background

Thailand which created PTT to secure energy supplies during the oil crunch of the late 1970s sold a third of the company in a 2001 IPO.

In 2008 as part of PTT's energy diversification drive the company opened the world's largest NGV (natural gas vehicle) gas station in Thailand to respond to the growing number of NGV vehicles in the country.

EXECUTIVES

Senior Executive Vice President, Office of General Counsel, Peangpanor Boonklum
Senior Executive Vice President, Corporate Strategy, Arawadee Photisaro
Executive Vice President, Group Accounting and Tax Policy, Wilaiwan Kanjanakanti
Senior Executive Vice President, Gas Business Unit, Wuttikorn Stithit
Senior Executive Vice President, Corporate Governance and Regulatory Affairs, Duangporn Thiengwatanatham
Director, Phongsthorn Thavisin
Senior Executive Vice President, International Trading Business Unit, Disathat Panyarachun
President and Chief Executive Officer,Global Power Synergy Public Company Limited, Worawat Pitayasiri
Chief Technology and Engineering Officer, Wittawat Svasti-xuto
Chief Operating Officer, Downstream Petroleum Business Group, Auttapol Rerkpiboon
Senior Executive Vice President, Downstream Business Group Alignment, Kris Imsang
President and Chief Executive Officer, Chansin Treenuchagron
Chief Financial Officer, Pannalin Mahawongtikul
Chief Operating Officer, Upstream Petroleum and Gas Business Group, Atikom Terbsiri
President and Chief Executive Officer, Global Power Synergy Public Company Limited, Chawalit Tippawanich
Independent Chairman of the Board, Thosaporn Sirisumphand
Acting President and Chief Executive Officer, PTT Oil and Retail Business Public Company Limited, Jiraponr Khaosawas
Auditors: EY Office Limited

LOCATIONS

HQ: PTT Public Co Ltd
   555 Vibhavadi-Rangsit Road, Chatuchak, Bangkok 10900
Phone: (66) 2 537 2000   **Fax:** (66) 2 537 3498 9
Web: www.pttplc.com

PRODUCTS/OPERATIONS

2011 Sales

	% of total
International trading	53
Oil	21
Natural gas	16
Exploration & production	6
Petrochemical	3
Coal	1
Other	-
Total	**100**

Selected Subsidiaries and Affiliates:

PetroAsia (Huizhou) Co. Ltd. (25%)
PTT Exploration and Production Public Co. Ltd. (66%)
PTT Mart Co. Ltd. (49%)
PTT Natural Gas Distribution Co. Ltd. (58%)
Star Petroleum Refining Co. Ltd. (36%)
Thai Lube Blending Co. Ltd. (49%)
Thai Oil Plc. (50%)

COMPETITORS

AltaGas Ltd
BHARAT PETROLEUM CORPORATION LIMITED
CHIYODA CORPORATION
Canadian Natural Resources Ltd
China National Petroleum Corporation
ECOPETROL S A
ENEOS HOLDINGS INC.
EXTERRAN CORPORATION
Equinor ASA
INDIAN OIL CORPORATION LIMITED
IRPC PUBLIC COMPANY LIMITED
NOBLE ENERGY INC.
Petr   leos Mexicanos E.P.E.
REPSOL SA.
THE PARKMEAD GROUP PLC

HISTORICAL FINANCIALS

Company Type: Public

Income Statement				FYE: December 31
	REVENUE ($ mil.)	NET INCOME ($ mil.)	NET PROFIT MARGIN	EMPLOYEES
12/20	53,967	1,261	2.3%	0
12/19	74,518	3,120	4.2%	0
12/18	72,215	3,699	5.1%	0
12/17	61,259	4,149	6.8%	0
12/16	48,019	2,643	5.5%	0
Annual Growth	3.0%	(16.9%)	—	—

2020 Year-End Financials

Debt ratio: 0.9%	No. of shares (mil.): —
Return on equity: 4.2%	Dividends
Cash ($ mil.): 11,090	Yield: —
Current ratio: 2.42	Payout: —
Long-term debt ($ mil.): 22,203	Market value ($ mil.): —

Public Bank Berhad (Malaysia)

Public Bank stakes its success on providing banking services to the public. The company has about 250 branches throughout Malaysia where it is one of the top lenders and fund operators. Offerings include deposit accounts credit cards home loans and insurance plans. In addition to retail and commercial services it provides corporate banking brokerage investment banking wealth management and Islamic banking. Public Bank has more than 100 overseas branches in countries including Cambodia China Hong Kong Laos Sri Lanka and Vietnam. The company was founded in 1966 by chairman Tan Sri Dato' Sri Dr. Teh Hong Piow.

EXECUTIVES

Chief Executive Officer of Public Investment Bank Berhad, Yo-hunn Lee
General Manager - Human Capital Management, Poh Lyn Ng
Independent Non-Executive Director, Chao Li Lim
General Director - Public Bank Vietnam Ltd, Keng Eng Chee
Chief Executive Officer - Cambodian Public Bank Plc, Ming Teck Ong
Director - Overseas Operations, Say Huat Lim
Director - Corporate Planning, Strategy & Economics, Soo Loong Chong
Independent Non-Executive Director, Gladys Leong
Independent Non-Executive Director, Mohd Hanif Bin Sher Mohamed
Independent Non-Executive Director, Chai Fhong Tham
Director - Branch Business Review & Support/Loan Product Development & Trade Finance, Yuew Sim Poon
Non-Independent Non-Executive Director, Chin Guan Lee
Senior Chief Operating Officer, Siew Yen Chang
General Manager - Information Technology, Yoke Fong Fam
Chief Financial Officer, Sook Ling Yik
Director - Security, A Wahab bin A Raman
Chief Executive Officer of Public Mutual Berhad, Kim Hong Yeoh
Director - PB Card Services & Support, Chui Chee Tee
Independent Non-Executive Director, Kim Ling Cheah
Chief Compliance Officer, Shien Doon Tan
General Manager - HP Operations, Man Hoe Wong
Director - HP Credit Control, See Choi Chan
Chief Executive Officer, Managing Director, Executive Director, Ah Lek Tay, $2,501,561 total compensation
Senior Chief Operating Officer, Sulaiman bin Abd Manap
Director - Corporate Banking, Boon Leong Soh
Chief Executive Officer, Executive Director - Public Bank (Hong Kong) Limited, Yoke Kong Tan
Senior General Manager - Corporate Banking, Credit Operations, HP Operations and Share Investment, Chew Fung Chan
General Manager - Credit Administration & Supervision, Kok Kwai Chan
Deputy Chief Executive Officer, Kat Kiam Chang
Group Chief Internal Auditor, Then Fui Lim
Senior General Manager - Retail Financial Services, Chiew Peng Chan
Chief Risk Officer, Sook Ling Loh
Director - Wealth Management & Transaction Banking, Geok Kheng Khoo
Senior General Manager - Knowledge & Learning, Seok Khim Koay
Head - Credit Operations, Kok Keong Lee
Chief Executive and Executive Director of Public Finance Limited, Yam Kiang Chong
Head - Treasury, Bacil Fernandez
Director - Banking Operations, Cheong San Ng
Chief Executive Officer of Public Islamic Bank Berhad, Syamsul Azuan bin Ahmad Fauzi
Senior General Manager - Public Affairs Division, Ab. Razak Bin Md Dali
Head - Property, Yew Hui Lim
Company Secretary, Wan Marhanim Binti Wan Muhammad
Auditors: Ernst & Young PLT

COMPETITORS

BANK OF AYUDHYA PUBLIC COMPANY LIMITED
BANK OF EAST ASIA LIMITED THE
DBS GROUP HOLDINGS LTD
TMB THANACHART BANK PUBLIC COMPANY
LIMITED
UNITED OVERSEAS BANK LIMITED

HISTORICAL FINANCIALS

Company Type: Public

Income Statement				FYE: December 31
	ASSETS ($ mil.)	NET INCOME ($ mil.)	INCOME AS % OF ASSETS	EMPLOYEES
12/20	112,073	1,209	1.1%	19,414
12/19	105,797	1,347	1.3%	19,260
12/18	101,544	1,352	1.3%	18,721
12/17	97,377	1,347	1.4%	18,553
12/16	84,719	1,160	1.4%	18,651
Annual Growth	7.2%	1.0%	—	1.0%

2020 Year-End Financials

Return on assets: 1.1%
Return on equity: 10.7%
Long-term debt ($ mil.): —
No. of shares (mil.): —
Sales ($ mil): 4,744

Dividends
  Yield: —
  Payout: 51.7%
Market value ($ mil.): —

Publicis Groupe S.A.

Publicis is one of the world's largest advertising and media firms. The European holding company provides a range of marketing services through four operating segments: Publicis Communications Publicis Sapient Publicis Media and Publicis Health. Well-known agency brands include Leo Burnett Digitas BBH Fallon and Saatchi & Saatchi. Marcel Bleustein-Blanchet founded Publicis in 1926 and named it after the French word for advertising combined with the French word for six his favorite number. The firm serves clients in over 100 countries but generates majority of the company's sales in North America.

Operations

Publicis is organized into four segments. Its Publicis Communications segment is the creative communications hub and includes Leo Burnett and Saatchi & Saatchi among several other creative agencies. Publicis Sapient is the company's digital and technology arm. Publicis Media operates media planning and buying services through agencies such as Zenith Digitas and Starcom. It creates value for clients through global media agency brands and scaled capabilities across investment strategy insights and analytics data and technology commerce performance marketing and content. Publicis Health's mission is to be the indispensable force for health and wellness business transformation through the alchemy of creativity and technology.

Geographic Reach

Publicis is headquartered in Paris and has operations in more than 100 countries. North America accounts for the largest share of the company's revenue at around 60% of total followed by Europe (nearly 25%) Asia/Pacific (some 10%) and Latin America and Middle East/Africa (less than 5% each).

Sales and Marketing

Publicis serves some 3620 clients in financial sector automotive TMT non-food consumer products food and beverages healthcare and leisure/energy/luxury and retail.

Automotive is Publicis's largest sector accounting for some 15% of total revenue.

Financial Performance

The company's revenue for fiscal 2020 decreased to 1% to ?9.7 billion compared with ?9.8 billion in the prior year.

Net income for fiscal 2020 decreased to ?571 million compared to ?844 million in the prior year.

Cash held by the company at the end of fiscal 2020 increased to ?3.7 billion. Cash provided by operations was ?3.0 billion while investing and financing activities used ?309 million and ?2.0 billion respectively. Main cash uses were acquisitions of subsidiaries and repayment of borrowings.

Strategy

The company's investments focus on digital expertise and creative excellence in order to enrich content strengthen its teams and promote innovation and new service offerings. The strengthening of its agencies and the development of strategic partnerships and initiatives with major internet players allows Publicis Groupe to anticipate the changes and evolution of communications industries towards digital technologies. The aim is to offer the most innovative solutions to its clients in phase with the rapid changes in consumer behavior and technologies.

Mergers and Acquisitions

In 2021 Publicis acquired Australian-based CitrusAd a software as a services (SaaS) platform optimizing brands marketing performances directly within retailer websites. CitrusAD's onsite expertise complemented with Epsilon's offsite retail media offering both powered by the CORE ID uniquely positions Publicis to lead the new generation of identity-led retail media with transparent measurement validated by transactions.

Company Background

In 1926 Marcel Bleustein then 19 years old started France's first advertising agency which he called Publicis (a takeoff on "publicity" and "six"). The company has spent the subsequent decades expanding globally through partnerships and acquisitions.

A major purchase was Saatchi & Saatchi which it acquired in 2000 for about $1.9 billion. Along with the deal the company inherited Saatchi's 50% of media buying unit Zenith Media (jointly owned by Cordiant Communications). In 2001 it merged Optimedia and Zenith with Publicis owning 75% of the new business.

HISTORY

In 1926 Marcel Bleustein then 19 years old started France's first advertising agency which he called Publicis (a takeoff on "publicity" and "six"). He launched his own radio station Radio Cite after the French government banned all advertising on state-run stations and by 1939 he had expanded into film distribution and movie theaters. With the outbreak of WWII Bleustein fled to London to serve with the Free French Forces.

Having adopted the name Bleustein-Blanchet he returned to France following the liberation and revived his advertising business. In 1958 he bought the former Hotel Astoria on the Champs-Elys es and opened the first Le Drugstore. The original structure burned in a 1972 fire and legend has it that Bleustein-Blanchet tapped Maurice L vy to lead the company after he found L vy salvaging records amid the ruins.

To expand its business Publicis formed an alliance — Chicago-based Foote Cone & Belding Communications (FCB) — in 1988. The partnership soured five years later however when Publicis acquired France's Groupe FCA. (FCB claimed the acquisition was a breach of contract and countered by establishing a new holding company for itself True North Communications.) Bleustein-Blanchet died in 1996 and his daughter Elisabeth Badinter was named chair of the supervisory board.

In 1997 Publicis and True North divided their joint network Publicis Communications with True North getting the European offices and Publicis getting Africa Asia and Argentina. Later that year Publicis attempted a $700 million hostile bid for the 81.5% of True North it didn't already own to stop True North's acquisition of Bozell Jacobs Kenyon & Eckhardt. The bid failed and Publicis' stake in True North was reduced to 11%. (True North was later acquired by Interpublic Group in 2001.)

The company gained new ground in the US through its acquisitions of Hal Riney & Partners and Evans Group in 1998. That year L vy helped soothe a bitter feud among the descendants of Marcel Bleustein: Elisabeth Badinter had battled with her sister Michele Bleustein-Blanchet over Bleustein-Blanchet's desire to sell her stake in Publicis' holding company. L vy's solution allowed Bleustein-Blanchet to sell her shares and left Badinter with control of the company.

Continuing its US expansion in 1999 Publicis bought a 49% stake in Burrell Communications Group (one of the largest African-American-owned ad agencies in the US).

In 2000 the company bought advertising outfit Fallon McElligott (now Fallon Worldwide) marketing firm Frankel & Co. and media buyer DeWitt Media (which was merged into Optimedia). Publicis capped off the year by acquiring Saatchi & Saatchi for about $1.9 billion. Along with the deal it inherited Saatchi's 50% of media buying unit Zenith Media (jointly owned by Cordiant Communications). In 2001 it merged Optimedia and Zenith with Publicis owning 75% of the new business.

2002 was a big year for Publicis and the ad industry in general; the decision to acquire Bcom3 catapulted the company into the really big leagues and created a distinct size difference between the top four advertising conglomerates and everyone else.

From 2002 to 2005 the company worked on integrating Bcom3 and Saatchi & Saatchi into its operational infrastructure as well as making small but selective acquisitions in order to maximize debt reduction.

In 2007 Publicis substantially beefed up its digital offerings when it bought US-based Digitas for $1.3 billion. A few months later Publicis acquired Business Interactif an interactive marketing agency based in France. The acquisition bolstered its French Digitas operations.

About that same time Publicis also snatched up Communication Central Group (CCG) one of the largest interactive marketing agencies in China. CCG was later rebranded as Digitas Greater China. In late 2008 Publicis acquired the search marketing business of DoubleClick's Performics operations. The deal gave Publicis 130 additional clients and 200 specialists in the Internet search marketing arena. Also in 2008 Leo Burnett's Asia/Pacific network got a boost when Publicis acquired W&K Communications an agency specializing in advertising promotion television production and media buying services and owning a presence in Beijing and Guangzhou China. W&K was later renamed Leo Burnett W&K Beijing Advertising Co.

EXECUTIVES

Executive Chairman, Publicis Health and COO, Publicis Communtcations North America, Nick Colucci

Chief Executive Officer Publicis Northern & Central Europe, Member of the Executive Committee, Jarek Ziebinski

General Manager, Véronique Weill

Global Chief Marketing Officer, Chairman of Publicis Emil and Publicis One Touch, Member of the Executive Board, Justin Billingsley

CEO, Publicis Communications North America, Andrew Bruce

Regional CEO, Americas Publicis Media, Tim Jones

Digital Business Transformation Lead Publicis Groupe, Chief Executive Officer EMEA & APAC Publicis.Sapient, Member of the Management Committee, Member of the Executive Committee, Nigel Vaz

Chief Executive Officer Publicis Health, Member of the Executive Committee, Alexandra Von Plato

Chief Executive Officer APAC & EMEA Publicis Media, Member of the Executive Committee, Gerry Boyle

Independent Member of the Supervisory Board, Enrico Letta

Executive Vice President - Global Clients, Member of the Executive Board, Ros King

Independent Member of the Supervisory Board, Antonella Mei-pochtler

Independent ember of the Supervisory Board, Suzan LeVine

Secretary General, Member of the Management Board, Member of the Management Committee, Member of the Executive Committee, Anne-Gabrielle Heilbronner, $615,279 total compensation

President, Agathe Bousquet

Chief Strategy Officer, Member of the Management Committee, Member of the Executive Committee, Carla Serrano

Chief Talent Officer, Member of the Executive Committee, Emmanuel Andre

CEO, Publicis Groupe UK, Annette King

Co-Vice Chair, Supervisory Board, Elisabeth Badinter

Chairman of the Supervisory Board, Maurice Levy, $2,164,871 total compensation

Member of the Supervisory Board, Sophie Dulac

Chief Operating Officer, CEO Publics Media, Member of the Management Board, Member of the Executive Board, Steve King, $1,038,662 total compensation

CEO, Publicis Group APAC and COO, Publicis Communications APAC, Loris Nold

Chief Executive Officer, Epsilon, Bryan Kennedy

Member of the Supervisory Board - Employee Representative, Patricia Velay-Borrini

Chief Creative Officer - Asia Pacific, Middle East and Africa, Natalie Lam

Chief Financial Officer, Member of the Management Board, Michel-Alain Proch

Chief Executive Officer of South East Asia - Public Technologies, Amrita Randhawa

Chief Executive Officer and CCO of Leo Burnett Taiwan, Kevin Yang

Chairman of the Management Board, Member of the Management Committee, Chief Executive Officer, Member of the Executive Committee, Arthur Sadoun, $968,494 total compensation

Auditors: ERNST & YOUNG et Autres

LOCATIONS

HQ: Publicis Groupe S.A.
133, avenue des Champs-Elysees, Paris 75008
Phone: (33) 1 44 43 77 88
Web: www.publicisgroupe.com

2016 Sales

	% of total
North America	54
Europe	28
Asia Pacific	11
Latin America	4
Middle East Africa	3
Total	**100**

COMPETITORS

Bertelsmann SE & Co. KGaA	OMNICOM GROUP INC.
COMPUTACENTER PLC	TECHNICOLOR
DENTSU INTERNATIONAL LIMITED	THE INTERPUBLIC GROUP OF COMPANIES INC.
HAVAS	VIVENDI SE
M&C SAATCHI PLC	WPP PLC

HISTORICAL FINANCIALS

Company Type: Public

Income Statement   FYE: December 31

	REVENUE ($ mil.)	NET INCOME ($ mil.)	NET PROFIT MARGIN	EMPLOYEES
12/20	13,240	706	5.3%	79,051
12/19	12,351	944	7.6%	83,235
12/18	11,395	1,052	9.2%	75,588
12/17	11,615	1,033	8.9%	77,767
12/16	10,276	(556)	—	78,913
Annual Growth	**6.5%**	**—**	**—**	**0.0%**

2020 Year-End Financials

Debt ratio: 18.3%	No. of shares (mil.): 245
Return on equity: 7.8%	Dividends
Cash ($ mil.): 4,540	Yield: 2.7%
Current ratio: 0.90	Payout: 11.9%
Long-term debt ($ mil.): 4,483	Market value ($ mil.): 3,030

	STOCK PRICE ($) FY Close	P/E High/Low		PER SHARE ($) Earnings	Dividends	Book Value
12/20	12.34	6	3	2.92	0.34	35.89
12/19	11.32	4	3	3.99	0.59	35.07
12/18	14.16	5	3	4.49	0.59	33.94
12/17	16.99	5	4	4.48	0.56	31.55
12/16	17.20	—	—	(2.49)	0.33	28.37
Annual Growth	**(8.0%)**	**—**	**—**	**—**	**0.5%**	**6.1%**

Qatar Islamic Bank

EXECUTIVES

Member of the Shariah Supervisory Board, Abdul Sattar Abdul Karim Abou Godda

Chief Operating Officer, Operations & IT Group, Lav Kataria

Executive Chairman of the Board, representing Al Mirqab Capital, Jassim Bin Al-thani

Executive Non-Independent Deputy Chairman of the Board, Abdullatif bin Abdullah Al Mahmoud

Non-Executive, Non-Independent Director, representing Brooq Trading Company, Abdullah Al Eidah

Non-Executive, Non-Independent Director, representing Ali Bin Ghanem Bin Ali Althani Group, Ali Al Thani

General Manager - Wholesale Banking Group, Tarek Fawzi

Non-Executive Director, representing Al Na'era Investment Co., Abdullah Al Thani

Member of the Shariah Supervisory Board, Mohammed Ahmaine

Head - Human Capital Group, Khalefa Al Mesalam

Chief Risk Officer, Rakesh Sanghvi

Group Chief Executive Officer, Bassel Gamal

Chief Financial Officer, Gourang Hemani

General Manager - Personal Banking Group, Dorai Anand

Executive Non-Independent Director, representing AlSraiya Group, Nasser Al-Kaabi

Chief Strategy & Digital Officer, Constantinos Constantinides

Executive Non-Independent Deputy Chairman of the Board, Mohammed Bin Issa Al Mohanadi

Executive Non-Independent Director, Mansour Al Muslah

Executive Non-Independent Director, Abdul Rahman Al-Abdul Ghani

Auditors: KPMG

LOCATIONS

HQ: Qatar Islamic Bank
Grand Hamad Ave., P.O. Box 559, Doha
Phone: (974) 4409409   **Fax:** (974) 4412700
Web: www.qib.com.qa

HISTORICAL FINANCIALS

Company Type: Public

Income Statement   FYE: December 31

	ASSETS ($ mil.)	NET INCOME ($ mil.)	INCOME AS % OF ASSETS	EMPLOYEES
12/20	47,900	842	1.8%	0
12/19	44,938	839	1.9%	0
12/18	42,111	757	1.8%	0
12/17	41,326	661	1.6%	0
12/16	38,429	592	1.5%	0
Annual Growth	**5.7%**	**9.2%**		

2020 Year-End Financials

Return on assets: 1.8%	Dividends
Return on equity: 2.5%	Yield: —
Long-term debt ($ mil.): —	Payout: 33.0%
No. of shares (mil.): —	Market value ($ mil.): —
Sales ($ mil): 1,666	

Qatar National Bank

Auditors: Global Balasubramaniam

LOCATIONS

HQ: Qatar National Bank
P.O. Box 1000, Doha
Phone: (974) 44425 444   **Fax:** (974) 4441 3753
Web: www.qnb.com.qa

HISTORICAL FINANCIALS

Company Type: Public

Income Statement   FYE: December 31

	ASSETS ($ mil.)	NET INCOME ($ mil.)	INCOME AS % OF ASSETS	EMPLOYEES
12/20	281,597	3,297	1.2%	0
12/19	259,621	3,943	1.5%	0
12/18	236,949	3,789	1.6%	0
12/17	222,900	3,607	1.6%	0
12/16	197,786	3,398	1.7%	0
Annual Growth	**9.2%**	**(0.7%)**	**—**	**—**

2020 Year-End Financials

Return on assets: 1.2%
Return on equity: 12.6%
Long-term debt ($ mil.): —
No. of shares (mil.): —
Sales ($ mil): 13,526

Dividends
Yield: —
Payout: 37.8%
Market value ($ mil.): —

QBE Insurance Group Ltd.

QBE Insurance Group may be one of Australia's leading insurers but it also has a hefty global reach. The company offers a variety of insurance and reinsurance products through offices in more than 25 countries. QBE provides general property/casualty policies as well as liability auto marine accident and health insurance workers' compensation and cybersecurity coverage.

Operations

QBE operates through three primary divisions: North America International and Australia Pacific.

North America writes general insurance reinsurance and Crop business in the United States.

International writes general insurance business in the United Kingdom Europe and Canada. It also writes general insurance and reinsurance business through Lloyd's; worldwide reinsurance business through offices in the United Kingdom United States Ireland Bermuda and mainland Europe; and provides personal and commercial insurance covers in Hong Kong Singapore Malaysia and Vietnam.

Australia Pacific primarily underwrites general insurance risks throughout Australia New Zealand and the Pacific region providing all major lines of insurance for personal and commercial risks.

Geographic Reach

QBE is headquartered in Sydney Australia. It operates in more than 25 countries in the Asia/Pacific region the Americas and Europe.

Financial Performance

Company's revenue in fiscal 2020 increased by 17% to $17.8 billion compared from the prior year with $15.2 billion mainly due to the higher reinsurance and other recoveries revenue.

The net loss after tax was $1.5 billion for the year ended 31 December 2020 compared with a net profit after tax of $550 million last year. The result included an estimated $655 million underwriting result impact from COVID-19 adverse prior accident year claims development elevated catastrophe claims a significantly reduced investment return as a result of extreme first-half market volatility and goodwill and deferred tax asset impairments in North America of $390 million and $120 million respectively.

Cash held by the company at the end of fiscal 2020 increased to $766 million. Cash provided by operations and financing activities were $1.2 billion each. Cash used for investing activities was $2.2 billion mainly for net payments for purchase of interest.

Strategy

All of the company's activities throughout 2021 and the longer term are anchored around QBE's four strategic priorities: performance customer focus modernisation and talent & culture underpinned by its DNA.

In 2021 the company will remain focused on creating a customer centric business that is more digitally enabled and supported by a modern tech-

nology infrastructure. QBE are streamlining and modernizing its technology estate to better support the evolving needs of its customers people and business.

Company Background

QBE was formed in 1973 with the merger of Australia's Queensland Insurance Bankers' and Traders' Insurance and Equitable Probate and General Insurance.

Queensland Insurance was founded in 1886 and by 1890 operated more than 36 agencies in London Hong Kong Singapore New Zealand and the Pacific Islands. In 1904 it opened its own offices in London and New York. Bankers' and Traders' started operations in 1921.

QBE is now one of the top 20 global insurance companies.

EXECUTIVES

Independent Non-Executive Director, Brian Walter Pomeroy, $226,000 total compensation
Group Executive, People & Change, Amanda Hughes
Independent Non-Executive Director, Eric Smith, $66,000 total compensation
Independent Non-Executive Director, Tan Le, $66,000 total compensation
Chief Executive Officer - Australia & Pacific (AUSPAC), Sue Houghton
Chief Executive Officer, International, Jason Harris, $60,000 total compensation
Independent Non-Executive Vice Chairman of the Board, John Green, $263,000 total compensation
Group Executive - Corporate Affairs and Sustainability, Vivienne Bower
Group Chief Underwriting Officer, Jason Brown, $641,000 total compensation
IR Contact Officer, Tony Jackson
Group Chief Financial Officer, Inder Singh, $743,000 total compensation
Group Chief Information Officer, Matt Mansour
Chief Executive Officer - North America, Todd Jones, $1,000,000 total compensation
Group Chief Risk Officer, Fiona Larnach
Group Chief Executive, Director, Andrew Horton
Group General Counsel, Group Company Secretary, Carolyn Scobie
Auditors: PricewaterhouseCoopers

LOCATIONS

HQ: QBE Insurance Group Ltd.
Level 27, 8 Chifley Square, Sydney, New South Wales 2000
Phone: (61) 2 9375 4444   **Fax:** (61) 2 9231 6104
Web: www.qbe.com

COMPETITORS

AMERICAN FINANCIAL GROUP INC.
AMERICAN INTERNATIONAL GROUP INC.
AVIVA PLC
BROWN & BROWN INC.
Chubb Limited
NORTH OF ENGLAND PROTECTING AND INDEMNITY ASSOCIATION
ODYSSEY RE HOLDINGS CORP.
UNIVERSAL INSURANCE HOLDINGS INC.
XL GROUP PUBLIC LIMITED COMPANY

HISTORICAL FINANCIALS

Company Type: Public

Income Statement

FYE: December 31

	ASSETS ($ mil.)	NET INCOME ($ mil.)	INCOME AS % OF ASSETS	EMPLOYEES
12/20	46,624	(1,517)	—	11,000
12/19	40,035	550	1.4%	11,704
12/18	39,582	390	1.0%	0
12/17	43,862	(1,249)	—	14,140
12/16	41,583	844	2.0%	14,226
Annual Growth	2.9%	—		(6.2%)

2020 Year-End Financials

Return on assets: (-3.4%)
Return on equity: (-18.1%)
Long-term debt ($ mil.): —
No. of shares (mil.): 1,471
Sales ($ mil.): 11,793

Dividends
Yield: 2.7%
Payout: —
Market value ($ mil.): 9,591

	STOCK PRICE ($) FY Close	P/E High/Low	PER SHARE ($) Earnings	Dividends	Book Value
12/20	6.52	— —	(1.09)	0.18	5.77
12/19	9.09	22 17	0.42	0.35	6.25
12/18	7.02	31 23	0.29	0.18	6.32
12/17	8.35	— —	(0.92)	0.40	6.52
12/16	8.96	15 11	0.61	0.37	7.51
Annual Growth	(7.6%)	— —	—	(16.4%)	(6.4%)

Rakuten Group Inc

Auditors: Ernst & Young ShinNihon LLC

LOCATIONS

HQ: Rakuten Group Inc
Rakuten Crimson House, 1-14-1 Tamagawa, Setagaya-ku, Tokyo 158-0094
Phone: (81) 50 5581 6910
Web: corp.rakuten.co.jp

HISTORICAL FINANCIALS

Company Type: Public

Income Statement

FYE: December 31

	REVENUE ($ mil.)	NET INCOME ($ mil.)	NET PROFIT MARGIN	EMPLOYEES
12/20	14,121	(1,107)	—	23,841
12/19	11,641	(293)	—	20,053
12/18	10,016	1,293	12.9%	17,214
12/17	8,393	982	11.7%	14,845
12/16	6,685	324	4.9%	14,134
Annual Growth	20.6%	—	—	14.0%

2020 Year-End Financials

Debt ratio: —
Return on equity: (-16.9%)
Cash ($ mil.): 44,483
Current ratio: 723.98
Long-term debt ($ mil.): —

No. of shares (mil.): 1,362
Dividends
Yield: 0.4%
Payout: —
Market value ($ mil.): 13,175

	STOCK PRICE ($) FY Close	P/E High/Low	PER SHARE ($) Earnings	Dividends	Book Value
12/20	9.67	— —	(0.81)	0.04	4.33
12/19	8.51	— —	(0.22)	0.04	5.00
12/18	6.65	0 0	0.95	0.04	5.21
12/17	9.19	0 0	0.70	0.04	4.51
12/16	9.79	0 0	0.23	0.00	4.08
Annual Growth	(0.3%)	— —	—	—	1.5%

Randstad NV

Founded in 1960 in the Netherlands Randstad is the global leader in the HR services industry. It operates primarily in Europe but also in Asia and North America under the Randstad brand and several others including Monster Ausy GULP Twago Spherion Yacht and Tempo Team. The company has over 4700 outlets and nearly 40 markets with almost 35000 corporate employees. In 2020 it helped nearly two million candidates find a meaningful job with more than 236000 clients. Furthermore it rained close to 350000 people.

Operations

Randstad's operations are divided across four business segments: staffing professionals in-house services and global businesses.

The largest segment bringing in almost half of all revenue is the staffing business. It is focused on recruiting candidates for manufacturing logistics and administrative jobs.

The in-house services segment which brings almost 25% of sales is a unique on-site solution for managing a client's workforce with specific skill sets and a fluctuating level of demand.

The professionals segment also around 20% of sales sources experienced staff for managerial and professional roles across different sectors and disciplines including IT engineering sales marketing & communications finance & accounting healthcare HR education and legal.

Global businesses which brings in 5% of revenue provides range of services such as online talent acquisition managed services programs recruitment process outsourcing and outplacement.

Randstad made 202800 permanent placements in 2020.

Geographic Reach

Randstad has over 4700 outlets in almost 40 markets. Its largest single market is North America which accounts for about 20% of total sales. France and Netherlands account for about 15% of sales each. Germany brings in nearly 10%.

Sales and Marketing

Randstad serves clients from multi-national blue-chip firms and government agencies to consulting firms and SMEs.

The company will connect with people beyond search selection staffing and recruitment. Through their smart solutions and online platforms they aim to be present at all stages in people's careers consistently improving their employability and providing training opportunities where this is appropriate. In today's fast changing world new technologies tools and solutions are redefining the way they interact with people. They combine this with the most important they have to offer: their human touch.

Financial Performance

Note: Growth rates may differ after conversion to US Dollars.

Randstad experienced a spike in revenue in 2018 followed by two consecutive years of revenue decrease.

The company's revenue fell further in 2020 to ?20.7 billion or a decrease of 12% from the prior year. Revenue across all segments also declined in 2020.

Net income also fell to ?304 million in 2020 compared to the prior year.

The company ended 2020 with cash of ?474 million an increase of 110% compared to ?225 million at the end of 2019. Operating activities provided ?1.5 billion in net cash while investing activities used ?112 million. Financing activities used another ?1.1 billion primarily for repayments of other non-current borrowings.

Strategy

Randstad's strategy centers around three basic pillars that reinforce each other: operational excellence digital and accelerating growth. The company commits significant resources to continue strengthening and innovating its concepts and ways of working that span the entire employer and employee journey and lifecycle. As operational excellence depends on the excellence of its people the company also attaches great value to the training and development of its employees. Transcending internal boundaries and geographical borders the company aims to leverage its global presence by sharing data and further rolling out best practices and standards as a more connected Randstad.

Randstad's digital strategy focuses on building a solid technological and data-driven foundation that enables them to 'see the possible in people'. The company aims to use data and insights to help identify new opportunities for talent that would have otherwise been overlooked. By combining this technology with the distinctive human touch of its HR professionals the company will engender lifelong relationships with people.

Randstad will proactively seek to expand their concepts and geographic reach and invest across multiple horizons putting them at the forefront of even more conversations about work. Through the global rollout of their Randstad RiseSmart concept the company will be able to provide career development and coaching services as part of a unique and leading value proposition. The company is also accelerating the growth of its offerings in Statement of Work (SOW) career coaching and talent mobility at an international scale.

Mergers and Acquisitions

In 2020 Randstad acquired 100% of the shares of the companies in the M hlenhoff + Partner Group a group of companies located in Germany with activities in the outplacement sector. The acquisition was made in line with the company's mid-to long-term strategy to grow in specialist activities and to strengthen their market position in certain markets and/or countries.

Company Background

Frits Goldschmeding founded Randstad Holding as Uitzendbureau Amstelveen near Amsterdam in 1960. Originally part of a student project the company turned a small profit its first year and was renamed Randstad Uitzendbureau in 1964. ("The Randstad" is the densely populated area including Amsterdam Rotterdam and the Hague.)

By 1970 Randstad had 32 branches in four countries including Germany and the UK. The company was recast as Randstad Holding in 1978. In 1985 Randstad celebrated its silver anniversary with 250 branches.

The company went public in 1990 listing its shares on the Amsterdam Stock Exchange. That year it moved its headquarters to the Amsterdam suburb of Diemen.

In 1993 Randstad entered the US market. By 1997 the company had more than 1000 branches in Europe and North America.

HISTORY

Frits Goldschmeding founded Randstad Holding as Uitzendbureau Amstelveen near Amsterdam in 1960.

Originally part of a student project the company turned a small profit its first year and was renamed Randstad Uitzendbureau in 1964. ("The Randstad" is the densely populated area including Amsterdam Rotterdam and the Hague.)

It launched its first operation outside the Netherlands the next year establishing Interlabor Interim in Belgium. By 1970 Randstad had 32 branches in four countries including Germany and the UK.

Continuing its expansion across Europe (it entered France in 1973) the company was recast as Randstad Holding in 1978. The next year it opened its 100th branch and launched its Randon security business in the Netherlands in 1980. In 1985 Randstad celebrated its silver anniversary with 250 branches.

The company went public in 1990 listing its shares on the Amsterdam Stock Exchange. That year it moved its headquarters to the Amsterdam suburb of Diemen.

In 1993 Randstad entered the US market when it bought Atlanta-based Temp Force and later acquired Nashville-based Jane Jones Enterprises. It also expanded its staffing business into Spain that year. Randstad's US business later scored a coup when it became a sponsor of the 1996 Olympic Games in Atlanta. The company placed more than 16000 temporary employees to help out during the games. By 1997 the company had more than 1000 branches in Europe and North America.

Founder and CEO Goldschmeding resigned his post in 1998 and was replaced by Hans Zwarts. That year Randstad bought Strategix Solutions the commercial staffing unit of US-based AccuStaff (later MPS Group) for $850 million. The next year the company bought Germany's Time Power Personal-Dienstleistungen and Spain's Tempo Grup. Randstad and Dutch publisher VNU announced plans to create an online employment site covering Europe in 2000 (the site was closed in 2001).

The following year Randstad bought Spanish staffing firm Umano giving the company 150 additional locations throughout Spain. It also sold its security and cleaning businesses in 2001. Zwarts retired in 2002 and was replaced by 30-year company veteran Cleem Farla. In 2003 Ben Noteboom took over as CEO. In 2004 Randstad opened an office in Poland and bought staffing firm Take Air.

In 2007 Randstad almost doubled Randstad Switzerland's revenue through the acquisition of Job One. The Swiss staffing firm operated about two dozen branches and focuses on the technology health care and construction industries. In the biggest acquisition in its company's history Randstad acquired rival staffing agency Vedior in mid-2008. The deal catapulted Randstad ahead of other staffing rivals making it one of the largest in the world.

Striving to improve its position in Canada and the US Randstad purchased rival SFN Group for about $770 million in 2011.

EXECUTIVES

Member of the Executive Board, Karen Fichuk, $781,632 total compensation

Member of the Supervisory Board, Helene Potier

Member of the Executive Board, Rene Steenvoorden, $426,137 total compensation

Chairman of the Executive Board, Chief Executive Officer, Jacques van den Broek, $1,139,406 total compensation

Member of the Executive Board, Chris Heutink, $786,189 total compensation

Independent Member of the Supervisory Board, Frank Dorjee

Vice Chairman of the Supervisory Board, Jaap Winter

Independent Member of the Supervisory Board, Barbara Borra

Independent Member of the Supervisory Board, Rudy Provoost

Independent Chairman of the Supervisory Board, Wout Dekker

Chief Financial Officer, Member of the Executive Board, Henry Schirmer, $864,808 total compensation

Independent Member of the Supervisory Board, Annet Aris

Member of the Executive Board, Rebecca Henderson, $781,632 total compensation
Auditors: Deloitte Accountants B.V.

LOCATIONS

HQ: Randstad NV
  Diemermere 25, Diemen 1112 TC
Phone: (31) 20 569 59 11   **Fax:** (31) 20 569 55 20
Web: www.randstad.com

2017 Sales

	% of total
Europe	
France	16
Netherlands	14
Germany	10
Italy	7
Belgium & Luxembourg	7
Iberia	6
Other	9
North America	18
Rest of world	8
Global businesses	5
Total	**100**

PRODUCTS/OPERATIONS

2017 Sales by Segment

	% of total
Staffing	53
In-house services	22
Professionals	20
Global businesses	5
Total	**100**

COMPETITORS

Airbus SE	NN Group N.V.
Chicago Bridge & Iron	PAGEGROUP PLC
Company N.V.	Redefine International
Expro Group Holdings	P.L.C.
N.V.	Victoria Retail Group
HAYS PLC	B.V.
IGATE CORP.	Wolters Kluwer N.V.
Koninklijke Vopak N.V.	

HISTORICAL FINANCIALS
Company Type: Public

Income Statement

	REVENUE ($ mil.)	NET INCOME ($ mil.)	NET PROFIT MARGIN	EMPLOYEES
12/20	25,426	363	1.4%	603,480
12/19	26,582	666	2.5%	687,280
12/18	27,269	791	2.9%	709,720
12/17	27,898	741	2.7%	706,730
12/16	21,839	607	2.8%	658,580
Annual Growth	3.9%	(12.1%)	—	(2.2%)

FYE: December 31

2020 Year-End Financials

Debt ratio: 4.2%
Return on equity: 6.4%
Cash ($ mil.): 581
Current ratio: 1.17
Long-term debt ($ mil.): —

No. of shares (mil.): 183
Dividends
  Yield: 1.4%
  Payout: 201.2%
Market value ($ mil.): 5,994

	STOCK PRICE ($) FY Close	P/E High/Low		PER SHARE ($) Earnings	Dividends	Book Value
12/20	32.70	21	10	1.98	0.47	31.25
12/19	30.32	10	6	3.63	1.50	27.45
12/18	22.90	9	6	4.32	1.33	28.01
12/17	30.60	10	9	4.03	0.90	27.87
12/16	27.03	10	6	3.30	0.70	23.96
Annual Growth	4.9%	—	—	(12.1%)	(9.5%)	6.9%

RCI Banque S.A.

Parisians who turn their noses up on riding SNCF's passenger trains might want to sniff out a deal with RCI Banque the auto financing subsidiary of French car manufacturer Renault. The company provides loans for new and used Renault Nissan Dacia and Renault Samsung Motors vehicles. RCI Banque finances its loans to the general public its dealerships and to third-party companies in need of fleet management. The company finances almost 1 million vehicle loans per year from offices in some 35 countries across Europe Asia and the Americas.

EXECUTIVES

VP, Finance and Group Treasury, Jean-Marc Saugier
VP, Company Secretary and Chief Risk Officer, Patrick Claude
Vice President - Credit, Marc Lagrene
Deputy Chief Executive Officer, Vice President - Territories and Performance, Francois Guionnet
Chief Compliance Officer, Pierre-Yves Beaufils
Chief Executive Officer, Senior Vice President, Joao Miguel Leandro

LOCATIONS

HQ: RCI Banque S.A.
  15 rue d'Uzes, Paris 75002
Phone: (33) 1 49 32 80 00
Web: www.rcibs.com

PRODUCTS/OPERATIONS

2016 Sales

	% of total
Interest and similar income	63
Income of other activities	36
Fees and commission income	1
Total	**100**

COMPETITORS

BNP PARIBAS	LeasePlan Corporation
HUNTINGTON BANCSHARES	N.V.
INCORPORATED	Royal Bank of Canada
LENLYN HOLDINGS	
LIMITED	

HISTORICAL FINANCIALS
Company Type: Public

Income Statement

	ASSETS ($ mil.)	NET INCOME ($ mil.)	INCOME AS % OF ASSETS	EMPLOYEES
12/19	65,210	1,013	1.6%	3,700
12/18	61,146	982	1.6%	3,481
12/16	45,740	635	1.4%	3,054
12/15	40,380	587	1.5%	2,913
12/14	38,919	511	1.3%	2,850
Annual Growth	10.9%	14.7%	—	5.4%

FYE: December 31

2019 Year-End Financials

Return on assets: 1.6%
Return on equity: 16.5%
Long-term debt ($ mil.): —
No. of shares (mil.): 1
Sales ($ mil): 4,345

Dividends
  Yield: —
  Payout: 22.1%
Market value ($ mil.): —

Reckitt Benckiser Group Plc

Auditors: KPMG LLP

LOCATIONS

HQ: Reckitt Benckiser Group Plc
  103 105 Bath Road, Slough, Berkshire SL1 3UH
Phone: (44) 1753 217800
Web: www.rb.com

HISTORICAL FINANCIALS
Company Type: Public

Income Statement

	REVENUE ($ mil.)	NET INCOME ($ mil.)	NET PROFIT MARGIN	EMPLOYEES
12/20	19,096	1,619	8.5%	43,900
12/19	16,963	(4,863)	—	42,400
12/18	16,083	2,759	17.2%	42,400
12/17	15,549	8,336	53.6%	40,400
12/16	12,167	2,253	18.5%	34,700
Annual Growth	11.9%	(7.9%)	—	6.1%

FYE: December 31

2020 Year-End Financials

Debt ratio: 44.9%
Return on equity: 12.8%
Cash ($ mil.): 2,246
Current ratio: 0.77
Long-term debt ($ mil.): 13,037

No. of shares (mil.): 712
Dividends
  Yield: 2.2%
  Payout: 19.2%
Market value ($ mil.): 12,915

	STOCK PRICE ($) FY Close	P/E High/Low		PER SHARE ($) Earnings	Dividends	Book Value
12/20	18.12	13	8	2.27	0.41	17.45
12/19	16.56	—	—	(6.86)	0.41	17.42
12/18	15.13	6	5	3.89	0.42	26.60
12/17	19.01	3	2	11.72	0.43	25.97
12/16	16.80	7	6	3.16	0.34	14.06
Annual Growth	1.9%	—	—	(7.9%)	4.3%	5.5%

Recruit Holdings Co Ltd

Auditors: Ernst & Young ShinNihon LLC

LOCATIONS

HQ: Recruit Holdings Co Ltd
  1-9-2 Marunouchi, Chiyoda-ku, Tokyo 100-6640
Phone: (81) 3 6835 1111
Web: www.recruit.co.jp

HISTORICAL FINANCIALS

Company Type: Public

Income Statement
FYE: March 31

	REVENUE ($ mil.)	NET INCOME ($ mil.)	NET PROFIT MARGIN	EMPLOYEES
03/21	20,495	1,186	5.8%	48,520
03/20	22,104	1,657	7.5%	51,900
03/19	20,865	1,573	7.5%	48,305
03/18	20,467	1,428	7.0%	42,483
03/17	16,456	764	4.6%	47,966
Annual Growth	5.6%	11.6%	—	0.3%

2021 Year-End Financials

Debt ratio: 0.0%
Return on equity: 12.6%
Cash ($ mil.): 4,525
Current ratio: 1.54
Long-term debt ($ mil.): 524

No. of shares (mil.): 1,635
Dividends
  Yield: 0.4%
  Payout: 6.1%
Market value ($ mil.): 16,094

	STOCK PRICE ($) FY Close	P/E High/Low		PER SHARE ($) Earnings	Dividends	Book Value
03/21	9.84	0	0	0.72	0.05	6.03
03/20	5.16	0	0	1.00	0.05	5.52
03/19	5.70	0	0	0.94	0.05	5.22
Annual Growth	31.4%	—		(6.5%)	0.2%	3.7%

Reliance Industries Ltd

Auditors: DTS & Associates

LOCATIONS

HQ: Reliance Industries Ltd
3rd Floor, Maker Chambers IV, 222, Nariman Point, Mumbai 400 021
Phone: (91) 22 3555 5000   **Fax:** (91) 22 2204 2268
Web: www.ril.com

HISTORICAL FINANCIALS

Company Type: Public

Income Statement
FYE: March 31

	REVENUE ($ mil.)	NET INCOME ($ mil.)	NET PROFIT MARGIN	EMPLOYEES
03/21	68,699	6,714	9.8%	236,334
03/20	82,823	5,210	6.3%	26,488
03/19	85,216	5,721	6.7%	28,967
03/18	64,280	5,544	8.6%	29,533
03/17	52,369	4,610	8.8%	24,167
Annual Growth	7.0%	9.9%	—	76.8%

2021 Year-End Financials

Debt ratio: 0.2%
Return on equity: 8.5%
Cash ($ mil.): 2,377
Current ratio: 1.34
Long-term debt ($ mil.): 22,371

No. of shares (mil.): —
Dividends
  Yield: —
  Payout: 32.1%
Market value ($ mil.): —

RenaissanceRe Holdings Ltd.

If insurers help save for a rainy day RenaissanceRe Holdings builds an ark. Through its Renaissance Reinsurance subsidiary the Bermuda-based firm indemnifies insurance companies around the globe against excess losses on natural catastrophes paying insurance claims after they exceed a certain retained amount. Its Syndicate 1458 offers insurance through Lloyd's of London. Top Layer Re a joint venture with State Farm provides excess non-US property catastrophe reinsurance. Another RenaissanceRe venture DaVinci Reinsurance covers catastrophes and specialty risks such as terrorism.

Operations

RenaissanceRe operates in two primary segments — the Property segment and the Casualty and Specialty segment.

Property operations include catastrophe and other property reinsurance as well as certain joint venture activities. The segment brings in more than half of the company's gross premiums written.

The Casualty and Specialty segment brings in about 50% of gross premiums written.

About 80% of its revenues came from net premiums earned.

Geographic Reach

RenaissanceRe is headquartered in Bermuda. The group leases office space in the US Australia Ireland Singapore Switzerland and the UK.

The US and Caribbean bring in around 55% of RenaissanceRe's gross premiums written.

Sales and Marketing

RenaissanceRe primarily markets its products through reinsurance brokers. Three brokerage firms — AON Marsh and Willis Towers Watson — account for more than 85% of the company's business.

Financial Performance

RenaissanceRe's revenue in 2019 was $4.2 billion a 103% jump from $2.1 billion in 2018. This resulted from an increase in most of its segment revenues.

Net income increased 229% or $521.4 million to $748.8 million in 2019.

Cash and cash equivalents at the end of the year were $1.4 billion 24% higher compared to $1.1 billion in the previous year. Cash provided by operating activities was $2.1 billion. Investing activities used $3 billion primarily for purchases of equity investments trading while financing activities provided $1.1 billion primarily from net third-party redeemable noncontrolling interest share transactions.

Strategy

RenaissanceRe's strategy focuses on superior risk selection superior customer relationships and superior capital management. It provides value to its customers and joint venture partners in the form of financial security innovative products and responsive service. The company is known as a leader in paying valid claims promptly. It principally measures its financial success through long-term growth in tangible book value per common share plus the change in accumulated dividends which is believed as the most appropriate measure of its financial performance and in respect of which the company believes to have delivered superior performance over time.

In recent years through the strategic execution of several initiatives including organic growth and acquisitions the company has expanded and diversified its casualty and specialty platform and products and believes it is a leader in certain casualty and specialty lines of business. RenaissanceRe also pursues a number of other opportunities through its ventures unit which has responsibility for creating and managing the company's joint ventures executing customized reinsurance transactions to assume or cede risk and managing certain strategic investments directed at classes of risk other than catastrophe reinsurance. From time to time the company considers diversification into new ventures either through organic growth the formation of new joint ventures or the acquisition of or the investment in other companies or books of business of other companies.

Mergers and Acquisitions

In early 2020 France-based AXA Liabilities Managers an acquirer and manager of legacy insurance and reinsurance business agreed to acquire RenaissanceRe (UK) Limited a company currently in run-off from RenaissanceRe Holdings Ltd. The acquisition which is expected to close later this year is subject to regulatory approval and will be made through an investment vehicle managed by AXA LM.

In 2019 RenaissanceRe Holdings Ltd. announced that it has concluded its acquisition of Tokio Millennium Re ("TMR"). The acquisition was originally announced on October 2018 and the completion follows the receipt of all necessary regulatory approvals.

EXECUTIVES

President, Chief Executive Officer, Director, Kevin O'Donnell, $1,100,000 total compensation
Chairman, James Gibbons
Independent Director, David Bushnell
Independent Director, Brian Gray
Independent Director, Anthony Santomero
Independent Director, Valerie Rahmani
Independent Director, Duncan Hennes
Chief Financial Officer, Executive Vice President, Robert Qutub, $635,000 total compensation
Independent Director, Carol Sanders
Independent Director, Cynthia Trudell
Independent Director, Jean Hamilton
Executive Vice President and Group Chief Risk Officer, Ian Branagan, $609,900 total compensation
Executive Vice President and Group Chief Underwriting Officer, Ross Curtis, $675,000 total compensation
Senior Vice President, Chief Accounting Officer, James Fraser
SVP, Sean Brosnan
Senior Vice President, Group General Counsel and Corporate Secretary, Shannon Bender
Auditors: Ernst & Young Ltd.

LOCATIONS

HQ: RenaissanceRe Holdings Ltd.
Renaissance House, 12 Crow Lane, Pembroke HM 19
Phone: (1) 441 2954513   **Fax:** (1) 441 2959453
Web: www.renre.com

PRODUCTS/OPERATIONS

2017 Sales by Segment

	% of total
Casualty and Specialty	52
Property	48
Total	**100**

2017 Sales

	$ mil.	% of total
Net premiums earned	1,717	82
Net investment income	222	11
Net realized and unrealized gains on investments	135	6
Net foreign exchange gains	10	1
Equity in earnings of other ventures	8	-
Other	9	-
Total	**2,095**	**100**

COMPETITORS

ALLIANCEBERNSTEIN HOLDING L.P.
ALLIANZ INSURANCE PLC
ARTHUR J. GALLAGHER & CO.
Argo Group International Holdings Ltd.
Aspen Insurance Holdings Limited

EMPLOYERS HOLDINGS INC.
FIDELITY NATIONAL FINANCIAL INC.
Fairfax Financial Holdings Limited
HALLMARK FINANCIAL SERVICES INC.
HCI GROUP INC.
Manulife Financial Corporation
OLD REPUBLIC INTERNATIONAL CORPORATION
SELECTIVE INSURANCE GROUP INC.
Talanx AG

HISTORICAL FINANCIALS

Company Type: Public

Income Statement   FYE: December 31

	ASSETS ($ mil.)	NET INCOME ($ mil.)	INCOME AS % OF ASSETS	EMPLOYEES
12/21	33,959	(40)	—	649
12/20	30,820	762	2.5%	604
12/19	26,330	748	2.8%	566
12/18	18,676	227	1.2%	411
12/17	15,226	(222)	—	384
Annual Growth	**22.2%**	—	—	**14.0%**

2021 Year-End Financials

Return on assets: (-0.1%)	Dividends
Return on equity: (-0.5%)	Yield: 0.8%
Long-term debt ($ mil.): —	Payout: —
No. of shares (mil.): 44	Market value ($ mil.): —
Sales ($ mil): 5,277	

Renault S.A. (France)

Auditors: KPMG Audit

LOCATIONS

HQ: Renault S.A. (France)
13-15, quai Le Gallo, Boulogne-Billancourt, Cedex 92513
Phone: (33) 1 76 84 04 04
Web: www.groupe.renault.com

HISTORICAL FINANCIALS

Company Type: Public

Income Statement   FYE: December 31

	REVENUE ($ mil.)	NET INCOME ($ mil.)	NET PROFIT MARGIN	EMPLOYEES
12/20	53,355	(9,828)	—	170,158
12/19	62,355	(158)	—	179,565
12/18	65,755	3,781	5.8%	183,002
12/17	70,450	6,130	8.7%	181,344
12/16	54,106	3,610	6.7%	124,849
Annual Growth	**(0.3%)**	—	—	**8.0%**

2020 Year-End Financials

Debt ratio: 66.9%	No. of shares (mil.): 291
Return on equity: (-26.9%)	Dividends
Cash ($ mil.): 26,628	Yield: —
Current ratio: 1.04	Payout: —
Long-term debt ($ mil.): 14,291	Market value ($ mil.): 2,542

	STOCK PRICE ($) FY Close	P/E High/Low		PER SHARE ($) Earnings	Dividends	Book Value
12/20	8.73	—	—	(36.22)	0.00	104.41
12/19	9.42	—	—	(0.58)	0.80	133.28
12/18	12.30	2	1	13.89	0.83	140.05
12/17	20.13	1	1	22.39	0.76	137.35
12/16	17.83	2	1	13.16	0.50	111.52
Annual Growth	**(16.4%)**	—	—	—	—	**(1.6%)**

Repsol S.A.

Repsol is a global multi-energy provider that has an integrated business model that ranges from oil and gas exploration and production to the commercialization of energy solutions for the home and mobility. The company sells its products in more than 95 countries and serves approximately 24 million customers.

Operations
Repsol has revised the definition of its operating segments in 2020 to bring it into line with the renewed strategic vision of the businesses and with the company's commitment to be CO2 neutral by 2050.

The company's reporting segments are: Exploration and Production; Industrial; and Commercial and Renewables.

The Exploration and Production segment include activities for the exploration development and production of crude oil and natural gas reserves.

The Industrial segment includes refining activities petrochemicals trading and transportation of crude oil and oil products and sale transportation and regasification of natural gas and liquefied natural gas (LNG).

Commercial and Renewables segment integrates the businesses of low-carbon power generation and renewable sources sale of electricity and gas mobility and sale of oil products and liquefied petroleum gas (LPG).

The company's commercial and renewables business activity accounted for the largest share (80%) in the company's total revenue followed by industrial and upstream business activities.

Geographic Reach
Repsol sells its products in over 95 countries and has seven industrial complexes in Spain Portugal and Peru.

Sales and Marketing
The company serves 24 million customers with 1.2 electricity and gas customers. Repsol also operates more than 4600 service stations in Spain Portugal Peru and Mexico.

Financial Performance
The company's sales decreased to ?32.9 billion in 2020 compared to ?49 billion in the prior year. The reduction in revenue in 2020 is explained by the economic impacts of the COVID-19 pandemic and in particular a decline in realization prices and production volumes in the assets of the Exploration and Production segment mainly the US Brazil Norway and Algeria lower activity in industrial complexes due to slack demand for oil products and a drop in sales in the commercial businesses as a result of the decline in demand due to mobility restrictions.

Repsol reported a net loss of ?3.3 billion in 2020. Cash held by the company at the end of 2020 increased by ?1.4 billion to $4.3 billion compared to ?2.9 billion in the prior year. Cash provided by operations was ?2.7 billion while investing activities provided ?222 million. Financing activities used ?1.6 billion.

Strategy
In November 2020 Repsol unveiled a new strategic plan the 2021-2025 Strategic Plan (21-25 SP). This will shape the transformation of the company in the coming years involving an accelerated energy transition by a profitable and realistic pathway that ensures profitability secures the future and creates maximum value for stockholders.

This comprises two periods: the first (2021-2022) will focus on ensuring financial robustness and will thus prioritize efficiency investment reduction and capital optimization while developing

projects to lead the energy transition; the second (2023-2025) once the impact of the COVID-19 crisis is behind us will focus on accelerating transformation and growth. The Plan envisages investments totaling 18.3 billion euros. Investments in low-carbon initiatives will come to 5.5 billion euros from 2021 and 2025 or 30% of the total.

To implement the Plan the organization will evolve by deploying four business areas (Upstream Industrial Customer and Low Emission Generation Businesses) supported by a more flexible and efficient Corporate division thus enhancing performance and value creation.

Mergers and Acquisitions
In early 2021 Repsol signed an agreement to acquire 40% of Hecate Energy a US-based PV solar and battery storage project developer. The transaction is Repsol's first foray into the US renewables market and complements the company's capabilities and portfolio and adds a solid platform with strong growth potential.

HISTORY

The Repsol Group emerged during Spain's negotiations to join the European Union named after REPESA's premium lubricant brand Repsol.

It was created in 1987 by the National Hydrocarbons Institute during the reorganization of the Spanish energy sector. The company went fully private in 1997.

EXECUTIVES

Non-Executive Independent Director, Henri Reichstul, $201,212 total compensation
Executive Managing Director, Communication and Chairman's Office, Begona Elices Garcia
Non-Executive Deputy Chairman of the Board, Manuel Manrique Cecilia, $201,212 total compensation
Chairman of the Board, Antonio Brufau Niubo, $2,848,514 total compensation
Chief Executive Officer, Executive Director, Josu Jon Imaz San Miguel, $201,212 total compensation
Executive Managing Director, Legal Affairs, Miguel Klingenberg Calvo
Executive Managing Director, People and Organization, Arturo Gonzalo Aizpiri
Executive Managing Director, Downstream Business, Maria Victoria Zingoni Dominguez
Chief Financial Officer, Antonio Lorenzo Sierra
General Director of Technological Development, Digitalization, Resources and Sustainability, Luis Cabra Duenas
Non-Executive Independent Director, Carmina Ganyet Cirera, $201,212 total compensation
Director of Industrial Businesses and Trading, Juan Carrillo de Albornoz Tejedor
Non-Executive Independent Director, Teresa Lloveras, $201,212 total compensation
Non-Executive Independent Director, Arantza Larranaga, $131,798 total compensation
Non-Executive Independent Director, Maite Fornes
Executive Director, Secretary, Luis Suarez de Lezo Mantilla, $201,212 total compensation
Auditors: PricewaterhouseCoopers Auditores, S.L.

LOCATIONS

HQ: Repsol S.A.
Calle Mendez Alvaro 44, Madrid 28045
Phone: (34) 91 75 38 100
Web: www.repsol.com

2018 sales

	%
Spain	51
US	6
Peru	6
Portugal	5
Other	32
Total	**100**

PRODUCTS/OPERATIONS

2018 Sales

	% of total
Downstream	90
Upstream	10
Total	**100**

COMPETITORS

BayWa AG	NATURGY ENERGY GROUP
Borealis AG	SA.
COMPA 'IA ESPA 'OLA DE	ROYAL DUTCH SHELL plc
PETROLEOS SAU	RUBIS
ESSAR ENERGY LIMITED	SASOL LTD
FUELCELL ENERGY INC.	SEMBCORP INDUSTRIES
GLENCORE PLC	LTD
INDIAN OIL CORPORATION	SNAM SPA
LIMITED	SURGUTNEFTEGAZ PAO
KINDER MORGAN INC	Suncor Energy Inc
LUKOIL PAO	TRICORN GROUP PLC
LyondellBasell	Ultrapar Participacoes
Industries N.V.	S/A

HISTORICAL FINANCIALS

Company Type: Public

Income Statement   FYE: December 31

	REVENUE ($ mil.)	NET INCOME ($ mil.)	NET PROFIT MARGIN	EMPLOYEES
12/20	40,080	(4,036)	—	23,739
12/19	55,396	(8,568)	—	24,634
12/18	57,263	2,680	4.7%	24,506
12/17	50,196	2,542	5.1%	24,226
12/16	36,763	1,833	5.0%	24,535
Annual Growth	**2.2%**	—	—	**(0.8%)**

2020 Year-End Financials

Debt ratio: 33.7%
Return on equity: (-14.5%)
Cash ($ mil.): 5,303
Current ratio: 1.29
Long-term debt ($ mil.): 11,858

No. of shares (mil.): 1,507
Dividends
 Yield: 7.1%
 Payout: —
Market value ($ mil.): 15,093

	STOCK PRICE ($) FY Close	P/E High/Low	PER SHARE ($) Earnings	Dividends	Book Value
12/20	10.01	— —	(2.61)	0.71	16.52
12/19	15.68	— —	(2.78)	0.82	19.35
12/18	16.03	14 11	1.66	0.83	23.33
12/17	17.72	14 12	1.62	0.80	23.43
12/16	14.10	12 7	1.22	0.54	22.24
Annual Growth	**(8.2%)**	— —	—	**7.4%**	**(7.2%)**

Resona Holdings Inc Osaka

Resona Holdings resonate in Japan's retail banking market. It's the holding company of Resona Bank and smaller regional banks Kinki Osaka Bank and Saitama Resona Bank which operate nearly 1450 branches across Japan mainly in the greater Tokyo area and the Kansai region. While it focuses on consumer and small business banking services Resona Bank also provides corporate pension management and real estate services corporate and personal trust services personal loans asset management and estate planning services. Altogether Resona Holdings boasts over 45 trillion ($375 billion) in total assets and 24 trillion ($20 billion) in trust assets.

Operations

Resona Holdings operates three core business segments: Consumer Banking which provides consumer loans asset management and asset succession services; Corporate Banking which provides corporate loans trust asset management real estate services corporate pension management and asset succession services; and Market Trading which provides short-term lending borrowing bond purchase and sale and derivatives trading in financial markets.

About 54% of its total revenue came from interest income in fiscal 2015 (ended March 31) while 23% came from non-trust fees and commissions and 3% came from trust fees. About 85% of its total loans and bills discounted were loans to small and medium-sized enterprises (SMEs). More than 60% of its deposits were from individuals.

Geographic Reach

Tokyo-based Resona Holdings has more than 1440 branches across Japan including more than 820 in the Kanto region and 579 in the Kansai region. Its Kinki Osaka Bank subsidiary has 128 manned branches mainly in the Kinki region. About 40% of its branches are manned while the majority are unmanned.

Financial Performance

Note: Growth rates may differ after conversion to US dollars.

Resona Holdings' revenues and profits have trended lower over the past several years mostly due to shrinking interest margins on loans amidst the low-interest environment.

The company had a breakout year in fiscal 2015 (ended March 31) however as its revenue rose by 4% to 861.4 billion ($7.2 billion) on higher fee and commission income from sales of its investment trust and insurance products. Its interest income continued to slide downward due to low interest margins.

Despite generating higher revenue in FY2015 the group's net income fell by 4% to 211.4 billion ($1.77 billion) mostly due to higher income taxes and a 23 billion charge related to the reversal of deferred tax assets in line with the reduction of the effective corporate tax rate. Resona's operating cash levels fell in half to 1103 billion ($9 billion) for the year mostly as it extended more of its cash toward loans and bills discounted.

Strategy

Resona Holdings in early 2015 launched its "New Mid-term Management Plan" for the next decade which set its sights on becoming the "No. 1 Retail Bank" through more proactive measures toward continued growth. Continuing to focus on its retail banking business and lending to SMEs the bank planned to "maximize customer value by maintaining its fundamental stance that 'Customers' joy and happiness are Resona's.'

The company also in 2015 outlined its three "ACL" initiatives which included: "All Resona" which aimed to offer collaboration of companies and services to provide SME customers with management consulting and other services as they grew; "Cross-selling promotion" which aimed to cross sell life insurance to the group's mortgage customers which numbered 560000 borrowers and grew by 40000 new borrowers annually; and "Low-cost operations" which rely on productivity-boosting initiatives such as installed communication terminals that allow tellers to serve customers more securely and efficiently.

Resona Holdings has significant market strength in its key markets in the greater Tokyo metro area and the Kansai region (the most populated and economically active parts of Japan). During 2015 it held 40% of the deposit market in the Saitama and Osaka Prefectures and nearly 20% of the loan market in the region as well.

Auditors: Deloitte Touche Tohmatsu LLC

LOCATIONS

HQ: Resona Holdings Inc Osaka
 1-5-65 Kiba, Koto-ku, Tokyo 135-8582
Phone: (81) 3 6704 3111
Web: www.resona-gr.co.jp

PRODUCTS/OPERATIONS

2014 Sales

	% of total
Interest income	57
Fees and commissions	23
Other operating income	4
Trust fees	3
Other	13
Total	**100**

Selected Subsidiaries

Daiwa Guarantee Co. Ltd. (credit guarantee)
Resona Bank Ltd. (bank)
Resona Guarantee Co. Ltd. (credit guarantee)
Saitama Resona Bank Ltd. (bank)
Kinki Osaka Shinyo Hosho Co. Ltd. (credit guarantee)
The Kinki Osaka Bank Ltd. (bank)
P.T. Bank Resona Perdania (bank)
Resona Kessai Service Co. Ltd. (collections agency)
Resona Card Co. Ltd. (credit cards)
Resona Capital Co. Ltd. (private equity)
Resona Research Institute Co. Ltd. (consulting)
Resona Business Service Co. Ltd. (staffing)

COMPETITORS

BANKIA SA (EXTINGUIDA)
DAIWA SECURITIES GROUP INC.
ENTERPRISE FINANCIAL SERVICES CORP
FIRST EAGLE ALTERNATIVE CAPITAL BDC INC.
MIZUHO FINANCIAL GROUP INC.
NOMURA HOLDINGS INC.
PERMIRA ADVISERS LLP
PROSPECT CAPITAL CORPORATION
Shinhan Financial Group Co. Ltd.

HISTORICAL FINANCIALS

Company Type: Public

Income Statement   FYE: March 31

	ASSETS ($ mil.)	NET INCOME ($ mil.)	INCOME AS % OF ASSETS	EMPLOYEES
03/21	665,594	1,124	0.2%	30,626
03/20	557,460	1,404	0.3%	31,425
03/19	533,754	1,581	0.3%	32,924
03/18	473,163	2,224	0.5%	27,082
03/17	433,392	1,444	0.3%	27,704
Annual Growth	**11.3%**	**(6.1%)**	—	**2.5%**

2021 Year-End Financials

Return on assets: 0.1%
Return on equity: 5.6%
Long-term debt ($ mil.): —
No. of shares (mil.): —
Sales ($ mil): 7,453

Dividends
 Yield: —
 Payout: 38.7%
Market value ($ mil.): —

Rexel S.A.

France-based Rexel distributes electrical parts and supplies that include wiring devices cabling systems lighting products electrical tools and climate control and security equipment. The company serves customers in the commercial sector (its largest market); industrial markets such as mining oil and gas and energy; and the residential market including new construction and upgrade projects. Subsidiaries include Conectis (voice and networking products) as well as North American units Rexel USA and Rexel Canada Electrical. The company has over 1900 branches and logistics centers in more than 25 countries around the world. Rexel generates around 55% of revenue in Europe operations.

Geographic Reach

Rexel operates through a network of more than 1900 branches in 25 countries. The company's largest market was around 55% from Europe followed by North America and Asia-Pacific were around 35% and around 10% respectively.

Sales and Marketing

The company operates through a network of more than 1900 branches.

Financial Performance

Note: Growth rates may differ after conversion to US Dollars.

The company's revenue for fiscal 2020 decreased to ?12.6 billion compared to ?13.7 billion in the prior year.

Net loss for fiscal 2020 was ?261.3 million compared to a net income of ?204.4 million in the prior year.

Cash held by the company at the end of fiscal 2020 increased to ?685.4 million. Cash provided by operations and investing activities was ?706.9 million and ?67.6 million respectively. Financing activities used ?580.2 million mainly for early repayment of senior notes.

Strategy

The organic growth was supplemented by a strategy of selective external growth. The Rexel Group acquired companies of regional national or international scale enabling it to reinforce its position in targeted zones as well as companies in countries with strong growth potential. Since 2010 the Rexel Group completed 44 consolidating acquisitions.

Mergers and Acquisitions

In 2021 Rexel announces the closing of the acquisition of 100% of Mayer a major distributor of electrical products and services operating in the Eastern part of the US. This move is an important step in expanding Rexel's footprint in the US the world's leading market for electrical supplies.

Company Background

Rexel was founded in 1967 as Compagnie de Distribution de Materiel Electrique (CDME) and went public on the Paris bourse in 1983. It entered the US market in 1986. CDME was acquired by Pinault in 1990 and changed its name to Rexel in 1993. The company entered international markets in South America Asia Pacific and Eastern Europe in the late 1990s.

EXECUTIVES

Member of the Executive Committee, Chief Strategy Officer, Constance Grisoni
Company Secretary, Isabelle Hoepfner-leger
Director - Employees Representative, Toni Killebrew
Group Purchasing and Supplier Relationship Director, Member of the Executive Committee, Guillaume Dubrule
Independent Director, Hendrica Verhagen
Chief Executive Officer, Guillaume Texier
Deputy Chairman of the Board, Senior Independent Director, Francois Henrot
Independent Director, Elen Phillips
Non-Executive Independent Chairman of the Board, Ian Meakins, $512,732 total compensation
Independent Director, Agnes Touraine
Independent Director, Maria Richter
Director, Marcus Alexanderson
Director, Employee Representative, Julien Bonnel
Group Digital and IT Transformation Director & Chief Executive Officer Nordics, Member of the Executive Committee, Nathalie Wright
Group Chief Financial Officer, Member of the Executive Committee, Laurent Delabarre
Chief Executive Officer and Senior Vice President of Rexel USA, Member of the Executive Committee, Jeff Baker
Chief Executive Officer Canada, Member of the Executive Committee, Roger Little
Chief Executive Officer United Kingdom/Ireland-Benelux, Member of the Executive Committee, Pierre Benoit
Independent Director, Francois Auque
Independent Director, Brigitte Cantaloube
Group Chief Human Resources and Communications Officer, Member of the Executive Committee, Luc Dallery
Chief Executive Officer of Rexel France, Member of the Executive Committee, Thomas Moreau
Auditors: PricewaterhouseCoopers Audit

LOCATIONS

HQ: Rexel S.A.
13 boulevard du Fort-de-Vaux, CS 60002, Paris, Cedex 17 75838
Phone: (33) 1 42 85 85 00   **Fax:** (33) 1 42 85 92 02
Web: www.rexel.com

2018 Sales

	% of total
Europe	55
North America	36
Asia/Pacific	9
Total	**100**

Rexel distributes electrical products in more than 30 countries around the world.

PRODUCTS/OPERATIONS

2018 Sales

	% of total
Commercial	45
Industrial	30
Residential	25
Total	**100**

Selected Solutions:
Smart Building
Lighting
Climate Control
Security
Datacom
Photovoltaics
Home Automation
Electric Vehicles
Industrial Solutions
Production Parts

COMPETITORS

ACCIONA SA
AGGREKO LIMITED
ANIXTER INTERNATIONAL INC.
ASHTEAD GROUP PUBLIC LIMITED COMPANY
FLEX LTD.
GOODWIN PLC
HONG KONG AND CHINA GAS COMPANY LIMITED THE
ITRON INC.
Itausa S/A
JABIL INC.
Jungheinrich AG
KION GROUP AG
KOC HOLDING ANONIM SIRKETI
LATECOERE
MANUTAN INTERNATIONAL
PREFORMED LINE PRODUCTS COMPANY
THE ALUMASC GROUP PLC
TITON HOLDINGS PLC
WORLEY LIMITED

HISTORICAL FINANCIALS
Company Type: Public

Income Statement
FYE: December 31

	REVENUE ($ mil.)	NET INCOME ($ mil.)	NET PROFIT MARGIN	EMPLOYEES
12/20	15,454	(320)	—	24,818
12/19	15,429	229	1.5%	26,537
12/18	15,306	172	1.1%	27,015
12/17	15,955	126	0.8%	27,530
12/16	13,897	145	1.0%	27,550
Annual Growth	**2.7%**	**—**		**(2.6%)**

2020 Year-End Financials

Debt ratio: 37.4%
Return on equity: (-6.4%)
Cash ($ mil.): 841
Current ratio: 1.59
Long-term debt ($ mil.): 3,388
No. of shares (mil.): 303
Dividends
  Yield: 0.0%
  Payout: —
Market value ($ mil.): 4,534

	STOCK PRICE ($) FY Close	P/E High/Low	PER SHARE ($) Earnings	Dividends	Book Value
12/20	14.95	— —	(1.06)	0.56	15.36
12/19	13.16	20 14	0.76	0.44	15.71
12/18	10.27	36 20	0.57	0.49	16.04
12/17	18.30	58 41	0.42	0.48	16.52
12/16	16.05	36 19	0.49	0.38	15.34
Annual Growth	**(1.8%)**	**— —**	**—**	**10.6%**	**0.0%**

RHB Bank Berhad

RHB Capital is the holding company for RHB Banking Group which offers retail small business and commercial banking services (through RHB Bank) and insurance securities asset management unit trusts derivatives corporate finance and underwriting (through RHB Investment Bank and RHB Insurance). The group's RHB Islamic Bank unit offers retail and commercial banking services that are sensitive to Islamic and regional laws. RHB Capital operates through more than 200 locations mainly in Malaysia but also Brunei Cambodia Hong Kong Indonesia Singapore Thailand and Vietnam. In 2013 RHB Investment Bank bought OSK Investment Bank. RHB Capital acquired and merged Kwong Yik Bank with DCB Bank in 1997.
Auditors: PricewaterhouseCoopers PLT

LOCATIONS

HQ: RHB Bank Berhad
Level 10, Tower One, RHB Centre, Jalan Tun Razak, Kuala Lumpur 50400
Phone: (60) 3 9287 8888   **Fax:** (60) 3 9281 9314
Web: www.rhbgroup.com

COMPETITORS

CIBC World Markets Inc
EGYPTIAN FINANCIAL GROUP HERMES HOLDING
FARGO WELLS SECURITIES LLC

HISTORICAL FINANCIALS

Company Type: Public

Income Statement				FYE: December 31
	ASSETS ($ mil.)	NET INCOME ($ mil.)	INCOME AS % OF ASSETS	EMPLOYEES
12/20	67,342	504	0.7%	14,000
12/19	62,963	606	1.0%	14,345
12/18	58,833	557	0.9%	14,425
12/17	56,713	480	0.8%	14,435
12/16	52,759	374	0.7%	14,790
Annual Growth	6.3%	7.7%	—	(1.4%)

2020 Year-End Financials

Return on assets: 0.7%
Return on equity: 7.6%
Long-term debt ($ mil.): —
No. of shares (mil.): —
Sales ($ mil): 2,689

Dividends
Yield: —
Payout: 34.8%
Market value ($ mil.): —

Ricoh Co Ltd

Ricoh is one of the world's leading manufacturers of printers copiers and supplies as well as fax machines video and web conferencing systems scanners and interactive whiteboards. Other products from the company which operates in about 200 countries include digital cameras servers software semiconductors printed circuit boards and optical equipment. Primarily serving its customers office needs Ricoh also has products for the healthcare education finance and manufacturing industries. Most of Japan-based Ricoh's revenue comes from international customers.

Operations

Ricoh operates through five segments: Office Printing some 50% of revenue Office Services about 30% of revenue Commercial Printing about 10% of revenue Thermal Media less than 5% of revenue Industrial Printing about 5% of revenue and Other about 10% of revenue.

Office Printing offers multifunctional printers imaging machines and related services.

Office Services provides teleconferencing products as well asPCs network support and user support services.

The Commercial Printing segment sells equipment such as cut sheet PP (production printer) continuous book PP related consumables services support software etc.

The Thermal Media segment manufactures and sells thermal paper used in point-of-sale labels for food products barcode labels and delivery labels as well as thermal transfer ribbon used to print clothing price tags brand tags and tickets.

Industrial Printing makes and sells industrial inkjet heads inkjet ink industrial printers and other items for printing on a range of surfaces that include furniture wallpaper automobile exteriors and furnishing fabric.

The Other segment encompasses optical equipment electrical equipment units semiconductors digital cameras industrial cameras 3D printing environment healthcare etc.

Geographic Reach

Sales in Ricoh's home country Japan account for about 45% of the company's revenue followed by the Americas over 25% Europe the Middle East and Africa over 20% and other (China South East Asia and Oceania) about 10%.

Financial Performance

Note: Growth rates may differ after currency conversion.

The company's revenue has been fluctuating in the last five years with an overall decline of 9% between 2016 and 2020.

Consolidated sales for the year ended 2020 declined 0.2% to 2 trillion reflecting the impact of what was by the fourth quarter a global pandemic.

The company's profit for 2020 was 39.5 billion a 20% decrease compared to the previous year. This was primarily due to the lower sales volume for the year coupled with a higher cost of sales.

The company's cash for the year ended 2020 was 263.7 billion. Operating activities generated 116.7 billion while investing activities used 164.6 billion primarily for capital expenditures. Financing activities provided another 75.8 billion.

Strategy

The company formulated growth strategies #0 #1 and #2 to leverage the company's strengths under RICOH Ignite. Growth Strategy #0 entails expanding customer value in core Office Printing business and streamlining operations to become more profitable.

The company created Growth Strategy #1 and #2 to draw on advanced combinations of these technologies with the company's printing technology and its base of 1.4 million corporate customers worldwide and cultivate fields that can become new earnings sources.

HISTORY

Ricoh began in 1936 as the Riken Kankoshi Company making photographic paper. With founder Kiyoshi Ichimura at the helm the company soon became the leader in Japan's sensitized paper market. It changed its name to Riken Optical Company in 1938 and started making cameras. Two years later it produced its first camera under the Ricoh brand.

By 1954 Ricoh cameras were Japan's #1 seller and also popular abroad. The next year it entered the office machine market with its compact mimeograph machine. Ricoh followed that in 1960 with an offset duplicator.

Ricoh built its business in the 1960s with a range of office machines including reproduction and data processing equipment and retrieval systems. The company began establishing operations overseas including US subsidiary Ricoh Industries U.S.A. in 1962. The US unit started marketing cameras but found greener pastures in the copier industry where Ricoh's products were sold under the Pitney Bowes and Savin brand names. It changed its name to Ricoh Company in 1963. Two years later Ricoh entered the emerging field of office computers and introduced an electrostatic copier. In 1968 Ichimura died and Mikio Tatebayashi took over as president for the next eight years.

EXECUTIVES

Chief Technology Officer, Corporate Senior Managing Executive Officer, Director of Advanced Technology Research Institute, Director, Seiji Sakata
Executive President, Chief Executive Officer, Chief Human Resource Officer, Representative Director, Yoshinori Yamashita
Chairman of Board of Directors, Director, Nobuo Inaba
Independent Director, Keisuke Yokoo
Corporate Executive Officer, Director of Professional Service, Kazuo Nishinomiya
Corporate Senior Executive Officer, President of Ricoh Digital Products Business Unit, Katsunori Nakata

Corporate Executive Office, President Ricoh Indal Trial Solutions Business Unit, President of Subsidiary, Yasutomo Mori
Corporate Senior Executive Officer, Senior Manager of Ricoh Digital Service Business UnitEuropean Extreme Headquarters, Chairman & CEO of subsidiary, David Mills
Corporate Senior Managing Executive Officer, Chief Financial Officer, Chief Director of Business Planning, Director, Hidetaka Matsuishi
Corporate Senior Managing Executive Officer, President of Ricoh Digital Services Business Unit, Director, Akira Ohyama
Independent Director, Kazuhiro Mori
Corporate Senior Executive Officer, Senior Manager of Ricoh Digital Services Business Unit in Japan Pole Supervision, President of Subsidiary, Tomohiro Sakanushi
Independent Director, Sadafumi Tani
Auditors: Deloitte Touche Tohmatsu LLC

LOCATIONS

HQ: Ricoh Co Ltd
1-3-6 Nakamagome, Ota-ku, Tokyo 143-8555
Phone: (81) 3 3777 8111
Web: www.ricoh.co.jp

2019 Sales

	% of total
Japan	39
The Americas	28
Europe Middle East Africa	23
Other	10
Total	**100**

PRODUCTS/OPERATIONS

2019 Sales

	% of total
Office Printing	55
Office Services	22
Commercial Printing	9
Industrial Printing	1
Thermal Media	3
Other	10
Total	**100**

Selected Products

Imaging and Solutions
  Imaging Solutions
  Diazo copiers
  Digital duplicators
  Digital monochrome and color copiers
  Fax machines
  Imaging supplies and consumables
  Wide-format copiers
  Printing systems (laser multifunction)
  Scanners
  Network System Solutions
  Document management software
  Networking and applications software
  Network systems
  Personal computers
  Servers
  Services and support
Industrial
  Electronic components
  Measuring equipment
  Optical equipment
  Semiconductor devices
  Thermal media
Other
  Digital cameras and other photographic equipment
  Financing and logistics services
  Optical disks

COMPETITORS

ASTRONOVA INC.
CANON INC.
EASTMAN KODAK COMPANY
ENTRUST CORPORATION
FUJIFILM HOLDINGS CORPORATION

QUADIENT INC.
SEIKO EPSON CORPORATION
TELLERMATE LIMITED
TRANSACT TECHNOLOGIES INCORPORATED

HISTORICAL FINANCIALS

Company Type: Public

Income Statement   FYE: March 31

	REVENUE ($ mil.)	NET INCOME ($ mil.)	NET PROFIT MARGIN	EMPLOYEES
03/21	15,191	(295)	—	81,184
03/20	18,503	364	2.0%	90,141
03/19	18,179	447	2.5%	92,663
03/18	19,431	(1,274)	—	97,878
03/17	18,146	31	0.2%	105,613
Annual Growth	(4.3%)			(6.4%)

2021 Year-End Financials

Debt ratio: 0.1%
Return on equity: (-3.5%)
Cash ($ mil.): 3,023
Current ratio: 1.61
Long-term debt ($ mil.): 1,261

No. of shares (mil.): 718
Dividends
Yield: 1.8%
Payout: —
Market value ($ mil.): 7,438

	STOCK PRICE ($) FY Close	P/E High/Low		PER SHARE ($) Earnings	Dividends	Book Value
03/21	10.35			(0.41)	0.19	11.57
03/20	6.84	0	0	0.50	0.24	11.70
03/19	10.30	0	0	0.62	0.16	11.62
03/18	9.64	—	—	(1.76)	0.19	11.82
03/17	8.17	2	2	0.04	0.36	12.86
Annual Growth	6.1%			—(14.7%)	(2.6%)	

Rio Tinto Ltd

Rio Tinto Limited one of the world's largest mining operations (along with BHP Billiton and Vale) is the Australian half of dual-listed sister companies with Rio Tinto plc taking up residence in London. Although each company trades separately the two Rio Tintos operate as one business. The company explores for a variety of commodities: bauxite copper diamonds gold iron ore minerals (borates and titanium dioxide) and potash. Iron ore makes up approximately 65% of the company's sales. Operates in approximately 35 countries worldwide the company has a major carbon footprint significant scope 1 and 2 emissions and material indirect scope 3 emissions. China accounts for about 60% of the company's revenue.

Operations

Rio Tinto's iron ore accounts for approximately 65% of the company's revenue followed by aluminum alumina and bauxite providing some 20% while copper industrial minerals gold gold uranium and others represent the remaining.

Iron ore is the primary raw material used to make steel. Steel is strong long-lasting and cost-efficient ? making it perfect for everything from washing machines to cars bridges and skyscrapers. It operates about 15 integrated mines in Western Australia four port terminals and three solar salt operations. Aluminum is one of the world's fastest-growing major metals. Lightweight and recyclable it is found in everything from jet engines to electric vehicles to smartphones. Its vertically integrated aluminum portfolio spans high-quality bauxite mines to alumina refineries to smelters.

Copper is essential to the transition to a low-carbon future as it plays a key role in electrification and power generation including in renewable energy and electric vehicles. Its white and colored diamonds are some of the world's most sought-after gems. Energy and minerals product group provides materials essential to a wide variety of industries ranging from agriculture to renewable energy and electric vehicles. It produces high-grade low impurity iron ore pellets and concentrate titanium dioxide and borates.

Geographic Reach

With corporate office in Melbourne Rio Tinto operates in some 35 countries worldwide. China accounts for about 60% of the company's revenue US and Asia (excluding China and Japan) bring in about 10% each Japan and Europe (Excluding UK) provide more than 5% each Canada Australia UK and others countries represent less than 5% each.

The company operates four bauxite mines and four alumina refineries in Australia Brazil and Guinea; about 15 aluminum smelters in Canada Australia New Zealand Iceland and Oman; seven hydropower plants in Canada; and three research & development centers in Canada France and Australia.

It also operates three copper operations in the US Mongolia and Chile; and two copper growth projects in the US Mongolia and Australia. The company also has a network of about 15 iron ore mines four port terminals a 1700-kilometre rail network and related infrastructure in the Pilbara region of Western Australia.

Sales and Marketing

Serving approximately 2000 customers worldwide the company serves clients in electrification and power generation sectors that include renewable energy agriculture and electric vehicles among other sectors. Its iron ore customers include Baowu Steel in China and Nippon Steel Corporation in Japan.

Financial Performance

The company's revenue for the year ended 2020 was $44.6 billion a 3% increase from the previous year's revenue of $43.2 billion.

The net profit attributable to the owners of Rio Tinto in 2020 was $9.8 billion compared to 2019's $8.0 billion.

The company's cash at the end of 2020 was $10.4 billion. Operating activities generated $15.9 billion while investing activities used $6.6 billion mainly for purchases of property plant and equipment and intangible assets. Financing activities used another $7.1 billion primarily for equity dividends paid.

Strategy

The company's strategy is to create superior sustainable value for shareholders in partnership with its stakeholders by meeting customers' needs maximizing cash from world-class assets and allocating capital with discipline.

In 2020 the company continued to evolve and strengthen its portfolio in part by progressing important growth options including those in Mongolia (the Oyu Tolgoi underground project) Australia (Winu Gudai-Darri) Serbia (Jadar) Guinea (Simandou iron ore) and the United States (Resolution Copper). In 2021 the company will also begin producing scandium oxide at a new plant in Quebec Canada.

The company has also announced a new electricity agreement that makes the Tiwai Point aluminium smelter operated by New Zealand Aluminium Smelter (NZAS) economically viable and competitive over the next four years. The smelter will continue operating until 31 December 2024 providing certainty to employees the local community and customers while providing more time for all stakeholders to plan for the future.

Company Background

Rio Tinto Limited began life as the Zinc Corporation in 1905 to recover zinc from the tailings of the silver and lead mines around Australia's mineral-rich Broken Hill area. The company expanded steadily extending its operations into a wide range of mining and metallurgical activities primarily in Australia. By 1914 it had changed its name to Consolidated Zinc Corporation. The company discovered the world's largest deposit of bauxite (1955) and formed Hamersley Holdings with Kaiser Steel (1962) to mine iron ore.

Rio Tinto plc (UK) began with mining operations in Spain in 1873. It sold most of its Spanish holdings in 1954 and branched out to Australia Africa and Canada. In 1962 Rio Tinto and Australia's Consolidated Zinc merged to form RTZ. The companies merged their Australian interests as a partially owned subsidiary CRA (from Conzinc Riotinto of Australia).

In 1968 RTZ bought U.S. Borax which was built on one of the earth's few massive boron deposits. (The use of boron in cleansers was widespread in the late 19th century.) A 1927 discovery in the Mojave Desert led to development of a large boron mine. Until its Turkish mine was nationalized RTZ controlled the world's boron supply. It sold U.S. Borax's consumer products operations in 1988.

RTZ opened a large copper mine at Bougainville in Papua New Guinea in 1969. Subsidiary CRA discovered diamonds in Western Australia's Argyle region three years later. CRA then opened Australia's largest thermal-coal development at Blair Athol in 1984.

RTZ bought Kennecott Corporation in 1989 and expanded its copper operations. Kennecott had been formed by Stephen Birch and named for Robert Kennicott (a typo altered the spelling of the company's name); it had begun mining at Bingham Canyon Utah in 1904. Kennicott had died in Alaska while trying to establish an intercontinental telegraph line. Backed by J.P. Morgan and the Guggenheims Birch also built a railroad to haul the ore. Kennecott merged its railroad and mine operations in 1915. Kennecott consolidated its hold on Chile's Braden copper mine (1925) and on the Utah Copper Company (1936) and other US mines. When copper prices slumped British Petroleum's Standard Oil of Ohio subsidiary bought Kennecott (1981). In 1989 RTZ purchased British Petroleum's US mineral operations including Kennecott.

By the 1990s RTZ and CRA (by then 49%-owned by RTZ) were increasingly competing for mining rights to recently opened areas of Asia and Latin America. RTZ sold the last of its nonmining holdings (building products group) in 1993. In 1995 RTZ brought CRA into its operations. Through Kennecott RTZ purchased US coal mine operators Nerco Cordero Mining Company and Colowyo Coal Company. Also in 1995 the company acquired 13% of Freeport-McMoRan Copper & Gold (sold in 2004).

The RTZ and CRA company names were changed to Rio Tinto plc and Rio Tinto Limited respectively in 1997. Rio Tinto bought a Wyoming coal mine from Kerr-McGee for about $400 million in 1998. The next year Rio Tinto bought 80% of Kestrel (coal Australia) increased its ownership of Blair Athol from 57% to 71% and increased its stake in Comalco (aluminum) to 72%.

In 2000 CEO Leon Davis retired; his position passed to energy group executive Leigh Clifford. In a move that sparked an outcry from union officials Davis accepted a position as non-executive deputy chairman (he retired from the board in 2005). Later that year Rio Tinto acquired both North Limited and Ashton Mining. The company also bought Comalco's outstanding shares and the Peabody Group's Australian subsidiaries.

Rio Tinto sold its Norzink Zink Smelter to Outokumpu in 2001. It also increased its holdings in Queensland Alumina Coal & Allied Industr

HISTORY

Rio Tinto Limited began life as the Zinc Corporation in 1905 to recover zinc from the tailings of the silver and lead mines around Australia's mineral-rich Broken Hill area. The company expanded steadily extending its operations into a wide range of mining and metallurgical activities primarily in Australia. By 1914 it had changed its name to Consolidated Zinc Corporation. The company discovered the world's largest deposit of bauxite (1955) and formed Hamersley Holdings with Kaiser Steel (1962) to mine iron ore.

Rio Tinto plc (UK) began with mining operations in Spain in 1873. It sold most of its Spanish holdings in 1954 and branched out to Australia Africa and Canada. In 1962 Rio Tinto and Australia's Consolidated Zinc merged to form RTZ. The companies merged their Australian interests as a partially owned subsidiary CRA (from Conzinc Riotinto of Australia).

In 1968 RTZ bought U.S. Borax which was built on one of the earth's few massive boron deposits. (The use of boron in cleansers was widespread in the late 19th century.) A 1927 discovery in the Mojave Desert led to development of a large boron mine. Until its Turkish mine was nationalized RTZ controlled the world's boron supply. It sold U.S. Borax's consumer products operations in 1988.

RTZ opened a large copper mine at Bougainville in Papua New Guinea in 1969. Subsidiary CRA discovered diamonds in Western Australia's Argyle region three years later. CRA then opened Australia's largest thermal-coal development at Blair Athol in 1984.

RTZ bought Kennecott Corporation in 1989 and expanded its copper operations. Kennecott had been formed by Stephen Birch and named for Robert Kennicott (a typo altered the spelling of the company's name); it had begun mining at Bingham Canyon Utah in 1904. Kennicott had died in Alaska while trying to establish an intercontinental telegraph line. Backed by J.P. Morgan and the Guggenheims Birch also built a railroad to haul the ore. Kennecott merged its railroad and mine operations in 1915. Kennecott consolidated its hold on Chile's Braden copper mine (1925) and on the Utah Copper Company (1936) and other US mines. When copper prices slumped British Petroleum's Standard Oil of Ohio subsidiary bought Kennecott (1981). In 1989 RTZ purchased British Petroleum's US mineral operations including Kennecott.

By the 1990s RTZ and CRA (by then 49%-owned by RTZ) were increasingly competing for mining rights to recently opened areas of Asia and Latin America. RTZ sold the last of its nonmining holdings (building products group) in 1993. In 1995 RTZ brought CRA into its operations. Through Kennecott RTZ purchased US coal mine operators Nerco Cordero Mining Company and Colowyo Coal Company. Also in 1995 the company acquired 13% of Freeport-McMoRan Copper & Gold (sold in 2004).

The RTZ and CRA company names were changed to Rio Tinto plc and Rio Tinto Limited respectively in 1997. Rio Tinto bought a Wyoming coal mine from Kerr-McGee for about $400 million in 1998. The next year Rio Tinto bought 80% of Kestrel (coal Australia) increased its ownership of Blair Athol from 57% to 71% and increased its stake in Comalco (aluminum) to 72%.

In 2000 CEO Leon Davis retired; his position passed to energy group executive Leigh Clifford. In a move that sparked an outcry from union officials Davis accepted a position as non-executive deputy chairman (he retired from the board in 2005). Later that year Rio Tinto acquired both North Limited and Ashton Mining. The company also bought Comalco's outstanding shares and the Peabody Group's Australian subsidiaries.

Rio Tinto sold its Norzink Zink Smelter to Outokumpu in 2001. It also increased its holdings in Queensland Alumina Coal & Allied Industries and Palabora Mining and it began developing the Hail Creek Coal Project in Australia which is based on one of the l

EXECUTIVES

Chief Executive - Rio Tinto Copper, Bold Baatar, $719,000 total compensation

Chief Operating Officer, Arnaud Soirat, $719,000 total compensation

Senior Non-Executive Independent Director, Simon Mckeon

Non-Executive Independent Director, Hinda Gharbi

Chief Financial Officer, Executive Director, Peter Cunningham

Chief People Officer, James Martin

Chief Executive - Rio Tinto Minerals, Sinead Kaufman

Chief Legal Officer and External Affairs, Isabelle Deschamps

Group Executive - Safety, Technical and Projects, Mark Davies, $159,000 total compensation

Senior Independent Non-Executive Director, Sam Laidlaw

Independent Non-Executive Director, Simon Henry

Chief Executive, Executive Director, Jakob Stausholm, $1,012,000 total compensation

COO, Rio Tinto Aluminium, Kellie Parker

Non-Executive Independent Director, Jennifer Nason

Non-Executive Independent Director, Ngaire Woods

Joint Company Secretary, Tim Paine

Independent Non-Executive Director, Michael L'Estrange

Chief Commercial Officer, Alfredo Barrios, $777,000 total compensation

Chief Executive - Rio Tinto Iron Ore, Simon Trott, $704,000 total compensation

Joint Company Secretary, Steve Allen

Auditors: KPMG LLP

LOCATIONS

HQ: Rio Tinto Ltd
Level 7, 360 Collins Street, Melbourne, Victoria 3000
Phone: (61) 3 9283 3333   **Fax:** (61) 3 9283 3707
Web: www.riotinto.com

2015 Sales

	% of total
China	42
US	15
Other Asia	14
Japan	11
Europe (Excluding UK)	8
Canada	4
Australia	3
UK	1
Other	2
Total	**100**

PRODUCTS/OPERATIONS

2015 Sales

	% of total
Iron Ore	41
Aluminum	27
Copper	9
Coal	8
Industrial Minerals	6
Gold	3
Diamonds	2
Other	4
Total	**100**

Selected Holdings

Aluminum
  Bell Bay
  Boyne Island (59% smelting)
  Queensland Alumina Ltd. (80%)
  Tiwai Point (79% New Zealand)
  Weipa (Australia)
Iron Ore
  Hamersley Iron Pty. Ltd.
  Channar (60%)
  Marandoo mine (Pilbara Australia)
  Nammuldi
  Iron Ore Co. of Canada (59%)
  Robe River Iron Associates (53%)
Energy & Minerals
  Coal
  Bengalla (30% Australia)
  Blair Athol Coal (71%)
  Hail Creek Coal (82%)
  Hunter Valley Operations (76%)
  Kestrel (80%)
  Mt Thorley (61%)
  Warkworth (42%)
  Rio Tinto Diamonds & Minerals
  Rio Tinto Diamond (diamonds Australia Canada Zimbabwe)
  Rio Tinto Minerals (borates titanium dioxide Argentina/Australia/US)
Copper Products
  Escondida (30% Chile)
  Grasberg (40% Indonesia)
  Kennecott Utah Copper (US)
  Northparkes (80%)
  Palabora (58% South Africa)
Gold
  Barneys Canyon (US)
  Bingham Canyon (US)
  Escondida (30% Chile)
  Rawhide (51% US)

COMPETITORS

ANGLO AMERICAN PLC	SOUTH32 LIMITED
ASARCO LLC	Sherritt International
BHP GROUP PLC	Corporation
FREEPORT-MCMORAN INC.	Turquoise Hill
Hudbay Minerals Inc	Resources Ltd
MAG Silver Corp	VEDANTA LIMITED
Magellan Minerals Ltd	Vale Canada Limited
Nevsun Resources Ltd	Vale S/A
Orvana Minerals Corp	Veris Gold Corp

HISTORICAL FINANCIALS
Company Type: Public

Income Statement   FYE: December 31

	REVENUE ($ mil.)	NET INCOME ($ mil.)	NET PROFIT MARGIN	EMPLOYEES
12/20	41,848	9,769	23.3%	47,474
12/19	43,165	8,010	18.6%	46,007
12/18	40,522	13,638	33.7%	47,458
12/17	40,030	8,762	21.9%	46,807
12/16	33,781	4,617	13.7%	51,029
Annual Growth	5.5%	20.6%	—	(1.8%)

2020 Year-End Financials

Debt ratio: 12.3%	No. of shares (mil.): 370
Return on equity: 22.2%	Dividends
Cash ($ mil.): 10,381	Yield: —
Current ratio: 1.80	Payout: 122.3%
Long-term debt ($ mil.): 12,069	Market value ($ mil.): —

Rio Tinto Plc

Rio Tinto plc's Australian counterpart is Rio Tinto Limited which has its headquarters in Melbourne. Rio Tinto explores for a variety of commodities: bauxite copper diamonds gold iron ore minerals (borates and titanium dioxide) and nickel. The company also produces aluminum through its Rio Tinto Alcan unit. Majority of the company's sales generates from China.

Operations

Rio Tinto consists of four business units based on their primary products: Iron Ore Aluminum Copper & Diamonds and Energy & Minerals.

The Energy & Minerals product group includes businesses with products such as uranium borates and titanium dioxide feedstock together with Iron Ore Company of Canada and the Simandou iron ore project. The Copper & Diamonds product group also produces gold silver molybdenum and other by-products.

Sales of iron ore account for around 60% of the total aluminum nearly 20% industrial minerals and coppers and diamonds less than 5%.

Geographic Reach

Based in London Rio Tinto has mining and corporate functions spanning the world but its areas of particular strength are Australia where it mines all the company's major ores and North America with significant additional other businesses in Asia Europe Africa and South America. China is Rio Tinto's largest geography by sales accounting for more than 50% of the total. Followed by the US with about 10% of total sales. The remaining sales are generated from: Asia excluding China and Japan (more than 10%); Japan (nearly 10%); Europe excluding the UK (over 5%); Canada Australia the UK and other countries (almost 10% combined).

Sales and Marketing

The Energy and Minerals portfolio includes titanium dioxide; rutile and zircon; borates; iron ore concentrate and pellets; and uranium.

The company's operations around the world are at various stages in the mining lifecycle from exploration to programme rehabilitation. Alongside copper the company also produce gold silver molybdenum and other materials such as rhenium. Rio Tinto supply customers in China Japan and the US.

Financial Performance

Rio Tinto' performance continues to grow and has an upward trend in its overall financial performance since 2016 and up to this year 2020.

Rio Tinto's revenue rose by $1.5 billion to $44.6 billion in 2020 compared to $43.2 billion in 2019.

The company's net income increased by $1.8 billion from $8 billion in 2019 to $9.8 billion in 2020. The increase was due to $1.1 billion of impairments most of which were taken in the first half of 2020 (five aluminum smelters and the Diavik diamond mine) and $1.3 billion of exchange losses.

Cash at the end of the year totaled $10.4 billion another $2.4 billion increase from the previous year. Cash from operations generated $15.9 billion. Investing and financing activities used $6.6 billion and $7.1 billion respectively.

Strategy

As part of the company's strategy it aims to create superior sustainable value for shareholders. Four pillars of its strategy: Portfolio People Partners and Performance.

Portfolio ? Rio Tinto's portfolio of low-cost long-life assets delivers attractive returns throughout the cycle. After a significant portfolio reshaping the company invested in commodities with strong long-term fundamentals and material growth opportunities.

People ? Rio Tinto continues strengthen its technical and commercial capabilities through its centres of excellence and are committed to building a diverse and inclusive workforce across its global business.

Partners - Partnerships and collaboration are essential to the long-term success of its business. It works closely with technology partners local suppliers governments community groups industry leaders and NGOs at all stages of the mining lifecycle from exploration to rehabilitation and closure.

Performance ? Rio Tinto looks to generate value from mine to market and also to prioritise value over volume in its investment decisions. It works to maximise value in other ways ? for example by developing new markets for its materials and by focusing on operating excellence to improve efficiency.

As part of the company's strategy to attract and retain the best personnel for their operations. The company aims to achieve gender balance in their business. The company is currently comprised of 20% as well as increased number of women in the senior leadership roles.

In 2020 Rio Tinto continued to broaden its portfolio through new projects in Mongolia (the Oyu Tolgoi underground project) Australia (Winu Gudai-Darri) Serbia (Jadar) Guinea (Simandou iron ore) and the United States (Resolution Copper). In 2021 the company will also begin producing scandium oxide at a new plant in Quebec Canada.

HISTORY

Following a tough 2009 in which the global recession depressed commodity prices Rio Tinto rebounded strongly in 2010 posting a 35% increase in overall revenues due primarily to increased sales volumes and prices generated by the beginnings of an economic recovery. Leading the pack for Rio Tinto was its Iron Ore segment which saw an increase of 91% over the previous year followed by the Copper segment with a hike of 24% and the Energy unit with 15%. Profitability soared in 2010 as net income jumped more than 184% due to lower operating costs and significant reductions in debt.

Despite its failed effort the previous year to hike its 9% stake in Rio Tinto to 19% Aluminum Corporation of China (Chinalco) formed a joint venture with Rio Tinto in 2010 to operate an iron ore project in Guinea West Africa. A Chinalco subsidiary will hold 47% of Rio Tinto's Simandou project which is expected to begin producing up to 70 million tons of ore per year by 2015.

In 2011 Rio Tinto and Chinalco teamed up again on a new joint venture that will focus on mineral exploration in China. Chinalco is seeking to find and develop domestic sources of copper coal and potash to offset the cost of importing those raw materials. Chinalco will hold a 51% interest in the joint venture Chinalco Rio Tinto Exploration with Rio Tinto holding the remaining 49%.

One of the world's largest producers of copper Rio Tinto operates the Oyu Tolgoi project in Mongolia along with Canada's Ivanhoe Mines and the Mongolian government. Vancouver-based Ivanhoe controlled one of the world's largest untapped copper and gold deposits in Mongolia and Rio Tinto expects the mine to be one of the world's top 10 copper producers as well as one of the top gold producers by 2018. In 2012 Rio Tinto upped its holding in Ivanhoe from 49% to 51% to become the majority owner.

Also in early 2012 Rio Tinto completed its offer for Canada-based uranium producer Hathor Exploration valued at $578 million after rival Cameco Corp. made a takeover bid for the company in 2011. Hathor supplies about a fifth of the world's uranium.

In 2011 the company also started slimming its aluminum operations. It placed 13 assets on the chopping block allowing Rio Tinto Alcan to focus

on its high-quality tier one assets (mostly in Canada) and improve performance. The company also planned to transfer its stakes in six Australian and New Zealand operations to a new business unit Pacific Aluminium.The new unit managed and reported separately from Rio Tinto Alcan would include the company's Gove bauxite mine and alumina refinery Boyne Smelters and Gladstone Power Station Tomago smelter and Bell Bay smelter in Australia. In New Zealand it would include the New Zealand Aluminium Smelters.

For at least a while longer the company is holding on to seven noncore assets managed by Rio Tinto Alcan including operations in France Germany the UK and the US. The company is in no hurry to sell and may wait until the economy improves before divesting certain operations. Rio Tinto has tried a similar divestment strategy before. It embarked on a divestment plan in the mid-2000s with the long-term goal of turning out $15 billion from its divestments. By 2010 the company had gained more than $10 billion from the divestment program.

Rio Tinto was formed in 1972.

EXECUTIVES

Chief Financial Officer, Peter Cunningham
Chief People Officer, James Martin
Chief Executive, Rio Tinto Iron Ore, Simon Trott, $704,000 total compensation
Chief Executive, Rio Tinto Copper, Bold Baatar, $719,000 total compensation
Chief Commercial Officer, Alfredo Barrios, $777,000 total compensation
Chief Operating Officer, Arnaud Soirat, $719,000 total compensation
Chief Executive Officer and Director, Jakob Stausholm, $1,012,000 total compensation
Chief Technical Officer, Mark Davies, $159,000 total compensation
Chief Executive, Rio Tinto Minerals, Sinead Kaufman
Chief Executive Officer, Australia, Kellie Parker
Group Executive, Strategy and Development, Peter Toth, $141,000 total compensation
Chief Executive, Rio Tinto Aluminium, Ivan Vella, $117,000 total compensation
Chief Legal Officer & External Affairs, Isabelle Deschamps
Auditors: PricewaterhouseCoopers LLP

LOCATIONS

HQ: Rio Tinto Plc
6 St. James's Square, London SW1Y 4AD
Phone: (44) 20 7781 2000   **Fax:** (44) 20 7781 1800
Web: www.riotinto.com

2017 Sales by Destination

	% of total
China	44
US	14
Asia (excl. China and Japan)	13
Japan	12
Europe (excl. UK)	7
Canada	3
Australia	2
UK	1
Other Countries	4
Total	**100**

PRODUCTS/OPERATIONS

2017 sales

	% of total
Iron ore	50
Aluminum	27
Copper	4
Coal	7
Industrial minerals	5
Gold	1
Diamonds	2
Other	4
Total	**100**

COMPETITORS

ANGLO PACIFIC GROUP PLC
ASA RESOURCE GROUP PLC
FRESNILLO PLC
Hudbay Minerals Inc
Nexa Resources
Vale S/A
WEATHERLY INTERNATIONAL PUBLIC LIMITED
  COMPANY
Yamana Gold Inc

HISTORICAL FINANCIALS
Company Type: Public

Income Statement — FYE: December 31

	REVENUE ($ mil.)	NET INCOME ($ mil.)	NET PROFIT MARGIN	EMPLOYEES
12/20	44,611	631	1.4%	47,474
12/19	43,165	(1,038)	—	46,007
12/18	40,522	287	0.7%	47,458
12/17	40,030	89	0.2%	46,807
12/16	33,781	159	0.5%	51,029
Annual Growth	7.2%	41.1%	—	(1.8%)

2020 Year-End Financials

Debt ratio: 13.7%
Return on equity: 1.4%
Cash ($ mil.): 10,381
Current ratio: 1.80
Long-term debt ($ mil.): 13,408

No. of shares (mil.): 1,246
Dividends
  Yield: 5.1%
  Payout: 64.3%
Market value ($ mil.): 93,792

	STOCK PRICE ($) FY Close	P/E High/Low		PER SHARE ($) Earnings	Dividends	Book Value
12/20	75.22	13	6	6.00	3.86	37.74
12/19	59.36	13	9	4.88	6.35	32.43
12/18	48.48	8	6	7.88	3.08	34.18
12/17	52.93	11	8	4.87	2.37	33.32
12/16	38.46	16	9	2.55	1.51	28.58
Annual Growth	18.3%	—	—	23.8%	26.4%	7.2%

Riyad Bank (Saudi Arabia)

One of the largest financial institutions in the Middle East Riyad Bank's palette of services includes something for just about every customer including those who require Sharia-compliant banking. The Saudi financial services firm offers retail and corporate banking services including credit cards mutual fund products electronic trade financing treasury services financing and IPO advice for the oil gas and petrochemical sector. The Riyad Bank network includes more than 300 branches with 81 dedicated branches for women as well as 19 self-service electronic branches and more than 2700 automated teller machines. It also has offices in London Houston and Singapore.

Operations
The bank operates an investment arm Riyad Capital that provides asset management services. The firm is also a major player in IPO advisory business in Saudi Arabia.

EXECUTIVES

Independent Member of the Board, Talal Al-Qudaibi, $96,000 total compensation
Independent Member of the Board, Mohammed Talal Al-Nahas, $106,666 total compensation
Independent Vice Chairman of the Board, Moutaz Al-Azzawi, $94,666 total compensation
Non-Executive Member of the Board, Mohammed Al-Otaibi, $106,666 total compensation
Independent Member of the Board, Jamal Al-Rammah, $106,666 total compensation
Independent Member of the Board, Ibrahim Sharbatly, $106,666 total compensation
Non-Executive Member of the Board, Mohammed Al Afaleq, $97,333 total compensation
Non-Executive Member of the Board, Abdul Rahman Jawa, $105,333 total compensation
Non-Executive Chairman of the Board, Abdullah Bin Mohammed Al Issa, $121,333 total compensation
Chief Executive Officer, Tareq Al-Sadhan
Non-Executive Member of the Board, Nader Al Wehibi, $97,333 total compensation
Chief Retail Banking Officer, Riyadh Al-zahrani
Chief Corporate Banking Officer, Mohammed Abo Al-Naja
Chief Human Capital Officer, Mazen Mohammed Khalifa
Chief Customer Officer, Khaled Walid Al-khudair
Chief Financial Officer, Abdullah Ali Al-Oraini
Chief Treasury and Investment Officer, Nader Al-koraya
Chief Operating Officer, Business Technology and Support Services, Mohammed Al-yahya
Chief Digital Officer, Mazen Pharaoh
Chief Risk Officer, Grant Lowen
Auditors: PricewaterhouseCoopers

LOCATIONS

HQ: Riyad Bank (Saudi Arabia)
Granada Oasis - A1 Tower, Riyadh - Al Shuhada District, Riyadh 11416
Phone: (966) 1 401 3030   **Fax:** (966) 1 404 2707
Web: www.riyadbank.com

COMPETITORS

AWA BANK LTD. THE
METROPOLITAN BANK &
  TRUST COMPANY
MIZUHO BANK LTD.

HISTORICAL FINANCIALS
Company Type: Public

Income Statement — FYE: December 31

	ASSETS ($ mil.)	NET INCOME ($ mil.)	INCOME AS % OF ASSETS	EMPLOYEES
12/19	70,877	1,493	2.1%	5,955
12/18	61,306	1,257	2.1%	5,973
12/17	57,675	1,052	1.8%	6,332
12/16	58,023	891	1.5%	6,337
12/15	59,483	1,078	1.8%	6,167
Annual Growth	4.5%	8.5%	—	(0.9%)

2019 Year-End Financials

Return on assets: 2.2%
Return on equity: 14.4%
Long-term debt ($ mil.): —
No. of shares (mil.): —
Sales ($ mil): 3,801

Dividends
  Yield: —
  Payout: 57.2%
Market value ($ mil.): —

Roche Holding Ltd

One of the world's largest pharmaceutical companies Roche has operations in over 100 countries. Roche's prescription drugs include cancer therapies MabThera/Rituxan and Avastin Perjeta and Kadcyla for HER2-positive breast cancer idiopathic pulmonary fibrosis drug Esbriet macular degeneration therapy Lucentis and Tamiflu which is used for infectious diseases. The company markets many of its bestsellers through California-based subsidiary Genentech and Japanese affiliate Chugai Pharmaceutical. Roche generates majority of sales from North America.

Operations
Roche operates in two divisions: Pharmaceuticals and Diagnostics.

Its pharmaceuticals division accounts for about 75% of annual revenue with oncology drugs making the largest sales contribution (around 40%). It is also active in neuroscience infectious diseases immunology haemophilia A and ophthalmology.

Diagnostics segment which accounts for nearly 25% of annual revenue is a leading maker of in vitro (test tube) clinical diagnostic tests through its professional diagnostics segment; it is also an established provider of diabetes tests and glucose monitors.

Geographic Reach
Roche based in Basel Switzerland generates around 50% of its annual sales in North America and some 25% in Europe.

In the Asia/Pacific region it operates in about a dozen markets: Hong Kong India Indonesia Japan Philippines Taiwan Thailand UAE Vietnam Pakistan Singapore China and Malaysia. The company also has a solid stance in the Japanese drug market through its 61.2% stake in Chugai Pharmaceutical.

Sales and Marketing
Roche's product marketing efforts in the US are conducted through its main US subsidiary Genentech which is one of the world's largest biotech companies.

In total three US national wholesale distributors represents approximately a third of total revenues.

Financial Performance
Note: Growth rates may vary after conversion to US Dollars.

The company's sales increased by 1% (CER) to CHF 58.3 billion (5% decline in CHF terms). Pharmaceuticals sales declined by 2% (CER) mainly due to the impact of biosimilars notably in the US and the impacts of the COVID-19 pandemic leading to reduced hospitalisations and outpatient visits.

Net income for fiscal 2020 increased to CHF 14.3 billion compared from the prior year with CHF 13.5 billion.

Cash held by the company at the end of 2020 decreased to CHF 5.7 billion. Cash provided by operations was CHF 18.6 billion while cash used for investing and financing activities were CHF 9.1 billion and CHF 9.7 billion respectively. Main uses of cash were Ppurchase of property plant and equipment; and dividends paid.

Strategy
Roche has entered into strategic alliances with various companies in order to gain access to potential new products or to utilize other companies to help develop the group's own potential new products. Potential future payments may become due to certain collaboration partners achieving certain milestones as defined in the collaboration agreements.

Mergers and Acquisitions
Acquisitions are also key elements in Roche's R&D growth strategy and have expanded its pharmaceutical segment in focused therapeutic areas.

In mid-2020 Roche acquired Stratos Genomics an early-stage sequencing technology company based in the US. The acquisition provides Roche access to Stratos Genomics unique chemistry Sequencing by Expansion (SBX). The Roche nanopore sequencer once developed will utilise a novel approach that combines electronic and biological components to sequence DNA for fast flexible and cost-effective clinical diagnostic testing.

Company Background

Roche can trace a direct line back to the foundation in 1896 of F.Hoffmann-La Roche & Co by entrepreneur Fritz Hoffman-La Roche. Pharmacist Carl Schaerges the first head of research together with chemist Emil C. Barell demonstrated the presence of iodine in thyroid extracts. This results in Roche's first patent and scientific publications. The company became the first to synthetic vitamin C on a mass scale in 1934 and in 1957 developed the benzodiazepines class of tranquilizers. Over the years Roche has expanded in Switzerland and abroad by making numerous acquisitions including Genentech in the US for a whopping $46.8 billion.

HISTORY

Fritz Hoffmann-La Roche backed by family wealth began making pharmaceuticals in a lab in Basel Switzerland in 1894. At the time drug compounds were mixed at pharmacies and lacked uniformity. Hoffmann was not a chemist but saw the potential for mass-produced standardized branded drugs.

By WWI Hoffman had become successful selling Thiocal (cough medicine) Digalen (digitalis extract) and other products on four continents. During the war the Bolsheviks seized the firm's St. Petersburg Russia facility and its Warsaw plant was almost destroyed. Devastated Hoffmann sold company shares outside the family in 1919 and died in 1920.

As WWII loomed Roche divided its holdings between F. Hoffman-La Roche and Sapac which held many of Roche's foreign operations. US operations became more important during the war. Roche synthesized vitamins C A and E (eventually becoming the world's top vitamin maker) and built plants and research centers worldwide.

Roche continued to develop such successful products as tranquilizers Librium (1960) and Valium (1963) — the world's best-selling prescription drug prior to anti-ulcer successors Tagamet (SmithKline Beecham now part of GlaxoSmithKline) and Prilosec (AstraZeneca). Roche made its first fragrance and flavor buy Givaudan in 1963.

In the 1970s after several governments accused it of price-gouging on Librium and Valium Roche agreed to price restraints. The company was fined for vitamin price-fixing in 1976. It was also rapped that year for its slow response to an Italian factory dioxin leak that killed thousands of animals and forced hundreds of families to evacuate.

Roche became one of the first drugmakers to sell another's products when it agreed to sell Glaxo's Zantac ulcer treatment in the US in 1982. The move let Roche maintain its large US sales force at the time when Valium went off patent decimating the company's drug sales.

Roche acquired a product pipeline when it bought a majority stake in genetic engineering firm Genentech in 1990. In 1994 it bought the struggling Syntex solidifying its position in North America. The company gained Aleve and other products in 1996 when it bought out its joint venture with Procter & Gamble and also acquired Cincinnati-based flavors and fragrances firm Tastemaker.

In its biggest acquisition ever Roche bought Corange in 1998 for $10.2 billion; its subsidiary Boehringer Mannheim was renamed Roche Molecular Biochemicals. In 1999 Roche announced it had located the gene that causes osteoarthritis. The company began to market anti-obesity pharmaceutical Xenical in the US that year despite reports of some unpleasant side effects.

EXECUTIVES

Chairman, Corporate Executive Committee, Chief Executive Officer, Executive Director, Severin Schwan, $3,726,670 total compensation

Head CEO Office and Secretary,Corporate Executive Committee, Per-Olof Attinger

Vice Chairman, Andre Hoffmann, $425,905 total compensation

Member of the Enlarged Corporate Executive Committee, General Counsel, Claudia Boeckstiegel

Chairman, Christoph Franz, $3,726,670 total compensation

Member of the Corporate Executive Committee, Chief People Officer, Cristina Wilbur, $1,072,489 total compensation

Member of the Enlarged Corporate Executive Committee, Head Group Communications, Barbara Schaedler

Member of the Enlarged Corporate Executive Committee, Head Genentech Research & Early Development (gRED), Aviv Regev

Member of the Corporate Executive Committee, Chief Financial and Information Officer, Alan Hippe, $1,703,621 total compensation

Member of the Corporate Executive Committee, Chief Executive Officer Roche Pharmaceuticals, William Anderson, $2,280,352 total compensation

Member of the Enlarged Corporate Executive Committee, Global Head Pharma Partnering, James Sabry

Member of the Enlarged Corporate Executive Committee, Head Roche Pharma Research & Early Development (pRED), William Pao

Member of the Corporate Executive Committee, Chief Executive Officer Roche Diagnostics, Thomas Schinecker, $936,379 total compensation

Auditors: KPMG AG

LOCATIONS

HQ: Roche Holding Ltd
Grenzacherstrasse 124, Basel CH-4070
Phone: (41) 61 688 11 11   **Fax:** (41) 61 688 13 96
Web: www.roche.com

2017 Sales

	% of total
America	50
Europe	26
Asia	21
Africa Australia & Oceania	3
Total	**100**

PRODUCTS/OPERATIONS

2017 Sales

	% of total
Pharmaceuticals	
Oncology	48
Immunology	14
Neuroscience	3
Ophthalmology	3
Infectious disease	2
Other	7
Diagnostics	23
Total	**100**

Selected Products

Top Products (listed alphabetically)
Actemra/RoActemra (rheumatoid arthritis)
Activase/TNKase (cardiovascular)
Alecensa
Avastin (colorectal cancer non-small cell lung cancer breast cancer kidney cancer)
Bactrim (anti-infective)
Bondronat (bone disease in breast cancer patients)
Bonviva/Boniva (osteoporosis)
CellCept (transplantation)
Cotellic
Dilatrend
Dormicum (sedation)
Erivedge (basal cell carcinoma)

ESBRIET
FoundationOne
FoundationOne Heme
Fuzeon (HIV)
Gazyva/Gazyvaro
Harmony Prenatal test
Hemlibra
Herceptin (HER2-positive breast cancer)
Invirase (HIV)
Kadcyla
Kytril (nausea and vomiting induced by chemotherapy or radiation therapy)
Lariam
Lucentis (wet age-related macular degeneration diabetic macular edema)
MabThera SC/Rituxan Hycela
MabThera/Rituxan (non-Hodgkin's lymphoma rheumatoid arthritis chronic lymphocytic leukemia)
Madopar (Parkinson's disease restless leg syndrome)
MIRCERA (predialysis)
NeoRecormon (anemia oncology)
Neupogen
Ocrevus
Pegasys (hepatitis B and C)
Perjeta (breast cancer)
Pulmozyme (cystic fibrosis)
Roaccutane/Accutane (acne)
Rocaltrol (osteoporosis)
Rocephin (bacterial infections)
Roferon-A (hepatitis C hairy cell leukemia AIDS-related Kaposi's sarcoma)
Tamiflu (treatment and prevention of influenza)
Tarceva (advanced non-small cell lung cancer advanced pancreatic cancer)
Tecentriq
Toradol (acute pain)
Valcyte (cytomegalovirus infection)
Valium (anxiety disorders)
Vesanoid (leukemia)
Viracept (HIV)
Xeloda
Xenical (weight loss weight control)
Xolair (asthma)
Zelboraf (metastatic melanoma)

COMPETITORS

AMDIPHARM MERCURY HOLDCO UK LIMITED	Clariant AG
BUNZL PUBLIC LIMITED COMPANY	ELI LILLY AND COMPANY
Boehringer Ingelheim International GmbH	NORGINE LIMITED
	PFIZER INC.
	RELX GROUP PLC
	SANOFI

HISTORICAL FINANCIALS

Company Type: Public

Income Statement   FYE: December 31

	REVENUE ($ mil.)	NET INCOME ($ mil.)	NET PROFIT MARGIN	EMPLOYEES
12/20	68,514	16,230	23.7%	101,465
12/19	65,947	13,961	21.2%	97,735
12/18	60,482	10,673	17.6%	94,442
12/17	57,118	8,845	15.5%	93,734
12/16	51,710	9,407	18.2%	94,052
Annual Growth	7.3%	14.6%	—	1.9%

2020 Year-End Financials

Debt ratio: 18.7%
Return on equity: 41.2%
Cash ($ mil.): 6,502
Current ratio: 1.30
Long-term debt ($ mil.): 11,603

No. of shares (mil.): 862
Dividends
  Yield: 1.6%
  Payout: 4.2%
Market value ($ mil.): 37,815

	STOCK PRICE ($) FY Close	P/E High/Low		PER SHARE ($) Earnings	Dividends	Book Value
12/20	43.84	3	2	18.76	0.72	47.84
12/19	40.66	3	2	16.16	0.68	39.27
12/18	31.08	3	2	12.41	1.08	32.55
12/17	31.58	3	3	10.29	1.06	31.41
12/16	28.53	3	2	10.93	1.00	27.23
Annual Growth	11.3%		—	14.4%	(7.9%)	15.1%

Rolls-Royce Holdings Plc

Rolls-Royce Holdings doesn't make cars so luxurious you'll cry (see Motor Cars) but it sure can make an aircraft engine whine. One of the world's largest aircraft engine makers Rolls-Royce through its Civil and Defense Aerospace businesses makes commercial and military engines for a broad customer base including airlines corporate and utility aircraft and helicopter operators and armed forces around the world. Beyond aviation its Energy unit supplies gas turbine power generation to the oil and gas industry while its Marine segment makes propulsion systems that power 70 navies worldwide. Rolls-Royce has operations in North America Europe and Asia with an emerging presence in the Middle East.

Operations

The company operates two divisions: Aerospace and Land & Sea.

The Aerospace division covers both civil and military aviation for which it develops manufactures markets and sells engines and power systems. The division's engines are found in the aircraft such as the Airbus A380 and on the defense side of things Rolls-Royce commands approximately one-quarter of the world's military engine manufacturing market share. Its portfolio covers all major sectors — combat helicopters unmanned and tactical aircraft training and transport. The Land & Sea division has three interests of power systems marine propulsion and nuclear power generation and propulsion. Its PWR2 nuclear propulsion system is found in the Royal Navy's Trident submarine fleet.

Geographic Reach

Headquartered in London Rolls-Royce has operations in over 50 countries and customers in over 150 worldwide. Europe is the company's biggest market at around 35% of sales followed by North America at 30% and Asia at 20%.

Financial Performance

Note: Growth rates may differ after conversion to US Dollars.

After a few years of growth from 2011 sales have flattened coming in at 13.7 billion in 2014 and 2015. Sales in Land & Sea were marginally lower than prior year due to weakness in Marine sales. Net income nudged up 14 million in 2015 to 83 million due to a decrease in taxation and commercial and administrative costs. Cash flow from operations fell 16% to 1.1 billion due to changes in provisions.

Strategy

Rolls-Royce is carrying out a streamlining process to enhance operational efficiency which included the axing of 600 management jobs since mid-2015 and the consolidation of its Civil Aerospace repair and overhaul activities allowing for the closure of sites in Brazil and the UK. It also sold its Michell Bearings business in November 2015 for 12.6 million and its L'Orange diesel parts maker to Woodward a US company for $859 million.

Rolls-Royce expects to see an uptick in its overseas business following the sharp fall in value of the Pound Sterling subsequent to the EU referendum in mid-2016.

Rolls-Royce is possibly weighing up an escalation of its nuclear activities after the UK government announced a 250 million competition to encourage development of small modular reactor (SMR) technologies which have potential uses as part of a 7 gigawatt network of SMRs.

Mergers and Acquisitions

In mid-2016 Rolls-Royce announced the purchase of the remaining 53% of shares in Industria de Turbo Propulsores (ITP) for ?720 million in order to strengthen its large engine growth program. ITP brings with it long-term aftermarket revenue including the high volume Trent 1000 and Trent XWB engines. The acquisition completed at the end of 2017.

In 2015 the company acquired R.O.V Technologies which makes products that allow for the remote inspection and cleaning of boiling/pressurized water reactors complementing Rolls-Royce's existing nuclear activities.

HISTORY

In 1906 automobile and aviation enthusiast Charles Rolls and engineer Henry Royce unveiled the Silver Ghost an automobile that earned Rolls-Royce a reputation as maker of the best car in the world.

A year after Rolls' 1910 death in a biplane crash Royce suffered a breakdown. From his home Royce continued to design Rolls-Royce engines such as the Eagle its first aircraft engine in 1914 and other engines used to power airplanes during WWI — but management of the company fell to Claude Johnson who remained chief executive until 1926.

Although the company returned primarily to making cars after WWI its engines were used in several history-making flights and in 1931 set world speed records for land sea and air. Rolls-Royce bought the Bentley Motor Company that year. In 1933 it introduced the Merlin engine which powered the Spitfire Hurricane and Mustang fighters of WWII. Rolls-Royce began designing a jet engine in 1938 and over the years it pioneered the turboprop engine turbofan and vertical takeoff engine.

Realizing that it had to break into the lucrative US airliner market to stay alive Rolls-Royce bought its main British competitor Bristol-Siddley Engines in 1966. With Bristol-Siddley came its contract to build the engine for the Anglo-French Concorde in 1976 and a US presence.

Lockheed ordered the company's RB211 engine for its TriStar in 1968 but Rolls-Royce underestimated the project's technical and financial challenges and entered bankruptcy in 1971. The British government stepped in and nationalized the aerospace division and sold the auto group. The RB211 entered service on the TriStar in 1972 and on the Boeing 747 in 1977.

Rolls-Royce was reprivatized in 1987. In a diversification effort two years later the company bought mining marine and power plant specialist Northern Engineering Industries. In the early 1990s the aerospace market was hurt by military spending cutbacks and a recession; the company cut more than 18000 jobs.

A joint venture with BMW launched the BR710 engine for Gulfstream and Canadair's long-range business jets in 1990. The company bought Allison Engine in 1995.

Rolls-Royce sold Parsons Power Generation Systems to Siemens in 1997. Also that year it won a contract to supply Trent 892 engines for Boeing 777 jets being built for American Airlines (a subsidiary of AMR Corporation) in a deal worth $1 billion.

In 1998 the British government approved a repayable investment of about $335 million in the company to develop a new model of Trent aircraft engines. Narrowing its focus the company sold its power transmission and distribution business to Austria-based VA Technologie.

Rolls-Royce pumped up its gas and oil equipment business in 1999 by buying the rotating compression equipment unit of Cooper Cameron (now Cameron International); it became one of the world leaders in marine propulsion by acquiring Vickers . The company then bought the aero and industrial engine repair service of First Aviation Services and took full control of its aircraft-engine joint venture with BMW; in return BMW received a 10% stake in Rolls.

In 2000 subsidiary Rolls-Royce Energy Systems India Private was awarded its first order: producing a Bergen gas engine for Garden Silk Mills for powering a textile plant in India. That year Rolls-Royce won a contract to supply engines for Israel's El Al airline's Boeing 777s. Late in 2000 it was reported that the company would cut about 5000 jobs over three years.

Early in 2001 Rolls-Royce sold most of its Vickers Turbine Components business. In October the company cut about 11% of its workforce in response to the worldwide crisis in the commercial jet business.

In 2002 the company announced that it had inked a 10-year $2 billion deal to supply engines to Gulfstream Aerospace. That year Rolls-Royce sold its Vickers Defence Systems unit which made tanks and armored vehicles to Alvis Plc. In 2003 Sir Ralph Robins who had been executive chairman for more than a decade retired from his post.

Early in 2004 Rolls-Royce and GE Aircraft Engines were picked to supply engines for Boeing's upcoming 787 Dreamliner. Rolls-Royce was also selected to supply engines for Airbus' upcoming behemoth A380.

In late 2007 it scored one of its largest contracts a $42 million project to provide steering gear and deck machinery for Chinese shipbuilder Sinopacific.

In 2008 it entered into a joint venture with Goodrich Corporation called Aero Engine Controls to produce engine controls for Rolls-Royce aircraft. It also partnered with France's AREVA to construct the first new nuclear reactors built in the UK in more than 20 years.

In 2009 the company focused on developing four advanced manufacturing research centers in the US the UK and Singapore. Rolls-Royce invested 300 million (more than $450 million) in its UK factories as part of its almost 2 billion (over $3 billion) capital replacement plan to be carried out over a period of 10 years. That year Rolls-Royce engines allowed the BAE Systems' Mantis UAV and AgustaWestland's Lynx Wildcat helicopter to take flight.

Rolls-Royce's nuclear market was strengthened in 2009 by its agreement with electric service provider EDF Energy (formerly known as London Electricity Group) to enter into a joint venture with EDF Energy giving support to the UK facility. The following year the company introduced its STOVL (short take-off and vertical landing) Rolls-Royce LiftSystem.

The bell of financial crisis knelled in 2008 causing the company to implement cost-cutting measures which included headcount reductions of almost 10%. The company in partnership with GE Aviation continued development of the F136 engine for the F-35 Joint Strike Fighter and its Trent 1000 engine took its first flight in the Boeing 787 Dreamliner. Also in 2008 Rolls-Royce established its civil nuclear business to tap a growing global market.

EXECUTIVES

Non-Executive Independent Director, Hsien Yang Lee, $83,366 total compensation
Company Secretary, Chief Governance Officer, Pamela Coles

Non-Executive Independent Director, Irene
Dorner, $124,408 total compensation
Senior Independent Non-Executive Director,
Kevin Smith, $124,408 total compensation
Non-Executive Independent Director, Beverly
Goulet, $83,366 total compensation
Chief People Officer, Sarah Armstrong
Non-Executive Independent Director, Nicholas
Luff, $83,366 total compensation
Non-Executive Independent Director, George
Culmer, $83,366 total compensation
Non-Executive Independent Director, Angela
Strank, $53,867 total compensation
Non-Executive Independent Director, Paul Adams
Chief Financial Officer, Executive Director, Panos
Kakoullis
**Non-Executive Independent Chairman of the
Board,** Anita Frew
Non-Executive Director, Mike Manley
Chief Technology Officer, Grazia Vittadini
Non-Executive Director, Wendy Mars
President - Electrical, Robert Watson
CEO and Director, Warren East, $1,119,675 total
compensation
Auditors: PricewaterhouseCoopers LLP

LOCATIONS

HQ: Rolls-Royce Holdings Plc
Kings Place, 90 York Way, London N1 9FX
Phone: (44) 20 7222 9020
Web: www.rolls-royce.com

2015 Sales

	% of total
Europe	36
North America	30
Asia	21
Middle East	6
South America	3
Australasia	2
Africa	1
Other	1
Total	**100**

PRODUCTS/OPERATIONS

2015 Sales (by market)

	% of total
Civil Aerospace	52
Power Systems	18
Defence Aerospace	15
Marine	10
Nuclear	5
Total	**100**

Selected Products and Services

Aircraft engines
Automation and control equipment
Bearings and seals
Diesel and gas turbine engines
Electric propulsion systems
Engine support services
Helicopter engines
Fuel cells
Generators
Offshore drilling equipment
Overhaul and repair services
Ship designs
Technical publications
Training

Selected Subsidiaries

Civil aerospace
  Optimized Systems and Solutions Limited (OSyS)
  (advanced controls and predictive data management)
  Rolls-Royce Leasing Limited (engine leasing)
  Rolls-Royce Total Care Services Limited (aftermarket
  support services)
Corporate
  Rolls-Royce International Limited (international
  support and commercial information services)
  Rolls-Royce Power Engineering plc (power generation
  and marine systems)
Energy

Rolls-Royce Fuel Cell Systems Limited (fuel cell
  system development)
Rolls-Royce Power Development Limited (project
  development)
Tidal Generation Limited (development of tidal
  generation systems)
Marine
  ODIM ASA (offshore drilling naval and power
  generation equipment)
  Rolls-Royce Marine Electrical Systems Limited
  (marine electrical systems)
  Rolls-Royce Power Development Limited (generation
  of electricity from independent power projects)
  Rolls-Royce Marine Power Operations Limited
  (nuclear submarine propulsion systems)
  Rolls-Royce Power Engineering plc (energy and
  marine systems)
p>#

COMPETITORS

Bombardier Inc	SAFRAN
COBHAM LIMITED	Scania AB
FAURECIA	VALEO
GKN LIMITED	Voith GmbH & Co. KGaA
PEUGEOT SA	
Pratt & Whitney Canada	
Corp	

HISTORICAL FINANCIALS

Company Type: Public

Income Statement

FYE: December 31

	REVENUE ($ mil.)	NET INCOME ($ mil.)	NET PROFIT MARGIN	EMPLOYEES
12/20	16,136	(4,326)	—	48,200
12/19	21,904	(1,736)	—	51,700
12/18	20,082	(3,065)	—	54,500
12/17	22,025	5,682	25.8%	50,000
12/16	18,396	(4,959)	—	49,900
Annual Growth	(3.2%)	—	—	(0.9%)

2020 Year-End Financials

Debt ratio: 33.8%
Return on equity: —
Cash ($ mil.): 4,710
Current ratio: 1.05
Long-term debt ($ mil.): 8,267

No. of shares (mil.): —
Dividends
  Yield: 0.4%
  Payout: —
Market value ($ mil.): —

	STOCK PRICE ($) FY Close	P/E High/Low		Earnings	PER SHARE ($) Dividends	Book Value
12/20	1.58	—	—	(0.72)	2.00	(0.80)
12/19	9.01	—	—	(0.31)	0.29	(0.79)
12/18	10.46	—	—	(0.57)	0.22	(0.25)
12/17	11.42	17	11	1.06	0.30	1.56
12/16	8.26	—	—	(0.93)	0.26	0.43
Annual Growth	(33.9%)	—	—	—	66.8%	—

Rosneft Oil Co OJSC (Moscow)

Rosneft is one of the world's largest public energy companies accounting for about 5% of the world's oil production. With assets in around 25 countries the Russian giant maintains one of the world's largest hydrocarbon reserves (approximately 5.19 million barrels per day). Its wide range of activities include exploration and production of offshore hydrocarbon deposits gas extraction and processing as well as marketing of petrochemical products in Russia and neighboring countries. The

company also has a dozen or so joint ventures in Europe and Asia. Though strongly Russian in its roots about 40% of Rosneft is owned by foreign shareholders primarily ROSNEFTEGAZ JSC BP and QH Oil Investments.

Operations

Rosneft's core activities include hydrocarbon prospecting and exploration production of oil gas and gas condensate implementation of offshore field development projects refining sales of oil gas and refined products in Russia and in some other countries.

The largest refining company in the Russian Federation's refining block includes nearly 15 large refineries as well as petrochemical and gas processing facilities located in five Federal Districts: Central Volga Southern Siberian and Far Eastern. Its refining business is primarily focused on the strategic goal of providing the domestic market with high-quality petroleum products including remote regions of the country. In addition about 1500 filling stations were connected to the company's contactless fuel payment service; the contactless food payment service is available at 50 BP filling stations.

Overall the company generates more than 40% of revenue from oil followed by oil products and petrochemicals providing nearly 40% and gas brings in about 5%. The remaining nearly 15% of revenue is generated from other sales.

Generates most of its revenue from oil gas petroleum products and petrochemicals support services and other and equity share in profits of associates and joint ventures account for the remaining.

Geographic Reach

Headquartered in Moscow Rosneft has a strong presence across nearly 80 regions of Russia plus parts of Abkhazia Kyrgyzstan and Belarus. The company's assets however are highly dispersed in about 25 countries across the world from Brazil and Canada to Egypt and Indonesia.

Sales and Marketing

The Rosneft trademark is one of the most recognizable in the oil products market of Russia. Operating the country's largest retail chain Rosneft has more than 3000 oil filling stations. The company also serves jet fuel marine fuels and lubricant markets plus more than 2090 shops and about 130 oil depots.

Financial Performance

Note: Growth rates may differ after conversion to US Dollars.

In 2020 the company's revenue decreased by 34% year-on-year to ?5.6 trillion on the back of a drop in global oil prices cuts in oil production and sales under the OPEC+ deal and COVID-19-related decline in global oil demand.

In 2020 the company had a net income of ?147 billion a 79% decrease from the previous year's net income of ?705 billion.

The company's cash at the end of 2020 was ?806 billion. Operating activities generated ?1.7 trillion while investing activities used ?1.7 trillion mainly for capital expenditures. Financing activities provided another ?530 billion.

Strategy

In pursuing its climate agenda Rosneft focuses on protecting the environment in line with Russia's Energy Strategy to 2035 and the Paris Agreement goals. In 2020 it approved the Carbon Management Plan for the period until 2035 underlying its environmental agenda to contribute to low-carbon economy. It covers climate risk management and seeks to unlock opportunities associated with future demand for energy. The Carbon Management Plan also seeks to find potential ways of achieving carbon neutrality by 2050.

HISTORY

Rosneft was formed in 1993.

In 2004 Rosneft acquired YUKOS' main oil unit — Yugansk — in a controversial $9.4 billion deal. The acquisition of Yugansk (also known as Yuganskneftegaz) has been more complicated than Rosneft may have wished as questions were raised about how the deal was handled and how the transaction was funded. In 2004 the company agreed to merge with Russian energy giant Gazprom. The Yugansk acquisition threw the merger with Gazprom into disarray with Rosneft claiming that terms of the deal should be renegotiated to account for the change in value of Rosneft's assets. In addition Group Menatep (majority owner of YUKOS) called for Rosneft to repay a loan estimated at about $900 million that is secured by Yugansk assets. In response Rosneft filed an $11 billion suit against YUKOS for unpaid taxes related to Yugansk.

In 2005 Rosneft approved the deal with Gazprom though the acquisition would exclude the Yugansk assets acquired from YUKOS. After months of conflicting reports state-controlled Gazprom abandoned the deal.

In 2006 Rosneft and BP teamed up to develop energy projects in Russia's Arctic. Rosneft raised $10.4 billion in a 2006 IPO (during which BP acquired a $1 billion stake).

In a move toward becoming a global oil company in 2011 Rosneft formed a strategic alliance with BP (involving a stock swap of 5% of BP's shares for 9.5% of Rosneft's) to help fund the exploration of three blocks on the Russian Arctic continental shelf. The blocks have a production capacity on a par with the UK North Sea. However rival Russian partners at TNK-BP (BP's established Russian joint venture) objected to the proposed deal saying that have the legal right to have first choice on BP expansion activities in Russia. An arbitration tribunal in the UK supported their position. BP subsequently agreed to pursue the Rosneft deal through TNK BP. This move was unsuccessful and in May 2011 the BP/Rosneft deal fell through.

It followed this by forming a joint venture with Exxon Mobil to explore oil and gas fields in the Arctic. (This plan was stymied by US sanctions imposed in 2014).

Growing its European refinery footprint in 2011 it also acquired a 50% stake in German refinery Ruhr Oel from PDVSA for about $1.6 billion. BP owns the other 50%.

Beefing up its Russian assets in 2012 also bought 51% of NGK ITERA LLC one of the largest independent producers and traders of natural gas in Russia for RUB 7 billion (US $227 million).

EXECUTIVES

Chief Executive Officer, Chairman of the Management Board, Deputy Chairman of the Board, Executive Director, Igor Sechin
Non-Executive Director, Bernard Looney
Member of the Management Board, Vice President - Refining, Petrochemicals, Commerce and Logistics, Didier Casimiro
Independent Director, Hans-Joerg Rudloff
Independent Deputy Chairman of the Board, Matthias Warnig
Member of the Management Board, First Vice President for Oil, Gas, and Offshore Business Development, Zeljko Runje
Non-Executive Director, Robert Dudley
Non-Executive Director - Representative of Qatar Investments Authority, Faisal Alsuwaidi
Non-Executive Director, Hamad Al-Mohannadi
Independent Director, Oleg Vyugin

Member of the Management Board, Vice President - In-House Services of Rosneft, Eric Liron
Member of the Management Board, Vice President - Chief Geologist, Andrey Polyakov
Non-Executive Director, Maxim Oreshkin
Member of the Management Board, Ilgam Kuchukov
Independent Chairman of the Board, Gerhard Schroeder
Non-Executive Director, Alexander Novak
Auditors: Ernst & Young LLC

LOCATIONS

HQ: Rosneft Oil Co OJSC (Moscow)
26/1, Sofiyskaya Embankment, Moscow 117997
Phone: (7) 499 517 88 99   **Fax:** (7) 499 517 72 35
Web: www.rosneft.com

PRODUCTS/OPERATIONS

2016 Sales

	% of total
Oil gas Petroleum products & petrochemicals	98
Support services & other	2
Equity share in profits of associates & joint ventures	-
Total	**100**

2016 Sales

	% of total
Refining and distribution	66
Exploration and production	33
Other	1
Total	**100**

COMPETITORS

ANADARKO PETROLEUM CORPORATION
CHEVRON CORPORATION
CIMAREX ENERGY CO.
COMPA 'IA ESPA 'OLA DE PETROLEOS SAU
Cequence Energy Ltd
DEVON ENERGY CORPORATION
EVOLUTION PETROLEUM CORPORATION
Equinor ASA
GAZPROM NEFT PAO
GAZPROM PAO
HESS CORPORATION
INDIAN OIL CORPORATION LIMITED
LUKOIL PAO
MARATHON OIL CORPORATION
MOL Magyar Olaj- es G zipari Nyilv nosan
  M k ¶d
OMV Aktiengesellschaft
TOTALENERGIES SE

HISTORICAL FINANCIALS

Company Type: Public

Income Statement   FYE: December 31

	REVENUE ($ mil.)	NET INCOME ($ mil.)	NET PROFIT MARGIN	EMPLOYEES
12/20	76,960	1,965	2.6%	355,900
12/19	139,403	11,375	8.2%	334,600
12/18	118,199	7,877	6.7%	325,600
12/17	104,023	3,839	3.7%	318,000
12/16	81,460	2,955	3.6%	0
Annual Growth	(1.4%)	(9.7%)	—	—

2020 Year-End Financials

Debt ratio: 0.4%	No. of shares (mil.): —
Return on equity: 3.1%	Dividends
Cash ($ mil.): 10,774	Yield: 0.0%
Current ratio: 0.95	Payout: 117.6%
Long-term debt ($ mil.): 50,932	Market value ($ mil.): —

	STOCK PRICE ($) FY Close	P/E High/Low		PER SHARE ($) Earnings	Dividends	Book Value
12/20	5.98	0	0	0.20	0.23	5.94
12/19	7.33	0	0	1.07	0.43	6.85
12/18	6.10	0	0	0.74	0.31	5.49
12/17	5.05	0	0	0.36	0.17	5.91
12/16	6.43	0	0	0.28	0.20	5.10
Annual Growth	(1.8%)	—	—	(8.1%)	4.3%	3.9%

Royal Bank of Canada (Montreal, Quebec)

Royal Bank of Canada (RBC) is Canada's largest bank and one of the largest in the world by market capitalization. The bank provides a diversified set of personal and commercial banking wealth management insurance investor and treasury services and capital markets globally. It serves more than 17 million customers ? businesses and group clients individual and institutional clients — through offices in Canada the US and about 35 other countries including the UK and other selected parts of Europe the Asia/Pacific region and the Caribbean. RBC which generates about 60% of revenue from Canada.

Operations

RBC operates six business segments: Personal & Commercial Banking Wealth Management Capital Markets Insurance Investor & Treasury Services and Corporate support.

Personal & Commercial Banking generates more than 35% of total revenue. It provides a broad suite of financial products and services.

Wealth Management provides a comprehensive suite of investment trust banking credit and other wealth solutions to high net worth and ultra-high net worth clients. It also offers asset management services to institutional and individual clients. The segment accounts about 25% of revenue.

Capital Markets segment brings in more than 20% of revenue and provides the technological and operational foundation required to effectively deliver products and services to its clients.

More than 10% of revenue comes from Insurance — life health home auto and other kinds of insurance. It includes insurance for individuals as well as reinsurance advice and solutions and business insurance services to business and group clients.

The Investor & Treasury Services accounts for about 5% of the company's revenue. It is a provider of asset services a leader in Canadian cash management and transaction banking services and a provider of treasury services to institutional clients worldwide.

The Corporate Support consists of Technology and Operations which provides the technological and operational requirements needed to deliver services and products to the company's customers. Overall net interest income accounts for more than 55% of total revenue.

Geographic Reach

Ontario-based RBC has more than 17 million clients in Canada the US and about 35 other countries. The company's Personal & Commercial Banking segment provides products and services in Canada the Caribbean and the US.

Overall the company generates about 60% of its revenue from Canada about 25% from the US and some 15% from other international sources.

Sales and Marketing

Royal Bank of Canada serves a wide range of customers including individuals institutional groups business clients high-net-worth and ultra-high-net-worth individuals and institutional clients.

Through its capital markets the company also serves the energy mining and infrastructure industrial consumer health care and technology markets and financial services.

Financial Performance

Note: Growth rates may differ after conversion to US dollars.

Total revenue for 2020 increased by 3% or amounting to C$1.1 billion which is higher than that of the prior year. This result is due to higher net interest income; underwriting and other advisory fees; investment management and custodial fees and higher trading revenue.

RBC's net income for 2020 was C$11.4 billion an 11% decrease from the previous year. The decrease is attributable to the effects of the COVID-19 pandemic on performing loans and lower spreads.

Cash and due from banks at end of 2019 was C$118.8 billion. Operating activities generated C$38.8 billion while investing activities used C$39.6 billion. Financing activities used another C$7.7 billion.

Strategy

RBC will sustain its technological leadership by investing significantly in its digital and innovation strategies enabling RBC to deliver even more insights and advice that create meaningful value for clients. RBC's differentiated technology platform and strong data foundation are supporting business growth operational efficiencies and leading-edge capabilities. RBC's next-generation delivery platform including a multi-cloud strategy accelerates its ability to bring products and services to market quickly scale across businesses and leverage world-class artificial intelligence (AI) and analytics to deliver superior business outcomes.

Company Background

Royal Bank of Canada (RBC) was created as Merchants Bank in 1864 and incorporated in 1869. It changed its name to The Royal Bank of Canada in 1901 and to Royal Bank of Canada in 1990.

HISTORY

Royal Bank of Canada (RBC) has looked south of the border ever since its 1864 creation as Merchants Bank in Halifax Nova Scotia a port city bustling with trade spawned by the US Civil War. After incorporating in 1869 as Merchants Bank of Halifax the bank added branches in eastern Canada. Merchants opened a branch in Bermuda in 1882. Gold strikes in Canada and Alaska in the late 1890s pushed it into western Canada.

Merchants opened offices in New York and Cuba in 1899 and changed its name to Royal Bank of Canada in 1901. RBC moved into new Montreal headquarters in 1907 and grew by purchasing such banks as Union Bank of Canada (1925). In 1928 it moved into the 42-story Royal Bank Building then the tallest in the British Empire.

The bank faltered during the Depression but recovered during WWII. After the war RBC financed the expanding minerals and oil and gas industries. When Castro took power in Cuba RBC tried to operate its branches under communist rule but sold out to Banco Nacional de Cuba in 1960.

RBC opened offices in the UK in 1979 and in West Germany Puerto Rico and the Bahamas in 1980. As Canada's banking rules relaxed RBC bought Dominion Securities in 1987. The US Federal Reserve approved RBC's brokerage arm for participation in stock underwriting in 1991.

The bank faced a $650 million loss in 1992 after backing the Reichmann family's Olympia & York property development company which failed under the weight of its UK projects. The next year an ever-diversifying RBC bought Royal Trustco Canada's #2 trust company and Voyageur Travel Insurance its largest retail travel insurer. A management shakeup in late 1994 ended with bank president John Cleghorn taking control of the company.

In 1995 RBC listed on the New York Stock Exchange and the next year joined with Heller Financial (an affiliate of Japan's Fuji Bank) to finance trade between Canada and Mexico. It began offering PC home banking in 1996 and Internet banking in 1997. That year RBC became one of the world's largest securities-custody service providers with its acquisition of The Bank of Nova Scotia's institutional and pension custody operations.

The company and Bank of Montreal agreed to merge in 1998 but Canadian regulators fearing the concentration of banking power seen in the US rejected the merger. In response the bank trimmed its workforce and orchestrated a sale-leaseback of its property portfolio (1999).

In the late 1990s RBC grew its online presence by purchasing the Internet banking operations of Security First Network Bank (now Security First Technologies 1998) the online trading division of Bull & Bear Group (1999) and 20% of AOL Canada (1999). It also bought several trust and fiduciary services businesses from Ernst & Young.

It acquired US mortgage bank Prism Financial and the Canadian retail credit card business of BANK ONE in 2000. RBC also sold its commercial credit portfolio to U.S. Bancorp. The company agreed to pay a substantial fine after institutional asset management subsidiary RT Capital Management came under scrutiny from the Ontario Securities Commission for alleged involvement in illegal pension-fund stock manipulation. RBC ended up selling RT Capital to UBS AG the following year.

Also in 2001 RBC made another US purchase: North Carolina's Centura Banks (now RBC Centura Banks). It sold Houston-based home lender RBC Mortgage to New Century Financial in 2005. Also that year it acquired private bank Abacus Financial which adding locations in the UK and Amsterdam.

RBC spent the decade prior to the global recession building up its US operations. The company moved into the US trust business in 2006 when it purchased American Guaranty & Trust a unit of National Life Insurance Company. In 2007 it bought the electronic brokerage business of New York boutique Carlin Financial Group. Other acquisitions made during that period include debt securities investor Access Capital Strategies energy advisory firm Richardson Barr and DC-area investment bank Ferris Baker Watts.

In 2008 RBC acquired community banks in Alabama Georgia and Florida including Alabama National BanCorporation. That same year RBC agreed to buy back some $850 million in auction-rate securities and pay the New York State attorney general's office a nearly $10 million fine. Auction-rate securities were sold to investors as a low-risk investment but as the economy worsened in 2007 and 2008 banks canceled the regular auctions rendering the securities worthless. Customers and regulators claimed that banks continued to sell them the securities even though they knew the investments had become very high risk.

Also in 2008 RBC Bank expanded its finance operations when it bought the Canadian commercial leasing business of ABN AMRO. It renamed the unit RBC Equipment Finance Group.

To cement its place among the world's 10 largest wealth managers RBC bought UK-based fixed income specialist BlueBay Asset Management for some $1.5 billion in 2010. Also that year it bought BNP Paribas Fortis' Hong Kong wealth management business.

In 2010 it also sold Liberty Life its US life insurance subsidiary that had posted losses for two years to Apollo affiliate Athene Holding. To boost brand recognition of another US unit the company changed the name of Voyageur Asset Management to RBC Global Asset Management (US).

EXECUTIVES

Corporate Director, Roberta Jamieson
President and Chief Executive Officer, David Mckay, $1,115,105 total compensation
Independent Director, David Denison
Independent Director, Andrew Chisholm
Chief Risk Officer, Graeme Hepworth
Chief Financial Officer, Nadine Ahn
Chief Legal Officer, Maria Douvas
Group Head - Personal, Commercial Banking and RBC Ventures, Neil McLaughlin, $551,594 total compensation
Chief Administrative Officer and Strategy Officer, Christoph Knoess
Independent Director, Maryann Turcke
Group Head and Chief Executive Officer - Capital Markets, Derek Neldner, $520,382 total compensation
Independent Director, Frank Vettese
Independent Director, Cynthia Devine
Independent Director, Bridget van Kralingen
Group Head - Wealth Management, Insurance, Investor and Treasury Services, Douglas Guzman, $520,382 total compensation
Group Head - Technology and Operations, Bruce Ross
Independent Director, Jacynthe Cote
Independent Director, Toos Daruvala
Chief Human Resource Officer, Helena Gottschling
Independent Director, Jeffery Yabuki
Independent Director, Thierry Vandal
Independent Chairman of the Board, Kathleen Taylor
Auditors: PricewaterhouseCoopers LLP

LOCATIONS

HQ: Royal Bank of Canada (Montreal, Quebec)
  200 Bay Street, Toronto, Ontario M5J 2J5
Phone: 416 974-6715
Web: www.rbc.com

2018 Sales

	% of total
Canada	60
US	23
Other international	17
Total	**100**

PRODUCTS/OPERATIONS

2018 Sales

	% of total
Net interest income	43
Non-interest income	57
Total	**100**

2018 Sales

	% of total
Personal & commercial banking	39
Wealth management	25
Capital markets	20
Insurance	10
Investor & treasury services	6
Total	**100**

COMPETITORS

COMMONWEALTH BANK OF
  AUSTRALIA
Credit Suisse Group AG
HSBC HOLDINGS PLC
HUNTINGTON BANCSHARES
  INCORPORATED

ING Groep N.V.
KEYCORP
U.S. BANCORP
UBS AG

HISTORICAL FINANCIALS

Company Type: Public

Income Statement				FYE: October 31
	ASSETS ($ mil.)	NET INCOME ($ mil.)	INCOME AS % OF ASSETS	EMPLOYEES
10/21	1,381,341	12,983	0.9%	85,301
10/20	1,221,243	8,593	0.7%	83,842
10/19	1,084,825	9,763	0.9%	82,801
10/18	1,016,511	9,443	0.9%	84,000
10/17	944,094	8,895	0.9%	78,210
Annual Growth	10.0%	9.9%	—	2.2%

2021 Year-End Financials

Return on assets: 0.9%
Return on equity: 17.3%
Long-term debt ($ mil.): —
No. of shares (mil.): 1,424
Sales ($ mil): 46,820

Dividends
  Yield: 0.0%
  Payout: 39.0%
Market value ($ mil.): 148,165

	STOCK PRICE ($) FY Close	P/E High/Low		PER SHARE ($) Earnings	Dividends	Book Value
10/21	104.01	10	7	8.95	3.50	56.07
10/20	69.99	11	7	5.88	3.22	45.80
10/19	80.66	9	8	6.64	3.07	44.34
10/18	72.84	10	9	6.37	2.94	42.27
10/17	78.15	10	8	5.88	2.68	39.56
Annual Growth	7.4%	—	—	11.1%	6.9%	9.1%

Royal Mail Plc

Be it fan mail business mail or junk mail Royal Mail seldom fails to deliver it in the UK. The company carries approximately 13 billion letters and other items daily to some 30 million addresses in the UK and around 45 countries internationally including the US. Royal Mail maintains a retail presence through its Post Office unit which oversees a network of some 11500 branches and provides postal as well as financial and travel services. Through Parcelforce Worldwide and the main Royal Mail brand the company delivers 1.3 billion packages in the UK and through Netherlands-based subsidiary General Logistics Systems some 650 million parcels in Europe and North America. The enterprise long government-owned went public in late 2013.

Financial Performance

Note: Growth rates may differ after conversion to US Dollars.

Royal Mail's revenue has been growing over the past four years but profits have been middling. In fiscal 2019 (ended March 31) the company's sales grew 4% to 10.6 billion due to the effect of a 53rd trading week and higher sales in Dutch subsidiary General Logistics Systems (GLS). The main Royal Mail business and GLS saw growth in parcels more than offset the continued structural decline in letter sending. Parcels accounted for 63% of sales in 2018 up on 59% in 2017.

Net income fell 32% to 175 million largely as a result of a tax benefit recorded in 2018 compared to a 66 million expense in fiscal 2019. Operating profits were impacted by impairments in the Golden State Overnight and Postal Express businesses in GLS.

Royal Mail's cash balance weakened during fiscal 2019 ending the year 362 million lower at 236 million. The company's operations generated 492 million while its investing activities used 543 million and its financing used 312 million.

Strategy

Royal Mail is transforming from a UK letter delivery company that delivers parcels to an international parcel-first company that also delivers letters in the UK. International expansion is pursued mostly through its international division General Logistics Systems (GLS) which acquired Golden State Overnight and Postal Express in 2016 bringing Royal Mail into the US and Canadian markets. It continues to buy its way into new markets and expand organically. In recent years GLS has launched a cross-border returns service introduced a flexible delivery service (FlexDeliveryService) in Spain and invested more than ?100 million in expanding capacity in its European network. It also connected the British Isles to its international FlexDeliveryService.

HISTORY

Though the British Post Office was officially born in 1635 a royal postal service had been in operation long before that time. Organized by Henry VIII in 1512 it originally served only noblemen and merchants. But the public appetite for mail led to the 1635 Act of Parliament (under Charles I) that officially opened the service to the entire British public to operate under the name Post Office.

During his reign Charles II passed the Post Office Charter of 1660 and dubbed Henry Bishop as Postmaster General. Bishop introduced the postmark to expedite delivery. Intracity delivery was launched in London in 1680 along with a citywide penny post.

Two problems over the years were the complex distance-based pricing schedule and the burden unexpected mail placed on the poor at a time when postage was paid cash on delivery. Rowland Hill burst onto the scene in 1837 with a treatise on postal reform: He pushed a cheap uniform rate unrelated to distance with postage to be prepaid.

Hill joined The Post Office to oversee his reforms and the nationwide flat-rate penny post was passed in 1840. He also introduced postage stamps to effect prepayment. Hill was finally named Post Office Secretary in 1854 and in the 1860s he introduced The Post Office savings banks to address underserved small savers. He retired in 1864 a giant of postal history.

A Hill contemporary was Anthony Trollope: Better known today for his novels Trollope enjoyed a successful postal career from 1834 to 1867 introducing roadside postboxes to Britain in the mid-1850s.

The state bought out Britain's telegraph firms in 1870 assigning the operations to The Post Office. When the government acquired the UK's remaining private telephone operator National Telephone Company in 1912 the service became a model European PTT (postal telephone and telegraph monopoly).

After WWII The Post Office enjoyed a decade of profits. But losses in 1955 made The Post Office realize its operations were too labor-intensive. It began using sorting machines in the mid-1950s and the postcode in 1959. The telephone arm rolled out subscriber trunk dialing in 1958 which enabled phone callers to dial without operator help.

The postal service initiated a modern banking service in 1968 called the Girobank. The next year The Post Office was established as an independent corporation (though still state-owned).

Margaret Thatcher's government spun off the telecommunications arm as British Telecom (now BT Group) in 1981; parts of the postal market were opened to competition. In 1986 The Post Office reorganized into four departments: Royal Mail Letters Parcelforce Girobank (sold in 1990) and Post Office Counters (which ran post offices as retail outlets).

During the 1990s the Royal Mail maintained a monopoly on mail costing less than a pound (until 2001 when EU regulations opened up this area to competition) but with other competition mounting The Post Office began to develop opportunities abroad. In 1994 it launched a US subsidiary to handle international bulk mail and in 1999 it bought German Parcel and Der Kurier. Other acquisitions included the Williames group (Ireland 1999) Citipost (US 1999) and express mail carrier Crie (France 2000). That year the company also agreed to create a joint venture with TNT Post Group and Singapore Post for international mail delivery.

Profits were hit in 2000 when The Post Office swallowed a write-down of some 570 million after the state decided to send benefits payments by direct deposit instead of by mail. The next year The Post Office changed its name to Consignia (derived from "consign") in tandem with its reorganization as a public limited company. The new name proved to be unpopular however and the company changed its name to Royal Mail Holdings in 2002.

The UK mail delivery market was officially opened to competition in 2006.

EXECUTIVES

Senior Non-Executive Independent Director, Sarah Hogg, $92,607 total compensation
Non-Executive Independent Director, Michael Findlay, $97,824 total compensation
Non-Executive Independent Director, Maria da Cunha, $84,781 total compensation
Chief Risk and Governance Officer, Group General Counsel, Company Secretary, Mark Amsden
Group Chief Financial Officer, Michael Jeavons, $122,606 total compensation
Chairman and Interim CEO, Keith Williams, $391,297 total compensation
Non-Executive Director, Shashi Verma
Chief Executive Officer, GLS, Martin Seidenberg
Non-Executive Independent Director, Lynne Peacock, $97,824 total compensation
Auditors: KPMG LLP

LOCATIONS

HQ: Royal Mail Plc
  185 Farringdon Road, London EC1A 1AA
Phone:
Web: www.royalmailgroup.com

PRODUCTS/OPERATIONS

2019 Sales

	% of total
UK Parcels International & Letters	73
General Logistics Systems	27
Total	**100**

COMPETITORS

AUSTRALIAN POSTAL
  CORPORATION
Deutsche Post AG
FEDEX OFFICE AND PRINT
  SERVICES INC.
Koninklijke PostNL
  B.V.

LA POSTE
POSTE ITALIANE SPA
PostNL N.V.
SINGAPORE POST LIMITED

HISTORICAL FINANCIALS

Company Type: Public

Income Statement
FYE: March 28

	REVENUE ($ mil.)	NET INCOME ($ mil.)	NET PROFIT MARGIN	EMPLOYEES
03/21	17,407	854	4.9%	158,592
03/20	13,242	196	1.5%	160,772
03/19	13,860	229	1.7%	161,978
03/18	14,358	365	2.5%	159,117
03/17	12,216	339	2.8%	158,955
Annual Growth	9.3%	25.9%	—	(0.1%)

2021 Year-End Financials

Debt ratio: 12.3%	No. of shares (mil.): 999
Return on equity: 11.9%	Dividends
Cash ($ mil.): 2,166	Yield: —
Current ratio: 1.19	Payout: —
Long-term debt ($ mil.): 1,232	Market value ($ mil.): 14,292

	STOCK PRICE ($) FY Close	P/E High/Low		PER SHARE ($) Earnings	Dividends	Book Value
03/21	14.30	24	5	0.85	0.00	6.62
03/20	3.27	41	20	0.20	0.51	6.87
03/19	6.21	95	35	0.23	0.55	6.05
03/18	14.86	63	40	0.36	0.58	6.26
03/17	10.63	50	37	0.34	0.48	6.30
Annual Growth	7.7%	—	—	25.7%	—	1.2%

RWE AG

RWE has become an electricity generation from renewables as the result of an asset swap with E.ON. Through its subsidiaries RWE AG is a player in the field of renewable energy. Through innovation and investment the new RWE is creating the foundation for a carbon neutral future. It also owns major UK and Netherlands-based utilities and Germany-based electricity and gas supplier RWE Power. It generates about 30% of its revenue in Germany.

Operations

In their 2020 financial report the company divided its operations to the following segments: Offshore Wind (less than 5% of revenue) is overseen by the RWE Renewables the company's group; Onshore wind/Solar (some 15% of revenue) where the company pools their onshore wind solar power and battery storage activities; Hydro/Biomass/Gas (nearly 10% of revenue) which is responsible for the run-of-river pumped storage biomass and gas power stations; Supply & trading (more than 5% of revenue) where the company trades their energy commodities and is managed by RWE Supply and Trading; and Coal/Nuclear (about 5% of revenue) which was previously lignite and is the generating electricity in Germany produced from lignite hard coal and nuclear fuel.

Geographic Reach

RWE operates in Germany the Netherlands/Belgium the UK Asia and in Central Eastern and South Eastern Europe. Germany and UK accounted for about 30% of the company's revenue each.

Financial Performance

RWE's revenue has seen poor performance for the span of five years and have continued to decrease with 2020 being slightly higher than 2019 and 2018.

Revenue increased 4% to ?13.7 billion in 2020 as compared to 2019's revenue of ?13.1 billion.

The company recorded a net income of ?995 million which is ?7.5 billion lower than the prior year's net income of ?8.5 billion.

RWE ended 2020 with ?34.8 billion. Operating activities and financing provided ?4.1 billion and ?1.8 billion respectively. While investing activities used ?4.3 billion.

Strategy

RWE's strategy revolves around the goal of becoming carbon neutral by 2040 through the development of their portfolio and segments. The company has continued to develop their portfolio and services since 2016 by pooling their Renewables Retail and Grid & Infrastructure divisions. For 2020 the company introduced a new segment structure wherein their main business electricity generation is now broken down by energy source whereas energy trading is still presented separately. This resulted in the following five segments: Offshore Wind; Onshore Wind?/?Solar; Hydro?/?Biomass?/?Gas; Supply?&?Trading; which all represent the core business and lastly the Coal?/?Nuclear segment.

Company Background

RWE traces its roots back to 1898 when Rheinisch-Westf ⬚lisches Elektrizit ⬚tswerk — or RWE for short — was established. In 1902 Hugo Stinnes an industrialist from M lheim acquired control of the company. He worked to build a large-scale efficient electricity supply.

HISTORY

Founded at the end of the 19th century RWE mirrored the industrialization of Germany in its growth. It was formed as Rheinisch-Westfalisches Elektrizitatswerk in 1898 by Erich Zweigert the mayor of Essen and Hugo Stinnes an industrialist from Mulheim to provide electricity to Essen and surrounding areas. The company began supplying power in 1900.

Stinnes persuaded other cities — Gelsenkirchen and Mulheim — to buy shares in RWE in 1905. In 1908 RWE and rival Vereinigte Elektrizitatswerk Westfalen (VEW) agreed to divide up the territories that each would supply.

Germany's coal shortages caused by WWI prompted RWE to expand its coal operations and it bought Rheinische Aktiengesellschaft f r Braunkohlenbergbau a coal producer in 1932. RWE also built a power line network completed in 1930 to connect populous northern Germany with the south. By 1939 as WWII began the company had plants throughout most of western Germany. However the war destroyed much of its infrastructure and RWE had to rebuild.

The company continued to rely on coal for most of its fuel needs in the 1950s but in 1961 RWE and Bayern Atomkraft sponsored the construction of a demonstration nuclear reactor the first of several such projects at Gundremmingen. The Gundremmingen plant was shut down in 1977 and to replace it RWE built two 1300-MW reactors that began operation in 1984.

RWE began to diversify and in 1988 it acquired Texaco's German petroleum and petrochemical unit which became RWE-DEA. By 1990 RWE's operations also included waste management and construction. RWE reorganized creating RWE Aktiengesellschaft as a holding company for group operations.

RWE-DEA acquired the US's Vista Chemical in 1991 and RWE's Rheinbraun mining unit bought a 50% stake in Consolidation Coal from DuPont. (The mining venture went public in 1999 as CONSOL Energy.) RWE led a consortium that acquired major stakes in three Hungarian power companies in 1995.

Hoping to play a role in Germany's telecommunications market RWE teamed with VEBA in 1997 to form the o.tel.o joint venture and RWE and VEBA gained control of large German mobile phone operator E-Plus. The nation's telecom market was deregulated in 1998 but Mannesmann and former monopoly Deutsche Telekom proved to be formidable competitors. In 1999 RWE and VEBA sold o.tel.o's fixed-line business (along with the o.tel.o brand name) and cable-TV unit Tele Columbus. The next year the companies sold their joint stake in E-Plus.

Faced with deregulating German electricity markets RWE Energie had begun restructuring as soon as the market opened up in 1998. It agreed to buy fellow German power company VEW in a $20 billion deal that closed in 2000. RWE also joined with insurance giant Allianz and France's Vivendi in a successful bid for a 49.9% stake in state-owned water distributor Berliner Wasserbetriebe (Vivendi later spurned an RWE offer to buy its energy businesses).

After taking advantage of deregulating markets in Germany RWE moved to pick up other European utilities: It acquired UK-based Thames Water (later renamed RWE Thames Water) in 2000 and bought a majority stake in Dutch gas supplier Intergas the next year. In 2002 the company issued an exchange offer to acquire UK electricity supplier Innogy (later renamed RWE npower) for a total of about $4.4 billion in cash and $3 billion in assumed debt. It also completed a $3.7 billion purchase of Czech Republic gas supplier Transgas.

In a move to further streamline operations RWE sold its 50% stake in refinery and service station subsidiary Shell & DEA Oil to Deutsche Shell and Shell Petroleum. To do battle in an increasingly competitive utility industry RWE is acquiring stakes in other European utilities. In 2003 RWE also acquired North American utility American Water Works which was combined with the US operations of RWE Thames Water for $4.6 billion in cash and $4 billion in assumed debt.

Recognizing that its international acquisitions of water utilities in the early 2000s had left it overextended RWE has been to selling its water assets in order to save cash and streamline its operations around its core power businesses. Overextended in 2006 the company sold its Thames Water unit to Kemble Water Limited a consortium led by Macquarie Bank's European Infrastructure Funds. It spun off its American Water unit in 2008.

The company saw its revenues drop in 2009 as the global recession hammered gas prices. However the same lower gas prices helped RWE to save costs enabling it to post an improved net income that year.

After being outmaneuvered by EDF in its plan to grow its Pan-European power footprint by acquiring British Energy RWE in 2009 acquired top Dutch power utility Essent for $10.7 billion. The deal boost its position as one of the top electricity and gas utilities in Europe.

Growing its energy sources in 2009 it also formed a joint venture with E.ON to develop 6000 MW of nuclear power capacity in the UK. In a move to reduce its dependency on the wholesale gas markets in 2009 RWE acquired 70% of the Breagh North Sea gas field for about $350 million.

The company announced CEO J rgen Gro mann who fought Germany's decision to phase out nuclear power stepped down in July 2012. Gro mann was replaced by Peter Terium the CEO of Essent. COO Rolf Martin Schmitz was named Deputy CEO.

EXECUTIVES

Chief Human Resource Officer and Labour Director, Zvezdana Seeger, $123,055 total compensation

Chairman of the Supervisory Board, Werner Brandt, $341,821 total compensation

Deputy Chairman of the Supervisory Board, Ralf Sikorski, $113,940 total compensation

Chairman, General Works Council, RWE Power AG, Harald Louis, $113,940 total compensation

Chief Executive Officer and Director, Markus Krebber, $911,524 total compensation

Chairman, Works Council of RWE AG,, Sandra Bossemeyer, $113,940 total compensation

Deputy Chairman, General Works Council, RWE Power AG, Michael Bochinsky, $113,940 total compensation

Auditors: PricewaterhouseCoopers GmbH

LOCATIONS

HQ: RWE AG
Altenessener Strasse 35, Essen D-45141
Phone: (49) 201 5179 0   **Fax:** (49) 201 5179 5005
Web: www.rwe.com

2017 Sales

	% of total
European Union	
Germany	62
UK	17
Other	19
Rest of Europe	1
Other	1
Total	**100**

PRODUCTS/OPERATIONS

2017 Sales by Segment

	% of total
innogy	88
Supply & Trading	7
European Power	2
Lignite & Nuclear	3
Other	
Total	**100**

COMPETITORS

ACCIONA SA
E.ON SE
EDP - ENERGIAS DE PORTUGAL S.A.
ENEL SPA
Fortum Oyj
INTERNATIONAL POWER LTD.
LUKOIL PAO
NATIONAL GRID PLC
ROYAL DUTCH SHELL plc
TOKYO ELECTRIC POWER COMPANY HOLDINGS INCORPORATED
UNITED UTILITIES GROUP PLC
Vattenfall AB

HISTORICAL FINANCIALS
Company Type: Public

Income Statement
FYE: December 31

	REVENUE ($ mil.)	NET INCOME ($ mil.)	NET PROFIT MARGIN	EMPLOYEES
12/19	14,736	9,541	64.7%	38,082
12/18	15,331	383	2.5%	58,441
12/17	50,867	2,775	5.5%	59,333
12/16	46,025	(6,029)	—	59,073
12/15	50,492	(185)	—	59,350
Annual Growth	**(26.5%)**	**—**	**—**	**(10.5%)**

2019 Year-End Financials
Debt ratio: 10.0%
Return on equity: 63.8%
Cash ($ mil.): 3,583
Current ratio: 1.43
Long-term debt ($ mil.): 4,405
No. of shares (mil.): 614
Dividends
  Yield: 1.8%
  Payout: 3.6%
Market value ($ mil.): 18,848

	STOCK PRICE ($) FY Close	P/E High/Low		PER SHARE ($) Earnings	Dividends	Book Value
12/19	30.66	2	2	15.52	0.56	30.95
12/18	21.89	48	32	0.62	1.30	19.25
12/17	20.29	9	5	3.70	1.80	16.03
12/16	12.36	—	—	(9.81)	0.00	6.78
12/15	12.63	—	—	(0.30)	0.79	12.86
Annual Growth	**24.8%**	—	—	—	**(8.2%)**	**24.6%**

Safran SA

Auditors: ERNST & YOUNG et Autres

LOCATIONS

HQ: Safran SA
2, boulevard du General Martial-Valin, Paris, Cedex 15 75724
Phone: (33) 1 40 60 80 80   **Fax:** (33) 1 40 60 81 02
Web: www.safran-group.com

HISTORICAL FINANCIALS
Company Type: Public

Income Statement
FYE: December 31

	REVENUE ($ mil.)	NET INCOME ($ mil.)	NET PROFIT MARGIN	EMPLOYEES
12/20	20,139	432	2.1%	78,900
12/19	29,697	2,747	9.3%	95,443
12/18	25,177	1,469	5.8%	92,639
12/17	21,697	5,742	26.5%	58,324
12/16	18,771	2,014	10.7%	66,490
Annual Growth	**1.8%**	**(32.0%)**	**—**	**4.4%**

2020 Year-End Financials
Debt ratio: 18.5%
Return on equity: 2.8%
Cash ($ mil.): 4,598
Current ratio: 0.96
Long-term debt ($ mil.): 4,263
No. of shares (mil.): 426
Dividends
  Yield: 0.0%
  Payout: 53.7%
Market value ($ mil.): 15,138

	STOCK PRICE ($) FY Close	P/E High/Low		PER SHARE ($) Earnings	Dividends	Book Value
12/20	35.46	55	20	0.98	0.53	35.50
12/19	38.70	7	5	6.32	0.51	32.71
12/18	29.89	12	8	3.37	0.47	31.52
12/17	25.75	2	2	13.75	0.25	30.23
12/16	17.97	4	3	4.84	0.39	16.58
Annual Growth	**18.5%**	—	—	**(32.9%)**	**8.2%**	**21.0%**

SAIC Motor Corp Ltd

SAIC Motor Corporation (SAIC Motor) is one of the largest automotive manufacturer listed on the A-Shares market in China. The company's subsidiary Shanghai Automotive Industry Corporation manufactures develops sells and invests on auto-

mobiles motorcycles and tractors. SAIC Motor's principal activities include research and development (R&D) and production and sale of spare parts (including engines transmissions powertrain chassis interior and exterior trim electronic appliances and intelligent products system). It is also engaged in auto service and trading business including logistics auto E-commerce mobility services energy-saving and recharging services; automobile-related finance insurance and investment businesses; overseas operations and international commerce; and trade business. Its operations include Shanghai Volkswagen SAIC-GM-Wuling SAIC-Iveco-Hongyan and Sunwin. It was founded in 1978 in Shanghai China.

Operations

SAIC Motor has two reportable segments: vehicles and parts (more than 95%) and financing (less than five percent). The reporting segments are determined based on the company's operating structure.

The vehicles and parts segment's products and services includes vehicles (about 75% of total sales) parts (around 20%) and trading and service which both account for some 5% of total sales. The company also offers loans and deposits to its customers.

Geographic Reach

SAIC Motor is based in Shanghai China. The country China also generates vast majority of its sales. The company's products are present in various countries including the UK the Netherlands Norway Hong Kong Thailand and Indonesia.

Sales and Marketing

SAIC Motor's major customers are from Automotive manufacturing industry which generates almost all of its sales. The company's advertising expenses were RMB 13.4 billion and RMB 13.5 billion in 2019 and 2018 respectively.

Financial Performance

The company's revenue increased 15% from RMB 730.6 billion in 2018 to RMB 843.3 billion 2019. The increase was due to the sales increase in all of its product segments.

Net profit attributable to shareholders of listed companies declined 29% from RMB 36 billion in 2018 to RMB 25.6 billion.

Cash at the end of 2019 was RMB 109.8 billion. Operating activities generated RMB 46.3 billion while investing activities used RMB 39.3 billion. Financing activities used another RMB 3.1 billion.

Strategy

The company will firmly grasp the major orientation of progress in science and technology the bigger picture of market evolution the general trend of changes in the industry make a deeper advancement of "new four modernizations?electrification intelligent networking sharing and internationalization" strategy insist in the philosophy of "innovation-leading a breakthrough at key points promotion with successful experiences in selected units and advancement in proper order" deeply layout and carry forward innovation chain construction while grasping market structured opportunity and promoting operational performance to spare no effort to seize vantage ground and commanding height and accelerate to push the business transformation and upgrading in the process of reconstitution of global automobile industry value chain striding forward globally competitive and influential comprehensive provider for traffic service and products.

To accelerate the innovation-driven development strategy SAIC Motor Corporation Limited made a non-public offering of shares on the domestic A-share market in 2017 and simultaneously implemented a core employee stock ownership plan.

Mergers and Acquisitions

In mid-2019 SAIC Motor's subsidiary HASCO acquired the remaining 50% equity of HASCO

Powertrain Components held by ZF China for RMB 65.2 million. HASCO Powertrain Components was a joint venture of HASCO and ZF China. HASCO includes HASCO Powertrain Components into the scope of consolidation of the consolidated financial statements since the acquisition.

In early 2019 HASCO's subsidiary HASCO Shanghai acquired 80% equity of Seeyao Electronics from Shanghai Changhui Industry Development Co. Ltd. for RMB 156.3 million. Seeyao Electronics and its subsidiary Shanghai Xinyu Electronic Technology Co. Ltd. became subsidiaries of HASCO Shanghai.

Also in early 2019 SAIC Motor's subsidiary Industry Sales acquired 50% equity of Anji Car Rental & Leasing from Avis Europe Group Holdings BV (Avis) for RMB 460.0 million. Anji Car Rental & Leasing was a joint venture of Industry Sales and Avis.

Company Background

SAIC Motor Corporation was established in 1984 as Shanghai Volkswagen Automotive a 50-50 joint venture with Volkswagen.

Auditors: Deloitte Touche Tohmatsu

LOCATIONS

HQ: SAIC Motor Corp Ltd
No. 489, Weihai Road, Jingan District, Shanghai 200041
Phone: (86) 21 22011138 **Fax:** (86) 21 22011199
Web: www.saicmotor.com

2015 Sales

	% of total
China	98
Others	2
Total	**100**

PRODUCTS/OPERATIONS

2015 Revenue by products

	% of total
Vehicles	75
Parts	19
Trading	1
Finance	1
Service and others	3
Total	**100**

2015 Revenue by Segment

	% of total
Vehicles and parts	99
Finance	1
Total	**100**

COMPETITORS

ADIENT PUBLIC LIMITED COMPANY
Crrc Corporation Limited
FIAT CHRYSLER AUTOMOBILES N.V.
MARUTI SUZUKI INDIA LIMITED
MERITOR INC.
NAVISTAR INTERNATIONAL CORPORATION
NTN CORPORATION
OSHKOSH CORPORATION
REV GROUP INC.
SKODA AUTO a.s.
TOYOTA INDUSTRIES CORPORATION
VOLKSWAGEN AG
VOXX INTERNATIONAL CORPORATION
Weichai Power Co. Ltd

HISTORICAL FINANCIALS

Company Type: Public

Income Statement

FYE: December 31

	REVENUE ($ mil.)	NET INCOME ($ mil.)	NET PROFIT MARGIN	EMPLOYEES
12/20	113,471	3,123	2.8%	0
12/19	121,198	3,679	3.0%	0
12/18	131,165	5,235	4.0%	0
12/17	133,791	5,287	4.0%	0
12/16	108,929	4,609	4.2%	0
Annual Growth	**1.0%**	**(9.3%)**		

2020 Year-End Financials

Debt ratio: 1.1%
Return on equity: 7.9%
Cash ($ mil.): 21,798
Current ratio: 1.11
Long-term debt ($ mil.): 7,201

No. of shares (mil.): —
Dividends
  Yield: —
  Payout: —
Market value ($ mil.): —

Samba Financial Group

The sound of money is music to Samba Financial Group's ears. The bank offers retail banking corporate banking investment banking asset management credit cards loans and related services through about 70 branches (25 are ladies only) and some 500 ATMs across Saudi Arabia and branches in London Dubai and Qatar. In Pakistan Samba Financial is the majority owner of Samba Bank Limited with about 30 branches. Its financial products are also Shariah-compliant. In 2014 the company launched a new SambaMobile app for smart phones and tablets. Samba Financial was set up in 1980 when it took over the two Saudi branches owned by Citibank; Citibank sold the last of its stake in the company in 2004.

Auditors: Ernst & Young & Co.

LOCATIONS

HQ: Samba Financial Group
King Abdul Aziz Road, P.O. Box 833, Riyadh 11421
Phone: (966) 1 477 4770 **Fax:** (966) 1 477 4770
Web: www.samba.com.sa

COMPETITORS

ARAB BANK PLC
AUSTRALIA AND NEW ZEALAND BANKING GROUP LIMITED
UNITED OVERSEAS BANK LIMITED

HISTORICAL FINANCIALS

Company Type: Public

Income Statement

FYE: December 31

	ASSETS ($ mil.)	NET INCOME ($ mil.)	INCOME AS % OF ASSETS	EMPLOYEES
12/19	68,161	1,062	1.6%	3,614
12/18	61,316	1,472	2.4%	3,497
12/17	60,696	1,338	2.2%	3,530
12/16	61,721	1,333	2.2%	3,560
12/15	62,659	1,388	2.2%	3,723
Annual Growth	**2.1%**	**(6.5%)**	**—**	**(0.7%)**

2019 Year-End Financials

Return on assets: 1.6%
Return on equity: 9.1%
Long-term debt ($ mil.): —
No. of shares (mil.): 2,000
Sales ($ mil): 2,896

Dividends
  Yield: —
  Payout: 71.3%
Market value ($ mil.): —

Samsung C&T Corp (New)

Auditors: Samil PricewaterhouseCoopers

LOCATIONS

HQ: Samsung C&T Corp (New)
123, Olympic-ro 35-gil, Songpa-gu, Seoul 05510
Phone: (82) 2 759 0290
Web: www.samsungcnt.com

HISTORICAL FINANCIALS

Company Type: Public

Income Statement

FYE: December 31

	REVENUE ($ mil.)	NET INCOME ($ mil.)	NET PROFIT MARGIN	EMPLOYEES
12/19	26,642	909	3.4%	0
12/18	27,945	1,536	5.5%	9,374
12/17	27,463	600	2.2%	9,422
12/16	23,392	89	0.4%	10,252
12/15	11,342	2,334	20.6%	12,083
Annual Growth	**23.8%**	**(21.0%)**		**—**

2019 Year-End Financials

Debt ratio: 0.0%
Return on equity: 4.7%
Cash ($ mil.): 2,342
Current ratio: 1.08
Long-term debt ($ mil.): 610

No. of shares (mil.): 163
Dividends
  Yield: —
  Payout: —
Market value ($ mil.): —

Samsung Electronics Co Ltd

Auditors: Deloitte Anjin LLC

LOCATIONS

HQ: Samsung Electronics Co Ltd
129, Samsung-ro, Yeongtong-gu, Suwon-si, Gyeonggi-do 16677
Phone: (82) 31 200 1114 **Fax:** (82) 31 200 7538
Web: www.sec.co.kr

HISTORICAL FINANCIALS

Company Type: Public

Income Statement

FYE: December 31

	REVENUE ($ mil.)	NET INCOME ($ mil.)	NET PROFIT MARGIN	EMPLOYEES
12/20	217,587	23,973	11.0%	0
12/19	199,547	18,625	9.3%	0
12/18	218,650	39,367	18.0%	0
12/17	224,719	38,780	17.3%	99,784
12/16	168,031	18,658	11.1%	93,200
Annual Growth	**6.7%**	**6.5%**	**—**	**—**

2020 Year-End Financials

Debt ratio: 0.0%
Return on equity: 9.9%
Cash ($ mil.): 26,997
Current ratio: 2.62
Long-term debt ($ mil.): 871

No. of shares (mil.): —
Dividends
  Yield: —
  Payout: 925.5%
Market value ($ mil.): —

San Miguel Corp

San Miguel Corporation (SMC) is one of the largest and most diversified conglomerates in the Philippines. It operates more than 100 facilities in Southeast Asia Australia New Zealand and China. The company's flagship unit is San Miguel Brewery (beer and liquor) while its Pure Food unit manufactures a variety of staples including meats dairy products and coffee. SMC also has packaging operations. It owns a major stake in the country's biggest oil refiner Petron. SMC has a portfolio of companies that is interwoven into the economic fabric of the Philippines benefiting from as well as contributing to the development and economic progress of the nation.

Operations

SMC has five operating segments: Fuel and Oil accounts for over 35% of total sales Food & Beverage more than 35% Energy representing some 15% Packaging unit drove almost 5% and Infrastructure less than 5%.

The Fuel and Oil segment is engaged in refining crude oil and marketing and distribution of refined petroleum products.

The food and beverage segment is engaged in the processing and marketing of branded value-added refrigerated processed meats and canned meat products manufacturing and marketing of butter margarine cheese milk ice cream jelly-based snacks and desserts specialty oils salad aids snacks and condiments marketing of flour mixes and the importation and marketing of coffee and coffee-related products; the production and sale of feeds;) the poultry and livestock farming processing and selling of poultry and fresh meats; and the milling production and marketing of flour and bakery ingredients grain terminal handling food services franchising and international operations.

The Energy segment sells retails and distributes power through power supply agreements (PSA) retail supply contracts (RSC) concession agreement and other power-related service agreements either directly to customers including Manila Electric Company (Meralco) other generators distribution utilities (DUs) electric cooperatives and industrial customers or through the Philippine Wholesale Electricity Spot Market (WESM).

The Packaging segment is involved in the production and marketing of packaging products including among others glass containers glass molds polyethylene terephthalate (PET) bottles and preforms PET recycling plastic closures corrugated cartons woven polypropylene kraft sacks and paperboard pallets flexible packaging plastic crates plastic floorings plastic films plastic trays plastic pails and tubs metal closures and two-piece aluminum cans woven products industrial laminates and radiant barriers.

The Infrastructure segment has investments in companies which hold long-term concessions in the infrastructure sector in the Philippines. It is engaged in the management and operation as well as construction and development of various infrastructure projects such as major toll roads airports railways bulk water and ports.

Overall the company generates almost all of its sales from its goods.

Geographic Reach

SMC is headquartered in the Philippines.

SMC's manufacturing operations extend beyond the Philippines to Hong Kong China Indonesia Vietnam Thailand and Malaysia. Its products are exported to major markets around the world.

Sales and Marketing

SMC's packaging segment serves manufacturers of food pharmaceutical chemical beverages and personal care customers.

Financial Performance

The company's revenue for fiscal 2020 decreased to PHP 725.8 billion compared with PHP 1.0 trillion in the prior year.

Net income for fiscal 2020 decreased to PHP 21.9 billion compared with PHP 48.6 billion in the prior year.

Cash held by the company at the end of fiscal 2020 increased to PHP 347.2 billion. Cash provided by operations and financing activities were PHP 50.9 billion and PHP 102.0 billion respectively. Cash used for investing activities was PHP 82.6 billion mainly for additions to property plant and equipment.

Strategy

The company has embarked on a diversification strategy and has expanded into new businesses through a number of acquisitions and investments resulting in the recognition of a significant amount of goodwill. The goodwill of the acquired businesses are reviewed annually to evaluate whether events or changes in circumstances affect the recoverability of the company's investments.

HISTORY

Don Enrique Barretto y de Ycaza opened La Fabrica de Cerveza de San Miguel a brewery in Manila in 1890. By 1900 the European-styled beers of San Miguel were outselling imported brands five to one. The company became a corporation in 1913. By WWI the brewery was selling beer in Hong Kong Shanghai and Guam.

Andres Soriano y Roxas joined San Miguel in 1918 and in the 1920s established the Royal Soft Drinks Plant (1922) the Magnolia Ice Cream Plant (1925) and the first non-US national Coca-Cola bottling and distribution franchise (1927). After WWII the company added additional facilities and factories as it modernized and expanded.

In the 1960s the firm changed its name to San Miguel Corporation (SMC). After the death of Andres in 1964 his son Andres Soriano Jr. became president. He decentralized operations into product segments. SMC continued to diversify in the 1970s.

A family feud erupted in 1983 when members of the controlling Soriano and Zobel families engaged in a proxy battle. Realizing he couldn't win the proxy fight Enrique Zobel sold all of his shares (about 20% of SMC) to Eduardo Cojuangco a Ferdinand Marcos ally and president of United Coconut Planters Bank. Upon Soriano's death in 1984 Cojuangco became chairman.

Cojuangco's estranged cousin Corazon Aquino won the 1986 national election and her government claimed assets associated with Marcos and his followers including Cojuangco's share of SMC. Cojuangco left the country with Marcos and Andres Soriano III became CEO. Cojuangco returned to the Philippines in 1989 to reclaim his share of the company. In mid-1998 immediately following Cojuangco-backed Joseph Estrada's election as president of the Philippines Andres Soriano III stepped down and Cojuangco returned to SMC's helm.

SMC sold Coca-Cola Bottlers Philippines to Sydney-based Coca-Cola Amatil (CCA) in 1995 in exchange for a 25% stake in CCA. Four years later SMC flirted with plans to sell its interest in CCA and then went on a buying binge. SMC and a company it majority owns La Tondeña Distillers jointly bought Filipino juice maker Sugarland. SMC then bought Australian brewer J. Boag & Son in 2000.

Estrada announced the government's plan to sell a 27% stake in SMC but those plans were altered dramatically after Estrada's ouster in early 2001. His successor President Gloria Arroyo said the government would seize 47% of the company's shares controlled by United Coconut Planters Bank (27%) and Cojuangco (20%).

Meanwhile company expansion continued. San Miguel agreed to buy the Philippines' largest processed-meat maker Pure Foods. The company bought 65% of bottler Coca-Coca Philippines from CCA in July giving up its stake in CCA as part of the deal. In August 2001 SMC then acquired 83% of rival RFM's Cosmos Bottling the Philippines' #2 soft drink company further consolidating its domestic beverage dominance. In September the company transferred its 49% stake in Sugarland to La Tondeña Distillers which then became the sole owner of the juice maker.

In 2002 Japanese brewer Kirin paid $530 million for 15% of San Miguel. Following an announced expansion plan into Asia San Miguel purchased a Thailand industrial complex for $20 million in September 2003 and Thai Amarit Brewery in April 2004. SMC snapped up a majority stake in Singapore-based ice-cream producer King's Creameries the following year and acquired control of Australia's National Foods for $1.45 billion.

In 2007 it sold its 65% stake in Coca-Cola Bottlers Philippines to The Coca-Cola Company which had previously owned 35% of the Philippine bottler. The deal was worth $590 million. SMC also sold National Foods a leading supplier of milk cheese and other dairy products in Australia to Kirin Holdings for about $2.6 billion in 2007.

EXECUTIVES

President, Chief Executive Officer, Ramon Ang
Chief Financial Officer, Treasurer, Ferdinand Constantino
Director, Estelito Mendoza
Director, Inigo Zobel
Director, Menardo Jimenez
Director, Leo Alvez
Director, Alexander Poblador
Senior Vice President, General Counsel, Corporate Secretary, Compliance Officer, Virgilio Jacinto
Independent Director, Teresita Leonardo-De Castro
Director, John Paul Ang
Director, Joselito Campos
Senior Vice President, Head of Treasury, Joseph Anthony Pineda
Senior Vice President, Senior Executive Assistant to the Office of the President and Chief Operating Officer, Director, Aurora Calderon
Independent Director, Reynato Puno
Independent Director, Margarito Teves
Director, Thomas Tan
Senior Vice President – Head of SMC Infrastructure Business, Lorenzo Formoso
Director, Jose de Venecia
Auditors: R.G. Manabat & Co.

LOCATIONS

HQ: San Miguel Corp
No. 40 San Miguel Avenue, Mandaluyong City, Metro Manila 1550
Phone: (63) 2 632 3000   **Fax:** (63) 2 632 3099
Web: www.sanmiguel.com.ph

PRODUCTS/OPERATIONS

2016 Sales

	% of total
Fuel and Oil	48
Beverage	16
Food	15
Energy	11
Packaging	4
Infrastructure	3
Others	3
Total	**100**

COMPETITORS

ANHEUSER-BUSCH
 COMPANIES LLC
ASSOCIATED BRITISH
 FOODS PLC
COCA-COLA AMATIL PTY
 LTD
CRAFT BREW ALLIANCE
 INC.
FOSTER'S GROUP PTY LTD
FULLER SMITH & TURNER
 PLC

GENERAL MILLS INC.
Grupo Bimbo S.A.B. de
 C.V.
MOLSON COORS BEVERAGE
 COMPANY USA LLC
THE BOSTON BEER
 COMPANY INC
THE COCA-COLA COMPANY

HISTORICAL FINANCIALS

Company Type: Public

Income Statement   FYE: December 31

	REVENUE ($ mil.)	NET INCOME ($ mil.)	NET PROFIT MARGIN	EMPLOYEES
12/19	20,153	421	2.1%	47,730
12/18	19,515	439	2.3%	28,598
12/17	16,583	566	3.4%	24,539
12/16	13,841	591	4.3%	22,396
12/15	14,384	265	1.8%	18,586
Annual Growth	8.8%	12.2%	—	26.6%

2019 Year-End Financials

Debt ratio: 1.0%
Return on equity: 6.3%
Cash ($ mil.): 5,657
Current ratio: 1.46
Long-term debt ($ mil.): 14,935

No. of shares (mil.): —
Dividends
 Yield: —
 Payout: —
 Market value ($ mil.): —

San-In Godo Bank, Ltd. (The) (Japan)

The San-in Godo Bank provides banking services in the Tottori and Shimane prefectures in western Japan. The bank also serves the adjacent Sanyo and Hyogo regions. It does business from more than 100 branches and 13 subsidiary companies. San-in Godo Bank operates overseas from offices in Dalian and Shanghai China and New York City. The bank was established in 1941.

EXECUTIVES

Chairman of the Board, Representative Director, Fumio Ishimaru
Independent Director, Tomoaki Seko
Director, Mamiko Nakamura
Independent Director, Yasuhiro Goto
Independent Director, Hideto Tago
President, Executive Officer, Representative Director, Toru Yamazaki
Director, Koji Miyauchi
Managing Executive Officer, Director of Business Planning, Director, Shuichi Ida
Managing Executive Officer, Director, Yuji Funo
Independent Director, Tamaki Adachi
Independent Director, Shoichi Imaoka
Independent Director, Yasuyuki Kuratsu
Auditors: Ernst & Young ShinNihon LLC

LOCATIONS

HQ: San-In Godo Bank, Ltd. (The) (Japan)
 10 Uomachi, Matsue, Shimane 690-8686
Phone: (81) 852 55 1000
Web: www.gogin.co.jp

COMPETITORS

BANK OF KYOTOLTD. THE
MUSASHINO BANK LTD.
 THE

HISTORICAL FINANCIALS

Company Type: Public

Income Statement   FYE: March 31

	ASSETS ($ mil.)	NET INCOME ($ mil.)	INCOME AS % OF ASSETS	EMPLOYEES
03/21	57,532	87	0.2%	3,217
03/20	52,431	96	0.2%	3,337
03/19	50,563	119	0.2%	3,366
03/18	52,253	128	0.2%	3,263
03/17	48,400	119	0.2%	3,217
Annual Growth	4.4%	(7.6%)	—	0.0%

2021 Year-End Financials

Return on assets: 0.1%
Return on equity: 2.6%
Long-term debt ($ mil.): —
No. of shares (mil.): 156
Sales ($ mil): 805

Dividends
 Yield: —
 Payout: 29.0%
 Market value ($ mil.): —

Sanofi

Auditors: ERNST & YOUNG et Autres

LOCATIONS

HQ: Sanofi
 54, rue La Boetie, Paris 75008
Phone: (33) 1 53 77 40 00   **Fax:** (33) 1 53 77 43 03
Web: www.sanofi.com

HISTORICAL FINANCIALS

Company Type: Public

Income Statement   FYE: December 31

	REVENUE ($ mil.)	NET INCOME ($ mil.)	NET PROFIT MARGIN	EMPLOYEES
12/20	45,862	15,112	33.0%	99,412
12/19	42,250	3,150	7.5%	100,409
12/18	40,857	4,931	12.1%	104,226
12/17	43,399	10,110	23.3%	106,566
12/16	36,647	4,972	13.6%	106,859
Annual Growth	5.8%	32.0%	—	(1.8%)

2020 Year-End Financials

Debt ratio: 24.1%
Return on equity: 20.1%
Cash ($ mil.): 17,077
Current ratio: 1.75
Long-term debt ($ mil.): 24,232

No. of shares (mil.): 1,258
Dividends
 Yield: 3.5%
 Payout: 14.1%
 Market value ($ mil.): 61,173

	STOCK PRICE ($) FY Close	P/E High/Low		PER SHARE ($) Earnings	Dividends	Book Value
12/20	48.59	6	4	11.99	1.70	61.42
12/19	50.20	23	18	2.50	1.72	52.77
12/18	43.41	13	11	3.93	1.79	54.14
12/17	43.00	8	6	7.98	5.36	55.54
12/16	40.44	11	10	3.83	4.63	47.78
Annual Growth	4.7%	—	—	33.0%	(22.2%)	6.5%

Sany Heavy Industry Co Ltd

Sany Heavy Industry (Sany) makes construction machinery to tame three of the earth's elements — earth wind and water. One of the world's top heavy equipment makers sells concrete pump and mixer trucks cranes excavators graders mining drill rigs and vehicles pile drivers road pavers steamrollers port machinery such as container lifts and even makes wind turbines for on- and offshore use. Sany (a unit of the SANY Group) operates about two dozen overseas subsidiaries. It has five manufacturing plants in China and four more in Brazil Germany India and the US.

Operations

Sany is one of the leading brands of concrete pumps cranes and land drilling machines in China. After years of development the company now has the largest producing capacity of concrete pumps in China and has established itself as one of the biggest manufacturers of concrete pumps in the world.

Sany is involved in all aspects of engineering machinery manufacturing with products as diversified as concrete machinery excavator crawler cranes truck cranes pile-driving machinery and road construction machinery.

Thecompany does not make all of the parts for its products. It uses Isuzu trucks as a base for its pumping rigs and engines and other components for its hydraulic shovels from Kawasaki Heavy Industries. About 80% of its procured parts come from Japan.

Geographic Reach

The company has six major industrial bases in China. Internationally it has a manufacturing base in India Germany US Brazil. The sells to more than 100 countries and regions.

Strategy

In response to growing exploitation of China's shale gas reserves in 2014 Sany launched a new field a set of petroleum equipment. During the 14th China International Petroleum & Petrochemical Technology and Equipment Exhibition Sany displayed a set of petroleum equipment including a Model 2500 fracturing truck a Model 2000 fracturing truck a 150-barrel fracturing blender and a measuring truck.

That year the company signed a $178.8 million sales contract with Venezuela's CORPOVEXS. to provide concrete machinery excavating machinery cranes and parts and components.

Company Background

The company's globalization efforts are relatively new. Sany America's US headquarters opened in 2011 in Peachtree City a suburb about 30 miles southwest of Atlanta. The company's 420000-sq.-ft. $60 million manufacturing plant employs 200 people and houses sales service assembly testing distribution and R&D operations. Workers there will build five concrete pump crane models. In order to grow the little-known brand in the US Sany America plans to make a name for itself at conventions participate in the government procurement bidding process and sponsor charity events.

Sany Brasil's $200 million plant in Sao Paulo opened in 2013. Its first operational plant in San Jose which opened in 2010 can assemble 700 excavators a year. Its plant in India also opened in 2010. In addition the company plans to build plants in Indonesia and Russia.

Sany was established in 1994 by the SANY Group.

EXECUTIVES

Senior Vice President, Xiangzhang Zhao
Senior Vice President, Ru'an Xiang
Director, Xiuguo Tang
Chairman of the Board, Wengen Liang
Director, Jianlong Huang
President, Vice Chairman of the Board, Wenbo Xiang
Senior Vice President, Qinghua Dai
Senior Vice President, Hongfu Yu
Senior Vice President, Director, Xiaogang Yi
Secretary of the Board, Shenglin Cai

LOCATIONS

HQ: Sany Heavy Industry Co Ltd
5th Floor, Block 6, No. 8 Beiqing Road, Changping District, Changsha, Hunan Province 102206
Phone: (86) 10 60738888   **Fax:** (86) 10 60738868
Web: www.sanyhi.com

COMPETITORS

AMERON INTERNATIONAL CORPORATION
BERGSTROM INC.
CATERPILLAR INC.
CLARK EQUIPMENT COMPANY
HYCO INTERNATIONAL INC.
Hyundai Doosan Infracore Co. Ltd.
KUBOTA CORPORATION
SUMITOMO HEAVY INDUSTRIES LTD.
Sichuan Tengzhong Heavy Industrial Machinery Co. Ltd.

HISTORICAL FINANCIALS

Company Type: Public

Income Statement   FYE: December 31

	REVENUE ($ mil.)	NET INCOME ($ mil.)	NET PROFIT MARGIN	EMPLOYEES
12/20	15,298	2,359	15.4%	0
12/19	10,874	1,610	14.8%	0
12/18	8,115	889	11.0%	0
12/17	5,890	321	5.5%	0
12/16	3,352	29	0.9%	0
Annual Growth	**46.2%**	**199.6%**	—	—

2020 Year-End Financials

Debt ratio: 1.5%
Return on equity: 30.4%
Cash ($ mil.): 1,925
Current ratio: 1.47
Long-term debt ($ mil.): 692

No. of shares (mil.): —
Dividends
Yield: —
Payout: —
Market value ($ mil.): —

SAP SE

SAP SE's enterprise resource planning software integrates back-office functions such as analytics accounting distribution and human resources and comes in on-premises and cloud-linked forms. SAP is going all-in on cloud computing and software-as-a-service with its flagship application suite S/4HANA. Besides enterprise software SAP Concur provides expenses management and SAP Fieldglasms provides external workforce management. The company's cloud portfolios serves more than 25 industries. Germany is the largest single market accounts for about 30% of total revenue.

Operations

SAP's largest software licenses and support generates some 60% of sales and comprises SAP's legacy on-premise software and support services.

SAP's Cloud subscriptions and support offerings which are growing as a proportion of the whole include S/4HANA and bring in roughly 30% of sales. Miscellaneous other services account for more than 15% of sales.

Broadly speaking SAP's products provide functionality such as analytics supply chain management financial management and customer relationship management among other things. The products are scaled and tailored to fit companies of varying size and in a diversity of industries.

SAP Concur is a leading cloud-based expenses management platform SAP Fieldglass helps companies manage contingent workforces and SAP Ariba is a B2B supply chain management platform that connects vendors and suppliers.

Geographic Reach

Headquartered in Walldorf Germany SAP caters to the EMEA region (Europe Middle East and Africa) which is SAP's biggest region about 45% of sales of which Germany represents about 30%. The US accounts more than 40% of sales and the Asia/Pacific region contributes roughly 15% of sales.

Sales and Marketing

Most of SAP's sales are generated by the employees within the organization although it also sells through partners.

Financial Performance

Note: Growth rates may differ after conversion to US Dollars.

SAP's performance for the span of five years continues to grow year by year although fluctuating between 2019 and 2020 with the slightly decreased 2020 performance from 2019.

Total revenue decreased from ?27.6 billion in 2019 to ?27.3 billion in 2020 representing a decrease of ?215 million or 1%.

The company's net income in 2020 increased by ?1.9 billion to ?5.3 billion as compared to the previous year's net income of ?3.3 billion.

SAP's cash on hand in 2020 was about the same with the previous year ending the year at ?5.3 billion as well. The company's operations generated ?7.1 billion. The company's financing activities and investing activities used ?4.0 billion and ?3.0 billion respectively. Main cash uses were for dividends paid purchase of treasury shares and purchase of intangible assets and property plant and equipment.

Strategy

SAP's strategy is to be the Experience Company powered by the Intelligent Enterprise. The company's vision for the intelligent enterprise an event-driven real-time business and technology that includes machine learning robotic process automation instead of blockchain of the Internet of Things and analytics. The company's "Intelligent Enterprise" focuses on bringing together cross-company business processes enable companies to quickly understand and improve businesses processes at scale and bringing experience data into an intelligent enterprise among other things. Further the company also focuses on its intelligent suite industry cloud sustainability management and business technology platform.

Mergers and Acquisitions

SAP bought Emarsys for about ?0.6 billion in 2020. Emarsys is a leading omnichannel customer engagement platform provider. The acquisition of Emarsys will enable the company to change how commerce is managed digitally through delivering hyperpersonalized omnichannel engagements in real time.

Company Background

The company was founded in 1972 by former IBM employees namely Dietmar Hopp Hasso Plattner Hans-Werner Hector Klaus Tchira und Claus Wellenreuther. Since then the company have continued to expand their portfolio through various

acquisitions. The company continues to grow through the SAP HANA which enables customers in-memory computing.

HISTORY

Former IBM software engineers Hasso Plattner Hans-Werner Hector Dietmar Hopp Claus Wellenreuther and Klaus Tschira started SAP in 1972 when the project they were working on for IBM was moved to another unit.

While rival software firms made many products to automate the various parts of a company's operations these engineers decided to make a single system that would tie a corporation together. In 1973 they launched an instantaneous accounting transaction-processing program called R/1. By 1979 they had adapted the program to create R/2 mainframe software that linked external databases and communication systems.

The company went public in 1988. That year Plattner began a project to create software for the computer network market. In 1992 as sales of its R/2 mainframe software lagged SAP introduced its R/3 software which would later become its flagship SAP ERP.

EXECUTIVES

Chief Marketing and Solutions Officer and Director, Julia White
Customer Success and Director, Scott Russell
Chief Executive Officer, Chief Operating Officer and Director, Christian Klein, $1,253,346 total compensation
Chief Technology Officer and Director, Juergen Mueller, $797,583 total compensation
Chief Financial Officer and Director, Luka Mucic, $797,583 total compensation
Deputy Chairman of the Supervisory Board, Margret Klein-Magar, $250,669 total compensation
SAP Product Engineering and Director, Thomas Saueressig, $797,583 total compensation
Chief People and Operating Officer and Labor Relations Director, Sabine Bendiek
Chairman of the Supervisory Board, Hasso Plattner, $313,336 total compensation
Auditors: KPMG AG Wirtschaftsprüfungsgesellschaft

LOCATIONS

HQ: SAP SE
Dietmar-Hopp-Allee 16, Walldorf 69190
Phone: (49) 0 6227 7 47474   **Fax:** (49) 0 6227 7 57575
Web: www.sap.com

2018 Sales

	% of total
Europe Middle East & Africa	
Germany	15
Other countries	30
Americas	39
Asia/Pacific	16
Total	**100**

PRODUCTS/OPERATIONS

2018 Sales

	% of total
Software & Support	
Support	44
Licenses	19
Cloud Subscription & Support	20
Services	17
Total	**100**

Selected Customers

Aigo
City of Cape Town South Africa
Danone

Beaumont Health System
McLaren Group

Selected Software
SAP Business All-in-One
SAP Business ByDesign
SAP Business One
SAP Business Suite
SAP ERP
SAP HANA
SAP NetWeaver

Selected Services
Application hosting
Business consulting
Custom development
Financing
Implementation
Maintenance
Training

Selected AcquisitionsConcur (2014) Travel and expense management software for companiesHybris (2014) Real-time customer engagement and commerce platformSeeWhy (2014) Cloud-based behavioral target marketing softwareTicket-Web (2013) Ticketing software and

Right Hemisphere (2012; enterprise visualization)
TechniData (2010; environmental health and safety)
Sybase (2010 business intelligence and database management)
Clear Standards (2009 environmental)
Highdeal (2009 billing)
Visiprise (2008 manufacturing process management)
Business Objects (2008 business intelligence)
OutlookSoft (2007 business performance management)
Pilot Software (2007 business performance management)

COMPETITORS
ALTERYX INC.
ASPEN TECHNOLOGY INC.
COGNIZANT TECHNOLOGY SOLUTIONS CORPORATION
CONCURRENT TECHNOLOGIES PLC
CRAY INC.
D4T4 SOLUTIONS PLC
DELL TECHNOLOGIES INC.
Diebold Nixdorf AG
HP INC.
INTERNATIONAL BUSINESS MACHINES CORPORATION
MICROSTRATEGY INCORPORATED
OMNICELL INC.
ORACLE CORPORATION
VERSANT CORPORATION
ZYTRONIC PLC

HISTORICAL FINANCIALS
Company Type: Public

Income Statement				FYE: December 31
	REVENUE ($ mil.)	NET INCOME ($ mil.)	NET PROFIT MARGIN	EMPLOYEES
12/20	33,551	6,314	18.8%	102,430
12/19	30,935	3,728	12.1%	100,330
12/18	28,295	4,675	16.5%	96,498
12/17	28,123	4,816	17.1%	88,543
12/16	23,294	3,849	16.5%	84,183
Annual Growth	9.6%	13.2%	—	5.0%

2020 Year-End Financials
Debt ratio: 33.4%
Return on equity: 16.9%
Cash ($ mil.): 6,518
Current ratio: 1.17
Long-term debt ($ mil.): 16,697
No. of shares (mil.): 1,179
Dividends
Yield: 0.9%
Payout: 23.3%
Market value ($ mil.): 153,805

	STOCK PRICE ($) FY Close	P/E High/Low	PER SHARE ($) Earnings	Dividends	Book Value
12/20	130.39	40 25	5.34	1.25	30.92
12/19	133.99	51 34	3.12	1.20	28.10
12/18	99.55	36 28	3.92	1.19	27.66
12/17	112.36	36 30	4.02	1.08	25.62
12/16	86.43	29 23	3.21	0.86	23.23
Annual Growth	10.8%	— —	13.6%	9.6%	7.4%

Sasol Ltd.

Sasol is a global chemicals and energy company that makes all manner of petrochemicals liquid and gaseous fuels (gasoline diesel jet fuel fuel alcohol and fuel oils) synthetic fuels and lubricants. The company also operates coal mines in South Africa and uses the coal as feedstock for its synthetic fuels and chemicals plants. Although one of the world's leaders in the development of coal gasification technology Sasol uses petroleum as a feedstock in some of its chemical products which include polymers and solvents. Most of the company's operations are based in South Africa but it also operates in numerous other countries throughout the world.

Operations
Sasol comprises two distinct market-focused businesses namely: Chemicals and Energy.

The Chemicals business is geared to grow by meeting evolving consumer needs including the demands of a growing and urbanizing middle class. It focuses its activities on specialty chemicals where it has differentiated capabilities and strong market positions that can be expanded over time. This business boasts a broad range of integrated alcohols and surfactants specialty alumina products which are strongly backed by a track record of collaborative innovation with customers.

The Energy business will position to be responsive to global trends by providing new energy and mobility solutions pursuing greenhouse gas emission reductions by developing and growing gas and renewables in Southern Africa and increase cash generation.

Base Chemicals produces polymers fertilizers and explosives phenolics methanol and some other products. Performance Solutions' products include Fisher Tropsch-based and paraffin wax solvents and comonomers.

Most of the company's revenue comes from the sales of products.

Geographic Reach
Headquartered in South Africa the company has presence in more than 30 countries.

Sales and Marketing
Through the company's operating business units Sasol makes use of direct sales models long-term marketing gas sales agreements and short-term crude oil sale and purchase agreements. Its marketing channels is divided into the main areas: liquid fuel sales to licensed wholesalers and liquid fuels sales to retailers and end-users and liquid fuels overland exports into other parts of Southern Africa. In its Chemical segment the company's products are sold to customers worldwide with a significant part under annual and multi-year contracts. For Base Chemicals polyethylene is produced and marketed on behalf of Sasol by its joint venture partner LyondellBasell. MEG is marketed and distributed on behalf of Sasol by another third

party while Phenolics are largely exported to international markets.

Financial Performance
Total turnover decreased by 2% from R12.7 billion in 2019 to R12.4 billion in 2020 due to subdued economic activity exacerbated by the unprecedented drop in demand because of COVID-19 lockdowns.

Earnings for fiscal 2020 was R9 billion compared from the prior year with a loss of $91.8 billion.

Cash provided by operations and investing activities were R34 billion and R25.1 billion respectively. Cash used for financing activities was R58.3 billion.

Strategy
In line with its strategic objectives Sasol divested its interest in the Gabon oil producing asset during February 2021 and successfully completed the divestment of its interest in the Canadian shale gas assets on 29 July 2021.

Company Background
The company through Sasol Synfuels International launched its first GTL plant with Qatar Petroleum in Qatar in 2007 and is constructing another in Nigeria. Although Sasol submitted a project application report in late 2009 for a CTL plant in China it is still waiting for approval from the Chinese government. The company began a feasibility study in 2011 for a GTL plant near Lake Charles Louisiana which would be larger than its plant in Qatar and would produce diesel and naphtha. Sasol and Talisman Energy also began a feasibility study in 2011 for a GTL plant in western Canada. That year Sasol agreed to develop a GTL project in Uzbekistan along with partners Uzbekneflegaz and PETRONAS.

In 2010 Sasol's fertilizer unit agreed to sell five blending plants and end ammonia imports in a deal struck with South Africa's Competition Commission to help cut fertilizer prices in South Africa. The company said it would dispose of its bulk blending and liquid fertilizer blending plants in Bellville Durban Endicott Kimberley and Potchefstroom by August 2011. The unit will continue producing limestone ammonium nitrate ammonium sulfate and a range of ammonium nitrate-and ammonium sulfate-based liquid and granular NPK fertilizer blends.

The company expanded its access to natural gas assets in Canada buying a 50% stake in Talisman Energy's Farrell Creek shale assets for more than C$1 billion in 2011. As part of the deal the two companies began the feasibility study to look into the viability of building a plant in western Canada to convert natural gas to liquid fuels using Sasol's proprietary technology. Sasol later completed a second C$1 billion deal with Talisman Energy in which it acquired 50% of the Cypress A shale gas asset in the Montney basin in British Columbia.

Also in 2011 a fuel sector strike in South Africa threatened the output of Sasol's basic chemicals production with unions demanding more pay and a 40-hour workweek. Although the company's rate of chemicals output was reduced at its Secunda plant that year Sasol experienced a 27% jump in earnings in 2011 over the previous year. Cost savings and higher global commodity prices helped it achieve higher margins especially in its chemicals business. Its Sasol Polymers unit's operating profit increased by 65% over the prior year.

Sasol was founded in 1979.

EXECUTIVES
Executive Vice President - Energy Operations,
Bernard Klingenberg, $391,944 total compensation

Non-Executive Independent Director, Katherine Harper

Executive Vice President - Technology and Sustainability, H C Brand, $272,273 total compensation

Group Company Secretary, Michelle Du Toit

Executive Director, Vuyo Kahla, $434,859 total compensation

Lead Non-Executive Independent Director, Stephen Westwell

President, CEO and Executive Director, Fleetwood Grobler, $650,344 total compensation

Non-Executive Independent Director, Muriel Dube

Non-Executive Independent Director, Martina Floel

Non-Executive Independent Director, Gesina Kennealy

Executive Vice President - Chemicals, Brad Griffith, $481,340 total compensation

Executive Vice President - Energy, Priscillah Mabelane, $363,420 total compensation

Executive Vice President - Human Resources and Stakeholder Relations, Charlotte Mokoena, $353,890 total compensation

Non-Executive Independent Director, Manuel Cuambe

Chief Financial Officer, Executive Director, Paul Victor, $484,970 total compensation

Non-Executive Independent Director, Nomgando Matyumza

Non-Executive Independent Director, Mpho Nkeli

Non-Executive Independent Chairman of the Board, Sipho Nkosi

Auditors: PricewaterhouseCoopers Inc.

LOCATIONS

HQ: Sasol Ltd.
Sasol Place, 50 Katherine Street, Sandton 2196
Phone: (27) 10 344 5000   Fax: (27) 11 788 5092
Web: www.sasol.com

2013 Sales by Geographic

	% of total
South Africa	48
Rest of South Africa	4
Europe	22
North America	11
Middle East and India	6
Far East	4
Southeast Asia and Australasia	3
South America	2
Total	**100**

PRODUCTS/OPERATIONS

2013 Sales

	% of total
Chemical cluster	55
South Africa energy cluster	41
International energy cluster	4
Total	**100**

Selected Locations

Asia
Australasia
Europe
Far East
Ireland
Middle East
Northern Asia
Rest of Africa
Southeast Asia
Southern Africa
The Americas
United Kingdom

COMPETITORS

ABENGOA SA
AIR PRODUCTS AND CHEMICALS INC.
ASPEN AEROGELS INC.
BP P.L.C.

COMPAÑIA ESPAÑOLA DE PETROLEOS SAU
ENEOS HOLDINGS INC.
ESSAR ENERGY LIMITED
Evonik Industries AG
FUCHS PETROLUB SE
GEVO INC.
GREENERGY INTERNATIONAL LIMITED
LUKOIL PAO
LyondellBasell Industries N.V.
REPSOL SA.
ROYAL DUTCH SHELL plc
RUBIS
THE CHEMOURS COMPANY
TOTALENERGIES SE
WARWICK INTERNATIONAL GROUP LIMITED

HISTORICAL FINANCIALS

Company Type: Public

Income Statement   FYE: June 30

	REVENUE ($ mil.)	NET INCOME ($ mil.)	NET PROFIT MARGIN	EMPLOYEES
06/21	14,122	631	4.5%	28,949
06/20	10,966	(5,248)	—	31,001
06/19	14,357	303	2.1%	31,429
06/18	13,191	634	4.8%	31,270
06/17	13,204	1,560	11.8%	30,900
Annual Growth	1.7%	(20.2%)	—	(1.6%)

2021 Year-End Financials

Debt ratio: 2.0%
Return on equity: 6.0%
Cash ($ mil.): 2,184
Current ratio: 1.76
Long-term debt ($ mil.): 6,794

No. of shares (mil.): 634
Dividends
  Yield: —
  Payout: —
Market value ($ mil.): 9,723

	STOCK PRICE ($) FY Close	P/E High/Low		PER SHARE ($) Earnings	Dividends	Book Value
06/21	15.33	1	0	1.02	0.00	16.16
06/20	7.71	—	—	(8.49)	0.00	14.06
06/19	24.85	6	4	0.49	0.74	24.58
06/18	36.54	3	2	1.03	0.70	25.75
06/17	27.95	1	1	2.55	1.14	24.78
Annual Growth	(13.9%)			— (20.5%)	—	
(10.1%)						

Saudi Basic Industries Corp - SABIC (Saudi Arabia)

Founded in 1976 Saudi Basic Industries Corp. (SABIC) is a public company based in Riyadh Saudi Arabia. SABIC is one of the biggest chemical companies in the world producing a range of polymers performance chemicals and fertilizers as well as steel products. The company sells chemicals to the agriculture automotive building and construction packaging industrial transportation and other industries. SABIC with over 12500 patent portfolio operates manufacturing and compounding plants in Saudi Arabia Europe the Americas and Asia. It also has distribution centers offices and storage facilities around the world. In 2020 70% of SABIC's stake acquired by its sibling company Saudi Aramco.

Operations

SABIC operates through three segments: Petrochemicals & Specialties Agri-Nutrients and (Metals) Hadeed.

The Petrochemicals & Specialties segment more than 85% of revenue uses hydrocarbon feedstock including methane ethane propane butane and light naphtha to make a range of products such as carbon dioxide ethylene methyl tert-butyl ether and other chemicals.

The Agri-Nutrients segment more than 5% of sales produces fertilizers that include urea ammonia and phosphate as well as compound fertilizers.

The Hadeed segment over 5% of sales makes steel products including rebar.

Geographic Reach

SABIC headquartered in Riyadh has global footprint serving its clients in 100 countries while operating in 50 countries with some 70 manufacturing and compounding plants across Americas Europe Middle-East & Africa and Asia-Pacific.

The company generates some 40% of revenue in Asia (nearly 20% of which is from China) roughly 25% in Europe more than 15% in Saudi Arabia and around 10% each in the Americas and other countries.

Sales and Marketing

SABIC's customers are in transportation agriculture construction medical devices packaging clean energy and electronics.

Financial Performance

SABIC's sales revenue in 2020 was SAR 117.0 billion a decrease of SAR 184 billion or 14% compared to SAR 135.4 billion in 2019 due to sharply lower average sales prices across key products; whereas the overall sales volume increased by 1%.

SABIC's net income for 2020 was SAR 67 million compared to SAR 5.2 billion in 2019. The decrease was mainly attributed to the decline in margins by 54% despite the increase in sales volume by 1%.

Cash and cash equivalent at the end of the year 2020 was SAR 28.8 billion a decrease of SAR 6.5 billion or 18% compared to 2019 which was mainly due to lower cash generated from operating activities. Cash provided by operations was SAR 22.0 billion while cash used for investing and financing activities were SAR 14.0 billion and SAR 14.5 billion respectively.

Strategy

SABIC's vision is to be the preferred world leader in chemicals and a true global powerhouse across key sectors of the chemical industry by delivering Chemistry that Matters.

In SABIC's core Petrochemical and Agri-Nutrients businesses the company invests to drive superior growth and increase the resilience of these differentiated commodity-based businesses. The company strive to become the leading global fully integrated Chemicals Plastics and Agri-Nutrients company.

In its Specialties business the company aim to build a position of strength over the medium term by building scale and innovative product offerings that can create a new growth platform for the group that is independent of feedstock dynamics that can support Saudi Vision 2030 designed to reduce Saudi Arabia's dependence on hydrocarbon exports.

SABIC's strategic ambitions rest on seven pillars: Customer Focus; Market Focus; Operational Excellence; Innovation; Portfolio Management; Transformation; and Localization Engine.

Company Background

SABIC was founded in 1976.

EXECUTIVES

Independent Member of the Board, Mohammed Talal Al-Nahas, $106,666 total compensation
Vice Chairman of the Board, Chief Executive Officer, Yousef Abdullah Al Benyan, $106,666 total compensation
Executive Vice President, Petrochemicals, Abdul Rahman Al Fageeh
Non-Executive Member of the Board, Olivier Thorel, $28,925 total compensation
Executive Vice President - Engineering & Project Management, Omar Bin Abdullah Al Amoudi
Independent Member of the Board, Khaled Hamza A. Nahas, $106,666 total compensation
Non-Executive Chairman of the Board, Khalid Hashim Aldabbagh, $28,925 total compensation
Executive Vice President, Shared Services, Abdulrahman Ahmed Shamsaddin
EVP Sustainability, Technology and Innovation and CTO and CSO, Bob Maughon
Executive Vice President - Manufacturing, Ahmed Al-Shaikh
Executive Vice President - Corporate Finance, Timothy Leveille
Executive Vice President, Corporate Human Resources, Abdulaziz Al-Oudan
Executive Vice President Agri-Nutrients, Samir A. Al Abdrabbuh
Independent Member of the Board, Nader Ibrahim Al-Wehibi, $106,666 total compensation
Non-Executive Member of the Board, Abdullah Bin Mohammed Al Issa, $106,666 total compensation
Non-Executive Member of the Board, Ziad Thamer Al-Murshed, $28,925 total compensation
Auditors: Ernst & Young

LOCATIONS

HQ: Saudi Basic Industries Corp - SABIC (Saudi Arabia)
Qurtubah District, Riyadh 11422
Phone: (966) 1 225 8000   **Fax:** (966) 1 225 9000
Web: www.sabic.com

2018 Sales

	% of total
Europe	23
Rest of Asia	22
China	17
Kingdom of Saudi Arabia	5
Americas	9
Others	14
Total	**100**

PRODUCTS/OPERATIONS

2018 Sales

	% of total
Petrochemicals & Specialties	89
Hadeed	6
Agri-Nutrients	5
Total	**100**

Selected Subsidiaries & Affiliates

Al-Jubail Petrochemical Co
Aluminum Bahrain
Arabian Industrial Fibers Co
Arabian Petrochemical Co
Eastern Petrochemical Co
Gulf Aluminum Rolling Mill Co
Gulf Petrochemical Industries Co
Jubail Fertilizer
Jubail United Petrochemical Co
Ma;aden Phosphate Co.
National Chemical Carrier Company
National Chemical Fertilizer Co
National Industrial Gases Co
National Methanol Co
SABIC Innovative Plastics
Saudi Arabian Fertilizer Co
Saudi Iron & Steel Co
Saudi Kayan Petrochemical Co
Saudi Methanol Co
Saudi Organometallic Chemicals Co
Saudi Petrochemical Co
Saudi Specialty Chemicals Co
Saudi-Yanbu Petrochemical Co
Saudi-European Petrochemical Co
Sinopec SABIC Tianjin Petrochemical Co
Yanbu National Petrochemical

COMPETITORS

Braskem S/A	NEWMARKET CORPORATION
CLARIANT CORPORATION	NISSAN CHEMICAL
FUTUREFUEL CORP.	CORPORATION
LANXESS SOLUTIONS US	PETROLOGISTICS LP
INC.	SHOWA DENKO K.K.
LG Chem Ltd.	Ultrapar Participacoes
LyondellBasell	S/A
Industries N.V.	VALLOUREC
MITSUBISHI CHEMICAL	
HOLDINGS CORPORATION	

HISTORICAL FINANCIALS

Company Type: Public

Income Statement   FYE: December 31

	REVENUE ($ mil.)	NET INCOME ($ mil.)	NET PROFIT MARGIN	EMPLOYEES
12/20	31,186	17	0.1%	0
12/19	37,263	1,483	4.0%	0
12/18	45,100	5,738	12.7%	0
12/17	39,937	4,914	12.3%	34,000
12/16	35,415	4,756	13.4%	35,000
Annual Growth	**(3.1%)**	**(75.3%)**	**—**	**—**

2020 Year-End Financials

Debt ratio: 3.6%	No. of shares (mil.): —
Return on equity: 0.0%	Dividends
Cash ($ mil.): 8,841	Yield: —
Current ratio: 2.17	Payout: —
Long-term debt ($ mil.): 8,895	Market value ($ mil.): —

Saudi British Bank (The)

The Saudi British Bank (SABB) provides personal private and corporate banking services to customers across Saudi Arabia. Founded in 1978 SABB operates a network of about 80 branches (including more than a dozen locations exclusively for women) offering deposits loans and Takaful (cooperative insurance that complies with Islamic law). It also issues VISA and MasterCard credit cards as well as the SABB Amanah card which offers monthly payment plans that adhere to Islamic principles. Corporate services include cash management treasury and investment banking through HSBC Saudi Arabia Limited. British banking giant HSBC owns about 40% of SABB; Saudi nationals own 60%.

Auditors: Ernst & Young & Co.

LOCATIONS

HQ: Saudi British Bank (The)
P.O. Box 9084, Riyadh 11413
Phone: (966) 1 405 0677   **Fax:** (966) 1 276 4809
Web: www.sabb.com

COMPETITORS

AIB GROUP (UK) P.L.C.
ARAB BANK PLC

BOC HONG KONG (HOLDINGS) LIMITED
CTBC Financial Holding Co. Ltd.
METROPOLITAN BANK & TRUST COMPANY
NATIONAL BANK OF KUWAIT S.A.K.P.
OVERSEA-CHINESE BANKING CORPORATION
LIMITED
UNION BANK OF INDIA
UNITED OVERSEAS BANK LIMITED

HISTORICAL FINANCIALS

Company Type: Public

Income Statement   FYE: December 31

	ASSETS ($ mil.)	NET INCOME ($ mil.)	INCOME AS % OF ASSETS	EMPLOYEES
12/19	70,792	754	1.1%	4,537
12/18	46,550	1,315	2.8%	3,171
12/17	50,030	1,054	2.1%	3,263
12/16	49,607	1,038	2.1%	3,317
12/15	50,009	1,153	2.3%	3,451
Annual Growth	**9.1%**	**(10.1%)**	**—**	**7.1%**

2019 Year-End Financials

Return on assets: 1.2%	Dividends
Return on equity: 6.4%	Yield: —
Long-term debt ($ mil.): —	Payout: 76.4%
No. of shares (mil.): 2,054	Market value ($ mil.): —
Sales ($ mil): 3,138	

Saudi Electricity Co

EXECUTIVES

Senior Vice President - Communications and Public Relations, Humoud Bin Awdah Al-ghubaini
Non-Executive Member of the Board, Abdulmalik Bin Abdullah Al-hogail
Senior Vice President - Human Resources, Abdulrahman Bin Mohammed Al-obayed
Chief Executive Officer, Fahad Bin Hussein Al-sudairi
Chief Executive Officer - Saudi Power Purchase Company, Osama Bin Abdulwahab Khawandanah
Executive Vice President - Distribution and Subscribers Services, Khalid Bin Hamad Al-gnoon
Chief Financial Officer, Executive Vice President, Manish Manchandya
Independent Member of the Board, Isam Bin Alwan Al-bayat
Non-Executive Vice Chairman of the Board, Najm Bin Abdull Ahal Zaid
Member of the Board, Sulaiman Bin Abdulaziz Al-twaijri
Director of Shareholders Director of Shareholders, Jamaan Bin Ali Al-zahrani
Member of the Board, Mohammed Bin Abdulrahman Al-bilaihed
Member of the Board, Yehia Bin Ali Al-jabr
Chief Executive Officer of National Grid SA, Ibrahim Bin Fahd Al Jarbou
Executive Vice President - Generation, Riyadh Bin Fahad Al-Zamil
Chief Executive Officer - Integrated Dawiyat Telecommunications & Information Technology Company, Ahmed Bin Abass Sindi
Senior Vice Chairman - Legal Affairs, Secretary of the Board of Directors, Faisal Bin Mohammed Al-lazzam
Chief Executive Officer - Saudi Electricity Company for Projects Development, Mahdi Nasser Al-dosary
Member of the Board, Walid Bin Ibrahim Shukri

Senior Vice President - Internal Audit, Abdulwahhab Hamza Bakr Khushayym
Head of Accounts Control Sector, Ibrahim Bin Abdullah Al-sada
Non-Executive Chairman of the Board, Khaled Bin Saleh Al Sultan
Auditors: KPMG Al Fozan & Partners

LOCATIONS

HQ: Saudi Electricity Co
P.O. Box 22955, Riyadh 11416
Phone: (966) 14053227   **Fax:** (966) 14032222
Web: www.se.com.sa

HISTORICAL FINANCIALS

Company Type: Public

Income Statement				FYE: December 31
	REVENUE ($ mil.)	NET INCOME ($ mil.)	NET PROFIT MARGIN	EMPLOYEES
12/19	17,344	370	2.1%	0
12/18	17,083	468	2.7%	34,599
12/17	13,497	1,842	13.6%	36,432
12/16	13,294	1,211	9.1%	38,329
12/15	11,064	411	3.7%	37,769
Annual Growth	11.9%	(2.6%)	—	—

2019 Year-End Financials

Debt ratio: 8.8%
Return on equity: 1.8%
Cash ($ mil.): 511
Current ratio: 0.33
Long-term debt ($ mil.): 37,189

No. of shares (mil.): —
Dividends
  Yield: —
  Payout: —
Market value ($ mil.): —

Saudi Telecom Co

Saudi Telecom Company (STC) is the leading provider of telecommunications services in the Kingdom of Saudi Arabia and it is among the largest operators in the Middle East. The company provides mobile and fixed telephone services along with Internet and other data services to residential and business customers. Operating the Jawal and Hatif networks STC also operates a submarine communications cable system connecting Saudi Arabia and Sudan in Africa through Arab Submarine Cables Company. The company generates majority of sales in its home country Kingdom of Saudi Arabia.

Operations

STC is engaged mainly in providing telecommunication services and related products. Majority of the company's revenues are from Saudi Telecom Company (stc) which accounts for more than 55% of total revenue; and stc Channels which produce approximately 25% of total.

Other operating segments (about 20% of total revenue) include: Kuwait Telecommunications Company (stc Kuwait) stc Bahrain Solutions by stc Specialized by stc stc Gulf Sapphire Aqalat Telecommunications Towers Company and Saudi Digital Payments Company

Geographic Reach

STC has a massive presence at home Kingdom of Saudi Arabia with more than 90% of total sales and it has expanded in the Middle East and nearby regions. It offers services in Turkey Kuwait Bahrain India Malaysia and South Africa.

Sales and Marketing

STC's customers primarily consist of local regional and international operators service providers and the regional business sector. The company's advertising and publicity expenses were SR 769.6 million in 2019 and SR 560.1 in 2018.

Financial Performance

Consolidated revenues increased by 5% in 2019 compared to the same period of the previous year to reach SAR 54.4 billion.

Cash held by the company at the end of 2019 decreased by SAR 124.1 million to SR 8.0 billion compared from the prior year with SAR 8.2 billion. Cash provided by operations was SAR 9.9 billion while cash used for investing and financing activities were SAR 2.0 billion and SAR 8.1 billion respectively. Main uses for cash were payments related to financial assets and movements in trade receivables and others.

Strategy

In 2019 the company culminated its strategy by launching STC's new brand in line with its leading position in the communications and information technology sector in the Kingdom. The new brand reflects the company's dynamism as a leading digital enabler locally regionally and globally. It also aligns with the company's progress in the field of digital transformation with digital payments media and entertainment in line with the digital data revolution and accelerating changes in the communications and information technology sector.

STC's vision is to be a leading digital services provider regionally thus enabling a diverse and digital economy in the Kingdom and the MENA region. STC's DARE strategy is a plan to achieve this vision by focusing on the following pillars: digitize STC; accelerate core asset performance; reinvent customer experience at world-class standards; and expand aggressively scale and scope.

Mergers and Acquisitions

In early 2020 STC entered in an agreement to acquire 55% stake in Vodafone Egypt for $2.4 billion. Vodafone Egypt is one of the leading player in the Egyptian mobile market and serves over 40 million customers. The potential acquisition of Vodafone Egypt is in line with STC expansion strategy in the MENA region. The company remains in discussions with Vodafone Group plc Vodafone Egypt's parent company to find a suitable agreement to enable the transaction to close.

EXECUTIVES

Chief Financial Officer, Ameen Al Shiddi
Chief Executive Officer, Nasser Al Nasser
Vice President - Enterprise Architecture, Abdullah Al Owini
Vice President, Corporate Analytics & Data, Khalid Al Barrak
Independent Member of the Board, Ibrahim Kadi, $53,333 total compensation
Vice President - Business Development, Sultan Bin Saeed
Vice President, Procurement & Support Services, Emad Alaoudah
Vice President - Wholesale, Alan Waylan
Senior Vice President - Enterprise Business Unit, Riyad Muawad
Vice President - People, Ahmed Alghamdi
Chief Internal Audit, Abdullah Al-Anzi
Senior Vice President - Technology and Operations, Haithem Alfaraj
Vice President - Wholesale Business Unit, Mohammed Alabbadi
Non-Executive Vice Chairman of the Board, Khaled Biyari, $53,333 total compensation
Vice President - Business Finance, Wjanand Van Till
Vice President - Customer Experience & Operations, Riyad Alonazi
Non-Executive Non Independent Member of the Board, Mohammed Al Nahhas, $53,333 total compensation

Senior Vice President - Corporate Affairs, Abdullah Abdulrahman Alkanhl
Auditors: Ernst & Young & Co.

LOCATIONS

HQ: Saudi Telecom Co
King Abdulaziz Complex, Imam Mohammed Bin Saud Street, Al Mursalat Area, P.O. Box 87912, Riyadh 11652
Phone: (966) 1 452 5881   **Fax:** (966) 1 452 5869
Web: www.stc.com.sa

PRODUCTS/OPERATIONS

2014 Sales

	% of total
GSM	62
Landline	11
Data services	27
Total	**100**

2014 Sales

	% of total
Usage Charges	60
Subscription fees	38
Activation fee & others	2
Total	**100**

COMPETITORS

AT&T INC.
BT GROUP PLC
Deutsche Telekom AG
EMIRATES TELECOMMUNICATIONS GROUP COMPANY (ETISAL
LEVEL 3 PARENT LLC
Oi S A Em Recuperacao Judicial
PT. TELKOM INDONESIA (PERSERO) TBK
Shaw Communications Inc
TELECOM ITALIA SPA
TELEFONICA SA
VODACOM GROUP LTD
VODAFONE GROUP PUBLIC LIMITED COMPANY

HISTORICAL FINANCIALS

Company Type: Public

Income Statement				FYE: December 31
	REVENUE ($ mil.)	NET INCOME ($ mil.)	NET PROFIT MARGIN	EMPLOYEES
12/19	14,498	2,843	19.6%	0
12/18	13,856	2,874	20.7%	0
12/17	13,532	2,702	20.0%	0
12/16	14,044	2,372	16.9%	0
12/15	13,491	2,466	18.3%	0
Annual Growth	1.8%	3.6%	—	—

2019 Year-End Financials

Debt ratio: 2.1%
Return on equity: 16.7%
Cash ($ mil.): 2,141
Current ratio: 1.35
Long-term debt ($ mil.): 2,379

No. of shares (mil.): 2,000
Dividends
  Yield: —
  Payout: 75.0%
Market value ($ mil.): —

Sberbank Of Russia

Sberbank is one of the largest banking institutions in Russia boasting assets of about 1.7 trillion divided among its Asset Management Insurance Private Pension fund and Life insurance segments. Its more than 14000 branches in Russia offer banking services ranging from savings to private and investment banking. The company also boasts more than 4000 agent network points and more than 70000 ATMs. More than 90% of the company's ATMs have contactless technologies. The company's online platform and mobile application is also a key driver to the growth of the digital audience of the company.

Operations

In addition to its main retail banking services Sberbank also boasts a trade finance and an investment banking business. It also provides health life third-party liability and other insurance products for both retail and corporate clients.

Sberbank's online banking services are accessed by about 65 million customers across the bank's app online portal and SMS service.

Sberbank is Russia's one of the leading credit card issuer with more than 15 million active credit cards in circulation. The bank's ATM network is over 70000 terminals.

Sberbank's Corporate and Investment Bank (Sberbank CIB) caters to about 200000 clients offering complex structured products to support major products in all sectors of the Russian economy (major large medium-sized corporate clients).

Geographic Reach

Sberbank based in Moscow Russia has over 10 Regional Banks that operate more than 14000 branches in nearly all of Russia's 85 regions. Internationally Sberbank has subsidiaries branches and representative offices in more than 20 countries including Russia the UK US CIS and Central and Eastern Europe.

Some of its primary foreign subsidiary banks are: SB SJC Sberbank (Kazakhstan) BPS-Sberbank OJSC (Belarus) Sberbank JSC (Ukraine) and Cetelem Bank LLC.

Sales and Marketing

Sberbank serves individuals institutions and medium to large-sized businesses and corporations. Overall Sberbank boast almost 100 million clients globally and holds more than 40% of consumer loans almost 55% of mortgages and about 15 million active credit cards.

Financial Performance

Note: Growth rates may differ after conversion to US dollars. This analysis uses operating income (sum of net interest income fee and commission and insurance premiums) in place of revenue.

Sberbank's revenues and profits have been on the uptrend in recent years thanks to continued growth in its corporate and retail loan businesses. Total revenue grew from RUB 2.3 trillion in 2019 to RUB 2.4 trillion in 2020.

Sberbank's coffers amounted to about RUB 2.4 trillion in 2020. The bank generated RUB 663.9 billion from its operations. The company's investing activities and financing used RUB 104.4 billion and RUB 450.5 billion respectively. Main cash uses were for acquisition of premises equipment and intangible assets and payment of dividends.

Strategy

The company is preparing to implement and incorporate its "Strategy 2023" which is a continuation of its prior strategy. In this new strategy the company gives attention to building a seamless customer experience and creating a unique customer proposition. Sberbank's goal for its Strategy 2023 includes the revenue growth of over 100% annually on its non-financial services and to be part of the top 3 on the e-commerce market among others.

EXECUTIVES

Chairman of the Executive Board, Chief Executive Officer, Executive Director, Member of the Supervisory Board, Herman Gref
Deputy Chairman Of The Board, Stanislav Kuznetsov

Chairman of the Supervisory Board, Non-Executive Director, Anton Siluanov
First Deputy Chairman of the Executive Board, Lev Khasis
Deputy Chairman of the Supervisory Board, Non-Executive Director, Sergey Ignatiev
Member of the Supervisory Board, Non-Executive Director, Vladimir Kolychev
Deputy Chairman of the Executive Board, Sergey Maltsev
Member of the Supervisory Board, Non-Executive Director, Dmitry Chernyshenko
Deputy Chairman of the Executive Board, Kirill Tsarev
Deputy Chairman of the Executive Board, Olga Golodets
Member of the Supervisory Board, Independent Director, Mikhail Kovalchuk
Senior Vice President of Sberbank and Head of the Wealth Management Block:, Natalya Alymova
Deputy Chairman of the Executive Board, Anatoly Popov
Chief Financial Officer & Head-Finance, Alexandra Buriko
Auditors: AO PricewaterhouseCoopers Audit

LOCATIONS

HQ: Sberbank Of Russia
19 Vavilova St., Moscow 117312
Phone: (7) 495 500 55 50   **Fax:** (7) 495 957 5731
Web: www.sberbank.com

PRODUCTS/OPERATIONS

Selected Subsidiary
DenizBank A.S.
Sberbank Europe AG
Sberbank Kazakhstan
BPS-Sberbank (Belarus)
Sberbank (Switzerland) AG

Selected Group companies
ActiveBusinessCollection LLC
Sberbank-Automated Trading System CJSC
Delovaya Sreda JSC
Sberbank Private Pension Funds JSC
Sberbank Leasing JSC
Sberbank-Services LLC
Sberbank Life Insurance LLC
Sberbank-Technology (Sbertech) JSC
Sovremennyye Tekhnologii LLC
Nonbanking Credit Institution Yandex.Money LLC

COMPETITORS

BANK OF INDIA
BANK VTB PAO
BPCE
Banco Bradesco S/A
Banco Santander Brasil S/A
Bank of Communications Co. Ltd.
Danske Bank A/S
DnB ASA
FIDESSA GROUP HOLDINGS LIMITED
ITAU UNIBANCO HOLDING SA
KEYCORP
MAPFRE SA

MUFG AMERICAS HOLDINGS CORPORATION
NATIONAL BANK HOLDINGS CORPORATION
QATAR NATIONAL BANK (Q.P.S.C.)
Shinhan Financial Group Co. Ltd.
Skandinaviska Enskilda Banken AB
Swedbank AB
THE CO-OPERATIVE BANK P.L.C.
The Bank of Nova Scotia
ZIONS BANCORPORATION

HISTORICAL FINANCIALS
Company Type: Public

Income Statement
FYE: December 31

	REVENUE ($ mil.)	NET INCOME ($ mil.)	NET PROFIT MARGIN	EMPLOYEES
12/20	42,910	10,174	23.7%	285,600
12/19	50,229	13,575	27.0%	281,300
12/18	39,817	11,950	30.0%	293,752
12/17	49,885	12,979	26.0%	310,277
12/16	45,941	8,827	19.2%	325,100
Annual Growth	(1.7%)	3.6%	—	(3.2%)

2020 Year-End Financials

Debt ratio: —	No. of shares (mil.): —
Return on equity: 15.9%	Dividends
Cash ($ mil.): 31,773	Yield: 6.7%
Current ratio: —	Payout: 223.1%
Long-term debt ($ mil.): —	Market value ($ mil.): —

	STOCK PRICE ($) FY Close	P/E High/Low		PER SHARE ($) Earnings	Dividends	Book Value
12/20	14.50	0	0	0.46	0.98	3.13
12/19	16.40	0	0	0.62	1.01	3.35
12/18	10.96	0	0	0.55	0.76	2.57
12/17	17.03	1	0	0.60	0.39	2.76
12/16	11.58	0	0	0.41	0.13	2.14
Annual Growth	5.8%	—	—	3.0%	64.9%	10.1%

Schaeffler AG

LOCATIONS

HQ: Schaeffler AG
Industriestr. 1-3, Herzogenaurach 91074
Phone:
Web: www.schaeffler.com

HISTORICAL FINANCIALS
Company Type: Public

Income Statement
FYE: December 31

	REVENUE ($ mil.)	NET INCOME ($ mil.)	NET PROFIT MARGIN	EMPLOYEES
12/20	15,463	(520)	—	83,297
12/19	16,198	480	3.0%	87,748
12/18	16,308	1,008	6.2%	92,478
12/17	16,807	1,174	7.0%	90,151
Annual Growth	(2.7%)	—	—	(2.6%)

2020 Year-End Financials

Debt ratio: 37.8%	No. of shares (mil.): 666
Return on equity: (-18.5%)	Dividends
Cash ($ mil.): 2,157	Yield: 0.0%
Current ratio: 1.75	Payout: —
Long-term debt ($ mil.): 4,943	Market value ($ mil.): 5,528

	STOCK PRICE ($) FY Close	P/E High/Low		PER SHARE ($) Earnings	Dividends	Book Value
12/20	8.30	—	—	(0.77)	0.60	3.22
12/19	0.00	—	—	0.73	1.00	4.76
Annual Growth (12.2%)		—	—	—	(15.6%)	

Schindler Holding AG

Schindler is one of the world's leading suppliers of escalators elevators and moving walkways for use in airports train and subway stations and other public and government buildings as well as in offices commercial properties and cruise ships. The company helps organize cities by moving people and goods and connecting vertical and horizontal transportation systems. Schindler has operations in more than 100 countries. The Schindler Group nets some 45% of its sales from Europe Middle East and Africa. It was founded in 1874 in Central Switzerland.

Operations

Schindler operates two divisions: Elevators and Escalators which accounts for all of the company's sales and Finance.

The Elevators & Escalators segment is managed as one global unit and comprises an integrated business that specializes in the production and installation of elevators and escalators as well as the modernization maintenance and repair of existing installations.

Finance comprises the expenses of Schindler Holding Ltd. and BuildingMinds as well as centrally managed financial assets and liabilities that have been entered into for Group investing and financing purposes.

Geographic Reach

The Swiss-based company has over 1000 branches in more than 100 countries as well as eight production sites and six R&D facilities in the US Brazil Europe China and India. Europe Middle East and Africa is its largest market at some 45% of revenue followed by the Asia-Pacific (about 30%) and the Americas region and Africa (over 25%).

Sales and Marketing

Schindler's lifts are found in malls offices hotels entertainment centers housing complexes and travel hubs.

Financial Performance

Schindler generated revenue of CHF 10.6 billion in 2020 from previous year's CHF 11.3 billion corresponding to a drop of 6%. In local currencies revenues increased slightly by 0.4%.

Profit of the company in 2020 decreased to CHF 1.0 billion from CHF 1.3 billion in 2019.

Cash held by the company at the end of fiscal 2020 increased to CHF 2.5 billion. Operating activities provided CHF 1.6 billion while investing and financing activities used CHF 607 million and CHF 804 million respectively. Main cash uses were current and non-current financial assets; and dividends paid.

Strategy

With a clear long-term perspective and a determination to generate sustained value for all the company's stakeholders Schindler has adapted to new market realities and continues to invest in the future. To preserve its competitiveness Schindler introduced structural realignments and cost optimization measures resulting in the factory closure in Zaragoza in 2020 and the reduction of about 2000 jobs globally over the course of two years. At the same time Schindler continues to invest in strategic initiatives aimed at enhancing the quality and customer centricity of its products and services as well as fostering innovation and connectivity. As one of the first results the modular elevator range was rolled out in key markets across Europe and Asia-Pacific in 2020 receiving a very positive customer response. Building on enhanced connectivity new digital services have been launched to provide our customers with tailored support and faster response times.

HISTORY

Robert Schindler and Eduard Villiger established Schindler & Villiger in 1874 to make lift equipment and machinery in Lucerne Switzerland. Villiger left the firm in 1892 and the enterprise became known as Robert Schindler Machinery Manufacturer. The company added an iron foundry in 1895.

Robert sold the business to his brother Alfred in 1901 and the company was renamed Alfred Schindler. The following year it delivered its first electric passenger elevator with automatic push-button controls.

Alfred Schindler took on a partner in 1906 by the name of Fritz Geilfuss. The company's name was changed to Schindler & Cie. Around this time the company's first subsidiary was established in Berlin. Other subsidiaries soon followed in France and another in Germany. Sales offices were opened in Argentina (1910) Belgium and Russia (1912) and Egypt Poland and Spain (1914).

Schindler & Cie. continued to grow adding elevator motor manufacturing (1915) and cranes (1920) to its product line. By 1923 the company had opened a factory in Mulhouse France. Geilfuss died in 1920 and Adolf Sigg became Alfred Schindler's partner in 1925.

During WWI the company's iron foundry produced munitions; it eventually became independent in 1925. By 1931 the company had expanded into Bulgaria China Colombia Ecuador Egypt Greece Lithuania Morocco South Africa and Yugoslavia. The firm was incorporated as Aufz ge und Elektromotorenfabrik Schindler & Cie. AG in 1932. Schindler delivered its first escalator in 1936.

Sales fell off during WWII as demand for elevators diminished but the company managed to expand modestly (Venezuela UK South Africa). By 1959 Schindler had become Europe's largest elevator company. Schindler acquired a stake in Dutch firm Westdijk in 1967 and bought Wertheim-Werk of Austria in 1969.

The company was restructured under the name Schindler Holding AG in 1970. By 1974 it had 56 subsidiaries throughout Europe South America and South Africa. Schindler entered the US in 1979 with the purchase of Reliance Electric Cleveland's Haughton Elevator division in Toledo Ohio.

The advent of the 1980s marked the beginning of a 15-year period of continued growth for Schindler. It established the first industrial joint venture with China in 1980 (another followed in 1988). Schindler went on to open an Australian subsidiary (1981) and strike a licensing deal with Bharat Bijlee Ltd. India's largest elevator company (1986). In 1987 Schindler bought a controlling interest in Japan's Nippon Elevator Industry Co. The company's 1988 purchase of a majority share of Swiss computer wholesaler ALSO Holding AG was deemed risky at the time but after some restructuring measures were taken the unit thrived. That year Schindler took over the North American elevator and escalator operations of Westinghouse.

During the first half of the 1990s Schindler began to emphasize its role as a service provider (maintenance and repair) and focused on growing in the Middle East and Eastern Europe. The second half of the 1990s saw Schindler introduce several elevating innovations. The machine room-less elevator debuted in 1997. That year the company made it possible to order elevators online.

By 1999 the company's 125th anniversary 40% of sales came from outside Europe and non-elevator operations climbed to 20% of sales. In 2000 Schindler inked a deal with Mitsubishi Electric to supply each other with elevator components.

In a move to tap new markets in 2002 Schindler acquired a 51% stake in Russian elevator maker Liftremont. The company closed factories in Brazil France Germany Japan Malaysia Poland and

Turkey that year. In 2003 Schindler acquired South Korea's Joong Ang Elevator Company and Austria's Doppelmayr Aufz ge.

The ALSO Group sold its Systems Business unit to Germany's Bechtle in 2004. A year later ALSO bought majority control of GNT Holding a Finnish distributor of IT products and consumer electronics.

2005 saw more acquisitions. Schindler bought Eletec Vytahy Spol (Czech Republic) and Mercury Ascensore (Japan). That year Schindler China opened an escalator factory in Shanghai capable of producing more than 6000 escalators a year.

In 2006 Schindler bought a one-quarter interest in Hyundai Elevator the second largest vendor of elevators and escalators in South Korea. It also took full ownership of Certus its long-time partner in Croatia and established a Schindler Adriatic organization to represent the group's interests in the Balkans. ALSO made GNT Holding a wholly owned subsidiary in 2008.

Schindler's momentum was affected by a decision made by European Union regulators in 2007. The company was among five elevator manufacturers fined following a three-year investigation into alleged anticompetitive practices in Belgium Germany Luxembourg and the Netherlands from 1995 to 2004.

During 2008 Schindler increased its ownership in its Korean subsidiary from 70% to 100% and bought a 49% stake in Al Doha Elevators & Escalators WLL in Qatar. The company has been an exclusive distributor of Schindler products in Qatar since 2005. It was renamed Al Doha Schindler Elevators & Escalators.

EXECUTIVES

Chairman of the Board, Silvio Napoli, $1,437,430 total compensation
Non-Executive Independent Member of the Board of Directors, Luc Bonnard, $372,667 total compensation
Executive Member of the Board of Directors, Erich Ammann, $783,665 total compensation
Non-Executive Independent Member of the Board of Directors, Rudolf Fischer, $255,543 total compensation
Non-Executive Independent Vice Chairman of the Board of Directors, Pius Baschera, $372,667 total compensation
Chairman of the Executive Committee, Chief Executive Officer, Thomas Oetterli, $1,119,066 total compensation
Non-Executive Independent Member of the Board of Directors, Monika Butler, $255,543 total compensation
Non-Executive Independent Member of the Board of Directors, Patrice Bula, $255,543 total compensation
Deputy Chief Executive Officer, Member of the Executive Committee for Corporate Human Resources, David Clymo
Chief Financial Officer, Member of the Executive Committee, Urs Scheidegger
Executive Member of the Board of Directors, Tobias Staehelin, $481,272 total compensation
Member of the Executive Committee responsible for Americas, Andre Inserra
Non-Executive Emeritus Chairman of the Board, Alfred Schindler, $381,185 total compensation
Member of the Executive Committee responsible for Europe North, Paolo Compagna
Member of the Executive Committee, Europe South, Julio Arce
Member of the Executive Committee, Asia-Pacific, Jujudhan Jena
Member of the Executive Committee, Field Quality and Excellence, Robert Seakins

Chief Technology Officer, Member of the Executive Committee, Karl-Heinz Bauer

Member of the Executive Committee responsible for Escalators and Supply Chain, Egbert Weisshaar

Non-Executive Independent Member of the Board of Directors, Carole Vischer, $255,543 total compensation

Member of the Executive Committee responsible for Operations, Christian Schulz

Member of the Executive Committee responsible for China, Daryoush Ziai

Chief Information Officer, Member of the Executive Board, Matteo Attrovio

Executive member of the Board of Directors, Orit Gadiesh, $551,547 total compensation

Auditors: PricewaterhouseCoopers AG

LOCATIONS

HQ: Schindler Holding AG
Seestrasse 55, Hergiswil CH-6052
Phone: (41) 41 632 85 50   **Fax:** (41) 41 445 31 44
Web: www.schindler.com

2015 Sales

	% of total
Europe	39
Americas	28
Asia-Pacific & Africa	33
Total	**100**

PRODUCTS/OPERATIONS

Selected Products & Services

Commercial elevators
Escalators (commercial public transportation) & moving walks
E-tools (planning analysis reporting)
Freight & special elevators
High-rise elevators
Modernization (elevators escalators)
Residential elevators
Service & maintenance

Selected Subsidiaries

Adams Elevator Equipment Company (US)
Administração e Comé;rcio Jaguar Ltda. (Brazil)
Ascensores Schindler (Chile) SA
Ascensores Schindler de Colombia SA
Ascensores Schindler SA (90% Argentina)
China-Schindler Elevator Co. Ltd. (63%)
Deve Hydraulic Lifts Pty. Ltd. (Australia)
Elevadores Schindler SA de CV (Mexico)
Elevator Car System (France)
Hovanes BV (The Netherlands)
Iran Schindler Lift Manufacturing Company Ltd. (15%)
Jardine Schindler Elevator Corp. (Philippines)
Jardine Schindler Lifts (Taiwan)
Jardine Schindler (Thai) Ltd.
Kibaek Specialfabrik Aps (Denmark)
Schindler Aufzügefabrik GmbH (Germany)
Schindler Elevator Corporation (Canada)
Schindler Elevator Corporation (US)
Schindler Elevator KK (Japan)
Schindler India PVT Ltd.
Schindler Ltd. (Egypt)
Schindler Ltd. (UK)
SA Schindler NV (Belgium)
Schindler SpA (Italy)
Stahl Heiser A/S (Norway)
Ternitz Druckguss GmbH (80% Austria)

COMPETITORS

Chocoladefabriken
  Lindt & Spr   ngli AG
INCHCAPE PLC
ISS World Services A/S
KONE Oyj
STRABAG SE

Swiss Life Holding AG
TCP International
  Holdings Ltd.
Zurich Insurance Group
  AG

HISTORICAL FINANCIALS

Company Type: Public

Income Statement

				FYE: December 31
	REVENUE ($ mil.)	**NET INCOME** ($ mil.)	**NET PROFIT MARGIN**	**EMPLOYEES**
12/20	12,080	819	6.8%	66,674
12/19	11,659	892	7.7%	66,306
12/18	11,059	958	8.7%	64,486
12/17	10,429	844	8.1%	61,019
12/16	9,512	750	7.9%	58,271
Annual Growth	**6.2%**	**2.2%**	**—**	**3.4%**

2020 Year-End Financials

Debt ratio: 9.8%
Return on equity: 18.7%
Cash ($ mil.): 2,819
Current ratio: 1.37
Long-term debt ($ mil.): 843

No. of shares (mil.): 107
Dividends
  Yield: —
  Payout: 59.6%
Market value ($ mil.): —

Schlumberger Ltd

Auditors: PricewaterhouseCoopers LLP

LOCATIONS

HQ: Schlumberger Ltd
42 Rue Saint-Dominique, Paris 75007
Phone: 713 513-2000
Web: www.slb.com

HISTORICAL FINANCIALS

Company Type: Public

Income Statement

				FYE: December 31
	REVENUE ($ mil.)	**NET INCOME** ($ mil.)	**NET PROFIT MARGIN**	**EMPLOYEES**
12/21	23,077	1,881	8.2%	92,000
12/20	23,868	(10,518)	—	86,000
12/19	33,250	(10,137)	—	105,000
12/18	33,179	2,138	6.4%	100,000
12/17	30,664	(1,505)	—	100,000
Annual Growth	**(6.9%)**	**—**	**—**	**(2.1%)**

2021 Year-End Financials

Debt ratio: 34.2%
Return on equity: 13.8%
Cash ($ mil.): 3,139
Current ratio: 1.22
Long-term debt ($ mil.): 13,286

No. of shares (mil.): 1,403
Dividends
  Yield: 1.6%
  Payout: 42.7%
Market value ($ mil.): 42,031

	STOCK PRICE ($) FY Close	**P/E** High/Low	**PER SHARE ($)** Earnings	Dividends	Book Value
12/21	29.95	27 16	1.32	0.50	10.69
12/20	21.83	— —	(7.57)	0.88	8.67
12/19	40.20	— —	(7.32)	2.00	17.16
12/18	36.08	52 23	1.53	2.00	26.15
12/17	67.39	— —	(1.08)	2.00	26.62
Annual Growth (20.4%)	**(18.4%)**	**— —**	**—**	**(29.3%)**	

Schneider Electric SE

Schneider Electric is a leading global manufacturer of equipment for energy management and industrial automation ? products like circuit breakers and switches switchgear and transformers motor starters and power grid automation and electric car charging systems. Its end markets span residential and commercial buildings utilities oil and gas infrastructures waste water plants machine manufacturers and data centers. Schneider Electric operates into two segment these are the energy management which provides a complete end-to-end technology offering enabled by EcoStruxure and industrial automation which includes industrial automation and industrial control activities across discrete process & hybrid industries. Majority of the company's sales come from outside Europe.

Operations

Schneider Electric's product groups are centered on two core offerings ? energy management and industrial automation. Within those groups are its four operating segments. Energy management encompasses the Low Voltage Medium Voltage and Secure Power segments. Schneider's Industrial automation segment offers products and software for the automation and control of machines for manufacturing and industrial processes. Energy management segment generates nearly 80% of the company's revenue and industrial automation accounts for more than 20%.

The Low Voltage offers electrical distribution products for residential and commercial buildings and data centers span all industries and include several building automation products such as circuit breakers power monitoring (EcoStruxure is its IoT- enabled power management solution) and network connectivity.

The Industrial automation provides comprehensive product and software solutions for the automation and control of machinery used in manufacturing and other industrial plants. Smart automation solutions combine sensors motion systems and motor controllers with software for distributed control systems safety systems machine and process control and human-machine interface. The division also offers software for the design maintenance and operation of industrial processes.

Medium Voltage products include switchgear transformers electrical network protection and automation controls. This business also offers connected products and software for grid automation and infrastructure and pipeline management.

The Secure Power specializes in critical power products for data centers and networks and sells products like uninterruptable power supplies (UPS) IT rack systems power distribution units and security and cooling systems.

Geographic Reach

Headquartered in Rueil Malmaison France Schneider has operations in more than 100 countries. The Asia Pacific region and North America generate nearly 30% each of the revenue while Western Europe accounts for more than 25%. The rest of the world contributes more than 15%.

Sales and Marketing

Distributors account for more than 40% of Schneider Electric's total revenues through an extensive network of more than 190 countries all over the world. The company serves some 75 global customers including Apple BHP Billiton ExxonMobil Nestle and Veolia Environment.

The company's main distributor includes electrical distributors (both global and regional players) such as Rexel Sonepar CED Edmunson Graybar Imelco Idee and Fegime buying groups with both online and offline presence Specialists in IT telecom and data center applications for critical infrastructures such as Tech Data and Ingram Micro DIY retailers such as Home Depot and Lowe's in the US Saint Gobain Distribution in France and Brazil and Adeo Group and Kingfisher in Europe and Russia Online marketplaces and e-tailers such as RS Components T-Mall and Grainger and specialist technical distributors for automation and industrial software solutions access control and security products.

Financial Performance

Note: Growth rates may differ after conversion to US Dollars.

Except for a dip in 2016 Schneider Electric's revenue has seen slow but steady growth the last five years rising about 2% between 2015 and 2019. The company's Energy Management segment has been the chief growth drivers since 2016.

Sales in 2019 increased about 6% to ?27.2 billion compared to ?25.7 billion in 2018. Growth in 2019 was due to consolidation of Aveva and disposal of Pelco and the US panels business and a positive exchange rate effect of +2% driven by the appreciation of the USD against the euro. Both businesses saw strong organic growth with Energy Management up 5% and with Industrial Automation at 1%.

Net income increased 4% to a record ?2.4 billion in 2019 compared to 2018 primarily due to lower net expenses to ?261 million driven by continued decrease in the cost of debt. The effective income tax rate was 22% down from 23% last year.

Cash at the end of 2019 was ?3.4 billion an increase of ?1.2 billion from the prior year. Cash from operations contributed ?4.3 billion to the coffers while investing activities used ?916 million mainly for long-term pension assets. Financing activities used ?2.2 billion primarily in the form of dividend payments.

Strategy

Schneider's strategy for growth hinges on four aspects?portfolio optimization open ecosystem innovation and culture. The company has already made substantial progress towards these goals and is further outlining ways it can continue achieving these.

As part of its portfolio optimization Schneider has made the following developments in 2019: it had double digit growth in Software; a 50% growth in connected assets under management; the Pelco divestment closed and the disposal of US panels business in Q2; and the completion of sale of Energy Projects GmbH in December. Its priorities for 2020 is to further scale digital offers; grow Services by twice its average growth; and continue portfolio optimization by about ?1.5 to ?2 billion in 2021.

Schneider also aims to empower its unrivalled network of partners with digital innovation to seize new market values and champion open connected and interoperable solutions. In 2019 it launched Schneider Electric Exchange the world's first cross-industry open ecosystem that unleashes the power of collaboration in an open environment. It also plans on enhancing its EcoStruxure platform capabilities as a digital model across end-user applications.

Furthermore Schneider plans on increasing its investment in R&D and innovation digital sales force skills and marketing and communication. It also strives to be the most diverse inclusive and equitable company globally. To this end Schneider prioritizes boosting a high performance and innovation culture creating more development and career opportunities for all and building the next generation of leaders to achieve the company's growth ambitions.

Company Background

Schneider Electric's predecessor was founded in 1782 to make industrial equipment. After the upheavals of the French Revolution and the Napoleonic Wars the company came under the control of brothers Adolphe and Eugene Schneider in 1836. Within two years they had built the first French locomotive (the country's first rail line opened in 1832).

Schneider became one of France's most important heavy industry companies branching into a variety of machinery and steel operations.

The company rebuilt after WWII aided by the French government. It was restructured as a holding company and its operating units were split into three subsidiaries: civil and electrical engineering industrial manufacturing and construction.

In 1963 Schneider concluded an alliance with the Empain Group of Belgium and by 1969 three years after Schneider went public the two companies merged to become Empain-Schneider.

Schneider began reorganizing in 1980. The effort entered its final phase in 1993 with a major recapitalization that saw the merger of its former parent company Societe Parisienne d'Entreprises et de Participations with Schneider SA and the issue of new stock to existing stockholders.

HISTORY

Schneider Electric's predecessor was founded in 1782 to make industrial equipment. After the upheavals of the French Revolution and the Napoleonic Wars the company came under the control of brothers Adolphe and Eugene Schneider in 1836. Within two years they had built the first French locomotive (the country's first rail line opened in 1832).

Schneider became one of France's most important heavy industry companies branching into a variety of machinery and steel operations. However the country's industrial development continued to trail that of Britain and Germany due to recurrent political strife including the revolution of 1848 and the Franco-Prussian War. France also possessed fewer coal and iron deposits.

During WWI Schneider was a key part of France's war effort. It entered the electrical contracting business in 1929 and fought off nationalization attempts in the mid-1930s. The blitzkrieg of 1939 brought much of France under Nazi occupation and the Schneider factories that were not destroyed were commandeered by the Germans.

The company rebuilt after the war aided by the French government. It was restructured as a holding company and its operating units were split into three subsidiaries: civil and electrical engineering industrial manufacturing and construction. Charles Schneider the last family member to lead the company died in 1950.

In 1963 Schneider concluded an alliance with the Empain Group of Belgium and by 1969 three years after Schneider went public the two companies merged to become Empain-Schneider. It was a period when the company made numerous non-core acquisitions entering such fields as ski equipment fashion publishing and travel.

Schneider began reorganizing in 1980. The effort entered its final phase in 1993 with a major recapitalization that saw the merger of its former parent company Societe Parisienne d'Entreprises et de Participations with Schneider SA and the issue of new stock to existing stockholders.

EXECUTIVES

Chief Financial Officer, Hilary Maxson, $242,123 total compensation

Independent Director, Jill Lee, $151,540 total compensation

Director - Employee Shareholders Representative, Rita Felix, $54,410 total compensation

President and CEO, North America, Annette Clayton

Director, Anna Ohlssonleijon

Independent Director, Lip-Bu Tan, $170,910 total compensation

Chief Governance Officer and Secretary General, Herve Coureil

Executive Vice President, Energy Management, Member of the Executive Committee, Philippe Delorme

Independent Director, Leo Apotheker, $310,464 total compensation

Chairman of the Board, Chief Executive Officer, Member of the Executive Committee, Jean-Pascal Tricoire, $996,979 total compensation

Auditors: ERNST & YOUNG et Autres

LOCATIONS

HQ: Schneider Electric SE
35, rue Joseph Monier, CS 30323, Rueil-Malmaison, Cedex 92506
Phone: (33) 1 41 29 70 00   **Fax:** (33) 1 41 29 71 00
Web: www.se.com

2017 Sales

	% of total
Asia/Pacific	28
Western Europe	27
North America	27
Rest of the world	18
Total	**100**

PRODUCTS/OPERATIONS

2017 Sales

	% of total
Low Voltage (Buildings)	44
Industrial Automation (Industry)	23
Medium Voltage (Infrastructure)	18
Secure Power (IT)	15
Total	**100**

Selected Products

Electrical Car Charging
Electrical Protection and Control
Home Automation and Security
Light Switches and Electrical Sockets
Surge Protection and Power Conditioning
Uninterruptible Power Supply (UPS)
Building Management
Emergency Lighting
Fire and Security
Network Infrastructure and Connectivity
Power Monitoring and Control
Variable Speed Drives and Soft Starters
Circuit Breakers and Switches
Contactors and Protection Relays
Electrical Car Charging
Electrical Protection and Control
Motor Starters and Protection Components
Surge Protection and Power Conditioning
Switchboards and Enclosures
Solar and Energy Storage
Grid Automation and SCADA Software
Switchgear Components and transformers
Protection Relays
Substation Automation
Critical Power Cooling and Racks
Data Center Software
IT Power Distribution
Prefabricated Data Center Modules
Security and Environmental Monitoring
Boxes Cabling and Interfaces
Human Machine Interfaces (HMI)
Measurement and Instrumentation
Motion Control and Robotics
Sensors and RFID System
Signaling Devices
Telemetry and Remote SCADA Systems

COMPETITORS

ABB Ltd	LAIRD LIMITED
ENERPAC TOOL GROUP CORP.	ROTORK P.L.C.
	SONEPAR
GEA Group AG	Siemens AG
GENUIT GROUP PLC	TT ELECTRONICS PLC
HALMA PUBLIC LIMITED COMPANY	Voith GmbH & Co. KGaA
	WEIR GROUP PLC(THE)
HONEYWELL INTERNATIONAL INC.	

HISTORICAL FINANCIALS

Company Type: Public

Income Statement

FYE: December 31

	REVENUE ($ mil.)	NET INCOME ($ mil.)	NET PROFIT MARGIN	EMPLOYEES
12/19	30,492	2,709	8.9%	151,297
12/18	29,454	2,672	9.1%	155,286
12/17	29,660	2,577	8.7%	153,124
12/16	26,072	1,847	7.1%	143,901
12/15	29,016	1,532	5.3%	181,362
Annual Growth	1.2%	15.3%	—	(4.4%)

2019 Year-End Financials

Debt ratio: 18.3%
Return on equity: 11.4%
Cash ($ mil.): 4,032
Current ratio: 1.37
Long-term debt ($ mil.): 7,189

No. of shares (mil.): 551
Dividends
  Yield: 2.5%
  Payout: 10.8%
Market value ($ mil.): 11,241

	STOCK PRICE ($) FY Close	P/E High/Low		PER SHARE ($) Earnings	Dividends	Book Value
12/19	20.40	5	3	4.86	0.53	43.93
12/18	13.52	4	3	4.76	0.48	43.31
12/17	16.95	5	4	4.57	0.43	42.56
12/16	13.81	4	3	3.26	0.37	38.99
12/15	11.35	7	4	2.68	0.43	40.16
Annual Growth	15.8%	—	—	16.1%	5.3%	2.3%

SCOR S.E. (France)

A global independent Tier 1 reinsurance company SCOR provides treaty (groups of risks) and facultative (individual risks) reinsurance covering the risks of insurance underwriters around the globe. The company reinsures property/casualty life accident and health insurance lines. SCOR's business is divided into three business units which provide a broad range of innovative reinsurance solutions: SCOR Global P&C (Property & Casualty) SCOR Global Life and SCOR Global Investments. The company is structured around three regional management platforms or organizational hubs: the EMEA Hub the Americas Hub and the Asia-Pacific Hub. SCOR the world's fourth largest reinsurer is established in around 30 countries and provides services to over 4400 clients worldwide.

Operations

The company's life insurance unit SCOR Global Life accounts for about 55% of gross written premiums while SCOR Global P&C (property and casualty) brings in about 45%. Outside of its reinsurance operations the company has a third smaller business named SCOR Global Investments which provides asset and investment management services to the other operating SCOR facilities.

The SCOR Global Life segment operates worldwide through the subsidiaries and branches of SCOR SE. Via this network SCOR Global Life is represented in three business regions EMEA the Americas and Asia-Pacific reinsuring Life and Health insurance risks along the three product lines Protection Longevity and Financial Solutions with a strong focus on biometric risks. In order to achieve this SCOR Global Life manages and optimizes the in-force book deepens the franchise and aims at having the best team organization and tools.

SCOR Global P&C is represented in three business regions EMEA the Americas and Asia-Pacific

and operates in three business areas: Specialties Insurance (large corporate accounts underwritten through facultative insurance contracts direct insurance SCOR Channel for which SCOR is the sole capital provider and MGA business a specialized type of insurance agent/broker vested with underwriting authority from an insurer) Reinsurance (including Property Casualty Motor Credit and Surety Decennial Insurance Aviation Marine Engineering and Agricultural risks) and P&C Partners (including Cyber and Alternative Solutions).

Geographic Reach

SCOR has about 35 offices throughout in the Americas Europe Middle East Africa (EMEA) and Asia-Pacific. SCOR generated about one-third of its gross written premiums in Europe Middle East and Africa (EMEA) with significant market positions in France Germany Spain and Italy about half of its gross written premiums in the Americas and some one-fifth in Asia.

Sales and Marketing

Reinsurance is written either through brokers or directly. The Non-Life business unit wrote some 70% of gross written premiums through brokers and about 30% through direct business while the Life business unit wrote more than 5% through brokers and around 95% through direct business.

Financial Performance

Revenue for fiscal 2020 decreased to ?1.6 billion compared from the prior year with ?1.9 billion.

Net income for fiscal 2020 decreased to ?110 million compared from the prior year with ?908 million.

Cash held by the company at the end of fiscal 2020 increased to ?1.8 billion. Cash provided by operations was ?988 million while cash used for investing and financing activities were ?464 million and ?41 million respectively. Main cash uses were acquisitions and cash used to redeem financial liabilities.

Strategy

In September 2019 SCOR launched its strategic plan "Quantum Leap". This plan covers the period from mid-2019 to the end of 2021. It respects SCOR's four strategic cornerstones which are: a strong franchise achieved by deepening its presence in the local Non-Life and Life reinsurance markets in which SCOR operates with recognized expertise and strengthening proactive client relationships through best-in-class services and product innovation; a high degree of diversification of Non-Life and Life business and geographical presence providing more stable results and robust capital diversification benefits with the use of financial market instruments; a controlled risk appetite on both sides of the balance sheet; and a robust capital shield policy.

This plan aims to create the reinsurance company of tomorrow. To this end SCOR is transforming profoundly accelerating its use of new technologies such as artificial intelligence robots big data multi-cloud and e-business to innovate expand its product and services offering and increase its efficiency for the benefit of its clients throughout the world.

HISTORY

SCOR was founded in 1970 by the French government to compete against reinsurers like Munich Re and Swiss Reinsurance; the government eventually ceded control to a group of French insurers including AXA UAP Re and Groupe des Assurances Nationales. By 1972 SCOR was expanding internationally.

Growth continued throughout the 1970s and '80s. In 1989 the firm acquired Deutsche Continental R ckversicherungs in Germany. A year later the firm listed on the Paris stock exchange.

In the early 1990s SCOR's owners began setting up their own reinsurance operations and selling off their holdings in the company. In 1995 AXA and Assurances Generales de France were the last to sell their stakes. Also that year SCOR consolidated ownership in its subsidiaries and streamlined its Asian operations.

The year 1996 was a big one in the US for SCOR. It acquired the reinsurance business of Allstate and also listed on the New York Stock Exchange. As worldwide property/casualty markets took a downturn in 1996 and 1997 SCOR began expanding its life accident and health reinsurance.

Numerous natural disasters in 1998 and 1999 hobbled SCOR's already slumping property/casualty unit; losses were offset by increased business in other lines. SCOR acquired full control of its Commercial Risk Partners subsidiary in 1999 bolstering its specialty reinsurance business. In 2000 SCOR reorganized its industrial risk business to further offset recent losses. That year the company bought Partner Re's US subsidiary PartnerRe Life and Switzerland-based Veritas property/casualty reinsurance portfolio.

In 2001 SCOR joined Inreon an online reinsurance exchange set up by industry bigwigs Swiss Re and Munich Re. In 2002 it liquidated and sold off subsidiary Commercial Risk Partners to reduce costs. Expanding internationally the company opened offices in Korea and India in 2004 and 2005.

In 2007 SCOR acquired Swiss reinsurer Converium Holding beginning with a buy-up of about a third of the company's shares. The purchase agreement went through several drafts (one resulting in a lawsuit alleging that SCOR had deliberately undervalued Converium) but was eventually accepted by both boards of directors. The acquisition added customers in Austria Germany Switzerland and the UK and boosted SCOR into a spot among the top five global life reinsurers.

Also in 2007 SCOR transformed itself into a Societas Europaea a legal structure that allows it more financial freedom in its European operations. In addition the company voluntarily delisted from the New York Stock Exchange.

EXECUTIVES

Director, Employee representative, Fiona Camara, $62,667 total compensation

Independent Director, Adrien Couret, $4,853 total compensation

Director, Employee representative, Lauren Carraud, $34,357 total compensation

Independent Director, Natacha Valla, $44,436 total compensation

Member of the Executive Board, Group General Secretary, Chief Compliance Officer, Claire Le Gall-Robinson

Independent Director, Jane Wicker-Miurin, $174,329 total compensation

Independent Director, Wang Zhen, $95,710 total compensation

Independent Director, Fabrice Bregier, $91,152 total compensation

Independent Director representing Malakoff Mederic Assurances, Thomas Saunier, $62,667 total compensation

Chief Executive Officer of SCOR Global Life, Member of the Group Executive Committee, Frieder Knuepling, $972,916 total compensation

Deputy Chief Executive Officer of SCOR Global Life, Member of the Executive Committee, Brona Magee

Chief Executive Officer, Laurent Rousseau

Deputy Chief Executive Officer of SCOR Global P and C and CEO of Specialty Insurance, Member of the Executive Committee, Romain Launay

Chief Financial Officer, Member of the Executive Board, Ian Kelly

Chief Executive Officer of SCOR Global P&C, Member of the Executive Committee, Jean-Paul Conoscente

Independent Director, Bruno Pfister, $177,747 total compensation

Independent Director, Vanessa Marquette, $160,656 total compensation

Independent Director, Kory Sorenson, $133,310 total compensation

Lead Independent Director, Augustin de Romanet de Beaune, $183,444 total compensation

Chief Executive Officer of SCOR Global Investments SE, Member of the Executive Committee, Francois De Varenne, $2,045,671 total compensation

Director, Claude Tendil, $125,334 total compensation

Non-Executive Chairman of the Board, Denis Kessler, $2,301,531 total compensation

Auditors: Mazars

LOCATIONS

HQ: SCOR S.E. (France)
5 avenue Kleber, Paris 75116
Phone: (33) 1 58 44 70 00   Fax: (33) 1 58 44 85 00
Web: www.scor.com

2013 Gross Written Premiums

	% of total
Europe	42
Americas	39
Asia-Pacific & other regions	19
Total	**100**

PRODUCTS/OPERATIONS

2013 Premiums

	% of total
Global P&C	53
Global Life	47
Total	**100**

COMPETITORS

ADMIRAL GROUP PLC
AIG EUROPE (SERVICES) LIMITED
AON GLOBAL LIMITED
ATRIUM UNDERWRITERS LIMITED
Baloise Holding AG
Hannover Rück SE
LIBERTY MUTUAL HOLDING COMPANY INC.
München er
Ping An Insurance (Group) Company Of China Ltd.
RFIB GROUP LIMITED
Talanx AG
WARRANTECH CORPORATION
Zurich Insurance Group AG

HISTORICAL FINANCIALS

Company Type: Public

Income Statement

	ASSETS ($ mil.)	NET INCOME ($ mil.)	INCOME AS % OF ASSETS	EMPLOYEES
				FYE: December 31
12/20	56,721	287	0.5%	3,123
12/19	52,633	473	0.9%	3,028
12/18	50,827	368	0.7%	2,887
12/17	51,826	342	0.7%	2,955
12/16	45,712	636	1.4%	2,802
Annual Growth	5.5%	(18.0%)	—	2.7%

2020 Year-End Financials

Return on assets: 0.5%
Return on equity: 3.7%
Long-term debt ($ mil.): —
No. of shares (mil.): 186
Sales ($ mil) 20,909

Dividends
Yield: 0.6%
Payout: 144.0%
Market value ($ mil.): 597

	STOCK PRICE ($) FY.Close	P/E High/Low		PER SHARE ($) Earnings	Dividends	Book Value
12/20	3.20	4	2	1.53	2.21	40.51
12/19	4.28	2	2	2.53	0.20	38.24
12/18	4.41	3	2	1.95	0.20	36.11
12/17	4.06	3	2	1.81	0.20	39.58
12/16	3.50	1	1	3.38	0.16	38.05
Annual Growth	(2.2%)	—		(17.9%)	92.4%	1.6%

Sekisui House, Ltd. (Japan)

Sekisui House could have written the book on Zen and the art of house building. One of Japan's leading homebuilders Sekisui House designs prefabricates and builds steel wooden and concrete houses and condominiums. It has built 2.2 billion homes. It is also involved in selling land detached houses and condominiums. Its real estate operations include leasing and managing houses low-rise apartments and commercial and retail buildings. Other operations include contract remodeling and landscaping. The company is also focusing on green building and sustainability in its new line of homes and adds such features as fuel cells to its houses. Sekisui Chemical owns 10% of the company which dates back to 1929.

EXECUTIVES

Vice Chairman of the Executive Board, Representative Director, Yosuke Horiuchi
Senior Managing Executive Officer, Director, Toru Ishii
Senior Managing Executive Officer, Director, Toshiharu Miura
Executive President, Chief Executive Officer, Representative Director, Yoshihiro Nakai
Independent Director, Yukiko Yoshimaru
Executive Vice President, Director, Kumpei Nishida
Independent Director, Keiko Takegawa
Independent Director, Yoshimi Nakajima
Executive Vice President, Representative Director, Satoshi Tanaka
Independent Director, Toshifumi Kitazawa
Auditors: Ernst & Young ShinNihon LLC

LOCATIONS

HQ: Sekisui House, Ltd. (Japan)
1-1-88 Oyodonaka, Kita-ku, Osaka 531-0076
Phone: (81) 6 6440 3111   Fax: (81) 6 6440 3331
Web: www.sekisuihouse.co.jp

PRODUCTS/OPERATIONS

Selected Subsidiaries and Affiliates

Sekisui House Umeda Operation Co. Ltd.
Sekiwa Real Estate Chubu Ltd.
Sekiwa Real Estate Chugoku Ltd.
Sekiwa Real Estate Kansai Ltd.
Sekiwa Real Estate Kyushu Ltd.
Sekiwa Real Estate Sapporo Ltd.
Sekiwa Real Estate Tohoku Ltd.
SGM Operation Co. Ltd

COMPETITORS

BORAN CRAIG BARBER ENGEL CONSTRUCTION CO. INC.
CADUS CORPORATION
CHRIS FREEMAN DESIGN LIMITED
CROWELL DON INC
DAVIDSON COMMUNITIES LLC
ENVOLVE CLIENT SERVICES GROUP LLC
HOVNANIAN ENTERPRISES INC.
HUNT BUILDING COMPANY LTD
KEEPMOAT HOMES LIMITED
LLANMOOR DEVELOPMENT CO. LIMITED
MERITAGE HOMES CORPORATION
SEDDON HOMES LIMITED
ST JAMES GROUP LIMITED
SUMITOMO REALTY & DEVELOPMENT CO. LTD.
TOLL BROTHERS INC.
WARINGS CONTRACTORS LIMITED
WESTON HOMES PLC

HISTORICAL FINANCIALS

Company Type: Public

Income Statement

	REVENUE ($ mil.)	NET INCOME ($ mil.)	NET PROFIT MARGIN	EMPLOYEES
				FYE: January 31
01/21	23,358	1,179	5.0%	28,362
01/20	22,172	1,296	5.8%	27,397
01/19	19,886	1,183	6.0%	24,775
01/18	19,852	1,224	6.2%	24,391
01/17	17,843	1,072	6.0%	23,299
Annual Growth	7.0%	2.4%	—	5.0%

2021 Year-End Financials

Debt ratio: 0.2%
Return on equity: 9.5%
Cash ($ mil.): 5,730
Current ratio: 2.13
Long-term debt ($ mil.): 2,889

No. of shares (mil.): 681
Dividends
Yield: 0.0%
Payout: 47.2%
Market value ($ mil.): 13,261

	STOCK PRICE ($) FY Close	P/E High/Low		PER SHARE ($) Earnings	Dividends	Book Value
01/21	19.47	0	0	1.73	0.82	18.60
01/20	21.51	0	0	1.89	0.73	17.01
01/19	15.09	0	0	1.71	0.71	15.83
01/18	18.44	0	0	1.77	0.62	15.93
01/17	16.13	0	0	1.54	0.56	14.08
Annual Growth	4.8%	—		2.9%	9.7%	7.2%

Seven & i Holdings Co. Ltd.

Seven & I Holdings Co. generates more than half its sales from convenience store operations both in Japan and elsewhere operating primarily under the 7-Eleven name. The company also has general merchandise superstores department stores and specialty stores (including Denny's restaurants) as well as a smaller division that provides financial services. All told Seven & I Holdings owns about 23000 stores in Japan and about 72000 stores worldwide. Its major subsidiaries include Seven-Eleven Japan and 7-Eleven Inc. Ito-Yokado Co. Sogo & Seibu Seven & i Food Systems and Seven Bank. The company generates about 40% sales outside Japan.

Operations

Illustrating its name Seven & i Holdings operates through seven segments: domestic convenience stores overseas convenience stores super-stores department stores specialty stores financial services and other.

Domestic and overseas convenience stores together contribute more than 50% to total revenue with overseas operations representing about two-thirds of that.

Superstores department stores and specialty stores located mostly in Japan together add another more than 40%. Superstores include general merchandise stores serving local communities (ItoYokado) and supermarkets such as York Mart and York Benimaru. Seven & i Holdings' leading department store is the Sogo & Seibu chain while its specialty stores include Seven & i Food Systems (operator of Denny's and other restaurants chains in Japan).

The financial services and other segments which bring in less than 5% of revenue.

Geographic Reach
Seven & I Holdings owns about 23000 stores in Japan and about 72000 stores in about 20 countries and territories internationally.

Sales and Marketing
Seven & i Holdings Co. Ltd. have developing stores that provide different kinds of value to meet the needs of society and customers. All deliveries from distribution centers to stores are made using environmentally-friendly delivery trucks (either hybrid vehicles or electric vehicles). Approximately 24 million customers visit the store per day

Financial Performance
The company's performance has seen a downward trend for the past three years starting from 2019 with 2021 as the lowest performing year even when compared with 2017 performance levels.

The company's revenue in 2021 decreased by 878 billion to 5.7 trillion as compared to 2020's revenue of about 6.6 billion.

Net income in 2021 also decreased by 38.9 billion to 179.2 billion as compared to the prior year's net income of about 218 billion.

Cash held by the company at the end of 2021 amounted to about 2.2 trillion. Cash provided by operations was 539.9 billion. Investing activities used 394 billion while financing activities provided 690 billion. Main cash uses were for acquisition of property and equipment and acquisition of intangible assets.

Strategy
Seven & I's growth strategy is comprised of three main points: opening the next "convenience" door; challenge for "food that are needed by customers; and the creation of affluent "lifestyle hubs".

In 2021 the company introduced new layouts in their operations that are more reflective of the emerging customer need. The company continues to work with its franchisees to create stores that offer products and services that adapts to its location. In addition growth is further enhanced through product development store expansion and the introduction of new services.

The group also targets the food business in the Tokyo metropolitan area capitalizing on the potential of this market focusing on integration and realignment of food supermarkets under the group's organization. A system was also created to supply prepared dished and semi-prepared foods across the group.

The group's largest stores Ito-Yokado and Sogo & Seibu are reviewing their existing store networks and restructuring them. The restructuring of these stores were able to address the demand for one-stop sopping that has been more common during the COVID-19 pandemic.

Company Background
Seven & i Holdings was founded in late 2005 to provide infrastructure and business services to its group of operating companies. 7-Eleven Inc. became a wholly owned subsidiary shortly thereafter.

EXECUTIVES
Executive Vice President, Vice President, Representative Director, Katsuhiro Goto
Managing Executive Officer, Chief Director of Business Promotion, Director, Junro Ito
President, Executive President, Representative Director, Ryuichi Isaka
Executive Officer, Chief Director of Corporate Communication, Director, Kimiyoshi Yamaguchi
President & Chief Executive Officer of Subsidiary, Director, Joseph DePinto
Executive Officer, Chief Director of Finance & Accounting, President of Subsidiaries, Director, Yoshimichi Maruyama
President of Subsidiary, Director, Fumihiko Nagamatsu
Director, Shigeki Kimura
Independent Director, Kazuko Rudy
Auditors: KPMG AZSA LLC

LOCATIONS
HQ: Seven & i Holdings Co. Ltd.
8-8 Nibancho, Chiyoda-ku, Tokyo 102-8452
Phone: (81) 3 6238 3000
Web: www.7andi.com

2018 Sales

	% of total
Japan	65
North America	33
Other regions	2
Total	**100**

PRODUCTS/OPERATIONS

2018 Sales

	% of total
Overseas convenience stores	33
Superstores	31
Domestic convenience stores	15
Department stores	11
Specialty stores	7
Financial services	3
Other	-
Total	**100**

Selected Subsidiaries and Affiliates
Convenience stores
  7-Eleven Inc.
  Seven-Eleven (Beijing) Co.
  Seven-Eleven China Co.
  Seven-Eleven Hawaii Inc.
  Seven-Eleven Japan Co.
Superstores
  Chengdu Ito-Yokado Co.
  Hua Tang Yokado Commercial Co.
  Ito-Yokado Co.
  KK. Sanei
  Marudai Co.
  SHELL GARDEN CO.
  York Mart Co.
  York-Benimaru Co.
Department stores
  Sogo & Seibu Co.
Specialty stores
  Barneys Japan
  Francfranc Corporation
  The Loft Co.
  Oshman's Japan Co.
  Seven & i Food Systems Co.
  Tower Records Japan
Financial services
  Seven Bank
  Seven Card Service Co.
  Seven Financial Service Co.

COMPETITORS
ALFRESA HOLDINGS CORPORATION
ANA HOLDINGS INC.
Brenntag Holding GmbH
CORE-MARK HOLDING COMPANY INC.
DAI-ICHI LIFE HOLDINGS INC.
FAST RETAILING CO. LTD.
Falabella S.A.
HIBBETT INC.
ISETAN MITSUKOSHI HOLDINGS LTD.
J.FRONT RETAILING CO.LTD.
JAPAN POST HOLDINGS CO.LTD.
LIFETIME BRANDS INC.
LIXIL CORPORATION
MEDIPAL HOLDINGS CORPORATION
METCASH LIMITED
SOMPO HOLDINGS INC.
SPARTANNASH COMPANY
T&D HOLDINGS INC.
TITON HOLDINGS PLC

HISTORICAL FINANCIALS
Company Type: Public

Income Statement — FYE: February 28

	REVENUE ($ mil.)	NET INCOME ($ mil.)	NET PROFIT MARGIN	EMPLOYEES
02/21	54,237	1,686	3.1%	135,332
02/20	61,118	2,006	3.3%	138,808
02/19	61,296	1,832	3.0%	144,628
02/18	56,373	1,691	3.0%	149,414
02/17	51,986	861	1.7%	140,938
Annual Growth	1.1%	18.3%	—	(1.0%)

2021 Year-End Financials
Debt ratio: 0.2%
Return on equity: 6.8%
Cash ($ mil.): 20,589
Current ratio: 1.20
Long-term debt ($ mil.): 8,724
No. of shares (mil.): 884
Dividends
  Yield: 0.0%
  Payout: 24.1%
Market value ($ mil.): 16,930

	STOCK PRICE ($) FY Close	P/E High/Low		PER SHARE ($) Earnings	Dividends	Book Value
02/21	19.14	0	0	1.91	0.46	28.38
02/20	16.85	0	0	2.27	0.44	27.06
02/19	21.98	0	0	2.07	0.42	25.76
02/18	20.83	0	0	1.91	0.40	25.65
02/17	19.55	0	0	0.97	0.42	23.56
Annual Growth	(0.5%)	—	—	18.3%	2.5%	4.8%

Shaanxi Yanchang Petroleum Chemical Engineering Co., Ltd.

Auditors: Xi'an Xigema Certified Public Accountant Film Limited

LOCATIONS
HQ: Shaanxi Yanchang Petroleum Chemical Engineering Co., Ltd.
No. 2, Xinqiao North Road, Yangling Agriculture Hi-tech Industry Demo Zonee, Xian, Shaanxi 712100
Phone: (86) 29 87033019   **Fax:** (86) 29 87031001
Web: www.qfny.com

HISTORICAL FINANCIALS
Company Type: Public

Income Statement   FYE: December 31

	REVENUE ($ mil.)	NET INCOME ($ mil.)	NET PROFIT MARGIN	EMPLOYEES
12/20	19,528	432	2.2%	0
12/19	1,159	42	3.7%	0
12/18	1,100	40	3.7%	0
12/17	598	20	3.4%	0
12/16	522	17	3.4%	0
Annual Growth	147.3%	122.4%	—	—

2020 Year-End Financials
Debt ratio: 1.7%
Return on equity: 30.2%
Cash ($ mil.): 3,016
Current ratio: 1.07
Long-term debt ($ mil.): 1,901
No. of shares (mil.): —
Dividends
  Yield: —
  Payout: —
Market value ($ mil.): —

Shandong Iron & Steel Co Ltd

EXECUTIVES

Deputy General Manager, Youfang Xu
Vice Chairman of the Board, Xiangyang Chen
Independent Director, Aiguo Wang
Independent Director, Xiaofeng Ping
General Manager, Director, Dengwu Luo
Deputy General Manager, Xiangdong Wang
Secretary of the Board, Lishan Jin
Auditors: Crowe Horwath CPA Limited (Special General Partner)

LOCATIONS

HQ: Shandong Iron & Steel Co Ltd
  Building 4, Shun Tai Plaza, No. 2000, Shun Hua Road, High-Tech Zone, Jinan, Shandong Province 250101
Phone: (86) 531 67606889   **Fax:** (86) 531 67606881
Web: www.sdsteel.cc

HISTORICAL FINANCIALS
Company Type: Public

Income Statement   FYE: December 31

	REVENUE ($ mil.)	NET INCOME ($ mil.)	NET PROFIT MARGIN	EMPLOYEES
12/20	13,350	110	0.8%	0
12/19	10,216	83	0.8%	0
12/18	8,128	306	3.8%	0
12/17	7,360	295	4.0%	0
12/16	7,220	(86)	—	0
Annual Growth	16.6%			

2020 Year-End Financials
Debt ratio: 3.1%
Return on equity: 3.4%
Cash ($ mil.): 1,044
Current ratio: 0.59
Long-term debt ($ mil.): 924
No. of shares (mil.): —
Dividends
  Yield: —
  Payout: —
Market value ($ mil.): —

Shanghai Construction Group Co., Ltd.

Auditors: PricewaterhouseCoopers Zhong Tian CPAs Limited Company

LOCATIONS

HQ: Shanghai Construction Group Co., Ltd.
  No. 666, Dongdaming Road, Shanghai 200080
Phone: (86) 21 35100838   **Fax:** (86) 21 55886222
Web: www.shconstruction.cn

HISTORICAL FINANCIALS
Company Type: Public

Income Statement   FYE: December 31

	REVENUE ($ mil.)	NET INCOME ($ mil.)	NET PROFIT MARGIN	EMPLOYEES
12/20	35,369	512	1.4%	0
12/19	29,532	564	1.9%	0
12/18	24,794	404	1.6%	0
12/17	21,833	397	1.8%	0
12/16	19,247	301	1.6%	0
Annual Growth	16.4%	14.1%	—	—

2020 Year-End Financials
Debt ratio: 3.8%
Return on equity: 9.5%
Cash ($ mil.): 11,997
Current ratio: 1.16
Long-term debt ($ mil.): 8,175
No. of shares (mil.): —
Dividends
  Yield: —
  Payout: —
Market value ($ mil.): —

Shanghai Electric Group Co Ltd

Auditors: PricewaterhouseCoopers Zhong Tian LLP

LOCATIONS

HQ: Shanghai Electric Group Co Ltd
  No. 212 Qinjiang Road, Shanghai 200233
Phone: (86) 21 33261888   **Fax:** (86) 21 34695780
Web: www.shanghai-electric.com

HISTORICAL FINANCIALS
Company Type: Public

Income Statement   FYE: December 31

	REVENUE ($ mil.)	NET INCOME ($ mil.)	NET PROFIT MARGIN	EMPLOYEES
12/20	20,990	574	2.7%	0
12/19	18,324	503	2.7%	0
12/18	14,706	438	3.0%	0
12/17	12,223	408	3.3%	0
12/16	11,387	296	2.6%	0
Annual Growth	16.5%	18.0%	—	—

2020 Year-End Financials
Debt ratio: 2.1%
Return on equity: 5.7%
Cash ($ mil.): 3,706
Current ratio: 1.24
Long-term debt ($ mil.): 2,735
No. of shares (mil.): —
Dividends
  Yield: —
  Payout: —
Market value ($ mil.): —

	STOCK PRICE ($) FY Close	P/E High/Low	PER SHARE ($) Earnings	Dividends	Book Value
12/20	5.58	29 20	0.04	0.00	(0.00)
12/19	6.09	32 26	0.03	0.14	(0.00)
12/18	6.84	38 30	0.03	0.22	(0.00)
12/17	8.11	59 43	0.03	0.00	(0.00)
12/16	8.65	63 47	0.02	0.00	(0.00)
Annual Growth	(10.4%)	— —	13.1%	—	—

Shanghai Jinfeng Investment Co Ltd

Auditors: Ernst & Young Hua Ming Certified Public Accountants

LOCATIONS

HQ: Shanghai Jinfeng Investment Co Ltd
  29th Floor, Tianan Center, No. 338, Nanjing West Road, Shanghai 200003
Phone: (86) 21 63592020   **Fax:** (86) 21 63586115
Web: www.ehousee.com

HISTORICAL FINANCIALS
Company Type: Public

Income Statement   FYE: December 31

	REVENUE ($ mil.)	NET INCOME ($ mil.)	NET PROFIT MARGIN	EMPLOYEES
12/20	69,731	2,293	3.3%	0
12/19	61,521	2,118	3.4%	0
12/18	50,700	1,653	3.3%	0
12/17	44,628	1,388	3.1%	0
12/16	35,627	1,037	2.9%	0
Annual Growth	18.3%	21.9%	—	—

2020 Year-End Financials
Debt ratio: 3.4%
Return on equity: 18.2%
Cash ($ mil.): 15,820
Current ratio: 1.20
Long-term debt ($ mil.): 31,653
No. of shares (mil.): —
Dividends
  Yield: —
  Payout: —
Market value ($ mil.): —

Shanghai Pharmaceuticals Holding Co Ltd

EXECUTIVES

Chairman, Jun Zhou
Vice President, Haoliang Gu
Independent Non-Executive Director, Liang Hong
President, Executive Director, Min Zuo
Vice President, Yaohua Zhang
Vice President, Jianyi Mao

Chief Financial Officer, Vice President, Executive Director, Bo Shen

Independent Non-Executive Director, Wenxun Huo

Independent Non-Executive Director, Chaoyang Gu

Vice President, Yong Zhao

Vice Chairman of the Board, Non-Executive Director, Dawei Ge

Joint Company Secretary, Jinzhu Chen

Auditors: PricewaterhouseCoopers Zhong Tian LLP

LOCATIONS

HQ: Shanghai Pharmaceuticals Holding Co Ltd
Shanghai Pharmaceutical Building, No. 200, Taicang Road, Shanghai 200020
Phone: (86) 21 63730908   **Fax:** (86) 21 63289333
Web: www.sphchina.com

HISTORICAL FINANCIALS

Company Type: Public

Income Statement   FYE: December 31

	REVENUE ($ mil.)	NET INCOME ($ mil.)	NET PROFIT MARGIN	EMPLOYEES
12/20	29,342	687	2.3%	0
12/19	26,812	586	2.2%	0
12/18	23,128	564	2.4%	0
12/17	20,107	541	2.7%	0
12/16	17,391	460	2.6%	0
Annual Growth	14.0%	10.5%	—	—

2020 Year-End Financials

Debt ratio: 2.1%
Return on equity: 10.3%
Cash ($ mil.): 3,409
Current ratio: 1.22
Long-term debt ($ mil.): 181

No. of shares (mil.): —
Dividends
Yield: 0.0%
Payout: 108.7%
Market value ($ mil.): —

	STOCK PRICE ($) FY Close	P/E High/Low		PER SHARE ($) Earnings	Dividends	Book Value
12/20	8.35	7	5	0.24	0.26	(0.00)
12/19	9.84	8	6	0.21	0.24	(0.00)
12/18	12.92	10	8	0.20	0.23	(0.00)
12/17	12.64	11	10	0.20	0.22	(0.00)
12/16	13.32	12	7	0.17	0.19	(0.00)
Annual Growth	(11.0%)	—	—	9.0%	8.3%	—

Sharp Corp (Japan)

Sharp is a recognized brand for electronic components and computer hardware and peripherals. The company's flagship products are LCDs and PCs. The company also produces solar cells laser diodes and optical sensors. Other Sharp offerings are printers and cell phones; consumer audio and video products such as Blu-ray disc players and LCD TVs; and a variety of appliances such as air purifiers and steam ovens. Founded by Tokuji Hayakawa Sharp traces its roots back to 1912 as metalworking shop in Matsui-cho Honjo Tokyo.

Operations

Sharp operates in three reportable segments: 8K Ecosystem (about 50% of total sales) Smart Life (some 35%) and ICT (around 15%).

8K Ecosystem's products is comprised of automotive cameras commercial projectors POS systems and audio equipment among others. The Smart Life segment includes home appliances telephones storage batteries and water foundries while

ICT's products are mobile phones and personal computers.

Geographic Reach

Based in Osaka Japan Sharp has ten branches and eight R&D facilities in Japan. It also has overseas R&D in US UK China Malaysia and India.

Financial Performance

In 2021 (ended March) Sharp reported 2.4 trillion in revenue down about 163.7 billion from the year before due to lower sales from Smart Life.

In 2021 the company had a net profit of 53.2 billion a 28% increase from the previous year's net income of 13.7 billion.

Strategy

In mid-2021 Sharp Solar Solution Asia Co. Ltd. (SSSA) has concluded an agreement with Fuyo General Lease Co. Ltd. to establish S-Solar Generation Thailand Co. Ltd. which will sell electricity in Thailand. This is the first time that Sharp Corporation or one of its subsidiaries has entered the business of selling power to private companies. Under a PPA*3 customer companies signing contracts with the new joint venture will be able to have a solar power system installed with zero initial investment and use solar-generated power at a reduced rate.

Recent years have seen growing demand for solar power systems in Thailand as the country moves to become carbon free. The service provided by this new joint venture will lower the cost barriers normally faced at time of solar power system installation and will contribute to the further spread of renewable energy.

The new joint venture will install solar power systems on customers' facilities (building roofs for example) and sell the electricity generated to the customer at a rate lower than electricity from the grid. SSSA will be in charge of installing and maintaining the solar panels. Operation of a solar power generation system is scheduled to begin in March 2022 at an appliances factory the first customer of the new joint venture.

Company Background

Tokuji Hayakawa established Hayakawa Electric Industry in 1912 to make a type of belt buckle he had designed. Three years later he invented the first mechanical pencil named the Ever-Sharp which was a commercial success. After an earthquake leveled much of Tokyo in 1923 including Hayakawa's business he moved to Osaka and sold the rights to his pencil to finance a new factory. He introduced Japan's first crystal radio sets in 1925 and four years later debuted a vacuum tube radio.

Following WWII Hayakawa Electric developed an experimental TV which it began mass-producing in 1953. The company was ready with color TVs when Japan initiated color broadcasts in 1960. Hayakawa Electric grew tremendously during the 1960s introducing microwave ovens (1962) solar cells (1963) the first electronic all-transistor-diode calculator (1964) and the first gallium arsenide LED (1969). The firm opened a US office in 1962. In 1970 the company began to make its own semiconductor devices and changed its name to Sharp Corp. a nod to the name of its first product.

HISTORY

Tokuji Hayakawa got started in manufacturing in 1912 when he established Hayakawa Electric Industry to make a type of belt buckle he had designed. Three years later he invented the first mechanical pencil named the Ever-Sharp which was a commercial success. After an earthquake leveled much of Tokyo in 1923 including Hayakawa's business he moved to Osaka and sold the rights to his pencil to finance a new factory. He introduced Japan's first crystal radio sets in 1925 and four years later debuted a vacuum tube radio.

Following WWII Hayakawa Electric developed an experimental TV which it began mass-producing in 1953. The company was ready with color TVs when Japan initiated color broadcasts in 1960. Hayakawa Electric grew tremendously during the 1960s introducing microwave ovens (1962) solar cells (1963) the first electronic all-transistor-diode calculator (1964) and the first gallium arsenide LED (1969). The firm opened a US office in 1962.

In 1970 the company began to make its own semiconductor devices and changed its name to Sharp Corporation a nod to the name of its first product. It began mass production of LCDs in 1973. Sharp later introduced the first electronic calculator with an LCD (1973) solar-powered calculators (1976) and a credit card-sized calculator (1979).

EXECUTIVES

Executive President, Chief Operating Officer, Chief Director of Administration Control, Representative Director, Katsuaki Nomura

Senior Managing Executive Officer, Chief Director of Smart Appliances & Solutions Business, Manager of Smart Life Group, Masahiro Okitsu

Senior Managing Executive Officer, Manager of Chairman Office, Yoshihiro Hashimoto

Senior Managing Executive Officer, Manager of ICT Group, Yoichi Tsusue

Independent Director, Hse-Tung Lu

Independent Director, Yasuo Himeiwa

Independent Director, Yutaka Nakagawa

Independent Director, Ting-Chen Hsu

Director, Hong-Jen Chuang

Chairman of the Board, Executive Chairman, Chief Executive Officer, Representative Director, Jeng-Wu Tai

Senior Managing Executive Officer, Chief Director of Smart Business Solution Business, Manager of 8K Ecosystem Group, Fujikazu Nakayama

Auditors: PricewaterhouseCoopers Aarata LLC

LOCATIONS

HQ: Sharp Corp (Japan)
1 Takumi-cho, Sakai-ku, Sakai, Osaka 590-8522
Phone: (81) 72 282 1221   **Fax:** 201 529-8425
Web: www.sharp.co.jp

PRODUCTS/OPERATIONS

2015 Sales

	% of total
Products business	54
Device business	46
Total	**100**

Selected Products

Consumer/information products
  Audiovisual and communication equipment
  Audio amplifiers
  Blu-ray disc players
  Digital cameras
  High-definition televisions
  Liquid crystal display DVD televisions
  Liquid crystal display televisions
  Liquid crystal display video projectors
  Mobile phones
  Video cameras
  Information equipment
  Calculators
  Digital copiers
  Fax machines
  Mobile business tools
  Personal computers
  Printers
  Home appliances
  Air cleaning systems
  Superheated steam ovens
Electronic components

Flash memory
Integrated circuits
Laser diodes and other optoelectronic devices
Radio-frequency components
Satellite broadcasting components
Solar cells and other photovoltaic devices

COMPETITORS

AMPEX CORPORATION	PARKERVISION INC.
ANDREA ELECTRONICS	PGI INC.
CORPORATION	QUALCOMM INCORPORATED
APPLE INC.	Quanta Computer Inc.
CASIO COMPUTER CO.	RF MONOLITHICS INC.
LTD.	SANYO ELECTRIC CO.
CLEARONE INC.	LTD.
FUNAI ELECTRIC CO.LTD.	TDK CORPORATION
KOSS CORPORATION	TEXAS INSTRUMENTS
MOTOROLA SOLUTIONS	INCORPORATED
INC.	UNIVERSAL ELECTRONICS
PANASONIC MOBILE	INC.
CO.LTD.	VARTA AG

HISTORICAL FINANCIALS

Company Type: Public

Income Statement				FYE: March 31
	REVENUE ($ mil.)	NET INCOME ($ mil.)	NET PROFIT MARGIN	EMPLOYEES
03/21	21,909	481	2.2%	50,478
03/20	20,923	193	0.9%	52,876
03/19	21,672	670	3.1%	54,156
03/18	22,858	661	2.9%	47,171
03/17	18,340	(222)	—	41,898
Annual Growth	4.5%	—		4.8%

2021 Year-End Financials

Debt ratio: 0.3%
Return on equity: 17.0%
Cash ($ mil.): 3,088
Current ratio: 1.34
Long-term debt ($ mil.): 5,074

No. of shares (mil.): 610
Dividends
  Yield: 0.9%
  Payout: —
Market value ($ mil.): 2,620

	STOCK PRICE ($) FY Close	P/E High/Low		PER SHARE ($) Earnings	Dividends	Book Value
03/21	4.29	0	0	0.79	0.04	5.18
03/20	2.59	0	0	0.30	0.05	4.77
03/19	2.74	0	0	0.83	0.02	5.95
03/18	7.44	0	0	0.81	0.00	7.15
03/17	4.19	—	—	(0.61)	0.00	5.29
Annual Growth	0.6%	—	—	—	—	(0.5%)

Shell plc

Royal Dutch Shell (Shell) boasts worldwide proved reserves of 1.3 billion barrels of oil equivalent. Operating in over 70 countries the British-Dutch company pumps out 3.6 million barrels of crude oil liquefied natural gas (LNG) natural gas synthetic crude oil and bitumen. Among the company's many and varied operations it boasts the world's deepest oil and gas project in the Gulf of Mexico the world's largest offshore floating LNG production plant off the Australian coast and the world's largest retail fuel network at about 46000 stations. Royal Dutch Shell also runs over 20 refineries transports natural gas trades gas and electricity and develops renewable energy.

Operations

Shell divides its operations into five segments: Integrated Gas Upstream Oil Products Chemicals and Corporate.

Its Oil Products business is part of an integrated value chain that refines crude oil and other feedstocks into products that are moved and marketed around the world for domestic industrial and transport use. The products it sells include gasoline diesel heating oil aviation fuel marine fuel low-carbon fuels lubricants bitumen and sulphur. It also trade crude oil oil products and petrochemicals. It provides access to electric vehicle charge points at home at work and on-the-go including at its forecourts and at a range of public locations. The Oil Products generate some 70% of total sales.

Integrated Gas comprises the company's liquefied natural gas (LNG) operations including exploration extraction and transportation. Other activities include the marketing and trading of crude oil natural gas LNG electricity and carbon-emission rights and the sale of LNG as a fuel for heavy-duty vehicles and vessels. Shell's investments in renewable and other low-carbon energy forms its New Energies business are housed in this segment. The Integrated Gas segment accounts for nearly 20% of total sales.

Chemicals business supplies customers with a range of base and intermediate chemicals used to make products that people use every day. It has a major manufacturing plants which are located close to refineries and its own marketing network. Chemicals represent more than 5% of total sales.

Shell's Upstream segment explores for and extracts crude oil natural gas and natural gas liquids. It also markets oil and gas and delivers them to market. The Upstream segment generates some 5% of total sales.

The Corporate segment covers the non-operating activities supporting Shell. It comprises Shell's holdings and treasury organisation self-insurance activities and headquarters and central functions.

Geographic Reach

Listed in London but run out of The Hague in the Netherlands Royal Dutch Shell has enormous global reach producing oil and natural gas in more than 70 countries including Australia Brazil Brunei Canada China Denmark Germany Malaysia the Netherlands Nigeria Norway Oman Qatar Russia the UK and the US.

Shell operates about 46000 fuel stations across 70 countries. Royal Dutch Shell's lubricants business produces markets and sells products in over 160 market and has four base oil manufacturing plants more than 30 lubricant blending plants eight grease plants and four gas-to-liquid base oil storage hubs.

It makes about 35% of revenue from its Asia/Oceania/Africa reporting region roughly 30% each from Europe and US. Other Americas (Brazil in particular) account for the remainder.

Financial Performance

The company's revenue for fiscal 2020 decreased to $180.5 billion compared with $344.9 billion in the previous year.

Loss for fiscal 2020 was $21.7 billion compared to the prior year with an income of $15.8 billion.

Cash held by the company at the end of fiscal 2020 increased to $31.8 billion. Cash provided by operations was $34.1 billion while cash used for investing and financing activities were $13.3 billion and $7.2 billion respectively. Main cash uses were capital expenditures dividends paid and repurchases of shares.

Strategy

Powering Progress sets out Shell's strategy to accelerate the transition of its business to net-zero emissions in step with society. It is designed to deliver value for its shareholders for its customers and for wider society. Powering Progress serves four main goals: generating shareholder value achieving net-zero emissions powering lives and respecting nature.

The company is transforming its company across its three business pillars of Growth Transition and Upstream. The company's growth pillar includes its service stations traditional and low-carbon fuels integrated power hydrogen charging for electric vehicles nature-based solutions and carbon capture and storage. It focuses on working with its customers to accelerate the transition to net-zero emissions.

Shell's Transition pillar comprises its Integrated Gas and its Chemicals and Products businesses and produces sustainable cash flow. The company's Upstream pillar delivers the cash and returns needed to fund its shareholder distributions and the transformation of its company by providing vital supplies of oil and natural gas.

HISTORY

In 1870 Marcus Samuel inherited an interest in his father's London trading company which imported seashells from the Far East. He expanded the business and after securing a contract for Russian oil began selling kerosene in the Far East.

Standard Oil underpriced competitors to defend its Asian markets. Samuel secretly prepared his response and in 1892 unveiled the first of a fleet of tankers. Rejecting Standard's acquisition overtures Samuel created "Shell" Transport and Trading in 1897.

Meanwhile a Dutchman Aeilko Zijlker struck oil in Sumatra and formed Royal Dutch Petroleum in 1890 to exploit the oil field. Young Henri Deterding joined the firm in 1896 and established a sales force in the Far East.

Deterding became Royal Dutch's head in 1900 amid the battle for the Asian market. In 1903 Deterding Samuel and the Rothschilds (a French banking family) created Asiatic Petroleum a marketing alliance. With Shell's non-Asian business eroding Deterding engineered a merger between Royal Dutch and Shell in 1907. Royal Dutch shareholders got 60% control; "Shell" Transport and Trading 40%.

After the 1911 Standard Oil breakup Deterding entered the US building refineries and buying producers. Shell products were available in every state by 1929. Royal Dutch/Shell joined the 1928 "As Is" cartel that fixed prices for most of two decades.

The post-WWII Royal Dutch/Shell profited from worldwide growth in oil consumption. It acquired 100% of Shell Oil its US arm in 1985 but shareholders sued maintaining Shell Oil's assets had been undervalued in the deal. They were awarded $110 million in 1990.

Management's slow response to two 1995 controversies — environmentalists' outrage over the planned sinking of an oil platform and human rights activists' criticism of Royal Dutch/Shell's role in Nigeria — spurred a major shakeup. It began moving away from its decentralized structure and adopted a new policy of corporate openness.

In 1996 Royal Dutch/Shell and Exxon (now Exxon Mobil) formed a worldwide petroleum additives venture. Shell Oil joined Texaco (now part of Chevron) in 1998 to form Equilon Enterprises combining US refining and marketing operations in the West and Midwest. Similarly Shell Oil Texaco and Saudi Arabia's Aramco combined downstream operations on the US's East and Gulf coasts as Motiva Enterprises.

In 1999 Royal Dutch/Shell and the UK's BG plc acquired a controlling stake in Comgas a unit of Companhia Energ tica de S o Paulo and the largest natural gas distributor in Brazil for about $1 billion.

In 2000 the company sold its coal business to UK-based mining giant Anglo American for more than $850 million. To gain a foothold in the US power marketing scene Royal Dutch/Shell formed a joint venture with construction giant Bechtel (called InterGen). The next year the company agreed to combine its German refining and marketing operations with those of RWE-DEA. Royal Dutch/Shell tried to expand its US natural gas reserves in 2001 by making a $2 billion hostile bid for Barrett Resources but the effort was withdrawn after Barrett agreed to be acquired by Williams for $2.5 billion.

In 2002 in connection with Chevron's acquisition of Texaco Royal Dutch/Shell acquired ChevronTexaco's (now Chevron) stakes in the underperforming US marketing joint ventures Equilon and Motiva. That year the company through its US Shell Oil unit acquired Pennzoil-Quaker State for $1.8 billion. Also that year Royal Dutch/Shell acquired Enterprise Oil for $5 billion plus debt. In addition it purchased RWE's 50% stake in German refining and marketing joint venture Shell & DEA Oil (for $1.35 billion).

In 2004 the group signed a $200 million exploration deal with Libya signaling its return to that country after a more than decade-long absence. Also that year the company reported that it had overestimated its reserves by 24%. The bad news resulted in the ouster of the chairman and CFO.

The Anglo-Dutch entity restructured to stay competitive. Revelations of overestimated oil reserves in 2004 prompted a push for greater transparency in the company's organizational structure. This led to the 2005 merger of former publicly traded owners Royal Dutch Petroleum and The "Shell" Transport and Trading Company into Royal Dutch Shell.

Searching for new oil assets in 2006 the company acquired a large swath of oil sands acreage in Alberta Canada. Further boosting its oil sands business in 2007 the company acquired the 22% of Shell Canada that it did not already own. The company also began investing some $12 billion (in addition to the $2.6 billion already spent) in offshore projects near Dubai. In 2008 Royal Dutch Shell expanded its exploration assets in Alaska by acquiring 275 lease blocks in the Chukchi Sea for $2.1 billion.

In 2009 the company made significant oil discoveries in the deepwater eastern Gulf of Mexico at West Boreas Vito and the Cardamom Deep and in 2010 at the Appomattox prospect in the Mississippi Canyon block. The finds expanded Shell Oil's long-term development plans in the area.

Further expanding its unconventional natural gas resources in 2010 the company spent $4.7 billion to acquire East Resources which holds 1 million acres of Marcellus Shale one of the fastest-growing shale plays in the US.

On the conventional side of the oil business the Gulf of Mexico produces 370000 barrels of oil per day or about 15% of Royal Dutch Shell's worldwide production. In 2010 the company claimed an industry record starting production at the deepest floating drilling and production platform in the world. The Perdido Development operates in 8000 ft. of water in the Gulf of Mexico. In response to the BP oil rig disaster in the Gulf of Mexico the company joined forces with Exxon Mobil Chevron and ConocoPhillips to form a $1 billion rapid-response joint venture that will be able to better manage and contain future deepwater spills.

With an eye toward raising cash and focusing on its majority holdings and joint ventures rather than on minority held businesses in 2010 Royal Dutch Shell sold 10% of its 34% in Australian oil and gas enterprise Woodside Petroleum for $3.3 billion. Royal Dutch Shell also announced that it would seek to sell the rest of its stake in Woodside Petroleum over time. (Earlier in the year the company formed a $3.5 billion joint venture with PetroChina which acquired Arrow Energy a company with major natural gas assets in Northern Australia).

As part of its strategy of selling noncore downstream assets to raise cash in 2010 Royal Dutch Shell sold its Finnish and Swedish operations (including a refinery in Gothenburg and 565 gas stations) to Finland-based St1 for $640 million. In 2011 it sold its UK-based Stanlow refinery to India's Essar Group for $350 million.

In 2010 the company formed a $12 billion joint venture with Brazil's Cosan to ramp up ethanol production.

EXECUTIVES

Member of the Executive Committee, Upstream Director, Wael Sawan
Member of the Executive Committee, Legal Director, Donny Ching
Chief Executive Officer, Member of the Executive Committee, Executive Director, Ben Van Beurden, $1,809,376 total compensation
Non-Executive Independent Director, Abraham Schot
Chairman of the Board, Andrew Mackenzie
Member of the Executive Committee, Downstream Director, Huibert Vigeveno
Chairwoman, Euleen Goh
Director, Projects and Technology, Harry Brekelmans
Member of the Executive Committee, Integrated Gas, Renewables and Energy Solutions Director, Maarten Wetselaar
Chief Financial Officer, Member of the Executive Committee, Executive Director, Jessica Uhl, $1,179,285 total compensation
Member of the Executive Committee, Chief Human Resources and Corporate Officer, Ronan Cassidy
Director, Jane Lute
Company Secretary, Linda Coulter
Non-Executive Independent Director, Martina Hund Mejean
Non-Executive Independent Director, Dick Boer
Auditors: Ernst & Young LLP

LOCATIONS

HQ: Shell plc
Carel van Bylandtlaan 30, The Hague 2596 HR
Phone: (31) 70 377 9111
Web: www.shell.com

2018 Sales

	% of total
Asia Oceania Africa	39
Europe	31
USA	23
Other Americas	7
Total	**100**

PRODUCTS/OPERATIONS

2018 Sales

	% of total
Downstream	86
Integrated Gas	11
Upstream	3
Total	**100**

COMPETITORS

ABU DHABI NATIONAL ENERGY COMPANY - PJSC
ARD Holdings S.A.
BP P.L.C.
CHEVRON CORPORATION
ESSAR ENERGY LIMITED
EXXON MOBIL CORPORATION
Equinor ASA
Expro Group Holdings N.V.
HELLENIC PETROLEUM S.A. HOLDING
IBERDROLA SOCIEDAD ANONIMA
Koninklijke Vopak N.V.
LUKOIL PAO
Louis Dreyfus Holding B.V.
REPSOL SA.
RWE AG
SASOL LTD
TECHNIP
TOTALENERGIES SE

HISTORICAL FINANCIALS

Company Type: Public

Income Statement				FYE: December 31
	REVENUE ($ mil.)	NET INCOME ($ mil.)	NET PROFIT MARGIN	EMPLOYEES
12/20	183,195	(21,680)	—	86,000
12/19	352,106	15,842	4.5%	83,000
12/18	396,556	23,352	5.9%	81,000
12/17	311,870	12,977	4.2%	84,000
12/16	240,033	4,575	1.9%	92,000
Annual Growth	(6.5%)	—	—	(1.7%)

2020 Year-End Financials

Debt ratio: 20.9%
Return on equity: (-12.6%)
Cash ($ mil.): 31,830
Current ratio: 1.23
Long-term debt ($ mil.): 66,838

No. of shares (mil.): —
Dividends
  Yield: —
  Payout: —
Market value ($ mil.): —

Shenzhen Overseas Chinese Town Co Ltd

EXECUTIVES

Independent Director, Zhenquan Sha
Chief Accounting Officer, Wenhong Feng
Vice Chairman of the Board, Fengxi Liu
President, Director, Xiaowen Wang
Chairman of the Board, Xiannian Duan
Vice President, Jie Yang
Vice President, Dafan Zhang
Independent Director, Yijiang Wang
Secretary of the Board, Shan Guan
Vice President, Jingping Yuan
Vice President, Mingtao Ni
Auditors: RSM China Certified Public Accountants Co., Ltd.

LOCATIONS

HQ: Shenzhen Overseas Chinese Town Co Ltd
Overseas Chinese Town Office Building, Nanshan District, Shenzhen, Guangdong Province 518053
Phone: (86) 755 26909069   **Fax:** (86) 755 26600936
Web: www.octholding.com

HISTORICAL FINANCIALS
Company Type: Public

Income Statement   FYE: December 31

	REVENUE ($ mil.)	NET INCOME ($ mil.)	NET PROFIT MARGIN	EMPLOYEES
12/20	12,517	1,939	15.5%	0
12/19	8,626	1,773	20.6%	0
12/18	6,999	1,539	22.0%	0
12/17	6,506	1,328	20.4%	0
12/16	5,109	991	19.4%	0
Annual Growth	25.1%	18.2%	—	—

2020 Year-End Financials

Debt ratio: 4.7%
Return on equity: 17.2%
Cash ($ mil.): 9,250
Current ratio: 1.62
Long-term debt ($ mil.): 17,489

No. of shares (mil.): —
Dividends
  Yield: —
  Payout: —
Market value ($ mil.): —

Shenzhen Shenxin Taifeng Group Co Ltd

EXECUTIVES

Director, Xiaoyan Wang
Auditors: Shenzhen Nanfang-Minhe Certified Public Accountants Co., Ltd.

LOCATIONS

HQ: Shenzhen Shenxin Taifeng Group Co Ltd
Fengcai Room, Dabao Road, Baocheng Zone 23, Baoan District, Shenzhen, Guangdong Province 518101
Phone: (86) 755 2759 6453   **Fax:** (86) 755 2759 6456

HISTORICAL FINANCIALS
Company Type: Public

Income Statement   FYE: December 31

	REVENUE ($ mil.)	NET INCOME ($ mil.)	NET PROFIT MARGIN	EMPLOYEES
12/20	14,075	95	0.7%	0
12/19	12,474	100	0.8%	0
12/18	11,900	74	0.6%	0
12/17	9,560	111	1.2%	0
12/16	5,836	58	1.0%	0
Annual Growth	24.6%	13.2%	—	—

2020 Year-End Financials

Debt ratio: 6.0%
Return on equity: 13.7%
Cash ($ mil.): 626
Current ratio: 1.03
Long-term debt ($ mil.): 307

No. of shares (mil.): —
Dividends
  Yield: —
  Payout: —
Market value ($ mil.): —

Shiga Bank, Ltd.

Shiga Bank established in 1933 has grown to become the largest bank in the Shiga prefecture. The bank and its 14 subsidiaries provide customers with typical banking products and services credit card leasing and venture capital financing services and accepts negotiable certificates of deposits and installment-deposits fixed-term savings products. Shiga Bank's primary customers are individuals and small and medium-sized businesses. The bank which operates nearly 140 offices and branches in Japan Hong Kong and Thailand (as well as 10 agents) is banking on the region's expanding economy to improve local economies in the Kyoto and Shiga prefectures. Shiga Bank if controlled by Japan Trustee Service Bank.

EXECUTIVES

Non-Executive Independent Director, Rikiya Hattori
Non-Executive Independent Director, Minako Takeuchi
Director of Audit, Director, Katsuyuki Nishikawa
Senior Managing Director, Representative Director, Shinya Kubota
Manager of Kyoto Office, Director, Katsumi Horiuchi
Non-Executive Independent Director, Hajime Yasui
Managing Director, Takahiro Saito
Senior Managing Director, Representative Director, Motohiro Nishi
President, Representative Director, Shojiro Takahashi
Auditors: Deloitte Touche Tohmatsu LLC

LOCATIONS

HQ: Shiga Bank, Ltd.
1-38 Hamamachi, Otsu, Shiga 520-8686
Phone: (81) 77 521 9530
Web: www.shigagin.com

COMPETITORS

CHUGOKU BANKLIMITED THE
DAISHI HOKUETSU BANK LTD.

NISHI-NIPPON CITYBANKLTD.

HISTORICAL FINANCIALS
Company Type: Public

Income Statement   FYE: March 31

	ASSETS ($ mil.)	NET INCOME ($ mil.)	INCOME AS % OF ASSETS	EMPLOYEES
03/21	70,388	103	0.1%	3,439
03/20	57,899	114	0.2%	3,480
03/19	55,219	132	0.2%	3,487
03/18	55,327	130	0.2%	3,570
03/17	49,545	133	0.3%	3,627
Annual Growth	9.2%	(6.1%)	—	(1.3%)

2021 Year-End Financials

Return on assets: 0.1%
Return on equity: 2.6%
Long-term debt ($ mil.): —
No. of shares (mil.): 49
Sales ($ mil): 799

Dividends
  Yield: —
  Payout: 18.1%
Market value ($ mil.): —

Shikoku Bank, Ltd. (Japan)

Shikoku Bank is primarily a provider of banking services to customers in Japan's Shikoku prefecture. The bank's financial services include both commercial and retail banking and lending among others. Shikoku Bank serves local businesses individuals consumers and public agencies through about 110 branches. The bank also operates six domestic subsidiaries.

EXECUTIVES

President, Representative Director, Fumiaki Yamamoto
Managing Director, Kazuyuki Koro
Managing Director, Yasuyuki Yokoyama
Chairman of the Board, Tadashi Nomura
Managing Director, Masataka Yamamoto
Senior Managing Director, Representative Director, Akihiro Nishigawa
Senior Managing Director, Representative Director, Hideo Takahashi
Chief Director of Tokushima Sales, Director, Hisashi Takase
Auditors: Ernst & Young ShinNihon LLC

LOCATIONS

HQ: Shikoku Bank, Ltd. (Japan)
1-1-1 Minami-Harimayacho, Kochi 780-8605
Phone: (81) 88 823 2111
Web: www.shikokubank.co.jp

COMPETITORS

YAMAGATA BANKLTD. THE
YAMANASHI CHUO BANK LTD. THE

HISTORICAL FINANCIALS
Company Type: Public

Income Statement   FYE: March 31

	ASSETS ($ mil.)	NET INCOME ($ mil.)	INCOME AS % OF ASSETS	EMPLOYEES
03/21	30,083	59	0.2%	1,908
03/20	27,617	28	0.1%	1,952
03/19	27,801	56	0.2%	1,998
03/18	28,510	67	0.2%	2,028
03/17	27,213	79	0.3%	2,001
Annual Growth	2.5%	(6.8%)	—	(1.2%)

2021 Year-End Financials

Return on assets: 0.2%
Return on equity: 4.4%
Long-term debt ($ mil.): —
No. of shares (mil.): 41
Sales ($ mil): 376

Dividends
  Yield: —
  Payout: 19.1%
Market value ($ mil.): —

Shimao Group Holdings Ltd

EXECUTIVES

Vice President - Financial Control, Executive Director, Fei Tang, $467,212 total compensation
Non-Executive Director, Mingjie Ye
Non-Executive Independent Director, Hong Bing Lyu
President, Executive Vice Chairman of the Board, Sai Tan Hui, $1,016,976 total compensation
Non-Executive Independent Director, Ching Kam Lam
Company Secretary, Yee Mei Lam

Executive Chairman of the Board, Wing Mau Hui, $792,204 total compensation
Executive Director, Kun Xie
Executive Director, Yi Lu, $377,564 total compensation
Non-Executive Independent Director, Lai Kuen Kan
Auditors: PricewaterhouseCoopers

LOCATIONS

HQ: Shimao Group Holdings Ltd
38th Floor, Tower One, Lippo Centre, 89 Queensway,
Phone: (852) 2511 9968   **Fax:** (852) 2511 0287
Web: www.shimaoproperty.com

HISTORICAL FINANCIALS

Company Type: Public

Income Statement   FYE: December 31

	REVENUE ($ mil.)	NET INCOME ($ mil.)	NET PROFIT MARGIN	EMPLOYEES
12/19	16,026	1,566	9.8%	10,854
12/18	12,432	1,284	10.3%	9,814
12/17	10,822	1,204	11.1%	8,394
12/16	8,537	744	8.7%	7,880
12/15	8,889	941	10.6%	7,223
Annual Growth	15.9%	13.6%	—	10.7%

2019 Year-End Financials

Debt ratio: 3.8%
Return on equity: 17.3%
Cash ($ mil.): 7,524
Current ratio: 1.38
Long-term debt ($ mil.): 12,901

No. of shares (mil.): —
Dividends
    Yield: 0.0%
    Payout: 365.6%
Market value ($ mil.): —

	STOCK PRICE ($) FY Close	P/E High/Low		PER SHARE ($) Earnings	Dividends	Book Value
12/19	32.17	10	7	0.48	1.74	2.89
12/18	25.99	11	9	0.38	1.39	2.62
12/17	21.80	10	7	0.36	1.11	2.63
12/16	13.58	10	8	0.22	0.00	2.24
12/15	18.78	12	10	0.27	0.00	2.23
Annual Growth	14.4%	—	—	15.0%	—	6.7%

Shimizu Corp.

Shimizu provides architectural engineering construction and development services for commercial industrial infrastructure and residential projects around the world. One of Japan's largest general contractors the company has worked on major projects including Tokyo's Metro subway Singapore's Changi Airport and the Malaysia-Singapore Bridge. Other areas of specialization range from offices and power stations to railroads and dams. Shimizu has increasingly focused on green building and urban renewal projects. Needless to say earthquake-resistant technologies and earthquake restoration projects are key to Shimizu's business. The company also provides facilities management. Shimizu was founded in 1804.

Operations

The company is engaged in construction real estate development and other related businesses.

The Construction business is operated by branches located in various regions. The segment accounts for 90% of revenue.

The Real estate business involves in the development rental and sales. It is operated by the Investment and Development division. The segment accounts for the remaining 10% of revenue.

Geographic Reach

The company boasts more than 70 offices mostly across Japan though it also operates in other parts of Asia the Middle East Europe Africa and North America.

Sales and Marketing

Shimizu mostly serves the office medical and welfare educational and cultural production and research logistics and residential markets.

Financial Performance

Note: Growth rates may differ after conversion to US dollars.

The company's revenue increased to 1.70 billion in fiscal 2020 compared to 1.66 billion in the prior year.

Cash held by the company at the end of fiscal 2020 increased to 352.7 billion. Cash provided by operations and financing activities were 170.6 billion and 68.7 billion respectively. Cash used for investing activities was 115.7 billion.

Strategy

Shimizu has positioned the five years of Mid-Term Management Plan (2019? 2023) as a period of advance investment to establish a new profit base. The company is pushing forcefully ahead on implementing this plan to expand and evolve the construction business establish a profit base in non-construction businesses and strengthen the management base to support growth. Shimizu will accelerate global expansion and pursue ESG management to enhance Shimizu's corporate value and contribute to the achievement of SDGs as its basic policy.

The company currently focuses on expanding and evolving the construction business; establishing a profit base in non-construction businesses; accelerating global expansion; and strengthening the management platform to support growth.

EXECUTIVES

Executive Vice President, Vice President, Chief Director of General Construction, Representative Director, Toshiyuki Imaki
Independent Director, Tamotsu Iwamoto
Chairman of the Board, Representative Director, Yoichi Miyamoto
Executive Vice President, Vice President, Chief Director of LCV Business, Director, Toru Yamaji
President, Executive President, Representative Director, Kazuyuki Inoue
Senior Managing Executive Officer, Chief Director of General Civil Engineering, Director, Kentaro Ikeda
Director, Motoaki Shimizu
Executive Vice President, Vice President, Manager of Corporate Ethics Office, Representative Director, Kimio Handa
Executive Vice President, Vice President, Chief Director of General Sales, Assistant Manager of Yumeshima Project Office, Director, Hiroshi Fujimura
Independent Director, Mayumi Tamura
Independent Director, Junichi Kawada
Independent Director, Yumiko Jozuka
Auditors: Ernst & Young ShinNihon LLC

LOCATIONS

HQ: Shimizu Corp.
2-16-1 Kyobashi, Chuo-ku, Tokyo 104-8370
Phone: (81) 3 3561 1111
Web: www.shimz.co.jp

2014 Sales

	% of total
Japan	89
Asia	10
Other	1
Total	**100**

PRODUCTS/OPERATIONS

2014 Sales

	% of total
Construction contracts	90
Real estate development and other	10
Total	**100**

Selected Projects

Overseas Projects
Factory Toyota Industries Compressor Parts America Co. (TICA)HMSI 3rd FactoryKarawang Factory PT. SHARP ELECTRONICS INDONESIANipro Pharma Vietnam PlantUmiray BridgeUrban Suites
Domestic Project
Naoetsu LNG terminalOsaki Wiz CityShintakamatsu Data Center PowericoYomiuri Shimbun Tokyo Head OfficeSelected Subsidiaries
Daiichi Setsubi Engineering Corporation
Katayama Stratech Corp.
Milx Corporation
Shimizu Comprehensive Development Corporation
Super Regional Inc.
The Nippon Road Co. Ltd.
TTK Corporation

COMPETITORS

Aecon Group Inc
Beijing Urban Construction Group Co. Ltd
China Railway Engineering Group Co. Ltd.
DAIWA HOUSE INDUSTRY CO. LTD.
INSTALLED BUILDING PRODUCTS INC.
KAJIMA CORPORATION
LAING O'ROURKE PLC.
REDROW PLC
TAISEI CORPORATION
TAKENAKA CORPORATION

HISTORICAL FINANCIALS

Company Type: Public

Income Statement   FYE: March 31

	REVENUE ($ mil.)	NET INCOME ($ mil.)	NET PROFIT MARGIN	EMPLOYEES
03/21	13,154	697	5.3%	18,894
03/20	15,645	911	5.8%	18,475
03/19	15,034	899	6.0%	18,499
03/18	14,309	800	5.6%	18,732
03/17	14,019	884	6.3%	18,917
Annual Growth	(1.6%)	(5.8%)	—	(0.0%)

2021 Year-End Financials

Debt ratio: 0.2%
Return on equity: 9.9%
Cash ($ mil.): 1,935
Current ratio: 1.42
Long-term debt ($ mil.): 2,346

No. of shares (mil.): 764
Dividends
    Yield: 0.0%
    Payout: 125.4%
Market value ($ mil.): 26,495

	STOCK PRICE ($) FY Close	P/E High/Low		PER SHARE ($) Earnings	Dividends	Book Value
03/21	34.67	0	0	0.91	1.15	9.64
03/20	32.52	0	0	1.18	1.51	8.81
03/19	33.84	0	0	1.15	1.05	8.38
03/18	35.37	0	0	1.02	1.17	7.80
03/17	36.47	0	0	1.13	0.59	6.51
Annual Growth	(1.3%)	—	—	(5.1%)18.2%		10.3%

Shin-Etsu Chemical Co., Ltd.

The Shin-Etsu Group is creating unrivaled value through the provision of key material and technologies. The company's organic and inorganic chemicals unit makes polyvinyl chloride (PVC) and more than 5000 types of silicone while its electronics materials unit makes semiconductor silicon epoxy molding compounds and rare earth magnets. Shin-Etsu also produces synthetic quartz used for fiber-optic communications and in LCD panels. Shin-Etsu operates in the US as Shintech an integrated PVC production plant under construction in Louisiana.

Operations

The company's segment includes PVC/Chlor-Alkali (around 30% of sales) Semiconductor Silicon (some 25%) Electronics & Functional Materials (around 15%) Silicones (nearly 15%) Specialty Chemicals (roughly 10%) and Processing Trading & Specialized Services (approximately 5%).

The PVC resins are general-purpose resins used in a wide range of applications from everyday products to all kinds of industrial markets. With three production bases in the US Europe and Japan it has the capacity to produce some 4.15 million tons of PVC each year.

As the world's leading manufacturer of silicon wafers used as substrates for semiconductor devices it consistently leads the way in terms of wafer purification and flattening technologies. It also provides the market with superior products while continuing to steer the silicon wafer industry.

Its Electronics and Functional materials business provides photoresists photomask blanks encapsulation materials pellicles and other products used in the semiconductor manufacturing process.

Its Silicone business produces silicones a highly functional material that has both organic and inorganic characteristics. It has developed over 5000 silicone products that are used in a wide range of industries including electronics and electric applications automobiles construction cosmetics healthcare and food.

Its Specialty Chemicals include cellulose derivatives an environmentally friendly materials made from natural polymer cellulose. It is versatile with applications ranging from such fields as pharmaceuticals and foods to materials for constructions and civil engineering work coatings ceramics and toiletries.

The Shin-Etsu Polymer develops and supplies products that are easy use and highly functional products making use of materials processing technologies.

Geographic Reach

The company is headquartered in Tokyo Japan. The company has over 25 plants and around 15 companies in Japan and about 95 locations in about 20 countries overseas.

Financial Performance

Company's revenue for fiscal 2021 decreased to 1.49 trillion compared from the prior year with 1.54 trillion.

Cash held by the company at the end of fiscal 2021 increased to 801.6 billion. Cash provided by operations was 401.2 billion while cash used for investing and financing activities were 250.7 billion and 91.1 billion respectively. Main uses of cash were purchases of property plant and equipment; and cash dividends paid.

Strategy

The company continued to invest steadily for growth in fiscal 2020 with the aim of increasing its corporate value. In 2020 at Shintech in the US an integrated PVC production plant under construction in Louisiana is scheduled to start operations. Also the company have started the next PVC expansion project at the same site. In all its businesses such as the silicones business and the electronics & functional materials business the company are actively investing resources including human resources and capital into R&D and the enhancement of facilities for future growth.

EXECUTIVES

Managing Executive Officer, Chief Director of Electronic Materials Business, Yukihiro Matsui
Independent Director, Toshihiko Fukui
Executive Officer, Director of Accounting, Toshiyuki Kasahara
Vice Chairman of the Board, President of Subsidiary, Representative Director, Fumio Akiya
Independent Director, Frank Popoff
Director, Shunzo Mori
Managing Executive Officer, Manager of Digital Promotion Office, Toshiya Akimoto
Managing Executive Officer, Director of Organic Synthesis, President of Subsidiaries, Fumio Arai
Independent Director, Kuniharu Nakamura
President, President of Subsidiaries, Representative Director, Yasuhiko Saito
Independent Director, Tsuyoshi Miyazaki
Senior Managing Executive Officer, Director of Operation in Semiconductor Business Unit, Director, Masahiko Todoroki
Managing Executive Officer, Chief Director of Vinyl Chloride Business, Masaki Miyajima
Independent Director, Hiroshi Komiyama
Senior Managing Executive Officer, Chief Director of Silicone Business, Director, Susumu Ueno
Executive Officer, Director of New Functional Materials Business, Kazumasa Maruyama
Managing Executive Officer, Kenji Ikegami
Executive Officer, Deputy Chief Director of Electronics Materials Business, Toshio Shiobara
Executive Officer, Director of Corporate Development, Yoshimitsu Takahashi
Executive Officer, Chief Director of International Business, Kai Yasuoka
Chairman of the Board, Chairman of Subsidiary, Representative Director, Chihiro Kanagawa
Auditors: Ernst & Young ShinNihon LLC

LOCATIONS

HQ: Shin-Etsu Chemical Co., Ltd.
2-6-1 Ohtemachi, Chiyoda-ku, Tokyo 100-0004
Phone: (81) 3 3246 5011
Web: www.shinetsu.co.jp

2015 Sales

	% of total
Japan	28
US	22
Asia/Oceania (excluding china)	19
Europe	12
China	10
Others	9
Total	**100**

PRODUCTS/OPERATIONS

2015 Sales

	% of total
PVC/Chlor-Alkali	36
Semiconductor Silicon	18
Electronics & Functional Materials	15
Silicones	14
Speciality Chemicals	9
Diversified	8
Total	**100**

Selected products

PVC Chlor-Alkali
Polyvinyl chloride
Caustic soda
Chloromethane
Specialty Chemicals
Cellulose derivatives
Silicon metal
Poval (Polyvinyl alcohol)
Synthetic pheromones
Silicones
Semiconductor Silicon
Electronics & Functional Materials
Rare earth magnets
Encapsulation materials
Photoresists
Photomask blanks
Synthetic quartz products
Epoxy molding compounds
Pellicles
Diversified Business
Processed plastics
Export of plant equipment
International trading
Engineering
Information processing
Wafer container

COMPETITORS

AGC INC.
ARKEMA INC.
BioAmber Canada Inc
CLARIANT CORPORATION
DIXIE CHEMICAL COMPANY INC.
HEXION INC.
INDORAMA VENTURES PUBLIC COMPANY LIMITED
LANXESS SOLUTIONS US INC.
LG Chem Ltd.
MITSUI CHEMICALSINC.
MPM HOLDINGS INC.
NIPPON SYNTHETIC CHEMICAL INDUSTRY CO. LTD. THE
Orbia Advance Corporation S.A.B. de C.V.
SHINTECH INCORPORATED
TOKUYAMA CORPORATION
TORAY PLASTICS (AMERICA) INC.
UBE INDUSTRIES LTD.
UNION CARBIDE CORPORATION

HISTORICAL FINANCIALS

Company Type: Public

Income Statement				FYE: March 31
	REVENUE ($ mil.)	NET INCOME ($ mil.)	NET PROFIT MARGIN	EMPLOYEES
03/21	13,519	2,652	19.6%	26,524
03/20	14,219	2,892	20.3%	25,697
03/19	14,393	2,791	19.4%	24,380
03/18	13,574	2,507	18.5%	22,667
03/17	11,067	1,573	14.2%	21,303
Annual Growth	5.1%	14.0%	—	5.6%

2021 Year-End Financials

Debt ratio: 0.0%
Return on equity: 10.7%
Cash ($ mil.): 7,829
Current ratio: 5.27
Long-term debt ($ mil.): 144
No. of shares (mil.): 415
Dividends
Yield: 1.2%
Payout: 7.7%
Market value ($ mil.): 17,623

	STOCK PRICE ($) FY Close	P/E High/Low		PER SHARE ($) Earnings	Dividends	Book Value
03/21	42.41	0	0	6.38	0.52	61.18
03/20	24.45	0	0	6.96	0.49	58.80
03/19	21.03	0	0	6.55	0.40	53.44
03/18	25.98	0	0	5.88	0.30	51.92
03/17	21.71	0	0	3.69	0.27	44.74
Annual Growth	18.2%	—	—	14.6%	17.9%	8.1%

Shinhan Financial Group Co. Ltd.

Shinhan Financial Group one of South Korea's largest financial companies in terms of assets provides retail and corporate banking credit cards insurance asset management securities brokerage and credit reporting services to almost 30 million customers. Its primary subsidiary is Shinhan Bank which has one of the largest branch networks in the country with more than 900 locations. It also owns a stake in the 40-branch Jeju Bank. Shinhan Financial Group has international operations in about a half-dozen other countries including Shinhan Bank America in New York. Other units include Shinhan Investment Corp. (about 100 offices) and Shinhan Life Insurance (about 200 offices).

Operations

Shinhan Financial which operates mainly through Shinhan Bank centers its business around three core segments: Retail Banking which provides traditional banking products and services to retail and affluent individuals and non-profit organizations; Corporate and Investment Banking services which makes loans to corporations and small to medium-sized businesses; International Banking which counts the business of Shinhan's overseas branch operations and other international businesses along with securities trading and administrative operations. Through its more than 30 direct and indirect subsidiaries the bank also provides insurance brokerage and asset management services as well as credit card products and services. Shinhan Financial generated roughly 75% its 2014 operating income from interest income one-third of which came from its retail loan business one-fifth coming from its credit card business and just over one-tenth coming from its corporate loan business. The majority of the remaining 25% of total revenue came from fee and commission income mostly from its retail banking and credit card businesses.

Geographic Reach

Shinhan Financial generated 96% of its operating income from South Korea in 2014. It had three-fourths of its 1250 locations in Korea with more than one-third of the its offices in the Seoul metropolitan market alone and about 20% of offices in the Kyunggi province. The rest of the Korean branches in the cities of Incheon Busan Kwangju Taegu Ulsan and Taejon. Shinhan Bank's international branches are in some 16 countries including Cambodia Canada China Germany Hong Kong India Japan Kazakhstan Myanmar Poland Singapore the UK the US and Vietnam. It has representative offices in Mexico and Uzbekistan.

Sales and Marketing

The company serves retail and affluent individuals small and mid-sized businesses non-profit organizations (such as hospitals airports and schools) and corporations. Its Shinhan Card business primarily sells through the banking and credit card branch network sales agents and business partnerships and affiliations with vendors.

Altogether the firm spent Wan$229.64 billion ($208.9 million) on advertising in 2014 up from W$211.3 billion ($192.2 million) and W$188.36 billion ($171.4 million) in 2013 and 2012 respectively.

Financial Performance

Note: Growth rates may differ after conversion to US dollars.

Shinhan Financial's revenues and profits have been trending lower in recent years due to shrink-ing interest margins on loans amidst the low-interest environment.

The firm's revenue dipped by 2% to W$16135 billion ($15.43 billion) in 2014 mostly as its interest income on loans dipped by 4% due to a continued decline in interest margins on both its retail loans and corporate loans. Shinhan's net fees and commission income however grew by 6% as its credit card fee income increased with higher consumer credit balances.

Despite lower revenues in 2014 Shinhan's net income jumped by 10% to W$2.08 billion ($1.89 million) mostly thanks to significant unrealized fair value gains of the firm's available-for-sale financial assets. The firm's cash levels fell sharply despite higher earnings during the year with operations using W$2.08 billion ($1.89 million) after adjusting Shinhan's earnings for non-cash interest expenses net insurance loss and net trading loss items.

Strategy

Shinhan Financial Group reiterated in 2015 that its long-term strategy (which it's followed since 2001) included: balanced growth among its banking and non-banking businesses; expansion of its service offerings to grow revenues and differentiate the bank from competitors; and strengthening of its management systems and core expertise in effort to become the market leader in Korea and a world-class financial holding company.To that end in 2015 the company planned to introduce more differentiated financial services; and continue its international expansion efforts by localizing its product offerings and operations and bolstering its local marketing expertise and distribution channels.Shinhan Financial is also moving toward digital banking channels that are quickly taking the industry by storm allowing the bank to slow the growth of its costly branch network and cut operating costs significantly. Indeed more than 8.6 million Shinhan customers — about one-third of its customer base — were enrolled in the firm's smart phone banking service in 2014; nearly double the size of its "Smart" customer base in 2012. Additionally about 59% of all Shinhan bank transactions were done over the bank's internet or mobile banking services while just 5% of transactions were at physical branch locations.

Mergers and Acquisitions

In June 2015 Shinhan Bank purchased a 75% stake in Centratama Nasional Bank along with its $81 million in assets and 41 offices in Indonesia. Similarly in April 2015 Shinhan obtained regulatory approval to acquired a 40% equity interest in Jakarta-based Bank Metro Express a small bank in Indonesia and expected to close the transaction in late 2015. The bank planned to merge the two Indonesian banks in 2016 to strengthen its operations in the Southeast Asia region.

EXECUTIVES

Non-Executive Independent Director, Jae Ho Sung
Non-Executive Independent Director, Yong Hak Huh
Non-Executive Independent Director, Hirakawa Yuki
Non-Executive Independent Director, Cheol Park
Non-Executive Independent Director, An Sun Park
Non-Executive Independent Director, Gyeong Rok Choi
Vice President, Hyo Ryeol Ahn
Auditors: KPMG Samjong Accounting Corp.

LOCATIONS

HQ: Shinhan Financial Group Co. Ltd.
  20 Sejong-daero 9-gil Jung-gu, Seoul 04513
Phone: (82) 2 6360 3129   **Fax:** (82) 2 6360 3098
Web: www.shinhangroup.com

PRODUCTS/OPERATIONS

2014 Sales

	% of total
Interest income	
Loans	57
Available for sale financia assets	3
Held to maturity financial assets	5
Trading assets	3
Cash and due from banks	1
Other interest income	2
Non Interest income	
Fee and commission income	21
Dividend income	1
Net trading income	2
Net gain on sale of available for sale financial assets	1
Net foreign currency transaction gain	4
Total	**100**

2014 Sales

	% of total
Banking	67
Credit card	25
Securities	4
Life insurance	4
Other	-
Total	**100**

Selected Subsidiaries

Jeju Bank (68.9%)
SHC Management
Shinhan AITAS (99.8%)
Shinhan Bank
Shinhan BNP Paribas Asset Management (65%)
Shinhan Capital
Shinhan Card
Shinhan Credit Information
Shinhan Data System
Shinhan Investment Corp.
Shinhan Life Insurance
Shinhan Private Equity Investment Management
Shinhan Savings Bank

COMPETITORS

AKBANK TURK ANONIM SIRKETI
ALDERMORE GROUP PLC
BANK VTB PAO
BYLINE BANCORP INC.
CAIXABANK SA
CANARA BANK
China Construction Bank Corporation
INVESTEC PLC
ITAU UNIBANCO HOLDING SA

METROPOLITAN BANK HOLDING CORP.
RECORD PLC
STANDARD BANK GROUP LTD
Swedbank AB
TP ICAP FINANCE PLC
TURKIYE IS BANKASI ANONIM SIRKETI
YAPI VE KREDI BANKASI ANONIM SIRKETI

HISTORICAL FINANCIALS

Company Type: Public

Income Statement				FYE: December 31
	ASSETS ($ mil.)	NET INCOME ($ mil.)	INCOME AS % OF ASSETS	EMPLOYEES
12/20	556,113	3,137	0.6%	23,091
12/19	478,445	2,947	0.6%	22,204
12/18	412,238	2,831	0.7%	22,624
12/17	399,870	2,736	0.7%	143
12/16	329,360	2,309	0.7%	147
Annual Growth	14.0%	8.0%	—	254.0%

2020 Year-End Financials

Return on assets: 0.5%
Return on equity: 8.1%
Long-term debt ($ mil.): —
No. of shares (mil.): 515
Sales ($ mil): 24,710

Dividends
  Yield: 5.0%
  Payout: 24.6%
Market value ($ mil.): 15,353

STOCK PRICE ($)		P/E		PER SHARE ($)		
	FY Close	High/Low		Earnings	Dividends	Book Value
12/20	29.76	0	0	6.11	1.51	78.49
12/19	38.07	0	0	6.06	1.39	71.56
12/18	35.49	0	0	5.90	1.35	67.58
12/17	46.40	0	0	5.74	1.35	64.92
12/16	37.64	0	0	4.77	0.99	54.61
Annual Growth	(5.7%)	—	—	6.4%	11.0%	9.5%

Shinsei Bank Ltd

Shinsei Bank provides retail and corporate banking and several other financial services from 35 branches throughout Japan. Shinsei used to focus on financing Japan's large industrial firms but has been cultivating its retail and small business banking operations. It offers retail banking services such as deposits mortgages and investments as well as higher-margin services such as wealth management market services and institutional asset management bond sales and underwriting trust services and specialty financing in the public and real estate sectors. Founded as the Long-Term Credit Bank of Japan in 1952 the company was reborn as Shinsei (Japanese for "new birth") Bank in 2000.

Operations

Shinsei Bank group operates three main business segments. The Individual Group segment (which generated 58% of Shinsei Bank's total revenue and 22% of its profit in fiscal 2015 ended March 31) provides retail banking personal loans credit cards mutual funds insurance housing loans and overseas remittance services. The Institutional Group (which contributed 32% to revenue and 65% to profit) provides public sector finance real estate finance specialty finance health care finance private equity and credit trading (through Shinsei PI Group) leasing and property management services (through Showa Leasing Co) and trust services (through Shinsei Trust). The Global Markets Group (7% of revenue 8% of profit) provides market wealth management and asset management services through subsidiaries such as Shinsei Investment Management and Shinsei Securities.

Broadly about 53% of the bank's revenue came from interest income (mostly from loans) in FY2015 while 16% came from fee and commission income. Around 4% of its revenue came from net trading income while the remaining 23% of its revenue came from (non-recurring) net gains on sales of certain non-trading assets.

While Shinsei Bank lends to a variety of different industries across Japan about 27% of its entire loan portfolio's value was tied to loans to customers in the finance and insurance and real estate industries. About 7% of its portfolio went to customers in the services industries while another 15% was lent to customers in the manufacturing electric power/gas/heat/water and transportation/postal service industries.

Geographic Reach

Shinsei Bank had 35 branch outlets across Japan in fiscal 2015 (ended March 31) with about one-third of them around Tokyo nine in the Kinki region seven in the Konto region (excluding Tokyo) and one each in the Chugoku Tohoku Tokai Shikoku Kyushi Hokkaido and Hokuriku/Koshinetsu regions of Japan. The bank also had over 43960 ATM locations in Japan with nearly 40% of them located in the Kanto/Tokyo

region and another 15% in the Kinki region. Additionally it had ATMs in all the other regions where there were branches along with 434 ATM locations in Okinawa.

Financial Performance

Note: Growth rates may differ after conversion to US dollars. This analysis uses financials from the company's annual report.

In domestic currency terms Shinsei Bank's annual revenues and profits have been trending higher since fiscal 2013 (ended March 31 2013) thanks to loan business growth and non-interest growth from fees and commissions and sales of investment products.

The bank's total revenue (defined by the company as the total of net interest income and non-interest income) grew to 235.3 billion in FY2015 thanks to a combination of: higher net interest income as the bank decreased its funding costs and collected higher dividend income from securities investments in the Institutional Group; and non-interest income growth thanks to an improvement in market-related transaction revenues including ALM operations (the company's corporate internal trading division) as well as a rise in revenue from the installment sales finance business of the consumer finance business.

Higher revenue and a decline in loan loss provisions in FY2015 boosted Shinsei Bank's net income up 64% to 67.8 billion ($567 million) for the year. The bank's operating cash levels declined sharply despite higher earnings with operations using 509 billion or $4.25 billion (operations provided 524 billion in FY2014) as the bank's deposit levels fell and as its loan balances grew.

Company Background

During the late 2000s Shinsei had been battered by its exposure to toxic assets including loans to failed Lehman Brothers and structured asset-backed securities. It had also taken a hit in the domestic real estate market in which the company had been a significant lender. Record losses reported for 2008 sparked rumors that Shinsei would merge with Aozora Bank another struggling midsized bank that was nationalized in 2001. The two banks reached a merger agreement in 2009 but called those plans off due to strategic differences.

HISTORY

The Japanese government nationalized Shinsei Bank's debt-ridden Long-Term Credit Bank in 1998. It sold the bank to an international group led by US-based Ripplewood Holdings in 2000 making it one of the few major Japanese banks to come under foreign control. Ripplewood spun off the bank in 2004 placing it on the Tokyo Stock Exchange.

In 2007 Shinsei acquired a minority stake in global advisory firm Duff & Phelps.

In 2008 it acquired GE's consumer finance business in Japan consisting of credit card personal lending and mortgage operations. In 2010 Shinsei Bank sold Shinsei Asset Management its Mumbai-based asset management operation to Daiwa Bank. The company would use the proceeds to pay down its debt.

EXECUTIVES

Senior Managing Executive Officer, Sanjeev Gupta
Senior Managing Executive Officer, Chief Officer of Group Organization Strategy, Michiyuki Okano
Executive Officer, President of Subsidiary, Shinichiro Seto
Senior Managing Executive Officer, Chief Officer of Group Business Strategy, Yoshiaki Kozano
Independent Director, Jun Makihara
President, Chief Executive Officer, Representative Director, Hideyuki Kudo
Senior Managing Executive Officer, Chief Officer Group Legal & Compliance, Director, Akira Hirasawa
Executive Officer, Takahisa Komoda
Independent Director, Ernest Higa
Independent Director, Rie Murayama
Independent Director, Ryuichi Tomimura
Independent Director, Hiroko Sasaki
Auditors: Deloitte Touche Tohmatsu LLC

LOCATIONS

HQ: Shinsei Bank Ltd
2-4-3 Nihonbashi-Muromachi, Chuo-ku, Tokyo 103-8303
Phone: (81) 3 6880 7000
Web: www.shinseibank.com

PRODUCTS/OPERATIONS

2014 Sales

	% of total
Net interest income	54
Noninterest income	
Net fee and commission	12
Net trading income	7
Others	27
Total	**100**

COMPETITORS

AKBANK TURK ANONIM SIRKETI
BANK OF YOKOHAMALTD.THE
BANK VTB PAO
Bank of Communications Co. Ltd.
CANARA BANK
HDFC BANK LIMITED
HSBC USA INC.
MALAYAN BANKING BERHAD
PRIVATEBANCORP INC.
Shanghai Pudong Development Bank Co.Ltd.
Shinhan Financial Group Co. Ltd.
YAPI VE KREDI BANKASI ANONIM SIRKETI

HISTORICAL FINANCIALS

Company Type: Public

Income Statement				FYE: March 31
	ASSETS ($ mil.)	NET INCOME ($ mil.)	INCOME AS % OF ASSETS	EMPLOYEES
03/21	96,999	407	0.4%	7,066
03/20	94,210	419	0.4%	6,738
03/19	86,426	472	0.5%	6,340
03/18	89,056	484	0.5%	6,413
03/17	82,806	453	0.5%	6,521
Annual Growth	4.0%	(2.7%)	—	2.0%

2021 Year-End Financials

Return on assets: 0.4%
Return on equity: 4.9%
Long-term debt ($ mil.): —
No. of shares (mil.): 215
Sales ($ mil): 3,489
Dividends
Yield: 0.0%
Payout: 0.9%
Market value ($ mil.): 738

STOCK PRICE ($)		P/E		PER SHARE ($)		
	FY Close	High/Low		Earnings	Dividends	Book Value
03/21	3.43	0	0	1.83	0.02	38.70
03/20	2.69	0	0	1.76	0.02	36.06
03/19	2.82	0	0	1.91	0.02	32.84
03/18	3.16	0	0	1.87	0.02	31.81
03/17	3.69	0	0	1.74	0.02	28.32
Annual Growth	(1.8%)	—	—	1.2%	(0.6%)	8.1%

Shizuoka Bank Ltd (Japan)

Auditors: Deloitte Touche Tohmatsu LLC

LOCATIONS

HQ: Shizuoka Bank Ltd (Japan)
1-10 Gofuku-cho, Aoi-ku, Shizuoka 420-8761
Phone: (81) 54 261 3131
Web: www.shizuokabank.co.jp

HISTORICAL FINANCIALS

Company Type: Public

Income Statement				FYE: March 31
	ASSETS ($ mil.)	NET INCOME ($ mil.)	INCOME AS % OF ASSETS	EMPLOYEES
03/21	127,124	394	0.3%	6,311
03/20	115,548	356	0.3%	6,328
03/19	107,046	423	0.4%	6,422
03/18	108,607	472	0.4%	6,469
03/17	98,874	261	0.3%	6,504
Annual Growth	6.5%	10.8%	—	(0.8%)

2021 Year-End Financials

Return on assets: 0.3%	Dividends
Return on equity: 4.1%	Yield: —
Long-term debt ($ mil.): —	Payout: 34.1%
No. of shares (mil.): 574	Market value ($ mil.): —
Sales ($ mil): 2,092	

Shoko Chukin Bank (The) (Japan)

Auditors: PricewaterhouseCoopers Aarata LLC

LOCATIONS

HQ: Shoko Chukin Bank (The) (Japan)
2-10-17 Yaesu, Chuo-ku, Tokyo 104-0028
Phone: (81) 3 3272 6111   **Fax:** (81) 3 3272 6169
Web: www.shokochukin.co.jp

HISTORICAL FINANCIALS

Company Type: Public

Income Statement				FYE: March 31
	ASSETS ($ mil.)	NET INCOME ($ mil.)	INCOME AS % OF ASSETS	EMPLOYEES
03/19	106,719	139	0.1%	5,149
03/18	112,606	351	0.3%	5,141
03/17	114,886	290	0.3%	5,127
03/16	111,939	110	0.1%	5,120
03/15	105,299	140	0.1%	4,140
Annual Growth	0.3%	(0.2%)	—	5.6%

2019 Year-End Financials

Return on assets: 0.1%	Dividends
Return on equity: 1.6%	Yield: —
Long-term debt ($ mil.): —	Payout: —
No. of shares (mil.): —	Market value ($ mil.): —
Sales ($ mil): 1,642	

Siam Cement Public Co. Ltd.

The Siam Cement is a leading business conglomerate in the ASEAN region. It still makes cement (sold under the K-Cement and Tiger brands) petrochemicals paper and packaging; other lines of business include building products and distribution. Siam Cement also has real estate holdings. The company provides strong domestic distribution network through sales campaign and activities to approximately 500 dealers nationwide its cement products are also sold to affiliate companies such as ready mixed concrete concrete roof board major concrete building material producers and major contractors. About 60% of the company's revenue comes from Thailand.

Operations

The Siam Cement comprises three core business units namely Cement-Building Materials Business Chemicals Business and Packaging Business. Cement-Building Materials Business generates more than 40% of total revenue. It manufactures and sells grey cement ready-mixed concrete white cement dry mortar roof tiles concrete paving blocks ceramic tiles sanitary wares and sanitary fittings.

Chemicals Business generates about 35% of total revenue. It manufactures and sells olefins polyolefins and other chemical products.

Packaging Business brings in some 20% of total revenue. It is comprised of two main operating businesses: Integrated Packaging Chain; fiber-based packaging packaging paper and performance and polymer packaging and Fibrous Chain; foodservice products pulp and paper products comprising mainly printing and writing paper and pulp.

Geographic Reach

Bangkok-based Siam Cement operates in ASEAN countries ? Thailand China Indonesia and Vietnam. About 60% of total revenue comes from Thailand followed by Vietnam which gives in about 10% of total revenue Indonesia about 10% and China generates approximately 5% of total revenue. The remaining revenue amounting approximately 20% comes from other regions.

Sales and Marketing

The company markets its products through the internet including e-mail and social media.

Financial Performance

Consolidated revenue from sales decreased 9% from the previous year to 399.9 billion Baht largely from lower chemical prices and sales volume.

Profit for fiscal 2020 increased to 33.7 billion Baht compared from the prior year with 27.7 billion Baht.

Cash held by the company at the end of fiscal 2020 increased to 64.4 billion Baht. Cash provided by operations and financing activities were 70.4 billion Baht and 37.5 billion Baht respectively. Cash used for investing activities was 71.2 billion Baht mainly for acquisition of others' equity and debt instruments.

Strategy

The business rigorously creates value to customers through High Value Added products and services (HVA) to differentiate and respond to customers' needs and enhance construction industry to increase wealth in community such as continuing products improvement through R&D becoming a trendsetter and developing eco-friendly products to reduce natural resources consumption. In addition the business has its own Research and Development institution that allows business to efficiently develop its products and services to serve the needs of each customer segment. Moreover the business can flexibly support the trend changes toward cement industries and consumer's behaviors by improving better quality of products. For instance SCG hybrid cement (Eco-friendly) Tiger Plastering cement SCG Precast Cement SCG marine cement SCG Portland Pozzolan cement Tiger Mortar General and Lightweight Block Plastering Xpert Formula crack resistant mortar cement Tiger Tile Adhesive for ceramic granite marble granite tiles GreyWhite skim coat SCG wood plank cool plus SCG roof tile for low slope & modern style roofing thin ceramics technology 'COTTOCERAM TM" in COTTO sensation series which makes wash basins look slimmer Modern design toilet 'Simply Modish' Smart toilet Tunio Laconic series which combined design and technology together and soft paddle faucet designed with universal design concept. Not only core product offerings but the business also provides total range of products services and solutions to serve agricultural sector government infrastructure projects commercial buildings and residential segment by joining with various SCG alliances and partners.

Mergers and Acquisitions

In mid-2021 SCG announced the completion of the 85% share acquisition (Merger and Partnership: M&P) investment in Deltalab S. L. (Deltalab) as SCG Packaging Public Company Limited (or SCGP) a subsidiary of SCC has disclosed the information of completion of the 85% share acquisition of "Deltalab" in Spain to the Stock Exchange of Thailand as the details in the attachment. Payment for the 85% M&P stake is the immediate 84.9 million Euro (approximately 3270 million Baht).

In late 2020 SCC announced that SCG Chemicals Co. Ltd. (or SCG Chemicals) a wholly owned subsidiary of SCC to acquire an additional 70% shares in HTExplore S.R.L. (or HTExplore) in Italy for total consideration of approximately 1.4 million Euro (or approximately 55 million Baht). As SCG Chemicals already holds a 30% stake this acquisition will raise SCG Chemicals' shareholding in HTExplore to 100%. The transaction will allow SCG Chemicals to increase its capability in catalyst testing via High Throughput Experimentation which will significantly reduce catalyst development time.

Catalyst testing is an essential process in developing high value-added products. The acquisition will help increase research and development capability of SCG Chemicals.

Also in late 2020 SCC announced the signing of a share purchase agreement to acquire a 100% stake in the UK-based Go-Pak UK Limited (or Go-Pak). This acquisition of Go-Pak is an expansion of SCGP's foodservice packaging business which will elevate its consumer platform and give access to Go-Pak's client base in UK Europe and North America and will also broaden SCGP's total packaging solutions and strengthen its production capabilities to grow the ASEAN market.

Company Background

In addition to the acquisition of a 90% stake in PT Indoris Printingdo a high-value added packaging manufacturer in Indonesia with an annual capacity of 8000 tons in 2014 the company acquired Silathai Sanguan which operates a crushing plant in Thailand; 55% of Panel World Co. Ltd. which operates cement-bonded particleboard in Thailand; 51% of Norner Holding a leading Norway-based innovation and technology firm specializing in material and polymer industries; and D-In-Pack Company Limited which converts sheet boards to boxes and caters in Thailand.

In 2014 Siam Cement formed a joint venture with Florim Ceramiche S.p.A of Italy (with SCG Cement-Building Materials holding a 33% stake) to establish a plant to manufacture high-end ceramic tiles with an annual output capacity of 5 million square meters.

In 2013 the company acquired Prime Group a major ceramic tiles producer in Vietnam.

In a 2011 deal to enhance Siam Cement's presence in the Indonesian market the company acquired majority stakes in two firms Keramika Indonesia Asosiasi Tbk (94%) and Kokoh Inti Arebama Tbk (70%). Keramika is a ceramics manufacturer while Kokoh is a nationwide distributor of building materials. The transaction fits Siam Cement's strategy of acquiring assets that mesh closely with its existing business units. Also in 2011 it acquired Vietnam-based Alcamax Packaging for about $25 million.

Siam Cement has made major progress in its expansion in Southeast Asia including the 2009 opening of a $185 million packaging paper plant in Vietnam. In 2010 Siam Cement acquired New Asia Industries Company Vietnam's leading producer and distributor of corrugated containers for $30 million.

Siam Cement is putting its money where the petrochemicals and packaging paper companies are. The company in 2006 formed a partnership with Dow Chemical to build a plastics manufacturing facility that began operations in 2010.

Thailand's first cement manufacturer Siam Cement was founded in 1913 on orders from King Rama VI.

EXECUTIVES

Director, Kan Trakulhoon
Independent Director, Chumpol Na Lamlieng
President, Chief Executive Officer, Director, Roongrote Rangsiyopash
Director, Cholanat Yanaranop
President - Cement-Building Materials Business, In charge of Vice President-Living Solution and Housing Products Business, Cement-Building Materials Business, Nithi Phatrachok
Director, Thumnithi Wanichthanom
Vice President - Chemicals Business, Chief Technology Officer - Innovation and Technology, Chemicals Business, Suracha Udomsak
President - Cementhai Holding Company Limited, Aree Chavalitcheewingul
President - Chemicals Business, Tanawong Areeratchakul
Independent Director, Tarisa Watanagase
Independent Director, Pasu Decharin
Independent Director, Parnsiree Amatayakul
Independent Director, Prasarn Trairatvorakul
Vice President - Regional Business - Cement-Building Materials Business, Paramate Nisagornsen
Vice President - Corporate Administration, SCG, Yuttana Jiamtragan
Director, Kasem Wattanachai
Vice President - Polyolefins and Vinyl Business - Chemicals Business, Sakchai Patiparnpreechavud
Corporate Planning and Finance Director, Chantanida Sarigaphuti
Vice President - Olefins Business and Operations - Chemicals Business, Mongkol Hengrojanasophon
Corporate Accounting Director, Pichit Leelaphantmetha
Vice President - Cement and Construction Solution Business, Cement - Building Materials Business, Chana Poomee
Chairman of the Board, Satitpong Sukvimol
Company Secretary and Assistant Secretary to The Board Of Directors, Pattarawan Tunsakul
Chief Financial Officer, Vice President - Finance and Investment, Thammasak Sethaudom
Auditors: KPMG Phoomchai Audit Ltd.

LOCATIONS

HQ: Siam Cement Public Co. Ltd.
1 Siam Cement Road, Bangsue, Bangkok 10800
Phone: (66) 2 586 3333   **Fax:** (66) 2 586 2974
Web: www.scg.co.th

2014 Sales

	% of total
Thailand	61
China	7
Indonesia	6
Vietnam	6
Other	20
Total	**100**

PRODUCTS/OPERATIONS

2014 Sales

	% of total
Chemicals	50
Cement building materials	37
Paper	13
Other	-
Total	**100**

Selected Products

Chemicals
  Olefins
  Polyolefins
Paper & packaging
  Corrugated boxes
  Gypsum linerboard
  Industrial paper
  Printing paper
  Writing paper
Cement
  Dry mortar
  Gray cement
  Ready-mixed concrete
  White cement
Building products
  Ceramic tiles
  Concrete paving blocks
  Gypsum boards
  Roof tiles
  Sanitary fittings and wares

COMPETITORS

AVIENT CORPORATION
FRC FOUNDERS
  CORPORATION
GLATFELTER CORPORATION
HANWA CO.LTD.
Holcim AG
IMERYS
INA-Holding Schaeffler
  GmbH & Co. KG
MASTEC INC.

SKANSKA USA CIVIL INC.
SONOCO PRODUCTS
  COMPANY
SYNTHOMER PLC
TAIHEIYO CEMENT
  CORPORATION
WESCO AIRCRAFT
  HOLDINGS INC.
thyssenkrupp Materials
  Services GmbH

HISTORICAL FINANCIALS

Company Type: Public

Income Statement   FYE: December 31

	REVENUE ($ mil.)	NET INCOME ($ mil.)	NET PROFIT MARGIN	EMPLOYEES
12/20	13,358	1,140	8.5%	0
12/19	14,703	1,074	7.3%	0
12/18	14,789	1,383	9.4%	0
12/17	13,841	1,689	12.2%	0
12/16	11,829	1,566	13.2%	0
Annual Growth	**3.1%**	**(7.6%)**	**—**	**—**

2020 Year-End Financials

Debt ratio: 1.1%
Return on equity: 11.3%
Cash ($ mil.): 2,151
Current ratio: 1.33
Long-term debt ($ mil.): 5,362

No. of shares (mil.): 1,200
Dividends
  Yield: —
  Payout: —
Market value ($ mil.): —

Siam Commercial Bank Public Co Ltd (The)

One of Thailand's largest commercial banks by total assets deposits and loans The Siam Commercial Bank (SCB) hails from royal beginnings. It is the country's oldest bank established by King Rama V in 1906 in response to the proliferation of foreign financial institutions in Thailand. It offers a variety of financial services such as corporate and personal lending retail and wholesale banking credit cards life insurance foreign currency trading and investment banking among others. SCB operates through a network of about 1200 branches and 9140 ATMs; it is expanding regionally. In 2014 SCB had Baht 2553 billion in total assets Baht 1781 billion in deposits and Baht 1733 billion in loans.

EXECUTIVES

Non-Executive Chairman of the Board, Vichit Suraphongchai
Chief Executive Officer, Executive Director, Arthid Nanthawithaya
Senior Executive Vice President, Chief Financial Officer, Manop Sangiambut
Senior Executive Vice President, Chief Information and Operations Officer, Voranuch Dejakaisaya
Senior Executive Vice President, Chief Integrated Channels Officer, Vitoon Pornsakulvanich
Independent Director, Prasan Chuaphanich
Independent Director, Weerawong Chittmittrapap
Independent Director, Lackana Leelayouthayotin
Independent Director, Chaovalit Ekabut
Independent Director, Paillin Chuchottaworn
Non-Executive Director, Jareeporn Jarukornsakul
President of the Bank, Arak Sutivong
Independent Director, Krirk Vanikkul
Independent Director, Thaweesak Koanantakool
President of the Bank, Sarut Ruttanaporn
Senior Executive Vice President, Chief Risk Officer, Anucha Laokwansatit
Independent Director, Pasu Decharin
Non-Executive Director, Satitpong Sukvimol
Director, Chakkrit Parapuntakul
President of the Bank, Apiphan Charoenanusorn
Senior Executive Vice President, Chief SME Banking Officer, Pikun Srimahunt
Independent Director, Kan Trakulhoon
Senior Executive Vice President, Chief Strategy Officer, Sathian Leowarin
Non-Executive Director, Thumnithi Wanichthanom
Senior Executive Vice President, Chief Wholesale Banking Officer, Wasin Saiyawan
Senior Executive Vice President, Chief Wealth Banking Officer, Narong Srichukrin
Senior Executive Vice President, Chief Credit Officer, Chiradej Chakrabandhu
Senior Executive Vice President, Chief Data Officer, Chalee Asavathiratham
Senior Executive Vice President, Trirat Suwanprateeb
Senior Executive Vice President, Chief Insurance Business Officer, Poramasiri Manolamai
Senior Executive Vice President, Chief Economist, Yunyong Thaicharoen
Senior Executive Vice President, Chief Retail and Business Banking Officer, Auraratana Jutimitta
Senior Executive Vice President, Chief Audit Officer, Krieng Wongnongtaey

Senior Executive Vice President, Chief Legal and Control Officer and Acting Head of Compliance, Wallaya Kaewrungruang
Auditors: KPMG Phoomchai Audit Ltd.

LOCATIONS

HQ: Siam Commercial Bank Public Co Ltd (The)
9 Ratchadapisek Road, Jatujak, Bangkok 10900
Phone: (66) 2 544 1000   **Fax:** (66) 2 937 7721
Web: www.scb.co.th

PRODUCTS/OPERATIONS

2013 Sales

	% of total
Interest income	56
Net earned insurance premiums	23
Fees & service income	14
Net trading income	4
Dividend income	2
Net gain on investments	1
Total	**100**

Selected Group Companies

SCB Asset Management
SCB Life Assurance
SCB Securities
The Siam Commercial Bank

COMPETITORS

AKBANK TURK ANONIM SIRKETI
BANK OF AYUDHYA PUBLIC COMPANY LIMITED
BANK OF CHINA LIMITED
BANK OF INDIA
BOC HONG KONG (HOLDINGS) LIMITED
China Merchants Bank Co. Ltd.
HANG SENG BANK LIMITED
HDFC BANK LIMITED
The Busan Bank Co. Ltd.
UNITED OVERSEAS BANK LIMITED
WGZ BANK AG Westdeutsche Genossenschafts-Zentr
Woori Finance Holdings Co. Ltd.

HISTORICAL FINANCIALS

Company Type: Public

Income Statement
FYE: December 31

	ASSETS ($ mil.)	NET INCOME ($ mil.)	INCOME AS % OF ASSETS	EMPLOYEES
12/20	109,506	909	0.8%	0
12/19	99,495	1,357	1.4%	0
12/18	98,527	1,238	1.3%	0
12/17	92,823	1,324	1.4%	0
12/16	81,380	1,330	1.6%	0
Annual Growth	**7.7%**	**(9.1%)**	**—**	**—**

2020 Year-End Financials

Return on assets: 0.8%
Return on equity: 6.6%
Long-term debt ($ mil.): —
No. of shares (mil.): —
Sales ($ mil): 5,854

Dividends
Yield: 0.0%
Payout: —
Market value ($ mil.): —

	STOCK PRICE ($) FY Close	P/E High/Low		PER SHARE ($) Earnings	Dividends	Book Value
12/20	11.32	2	1	0.27	0.51	4.05
12/19	16.23	2	1	0.40	0.56	3.96
12/18	16.16	2	1	0.36	0.55	3.46
12/17	18.27	2	1	0.39	0.53	3.29
12/16	16.45	1	1	0.39	0.49	2.75
Annual Growth	**(8.9%)**	**—**	**—**	**(9.1%)**	**1.3%**	**10.2%**

Sichuan Chang Hong Electric Co Ltd

EXECUTIVES

Independent Director, Xiangdong Ning
Chairman of the Board, Yong Zhao
Secretary of the Board, Qilin Zhao
Deputy General Manager, Mingxian Tan
Deputy General Manager, Guangqing Zheng
Independent Director, Xiaoliang Jia
Independent Director, You Huang
Independent Director, Lang Gao
Deputy General Manager, Director, Yingjian Wu
Deputy General Manager, Dexuan Guo
Deputy General Manager, Director, Jiang Wu
Independent Director, Xiaosu Gao
Auditors: Shine Wing Certified Public Accountants

LOCATIONS

HQ: Sichuan Chang Hong Electric Co Ltd
No. 35, East Mianxing Road, High-Tech Park,
Mianyang, Sichuan Province 621000
Phone: (86) 816 2418486   **Fax:** (86) 816 2418518
Web: www.changhong.com

HISTORICAL FINANCIALS

Company Type: Public

Income Statement
FYE: December 31

	REVENUE ($ mil.)	NET INCOME ($ mil.)	NET PROFIT MARGIN	EMPLOYEES
12/20	14,441	6	0.0%	0
12/19	12,760	8	0.1%	0
12/18	12,122	46	0.4%	0
12/17	11,929	54	0.5%	0
12/16	9,673	79	0.8%	0
Annual Growth	**10.5%**	**(45.7%)**	**—**	**—**

2020 Year-End Financials

Debt ratio: 3.7%
Return on equity: 0.3%
Cash ($ mil.): 3,037
Current ratio: 1.03
Long-term debt ($ mil.): 254

No. of shares (mil.): —
Dividends
  Yield: —
  Payout: —
Market value ($ mil.): —

Siemens AG (Germany)

Siemens is a global powerhouse focusing on the areas of electrification automation and digitalization. One of the largest electronics and industrial engineering companies in the world. The German conglomerate makes everything from healthcare and building technologies to factory automation and power distribution equipment. Siemens has facilities in most corners of the world and serves a global customer base of manufacturers and construction energy and healthcare businesses. Formed in 1847 as Siemens & Halske the company's technological innovations include the first long-distance telegraph system in Europe a high-efficiency dynamo for generating electricity and the SIMATIC industrial machine automation technology.

Operations

Siemens operates its business through six reportable segments.

Publicly traded and separately managed company Siemens Healthineers generates about 30% of total sales. The division develops manufactures and sells health imaging and diagnostic technology and clinical consulting services globally to healthcare providers.

The Digital Industries segment offers automation technology industrial software and services and a cloud-based industrial internet of things (IoT) operating system primarily for manufacturing. This segment generates over 25% of sales.

Smart Infrastructure (roughly 25% of sales) connects energy systems buildings and industries. The company do this from the macro to the micro level physical products components and systems to connected cloud-based digital offerings and services. From intelligent grid control and electrification to smart storage solutions from building automation and control systems to switches valves and sensors.

Mobility segment (over 15%) combines all Siemens businesses in the area of passenger and freight transportation including rail vehicles rail automation systems rail electrification systems road traffic technology digital solutions and related services. It also provides its customers with consulting planning financing construction service and operation of turnkey mobility systems.

Other segments include Financial Services and Portfolio Companies which accounts for less than 10% of sales combined.

Geographic Reach

Headquartered in Munich Germany Siemens has offices warehouses and R&D facilities in nearly every country across the globe and has diverse geographic revenue streams.

Siemens generates around half its revenue from the geographic region comprising Europe CIS Africa and the Middle East. The Americas accounts for over 25% of sales most of which comes from Siemens' largest single country the US. It derives nearly 25% of sales from the Asia/Pacific region.

Sales and Marketing

Siemens serves a range of customers including infrastructure developers construction companies and contractors; owners operators and tenants of both public and commercial buildings including hospitals campuses airports and data centers; companies in heavy industries such as oil and gas mining and chemicals; companies in discrete manufacturing industries such as automotive and machine building; and utilities and power grid network operators (transmission and distribution).

In its Smart Infrastructure segment it serves its customers through a broad variety of channels including its global product and systems sales organization distributors panel builders original equipment manufacturers (OEM) value added resellers and installers as well as by direct sales through the branch offices of its regional solutions and services units worldwide.

Financial Performance

Note: Growth rates may differ after conversion to US Dollars.

Siemens' revenue has fluctuated for five years with 2017 as its highest performing year slightly recovering in 2021 compared with the other years over the period.

The company's revenue increased by 13% to ?62.3 billion in fiscal 2021 compared to ?55.3 billion in the prior year. Revenue went up significantly year-over-year led by double-digit growth in Siemens Healthineers and Digital Industries. Smart Infrastructure recorded a clear increase while Mobility posted slightly higher revenue year-over-year. The revenue increase in emerging markets was driven by substantially higher demand in China and to a lesser degree India.

The company's net income also increased to ?6.7 billion compared to ?4.2 billion in the prior year. This improvement was due mainly to the aforementioned significantly higher Adjusted EBITA Industrial Business and the lower loss outside Industrial Business. In addition discontinued operations largely related to the sale of Flender contributed income of ?1.1 billion in fiscal 2021.

Cash held by the company at the end of 2021 amounted to ?9.5 billion from 2020's cash held at about ?14.0 billion. Cash provided by operations was ?10.0 billion. Cash used for investing activities was ?15.5 billion while financing activities provided ?785 million. Main cash uses were for acquisition of businesses repayment of long-term debt dividends paid and additions to intangible assets and property plant and equipment.

Strategy

A part of the company's strategy includes divesting its activities in some business areas and strengthening other areas through portfolio measures including mergers and acquisitions. In addition the company is primarily focused on highly attractive growth markets that support the global economy such as industry infrastructure transportation and healthcare.

Mergers and Acquisitions

In 2021 Siemens Healthineers completed the acquisition of Varian Medical Systems Inc. (Varian) for US$16.4 billion. Varian becomes new business segment within Siemens Healthineers; important step in the implementation of its Strategy 2025. With Varian Siemens Healthineers will leverage AI-assisted analytics to advance the development and delivery of data-driven precision care and redefine cancer diagnosis care delivery and post-treatment survivorship. Through early and accurate detection as well as more efficient diagnosis increased treatment quality and access Siemens Healthineers will support and accelerate Varian's mission to reduce uncertainty for cancer patients and increase the level of cancer survivorship.

Company Background

Electrical engineer Werner von Siemens and craftsman Johann Halske formed Siemens & Halske in 1847. In 1874 the firm finished the first transatlantic telegraph cable which ran from Ireland to the US. The company also created Europe's first electric power transmission system (1876) the world's first electrified railway (1879) and one of the first elevators (1880).

HISTORY

In 1847 electrical engineer Werner von Siemens and craftsman Johann Halske formed Siemens & Halske. The firm's first major project linked Berlin and Frankfurt with the first long-distance telegraph system in Europe (1848). In 1870 it completed a 6600-mile telegraph line from London to Calcutta India and in 1874 it made the first transatlantic cable linking Ireland to the US.

The company's history of firsts includes Europe's first electric power transmission system (1876) the world's first electrified railway (1879) and one of the first elevators (1880). In 1896 it patented the world's first X-ray tube and completed the first European subway in Budapest Hungary.

By the next century it had formed light-bulb cartel OSRAM with German rivals AEG and Auer (1919) and created a venture with Furukawa Electric called Fuji Electric (1923). It developed radios and traffic lights in the 1920s and began producing electron microscopes in 1939.

Siemens & Halske played a critical role in Germany's war effort in WWII and suffered heavy losses. During the 1950s it recovered by developing data processing equipment silicates for semi-

conductors and the first implantable pacemaker. It moved into the nuclear industry in 1959 when its first reactor went into service at Munich-Garching. In 1966 the company reincorporated as Siemens AG.

EXECUTIVES

Independent Chairman of the Supervisory Board - Shareholder Representative, Jim Hagemann Snabe, $334,637 total compensation
Member of the Managing Board of Siemens AG and CEO Digital Industries, Cedrik Neike, $1,317,038 total compensation
President and Chief Executive Officer, Roland Busch, $2,115,387 total compensation
Chief Financial Officer, Member of the Management Board, Ralf Thomas, $1,317,038 total compensation
Auditors: Ernst & Young GmbH

LOCATIONS

HQ: Siemens AG (Germany)
Werner-von-Siemens-Str. 1, Munich D-80333
Phone: (49) 89 636 33443   **Fax:** (49) 89 636 30085
Web: www.siemens.com

2018 Sales

	% of total
Europe CIS Africa Middle East	51
Americas	27
Asia Australia	22
Total	**100**

PRODUCTS/OPERATIONS

2018 Sales

	% of total
Siemens Healthineers	16
Digital Factory	15
Power and Gas	15
Energy Management	14
Siemens Games Renewable Energy	11
Mobility	10
Process Industries and Drives	9
Building Technologies	8
Financial Services (SFS)	1
Total	**100**

Products & Services

Industrial Automation
Building Technologies
Drive Technology
Energy
Healthcare
Mobility
Financing
Consumer Products
Services
Solutions by Market
Aerospace
Automotive Manufacturing
Battery Manufacturing
Chemistry Industry
Cement
Cranes
Data Centers
Distributors
Electronics Industry
Fiber Industry
Food & Beverage
Glass Industry
Conveyor Technology
Machinery and Plant Construction
Marine
Mining Industry
Municipalities and DSOs
Oil & Gas
Panel Building
Pharmaceutical Industry
Power Utilities

COMPETITORS

AMETEK INC.
BARNES GROUP INC.
Beijing Hollysys Co. Ltd.
FORTIVE CORPORATION
FUJITSU LIMITED
HONEYWELL INTERNATIONAL INC.
HURCO COMPANIES INC.
KEYSIGHT TECHNOLOGIES INC.
MKS INSTRUMENTS INC.
RUBIX GROUP INTERNATIONAL LIMITED
SCHNEIDER ELECTRIC SE
VOLEX PLC

HISTORICAL FINANCIALS
Company Type: Public

Income Statement				FYE: September 30
	REVENUE ($ mil.)	NET INCOME ($ mil.)	NET PROFIT MARGIN	EMPLOYEES
09/21	72,072	7,131	9.9%	303,000
09/20	131,596	9,437	7.2%	656,000
09/19	94,740	5,644	6.0%	385,000
09/18	96,187	6,726	7.0%	379,000
09/17	98,120	7,143	7.3%	363,000
Annual Growth	(7.4%)	(0.0%)	—	(4.4%)

2021 Year-End Financials

Debt ratio: 40.3%
Return on equity: 10.5%
Cash ($ mil.): 11,048
Current ratio: 1.31
Long-term debt ($ mil.): 47,317

No. of shares (mil.): —
Dividends
　Yield: 9.3%
　Payout: 89.4%
Market value ($ mil.): —

	STOCK PRICE ($) FY Close	P/E High/Low		PER SHARE ($) Earnings	Dividends	Book Value
09/21	82.14	11	8	8.79	7.67	(0.00)
09/20	69.65	7	4	11.54	1.56	106.61
09/19	53.59	9	7	6.89	1.60	64.59
09/18	63.86	10	8	8.12	1.58	65.02
09/17	70.75	20	9	8.61	1.55	62.42
Annual Growth	3.8%	—	—	0.5% 49.1%		—

Siemens Energy AG

LOCATIONS

HQ: Siemens Energy AG
Otto-Hahn-Ring 6, Munich 81739
Phone: (49) 89 636 00
Web: www.siemens-energy.com

HISTORICAL FINANCIALS
Company Type: Public

Income Statement				FYE: September 30
	REVENUE ($ mil.)	NET INCOME ($ mil.)	NET PROFIT MARGIN	EMPLOYEES
09/20	32,148	(1,880)		92
09/19	31,413	172	0.5%	89
Annual Growth	2.3%	—	—	3.4%

2020 Year-End Financials

Debt ratio: 3.2%
Return on equity: (-11.9%)
Cash ($ mil.): 5,421
Current ratio: 1.04
Long-term debt ($ mil.): 867

No. of shares (mil.): 717
Dividends
　Yield: —
　Payout: —
Market value ($ mil.): —

	STOCK PRICE ($) FY Close	P/E High/Low	PER SHARE ($) Earnings	Dividends	Book Value
09/20	0.00	— —	(2.59)	0.00	24.39
09/19	0.00	— —	0.24	0.00	17.80
/0.00	—	—(0.00)	0.00	(0.00)	
Annual Growth					

Siemens Gamesa Renewable Energy SA

Created in 2017 by the merger of Siemens Wind Power and Gamesa Siemens Gamesa offers both offshore and onshore wind power technology as well as industry-leading service solutions. It supplies wind power solutions to customers all over the globe the company have installed over 107 GW in around 75 countries. Siemens Gamesa also offers comprehensive and flexible portfolios for the maintenance and optimization of wind turbines providing a holistic lifetime-care service through innovation and digitalization; from technical assistance to complete asset management not only for Siemens Gamesa wind turbines but also for third party assets.

EXECUTIVES

Director, Tim Dawidowsky
Chief Financial Officer, Beatriz Puente Ferreras
Chief Operations Officer, Christoph Wollny
Human Resources Director, Javier Fernndez-Combarro
Chief Strategy and Corporate Affairs Officer, Carlos Albi
Secretary non-member of the Board of Directors and Legal Counsel, Juan Antonio Garcia Fuente
Independent Director, Klaus Rosenfeld
Director, Mariel Von Schumann
Independent Director, Gloria Hernandez Garcia
Director, Maria Ferraro
Independent Director, Harald Von Heynitz
Vice Chairman of the Board, Tim Oliver Holt
Chief Executive Officer of Service Business Unit, Juan Gutierrez
Independent Director, Rudolf Kraemmer
Chairman of the Board, Miguel Angel Lopez Borrego
Chairman, Andreas Nauen, $873,642 total compensation
General Secretary, Juergen Bartl
Auditors: Ernst & Young, S.L.

LOCATIONS

HQ: Siemens Gamesa Renewable Energy SA
Parque Tecnologico de Bizkaia, Edificio 222, Vizcaya, Zamudio 48170
Phone: (34) 944 03 73 52
Web: www.siemensgamesa.com

2012 Sales

	% of total
Latin America	32
Europe & other	27
US	20
India	12
China	9
Total	**100**

COMPETITORS

ACCIONA SA
BayWa AG
CARR'S GROUP PLC
ELECTROCOMPONENTS PUBLIC LIMITED COMPANY
FUTUREN
IBERDROLA SOCIEDAD ANONIMA
MELROSE INDUSTRIES PLC
SYNECTICS PLC

HISTORICAL FINANCIALS

Company Type: Public

Income Statement — FYE: September 30

	REVENUE ($ mil.)	NET INCOME ($ mil.)	NET PROFIT MARGIN	EMPLOYEES
09/20	14,922	(1,444)	—	25,458
09/19	16,093	220	1.4%	23,882
09/18	14,354	110	0.8%	23,799
09/17*	10,288	(23)	—	22,432
12/16	7,452	474	6.4%	8,452
Annual Growth	**19.0%**	—	—	**31.7%**

*Fiscal year change

2020 Year-End Financials

Debt ratio: 11.3%
Return on equity: (-16.3%)
Cash ($ mil.): 2,552
Current ratio: 0.83
Long-term debt ($ mil.): 1,165
No. of shares (mil.): 679
Dividends
  Yield: 0.1%
  Payout: —
Market value ($ mil.): 3,703

	STOCK PRICE ($) FY Close	P/E High/Low	PER SHARE ($) Earnings	Dividends	Book Value
09/20	5.45	— —	(2.12)	0.01	11.43
09/19	2.77	17 10	0.33	0.00	14.52
09/18	2.57	35 22	0.16	0.00	13.73
09/17*	2.59	— —	(0.05)	0.61	14.93
12/16	4.00	4 3	1.71	0.02	9.94
Annual Growth	**8.0%**	— —	—	(22.7%)	3.5%

*Fiscal year change

Siemens Healthineers AG

Auditors: Ernst & Young GmbH

LOCATIONS

HQ: Siemens Healthineers AG
HenkestraBe 127, Erlangen 91052
Phone: (49) 800 188 188 5
Web: www.siemens-healthineers.com

HISTORICAL FINANCIALS

Company Type: Public

Income Statement — FYE: September 30

	REVENUE ($ mil.)	NET INCOME ($ mil.)	NET PROFIT MARGIN	EMPLOYEES
09/19	15,837	1,709	10.8%	52,000
09/18	15,554	1,465	9.4%	50,000
09/17*	16,159	1,629	10.1%	48,000
10/16	0	0	—	0
Annual Growth	—	—	—	—

*Fiscal year change

2019 Year-End Financials

Debt ratio: 0.7%
Return on equity: 17.0%
Cash ($ mil.): 1,003
Current ratio: 1.39
Long-term debt ($ mil.): 67
No. of shares (mil.): 1,000
Dividends
  Yield: 1.3%
  Payout: 14.3%
Market value ($ mil.): 19,660

	STOCK PRICE ($) FY Close	P/E High/Low	PER SHARE ($) Earnings	Dividends	Book Value
09/19	19.66	14 11	1.71	0.26	10.66
09/18	22.25	18 16	1.46	0.00	10.02
09/17*	0.00	— —	1.63	0.00	(0.00)
Annual Growth	—	—	1.7%	—	—

*Fiscal year change

SK Telecom Co Ltd (South Korea)

SK Telecom (SKT) a member of the SK Group chaebol is the leading wireless communication services provider in South Korea. The company serves more than 30 million mobile customers (good for a better than 40% market share). In addition to cellular and wireless data services SKT provides broadband internet access through a controlling stake in the #2 South Korean alternative local-exchange carrier and ISP SK Broadband. It also operates internet portal NATE.com. SKT has international offices in China California and Japan but almost all revenue is from South Korea. SK Group owns 25% of SKT.

Operations

SKT operates in four segments: cellular services about 75% of revenue fixed-line telecommunications services about 15% of revenue e-commerce services about 5% of revenue and other businesses less than 5% of revenue.

SKT's cellular services offer wireless voice and data transmission and its sells wireless devices and provides Internet of Things technologies.

The company's fixed-line segment provides telephone broadband internet and Internet Protocol TV (IPTV) and business communications through subsidiaries SK Broadband and SK Telink.

The E-commerce services segment consists of marketplace business operated by the SK Planet subsidiary. The company's 11st service is an online marketplace that offers products through online and mobile devices.

The Others segment offers complementary products and services.

Geographic Reach

SKT gets 99% of its revenue from South Korea. It has offices in the US China Malaysia and Japan.

Financial Performance

SKT's revenue has bounced up and down in a narrow range for the past five years as it tries to find growth opportunities in South Korea's saturated mobile phone market.

The company's sales rose about 3% in 2017 to 17.5 trillion Korean won (KWN) compared to 17.1 trillion KWN in 2016. The increase came from a rise in broadband internet service revenue from more overall subscribers and more premium IPTV subscribers. Further device revenue rose from sales of higher-priced handset models released in 2017.

SKT's profit increased to 2.6 trillion KWN from 1.6 trillion KWN in 2016.

SKT had about 1.4 KWN trillion in cash and equivalents 2018 compared to 1.5 trillion KWN in

2017. Operating activities produced 3.8 trillion KWN in 2018 and investing activities provided 456 billion KWN while financing activities used 3.5 trillion KWN.

Strategy

SKT's path to growth is through 5G networks the new generation of wireless service that promises to provide faster service with lower response times. Advocates have said 5G will enable a range of capabilities such as vehicle-to-vehicle communications required for self-driving cars. The new network's technology is the leading element of SK's strategy to combined mobile communication media the Internet of Things and an artificial intelligence-based service platform.

South Korea was the first country to switch on 5G technology when SKT and competitors KT and LG Uplus started service for corporate customers in late 2018. SKT's 5G service branded 5GX was available in 13 areas in South Korea.

While SKT remains the biggest wireless provider in South Korea its market share has declined in recent years. It dropped to about 42% from about 44% in 2018. KT remained in second place with about 25% while fast-growing LG Uplus reached about 20%.

Company Background

SKT was founded in 1984 and offered carphone service and pager service in its first year. In subsequent years the company added pay-TV and wireless phone service. SKT has been the dominant telecommunications company in South Korea throughout its history.

HISTORY

SK Telecom was South Korea's first wireless telecommunications service provider. Its new product front generated buzz in 2005 when it announced a new service that allows customers to repel mosquitoes within a range of one meter using their cell phones. The service — introduced in South Korea in 2004 — was rolled out to a smattering of Southeast Asian countries.

Through its WitherThan.com mobile phone content unit SK Telecom established new offices in the UK and Indonesia in 2005 to expand its cell phone Internet business abroad. A month later it announced plans to invest $490 million in building third-generation mobile phone networks utilizing a European standard. The networks would be installed in 84 cities around South Korea.

The company decided to sell its stake in handset manufacturer SK Teletech to Pantech (South Korea's second-largest handset maker) in 2005. The $299.1 million deal sealed the sale of a 60% interest held by SK Telecom and helped SK Teletech avoid government regulation. The company was prevented from selling more than 1.2 million handsets per year because it was a unit of SK Telecom previously a wireless monopoly. Regulators simultaneously fined the company $90 million for offering illegal handset subsidies.

SK Telecom also jointly launched a mobile phone production plant in China with Pantech in 2005 to help expand its market position in that country.

Legal troubles hounded the company in 2005. The Korea Baseball Organization sued over unauthorized broadcasts of baseball games on its mobile TV service. The organization claimed TU Media a unit of SK Telecom broadcasted the games for its mobile TV subscribers without permission. It was also fined $1.4 million for discriminating against other Internet portal companies in opening its wireless network to them.

Aiming for improved network quality SK Telecom said in 2005 it would invest $152.4 million to upgrade its mobile phone network infrastructure by year's end. The company also began exploring

opportunities in the entertainment industry. It announced plans to set up a joint $74.9 million fund with investment companies that would invest in entertainment-related ventures. The company also unveiled plans to open a research and development center in China.

In 2006 SK Telecom invested $1 billion in China Unicom taking a small stake in the company. The investment was seen as an endorsement of the advanced wireless technology known as CDMA2000.

SK Telecom effectively ended its activities in the North America when it sold its stake in joint wireless venture HELIO in 2008. The company had entered the US market in early 2005 when it formed HELIO with EarthLink to market wireless voice and data services. HELIO did not meet with the reception its parent companies had hoped however and both SK Telecom and Earthlink sold their interests in the struggling business to Virgin Mobile USA for about $39 million in 2008; SK Telecom took a 17% stake in Virgin Mobile USA as part of the deal. It eventually sold those shares to Sprint Nextel in late 2009.

The company in 2008 bought a stake in hanarotelecom which subsequently changed its name to SK Broadband; the company increased its stake in SK Broadand to just over 50% in 2009. The deal added broadband Internet and fixed-line telephone services to the company's portfolio enabling it to better compete with the country's largest fixed line carrier KT Corporation SK Telecom bought the leased line business of affiliate SK Networks later that year to improve the quality of its fixed-line voice calling.

Auditors: KPMG Samjong Accounting Corp.

LOCATIONS

HQ: SK Telecom Co Ltd (South Korea)
65 Eulji-ro, Jung-gu, Seoul 04539
Phone: (82) 2 6100 2114   **Fax:** (82) 2 6100 7830
Web: www.sktelecom.com

PRODUCTS/OPERATIONS

2017 Sales

	% of total
Cellular services	76
Fixed-line telecommunication services	16
E-commerce Services	6
Other Businesses	2
Total	**100**

COMPETITORS

China Telecom	T-MOBILE US INC.
Corporation Limited	TELSTRA CORPORATION
EIRCOM LIMITED	LIMITED
MTS PAO	VODAFONE IDEA LIMITED
NII HOLDINGS INC.	Vodafone GmbH
SPRINT CORPORATION	Vodafone Libertel B.V.
STARHUB LTD.	

HISTORICAL FINANCIALS

Company Type: Public

Income Statement   FYE: December 31

	REVENUE ($ mil.)	NET INCOME ($ mil.)	NET PROFIT MARGIN	EMPLOYEES
12/20	17,204	1,382	8.0%	41,097
12/19	15,457	770	5.0%	40,543
12/18	15,199	2,805	18.5%	39,909
12/17	16,433	2,438	14.8%	4,498
12/16	14,227	1,395	9.8%	4,399
Annual Growth	4.9%	(0.2%)	—	74.8%

2020 Year-End Financials

Debt ratio: 0.0%	No. of shares (mil.): 73
Return on equity: 6.4%	Dividends
Cash ($ mil.): 1,258	Yield: —
Current ratio: 1.07	Payout: —
Long-term debt ($ mil.): 8,884	Market value ($ mil.): 1,790

	STOCK PRICE ($) FY Close	P/E High/Low		PER SHARE ($) Earnings	Dividends	Book Value
12/20	24.48	0	0	18.80	0.00	298.30
12/19	23.11	0	0	10.52	8.66	276.65
12/18	26.80	0	0	39.53	8.97	280.44
12/17	27.91	0	0	34.31	9.38	237.02
12/16	20.90	0	0	19.56	8.32	188.28
Annual Growth	4.0%	—	—	(1.0%)	—	12.2%

Skandinaviska Enskilda Banken

Skandinaviska Enskilda Banken (SEB) provides merchant banking retail banking wealth management and life insurance in some 20 nations mostly in Northern Europe. Its merchant banking division provides lending debt capital markets trading finance and custody services to corporate clients and financial institutions. Its retail division provides business services including loans and card services. SEB Wealth Management offers asset management and private banking services to institutional and wealthy clients. Founded in 1856 the bank boasts nearly SK$3 trillion (around $350 billion) in assets.

Operations

The bank operates four main business segments: Merchant Banking which generated 43% of total revenue in 2020; Retail Banking (39% of revenue); Wealth Management (12% of revenue); and Life (6% of revenue) which provides life insurance products.

More broadly SEB generated 51% of its total revenue from interest income in 2020 while 36% came from fee and commission income and 13% came from net financial income.

Geographic Reach

The bank has a unique customer base and market position serving its customers in its home markets and beyond.

It serves large corporations and financial institutions in Sweden and hold a forefront position in providing corporate services in Norway Denmark Finland and the United Kingdom. It provides universal banking services in Sweden Estonia Latvia and Lithuania. In Germany operations have a strong focus on corporate and investment banking based on a full-service offering to corporations institutional customers and internationally operating real estate investors.

It also serves corporate customers from the Nordic countries United Kingdom and Germany around the globe with offices in international financial centers such as New York and London in Asia via offices in Shanghai Beijing Hong Kong and Singapore. Its international network is also instrumental in its ability to offer global financial institutions access to investment opportunities in Nordic assets.

Sales and Marketing

Retail Banking served about 4 million private customers and 400000 small and medium-sized businesses in 2020. Its Wealth Management division serves institutions life insurance companies and private individuals.

SEB's corporate customers come from a broad range of industries and sectors including manufacturing and service companies as well as investment and property companies.

Financial Performance

Note: Growth rates may differ after conversion to US dollars.

SEB's total operating income was steady at SEK 50 million after recording an increase in income from large corporate & financial institution and corporate & private customers segments offset by its Baltic and life & investment management. Seb's net profit fell 22% to SEK 15.7 million in 2020 compared to SEK 20.2 million in 2019.

Net change in cash and cash equivalents in 2020 was SEK 180 million. Operating activities generated SEK 190 million while financing and investing activities used SEK 10 million and SEK 56 thousand respectively.

Strategy

SEB's current long-term strategy named Vision 2025 has been adjusted along the way in order for it to continue to deliver long-term value to its customers shareholders and employees. The mega trends of digitalization and sustainability are expected to remain drivers of transformation and hence continue to require investments. The economic and societal consequences of the Covid-19 pandemic during 2020 have further accelerated transformation both in SEB and in society. This is presenting both challenges and opportunities that it incorporates into its strategic direction in order to ensure that it remains the preferred choice for its customers.

The bank's strategic work will remain concentrated to the areas of advisory leadership operational excellence and extended presence with particular emphasis on geographical expansion digitalization sustainability savings and investments as well as regulatory compliance ? all with the overarching ambition to become a leading northern European bank for corporates and institutions and the top universal bank in Sweden and the Baltic countries.

HISTORY

Skandinaviska Enskilda Banken (SEB) was incorporated in 1972 as a result of the merger between Stockholm's Enskilda Bank (founded in 1856 by the Wallenberg family) and Skandinaviska Banken (founded in 1864 and a pioneer in commercial lending in Scandinavia). By 1974 SEB had begun expanding its operations forming an investment management subsidiary. It then became one of the first Swedish banks to go international when it took a stake in the German Deutsch-Skandinavische Bank in 1976. By the end of the 1970s SEB had reached halfway around the world establishing a subsidiary in Singapore to handle Southeast Asian operations.

By the early 1980s SEB was leading the nation in industrial as well as private accounts largely due to deregulation and the introduction of new financial instruments including Swedish treasury bills a commercial paper market and market-rate state bonds. The bank continued to expand opening branches in the Cayman Islands Hamburg London and New York; it also began cross-border banking in Scandinavia through a regional alliance with Bergen Bank of Norway Privatbanken of Denmark and Union Bank of Finland.

In another step toward deregulation the Swedish government lifted the ban on foreign banking in 1985. Within a year a dozen international banks had established themselves in Sweden but SEB continued to expand; its investment banking subsidiary Enskilda Securities opened branches in

Hong Kong London New York Paris and Singapore in the latter half of the 1980s.

In 1990 the bank acquired an option to buy about a third of Skandia Sweden's largest private insurance company. But facing strong resistance from Skandia's management SEB accepted defeat and sold most of its option to two Scandinavian insurance companies. Winds of change blew through Sweden in the early 1990s as the country suffered a severe economic recession. Deregulation in the mid-1980s followed by excessive lending to the property market led to inflated real estate prices and then a collapse of the market. Banks investing in property experienced huge losses; many banks (including SEB) had to turn to the government for help to strengthen their capital bases. The mid-1990s saw the bank still trying to recover selling several of its subsidiaries including a vehicle finance unit to GE Capital.

1997 saw SEB acquire Trygg-Hansa (now SEB Trygg Liv) one of Sweden's major insurers. The bank remained acquisitive in 1998 expanding aggressively into the Baltic by buying major stakes in banks in Estonia (Eesti hlspank) Latvia (Latvija Unibanken) and Lithuania (Vilniaus Bankas).

In 1999 the bank further emphasized its Internet business making it a separate unit. Also that year SEB sold Trygg-Hansa's non-life business to Denmark's Codan Insurance in exchange for Codan's banking subsidiary and other assets. In 2000 the bank acquired Germany's almost 200-branch BfG Bank from Credit Lyonnais; it then used BfG to create a cross-selling and Internet alliance with German insurer Gerling. Also in 2000 SEB upped its stake in Eesti hispank Vilniaus Bankas and Latvijas Unibanka.

The following year SEB announced plans to acquire fellow Swedish bank F ¶reningsSparbanken to create SEB SwedBank. EU regulators investigated the proposal and demanded significant concession. As a result the two banks dropped plans for the merger later in 2001.

SEB continued to boost its offerings and services — largely through acquisitions — during the early years of the 21st century. Purchases included Europay in Norway (2002) Danish life insurer Codan Pension (2004) Ukraine's Bank Agio (2005) and Russia's PetroEnergoBank (2006). In 2007 it acquired nearly all of Factorial Bank adding 65 branches in Eastern Ukraine. The following year it bought London-based hedge fund Key Asset Management.

EXECUTIVES

Independent Chairman of the Board, Marcus Wallenberg
Deputy President and Chief Executive Officer and Group Data Privacy Senior Manager, Mats Torstendahl
Acting Chief Financial Officer, Peter Kessiakoff
Co-Head - Large Corporates and Financial Institutions division, Jonas Ahlstrom
Independent Director, Lars Ottersgard
Independent Director, Anne Berner
Senior Advisor to the CEO, Martin Johansson
Country Manager SEB, Germany, Johan Andersson
Head of the Life Division, David Teare
Independent Vice Chairman of the Board, Sven Nyman
Independent Director, Winnie Fok
Director, Employee Representative, Charlotta Lindholm
Director, Employee Representative, Anna-Karin Glimstrom
Chief Transformation Officer for Control and Staff Functions, Nina Korfu-Pedersen
Country Manager SEB, Denmark, Peter Hoeltermand
Country Manager SEB, Norway, John Turesson

Independent Director, Signhild Arnegard Hansen
Independent Director, Helena Saxon
Chief Transformation Office, Sara Ohrvall
Country Manager SEB, Finland, Marcus Nysten
Head of Business Support and Operations, Jeanette Almberg
Executive Vice President, Co-Head of the Large Corporates & Financial Institutions Division, Joachim Alpen
Head of Operations, Ausra Matuseviciene
Chief Information Officer, Nicolas Moch
Head of Group Technology, Group Outsourcing Senior Manager, Petra Alund
Head of division Corporate and Private Customer, Jonas Soederberg
Independent Vice Chairman of the Board, Jesper Ovesen
Deputy President and Chief Executive Officer, Magnus Carlsson
Executive Vice President, Co-Head of Private Wealth Management and Family Office division, William Paus
President, Chief Executive Officer, Director, Johan Torgeby, $1,356,964 total compensation
Auditors: Ernst & Young AB

LOCATIONS

HQ: Skandinaviska Enskilda Banken
  Kungstradgardsgatan 8, Stockholm SE-106 40
Phone: (46) 771 62 10 00
Web: www.sebgroup.com

2014 Operating Income

	% of total
Scandinavia	
Sweden	60
Norway	8
Denmark	7
Finland	4
Baltics	
Lithuania	3
Estonia	3
Latvia	2
Germany	7
Other	6
Total	**100**

PRODUCTS/OPERATIONS

2014 Sales by Segment

	% of total
Merchant Banking	38
Retail Banking	27
Life	10
Wealth Management	10
Baltic	8
Other	7
Total	**100**

COMPETITORS

Banque de Montreal	KEYCORP
Bayerische Landesbank	Landesbank
CIT GROUP INC.	Baden-W rttemberg
COMMONWEALTH BANK OF AUSTRALIA	STANDARD CHARTERED PLC
	Swedbank AB
Co ¶peratieve Rabobank U.A.	The Toronto-Dominion Bank
DEUTSCHE BANK AG	UBS AG
Danske Bank A/S	UniCredit Bank AG

HISTORICAL FINANCIALS

Company Type: Public

Income Statement
FYE: December 31

	ASSETS ($ mil.)	NET INCOME ($ mil.)	INCOME AS % OF ASSETS	EMPLOYEES
12/20	372,130	1,927	0.5%	16,193
12/19	307,085	2,169	0.7%	15,819
12/18	286,832	2,584	0.9%	15,562
12/17	311,976	1,979	0.6%	15,804
12/16	289,111	1,171	0.4%	16,087
Annual Growth	6.5%	13.3%	—	0.2%

2020 Year-End Financials

Return on assets: 0.5%
Return on equity: 9.5%
Long-term debt ($ mil.): —
No. of shares (mil.): —
Sales ($ mil): 8,079

Dividends
Yield: —
Payout: 56.7%
Market value ($ mil.): —

Skanska AB

Auditors: Ernst & Young AB

LOCATIONS

HQ: Skanska AB
Warfvinges vag 25, Stockholm SE-112 74
Phone: (46) 10 448 00 00   **Fax:** (46) 8 755 12 56
Web: www.group.skanska.com

HISTORICAL FINANCIALS

Company Type: Public

Income Statement
FYE: December 31

	REVENUE ($ mil.)	NET INCOME ($ mil.)	NET PROFIT MARGIN	EMPLOYEES
12/20	19,625	1,208	6.2%	32,463
12/19	18,580	648	3.5%	34,756
12/18	19,184	510	2.7%	38,650
12/17	19,242	499	2.6%	40,759
12/16	16,036	631	3.9%	42,903
Annual Growth	5.2%	17.6%	—	(6.7%)

2020 Year-End Financials

Debt ratio: 0.2%
Return on equity: 27.5%
Cash ($ mil.): 2,387
Current ratio: 1.52
Long-term debt ($ mil.): 323

No. of shares (mil.): 412
Dividends
Yield: 0.0%
Payout: 13.4%
Market value ($ mil.): 10,719

	STOCK PRICE ($) FY Close	P/E High/Low		Earnings	PER SHARE ($) Dividends	Book Value
12/20	26.00	1	1	2.92	0.39	11.46
12/19	22.90	2	1	1.57	0.64	8.60
12/18	15.76	2	1	1.24	0.97	7.98
12/17	20.56	3	2	1.21	1.00	8.07
12/16	23.89	2	1	1.53	0.83	7.37
Annual Growth	2.1%	—	—	17.5%	(17.1%)	11.7%

Societe Generale

Auditors: ERNST & YOUNG et Autres

LOCATIONS

HQ: Societe Generale
29, Boulevard Haussman, Paris 75009
Phone: (33) 1 42 14 20 00
Web: www.societegenerale.com

HISTORICAL FINANCIALS

Company Type: Public

Income Statement
FYE: December 31

	ASSETS ($ mil.)	NET INCOME ($ mil.)	INCOME AS % OF ASSETS	EMPLOYEES
12/20	1,794,238	(316)	—	133,251
12/19	1,523,026	3,646	0.2%	138,240
12/18	1,499,550	4,425	0.3%	149,022
12/17	1,528,565	3,363	0.2%	147,125
12/16	1,459,485	4,090	0.3%	145,672
Annual Growth	5.3%	—	—	(2.2%)

2020 Year-End Financials

Return on assets: (-0.0%)
Return on equity: (-0.4%)
Long-term debt ($ mil.): —
No. of shares (mil.): 853
Sales ($ mil): 56,071

Dividends
Yield: 0.1%
Payout: —
Market value ($ mil.): 3,550

	STOCK PRICE ($) FY Close	P/E High/Low		Earnings	PER SHARE ($) Dividends	Book Value
12/20	4.16	—	—	(1.25)	0.68	88.71
12/19	6.99	2	2	3.42	0.49	84.40
12/18	6.29	3	1	4.86	0.51	88.59
12/17	10.36	4	3	3.50	0.53	89.45
12/16	9.82	2	1	4.50	0.42	81.82
Annual Growth	(19.3%)	—	—	—	12.6%	2.0%

Sodexo

Founded in 1966 by Pierre Bellon Sodexo is the global leader in Quality of Life services. The company is a partner of over 100 million consumers in about 60 countries. With more than 410000 employees worldwide the company is the number one France-based private employer worldwide. The company has a wide range of services to meet the needs of clients and consumers. These services include on-site services benefits & rewards services and personal & home services. Sodexo's services contribute to the performance of their clients the satisfaction of the company's consumers the fulfillment of their teams and the economic social and environmental development of their local communities.

Operations
Sodexo operates through the following business segments: On-Site Services Benefits and Rewards Services and Personal & Home Services.

On-Site Services which accounts for about 95% of group sales and provides foodservice and facilities management. It increases the efficiency and well-being at the workplace care for patients at the hospital foster an optimal learning environment at schools and provide safety on a remote site.

The Benefits & Rewards segment provides rewards and benefits for companies' employees and travel and expense management through multi-advantage card solutions. It generates around 5% of sales.

Lastly Personal & Home Services is divided into Childcare services Concierge services and Homecare services. The segment's Childcare services have combined its operations with Grandir Group.

Geographic Reach
France-based Sodexo which operates in about 60 countries generates nearly 40% of its revenue in the US more than 40% in Europe and about 20% in Africa Asia Latin America and the Middle East.

Sales and Marketing
Sodexo's customers are diverse but include government departments (such as military and health)

onshore and offshore oil and gas companies sporting event organizers and companies with significant facilities and catering needs. Sodexo has around 100 million customers in total.

Financial Performance
Note: Growth rates may differ after conversion to US Dollars.

Sodexo has struggled to attain meaningful revenue growth in recent years while profits have fluctuated. Over a five-year period the company ended it with 2021 being the lowest performing year.

Sodexo's revenue has decreased by about 10% to ?17.4 billion in 2021 compared to ?19.3 billion in the prior year.

The company was able to record a net profit of about ?139 million compared to a net loss of about ?315 million.

Sodexo's cash balance is up ?2 billion during 2021 ending the year at ?3.5 billion. The company's operations produced ?982 million. Investing activities used another ?303 million while financing activities provided ?789 million. Main cash uses were acquisitions of property plant and equipment and intangible assets.

Strategy
Faced with various changes in the market that Sodexo operates in the company incorporates its strategy with some external factors: major long-term global trends such as aging populations increasing urbanization the development of the middle classes among other trends. This strategy enables the company to optimize its value proposition and to the position of its activities in the market as well as in the value chain. Further the company is starting on a program to simplify and optimize its central structures which includes the transition of operations from 12 regions to 7 regions. This also includes the exclusive negotiations that the company took with the Grandir Group's Liveli to combine its childcare activities.

HISTORY

The Bellon family had been luxury ship hospitality specialists since the turn of the century 60 years before Pierre Bellon founded Sodexho in 1966. By 1971 Bellon had his first contract outside France to provide foodservice to a Brussels hospital. Sodexho continued to expand its services into the late 1970s entering remote site management in Africa and the Middle East in 1975 and starting its service vouchers segment in Belgium and Germany in 1978.

Sodexho jumped the pond in 1980 expanding its businesses into North and South America. The company went public on the Paris Bourse exchange in 1983. Two years later it bought Seiler a Boston vending machine company-turned-restaurateur. Sodexho then bought San Francisco's Food Dimensions in 1987. After beefing up its American operations with four other US acquisitions the company merged Food Dimensions and Seiler in 1989. Sodexho's US river cruise company Spirit Cruises — an echo of the Bellon family's original calling — was also included in the merger. The merged US companies were renamed Sodexho USA in 1993.

The 1990s proved an era of growth and acquisitions for Sodexho. The company expanded into Japan Africa Russia and five Eastern European countries in 1993. The company acquired a 20% stake in Corrections Corporation of America the following year and virtually doubled its size with the acquisition of the UK's Gardner Merchant in 1995. The largest catering company in that region Gardner Merchant had holdings that spanned Australia Asia northern Europe the UK and the US — generally markets where Sodexho did not have a strong presence. That year the company also acquired Partena a Swedish security and care company from Volvo's Fortos.

Gardner Merchant's US business was officially merged with Sodexho USA in 1996 to make it the #4 foodservice company in the US. Also that year Sodexho acquired Brazilian service voucher company Cardapio. After a year of legal wrangling Sodexho also lost a fight for control of Accor's Eurest France to rival caterer Compass Group and sold off its minority interest. The next year Sodexho acquired 49% of Universal Ogden Services renamed Universal Services an American remote site manager. To signify its efforts to maintain the individuality of the companies it acquires Sodexho changed its name to Sodexho Alliance in 1997.

Marriott International merged its foodservice branch with Sodexho's North American foodservice operations in 1998. With a 48% stake Sodexho Alliance became the largest shareholder; former Marriott International stockholders took the rest with the Marriott family controlling 9%. Before the merger Sodexho USA was less than one-fourth the size of Marriott International's foodservice division. Sodexho acquired GR Servicios Hoteleros in 1999 thereby becoming the largest caterer in Spain. The following year it agreed to merge its remote site management operations with Universal Services and rename it Universal Sodexho (later Sodexo Remote Sites).

In 2001 its initial $900 million bid to buy the 52% of Sodexho Marriott Services it didn't already own was rebuffed by its subsidiary's shareholders. Sodexho Alliance made a better offer (about $1.1 billion) and finally reached an agreement to purchase the rest of Sodexho Marriott Services. The deal was completed later that year and Sodexho Marriott Services changed its name to Sodexho Inc. Also that year the company agreed to pay some $470 million for French rival Sogeres and US-based food management firm Wood Dining.

In 2002 the company announced it had detected accounting and management errors in its UK operations causing the value of its stock to fall by nearly one-third. In addition the company replaced its UK management team because of poor performance there.

Admitting no wrongdoing Sodexho settled an $80 million race-bias lawsuit just before it was to go to trial in 2005. The suit brought by the African-American employees of its American subsidiary Sodexho Inc. charged that African-Americans were routinely passed over for promotions and were segregated within the company. In addition to paying the monetary award Sodexho agreed to increase company diversity through promotion incentives monitoring and training.

In 2005 Bellon 75 stepped down as company CEO but remained chairman. He was replaced by Sodexho veteran Michel Landel. The company changed its name to Sodexo in 2008 a rebranding effort that eliminated both the word "Alliance" and the "h" from its name.

EXECUTIVES

Chief Executive Officer, Sports & Leisure worldwide, On-site Services, Member of the Executive Committee, Director, Nathalie Bellon-Szabo, $75,421 total compensation
Independent Director, Federico Gonzalez Tejera, $31,077 total compensation
Group Chief Digital & Innovation Officer, Member of the Executive Committee, Belen Moscoso Del Prado
Group Chief Sales and Marketing Officer, Member of the Executive Committee, Bruno Vanhaelst
Chief Executive Officer - Corporate Services, On-site Services, Member of the Executive Committee, Sunil Nayak

Group Chief Communications and Public Affairs Officer, Member of the Executive Committee, Anne Bardot
CEO, Benefits & Rewards Services, Member of the Executive Committee, Aurelien Sonet
CEO of Sedexo Energy & Resources Worldwide, Simon Seaton
Chairman of the Board, Interim Chief Executive Officer, Sophie Bellon, $806,811 total compensation
Region Chair, France, Anna Notarianni
CEO, Service Operations, Regional Chair, UK & Ireland, On-site Services, Member of the Executive Committee, Sean Haley
Chief Executive Officer, Corporate Responsibility and Personal & Home Services, Member of the Executive Committee, Didier Sandoz
Group Chief Financial Officer, Member of the Executive Committee, Marc Rolland
Region Chair, North America, On-site Services, Member of the Executive Committee, Sarosh Mistry
Independent Director, Luc Messier, $58,867 total compensation
Independent Director, Veronique Laury, $65,979 total compensation
CEO, Geographic Regions Region Chair, Asia Pacific, On-site Services, Member of the Executive Committee, John Dimech
Group Chief Growth Officer, Member of the Executive Committee, Sylvia Metayer
CEO, Healthcare & Seniors, On-site Services, Member of the Executive Committee, Marc Plumart
CEO, Government & Agencies, On-site Services, Member of the Executive Committee, Tony Leech
Auditors: KPMG Audit

LOCATIONS

HQ: Sodexo
255, quai de la Bataille de Stalingrad, Issy-les-Moulineaux, Cedex 9 92866
Phone: (33) 1 30 85 75 00
Web: www.sodexo.com

2018 Sales

	% of total
North America	45
Europe	39
Africa Asia Australia LatAm Middle East	16
Total	**100**

PRODUCTS/OPERATIONS

2018 Sales

	% of total
On-site Services	
Business & Administrations	54
Health Care and Seniors	23
Educations	10
Benefits & Services	4
Total	**100**

2018 sales

By type of service	% of total
On-site Services revenues	
Foodservices	65
Facilities management services	31
Benefits and Rewards Services	4
Total	**100**

COMPETITORS

CANNAE HOLDINGS INC.	DOMINO'S PIZZA GROUP
CERIDIAN CORPORATION	PLC
COMPUTACENTER PLC	HAYS PLC
DENNY'S CORPORATION	LUBY'S INC.
DINE BRANDS GLOBAL	MCDONALD'S CORPORATION
INC.	THE WENDY'S COMPANY

HISTORICAL FINANCIALS

Company Type: Public

Income Statement
FYE: August 31

	REVENUE ($ mil.)	NET INCOME ($ mil.)	NET PROFIT MARGIN	EMPLOYEES
08/20	23,013	(375)	—	422,712
08/19	24,235	734	3.0%	470,237
08/18	23,771	758	3.2%	460,663
08/17	24,504	855	3.5%	427,268
08/16	22,542	709	3.1%	425,594
Annual Growth	0.5%	—	—	(0.2%)

2020 Year-End Financials

Debt ratio: 34.3%	No. of shares (mil.): 146
Return on equity: (-8.7%)	Dividends
Cash ($ mil.): 2,414	Yield: 4.4%
Current ratio: 0.98	Payout: —
Long-term debt ($ mil.): 5,925	Market value ($ mil.): 2,102

	STOCK PRICE ($) FY Close	P/E High/Low		PER SHARE ($) Earnings	Dividends	Book Value
08/20	14.40	—		(2.57)	0.64	22.51
08/19	22.61	5	4	4.97	0.61	33.69
08/18	20.71	6	4	5.06	0.68	26.27
08/17	23.35	6	5	5.67	0.51	28.17
08/16	23.16	6	4	4.62	0.49	27.11
Annual Growth	(11.2%)	—	—	—	6.7%	(4.5%)

SoftBank Corp (New)

Auditors: Deloitte Touche Tohmatsu LLC

LOCATIONS

HQ: SoftBank Corp (New)
1-7-1, Kaigan, Minato-ku, Tokyo 105-7529
Phone: (81) 3 6889 2000
Web: www.softbank.jp

HISTORICAL FINANCIALS

Company Type: Public

Income Statement
FYE: March 31

	REVENUE ($ mil.)	NET INCOME ($ mil.)	NET PROFIT MARGIN	EMPLOYEES
03/21	47,013	4,437	9.4%	65,920
03/20	44,783	4,358	9.7%	50,950
03/19	33,828	3,889	11.5%	29,609
03/18	33,738	3,774	11.2%	25,889
Annual Growth	11.7%	5.5%	—	36.6%

2021 Year-End Financials

Debt ratio: 0.4%	No. of shares (mil.): —
Return on equity: 39.1%	Dividends
Cash ($ mil.): 14,313	Yield: 6.1%
Current ratio: 0.76	Payout: 82.8%
Long-term debt ($ mil.): 33,345	Market value ($ mil.): —

	STOCK PRICE ($) FY Close	P/E High/Low		PER SHARE ($) Earnings	Dividends	Book Value
03/21	13.12	0	0	0.93	0.81	2.91
03/20	12.90	0	0	0.90	0.39	1.94
03/19	11.50	0	0	0.81	0.34	2.35
03/18	0.00			0.92	1.71	(0.00)
Annual Growth	—	—	—	0.3%	(22.1%)	—

Sojitz Corp

Sojitz Corporation is general trading company that engaged in wide business globally such as buying selling importing and exporting goods manufacturing and selling of products providing services and planning and coordinating projects in Japan and overseas. The company invest in various sectors and financing activities and operates in related to Automobiles plants Aerospace medical infrastructure energy mineral resources chemicals foodstuff resources agriculture and forestry resources and more. In 2020 Sojitz Corporation acquired acquired a 33.46% stake in TDA Holdings B.V. ("TDA") and In 2021 Sojitz acquired 13.30% Royal Holdings common stock and also in same year 2021 Sojitz acquired has acquired a 100% ownership interest in Southwest Rail Industries Inc. ("SRI").

Operations

Sojitz reports ten business divisions.

Its leading segment is Chemicals (25% sales) which trades Organic chemicals; inorganic chemicals; functional chemicals fine chemicals; industrial salt; healthcare and natural. products; rare earths; commodity resins; advanced resins and more.

Metals & Coal (20%) includes coal steel and base metals trading and investment in rare metals such as niobium and steel-related businesses such as alumina refining.

Retail & Lifestyle Business (about 18%) is focused Cotton and synthetic fabrics; knitted fabrics and products; clothing; medical material; construction materials.

Automotive (about 13%) includes trading of completed automobiles; assembly and sales; retail; automobile and motorcycle parts simply parts assembly.

Foods & Agriculture Business (another 6%) sells fertilizer grain and feed marine products and other agricultural products.

Some 2% revenue comes from each of Sojitz's Machinery & Medical Infrastructure Includes Plant Projects (Fertilizer & chemical energy infrastructure and environmental projects); Industrial Machinery (Industrial machinery surface-mounting machines start-up.In addition some of 2% Aerospace & Transportation Project (Commercial aircraft defense and related equipment agency and sales business jets used aircraft and part-out business airport business).

Industrial Infrastructure & Urban Development (less than 2%) includes real estate development consignment sales rent administration and management business such as industrial park business housing and office.

Energy & Social Infrastructure (about 5%) Infrastructure & Environment (Renewable energy IPP projects); Power-related projects (IPP and IWP projects power plant EPC business); Energy (Oil and gas; petroleum products; NG and LNG-relarated business); Nuclear power related business (nuclear fuels; nuclear power-related equipment and machinery).

Other (less than 5%) business includes domestic branches logistics and insurance services.

Geographic Reach

The company has operations in Japan The Americas Europe and Asia and Oceania. In additions 5 domestic branches and 79 local corporation and representative offices.

Sales and Marketing

The company have engaged in wide variety of business in Japan and overseas such as food distribution business commercial facility business brand business consumer goods distribution business textile business and real estate business.

Financial Performance

Note: Growth rates may differ after conversion to US Dollars.

Revenue was down 6% year on year to 1.8 trillion due to lower revenue in the Chemicals Division a result of declines in the transaction volumes of plastic resins and in the price of methanol and in the Metals & Mineral Resources Division a result of fall in sales prices in overseas coal businesses.

Profit for the year 2020 (attributable to owners of the company) decreased 9.6 billion year on year to 60.8 billion.

The company's cash at the end of 2020 was 272.7 billion. Operating activities generated 40.5 million while investing activities used 35.7 billion. Financing activities used another 12.2 billion.

Strategy

Medium-Term Management Plan 2023—Start of the Next Decade Sojitz's new three-year medium-term management plan was launched in April 2021. This plan defines Sojitz vision for 2030 as becoming a general trading company that constantly fosters new businesses and human resources. To pursue this vision Sojitz will continue to fulfill its mission as a general trading company: delivering goods and services where necessary. At the same time the company will seek to increase corporate value by creating business and human resource value that responds to market needs and social issues. Accordingly the company looks to pursue competitiveness and growth by adopting market-oriented initiatives applying co-creation and sharing methodologies and striving for speed to propose solutions that respond to market needs and social issues. Organizations and human resources will be transformed to accommodate these undertakings.

Mergers and Acquisitions

In 2020 Sojitz has acquired a 33.46% stake in TDA Holdings B.V. ("TDA") the parent company to aircraft parts distributor Touchdown Aviation B. V. based in the Netherlands. TDA's business involves selling parts obtained from disassembled used aircraft.

In 2021 Sojitz Corporation has concluded an agreement with Royal Holdings Co. Ltd. to form a capital and business tie-up and Sojitz will acquire 13.30% of Royal Holdings' common stock and be issued 1st stock acquisition rights through third-party allotment.

In 2021 Sojitz Corporation has acquired a 100% ownership interest in Southwest Rail Industries Inc. ("SRI") through Sojitz Corporation of America a fully owned subsidiary of Sojitz. SRI is a U.S. company that operates a railcar leasing business*Å headquartered in Texas.

Company Background

In April 2003 Nichimen Corporation and Nissho Iwai Corporation established a joint holding company integrating their businesses the following year to become the Sojitz Group. Both companies trace their history back to three trading company titans (Japan Cotton Trading Co. Ltd. Iwai & Co. Ltd. and Suzuki & Co. Ltd.) who played an instrumental role in the development of modern Japan.

HISTORY

The Nissho and Iwai companies got their acts together as Nissho Iwai in 1968 but each company dates back to the middle of the 19th century. In 1863 Bunsuke Iwai opened a shop in Osaka to sell imported goods such as glass oil products silk and wine. The Meiji government which came to power in 1868 encouraged modernization and industrialization a climate in which Iwai's business flourished. In 1877 Iwajiro Suzuki established a similar trading concern Suzuki & Co. that eventually became Nissho.

After cotton spinning machines were introduced in Japan in the 1890s both Iwai and Suzuki imported cotton. Iwai began to trade directly with British trader William Duff & Son (an innovation in Japan where the middleman or shokan played the paramount role in international trade). Iwai became the primary agent for Yawata Steel Works in 1901 and was incorporated in 1912. Meanwhile Suzuki solely engaged in the import trade emerged as one of the top sugar brokers in the world and established an office in London.

To protect itself from foreign competition Iwai established a number of companies to produce goods in Japan including Nippon Steel Plate (1914) and Tokuyama Soda (1918). Stagnation after WWI forced Suzuki to restructure. In 1928 the company sold many of its assets to trading giant Mitsui and reorganized the rest under a new name Nissho Co.

Both Iwai and Nissho subsequently grew as they helped fuel Japan's military expansion in Asia in the 1930s. But Japan's defeat in WWII devastated the companies. When the occupation forces broke up Mitsui and other larger trading conglomerates both companies took advantage of the situation to move into new business areas. In 1949 Nissho established Nissho Chemical Industry Nissho Fuel and Nijko Shoji (a trading concern). It also opened its US operations Nissho American Corp. in 1952.

Poor management by the Iwai family led the company into financial trouble in the 1960s and prompted the Japanese government to instruct the profitable Nissho to merge with Iwai in 1968.

In 1979 Nissho Iwai was accused of funneling kickbacks from US aircraft makers to Japanese politicians. The scandal led to arrests the resignation of the company's chairman and the suicide of another executive. Nissho Iwai exited the aircraft marketing business in 1980.

Despite Japan's recession in the 1990s Nissho Iwai managed to make some significant investments. In 1991 the company teamed up with the Russian government to develop a Siberian oil refinery. A year later Nissho acquired a stake in courier DHL International and in 1995 it set up a unit to process steel plates in Vietnam.

However in the late 1990s rough economic conditions caught up with the firm. It dissolved its NI Finance unit (domestic financing) in 1998 after its disastrous performance. The large trading firm or sogo shosha also began a major restructuring effort to get back on track.

In 1999 Nissho Iwai sold its headquarters its 5% stake in DHL International and its stake in a Japanese ISP Nifty. CEO Masatake Kusamichi resigned. He was replaced by Shiro Yasutake who took charge of the firm's restructuring. In 2000 the company's ITX Corp. acquired five IT-related affiliates of Nichimen Corp.

As part of the group's streamlining efforts in 2001 Nissho Iwai spun off its nonferrous marketing unit (Alconix) and agreed to merge the group's LNG operations with Sumitomo's LNG business. The next year Hidetoshi Nishimura replaced Yasutake as CEO.

In 2003 Nissho Iwai merged with the smaller Nichimen Corp. to form Nissho Iwai-Nichimen Holdings. Hidetoshi Nishimura president and CEO of Nissho Iwai and Toru Hambayashi president of Nichimen became co-CEOs of the new holding company. Former board member Akio Dobashi took over the reins as president and sole CEO early in 2004; in April he moved over to the chairman's seat and Yutaka Kase assumed the president and CEO titles. In June the company changed its name from Nissho Iwai-Nichimen Holdings to Sojitz Holdings Corporation.

As part of its ongoing reorganization in 2005 the company renamed itself again when it merged the holding company into Sojitz Corporation.

The company formed a subsidiary in China in 2009 to enter key businesses such as the automotive ball bearing textiles and plastics industries. That year it transferred its domestic foodstuffs business to a wholly owned subsidiary called Sojitz Foods Corporation.

Sojitz also began searching in 2010 for sources other than China for rare earth metals. It signed a contract in mid-year with Lynas Corporation in Australia to purchase about 8500 tons a year some 30% of Japan's annual demand. It also entered a joint venture with Toyota Tusho to import another 3000 tons from Vietnam. Shipments from China which mines and sells most of the world's rare earth metals were delayed in 2010 in a move Japan said was a de facto blockade. Rare earth metals such as palladium are a key element in the production of electronic components and lithium-ion batteries.

EXECUTIVES

Senior Managing Executive Officer, Director, Masao Goto
Independent Director, Naoko Saiki
Senior Managing Executive Officer, President of Subsidiary, Shigeru Nishihara
Executive Vice President, Representative Director, Ryutaro Hirai
President, Chief Executive Officer, Representative Director, Masayoshi Fujimoto
Chief Financial Officer, Executive Vice President, Representative Director, Seiichi Tanaka
Independent Director, Kayoko Naito
Independent Director, Norio Otsuka
Independent Director, Ungyong Shu
Auditors: KPMG AZSA LLC

LOCATIONS

HQ: Sojitz Corp
2-1-1 Uchisaiwai-cho, Chiyoda-ku, Tokyo 100-8691
Phone: (81) 3 6871 5000   **Fax:** (81) 3 6871 2430
Web: www.sojitz.com

2018 Sales

	% of total
Japan	47
Asia and Oceania	35
The Americas	8
Europe	8
Others	2
Total	**100**

PRODUCTS/OPERATIONS

2018 Sales

	% of total
Chemicals	28
Metals & Coal	18
Foods & Agriculture Business	8
Retail & Lifestyle	16
Automotive	11
Industrial Infrastructure & Urban Development	3
Aerospace & IT Business	4
Infrastructure & Environment Business	7
Energy	3
Others	2
Total	**100**

COMPETITORS

ASHLAND GLOBAL HOLDINGS INC.
ASHLAND LLC
FORMOSA PLASTICS CORPORATION
Franz Haniel & Cie. GmbH
GEA Group AG
HELM AG
HeidelbergCement AG

ITOCHU CORPORATION
KOC HOLDING ANONIM SIRKETI
Kl ¶ckner & Co SE
MARUBENI CORPORATION
MITSUI & CO. LTD.
Neles Oyj
Posco Co. Ltd.
SEALASKA CORPORATION
SUMITOMO CORPORATION

HISTORICAL FINANCIALS

Company Type: Public

Income Statement   FYE: March 31

	REVENUE ($ mil.)	NET INCOME ($ mil.)	NET PROFIT MARGIN	EMPLOYEES
03/21	14,472	243	1.7%	24,141
03/20	16,166	560	3.5%	22,330
03/19	16,761	635	3.8%	21,909
03/18	17,106	535	3.1%	22,778
03/17	13,911	364	2.6%	17,311
Annual Growth	1.0%	(9.6%)	—	8.7%

2021 Year-End Financials

Debt ratio: 0.3%
Return on equity: 4.5%
Cash ($ mil.): 2,597
Current ratio: 1.63
Long-term debt ($ mil.): 6,771
No. of shares (mil.): 1,200
Dividends
   Yield: —
   Payout: 44.4%
Market value ($ mil.): —

Solvay SA

Solvay produces and sells chemicals advanced plastics and lightweight materials. End markets for its products are diverse and include automotive aerospace consumer goods electronics energy and the environment. Solvay operates in nearly 65 countries and has major operations in Europe North America and Asia as well as a smaller operation in Latin America. The Solvay process a method of producing sodium carbonate or soda ash is named after company founder Ernest Solvay who invented it in the 1860s. Its advance materials segment accounts for nearly 70% of sales. More than 30% of its sales were generated from Asia and the rest of the world.

Operations

Solvay is organized into four operating segments:

Materials (nearly 70% of sales) offer a unique portfolio of high-performance polymers and composite technologies used primarily in sustainable mobility applications. Its solutions enable weight reduction and enhance performance while improving CO2 and energy efficiency. Major markets served include next-generation mobility in automotive and aerospace healthcare and electronics.

Solutions (around 20%) offer a unique formulation & application expertise through customized specialty formulations for surface chemistry & liquid behavior maximizing yield and efficiency of the processes they are used in while minimizing the eco-impact. Novecare Technology Solutions Aroma and Special Chem focus on specific areas such as resources (improving the extraction yield of metals minerals and oil) industrial applications (such as coatings) or consumer goods and healthcare (including vanillin and guar for home and personal care).

Chemicals (over 10%) host chemical intermediate businesses focused on mature and resilient markets. Solvay is a world leader in soda ash and peroxides and major markets served include building and construction consumer goods and food. Its Silica Coatis and Rusvinyl businesses are also high quality assets with strong positions in their markets. This segment provides resilient cash flows and the company selectively invests in these businesses to become the #1 cash conversion chemical player.

Corporate & Business Services includes corporate and other business services such as Group re-

search & innovation or energy services whose mission is to optimize energy consumption and reduce CO2 emissions.

Geographic Reach

Headquartered in Belgium the company operates around 110 industrial sites across the world with the greatest concentration in Europe. Asia region is the largest by revenue accounting for over 30% of total followed by the Europe generating nearly 30% North America contributing more than 25% and Latin America for around 10%.

Financial Performance

Note: Growth rates may differ after conversion to US Dollars.

The company in 2020 had a net sales of ?9 billion a 13% decrease from the previous years as civil aero and oil & gas challenges were moderated by resilient demand in healthcare consumer goods personal care and electronics.

In 2020 the company suffered a net loss of ?929 million.

The company's cash at the end of 2020 was ?1 billion. Operating activities generated ?1.2 billion while financing activities used ?1.7 billion mainly for repayment of borrowings. Investing activities generated another ?711 million.

Strategy

Solvay has launched since the beginning of the year restructuring plans hence accelerating the alignment of its worldwide organization with its G.R.O.W. strategy and responding to the challenging economic environment. The plans are leading to approximately 1300 net redundancies including 620 for the Composite Materials launched in Q2 2020. A provision has been accrued for ?123 million during 2020.

In early 2020 Solvay divests its Performance Polyamides activities to BASF and Domo Chemicals. The transaction is based on an enterprise value of ? 1.6 billion and the selling proceeds net of costs of disposals on the combined transaction were ?1.3 billion (selling proceeds of ?1.5 billion received on January 31 2020). The capital gain after taxes was ?140 million after the agreement on the final purchase price with DOMO Chemicals finalized in Q4 2020 while the final agreement with BASF is pending and is expected to be finalized in Q1 2021 without significant changes.

In 2020 in line with its G.R.O.W. strategy Solvay began the process of exploring options to sell certain business lines. In October agreements were reached to sell Solvay's interests in a few business lines including the sodium chlorate business and related assets in Portugal (part of Peroxides) certain fluorine chemicals and its site in Korea (part of Special Chem).

HISTORY

Solvay began in the 1860s when founder Ernest Solvay perfected a method that created soda ash at a lower cost than the prevailing Leblanc process. In 1886 the company began to diversify into manufacturing chlorine and expanded beyond Belgium into the France Germany Russia the UK and the US. By the 1900s Solvay had reduced the price for soda ash by two-thirds what it had been before his entry into the field.

The company lost its Russia-based plants during the Russian Revolution. Ernest Solvay died shortly thereafter in 1922. To overcome its Russian losses the company modernized its remaining plants and added new businesses such as potassium mining.

During the 1930s and 1940s the company began to switch its plants to the electrolysis process and expanded into Italy Greece and other countries. Because of their locations the firm's plants suffered during WWII and the company lost several as the Iron Curtain descended across East Europe. The company rebuilt what facilities it could and once again diversified its product base.

Solvay began making plastic (polyvinyl chloride PVC) in 1949 at its plant in Jemeppe Belgium and throughout the 1950s and 1960s the company developed into a major manufacturer of bulk chemicals. In the late 1960s Baron Rene Boel who had married into the family managed the company; he took it public in 1971. Boel hired executives from outside the family and modernized the company's management structure. These changes kept the company financially healthy until 1976 when US companies began manufacturing soda ash from trona rock mine. Cheaper and more environmentally friendly the process forced Solvay to close its soda ash plants. (The company later returned to making soda ash.)

Despite these problems Solvay continued expansion during the 1980s which included creating Solvay America a holding company for its US companies. Recognizing its vulnerability from a reliance on bulk chemicals the company began to diversify into drug production.

In 1993 Solvay recorded a $198 million loss its first in more than a decade. Analysts questioned whether the company could compete against companies such as Akzo (now Akzo Nobel) which produced nothing but pharmaceuticals. Under the leadership of CEO Baron Daniel Janssen Solvay tried to kill off its reputation as an industrial dinosaur. With the fall of the Berlin Wall Solvay recovered many of the plants it had lost during WWII and the Cold War. It renovated them closed many of its unprofitable operations and sold off noncore businesses such as its animal health units to American Home Products (renamed Wyeth in 2002). To improve profits it teamed up with companies such as US pharmaceutical giant Upjohn (Pharmacia & Upjohn).

By 1996 Solvay concentrated on chemicals plastics pharmaceuticals and processing (manufacturing finished products such as pipes and fittings). In 1998 Solvay veteran Alo s Michielsen replaced Daniel Janssen who retired as executive committee chairman and CEO. The appointment marked the first time a non-family member was tapped to run the company. Michielsen went to work on improving the company's old-fashioned image which he considered partially to blame for depressing the firm's stock price.

The company's plastic division in 1999 suffered from low PVC prices which rebounded within the year when EVC International NV (now INEOS Vinyls) shut down its PVC plant in Italy. Solvay bought US-based Unimed Pharmaceuticals and a strategic stake in generic prescription drugmaker Duramed that year. In 2000 Solvay entered into a 50/50 venture with Plastic Omnium (plastics processing) called Inergy Automotive Systems; the new company is the largest maker of plastic fuel tanks in the world. In 2002 the company acquired Ausimont from Montedison and Longside International for about $1.1 billion. It also has acquired pharmaceuticals makers and products including hypertension medications Aceon and Teveten.

In 2008 Solvay acquired Egyptian chemicals maker Alexandria Sodium Carbonate Company (ASCC) for $130 million. The company viewed the acquisition as an entry not only into the Egyptian market but also into the greater Middle East and Northern African regions. Solvay began doubling the capacity at ASCC's manufacturing facility.

Solvay sold its manufactured pharmaceuticals unit to US-based Abbott Labs in 2010 for $7.6 billion.

EXECUTIVES

Chairman of the Board, Nicolas Boel
Group Corporate Secretary, Michel Defourny
Independent Director, Matti Lievonen
Independent Director, Agnes Lemarchand-Poirier
Chairman of the Management Board, Chief Executive Officer, Director, Ilham Kadri, $1,310,316 total compensation
Chief People Officer, Member of the Executive Committee, Herve Tiberghien, $366,888 total compensation
Independent Director, Philippe Tournay
Chief Digital Officer, Yan Beynon
Member of the Executive Committee, Vincent De Cuyper, $754,578 total compensation
Member of the Executive Committee, Chief Financial Officer, Karim Hajjar, $1,008,783 total compensation
Auditors: Deloitte Bedrijfsrevisoren / Reviseurs d'Entreprises CVBA/SCRL

LOCATIONS

HQ: Solvay SA
Rue de Ransbeek, 310, Brussels 1120
Phone: (32) 2 264 2111   **Fax:** (32) 2 264 3061
Web: www.solvay.com

2015 Sales

	% of total
Asia and Rest of the World	35
Europe	30
Other Europe	2
North America	23
Latin America	10
Total	**100**

PRODUCTS/OPERATIONS

2015 Sales

	% of total
Advanced Materials	32
Performance Chemicals	29
Advanced Formulations	25
Functional Polymers	14
Others	-
Total	**100**

COMPETITORS

AIR PRODUCTS AND CHEMICALS INC.	ELEMENTIS PLC
	N L INDUSTRIES INC.
BASF SE	OLIN CORPORATION
Braskem S/A INC.	ROCKWOOD HOLDINGS
Clariant AG	SOLUTIA INC.
ECOVYST INC.	

HISTORICAL FINANCIALS

Company Type: Public

Income Statement   FYE: December 31

	REVENUE ($ mil.)	NET INCOME ($ mil.)	NET PROFIT MARGIN	EMPLOYEES
12/19	12,605	132	1.1%	24,100
12/18	12,939	982	7.6%	24,500
12/17	13,055	1,271	9.7%	24,500
12/16	12,040	655	5.4%	27,000
12/15	12,032	442	3.7%	30,900
Annual Growth	**1.2%**	**(26.0%)**	**—**	**(6.0%)**

2019 Year-End Financials

Debt ratio: 21.8%
Return on equity: 1.1%
Cash ($ mil.): 908
Current ratio: 1.53
Long-term debt ($ mil.): 3,385

No. of shares (mil.): 103
Dividends
Yield: 0.0%
Payout: 20.4%
Market value ($ mil.): 1,188

	STOCK PRICE ($) FY Close	P/E High/Low		PER SHARE ($) Earnings	Dividends	Book Value
12/19	11.49	11	8	1.29	0.26	103.30
12/18	10.03	2	1	9.47	0.26	116.65
12/17	13.77	2	1	12.22	0.26	111.84
12/16	11.93	2	2	6.32	0.00	99.28
Annual Growth	**(1.2%)**	**—**	**—**	**(32.8%)**	**—**	**1.0%**

Sompo Holdings Inc

Sompo Holdings (formerly Sompo Japan Nipponkoa Holdings) owns several companies that are primarily engaged in the insurance sector. Its subsidiaries include property/casualty units Sompo Japan Nipponkoa Saison Automobile & Fire and Mysurance and a handful of overseas insurance companies. Domestic property/casualty insurance brings in about 65% of the group's total earnings. Other operations include asset and risk management services pension plans and some supplemental health insurance products. The company also owns SOMPO Care which provides nursing care services.

Operations

Sompo operates through four segments: Domestic P&C Insurance (which accounts for about 60% of total sales) Overseas Insurance Domestic Life Insurance and Nursing Care & Healthcare.

The Overseas Insurance segment which brings in nearly 15% of sales includes such units as Sompo International Holdings Sompo America Sompo Japan and Sompo Seguros. The Domestic Life Insurance segment brings in some 10% of sales and includes SOMPO Himawari Life Insurance. Nursing Care & Healthcare businesses bring in about 5% of sales include Sompo Care and Sompo Risk Management & Health Care.

Sompo consists of about 75 subsidiaries and approximately 15 affiliates.

Geographic Reach

Headquartered in Japan Sompo operates through around 1025 domestic bases and approximately 1000 nursing care facilities in about 30 countries and regions.

Financial Performance

The company's revenue for fiscal 2021 increased to 202.1 billion compared from the prior year with 150.8 billion.

Net income for fiscal 2021 increased to 194.9 billion compared from the prior year with 177.2 billion.

Cash held by the company at the end of fiscal 2021 increased to 1.1 trillion. Cash provided by operations was 626.2 billion while cash used for investing and financing activities were 359.5 billion and 94.5 billion respectively. Main uses of cash were purchase of securities and repayments of borrowings.

Strategy

Under the previous Mid-Term Management Plan which was started in fiscal 2016 the company achieved steady growth based on the efforts that had been made by each business accelerated new investments in growth areas and digital strategy for the future and made steady progress in qualitative evolution toward the realization of "A Theme Park for Security Health & Wellbeing." The Domestic P&C Insurance Business worked on structural reform of the business foundation to strengthen the profitability of existing business as well as the development of new businesses. The

Overseas Insurance and Reinsurance Business made progress toward the establishment of a global platform through reorganizing subsidiaries and expanding business scale through disciplined M&A such as the acquisition of Endurance Specialty Holdings Ltd (now Sompo International Holdings Ltd.).

The Domestic Life Insurance Business developed and sold new products and services to transform into a health support enterprise centered around InsurhealthÂ®. The Nursing Care & Healthcare Business implemented measures to improve the service quality and productivity of existing nursing facilities as well as worked on human resource development Initiatives in the digital field were stepped up with proactive formation of partnerships with a variety of players and appointing external talent.

Company Background
Sompo Holdings was created to hold two insurance companies: Sompo Japan and Nipponkoa Insurance. While already strong players in Japan's property/casualty and life insurance markets when merger mania hit the industry they didn't want to be left out and formed the joint holding company in 2010. The two companies merged into one entity Sompo Japan Nipponkoa Insurance in 2014.

Why merge in the first place? Sompo cited pressures on its industry from several sources including the country's declining birthrate its rapidly aging population and the effects of climate change. While those are real challenges to the industry the Sompo/Nipponkoa merger also took place at the same time as several other large mergers among Japanese insurance companies.

EXECUTIVES

Independent Director, Takashi Nawa
Independent Director, Misuzu Shibata
Independent Director, Kazuhiro Higashi
Independent Director, Kumi Ito
Independent Director, Meyumi Yamada
President, Group Chief Executive Officer, Representative Executive Officer, Director, Kengo Sakurada
Vice President, Group Chief Operating Officer, Representative Executive Officer, Director, Shinji Tsuji
Executive Officer, Domestic P&C Insurance Business Owner, Executive President & President of Subsidiary, Keiji Nishizawa
Independent Director, Isao Endo
Independent Director, Scott Davis
Director, Toshihiro Teshima
Group Chief Financial Officer, Senior Managing Executive Officer, Group Co-Chief Strategy Officer, Masahiro Hamada
Senior Managing Executive Officer, Group Co-Chief Strategy Officer, Chief Executive Officer of subsidiary, Mikio Okumura
Executive Officer, Domestic Life Insurance Business Owner, Executive President & President of Subsidiary, Yasuhiro Ohba
Independent Director, Naoki Yanagida
Auditors: Ernst & Young ShinNihon LLC

LOCATIONS

HQ: Sompo Holdings Inc
1-26-1 Nishi-Shinjuku, Shinjuku-ku, Tokyo 160-8338
Phone: (81) 3 3349 3000
Web: www.sompo-hd.com

2018 Sales by Segment

	% of total
Domestic P&C Insurance	59
Overseas Insurance	17
Domestic Life Insurance	9
Nursing Care & Healthcare	3
Other	1
Adjustments	11
Total	**100**

2018 Sales

	% of total
Japan	79
US	10
Other	11
Total	**100**

Selected Locations
Belgium
Bermuda
France
Germany
Italy
Mexico
Singapore
Spain
Switzerland
UK
US

COMPETITORS

AEON CO. LTD.
CNA FINANCIAL CORPORATION
China Life Insurance Company Limited
Extendicare Real Estate Investment Trust
FUKOKU MUTUAL LIFE INSURANCE COMPANY
Intact Corporation Financi're
JAPAN POST HOLDINGS CO.LTD.
MAPFRE SA
MITSUBISHI UFJ FINANCIAL GROUP INC.
MIZUHO FINANCIAL GROUP INC.
NOMURA HOLDINGS INC.
PERMIRA ADVISERS LLP
SOFTBANK GROUP CORP.
VERISK ANALYTICS INC.

HISTORICAL FINANCIALS
Company Type: Public

Income Statement				FYE: March 31
	REVENUE ($ mil.)	NET INCOME ($ mil.)	NET PROFIT MARGIN	EMPLOYEES
03/21	34,247	1,286	3.8%	82,118
03/20	34,115	1,128	3.3%	79,441
03/19	32,567	1,324	4.1%	81,115
03/18	35,228	1,316	3.7%	80,938
03/17	30,215	1,488	4.9%	80,667
Annual Growth	3.2%	(3.6%)	—	0.4%

2021 Year-End Financials

Debt ratio: —	No. of shares (mil.): 355
Return on equity: 7.8%	Dividends
Cash ($ mil.): 9,904	Yield: —
Current ratio: —	Payout: 42.8%
Long-term debt ($ mil.): —	Market value ($ mil.): —

Sony Group Corp

Sony develops designs produces manufactures and sells different kinds of electronic equipment instruments and devices for consumer professional and industrial markets such as network services game hardware and software televisions audio and video recorders and players still and video cameras mobile phones and image sensors. Sony is engaged in the development production manufacture and distribution of recorded music and the management and licensing of the words and music of songs as well as the production and distribution of animation titles including game applications based on animation titles. Sony is also engaged in the production acquisition and distribution of motion pictures and television programming and the operation of television and digital networks. In addition Sony has several financial services businesses (insurance and banking). Japan and the US are the company's largest single markets together accounting for more than half of sales.

Operations
Sony reports revenue through seven business segments.

Its largest accounting for 30% of sales is Game & Network Services (G&NS) includes network services businesses the manufacture and sales of home gaming products and production and sales of software.

The Electronics Products & Services (EP&S) accounting for more than 20% includes the Televisions business the Audio and Video business the Still and Video Cameras business the smartphone business and internet-related service business.

The Financial Services accounting for nearly 20% represents individual life insurance and non-life insurance businesses in the Japanese market and a bank business in Japan.

The Music segment accounting for 10% of sales includes the Recorded Music Music Publishing and Visual Media and Platform businesses.

The Pictures segment accounting for less than 10% includes the Motion Pictures Television Productions and Media Networks businesses.

The Imaging & Sensing Solutions (I&SS) accounting for more than 10% includes the image sensors business.

The All Other segment accounting for less than 5% consists of various operating activities including the disc manufacturing and recording media businesses.

Geographic Reach
Based in Tokyo Japan Sony has facilities throughout the world although its primary manufacturing plants are located in Japan. Other plant locations include China Malaysia Thailand Europe and the US.

Japan is also the company's single largest market by sales (more than 30%) with the US and Europe accounting for almost 25% and 20% of sales respectively.

Sales and Marketing
Sony's products are marketed worldwide by sales subsidiaries and unaffiliated distributors as well as direct online sales and offers via the internet. The company's electronics products and services are marketed under the trademark "Sony" which has been registered in approximately 200 countries and territories.

Along with its global corporate functions in Japan Sony Mobile also has sales and marketing operations in many major regions of the world as well as a major manufacturing site in Thailand and product development sites in Japan and Sweden.

Advertising costs were 385500 million 359458 million and 260068 million for years 2019 2020 and 2021 respectively.

Financial Performance
Sony's operating revenues fluctuated over the past three years with nearly 4% of revenue growth from 2019. The company's reported an operating revenue of 8.9 billion 2021 up by 9% from the prior year.

The company's net income increased by 589.6 billion in 2021. The increase in operating revenue was mainly due to significant increases in sales in the Game & Network Services (G&NS) and Financial Services segments partially offset primarily by a significant decrease in sales in the Pictures segment.

Sony ended 2021 with cash and cash equivalents of 1.8 trillion. Operating activities generated 1.4 trillion while investing activities used 1.8 trillion mainly for payments for investments and advancements by financial services business. Financing activities provided 666.9 billion.

Strategy

Sony's long-term corporate strategy as a creative entertainment company with a solid foundation of technology is to create value focusing on the keywords of creativity technology and the world (community). To realize this goal in the three years from 2022 through 2024 Sony plans to allocate 2 trillion yen for strategic investment and to continue to proactively engage in investment towards growth in the areas of IP/DTC technology and share repurchases in order of priority.

Sony intends to continue to work to secure components and make improvements to production in order to meet the strong demand from its customers despite the expected supply constraints of semiconductors and other components through 2022. Regarding software and network services Sony plans to continue the initiatives it undertook in 2021 including investing proactively in its own in-house studios as well as investing in or partnering with external studios while focusing on measures to further enhance the attractiveness of its network services such as PS Plus.

Sony has continued to proactively make investments to strengthen its content IP and its relationships with artists. In order to capitalize on the increase of streaming penetration in emerging markets Sony is strengthening its approach in emerging markets by proactively investing in local talent and collaborating with local companies.

Sony intends to continue to leverage its advantages as an independent studio investing in the development and revitalization of owned IP and strengthening its creative capacity to create new IP in order to continue to produce outstanding video content across diverse genres. The company plans to continue to focus on diversifying and expanding communities of interest through anime distribution development and distribution of kids' programming and family and faith-based films as well as Sony's network business in India.

Mergers and Acquisitions

Sony announced the acquisition of the independent Brazilian music label Som Livre in April 2021 and completed its acquisition of AWAL a music distribution business mainly for independent recording artists in May 2021.

In 2021 Sony invested in Bilibili Inc. and Epic Games Inc. (Epic) and acquired minority interests in both companies with the goal of accelerating business expansion in the area of entertainment. In the same month the company acquired 100% of the shares and related assets of certain subsidiaries of Kobalt Music Group Limited (Kobalt) relating to AWAL Kobalt's music distribution business mainly for independent recording artists and Kobalt Neighbouring Rights Kobalt's music neighboring rights management business. The consideration for this acquisition was 49.8 billion yen.

Company Background

Tokyo Telecommunications Engineering Corporation the predecessor of Sony was established in 1946 with about 20 employees. It listed on the over-the-counter market of the Toyko Stock Exchange (TSE) in 1955 and three years later changed its name to Sony Corporation. The company also listed on the TSE that year.

HISTORY

Akio Morita Masaru Ibuka and Tamon Maeda (Ibuka's father-in-law) started Tokyo Telecommunications Engineering in 1946 with funding from Morita's father's sake business. The company produced the first Japanese tape recorder in 1950. Three years later Morita paid Western Electric (US) $25000 for transistor technology licenses which sparked a consumer electronics revolution in Japan. His firm launched one of the first transistor radios in 1955 followed by the first Sony-trade-

marked product a pocket-sized radio in 1957. The next year the company changed its name to Sony (from "sonus" Latin for "sound" and "sonny" meaning "little man"). It beat the competition to newly emerging markets for transistor TVs (1959) and solid-state videotape recorders (1961).

Sony launched the first home video recorder (1964) and the first solid-state condenser microphone (1965). Its 1968 introduction of the Trinitron color TV tube began another decade of explosive growth. Sony bet wrong on its Betamax VCR (1976) which lost to rival Matsushita's (now Panasonic Corp.) VHS as the industry standard. However 1979 brought another success the Walkman personal stereo.

Pressured by adverse currency rates and competition worldwide Sony used its technology to diversify beyond consumer electronics and began to move production to other countries. In the 1980s it introduced Japan's first 32-bit workstation and became a major producer of computer chips and floppy disk drives. The purchases of CBS Records in 1988 ($2 billion) and Columbia Pictures in 1989 (a $4.9 billion deal which included TriStar Pictures) made Sony a major force in the rapidly growing entertainment industry.

The firm manufactured Apple's PowerBook but its portable CD player Data Discman was successful only in Japan (1991). In the early 1990s Sony joined Nintendo to create a new kind of game console combining Sony's CD-ROM drive with the graphic capabilities of a workstation. Although Nintendo pulled out in 1992 Sony released PlayStation in Japan (1994) and in the US (1995) to great success. Two years later in a joint venture with Intel it developed a line of PC desktop systems.

Rather than support an industry-wide standard in 1997 Sony teamed up with Philips Electronics to make another recording media called Super Audio CD which could replace videotapes and CDs. (Sony and Philips created the CD and continue to receive royalties from it.)

In 1998 Sony shipped its first digital high-definition TV to the US folded TriStar into Columbia Pictures merged its Loews Theatres unit with Cineplex Odeon and launched its Wega flat-screen TV.

Philips Sun Microsystems and Sony formed a joint venture in early 1999 to develop networked entertainment products. Also in 1999 Nobuyuki Idei became CEO and the company introduced a Walkman with the capability to download music from the Internet.

In 2000 Sony formed PlayStation.com Japan to sell game consoles and software online; it also introduced its 128-bit PlayStation 2 which plays DVD movies and connects to the Internet. The company later restructured placing all of its US entertainment holdings under a newly-formed umbrella company called Sony Broadband Entertainment.

In early 2001 Sony started an online bank with Japan's Sakura Bank and JP Morgan Chase. Struggling to coordinate its content units (music movies games etc.) with its manufacturing operations (TVs VCRs radios etc.) Sony announced yet another corporate restructuring plan; that move placed all electronics units under one upper-management group.

Adverse market conditions in 2001 aggravated by the September 11 attacks led Sony Pictures Entertainment to consolidate its two domestic television operations folding Columbia TriStar Network Television into Columbia TriStar Domestic Television (CTDT).

In February 2002 an investment group led by Onex Corporation acquired its Loews Theatres unit (which filed for bankruptcy in February 2001). In the course of the fiscal year ending March 2002

Sony laid off about 13700 employees primarily in its electronics and music businesses.

In an attempt to capitalize on the strength of its own brand Sony Pictures Entertainment renamed its Columbia TriStar Domestic Television (CTDT) and Columbia TriStar International Television (CTIT) divisions in September 2002 designating them as Sony Pictures Television (SPT) and Sony Pictures Television International (SPTI) respectively. In October 2002 Sony transformed its Aiwa unit into a wholly-owned subsidiary and absorbed the struggling firm in December 2002.

In 2003 Sony adopted a US-style corporate governance model (made possible by a revision in Japan's Commercial Code) and acquired CIS Corp. a Japanese information system consulting firm. In an effort to cut costs through manufacturing consolidation Sony closed its audio equipment plant in Indonesia that year.

Sony unveiled the Vaio Pocket in 2004 a portable music player designed to compete with Apple's iPod; Vaio Pocket debuted in the US later that year. Sony also introduced a similar product Network Walkman — its first Walkman with a hard drive — in 2004. In October 2004 the company launched a music download system in Japan dubbed MusicDrop. The system utilizes Microsoft's Windows Media Player.

To manage its financial units (Sony Life Insurance Company Sony Assurance and Sony Bank) it created Sony Financial Holdings in 2004. The company announced in 2005 that Idei would be succeeded by foreigner Howard Stringer who had been in charge of Sony's entertainment unit. In 2005 Sony sold its minority stake in music club Columbia House to BMG Direct a subsidiary of Germany's Bertelsmann. In December 2005 the company spun off Sony Communication Network the subsidiary that operates So-Net Internet service (which has nearly 3 million subscribers) through an IPO.

In June 2006 Sony created a holding company for its Japanese-based retail operations (Sony Plaza Sony Family Club B&C Laboratories CP Cosmetics Maxim's de Paris and Lifeneo) and sold 51% of the holding company to investment firm Nikko Principal Investments Japan.

In late 2008 Sony bought out NEC's 45% stake in joint venture Sony Optiarc.

The company in 2010 sold the measuring equipment business of Sony Manufacturing Systems to Mori Seiki a Japan-based precision tool maker in a deal valued at about 6 billion (nearly $70 million). It also sold off its 90% stake in Sony Baja California its main TV factory in North America located in Tijuana Mexico to Taiwanese company Hon Hai Precision Industry. It generated $217 million for its share in HBO Latin America which it sold to Time Warner.

In February 2012 Sony acquired Telefonaktiebolaget LM Ericsson's 50% stake in Sony Ericsson Mobile Communications AB marking the completion of the previously announced transaction. As a result Sony Ericsson became a wholly-owned subsidiary of Sony and was renamed "Sony Mobile Communications."

EXECUTIVES

Vice Chairman, charge of Electronics Products & Solutions Business In charge ofStorage Media BusinessSony Electronics Corporation President and CEOSony Imaging Products & Solutions Inc. President and Representative Director, Shigeki Ishizuka, $528,210 total compensation

Executive Deputy President; Officer in Charge, R&D and Medical Business; President, R&D Center; Representative Director and Deputy President, Sony Imaging Products and Solutions Inc., Toru Katsumoto, $547,075 total compensation

Executive Vice President, Officer in charge of Human Resources and General Affairs, Kazushi Ambe, $433,887 total compensation

Vice President and CFO, Hiroki Totoki, $622,534 total compensation

Independent Director, Adam Crozier

Independent Director, Keiko Kishigami

Independent Director, Joseph Kraft

Executive Vice President, Officer in charge of Legal, Compliance, Corporate Communications, CSR, External Relations, Quality, Environment, Information Security and Privacy, Shiro Kambe, $452,752 total compensation

Chairman, President and CEO, Kenichiro Yoshida, $1,839,306 total compensation

Auditors: PricewaterhouseCoopers Aarata LLC

LOCATIONS

HQ: Sony Group Corp
 1-7-1 Konan, Minato-ku, Tokyo 108-0075
Phone: (81) 3 6748 2111 **Fax:** 212 833-6849
Web: www.sony.co.jp

2018 Sales

	% of total
Japan	31
Europe	22
US	21
Asia/Pacific (except Japan and China)	12
China	8
Other	6
Total	**100**

PRODUCTS/OPERATIONS

2018 Sales

	% of total
Game & Network services	22
Home entertainment & sound	14
Mobile communications	8
Financial services	14
Semiconductors	10
Pictures	11
Imaging products & solutions	7
Music	9
Other	5
Total	**100**

COMPETITORS

ACORN ENERGY INC.
AEON CO. LTD.
ALCATEL LUCENT
ARRIS GLOBAL LTD.
Acer Incorporated
BANDAI NAMCO HOLDINGS INC.
Bilfinger SE
DENTSU GROUP INC.
DIALOG SEMICONDUCTOR LIMITED
FAST RETAILING CO. LTD.
IMI PLC
JACOBS ENGINEERING GROUP INC.
JAKKS PACIFIC INC.
JAPAN DISPLAY INC.
MATTHEWS INTERNATIONAL CORPORATION
MORGAN ADVANCED MATERIALS PLC
Mad Catz Interactive Inc
NINTENDO CO. LTD.
NIPPON TELEGRAPH AND TELEPHONE
 CORPORATION
NIPPON TELEVISION HOLDINGS INC.
Navico Holding AS
PIONEER CORPORATION
SOFTBANK GROUP CORP.
SOMPO HOLDINGS INC.
SPEED COMMERCE INC.
TECHNICOLOR

TOMY INTERNATIONAL INC.
TPG CAPITAL MANAGEMENT L.P.
WS ATKINS LIMITED

HISTORICAL FINANCIALS

Company Type: Public

Income Statement

	REVENUE ($ mil.)	NET INCOME ($ mil.)	NET PROFIT MARGIN	EMPLOYEES
03/21	81,277	10,582	13.0%	109,700
03/20	76,092	5,363	7.0%	111,700
03/19	78,249	8,273	10.6%	114,400
03/18	80,461	4,621	5.7%	117,300
03/17	68,003	655	1.0%	128,400
Annual Growth	**4.6%**	**100.5%**	**—**	**(3.9%)**

FYE: March 31

2021 Year-End Financials

Debt ratio: 0.0%
Return on equity: 24.1%
Cash ($ mil.): 16,138
Current ratio: 0.92
Long-term debt ($ mil.): 6,983

No. of shares (mil.): 1,239
Dividends
 Yield: 0.4%
 Payout: 5.5%
Market value ($ mil.): 131,371

	STOCK PRICE ($) FY Close	P/E High/Low		PER SHARE ($) Earnings	Dividends	Book Value
03/21	106.01	0	0	8.46	0.47	40.64
03/20	59.18	0	0	4.25	0.37	31.15
03/19	42.24	0	0	6.39	0.27	27.05
03/18	48.34	0	0	3.58	0.21	22.08
03/17	33.73	1	0	0.51	0.18	17.69
Annual Growth	**33.1%**			**—101.9%**	**27.3%**	**23.1%**

South African Reserve Bank

Auditors: SizweNtsalubaGobodo Grant Thornton Inc.

LOCATIONS

HQ: South African Reserve Bank
 370 Helen Joseph Street, Pretoria 0002
Phone: (27) 12 313 3911
Web: www.resbank.co.za

HISTORICAL FINANCIALS

Company Type: Public

Income Statement

	ASSETS ($ mil.)	NET INCOME ($ mil.)	INCOME AS % OF ASSETS	EMPLOYEES
03/21	63,472	242	0.4%	2,251
03/20	62,466	159	0.3%	2,189
03/18	62,701	182	0.3%	1,967
03/17	56,623	90	0.2%	2,186
03/16	55,884	99	0.2%	2,233
Annual Growth	**2.6%**	**19.4%**	**—**	**0.2%**

FYE: March 31

2021 Year-End Financials

Return on assets: 0.3%
Return on equity: 14.4%
Long-term debt ($ mil.): —
No. of shares (mil.): 2
Sales ($ mil): 1,318

Dividends
 Yield: —
 Payout: —
Market value ($ mil.): —

SpareBank 1 SR Bank ASA

EXECUTIVES

Director, Employee Representative, Sally Lund-Andersen

Independent Director, Tor Dahle

Independent Director, Kate Henriksen

Director, Employee Representative, Kristian Kristensen

Independent Chairman of the Board, Dag Mejdell

Independent Director, Jan Skogseth

Executive Vice President - Group Strategy and Projects, Jan Friestad, $251,558 total compensation

Chief Financial Officer, Inge Reinertsen, $248,477 total compensation

Executive Vice President, Customer Services and Marketing, Ella Skjorestad, $189,305 total compensation

Executive Vice President, Corporate Market, Tore Medhus, $248,796 total compensation

Executive Vice President, Communications and Sustainability, Thor-Christian Haugland, $191,005 total compensation

Executive Vice President, Risk Management, Frode Bo, $213,633 total compensation

Executive Vice President - Technology Development and Business Processes, Glenn Saether, $220,750 total compensation

Executive Vice President, Compliance, Signe Helliesen, $140,014 total compensation

Executive Vice President, Human Resources and Business Support, Gro Tveit, $195,255 total compensation

Director, Trine Romuld

Chief Executive Officer, Benedicte Schilbred Fasmer

Director, Ingrid Riddervold

Executive Vice President of Human Resources Communications and Sustainability, Nina Edvardsen

Auditors: PricewaterhouseCoopers AS

LOCATIONS

HQ: SpareBank 1 SR Bank ASA
 Christen Tranes Gate 35, Stavanger N-4007
Phone: (47) 915 02002 **Fax:** (47) 51 57 12 60
Web: www.sr-bank.no

HISTORICAL FINANCIALS

Company Type: Public

Income Statement

	ASSETS ($ mil.)	NET INCOME ($ mil.)	INCOME AS % OF ASSETS	EMPLOYEES
12/20	33,691	176	0.5%	1,378
12/19	29,118	350	1.2%	1,373
12/18	26,965	263	1.0%	1,271
12/17	26,419	254	1.0%	1,238
12/16	22,479	203	0.9%	1,127
Annual Growth	**10.6%**	**(3.6%)**	**—**	**5.2%**

FYE: December 31

2020 Year-End Financials

Return on assets: 0.5%
Return on equity: 6.3%
Long-term debt ($ mil.): —
No. of shares (mil.): 255
Sales ($ mil): 1,075

Dividends
 Yield: —
 Payout: —
Market value ($ mil.): —

Standard Bank Group Ltd

Standard Bank Group sets the standard for sub-Saharan banking. Standard Bank South Africa's largest bank offers a variety of retail and commercial banking corporate and investment banking investment management and life insurance services. The group operates in about 20 African nations through about 50000 employees. It operates as Stanbic Bank. It serves individuals and small to medium-sized business and corporate customers. Standard Bank holds a controlling stake in South African insurance firm Liberty Holdings along with The Standard Bank of South Africa (SBSA).

Operations

The company operates through five main business units: Personal & Business Banking; Corporate & Investment Banking; Central and other; Other banking interests; and Liberty.

The Personal & Business Banking segment caters to individual customers small to medium-sized enterprises and commercial banking in South Africa. The unit offers transactional products mortgage lending card products and vehicle and asset finance. The segment accounts for about 55% of total revenue.

Corporate & Investment Banking segment (more than 30%) serves clients in governments parastalsis larger corporates financial institutions and multinational corporates. Customer coverage trading and risk management comprehensive suites and advisory and financing solutions are some of the business unit's product offerings.

Representing more than 10% of total revenue the Liberty segment caters to life insurance and investment management activities.

Central and other is responsible for the group hedging activities while banking interests manages the equity investments held in the terms with the partnership with the ICBC Standard Bank.

Geographic Reach

Contributing almost 85% of Standard Bank's revenue South Africa is its largest market by far. Standard Bank also operates in more than 15 other African nations (from Angola to Zimbabwe).

Financial Performance

Standard Bank's total income for 2020 decreased by about R$10.4 billion to R$123.7 billion compared to R$134.0 billion.

Net income decreased by R$14.5 billion in 2020 compared from R$ 30.7 billion in the prior year.

Cash at the end of the year amounted to R$87.5 billion. Operating activities provided R$28.4 billion to the coffers. Investing activities provided R$430 million while financing activities used R$12.5 billion. Main cash uses were for payment of dividends and redemption of subordinated debt.

Strategy

Standard Bank Group's strategy remains unchanged but its execution is accelerated. The group aims to accelerate its strategies through the strengthening of its digital capabilities and integration of its business to transform client experiences and drive operational efficiency. The execution of the group's strategy is focused on delivering personalized and exceptional client experiences leveraging digital to drive engagement and efficiencies and co-creating integrated platform-based solutions in selected client networks.

Auditors: PricewaterhouseCoopers Inc.

LOCATIONS

HQ: Standard Bank Group Ltd
9th Floor, Standard Bank Centre, 5 Simmonds Street, Johannesburg 2001
Phone: (27) 11 636 9111   **Fax:** (27) 11 636 4207
Web: www.standardbank.com

2011 Total Income

	% of total
South Africa	84
Rest of Africa	10
Outside of Africa	5
Central and other	1
Total	**100**

Selected Markets

Africa
  Angola
  Botswana
  DRC
  Ghana
  Kenya
  Lesotho
  Malawi
  Mauritius
  Mozambique
  Namibia
  Nigeria
  South Africa
  Swaziland
  Tanzania
  Uganda
  Zambia
Americas
  Argentina
  Brazil
  US
Europe/Asia Pacific
  China
  Hong Kong
  Isle of Man
  Japan
  Jersey
  Russia
  Singapore
  Taiwan
  Turkey
  United Arab Emirates
  United Kingdom

PRODUCTS/OPERATIONS

2011 Revenue

	% of total
Liberty	45
Personal & business banking	34
Corporate & investment banking	21
Central & other	
Total	**100**

COMPETITORS

ABERDEEN ASSET MANAGEMENT PLC
BARCLAYS BANK PLC
CAPITACOMMERCIAL TRUST
DUCHOSSOIS TECHNOLOGY PARTNERS LLC
FIRSTRAND LTD
ICICI BANK LIMITED
IT WORX INC.
LLOYDS BANKING GROUP PLC
NATIONAL AUSTRALIA BANK LIMITED
Nordea Bank AB
PRYMAK LLC
QATAR NATIONAL BANK (Q.P.S.C.)
Restricted Data - Order Investigation 653708586
Restricted Data - Order Investigation 654703487
SANTANDER UK GROUP HOLDINGS PLC
STANDARD CHARTERED PLC
TP ICAP FINANCE PLC
W.H. IRELAND GROUP PLC
WIX.COM LTD
Woori Finance Holdings Co. Ltd.

HISTORICAL FINANCIALS

Company Type: Public

Income Statement

                                            FYE: December 31

	ASSETS ($ mil.)	NET INCOME ($ mil.)	INCOME AS % OF ASSETS	EMPLOYEES
12/20	172,614	842	0.5%	50,115
12/19	162,031	1,811	1.1%	50,691
12/18	147,921	1,909	1.3%	53,178
12/17	164,724	2,131	1.3%	54,558
12/16	142,297	1,616	1.1%	54,767
Annual Growth	4.9%	(15.0%)	—	(2.2%)

2020 Year-End Financials

Return on assets: 0.5%
Return on equity: 6.6%
Long-term debt ($ mil.): —
No. of shares (mil.): 1,592
Sales ($ mil): 14,263

Dividends
  Yield: 5.0%
  Payout: 49.2%
Market value ($ mil.): 13,763

	STOCK PRICE ($) FY Close	P/E High/Low		PER SHARE ($) Earnings	Dividends	Book Value
12/20	8.64	1	1	0.53	0.44	8.08
12/19	11.88	1	1	1.13	0.52	8.14
12/18	12.73	1	1	1.19	0.53	7.60
12/17	15.86	1	1	1.31	0.49	8.41
12/16	11.05	1	1	1.00	0.39	7.10
Annual Growth	(6.0%)	—	—	(14.7%)	3.3%	3.3%

Standard Chartered Plc

While the British Empire isn't as global as it used to be that hasn't stopped Standard Chartered. The UK-based banking group known as Stanchart primarily operates in its target markets of Asia the Middle East and Africa home to many of the world's fastest-growing economies. It also operates in Europe and the Americas. In all Stanchart has more than 1000 branches in 60 countries and serves customers in roughly 150. The company's activities center on retail banking (deposit accounts loans cards and investment products) and corporate and institutional banking (capital markets cash management international trade custody and clearing services); it also has commercial banking and private banking functions. Stanchart traces its roots back more than 160 years.

Operations

Because the bank's strategy is centered around client relationships Stanchart organizes its business around four client segment groups.

Corporate and Institutional Banking generates around 45% of Stanchart's annual sales providing transaction services corporate finance financial markets and borrowing. Retail banking which encompasses typical services such as current accounts loans cards and investment products pulls in some 35% of sales.

Stanchart's Commercial Banking (10%) unit provides international banking services to its client base of 45000 SMEs and local corporations who depend on Stanchart as their main international bank. The Private Banking segment which generates 5% of sales offers investment credit wealth planning and private wealth services to its 8000 clients.

Geographic Reach

UK-based Standard Chartered (Stanchart) does business from more than 1000 branches in around 60 markets mostly in Asia Africa and the Middle

East but also in Europe and the Americas. Stanchart's biggest territories are Greater China and North Asia (40% of sales) Southeast and South Asia (more than 25%) and Africa and the Middle East (20%). Stanchart's Private and International Banking activities are carried out mainly through its London office.

Stanchart divides its four business segments into two groups Global and Local. Global (Corporate & Institutional Banking and Private Banking) serves customers through relationship managers with a global remit while the Local business (Retail and Commercial Banking) deploys country-level relationship managers.

Sales and Marketing

The Corporate & Institutional business serves financial institutions and global and local corporate clients; while the Retail group serves individuals and small businesses. Private Banking clients include high-net-worth individuals and Commercial Clients include mid-sized companies. The bank serves clients from a variety of sectors: including energy manufacturing commercial real estate consumer durables and construction.

Since 2010 Stanchart has been the lead sponsor of Liverpool Football Club one of Europe's leading soccer teams and which has multitudes of fans in the company's target markets. The current deal runs until the end of the 2022/23 season.

Financial Performance

Standard Chartered has struggled to achieve sustained revenue growth in its recent past. In fiscal 2018 the company's revenue grew 3% to $14.8 billion due to strong increases in net interest income and net trading income partially offset by a reduction in miscellaneous operating income particularly the absence from the books of a $235 million gain on available-for-sale investments recorded in 2017.

Net income declined 13% to $1.1 billion as Stanchart's operating profits were impacted by the decision to put aside $900 million for fines that could arise from FX trading investigations and sanction breaches in the US and UK. Partially offsetting that item was a sharp reduction in impairment expenses.

Stanchart's cash balance strengthened during 2018 ending the year $11.8 billion higher at $97.5 billion. It generated $25.3 billion in cash from its operations while its investing activities absorbed $12.4 billion and its financing activities used $1.0 billion. The bank's primary cash uses were net purchases of investment securities debt repayments and dividend payouts.

Strategy

As major part of Standard Chartered's (Stanchart) investment program is in digital with the goal to accelerate internal transformation and develop new revenue channels. Company-wide investment reached $1.6 billion in 2018 up on $1.5 billion and $1.4 billion in the two preceding years. It is launching digital retail banking in Africa with an initial roll-out in Cote d'Ivoire followed up by Uganda Tanzania and Ghana in 2018 and Kenya and Stanchart's other African nations in 2019. Additionally more than 50 banking services are available on Stanchart's banking app in India while it established a challenger bank in Hong Kong in partnership with e-commerce giant Alibaba.

Stanchart sees great potential in developing its trade finance business by capitalizing on its virtually unrivaled position in emerging markets particularly Africa and Asia. The company has seen large multinationals in increasing numbers ask it to handle their trade finance requirements across multiple borders; some two-thirds of revenue in the Corporate and Institutional Banking segment now arises from its trade finance network. Going forward Stanchart will look to deepen its position in India South Korea the UAE and Indonesia.

Mergers and Acquisitions

Helping to position Stanchart as a top South African custodian the company in 2013 acquired the South African custody and trustee business of Absa Bank which had developed a profitable custody model across more than 20 sub-Saharan African countries.

Company Background

Asia Africa and the Middle East have been among Stanchart's targeted areas for growth. It owns First Africa Group which provides mergers and acquisitions advisory services to companies wanting to invest in Africa. Stanchart bought Barclays Bank's custody business in 2010 adding operations in eight African nations. In late 2011 the company bought the performing segment of Barclays' credit card business in India at a discount. In 2012 to expand its wholesale banking business in Turkey Stanchart purchased Credit Agricole Yatirim Bankasi Turk A.S. (CAYBT) a fully-owned subsidiary of Credit Agricole Corporate and Investment Bank. It exited the equity capital markets in 2015. The company's trans-border nature means it sometimes falls foul of sanction regimes; it faces $900 million in fines from the US Government for violating sanctions against Iran and other countries.

HISTORY

Standard Chartered began in 1853 as the Chartered Bank of India Australia and China to finance trade between the UK and its Asian colonies. It began establishing offices in 1858. Over the next 40 years The Chartered Bank expanded throughout Asia. In the 20th century the bank opened branches in Germany and the US. In 1957 Chartered entered the Middle East by acquiring Eastern Bank. In 1969 it agreed to merge with Standard Bank.

In 1862 schoolmaster John Paterson established the Standard Bank of British South Africa Ltd. to fund trade with mining businesses. Within two years the bank had 15 branches. Like Chartered Standard had moved into Germany and the US by 1905 and operated in central and southern Africa by 1912.

In 1962 the bank was renamed The Standard Bank Ltd. Three years later it expanded into Gambia Ghana Nigeria and Sierra Leone but the end of colonialism meant instability; business was threatened and ruling parties often nationalized Standard's banks. In 1969 the bank agreed to merge with Chartered Bank.

Asian and Middle Eastern business flourished in the early 1970s while South African branches struggled under growing international pressure on the country's apartheid regime. In response the company diversified into metals trading and consumer finance. It also expanded in the US market with the purchase of Union Bancorp of California.

Standard Chartered failed in a 1981 attempt to gain entry to the UK market through purchasing Royal Bank of Scotland. Four years later that bank went public.

In 1986 Lloyds Bank tried to take over Standard Chartered but investors Robert Holmes a Court Yue-Kong Pao and Khoo Teck Puat acquired enough of the company to block the play. Meanwhile overseas financial deregulation brought more competition and Hong Kong Singapore and Malaysia sank into recession.

Hit by trade sanctions against South Africa the bank in 1987 sold its operations there. As the world tumbled deeper into recession Standard Chartered's loan losses climbed. But the bank began to recover the next year as it trimmed its US bank holdings.

Scandal hit the bank in the 1990s. In 1992 Standard Chartered paid $515 million in restitution

after a broker in its Mumbai India office embezzled some $1.2 billion from Indian banks. In 1994 executives with Mocatta were convicted of bribery and the Hong Kong government banned Standard Chartered Securities (sold in 1996) from underwriting stock offerings for nine months after it falsified six IPOs.

In 1997 Standard Chartered refocused on retail banking with its 1998 purchase of what is now Banco Standard Chartered in Latin America and its bank/insurance tie-ups with CGU (now CGNU) and Prudential plc. The promotion of Rana Talwar to CEO brought a strategic focus on emerging markets from which other banks were withdrawing.

Standard Chartered in 1999 bought Thailand's Nakornthon Bank and the non-Swiss trade financing operations of UBS AG and expanded into China through a pact with the Bank of China. In 2000 the company bought Australia and New Zealand Banking Group's Grindlays operations in South Asia and the Middle East. The following year Stanchart began cutting 20% of its workforce. It also folded Grindlay's operations into its own while retaining the brand's name.

In 2004 Stanchart bought the majority of Australia and New Zealand Banking Group's project finance business which is headquartered in London. The business which cost Stanchart about $1.5 billion operates in four regions: the UK the US the Middle East and South Asia (especially India).

In 2005 the bank acquired Korea First Bank (now SC First Bank); the deal was the biggest foreign investment ever for South Korea's financial sector. The following year Stanchart paid about $1.2 billion for Taiwan's Hsinchu Bank making it the first foreign bank owner in that country. Also in 2006 the bank acquired 20% of China Bohai Bank.

In 2008 the UK government responded to the global financial crisis by investing 50 billion ($87.9 billion) in the nation's top banks including Stanchart. It agreed to guarantee another 250 billion ($438 billion) in bonds and provide additional liquidity of at least 200 billion ($350 billion) to the banks. The bailout plan was initiated to provide capital directly to the banks in order to revitalize lending activities.

Also in 2008 the company made some acquisitions for further international expansion. It bought Asia Trust and Investment Corporation which added some 10 branches in the lucrative Taipei market. Stanchart also bought some of the Brazil operations of Lehman Brothers after that company filed for bankruptcy protection.

EXECUTIVES

Independent Non-Executive Director, David Conner

Chief Executive Officer - Corporate & Institutional Banking, Simon Cooper

Chief Executive Office, Consumer, Private and Business Banking, Judy Hsu

Independent Non-Executive Director, Gay Evans

Independent Non-Executive Director, Carlson Tong

Independent Non-Executive Director, David Tang

Group Chief Operating Officer, David Whiteing

Group Head - Human Resources, Tanuj Kapilashrami

Independent Non-Executive Director, Phil Rivett

Independent Non-Executive Director, Maria Ramos

Interim Company Secretary, Scott Corrigan

Group General Counsel, David Fein

Independent Non-Executive Director, Byron Grote

Non-Executive Independent Deputy Chairman of the Board, Naguib Kheraj

Group Chief Financial Officer, Executive Director, Andy Halford, $1,928,970 total compensation

Regional Chief Executive Officer, Asia, Benjamin
  Hung
Regional Chief Executive Officer, Africa & Middle
  East, Sunil Kaushal
Group Chief Information Officer, Michael Gorriz
Independent Non-Executive Director, Jasmine
  Whitbread
Group Chief Executive Officer, Executive
  Director, William Winters, $3,039,667 total
  compensation
Group Chief Risk Officer, Mark Smith
Chairman, Jose Vinals
Group Head, Corporate Affairs, Brand &
  Marketing, Conduct, Financial Crime and
  Compliance, Tracey McDermott
Auditors: Ernst & Young LLP

LOCATIONS

HQ: Standard Chartered Plc
  32nd Floor, 4-4A Des Voeux Road, Central,
Phone: (44) 20 7885 8888   Fax: (44) 20 7885 9999
Web: www.sc.com

2018 Sales

	% of total
Greater China & North Asia	42
ASEAN & South Asia	27
Africa & the Middle East	18
Europe & Americas	11
Central and other	2
Total	**100**

PRODUCTS/OPERATIONS

2018 Sales

	% of total
Net Interest Income	59
Net Fee and Commission Income	24
Net Trading Income	11
Other Operating Income	6
Total	**100**

2018 Sales

	$mil	%
Corporate & Institutional Banking	6,606	45
Retail Banking	5,041	34
Commercial Banking	1,390	9
Private Banking	518	4
Central & Other Items	1,234	8
Total	**14,789**	**100**

COMPETITORS

ALLIED IRISH BANKS PUBLIC LIMITED COMPANY
E. SUN FINANCIAL HOLDING COMPANY LTD.
GENERAL ELECTRIC CAPITAL CORPORATION
HSBC HOLDINGS PLC
Islandsbanki hf.
NATWEST GROUP PLC
Nordea Bank AB
UniCredit Bank AG
YORKSHIRE BANK PUBLIC LIMITED COMPANY

HISTORICAL FINANCIALS

Company Type: Public

Income Statement				FYE: December 31
	ASSETS ($ mil.)	NET INCOME ($ mil.)	INCOME AS % OF ASSETS	EMPLOYEES
12/20	789,050	724	0.1%	83,657
12/19	720,398	2,303	0.3%	84,398
12/18	688,762	1,054	0.2%	85,402
12/17	663,501	1,219	0.2%	86,021
12/16	646,692	(247)	—	86,693
Annual Growth	**5.1%**	**—**	**—**	**(0.9%)**

Return on assets: 0.1%   Dividends
Return on equity: 1.4%   Yield: 0.0%
Long-term debt ($ mil.): —   Payout: 87.3%
No. of shares (mil.): —   Market value ($ mil.): —
Sales ($ mil): 21,050

	STOCK PRICE ($) FY Close	P/E High/Low		PER SHARE ($) Earnings	Dividends	Book Value
12/20	12.79	185	83	0.10	0.09	16.00
12/19	19.15	34	27	0.56	0.22	15.78
Annual Growth	**(33.2%)**	**—**		**—**	**(34.6%)**	**(20.0%)**	**0.4%**

State Bank of India

Auditors: Khandelwal Jain & Co.

LOCATIONS

HQ: State Bank of India
  Corporate Centre, Madam Cama Road, Mumbai 400
  021
Phone: (91) 22 2283 0535   Fax: (91) 22 2285 5348
Web: www.sbi.co.in

HISTORICAL FINANCIALS

Company Type: Public

Income Statement				FYE: March 31
	ASSETS ($ mil.)	NET INCOME ($ mil.)	INCOME AS % OF ASSETS	EMPLOYEES
03/21	662,268	3,062	0.5%	245,652
03/20	555,704	2,617	0.5%	249,448
03/19	561,960	332	0.1%	257,252
03/18	555,855	(700)	—	264,041
03/17	531,232	37	0.0%	209,567
Annual Growth	**5.7%**	**201.2%**	**—**	**4.1%**

2021 Year-End Financials

Return on assets: 0.5%   Dividends
Return on equity: 8.5%   Yield: —
Long-term debt ($ mil.): —   Payout: —
No. of shares (mil.): —   Market value ($ mil.): —
Sales ($ mil): 52,611

	STOCK PRICE ($) FY Close	P/E High/Low		PER SHARE ($) Earnings	Dividends	Book Value
03/21	52.70	2	1	0.34	0.00	4.22
03/20	25.60	2	1	0.29	0.00	3.72
03/19	43.95	17	13	0.04	0.00	3.80
03/18	40.11	—	—	(0.08)	0.38	3.97
03/17	43.17	140	84	0.00	0.38	4.20
Annual Growth	**5.1%**	**—**		**(191.1%)**	**—**	**0.1%**

Steinhoff International Holdings NV

LOCATIONS

HQ: Steinhoff International Holdings NV
  Building B2, Vineyard Office Park, Cnr Adam Tas &
  Devon Valley Road, Stellenbosch 7600
Phone: (27) 21 8080700   Fax: (27) 21 8080800
Web: www.steinhoffinternational.com

HISTORICAL FINANCIALS

Company Type: Public

Income Statement				FYE: September 30
	REVENUE ($ mil.)	NET INCOME ($ mil.)	NET PROFIT MARGIN	EMPLOYEES
09/19	13,081	(1,769)	—	108,361
09/18	14,857	(1,444)	—	123,054
09/17	22,233	(4,768)	—	125,501
09/16*	18,351	1,604	8.7%	105,866
06/15	10,969	1,090	9.9%	91,114
Annual Growth	**4.5%**	**—**	**—**	**4.4%**

*Fiscal year change

2019 Year-End Financials

Debt ratio: 84.9%   No. of shares (mil.): —
Return on equity: —   Dividends
Cash ($ mil.): 1,958   Yield: —
Current ratio: 1.42   Payout: —
Long-term debt ($ mil.): 11,313 Market value ($ mil.): —

Stellantis NV

Auditors: EY S.p.A

LOCATIONS

HQ: Stellantis NV
  Singaporestraat 92-100, Lijnden P7 1175 RA
Phone: (31) 20 3421 707
Web: www.stellantis.com

HISTORICAL FINANCIALS

Company Type: Public

Income Statement				FYE: December 31
	REVENUE ($ mil.)	NET INCOME ($ mil.)	NET PROFIT MARGIN	EMPLOYEES
12/20	106,376	35	0.0%	189,512
12/19	121,468	7,434	6.1%	191,752
12/18	126,443	4,131	3.3%	198,545
12/17	132,982	4,184	3.1%	235,915
12/16	117,222	1,903	1.6%	231,019
Annual Growth	**(2.4%)**	**(63.0%)**	**—**	**(4.8%)**

2020 Year-End Financials

Debt ratio: 25.9%   No. of shares (mil.): 1,574
Return on equity: 0.1%   Dividends
Cash ($ mil.): 29,265   Yield: —
Current ratio: 1.03   Payout: —
Long-term debt ($ mil.): 20,908 Market value ($ mil.): —

Storebrand ASA

Auditors: PricewaterhouseCoopers AS

LOCATIONS

HQ: Storebrand ASA
  Professor Kohts vei 9, Lysaker NO-1327
Phone: (47) 915 08880   Fax: (47) 22 48 98 90
Web: www.storebrand.no

HISTORICAL FINANCIALS

Company Type: Public

Income Statement

FYE: December 31

	ASSETS ($ mil.)	NET INCOME ($ mil.)	INCOME AS % OF ASSETS	EMPLOYEES
12/20	85,418	275	0.3%	1,824
12/19	72,048	235	0.3%	1,759
12/18	66,529	424	0.6%	1,789
12/17	69,389	289	0.4%	1,795
12/16	60,401	246	0.4%	1,745
Annual Growth	9.1%	2.8%	—	1.1%

2020 Year-End Financials

Return on assets: 0.3%	Dividends
Return on equity: 6.7%	Yield: 0.0%
Long-term debt ($ mil.): —	Payout: —
No. of shares (mil.): 467	Market value ($ mil.): —
Sales ($ mil): 9,510	

	STOCK PRICE ($) FY Close	P/E High/Low		PER SHARE ($) Earnings	Dividends	Book Value
12/20	0.00	2	2	0.59	0.38	9.02
12/19	12.07	3	3	0.50	0.67	8.11
12/18	16.57	2	2	0.91	0.56	8.09
12/17	15.50	3	2	0.64	0.25	8.03
Annual Growth	—	—	—	(2.2%)	11.4%	3.0%

Strabag SE-BR

Auditors: KPMG Austria GmbH Wirtschaftsprufungs- und Steuerberatungsgesellschaft

LOCATIONS

HQ: Strabag SE-BR
Triglavstrasse 9, Villach 9500
Phone: (43) 800 880 890
Web: www.strabag.com

HISTORICAL FINANCIALS

Company Type: Public

Income Statement

FYE: December 31

	REVENUE ($ mil.)	NET INCOME ($ mil.)	NET PROFIT MARGIN	EMPLOYEES
12/19	17,627	417	2.4%	76,919
12/18	17,394	404	2.3%	75,460
12/17	16,136	334	2.1%	72,904
12/16	13,152	293	2.2%	71,839
12/15	14,271	170	1.2%	73,315
Annual Growth	5.4%	25.1%	—	1.2%

2019 Year-End Financials

Debt ratio: —	No. of shares (mil.): 102
Return on equity: 9.9%	Dividends
Cash ($ mil.): 2,762	Yield: —
Current ratio: 1.16	Payout: 24.8%
Long-term debt ($ mil.): —	Market value ($ mil.): —

Subaru Corporation

Subaru Corporation (formerly Fuji Heavy Industries) is the parent of Subaru of America the automotive company known for its all-wheel-drive (AWD) technology found in crossover vehicles (a sedan drive with SUV looks) such as the Forester and Outback and in the Impreza Legacy and Tribeca models. In addition to Subaru of America based in the US the company operates through more than 75 subsidiaries in Japan China and Taiwan and 10 equity-method affiliated companies. The company also makes aircraft and structural components within its Aerospace Company. Its core business however is Subaru automobiles representing almost 90% of sales.

Operations

The company operates in three business units: the Automotive Business Unit the Aerospace Company and Other Businesses.

The Automotive Business Unit manufactures cars equipped with outstanding safety and driving performance in a variety of driving conditions. This is reflected in the vehicles the company makes which has the Symmetrical All-Wheel Drive (AWD) System which features a symmetrically-laid-out drivetrain and the horizontally-opposed engine. The automotive business unit accounts for roughly 90% of the company's total revenue.

The Aerospace Company develops and produces a wide variety of aircraft in various programs. It provides maintenance and repair for products such as the UH-1J utility helicopter used by the Japan Ground Self-Defense Force as well as the T-5 Maritime Self-Defense Force trainer unmanned aerial vehicles and flight simulators. It also participates in development projects for Boeing aircrafts such as its Center Wing and integration with main landing gear wheel wells and doors. This business unit accounts for about 10% of total revenue.

Geographic Reach

The head office of Subaru Corporation is located in Tokyo Japan. The company's Automotive Business Unit operates from three plants: Gunma Main Plant Yajima Plant and Oizumi Plant. The Aerospace Company has three manufacturing plants located across Japan: Handa Plant Handa West Plant and Utsunomiya Plant.

The company generates the majority of its revenue from North America which represents 70% of the company's sales followed by Japan which represents 20%.

Financial Performance

Note: Growth rates may differ after conversion to US Dollars.

Subaru Corporation has seen modest growth in sales over the past five years. Revenue in fiscal 2019 decreased 2% to 3.1 trillion compared with 3.2 trillion in 2018 mainly due to the fall in automobile unit sales as well as in the increase of quality-related expenses triggered by the recall of engine parts.

Net income declined significantly falling 40% in fiscal 2019 to 147.8 billion. This loss is mainly due to selling expenses as well as plant shutdown costs which amounted to 405.7 billion.

Cash at the end of fiscal 2019 was 702.3 billion an increase of 63 billion from the prior year. Cash from operations contributed 174 billion to the coffers while investing activities used 158.3 billion mainly for purchases of securities and non-current assets. Financing activities used another 96.6 billion for loan payments and dividends.

Strategy

Subaru recognizes that the automotive industry is in a period of transition to a new era and social demands for new technologies are increasing. The company is keen on determining business sectors in which it can leverage its strengths and intensively invest in necessary resources to the improvement of medium and long-term corporate value and sustained growth.

The company's engineering and product development divisions have studied and begun implementing fundamental quality reforms starting from the development planning and design stages. These reforms include a review of development schedules and supplier selection and collaboration to enable reliable confirmation of quality sharing of parts across models updating of durability testing facilities and increasing personnel.

The company also announced a target of unit sales of 1.3 million vehicles worldwide in 2025 as well as increasing its dealer network to about 650 dealers. To achieve this the company is securing dealer income through increasing unit sales per dealer. Since the US is its key market the company will continue to advance on its potential; the company has planned for a consolidated unit sales of more than 1 million vehicles particularly the Ascent Forester and Crosstrek.

Additionally the company aims to utilize its all-new Forester and Subaru XV models equipped with its e-BOXER system to support sales in the Chinese and European markets.

HISTORY

Chikuhei Nakajima started the Aircraft Research Laboratory north of Tokyo in 1917 renaming it the Nakajima Aircraft Company in 1931. Amid the ashes of WWII Nakajima formed Fuji Sangyo to make products with aircraft technology in 1945. His motor scooters used bomber tail wheels and he later added buses with unibody frames. Nakajima died in 1949.

Fuji Sangyo joined four other firms in 1953 and Fuji Heavy Industries was born. The Subaru car division debuted in 1958 and FHI went public two years later. The firm expanded product lines throughout the 1960s and in 1968 Nissan Motor invested in FHI. The relationship lasted more than 30 years.

Subaru expanded to the US in 1968 with the help of furniture retailer Harvey Lamm. Lamm visiting Japan saw Subaru's utilitarian front-wheel-drive station wagon and recognized its potential. He convinced FHI to make him its US importer and he set up Subaru of America. Lamm ultimately became chairman and CEO of the US subsidiary.

In 1975 FHI exported the four-wheel-drive Subaru GF to the US; it was the country's first four-wheel-drive car for the mass market. High energy prices and the appeal of a four-wheel-drive car drove sales in the 1970s and early 1980s. By 1986 Subaru achieved 12 straight years of record sales and profits.

The next year however a rising yen boosted Japanese car prices and sales dips fueled round after round of incentives. Profits tanked and Subaru responded by expanding trim levels and power train choices. The misstep confused shoppers and sales nose-dived.

Also in 1987 FHI and Isuzu teamed up to build an assembly plant (Subaru-Isuzu Automotive) in Indiana while other makers introduced minivans and sport utility vehicles. Focusing on cars Subaru missed the start of the SUV boom. Even the arrival of the Legacy in 1989 failed to jumpstart sales. Lamm left Subaru in 1990 and two years later Subaru's US arm posted a record loss of $250 million.

Veteran CFO George Muller took over as president and COO of Subaru of America in 1993. Saddled with inventory plummeting sales and a poor brand image he promptly launched one of the greatest turnarounds in US automotive history.

Muller refined the niche Lamm carved out in the 1970s. He cut every product from the lineup that lacked all-wheel-drive. Enlisting the Legacy a car-SUV hybrid (Outback) was created in 1995 by lifting the body a few inches and adding beefy-looking body attachments.

Muller took aggressive steps at the corporate level to cut costs and build a culture of risk-taking initiative and speed. By 1999 profits were back to record levels. In Japan though trouble at parent FHI overshadowed Subaru's rejuvenation.

In 1998 revelations surfaced that FHI bribed legislator Yojiro Nakajima (a former official in Japan's defense agency and grandson of Chikuhei) to secure government contracts for a sea rescue aircraft. FHI had also illegally funneled cash to Nakajima to help his 1996 election bid. Nakajima along with FHI's chairman and several former executives was arrested. He later committed suicide and FHI was barred from bidding on defense contracts for one year.

GM bought 20% of FHI for $1.5 billion in 1999. The deal included the 4% held by FHI's largest investor Nissan. GM won access to FHI's all-wheel-drive technology and provided FHI resources to develop more-efficient fuel systems. Midway through 2000 Muller resigned from Subaru.

FHI struck a deal with Airbus in 2001 develop the company's new Airbus A380 airliner. Subaru and GM also unveiled plans to jointly produce an all-wheel-drive sport wagon to be built at the Subaru-Isuzu plant in the US.

FHI announced in 2002 that it would cease production of bus bodies and railway cars by March 2003. Later that year FHI bought Isuzu Motors' 49% stake in the companies' carmaking joint venture Subaru-Isuzu Automotive. FHI renamed the company Subaru of Indiana Automotive.

That same year FHI implemented sweeping changes in an effort to focus on its core business — building cars. The Fuji Dynamic Revolution-1 plan (FDR-1) aimed to increase sales by 35% by 2007 and to remake Subaru as a luxury brand. Part of the original plan was for the company to leverage its relationship with GM to reduce procurement and purchasing costs. GM however decided largely to terminate its relationship with FHI and has sold its 20% stake in the Japanese manufacturer about 9% of it going to Toyota Motor. It sold the remaining 11% through Fuji's open-market share-buyback program and through regular market sales.

In the first product tie-up since Toyota became FHI's largest shareholder the two companies announced in early 2006 that Toyota Camrys would be built at FHI's Subaru of Indiana plant. That production began the following year.

In 2006 FHI made a few adjustments to its FDR-1 plan. The company restructured its sales networks and layed off about 700 workers to meet its cost reduction goals. The notion of transforming into a luxury brand however was deemed to be infeasible from a cost standpoint. FDR-1's successes were mixed. FHI managed to increase sales but profits were hurt by poor sales at home in Japan and meager sales of higher-end Subaru models in the US which were likely slowed by high fuel prices.

In 2007 FHI established its Overseas Sales and Marketing Divisions I & II. The first overseas division is dedicated to centralizing control of manufacturing and sales activities in the US. The move aimed to bring refinement and sophistication to the Subaru brand in the US while capitalizing on its reputation of offering affordable compelling AWD vehicles.

EXECUTIVES

President, Chief Executive Officer, Representative Director, Tomomi Nakamura
Senior Managing Executive Officer, Chief Director of Manufacturing, Director, Atsushi Ohsaki

Chief Financial Officer, Senior Managing Executive Officer, Chief Risk Management Officer, Director, Katsuyuki Mizuma
Senior Managing Executive Officer, Chief Director of Procurement, Director, Tetsuo Ohnuki
Senior Managing Executive Officer, Chief Director of 1st Overseas Sales, Chairman and Chief Executive Officer of Subsidiary, Director, Fumiaki Hayata
Independent Director, Natsunosuke Yago
Independent Director, Yasuyuki Abe
Independent Director, Miwako Doi
Auditors: KPMG AZSA LLC

LOCATIONS

HQ: Subaru Corporation
1-20-8 Ebisu, Shibuya-ku, Tokyo 150-8554
Phone: (81) 3 6447 8825   **Fax:** (81) 3 6447 8184
Web: www.subaru.co.jp

2018 Sales

	% of total
North America	68
Japan	20
Asia	4
Europe	3
Others	5
Total	**100**

PRODUCTS/OPERATIONS

2018 Sales

	% of total
Automobiles	94
Aerospace	4
Other	2
Total	**100**

Selected Products and Divisions

Aerospace
  AH-64D combat helicopter
  Center-wing section (Boeing B-777)
  Design and training simulators
  Fixed-wing aircraft
  T-1 Trainer
  Unmanned aircraft
Automobiles
  Dex
  Dias Wagon
  Exiga
  Forester
  Impreza (wagon sedan)
  Legacy (touring B4 Outback)
  Outback (sport wagon sedan)
  Sambar (van truck wagon)
  Stella (R1 R2 Pleo)
  Tribeca
Eco Technologies
  Clean Robot floor-cleaning system
  Intermediate refuse collection systems
  Maintenance and sanitation vehicles
  Refuse management systems
  Special purpose vehicles
  Sweepers and scrubbers
  Wind-power systems

Selected Subsidiaries:

Fuji Heavy Industries U.S.A. Inc.
Fuji Machinery Co. Ltd. (Japan)
Subaru Canada Inc.
Subaru of China Ltd.
Subaru Europe N.V./S.A. (Belgium)
Subaru of America Inc. (US)
Subaru of Indiana Automotive Inc.

COMPETITORS

Bayerische Motoren Werke AG	MITSUBISHI MOTORS CORPORATION
FORD MOTOR COMPANY	Magna International Inc
GENERAL MOTORS COMPANY	
Hyundai Motor Company	PEUGEOT SA
ISUZU MOTORS LIMITED	SUZUKI MOTOR CORPORATION
MAZDA MOTOR CORPORATION	

HISTORICAL FINANCIALS

Company Type: Public

Income Statement

FYE: March 31

	REVENUE ($ mil.)	NET INCOME ($ mil.)	NET PROFIT MARGIN	EMPLOYEES
03/21	25,560	690	2.7%	45,511
03/20	30,807	1,405	4.6%	44,747
03/19	28,538	1,334	4.7%	43,057
03/18	32,068	2,075	6.5%	41,998
03/17	29,747	2,525	8.5%	40,737
Annual Growth	(3.7%)	(27.7%)	—	2.8%

2021 Year-End Financials

Debt ratio: 0.0%
Return on equity: 4.3%
Cash ($ mil.): 8,138
Current ratio: 2.27
Long-term debt ($ mil.): 2,777

No. of shares (mil.): 767
Dividends
  Yield: 2.6%
  Payout: —
Market value ($ mil.): 7,673

	STOCK PRICE ($) FY Close	P/E High/Low		PER SHARE ($) Earnings	Dividends	Book Value
03/21	10.00	0	0	0.90	0.26	20.93
03/20	9.40	0	0	1.83	0.67	20.57
03/19	11.35	0	0	1.74	0.65	18.90
03/18	16.57	0	0	2.71	0.69	19.06
03/17	18.37	0	0	3.27	0.66	17.01
Annual Growth	(14.1%)		—	(27.6%)	(20.5%)	5.3%

SUEZ SA

SUEZ (formerly SUEZ Environnement) conducts a variety of activities including the treatment production and distribution of drinking water; the collection recovery and treatment of wastewater; and the collection and processing of nonhazardous and hazardous waste recycling of waste and street cleaning. SUEZ is the largest private O&M contractor in the municipal sector supplying drinking water to 7 million people and wastewater treatment services to 3.5 million people. It operates through subsidiaries such as Degremont (water treatment services) and SITA (waste management services). SUEZ was formed in 2002 by the regrouping of SITA (one of Europe's largest waste management companies) with French conglomerate SUEZ's Ondeo Degr mont water unit. Other operations include Safege (consulting engineering for water operations). Europe accounts for the majority of the company's sales.

Operations

SUEZ's subsidiaries are divided into the following operating segments: Recycling and Recovery Europe (around 35% of sales) Water Europe (over 25%) International (about 25%) WTS (nearly 15%).

The Recycling and Recovery Europe services include collection sorting recycling composting energy recovery and landfilling for both non-hazardous and hazardous waste. Water Europe is a water distribution and treatment services particularly under concession contracts (water management). International segment comprises the expansion of business segments depending on the opportunities that may arise in the areas of water waste and engineering services with a special focus on risk - management resulting from specific local environments by setting up partnerships entering into hedges and limiting invested capital or other investments in highly regulated environments. The

WTS includes all water services for the industrial customer segment. The "Other" segment is made up of holding companies including SUEZ as well as SUEZ Consulting a consulting subsidiary of the Group.

Geographic Reach
Headquartered in France Europe accounts for about 60% of sales North America with about 15% and South America Asia Oceania Africa as well as Middle East accounts for over 5% each.

Sales and Marketing
The company serves public authorities and private sector customers. It supplies drinking water to 7 million people and wastewater treatment services to 3.5 million people.

Financial Performance
The company's revenue in 2019 increased by 4% to ?18.0 billion compared to ?17.3 billion in the prior year. The increase was due to higher water technologies & solutions and recycling & recovery Europe revenues.

Net income for 2019 increased to ?352 million compared to ?335 million in the prior year.

Cash held by the company at the end of 2019 increased to ?2.9 billion. Cash provided by operations was ?2.5 billion while cash used for investing and financing activities were ?1.5 billion and ?860.7 million respectively. Main uses for cash were investments in property plant and equipment and intangible assets; and repayment of borrowings and financial debts.

Strategy
The Shaping SUEZ 2030 plan is based on three pillars that the company is already putting into practice in its daily work: a more selective path to growth simplified operational processes and a strong corporate culture centering on four cardinal values (passion for the environment customer first respect and team spirit) spearheading SUEZ's conquering spirit.

Mergers and Acquisitions
In late 2020 SUEZ Itochu Corporation and Five Capital Fund I (a Saudi CMA-regulated fund) successfully closed the acquisition of a majority stake in Environment Development Company (EDCO) a Saudi hazardous waste management company. This operation will position partners in the rapidly expanding hazardous waste market in Saudi Arabia where major petrochemical industrial projects are ongoing and planned. The transaction amount for SUEZ represents 113.4 MSAR (25.99 M?) enterprise value.

In mid-2020 SUEZ has signed an agreement to purchase the Reverse Osmosis (RO) membrane portfolio from specialty chemical company LANXESS. The membrane will become part of the company' Water Technologies & Solutions product portfolio and further enhances the business' ability to help customers address water treatment challenges. The acquisition falls in line with SUEZ's strategy to grow and invest in the industrial water market.

Auditors: Mazars

LOCATIONS
HQ: SUEZ SA
Tour CB21 - 16 place de l'Iris, Paris La Defense, Cedex 92040
Phone: (33) 1 58 81 20 00   **Fax:** (33) 1 58 81 25 00
Web: www.suez.com

2013 Sales

	% of total
Europe	69
Oceania	8
North America	6
South America	6
Africa & Middle East	6
Asia	5
Total	**100**

PRODUCTS/OPERATIONS

Selected Subsidiaries
Chine
Degré;mont
Lyonnaise des Eaux
Ondeo IS
Ondeo Systems
Safege
SITA France
SITA Trashco
SITA UK
United Water

COMPETITORS
AEGION CORPORATION
ASSYSTEM
EVOQUA WATER TECHNOLOGIES LLC
FCC ENVIRONMENT (UK) LIMITED
JOHN WOOD GROUP PLC
SECHE ENVIRONNEMENT
SEMBCORP INDUSTRIES LTD
SEVERN TRENT PLC
SOUTH STAFFORDSHIRE PLC
TECNICAS REUNIDAS SA
WASTE MANAGEMENT INC.

HISTORICAL FINANCIALS
Company Type: Public

Income Statement — FYE: December 31

	REVENUE ($ mil.)	NET INCOME ($ mil.)	NET PROFIT MARGIN	EMPLOYEES
12/19	20,226	394	2.0%	0
12/18	19,847	383	1.9%	88,775
12/17	19,025	361	1.9%	88,576
12/16	16,178	443	2.7%	83,921
12/15	16,484	443	2.7%	82,536
Annual Growth	**5.2%**	**(2.9%)**		

2019 Year-End Financials

Debt ratio: 39.4%	No. of shares (mil.): 618
Return on equity: 5.4%	Dividends
Cash ($ mil.): 4,157	Yield: —
Current ratio: 0.95	Payout: 135.4%
Long-term debt ($ mil.): 11,131	Market value ($ mil.): —

Sumitomo Chemical Co., Ltd.

Auditors: KPMG AZSA LLC

LOCATIONS
HQ: Sumitomo Chemical Co., Ltd.
2-27-1 Shinkawa, Chuo-ku, Tokyo 104-8260
Phone: (81) 3 5543 5160   **Fax:** (81) 3 5543 5901
Web: www.sumitomo-chem.co.jp

HISTORICAL FINANCIALS
Company Type: Public

Income Statement — FYE: March 31

	REVENUE ($ mil.)	NET INCOME ($ mil.)	NET PROFIT MARGIN	EMPLOYEES
03/21	20,654	415	2.0%	38,648
03/20	20,504	284	1.4%	37,453
03/19	20,936	1,065	5.1%	36,384
03/18	20,628	1,259	6.1%	35,829
03/17	17,479	764	4.4%	35,590
Annual Growth	**4.3%**	**(14.1%)**		**2.1%**

2021 Year-End Financials

Debt ratio: 0.3%	No. of shares (mil.): 1,634
Return on equity: 4.7%	Dividends
Cash ($ mil.): 3,259	Yield: 2.1%
Current ratio: 1.45	Payout:
Long-term debt ($ mil.): 9,940	Market value ($ mil.): 42,657

	STOCK PRICE ($) FY Close	P/E High/Low		PER SHARE ($) Earnings	Dividends	Book Value
03/21	26.09	1	0	0.25	0.56	5.63
03/20	14.58	1	1	0.17	1.01	5.20
03/19	23.36	0	0	0.65	1.04	5.52
03/18	29.07	1	0	0.77	0.80	5.34
03/17	28.03	1	0	0.47	0.58	4.49
Annual Growth	**(1.8%)**	—	—	**(14.1%)**	**(0.8%)**	**5.8%**

Sumitomo Corp. (Japan)

Auditors: KPMG AZSA LLC

LOCATIONS
HQ: Sumitomo Corp. (Japan)
2-3-2 Otemachi, Chiyoda-ku, Tokyo 100-8601
Phone: (81) 3 6285 5000   **Fax:** 212 207-0456
Web: www.sumitomocorp.co.jp

HISTORICAL FINANCIALS
Company Type: Public

Income Statement — FYE: March 31

	REVENUE ($ mil.)	NET INCOME ($ mil.)	NET PROFIT MARGIN	EMPLOYEES
03/21	41,951	(1,382)	—	103,443
03/20	48,823	1,578	3.2%	100,246
03/19	48,212	2,894	6.0%	91,362
03/18	45,460	2,905	6.4%	98,635
03/17	35,748	1,528	4.3%	91,365
Annual Growth	**4.1%**	—		**3.2%**

2021 Year-End Financials

Debt ratio: 0.3%	No. of shares (mil.): 1,249
Return on equity: (-6.0%)	Dividends
Cash ($ mil.): 5,409	Yield: 4.5%
Current ratio: 1.54	Payout: —
Long-term debt ($ mil.): 21,985	Market value ($ mil.): 18,071

	STOCK PRICE ($) FY Close	P/E High/Low		PER SHARE ($) Earnings	Dividends	Book Value
03/21	14.46	—	—	(1.11)	0.66	18.27
03/20	11.27	0	0	1.26	0.77	18.76
03/19	13.84	0	0	2.32	0.64	20.04
03/18	16.88	0	0	2.33	0.50	19.30
03/17	13.54	0	0	1.22	0.46	16.96
Annual Growth	**1.7%**	—	—	—	**9.3%**	**1.9%**

Sumitomo Electric Industries, Ltd. (Japan)

Sumitomo Electric Industries (SEI) is Japan's largest producer of wire and cable and makes several other products including wiring harnesses for cars flexible printed circuits and optical fiber for telecommunications. The company has around 415 subsidiaries and affiliates around the globe. It sells about 55% of its products to companies in the automotive industry; SEI also serves customers in the electronics telecommunications and environmental and energy industries. The company generates nearly 45% of its business in Japan.

Operations

SEI operates five business segments categorized according to the products offered: Automotive Environment and Energy Industrial Materials Electronics and Infocommunications (information and communications).

The Automotive business offers wiring harnesses anti-vibration rubbers automotive hoses and car electronic components. The business segment accounts for about 55% of the company's net sales.

Environment and Energy offers electric conductors power transmission wires/cables/equipment magnet wires air cushions for railroad vehicles power system equipment such as substation equipment/control systems charged beam equipment and processing electrical/power supply work and engineering and porous metals. The segment accounts for around 20% of sales.

Industrial Materials (approximately 10% of sales) includes tensioning materials for prestressed concrete precision spring steel wires steel tire cord cemented carbide tools diamond and CBN tools laser optics sintered powder metal parts and semiconductors heat-spreader materials. Electronics (nearly 10%) include wiring materials electric beam irradiation products flexible printed circuits fluorine resin products fasteners metal parts and chemical products. Infocommunications (roughly 10%) comprises optical fiber cables and transceiver modules and optical and wireless devices.

Geographic Reach

Headquartered in Japan SEI operates in about 415 companies located in 40 countries. The company's primary operating facilities in Japan are located in Osaka Tokyo Itami Yokohama and Ibaraki. The company's largest market is Japan with approximately 45% of revenue followed by Asia (excluding Japan) with around 30% of sales and the Americas with about 15%. Europe and others account for the rest.

Financial Performance

Net sales for fiscal 2020 decreased to 2.9 trillion compared from 3.1 trillion in the prior year due to impact of the COVID-19 pandemic.

Profit for fiscal 2020 increased to 133.2 billion compared with 110.3 billion.

Cash held by the company at the end of fiscal 2020 decreased to 249.0 billion. Cash provided by operations was 264.6 billion while investing and financing activities used 178.0 billion and 1.3 billion respectively. Main cash uses were purchase of property plant and equipment; and redemption of bonds and repayments of long-term debt.

Strategy

The business environment surrounding the company is constantly changing including the spreading of the COVID-19 infection. The digitalization of the economy and society the response to issues related to the global environment and the movement to strengthen efforts to enhance re-

silience are all rapidly accelerating. As part of its efforts to develop a system that can respond to these changes in the business environment the company established the DX Promotion Committee in April 2021 to further promote digital transformation (DX) which has so far been promoted mainly in manufacturing sites.

Company Background

Sumitomo Electric Industries as a part of the Sumitomo group business began nearly 400 years ago with the paired talents of spiritual founder Masatomo Sumitomo (who had received training as a Buddhist priest) and his disciple and brother-in-law Riemon Soga. Sumitomo wrote treatises on the conduct of commercial activity and Soga applied his technological skill in extracting silver from copper ore improving upon traditional Western methods and opened a copper business in Kyoto in 1590 that soon transformed the copper refining industry in Japan.

The company later diversified its business to include flexible printed circuits (1960s) fiber optic cables for telecommunications (1970s) and wiring harnesses for automobiles made with its newly-developed aluminum alloy wires (2010s).

HISTORY

Sumitomo Electric Industries as a part of the Sumitomo group business began nearly 400 years ago with the paired talents of spiritual founder Masatomo Sumitomo (who had received training as a Buddhist priest) and his disciple and brother-in-law Riemon Soga. Sumitomo wrote treatises on the conduct of commercial activity and Soga applied his technological skill in extracting silver from copper ore improving upon traditional Western methods and opened a copper business in Kyoto in 1590 that soon transformed the copper refining industry in Japan.

Soga's prosperous copper business became the founding company of the Sumitomo group. After Soga died in 1636 his son Tomomochi married Masatomo's daughter (entering into the Sumitomo family) and became the company's leader.

By the late 1600s the family was one of Japan's top copper producers. The house of Sumitomo entered several other businesses by the mid-1800s in order to insulate itself from waning copper production. The family established the Sumitomo Copper Rolling Works in 1897 to produce bare copper wire.

In 1909 production of cable for Japan's telecommunications industry began and in 1920 the family took their company public renaming it Sumitomo Electric Wire & Cable Works. The next year the company added high-carbon steel wire manufacturing. Its name changed to Sumitomo Electric Industries (SEI) in 1939.

The company began making rubber products for use in aircraft fuel tanks in 1943. The decade drew to a close with the addition of overhead transmission cable engineering operations.

SEI continued to move into new businesses in the 1960s. In 1960 SEI took a 25% stake in Sumitomo 3M a three-way joint venture with NEC (25%) and 3M (50%) to produce industrial cable in Japan. To capitalize on the boom in Japan's automobile and industrial equipment industries SEI introduced disc brakes to its lineup in 1963. Also SEI formally entered into management participation in Japan's Dunlop Tire Company which was then renamed Sumitomo Rubber Industries. (It had initially invested in the tire maker in 1960.)

SEI hit pay dirt with its automotive businesses producing brakes for manufacturers of passenger cars commercial vehicles motorcycles construction and industrial equipment and railcars. In the late 1960s SEI added traffic control systems.

With the introduction of compound semiconductors (used in wireless transmitters and electronic control devices) and cable television systems the 1970s brought SEI into the arena of value-added high-tech products. SEI began producing optical-fiber cable in 1974.

SEI expanded further into fiber optics when it introduced its first LAN in 1981 and set up its US-based Sumitomo Electric Lightwave unit in 1983.

In 1987 the company began producing antilock brakes (ABS) and invested $45 million in an evenly split ABS manufacturing US joint venture (Lucas Sumitomo) with a unit of Lucas Varity. Lucas Varity was later bought by TRW and Sumitomo eventually acquired its remaining 50%. SEI closed out the 1980s by adding satellite navigation systems to its growing automobile product offerings.

The 1990s saw wider global expansion through more alliances and acquisitions. In 1990 SEI teamed up again with Lucas Varity to establish a joint venture in the UK to make automobile wiring harnesses. (SEI together with one of its own affiliates bought Lucas' half share in the company in 1999.) That year SEI through its Sumitomo Electric Wiring Systems unit formed AutoNeural Systems a joint venture with Ford-affiliated Visteon for automobile wiring harnesses.

In 2000 SEI set up ExceLight Communications (spun off from Sumitomo Electric Lightwave) to make optical components and subsystems for telecommunications cable TV and broadband equipment industries. The company restructured its electric power cable operations in early 2001 forming a manufacturing joint venture with Hitachi Cable and shutting one of its plants in Japan. Early the following year SEI acquired the Japan-based Calsonic Kansei Corporation's wiring harness business. SEI closed its electric furnaces in Japan and spun off its Sumitomo Steel Wire Corp. in late 2002. In early 2003 the company joined efforts with Hitachi Cable and Tatsuta Electric Wire & Cable to form Sumiden Hitachi Cable Ltd. a company that specialized in the manufacture of low-voltage power cables.

In 2006 the company acquired the former Volkswagen Bordnetze (now called Sumitomo Electric Bordnetze) a Germany-based manufacturer of wire harnesses from its previous joint owners Volkswagen and VDO Automotive.

Continuing to strengthen its European operations the company along with subsidiary Sumitomo Electric Sintered Alloy acquired Germany-based Cloyes Europe a sintered parts maker in 2007. SEI will use this acquisition to supply Japanese auto parts makers that have manufacturing facilities in Europe.

Also in 2007 as part of a group realignment SEI increased its ownership in Nissin Electric to more than 50% and it acquired affiliate Toyokuni Electric Cable. The acquisitions are part of the company's efforts to position itself as a global player.

EXECUTIVES

Senior Managing Director, Chief Director of New Business Development, Deputy Chief Director of Automotive Business, Representative Director, Hideo Hato

Managing Director, Chief Director of Cable & Energy Business, Masaki Shirayama

Managing Director, Chief Director of Advanced Material Business, Toshiyuki Sahashi

Senior Managing Director, Representative Director, Yoshitomo Kasui

Managing Director, Nobuyuki Kobayashi

Independent Director, Hiroshi Sato

Managing Director, Chief Director of Electronics Sales, Yasuhiro Miyata

Independent Director, Michihiro Tsuchiya

Independent Director, Christina Ahmadjian
Independent Director, Atsushi Horiba
Independent Director, Katsuaki Watanabe
President, Chief Operating Officer, Representative Director, Osamu Inoue
Senior Managing Director, Chief Director of Research & Development, Representative Director, Akira Nishimura
Vice President, Chief Director of Automobile Business, Chairman of Subsidiary, Representative Director, Mitsuo Nishida
Chairman of the Board, Chief Executive Officer, Representative Director, Masayoshi Matsumoto
Auditors: KPMG AZSA LLC

LOCATIONS

HQ: Sumitomo Electric Industries, Ltd. (Japan)
Sumitomo Bldg., 4-5-33 Kitahama, Chuo-ku, Osaka 541-0041
Phone: (81) 6 6220 4141
Web: www.sei.co.jp

2018 sales

	% of total
Japan	48
Asia	30
Americas	14
Europe and Others	8
Total	**100**

PRODUCTS/OPERATIONS

2018 sales

	% of total
Automotive	54
Environment and Energy	22
Industrial materials & other	11
Electronics	7
Information & communications	6
Total	**100**

Products

Automotive
Information and Communication System
Electronics / Consumer Electronics Semiconduc
Energy
Environment
Infrastructure
 Industrial
Bankruptcy
Wiring harnesses
Vibration-proof rubber
Automotive hoses
Car electrical equipment
Electronic wire products
Compound semiconductors
Metallic material for electronic parts
Electric-beam irradiation products
Flexible printed circuits
Fluorine resin products
Electric conductors
Power transmission wires/ cables/equipment
Magnet wires
Air cushions for railroad vehicles
Power systems
Equipment such as substation equipment/control systems
Charged beam equipment and processing
Electrical/power supply work and engineering porous
 metals

COMPETITORS

EATON CORPORATION PUBLIC LIMITED COMPANY
ENERPAC TOOL GROUP CORP.
GKN LIMITED
HELLA GmbH & Co. KGaA
JTEKT CORPORATION
LEAR CORPORATION
METHODE ELECTRONICS INC.
MOTORCAR PARTS OF AMERICA INC.
NEWCOR INC.
NHK SPRING CO. LTD.

PULSE ELECTRONICS CORPORATION
TENNECO INC.
thyssenkrupp AG

HISTORICAL FINANCIALS

Company Type: Public

Income Statement

FYE: March 31

	REVENUE ($ mil.)	NET INCOME ($ mil.)	NET PROFIT MARGIN	EMPLOYEES
03/21	26,358	508	1.9%	325,011
03/20	28,622	669	2.3%	320,975
03/19	28,696	1,066	3.7%	312,930
03/18	29,026	1,133	3.9%	293,269
03/17	25,172	962	3.8%	286,498
Annual Growth	**1.2%**	**(14.7%)**	**—**	**3.2%**

2021 Year-End Financials

Debt ratio: 0.1%
Return on equity: 3.5%
Cash ($ mil.): 2,290
Current ratio: 1.72
Long-term debt ($ mil.): 2,709

No. of shares (mil.): 780
Dividends
 Yield: 1.9%
 Payout: —
Market value ($ mil.): 12,013

	STOCK PRICE ($) FY Close	P/E High/Low		PER SHARE ($) Earnings	Dividends	Book Value
03/21	15.40	0	0	0.65	0.30	18.86
03/20	10.26	0	0	0.86	0.44	17.93
03/19	13.37	0	0	1.37	0.44	17.95
03/18	15.03	0	0	1.44	0.41	18.58
03/17	16.73	0	0	1.23	0.32	16.23
Annual Growth	**(2.0%)**	**—**	**—**	**(14.6%)**	**(1.8%)**	**3.8%**

Sumitomo Life Insurance Co. (Japan)

Sumitomo Life is a life insurance company. The firm sells individual group life and specialized health policies through more than 85 branch offices and more than 1400 district offices. In addition the company includes quick and simple processing of insurance claims benefits and policyholder loans extension of the grace period on premium payments and interest rate reduction or exemption on policyholder loans. Along with its sales force Sumitomo Life sells its products through a network of financial institutions and affiliates. The company has a total of approximately $110 billion policies in force. Sumitomo Life has operations in other Asian and North American countries. Sumitomo Life was established in May 1907 under the name of Hinode Life Insurance Co. Ltd.

Geographic Reach

The company is based in Osaka Japan. It has operations in China Vietnam Indonesia and the US.

The company has representative offices in New York London Beijing and Hanoi.

Sales and Marketing

Sumitomo Life's principal selling channels are its sales force of over 30000 representatives.

The company focused on promoting insurance sales through channels such as "bancassurance" and "insurance outlets". The bancassurance network is highly effective and ranks as one of the industry's largest with over 300 participating banks and financial institutions.

Financial Performance

The company's revenue for fiscal 2020 increased to 3.52 trillion compared from the prior year with 3.49 billion.

Profit for fiscal 2020 increased to 118.2 billion compared from the prior year with 37.6 billion.

Cash held by the company at the end of fiscal 2020 decreased to 571.4 billion. Cash provided by operations and financing activities were 830.4 billion and 108.5 billion respectively. Cash used for investing was 947.6 billion mainly for purchase of securities.

Strategy

Sumitomo's basic strategy is to promote the Asset-Liability Management (ALM) framework. In order to secure stable earnings and reliably make payments such as insurance claims the company will invest mainly in yen-denominated interest-bearing assets such as long-term public and corporate bonds and loans. Furthermore the company aim to improve returns by investing in stocks and foreign bonds within acceptable risks. It will also manage its investments considering sustainability over the medium to long-term including ESG factors (responsible investment) thereby contributing to the realization of a sustainable society as well as securing stable earnings over the medium- to long-term as a responsible institutional investor.

Company Background

Predecessor Hinode Life Insurance was founded in 1907. It changed its name to Sumitomo Life Insurance after it was acquired by Sumitomo Goshi Company in 1925.

The company established its New York representative office in 1972.

Auditors: KPMG AZSA LLC

LOCATIONS

HQ: Sumitomo Life Insurance Co. (Japan)
1-4-35 Shiromi, Chuo-ku, Osaka 540-8512
Phone: (81) 6 6937 1435
Web: www.sumitomolife.co.jp

PRODUCTS/OPERATIONS

2018 Sales

	% of total
Insurance premiums & other	72
Investment income	24
Other ordinary income	4
Total	**100**

COMPETITORS

AMBAC FINANCIAL GROUP INC.
FUKOKU MUTUAL LIFE INSURANCE COMPANY
GENWORTH FINANCIAL INC.
GIBRALTAR LIFE INSURANCE CO. LTD. THE
LEGAL & GENERAL GROUP PLC
LIVERPOOL VICTORIA FRIENDLY SOCIETY LTD
METLIFE INC.
MS&AD INSURANCE GROUP HOLDINGS INC.
MUTUAL OF OMAHA INSURANCE COMPANY
NEW YORK LIFE INSURANCE COMPANY
NIPPON LIFE INSURANCE COMPANY
PRUDENTIAL FINANCIAL INC.
RenaissanceRe Holdings Ltd.
SYMETRA FINANCIAL CORPORATION
THE GUARDIAN LIFE INSURANCE COMPANY OF AMERICA
THE HARTFORD FINANCIAL SERVICES GROUP INC.
UNUM GROUP

HISTORICAL FINANCIALS

Company Type: Public

Income Statement
FYE: March 31

	ASSETS ($ mil.)	NET INCOME ($ mil.)	INCOME AS % OF ASSETS	EMPLOYEES
03/19	341,431	435	0.1%	42,954
03/18	339,368	657	0.2%	42,848
03/17	307,252	501	0.2%	42,835
03/16	283,151	588	0.2%	42,245
03/15	229,128	1,044	0.5%	42,115
Annual Growth	10.5%	(19.6%)	—	0.5%

2019 Year-End Financials

Return on assets: 0.1%	Dividends
Return on equity: 2.9%	Yield: —
Long-term debt ($ mil.): —	Payout: —
No. of shares (mil.): —	Market value ($ mil.): —
Sales ($ mil): 30,216	

Sumitomo Mitsui Financial Group Inc Tokyo

Sumitomo Mitsui Financial Group (SMFG) is the holding company for Sumitomo Mitsui Banking which boasts some 450 domestic branches and another nearly 20 locations abroad. As one of Japan's largest banks SMFG provides banking and leasing services as well as securities credit cards and consumer finance and asset management. Other units of SMFG include credit card firm Sumitomo Mitsui Card management consulting firm Japan Research Institute and Sumitomo Mitsui Finance and Leasing. SMFG also operates the California-based Manufacturers Bank.

Operations

SMFG Group operates four principal business segments: Wholesale Retail Global and Global Markets.

Wholesale provides financing investment management M&A advisory and leases. It consists of the wholesale businesses of SMBC (Sumitomo Mitsui Banking Corporation) SMBC Nikko Securities SMBC Trust Bank and SMFL (Finance and Leasing). It generates nearly 30% of Sumitomo Mitsui's gross profit.

Retail provides retail banking services such as wealth management payment service and consumer finance business. It primarily consists of the retail banking units of SMBC SMBC Nikko and SMBC Trust Bank as well as three consumer finance companies Sumitomo Mutsui Card SMBC Finance Service and SMBC Consumer Finance. Retail generates more than 15% of gross profit.

The Global Business Unit supports the global operations of domestic and overseas customers by leveraging SMBC's extensive global network and products and services.The segment accounts for more than 25% of gross profit.

Global Markets offers foreign exchange services derivatives bonds stocks and other financial products. It brings in 30% of gross profit.

Geographic Reach

About 60% of SMFG's operating income comes from its domestic business in Japan. The rest came from customers in the Europe and Middle East region (about 10%) the Asia and Oceania region (nearly 15%) and the Americas (more than 15%).

Financial Performance

Consolidated gross profit increased by 37.6 billion year-on-year to 2.8 trillion. This increase was primarily the result of the strong performance in the wealth management and overseas securities businesses as well as the success of nimble portfolio management in the Global Markets Business Unit which outweighed a decline in profit due to the COVID-19 pandemic.

Profit attributable to owners of parent decreased by 191.1 billion year-on-year to 512.8 billion because of impairment losses on goodwill in Sumitomo Mitsui DS Asset Management Company Limited and the recording of losses on forward dealings aimed at mitigating risks of stock price.

SMFG's net cash at the end of 2020 was 56.1 billion. Operations generated 7.1 billion while investing and financing activities used 3 billion and 1 billion respectively. Operating cash flow strengthened 30% to 11.2 trillion due to changes in loans and advances.

Strategy

Sumitomo Mitsui's Core Policy of the Medium-Term Management Plan (FY 2020-FY 2022) includes transformation of existing businesses seeking new growth opportunities and elevating quality in all aspects.

The SMBC Group has defined the development of digital solutions for corporate clients as one of the key strategies for its Medium-Term Management Plan. This aims to resolve the management issues of corporate clients and create new business values. The forerunners of their digital strategies are SMBC CLOUDSIGN Inc. and Plari Town Inc. SMBC Group is encouraging in-house entrepreneurial ventures by supporting the ambitious and unprecedented undertakings of employees through a CEO production project. Both SMBC CLOUDSIGN and Plari Town Inc. are led by CEOs in their 30s who have been appointed through this project.

SMFG along with SMBC and SMBC Nikko entered into a strategic alliance with Jefferies Financial Group to work on future corporate and investment banking business opportunities. Through the alliance the two companies will coordinate across highly accretive growth areas in the corporate and investment banking business. This partnership is expected to boost both company's current business lines and improve their ability to support client needs.

Mergers and Acquisitions

In July 2021 SMFC announced its plan to acquire a 74.9% stake in Fullerton India Credit Company (FICC) a non-banking finance company that offers credit to retail and small businesses. The transaction is worth $2 billion. The company plans to fully acquire FICC in the future. This investment provides SMFG a retail finance platform in India.

EXECUTIVES

Chairman of Subsidiary, Director, Yasuyuki Kawasaki
Senior Managing Executive Officer, Manager of Joint Business in Global Business Division, Ryuji Nishisaki
Senior Managing Executive Officer, Group Chief Risk Officer, Director, Teiko Kudo
Senior Managing Executive Officer, Manager of Retail Business, Takashi Yamashita
Director, Toshihiro Isshiki
Executive President, Group Chief Executive Officer, Representative Executive Officer, Director, Jun Ohta, $1,037,557 total compensation
Director, Atsuhiko Inoue
Vice Chairman, Vice Chairman of Subsidiary, Manabu Narita
Independent Director, Yoshinobu Tsutsui

President and Chief Executive Officer of Subsidiary, Director, Makoto Takashima, $150,917 total compensation
Independent Director, Katsuyoshi Shinbo
Independent Director, Masayuki Matsumoto
Independent Director, Eriko Sakurai
Independent Director, Arthur Mitchell
Independent Director, Shozo Yamazaki
Senior Managing Executive Officer, Group CDIO, Katsunori Tanizaki
Executive Vice President, Group Chief Human Resource Officer, Representative Executive Officer, Executive Vice President of Subsidiary, Toshikazu Yaku, $273,537 total compensation
Executive Vice President, Representative Executive Officer, Manager of Joint Business in Wholesale Business Division, Executive Vice President of Subsidiary, Masahiko Ohshima
Vice Chairman, Vice Chairman of Subsidiary, Gotaro Michihiro, $273,537 total compensation
Senior Managing Executive Officer, Group Chief Information Officer, Shoji Masuda
Group Chief Financial Officer, Senior Managing Executive Officer, Group CSO, Director, Toru Nakashima
Senior Managing Executive Officer, Manager of Market Business, Masamichi Koike
Senior Managing Executive Officer, Manager of Joint Business in Wholesale Business Division, Muneo Kanamaru
Senior Managing Executive Officer, Manager of Joint Business in Global Business Division, Akihiro Fukutome
Independent Director, Masaharu Kohno
Senior Managing Executive Officer, Group Chief Compliance Officer, Tetsuro Imaeda
Senior Managing Executive Officer, Group CAE, Fumiharu Kozuka
Chairman, Takeshi Kunibe, $962,098 total compensation
Auditors: KPMG AZSA LLC

LOCATIONS

HQ: Sumitomo Mitsui Financial Group Inc Tokyo
1-2 Marunouchi, 1-chome, Chiyoda-ku, Tokyo 100-0005
Phone: (81) 3 3282 8111   **Fax:** (81) 3 4333 9954
Web: www.smfg.co.jp

PRODUCTS/OPERATIONS

2013 Sales

	% of total
Interest	
Loans & advances	43
Investment securities	2
Other	1
Noninterest	
Fees & commissions	27
investment income	9
Trading profits	4
Other	14
Total	**100**

COMPETITORS

BARCLAYS BANK PLC
Bank of Communications Co. Ltd.
CONCORDIA FINANCIAL GROUP LTD.
DAIWA SECURITIES GROUP INC.
ICICI BANK LIMITED
Industrial And Commercial Bank Of China Limited
JEFFERIES FINANCIAL GROUP INC.
MIZUHO FINANCIAL GROUP INC.
MS&AD INSURANCE GROUP HOLDINGS INC.
NATIONAL AUSTRALIA BANK LIMITED
NOMURA HOLDINGS INC.
PERMIRA ADVISERS LLP
SONY FINANCIAL GROUP INC.
Woori Finance Holdings Co. Ltd.

HISTORICAL FINANCIALS

Company Type: Public

Income Statement — FYE: March 31

	ASSETS ($ mil.)	NET INCOME ($ mil.)	INCOME AS % OF ASSETS	EMPLOYEES
03/21	2,122,609	6,208	0.3%	98,100
03/20	1,954,473	1,842	0.1%	86,400
03/19	1,765,366	4,893	0.3%	99,800
03/18	1,809,786	7,157	0.4%	88,100
03/17	1,709,656	5,615	0.3%	93,200
Annual Growth	5.6%	2.5%	—	1.3%

2021 Year-End Financials

Return on assets: 0.3%
Return on equity: 5.9%
Long-term debt ($ mil.): —
No. of shares (mil.): 1,370
Sales ($ mil): 34,327

Dividends
Yield: 5.0%
Payout: 7.7%
Market value ($ mil.): 9,936

	STOCK PRICE ($) FY Close	P/E High/Low		PER SHARE ($) Earnings	Dividends	Book Value
03/21	7.25	0	0	4.53	0.37	80.45
03/20	4.79	0	0	1.34	0.34	73.15
03/19	7.03	0	0	3.50	0.32	72.98
03/18	8.50	0	0	5.07	0.30	75.19
03/17	7.25	0	0	4.10	0.28	65.86
Annual Growth	(0.0%)	—	—	2.5%	7.3%	5.1%

Sumitomo Mitsui Trust Holdings Inc

Auditors: KPMG AZSA LLC

LOCATIONS

HQ: Sumitomo Mitsui Trust Holdings Inc
1-4-1 Marunouchi, Chiyoda-ku, Tokyo 100-8233
Phone: (81) 3 6256 6000
Web: www.smth.jp

HISTORICAL FINANCIALS

Company Type: Public

Income Statement — FYE: March 31

	ASSETS ($ mil.)	NET INCOME ($ mil.)	INCOME AS % OF ASSETS	EMPLOYEES
03/21	561,428	1,284	0.2%	24,332
03/20	520,501	1,501	0.3%	23,807
03/19	514,963	1,570	0.3%	23,639
03/18	643,740	1,450	0.2%	24,898
03/17	585,418	1,086	0.2%	24,816
Annual Growth	(1.0%)	4.3%	—	(0.5%)

2021 Year-End Financials

Return on assets: 0.2%
Return on equity: 5.4%
Long-term debt ($ mil.): —
No. of shares (mil.): 374
Sales ($ mil): 12,808

Dividends
Yield: 3.8%
Payout: 3.9%
Market value ($ mil.): 1,339

	STOCK PRICE ($) FY Close	P/E High/Low		PER SHARE ($) Earnings	Dividends	Book Value
03/21	3.57	0	0	3.43	0.14	64.91
03/20	2.88	0	0	4.00	0.14	62.81
03/19	3.60	0	0	4.14	0.12	63.31
03/18	4.13	0	0	3.80	0.12	64.97
03/17	3.45	0	0	2.84	0.12	57.59
Annual Growth	0.9%	—	—	4.8%	3.7%	3.0%

Sun Life Financial Inc

Sun Life Financial offers insurance wealth and asset management products to individuals and business entities in Canada the US and Asia as well as Europe. Sun Life's products include individual and group life and health insurance individual and group annuities group pensions mutual funds and asset management services. The US subsidiaries include Massachusetts Financial Services Company Ryan Labs Asset Management and Prime Advisors. Sun Life's products and services are distributed through direct and independent sales agents and advisors as well as banks and consultants. With almost 126000 advisors Sun Life has about $1.1 trillion assets under management.

Operations

Sun Life Financial operates through five business segment: Sun Life Financial Canada (about 50% of total revenue) Sun Life Financial U.S. (around 20%) Sun Life Financial Asia (some 15%) Sun Life Financial Asset Management (more than 10% of total revenue) and Corporate (less than 5%).

Sun Life Financial's Canada segment (SLF Canada) operates through three business units: Individual Insurance & Wealth Group Retirement Services and Group Benefits. The Individual Insurance & Wealth unit provides insurance and investment products to individuals and families. Group Retirement Services provides pension plans and defined benefit solutions to employers while Group Benefits offers life dental extended health care disability and critical illness and other insurance products to employers.

The Sun Life Financial's U.S. operates through Group Benefits and In-force Management. The Group Benefits unit offers life disability absence management medical stop-loss dental vision and voluntary insurance products. In-force Management provides more than 100000 individual life insurance policies.

Sun Life Financial's Asset Management operates through MFS Investment Management and SLC Management. MFS Investment Management manages assets for institutional and retail investors; it has more than $527 million in assets under management. SLC Management delivers LDI alternative fixed income and real estate products in the US and Canada.

Sun Life Financial's Asia operates through two business units: Insurance and Wealth and International. The Insurance and Wealth unit offers a variety of financial planning products in seven Asian markets. International serves wealthy individuals outside of the US and Canada.

The Corporate segment includes the UK business (a run-off block of life and pension policies) and Corporate Support.

Geographic Reach

Sun Life has operations in a number of markets worldwide including Canada (its home market) the United States the United Kingdom Ireland Hong Kong the Philippines Japan Indonesia India China Australia Singapore Vietnam Malaysia and Bermuda.

Sales and Marketing

Sun Life Financial distributes its products through its own career sales force and through independent brokers sales representatives independent advisors and benefits consultants among others.

Financial Performance

Note: Growth rates may differ after conversion to US Dollars.

Sun Life Financial's revenue increased 47% in 2019 to $39.7 billion compared to 2018 primarily driven by increases in the fair value in FVTPL assets predominantly due to the impact of interest rates as well as equity market movements and increased net premium revenue in Canada Asia and the US. The impacts of foreign exchange translation increased revenue by $422 million.

Net income increased 4% in 2019 to $2.6 billion driven by less unfavorable assumption changes and management actions impacts partially offset by higher fair value adjustments on MFS's share-based payment awards and unfavorable market-related impacts.

Cash and equivalents at the end of the year were $9.5 billion a $143 million higher from the year prior. Operating activities generated $2.5 billion while investing and financing activities used $430 million and $2.4 billion respectively. Sun Life's main cash uses in 2019 were acquisitions dividends paid and redemption of senior debentures and subordinated debt.

Strategy

Sun Life Financial to provide outstanding value to its clients. The company's strategy places the client at the center of everything it does. Sun Life's four pillar approach defines the businesses and markets in which it competes. Currently in its four pillars Sun Life is a leader in insurance and wealth solutions in its Canadian Home Market; a leader in US group benefits; a leader in Global Asset Management; and a leader in Asia through distribution excellence in higher growth markets.

Sun Life's client-centric strategy has five key areas of focus that the company is pursuing across each of its four pillars. These areas of focus define how the company competes in its markets extends its competitive advantages fulfills its purpose and support its ambition to be one of the best insurance and asset management companies in the world.

One of Sun Life's key areas is its clients. The company is focused on building lasting and trusted client relationships by providing quality products and services that deliver on its purpose. The company achieves this by making it easier to do business with the company; being more proactive in contracting and engaging with its clients; and delivering consistently superior client service.

Another pillar is Distribution Excellence: Sun Life continues to invest in its distribution capabilities through digital channels and by enabling its advisors agents partners and brokers to deliver great client experiences and focus on meeting client needs.

For its Digital Data & Analytics Sun Life is investing in new capabilities across its businesses to reach its clients more effectively drive efficiencies and explore new business opportunities. Its focus in these areas is to digitize current processes and interactions; be more proactive predictive and personalized with its clients; and build and deploy new digital business models.

For its Financial Discipline Sun Life is focusing on delivering strong earnings growth and disciplined expense management to support the enterprise's medium-term objectives; and create a culture of accountability purpose and passion for long-term client and business value embodied by all employees including a strong focus on efficient use of resources to drive top and bottom line growth.

Lastly for its Talent and Culture Sun Life maintains its focus on attracting retaining and developing the best talent while also continuing to evolve its talent and culture to manage the increasing pace of change. Its talent goals are to continue to attract a disproportionate share of top talent across its geographies wrapped in an empowering culture; build on its high performance culture and support and reward its diverse talented workforce; ensure that its focus on its clients becomes deeply embedded in its unique and inclusive culture; and remain committed to the highest standards of business ethics and good governance.

Mergers and Acquisitions

In 2021 Sun Life Financial acquires 51% majority stake of US-based Crescent Capital Group a global alternative credit investment manager for up to US$338 million (approximately C$450 million). Crescent will form part of SLC Management Sun Life's alternatives asset management business. The acquisition will extend SLC Management's solutions in alternative credit which will benefit existing and prospective clients.

In 2020 Sun Life Financial completed the acquisition of majority stake of UK-based InfraRed a global infrastructure and real estate manager for cash consideration of 300 million (approximately US$390 million C$515 million). InfraRed advises institutional and pooled fund Clients on approximately US$12 billion (C$17 billion) in assets under management. InfraRed will be part of SLC Management Sun Life's alternatives asset management business. The acquisition will broaden SLC Management's investment solutions for institutional Clients to include infrastructure equity and advance sustainable investment options.

In 2019 Sun Life Financial completed the acquisition of majority stake BentallGreenOak. The acquisition adds organizational depth and a full spectrum of solutions including equity and debt real estate strategies while adding to the capabilities of its alternatives manager SLC Management.

Company Background

Sun Life was founded in 1865. It demutualized in 2000 and the money it raised as a publicly traded company helped finance growth. During the first 10 years of its public status it grew through a steady pace of acquisitions beginning with its buy of Clarica Life in 2002. Clarica's products were later rebranded with the Sun Life name. International acquisitions have included Assurant Employee Benefits (2016) Genworth's US employee benefits group (2007) and insurance and pension operations in Hong Kong from Commonwealth Bank of Australia (2005).

EXECUTIVES

Executive Vice President, Chief Risk Officer, Colm Freyne, $427,593 total compensation

Independent Director, Deepak Chopra

Independent Non-Executive Chairman of the Board, William Anderson

Independent Director, Barbara Stymiest

President - Sun Life U.S, Daniel Fishbein, $594,290 total compensation

Independent Director, Stephanie Coyles

Executive Vice President - Corporate Strategy and Global Marketing, Linda Dougherty

Independent Director, Margaret Harris

Independent Director, Ashok Gupta

Executive Vice President, Chief Information Officer, Laura Money

Chief Financial Officer, Executive Vice President, Manjit Singh

Independent Director, David Ho

Director, Marie-lucie Morin

Director, Helen Hicks

Chief Executive Officer of Sun Life Vietnam, Nhon Ly Luc

President - SLC Management, Stephen Peacher, $580,058 total compensation

Independent Director, Martin Glynn

Executive Vice President, Chief Legal and Public Affairs Officer, Melissa Kennedy

Independent Director, Scott Powers

President - Sun Life Canada, Jacques Goulet, $438,867 total compensation

Executive Vice President, Chief Human Resource and Communications Officer, Helena Pagano

President, Chief Executive Officer, Director, Kevin Strain, $476,156 total compensation

Auditors: Deloitte LLP

LOCATIONS

HQ: Sun Life Financial Inc
1 York Street, Toronto, Ontario M5J 0B6
Phone: 416 979-9966 **Fax:** 416 979-3209
Web: www.sunlife.com

PRODUCTS/OPERATIONS

2018 Sales by Segment

	% of total
SLF Canada	56
SLF U.S.	19
SLF Asset Management	15
SLF Asia	9
Corporate	1
Total	**100**

COMPETITORS

AMERICAN NATIONAL INSURANCE COMPANY
CANNAE HOLDINGS INC.
CLAYTON DUBILIER & RICE INC.
China Life Insurance Company Limited
DAIDO LIFE INSURANCE COMPANY
EUROMONEY INSTITUTIONAL INVESTOR PLC
Enstar Group Limited
Great-West Lifeco Inc
Kyobo Life Insurance Co. Ltd.
NIPPON LIFE INSURANCE COMPANY
Power Corporation of Canada
VOYA FINANCIAL INC.

HISTORICAL FINANCIALS

Company Type: Public

Income Statement				FYE: December 31
	ASSETS ($ mil.)	NET INCOME ($ mil.)	INCOME AS % OF ASSETS	EMPLOYEES
12/21	271,166	3,168	1.2%	24,589
12/20	253,690	1,961	0.8%	23,816
12/19	228,232	2,083	0.9%	40,600
12/18	199,610	1,921	1.0%	22,318
12/17	214,666	1,788	0.8%	21,495
Annual Growth	**6.0%**	**15.4%**	**—**	**3.4%**

2021 Year-End Financials

Return on assets: 1.2%
Return on equity: 14.9%
Long-term debt ($ mil.): —
No. of shares (mil.): 586
Sales ($ mil): 28,020

Dividends
Yield: 3.3%
Payout: 48.0%
Market value ($ mil.): 32,634

	STOCK PRICE ($) FY Close	P/E High/Low		PER SHARE ($) Earnings	Dividends	Book Value
12/21	55.69	8	7	5.25	1.85	37.53
12/20	44.46	13	7	3.22	1.64	34.68
12/19	45.57	11	8	3.38	1.58	31.99
12/18	33.19	10	8	3.04	1.47	30.15
12/17	41.26	12	10	2.78	1.39	30.01
Annual Growth	**7.8%**	**—**	**—**	**17.2%**	**7.3%**	**5.7%**

Sunac China Holdings Ltd

Auditors: PricewaterhouseCoopers

LOCATIONS

HQ: Sunac China Holdings Ltd
10/F, Building C7, Magnetic Plaza, Binshuixi Road, Nankai District, Tianjin 300381
Phone:
Web: www.sunac.com.cn

HISTORICAL FINANCIALS

Company Type: Public

Income Statement				FYE: December 31
	REVENUE ($ mil.)	NET INCOME ($ mil.)	NET PROFIT MARGIN	EMPLOYEES
12/19	24,333	3,740	15.4%	50,834
12/18	18,136	2,408	13.3%	38,040
12/17	10,122	1,690	16.7%	19,271
12/16	5,089	356	7.0%	13,294
12/15	3,543	507	14.3%	8,271
Annual Growth	**61.9%**	**64.7%**	**—**	**57.5%**

2019 Year-End Financials

Debt ratio: 4.8%
Return on equity: 35.1%
Cash ($ mil.): 11,201
Current ratio: 1.17
Long-term debt ($ mil.): 26,808

No. of shares (mil.): —
Dividends
Yield: —
Payout: 20.8%
Market value ($ mil.): —

Suncor Energy Inc

Suncor Energy is strategically focused on developing one of the world's largest petroleum resource basins ? Canada's Athabasca oil sands. Suncor explores for acquires develops produces and markets crude oil in Canada and internationally; the company transports and refines crude oil and markets petroleum and petrochemical products primarily in Canada. Suncor also operates a renewable energy business and conducts energy trading activities focused principally on the marketing and trading of crude oil natural gas byproducts refined products and power. Suncor reported gross proved and probable reserves of 6.7 billion barrels of oil equivalent.

Operations

Suncor operates in three main segments: Oil Sands Exploration and Production (E&P); and Refining and Marketing.

Suncor's Oil Sands segment (nearly 40% of total revenue) with assets located in the Athabasca oil sands of northeast Alberta produces bitumen from mining and in situ operations. Bitumen is either upgraded into SCO for refinery feedstock and diesel fuel or blended with diluent for refinery feedstock or direct sale to market through the company's midstream infrastructure and its marketing activities. The segment includes the marketing supply transportation and risk management of crude oil natural gas power and byproducts.

Suncor's E&P segment (some 5%) consists of offshore operations off the east coast of Canada and in the North Sea the Norwegian Sea and the Norwegian North Sea and onshore assets in Libya and Syria. This segment also includes the marketing and risk management of crude oil and natural gas.

Suncor's Refining and Marketing segment accounts for about 55% of total revenue consists of two primary operations the refining and supply and marketing operations discussed below as well as the infrastructure supporting the marketing supply and risk management of refined products crude oil natural gas power and byproducts. This segment also includes the trading of crude oil refined products natural gas and power.

Geographic Reach
The company has operations in Canada Germany Libya the Norway Syria the UK and the US. Canada accounted for about 85% of Suncor Energy's revenues.

Sales and Marketing
The company's primary markets for synthetic oil and bitumen production from Suncor's Oil Sands segment including PFT bitumen from Fort Hills include refining operations in Alberta Ontario Quebec the US Midwest and the US Rocky Mountain regions and markets on the US Gulf Coast. Diesel production from upgrading operations is sold primarily in Western Canada and the US.

Oil and gas production from East Coast Canada and Offshore U.K. & Norwayis either marketed by the company's Energy Trading business acting as a marketing agent or sold to its Energy Trading business which then markets the products to customers under direct sales arrangements.

Suncor's retail service station network operates nationally in Canada primarily under the Petro-Canada brand. This network consists of more than 1560outlets across Canada. In addition refined products are marketed through independent dealers and joint arrangements. Suncor's Canadian retail network had annual sales of gasoline motor fuels averaging approximately 4.1 million liters per site.

Suncor's Colorado retail network consists of some 45 owned or leased Shell Exxon or Mobil branded outlets. Suncor also has product supply agreements with about 135 Shell-branded sites in both Colorado and Wyoming and with more than 60 Exxon and Mobil-branded sites in Colorado.

Suncor's wholesale operations sell refined products into farm home heating paving small industrial commercial and truck markets. Through its PETRO-PASS network Suncor is a national marketer to the commercial road transport segment in Canada. Suncor also sells refined products directly to large industrial and commercial customers and independent marketers.

Financial Performance
The company's revenue for fiscal 2020 decreased to $25.1 billion compared from the prior year with $39.0 billion.

Net loss for fiscal 2020 increased to $4.3 billion compared from the prior year with a net income of $2.9 billion.

Cash held by the company at the end of fiscal 2020 decreased to $1.9 billion. Cash provided by operations and financing activities were $2.7 billion

and $1.8 billion respectively. Cash used for investing activities was $4.5 billion mainly for capital and exploration expenditures.

Strategy
Following a successful commercial-scale evaluation in 2018 the company began a phased implementation of AHS at its operated mine sites. AHS were deployed at the North Steepbank mine in 2018 and at Fort Hills in 2020. Full implementation at the Oil Sands Base Millennium mine is expected to be completed in 2024. Autonomous haul trucks which operate using GPS wireless communication and perceptive technologies have demonstrated an ability to maneuver safely effectively and efficiently in Suncor's operating environment and offer a number of advantages over existing truck and shovel operations including enhanced safety performance better operating efficiency and lower operating costs.

Company Background
To focus on its growth markets and to pay down debt in 2013 the company agreed to sell its conventional natural gas business in Western Canada to a Centrica and Qatar Petroleum partnership for $1 billion.

To further develop its oil sands assets in 2010 the company formed a strategic alliance with TOTAL. As part of the deal France-based TOTAL paid Suncor Energy about $1.7 billion to acquire 19% of Suncor Energy's 60% interest in the Fort Hills mining project and a 49% stake in the Voyageur Upgrader project near Fort McMurray. Suncor Energy acquired about 37% of TOTAL's stake in the Joslyn project.

Boosting its profile as an integrated energy company in 2009 the company acquired Petro-Canada in a $15 billion deal. The acquisition created an energy behemoth with extensive holdings in oil sands solid conventional exploration and production assets and a major refining and retailing network. Following the Petro-Canada deal the company divested about $1.5 billion of non-core assets in Western Canada the US Trinidad and Tobago and the North Sea. In 2010 Suncor Energy sold its North Sea exploration assets (of Petro Canada Netherlands) to Dana Petroleum for $393 million. Later that year it sold a pair of natural gas properties in Alberta to a subsidiary of Abu Dhabi National Energy Company for $285 million. It also sold its Wildcat Hills assets which produce some 80 million cu. ft. of natural gas per day to Direct Energy for about $360 million.

EXECUTIVES
President, Chief Executive Officer, Director, Mark Little, $738,803 total compensation
Chief People Officer, Paul Gardner
Executive Vice President - Downstream, Kristopher Smith, $431,509 total compensation
Chief Transformation Officer, Bruno Francoeur
Executive Vice President - Upstream, Michael MacSween, $431,509 total compensation
Independent Chairman of the Board, Michael Wilson
Chief Financial Officer, Alister Cowan, $452,893 total compensation
Independent Director, Patricia Bedient
Auditors: KPMG LLP

LOCATIONS
HQ: Suncor Energy Inc
    150 - 6th Avenue S.W., Calgary, Alberta T2P 3E3
Phone: 403 296-8000
Web: www.suncor.com

COMPETITORS
CNOOC Petroleum North   IDEMITSU KOSAN CO.LTD.

America ULC
DELEK US ENERGY INC.
DELEK US HOLDINGS INC.
ENTERPRISE PRODUCTS PARTNERS L.P.
EXXON MOBIL CORPORATION
Equinor ASA
GENESIS ENERGY L.P.
HOLLYFRONTIER CORPORATION
MARATHON PETROLEUM CORPORATION
NOBLE ENERGY INC.
NUSTAR ENERGY L.P.
PHILLIPS 66
VALERO ENERGY CORPORATION
WESTERN REFINING INC.

HISTORICAL FINANCIALS
Company Type: Public

Income Statement — FYE: December 31

	REVENUE ($ mil.)	NET INCOME ($ mil.)	NET PROFIT MARGIN	EMPLOYEES
12/20	19,675	(3,392)	—	12,591
12/19	29,941	2,226	7.4%	12,889
12/18	28,628	2,418	8.4%	12,480
12/17	25,666	3,556	13.9%	12,381
12/16	20,011	330	1.7%	12,837
Annual Growth	(0.4%)	—	—	(0.5%)

2020 Year-End Financials

Debt ratio: 17.4%
Return on equity: (-11.0%)
Cash ($ mil.): 1,480
Current ratio: 0.89
Long-term debt ($ mil.): 10,847
No. of shares (mil.): 1,525
Dividends
  Yield: 4.9%
  Payout: —
Market value ($ mil.): 25,592

	STOCK PRICE ($) FY Close	P/E High/Low		PER SHARE ($) Earnings	Dividends	Book Value
12/20	16.78	—	—	(2.22)	0.82	18.41
12/19	32.80	19	15	1.43	1.26	21.08
12/18	27.97	20	13	1.48	1.10	20.39
12/17	36.72	14	11	2.14	1.02	22.06
12/16	32.69	118	76	0.21	0.86	19.86
Annual Growth	(15.4%)	—	—	—	(1.1%)	(1.9%)

Suncorp Group Ltd.

Suncorp-Metway (aka Suncorp Group) wants to be a rising star in Australia's insurance and banking sectors. The group owns Suncorp Insurance which operates one of the country's largest general insurance companies as well as a small but growing life insurance and wealth management business. The general insurance business sells personal and commercial property/casualty insurance under its Suncorp AAMI GIO Vero and Shannons brands. In addition to its insurance business Suncorp also runs Suncorp Bank an operator of some 200 branches in eastern Australia. Among other products the bank offers personal and commercial banking accounts financial planning and loans to consumers and small to midsized businesses.
Auditors: KPMG

LOCATIONS
HQ: Suncorp Group Ltd.
    Level 28, Brisbane Square, 266 George Street, Brisbane, Queensland 4000
Phone: (61) 7 3362 1222   **Fax:** (61) 7 3135 2940
Web: www.suncorpgroup.com.au

PRODUCTS/OPERATIONS

2013 Sales

	% of total
General Insurance	
Personal	35
Commercial	23
Banking	19
Life and Wealth Management	13
New Zealand General Insurance	10
Total	**100**

Selected Subsidiaries

Asteron Group Ltd. (life insurance)
GIO General Ltd (general insurance products)
Suncorp Life & Superannuation Limited life (insurance products)
Suncorp Metway Insurance Ltd (general insurance products)
Suncorp Metway Investment Management Limited (investment schemes and provides investment management services)
Vero Insurance Ltd. (New Zealand general insurance)

COMPETITORS

BAKER BOYER BANCORP	TRAVELERS INSURANCE
BNCCORP INC.	COMPANY LIMITED
Cathay Life Insurance	UNIGARD INSURANCE
Co.Ltd.	COMPANY
EXTRACO CORPORATION	
PRINCETON NATIONAL	
BANCORP INC.	

HISTORICAL FINANCIALS

Company Type: Public

Income Statement
FYE: June 30

	ASSETS ($ mil.)	NET INCOME ($ mil.)	INCOME AS % OF ASSETS	EMPLOYEES
06/21	72,701	775	1.1%	13,505
06/20	65,611	625	1.0%	13,500
06/19	67,425	122	0.2%	0
06/18	73,346	781	1.1%	0
06/17	74,613	825	1.1%	0
Annual Growth	(0.6%)	(1.6%)	—	—

2021 Year-End Financials

Return on assets: 1.0%
Return on equity: 7.8%
Long-term debt ($ mil.): —
No. of shares (mil.): 1,282
Sales ($ mil): 10,648

Dividends
  Yield: 2.2%
  Payout: 38.5%
Market value ($ mil.): 10,623

	STOCK PRICE ($) FY Close	P/E High/Low		PER SHARE ($) Earnings	Dividends	Book Value
06/21	8.28	10	7	0.58	0.19	7.85
06/20	6.42	13	7	0.47	0.14	6.83
06/19	9.51	81	61	0.09	0.55	7.08
06/18	10.91	13	11	0.59	0.60	7.97
06/17	11.29	14	11	0.63	0.00	8.19
Annual Growth	(7.5%)	—	—	(2.3%)	—	(1.0%)

Suning.com Co Ltd

Auditors: PricewaterhouseCoopers

LOCATIONS

HQ: Suning.com Co Ltd
No. 68, Huaihai Road, Nanjing, Jiangsu Province 210005
Phone: (86) 25 84418888   **Fax:** (86) 25 84467008
Web: www.cnsuning.com

HISTORICAL FINANCIALS

Company Type: Public

Income Statement
FYE: December 31

	REVENUE ($ mil.)	NET INCOME ($ mil.)	NET PROFIT MARGIN	EMPLOYEES
12/20	38,575	(653)		0
12/19	38,692	1,414	3.7%	0
12/18	35,613	1,937	5.4%	0
12/17	28,878	647	2.2%	0
12/16	21,397	101	0.5%	0
Annual Growth	15.9%		—	—

2020 Year-End Financials

Debt ratio: 1.7%
Return on equity: (-5.1%)
Cash ($ mil.): 3,958
Current ratio: 0.86
Long-term debt ($ mil.): 76

No. of shares (mil.): —
Dividends
  Yield: —
  Payout: —
Market value ($ mil.): —

Sunshine City Group Co., Ltd.

Auditors: Fujian Shu Lun Pan Mindu Certified Public Accountants Co., Ltd.

LOCATIONS

HQ: Sunshine City Group Co., Ltd.
22/F Mingliu Building, No. 56, Gutian Road, Fuzhou, Fujian Province 350005
Phone: (86) 591 83353145   **Fax:** (86) 591 88089227

HISTORICAL FINANCIALS

Company Type: Public

Income Statement
FYE: December 31

	REVENUE ($ mil.)	NET INCOME ($ mil.)	NET PROFIT MARGIN	EMPLOYEES
12/20	12,563	798	6.4%	0
12/19	8,773	577	6.6%	0
12/18	8,209	438	5.3%	0
12/17	5,096	316	6.2%	0
12/16	2,822	177	6.3%	0
Annual Growth	45.3%	45.7%	—	—

2020 Year-End Financials

Debt ratio: 4.4%
Return on equity: 18.1%
Cash ($ mil.): 7,615
Current ratio: 1.38
Long-term debt ($ mil.): 11,086

No. of shares (mil.): —
Dividends
  Yield: —
  Payout: —
Market value ($ mil.): —

Surgutneftegas PJSC

Based in the Siberian provincial city of Surgut Surgutneftegas is one of Russia's top-five integrated oil and natural gas companies accounting for more than 10% of the country's oil production. Surgutneftegas assets include pipelines refineries oil storage tanks and about 300 gas stations. The company also constructs power transmission lines and builds roads as part of its business operations.

Operations are concentrated on the Russian regions of Western Siberia Eastern Siberia and Timano-Pechora. More than 70% of the company's sales comes from the domestic Russian market.

Operations

Surgutneftegas reports four core operations: Hydrocarbon Exploration and Production Manufacturing and Marketing of Oil Products Production of Petrochemicals and Gas Processing and Power Generation. The company reports its revenue under two broad segments: Exploration and Production accounts for almost 60% of total sales with the rest listed under Refining and Sale activities.

Its leading segment Exploration and Production engages in prospecting exploration and operation of oil and gas fields. Manufacturing and Marketing manages crude oil refining production of oil products and wholesale and retail trade in oil products. Hydrocarbons are converted into raw materials for chemicals under the Production of Petrochemicals segment. Lastly the segment Gas Processing and Power Generation includes processing of petroleum gas sale of commercial gas and liquid hydrocarbons and construction and operation of gas turbine power plants.

Geographic Reach

Surgutneftegas has substantial assets in three of the largest Russian oil and gas provinces? Western Siberia Eastern Siberia and Timano-Pechora. The key areas of hydrocarbon production are Khanty-Manyisky Yamalo-Nenetsky Tyumenskaya Oblast in Western Siberia and the Republic of Sakha in Eastern Siberia. Refining facilities are located in two regions? the oil refinery in the city of Kirishi Leningradskaya Oblast and the gas processing plant in Surgutsky District.

The company's oil products are sold in both wholesale and retail outlets in Saint Petersburg Leningradskaya Tverskaya Novgorodskaya Pskovskaya and Kaliningradskaya Oblasts. Some 30% of the company's sales comes from outside its Russian domestic market.

Sales and Marketing

Surgutneftegas is accreted at two of the biggest Russian exchange platforms: Saint-Petersburg International Mercantile Exchange and Exchange Saint-Petersburg. Wholesale contracts are often long-term. In addition the company has about 300 gas stations across Russia offering retail products.

Financial Performance

Note: Growth rates may differ after conversion to US Dollars.

Revenue for Surgutneftegas in 2017 improved some 15% to RUB 1.17 trillion climbing from RUB 1.02 trillion a year earlier.

In the 2015-17 period the company's operating profit has remained stable despite low oil prices and restricted production requirements by the OPEC. Net income jumped from a loss of RUB 62 billion posted in 2016 to a profit of RUB 194 billion a year later. The improved result was almost entirely due to a RUB 320 million reduction in net exchange rate differences for 2017.

The company's cash and cash equivalents surged by RUB 110 billion ending 2017 with $217 billion on hand. Cash from operations generated $356 billion while cash from investing used $290 billion ($160 billion on CAPEX). Financing activities saw a positive cash inflow of $43 million.

Strategy

As one of Russia's top five oil companies Surgutneftegas aims to maintain its upstream portfolio through new property leasing expand its midstream production output and stimulate growth that's led by R&D.

To replenish its production resource base Surgutneftegas secures new licenses for exploration or geological studies especially in the Western and Eastern Siberia. But a declining trend in the production rate of the company's mature oil fields in Western Siberia is a concern for the company.

The company also invests heavily on its refineries especially the KINEF facility. It completed the construction of a large high-octane gasoline plant there. These growth projects allow Surgutneftegas to remain a major producer of oil products in Saint Petersburg and neighboring states.

Organically the company grows through in-house research spending (96 projects carried out in 2017 in fields like oil recovery and field development) and cost reduction programs (RUB 5.3 billion in 2017).

Despite stringent growth efforts adverse external factors negatively affected the company. In 2017 it produced 60.5 mt of refined products (61.8 mt in 2016) due to OPEC constraints. Surgutneftgas like all Russian oil companies is also heavily dependent on government tax breaks for posting profits?more than half of the company's net income in 2017 came from it?that makes it vulnerable to changes in politics.

Company Background

Surgutneftegas traces its roots back to the 1970s when petroleum production associations were established in Surgut Nizhnevartovsk and Nefteyugansk. A 1992 reorganization led to the merger of Surgutneftegas with Kirishi oil refinery and petroleum product suppliers in Northwest Russia. The very next year it became a joint stock company as part of the privatization effort of Russia's oil industry.

The company takes pride in transforming some of the remotest parts of Russia into profitable oil and gas fields.

EXECUTIVES

Director, Viktor Krivosheev
Vice Chairperson of the Board of Directors, Nikolai Matveev
General Director (CEO), Director, Vladimir Bogdanov
Chairperson of the Board of Directors, Vladimir Erokhin
Director, Chief Engineer – First Deputy General Director, Alexander Bulanov
Auditors: Crowe Expertiza LLC

LOCATIONS

HQ: Surgutneftegas PJSC
ul.Grigoriya Kukuyevitskogo 1, bld. 1, Surgut, Khanty-Mansiysky Autonomous Okrug-Yugra, Tyumenskaya Oblast 628415
Phone: (7) 3462 42 60 28
Web: www.surgutneftegas.ru

2017 Sales

	% of total
Domestic market	72
Export	28
Total	**100**

PRODUCTS/OPERATIONS

2017 Sales

	% of total
Exploration and Production	61
Refining and Sale	39
Total	**100**

COMPETITORS

CONOCOPHILLIPS
Canadian Natural Resources Ltd
China National Offshore Oil Corporation
ECOPETROL S A
ENEOS HOLDINGS INC.
ISRAMCO INC.

LUKOIL PAO
OMV Aktiengesellschaft
Petr leos Mexicanos E.P.E.
REPSOL SA.
ROYAL DUTCH SHELL plc
Suncor Energy Inc

HISTORICAL FINANCIALS

Company Type: Public

Income Statement

FYE: December 31

	REVENUE ($ mil.)	NET INCOME ($ mil.)	NET PROFIT MARGIN	EMPLOYEES
12/20	14,373	9,930	69.1%	113,000
12/19	25,240	1,705	6.8%	114,000
12/18	22,325	12,200	54.7%	115,000
12/17	20,324	3,366	16.6%	116,000
12/16	16,671	(1,014)	—	114,275
Annual Growth	**(3.6%)**	**—**		**(0.3%)**

2020 Year-End Financials

Debt ratio: —	No. of shares (mil.): —
Return on equity: 15.4%	Dividends
Cash ($ mil.): 18,916	Yield: 2.3%
Current ratio: 7.10	Payout: 48.6%
Long-term debt ($ mil.): —	Market value ($ mil.): —

	STOCK PRICE ($) FY Close	P/E High/Low		Earnings	PER SHARE ($) Dividends	Book Value
12/20	5.51	0	0	0.26	0.13	1.97
12/19	6.21	3	2	0.04	1.16	2.04
12/18	5.49	0	0	0.32	0.21	1.81
12/17	4.91	1	1	0.09	0.10	1.75
12/16	5.13	—	—	(0.03)	1.10	1.57
Annual Growth	**1.8%**			**—**	**(41.2%)**	**5.7%**

Suruga Bank, Ltd.

Just like its namesake bay at the foot of Mount Fuji Suruga Bank wants to be deep and wide. Formed in 1895 the bank serves the greater Tokyo area through more than 125 branches. It offers mortgage loans personal loans credit cards and wealth management products deposit products home loans for foreign residents asset management and small and medium enterprise (SME) lending services. It caters to SME markets targeting the self-employed working women senior citizens and the newly wealthy. Through an alliance with Japan Post Bank it expanded its consumer loans business. Under the deal Japan Post (with its branch network of more than 230 locations) handles home loans in partnership with Suruga.

EXECUTIVES

Independent Director, Emi Noshita
Independent Director, Yoichi Namekata
Director, Yugo Minemura
Independent Director, Yoriyuki Kusaki
Independent Director, Yasumine Satake
Director, Kazumasa Itakura
Vice President, Representative Director, Kosuke Kato
President, Representative Director, Kosuke Saga
Managing Director, Tomoaki Tsutsumi
Director, Tomoki Toya
Auditors: Ernst & Young ShinNihon LLC

LOCATIONS

HQ: Suruga Bank, Ltd.
23 Toriyoko-cho, Numazu, Shizuoka 410-8689
Phone: (81) 55 962 0080
Web: www.surugabank.co.jp

COMPETITORS

AOZORA BANK LTD. THE
AUSTRALIA AND NEW ZEALAND BANKING GROUP LIMITED
HANG SENG BANK LIMITED
UniCredit Bank AG

HISTORICAL FINANCIALS

Company Type: Public

Income Statement

FYE: March 31

	ASSETS ($ mil.)	NET INCOME ($ mil.)	INCOME AS % OF ASSETS	EMPLOYEES
03/21	32,065	193	0.6%	2,280
03/20	32,073	233	0.7%	2,514
03/19	30,957	(877)	—	2,645
03/18	42,016	65	0.2%	2,661
03/17	39,995	381	1.0%	2,743
Annual Growth	**(5.4%)**	**(15.6%)**		**(4.5%)**

2021 Year-End Financials

Return on assets: 0.6%	Dividends
Return on equity: 7.9%	Yield: —
Long-term debt ($ mil.): —	Payout: —
No. of shares (mil.): 231	Market value ($ mil.): 9,324
Sales ($ mil.): 907	

	STOCK PRICE ($) FY Close	P/E High/Low		Earnings	PER SHARE ($) Dividends	Book Value
03/21	40.25	—	—	0.84	0.45	11.14
03/20	40.25	0	0	1.01	0.05	10.21
03/19	227.00	—	—	(3.79)	0.94	9.40
03/18	227.00	8	8	0.28	2.12	13.93
03/17	220.65	1	1	1.65	1.80	13.05
Annual Growth (3.9%)	**(34.6%)**			**—**	**(15.6%)(29.3%)**	

Suzuken Co Ltd

Auditors: Deloitte Touche Tohmatsu LLC

LOCATIONS

HQ: Suzuken Co Ltd
8 Higashi-Katahamachi, Higashi-ku, Nagoya, Aichi 461-8701
Phone: (81) 52 961 2331
Web: www.suzuken.co.jp

HISTORICAL FINANCIALS

Company Type: Public

Income Statement

FYE: March 31

	REVENUE ($ mil.)	NET INCOME ($ mil.)	NET PROFIT MARGIN	EMPLOYEES
03/21	19,223	71	0.4%	18,305
03/20	20,391	259	1.3%	18,998
03/19	19,254	272	1.4%	19,122
03/18	20,002	177	0.9%	19,459
03/17	19,024	190	1.0%	20,163
Annual Growth	**0.3%**	**(21.8%)**		**(2.4%)**

2021 Year-End Financials

Debt ratio: —
Return on equity: 1.9%
Cash ($ mil.): 1,364
Current ratio: 1.28
Long-term debt ($ mil.): —

No. of shares (mil.): 89
Dividends
  Yield: —
  Payout: —
Market value ($ mil.): —

Suzuki Motor Corp. (Japan)

Suzuki Motor Corporation is one of the leading Japanese carmakers and a global motorcycle manufacturer. Suzuki's passenger car models include the Alto Grand Vitara Swift and SX4. Its motorcycle products include cruiser motocross off-road scooter street and touring models as well as ATVs. Suzuki Motor's non-vehicle products include outboard motors for boats and motorized wheelchairs. It builds its lineup on its own and through numerous subsidiaries and joint ventures overseas. Japan accounts for nearly 35% of sales. Suzuki entered the US car market in 1985 with the Samurai the country's first compact SUV.

Operations

Suzuki divides its operations into three reportable segments: automobile (some 90%) motorcycles (more than 5%) and marine and other.

The group's automobile segment's main products are mini vehicles sub-compact vehicles standard-sized vehicles while its motorcycle products are all-terrain vehicles and motorcycles. The marine and other segment accounts for the remaining revenue and includes outboard motors and houses.

Geographic Reach

Suzuki's products are manufactured in more than 25 companies in about 20 overseas countries and serves more than 210 countries. Outside of Japan (around 35% of its total sales; headquarters) Asian consumers including India represent nearly 45% of its sales whereas North American and European purchases combined account for approximately 15%. Suzuki subsidiary Maruti Suzuki India is one of India's largest passenger car company.

Suzuki is headquartered in Hamamatsu-shi Japan.

Sales and Marketing

Suzuki distributes its products around the world through its dealers distributors and other partners. Some of the group's distributors are Derco Peru Apex Car Rental Uttara Motors Mirkat Lusolanda and Mayfairs W'Sale.

Financial Performance

The group's net sales at the end of 2019 decreased by 10% to 3.5 trillion yen. Sales in Asia decreased by 2% owing to the impact of COVID-19 despite an increase in India

Net income for the year 2019 decreased by 25% to 1342 billion yen compared to the prior year with 178.8 billion yen.

Cash held by the group at the end of 2019 decreased by 127.7 billion yen to 473.1 million. Cash provided by operations was 383.4 billion while cash used for investing and financing activities were 250.8 billion and 256.1 billion yen. Main uses for cash were purchase of short-term investment securities and purchase of convertible bond with stock acquisition rights.

Strategy

The group has established the New Mid-Term Management Plan SUZUKI NEXT 100 - Strengthening of management base toward the 100th anniversary of foundation and the next 100 years a five-year plan from 2015.

The group will be celebrating its 100th anniversary of foundation in 2020. In order for the group to continuously grow for the next 100 years the group will put efforts into strengthening of management base by positioning the next five years as the period to stabilize the foundation of management. The group will tackle as Team Suzuki to globally develop manufacturing base and overhaul working procedure.

HISTORY

In 1909 Michio Suzuki started Suzuki Loom Works in Hamamatsu Japan. The company went public in 1920 and continued producing weaving equipment until the onset of WWII when it began to make war-related products.

Suzuki began developing inexpensive motor vehicles in 1947 and in 1952 it introduced a 36cc engine to motorize bicycles. The company changed its name to Suzuki Motor and launched its first motorcycle in 1954. Suzuki's entry into the minicar market came in 1955 with the Suzulight followed by the Suzumoped (1958) a delivery van (1959) and the Suzulight Carry FB small truck (1961).

Suzuki's triumph in the 1962 50cc-class Isle of Man TT motorcycle race started a string of racing successes that brought international prominence to the Suzuki name. The company established its first overseas plant in Thailand in 1967.

In the 1970s Suzuki met market demand for motorcycles with large engines. Meanwhile a mid-1970s recession and falling demand for low-powered cars in Japan led the minicar industry there to produce two-thirds fewer minicars in 1974 than in 1970. Suzuki responded by pushing overseas beginning auto exports and expanding foreign distribution. In 1975 it started producing motorcycles in Taiwan Thailand and Indonesia.

Suzuki boosted capacity internationally throughout the 1980s through joint ventures. Motorcycle sales in Japan peaked in 1982 then tapered off but enjoyed a modest rebound in the late 1980s. In 1988 the company agreed to handle distribution of Peugeot cars in Japan.

Suzuki and General Motors began their long-standing relationship in 1981 when GM bought a small stake in Suzuki. The company began producing Swift subcompacts in 1983 and sold them through GM as the Chevy Sprint and later the Geo Metro. In 1986 Suzuki and GM of Canada jointly formed CAMI Automotive to produce vehicles including Sprints Metros and Geo Trackers (Suzuki Sidekicks) in Ontario; production began in 1989.

Although sales via GM increased through 1990 US efforts with the Suzuki nameplate faltered shortly after Suzuki formed its US subsidiary in Brea California in 1986. A 1988 Consumer Reports claim that the company's Samurai SUV was prone to rolling over devastated US sales. The next year Suzuki's top US executives quit apparently questioning the company's commitment to the US market.

Suzuki established Magyar Suzuki a joint venture with Hungarian automaker Autokonszern Rt. C. Itoh & Co. and International Finance Corporation in 1991 to begin producing the Swift sedan in Hungary. The company expanded a licensing agreement with a Chinese government partner in 1993 becoming the first Japanese company to take an equity stake in a Chinese carmaking venture. The next year Suzuki introduced the Alto van Japan's cheapest car at just over $5000 and the Wagon R miniwagon which quickly became one of Japan's top-selling vehicles.

In a case that was later overturned a woman was awarded $90 million from Suzuki after being paralyzed in a Samurai rollover in 1990. The company sued Consumers Union publisher of Consumer Reports in 1996 charging it had intended to fix the results in the 1988 Samurai testing.

GM raised its 3% stake in Suzuki to 10% in 1998. The company teamed up with GM and Fuji Heavy Industries (Subaru) in 2000 to develop compact cars for the European market. It was also announced that GM would spend about $600 million to double its stake in Suzuki to 20%. In 2001 Suzuki announced that it had agreed to cooperate with Kawasaki in the development of new motorcycles scooters and ATVs.

The following year Suzuki agreed to take control of Maruti Udyog Ltd. the state-owned India-based car manufacturer in an $80 million rights issue deal.

GM sold almost all of its 20% stake in Suzuki in early 2006 to raise cash for its own beleaguered operations. GM divested the remaining 3% stake in late 2008 for about $230 million as it endured a dire cash crisis.

EXECUTIVES

Independent Director, Hideaki Domichi
Representative Director and President, Toshihiro Suzuki
Representative Director and Senior Technical Executive, Osamu Honda
Independent Director, Osamu Kawamura
Director and Managing Officer, Masahiko Nagao
Director and Managing Officer, Toshiaki Suzuki
Managing Officer, Kinji Saito
Independent Director, Yuriko Kato
Managing Officer, Yukihiro Yamashita
Auditors: Seimei Audit Corp.

LOCATIONS

HQ: Suzuki Motor Corp. (Japan)
300 Takatsuka-cho, Minami-ku, Hamamatsu, Shizuoka 432-8611
Phone: (81) 53 440 2030
Web: www.suzuki.co.jp

2016 Sales

	% of total
Asia	44
Japan	41
Europe	10
Other regions	5
Total	**100**

PRODUCTS/OPERATIONS

2016 Salles

	% of total
Automobiles	91
Motorcycles	7
Marine and power products	2
Total	**100**

List of Items

Automobiles
  Alto/CELERIO
  APV
  Grand Vitara SUV
  Jimny
  Kizashi sport sedan
  Splash
  Swift
  SX4 Crossover Sport SportBack
Motorcycles/ATV
  Cruiser
  Dual purpose
  Motocross
  Offroad
  Scooter
  Sport Enduro Tourer
  Street
  Supersport
Outboard motors
  Carburetor

Electronic
Kerosene O

COMPETITORS

Bayerische Motoren	PEUGEOT SA
Werke AG	RENAULT
FORD MOTOR COMPANY	SUBARU CORPORATION
HONDA MOTOR CO. LTD.	YAMAHA MOTOR CO. LTD.
Hyundai Motor Company	
MITSUBISHI MOTORS	
CORPORATION	

HISTORICAL FINANCIALS

Company Type: Public

Income Statement

FYE: March 31

	REVENUE ($ mil.)	NET INCOME ($ mil.)	NET PROFIT MARGIN	EMPLOYEES
03/21	28,703	1,322	4.6%	103,891
03/20	32,136	1,236	3.8%	102,572
03/19	34,958	1,614	4.6%	101,523
03/18	35,383	2,031	5.7%	93,065
03/17	28,348	1,430	5.0%	86,969
Annual Growth	0.3%	(1.9%)	—	4.5%

2021 Year-End Financials

Debt ratio: 0.1%	No. of shares (mil.): 485
Return on equity: 9.2%	Dividends
Cash ($ mil.): 9,253	Yield: 1.7%
Current ratio: 1.28	Payout: 112.4%
Long-term debt ($ mil.): 1,824	Market value ($ mil.): 88,794

	STOCK PRICE ($) FY Close	P/E High/Low		PER SHARE ($) Earnings	Dividends	Book Value
03/21	182.84	1	0	2.72	3.20	31.38
03/20	94.75	1	0	2.64	2.73	28.23
03/19	177.25	1	0	3.57	2.95	27.25
03/18	217.61	1	0	4.46	2.15	27.66
03/17	168.75	0	0	3.24	1.24	20.40
Annual Growth	2.0%		— —	(4.3%)	26.7%	11.4%

Svenska Handelsbanken

Svenska Handelsbanken is Swedish for universal banking. The group provides corporate and individual clients with deposit products loans credit cards and other banking services. Subsidiaries operate in several related areas including life insurance mortgages pensions fund management and Internet banking. The bank boasts more than 830 branches in 25 countries with most in Sweden the UK Denmark Finland Norway and the Netherlands. Subsidiaries include corporate financing unit Handelsbanken Finans Handelsbanken Asset Management and Handelsbanken Liv. Founded in 1871 the bank's assets now exceed $360 billion.

Operations

The bank operates in seven business segments mostly based on geography. These include branch operation segments in Sweden the UK Denmark Finland Norway and the Netherlands as well as a Capital Markets segment.

The bank made more than 80% of its total revenue in 2014 from interest income mostly from corporate loans and mortgage loans but also from consumer loans. The majority of the remaining revenues came from fee and commission income

from its investment banking and other corporate finance services with a small portion (3% of revenues) coming from its insurance and pensions operations.

Geographic Reach

Svenska Handelsbanken generates more than 60% of its revenue in Sweden while its operations in Norway and the UK each bring in 10% of total revenue. The banks other top markets include Denmark Finland and the Netherlands. It also has a presence in countries including Austria China Hong Kong Russia and the US.

Financial Performance

The bank's net revenues and profits have been on the rise in recent years thanks to a combination of low borrowing rates on deposits growing investment banking and loan business from aggressive branch expansion rising investment gains and strong controls on staffing costs.

Svenska's revenue dipped by 5% to SK$63.5 billion ($8.14 billion) in 2014 despite higher loan volumes mostly as interest margins on loans and securities shrank amidst the low-interest environment. Despite lower revenues the bank's net income rose by 6% to SK$15 billion ($1.9 billion) thanks to a decline in interest expenses on deposits and a slower rise in staff costs.

The bank's operating cash fell by more than 50% to SK$52.8 billion ($6.76 billion) despite higher earnings in 2014 mostly as it used more cash toward loans to the public and other credit institutions.

Strategy

With its focus on being as local to its customer as possible Svenska Handelsbanken continues to grow its digital banking and its physical branch network in new markets around the world. During 2014 the bank opened 24 new branches across several countries including 17 in the UK two in each Norway and the Netherlands and one branch in each of Denmark and Finland.

HISTORY

Svenska Handelsbanken (roughly translated as The Swedish Commercial Bank) was founded as Stockholms Handelsbank in 1871 by former directors of Stockholms Enskilda Bank who lost an internal power struggle. Industrialization in the latter stages of the 19th century saw Stockholms Handelsbank expand nationwide with the bank pursuing an aggressive lending policy. Larger companies required larger financing resulting in smaller local banks running into trouble and forcing them to merge with bigger ones. Through a series of mergers of this kind Stockholms Handelsbank exploded in size and branches increased from seven (all Stockholm-based) to 250 nationwide by 1919. To reflect this growth the company changed its name to Svenska Handelsbanken the same year.

Sweden remained neutral during WWI allowing business to prosper but the depression hit hard. The bank had to write off millions in bad loans and additions to its reserves. During the 1930s Handelsbanken regained stability largely thanks to its geographical diversity; operations in areas with high economic activity made up for struggling regions.

Sweden once again remained neutral during WWII but political uncertainty kept deposits high and it became difficult to maintain profitable loan volumes. In the 1940s Svenska Handelsbanken divested many of its industrial holdings and began to rededicate itself to small- and medium-scale lending.

Through a string of purchases in the 1950s and 1960s the bank became the largest bank in Scandinavia and began looking to expand internationally. Joint ventures and acquisitions saw the company move into other parts of Europe and the US in the 1970s. Nordic American Banking a US subsidiary was set up to handle import and export financing for North and South American clients doing business with Scandinavian countries. The 1980s saw the company establish a merchant-banking subsidiary in London and enter the Asian market forming Svenska Handelsbanken Asia (based in Singapore).

The bank remained acquisitive during the first half of the 1990s including a purchase of life insurance company RKA (later renamed Handelsbanken Liv) and parts of the Finnish Skopbank. In 1996 Handelsbanken acquired Swedish mortgage company Stadshypotek.

During the latter half of the 1990s it ventured into e-business and increased its presence in the Nordic countries and the UK. In 1999 the company acquired the Norwegian Bergensbanken after having been beaten by MeritaNordbanken in the chase for Christiania Bank (which was Norway's second-largest at the time). The next year Handelsbanken acquired Spartacus a Danish consumer finance company. In 2001 it made another Danish purchase Midtbank making it one of Denmark's largest bankers. That year it also acquired Swedish life insurance company SPP.

In 2004 Handelsbanken bought Swedish fund manager XACT Fonder from OMHEX (now OMX).

The company bought Lokallbanken in Denmark in 2008. The deal added about 15 branches to Handelsbanken's network.

EXECUTIVES

Head - Swedish Branch Operations, Michael Green, $853,971 total compensation
Deputy Chairman of the Board, Fredrik Lundberg
Head - Financing, Goran Stille, $716,774 total compensation
Chief Executive Officer, Handelsbanken Norway, Dag Tjernsmo, $434,228 total compensation
Director, Ulf Riese
Chairman of subsidiary, Mikael Hallaker
Acting Head - Handelsbanken Finland, Hanne Katrama
Chief Information Officer (IT and Infrastructure), Mattias Forsberg
Head of Group Communication and Sustainability, Jan Larsson
Independent Director, Jon Baksaas
Head - Handelsbanken Digital, Katarina Ljungqvist, $148,051 total compensation
Company Secretary and Chief Legal Officer, Group Legal, Martin Wasteson
Chief Risk Officer, Group Risk Control, Maria Hedin
Chief Executive Officer, Handelsbanken UK, Mikael Sorensen, $1,020,437 total compensation
Chief Human Resources, Group HR, Magnus Ericson
Chief Executive Officer, Handelsbanken Denmark, Lars Moesgaard, $466,795 total compensation
Chief Financial Crime Prevention Officer, Group Financial Crime Prevention, Hannu Saari
Independent Director, Hans Biorck
Head of Central Sweden, Pontus Ahlund, $579,577 total compensation
Head of Investment Bank, Pal Bergstrom
Head of Capital Markets, Dan Lindwall
Head, Handelsbanken Southern UK, John Hodson
Head, Handelsbanken South West UK, Chris Teasdale
Head, Handelsbanken Yorkshire and North East UK, Suzanne Minifie
Chief Compliance Officer, Martin Noreus
Deputy Director - Employee representative, Stefan Henricson
Independent Director, Arja Taaveniku

Director - Employee representative, Lena Renstroem
Deputy Director - Employee representative, Charlotte Uriz
Director - Employee representative, Anna Hjelmberg
Chairman of the Board, Paer Boman
President, Group Chief Executive Officer, Director, Carina Akerstroem, $1,356,964 total compensation
Chief Operating Officer, Handelsbanken Sweden, Katarina Berner Frosdal, $853,971 total compensation
Independent Director, Kerstin Hessius
Head, Handelsbanken South East Sweden, Anders Fagerdahl
Auditors: Ernst & Young AB

LOCATIONS

HQ: Svenska Handelsbanken
Kungstradgardsgatan 2, Stockholm SE-106 70
Phone: (46) 8 701 10 00
Web: www.handelsbanken.se

2014 Sales

	% of total
Sweden	63
Norway	10
UK	10
Denmark	6
Finland	6
Netherlands	4
Other countries	1
Total	**100**

PRODUCTS/OPERATIONS

2014 Sales by Segment

	% of total
Branch operations	
Sweden	52
Other countries	33
Capital markets	15
Total	**100**

COMPETITORS

Banque de Montreal	NATWEST GROUP PLC
Bayerische Landesbank PLC	STANDARD CHARTERED
Co ¶perative Rabobank U.A.	Swedbank AB
Danske Bank A/S	U.S. BANCORP
NATIONAL BANK OF GREECE S.A.	UNICREDIT SPA
	UniCredit Bank AG

HISTORICAL FINANCIALS

Company Type: Public

Income Statement				FYE: December 31
	ASSETS ($ mil.)	NET INCOME ($ mil.)	INCOME AS % OF ASSETS	EMPLOYEES
12/20	383,740	1,907	0.5%	12,474
12/19	329,984	1,819	0.6%	12,548
12/18	332,708	1,938	0.6%	12,307
12/17	337,253	1,962	0.6%	11,832
12/16	289,876	1,792	0.6%	11,759
Annual Growth	7.3%	1.6%	—	1.5%

2020 Year-End Financials

Return on assets: 0.5%
Return on equity: 9.3%
Long-term debt ($ mil.): —
No. of shares (mil.): 1,980
Sales ($ mil): 7,342

Dividends
Yield: 0.1%
Payout: 104.1%
Market value ($ mil.): 9,851

STOCK PRICE ($)	P/E		PER SHARE ($)		
FY Close	High/Low		Earnings	Dividends	Book Value
12/20 4.98	1	1	0.96	1.00	10.60
12/19 5.31	1	1	0.92	0.30	8.68
12/18 5.55	1	1	0.99	0.45	8.17
12/17 6.78	1	1	1.00	0.30	8.88
12/16 6.91	1	1	0.92	0.33	7.74
Annual Growth (7.9%)	—	—	1.2%	31.7%	8.2%

Swedbank AB

Auditors: PricewaterhouseCoopers AB

LOCATIONS

HQ: Swedbank AB
Landsvaegen 40, Sundbyberg SE-172 63
Phone: (46) 8 585 900 00   **Fax:** (46) 8 796 80 92
Web: www.swedbank.com

HISTORICAL FINANCIALS

Company Type: Public

Income Statement				FYE: December 31
	ASSETS ($ mil.)	NET INCOME ($ mil.)	INCOME AS % OF ASSETS	EMPLOYEES
12/20	317,568	1,582	0.5%	17,373
12/19	258,880	2,117	0.8%	16,327
12/18	250,923	2,364	0.9%	15,879
12/17	269,687	2,358	0.9%	14,588
12/16	237,652	2,155	0.9%	14,061
Annual Growth	7.5%	(7.4%)	—	5.4%

2020 Year-End Financials

Return on assets: 0.5%
Return on equity: 8.7%
Long-term debt ($ mil.): —
No. of shares (mil.): 1,119
Sales ($ mil): 7,260

Dividends
Yield: 0.0%
Payout: 25.2%
Market value ($ mil.): 19,757

STOCK PRICE ($)	P/E		PER SHARE ($)		
FY Close	High/Low		Earnings	Dividends	Book Value
12/20 17.64	2	1	1.41	0.35	16.96
12/19 14.88	1	1	1.89	1.53	13.32
12/18 22.39	1	1	2.11	1.55	13.75
12/17 24.05	2	1	2.11	1.59	14.60
12/16 24.15	1	1	1.93	1.19	12.86
Annual Growth (7.6%)	—	—	(7.6%)	(26.1%)	7.2%

Swire (John) & Sons Ltd. (United Kingdom)

LOCATIONS

HQ: Swire (John) & Sons Ltd. (United Kingdom)
Swire House, 59 Buckingham Gate, London SW1E 6AJ
Phone:

HISTORICAL FINANCIALS

Company Type: Public

Income Statement				FYE: December 31
	REVENUE ($ mil.)	NET INCOME ($ mil.)	NET PROFIT MARGIN	EMPLOYEES
12/19	22,781	1,035	4.5%	91,022
12/18	21,142	801	3.8%	92,256
12/17	20,891	841	4.0%	94,235
12/16	15,909	49	0.3%	80,820
12/15	13,860	231	1.7%	0
Annual Growth	13.2%	45.4%	—	—

2019 Year-End Financials

Debt ratio: 38.9%
Return on equity: 3.8%
Cash ($ mil.): 4,740
Current ratio: 1.10
Long-term debt ($ mil.): 11,870

No. of shares (mil.): 100
Dividends
Yield: —
Payout: —
Market value ($ mil.): —

Swiss Life (UK) plc (United Kingdom)

Auditors: PricewaterhouseCoopers AG

LOCATIONS

HQ: Swiss Life (UK) plc (United Kingdom)
General-Guisan-Quai 40, P.O. Box 2831, Zurich CH-8022
Phone: (41) 43 284 33 11
Web: www.swisslife.com

HISTORICAL FINANCIALS

Company Type: Public

Income Statement				FYE: December 31
	ASSETS ($ mil.)	NET INCOME ($ mil.)	INCOME AS % OF ASSETS	EMPLOYEES
12/19	235,951	1,240	0.5%	9,330
12/18	216,508	1,093	0.5%	8,624
12/17	218,040	1,031	0.5%	7,979
12/16	196,218	905	0.5%	7,801
12/15	190,566	878	0.5%	7,595
Annual Growth	5.5%	9.0%	—	5.3%

2019 Year-End Financials

Return on assets: 0.5%
Return on equity: 7.6%
Long-term debt ($ mil.): —
No. of shares (mil.): 31
Sales ($ mil): 19,111

Dividends
Yield: —
Payout: —
Market value ($ mil.): —

Swiss Life Holding AG

Auditors: PricewaterhouseCoopers AG

LOCATIONS

HQ: Swiss Life Holding AG
General-Guisan-Quai 40, P.O. Box 2831, Zurich CH-8022
Phone: (41) 43 284 33 11   **Fax:** (41) 43 284 63 11
Web: www.swisslife.com

HISTORICAL FINANCIALS

Company Type: Public

Income Statement FYE: December 31

	REVENUE ($ mil.)	NET INCOME ($ mil.)	NET PROFIT MARGIN	EMPLOYEES
12/20	24,670	1,187	4.8%	9,823
12/19	25,157	1,240	4.9%	9,330
12/18	20,394	1,093	5.4%	8,624
12/17	19,231	1,031	5.4%	7,979
12/16	19,360	905	4.7%	7,801
Annual Growth	6.2%	7.0%	—	5.9%

2020 Year-End Financials

Debt ratio: —
Return on equity: 6.2%
Cash ($ mil.): 8,930
Current ratio: —
Long-term debt ($ mil.): —

No. of shares (mil.): 31
Dividends
  Yield: 1.0%
  Payout: 0.6%
Market value ($ mil.): 721

	STOCK PRICE ($) FY Close	P/E High/Low		PER SHARE ($) Earnings	Dividends	Book Value
12/20	22.67	1	0	37.22	0.24	613.14
12/19	25.34	1	1	37.74	0.53	530.51
12/18	18.70	1	1	32.01	0.63	449.48
12/17	16.94	1	0	30.36	0.51	465.67
12/16	13.88	0	0	26.79	0.38	420.70
Annual Growth	13.0%	—	—	8.6%	(10.8%)	9.9%

Swiss Re Ltd

Auditors: PricewaterhouseCoopers Ltd.

LOCATIONS

HQ: Swiss Re Ltd
  Mythenquai 50/60, Zurich 8022
Phone: (41) 43 285 2121   **Fax:** (41) 43 285 2999
Web: www.swissre.com

HISTORICAL FINANCIALS

Company Type: Public

Income Statement FYE: December 31

	ASSETS ($ mil.)	NET INCOME ($ mil.)	INCOME AS % OF ASSETS	EMPLOYEES
12/20	182,622	(878)	—	13,401
12/19	238,567	727	0.3%	15,401
12/18	207,570	462	0.2%	14,943
12/17	222,526	398	0.2%	14,485
12/16	215,065	3,626	1.7%	14,053
Annual Growth	(4.0%)	—	—	(1.2%)

2020 Year-End Financials

Return on assets: (-0.4%)
Return on equity: (-3.1%)
Long-term debt ($ mil.): —
No. of shares (mil.): 317
Sales ($ mil): 43,338

Dividends
  Yield: 6.3%
  Payout: —
Market value ($ mil.): 7,522

	STOCK PRICE ($) FY Close	P/E High/Low		PER SHARE ($) Earnings	Dividends	Book Value
12/20	23.69	—	—	(3.04)	1.51	85.47
12/19	28.12	11	9	2.39	1.40	89.34
12/18	22.91	19	16	1.37	1.27	82.48
12/17	23.38	24	21	1.03	1.22	97.65
12/16	23.76	2	2	9.82	0.97	109.31
Annual Growth	(0.1%)	—	—	—	11.6%	(6.0%)

SwissCom AG

Auditors: PricewaterhouseCoopers AG

LOCATIONS

HQ: SwissCom AG
  Alte Tiefenaustrasse 6, Worblaufen CH-3048
Phone: (41) 58 221 99 11   **Fax:** (41) 58 221 81 54
Web: www.swisscom.com

HISTORICAL FINANCIALS

Company Type: Public

Income Statement FYE: December 31

	REVENUE ($ mil.)	NET INCOME ($ mil.)	NET PROFIT MARGIN	EMPLOYEES
12/20	12,603	1,737	13.8%	19,062
12/19	11,847	1,729	14.6%	19,317
12/18	11,907	1,552	13.0%	19,845
12/17	11,949	1,608	13.5%	20,506
12/16	11,438	1,575	13.8%	21,127
Annual Growth	2.5%	2.5%	—	(2.5%)

2020 Year-End Financials

Debt ratio: 32.5%
Return on equity: 16.6%
Cash ($ mil.): 386
Current ratio: 0.89
Long-term debt ($ mil.): 6,994

No. of shares (mil.): 51
Dividends
  Yield: 2.7%
  Payout: 4.8%
Market value ($ mil.): 2,784

	STOCK PRICE ($) FY Close	P/E High/Low		PER SHARE ($) Earnings	Dividends	Book Value
12/20	53.75	2	2	33.54	1.46	208.01
12/19	52.86	2	1	33.39	2.20	177.17
12/18	47.95	2	1	29.97	2.30	161.37
12/17	53.33	2	1	31.06	2.25	151.43
12/16	44.74	2	1	30.43	2.14	123.54
Annual Growth	4.7%	—	—	2.5%	(9.1%)	13.9%

T&D Holdings Inc

No mystery in a name here: T&D Holdings serves as the holding company for Japanese insurance companies Taiyo Life and Daido Life. Combined the companies constitute one of Japan's top life insurers. Taiyo Life gears its products to individuals while Daido Life's products are targeted toward small businesses. Another subsidiary T&D Financial Life sells whole life policies through financial institutions the likes of banks securities firms and insurance shop agents. Other businesses under the T&D umbrella include T&D Asset Management T&D Customer Services (administrative services) and Pet & Family (pet insurance) and T&D Information Systems (computer processing).

Operations

T&D Holdings' Taiyo Life division which accounts for 40% of the holding company's annual revenues serves households with comprehensive life products including death benefits and medical or nursing care coverage. Meanwhile the Daido Life unit (another 40% of sales) focuses on the sale of term life insurance and illness policies through business accounts. The third-largest business unit T&D Financial Life sells whole life policies.

Geographic Reach

The company operates in Japan.

Sales and Marketing

The operating units of T&D Holdings use targeted sales techniques. With a focus on selling to housewives and middle-aged women Taiyo Life employs a sales force made up of some 8600 women (similar in age to their target market base) who visit homes to present tailor-made coverage options. Daido Life gears its marketing efforts towards small and midsized businesses by partnering with enterprise associations (such as the National Federation of Corporate Taxpayers Association); it has some 3800 in-house sales representatives. The company's T&D Financial Life unit markets through a network of some 120 agencies including financial institutions.

Financial Performance

In fiscal 2014 (ended March) revenue decreased 14% to 2085 billion as new policy sales in the Taiyo Life and Daido Life units declined. The decline in new policies primarily reflected the impact of an increase in insurance premiums in 2013. It was partially offset by an increase in revenue from T&D Financial Life.

Net income rose 24% to 78.9 billion in fiscal 2014 as provisions for policy and other reserves declined and operating expenses decreased. Cash flow from operations fell 75% to 159 billion.

Strategy

T&D Holdings is seeking to grow by branching out beyond its traditional market segments. Its Taiyo Life unit is working to expand policy sales by marketing policies geared at men and children. Daido Life is adding products for business owners such as living protection coverage while T&D Financial Life is introducing new products for bereaved families and retirees. The group is also seeking to expand its international operations.

T&D Holdings is also growing its operations into the provision of short-term small-amount policies for pet shops. The company seeks to expand in new and existing business fields through alliances and acquisitions as well.

In 2014 Daido Life launched a new whole life product Life Gift which meets the growing demand for inheritance planning as Japan's population ages.

Company Background

T&D Holdings was formed through the merger of Taiyo Life and Daido Life in 2004. The companies first began working together through an alliance formed in 1999.

EXECUTIVES

President of Subsidiary, Director, Naoki Soejima
Vice President, Representative Director, Kanaya Morinaka
Independent Director, Shinnosuke Yamada
President, Representative Director, Hirohisa Uehara
Independent Director, Haruka Matsuyama
Director, Yasuo Teraoka
Managing Executive Officer, Hotaka Nagai
Managing Executive Officer, Tomoyasu Isobe
Senior Managing Executive Officer, Yasuro Tamura
President of Subsidiary, Director, Mutsuro Kitahara
Independent Director, Seiji Higaki
Chairman of Subsidiary, Director, Minoru Kudo
Independent Director, Naoki Ohgo
Managing Executive Officer, Director, Yoshihisa Tanaka
Independent Director, Kensaku Watanabe
Senior Managing Executive Officer, Director, Mitsuhiro Nagata
Director, Junichi Yanai
Auditors: Ernst & Young ShinNihon LLC

LOCATIONS

HQ: T&D Holdings Inc
2-7-1 Nihonbashi, Chuo-ku, Tokyo 103-6031
Phone: (81) 3 3272 6104   **Fax:** (81) 3 3272 6552
Web: www.td-holdings.co.jp

PRODUCTS/OPERATIONS

2014 Sales

	% of total
Daido Life	40
Taiyo Life	37
T&D Financial Life	20
Other	3
Total	**100**

Selected Subsidiaries and Affiliates

AIC Private Equity Fund General Partner Ltd
Alternative Investment Capital Ltd.
Daido Life Insurance Company
Daido Management Service Co. Ltd.
Nihon System Shuno Inc.
Pet & Family Small-amount Short-term Insurance
  Company
T&D Asset Management Cayman Inc.
T&D Asset Management Co. Ltd.
T&D Confirm Ltd.
T&D Customer Services Co. Ltd.
T&D Financial Life Insurance Company
T&D Information System Ltd.
T&D Lease Co. Ltd.
Taiyo Credit Guarantee Co. Ltd.
Taiyo Life Insurance Company
Toyo Insurance Agency Co. Ltd.
Zenkoku Business Center Co. Ltd.

COMPETITORS

AEON CO. LTD.
DAIDO LIFE INSURANCE COMPANY
Extendicare Real Estate Investment Trust
FUKOKU MUTUAL LIFE INSURANCE COMPANY
Kyobo Life Insurance Co. Ltd.
LIVERPOOL VICTORIA FRIENDLY SOCIETY LTD
MITSUBISHI UFJ FINANCIAL GROUP INC.
MIZUHO FINANCIAL GROUP INC.
NIPPON LIFE INSURANCE COMPANY
PERMIRA ADVISERS LLP
SOFTBANK GROUP CORP.

HISTORICAL FINANCIALS

Company Type: Public

Income Statement — FYE: March 31

	ASSETS ($ mil.)	NET INCOME ($ mil.)	INCOME AS % OF ASSETS	EMPLOYEES
03/21	161,457	1,465	0.9%	20,610
03/20	152,188	618	0.4%	20,106
03/19	142,623	657	0.5%	20,576
03/18	143,731	730	0.5%	20,960
03/17	133,186	672	0.5%	21,109
Annual Growth	**4.9%**	**21.5%**	**—**	**(0.6%)**

2021 Year-End Financials

Return on assets: 0.9%
Return on equity: 12.1%
Long-term debt ($ mil.): —
No. of shares (mil.): 591
Sales ($ mil): 20,895
Dividends
 Yield: 3.3%
 Payout: 8.0%
Market value ($ mil.): 3,700

	STOCK PRICE ($) FY Close	P/E High/Low		Earnings	PER SHARE ($) Dividends	Book Value
03/21	6.26	0	0	2.45	0.21	23.62
03/20	3.95	0	0	1.00	0.20	17.11
03/19	5.24	0	0	1.05	0.18	17.01
03/18	8.00	0	0	1.15	0.17	17.39
03/17	7.27	0	0	1.03	0.21	15.47
Annual Growth	**(3.7%)**	**—**	**—**	**24.1%**	**(0.4%)**	**11.2%**

Taisei Corp

Auditors: KPMG AZSA LLC

LOCATIONS

HQ: Taisei Corp
1-25-1 Nishi-Shinjuku, Shinjuku-ku, Tokyo 163-0606
Phone: (81) 3 3348 1111
Web: www.taisei.co.jp

HISTORICAL FINANCIALS

Company Type: Public

Income Statement — FYE: March 31

	REVENUE ($ mil.)	NET INCOME ($ mil.)	NET PROFIT MARGIN	EMPLOYEES
03/19	14,907	1,016	6.8%	18,082
03/18	14,931	1,194	8.0%	17,672
03/17	13,302	810	6.1%	17,933
03/16	13,766	686	5.0%	17,759
03/15	13,112	318	2.4%	17,634
Annual Growth	**3.3%**	**33.7%**	**—**	**0.6%**

2019 Year-End Financials

Debt ratio: 0.1%
Return on equity: 16.2%
Cash ($ mil.): 4,223
Current ratio: 1.30
Long-term debt ($ mil.): 1,142
No. of shares (mil.): 218
Dividends
 Yield: 0.0%
 Payout: —
Market value ($ mil.): 2,617

	STOCK PRICE ($) FY Close	P/E High/Low		Earnings	PER SHARE ($) Dividends	Book Value
03/19	12.00	0	0	4.62	0.31	29.82
03/18	13.00	0	0	5.29	0.26	28.02
03/17	6.92	0	0	3.51	0.22	22.21
03/16	5.95	—	—	2.93	0.11	19.71
03/15	5.95	0	—	1.40	0.07	17.45
Annual Growth	**19.2%**	**—**	**—**	**34.9%**	**46.1%**	**14.3%**

Taiwan Semiconductor Manufacturing Co., Ltd.

Taiwan Semiconductor Manufacturing Co. (TSMC) is the largest dedicated contract semiconductor manufacturer in the world with roughly 50% market share. The company handles manufacturing for semiconductor and integrated device companies that don't have their own manufacturing facilities. Overall it makes which make more than 10760 products using more than 270 technologies for about 500 customers. Taiwan Semiconductor Manufacturing Co's fabless customers include AMD Broadcom NVIDIA and QUALCOMM and among its integrated device manufacturer customers are Broadcom Limited Hisilicon Technologies Co. Ltd. and Intel Corporation. Geographically TSMC has factories in Taiwan China and the US and US customers account for about 60% of revenue.

Operations

Wafer manufacturing makes up more than 85% of sales and Taiwan Semiconductor Manufacturing Co. also makes fabricating masks and provides services such as design probing and testing and assembly. Constituting its largest-selling product logic semiconductors are standard logic devices such as microprocessors microcontrollers digital signal processors graphic chips and chip sets.

About 50% of revenue comes from Smartphone Roughly 30% is from High performance computing Internet of Things generates nearly 10% of revenue and Digital consumer electronics Automotive and Others generates about 5% of revenue each.

Geographic Reach

Taiwan Semiconductor Manufacturing Co. headquartered in Hsinchu City Taiwan has offices around the world. Customers in the US account for about 60% of the company's revenue followed by China with approximately 20% of company's revenue and Taiwan with about 10% of company's revenue.

Most of Taiwan Semiconductor Manufacturing Co.'s production capacity is in Taiwan but it also has facilities in the US Shanghai and Nanjing China.

Sales and Marketing

Taiwan Semiconductor Manufacturing Co.'s revenue is tied to its 10 largest customers who accounts for more than 70% of company's net revenue. The company's largest customer supplies about 25% of revenue. Taiwan Semiconductor Manufacturing Co. Is also a major supplier of chips used in Apple's iPhones and a slowdown in iPhone sales could have an impact of the company. Taiwan Semiconductor Manufacturing Co. spent NT$6 million NT$6 million and NT$6.3 million for marketing expense for fiscal year 2017 2018 and 2019 respectively

Financial Performance

Note: Growth rates may differ after conversion to US Dollars.

The company's revenue increased by 4% compared to 2018 mainly attributed to the growing demand for 7-nanometer products and the depreciation of NT dollar against the US dollar on a weighted average basis from 2018 to 2019 partially offset by the decline in demand for most mature technology products.

Net income decreased about 3%.

Taiwan Semiconductor Manufacturing Co.'s cash and equivalents declined 21% in 2019 from 2018. In 2019 cash from operations increased 5% and the company used 46% more cash for investing activities and 10% more cash for financing activities than in 2019.

Strategy

Taiwan Semiconductor Manufacturing Co. manages its overall capacity and technology upgrade plans based on long term market demand forecasts for its products and services. According to its current market demand forecasts the company intends to maintain the strategy of expanding manufacturing capacity and upgrading manufacturing technologies to meet both the fabrication and the technology needs of customers.

Taiwan Semiconductor Manufacturing Co.'s capital expenditures in 2017 2018 and 2019 were NT$330.6 billion NT$315.6 billion and NT$460.4 billion (US$14.9 billion translated from a weighted average exchange rate of NT$30.90 to US$1.00) respectively. Its capital expenditures in 2020 are expected to be between US$15 billion to US$16 billion which depending on market conditions may be adjusted later. The company's capital expenditures for 2020 are expected to be funded primarily by its operating cash flow and partially by the issuance of corporate bonds. In 2020 Taiwan Semiconductor Manufacturing Co. anticipates its capital expenditures to focus primarily on the following: installing and expanding capacity mainly for 5-nanometer and 3-nanometer nodes; expanding capacity for advanced packaging and mask operations; expanding buildings/facilities for Fab 18 in Southern Taiwan Science Park; and investing in research and development projects for new process technologies.

Company Background

Morris Chang learned early to adapt to rapid change. The future founder and chairman of Taiwan Semiconductor Manufacturing Company (TSMC) lived in six cities before age 18 as his family fled the ravages of the Sino-Japanese War and WWII in China. Chang immigrated to the US to attend MIT and Stanford where he ultimately earned a Ph.D. in electrical engineering.

In 1987 Chang founded TSMC as the world's first dedicated contract semiconductor manufacturer — the first silicon foundry. Chang's pioneering role in the foundry industry has earned him many accolades including the first-ever Robert N. Noyce Medal of the Institute of Electrical and Electronics Engineers and the first-ever Exemplary Leadership award (subsequently named in his honor) of the Fabless Semiconductor Association (now the Global Semiconductor Alliance). Known for his analytical mind Chang was once ranked among the top 1000 players of contract bridge in the world.

TSMC became profitable within 15 months of its founding. Throughout the 1990s it continued to be among industry leaders both in production capacity and in deployment of cutting-edge technology.

HISTORY

The big foundries — including TSMC's Taiwanese archrival United Microelectronics Corporation (UMC) — played a major role in the growth of the worldwide fabless semiconductor industry in the 21st century. Foundries aim to save clients the costs and time associated with building expensive wafer fabrication plants (fabs) of their own. Their services are especially vital for fabless companies whose entire business model is predicated on outsourcing all manufacturing.

Morris Chang learned early to adapt to rapid change. The future founder and chairman of Taiwan Semiconductor Manufacturing Company (TSMC) lived in six cities before age 18 as his family fled the ravages of the Sino-Japanese War and WWII in China. Chang immigrated to the US to attend MIT and Stanford where he ultimately earned a Ph.D. in electrical engineering.

In 25 years at Texas Instruments (TI) Chang worked his way up from the ranks of technical management into the executive suite. In 1983 he resigned from TI to become CEO of General Instrument but in 1985 the Taiwanese government recruited him to head its Industrial Technology Research Institute (ITRI). He remained chairman of ITRI from 1988 to 1994.

Working from his position at ITRI Chang became chairman of contract electronics manufacturer United Microelectronics Corporation (UMC) in 1987. Also that year he founded TSMC as the world's first dedicated contract semiconductor manufacturer — the first silicon foundry. Chang's pioneering role in the foundry industry has earned him many accolades including the first-ever Robert N. Noyce Medal of the Institute of Electrical and Electronics Engineers and the first-ever Exemplary Leadership award (subsequently named in his honor) of the Fabless Semiconductor Association (now the Global Semiconductor Alliance). Known for his analytical mind Chang was once ranked among the top 1000 players of contract bridge in the world.

TSMC became profitable within 15 months of its founding. Throughout the 1990s it continued to be among industry leaders both in production capacity and in deployment of cutting-edge technology.

EXECUTIVES

SVP, Operations, Product Development, Y. Chin
Independent Director, Rafael Reif
SVP, Information Technology and Materials Management, J.K. Lin
VP, Research and Development, Design and Technology Platform, Cliff Hou
SVP, Research and Development, Technology Development, Y. Mii
VP, Research and Development, Technology Development, Y. Wang
General Counsel, Deputy General Manager-Legal, Secretary of the Board, Sylvia Fang
VP, Research and Development, Integrated Interconnect and Packaging, Douglas Yu
VP, HR, Connie Ma
VP, Business Development, Kevin Zhang
Deputy General Manager-Operations / Advanced Packaging Technology & Service, Marvin Liao
Deputy General Manager-Operations / Fab Operations II, Y.H. Liaw
Chief Financial Officer, Deputy General Manager-Finance, Wendell Huang, $140,002 total compensation
Independent Director, Moshe Gavrielov
Director, Ming-Hsin Kung
Independent Director, Yancey Hai
Chief Information Officer, Deputy General Manager-Information Technology & Materials Management & Risk Management / Corporate Information Technology, Horng-Dar Lin
Deputy General Manager-Quality & Reliability, Jun He
Deputy General Manager-Research & Development / More than Moore Technologies, C.S. Yoo
Deputy General Manager-Research & Development / Platform Development, Geoffrey Yeap
VP, Operations, Product Development, Fab 12B and TSMC Fellow, T. Chang
VP, Research and Development, Technology Development, N3 Platform Development Division, Michael Wu
VP, Research and Development, Technology Development, Pathfinding, Min Cao
Deputy General Manager-Research & Development / Advanced Tool & Module Development, Simon Jang
Senior Deputy General Manager-Corporate Strategy Office, Rick Cassidy
Senior Deputy General Manager-Europe & Asia Sales, Lora Ho
President, Vice Chairman of the Board, C.C. Wei, $356,133 total compensation
Chairman of the Board, Mark Liu, $450,000 total compensation
SVP, Research and Development, Technology Development, Wei-Jen Lo
VP, Operations, 300mm Fabs, J. Wang
Auditors: Deloitte & Touche

LOCATIONS

HQ: Taiwan Semiconductor Manufacturing Co., Ltd.
No. 8, Li-Hsin Road 6, Hsinchu Science Park, Hsinchu 300
Phone: (886) 3 563 6688   **Fax:** (886) 3 563 7000
Web: www.tsmc.com

2017 Sales by Geography

	% of total
United States	64
Asia	20
Taiwan	9
Europe the Middle East and Africa	7
Total	**100**

2017 Sales by Region

	% of total
North America	64
China	12
Asia/Pacific	11
Europe Middle East and Africa	7
Japan	6
Total	**100**

PRODUCTS/OPERATIONS

2017 Sales

	% of total
Wafer	89
Others	11
Total	**100**

2017 Sales

	% of total
Fabless semiconductor companies/systems companies	80
Integrated device manufacturers	20
Total	**100**

2017 Sales

	% of total
Communication	59
Industrial/Standard	23
Computer	10
Consumer	8
Total	**100**

COMPETITORS

ADVANCED ENERGY INDUSTRIES INC.
AMKOR TECHNOLOGY INC.
COHERENT INC.
FLEX LTD.
INTEGRATED SILICON SOLUTION INC.

Infineon Technologies AG
LINEAR TECHNOLOGY LLC
MAXIM INTEGRATED PRODUCTS INC.
XCERRA CORPORATION

HISTORICAL FINANCIALS

Company Type: Public

Income Statement   FYE: December 31

	REVENUE ($ mil.)	NET INCOME ($ mil.)	NET PROFIT MARGIN	EMPLOYEES
12/20	47,656	18,428	38.7%	29,847,196
12/19	35,739	11,822	33.1%	51,297
12/18	33,721	11,480	34.0%	48,752
12/17	32,963	11,571	35.1%	48,602
12/16	29,299	10,331	35.3%	0
Annual Growth	12.9%	15.6%	—	—

2020 Year-End Financials

Debt ratio: 0.4%
Return on equity: 29.8%
Cash ($ mil.): 23,491
Current ratio: 1.77
Long-term debt ($ mil.): 9,112

No. of shares (mil.): —
Dividends
  Yield: 1.2%
  Payout: 191.2%
Market value ($ mil.): —

	STOCK PRICE ($) FY Close	P/E High/Low		PER SHARE ($) Earnings	Dividends	Book Value
12/20	109.04	5	2	0.71	1.36	2.54
12/19	58.10	4	3	0.46	1.60	2.08
12/18	36.91	3	3	0.44	1.04	2.11
12/17	39.65	3	2	0.45	0.94	1.98
12/16	28.75	2	2	0.40	0.76	1.66
Annual Growth	39.6%	—	—	15.6%	15.8%	11.3%

Takeda Pharmaceutical Co Ltd

The work of Takeda Pharmaceutical Company started way back in 1781 when its predecessor began selling traditional Japanese and Chinese remedies. These days Takeda is a global values-based research and development (R&D) driven biopharmaceutical company which operates in approximately 80 countries and regions across the world. Top-selling products include ulcerative colitis drug Entyvio anti-cancer agent Adcetris and antidepressant Trintellix. The company is also a leading maker of over-the-counter medications such as cold remedies and vitamins. Its largest market is the US which brings in about 50% of revenue.

Operations

Product sales contribute more than 95% of Takeda's total revenue. The company also makes money on out-licensing and service.

The company is focused on four therapeutic areas: oncology rare genetics and hematology neuroscience and gastroenterology (GI). The company also makes targeted R&D investments in plasma-derived therapies (PDT) and vaccines.

Gastroenterology provides about 25% of the company's total revenue. PDT immunology oncology neuroscience account for about 15% each rare hematology brings in nearly 10% rare metabolic and hereditary angioedema represent approximately 5% each while other products generate the remaining.

Geographic Reach

Headquartered in Japan Takeda also has major regional locations in Austria Japan Singapore Switzerland and the US.

The company's network span in more than 80 countries and regions in the Asia Pacific the Americas Europe and Africa. The US is Takeda's largest market bringing in nearly 50% of revenue followed by Europe and Canada with about 20% of revenue. Japan accounts for more than 15% Asia and Latin America generate about 5% each and Russia/CIS and other provide the remaining.

Sales and Marketing

Takeda sells its products to retail customers government agencies wholesalers health insurance companies and managed healthcare organizations.

Financial Performance

Revenue for the fiscal year ended March 31 2021 was 3.2 trillion a decrease of 93.4 billion or 3% compared to the previous fiscal year. Gastroenterology ("GI") and Plasma-Derived Therapies ("PDT") Immunology contributed to positive revenue growth however this was offset by intensified competition and generic erosion in Rare Diseases and the negative impact across the portfolio from changes in foreign exchange rates.

In 2020 the company had a net profit of 44.3 billion a 67% decrease from the previous year's net profit of 135.1 billion.

The company's cash at the end of 2020 was 637.6 billion. Operating activities generated 669.8 billion while investing activities provided 292.1 trillion. Financing activities used 1 trillion mainly for repayments of bonds and long-term loans.

Strategy

The company's business is organized as a single operating segment reflecting the presentation of information to its management for the purposes of allocating resources measuring performance and forecasting future periods.

The company may also acquire new businesses to expand its R&D capabilities (including expanding into new methodologies) and to acquire new products (whether in the development pipeline or at the marketing stage) or enter other strategic regions. Similarly the company divests from businesses and product lines to maintain its focus on key growth drivers and to manage its portfolio.

Mergers and Acquisitions

In late 2021 Takeda announced to acquire GammaDelta Therapeutics Limited (GammaDelta) a company focused on exploiting the unique properties of gamma delta (?d) T cells for immunotherapy. The acquisition expands Takeda's immuno-oncology and innate immune cell therapy portfolio with novel platforms leveraging ?dT cells for the potential treatment of solid tumors and hematological malignancies. In addition to early-stage cell therapy programs Takeda will obtain GammaDelta's allogeneic variable delta 1 (Vd1) gamma-delta (?d) T cell therapy platforms which includes both blood-derived and tissue-derived platforms.

In early 2021 Takeda announced to acquire Maverick Therapeutics a private biopharmaceutical company pioneering conditionally active bispecific T-cell targeted immunotherapies for up to approximately $525 million in upfront and potential milestone payments subject to certain adjustments. Under the agreement Takeda will obtain Maverick's T-cell engager COBRA platform and a broad development portfolio including Maverick's lead development candidate TAK-186 (MVC-101) currently in a Phase 1/2 study for the treatment of EGFR-expressing solid tumors and TAK-280 (MVC-280) which is anticipated to enter the clinic in the second half of Takeda's fiscal year 2021 for the treatment of patients with B7H3-expressing solid tumors.

In early 2020 Takeda acquired PvP Biologics following the conclusion of a Phase 1 proof-of-mechanism study of investigational medicine TAK-062 (Kuma062) for the treatment of uncontrolled celiac disease. TAK-062 is a potential best-in-class highly potent super glutenase ? a protein that degrades ingested gluten ? that was computationally engineered to treat celiac disease a serious autoimmune disease where the ingestion of gluten leads to inflammation and damage in the small intestine. The Phase 1 study investigated TAK-062's safety and tolerability in both healthy volunteers and people with celiac disease. The ability of TAK-062 to degrade ingested gluten was studied in healthy volunteers. Takeda plans to submit data from the Phase 1 study for presentation at an upcoming medical congress.

Company Background

In 1787 Chobei Takeda I started a business selling tradition Japanese and Chinese herbal medicines in Osaka Japan. In the 1860s with his great-grandson at the helm the business started importing western medicines. The company entered the manufacturing business in 1895 and in 1914 it established a research division so that it could develop its own products.

The company was incorporated as Chobei Takeda & Co. in 1925 transitioning from an individually owned business to a corporate organization. Chobei Takeda was renamed Takeda Pharmaceutical in 1943. It went public in 1949. In the 1960s Takeda began operating in other Asian markets. It entered the US and European markets in the 1990s.

EXECUTIVES

Representative Director, Masato Iwasaki
Chairman, Masahiro Sakane
Independent Director, Steven Gillis
Independent Director, Ian Clark
Independent Director, Olivier Bohuon
Independent Director, Masami Iijima
Independent Director, Emiko Higashi
President, Chief Executive Officer, Representative Director, Christophe Weber
President of Research & Development, Vice President of Subsidiary, Director, Andrew Plump
Auditors: KPMG AZSA LLC

LOCATIONS

HQ: Takeda Pharmaceutical Co Ltd
2-1-1 Nihonbashi-Honcho, Chuo-ku, Tokyo 103-8668
Phone: (81) 3 3278 2111   **Fax:** (81) 3 3278 2000
Web: www.takeda.co.jp

2018 Sales

	% of total
US	34
Japan	33
Europe & Canada	18
Latin America	6
Russia/CIS	4
Asia (excluding Japan) & other	4
Other	2
Total	**100**

PRODUCTS/OPERATIONS

Selected Products

Prescription drugs
  Actos (type 2 diabetes)
  Adecut (high blood pressure)
  Amasulin (anti-infective)
  Blopress (high blood pressure)
  Bronica (asthma)
  Ceuleuk (angiosarcoma)
  Dexilant (acid reflux)
  Eurodin (central nervous system)
  Lupron Depot (prostate cancer endometriosis)
  Osten (osteoporosis)
  Pansporin (anti-infective)
  Prevacid (peptic ulcers)
  Rozerem (insomnia)
  Takesulin (anti-infective)
  Uloric (gout)
  Velcade (multiple myeloma)
Consumer health care
  Alinamin (vitamins)
  Benza (cold remedy)
  Scorba (athlete's foot)

Selected Subsidiaries

Amato Pharmaceutical Products Ltd. (30%)
Millennium Pharmaceuticals Inc. (US)
Nihon Pharmaceutical Co. Ltd. (88%)
Laboratoires Takeda (France)
Takeda America Holdings Inc. (US)
Takeda Europe Holdings B.V. (Netherlands)
Takeda Cambridge Limited (UK)
Takeda Healthcare Products Co. Ltd.
Takeda Italia Farmaceutici S.p.A. (77%)
Takeda Pharma AG (Switzerland)
Takeda Pharma GmbH (Germany)
Takeda Pharma Ireland Limited
Takeda Pharmaceuticals Europe Limited (UK)
Takeda Pharmaceuticals North America Inc. (US)
Takeda Research Investment Inc. (US)
Takeda San Diego Inc. (US)
Takeda San Francisco Inc. (US)
Takeda Singapore Pte Limited
Takeda (Thailand) Ltd. (48%)
Tianjin Takeda Pharmaceuticals Co. Ltd. (75% China)

COMPETITORS

ALEXION PHARMACEUTICALS INC.
ALMIRALL SA
ASTRAZENECA PLC
BIOVERATIV INC.
BRISTOL-MYERS SQUIBB COMPANY
CELGENE CORPORATION
CUBIST PHARMACEUTICALS LLC
DYAX CORP.
EISAI CO. LTD.
ENDO HEALTH SOLUTIONS INC.
ENDO INTERNATIONAL PUBLIC LIMITED COMPANY
GILEAD SCIENCES INC.

INCYTE CORPORATION
LES LABORATOIRES SERVIER
LIGAND PHARMACEUTICALS INCORPORATED
Leo Pharma A/S
PFIZER INC.
SANOFI
SUCAMPO PHARMACEUTICALS INC.
TEVA PHARMACEUTICAL INDUSTRIES LIMITED
VERTEX PHARMACEUTICALS INCORPORATED

HISTORICAL FINANCIALS

Company Type: Public

Income Statement   FYE: March 31

	REVENUE ($ mil.)	NET INCOME ($ mil.)	NET PROFIT MARGIN	EMPLOYEES
03/21	28,880	3,395	11.8%	47,099
03/20	30,319	407	1.3%	47,495
03/19	18,937	985	5.2%	49,578
03/18	16,673	1,759	10.6%	27,230
03/17	15,491	1,028	6.6%	29,900
Annual Growth	16.9%	34.8%	—	12.0%

2021 Year-End Financials

Debt ratio: 0.3%	No. of shares (mil.): 1,576
Return on equity: 7.6%	Dividends
Cash ($ mil.): 3,025	Yield: 4.6%
Current ratio: 1.53	Payout: 37.6%
Long-term debt ($ mil.): 41,663	Market value ($ mil.): 28,782

	STOCK PRICE ($) FY Close	P/E High/Low		PER SHARE ($) Earnings	Dividends	Book Value
03/21	18.26	0	0	2.16	0.85	29.64
03/20	15.18	1	0	0.26	0.83	27.61
03/19	20.37	0	0	1.02	0.81	29.77
03/18	24.41	0	0	2.24	0.86	23.68
03/17	23.64	0	0	1.31	0.83	21.44
Annual Growth	(6.2%)	—	—	13.3%	0.6%	8.4%

Talanx AG

Talanx Group is Germany's third-largest and one of the major European insurance groups by premium income. Also known as Talanx it operates in property/casualty insurance life insurance and financial services as well as reinsurance in both the property/casualty and life categories. Brands include HDI which provides insurance policies to both private and industrial customers; Hannover Re one of the world's largest reinsurers; and asset manager Ampega among others. Talanx has operations in more than 150 countries worldwide. The group is controlled by HDI Haftpflichtverband der Deutschen Industrie. Europe is its largest market giving approximately 60% of its gross written premiums.

Operations

Talanx reports its business in six insurance segments: Industrial Lines Retail Germany ? Property Casualty Retail Germany ? Life Retail International Property/Casualty Reinsurance and Life/Health Reinsurance. The group also has a Corporate Operations segment. The group's primary brands include HDI Hannover Re Targo Versicherungen PB Versicherungen Neue Leben Warta and Ampega.

Property/Casualty Reinsurance leads the pack with more than 35% of total gross written premiums. Life/Health Reinsurance (about 20%) and Industrial lines (around 15%) follow.

Property/Casualty Reinsurance is primarily handled by subsidiary Hannover R ck. Its target markets are North America and Continenal Europe.

Retail Germany consists of the Property/Casualty Insurance and Life Insurance segments.

Retail International covers its foreign insurance business with retail and commercial customers in various lines of insurance including our bancassurance activities.

The Industrial Lines segment reports the group's global industrial business. Its business operations encompass a wide selection of insurance products such as liability motor casualty fire property legal protection marine financial lines agency and specialty (including in lines such as errors and omissions liability insurance directors' and officers' (D&O) liability insurance sports and entertainment aviation offshore energy and livestock insurance) and engineering insurance for large and medium-sized enterprises in Germany and abroad.

Geographic Reach

Europe accounts for approximately 60% of Talanx's gross premiums written with Germany bringing in about 20% on its own. The US is the group's largest non-European region with approximately 20% of total gross written premiums.

The group also does business in the rest of the Americas Africa and the Asia Pacific region.

Based in Hannover the group operates in more than 150 countries.

Sales and Marketing

Talanx sells its products by its own field organisation independent brokers and multiple agents via partnerships online and direct channels.

Financial Performance

Note: Growth rates may differ after conversion to US Dollars.

The company's revenue for fiscal 2020 increased to ?407 million compared to ?405 million in the prior year.

Net income for fiscal 2020 decreased to ?1.2 billion compared from the prior year with ?1.7 billion.

Cash held by the company at the end of fiscal 2020 decreased to ?3.48 billion. Cash provided by operations was ?6.3 billion while investing and financing activities used ?5.2 billion and ?1.0 billion respectively. Main cash uses were sale and maturity of financial instruments; and capital reductions.

Strategy

The company's strategy is geared towards achieving its ambitious and clearly defined growth and profitability targets by systematically expanding its strengths ("strengthen") and adopting a focused approach to its development areas ("develop"). The company as a whole aim for a return on equity of at least 800 basis points above the risk-free interest rate in order to ensure long-term value creation. Its objective is to increase earnings per share (EPS) by an average of at least 5% a year by 2022 underpinned by focused divisional strategies and a host of strategic growth initiatives. Talanx also intends to continue to distribute no less than 35% to 45% of its consolidated earnings under IFRS to its shareholders with future dividends remaining at least at the prior year's level in absolute terms. As strategic subsidiary conditions the company has also set itself the goal of achieving limited market risk (= 50%) and a high regulatory solvency ratio (150%?200%).

Areas that Talanx is continuing to develop include optimizing capital management in order to maximize financial flexibility within the company providing solid capital resources at all times and ensuring dividend stability in the long run.

Mergers and Acquisitions

In late 2020 Talanx expanded its business in Italy by making a bolt-on acquisition. HDI Assicurazioni a subsidiary of HDI International AG the Talanx' retail international division is buying all the shares of Italian non-life insurer Amissima Assicurazioni from Amissima Holdings (indirectly owned by investment funds managed by affiliates of Apollo Global Management Inc.). In line with its strategy HDI's purchase enhances its diversification by expanding its non-life insurance business and will lift its Italian premium volume by approximately EUR 300 million to roughly EUR 2 billion. Roughly 30% of this figure will be attributable to the local non-life insurance business. The acquisition moves HDI up from 17th place to 11th place among Italy's non-life insurers measured in terms of market share giving it the chance to reach the top 10 through organic growth. It was agreed not to disclose the amount of the purchase price.

Company Background

The company traces its roots back over a century but began operating as a holding company under the name HDI Beteilgung AG in 1996. In 1998 it was renamed Talanx which is a blend of the words "talent" and "phalanx" (a Greek word referring to a battle formation).

In 2012 the company completed its IPO and began trading on Germany's Frankfurt Stock Exchange. The company raised about €817 million which it used to grow its business. Post-IPO HDI Haftpflichtverband der Deutschen Industrie maintained a majority stake in Talanx.

EXECUTIVES

Member of the Management Board, Edgar Puls, $410,186 total compensation
Member of the Management Board, Wilm Langenbach, $51,273 total compensation
Member of the Management Board, Christopher Lohmann, $260,923 total compensation
Chairman and Chief Executive Officer, Torsten Leue, $968,494 total compensation
Member of the Management Board, Jan Wicke, $773,656 total compensation
Member of the Management Board, Jean-Jacques Henchoz, $1,002,677 total compensation
Auditors: PricewaterhouseCoopers GmbH

LOCATIONS

HQ: Talanx AG
    HDI-Platz 1, Hannover D-30659
Phone: (49) 511 3747 0   **Fax:** (49) 511 3747 2525
Web: www.talanx.com

2017 Gross Written Premiums

	% of total
Germany	26
Central & Eastern Europe including Turkey	9
UK	8
Rest of Europe	15
US	18
Rest of North America	2
Asia & Australia	12
Latin America	8
Africa	2
Total	**100**

PRODUCTS/OPERATIONS

2017 Gross Written Premiums by Segment

	% of total
Property/Casualty Reinsurance	31
Life/Health Reinsurance	21
Retail International	16
Retail Germany — Life Insurance	14
Industrial Lines	13
Retail Germany — Property/Casualty Insurance	5
Total	**100**

COMPETITORS

AA LIMITED
ABRDN PLC
Allianz SE

Argo Group International Holdings Ltd.
Baloise Holding AG
COMPUTACENTER PLC
ESURE GROUP PLC
Enstar Group Limited
Fairfax Financial Holdings Limited
Hiscox Ltd
LIVERPOOL VICTORIA FRIENDLY SOCIETY LTD
METLIFE INC.
RSA INSURANCE GROUP LIMITED
RenaissanceRe Holdings Ltd.
SBERBANK PAO
SCOR SE
Zurich Insurance Group AG

HISTORICAL FINANCIALS

Company Type: Public

Income Statement				FYE: December 31
	REVENUE ($ mil.)	NET INCOME ($ mil.)	NET PROFIT MARGIN	EMPLOYEES
12/19	42,032	1,036	2.5%	21,516
12/18	38,257	805	2.1%	20,780
12/17	38,386	805	2.1%	22,059
12/16	32,815	957	2.9%	21,649
12/15	33,888	799	2.4%	21,965
Annual Growth	5.5%	6.7%	—	(0.5%)

2019 Year-End Financials

Debt ratio: —
Return on equity: 9.7%
Cash ($ mil.): 3,949
Current ratio: —
Long-term debt ($ mil.): —

No. of shares (mil.): 252
Dividends
  Yield: —
  Payout: —
Market value ($ mil.): —

Tata Motors Ltd

Tata Motors is an automobile maker. The company produces passenger cars including popular models such as Jaguar Land Rover Safari and Sumo and commercial vehicles such as buses trucks tractor-trailers light commercial vehicles and defense and construction equipment. Furthermore Tata Motors has OEMs offering an extensive range of integrated smart and e-mobility solutions. Tata Motors sells its vehicles through an extensive dealer network in India and exports vehicles to countries in Africa Asia Europe the Middle East and South America. In addition the company distributes Fiat-brand cars in India through its joint venture with Fiat. Tata Motors rolled out its first commercial truck in 1945. Its vehicles can now be found on the roads in more than 125 countries. The company generates majority of sales from international markets.

Operations

Tata Motors' business segments are primarily divided by its automotive operations and other all other operations.

Automotive operations represent the company's primary segment which includes Tata Commercial Vehicles Tata Passenger Vehicles Jaguar Land Rover and Vehicle financing. Jaguar and Land Rover brands account for around 80% of total revenue with Tata and other brand vehicles including vehicle financing bringing in the rest. Vehicles are categorized as car and sport utility vehicles (SUVs) trucks and buses and defense vehicles and equipment.

Car models include the Tigor Tiago Bolt and the smaller GenX Nano; SUVs are the Harrier Nexon Hexa Safari Storme and Sumo Gold.

Tata Motors' trucks include its Prima Ace Mega ICV truck Super Ace Mint Ultra and Zip Gold

trucks which are used for various applications such as refuse trucks road sweepers and suction machine trucks. Part of its truck business operates through subsidiary Tata Daewoo Commercial Vehicle Company (TDCV) which is South Korea's second largest manufacturer of medium- and heavy-duty trucks exporting vehicles to more than 60 countries. Tata Motors also makes buses including city buses school buses coaches and what it calls its "Smart City" STARBUS electric and hybrid buses.

Its defense vehicles include troop carriers water tankers tippers load carriers prison vans and fire tenders.

Other operations include information technology services machine tools and factory automation services.

Geographic Reach

Through subsidiaries and affiliated companies Tata Motors has operations in India the UK South Korea Thailand Spain and South Africa. The US is its largest market representing around 20% of its total sales. It is followed by India for almost 20%. The UK generates more than 15% of total sales and China for more than 10%. Other European countries also account for over 15% of total sales while the rest of the world contributes the remaining revenue.

Tata Motors has manufacturing facilities across India; Jaguar Land Rover has manufacturing facilities in the UK as well as in Austria Brazil China Slovakia and India; Daewoo manufacturing facilities are located in South Korea. In addition the company operates R&D and design facilities across Asia and Europe. Tata Motors is headquartered in Mumbai India.

Sales and Marketing

Tata Motors' vehicles are sold through a network of authorized dealers and service centers across the Indian market and a network of distributors and local dealers in international markets. All told the company has more than 6500 sales and service points worldwide.

Moreover digital channels such as online sales and remote servicing via SOTA are helping improve customer service.

Financial Performance

Note: Growth rates may differ after conversion to US Dollars.

Tata Motors has seen significant growth in the past years despite it falling considerably in fiscal 2020. Revenue fell by 11% between fiscal 2018 and fiscal 2020 with ?3.01 trillion in fiscal 2019. A steep volume decline a general economic slowdown the impact of the COVID-19 pandemic towards the year-end and the resulting negative operating leverage of the company impacted profitability and cash flows.

Revenue fell by 14% in fiscal 2020 to ?2.6 trillion compared to ?3.01 the prior year due to a decrease in wholesale volumes in both Tata and Jaguar Land Rover brands.

Tata Motors did not fare better in terms of profits either. The company experienced consecutive net loss of ?12.1 trillion in fiscal 2020 following the loss of ?28.8 trillion the year prior. The COVID-19 pandemic has severely affected the company's performance as well as lower demand thus disrupting its steady delivery of profit in the past years.

Cash at the end of the period was ?184.7 trillion. Cash from operations generated ?266.3 billion and financing activities added another ?33.9 billion from proceeds from issue of shares and long-term borrowings. Investing activities used ?341.7 billion mainly for payments for assets and purchase of investments.

Strategy

Tata Motors continues its Turnaround 2.0 strategy which was launched in FY19 by emphasizing

operational efficiency using common platforms initiating cost reduction and capex rationalization programmes leveraging on developments in EV markets and launching a new BSVI portfolio that offers exciting features and delivers an enhanced value proposition. Key priorities include enhancing retail sales efficiently managing dealer network inventories and improving dealer performance profitability and network expansion.

Tata Motors introduced 'Click to drive' an end-to-end online sales experience enabling customers to buy the car of their choice with a click of a button from the comfort of their homes as a response to customer uncertainty due to the pending transition from BSIV to BSVI the liquidity crisis and the rising cost of vehicle ownership among other reasons.

In terms of electric vehicles Tata Motors launched the Nexon EV in January 2020 which is powered by the state-of-the-art EV technology 'ZIPTRON' a high voltage high performance technology designed specifically for Indian conditions. It also launched the Tigor EV+ with 213 km range which has received a strong market response and is the highest selling EV in India.

Company Background

Tata Motors is part of the Tata Group which was founded in 1868 by Jamsetji Tata. Tata Motors began manufacturing locomotives and other engineering products in 1945 and rolled out its first commercial truck?the TMB 312?in 1954. Tata Motors' 1210 series of vehicles began production in 1964 and in 1975 the company began producing the Tata 1210 semi-forward model.

In 1983 the company started making heavy commercial vehicles and in 2005 it launched its first fully built buses and coaches called GLOBUS and STARBUS brands. The popular Tata Nano mini car and Jaguar Land Rover were both introduced in 2009. In 2014 the company started making defense vehicles the first being the Armoured Personnel Carrier (APC). Its first electric vehicle the Tata Tigor was launched in 2017.

EXECUTIVES

Additional Non-Executive Independent Director, Kosaraju Chowdary, $26,937 total compensation
Additional Executive Director, Girish Wagh
Non-Executive Independent Director, Vedika Bhandarkar, $60,609 total compensation
Additional Non-Executive Non-Independent Director, Thierry Bollore
Non-Executive Independent Director, Om Bhatt, $60,609 total compensation
Non-Executive Chairman of the Board, Natarajan Chandrasekaran
Additional Non-Executive Non-Independent Director, Mitsuhiko Yamashita, $26,937 total compensation
Auditors: KPMG Assurance and Consulting Services LLP

LOCATIONS

HQ: Tata Motors Ltd
  Bombay House, 24, Homi Mody Street, Mumbai, Maharashtra 400 001
Phone: (91) 22 6665 7219   **Fax:** (91) 22 6665 7790
Web: www.tatamotors.com

2018 Sales

	% of total
India	20
UK	17
Rest of Europe	16
United States	15
China	15
Rest of the World	17
Total	**100**

PRODUCTS/OPERATIONS

2018 Sales

	% of total
Jaguar Land Rover Vehicles	76
Tata and Flat Vehicles	20
Tata Daewoo Commercial Vehicles	2
Financial Revenues	1
Others	1
Total	**100**

Selected Products and Services

Cars and Sport Utility Vehicles
  Hatchbacks
  Sedans
  Sport Utility Vehicles
Defence
  Logistic
  Troop Carriers
  Water Tankers
  Tippers
  Load Carriers
  Prison Vans
  Fire tenders
  Aid & Development Vehicles
  Ambulances
  Buses
  Recovery Trucks
  Refrigerated Trucks
  Utility Trucks/Troop Carriers
  Armored Trucks
  Combat Vehicles
  Combat Support Vehicles
Trucks and Buses
  Trucks and Buses
  Municipal Solutions

Selected Subsidiaries

Concorde Motors (India) Limited
Jaguar Land Rover PLC-UK
PT Tata Indonesia
Sheba Properties Ltd-India
TAL Manufacturing Solutions Ltd-India
Tata Daewoo Commercial Vehicle Co Ltd- South Korea
Tata Hispano Motors Carrocera SA- Spain
Tata Marcopolo Motors Ltd-India.
Tata Motors (SA) Proprietary Ltd -South Africa.
Tata Motors European Technical center PLC -UK
Tata Motors Finance Ltd -India
Tata Motors Insurance Broking and Advisory Services
  Ltd-India
Tata Motors(Thailand) Ltd
Tata Precision Industries Pts Ltd-Singapore
Tata Technologies Ltd-India
TML Distribution Company Ltd-India
TML Drivelines Ltd-India
TML Holdings Pte Ltd- Singapore

COMPETITORS

AB Volvo	MITSUBISHI MOTORS
Bayerische Motoren	CORPORATION
Werke AG	NAVISTAR INTERNATIONAL
China Faw Group Co.	CORPORATION
Ltd.	VOLKSWAGEN AG
HONDA MOTOR CO. LTD.	WABCO HOLDINGS INC.
Hyundai Mobis Co. Ltd.	
MARUTI SUZUKI INDIA	
LIMITED	

HISTORICAL FINANCIALS

Company Type: Public

Income Statement
FYE: March 31

	REVENUE ($ mil.)	NET INCOME ($ mil.)	NET PROFIT MARGIN	EMPLOYEES
03/21	33,917	(1,950)	—	75,278
03/20	34,345	(1,508)	—	78,906
03/19	43,264	(4,236)	—	82,797
03/18	44,311	1,024	2.3%	81,090
03/17	40,962	943	2.3%	79,558
Annual Growth	**(4.6%)**	**—**		**(1.4%)**

Debt ratio: 0.5%
Return on equity: (-26.1%)
Cash ($ mil.): 6,293
Current ratio: 0.94
Long-term debt ($ mil.): 12,724
No. of shares (mil.): —
Dividends
  Yield: —
  Payout: —
Market value ($ mil.): —

	STOCK PRICE ($) FY Close	P/E High/Low		PER SHARE ($) Earnings	Dividends	Book Value
03/21	20.79	—	—	(0.54)	0.00	1.80
03/20	4.72	—	—	(0.44)	0.00	2.17
03/19	12.56	—	—	(1.25)	0.00	2.35
03/18	25.70	2	1	0.30	0.00	4.11
03/17	35.65	3	2	0.28	0.01	2.43
Annual Growth	**(12.6%)**	**—**	**—**	**—**	**—**	**(7.2%)**

Tata Steel Ltd

Tata Steel is one of the most geographically diversified steel producers around the world. The company's steelmaking and finishing facilities have the capacity to produce approximately 28.54 million tons of crude steel a year. Tata Steel's products include hot and cold rolled coils and sheets tubes wire rods rings and bearings. Its domestic facilities are located in Jamshedpur in eastern India and Tata Steel's international operations include UK-based subsidiary Tata Steel Europe Singapore's NatSteel and Tata Steel Thailand. The company also owns interests in coal and iron projects that supply the steelmaker with raw materials. About half of the company's total revenue comes from domestic operations. Tata Steel was established in in 1907.

Operations
The company is primarily engaged in the business of manufacture and distribution of steel products across the globe. Operating segments are based on the different geographical areas: Tata Steel India (about 35% of revenue); Tata Steel Europe (nearly 30%); Bamnipal steel (almost 10% of revenue; including Tata Steel BSL); South-East Asian operations (approximately 5%); Tata Steel long products (less than 5%); other Indian operations (some 5%); and rest of the world and other trade related operations (account for the remaining).

Overall about 95% of Tata Steel's revenue comes from steel products.

Geographic Reach
India-based Tata Steel generates about half of the total revenue from India. Its global offices are located in London Singapore and Thailand.

Sales and Marketing
Tata Steel has diversified offerings across market segments: agriculture; automotive; construction; and industrial and general engineering. Its online and channel sales enabled through digital platforms such as Aashiyana COMPASS DigEca enabled digital sales of products and services.

Financial Performance
Note: Growth rates may differ after conversion to US Dollars.

The turnover during the current period was ?64869 crores higher by 7% over the previous year primarily due to an increase in steel prices while the deliveries were at par.

In 2021 the company had a net profit of ?17795.1 crores a 169% increase from the previous year's net profit of ?6610.98 crores.

The company's cash for the year ended 2021 was ?1501.7 crores. Operating activities generated

?29368.6 crores while investing activities used ?13008.5 crores mainly for the purchase of capital assets. Financing activities used another ?15852 crores mainly for repayment of long-term borrowings.

Strategy
In FY2021 the company slowed down the growth in capital expenditure and focused on sustainable capital expenditure across its production facilities.

The company also focused on deleveraging during the second half of the current year therefore made repayment of borrowings (net of proceeds) amounting to ?13229 crores.

In anticipation of severe disruption in business cash flows management focused on cash flows and shore up liquidity to ensure the sustainability of operations for an elongated pandemic scenario;

Strategic cash war room for strict ground-level monitoring of the cash targeted on fixed cost reduction monitoring of working capital; and

The key emphasis of the Management is on balancing growth ambitions and maintaining liquidity and a healthy balance sheet.

Company Background
Tata Steel was founded in 1907 as Asia's first private sector integrated steel company.

EXECUTIVES

Additional Non-Executive Independent Director, David Crane
Non-Executive Independent Director, Mallika Srinivasan
Non-Executive Chairman of the Board, Natarajan Chandrasekaran
Non-Executive Independent Director, Deepak Kapoor
Non-Executive Director, Saurabh Agrawal
Non-Executive Director, Vijay Sharma
Chief Executive Officer, Managing Director, Executive Director, Thachat Narendran, $202,033 total compensation
Additional Non-Executive Independent Director, Farida Khambata
Chief Financial Officer, Executive Director, Koushik Chatterjee, $181,829 total compensation
Non-Executive Independent Director, Om Bhatt
Chairman Emeritus, Ratan Tata
Auditors: Price Waterhouse & Co. Chartered Accountants LLP

LOCATIONS

HQ: Tata Steel Ltd
Bombay House, 24 Homi Mody Street, Fort Mumbai 400 001
Phone: (91) 22 6665 8282   **Fax:** (91) 22 6665 7724
Web: www.tatasteel.com

2016 Sales

	% of total
Outside India	68
Within India	32
Total	**100**

PRODUCTS/OPERATIONS

2016 Sales

	% of total
Steel	91
Others	9
Total	**100**

Selected Operations

Steel
Ferroalloys & Minerals (chrome mines & manufacturing ferro chrome & ferro manganese)
Bearings (ball bearings clutch release bearings & double row self-aligning bearings)
Tubes
Wire

COMPETITORS

ArcelorMittal
BLUESCOPE STEEL
  LIMITED
CHINA STEEL
  CORPORATION
HAYNES INTERNATIONAL
  INC.
JSW STEEL LIMITED
KOBE STEEL LTD.
MECHEL PAO
Metal rgica Gerdau
  S/A

NIPPON STEEL TRADING
  CORPORATION
NLMK PAO
SEVERSTAL PAO
SSAB AB
TERNIUM S.A.
TIMKENSTEEL
  CORPORATION
UNITED STATES STEEL
  CORPORATION

HISTORICAL FINANCIALS

Company Type: Public

Income Statement
FYE: March 31

	REVENUE ($ mil.)	NET INCOME ($ mil.)	NET PROFIT MARGIN	EMPLOYEES
03/21	21,361	1,023	4.8%	73,962
03/20	18,510	206	1.1%	70,212
03/19	22,786	1,476	6.5%	75,294
03/18	20,444	2,064	10.1%	65,144
03/17	18,187	(653)	—	67,902
Annual Growth	4.1%	—	—	2.2%

2021 Year-End Financials

Debt ratio: 0.4%
Return on equity: 10.1%
Cash ($ mil.): 790
Current ratio: 0.85
Long-term debt ($ mil.): 8,979

No. of shares (mil.): 1,202
Dividends
  Yield: 0.0%
  Payout: 11.6%
Market value ($ mil.): —

	STOCK PRICE ($) FY Close	P/E High/Low		PER SHARE ($) Earnings	Dividends	Book Value
03/21	0.00	0	0	0.87	0.10	8.43
03/20	4.35	0	0	0.16	0.15	8.10
03/19	15.00	—	—	1.27	0.12	8.28
03/18	15.00	—	—	1.97	0.35	7.78
Annual Growth	—	—	—	(18.4%)	(26.4%)	2.0%

TDK Corp

TDK Corporation branched out from its original focus in the 1930s of commercializing ferrite a magnetic material. TDK is a world leader in electronic solutions for the smart society. TDK's comprehensive innovation-driven portfolio features passive components such as ceramic aluminum electrolytic and film capacitors as well as magnetics high-frequency and piezo and protection devices. The product spectrum also includes sensors and sensor systems such as temperature and pressure magnetic and MEMS sensors. In addition TDK provides power supplies and energy devices magnetic heads and more. These products are marketed under the product brands TDK EPCOS InvenSense Micronas Tronics and TDK-Lambda. TDK focuses on demanding markets in automotive industrial and consumer electronics and information and communication technology. With operations around the world Japan-based TDK generates about 90% of its sales outside of its home country.

Operations

TDK's four major reporting segments are Energy Application Products Passive Components Magnetic Application Products and Sensor Application Components.

Energy application products (nearly 45% of total revenue) include energy devices such as lithium polymer batteries for smartphones tablet devices notebook computers wearable devices game consoles drones and residential energy storage systems and power supplies (DC-DC converters onboard chargers and POL converters).

About 30% of revenue comes from passive components which include ceramic chip capacitors aluminum electrolytic capacitors film capacitors and 3-terminal feed-through capacitors.

Magnetic application products some 15% of revenue hard disk drive (HDD) heads HDD suspension assemblies power supplies and magnet products.

Sensor application products (around 5%) makes sensors for automotive ICT and industrial and energy.

Geographic Reach

TDK based in Tokyo has more than 250 factories research and development and sales offices in more than 30 countries.

Most of TDK's revenue — some 75% — comes from customers in Asia more than 10% comes from Europe with the US and Japan supplying 15% of combined revenue.

Financial Performance

As a result of the deterioration of the US?China relations economic downturns and restrictions on production activities due to the COVID-19 pandemic and rising value of the yen against the dollar and other factors net sales in fiscal 2020 were down 1% year on year to 1.4 trillion.

In 2020 the company had a net income of 57.8 billion a 30% decrease from the previous year's net income of 82.2 billion.

The company's cash at the end of 2020 was 332.7 billion. Operating activities generated 222.4 billion while investing activities used 42 billion. Financing activities used another 121.8 billion.

Strategy

Against the backdrop of redoubled demand for customization and modularization in the smartphone market needs have grown for coordination of the various electronic components mounted in those products. To constantly supply customers with optimum solutions TDK moved from traditional in-house self-sufficiency to cooperation with IC manufacturers transferring one portion of its high-frequency component business to Qualcomm Incorporated (Qualcomm). Similarly in gearing up to meet the next stage of social needs it pursued sensor-focused M&As as a means to field a wide-ranging arsenal of technologies while solid growth investments expanded sales to the automotive market.

Mergers and Acquisitions

In 2016 TDK strengthened its position in the sensor market. in December 2016 it agreed to acquire InvenSense a maker of motion sensors for $1.3 billion. InvenSense makes among other things gyroscopes for smartphones and other devices. The company's biggest customer is Apple. Earlier in 2016 TDK subsidiary EPCOS agreed to acquire Tronics Microsystems SA another sensors company. TDK looks for the addition of InvenSense and Tronics to increase it appeal to the automotive consumer and industrial markets.

In 2015 TDK acquired HDD suspension manufacturer Hutchinson Technology Inc. Hutchinson manufactures components for HDD suspensions (mount plate trace-gimbal circuit and stainless steel etching parts) and assembles these components into HDD suspensions a key component of HDD heads.

HISTORY

Kanzo Saito who had previously raised rabbits for their fur took out a patent in 1935 on ferrite a type of ceramic made mainly from iron oxide that held promise for electronics applications. (Japan's Yogoru Kato is credited with inventing the material.) Saito founded Tokyo Denkikagaku Kogyo K.K. (TDK) to pioneer the mass production of ferrite and output rose quickly as developers found countless new uses for the substance. Saito handed over the presidency of the company in 1946 to Teiichi Yamazaki who expanded TDK's portfolio into products such as magnetic recording tape (1952).

The company's global thrust began when it opened a Los Angeles office in 1959. Two years later it was listing shares on the Tokyo Stock Exchange. TDK branched into cassette tapes in 1966 and electromagnetic wave absorbers in 1968 the year the company opened its first overseas manufacturing center in Taiwan.

During the 1970s TDK launched operations in Australia Europe and South America. It began listing its shares on the New York Stock Exchange in 1982. That year the company also introduced a solar battery. In 1983 TDK officially changed its name to TDK Corporation.

In 1987 Hiroshi Sato was appointed president of the company. TDK bought integrated circuit maker Silicon Systems in 1989 (sold in 1996 to Texas Instruments) as Sato began to modernize the company's offerings and organization. With a conservative management style he'd often wait to see how other companies fared in new markets before committing TDK prompting the industry to label him the "gambler who follows someone else." During his tenure Sato gave the company solid footholds in niches such as optical disks high-density heads and cellular phone components.

EXECUTIVES

Independent Director, Kozue Nakayama
Senior Managing Executive Officer, Chief Director of Strategy, Director, Seiji Osaka
Managing Executive Officer, Chief Executive Officer of Sensor System Business Company, Noboru Saito
Chairman of the Board, Makoto Sumita
Global Chief Compliance Officer, Senior Managing Executive Officer, Chief Director of Accounting & Finance, Representative Director, Tetsuji Yamanishi
President, Chief Executive Officer, Chief Director of Humidifier Measure, Representative Director, Shigenao Ishiguro
Managing Executive Officer, Chief Director of Technology & Intellectual Property, Director, Shigeki Sato
Independent Director, Mutsuo Iwai
Auditors: KPMG AZSA LLC

LOCATIONS

HQ: TDK Corp
  2-5-1 Nihonbashi, Chuo-ku, Tokyo 103-6128
Phone: (81) 3 6778 1055   Fax: 516 294-8318
Web: www.jp.tdk.com

PRODUCTS/OPERATIONS

2019 Sales

	% of total
Energy Application Products	39
Passive Application Products	31
Magnetic Application Products	20
Sensor Application Products	6
Other	4
Total	100

2019 Sales

	% of total
Asia and others	72
Europe	12
Americas	8
Japan	8
Total	100

Selected Products

Data Storage
  Magnetic heads (hard disk drives)
  Thermal-assist magnetic heads (scheduled to begin production in March 2013)
Electronic Components
  Anechoic chambers
  Capacitors
  Converters
  Cores and magnets
  Ferrite
  Metal
  Inductors
  Power supplies
  Sensors
  Transformers
  Varistors
Other
  Factory automation equipment
  Organic EL displays

COMPETITORS

ADVANCED ENERGY
  INDUSTRIES INC.
ASM International N.V.
INFINEON TECHNOLOGIES
  AMERICAS CORP.
KYOCERA CORPORATION
LITTELFUSE INC.
METHODE ELECTRONICS
  INC.
MICRON TECHNOLOGY INC.

MINI-SYSTEMS INC.
MOLEX LLC
NIDEC CORPORATION
SHARP CORPORATION
ULTRALIFE CORPORATION
VEECO INSTRUMENTS INC.
VISHAY PRECISION GROUP
  INC.
XCERRA CORPORATION

HISTORICAL FINANCIALS

Company Type: Public

Income Statement				FYE: March 31
	REVENUE ($ mil.)	NET INCOME ($ mil.)	NET PROFIT MARGIN	EMPLOYEES
03/21	13,357	716	5.4%	129,284
03/20	12,556	532	4.2%	107,138
03/19	12,477	742	5.9%	104,781
03/18	11,976	597	5.0%	102,883
03/17	10,538	1,297	12.3%	99,693
Annual Growth	6.1%	(13.8%)	—	6.7%

2021 Year-End Financials

Debt ratio: 0.1%
Return on equity: 8.5%
Cash ($ mil.): 3,435
Current ratio: 1.22
Long-term debt ($ mil.): 1,402

No. of shares (mil.): 378
Dividends
  Yield: 3.6%
  Payout: 28.7%
Market value ($ mil.): 53,094

	STOCK PRICE ($) FY Close	P/E High/Low		PER SHARE ($) Earnings	Dividends	Book Value
03/21	140.10	1	0	1.89	1.70	23.92
03/20	76.50	1	0	1.40	1.57	20.52
03/19	78.50	1	0	1.95	0.45	20.91
03/18	89.47	1	0	1.57	0.38	20.50
03/17	63.58	0	0	3.42	1.11	18.75
Annual Growth	21.8%	—	—	(13.8%)	11.3%	6.3%

TE Connectivity Ltd

TE Connectivity is a global industrial technology leader creating a safer sustainable productive and connected future. Its devices are used in aerospace automotive data and devices commercial transportation energy and medical applications. The company operates about 105 manufacturing sites around the world and sells its products in some 140 countries primarily through direct selling ef-

forts to manufacturers. Majority of its sales were generated outside the US.

Operations

TE Connectivity sorts its businesses into Transportation Industrial and Communications.

Transportation delivers some 60% of the company's revenue. It makes terminals and connector systems and components sensors relays application tooling and wire and heat shrink tubing.

Industrial accounts for around 25% of revenue with its products that connect and distribute power data and signals.

Communications makes components for the data and devices and appliances markets and generates about 15% of revenue.

Geographic Reach

TE Connectivity is a worldwide operation with approximately 18 million square feet and leased approximately 10 million square feet of aggregate floor space used primarily for manufacturing warehousing and offices in more than 50 countries.

In terms of revenue source the US accounts for about 25% followed by Switzerland nearly 25% China over 20% and other countries in the Asia-Pacific region roughly 15%.

While headquartered in Switzerland for tax purposes its corporate office is in Pennsylvania.

Sales and Marketing

TE Connectivity connects directly with its customers most of the time with 80% of revenue coming from its own sales force. The company also sell through distributors.

Its largest end market was automotive accounting for about 45% of sales followed by commercial transportation sensors industrial equipment and data and devices (around 10% each) and aerospace defense oil and gas energy medical and appliances account for the rest.

Financial Performance

Net sales increased $2.8 billion or 23% in fiscal 2021 as compared to fiscal 2020. The increase in net sales resulted primarily from organic net sales growth of 18% and the positive impact of foreign currency translation of 4% due to the strengthening of certain foreign currencies.

Net income for fiscal 2021 was $2.3 billion compared to a net loss of $241 million.

Cash held by the company at the end of fiscal 2021 increased to $1.2 billion. Net cash provided by operating activities were $2.7 billion while investing and financing activities used $1.0 billion and $1.4 billion respectively. Main cash uses were capital expenditures and repurchase of common shares.

Mergers and Acquisitions

In early 2020 TE Connectivity completed its public takeover of Berlin-based First Sensor AG a global player in sensor technology. TE now holds 71.87% shares of First Sensor. In combining the First Sensor and TE portfolios TE will be able to offer an even broader product base including innovative market-leading sensors connectors and systems plus best-in-class capabilities that supports the growth strategy of TE's sensors business and TE Connectivity as a whole. Terms were not disclosed.

Company Background

TE Connectivity undertook its solo role on the world's stage of passive electronics in 2007. Tyco International had rewritten its corporate script and moved to split off Tyco Electronics and Covidien (formerly Tyco Healthcare Group) from its security and engineered products operation; three standalone public companies resulted. The company changed its name to TE Connectivity in 2011 to better reflect its operations after the ADC acquisition.

EXECUTIVES

Independent Director, Mark Trudeau
Senior Vice President, Chief Human Resources Officer, Global Human Resources, Timothy Murphy
Vice President, Chief Supply Chain Officer, Jimmy McDonald
Senior Vice President, Chief Strategy Officer, Arvind Kaushal
Senior Vice President, Chief Information Officer, Joseph Eckroth
Vice President, Chief Continuous Improvement Officer, Claudia Anderson
Independent Director, Carol Davidson
Senior Vice President of Operations, Joel Dubs
Independent Director, Abhijit Talwalkar
Senior Vice President, Mergers and Acquisitions, Jeanne Quirk
Lead Independent Director, Pierre Brondeau
Independent Director, Lynn Dugle
President - Communications Solutions, Aaron Stucki
Senior Vice President, General Manager, Channel, Karen Leggio
Senior Vice President, Corporate Controller, Robert Ott
Chief Financial Officer, Executive Vice President, Executive Director, Heath Mitts, $673,111 total compensation
SVP, Eric Resch
Chairman, Thomas Lynch
Chief Executive Officer, Executive Director, Terrence Curtin, $1,200,000 total compensation
Independent Director, William Jeffrey
Independent Director, Dawn Willoughby
President - Industrial Solutions, Shadrak Kroeger, $573,250 total compensation
Independent Director, Yong Nam
President - Transportation Solutions, Steven Merkt, $654,136 total compensation
Executive Vice President, General Counsel, John Jenkins, $573,513 total compensation
Independent Director, Laura Wright
Auditors: DELOITTE & TOUCHE LLP

LOCATIONS

HQ: TE Connectivity Ltd
  Muhlenstrasse 26, Schaffhausen CH-8200
Phone: (41) 52 633 6661
Web: www.te.com

2018 Sales

	$ mil.	% of total
EMEA	5,255	38
APAC	4,762	34
Americas	3,971	28
Total	13,988	100

PRODUCTS/OPERATIONS

2018 Sales

	$ mil.	% of total
Transportation Solutions	8,290	59
Industrial Solutions	3,856	28
Communications Solutions	1,842	23
Total	13,988	100

Selected Products

Antennas
Application tooling
Circuit protection devices
Connector systems
Fiber optics
Heat shrink tubing
Intelligent building controls
Network interface devices
Racks and panels
Relays
Touch screens
Undersea telecommunication systems
Wire and cable

COMPETITORS

Alpiq Holding SA
CTS CORPORATION
Canadian Apartment Properties Real Estate Investment Tru
DEXUS PROPERTY SERVICES PTY LIMITED
EXAR CORPORATION
FORMFACTOR INC.
GROUPE CRIT
ICAHN ENTERPRISES L.P.
INVENTEC CORPORATION
MACOM TECHNOLOGY SOLUTIONS HOLDINGS INC.
MAXLINEAR INC.
SANMINA CORPORATION
TCP International Holdings Ltd.
VIAVI SOLUTIONS INC.
VOLEX PLC

HISTORICAL FINANCIALS

Company Type: Public

Income Statement				FYE: September 24
	REVENUE ($ mil.)	NET INCOME ($ mil.)	NET PROFIT MARGIN	EMPLOYEES
09/21	14,923	2,261	15.2%	89,000
09/20	12,172	(241)	—	82,000
09/19	13,448	1,844	13.7%	78,000
09/18	13,988	2,565	18.3%	80,000
09/17	25,298	3,366	13.3%	78,000
Annual Growth	(12.4%)	(9.5%)	—	3.4%

2021 Year-End Financials

Debt ratio: 19.0%
Return on equity: 22.6%
Cash ($ mil.): 1,203
Current ratio: 1.56
Long-term debt ($ mil.): 3,589

No. of shares (mil.): 329
Dividends
  Yield: 1.3%
  Payout: 38.6%
Market value ($ mil.): —

TechnipFMC plc

Auditors: PricewaterhouseCoopers LLP

LOCATIONS

HQ: TechnipFMC plc
Hadrian House, Wincomblee Road, Newcastle Upon Tyne NE6 3PL
Phone: (44) 191 295 0303
Web: www.technipfmc.com/

HISTORICAL FINANCIALS

Company Type: Public

Income Statement				FYE: December 31
	REVENUE ($ mil.)	NET INCOME ($ mil.)	NET PROFIT MARGIN	EMPLOYEES
12/20	13,050	(3,287)	—	35,000
12/19	13,409	(2,415)	—	37,000
12/18	12,552	(1,921)	—	37,000
12/17	15,056	113	0.8%	37,000
12/16	0	(0)	—	0
Annual Growth	—	—	—	—

2020 Year-End Financials

Debt ratio: 20.2%
Return on equity: (-55.5%)
Cash ($ mil.): 4,832
Current ratio: 1.10
Long-term debt ($ mil.): 3,317

No. of shares (mil.): 449
Dividends
  Yield: 7.4%
  Payout: —
Market value ($ mil.): —

Telecom Italia SpA

Telecom Italia SpA (TIM) is Italy's #1 telephone operator with more than 17100 fixed retail and wholesale access lines and more than 30800 mobile lines for retail and wholesale customers. The company has the largest customer base in Italy. It also operates in Brazil where it boasts about 55000 subscribers to its mobile services. Subsidiary Inwit is responsible for the management and operations of telecom towers used by TIM and other operators. Besides telecommunications TIM's Olivetti brand makes IT products such as printers calculators cash registers and digital school equipment for businesses and other organizations. TIM generates more than 75% of its sales in Italy.

Operations
TIM operates in three reportable segments: Domestic Brazil and Other Operations.

TIM's domestic segment generates about 80% of revenue. The segment also includes Olivetti (products and services for IT) INWIT (electronic communications) and Telecom Italia Sparkle Group (fiber-optic networks for wholesale).

The Brazil business unit generates about 20% of TIM's revenue. It provides mobile telephone service using UMTS GSM and LTE Technologies.

Other operations segment includes the financial companies (Telecom Italia Capital S.A. and Telecom Italia Finance S.A.) and other minor companies not strictly related to the TIM Group's core business.

Overall The company's services account for about 90% of total revenue while equipment sales and construction contracts account for the remaining.

Geographic Reach
Based in Rome TIM's main geographies are Italy (80% of sales) and Brazil (20%). Through subsidiary Sparkle the company operates in Europe the Mediterranean South America.

Sales and Marketing
TIM divides its sales organizations for consumers business wholesale and other.

The consumer unit is made up of fixed and mobile voice and internet services and products for individuals families and public telephony. The segment includes TIM Retail.

The business unit consists of voice data and internet services and products as well as ICT technologies for small and medium businesses home offices public sector large. accounts and enterprises in the fixed and mobile telecoms markets. The segment includes Olivetti TI Trust Technologies and Tesly.

Wholesale manages and develops of the portfolio of the regulated and unregulated whole services for fixed-line and mobile telecommunications operators in the domestic market and open access operations. The segment includes TN Fiber TI San Marino and Telefonia Mobile Sammarinese.

Financial Performance
Note: Growth rates may differ after conversion to US Dollars.

Total TIM Group revenues decreased 5% to 17974 million euros for 2019 compared with the previous year. This was primarily due to lower sales in the company's services segment.

2019 Net profit for the year attributable to owners of the parent amounted to 916 million euros (while a net loss of 1.4 billion euros was posted in 2018).

Cash at the end of 2019 was 3.2 billion euros. Operating activities generated 5.9 billion euros while investing activities used 3.2 billion euros mainly for purchases of intangible tangible and rights of use assets on a cash basis. Financing activities used another 1.1 billion euros primarily for repayments of non-current financial liabilities.

Strategy
TIM has four strategic initiatives consist of:

Network-sharing partnership with INWIT and Vodafone Italia: following the green light from the European antitrust authority the creation of the new INWIT and the implementation of the planned programs for the sharing of passive mobile network infrastructure with Vodafone will be monitored with benefits in terms of lower capital invested and shorter development times for 5G networks.

Fiber networks: a period of exclusivity has been granted to the KKR Infrastructure fund as a financial partner for the development of the fiber network in Italy following the submission of a non-binding offer for the purchase of approximately 40% of TIM's secondary fiber/copper network and given the desired integration with Open Fiber.

Partnership for Cloud Services: signed the final agreements with Google Cloud which start a technological collaboration to create cloud services and enrich TIM's technological services offering which will lead to the development of business of about 1 billion euros in revenues and 400 million euros in EBITDA up to 2024.

Exclusive deal with Disney: the big world player in the content industry has chosen TIM Vision for the exclusive distribution of Disney+ in Italy confirming TIM Vision as the reference operator in the aggregation of premium content in Italy a position achieved in just one year.

Company Background
Telecom Italia S.p.A. is a leader in fixed-line and wireless telecommunication services in Italy. As a holding company with majority ownership in numerous subsidiaries it provides domestic and international fixed-line and wireless telecommunication operations as well as Internet information technology and satellite communication services. Its international operations include fixed-line and wireless communications in Latin America and the Mediterranean region. It is the majority owner of Telecom Italia Mobile (TIM) Italy's leading provider of wireless communications. Telecom Italia is the former government telephone monopoly which was privatized in 1997 and controlled by Olivetti in 1999 in a hostile takeover. Telecom Italia faces increasing competition in both domestic and international markets.

HISTORY

After gaining political power in Italy Benito Mussolini began a program of nationalization focusing first on three major banks and their equity portfolios. Included were three local phone companies that became the core of Societ Finanziaria Telefonica (STET) created in 1933 to handle Italy's phone services under the state's industrial holding company Istituto per La Ricostruzione Industriale (IRI).

Germany and Italy grew closer in the years leading up to WWII and Italian equipment makers entered a venture with Siemens to make phone equipment. STET came through the war with most of its infrastructure intact and a monopoly on phone service in Italy. Siemens' properties along with those of other equipment makers were taken over by another company TETI which was nationalized and put under STET's control in 1958. This expanded STET's monopoly to include equipment manufacturing.

Italy's industries were increasingly nationalized under IRI. Companies within the IRI family forged alliances with each other and with independent companies which frequently were absorbed into STET.

STET's scope expanded during the 1960s and 1970s to include satellite and data communications but its monopoly was undermined by new technologies such as faxes PCs and teleconferencing. In the technology race among equipment makers STET fell behind. And in a satellite communications era STET's status as a necessary long-distance carrier was threatened. Despite these pressures change did not come easily to STET. State monopolies maintained popular support not only on nationalistic grounds but also because of labor's strong anticompetitive stance.

Anticipating privatization however IRI reorganized STET in 1994 and poured new capital into the company. STET's five telecom companies — SIP (domestic phone operator) Italcable (intercontinental) Telespazio (satellite) SIRM (maritime) and Iritel (domestic long distance) — were merged into one Telecom Italia. Its mobile phone business was spun off as Telecom Italia Mobile (TIM) in 1995.

To end political feuding the government abruptly replaced the heads of STET and Telecom Italia in 1997. Telecom Italia was merged with STET which took the Telecom Italia name and was privatized that year. Berardino Libonati became chairman and Franco Bernabe formerly CEO of oil company ENI took the helm as CEO. The company began taking stakes in foreign telecom companies including mobilkom austria Spanish broadcaster Retevision and — as European Union competition began in 1998 — Telekom Austria.

Erstwhile rival Olivetti launched a hostile takeover bid for Telecom Italia in 1999. Though Telecom Italia tried to fend off the smaller firm with various maneuvers including a proposed merger with Deutsche Telekom Olivetti gained 55% of Telecom Italia. Olivetti CEO Roberto Colaninno took over as chairman and CEO.

That year Telecom Italia sold 50% of Stream its pay TV unit to an investor group led by News Corp. The company also announced plans to spin off and sell a stake in its ISP Tin.it. In 2000 however Telecom Italia instead combined Tin.it with SEAT Pagine Gialle a yellow pages directory publisher and Internet portal operator (spun off from the parent company and sold in 2003). Also that year the company sold off 81% of its telecom equipment unit Italtel and its 49% stake in installations firm Sirti.

In 2001 Colaninno and several other Telecom Italia officials were named as suspects in an investigation of whether the company had violated accounting conflict of interest and share manipulation laws. Colaninno was replaced when tire maker Pirelli and Edizione Holding the parent company of the Benetton Group acquired a 23% stake in Olivetti.

Telecom Italia teamed up with News Corp. to develop the Stream pay TV joint venture renamed Sky Italia. The venture gained a kick-start when the two companies teamed to buy Italian pay-TV business Telepiu from Vivendi Universal in a cash and debt assumption deal that was valued at $871 million. The deal included agreements to drop disputes between Telepiu and Stream. Telecom Italia then sold a 30% stake in the venture to News Corp. It retained a 20% share with News Corp. controlling 80%.

In 2003 the company abandoned plans to acquire phone directories group Pagine Utili from Fininvest in a deal that would have been worth more than $130 million because of protests by Italian regulators who claimed the deal would breach competition laws. It also spun off its international services division starting in 2003 into a separate company Telecom Italia Sparkle which concentrated on services to other fixed-line operators ISPs and international corporations and sold its nearly 62% stake in SEAT Pagine Gialle to an investor group for $3.55 billion.

Once the subsidiary Telecom Italia became the parent company after the 2003 merger with former parent Olivetti. The reorganization simplified a corporate structure that was at best confusing: Olivetti through its Tecnost unit had acquired a controlling 55% stake in Telecom Italia in 1999. Two years later tire maker Pirelli and the Benetton family teamed up to take control of Olivetti. Olivetti's largest shareholder was Olimpia a company owned by Pirelli and the Benetton Group among others.

Because Telecom Italia accounted for more than 95% of the revenues of Olivetti the reorganization also kept the focus on the core business. The merger was met with favor among market watchers and some shareholders although a group of international investors opposed the restructuring.

Reorganization continued at the company and it began selling some international fixed-line assets and putting some wireless operations outside Italy on the market. Disposals included Digitel the Venezuelan wireless carrier to Oswaldo Cisneros' Telvenco in a deal valued at about $425 million. It also sold its 81% stake in Greek wireless carrier Hellas Telecommunications to US-based private equity firms Texas Pacific Group and Apax Partners in a deal valued at $1.4 billion; stakes in Spanish joint venture Auna and satellite unit Telespazio (to Leonardo - Finmeccanica); and in 2005 it sold its holdings in IT services and consulting company Finsiel to Italian outsourcing firm Gruppo COS.

After spurning an offer from AT&T to buy the company Telecom Italia named Pasquale Pistorio chairman in 2007 replacing Guido Rossi who had held the position for only seven months. Telefonica subsequently won control of the company. Later that year Pistorio was replaced by Gabriele Galateri as chairman; Galateri was nominated by another top shareholder Mediobanca.

In 2010 the company began selling off interests not related to its businesses in Italy or Brazil. It sold its 70% stake in Elettra which specialized in laying submarine cables to France Telecom (later renamed Orange) for ?20 million ($27 million); its Netherlands fixed-line provider BBNed to Tele2 for ?50 million ($64 million); and its German broadband unit HanseNet to Telef "nica for the tidy sum of ?900 million ($1.2 billion) in cash. The following year Telecom Italia sold its 27% stake in the state-run Cuban phone company ETECSA for $706 million to Rafin SA a financial services firm in that country. Also in 2011 the company sold subsidiary Loquendo to US-based Nuance Communications. The sales were part of Telecom Italia's ongoing effort to sell non-core businesses in order to reduce debt.

EXECUTIVES

Chairman, Salvatore Rossi
Non-Executive Director, Frank Cadoret
Director Presidente Tim Participaç es S.A., Pietro Labriola
Head of IT and Security Compliance, Roberto Mazzilli
Head of Legal, Regulatory and Tax, General Counsel, Secretary and Director, Agostino Nuzzolo
Chief Technology and Information Office, Michele Gamberini
Chairman, Arnaud Roy de Puyfontaine
Auditors: EY S.p.A.

LOCATIONS

HQ: Telecom Italia SpA
Via Gaetano Negri 1, Milan 20123
Phone: (39) 06 36 88 1
Web: www.telecomitalia.com

2018 Sales

	% of total
Italy	79
Other regions	21
Total	**100**

PRODUCTS/OPERATIONS

2018 Sales

	% of total
Services	92
Equipment sales	8
Total	**100**

2017 Sales

	% of total
Domestic	79
Brazil	21
Total	**100**

COMPETITORS

1&1 AG	Proximus
AT&T INC.	SBA COMMUNICATIONS
BT GROUP PLC	CORPORATION
Deutsche Telekom AG	SPIRENT COMMUNICATIONS
IDT CORPORATION	PLC
JAZZ TELECOM SAU	VODAFONE GROUP PUBLIC
(EXTINGUIDA)	LIMITED COMPANY
Nortel Networks	VODAFONE ITALIA SPA
Corporation	WIND TELECOMUNICAZIONI
PCCW LIMITED	SPA

HISTORICAL FINANCIALS

Company Type: Public

Income Statement   FYE: December 31

	REVENUE ($ mil.)	NET INCOME ($ mil.)	NET PROFIT MARGIN	EMPLOYEES
12/20	20,272	8,865	43.7%	52,347
12/19	21,831	1,028	4.7%	55,198
12/18	22,733	(1,615)	—	57,901
12/17	25,146	1,343	5.3%	59,429
12/16	21,091	1,909	9.1%	61,229
Annual Growth	**(1.0%)**	**46.8%**	**—**	**(3.8%)**

2020 Year-End Financials

Debt ratio: 42.6%
Return on equity: 30.9%
Cash ($ mil.): 5,926
Current ratio: 0.97
Long-term debt ($ mil.): 26,770

No. of shares (mil.): —
Dividends
Yield: 1.8%
Payout: 22.5%
Market value ($ mil.): —

	STOCK PRICE ($) FY Close	P/E High/Low	Earnings	Dividends	Book Value
12/20	4.57	20 10	0.41	0.08	2.12
12/19	6.18	162121	0.04	0.01	1.51
12/18	5.55	—	(0.08)	0.00	1.49
12/17	8.63	221160	0.06	0.00	1.72
12/16	8.89	151 83	0.08	0.00	1.49
Annual Growth	**(15.3%)**	**— —**	**48.0%**	**—**	**9.3%**

Telefonica SA

Auditors: PricewaterhouseCoopers Auditores, S.L.

LOCATIONS

HQ: Telefonica SA
Distrito Telefonica, Ronda de la Comunicacion, s/n, Madrid 28050
Phone: (34) 91 482 3733   **Fax:** (34) 91 482 3817
Web: www.telefonica.com

HISTORICAL FINANCIALS

Company Type: Public

Income Statement

	REVENUE ($ mil.)	NET INCOME ($ mil.)	NET PROFIT MARGIN	EMPLOYEES
12/20	52,866	1,941	3.7%	112,797
12/19	54,366	1,282	2.4%	113,819
12/18	55,762	3,814	6.8%	120,138
12/17	62,344	3,754	6.0%	122,718
12/16	54,943	2,501	4.6%	127,323
Annual Growth	(1.0%)	(6.1%)	—	(3.0%)

FYE: December 31

2020 Year-End Financials

Debt ratio: 58.9%
Return on equity: 11.1%
Cash ($ mil.): 6,877
Current ratio: 1.20
Long-term debt ($ mil.): 51,910

No. of shares (mil.): —
Dividends
 Yield: 11.2%
 Payout: 154.5%
Market value ($ mil.): —

	STOCK PRICE ($) FY Close	P/E High/Low	PER SHARE ($) Earnings	Dividends	Book Value
12/20	4.04	33 14	0.29	0.46	2.54
12/19	6.97	52 39	0.19	0.45	3.76
12/18	8.46	17 13	0.65	0.46	4.01
12/17	9.68	23 17	0.67	0.48	3.96
12/16	9.20	26 19	0.44	0.77	3.92
Annual Growth	(18.6%) (10.3%)	— —	(9.7%)	(12.3%)	

Telenor ASA

Telenor is a leading Scandinavian telecommunications provider offering mobile broadband and TV services. The Norway-based company's mobile business has about 174 million subscribers in its home country Sweden and Denmark and across the world in Pakistan Bangladesh Thailand Malaysia and Myanmar. Telenor entered Finland's telecom market in 2019 by taking a controlling stake in DNA the country's third-largest mobile firm. Norway is Telenor's biggest market accounting for about a quarter of revenue while Southeast Asian operations combine to provide more than 50% of revenue.

Financial Performance

Telenor's annual revenue peaked at more than $128 billion Norwegian krone (NOK) in 2015 and has declined since as its number of landline customers has shrunk. Paring cost helped strengthen the company's profits in 2017 and 2018.

Revenue in 2018 dipped to NOK 110.4 billion down 1.5% dip from 2017 due to lower handset sales a diminished customer base for legacy products and interconnect revenue. The company reported growth in mobile subscriptions and traffic revenue as well as in the number of high-speed internet customers.

Net income rose to NOK 14.7 billion in 2018 up NOK 2.7 billion from 2017 boosted by the partial sale of ownership of Telenor Microfinance Bank and the disposal of assets in Central and Eastern Europe.

In 2018 Telenor's cash coffers had NOK 18.3 billion compared to NOK 22.3 billion the year before. In 2018 operating activities generated NOL 36.4 billion while investing and financing activities used NOK 613 million and NOK 39.5 billion.

Strategy

Telenor's far-flung operations are governed by three strategic watchwords: Growth efficiency and

simplification. Seeking efficiency the company continues to cut expenses reducing its operational costs 3% in 2018. Telenor has saved some money by outsourcing network and IT operations and sharing infrastructure in some Asian markets.

In simplifying Telenor divested its operations in India sharply reduced its stake in VEON (a telecom firm with businesses in Asia Africa and Europe) and sold its operations in Central and Eastern Europe including the merger of its 701Search business with Carousell a fast-growing Asian classifieds marketplace.

Those actions free Telenor to concentrate on its businesses in Scandinavia and Southeast Asia. By claiming a controlling interest in DNA the third-ranking telecom in Finland Telenor now has operations throughout the region. In Scandinavia Telenor is upgrading networks adding base stations and offering new subscription plans designed to keep customers and attract new ones.

In Southeast Asia Telenor is upgrading networks and offering more services. In Pakistan where the company has built a 2.3 gHz network it is developing mobile financial services through a joint venture with Ant Financials.

Further Telenor invests in developing capabilities in artificial intelligence robotics and security.

Telenor faces competition from Telia Co. its Sweden-based rival for Nordic domination. Telia divested holdings in Central and Eastern Europe to focus on the Nordic countries. Telia last year widened its presence in Norway in 2018 by buying TDC A/S's Norwegian business. And Telia bolstered its TV holdings in buying Bonnier AB's TV operations in Sweden and Finland.

Mergers and Acquisitions

In 2019 Telenor increased its stake in DNA a mobile carrier in Finland to more than 50% with the intention of eventually owning it outright. The deal will give Telenor control of the third-largest mobile operator in Finland a country with the world's highest mobile data use in the world. DNA is also Finland's second-largest broadband service provider and operates its biggest cable-TV service.

HISTORY

Telecommunications arrived in Norway in 1855 when the first telegraph line was opened and the Norwegian Telegraph Administration was created. By 1880 telephone systems were being installed followed by the first automatic phone exchange (1918) Telex services (1946) and a transmitter network for television which debuted in 1960. Mobile phone service was introduced in 1966 but it was not until 1969 that the agency's name was changed to Norwegian Telecommunications Administration.

Norway had progressed to its first computer-controlled phone exchange by the mid 1970s and in 1976 launched a national satellite system (NORSAT) that linked North Sea oil explorers with Norway's mainland. It opened the world's first fully automated coastal earth station in 1982 to carry maritime traffic as part of the INMARSAT system and a year later automated its last manually operated phone exchange. (Telenor held a stake in INMARSAT until it sold it in 2006.)

In the mid-1980s the national carrier became known as Norwegian Telecom (Televerket). In 1984 it introduced an upgraded mobile phone system and a numeric paging system (alphanumeric paging followed in 1991). The first digital phone exchanges arrived in 1986 and two years later Televerket was reorganized into three units: the national operator (Televerket) a sales subsidiary (TBK) and a state regulatory agency for equipment approval (STF).

The company in 1990 organized its mobile services under a single division (Tele-mobil) which a

year later became a limited company. Two years later data transmission was opened to competition and the resale of surplus leased line capacity was allowed.

In 1993 Televerket reorganized under the name Norwegian Telecom Group and joined a consortium of Nordic and Hungarian companies to win a mobile operator license in Hungary. A year later it became a state-owned company and in 1995 was renamed Telenor. That year it teamed up with British Telecommunications (now BT Group) and Tele Danmark (now TDC) to create the Swedish telecom competitor Telenordia (Telenor and BT became 50-50 owners in 2000).

EXECUTIVES

EVP and Head, Nordics, Jukka Leinonen, $660,446 total compensation

Independent Director, Pieter Knook

Independent Director, Astrid Joos

President, Chief Executive Officer, Sigve Brekke, $714,518 total compensation

Executive Vice President, Head of Telenor Asia, Jorgen Arentz Rostrup, $571,848 total compensation

Executive Vice President, Chief People & Sustainability Officer, Cecilie Heuch, $337,393 total compensation

EVP, Chief People and Sustainability Officer, Tone Bachke, $291,501 total compensation

Independent Chair of the Board, Gunn Waersted

Independent Deputy Chair of the Board, Jorgen Kildahl

Executive Vice President, Chief Technology Officer, Ruza Sabanovic, $435,871 total compensation

Auditors: Ernst & Young AG

LOCATIONS

HQ: Telenor ASA
 Snaroyveien 30, Fornebu N-1360
Phone: (47) 678 90 000
Web: www.telenor.com

2018 Sales

	% of total
Norway	26
Sweden	13
Other Nordic	5
Thailand	17
Malaysia	12
Bangladesh	12
Other Asia	13
Other Countires	2
Total	100

PRODUCTS/OPERATIONS

2018 Sales

	% of total
Mobile Subscription and Traffic	63
Fixed Internet/TV	8
Canal Digital DTH	4
Fixed Telephony	1
Fixed Data Services	1
Other Revenue	23
Total	100

COMPETITORS

Deutsche Telekom AG
EIRCOM LIMITED
KCOM GROUP LIMITED
NETIA S A
NIPPON TELEGRAPH AND TELEPHONE CORPORATION
Proximus
TELSTRA CORPORATION LIMITED
Tele2 AB
Telekom Austria Aktiengesellschaft
Telia Company AB

HISTORICAL FINANCIALS

Company Type: Public

Income Statement   FYE: December 31

	REVENUE ($ mil.)	NET INCOME ($ mil.)	NET PROFIT MARGIN	EMPLOYEES
12/20	14,414	2,035	14.1%	18,000
12/19	12,934	884	6.8%	20,000
12/18	12,714	1,697	13.3%	21,000
12/17	15,215	1,461	9.6%	31,000
12/16	15,275	329	2.2%	36,000
Annual Growth	(1.4%)	57.7%	—	(15.9%)

2020 Year-End Financials

Debt ratio: 5.0%	No. of shares (mil.): 1,399
Return on equity: 45.2%	Dividends
Cash ($ mil.): 2,415	Yield: 5.3%
Current ratio: 0.83	Payout: 71.8%
Long-term debt ($ mil.): 11,748	Market value ($ mil.): 23,791

	STOCK PRICE ($) FY Close	P/E High/Low		PER SHARE ($) Earnings	Dividends	Book Value
12/20	17.00	2	1	1.45	0.91	3.21
12/19	17.91	4	3	0.61	0.94	3.04
12/18	19.37	2	2	1.15	1.52	3.91
12/17	21.39	3	2	0.97	0.97	4.67
12/16	14.92	27	8	0.22	0.85	3.94
Annual Growth	3.3%	—	—	60.2%	1.5%	(5.0%)

Telstra Corp., Ltd.

Telstra is Australia's #1 telecommunications carrier serving more than 18.3 million retail mobile phone customers 3.7 million fixed-line bundle and standalone data subscribers and about 1.4 million standalone voice subscribers. It is also a leading ISP with more than 7.3 million fixed line broadband subscribers. Telstra's largest market is consumer and residential customers. The company also provides wholesale network services to other communications companies. Telstra has installed fifth generation (5G) network services in 10 Australian cities preparing for the broader roll out of the technology in the coming years. Telstra has the Asia/Pacific region's largest subsea cable network measuring about 400000 kilometers.

Operations

Telstra operates through four segments: Telstra Consumer and Small Business (TC&SB) Telstra Enterprise (TE) Telstra InfraCo and Networks and IT (N&IT).

The TC&SB segment 55% of revenue provides telecommunications products and mobile services fixed and mobile broadband telephone and Pay TV/IPTV and digital content.

The TE segment about a third of sales manages Telstrós business with larger companies. It manages data and internet protocol (IP) networks mobility services and network applications and services products such as managed network unified communications cloud and integrated services

The Telstra InfraCo segment about 10% of revenue provides telecommunication products and services delivered over Telstra's network to other carries carriage services providers and inter-service providers.

The N&IT segment builds and manages the shared platforms infrastructure cloud services software and technologies for internal functions.

Geographic Reach

Australia accounts for 95% of Telstra's revenue. The company's international operations headquartered in Hong Kong provide services to customers across the Asia/Pacific region Europe the Americas the Middle East and Africa.

Sales and Marketing

Telstra has many ways to reach its customers and prospective customers. It operates 362 branded retail stores 90 Telstra Business Centers and it has 127 business and enterprise partners. Its products are available in more 15000 partner retail locations. A company initiative is to improve and expedite customer service. About 52% of its customer service interactions are handled online and 2.3 million customers use Telstra's smartphone app.

Financial Performance

Australian dollars are used in this financial report.

Telstra's revenue has been stagnant in the past five years as it has coped with increased competition in the Australian communications market.

In 2019 (ended June) revenue dropped to $27.8 billion down about $1 billion from 2018. The company blamed the decrease on the National Broadband Network (nbn) a national wholesaler of broadband service that Telstra and other carriers buy service from. The company reported growth in its mobile wholesale and fixed-line businesses.

Telstra's profit also decreased dropping to $2.1 billion in 2019 about 40% lower than the previous year despite cost reductions made in 2019.

The company's coffers held $604 million in cash and equivalents at the end of 2019 compared to $620 million at the close of 2018. In 2019 operations generated $6.7 billion while investing activities used $3.6 billion and financing activities used about $3 billion.

Strategy

The launch of a national broadband network known as nbn has meant headaches for Telstra. In 2019 (ended June) the network cost the company about $600 million in revenue. As the top telecom provider in Australia Telstra had been the de facto broadband provider in the country. But that role will go to nbn when the transition is complete. Telstra created its InfraCo segment in response to nbn and it positions the unit as an alternative infrastructure provider.

In the meantime Telstra aims to improve its overall business through a plan of simplification. It is simplifying its business structure cutting about $456 million in costs in 2019. It has made its offerings to consumers and businesses less complex reducing the number of plans available to 20 from some 1800.

Telstra is rolling out 5G service to more Australian cities and has begun selling 5G handsets. The emergence of the faster network could leapfrog the technologies sold by nbn and feed Telstra's revenue in the coming years.

Mergers and Acquisitions

The company acquired Pacnet Ltd. which operates undersea cables through Asia and from North America to Asia across the Pacific Ocean. The $697 million transaction brings Telstra an expanded data center network more submarine cables and major customers across the region. The move boosts Telstra's engagement with corporate customers.

HISTORY

When Australia gained independence in 1901 telecommunications were assigned to the new state-owned Postmaster-General's Department (PMG). Engineer H. P. Brown who had managed the UK's telegraph and telephone system became head of PMG in 1923. He set up research labs that

year oversaw the first overseas call to London in 1930 and streamlined operations until his reign ended in 1939.

During WWII Australia quickly expanded its communications infrastructure to assist the Allied Front in the South Pacific. Following the war the government formed the Overseas Telecommunications Commission (OTC) in 1946 to handle international operations independent of PMG.

Even as new technology connected the continent and boosted the productivity of PMG its postal operations steadily recorded losses in the postwar era. In 1974 a Royal Commission recommended that postal and telecom services be split. Australian Telecommunications Commission (Telecom Australia) was launched in 1975 (OTC retained overseas services); it turned a profit in its first year.

Looking to connect residents in the outback the firm signed Japan's Nippon Electric (now NEC) in 1981 to set up a digital radio transmission system; by the next decade it connected some 50000 outback users. Also in 1981 Telecom Australia took a 25% stake in government-owned satellite operator AUSSAT and launched nationwide paging and mobile phone service in Melbourne and Sydney.

Renamed Australian Telecommunications in 1989 the carrier got its first whiff of competition as others were allowed to provide phone equipment. Two years later Optus Communications began competing with Telecom Australia; for the privilege it was forced to buy the unsuccessful AUSSAT. Long-distance competition began in 1991 and mobile phone competition began in 1992. In response Telecom Australia merged with OTC to become Australian and Overseas Telecommunications Corporation (AOTC).

AOTC became Telstra Corporation in 1993 and launched a digital wireless GSM-based network. It joined with Rupert Murdoch's News Corp. to form pay TV operator FOXTEL in 1995.

EXECUTIVES

Non-Executive Independent Director, Nora Scheinkestel, $211,777 total compensation

Chief Executive Officer - Telstra InfraCo, Group Executive, Brendon Riley, $1,027,567 total compensation

Chief Executive Officer and Managing Director, Andrew Penn, $1,765,805 total compensation

Non-Executive Independent Director, Elana Rubin, $199,846 total compensation

Non-Executive Independent Director, Bridget Loudon, $140,936 total compensation

Non-Executive Independent Director, Eelco Blok, $172,255 total compensation

Group Executive - Telstra Enterprise, David Burns, $805,350 total compensation

Group Executive - Transformation, Communications and People, Alexandra Badenoch, $677,090 total compensation

CFO and Group Executive, Strategy and Finance, Vicki Brady, $878,428 total compensation

Non-Executive Independent Director, Roy Chestnutt, $197,609 total compensation

Group Executive - Networks and IT, Nikos Katinakis, $803,858 total compensation

Company Secretary, Sue Laver

Group Executive - Product and Technology, Kim Krogh Andersen, $729,289 total compensation

Non-Executive Independent Director, Niek Jan van Damme, $192,389 total compensation

Group General Counsel and Group Executive, Sustainability, External Affairs & Legal, Lyndall Stoyles

Non-Executive Independent Chairman of the Board, John Mullen, $561,508 total compensation

Non-Executive Independent Director, Craig Dunn, $220,725 total compensation

Head, Consumer and Small Business Segment, Michael Ackland, $836,669 total compensation
Auditors: Ernst & Young

LOCATIONS

HQ: Telstra Corp., Ltd.
Level 41, 242 Exhibition Street, Melbourne, Victoria 3000
Phone: (61) 3 8647 4838   **Fax:** (61) 3 9650 0989
Web: www.telstra.com

2019 Sales

	% of total
Australia	94
Other countries	6
Total	**100**

PRODUCTS/OPERATIONS

2019 Sales

	% of total
Fixed	21
Mobile	42
Data & IP	9
Network applications & services	14
Media	3
Global connectivity	7
Other	4
Total	**100**

2015 Sales

	% of total
TC&SB	56
TE	33
Telstra InfraCo	11
N&IT	-
Other	-
Total	**100**

Selected Services

Advertising and directory services
Audio video and Internet conferencing
Broadband ISP
Cable TV
Data transmission
E-mail
Enhanced fax products and services
Freecall (toll-free 1-800 phone service)
Information technology (IT) services
Internet access
Mobile phone service
Prepaid telephony
Satellite transmission

COMPETITORS

AT&T INC.
CHARTER COMMUNICATIONS INC.
Deutsche Telekom AG
HAWAIIAN TELCOM HOLDCO INC.
IDT CORPORATION
SINGAPORE TELECOMMUNICATIONS LIMITED
SK Telecom Co. Ltd.
VIRGIN MEDIA INC.
VODAFONE GROUP PUBLIC LIMITED COMPANY
XO HOLDINGS INC

HISTORICAL FINANCIALS

Company Type: Public

Income Statement   FYE: June 30

	REVENUE ($ mil.)	NET INCOME ($ mil.)	NET PROFIT MARGIN	EMPLOYEES
06/21	16,181	1,393	8.6%	27,015
06/20	16,248	1,246	7.7%	28,959
06/19	17,697	1,509	8.5%	29,769
06/18	19,206	2,630	13.7%	32,293
06/17	19,986	2,989	15.0%	32,293
Annual Growth	(5.1%)	(17.4%)	—	(4.4%)

2021 Year-End Financials

Debt ratio: 24.2%
Return on equity: 12.7%
Cash ($ mil.): 844
Current ratio: 0.68
Long-term debt ($ mil.): 7,575

No. of shares (mil.): —
Dividends
  Yield: 4.1%
  Payout: 499.4%
Market value ($ mil.): —

	STOCK PRICE ($) FY Close	P/E High/Low		PER SHARE ($) Earnings	Dividends	Book Value
06/21	14.04	88	64	0.12	0.59	0.92
06/20	10.80	90	66	0.10	0.49	0.83
06/19	13.44	75	51	0.13	0.64	0.86
06/18	9.74	54	32	0.22	0.92	0.93
06/17	16.52	69	47	0.25	1.14	0.94
Annual Growth (0.5%)	(4.0%)			—	(17.2%)	(15.3%)

TELUS Corp

Auditors: Deloitte LLP

LOCATIONS

HQ: TELUS Corp
Floor 23, 510 West Georgia, Vancouver, British Columbia V6B 0M3
Phone: 604 697-8044   **Fax:** 604 899-1289
Web: www.telus.com

HISTORICAL FINANCIALS

Company Type: Public

Income Statement   FYE: December 31

	REVENUE ($ mil.)	NET INCOME ($ mil.)	NET PROFIT MARGIN	EMPLOYEES
12/20	12,048	947	7.9%	78,100
12/19	11,203	1,340	12.0%	65,600
12/18	10,350	1,174	11.4%	58,000
12/17	10,531	1,164	11.1%	0
12/16	9,442	907	9.6%	51,250
Annual Growth	6.3%	1.1%	—	11.1%

2020 Year-End Financials

Debt ratio: 36.9%
Return on equity: 10.6%
Cash ($ mil.): 666
Current ratio: 0.79
Long-term debt ($ mil.): 14,809

No. of shares (mil.): 1,291
Dividends
  Yield: 4.5%
  Payout: 160.5%
Market value ($ mil.): 25,562

	STOCK PRICE ($) FY Close	P/E High/Low		PER SHARE ($) Earnings	Dividends	Book Value
12/20	19.80	46	16	0.74	0.89	7.35
12/19	38.73	27	24	1.11	0.85	6.69
12/18	33.14	27	24	0.98	0.80	6.29
12/17	37.87	32	27	0.98	0.79	5.51
12/16	31.85	32	26	0.76	0.68	4.98
Annual Growth (11.2%)				—	(0.9%)	7.0% 10.2%

Tencent Holdings Ltd.

Auditors: PricewaterhouseCoopers Certified Public Accountants

LOCATIONS

HQ: Tencent Holdings Ltd.
Tencent Binhai Towers, No. 33 Haitian 2nd Road, Nanshan District, Shenzhen, Guangdong Province 518054
Phone: (86) 755 86013388   **Fax:** (86) 755 86013399
Web: www.tencent.com

HISTORICAL FINANCIALS

Company Type: Public

Income Statement   FYE: December 31

	REVENUE ($ mil.)	NET INCOME ($ mil.)	NET PROFIT MARGIN	EMPLOYEES
12/20	73,707	24,440	33.2%	85,858
12/19	54,221	13,410	24.7%	62,885
12/18	45,461	11,444	25.2%	54,309
12/17	36,536	10,988	30.1%	44,796
12/16	21,880	5,918	27.0%	38,775
Annual Growth	35.5%	42.6%	—	22.0%

2020 Year-End Financials

Debt ratio: 2.8%
Return on equity: 28.0%
Cash ($ mil.): 23,362
Current ratio: 1.18
Long-term debt ($ mil.): 35,809

No. of shares (mil.): —
Dividends
  Yield: 0.1%
  Payout: 5.8%
Market value ($ mil.): —

	STOCK PRICE ($) FY Close	P/E High/Low		PER SHARE ($) Earnings	Dividends	Book Value
12/20	71.89	5	3	2.53	0.14	11.32
12/19	48.01	5	4	1.39	0.12	6.56
12/18	39.47	7	4	1.20	0.10	4.97
12/17	51.92	8	3	1.15	0.07	4.14
12/16	24.22	6	4	0.62	0.05	2.65
Annual Growth 31.3%				—	41.9%	28.5% 43.7%

Tesco PLC (United Kingdom)

Auditors: Deloitte LLP

LOCATIONS

HQ: Tesco PLC (United Kingdom)
Tesco House, Shire Park, Kestrel Way, Welwyn Garden City AL7 1GA
Phone: (44) 1992 632222   **Fax:** (44) 1992 630794
Web: www.tescoplc.com

HISTORICAL FINANCIALS

Company Type: Public

Income Statement   FYE: February 27

	REVENUE ($ mil.)	NET INCOME ($ mil.)	NET PROFIT MARGIN	EMPLOYEES
02/21	80,586	8,551	10.6%	367,321
02/20	83,354	1,249	1.5%	423,092
02/19	83,156	1,720	2.1%	464,505
02/18	80,368	1,685	2.1%	448,988
02/17	70,173	(50)	—	464,520
Annual Growth	3.5%	—	—	(5.7%)

2021 Year-End Financials

Debt ratio: 22.1%
Return on equity: 48.0%
Cash ($ mil.): 3,494
Current ratio: 0.69
Long-term debt ($ mil.): 8,614

No. of shares (mil.): —
Dividends
  Yield: 0.0%
  Payout: 94.4%
Market value ($ mil.): —

STOCK PRICE ($)		P/E	PER SHARE ($)		
	FY Close	High/Low	Earnings	Dividends	Book Value
02/21	9.38	16 13	0.89	0.84	2.22
02/20	8.77	79 65	0.16	0.15	2.21
02/19	8.71	60 42	0.22	0.10	2.50
02/18	8.64	48 38	0.26	0.05	2.27
02/17	7.10	— —	(0.01)	0.00	1.25
Annual Growth	7.2%	— —	—	—	15.4%

Teva Pharmaceutical Industries Ltd

Teva Pharmaceutical Industries is a global leader in generics biopharmaceuticals and specialty medicines with a portfolio consisting of more than 3500 products in nearly every therapeutic area. Headquartered in Israel Teva has more than 1160 generic products in its pre-approved global pipeline which includes products in all stages of the approval process: pre-submission post-submission and after tentative approval. In specialty medicines the company focuses on three main areas ? the central nervous system (CNS) and pain respiratory and oncology. The company operates in three segments: North America Europe and International Markets. Around half of the company's total sales were generated from the North America.

Operations

Teva operates its business through three segments: North America (accounts nearly 50% of company's revenue) Europe (about 30% of revenue) and International Markets (nearly 15% of revenue).

The North America segment includes the US and Canada. Its specialty portfolio has an established presence in central nervous system (CNS) medicines and pain respiratory and oncology.

Europe segment includes the European Union and certain other European countries. Its specialty portfolio focuses on three main areas: CNS and pain (including migraine) respiratory and oncology. Its OTC portfolio in Europe includes global brands such as SUDOCREM as well as local and regional brands such as NasenDuo in Germany and Flegamina in Poland.

The International Markets segment includes all countries in which the company operate other than those in its North America and Europe segments. These markets comprise more than 35 countries covering a substantial portion of the global pharmaceutical market. Its specialty portfolio in International Markets focuses on three main areas: CNS and pain respiratory and oncology.

Generic medicines produced by Teva include chemical and therapeutic versions of tablets capsules injectables inhalants liquids ointments and creams. It also offers a broad range of basic chemical entities as well as specialized product families such as sterile products hormones high-potency drugs and cytotoxic substances in both parenteral and solid dosage forms. Specialty medicines include Copaxone Ajovy Austedo Bendeka and Treanda ProAir (ProAir HFA ProAir Digihaler and ProAir RespiClick) QVAR (QVAR and QVAR Redi-Haler) Cinqair/Cinqaero AirDuo RespiClick/ArmonAir RespiClick/AirDuo Digihaler and Braltus. In addition to focusing on therapeutic areas of CNS and respiratory medicines Teva provides specialty medicines in oncology and selected other areas.

The company also supplies active pharmaceutical ingredients (APIs) the essential raw materials used in drug manufacturing.

Teva operates about 45 finished dosage and packaging pharmaceutical plants in more than 20 countries. These plants manufacture solid dosage forms sterile injectables liquids semi-solids inhalers transdermal patches and other medical devices. It produces approximately 68 billion tablets and capsules and approximately 646 million sterile units.

Overall the company's sales of goods account for nearly 85% of the company's total sales distribution generates nearly 10% licensing arrangements and other represent the remaining.

Geographic Reach

Based in Israel Teva operates about 85 manufacturing and R&D facilities. It also has principal executive offices in Parsippany New Jersey and Amsterdam the Netherlands. The company is structured into three geographic segments ? North America (which accounts for about half of total sales) Europe (less than 30% of sales) and International Markets (about 15% of sales).

Its primary manufacturing technologies solid dosage forms injectables and blow-fill-seal are available in North America Europe Latin America India and Israel. The manufacturing sites located in Israel Germany Hungary Croatia Bulgaria India Spain Poland and the Czech Republic make up the majority of its production capacity.

Sales and Marketing

Teva's generic sales in the US are made directly to retail drug chains mail order distributors and wholesaler.

In North America the company participates in pharmaceutical conferences and advertises in professional journals and on pharmacy websites.

The company's advertising costs for the years 2020 2019 and 2018 were approximately $225 million $213 million and $256 million respectively.

Financial Performance

The company's revenues in 2020 were $16.7 billion a decrease of 1% mainly due to a decline in revenues from certain oncology products COPAXONE and certain respiratory products partially offset by higher revenues from AUSTEDO and AJOVY. The decline in revenues was also affected by reduced demand for certain products resulting from the impact of the COVID-19 pandemic.

Net loss for fiscal 2020 increased to $4.1 billion compared from the prior year with $1.0 billion.

Cash held by the company at the end of fiscal 2020 increased to $2.2 billion. Cash provided by operations and investing activities was $1.2 billion and $863 million respectively. Cash used for financing activities was $1.9 billion mainly for repayment of senior notes and loans and other long term liabilities.

Strategy

The key areas of focus for its respiratory R&D is the development of differentiated respiratory therapies for patients using innovative delivery systems to deliver chemical and biological therapies. Teva's device strategy is intended to result in "device consistency" allowing physicians to choose the device that best matches a patient's needs both in terms of ease of use and effectiveness of delivery of the prescribed molecule and includes three main types of devices.

Mergers and Acquisitions

Acquisitions around the globe have helped the company enter new markets and secure market dominance in others. In 2014 Teva acquired biotech company Labrys Biologics which is focused on migraine treatments for $207 million.

The company now plans to buy California-based Auspex Pharmaceuticals which is developing drugs for central nervous system disorders including Huntington's disease and Tourette's syndrome for some $3.2 billion. It is also buying US-based private software firm Gecko Health Innovations which makes products that alert respiratory patients when it's time to take their medicine.

And in yet another deal aimed at growing its emerging market operations Teva acquired Mexico-based drugmaker Representaciones e Investigaciones Medicas SA (more simply known as Rimsa) for $2.3 billion in 2016. That purchase makes Teva one of Mexico's top pharmaceutical firms.

Shortly after buying Allergan's generics business in 2016 Teva bought that firm's Anda distribution business for $500 million. Anda distributes branded generic OTC and specialty products from more than 300 manufacturers in the US. The deal included three distribution centers and fits in well with Teva's strategy to build up its supply chain network.

HISTORY

Teva traces its origins to Salomon Levin and Elstein Ltd. a drug distribution firm based in Jerusalem which at the time was a Jewish section of British-controlled Palestine.

Ironically in the 1930s the company benefited from the emigration of Jewish people many of whom were scientists seeking to escape the Nazi regime in Germany which at the time was the global leader in drug development. The company went public in 1951.

In 1968 Eli Hurvitz was appointed to Teva's board of directors and scripted much of the company's growth. In 1970 Teva merged with Assia Chemical Laboratories (Hurvitz's old employer) and another company to form Teva Pharmaceutical Industries.

Ten years later Teva sold a 20% stake of itself to Koor Industries in exchange for Koor subsidiary Ikapharm Teva's closest competitor. (Koor later launched a takeover bid but the Founders Group Teva's controlling shareholders foiled the attempt.)

In 1985 Teva moved into the US. It formed a joint venture with W. R. Grace called TAG Pharmaceuticals (Teva bought out W. R. Grace's portion in 1991). In 1985 TAG bought Lemmon Co. famous — or infamous — for its tranquilizer Quaalude which had gained notoriety as the recreational drug of choice for many young people. Lemmon which ceased production of Quaalude prior to Teva's purchase became the acquirer's generic manufacturing division.

Teva bought Abic Israel's #2 drugmaker in a complex 1988 transaction that gave Canadian investor and Seagram's heir Charles Bronfman a stake in the company. British publisher Robert Maxwell also bought a substantial stake in Teva. (Following Maxwell's mysterious death in 1993 his estate sold his stake.)

In the 1990s Teva turned its attention to Europe buying companies in France Hungary Italy and the UK. In 1996 the company bought US firm Biocraft Laboratories merging it with Lemmon and forming Teva Pharmaceuticals USA.

In 1998 the company reorganized after officials realized that it had to evolve from being a collection of disparate operating entities to a more centralized operation. It also divested several operations — including its Russian joint venture its yeast and alcohol fermentation business and some of its German operations — in order to concentrate on pharmaceuticals.

EXECUTIVES

Senior Vice President, Chief Accounting Officer,
Amir Weiss

Independent Director, Amir Elstein

Chief Financial Officer, Executive Vice President, Eliyahu Kalif, $681,281 total compensation

Independent Director, Janet Vergis

Executive Vice President - Global Marketing and Portfolio, Eli Shani

Independent Director, Ronit Satchi-Fainaro

Independent Chairman of the Board, Sol Barer

Independent Director, Jean-Michel Halfon

Independent Director, Nechemia Peres

Independent Director, Roberto Mignone

Executive Vice President - North America Commercial, Sven Dethlefs

Independent Director, Perry Nisen

Executive Vice President - European Commercial, Richard Daniell

Executive Vice President - Global R&D, Hafrun Fridriksdottir, $720,000 total compensation

Independent Director, Gerald Lieberman

Executive Vice President - Global Operations, Eric Drape, $708,010 total compensation

Executive Vice President - Global Communications, Brand and ESG, Chief Human Resource Officer, Galia Inbar

Independent Director, Tal Zvi Zaks

Executive Vice President - International Markets Commercial, Mark Sabag, $605,749 total compensation

Executive Vice President, Chief Legal Officer, David Stark

Auditors: Kesselman & Kesselman (member of PricewaterhouseCoopers International Limited)

LOCATIONS

HQ: Teva Pharmaceutical Industries Ltd
124 Dvora HaNevi'a St., Tel Aviv 6944020
Phone: (972) 3 914 8213
Web: www.tevapharm.com

2018 Sales

	$ mil.	% of total
North America	927	49
Europe	5,187	28
International Markets	3,005	16
Other activities	1,366	7
Total	**18,854**	**100**

PRODUCTS/OPERATIONS

2018 Sales

	$ mil.	% of total
Sales of goods	15,881	84
Distribution	1,956	10
Licensing arrangements	165	1
Other	852	5
Total	**18,854**	**100**

Selected Products

Branded products
  Central nervous system
  Azilect (Parkinson's)
  Copaxone (multiple sclerosis)
  Provigil (narcolepsy)
  Specialty respiratory
  ProAir (bronchial spasms)
  Qvar (chronic asthma)
Biosimilars
  Eporatio (erythopoietin treatment for chemotherapy-induced anemia)
  Granulocyte Colony Stimulating Factor (anti-infective for oncology patients)
  Tev-Tropin (human growth hormone)
Generic products
  Amoxicillin (Amoxil)
  Atorvastatin (Lipitor)
  Bromatapp (Dimetapp)
  Candesartan (Atacand)
  Cimetidine (Tagamet)
  Ciprofloxacin (Cipro)
  Clemastine fumarate (Tavist)
  Clotrimazole (Lotrimin)
  Diclofenac extended release (Voltaren XR)
  Diltiazem HCl (Cardizem)

Donepezil (Aricept)
Fluconazole Injection (Diflucan)
Fluoxetine (Prozac)
Galantamine (Reminyl)
Ketoconazole cream (Nizoral Cream)
Lamivudine (Epivir)
Lovastatin (Mevacor)
Metronidazole (Flagyl)
Quetiapine (Seroquel)
Sotalol hydrochloride (Betapace)
Sulfamethoxazole and Trimethoprim (Bactrim)
Tizanidine (Zanaflex)
Tramadol hydrochloride (Ultram/Ultracet)

COMPETITORS

Bausch Health Companies Inc
CIPLA LIMITED
HIKMA PHARMACEUTICALS PUBLIC LIMITED COMPANY
INDIVIOR PLC
MALLINCKRODT PUBLIC LIMITED COMPANY
MANNATECH INCORPORATED
NATURAL ALTERNATIVES INTERNATIONAL INC.
PFIZER INC.
SANOFI
USANA HEALTH SCIENCES INC.

HISTORICAL FINANCIALS

Company Type: Public

Income Statement — FYE: December 31

	REVENUE ($ mil.)	NET INCOME ($ mil.)	NET PROFIT MARGIN	EMPLOYEES
12/21	15,878	417	2.6%	37,537
12/20	16,659	(3,990)	—	40,216
12/19	16,887	(999)	—	40,039
12/18	18,854	(2,150)	—	42,535
12/17	22,385	(16,265)	—	51,792
Annual Growth	**(8.2%)**	**—**		**(7.7%)**

2021 Year-End Financials

Debt ratio: 48.3%
Return on equity: 4.1%
Cash ($ mil.): 2,165
Current ratio: 1.14
Long-term debt ($ mil.): 21,617

No. of shares (mil.): 1,103
Dividends
  Yield: —
  Payout: —
Market value ($ mil.): 8,835

	STOCK PRICE ($) FY Close	P/E High/Low		PER SHARE ($) Earnings	Dividends	Book Value
12/21	8.01	34	21	0.38	0.00	9.32
12/20	9.65	—	—	(3.64)	0.00	9.15
12/19	9.80	—	—	(0.91)	0.00	12.79
12/18	15.42	—	—	(2.35)	0.43	13.49
12/17	18.95	—	—	(16.26)	0.72	17.07
Annual Growth	**(19.4%)**			**—**	**—**	**(14.0%)**

Thales

Thales develops and manufactures weapons munitions and equipment for waging war across all defensible spheres: land air water space and digital. Thales' primary customers are national defense forces across the globe with a particular focus on Europe which accounts for nearly 55% of sales. Besides defense and security products Thales' aerospace division outfits commercial planes with in-flight entertainment and connectivity equipment and provides flight simulator-based pilot training while a transport division provides rail signaling monitoring and ticketing for rail networks. Thales signaled its intent to grow in cybersecurity with

the 2019 acquisition of Gemalto. The French government owns about 25% of Thales and aerospace company Dassault holds nearly 25%.

Operations

Thales is divided into four reportable segments.

The largest Defense & Security accounts for about 45% of sales. It provides air land and naval defense capabilities for a wide range of scenarios. These include guns ammunition missiles mortars and information and communication systems on land; short- and medium-range missiles missile electronic sub-systems rockets jet and helicopter optronics and support and repair services for air forces; and above water and underwater warfare such as radar sonar communications at sea.

The Aerospace segment generates around a third of sales. It's divided in two: Aeronautics makes in-flight entertainment connectivity equipment and civil and military flight simulators; and Space a joint-venture with Italy's Leonardo makes orbital infrastructure satellite systems and navigation and earth observation systems.

The Transport segment (about 10% of sales) provides urban transport systems (subways and trams) and mainline networks with signaling monitoring control and ticketing.

The Digital Identity and Security (about 15%) segment includes certification of physical and digital identities various authentication methods (including biometrics) IoT connectivity and data encryption.

Geographic Reach

Based in Paris France Thales' customers in Europe represent nearly 55% of sales. The Asia/Pacific region generates nearly 15% of sales while North America accounts for more than 10% of sales and Middle East some 10%. Australia/New Zealand and all other countries generates around 5% each.

The company has operations in nearly 70 countries including Europe in France Germany the Netherlands Spain and the UK as well as in Australia and the US. The company extends its global presence through joint ventures and partnerships.

Sales and Marketing

Customers include some of the world's largest corporations as well as government. Almost 60% of Thales' revenues comes from government customers and more than 40% of its revenue comes from non-government customers (private operators of critical infrastructure aircraft manufactures etc.).

Financial Performance

Note: Growth rates may differ after conversion to US Dollars.

2019 sales amounted to ?18.4 billion compared to ?15.9 billion in 2018 an increase of 16% after the consolidation of Gemalto.

The company had a consolidated net income of ?1.1 billion a 14% increase from the previous year.

The company's cash for the year ended 2019 totaled ?2.9 billion. Operating activities generated ?1.8 billion while investing activities used ?4.6 billion mainly for investments in subsidiaries and affiliates. Financing activities generated ?128.3 million.

Strategy

The company's strategic priorities for the year consists of:

Accelerating the sales transformation project; Streamlining the organization of international development; Implementing a new management for key accounts; and Paying increased attention to opportunities in the support and maintenance of installed bases.

Thales Alenia Space continued to develop a strategic partnership to meet the new needs of the market particularly with the signing of a partnership agreement with Hemeria to target the nanosatellite market. In 2019 LeoStella a joint venture between Thales Alenia Space and SpaceFlight Industries opened its new small satellite production facility in Seattle in the United States where it began the integration of the BlackSky constellation for low - orbit Earth observation with a high revisit rate. Thales Alenia Space also opened its new automated production site for assembling photovoltaic cells on satellite solar panels in Hasselt Belgium.

Mergers and Acquisitions

In 2019 Thales acquired Franco-Dutch digital security company Gemalto for around $4.6 billion. The deal which will see Gemalto combined with Thales' digital security business and will add around $19 billion to sales.

Also in 2019 Thales acquired Psibernetix (Ohio-based) a company known for its aerial combat AI; Ercom a communication and device security expert; and Suneris a provider of solutions for supervision and control of telecommunication network traffic.

HISTORY

Compagnie Fran Şaise Thomson-Houston (CFTH) began as a subsidiary for US-based tramway-equipment maker Thomson-Houston Electric Corporation in 1893. French investors bought the subsidiary when Thomson-Houston and Edison General Electric merged to become General Electric (GE). The fledgling company kept its founder's name and maintained a licensing agreement with GE. Early interests included power stations and the electrification of tramways. Diversification in the 1920s included the acquisition of Societe des Usines du Pied-Selle (kitchen and heating equipment 1920) and the formation of a finance company Financiere lectricite (1925).

Alsthom was created in 1928 when Thomson and Societe Alsacienne de Constructions Mecaniques joined to make industrial electrical equipment. Radio and TV receivers were added in 1929 when Thomson acquired tablissements Ducretet.

The 1930s brought the acquisition of tablissement Kraemer (radio equipment 1936). During WWII however operations not used by the German military sat idle.

Postwar political conflict between France and the US plus Thomson's involvement in defense and nuclear technology caused it to end association with GE in 1953. A 1959 agreement with Pathe-Marconi began radio and TV production.

A 1966 merger with Hotchkiss-Brandt resulted in a new name Thomson-Brandt. In 1968 another merger and another name change Thomson-CSF occurred when Compagnie Generale de TSF joined Thomson. In 1981 the French nationalized Thomson-Brandt and in 1982 created holding company Thomson S.A. to manage it. Opposition to the government's nationalization in 1987 forced Thomson's return to the private sector and the company formed semiconductor unit SGS-Thomson Microelectronics. In 1989 the company acquired defense electronics businesses MBLE (Belgium) and Signaal (Denmark) from Philips.

Arms sales declined in 1991 and the company began to produce consumer goods such as satellite TV dishes. A 1992 agreement introduced IBM technology to Thomson defense and space products. UK-based GEC and Thomson began making sonar and antisubmarine systems after a 1995 agreement.

Thomson sold its interests in Credit Lyonnais Securities to the French government in 1996. The company sold its semiconductor unit in 1997. Thomson strengthened its defense business by taking a majority interest in Siemens Forvarssystemer (military communications Norway) in 1998 and striking a $500 million deal with Raytheon to make control systems for NATO in 1999. That year Thomson also purchased a 42% stake in Singapore-based optronics company Avimo Group.

Late in 1999 Shorts Missile Systems Ltd. (SMS) – Thomson's joint venture with Canada-based Bombardier– won a long-term $319 million contract to make short-range Starstreak anti-aircraft missiles for the UK. In 2000 Thomson-CSF acquired UK-based Racal Electronics a defense electronics firm for $2.17 billion and bought out Bombardier's share in the SMS venture. Also in 2000 the company announced plans to sell Crouzet-Automatismes (its electro-mechanical components division) to Schneider Electric. In December Thomson-CSF changed its name to Thales and agreed to form a joint air-defense venture (Thales-Raytheon Systems) with Raytheon.

In 2001 the company acquired majority control over optronics company Avimo. The same year Thales sold its 48.8% stake in Alcatel Space to joint venture partner Alcatel for about $700 million. (That deal and another sale of Thales' stock late in the year reduced Alcatel's stake to about 16%.) Thales also agreed to buy Orbital Science's GPS businesses Magellan Corporation and Navigation Solutions LLC (NavSol) a joint venture with Hertz for about $70 million. In November the company sold Thales Instruments (the former instruments business of Racal) to an investment firm consortium for about $120 million.

Thales agreed to sell its computer services arm Thales IS to French IT company GFI Informatique in 2002. However GFI abandoned the deal which would have been worth more than $300 million soon after it was announced.

In 2004 Thales gained ground when BAE lost prime contractor status in building the Royal Navy's new carriers; but the two companies would ultimately work together with US-based KBR coordinating things. The following year Thales inked a ?236 million deal to supply 18 facilities with Tiger combat helicopter simulators.

In 2006 Thales and Germany's Diehl Stiftung & Co. merged their aerospace activities specifically cockpit avionics systems and flight and engine control to create a new joint venture company Diehl Aerospace GmbH. The two companies teamed up again to form Junghans Microtec GmbH a combination of the two companies' ammunition fuse and safety device operations.

In exchange for a near 21% stake in Thales plus cash Thales acquired the satellite-building and homeland security businesses of telecom-equipment maker Alcatel-Lucent in 2006. The deal included Alcatel-Lucent's transport systems division which makes signaling systems for railways and subway systems. As part of the acquisition the French government's stake in Thales decreased.

Thales acquired a 25% slice of shipyard concern Direction des Constructions Navales (DCN) in 2007 with an option to increase its stake to as much as 35%. In return Thales handed over its Naval France business to DCN and a stake in three of Thales's concerns. The tie-up pushes Thales's system capabilities to the front of the European naval market. Also that same year ITT Gilfillan and Thales inked a deal that would enable ITT radar systems to have the exclusive right to market and produce the Smart SMK II radar system for the US market. Thales also has a manufacturing facility in Maryland where it works on the Joint Tactical Radio System.

The company sold its Thales Computers unit to Kontron Modular Computers in 2008 for ?11 million (over $14 million). It also divested its electronic payment business that same year; American Group Hypercom purchased it for over ?93 million (almost $125 million).

To expand its information and communications systems security business the company pocketed nCipher in 2008 a supplier of encryption products for government financial institutions and enterprises that need to protect sensitive data. Also in 2008 Thales joined Emirates Advanced Investments subsidiary C4 Advanced Solutions (C4AS) to step up military communication systems and equipment in the Middle East and Northern Africa. Holding a 49% stake in the Abu Dhabi-based joint venture (Thales Advanced Solutions) Thales supplies tactical radio maintenance in-service support for products and systems and software for communications systems to UAE armed forces. The joint venture extended Thales's regional influence; the company already won a deal to integrate communications at Abu Dhabi International Airport's air traffic control center tower. India is a customer too and operates combat aircraft built by Dassault and Thales.

Thales purchased Israel-based medical imaging company CMT Medical Technologies in 2009 for about ?20 million (more than $28 million). While its medical imaging business took a giant hit during the recession its joint venture with Philips and Siemens (Thales holds 51%) to make digital X-ray detectors offset the impact. The acquisition of CMT satisfies all the needs of OEM requirements.

EXECUTIVES

Non-Executive Director representing Employees, Anne-Marie Hunot-Schmit, $38,739 total compensation

Non-Executive Director representing Employees, Frederique Sainct, $48,709 total compensation

Executive Vice President, General Counsel, Member of the Executive Committee, Group Secretary, Isabelle Simon

Executive Vice President, Strategy, Research and Technology, Member of the Executive Committee, Philippe Keryer

Non-Executive Director proposed by the Public Sector, Delphine d'Amarzit, $28,086 total compensation

Non-Executive Director proposed by the Public Sector, Bernard Fontana, $36,560 total compensation

Non-Executive Independent Director, Philippe Knoche, $22,859 total compensation

Auditors: Mazars

LOCATIONS

HQ: Thales
Tour Carpe Diem, Place des Corolles Esplanade Nord, Courbevoie 92400
Phone: (33) 1 57 77 80 00
Web: www.thalesgroup.com

2018 Sales

	% of total
Europe	55
Asia	14
Middle East	10
North America	9
Australia & New Zealand	5
Rest of the World	6
Total	**100**

PRODUCTS/OPERATIONS

2018 Sales

	% of total
Defense & Security	51
Aerospace	36
Transport	13
Total	**100**

Selected Divisions

Air operations
Avionics
Defense & security C4I systems
Defense mission systems
Land defense
Space
Transportation systems

Selected Subsidiaries

TDA Armements
Thales Air Systems
Thales Alenia Space
Thales Avionics
Thales Communications
Thales Electron Devices (TED)
Thales Optronique
Thales Raytheon Systems
Thales Security Solutions & Services SAS
Thales Services
Thales Systèmes Aé;roporté;s
Thales Underwater Systems

COMPETITORS

CAPGEMINI
COMPUTACENTER PLC
GRIFFON CORPORATION
INMARSAT GROUP
  HOLDINGS LIMITED
L-3 COMMUNICATIONS
  HOLDINGS INC.

L3 TECHNOLOGIES INC.
L3HARRIS TECHNOLOGIES
  INC.
QINETIQ GROUP PLC
SMITHS GROUP PLC
SPECTRIS PLC
TECHNICOLOR

HISTORICAL FINANCIALS

Company Type: Public

Income Statement

FYE: December 31

	REVENUE ($ mil.)	NET INCOME ($ mil.)	NET PROFIT MARGIN	EMPLOYEES
12/20	20,850	593	2.8%	80,702
12/19	20,660	1,259	6.1%	82,605
12/18	18,156	1,124	6.2%	66,135
12/17	18,934	985	5.2%	64,860
12/16	15,716	999	6.4%	63,783
Annual Growth	**7.3%**	**(12.2%)**	**—**	**6.1%**

2020 Year-End Financials

Debt ratio: 29.3%	No. of shares (mil.): 212
Return on equity: 9.1%	Dividends
Cash ($ mil.): 6,141	Yield: 0.5%
Current ratio: 1.01	Payout: 3.5%
Long-term debt ($ mil.): 6,393	Market value ($ mil.): 3,908

	STOCK PRICE ($) FY Close	P/E High/Low	PER SHARE ($) Earnings	Dividends	Book Value
12/20	18.36	11 6	2.79	0.10	29.49
12/19	21.07	2314361	0.06	0.48	28.76
12/18	118.00	28 26	5.27	0.52	30.72
Annual Growth	**(60.6%)**	**—**	**—(14.7%)**	**(34.2%)**	**(1.0%)**

ThyssenKrupp AG

Thyssenkrupp (pronounced TISS-in kroop) is an international group of companies consisting largely of independent industrial and technology businesses. The German company's operations span about 80 sites and numerous sectors and fields including industrial components automotive technology marine systems material services multi tracks and steel manufacture. Thyssenkrupp is active in about 55 countries worldwide but gets about 50% of total sales outside German-speaking areas. With approximately 890 locations the company has four regional platforms. The company was formed in 1999 via the merger of German industrial companies Thyssen and Krupp.

Operations

The truly vast operations of Thyssenkrupp are organized into six segments ? Materials Services Steel Europe Multi Tracks Automotive Technology Industrial Components and Marine Systems.

The Materials Services segment Thyssenkrupp's biggest earner at around 35% of annual sales offers an extensive range of services. The company's portfolio ranges from high-quality materials and raw materials to technical services through the development of intelligent processes for automation extended supply chains warehousing and inventory management.

Steel Europe (approximately 25% of sales) concentrates on the market for high-quality flat carbon steel. The product range comprises hot-rolled coil thick sheet premium strips coated products non-oriented electrical steel tinplate medium coil and grain-oriented electrical steel.

Providing about 15% of sales Multi Tracks segment is a new independent segment in which the company bundle businesses for which Thyssenkrupp is considering a different ownership structure in the short- to mid-term.

Automotive Technology (more than 10%) develops and manufactures high-tech components and systems for the auto industry. It also develops automated production systems such as system engineering.

Industrial Components accounts for more than 5% of sales. It comprises two business units: the bearings business and forgings business. Bearings is the global market leader and also one of the biggest manufacturers of seamless rolled slewing rings. Its slewing bearings and rings are used in a wide range of forward-looking applications. Forged Technologies is a specialist in the forgings business and is among the leading global manufacturers of components for engines undercarriages and construction machinery supplying customers in the truck automotive and construction machine sectors.

Marine Systems accounts for around 5% of sales. It supplies system for submarines and surface vessels and for maritime electronics and security technology.

Geographic Reach

Thyssenkrupp is headquartered in Essen Germany and has regional headquarters in North and South America Greater China India the Asia Pacific region and the Middle East & Africa region as well as the regional offices. It operates from some 890 locations in about 55 countries. Generating about 50% of revenue from outside Germany the company's geographic sales mix is diversified drawing about 35% of sales from Germany nearly 15% from the US and China represents the remaining.

Sales and Marketing

Thyssenkrupp sells its products to industries including the automotive sector (some 30% of annual sales) steel and processing (about 15%) trading (around 10%) engineering (about 10%) public sector (around 5%) packaging (nearly 5%) construction and energy and utility (less than 5%) and other customer groups generates more than 20%.

Financial Performance

The company's revenue for fiscal 2021 increased by 18% to ?34.0 billion compared from the prior year with ?28.9 billion.

Loss for fiscal 2021 was ?25 million compared from the prior year with a net income of ?9.6 billion.

Cash held by the company at the end of fiscal 2021 increased to ?9.0 billion. Cash provided by operations was ?92 million while cash used for investing and financing activities were ?510 million and ?1.3 billion respectively. Main uses of cash were for capital expenditures and repayment of liabilities.

Strategy

Thyssenkrupp is in the midst of the corporate transformation adopted in May 2019 which was further concertized in May 2020. The aim is to realign Thyssenkrupp as a sustainable and high-performing group of companies with a lean management model and clearly structured portfolio.

In company's transformation process the company are guided at all times by its three action three action areas: performance portfolio and people.

HISTORY

Formed separately in the 1800s both Thyssen and Krupp flourished in their early years under family control. Friedrich Krupp opened his steel factory in 1811. He died in 1826 and left the nearly bankrupt factory in the hands of his 14-year-old son Alfred who turned the business around. At the first World's Fair in 1851 Alfred unveiled a steel cannon far superior to earlier bronze models.

Twenty years later August Thyssen founded a puddling and rolling mill near Mulheim. He bought small factories and mines and by WWI he ran Germany's largest iron and steel company. During the world wars the resources of both companies were turned toward military efforts.

Post-WWII years were tough for both companies. Thyssen was split up by the Allies and when it began production again in 1953 it consisted of one steel plant. In the Krupp camp Alfred's great-grandson Alfried was convicted in 1948 of using slave labor during WWII. Released from prison in 1951 Alfried rebuilt Krupp. After near ruin following WWII both companies emerged and enjoyed a resurgence along with the German economy in which they prospered and expanded during the 1950s.

By the 1980s Thyssen's businesses included ships locomotives offshore oil rigs specialty steel and metals trading and distribution. Krupp continued to grow and in 1992 it took over engineering and steelmaking concern Hoesch AG. (Eberhard Hoesch had begun making railroad tracks in the 1820s. The company grew and expanded into infrastructure and building products.)

The new Fried. Krupp AG Hoesch-Krupp bought Italian specialty steelmaker Acciai Speciali Terni chemical-plant builder Uhde and South African shipper J.H. Bachmann. Its automotive division formed a joint venture in Brazil and added production sites in China Mexico Romania and the US.

In 1997 Thyssen expanded in North America with its $675 million acquisition of Giddings & Lewis (machine tools US) and the purchase of Copper & Brass Sales (metals processing and distributing).

Krupp attempted a hostile takeover of Thyssen in 1997. The takeover failed but the companies soon agreed to merge their steel operations to form Thyssen Krupp Stahl. Bigger plans were in the works and in 1998 the two companies agreed to merge. That year Thyssen sold its Plusnet fixed-line phone business to Esprit Telecom Group.

In 1999 Krupp's automotive division (Krupp Hoesch Automotive) bought Cummins' Atlas Crankshaft subsidiary. Thyssen also bought US-based Dover's elevator business for $1.1 billion. Krupp and Thyssen completed their merger in 1999. The company planned to spin off its steel operations but held off due to its success in 2000. ThyssenKrupp did however sell its Krupp Kunststofftechnik unit (plastic molding machines) for about $183 million. To speed corporate decision-making the company made plans to scrap its dual-management structure in 2001.

Early in 2001 ThyssenKrupp agreed to buy 51% of Fiat unit Magneti Marelli's suspension-systems and shock-absorbers business. It also had the option of buying the remainder after 2004. In 2002 the company formed alliances with NKK and Kawasaki Steel to share its steel sheet making technologies while expanding its business with Japanese automotive makers in Europe. ThyssenKrupp's joint venture with Chinese steelmaker ANSC Angang New Steel known as TAGAL began producing galvanized coil of which about 80% will be used in China's burgeoning automotive industry.

In 2004 ThyssenKrupp sold its residential real estate unit for around $2.8 billion to a consortium of real estate funds operated by Morgan Stanley and Corpus-Immobiliengruppe. It divested the automotive segment of the capital goods unit in 2006 selling it off in pieces.

ThyssenKrupp opened three major new steel facilities in the Americas in 2010. A new integrated steel mill in Santa Cruz Brazil started production in mid-year. The $7 billion plant the company's biggest project ever is a partnership with South American giant Vale SA which owns a 25% stake in the venture. The company also began production at two plants in Calvert Alabama: a $3.6 billion carbon steel plant and a $1.4 billion stainless steel rolling plant. The company also constructed — and

consolidated its corporate staff in — a new headquarters building in Essen Germany in 2010.

EXECUTIVES

Chief Human Resources and Labor Director, Oliver Burkhard, $836,593 total compensation
Chief Executive Officer and Chairwoman of the Board of Management, Martina Merz, $1,601,480 total compensation
Chairman of the Supervisory Board, Siegfried Russwurm
Chief Financial Officer and Chairman, Supervisory Board, thyssenkrupp Steel Europe AG, Klaus Keysberg, $836,593 total compensation
Auditors: PricewaterhouseCoopers GmbH Wirtschaftsprufungsgesellschaft

LOCATIONS

HQ: ThyssenKrupp AG
ThyssenKrupp Allee 1, Essen 45143
Phone: (49) 201 844 0   **Fax:** (49) 201 844 53600
Web: www.thyssenkrupp.com

Sales 2018

	%
Germany	29
USA	16
China	7
Other	48
Total	**100**

PRODUCTS/OPERATIONS

Sales 2018

	%
Components Technology	17
Elevator Technology	17
Industrial Solutions	11
Materials Services	33
Steel Europe	21
Corporate	1
Total	**100**

COMPETITORS

ArcelorMittal	SPECTRIS PLC
BODYCOTE PLC	TARKETT
GKN LIMITED	VALEO
KOC HOLDING ANONIM SIRKETI	Voith GmbH & Co. KGaA
Kl ¶ckner & Co SE	WEIR GROUP PLC(THE)
RENOLD PUBLIC LIMITED COMPANY	voestalpine AG

HISTORICAL FINANCIALS

Company Type: Public

Income Statement   FYE: September 30

	REVENUE ($ mil.)	NET INCOME ($ mil.)	NET PROFIT MARGIN	EMPLOYEES
09/20	33,836	11,222	33.2%	103,598
09/19	45,811	(331)	—	162,372
09/18	40,281	9	0.0%	161,096
09/17	48,968	(766)	—	158,739
09/16	43,829	330	0.8%	156,487
Annual Growth	(6.3%)	141.4%	—	(9.8%)

2020 Year-End Financials

Debt ratio: 19.1%   No. of shares (mil.): 622
Return on equity: 165.3%   Dividends
Cash ($ mil.): 13,519   Yield: —
Current ratio: 2.26   Payout: —
Long-term debt ($ mil.): 5,599   Market value ($ mil.): 3,115

	STOCK PRICE ($) FY Close	P/E High/Low	PER SHARE ($) Earnings	Dividends	Book Value
09/20	5.00	1 0	18.03	0.00	18.45
09/19	13.98	— —	(0.53)	0.11	3.07
09/18	25.24	30652176	0.01	0.11	5.22
09/17	29.44	— —	(1.36)	0.11	5.48
09/16	24.89	— —	0.58	0.00	4.15
Annual Growth	(33.0%)	—	—136.1%	—	45.2%

Tianjin Tianhai Investment Co Ltd

EXECUTIVES

Director, Zhipeng Luo
Independent Director, Weili Chen
President, Director, Xuefeng Chen
Independent Director, Baocheng Zhou
Independent Director, Yu Huang
Auditors: Zhong He Zheng Xin CPAs Co., Ltd.

LOCATIONS

HQ: Tianjin Tianhai Investment Co Ltd
No. 207, Machang Road, Hexi District, Tianjin 300204
Phone: (86) 22 23281780   **Fax:** (86) 22 23286115

HISTORICAL FINANCIALS

Company Type: Public

Income Statement   FYE: December 31

	REVENUE ($ mil.)	NET INCOME ($ mil.)	NET PROFIT MARGIN	EMPLOYEES
12/20	51,480	(1,496)	—	0
12/19	47,016	75	0.2%	0
12/18	48,917	8	0.0%	0
12/17	48,476	126	0.3%	0
12/16	5,409	46	0.9%	0
Annual Growth	75.6%	—	—	—

2020 Year-End Financials

Debt ratio: 4.4%   No. of shares (mil.): —
Return on equity: (-110.2%)   Dividends
Cash ($ mil.): 1,590   Yield: —
Current ratio: 0.94   Payout: —
Long-term debt ($ mil.): 980   Market value ($ mil.): —

TMBThanachart Bank Public Co Ltd

TMB Bank provides commercial banking services to customers in Thailand. Its services include deposits personal loans credit cards life insurance and currency exchange. The bank operates hundreds of locations thoughout the country in addition to foreign branches in Hong Kong and Vietnam. Formerly known as the Thai Military Bank TMB began operations in 1957; Thai Military Bank Thai Danu Bank and the Industrial Finance Corporation of Finance merged in 2004 to form the latest incarnation of TMB Bank. The Netherlands-based financial services firm ING Groep owns around 30% of the company while Thailand's Ministry of Finance holds about a quarter.

EXECUTIVES

Independent Director, Chananyarak Phetcharat
Chief Executive Officer, Director, Piti Tantakasem
Independent Director, Willem Nagel
Executive Director, Yokporn Tantisawetrat
Chief Risk Officer, Johannes Grisel
Head of Market Conduct Risk Management, Varoon Kanjanapoo
Chief Commercial Banking Officer, Senathip Sripaipan
Head of Audit, Sunthorn Rukpanich
Independent Director, Teeranun Srihong
Independent Director, Prinya Hom-anek
Chairman of the Board, Eknisi Nitithanprapas
Chief Marketing Officer, Kanchana Rojvatunyu
Vice Chairman of the Board, Vice Chairman of the Executive Board, Suphadej Poonpipat
Director, Somjate Moosirilert
Director, Michal Szczurek
Chairman of the Executive Board, Director, Philippe Damas
Auditors: KPMG Phoomchai Audit Ltd.

LOCATIONS

HQ: TMBThanachart Bank Public Co Ltd
3000 Phaholyothin Road, Chomphon, Chatuchak, Bangkok 10900
Phone: (66) 2 299 1111   **Fax:** (66) 2 299 1211
Web: www.tmbbank.com

COMPETITORS

BANGKOK BANK PUBLIC COMPANY LIMITED
HACHIJUNI BANK LTD. THE
KRUNG THAI BANK PUBLIC COMPANY LIMITED

HISTORICAL FINANCIALS

Company Type: Public

Income Statement				FYE: December 31
	ASSETS ($ mil.)	NET INCOME ($ mil.)	INCOME AS % OF ASSETS	EMPLOYEES
12/20	60,402	337	0.6%	0
12/19	62,381	242	0.4%	0
12/18	27,564	358	1.3%	0
12/17	25,902	266	1.0%	0
12/16	22,936	229	1.0%	0
Annual Growth	27.4%	10.1%	—	—

2020 Year-End Financials

Return on assets: 0.5%
Return on equity: 5.0%
Long-term debt ($ mil.): —
No. of shares (mil.): —
Sales ($ mil): 3,094
Dividends
  Yield: —
  Payout: 42.9%
Market value ($ mil.): —

Toho Bank, Ltd. (The)

The Toho Bank is a regional bank serving the Fukushima Prefecture in Japan. Armed with more than 115 branches and ATMs installed at more than 230 locations the bank offers local customers businesses and public institutions the traditional array of banking services including savings lending real estate venture firm support and financing and foreign and domestic exchange products. Toho Bank was established in 1941 and owns subsidiaries and affiliated companies such as The Toho Real Estate Service Co. The Toho Card Co. and The Toho Staff Service Co.

EXECUTIVES

Independent Director, Satoshi Nagano
Director, Masayuki Sakaji
President, Representative Director, Minoru Sato
Managing Director, Chief Director of Business, Michio Sakai
Senior Managing Director, Representative Director, Hideho Suto
Independent Director, Asao Aono
Independent Director, Hayao Watanabe
Independent Director, Takashi Fujiwara
Director, Takayuki Ishii
Managing Director, Chief Director of Sales, Kiichi Yokoyama
Managing Director, Director of Koriyama Sales, Shigeki Nanami
Auditors: Ernst & Young ShinNihon LLC

LOCATIONS

HQ: Toho Bank, Ltd. (The)
3-25 Ohmachi, Fukushima 960-8633
Phone: (81) 24 523 3131
Web: www.tohobank.co.jp

COMPETITORS

CHUKYO BANK LIMITED.   NANTO BANKLTD. THE

HISTORICAL FINANCIALS

Company Type: Public

Income Statement				FYE: March 31
	ASSETS ($ mil.)	NET INCOME ($ mil.)	INCOME AS % OF ASSETS	EMPLOYEES
03/21	61,344	(42)	—	2,617
03/20	55,465	25	0.0%	2,725
03/19	53,367	32	0.1%	2,821
03/18	56,759	69	0.1%	2,927
03/17	53,872	63	0.1%	2,951
Annual Growth	3.3%	—	—	(3.0%)

2021 Year-End Financials

Return on assets: (-0.0%)
Return on equity: (-2.4%)
Long-term debt ($ mil.): —
No. of shares (mil.): 252
Sales ($ mil): 526
Dividends
  Yield: —
  Payout: —
Market value ($ mil.): —

Tohoku Electric Power Co., Inc. (Japan)

Tohoku Electric Power keeps the factories humming and the lights on in northern Japan. The people of Tohoku the northern part of Japan's main island rely on Tohoku Electric Power for their electricity needs. Founded in 1951 the company produces power primarily through its thermal hydroelectric and nuclear power plants although it is also developing solar and geothermal power plants to cut carbon emissions. Overall it has a generating capacity of some 16720 MW. Tohoku Electric Power one if Japan's top electric utilities delivers electricity to roughly customers in Tohoku and Niigata.

Operations

Tohoku Electric Power generates transmits and sells electricity. It generates power via a variety of sources such as hydroelectric thermal (coal gas) geothermal solar and nuclear. In total it has capacity to produce some 16720 MW of electrical through about 225 generating stations. Its transmission facilities include about 15365 km of transmission lines.

Its electricity business accounts for some 90% of total revenue.

Geographic Reach

Sendai Japan-headquartered Tohoku Electric Power serves prefectures (similar to counties in the US) in northern Japan including Aomori Iwate Akita Miyagi Yamagata Fukushima and Niigata. Its power generation facilities are generally located in the same service area.

The company has a foothold in a few overseas projects in Mexico Indonesia and Vietnam focusing on energy production via coal gas and geothermal sources.

Sales and Marketing

The company's customers have included fuel futures market electricity futures market Japan Electric Power Exchange and negotiated markets.

Financial Performance

Revenue for 2019 increased to 2.25 billion compared from to 2.24 billion in the prior year.

The Company's net income increased to 65.1 billion while cash in the prior year was 50.9 billion.

Cash held by the Company at the end of 2019 increased to 252.3 billion compared to 184.9 billion in the prior year. Cash provided by operations and financing activities were 371.5 billion and 6.7 billion respectively. Cash used for investing was 310.6 billion mainly for purchase of property plant and equipment.

Strategy

In 2020 the Company published the Tohoku Electric Power Group Medium-/Long-term Vision. This will lend energy needed to achieve the company's ideal for the 2030s: to work as a group of enterprises to the company closer to a smart society starting from Tohoku and keeping pace with sustainable societal progress.

The Company's strategy focuses on: solutions to meet the needs of the customers and communities the company serve; seeking new business growth opportunities; and establishing solid business foundations through transformation.

EXECUTIVES

Independent Director, Ikuko Miyahara
Managing Executive Officer, Chief Director of Nuclear Power, Director, Isao Kato
Director, Koki Kato
Executive Vice President, Vice President, President of Subsidiary, Representative Director, Shinichi Okanobu
Executive Vice President, Vice President, Chief Director of Business Support, Representative Director, Shunji Yamamoto
Chairman of the Board, Representative Director, Jiro Masuko
Vice President, Executive Vice President, Representative Director, Toshinori Abe
Independent Director, Shiro Kondo
Independent Director, Tsutomu Kamijo
President, Executive President, Representative Director, Kojiro Higuchi
Independent Director, Osamu Kawanobe
Independent Director, Kazuo Kobayashi
Managing Executive Officer, Assistant Manager of Power Generation and Marketing Company, Director, Hiromitsu Takano

LOCATIONS

HQ: Tohoku Electric Power Co., Inc. (Japan)
  1-7-1 Honcho, Aoba-ku, Sendai, Miyagi 980-8550
Phone: (81) 22 225 2111
Web: www.tohoku-epco.co.jp

2016 Sales

	% of total
Electric Power Business	77
Construction Business	13
Other	10
Total	**100**

COMPETITORS

ALLETE INC.
EDF ENERGY LIMITED
EXELON CORPORATION
HOKKAIDO ELECTRIC POWER COMPANY
  INCORPORATED
PACIFICORP
SSE PLC
THE SOUTHERN COMPANY
TOKYO ELECTRIC POWER COMPANY HOLDINGS
  INCORPORATED
Vattenfall AB

HISTORICAL FINANCIALS

Company Type: Public

Income Statement				FYE: March 31
	REVENUE ($ mil.)	NET INCOME ($ mil.)	NET PROFIT MARGIN	EMPLOYEES
03/21	20,653	265	1.3%	24,717
03/20	20,694	581	2.8%	24,870
03/19	20,265	419	2.1%	25,032
03/18	19,506	444	2.3%	25,058
03/17	17,437	625	3.6%	24,771
Annual Growth	4.3%	(19.3%)	—	(0.1%)

2021 Year-End Financials

Debt ratio: 0.4%
Return on equity: 3.6%
Cash ($ mil.): 1,854
Current ratio: 0.70
Long-term debt ($ mil.): 19,350

No. of shares (mil.): 500
Dividends
  Yield: —
  Payout: 71.5%
Market value ($ mil.): —

Tokio Marine Holdings Inc

Japan's oldest property/casualty insurance company Tokio Marine Holdings has one of the largest insurance sales networks in the country. The company also serves customers in about 45 additional countries in Asia Oceania Europe Africa the Middle East and the Americas. Through Tokio Marine & Nichido Fire (TMNF) and other subsidiaries Tokio Marine provides property/casualty policies including specialty marine personal accident fire and auto coverage. It also offers life insurance and financial services such as asset management investment consulting and staffing.

Operations

Tokio Marine operates in four segments: Domestic Non-Life Insurance Domestic Life Insurance International Insurance and Financial and Other.

The Domestic Non-Life Insurance segment accounting for about half of sales provides property/casualty insurance policies including fire marine accident and voluntary and compulsory auto coverage. Subsidiaries include core unit Tokio Marine & Nichido Fire Nishin Fire E.design Tokio Marine Millea and Tokio Marine West.

The International Insurance segment (about 35% of sales) provides property/casualty coverage in about 45 countries worldwide. Its subsidiaries include Philadelphia Insurance (US) Delphi Financial (US) Tokio Marine HCC (US) Tokio Marine Kiln (UK) Tokio Marine Asia (Singapore) and Tokio Marine Seguradora (Brazil).

The Domestic Life Insurance segment (15% of sales) provides life policies and annuities to individuals and groups in Japan. Tokio Marine's core life unit is Tokio Marine & Nichido Life (established in 1996).

The Financial and Other segment provides asset management consulting and human resource services.

Geographic Reach

Tokio Marine has insurance operations in about 45 countries throughout Asia Oceania Europe Africa the Middle East and the Americas. The majority of Tokio Marine's revenue comes from Japan (more than 60%) followed by the US (25%).

Financial Performance

The company's revenue for fiscal 2020 decreased for 5.46 trillion compared from the prior year with 5.47 trillion.

Net income for fiscal 2020 decreased to 161.8 billion compared from the prior year with 259.8 billion.

Cash held by the company at the end of fiscal 2020 decreased to 924.7 billion. Cash provided by operations was 1.2 trillion while cash used for investing and financing activities were 731 billion and 513 billion respectively. Main uses of cash were purchases of securities and repayments of borrowings.

Strategy

The COVID-19 pandemic has accelerated digital transformation (DX) across industries and sectors. Customer needs have also shifted dramatically. Such changes were in progress but the pandemic has brought them into focus. Although the pre- and post-pandemic issues are largely unchanged the speed of change has doubled or tripled constraining projections and ruling out predictions even two or three years ahead. In this age of high discontinuity neither received wisdom nor past success apply. Rather outcomes that defy logic and expectations are the norm.

The 2+1 Growth Strategy is first about identifying new markets and designing new approaches based on accurate and insightful understanding of how customer needs are changing. The global shift to renewable energy and the rise in cyber risks are but two examples that demand attention. Another is Japan's declining birthrate and aging population which has put enormous pressure on healthcare where issues are snowballing and rural industries and economies are on a steep downhill slope. The importance of these social issues will only increase over the next two decades. The company are intent therefore upon discovering new opportunities and markets created by this evolving environment.

Company Background

Japan's first insurance company Tokio Marine and Fire Insurance was founded in 1879 to provide marine insurance in Japan. The firm expanded overseas rapidly establishing offices in London Paris and New York. It later added fire personal accident theft and auto coverage.

In 1944 Tokio merged with Mitsubishi Marine Insurance and Meiji Fire Insurance. After the war Tokio slowly recovered and resumed overseas operations. During the 1950s and 1960s the company grew its personal lines adding homeowners coverage. Domestic business slowed during the 1970s and 1980s and Tokio boosted operations overseas.

Millea Holdings was created in 2002 as the holding company for the merger between Tokio Marine and Fire and Nichido Fire and Marine. The two companies combined to become main operating subsidiary Tokio Marine & Nichido Fire Insurance in 2004. In 2008 Millea Holdings changed its name to Tokio Marine Holdings to reflect positive brand recognition associated with the Tokio Marine name.

Later acquisitions included Real Seguros (Brazil 2005) Nisshin Fire and Marine (Japan 2006) Asia General (Singapore 2007) Nihon Kousei (Japan 2007) Kiln (UK 2008) Philadelphia Consolidated (US 2008) Delphi Financial (US 2012) and HCC (US 2015).

HISTORY

After the US forced Japan to open to trade in 1854 Western marine insurers began operating there. In 1878 Japan's government organized backers for a Japanese marine insurance firm. Tokio Marine and Fire Insurance was founded the next year.

Tokio grew quickly insuring trading companies like Mitsubishi and Mitsui; it soon had offices in London Paris and New York. Increased competition in the 1890s forced it to curtail its foreign operations and begin using brokers in most other countries.

Victory in the Russo-Japanese War of 1904-05 buoyed the country but the economy slowed as it demobilized. Businesses responded by forming cooperative groups known as zaibatsu. Tokio Marine and Fire was allied with the Mitsubishi group.

Before WWI Tokio expanded by adding fire personal accident theft and auto insurance and it continued to buy foreign sales brokers. Japan's insurance industry consolidated in the 1920s and the company bought up smaller competitors. The 1923 Tokyo earthquake hit the industry hard but Tokio's new fire insurance operations had little exposure.

Most of Tokio's foreign operations were seized during WWII. In 1944 Tokio merged with Mitsubishi Marine Insurance and Meiji Fire Insurance. Business grew in WWII but wartime destruction left Tokio with nothing to insure and no money to pay claims.

After the war Tokio slowly recovered and resumed overseas operations. Although the US had dismantled the zaibatsu during occupation Tokio allied once again with Mitsubishi when Japan's government rebuilt most of the old groups as keiretsu.

During the 1950s and 1960s the company grew its personal lines adding homeowners coverage. Domestic business slowed during the 1970s and 1980s and Tokio boosted operations overseas. It added commercial property/casualty insurer Houston General Insurance (a US company sold in 1997) Tokio Reinsurance and interests in insurance and investment management firms.

In the 1980s the firm invested heavily in real estate through jusen (mortgage companies). Japan's overheated real estate market collapsed in the early 1990s dumping masses of nonperforming assets on jusen and their investors (the country's major banks and insurers including Tokio).

Deregulation began in 1996 and economic recession soon followed. In 1998 Tokio joined other members of the Mitsubishi group including Bank of Tokyo-Mitsubishi and Meiji Life Insurance to form investment banking pension and trust joint ventures. The firm also formed its own investment trust and allied with such foreign financial companies as BANK ONE and United Asset Management to develop new investment products. Brokerage firm Charles Schwab Tokio Marine Securities a joint venture was launched in 1999. That year Tokio consolidated its foreign reinsurance operations into Tokio Marine Global Re in Dublin Ireland and kicked off a business push that included reorganizing its agent force and planning for online sales.

Millea Holdings was created in 2002 as the holding company for the merger between Tokio Marine and Fire and Nichido Fire and Marine. The two were combined and renamed Tokio Marine & Nichido Fire Insurance a subsidiary of Millea Holdings.

The company's 2005 acquisition of Real Seguros allowed the company to bring its life insurance products to Brazil (renamed Tokio Marine Seguradora). In 2006 Millea acquired Nisshin Fire and Marine Insurance Company as a separately operated subsidiary. In 2007 the firm purchased Asia General Holdings and its life insurance subsidiaries which operated in Singapore and Malaysia. It also purchased Japanese fire insurance provider Nihon Kousei Kyousaikai.

In 2008 Millea Holdings changed its name to Tokio Marine Holdings to reflect the positive brand recognition associated with the Tokio Marine name.

The company made several key acquisitions to further expand its international operations including purchases of Kiln (UK 2008) Philadelphia Consolidated (US 2008) Delphi Financial (US 2012) and HCC (US 2015).

In late 2017 Tokio Marine subsidiary HCC acquired the medical stop-loss insurance operations of US giant AIG. The acquired business included some 40.8 billion in gross written premiums.

EXECUTIVES

Chairman of the Board, Tsuyoshi Nagano
Managing Director, Managing Executive Officer, Kenji Okada
Senior Managing Executive Officer, Shingo Kawaguchi
Managing Executive Officer, Makoto Yoda
Executive Officer, Director of Internal Audit, Shumpei Takizawa
Managing Executive Officer, Kenichi Kitazawa
Independent Director, Shinya Katanozaka
President & CEO of Tokio Marine & Nichido (Representative Director), Shinichi Hirose
Vice President, Executive Vice President, Group Chief Financial Officer, Representative Director, Takayuki Yuasa
Senior Managing Director, Senior Managing Executive Officer, Co-Head of International Business, Representative Director, Akira Harashima
Senior Managing Director, Tadashi Handa
Managing Executive Officer, Susumu Harada
Managing Executive Officer, Robert O'Leary
Managing Executive Officer, Kichiichiro Yamamoto
Senior Managing Executive Officer, Donald Sherman
Senior Managing Executive Officer, Co-Head of International Business, Christopher Williams
President, Group Chief Executive Officer, Chairman of Subsidiary, Representative Director, Satoru Komiya
Managing Director, Managing Executive Officer, Yoshinari Endo
Managing Director, Managing Executive Officer, Yoichi Moriwaki

Executive Officer, CEO of Subsidiary, Jose Ferrara
Executive Officer, Tetsufumi Kawamoto
Managing Executive Officer, Masashi Namatame
Managing Executive Officer, Noboru Yamagata
Executive Officer, Director of Legal Compliance, Yoshinori Ishii
Managing Executive Officer, Yoshihiko Shima
Executive Officer, Tomoya Kittaka
Executive Officer, Director of Human Resources, Mika Nabeshima
Independent Director, Emi Osono
CEO, Tokio Marine HCC, Susan Rivera
Auditors: PricewaterhouseCoopers Aarata LLC

LOCATIONS

HQ: Tokio Marine Holdings Inc
  1-2-1 Marunouchi, Chiyoda-ku, Tokyo 100-0005
Phone: (81) 3 6212 3333
Web: www.tokiomarinehd.com

PRODUCTS/OPERATIONS

Selected Mergers and Acquisitions

COMPETITORS

AMERICAN INTERNATIONAL GROUP INC.	MIZUHO FINANCIAL GROUP INC.
ANA HOLDINGS INC.	NOMURA HOLDINGS INC.
AVIVA PLC	T&D HOLDINGS INC.
Axis Capital Holdings Limited	TOKIO MARINE KILN GROUP LIMITED
DAI-ICHI LIFE HOLDINGS INC.	TPG CAPITAL MANAGEMENT L.P.
JAPAN POST HOLDINGS CO.LTD.	Zurich Insurance Group AG

HISTORICAL FINANCIALS

Company Type: Public

Income Statement   FYE: March 31

	ASSETS ($ mil.)	NET INCOME ($ mil.)	INCOME AS % OF ASSETS	EMPLOYEES
03/21	232,697	1,461	0.6%	43,257
03/20	232,647	2,393	1.0%	41,101
03/19	203,454	2,479	1.2%	40,848
03/18	215,939	2,676	1.2%	39,191
03/17	202,202	2,449	1.2%	36,842
Annual Growth	3.6%	(12.1%)	—	4.1%

2021 Year-End Financials

Return on assets: 0.6%	Dividends
Return on equity: 4.6%	Yield: 4.5%
Long-term debt ($ mil.): —	Payout: 98.5%
No. of shares (mil.): 693	Market value ($ mil.): 33,034
Sales ($ mil): 48,518	

	STOCK PRICE ($) FY Close	P/E High/Low		PER SHARE ($) Earnings	Dividends	Book Value
03/21	47.65	0	0	2.10	2.18	47.76
03/20	45.50	0	0	3.40	2.03	44.55
03/19	48.50	0	0	3.46	2.16	45.71
03/18	45.68	0	0	3.60	1.45	49.43
03/17	42.35	0	0	3.25	1.15	42.26
Annual Growth	3.0%		—	(10.4%)	17.2%	3.1%

Tokyo Electric Power Company Holdings Inc

Tokyo Electric Power Company (TEPCO) is known as Japan's largest electricity operator which supplies power to the Kanto region including the Tokyo Metropolitan Area. The company has total assets of about 12.1 billion and electricity sales of about 204.5 TWh. Overall the company has roughly 25 companies as its consolidated subsidiaries. TEPCO is still committed to carrying out the complex multilayer and largescale decommissioning project followed by the major crisis in 2011 when its Fukushima Dai-ichi nuclear plant complex experienced a partial meltdown at three reactors and radioactive material was released in the wake of a major earthquake and tsunami.

Operations

TEPCO holds three independent business entities: TEPCO Energy Partner TEPCO Power Grid TEPCO Fuel & Power and TEPCO Renewable Power.

TEPCO Energy Partner Inc. engages in the retail sale of electricity and gas in the Tokyo Metropolitan area. TEPCO Power Grid is a general power transmission and distribution operator in charge of providing a stable supply of power to the Tokyo Metropolitan area. TEPCO Fuel & Power handles the company's fuel and thermal power generation businesses. Lastly TEPCO Renewable Power Inc. manages the generation of power from renewable energies such as hydro wind and solar power.

Geographic Reach

TEPCO is headquartered in Tokyo Japan and has offices in Washington DC and London.

Financial Performance

TEPCO's performance for the span of five years has fluctuated with 2017 to 2019 having an upward trend then decreasing annually since then.

Revenue for the year ended 2021 decreased by 375 billion to 5.9 trillion compared to 6.2 trillion in the previous fiscal year.

Net Income attributable to owners of the parent increased by 130 billion to 180.9 billion in 2021 compared to the prior year's net income of 50.7 billion.

The company's cash for the year ended 2021 was 239.8 billion. Operating activities generated 239.8 billion. Investing activities and financing activities used 577.2 billion and 20.3 billion respectively. Main cash uses were for purchases of property plant and equipment and repayment of short-term loans.

Strategy

TEPCO's strategies are centered and focused on its different operating segments. TEPCO Power Grid's strategy aims to strengthen transmission and distribution infrastructure and to create new value from these networks. TEPCO Renewable Power Inc. aims to strengthen domestic hydroelectric power infrastructure promote overseas hydroelectric power projects and promote domestic and overseas offshore wind power projects. In addition the company also has a strategy to develop a presence in areas with potential substantial growth expand the scope of investments and strengthen overseas transmission and distribution projects.

HISTORY

The Tokyo Electric Power Company (TEPCO) descended from Tokyo Electric Light which was formed in 1883. In 1887 the company switched on Japan's first power plant a 25-KW fossil fuel generator. Fossil fuels were the main source of electricity in Japan until 1912 when long-distance transmission techniques became more efficient making hydroelectric power cheaper.

In 1938 Japan nationalized electric utilities despite strong objections from Yasuzaemon Matsunaga a leader in Japan's utility industry and former president of the Japan Electric Association. After WWII Matsunaga championed public ownership of Japan's power companies which helped in 1951 to establish the current system of 10 regional companies each with a service monopoly. Tokyo Electric Power was the largest. That year it was listed on the Tokyo Stock Exchange and was regulated by the Ministry of International Trade and Industry. (The ministry has regulated electric utilities since 1965.)

Fossil fuel plants made a comeback in Japan in the postwar era because they could be built more economically than hydroelectric plants. When the OPEC oil embargo of the 1970s demonstrated Japan's dependence on foreign oil TEPCO increased its use of liquefied natural gas (LNG) and nuclear energy sources. (It brought its first nuke online in 1971.) In 1977 it formed the Energy Conservation Center to promote conservation and related legislation.

To further reduce its oil dependence TEPCO joined other US and Japanese firms in building a coal gasification plant in California's Mojave Desert in 1982. Two years later TEPCO announced it would begin building its first coal-burning generator since the oil crisis. It established Tokyo Telecommunication Network (TTNet) a partnership to provide telecommunications services in 1986 and TEPCO Cable TV in 1989.

As part of its interest in alternative energy systems TEPCO established a global environment department in 1990 to conduct R&D on energy and the environment. Its environmental program has included reforestation and fuel cell research.

Liberalization in 1995 allowed Japan's electric utilities to buy power from independent power producers; TEPCO quickly lined up 10 suppliers. The company proceeded with energy experimentation in 1996 trying a 6000-KW sodium-sulfur battery at a Yokohama transformer station. The next year the company announced that it would become the first electric utility to sell liquefied natural gas as part of its energy mix and finished building the world's largest nuclear plant.

To gain experience in deregulating markets TEPCO invested in US power generating company Orion Power in 1999. (It agreed to sell its 5% stake to Reliant Energy in 2001.) At home the firm joined Microsoft and SOFTBANK to form SpeedNet which provides Internet access over TTNet's network. In 2000 TEPCO got its first taste of deregulation when large customers (accounting for about a third of the market) began choosing their electricity suppliers. Also in 2000 TEPCO joined a group of nine Japanese electric companies to create POWEREDCOM. (In 2005 TEPCO sold its stake in POWEREDCOM to KDDI in order to focus on its core power business).

In 2001 TEPCO joined up with Sumitomo and Electricite de France to build Vietnam's first independent power plant.

To raise cash in 2006 Mirant (now GenOn Energy) sold its power plants in the Philippines to TEPCO and Marubeni for $3.4 billion.

Public confidence was shaken by a rash of accidents within Japan's nuclear industry. The company had struggled to restore its credibility after the Japanese government shut down TEPCO's 17 nuclear reactors due to safety concerns prompted by the company's admittance of falsifying safety data to cover up faults at several of its nuclear facilities in 2002. In 2009 it reopened the Kashiwazaki-Kariwa Nuclear Power Station which was closed in 2007 due to a major earthquake in the region.

Through affiliates TEPCO also offers cable TV and Internet services international consulting and investing in non-Japan-based independent power producers. Other businesses include construction real estate and transportation companies.

The company is developing new green energy sources such as wind and solar in order to meet carbon emission reduction targets. In 2009 the company agreed to build a major solar project in Kawasaki Kanagawa to serve about 5900 households. In 2010 it teamed up with Toyota Tsusho to fund wind power company Eurus Energy Holdings which acquired solar power company Jindosun Park in 2011. Jindosun oversees the generation of 2974 KW of electricity mostly in South Korea and activated a 45000 KW plant in the US in mid-2011.

Broadening its international power assets in 2011 the company agreed to buy 12% of Thailand-based independent power producer Electricity Generating PCL for about $274 million. However the daunting financial impact of the Fukushima disaster has cast a pall over the company's international expansion plans.

In 2012 it agreed to sell its 67.5% stake in Australian power station Loy Yang A to the plant's minority owner AGL Resources for $1.6 billion.

EXECUTIVES

Executive Officer, Director, Shigehiro Yoshino
Chairman of the Board, Independent Director, Yoshimitsu Kobayashi
Independent Director, Hideko Kunii
Executive President, Chief Executive Officer, Representative Executive Officer, Manager of Nuclear Reform Special Taskforce, Director, Tomoaki Kobayakawa
Managing Executive Officer, Ryutaro Yamamoto
Executive Vice President, Mitsushi Saiki
Managing Executive Officer, Chief Director of Niigata, Deputy Chief Director of Nuclear Power & Location, Masaya Kitta
Managing Executive Officer, Chief Director of Nuclear & Location, Manager of Nuclear Reform Special Task Force, Director, Shigenori Makino
Chief Financial Officer, Executive Vice President, Representative Executive Officer, President of Subsidiary, Director, Seiji Moriya
Managing Executive Officer, Chief Information Officer, Chief Information Security Officer, Tomomichi Seki
Managing Executive Officer, Chief Director of Aomori Business in Main Nuclear Power and Location Unit, Deputy Chief Director of Nuclear Power & Location, Issei So
Executive Vice President, Representative Executive Officer, President of Subsidiary, Director, Seiichi Fubasami
Managing Executive Officer, Chief Decommissioning Officer, President of Fukushima Daiichi Decontamination and Decommissioning Engineering Company, Akira Ono
Independent Director, Hideo Takaura
Director, Yoshihito Morishita
Managing Executive Officer, Chief Director of Fukushima, Deputy Chief Director of Manager of Nuclear Power & Location, Kazuyoshi Takahara
President of Subsidiary, Director, Nobuhide Akimoto
Managing Executive Officer, Chief Marketing Officer, Momoko Nagasaki
Independent Director, Shigeo Oyagi
Independent Director, Shoichiro Onishi
Independent Director, Asa Shinkawa
Managing Executive Officer, Hiroyuki Yamaguchi
Auditors: Ernst & Young ShinNihon LLC

LOCATIONS

HQ: Tokyo Electric Power Company Holdings Inc
1-1-3 Uchisaiwai-cho, Chiyoda-Ku, Tokyo 100-8560
Phone: (81) 3 6373 1111
Web: www.tepco.co.jp

PRODUCTS/OPERATIONS

Selected Subsidiaries
TEPCO CABLE TELEVISION Inc. (85% cable television)
TEPCO SYSTEMS CORPORATION (information software and services)
Toden Kogyo Co. Ltd. (facilities construction and maintenance)
Toden Real Estate Co. Inc. (property management)
Tokyo Densetsu Service Co. Ltd. (facilities construction and maintenance)
Tokyo Electric Power Environmental Engineering Company Incorporated (facilities construction and maintenance)
Tokyo Electric Power Services Company Limited (facilities construction and maintenance)

COMPETITORS

ABU DHABI NATIONAL ENERGY COMPANY - PJSC
ACCIONA SA
AEON CO. LTD.
ANA HOLDINGS INC.
EDF ENERGY LIMITED
EDP - ENERGIAS DE PORTUGAL S.A.
ENEOS HOLDINGS INC.
Fortum Oyj
GLOBAL INFRASTRUCTURE MANAGEMENT LLC
INTERNATIONAL POWER LTD.
JAPAN POST HOLDINGS CO.LTD.
JFE HOLDINGS INC.
KANSAI ELECTRIC POWER COMPANY INCORPORATED THE
MITSUBISHI CHEMICAL HOLDINGS CORPORATION
NATIONAL GRID PLC
NIPPON TELEGRAPH AND TELEPHONE CORPORATION
OJI HOLDINGS CORPORATION
Riverstone Energy Limited
SOFTBANK GROUP CORP.
SOMPO HOLDINGS INC.
TOHOKU ELECTRIC POWER COMPANYINCORPORATED
UNITED UTILITIES GROUP PLC

HISTORICAL FINANCIALS

Company Type: Public

Income Statement				FYE: March 31
	REVENUE ($ mil.)	NET INCOME ($ mil.)	NET PROFIT MARGIN	EMPLOYEES
03/21	52,985	1,633	3.1%	40,530
03/20	57,498	467	0.8%	40,734
03/19	57,235	2,098	3.7%	44,042
03/18	55,100	2,995	5.4%	44,610
03/17	47,919	1,187	2.5%	45,217
Annual Growth	2.5%	8.3%	—	(2.7%)

2021 Year-End Financials

Debt ratio: 0.3%
Return on equity: 6.0%
Cash ($ mil.): 4,108
Current ratio: 0.44
Long-term debt ($ mil.): 22,831

No. of shares (mil.): 1,603
Dividends
  Yield: —
  Payout: —
Market value ($ mil.): —

Tokyo Electron, Ltd.

Auditors: KPMG AZSA LLC

HQ: Tokyo Electron, Ltd.
  5-3-1 Akasaka, Minato-ku, Tokyo 107-6325
Phone: (81) 3 5561 7000   **Fax:** 512 424-1001
Web: www.tel.co.jp

HISTORICAL FINANCIALS

Company Type: Public

Income Statement   FYE: March 31

	REVENUE ($ mil.)	NET INCOME ($ mil.)	NET PROFIT MARGIN	EMPLOYEES
03/21	12,635	2,194	17.4%	14,479
03/20	10,384	1,706	16.4%	13,837
03/19	11,542	2,241	19.4%	12,742
03/18	10,648	1,924	18.1%	11,946
03/17	7,152	1,030	14.4%	11,241
Annual Growth	15.3%	20.8%	—	6.5%

2021 Year-End Financials

Debt ratio: —
Return on equity: 26.2%
Cash ($ mil.): 1,684
Current ratio: 3.10
Long-term debt ($ mil.): —

No. of shares (mil.): 156
Dividends
  Yield: 1.5%
  Payout: 11.2%
Market value ($ mil.): 17,061

	STOCK PRICE ($) FY Close	P/E High/Low		PER SHARE ($) Earnings	Dividends	Book Value
03/21	109.25	0	0	14.03	1.66	59.25
03/20	46.55	0	0	10.72	1.35	49.00
03/19	36.37	0	0	13.61	1.73	48.84
03/18	46.16	0	0	11.69	1.19	44.27
03/17	27.38	0	0	6.26	0.54	35.20
Annual Growth	41.3%	—		22.3%	32.4%	13.9%

Tokyo Gas Co Ltd

Auditors: KPMG AZSA LLC

LOCATIONS

HQ: Tokyo Gas Co Ltd
  1-5-20 Kaigan, Minato-ku, Tokyo 105-8527
Phone: (81) 3 5400 7736   **Fax:** 646 865-0592
Web: www.tokyo-gas.co.jp

HISTORICAL FINANCIALS

Company Type: Public

Income Statement   FYE: March 31

	REVENUE ($ mil.)	NET INCOME ($ mil.)	NET PROFIT MARGIN	EMPLOYEES
03/21	15,941	447	2.8%	16,858
03/20	17,735	399	2.3%	16,591
03/19	17,719	763	4.3%	16,708
03/18	16,737	706	4.2%	17,138
03/17	14,194	475	3.3%	16,823
Annual Growth	2.9%	(1.5%)	—	0.1%

2021 Year-End Financials

Debt ratio: 0.3%
Return on equity: 4.3%
Cash ($ mil.): 1,425
Current ratio: 1.33
Long-term debt ($ mil.): 8,434

No. of shares (mil.): 441
Dividends
  Yield: 2.5%
  Payout: —
Market value ($ mil.): 4,939

	STOCK PRICE ($) FY Close	P/E High/Low		PER SHARE ($) Earnings	Dividends	Book Value
03/21	11.20	0	0	1.01	0.28	23.63
03/20	11.55	0	0	0.90	0.29	23.98
03/19	13.54	0	0	1.69	0.25	23.26
03/18	13.04	0	0	1.55	0.26	23.43
03/17	18.19	0	0	1.03	0.43	21.45
Annual Growth	(11.4%)	—		(0.4%)	(9.8%)	2.4%

Tongling Nonferrous Metal Group Co Ltd

They may not make copper pennies in China but the metal has still been lucky for Tongling Nonferrous Metals. The company ranks among China's largest copper producers. Its products include alloy powder tubes coils and cathodes; other non-ferrous items include brass wires and tubes gold and silver ingots palladium platinum silver nitrate and sulfuric acid. Tongling distributes its copper and other products in the provinces of eastern China. It is owned by the Anhui provincial government. The company joined with China Railway Construction Corp. in 2009 to buy Canadian copper company Corriente Resources for C$680 million (US$650 million).

Operations
Tongling is engaged in geological exploration mining mineral processing copper lead and zinc smelting and refining copper gold silver and alloy products processing.

Geographic Reach
The company is based in Tongling Anhui in China and exports its products to more than 10 countries including Japan Germany the US and Singapore.

Sales and Marketing
The company serves industries such as construction and installation shaft and drift construction scientific research and design transportation and real estate development.

Auditors: Huapu Tianjian Certified Public
  Accountants (Beijing) Co., Ltd.

LOCATIONS

HQ: Tongling Nonferrous Metal Group Co Ltd
  Colored West Yard Building, Changjiang West Road,
  Tongling, Anhui Province 244000
Phone: (86) 562 5860159   **Fax:** (86) 562 2825082
Web: www.tlys.cn

COMPETITORS

ANGLE RING HOLDINGS LIMITED
China Gerui Advanced Materials Group Limited
MITSUI MINING AND SMELTING COMPANY LIMITED
MORTON INDUSTRIAL GROUP INC.

HISTORICAL FINANCIALS

Company Type: Public

Income Statement   FYE: December 31

	REVENUE ($ mil.)	NET INCOME ($ mil.)	NET PROFIT MARGIN	EMPLOYEES
12/20	15,204	132	0.9%	0
12/19	13,358	122	0.9%	0
12/18	12,297	103	0.8%	0
12/17	12,667	84	0.7%	0
12/16	12,481	25	0.2%	0
Annual Growth	5.1%	50.3%		

2020 Year-End Financials

Debt ratio: 4.9%
Return on equity: 4.6%
Cash ($ mil.): 929
Current ratio: 1.13
Long-term debt ($ mil.): 765

No. of shares (mil.): —
Dividends
  Yield: —
  Payout: —
Market value ($ mil.): —

Toppan Inc

Toppan Printing operates in three business segments: Information & Communication (marketing materials business forms magazines and books) Living & Industry (packaging and labels) and Electronics (materials for digital displays and semiconductors). Toppan boasts about 225 group companies across the Asia/Pacific region as well as in Europe and North America. Japan accounts for more than 80% of sales and the company is working to grow its business outside the country. The company was founded in 1900 by engineers from the printing bureau of Japan's Ministry of Finance.

Operations
Company reports in three reporting segments: information & communication; living & industry; and electronics.

Information & communication segment offers securities-related documents passbooks cards business forms catalogues and other commercial printing magazines books and other publication printing and BPO. The segment accounts for 60% of the company's total revenue.

Living & industry segment includes flexible packaging folding cartons and other packaging products plastic molded products ink transparent barrier film decorative paper/film wallpaper and other decorative material. The segment accounts for about 30% of the company's total revenue.

Electronics segment offers color filters for LCDs TFT LCDs anti-reflection films photomasks and semiconductors packaging products. Electronics segment accounts for more than 10% of revenue.

Geographic Reach
Based in Tokyo Japan Toppan earns majority of its revenue locally with around 80% of revenue.

Financial Performance
Company revenue for fiscal 2021 decreased by 1% to 1.47 trillion compared from the prior year with 1.49 trillion.

Cash held by the company in fiscal 2021 increased to 497.2 billion. Cash provided by operations investing and financing activities were 76.9 billion 81.2 billion and 42.2 billion respectively.

Strategy
Toppan Printing will strengthen its business continuity planning in light of the COVID-19 pandemic and will take steps to respond to changes in consumer behavior and values after the pandemic subsides. In the medium term the company positions "transforming the business portfolio" to enhance profitability "strengthening management foundations" to generate new growth and "expanding ESG initiatives" to support sustainable value enhancement as key managements challenges. Under the key concept of "digital & sustainable transformation" the company will optimally allocate and effectively use management resources to further expand business by pursuing the following initiatives.

HISTORY

Toppan Printing was established as Toppan Printing Limited Partnership in 1900 by engineers from Japan's Ministry of Finance who used the most advanced printing techniques of the day. It was renamed Toppan Printing Co. in 1908. In its early days the company focused primarily on securities (for the Ministry of Finance) books and business forms.

Toppan flourished during and immediately after WWI as book and magazine publishing increased. In 1926 it opened the Koishikawa Paper Container Plant. Printing declined in the 1930s however as the Japanese dictatorship banned books and stifled writers and publishers. WWII brought a paper shortage and recession which further depressed Japan's printing industry.

As the printing industry began to recover after the end of WWII Toppan expanded into specialty packaging materials (1952) and industrial materials (1958). It also acquired children's book publisher Froebel-Kan in 1961 and became the first Japanese printer to open a Hong Kong plant in 1963. The company grew at a steady pace throughout the 1960s eventually adding planning and designing to its stable of services. Toppan Moore Business Forms a joint venture between Toppan and Canada's Moore Corporation was established in 1965 (it would become Japan's largest business form printer by the 1980s).

Toppan formed a US subsidiary Toppan Printing (America) in New York City in 1971 and became the first Japanese printer to establish a production plant in the US with the 1979 opening of a separation plant in Mountainside New Jersey. During the late 1970s and early 1980s the company made several important breakthroughs in containers and packing products; it developed long-term liquid storage containers (1976) easy-to-uncap heat seals for packaging (1978) and long-term food storage containers (1980). In 1983 Toppan Moore developed a smart card with two embedded integrated circuits. Two years later the company purchased decorating products manufacturer Kyodo Kako. By the end of the decade Toppan had moved into the production of videotext batteries compact discs liquid crystal display filters lottery tickets postage stamps and portable smart card systems. It also began emphasizing distribution and direct marketing services and created an industrial materials division.

By 1990 Toppan had 21 printing plants and more than 50 sales offices throughout Japan as well as 21 international offices. That year the company formed a photomask joint venture company with Dallas-based Texas Instruments. Toppan executive Hiromichi Fujita was named president of the firm in 1991 (he later became chairman). The company established a multimedia unit in 1996 and acquired all of Toppan Moore — renamed Toppan Forms — the following year (it spun off Toppan Forms in a public offering in 1998).

In 1999 Toppan joined with Internet Initiative Japan Intel Sun Microsystems and IBM Japan to create Bitway which focuses on Internet marketing and distribution of digital content. The following year Toppan entered into a variety of partnerships and joint ventures with such firms as Chughwa Picture Tubes (photomasks) Gemplus (smart cards) and Baltimore Technologies Japan Co. (electronic authentication). Also in 2000 the company celebrated the 100th anniversary of its founding. In 2001 the company partnered with Taiwan's Powerchip Semiconductor Corp. to make chips for other companies.

That year the company invested in another Internet opportunity joining with NEC Corp. and SGI Japan Ltd. to support businesses using broadband Internet services.

EXECUTIVES

President, Representative Director, Hideharu Maro

Chairman of the Board, Representative Director, Shingo Kaneko
Executive Vice Presidents, Director, Shinichi Ohkubo
Independent Director, Yoshinobu Noma
Managing Executive Officer, Chief Director of Eastern Japan Business, Yuichiro Kotani
Managing Executive Officer, Mitsuhiro Nakao
Managing Executive Officer, Director of Environmental Design Business in Main Living & Industry Business Unit, Norio Yamanaka
Managing Executive Officer, Director of Chubu Business, Haruhiko Noguchi
Senior Managing Executive Officer, Director, Kazunori Sakai
Independent Director, Ryoko Toyama
Senior Managing Executive Officer, Chief Director of Electronics Business, Tetsuro Ueki
Senior Managing Executive Officer, Chief Director of Information & Communication Business, Masanori Saito
Executive Officer, Chief Director of Finance & Accounting, Director, Takashi Kurobe
Executive Officer, Chief Senior Director of Manufacturing, Director, Hironori Majima
Independent Director, Mieko Nakabayashi
Auditors: KPMG AZSA LLC

LOCATIONS

HQ: Toppan Inc
  1-3-3 Suido, Bunkyo-ku, Tokyo 112-8531
Phone: (81) 3 3835 5665   **Fax:** 770 467-5905
Web: www.toppan.co.jp

2016 Sales

	% of total
Japan	85
Asia	11
Other	4
Total	**100**

PRODUCTS/OPERATIONS

Selected Offerings
Information & Networks
  Publications Printing
  Magazines
  Books
  Electronic publications
  Publication planning & editing
  Advertising
  Commercial Printing
  Posters
  Catalogs
  Brochures
  Flyers
  Direct mail
  Calendars
  Corporate communications materials
  Business Forms
  Cards
  Envelopes
  Continuous forms
Living Environment
  Packaging & industrial materials
  Interior decor materials
Electronics
  Displays
  Semiconductors

COMPETITORS

BUNZL PUBLIC LIMITED COMPANY
CCL Industries Inc
CLIPPER MAGAZINE LLC
DAI NIPPON PRINTING CO. LTD.
FORT DEARBORN COMPANY
KRONES AG
MACDERMID INCORPORATED
MPAC Industries Corporation

MPS CHICAGO INC.
NELSONS LABELS (MANCHESTER) LIMITED
PANTONE LLC
RENISHAW P L C
THE SEGERDAHL CORP
WALSWORTH PUBLISHING COMPANY INC.
WESTROCK PACKAGING INC.
XEROX CORPORATION

HISTORICAL FINANCIALS
Company Type: Public

Income Statement				FYE: March 31
	REVENUE ($ mil.)	NET INCOME ($ mil.)	NET PROFIT MARGIN	EMPLOYEES
03/21	13,248	740	5.6%	58,203
03/20	13,689	801	5.9%	58,102
03/19	13,226	370	2.8%	57,147
03/18	13,681	398	2.9%	57,878
03/17	12,804	290	2.3%	57,017
Annual Growth	0.9%	26.3%	—	0.5%

2021 Year-End Financials

Debt ratio: 0.1%
Return on equity: 6.5%
Cash ($ mil.): 4,641
Current ratio: 2.44
Long-term debt ($ mil.): 2,561

No. of shares (mil.): 343
Dividends
  Yield: 0.0%
  Payout: —
Market value ($ mil.): 3,032

	STOCK PRICE ($) FY Close	P/E High/Low		PER SHARE ($) Earnings	Dividends	Book Value
03/21	8.82	0	0	2.14	0.27	34.76
03/20	8.26	0	0	2.40	0.18	31.26
03/19	7.41	0	0	1.09	0.18	32.53
03/18	8.03	0	0	1.17	0.19	33.04
03/17	10.36	0	0	0.86	0.17	28.15
Annual Growth	(4.0%)	—		25.7%	11.9%	5.4%

Toray Industries, Inc.

Auditors: Ernst & Young ShinNihon LLC

LOCATIONS

HQ: Toray Industries, Inc.
  2-1-1 Nihonbashi-Muromachi, Chuo-ku, Tokyo 103-8666
Phone: (81) 3 3245 5201   **Fax:** (81) 3 3245 5054
Web: www.toray.co.jp

HISTORICAL FINANCIALS
Company Type: Public

Income Statement				FYE: March 31
	REVENUE ($ mil.)	NET INCOME ($ mil.)	NET PROFIT MARGIN	EMPLOYEES
03/21	17,011	413	2.4%	46,267
03/20	20,401	513	2.5%	48,031
03/19	21,570	716	3.3%	48,320
03/18	20,763	903	4.4%	45,762
03/17	18,124	889	4.9%	46,248
Annual Growth	(1.6%)	(17.4%)	—	0.0%

2021 Year-End Financials

Debt ratio: 0.3%
Return on equity: 3.9%
Cash ($ mil.): 2,165
Current ratio: 1.73
Long-term debt ($ mil.): 5,912

No. of shares (mil.): 1,601
Dividends
  Yield: 1.8%
  Payout: 87.6%
Market value ($ mil.): 20,753

	STOCK PRICE ($) FY Close	P/E High/Low		PER SHARE ($) Earnings	Dividends	Book Value
03/21	12.96	0	0	0.26	0.24	6.98
03/20	8.52	0	0	0.32	0.29	6.30
03/19	12.72	0	0	0.45	0.29	6.39
03/18	19.03	0	0	0.56	0.26	6.43
03/17	17.75	0	0	0.56	0.26	5.72
Annual Growth	(7.6%)	—		(17.4%)	(2.3%)	5.1%

Toronto Dominion Bank

The Toronto-Dominion Bank wants to score financial TDs at home and abroad. Also known as TD Bank Group (or just plain "TD" for short) it is the sixth largest bank in North America by number of branches. The bank serves more than 26 million customers through three business segments: Canadian Retail which includes TD Canada Trust TD Auto Finance Canada TD Wealth TD Direct Investing and TD Insurance; US Retail which includes TD Bank America's Most Convenient Bank TD Auto Finance TD Wealth and an investment in The Charles Schwab Corporation; and Wholesale Banking (operating as TD Securities). TD also provides financial services to online and mobile customers. The bank had some C$1.7 trillion in assets in fiscal 2020.

Operations

The company has three key business segments: Canadian Retail U.S. Retail and Wholesale Banking.

TD Bank generates about 55% of revenue from Canadian Retail which offers a full range of financial products and services to over 16 million customers in the Canadian personal and commercial banking wealth and insurance businesses. The credit cards business provides a comprehensive line-up of credit cards including proprietary co-branded and affinity credit card programs.

US Retail which brings in around 35% of revenue operates under the brand TD Bank and comprises the T-D Bank's US-based retail commercial and wealth management services. Retail provides a full suite of financial products and services through its network of over 1200 branches located along the east coast from Maine to Florida.

Wholesale Banking operating under the brand name TD Securities contributes about 10% of TD Bank's revenue. The unit provides a variety of capital market investment banking and corporate banking products and services. TD Securities also offers underwriting and distribution of new debt and equity issues advice on strategic acquisitions and divestitures and various assistance with trading and investment activities.

Geographic Reach

Calling its namesake Canadian city home the Toronto-based Toronto-Dominion Bank operates across the entire country of Canada. It also operates within the US (particularly up and down the East Coast) and has offices in Ireland Japan Netherlands Singapore and the UK. The Canada accounts for over 55% of company's sales and US for about 35% while other countries account for the remaining.

Sales and Marketing

Canadian Retail serves over 16 million customers in the Canadian personal and commercial banking wealth and insurance businesses. Personal Banking provides a full range of financial products and services through its network of nearly 1100 branches more than 3400 automated teller machines (ATMs) telephone internet and mobile banking. US Retail provides products and services to nearly 10 million retail customers through multiple delivery channels including a network of nearly 1200 stores located along the east coast from Maine to Florida mobile and internet banking ATM and telephone. Wholesale Banking clients include companies governments and institutions in key financial markets around the world.

Financial Performance

TD Bank's revenue and net income have grown steadily year-to-year over the past five years.

TD Bank's revenue in 2020 reached over C$43 billion from C$41.1 billion in 2019.

Reported net income for 2020 was C$11.9 billion compared to C$11.7 in 2019. The increase reflects a net gain on sale of the Bank's investment in TD Ameritrade and charges in the prior year related to the agreement with Air Canada.

Cash on hand at the end of 2020 was C$6.4 billion. Cash from operations was C$231.8 billion while investing activities used $224.1 billion. Financing activities used C$6.1 billion.

Strategy

TD Bank continues to invest in personalized customer service while strengthening its omni-channel strategy to allow customers to move seamlessly across channels. The company is also looking to expand its advisory capabilities through TD Ready Advice and continue to help its customers navigate the impact of the coronavirus pandemic and plan their financial futures. The company continues to grow with and support its TD partners invest in an efficient and agile infrastructure innovation and data capabilities and adapt to industry and regulatory changes.

Mergers and Acquisitions

In 2021 TD Bank and Wells Fargo announced a definitive agreement subject to specific closing conditions for TD to acquire Wells Fargo's Canadian Direct Equipment Finance business. This move is anticipated to enhance TD's Canadian Equipment Financing business and expand TD's presence in core markets.

Company Background

The Bank of Toronto was established in 1855 by flour traders who wanted their own banking facilities. Its growth encouraged another group of businessmen to found the Dominion Bank in 1869. Dominion emphasized commercial banking and invested heavily in railways and construction.

As the new nation expanded westward both banks established branch networks. They helped fund Canada's primary industries — dairy mining oil pulp and textiles. After growing during and after WWII The Bank of Toronto and Dominion Bank decided to increase their capital base merging into a 450-branch bank in 1955.

HISTORY

The Bank of Toronto was established in 1855 by flour traders who wanted their own banking facilities. Its growth encouraged another group of businessmen to found the Dominion Bank in 1869. Dominion emphasized commercial banking and invested heavily in railways and construction.

As the new nation expanded westward both banks established branch networks. They helped fund Canada's primary industries — dairy mining oil pulp and textiles. True to its pioneering spirit a Bank of Toronto official claimed to be the first to have set up a branch office with the help of aviation (in Manitoba in the 1920s).

The demand for agricultural products and commodities dropped after WWI but production continued full throttle creating a world grain glut that helped trigger the stock market crash of 1929. Both the Bank of Toronto and Dominion Bank contracted during the 1930s. After growing during and subsequent to WWII The Bank of Toronto and Dominion Bank decided to increase their capital base merging into a 450-branch bank in 1955.

In the 1970s TD Bank opened offices in Bangkok Beirut and Frankfurt among other cities abroad. During the 1980s it was active in making loans to less-developed countries. After the deregulation of the Canadian securities industry in 1987 then-CEO Richard Thomson reduced international lending and began focusing on brokerage activities. The strategy paid off when several Latin American countries fell behind on their loans in the late 1980s.

As the North American economy slowed in the early 1990s TD Bank's nonperforming loans increased and with it its loan loss reserves. The bank still made acquisitions including Central Guaranty Trust (1993) and Lancaster Financial Holdings (1995 investment banking). It worked to build its financial services expanding its range of service offerings and geographic coverage and buying New York-based Waterhouse Investor Services (1996); 97% of Australia-based Pont Securities (1997); and California-based Kennedy Cabot & Co. (1997). In 1998 the bank sold its payroll services to Ceridian and its Waterhouse Securities unit bought US discount brokerage Jack White & Co.

That year the government nixed TD Bank's merger with Canadian Imperial on the same day it voided the Royal Bank of Canada/ Bank of Montreal deal. The banks believed the consolidation was necessary to stave off foreign banks' encroachment into Canada but the government had domestic antitrust concerns: Though Canada has one-tenth the population of the US its five top banks all ranked in the top 15 in North America.

In 1999 TD Bank bought Trimark Financial's retail trust banking business and spun off part of Waterhouse Investor Services which would become part of TD Waterhouse Group. That year the bank ramped up its focus on Internet banking.

Not giving up on acquisition-fueled growth in 2000 the company bought CT Financial Services (now TD Canada Trust) from British American Tobacco. As a condition for government approval TD Bank had to sell its MasterCard credit portfolio (sold to Citibank Canada) and a dozen southern Ontario branches (to Bank of Montreal).

The company's plans to hitch a ride on the Wal-Mart gravy train derailed in 2001. Arrangements to open bank branches in some US-based Wal-Mart stores were squelched by regulators enforcing the banking and commerce barrier. TD Bank later closed all of its existing branches (more than 100 in all) inside Canadian Wal-Marts as part of a broader restructuring.

TD Bank suffered its first-ever annual loss during fiscal year 2002. Write-downs on loans to telecommunications technology and energy firms contributed mightily to the dismal results.

Frustrated by limited growth opportunities at home in 2005 TD Bank ventured south of the border with its purchase of a stake in Banknorth. TD Bank paid about $4.8 billion in cash and stock for its original 51% stake (it bought the rest in 2007). Additionally in 2006 the company assumed about a 40% ownership in TD AMERITRADE as part of the sale of TD Waterhouse.

In 2008 the company acquired New Jersey-based Commerce Bancorp. The $8.5 billion acquisition deal added some 450 branches along the eastern seaboard to TD Bank's US network and exemplified the company's plans to expand abroad. TD merged Commerce with its TD Banknorth unit to create TD Bank.

EXECUTIVES

Head, Wholesale Banking and CEO, TD Securities, Riaz Ahmed, $557,552 total compensation

Group President, Chief Executive Officer, Non-Independent Director, Bharat Masrani, $1,077,935 total compensation

Group Head, Customer and General Counsel, TD Bank Group, Norie Campbell

Group Head, Canadian Personal Banking, TD Bank Group, Michael Rhodes

Group Head, Canadian Business Banking, TD Bank Group, Paul Douglas

Independent Director, Alan MacGibbon

Group Head, Chief Risk Officer, Ajai Bambawale

Group Head - Wealth Management and TD Insurance, Leovigildo Salom
Independent Director, S. Jane Rowe
Auditors: Ernst & Young LLP

LOCATIONS

HQ: Toronto Dominion Bank
66 Wellington Street West, Toronto, Ontario M5K 1A2
Phone: 416 944-6367　　**Fax:** 416 982-6166
Web: www.td.com

PRODUCTS/OPERATIONS

FY2017 Revenue

	% of total
Interest	
Loans	53
Securities:	
Interest	9
Dividends	2
Deposits with banks	1
Non interest	
Investment and securities services	10
Insurance revenue	9
Service charges	6
Card services	6
Credit fees	3
Trading income	1
Total	**100**

FY2017 Revenue by Segment

	% of total
Canadian Retail	59
US Retail	28
Wholesale Banking	9
Corporate	4
Total	**100**

FY2017 Revenue by Country

	% of total
Canada	59
US	36
Other	5
Total	**100**

Selected Canadian Subsidiaries

CT Financial Assurance Company (99.9%)
Meloche Monnex Inc.
　Security National Insurance Company
　Primmum Insurance Company
　TD Direct Insurance Inc.
　TD General Insurance Company
　TD Home and Auto Insurance Company
TD Asset Finance Corp.
TD Asset Management Inc.
　TD Waterhouse Private Investment Counsel Inc.
TD Investment Services Inc.
TD Life Insurance Company
TD Mortgage Corporation
　The Canada Trust Company
　TD Pacific Mortgage Corporation
TD Mortgage Investment Corporation
TD Nordique Investments Limited
TD Parellel Private Equity Investors Ltd.
TD Securities Inc.
TD Timberlane Investments Limited
　TD McMurray Investments Limited
　TD Redpath Investments Limited
　TD Riverside Investments Limited
TD Vermillion Holdings ULC
　TD Financial International Ltd. (Bermuda)
　Canada Trustco International Limited (Barbados)
　TD Reinsurance (Barbados) Inc.
　Toronto Dominion International Inc. (Barbados)
TD Waterhouse Canada Inc.
　thinkorswim Canada
Truscan Property Corporation

Selected US Subsidiaries

TDAM USA Inc.
TD Prime Services
Toronto Dominion Holdings (U.S.A.) Inc.
　TD Holdings II Inc.
　TD Securities (USA) LLC
　Toronto Dominion (Texas) LLC
　Toronto Dominion Capital (U.S.A.) Inc.
　Toronto Dominion Investments Inc.

Selected Other International Subsidiaries

Internaxx Bank S.A. (Luxembourg)
NatWest Personal Financial Management Limited (50% UK)
　NatWest Stockbrokers Limited
TD Ireland
　TD Global Finance
TD Waterhouse Bank N.V. (The Netherlands)
TD Waterhouse Investor Services (UK) Limited
　TD Waterhouse Investor Services (Europe) Limited (UK)
Toronto Dominion (South East Asia) Limited (Singapore)

COMPETITORS

CIT GROUP INC.
COMMONWEALTH BANK OF AUSTRALIA
HSBC HOLDINGS PLC
HUNTINGTON BANCSHARES INCORPORATED
ING Groep N.V.
KEYCORP
Nordea Bank AB
STANDARD CHARTERED PLC
U.S. BANCORP

HISTORICAL FINANCIALS

Company Type: Public

Income Statement

FYE: October 31

	ASSETS ($ mil.)	NET INCOME ($ mil.)	INCOME AS % OF ASSETS	EMPLOYEES
10/21	1,399,434	11,373	0.8%	89,464
10/20	1,289,890	8,741	0.7%	89,598
10/19	1,074,466	8,666	0.8%	89,031
10/18	1,016,639	8,413	0.8%	84,383
10/17	995,579	7,942	0.8%	83,160
Annual Growth	**8.9%**	**9.4%**	**—**	**1.8%**

2021 Year-End Financials

Return on assets: 0.8%
Return on equity: 14.3%
Long-term debt ($ mil.): —
No. of shares (mil.): 1,822
Sales ($ mil): 39,609
Dividends
　Yield: 0.0%
　Payout: 40.9%
　Market value ($ mil.): 132,113

	STOCK PRICE ($) FY Close	P/E High/Low		PER SHARE ($) Earnings	Dividends	Book Value
10/21	72.51	9	6	6.25	2.56	44.35
10/20	44.23	9	6	4.83	2.34	39.54
10/19	57.07	9	8	4.74	2.17	36.75
10/18	55.46	10	9	4.58	2.03	32.93
10/17	56.85	10	8	4.28	1.81	31.40
Annual Growth	**6.3%**	**—**	**—**	**9.9%**	**9.1%**	**9.0%**

Toshiba Corp

Auditors: PricewaterhouseCoopers Aarata LLC

LOCATIONS

HQ: Toshiba Corp
1-1-1 Shibaura, Minato-ku, Tokyo 105-8001
Phone: (81) 3 3457 4511　　**Fax:** (81) 3 3456 1631
Web: www.toshiba.co.jp

HISTORICAL FINANCIALS

Company Type: Public

Income Statement

FYE: March 31

	REVENUE ($ mil.)	NET INCOME ($ mil.)	NET PROFIT MARGIN	EMPLOYEES
03/21	28,442	1,029	3.6%	117,300
03/20	31,541	(1,056)	—	125,648
03/19	33,971	9,149	26.9%	128,697
03/18	39,084	7,571	19.4%	141,256
03/17	44,354	(8,636)	—	153,492
Annual Growth	**(10.5%)**	**—**	**—**	**(6.5%)**

2021 Year-End Financials

Debt ratio: 0.1%
Return on equity: 10.8%
Cash ($ mil.): 4,745
Current ratio: 1.70
Long-term debt ($ mil.): 3,417
No. of shares (mil.): 453
Dividends
　Yield: 0.5%
　Payout: 3.9%
　Market value ($ mil.): 7,715

	STOCK PRICE ($) FY Close	P/E High/Low		PER SHARE ($) Earnings	Dividends	Book Value
03/21	17.00	0	0	2.27	0.09	23.17
03/20	10.84	—	—	(2.18)	0.18	19.09
03/19	15.86	0	0	14.83	0.09	24.30
03/18	17.24	0	0	15.34	0.00	11.32
03/17	12.79	—	—	(20.40)	0.00	(11.68)
Annual Growth	**7.4%**					

TotalEnergies SE

Total SE is a broad energy company that produces and markets fuels natural gas and electricity. The company operates in more than 130 countries. In 2020 the company finalized the acquisition of a 37.4% interest in Adani Gas. In terms of sales Europe accumulated almost 50% of the total revenue. In early 2021 Total SE proposes to change its name to TotalEnergies as part of its plan to become a broad energy company amid the global clean energy transition.

Operations

TotalEnergies has four business segments: Exploration & Production; Integrated Gas Renewables & Power; Refining & Chemicals; Marketing & Services.

The Refining & Chemicals segment collecting 40% of annual sales constitutes a major industrial hub comprising the activities of refining petrochemicals and specialty chemicals. This segment also includes the activities of oil Supply Trading and marine Shipping.

The Marketing and Services segments accounts for 45%. This segment includes the global activities of supply and marketing in the field of petroleum products.

The Integrated Gas Renewables & Power segment is comprised of integrated gas (including LNG) and low carbon electricity businesses. It includes the upstream and midstream LNG activity that was previously reported in the Exploration & Production segment. The segment accounts for more than 10% of total revenue.

The Exploration & Production segment brings in nearly 5% of revenue.

Geographic Reach

France-based TotalEnergies has presence in more than 130 countries across five continents. Largest sales are evident in Europe for nearly 50% of the total revenue followed by France with around 20%.

Sales and Marketing

TotalEnergies serves both businesses and consumers offering increasingly innovative high-quality solutions. For businesses the company offers additives and special fuels; batteries; specialty chemicals; special fluids; natural gas and power; lubricants; and polymers among other things. TotalEnergies also provides dedicated products and solutions for aviation heating and marine. Consumer products and solutions include home heating natural gas and power solutions and solar energy.

Financial Performance

The company's revenue decreased by $56.5 billion in 2020 to $119.7 billion from $176.2 billion in the prior year. Non-Group sales were $140.7 billion in 2020 compared to $200.3 billion in 2019 a decrease of 30% reflecting the decreased hydrocarbon prices and the decrease in global energy demand due to the COVID-19 pandemic. In 2020 Non-Group sales decreased by 32% for the Exploration & Production segment 14% for the Integrated Gas Renewables & Power segment 35% for Refining & Chemicals segment and 27% for the Marketing & Services segment.

The company's net income in 2020 decreased by $4.1 million to $7.3 billion compared to $11.4 billion in 2019 due to exceptional asset impairments notably on Canadian oil sands assets.

Cash held by the company at the end of 2020 increased by $3.9 million to $31.3 billion compared to $27.4 billion in the prior year. Cash provided by operations was $14.8 billion while investing activities used $13.1 billion and financing activities generated $1.4 billion.

Strategy

2020 represents a pivotal year for TOTAL's strategy with the announcement of its ambition to get to net zero emissions (Net Zero) together with society. The company affirms its plan to transform itself into a broad energy company to meet the dual challenge of the energy transition: more energy fewer emissions. Thus TOTAL's profile will be transformed over the 2020-30 decade: the growth of energy production will be based on two pillars LNG and Renewables & Electricity while oil products are expected to fall from 55% to 30% of sales. To anchor this transformation the company will propose to its shareholders at the Annual General Meeting to be held on May 28 2021 changing its name to TotalEnergies. They will thus have the opportunity to endorse this strategy and the underlying ambition to transition to carbon neutrality.

In 2020 TotalEnergies secured its investments in Renewables & Electricity ($2 billion) and accelerated the implementation of its strategy to grow renewables adding 10 GW to its portfolio. With the acquisition at the start of 2021 of a 20% stake in Adani Green Energy Limited (AGEL) one of the largest solar developers in the world and of portfolios of projects in the United States the company now has a portfolio of gross installed capacity under construction and in development of 35 GW by 2025 with more than 20 GW already benefiting from long-term power purchase agreements.

Mergers and Acquisitions

In 2021 TotalEnergies has signed a Sale and Purchase Agreement (SPA) with Novatek to acquire 10% of Arctic Transshipment LLC a wholly owned subsidiary of Novatek which owns and will operate two liquefied natural gas (LNG) transshipment terminals being built in the Murmansk and Kamchatka regions of Russia. These terminals will provide export logistics services including to the Arctic LNG 2 project under construction and will each initially include a 360000 m3 floating storage unit (FSU) and two ship-to-ship transfer kits (STS). TotalEnergies is a 19.4% shareholder in Novatek and holds a 20% stake in Yamal LNG a project

that started up in December 2017 and produced more than 18.8 million tons of LNG in 2020. The company also holds a 10% stake in Arctic LNG 2 a project currently under construction and on track to deliver its first LNG cargo in 2023.

In early 2021 TotalEnergies announces the acquisition of a 20% minority interest in Adani Green Energy Limited (AGEL) from Adani Group. The transaction marks the deepening partnership between the Adani Group ? India's leading infrastructure platform - and Total in the transition and green energy fields in India. The investment in AGEL is another step in the strategic alliance between Adani Group and Total which covers investments in LNG terminals gas utility business and renewable assets across India. This is in line with the commitment of both Adani and Total to be leading participants in the sustainable economy of the future and help India in its quest for development of renewable energy.

HISTORY

A French consortium formed the Compagnie Fran Saise des Petroles (CFP) in 1924 to develop an oil industry for the country. Lacking reserves within its borders France had a 24% stake in the Turkish Petroleum Company (TPC) acquired from Germany in 1920 as part of the spoils from WWI. When oil was discovered in Iraq in 1927 the TPC partners (CFP; Anglo-Persian Oil later BP; Royal Dutch Shell; and a consortium of five US oil companies) became major players in the oil game.

After WWII CFP diversified its sources for crude opening a supply in 1947 from the Venezuelan company Pantepec and making several major discoveries in colonial Algeria in 1956. It also began supplying crude to Japan South Korea and Taiwan in the 1950s. To market its products in North Africa and France and other European areas it introduced the brand name TOTAL in 1954. It began making petrochemicals in 1956. Decades later in 1985 the company adopted its brand name as part of its new name TOTAL Compagnie Fran Saise des Petroles shortened in 1991 to TOTAL.

Auditors: Ernst & Young Audit

LOCATIONS

HQ: TotalEnergies SE
2, place Jean Millier, La Defense 6, Courbevoie 92400
Phone: (33) 1 47 44 45 46   **Fax:** (33) 1 47 44 49 44
Web: www.total.com

2018 Sales

	% of total
Europe	
France	23
Other countries	48
Africa	11
North America	11
Other regions	8
Total	**100**

PRODUCTS/OPERATIONS

2018 Sales

	% of total
Refining & Chemicals	49
Marketing & Services	27
Exploration & Production	17
Gas Renewables & Power	7
Total	**100**

COMPETITORS

Borealis AG
COMPA 'IA ESPA 'OLA DE PETROLEOS SAU
ENEOS HOLDINGS INC.

HONG KONG AND CHINA GAS COMPANY LIMITED THE
INDIAN OIL CORPORATION LIMITED
KINDER MORGAN INC
LUKOIL PAO
MRC GLOBAL INC.
NATURGY ENERGY GROUP SA.
NK ROSNEFT PAO
RUBIS
SASOL LTD
SEMBCORP INDUSTRIES LTD
SNAM SPA
TRICORN GROUP PLC
TransAlta Corporation
Ultrapar Participacoes S/A

HISTORICAL FINANCIALS
Company Type: Public

Income Statement

	REVENUE ($ mil.)	NET INCOME ($ mil.)	NET PROFIT MARGIN	EMPLOYEES
12/20	119,704	(7,242)	—	105,476
12/19	176,249	11,267	6.4%	107,776
12/18	184,106	11,446	6.2%	104,460
12/17	149,099	8,631	5.8%	98,277
12/16	127,925	6,196	4.8%	102,168
Annual Growth	(1.6%)	—	—	0.8%

FYE: December 31

2020 Year-End Financials

Debt ratio: 26.1%
Return on equity: (-6.5%)
Cash ($ mil.): 31,268
Current ratio: 1.23
Long-term debt ($ mil.): 52,467
No. of shares (mil.): —
Dividends
Yield: 7.3%
Payout: —
Market value ($ mil.): —

	STOCK PRICE ($) FY Close	P/E High/Low	PER SHARE ($) Earnings	Dividends	Book Value
12/20	41.91	—	(2.90)	3.09	39.45
12/19	55.30	14 11	4.17	2.89	45.15
12/18	52.18	15 12	4.24	2.95	44.34
12/17	55.28	17 14	3.34	5.64	44.26
12/16	50.97	20 16	2.52	5.40	40.78
Annual Growth	(4.8%)	—	—	(13.0%)	(0.8%)

Toyota Industries Corporation (Japan)

If you're in the market for a forklift call Toyota Industries. Those on the hunt for a Corolla should call Toyota Motor. Toyota Industries builds forklifts and other lift trucks automotive parts (engines air-conditioning compressors and electronics) and textile machinery (which established the company in 1926). It also offers logistics services. Toyota Industries have more nearly 60 subsidiaries in and outside Japan. Its largest shareholders are Toyota Motor which owns nearly 25% of the company and DENSO which has around 9% stake. The company's largest business activity Material Handling Equipment accounts for more than 65% of total sales.

Operations

The company has three business activities: Material Handling Equipment (more than 65% of total sales) Automobile (nearly 30%) and Textile Machinery (less than 5%).

Materials Handling Equipment business activity provides materials handling products and service to customers around the world through Toyota Material Handling Group (TMHG) under the brands of TOYOTA RAYMOND and CESAB. Toyota Industries develops manufactures and markets industrial vehicles such as lift trucks and other materials handling equipment and systems related to transportation storage and sorting of goods. In order to help customers overcome logistics challenges it offers optimized materials handling solutions based on our technological capabilities and materials handling know-how. Under the AICHI brand the company provides aerial work platforms.

Automobile business activity develops and manufactures automobiles and automobile-related products such as vehicles engines car air-conditioning compressors car electronics components and devices and stamping dies.

Textile Machinery business activity develops manufactures and markets textile machinery the majority of which has been supplied to customers outside Japan. It has two main categories: spinning machinery and weaving machinery. Its textile machinery receives high praise from customers around the world for its high reliability and productivity as our products are developed through technological expertise accumulated over the years.

Geographic Reach
Headquartered in Kariya-shi the company operates through its subsidiaries in over 70 facilities located in Europe Asia North and Latin America and Oceania and has about 10 manufacturing plants in Japan.

Financial Performance
Total consolidated net sales amounted to 2171.3 billion yen a decrease of 43.6 billion yen or 2% from the previous fiscal year.

Profit attributable to owners of the parent totaled 145.8 billion yen a decrease of 6.9 billion yen or 4%.

The company's cash for the year ended 2020 totaled 358.1 billion. Operating activities generated 313.2 billion while investing activities used 182.6 billion mainly for payments for bank deposits. Financing activities used another 7.1 billion.

Mergers and Acquisitions
In 2013 Toyota Industries made a move to strengthen its forklift portfolio when it acquired Cascade Corporation for $759 million. Cascade makes a variety of forklift attachments handling forks cylinders and other related parts to dealers and manufacturers of lift trucks in North America Europe China and the Asia/Pacific region. It now operates as a wholly owned subsidiary of Toyota Industries.

EXECUTIVES

Chairman of the Board, Representative Director, Tetsuro Toyoda
President, Representative Director, Akira Onishi
Vice President, President of Toyota L&F Company, Representative Director, Yojiro Mizuno
Managing Executive Officer, Director of Compressor Business, Director, Yuji Ishizaki
Independent Director, Kenichiro Yamanishi
Independent Director, Shuzo Sumi
Vice President, Chief Director of Corporate, Representative Director, Takuo Sasaki
Independent Director, Masahiko Maeda
Auditors: PricewaterhouseCoopers Aarata LLC

LOCATIONS

HQ: Toyota Industries Corporation (Japan)
2-1 Toyoda-cho, Kariya, Aichi 448-8671
Phone: (81) 566 22 2511   **Fax:** (81) 566 27 5650
Web: www.toyota-shokki.co.jp

PRODUCTS/OPERATIONS

Selected Products
Automobile
  Car air-conditioning compressors
  Diesel and gasoline engines
  Electronics components
  Foundry parts
  Passenger vehicles
Materials Handling Equipment
  Aerial work platforms
  Automated storage and retrieval systems
  Automatic guided vehicles
  Counterbalanced lift trucks
  Warehouse trucks
Logistics
  Collection and delivery of cash and management of sales proceeds
  Logistics planning
  Management collection and delivery of corporate documents
  Operation of distribution centers
  Secure storage
  Transportation services
Textile Machinery
  Air-jet looms
  High-speed ring spinning frames
  High-speed roving frames
Other
  Semiconductor package substrates

COMPETITORS

CATERPILLAR INC.	NTN CORPORATION
GENERAL MOTORS COMPANY	PACCAR INC
HONDA MOTOR CO. LTD.	REV GROUP INC.
MAHINDRA AND MAHINDRA	SUMITOMO HEAVY
LIMITED	INDUSTRIES LTD.
MYERS INDUSTRIES INC.	TATA MOTORS LIMITED
NAVISTAR INTERNATIONAL	
CORPORATION	

HISTORICAL FINANCIALS

Company Type: Public

Income Statement   FYE: March 31

	REVENUE ($ mil.)	NET INCOME ($ mil.)	NET PROFIT MARGIN	EMPLOYEES
03/21	19,131	1,234	6.5%	78,343
03/20	20,003	1,343	6.7%	79,266
03/19	20,000	1,379	6.9%	77,266
03/18	18,872	1,583	8.4%	72,857
03/17	14,982	1,175	7.8%	63,618
Annual Growth	6.3%	1.2%		5.3%

2021 Year-End Financials

Debt ratio: 0.1%	No. of shares (mil.): 310
Return on equity: 4.8%	Dividends
Cash ($ mil.): 5,347	Yield: 0.0%
Current ratio: 1.64	Payout: —
Long-term debt ($ mil.): 8,219	Market value ($ mil.): 28,145

	STOCK PRICE ($) FY Close	P/E High/Low		PER SHARE ($) Earnings	Dividends	Book Value
03/21	90.65	0	0	3.98	1.36	94.13
03/20	47.34	0	0	4.33	1.47	72.36
03/19	50.50	0	0	4.44	1.40	72.12
03/18	61.77	0	0	5.10	1.30	77.45
03/17	50.05	0	0	3.76	1.06	64.53
Annual Growth	16.0%	—	—	1.4%	6.5%	9.9%

Toyota Motor Corp

Toyota Motor also known as Toyota is among the world's largest automotive manufacturers. The company designs and manufactures a diverse product line-up that ranges from subcompacts to luxury and sports vehicles to SUVs trucks minivans and buses. Its vehicles are produced either with combustion engines or hybrid-electric propulsion systems as with the iconic Prius. Popular models include the Camry Corolla Land Cruiser and luxury Lexus line as well as the Tundra truck. Toyota's subsidiaries also manufacture vehicles: Daihatsu Motor produces mini-vehicles while Hino Motors produces trucks and buses. Additionally Toyota makes automotive parts for its own use and for sale to others. The company's domestic sales account for nearly 45% of the company's revenue.

Operations
Major Toyota subsidiaries include Toyota Auto Body Co. Ltd. Toyota Motor Sales U.S.A. Toyota Motor North America Toyota Motor Engineering & Manufacturing North America Toyota Financial Services Corporation and Toyota Motor Credit Corporation.

Toyota divides its operations into the three segments of automotive (about 90% of total sales) financial services (more than 5%) and all other (nearly 5%). Automotive is obviously Toyota's bread and butter; the segment makes passenger and commercial vehicles minivans trucks and related parts and accessories. It's less known financial services segment provides financing to dealers and their customers for the lease or purchase of Toyota vehicles. The financial services business also provides retail installment credit and leasing through loans and contracts originated by Toyota dealers. Toyota's all other operations include the design and manufacture of prefabricated housing and information technology-related businesses such as GAZOO.com which offers a web portal for general automobile information and car racing.

Overall its sales of production accounts nearly 95% of total sales while financing operation accounts the remainder.

Geographic Reach
Toyota maintains a vast geographic reach selling to approximately 200 countries and regions through nearly 530 consolidated subsidiaries and some 200 affiliated companies. More than 55% of its sales come from Asia (Japan counts for nearly 45%) while North America generates nearly 30% of sales. Countries in Europe Africa the Middle East Oceania Central and South America account for the remainder.

Toyota and affiliated companies produce automobiles and related parts and components through more than 50 overseas manufacturing companies in more than 25 countries and regions besides Japan. Toyota's major manufacturing facilities include plants in Japan the US Canada the UK France Turkey Thailand China Taiwan India Indonesia South Africa and Argentina.

Daihatsu brand vehicles are produced in nearly five factories in Japan and two in Indonesia and Malaysia. Hino brand vehicles are produced at four factories in Japan and at about a dozen facilities in more than ten countries including Indonesia and Thailand.

Sales and Marketing
Toyota sells its products mainly through dealers and distributors as well as certain of Toyota's third-party suppliers and business partners. The company spent 470.8 billion 490.1 billion and 509.7 billion in advertising for the years ended in 2020 2019 and 2018 respectively.

Financial Performance

Toyota had net revenues for fiscal 2020 of 29.9 trillion a decrease of 295.6 billion or 1.0% compared to the prior fiscal year. The decrease resulted mainly from the 880.0 billion unfavorable impact of changes in exchange rates partially offset by the 440.0 billion impact of changes in vehicle unit sales and sales mix.

Net income attributable to the shareholders of Toyota Motor Corporation increased by 193.3 billion or 10% to 2.1 trillion during fiscal 2020 compared to the prior fiscal year.

Cash held by the company at the end of 2020 increased to 4.4 trillion compared to 3.7 trillion in the prior year. Cash provided by operations and financing activities were 3.6 trillion and 397.1 billion respectively. Cash used for investing activities 3.2 trillion mainly for additions to finance receivables.

Strategy

In promoting a sustainable growth strategy establishing a system capable of providing optimal supply of products in the global market is integral to Toyota's strategy.

In line with its basic policy of manufacturing in countries or regions where there is demand and where Toyota is truly competitive Toyota will make efficient use of and maximize capacity utilization at its existing plants to respond to the expanding market and will continue to focus on making efficient capital investments as necessary. Furthermore Toyota will continue to place top priority on safety and quality in strengthening true competitiveness with the aim of achieving sustainable growth.

Company Background

Toyota was founded in 1937. During World War II the company made military trucks and in the 1950s it launched the four-wheel-drive Land Cruiser full-sized Crown and the small Corona. Toyota Motor Sales U.S.A. debuted the Toyota Corolla which became the best-selling car of all time in 1968. By 1970 Toyota was the world's fourth-largest automaker.

Toyota expanded rapidly in the US. During the 1970s the oil crisis caused demand for fuel-efficient cars and Toyota was there to grab market share from US makers. In 1975 Toyota displaced Volkswagen as the US's #1 auto importer. Toyota began auto production in the US in 1984 through NUMMI its joint venture with General Motors. The Lexus line was launched in the US in 1989.

Because of European restrictions on Japanese auto imports until 2000 Toyota's European expansion slowed. Toyota responded in 1992 by agreeing to distribute cars in Japan for Volkswagen and also by establishing an engine plant (later moved to full auto production) in the UK.

The SUV mania of the 1990s spurred Toyota's introduction of luxury minivans and light trucks. In 1997 Toyota introduced the Prius a hybrid electric- and gas-powered car. That was the beginning of Toyota's push to provide an electrified version of all its models by 2025.

HISTORY

In 1926 Sakichi Toyoda founded Toyoda Automatic Loom Works. In 1930 he sold the rights to the loom he invented and gave the proceeds to his son Kiichiro Toyoda to begin an automotive business. Kiichiro opened an auto shop within the loom works in 1933. When protectionist legislation (1936) improved prospects for Japanese automakers Kiichiro split off the car department took it public (1937) and changed its name to Toyota.

During WWII the company made military trucks but financial problems after the war caused Toyota to reorganize in 1950. Its postwar commitment to R&D paid off with the launch of the four-wheel-drive Land Cruiser (1951); full-sized Crown (1955); and the small Corona (1957).

Toyota Motor Sales U.S.A. debuted the Toyopet Crown in the US in 1957 but it proved underpowered for the US market. Toyota had better luck with the Corona in 1965 and with the Corolla (which became the best-selling car of all time) in 1968. By 1970 Toyota was the world's fourth largest carmaker.

Toyota expanded rapidly in the US. During the 1970s the oil crisis caused demand for fuel-efficient cars and Toyota was there to grab market share from US makers. In 1975 Toyota displaced Volkswagen as the US's #1 auto importer. Toyota began auto production in the US in 1984 through NUMMI its joint venture with General Motors. The Lexus line was launched in the US in 1989.

Because of European restrictions on Japanese auto imports until 2000 Toyota's European expansion slowed. Toyota responded in 1992 by agreeing to distribute cars in Japan for Volkswagen and also by establishing an engine plant (later moved to full auto production) in the UK.

The SUV mania of the 1990s spurred Toyota's introduction of luxury minivans and light trucks. Hiroshi Okuda a 40-year veteran with Toyota and the first person from outside the Toyoda family to run the firm succeeded Tatsuro Toyoda as president in 1995. The next year Toyota consolidated its North American production units into Cincinnati-based Toyota Motor Manufacturing North America.

In 1997 Toyota introduced the Prius a hybrid electric- and gas-powered car. The next year Toyota boosted its stake in affiliate Daihatsu Motor (mini-vehicles) to about 51% and started Toyota Mapmaster (51% owned) to make map databases for car navigation systems. Okuda became chairman in 1999 replacing Shoichiro Toyoda and Fujio Cho became president (later chairman). Also that year Toyota agreed to form a joint venture with Isuzu Motors to manufacture buses.

In 2000 Toyota launched the WiLL Vi a sedan aimed at young people. It announced that it was building an online replacement parts marketplace with i2 Technologies and formed a financial services company (Toyota Financial Service) and a brokerage firm (Toyota Financial Services Securities Corp.). Toyota also bought a 5% stake in Yamaha Motor (the world's #2 motorcycle maker) and raised its stake in truck maker Hino Motors from about 20% to around 34%.

International developments included Toyota's agreement with the Chinese government to produce passenger cars for sale in China built by Tianjin Toyota Motor Corp. a joint venture between Chinese carmaker Tianjin Automobile Xiali and Toyota. In 2001 Toyota opened a plant in France. Later that year Toyota also increased its stake in Hino Motors to 50%. With partners Toyoda Gosei and Horie Metal Co. Ltd. Toyota formed a joint venture in 2002 to manufacture resin fuel tank systems. In 2004 Toyota forged a joint venture agreement with Guangzhou Automobile Group to build engines in China. The following year Toyota established 14 Lexus dealerships in China. The company began joint car production in Europe with Peugeot S.A. in 2005. Also in 2005 Toyota bought just under 9% of Fuji Heavy Industries — the Japanese maker of Subaru passenger vehicles. The two companies began production of Toyota Camrys at Fuji Heavy Industries' underutilized Subaru of Indiana plant in 2007.

After suffering through the Great Recession from 2008 to 2010 Toyota faced another unforeseen crisis. In March 2011 its business suffered unexpectedly from the Great East Japan Earthquake which triggered a deadly tsunami and subsequent nuclear crisis that forced Tokyo Electric Power (Tepco) to shut down reactors at two nuclear power plants and five other conventional power plants. The events forced manufacturers to reduce their output or move production to other regions. Toyota along with its rivals (Nissan Honda and Mazda) were forced to close their factories days after the devastation.

EXECUTIVES

Vice Chairman, Shigeru Hayakawa
President, Chief Executive Officer, Representative Director, Akio Toyoda
Chairman of the Board, Representative Director, Takeshi Uchiyamada
Executive Officer, Chief Risk Officer, Representative Director, Koji Kobayashi
Executive Officer, Chief Information & Security Officer, Chief Product Integration Officer, President of Connected Company, Keiji Yamamoto
Chief Financial Officer, Executive Officer, Chief Director of Accounting, Director, Kenta Kon
Executive Officer, Chief Branding Officer, President of Subsidiaries, Koji Sato
Executive Officer, Chief Human Resource Officer, Chief Planning Officer, Chief Director of Business Development, Masanori Kuwata
Executive Officer, Chief Sustainability Officer, Yumi Otsuka
Managing Officer, Plant GM, Miyoshi Plant and Plant GM, Myochi Plant, Masamichi Okada
Executive Officer, Chief Technology Officer, Chief Director of Toyota ZEV Factory, Manager of Car Development Center, Masahiko Maeda
Managing Officer and Deputy Chief Officer, Japan Sales Business Group, Jun Nagata
Chief, Toyota Research Institute-Advanced Development, James Kuffner
Auditors: PricewaterhouseCoopers Aarata LLC

LOCATIONS

HQ: Toyota Motor Corp
1 Toyota-cho, Toyota, Aichi 471-8571
Phone: (81) 565 28 2121   **Fax:** (81) 565 23 5800
Web: www.toyota.co.jp

2018 Sales

	% of total
Japan	43
North America	28
Asia	14
Europe	9
Other	6
Total	**100**

PRODUCTS/OPERATIONS

2018 Sales

	% of total
Automotive	88
Financial services	7
Other	5
Total	**100**

2018 Sales

	% of total
Sales of products	93
Financing operations	7
Total	**100**

Selected Products

Vehicles
  4Runner
  Allion (sold in Japan)
  Alphard (minivan sold in Japan)
  Aurus (hybrid)
  Avalon
  Camry (also hybrid)
  Corolla
  Corolla Rumion
  Crown
  FJ Cruiser

Highlander (also hybrid)
Land Cruiser
Lexus
GX
LS600h (hybrid)
LX (SUV)
RX
SC
Mark X (sold in Japan)
Matrix
Premio (sold in Japan)
Prius (hybrid)
RAV4
Scion
Sequoia
Sienna (minivan)
Tacoma (truck)
Tundra (truck)
Vanguard
Vellfire (minivan)
Venza
Wish (minivan sold in Japan)
Yaris (marketed in Japan as the Vitz)
Other products
Factory automation equipment
Forklifts and other industrial vehicles
Housing products

COMPETITORS

FORD MOTOR COMPANY
FORD MOTOR COMPANY
  LIMITED
HONDA MOTOR CO. LTD.
MAZDA MOTOR OF AMERICA
  INC.
NISSAN MOTOR CO.LTD.

PEUGEOT SA
SUBARU CORPORATION
SUZUKI MOTOR
  CORPORATION
TOYOTA MOTOR NORTH
  AMERICA INC.

HISTORICAL FINANCIALS
Company Type: Public

Income Statement				FYE: March 31
	REVENUE ($ mil.)	NET INCOME ($ mil.)	NET PROFIT MARGIN	EMPLOYEES
03/19	272,933	17,002	6.2%	370,870
03/18	276,677	23,486	8.5%	369,124
03/17	246,829	16,377	6.6%	364,445
03/16	252,928	20,594	8.1%	348,877
03/15	226,993	18,114	8.0%	344,109
Annual Growth	4.7%	(1.6%)	—	1.9%

2019 Year-End Financials
Debt ratio: 0.3%
Return on equity: 9.6%
Cash ($ mil.): 52,627
Current ratio: 1.04
Long-term debt ($ mil.): 95,273

No. of shares (mil.): —
Dividends
  Yield: 0.0%
  Payout: 67.8%
Market value ($ mil.): —

	STOCK PRICE ($) FY Close	P/E High/Low		PER SHARE ($) Earnings	Dividends	Book Value
03/19	118.02	0	0	5.83	3.95	63.27
03/18	130.37	0	0	7.84	3.96	62.23
03/17	108.62	0	0	5.36	3.79	54.12
03/16	106.32	0	0	6.55	3.64	50.50
03/15	139.89	0	0	5.73	3.22	44.47
Annual Growth	(4.2%)	—	—	0.4%	5.3%	9.2%

Toyota Tsusho Corp

Auditors: PricewaterhouseCoopers Aarata LLC

LOCATIONS

HQ: Toyota Tsusho Corp
  Century Toyota Bldg., 4-9-8 Meieki, Nakamura-ku,
  Nagoya, Aichi 450-8575
Phone: (81) 52 584 5482   **Fax:** (81) 52 584 5659
Web: www.toyota-tsusho.com

HISTORICAL FINANCIALS
Company Type: Public

Income Statement				FYE: March 31
	REVENUE ($ mil.)	NET INCOME ($ mil.)	NET PROFIT MARGIN	EMPLOYEES
03/21	56,981	1,215	2.1%	68,877
03/20	61,667	1,248	2.0%	71,033
03/19	61,066	1,197	2.0%	63,728
03/18	61,128	1,226	2.0%	62,269
03/17	51,851	965	1.9%	61,472
Annual Growth	2.4%	5.9%	—	2.9%

2021 Year-End Financials
Debt ratio: 0.2%
Return on equity: 10.1%
Cash ($ mil.): 6,118
Current ratio: 1.50
Long-term debt ($ mil.): 9,681

No. of shares (mil.): 352
Dividends
  Yield: —
  Payout: —
Market value ($ mil.): —

Trane Technologies plc

Auditors: PricewaterhouseCoopers LLP

LOCATIONS

HQ: Trane Technologies plc
  170/175 Lakeview Dr., Airside Business Park, Swords,
  Co. Dublin
Phone: (353) 0 18707400
Web: www.tranetechnologies.com

HISTORICAL FINANCIALS
Company Type: Public

Income Statement				FYE: December 31
	REVENUE ($ mil.)	NET INCOME ($ mil.)	NET PROFIT MARGIN	EMPLOYEES
12/21	14,136	1,423	10.1%	37,000
12/20	12,454	854	6.9%	35,000
12/19	16,598	1,410	8.5%	50,000
12/18	15,668	1,337	8.5%	49,000
12/17	14,197	1,302	9.2%	46,000
Annual Growth	(0.1%)	2.2%	—	(5.3%)

2021 Year-End Financials
Debt ratio: 26.8%
Return on equity: 22.4%
Cash ($ mil.): 2,159
Current ratio: 1.36
Long-term debt ($ mil.): 4,491

No. of shares (mil.): 235
Dividends
  Yield: 1.1%
  Payout: 42.3%
Market value ($ mil.): —

Transneft

Transneft operates one of the largest networks of oil pipelines in the world. The company moves crude oil through more than 51000 km and petroleum through some 14600 km of pipeline stretching across Eastern Europe and Asia. After the breakup of the Soviet Union the government agency that controlled the Russian oil industry and the pipeline system (Glavtransneft) reorganized and in 1931 formed the joint-stock company Transneft. Transneft operates a transportation network consisting of more than 67000 km of pipeline over 500 oil refilling (pump) stations and

---

reservoirs capable of storing more than 24 million cu. meters of storage tanks. The company transports about 85% of the oil produced in Russia.

Operations

The core business activity of Transneft is rendering services of oil and petroleum products transportation via trunk pipelines in the Russian Federation and beyond including transportation outside of Russia on the basis of interstate and intergovernmental agreements. Apart from the core activity of transporting oil across Russia the Company plans and supervises oil transportation and supply to other countries ensures acceptance at foreign custody transfer points collects and compiles data.

Approximately two-thirds of total sales were generated from oil transportation services and about a fifth came from oil sales for export while petroleum products transportation services compounding services sales of oil on the domestic market sales of petroleum products and other accounts for the rest.

Geographic Reach

The company is headquartered in Moscow Russia.

Financial Performance

The company's revenue in 2019 was RMB 1.1 trillion up by RUB 83871 million or 9% compared to 2018 mainly due to the revenues growth from oil transportation services and the inclusion of NCSP Group and NFOT in Transneft Group's consolidated indicators.

EBITDA in 2019 increased by 12% to RUB 486.3 billion compared from the prior year with RUB 433.4 billion.

Strategy

The strategy provides for: ensuring systematic development of the trunk pipeline system; ensuring reception and transportation of petroleum products from newly connected refineries; reducing accident rate at trunk pipelines; excluding discharge of insufficiently treated wastewater; keeping the sulfur contents in the crude oil pumped via the Transneft system within the limits set in the rational routing scheme; reducing expenses related to pipeline construction and operation; maintaining the optimum expenditure level; and decreasing the purchase volumes of imported products.

The Long-Term Development Programme of Transneft by the resolution of the Board of Directors of Transneft in 2014 and is updated every year. It specifies the lists of means and specific measures to ensure the achievement of development goals of Transneft defined in the Strategy within the set deadlines with indication of the level and sources of their financing. The LDP updated in 2019 indicates the current and expected performance of the Company till 2024.

EXECUTIVES

Member of the Management Board, Vice President, Larisa Kalanda
Chairman of the Board of Directors - Representative of the Russian Federation, Alexander Novak
Member of the Management Board, Vice President, Vyacheslav Skvortsov
Member of the Management Board, Vice President, Pavel Revel-Muroz
President, Chairman of the Management Board, Member of the Board of Directors - Representative of the Russian Federation, Nikolay Tokarev, $75,823 total compensation
Member of the Board of Directors - Representative of the Russian Federation, Matthias Warnig, $75,823 total compensation
Member of the Management Board, First Vice President, Maksim Grishanin

Member of the Management Board, Vice
President, Boris Korol
Member of the Management Board, Vice
President, Sergey Andronov
Member of the Board of Directors -
Representative of the Russian Federation, Kirill
Dmitriev, $75,823 total compensation
Member of the Board of Directors, Independent
Director, Ilya Klebanov, $75,823 total
compensation
Member of the Board of Directors -
Representative of the Russian Federation, Valery
Shantsev, $75,823 total compensation
Member of the Management Board, Vice
President, Rashid Sharipov
Member of the Board of Directors, Independent
Director, Aleksandr Korsik, $75,823 total
compensation
Member of the Board of Directors -
Representative of the Russian Federation, Alexey
Kozlov
Member of the Board of Directors, Independent
Director, Genadii Shmal, $75,823 total
compensation
Member of the Management Board, Vice
President, Sergey Shotsky
Auditors: JSC KPMG (member of KPMG
International)

LOCATIONS

HQ: Transneft
    4 bldg. 2, Presnenskaya Embankment, Moscow 123112
Phone: (7) 495 9508178   **Fax:** (7) 495 9508900
Web: www.transneft.ru

2015 Sales

	% in total
Russian Federation	80
China	17
Other Countries	3
Total	**100**

PRODUCTS/OPERATIONS

2015 Sales

	% of total
Oil transportation services	71
Oil products transportation services	8
Trading operations for sale of oil and oil products	21
Total	**100**

Selected Subsidiaries

Baltnefteprovod Ltd
CJSC Transneft
JSC Center for metrology maintenance
OJSC Chernomortransneft (CHMT)
OJSC Diascan Center for Technical Diagnosis
OJSC Druzhba MN
ОJSC Giprotruboprovod
OJSC Privolzhskneфteprovod
OJSC Severny MN
OJSC Severo-Zapadny MN
OJSC Sibnefteprovod
OJSC Svyaztransneft
OJSC Transsibneft
OJSC Tsentrsibnefteprovod (CSN)
OJSC Uralsibnefteprovod
OJSC Verkhnevolzhskneфteprovod
OJSC Volzhsky podvodnik
Strojneft TSUP Ltd.
Transneft Trade House Ltd.
Transneft UK Limited
Transpress Ltd.

COMPETITORS

BEIJING ENTERPRISES	Inter Pipeline Ltd
HOLDINGS LIMITED	NOBLE MIDSTREAM
China Shenhua Energy	PARTNERS LP
Company Limited	NUSTAR ENERGY L.P.
ENBRIDGE ENERGY	PLAINS ALL AMERICAN
PARTNERS L.P.	PIPELINE L.P.
ENEOS HOLDINGS INC.	PLAINS GP HOLDINGS

Enbridge Inc   L.P.
GENESIS ENERGY L.P.   SURGUTNEFTEGAZ PAO

HISTORICAL FINANCIALS

Company Type: Public

Income Statement				FYE: December 31
	REVENUE ($ mil.)	NET INCOME ($ mil.)	NET PROFIT MARGIN	EMPLOYEES
12/19	17,093	2,882	16.9%	0
12/18	14,060	3,218	22.9%	1,322
12/17	15,296	3,320	21.7%	0
12/16	13,851	3,802	27.5%	0
12/15	11,045	1,941	17.6%	0
Annual Growth	11.5%	10.4%		

2019 Year-End Financials

Debt ratio: 0.3%
Return on equity: 8.6%
Cash ($ mil.): 1,343
Current ratio: 1.56
Long-term debt ($ mil.): 8,927

No. of shares (mil.): 5
Dividends
  Yield: —
  Payout: —
Market value ($ mil.): —

Traton SE

LOCATIONS

HQ: Traton SE
    Dachauer Str. 641, Munich 80995
Phone: (49) 89 36098 303
Web: www.traton.com

HISTORICAL FINANCIALS

Company Type: Public

Income Statement				FYE: December 31
	REVENUE ($ mil.)	NET INCOME ($ mil.)	NET PROFIT MARGIN	EMPLOYEES
12/19	30,203	1,704	5.6%	82,981
12/18	29,691	1,591	5.4%	79,674
Annual Growth	1.7%	7.1%	—	4.2%

2019 Year-End Financials

Debt ratio: —
Return on equity: 9.9%
Cash ($ mil.): 2,147
Current ratio: 1.01
Long-term debt ($ mil.): —

No. of shares (mil.): 500
Dividends
  Yield: —
  Payout: 32.8%
Market value ($ mil.): —

	STOCK PRICE ($) FY Close	P/E High/Low		PER SHARE ($) Earnings	Dividends	Book Value
12/19	0.00	—	—	3.41	1.12	31.13
12/18	0.00	—	—	3.18	0.00	
1,923.77						
/0.00		—	(0.00)	0.00	(0.00)	
Annual Growth		—	—	—	—	

TSB Banking Group Plc

Auditors: KPMG LLP

LOCATIONS

HQ: TSB Banking Group Plc
    20 Gresham Street, London EC2V 7JE
Phone: (44) 20 7003 9000
Web: www.tsb.co.uk

HISTORICAL FINANCIALS

Company Type: Public

Income Statement				FYE: December 31
	ASSETS ($ mil.)	NET INCOME ($ mil.)	INCOME AS % OF ASSETS	EMPLOYEES
12/21	62,921	175	0.3%	6,137
12/20	57,872	(217)	—	7,068
12/19	52,189	34	0.1%	8,198
12/18	52,505	(80)	—	8,439
12/17	57,438	160	0.3%	8,583
Annual Growth	2.3%	2.3%	—	(8.0%)

2021 Year-End Financials

Return on assets: 0.2%
Return on equity: 7.3%
Long-term debt ($ mil.): —
No. of shares (mil.): 500
Sales ($ mil): 1,409

Dividends
  Yield: —
  Payout: —
Market value ($ mil.): —

Turkiye Garanti Bankasi AS

Turkiye Garanti Bankasi (Garanti Bank Turkey)
is Turkey's second largest private bank. The bank
is operating in all business lines of the banking
sector including corporate commercial SME payment systems retail private and investment banking. Garanti Bank has an extensive distribution
network consisting of over 900 domestic branches
and about 10 branches across Cyprus Malta London D sseldorf and Shanghai. Garanti Bank provides factoring insurance leasing investment private pension plans portfolio management and
other services. As Turkey's second-largest private
bank Garanti serves more than 15 million customers. The bank was founded in 1946.
Auditors: KPMG Bagimsiz Denetim ve Serbest
    Muhasebeci Mali Musavirlik A.S. (a member firm
    of KPMG International Cooperative)

LOCATIONS

HQ: Turkiye Garanti Bankasi AS
    Levent Nispetiye Mah., Aytar Cad., No. 2 Besiktas,
    Istanbul, Istanbul Province 34340
Phone: (90) 212 318 18 18   **Fax:** (90) 212 216 64 22
Web: www.garantibbva.com.tr

PRODUCTS/OPERATIONS

2014 Sales

	% of total
Interest income	80
Net fee and commission income	15
Other operting income	5
Total	**100**

2014 Sales

	% of total
Corporate Banking	33
Retail Banking	31
Investment Banking	13
Others	23
Total	**100**

COMPETITORS

AXIS BANK LIMITED
BANK OF AYUDHYA PUBLIC COMPANY LIMITED
BANK VTB PAO

BINBANK PAO
CANARA BANK
China Construction Bank Corporation
HSBC USA INC.
RIYAD BANK
Shinhan Financial Group Co. Ltd.
Swedbank AB
UniCredit Bank Austria AG
VIETNAM JOINT STOCK COMMERCIAL BANK FOR
 INDUSTRY AND TRADE

HISTORICAL FINANCIALS

Company Type: Public

Income Statement				FYE: December 31
	ASSETS ($ mil.)	NET INCOME ($ mil.)	INCOME AS % OF ASSETS	EMPLOYEES
12/20	72,760	848	1.2%	18,656
12/19	72,018	1,036	1.4%	18,784
12/18	74,953	1,263	1.7%	22,024
12/17	93,101	1,596	1.7%	21,840
12/16	87,385	1,419	1.6%	23,692
Annual Growth	(4.5%)	(12.1%)	—	(5.8%)

2020 Year-End Financials

Return on assets: 1.3%
Return on equity: 10.8%
Long-term debt ($ mil.): —
No. of shares (mil.): —
Sales ($ mil): 7,393

Dividends
 Yield: —
 Payout: —
Market value ($ mil.): —

	STOCK PRICE ($) FY Close	P/E High/Low	PER SHARE ($) Earnings	Dividends	Book Value
12/20	1.43	108 57	0.00	0.00	0.02
12/19	1.81	124 83	0.00	0.00	0.02
12/18	1.46	1 1	0.30	0.08	0.02
12/17	2.83	2 1	0.38	0.06	0.03
12/16	2.09	2 2	0.34	0.03	0.02
Annual Growth	(9.1%)	—	—(72.2%)	—	(5.0%)

Turkiye Is Bankasi AS

T rkiye Is Bankas? or Isbank is banking in Turkey. Serving some 15 million customers the institution known as Isbank is the country's largest publicly-traded bank and provides corporate banking commercial lending treasury banking private banking and traditional retail banking products and services through more than 1300 branches and 6300-plus ATMs across Turkey. It also boasts insurance investment advisory and real estate investment businesses. Founded in 1924 by mandate of the Turkish Republic's founding father Mustafa Kemal Atat rk employees now own a roughly 40% stake in the bank while the Republican People's Party owns a 28% stake in the name of the founder.

Operations

The bank operates through five main banking businesses. Its Commercial Banking and Corporate Banking businesses which made up 36% and 18% of the bank's total revenue in 2014 respectively provides large corporations SMEs and other trading companies with project financing traditional account and card products operating and investment loans foreign trade transactions and financing letters of guarantee and credit and other corporate banking services.

Isbank's Retail Banking (20% of revenue) provides traditional banking services to individuals while its Treasury Banking business (20% of rev-

enue) provides medium and long-term funding tools including securities and foreign currency trading money market transactions swaps futures and other complex financial transactions. The bank's small Private Banking business (less than 1% of revenue) serves high-net worth individuals with cash management and wealth management services.

Its non-banking operations (5% of revenue) include: insurance; 'investment and finance' which provides leasing factoring brokerage corporate finance investment advisory private portfolio management and real estate investments; and the 'manufacturing and trading' business which involves glass production and complementary industrial and commercial operations and food production. In 2015 the bank also had equity investments in 25 companies operating mainly in the industry and financial sector.

The bank generated more than 80% of its total revenue in 2014 from interest income (mostly from loans) while about 12% came from fee and commission based income. The rest of revenue mostly came from non-banking business (mostly manufacturing and insurance) and securities trading income.

Geographic Reach

Isbank boasts more than 1330 branches across Turkey (it's home country) but also has foreign branches in London The Turkish Republic of Northern Cyprus Baghdad Batumi Tbilisi Pristine and Prizren. It also has banking subsidiaries in Germany and Russia.

Financial Performance

Note: Growth rates may differ after conversion to US dollars.

Isbank has struggled to consistently grow its revenue profit in recent years though its financials have been relatively stable in the years following the financial crisis. Isbank enjoyed a breakout year in 2014 however with revenue growing by double digits to 33.37 billion Turkish Lira (about $14.4 billion) as the bank grew its loan business across its Corporate Commercial and Retail Banking businesses. Commercial banking led most of the growth with its revenue spiking by more than 50% during the year while income from Commercial and Retail banking swelled by 31% and 23% respectively. The bank also saw 30%-plus growth in its Investment and Finance and Manufacturing and Trading divisions during the year as well.

Higher revenue in 2014 drove Isbank's net income up by 4% to TL$4.57 billion (roughly $1.96 billion) while the bank's operations used more cash than in the prior year as it took in fewer deposits and used more cash toward repurchase agreements.

Strategy

Isbank stated in 2015 that its top three objectives were to: provide fast and efficient services that meet its customers needs; consistently enhance its shareholder value; and motivate its employees to maximize their performance.

The bank has been expanding its branch and ATM network in recent years to grow its loan business focusing mostly on growing relationships with large corporate as well as small-to-midsize enterprise (SME) customers. In 2014 alone the bank added 44 new branches to its network and more than 600 new ATMs growing its total network by more than 3%.

EXECUTIVES

Deputy Chief Executive, Gamze Yalcin
Non-Executive Independent Director, Ersin Onder Ciftcioglu
Deputy Chief Executive, Nevzat Seyrek
Deputy Chief Executive, Sezgin Yilmaz

Non-Executive Director, Fazli Bulut
Non-Executive Independent Director, Ahmet Sungur
Non-Executive Director, Durmus Oztek
Non-Executive Director, Mustafa Selcuk
Non-Executive Director, Recep Ozyildiz
Non-Executive Director, Sadrettin Yurtsever
Non-Executive Independent Vice Chairman of the Board, Yusuf Toprak
Deputy Chief Executive, Serkan Kaygalak
Deputy Chief Executive, Ozan Gursoy
Deputy Chief Executive, H. Cahit Cinar
Chief Executive Officer, Member of the Board, Hakan Aran
Non-Executive Chairperson of the Board, Fusun Tumsavas
Deputy Chief Executive, Yalcin Sezen
Deputy Chief Executive, Senar Akkus
Non-Executive Director, Feray Demir
Deputy Chief Executive, Murat Bilgic
Deputy Chief Executive, Sahismail Simsek
Deputy Chief Executive, Ebru Ozsuca
Auditors: Guney Bagimsiz Denetim ve Serbest Muhasebeci Mali Musavirlik A.S. (member of member firm of Ernst & Young Global Limited)

LOCATIONS

HQ: Turkiye Is Bankasi AS
Is Kuleleri, Istanbul, Levent 34330
Phone: (90) 212 316 00 00   **Fax:** (90) 212 316 09 00
Web: www.isbank.com.tr

PRODUCTS/OPERATIONS

2014 Sales

	% of total
Interest income	52
Non-interest income	
Income from manufacturing operations	21
Income from insurance operations	11
Fee and commission income	7
Securities trading income	3
Income from other operations	2
Foreign exchange gains	2
Others	2
Total	**100**

2014 Sales

	% of total
Banking business	
Commercial	35
Retail	20
Treasury investment	19
Corporate	18
others	2
Non-banking business	
Investment and finance	3
Insurance	2
Manufacturingtrading and service	1
Total	**100**

COMPETITORS

AL RAJHI BANKING AND INVESTMENT
 CORPORATION
Agricultural Bank of China Limited
BANK VTB PAO
Bank of Communications Co. Ltd.
CAIXABANK SA
CANARA BANK
HSBC USA INC.
Industrial And Commercial Bank Of China Limited
SHINSEI BANK LIMITED
Shinhan Financial Group Co. Ltd.
TURKIYE GARANTI BANKASI ANONIM SIRKETI
UNITED OVERSEAS BANK LIMITED
Woori Finance Holdings Co. Ltd.

HISTORICAL FINANCIALS
Company Type: Public

Income Statement				FYE: December 31
	ASSETS ($ mil.)	NET INCOME ($ mil.)	INCOME AS % OF ASSETS	EMPLOYEES
12/20	95,398	894	0.9%	0
12/19	94,045	992	1.1%	0
12/18	94,083	1,273	1.4%	0
12/17	114,421	1,520	1.3%	24,868
12/16	105,241	1,541	1.5%	0
Annual Growth	(2.4%)	(12.7%)	—	—

2020 Year-End Financials

Return on assets: 1.0%
Return on equity: 10.4%
Long-term debt ($ mil.): —
No. of shares (mil.): —
Sales ($ mil): 10,685

Dividends
  Yield: —
  Payout: —
Market value ($ mil.): —

Turkiye Petrol Rafinerileri AS

Türkiye Petrol Rafinerileri (Turkish Petroleum Refineries) also known as T PRAS makes petroleum products including naphtha gasoline and lubricants for civilian and military customers and operates four crude oil refineries in Turkey. T PRAS which has a processing capacity of about 28.1 million tons of crude oil a year obtains its supply primarily from sources in Algeria Iran Iraq Libya Russia Saudi Arabia and Syria. The company also owns 80% of petroleum shipping company DITAS and 40% of Opet Petrolc l k which operates more than 1390 gas stations in Turkey and holds a market share of 14%. A consortium led by Turkish conglomerate Ko § Holding controls 51% of the company.

Operations
T PRAS is engaged in providing and refining crude oil importing and exporting petroleum products operating domestic and foreign refineries. T PRAS supplies Turkey with about 70% of its fuel and controls about 60% of Turkey's total petroleum storage capacity. It also has a petrochemical plant that produces emulsion styrene butadiene rubber polystyrene and carbon black.

In 2014 Kirikkale Refinery processed 3.1 million tons of crude oil - a total of 3.3 million tons of material including semi-finished products; the refinery's capacity utilization rate stood at 66.5%.

That year a total of 8.3 million tons of material including semi-finished products was processed at Izmir Refinery; the refinery's capacity utilization rate stood at 75.1%.

Batman Refinery has a capacity utilization rate 37.2% and a storage capacity of 253 million.

In 2014 T PRAS produced 20.1 million tons of products.

Serving customers through nearly 1400 Opet and Sunpet dealers Opet is engaged in retail commercial and industrial sales operations and international trade of petroleum products. The company manufactures and sells lubricating oil through Opet-Fuchs its 50/50 joint venture company with Fuchs the German lubricant manufacturer.

The company also engages in jet fuel supply and sales through THY-Opet a 50/50 partnership between Opet and Turkish Airlines. THY-Opet provides service to domestic and international airline companies at 51 airports in Turkey.

In 2014 DITAS transported 4.8 million tons of crude oil and 3.5 million tons of petroleum products 8.3 million tons in total.

Geographic Reach
The company has offices across Turkey and a presence elsewhere in Europe and in the US.

Financial Performance
The slump in crude oil prices and lower volumes led to T PRAS' net sales falling by 3% in 2014.

Net income increased by 21% due to lower cost of sales (marketing selling and distribution expenses and research and development costs).

T PRAS' cash from operating activities increased by 6% in 2014 due to changes in inventories and trade receivables.

Strategy
The company is focused on upgrading its aging refineries and streamlining other operations to better compete with its peers across Europe. The Residuum Upgrading Facility is the largest single industrial investment ever made in Turkey with a total capital investment of $ 3 billion including pier railroad links and financing costs.

This completed project at Izmit Refinery allows T PRAS to process about 4.2 million tons of high-sulfur fuel oil and related heavy products consumption of which has been falling rapidly in recent years. This will yield 2.9 million tons of diesel/jet fuel 522000 tons of gasoline and 69000 tons of LPG for a total of 3.5 million tons of valuable white products at Euro-V standards as well as 690000 tons of petroleum coke and 86000 tons of sulfur.

As part of its R&D efforts in 2014 the company continued to work on 12 major projects.

T PRAS aims to increase its competitive power in Turkey through its existing infrastructure and customer relations while it aims to increase market share in the imported products alongside production. It also plans to make use of the growing international market prospects.

Company Background
In 2006 a private consortium of Turkish companies acquired the Turkish government's controlling stake in T PRAS for more than $4.1 billion.

EXECUTIVES

Non-Executive Chairman of the Board of Directors, Omer Koc
General Manager, Ibrahim Yelmenoglu
Non-Executive Member of the Board of Directors, Semahat Arsel
Non-Executive Member of the Board of Directors, Rahmi Koc
Non-Executive Member of the Board of Directors, Levent Cakiroglu
Assistant General Manager (Technical), Ihsan Kemaloglu
Assistant General Manager (Sales & Marketing), Ozgur Kahramanzade
Independent Non-Executive Member of the Board of Directors, Kamil Bozer
Independent Non-Executive Member of the Board of Directors, Muharrem Kayhan
Non-Executive Member of the Board of Directors, Yagiz Eyuboglu
Assistant General Manager (Crude Oil Supply & Foreign Trade), Atilla Ulusu
Independent Non-Executive Member of the Board of Directors, Ayse Ediboglu
Assistant General Manager (Financial), Dogan Korkmaz
Non-Executive Vice Chairman of the Board of Directors, Ali Koc
Assistant General Manager (Investments & Planning), Levent Zagra

Non-Executive Member of the Board of Directors and Privatization Administration Representative, Fatih Kilinc
Independent Director, Tufan Erginbilgic
Non-Executive Member of the Board of Directors, Erol Memioglu

LOCATIONS
HQ: Turkiye Petrol Rafinerileri AS
  Petrol Caddesi No. 25, Korfez, Kocaeli 41790
Phone: (90) 262 316 30 00   **Fax:** (90) 262 316 30 10
Web: www.tupras.com.tr

COMPETITORS
CALUMET SPECIALTY PRODUCTS PARTNERS L.P.
CVR ENERGY INC.
GLOBAL PARTNERS LP
IDEMITSU KOSAN CO.LTD.
INDIAN OIL CORPORATION LIMITED
MANGALORE REFINERY AND PETROCHEMICALS LIMITED
Neste Oyj
SPRAGUE RESOURCES LP
SURGUTNEFTEGAZ PAO
Suncor Energy Inc
TOTALENERGIES SE

HISTORICAL FINANCIALS
Company Type: Public

Income Statement				FYE: December 31
	REVENUE ($ mil.)	NET INCOME ($ mil.)	NET PROFIT MARGIN	EMPLOYEES
12/19	15,057	88	0.6%	6,098
12/18	16,736	701	4.2%	5,952
12/17	14,263	1,007	7.1%	5,499
12/16	9,878	508	5.1%	5,296
12/15	12,629	873	6.9%	5,131
Annual Growth	4.5%	(43.6%)	—	4.4%

2019 Year-End Financials

Debt ratio: 5.7%
Return on equity: 4.6%
Cash ($ mil.): 1,790
Current ratio: 0.99
Long-term debt ($ mil.): 2,335

No. of shares (mil.): —
Dividends
  Yield: —
  Payout: —
Market value ($ mil.): —

UBS Group AG

Auditors: Ernst & Young Ltd.

LOCATIONS
HQ: UBS Group AG
  Bahnhofstrasse 45, Zurich CH-8001
Phone: (41) 44 234 11 11
Web: www.ubs.com

HISTORICAL FINANCIALS
Company Type: Public

Income Statement				FYE: December 31
	REVENUE ($ mil.)	NET INCOME ($ mil.)	NET PROFIT MARGIN	EMPLOYEES
12/20	39,106	6,557	16.8%	71,551
12/19	41,562	4,304	10.4%	68,601
12/18	43,077	4,516	10.5%	66,888
12/17	20,158	1,078	5.4%	61,253
12/16	18,993	3,147	16.6%	59,387
Annual Growth	19.8%	20.1%	—	4.8%

Debt ratio: —
Return on equity: 11.4%
Cash ($ mil.): 158,231
Current ratio: —
Long-term debt ($ mil.): —

No. of shares (mil.): —
Dividends
Yield: —
Payout: —
Market value ($ mil.): —

Ultrapar Participacoes SA

Brazil-based Ultrapar Participa § µes is a holding company for a number of midstream and downstream liquefied petroleum gas (LPG) companies. Ultragaz distributes LPG to residential commercial and industrial customers; Ipiranga distributes gasoline ethanol disel fuel oil kerosene natural gas for vehicles and lubricants from 7090 service stations in Brazil and directly to large customers; Oxiteno manufactures ethylene oxide (plus derivatives) and specialty chemicals including surfactants; and Ultracargo provides liquid storage via six terminals. Ultrapar also operates a chain of more than 415 drugstores under the Extrafarma banner. Ultra S.A holds a 20% stake in Ultrapar.

Operations

Ultrapar operates five main business segments: gas distribution fuel distribution chemicals storage and drugstores.

The fuel distribution segment (Ipiranga) operates the distribution and marketing of gasoline ethanol diesel fuel oil kerosene natural gas for vehicles and lubricants and related activities throughout all the Brazilian territory. Ipiranga sells fuel at 7090 service stations and accounts for 85% of total sales.

The gas distribution segment (Ultragaz) distributes LPG to residential commercial and industrial consumers especially in the South Southeast and Northeast regions of Brazil. Ultragaz has a roughly 25% share of the Brazilian market and generates about 10% of sales.

The chemicals segment (Oxiteno) produces ethylene oxide and its main derivatives and fatty alcohols which are raw materials used in cosmetics detergents crop protection chemicals packaging textiles and coatings. Oxiteno generates 5% of sales.

Extrafarma the drugstore segment retails pharmaceutical hygiene and beauty products through 415-plus drugstores in the states of Par ˜ Amap ˜ Maranh o Tocantins Pernambuco Cear ˜ Bahia Rio Grande do Norte Para ba Sergipe and S o Paulo. Extrafarma operates three distribution centers.

The storage segment (Ultracargo) operates liquid bulk terminals especially in the Southeast and Northeast regions of Brazil. Accounting for one percent of sales.

The company also manufactures approximately 1000 products used in various industrial sectors such as cosmetics detergents crop protection chemicals packaging textiles and coatings.

Geographic Reach

Ultrapar is headquartered in Sao Paulo and generates virtually all its revenue within Brazil. Subsidiary Ultragaz operates in all regions of Brazil through a distribution network comprising about 20 filling plants. Ipiranga's 7090 service stations are spread across the country. Extrafarma operates in more than 10 states in Brazil and has three distribution centers in Benevides Aquiraz and Guarulhos.

Subsidiary Oxiteno operates three plants in Mexico. Oxiteno's more than 10 international plants produce specialty chemicals. It also has commercial offices in Argentina Belgium China and Colombia.

Sales and Marketing

Ultragaz distributes LPG to residential commercial and industrial market segments. Ipiranga distributes gasoline ethanol diesel NGV fuel oil kerosene and lubricants through a network of 7090 service stations and directly to large customers. It delivers LPG to 11 million households and 55000 business customers.

Financial Performance

Note: Growth rates may differ after conversion to US Dollars.

Ultrapar's fortunes are tied to commodity prices fluctuations in the local currency (the reais) and the health of the Brazilian economy. Its revenues have steadily grown in the past years despite a slight drop in 2019. Overall revenue grew 18% between 2015 and 2019. Net income has also declined in 2019 following four years of profits averaging R$1.5 billion; net income fell 73% in the last five years.

Ultrapar's net revenue from sales and services decreased 2% from R$90.7 billion in 2018 to R$89.3 billion in 2019. This was due to decreases in revenues from Ipiranga and Oxiteno offset by minimal increases in revenues from Utragaz Ultracargo and Extrafarma.

Net income in 2019 was R$402.9 million a 64% decrease from R$1.1 billion in 2018 mainly due to the decline in operating income and share of profit of joint-ventures and associates between the periods and higher net financial expenses.

Ultrapar's cash on hand fell by R$1.8 billion during 2019 ending the year at $2.1 billion. The company's operations generated R$2.9 billion while its investing activities used R$1.8 billion and its financing used R$2.9 billion. Ultrapar's main cash uses in 2019 were capital increase in joint ventures paid interests lease payments and redemption of non-controlling shares of Oxiteno Nordeste.

Strategy

Ultrapar has a multi-faceted strategy each focusing on the company's key aspects for growth and development. The company intends to reinforce its high brand recognition associated with quality safety and efficiency by continuing to supply high-quality products and services and to introduce new services and distribution channels.

The company also aims to maintain strong relationships with its resellers in the LPG and fuel distribution business. It plans to continue to invest in training its dealers in order to maximize efficiency to further strengthen its relationship and to promote the high standards for its distribution network. In parallel it plans to continue to increase its operational efficiency and productivity at Ultragaz and Ipiranga.

Its sales strategy is to increase Ipiranga's market by improving the performance of the existing resale and expanding its network of service stations with high profitability and lower market share. Ipiranga's strategy also includes expanding its logistics infrastructure to support the growing demand for fuels in Brazil and initiatives aiming at differentiating its products and services.

It also aims to enhance its retail network. In 2019 Ipiranga launched Km de Vanatgens (KVM) a loyalty program through which customers and resellers may redeem rewards and benefits in areas of entertainment tourism magazines airline tickets car rental and others. With over 32 million participants in 2019 KMV has served as an important platform strengthening relationships with Ipiranga's customers and resellers.

Company Background

In 2008 Ultrapar acquired Chevron's Texaco-branded fuel distribution business (2000 gas stations) in Brazil for $720 million.

In 2010 it bought fuel distributor Distribuidora Nacional de Petroleo (DNP) for about $50 million. DNP has a network of 110 gas stations in the northern Brazilian states of Acre Amazonas Mato Grosso Para Rondonia and Roraima.

EXECUTIVES

Chairman of the Board, Pedro Wongtschowski
President - Ultracargo, Decio de Sampaio Amaral
Independent Director, Jose Mauricio Pereira Coelho
Chief Operating Officer of Oxiteno, Joao Benjamin Parolin
Vice Chairman of the Board, Lucio de Castro Andrade
Independent Director, Jorge Marques de Toledo Camargo
President - Ipiranga, Marcelo de Araujo
Independent Director, Jose Gallo
Independent Director, Ana Paula Vitali Janes Vescovi
Chief Financial Officer, Investor Relations Officer, Rodrigo de Almeida Pizzinatto
President - Ultragaz, Tabajara Bertelli Costa
Independent Director, Flavia Buarque De Almeida
Chief Executive Officer, Frederico Pinheiro Fleurycurado
Independent Director, Marcos Marinho Lutz
Independent Director, Alexandre Teixeira de Assumpcao Saigh
Independent Director, Otavio Lopes Castello Branco Neto
Independent Director, Jose Luiz Alqueres
Auditors: KPMG Auditores Independentes

LOCATIONS

HQ: Ultrapar Participacoes SA
Brigadeiro Luis Antonio Avenue, 1343, 9th Floor, Sao Paulo 01317-910
Phone: (55) 11 3177 3820
Web: www.ultra.com.br

PRODUCTS/OPERATIONS

2018 Sales

	% of total
Ipiranga	84
Ultragaz	8
Oxiteno	5
Extrafarma	2
Ultracargo	1
Total	**100**

Selected Subsidiaries

Ipiranga (fuels & lubricants)
Oxiteno (petrochemicals)
Ultracargo (transportation logistics)
Ultragaz (LPG distribution)

COMPETITORS

Alpek S.A.B. de C.V.	LyondellBasell
Brenntag Holding GmbH	Industries N.V.
DXP ENTERPRISES INC.	MRC GLOBAL INC.
GLENCORE PLC	PHILLIPS 66
Grupo Carso S.A.B. de C.V.	Parkland Corporation
	REPSOL SA.
IRPC PUBLIC COMPANY LIMITED	SASOL LTD
	VALLOUREC

Company Type: Public

Income Statement				FYE: December 31
	REVENUE ($ mil.)	NET INCOME ($ mil.)	NET PROFIT MARGIN	EMPLOYEES
12/20	15,642	172	1.1%	15,946
12/19	22,215	92	0.4%	16,024
12/18	23,369	296	1.3%	17,034
12/17	24,151	475	2.0%	16,448
12/16	23,766	479	2.0%	15,173
Annual Growth	(9.9%)	(22.6%)	—	1.3%

2020 Year-End Financials

Debt ratio: 9.2%
Return on equity: 9.3%
Cash ($ mil.): 512
Current ratio: 1.89
Long-term debt ($ mil.): 2,718

No. of shares (mil.): 1,090
Dividends
Yield: 2.0%
Payout: 57.9%
Market value ($ mil.): 4,939

	STOCK PRICE ($) FY Close	P/E High/Low	PER SHARE ($) Earnings	Dividends	Book Value
12/20	4.53	6 2	0.16	0.09	1.68
12/19	6.26	42 11	0.09	0.13	2.17
12/18	13.54	20 9	0.27	0.20	2.24
12/17	22.73	17 13	0.44	0.26	2.61
12/16	20.74	17 12	0.44	0.25	2.41
Annual Growth	(31.6%) (8.6%)	—	—	(22.7%)	(22.5%)

Umicore SA

Umicore provides clean-mobility solutions for all platform types and recycles these materials when they reach the end of their useful life. It also provides automotive catalysts for lightduty and heavy-duty vehicles of all fuel types and the rechargeable battery materials and automotive catalysts that are required to power. Operating one of the world's most sophisticated precious metals recycling facilities and across its activities Umicore can recover about 30 precious and non-ferrous metals from industrial residues used electronic scrap batteries automotive and industrial catalysts fuel cells and more. The company owns around 40% of Element Six Abrasives a joint venture with industrial diamond producer Element Six. Majority of its sales comes from Europe.

Operations

Umicore's diversified business includes segments including: Recycling (some 60% of sales) Catalysis (about 30%) and Energy & Surface Technologies (nearly 15%).

The Recycling segment treats complex waste streams containing precious and other specialty metals. The operations can recover some 20 of these metals from a wide range of input materials ranging from industrial residues to end-of-life materials. Other activities include production of precious metals-based materials that are essential for applications as diverse as high-tech glass production electrics and electronics.

The Catalysis segment provides automotive catalysts to clean the exhaust gases from internal combustion engines for gasoline and diesel light- and heavy-duty diesel applications including on-road and non-road vehicles. The business group also offers stationary catalysis for industrial emissions control and produces precious metals-based compounds and catalysts for use in the pharmaceutical and fine chemicals industries.

The Energy & Surface Technologies segment is focused on products that are found in applications used in the production and storage of clean energy and in a range of applications for surface technologies that bring specific properties and functionalities to end products. All the activities offer a closed loop service for the customers.

Geographic Reach

The Brussels Belgium-based company has regional management platforms in China North America Japan and South America. Its business is global in nature with more than 45 production sites and some 15 research and development centers in approximately 30 countries.

Around 55% of sales were generated in Europe about 25% in Asia Pacific and nearly 20% in North America while South America and Africa accounts for less than 5% combined.

Sales and Marketing

Umicore serves customers in a diverse array of industries including automotive chemicals electronics energy metals and finance sectors.

Financial Performance

The company's revenue for fiscal 2020 decreased to ?3.2 billion compared form the prior year with ?3.4 billion.

Profit for fiscal 2020 decreased to ?131 million compared from the prior year with ?288 million.

Cash held by the company at the end of fiscal 2020 increased to ?1.0 billion. Cash provided by operations and financing activities were ?602.6 million and ?636.1 million respectively. Cash used for investing activities was ?429.5 million.

Strategy

Umicore aims to generate a return on capital employed of more than 15%. One of its Horizon 2020 goals is to double its earnings mainly through growth in recycling and materials for clean mobility. While the primary focus is on organic growth acquisitions are also considered if they fit the strategy and can add value for shareholders.

HISTORY

Created in 1906 to exploit the rich mineral resources of the Belgian Congo (later called the Congo then Za re now simply Congo) the company then known as Union Mini˝re du Haut Katanga (UM) mined cobalt copper precious metals tin and zinc in Belgium's African colony. UM smelted the mined ores in Africa and then transported them to Belgium for refining.

UM first cast copper in the Belgian Congo at Elisabethville (now Lubumbashi) in 1911; tin production began in 1918 gold and silver recovery in 1921 and radium production in 1922. In 1924 the company began smelting cobalt at its Jadotville-Panda plant. It added production of zinc in 1937 and uranium in 1943. (It exited the uranium business in 1960.) That year the Congo gained independence from Belgium and when widespread violence and unrest swept the country the United Nations sent in troops to restore order. UN forces withdrew from the country in 1964.

In 1965 Joseph Mobutu rose to power and began a reign of terror. He nationalized UM's mines and smelting operations in 1968. Mobutu's action forced the company to develop new mining operations in the 1970s and 1980s. During that period the company became a subsidiary of conglomerate Societe Generale de Belgique.

UM grew substantially in 1989 when it merged with Metallurgie Hoboken-Overplet (nonferrous and precious metals) Vielle-Montagne (zinc) and Mechim (engineering). Growth proved troublesome however and in 1995 saddled with high labor costs and too many noncore assets the company began to sell off operations. By 1999 UM had sold Asturienne Penamet Cananea its CSO trading companies Diamant Boart Overpelt-Plascobel Union Mines and Zinkgruvan. The divestitures lowered sales but returned the company to profitability.

With restructuring behind it UM acquired a controlling interest in four businesses in 2000: Padaeng Industry (zinc Thailand) Larvik Pigment (zinc for paint; Australia Malaysia Norway) and V&S Scientific and Tayside Optical Technology (both UK-based producers of finished optics products).

In 2001 UM acquired the 60% of optical materials maker Vertex (France) that it didn't own and sold its Sogemin metals trading unit to Belgian Natexis Banques Populaires (now called simply Natixis). That September UM changed its name to Umicore. The company continued its global growth in 2002 buying a zinc alloy processor in France and China's leading producer of zinc dust (used to make paint).

In 2003 the company acquired OM Group's precious metals group (PMG) for about $750 million diversifying its business and expanding its operations in North and South America. Also that year Franco-Belgian utility Suez divested its 15% stake in the company (Suez had acquired a controlling stake when it bought Societe Generale de Belgique).

In 2005 the company spun off its copper business as a separate company called Cumerio.

EXECUTIVES

Executive Vice President - Energy & Surface, Member of the Management Board, Denis Goffaux, $501,338 total compensation

Chief Executive Officer, Member of the Management Board, Marc Grynberg, $820,372 total compensation

Honorary Chairman, Karel Vinck, $108,124 total compensation

Chairman of the Supervisory Board, Thomas Leysen, $68,364 total compensation

Executive Vice President, Chief Counsel, Board Secretary, Member of the Management Board, Geraldine Nolens, $501,338 total compensation

Independent Member of the Supervisory Board, Mark Garrett, $30,763 total compensation

Independent Member of the Supervisory Board, Ines Kolmsee, $30,763 total compensation

Chief Financial Officer, Member of the Management Board, Filip Platteeuw, $501,338 total compensation

Independent Member of the Supervisory Board, Eric Meurice, $30,763 total compensation

Senior Vice President - Umicore Greater China, David Fong

Independent Member of the Supervisory Board, Francoise Chombar, $30,763 total compensation

Independent Member of the Supervisory Board, Liat Ben-Zur, $30,763 total compensation

Independent Member of the Supervisory Board, Koenraad Debackere, $30,763 total compensation

Executive Vice President - Energy & Surface Technology, Member of the Management Board, Ralph Kiessling, $501,338 total compensation

Member of the Supervisory Board, Laurent Raets, $30,763 total compensation

Member of the Supervisory Board, Mario Armero, $20,593 total compensation

Executive Vice President - Catalysis, Member of the Management Board, Bart Sap

Auditors: PricewaterhouseCoopers Bedrijfsrevisoren/Réviseurs d'Entreprises

LOCATIONS

HQ: Umicore SA
Rue du Marais 31 Broekstraat, Brussels B-1000
Phone: (32) 2 227 71 11   Fax: (32) 2 227 79 00
Web: www.umicore.com

2015 Sales

	% of total
Europe	65
Asia pacific	17
North America	13
South America	3
Africa	2
Total	**100**

PRODUCTS/OPERATIONS

2015 Sales

	% of total
Recycling	60
Catalysis	26
Energy & Surface Technologies	14
Total	**100**

Selected Business Units

Catalysis
Automotive Catalysts
Precious Metals Chemistry
Energy & Surface Technologies
Cobalt & Specialty Materials
Electro-Optic Materials
Electroplating
Rechargeable Battery Materials
Thin Film Products
Recycling
Battery Recycling
Jewellery & Industrial Metals
Platinum Engineered Materials
Precious Metals Management
Precious Metals Refining
Technical Materials
Other
Zinc Chemicals
Building Products - VMZINC

COMPETITORS

AIR PRODUCTS AND CHEMICALS INC.
AMPCO SERVICES L.L.C.
BODYCOTE PLC
EASTMAN CHEMICAL COMPANY
IMERYS
INDORAMA VENTURES PUBLIC COMPANY LIMITED
JOHNSON MATTHEY PLC
Methanex Corporation
NISSAN CHEMICAL CORPORATION
PETROLOGISTICS LP
SUMITOMO CHEMICAL COMPANY LIMITED
Solvay
UNION CARBIDE CORPORATION

HISTORICAL FINANCIALS

Company Type: Public

Income Statement				FYE: December 31
	REVENUE ($ mil.)	NET INCOME ($ mil.)	NET PROFIT MARGIN	EMPLOYEES
12/20	25,516	160	0.6%	10,859
12/19	19,767	323	1.6%	11,152
12/18	15,824	363	2.3%	13,600
12/17	14,408	254	1.8%	13,129
12/16	11,090	138	1.2%	13,117
Annual Growth	**23.2%**	**3.8%**	**—**	**(4.6%)**

2020 Year-End Financials

Debt ratio: 34.8%	No. of shares (mil.): 240
Return on equity: 5.0%	Dividends
Cash ($ mil.): 1,239	Yield: 0.3%
Current ratio: 1.62	Payout: 7.1%
Long-term debt ($ mil.): 2,027	Market value ($ mil.): 2,864

	STOCK PRICE ($)	P/E	PER SHARE ($)		
	FY Close	High/Low	Earnings	Dividends	Book Value
12/20	11.90	27 16	0.66	0.05	13.04
12/19	12.15	10 6	1.34	0.13	12.09
12/18	9.86	11 7	1.50	0.13	12.40
12/17	11.94	50 12	1.16	0.13	9.85
12/16	27.53	52 29	0.63	0.11	8.64
Annual Growth	**(18.9%)**	**— —**	**1.3%**	**(19.9%)**	**10.8%**

Unicredito SpA

UniCredit is one of the world's best bank for small and medium-sized enterprises. The financial services group operates in some 15 core European countries plus some 15 international markets. Germany and Austria operates as UniCredit Bank and UniCredit Bank Austria. UniCredit's structure is based on four geographic-focused retail banking divisions plus a corporate and investment bank and others. The bank has assets of approximately ?930 billion and generates majority of sales in Italy. UniCredit is the result of the merger of several Italian banks in the late 1990s.

Operations

UniCredit operates through five main divisions: Commercial Banking (CB) Italy CB Germany CB Austria Central and Eastern Europe division and Corporate & Investment Bank (CIB).

CB Italy Germany and Austria carry out comparable activities in their respective territories including commercial banking via a branch network and online private banking and other functions typical of a large bank. CB Italy generates more than 35% of UniCredit's revenue CB Germany roughly 15% and CB Austria nearly 10%.

The CIB segment serves multinational and large corporations with structured financing hedging and treasury solutions for corporate and investment products. It accounts for around 25% of sales.

The Central and Eastern Europe segment offers products and services to retail corporate and institutional clients in the region: Bosnia-Herzegovina Bulgaria Croatia Czech Republic Hungary Romania Russia Serbia Slovakia and Slovenia. The segment accounts for about 20% of total revenue.

Net interest income accounts for about 55% of sales while fees and commissions generate about 35%.

Geographic Reach

From its Milan base UniCredit's international branch network numbers around 3490 across its some 15 core markets (about 2230 branches in Italy). UniCredit reaches customers in more than 15 countries via a network of international representative offices and branches. Italy accounts for about 45% of UniCredit's sales followed by Germany for nearly 25%. The remaining sales are from Other European countries (exceeding 20%) Austria (about 10%) America and Asia Pacific.

Sales and Marketing

UniCredit boasts more than 16 million clients.

Financial Performance

Note: Growth rates may differ after conversion to US dollars.

In 2020 company's revenues were ?17.1 billion decreasing by 9% versus 2019. The decrease was widespread among all the revenues items mainly because of the different economical-financial con-

ditions resulted from the Covid-19 crisis and the related lockdown measures.

Loss for fiscal 2020 was ?2.8 billion compared from the prior year with a profit of ?3.4 billion.

Strategy

The company's strategy remains "One Bank One UniCredit" and its mission is unchanged: UniCredit is a simple successful pan-European commercial bank with a fully plugged in CIB delivering a unique Western Central and Eastern European network to its extensive and growing client franchise. The company will continue to build on its existing competitive advantages. The company's four strategic focuses are: grow and strengthen client franchise; transform and maximize productivity; and capital and balance sheet management.

HISTORY

UniCredito Italiano's ancestor Banca di Genova was formed in 1870 just after Italy unified. Within a year the bank was in a South American venture Banco de Italia y Rio de la Plata. A banking crisis beginning in the late 1880s threatened the company which was saved and reorganized with the aid of German banking interests. The changes gave the bank — which was renamed Credito Italiano — an advantage over home-grown rivals and pointed it in the direction of German-style universal banking including making direct investments in Italy's late-blooming industrial sector.

In the early 20th century Credito Italiano joined other banks in foreign ventures in Albania Brazil and China and opened offices in London and New York.

After the 1929 crash Credito Italiano acquired several failed banks. But Credito Italiano itself was none too healthy: Government attempts in the 1920s to peg the lira to the pound led to industrial stagnation leaving the bank holding highly illiquid industrial investments and by the early 1930s it was essentially an industrial holding company.

Credito Italiano's existence was threatened when the Depression hit in earnest. To save the bank and its peers Mussolini established the Istituto per la Ricostruzione Industriale (IRI) in 1933 as a "temporary" Resolution Trust-style holding company (IRI was finally liquidated in 2000) to take over the industrial assets of Credito Italiano and several other banks. IRI was instantly a major shareholder in Credito Italiano. IRI-held banks were designated "banks of national interest" three years later and were allowed to provide only short-term commercial banking services a limit that remained in effect for more than 50 years.

In 1946 to fill the need for long-term industrial credit to rebuild war-torn Italy Credito Italiano joined with Banca Commerciale Italiana (now part of IntesaBci) and Banco di Roma to form Mediobanca.

Credito Italiano went public in 1969 (IRI sold its interest in the bank in 1993). As a bank of national interest Credito Italiano was called upon to help bail out several of the country's industrial groups in 1979 (it did so reluctantly).

Changing laws allowed the company to expand its branch network in 1980 and in 1982 IRI allowed Credito Italiano to raise capital (although it was still obliged to prop up struggling state industries). But the 1987 US stock market crash caused Credito Italiano's earnings to plunge 33%. Two years later it bought a stake in Banca Nazionale dell'Agricoltura then Italy's largest private bank.

In 1995 the company joined forces with Rolo Banca 1473 (named for the year its progenitor was founded) to form Credito Italiano Group. Two years later Alessandro Profumo became CEO. He would usher in more than a decade of rapid and agressive expansion.

Credito Italiano merged in 1998 with UniCredito a collection of several northern Italian banks. One Cassa di Risparmio di Verona Vicenza Belluno e Ancona (Cariverona) began in 1501 as a pawnshop operated by monks.

Foreshadowing the bank's shift to an Internet growth strategy (announced after talks with Spain's Banco Bilbao Vizcaya Argentaria fell through) UniCredit in 1999 announced plans for an electronic stock market to include after-hours trading. It also continued to boost holdings in Eastern European banks. In 2000 the company entered into securities brokerage and mutual fund administration with its purchase of US-based Pioneer Investment Management.

In 2001 UniCredito bought 10% of the Pirelli/Benetton-owned holding company formed to control Italian telecommunications company Olivetti. The following year the company partnered with Ko § Holding to take a majority stake in Yapi Kredi.

The bank acquired HVB and Bank Austria in 2005 in an $18 billion cross-border deal one of the largest such deals ever seen in Europe. The bank strengthened its hold at home in 2007 with the nearly $30 billion purchase of Italian bank Capitalia. Antitrust authorities ordered UniCredit to sell its stake in Assicurazioni Generali following the Capitalia transaction.

EXECUTIVES

Co-CEO - Commercial Banking WEu, Francesco Giordano
Interim General Manager, Co-Chief Operating Officer, Ranieri De Marchis
Non-Executive Independent Director, Elena Carletti
Group Chief Risk Officer, TJ Lim
Deputy COO, Group Chief Transformation Officer, Finja Kutz
Head of Group HR, Paolo Cornetta
Co-CEO Commercial Banking Italy, Remo Taricani
Head of Group Legal - Secretary of the Board of Directors, Gianpaolo Alessandro
CEO of Group Wealth Management & Private Banking, Mirko Bianchi
Co-CEO Commercial Banking Italy, Andrea Casini
Co-CEO Commercial Banking, Central Eastern Europe, Gianfranco Bisagni
CEO of Commercial Banking Austria, Robert Zadrazil
Co-Chief Operating Officer, Carlo Vivaldi
Co-CEO - Commercial Banking WEU, Olivier Khayat
Non-Executive Independent Director, Maria Pierdicchi
Non-Executive Independent Director, Francesca Tondi
Non-Executive Independent Director, Vincenzo Cariello
Head of Group Identity & Communication, Maximilian Hohenberg
Co-CEO - Commercial Banking CEE, Niccolo Ubertalli
CEO of Corporate and Investment Banking, Richard Burton
Co-Group Chief Financial Officer, Stefano Porro
Independent Non-Executive Deputy Chairman of the Board, Director, Lamberto Andreotti
Non-Executive Independent Director, Stefano Micossi
Non-Executive Independent Director, Diego Giorgi
Non-Executive Independent Director, Beatriz Bartolome
Head of Finance & Accounts, Wouter Devriendt
Head of Group ESG Strategy & Impact Banking, Roberta Marracino
Chairman of the Board, Pietro Padoan

Head of Group Regulatory Affairs, Adeline De Metz
Group Data & Analytics Officer, Marco Bressan
Head of Group Institutional Affairs and Sustainability, Maurizio Beretta
Chief Compliance Officer, Serenella De Candia
Head of Strategy and M&A, Andrea Maffezzoni
CEO Commercial Banking Germany, Michael Diederich
Chief Lending Officer, Aurelio Maccario
Auditors: Deloitte & Touche S.p.A.

LOCATIONS

HQ: Unicredito SpA
 Piazza Gae Aulenti 3 - Tower A, Milano 20154
Phone: (39) 2 88 621   **Fax:** (39) 2 8862 3463
Web: www.unicreditgroup.eu

2014 Sales

	% of total
Italy	48
Germany	20
Austria	9
Poland	7
Other countries	16
Total	**100**

PRODUCTS/OPERATIONS

2017 Sales

	% of total
Commercial banking Italy	36
Corporate & investment banking	20
Central & Eastern Europe	20
Commercial Banking Germany	13
Commercial Banking Austria	8
Asset gathering	3
Total	**100**

COMPETITORS

BANCO BILBAO VIZCAYA ARGENTARIA SOCIEDAD ANONIMA
BANCO SANTANDER SA
BANKINTER SOCIEDAD ANONIMA
BNP PARIBAS
Danske Bank A/S
Nordea Bank AB
STANDARD CHARTERED PLC
Skandinaviska Enskilda Banken AB
Svenska Handelsbanken AB
UniCredit Bank AG

HISTORICAL FINANCIALS
Company Type: Public

Income Statement
FYE: December 31

	ASSETS ($ mil.)	NET INCOME ($ mil.)	INCOME AS % OF ASSETS	EMPLOYEES
12/20	1,143,166	(3,418)		90,836
12/19	960,691	3,787	0.4%	94,514
12/18	952,193	4,457	0.5%	97,775
12/17	1,003,105	6,560	0.7%	103,771
12/16	907,566	(12,448)	—	130,931
Annual Growth	**5.9%**	—	—	**(8.7%)**

2020 Year-End Financials

Return on assets: (-0.3%)	Dividends
Return on equity: (-4.5%)	Yield: —
Long-term debt ($ mil.): —	Payout: —
No. of shares (mil.): —	Market value ($ mil.): —
Sales ($ mil): 25,593	

	STOCK PRICE ($) FY Close	P/E High/Low		PER SHARE ($) Earnings	Dividends	Book Value
12/20	4.53	—	—	(1.59)	0.00	32.64
12/19	7.25	5	3	1.63	0.10	30.88
12/18	5.62	6	3	1.95	0.12	28.67
12/17	9.60	4	3	3.33	0.00	31.96
Annual Growth	**(22.1%)**	—	—	—	—	**0.5%**

Unilever Plc (United Kingdom)

Unilever PLC along with its Dutch counterpart Unilever N.V. constitute a global food & refreshment beauty &personal care and home care products powerhouse. The group's vast portfolio of consumer products includes about 30 global brands — including Hellmann's (mayonnaise) Knorr (soups) Lipton (tea) Axe (deodorant) and Dove (soaps) — that each brings up more than EUR1 billion in sales. Unilever's consumer goods are sold in more than 190 countries and its largest market is in the US. Based in the UK Unilever PLC trades on the London and New York stock exchanges.

Operations
Unilever's over 400 brands are divided into three groups.

The Beauty & Personal Care product category sells skin cleansing (soap shower) skin care (face hand and body moisturisers) hair care (shampoo conditioner styling) and deodorants ?Brands include Axe Dove Lux Rexona and Sunsilk — as well as other household names such as TRESemme Signal Lifebuoy and Vaseline. It generates more than 40% of Unilever's total sales.

The Food & Refreshment primarily sells ice cream savoury (soups bouillons seasoning) dressing (mayonnaise ketchup) and tea. It comprises of brands Knorr stocks Hellmann's mayonnaise Heartbrand Lipton Magnum Pukka and more. The segment accounts for about 40% of sales.

The Home Care segment produces cleaning products of various kinds led by the billion-euro Dirt is Good (Persil and Omo) and Surf brands alongside Seventh Generation Domestos Sunlight Cif and more. It brings in some 20% of overall sales.

Geographic Reach
Based in London UK Unilever has operations in more than 190 countries.

Geographically Unilever's revenue is highly diversified. The US is its single largest market that generates about 20% of sales while the UK and India accounts for some 15% combined. Other countries generated the remaining over 65%.

Sales and Marketing
Unilever sells its products through around 25 million retail stores globally. Its diverse line of customers range: from large traditional 'bricks and mortar' store partners (the largest group in terms of sales) to online-only retailers small family-owned shops and value retailers.

Financial Performance
The company generated a turnover of EUR 50.7 billion a decline of 2% from the previous year. This included an unfavorable currency impact of 5% driven by weakening of currencies in our key markets such as Brazil Argentina and India.

In 2020 the company had a net income of EUR 6.1 billion a 1% increase from the previous year's net income of EUR 6 billion.

The company's cash at the end of 2020 was EUR 5.5 billion. Operating activities generated EUR 9.1 billion while investing activities used EUR 1.5 billion mainly for acquisition of businesses and investments in joint ventures and associates. Financing activities used another EUR 5.8 billion primarily for dividends paid.

Strategy

Unilever's strategy consists of: Developing its portfolio into high growth spaces; Winning with its brands as a force for good powered by purpose and innovation; Accelerate in USA India China and key growth markets; Lead in the channels of the future; and Build a purpose-led future-fit organization and growth culture.

Mergers and Acquisitions

In early 2021 Unilever has completed the acquisition of Paula's Choice the digital-led skin care brand. Paula's Choice offers powerful content and digital tools to demystify the science behind skin care including an extensive "Ingredient Dictionary" that breaks down the research behind nearly 4000 ingredients and Expert Advice a curated online hub of skin care and ingredient knowledge. Terms of the deal were not disclosed.

Also in 2021 Unilever has signed an agreement to acquire Onnit a holistic wellness and lifestyle company based in Austin Texas. Onnit's supplements are the foundation of the brands' offering and are made with scientifically proven and high-quality ingredients to provide improved cognitive function mood and relaxation gut health and immunity support. With its holistic health offering and digital-first model Onnit perfectly complements the company's growing portfolio of innovative wellness and supplement brands that include OLLY Equilibra Liquid I.V. and SmartyPants Vitamins. Terms were not disclosed.

In 2020 Unilever has signed an agreement to acquire Liquid I.V. a U.S-based health-science nutrition and wellness company. Liquid I.V. provides a 360-degree approach to wellness with a product range that includes Hydration Energy and Sleep. Liquid I.V. is also non-GMO vegan gluten free soy free and dairy free. Terms of the deal were not disclosed.

In early 2020 Hindustan Unilever Limited (HUL) India's largest fast-moving consumer goods company and Unilever's listed subsidiary in India has successfully completed the merger of Singapore-based GlaxoSmithKline Consumer Healthcare Limited (GSKCH) with HUL. Unilever has also completed the related acquisition of Horlicks brands rights and other Consumer Healthcare nutrition assets from GSK in other predominantly Asian markets.

Company Background

Unilever traced its roots 1890's Although Unilever wasn't formed until 1930 the companies that joined forces to create the business we know today were already well established before the start of the 20th century. In 1929 With businesses expanding fast companies set up negotiations intending to stop others producing the same types of products. But instead they agree to merge and so Unilever is created.

EXECUTIVES

Chief Research and Development Officer, Richard Slater
President, Home Care, Peter Ter Kulve
Chief Executive Officer and Executive Director, Alan Jope, $1,718,224 total compensation
Chief Supply Chain Officer, Marc Engel
Chief Human Resources Officer, Leena Nair

Chief Operating Officer, Nitin Paranjpe
Non-Executive Independent Chairman of the Board, Nils Andersen
President, Unilever South Asia and Chair and Managing Director, Hindustan Unilever Limited, Sanjiv Mehta
Non-Executive Independent Director, Strive Masiyiwa
Vice-Chair, Youngme Moon
President - Foods & Refreshment, Hanneke Faber
Non-Executive Independent Director, Andrea Jung
Chief Digital & Marketing Officer, Conny Braams
President - North America, Fabian Garcia
Non-Executive Independent Director, Susan Kilsby
Non-Executive Director, Adrian Hennah
Group Secretary, Chief Legal Officer, Ritva Sotamaa
Chief Financial Officer, Executive Director, Graeme Pitkethly, $1,294,365 total compensation
President, Beauty and Personal Care, Sunny Jain
Auditors: KPMG LLP

LOCATIONS

HQ: Unilever Plc (United Kingdom)
100 Victoria Embankment, London EC4Y 0DY
Phone: (44) 20 7822 5252   **Fax:** (44) 20 7822 5464
Web: www.unilever.com

2016 Sales

	% total
US	16
Netherlands / UK	7
Others	77
Total	**100**

PRODUCTS/OPERATIONS

2017 Sales

	% total
Personal Care	39
Foods	23
Refreshment	18
Home Care	20
Total	**100**

Selected Global Brands

Axe
Dirt is Good (OMO)
Dollar Shave Club
Dove
Family Goodness (Rama)
Hellmann's
Knorr
Lipton
Lux
Magnum
Rexona
Sunsilk
Surf

COMPETITORS

BAKKAVOR GROUP PLC
CRODA INTERNATIONAL PUBLIC LIMITED COMPANY
DECHRA PHARMACEUTICALS PLC
FRASERS GROUP PLC
HINDUSTAN UNILEVER LIMITED
ITC LIMITED
KERRY GROUP PUBLIC LIMITED COMPANY
PRESTIGE CONSUMER HEALTHCARE INC.
RECKITT BENCKISER GROUP PLC
THE PROCTER & GAMBLE COMPANY
Unilever N.V.

HISTORICAL FINANCIALS

Company Type: Public

Income Statement				FYE: December 31
	REVENUE ($ mil.)	NET INCOME ($ mil.)	NET PROFIT MARGIN	EMPLOYEES
12/20	62,253	6,849	11.0%	150,000
12/19	58,361	6,315	10.8%	153,000
12/18	58,384	10,752	18.4%	155,000
12/17	64,391	7,256	11.3%	165,000
12/16	55,658	5,473	9.8%	168,832
Annual Growth	2.8%	5.8%		(2.9%)

2020 Year-End Financials

Debt ratio: 45.3%	No. of shares (mil.): —
Return on equity: 39.1%	Dividends
Cash ($ mil.): 6,809	Yield: 3.0%
Current ratio: 0.78	Payout: 76.5%
Long-term debt ($ mil.): 25,883	Market value ($ mil.): —

	STOCK PRICE ($) FY Close	P/E High/Low		PER SHARE ($) Earnings	Dividends	Book Value
12/20	60.36	32	23	2.60	1.83	7.13
12/19	57.17	31	24	2.40	1.80	5.66
12/18	52.25	16	14	3.99	1.81	5.07
12/17	55.34	28	21	2.58	1.65	5.97
12/16	40.70	25	21	1.92	1.33	6.04
Annual Growth	10.4%	—	—	7.9%	8.4%	4.2%

Union Bank Of India

LOCATIONS

HQ: Union Bank Of India
Union Bank Bhavan, 239, Vidhan Bhavan Marg,
Nariman Point, Mumbai 400 021
Phone: 1800 208 2244
Web: www.unionbankofindia.co.in

HISTORICAL FINANCIALS

Company Type: Public

Income Statement				FYE: March 31
	ASSETS ($ mil.)	NET INCOME ($ mil.)	INCOME AS % OF ASSETS	EMPLOYEES
03/20	73,543	(413)	—	37,318
03/19	72,054	(422)	—	37,262
03/18	75,490	(801)	—	37,587
03/17	70,263	88	0.1%	36,877
03/16	61,599	205	0.3%	35,473
Annual Growth	4.5%	—		1.3%

2020 Year-End Financials

Return on assets: (-0.5%)	Dividends
Return on equity: (-10.2%)	Yield: —
Long-term debt ($ mil.): —	Payout: —
No. of shares (mil.): —	Market value ($ mil.): —
Sales ($ mil): 5,717	

Unipol Gruppo SpA

Unipol Gruppo is an Italian firm with dozens of subsidiaries in the insurance real estate banking and other industries. It primarily operates through subsidiary UnipolSai Assicurazioni. That unit provides property/casualty and life insurance and reinsurance as well as financial investment services. Unipol Gruppo also has operations in the bancassurance channel through Arca Vita and Arca Assicurazioni held by the subsidiary UnipolSai which distribute Life and Non-Life policies through the corporate groups of Banca Popolare dell'Emilia Romagna. Other businesses include agriculture and hospitality. In the financial area it operates through UnipolRec a company specializing in the management of non-performing loans.

EXECUTIVES

Non-Executive Chairman of the Board, Pierluigi Stefanini, $1,015,233 total compensation
Chief Executive Officer, Group Chief Executive Officer, General Manager, Executive Director, Carlo Cimbri
Non-Executive Deputy Chairman of the Board, Ernesto Dalle Rive
Non-Executive Director, Milo Pacchioni
General Manager - Administration, Controlling and Operations, Maurizio Castellina
Non-Executive Director, Adriano Turrini
General Manager - Insurance Group, Matteo Laterza
Group Global Counselor, Giuseppe Santella
Non-Executive Independent Director, Maria Pasquariello
Non-Executive Independent Director, Giuseppina Gualtieri
Non-Executive Director, Daniele Ferre
Non-Executive Independent Director, Patrizia De Luise
Non-Executive Independent Director, Gianmaria Balducci
Non-Executive Independent Director, Antonietta Mundo
Non-Executive Independent Director, Annamaria Trovo
Non-Executive Independent Director, Massimo Desiderio
Non-Executive Independent Director, Pier Morara, $98,741 total compensation
Non-Executive Independent Director, Roberta Datteri
General Manager - Business Development and Corporate Communication, Gian Luca Santi
Auditors: PricewaterhouseCoopers S.p.A.

LOCATIONS

HQ: Unipol Gruppo SpA
Via Stalingrado, 45, Bologna 40128
Phone: (39) 051 5076111   **Fax:** (39) 051 5076666
Web: www.unipol.it

PRODUCTS/OPERATIONS

Selected Subsidiaries
Atahotels (hotels)
DDOR Novi Sad (Serbia insurance)
Linear Assicurazioni (direct insurance)
Marina di Loano (port management)
Tenute de Cerro (agriculture)
UNA Hotels & Resorts (hotels)
Unipol Banca (banking)
UnipolSai Assicurazioni S.p.A. (insurance holding company)UniSalute (health care insurance)

COMPETITORS

ALEXANDER FORBES LTD	LSL PROPERTY SERVICES PLC
AON GLOBAL LIMITED	
CHARLES TAYLOR LIMITED	MAPFRE SA
Everest Re Group Ltd.	SOMPO HOLDINGS INC.
Guardian Holdings Limited	Sampo Oyj
	Talanx AG

HISTORICAL FINANCIALS
Company Type: Public

Income Statement   FYE: December 31

	REVENUE ($ mil.)	NET INCOME ($ mil.)	NET PROFIT MARGIN	EMPLOYEES
12/19	18,638	1,013	5.4%	12,337
12/18	16,282	459	2.8%	14,241
12/17	15,787	(414)	—	14,188
12/16	17,565	348	2.0%	0
12/15	20,241	296	1.5%	13,864
Annual Growth	(2.0%)	36.0%		(2.9%)

2019 Year-End Financials

Debt ratio: —	No. of shares (mil.): 716
Return on equity: 15.4%	Dividends
Cash ($ mil.): 1,130	Yield: —
Current ratio: —	Payout: 22.2%
Long-term debt ($ mil.): —	Market value ($ mil.): —

UnipolSai Assicurazioni SpA

Auditors: PricewaterhouseCoopers SpA

LOCATIONS

HQ: UnipolSai Assicurazioni SpA
Via Stalingrado 45, Bologna 40128
Phone: (39) 051 5077111   **Fax:** (39) 051 7096584
Web: www.unipolsai.com

HISTORICAL FINANCIALS
Company Type: Public

Income Statement   FYE: December 31

	REVENUE ($ mil.)	NET INCOME ($ mil.)	NET PROFIT MARGIN	EMPLOYEES
12/19	17,988	704	3.9%	12,274
12/18	15,591	1,036	6.6%	11,935
12/17	15,502	604	3.9%	11,529
12/16	14,625	525	3.6%	10,280
12/15	17,394	774	4.5%	9,951
Annual Growth	0.8%	(2.3%)	—	5.4%

2019 Year-End Financials

Debt ratio: —	No. of shares (mil.): —
Return on equity: 10.1%	Dividends
Cash ($ mil.): 838	Yield: —
Current ratio: —	Payout: —
Long-term debt ($ mil.): —	Market value ($ mil.): —

UNIQA Insurance Group AG

Auditors: PwC Wirtschaftspruefung GmbH

LOCATIONS

HQ: UNIQA Insurance Group AG
Untere Donaustrasse 21, Vienna 1029
Phone: (43) 1 211 75 3773   **Fax:** (43) 1 211 75 793773
Web: www.uniqagroup.com

HISTORICAL FINANCIALS
Company Type: Public

Income Statement   FYE: December 31

	ASSETS ($ mil.)	NET INCOME ($ mil.)	INCOME AS % OF ASSETS	EMPLOYEES
12/20	39,160	23	0.1%	13,408
12/19	32,255	260	0.8%	13,038
12/18	32,642	278	0.9%	12,818
12/17	34,456	193	0.6%	12,839
12/16	35,519	156	0.4%	12,855
Annual Growth	2.5%	(37.5%)	—	1.1%

2020 Year-End Financials

Return on assets: 0.0%	Dividends
Return on equity: 0.5%	Yield: —
Long-term debt ($ mil.): —	Payout: 300.0%
No. of shares (mil.): 306	Market value ($ mil.): —
Sales ($ mil): 6,722	

United Overseas Bank Ltd. (Singapore)

One of Singapore's top financial institutions United Overseas Bank (UOB) provides a range of commercial banking and personal financial services. The bank's offerings include asset management private equity fund management and insurance services. It is also one of the largest capital market issuers in the Asia-Pacific region. Altogether the bank has more than 500 branches and 1.3 million ATMs in almost 20 countries. Most of UOB's revenue comes from Singapore.

Operations

UOB is organized into three businesses - Retail Wholesale and Global Markets and Investment Management. Its retail business covers personal accounts private banking and small businesses. It accounts for about 45% of revenue. The wholesale division serves large corporations and financial institutions; it accounts for more than 40% of revenue. Global markets and investment management which provides asset management foreign exchange money market funds derivatives and other capital market activities accounts for more than 5% of revenue and the rest comes from other activities.

Overall UOB generates roughly 65% of its revenue from interest income and the rest comes from non-interest income.

Geographic Reach

Altogether the bank has operations in about 20 Asian countries. While its headquarters is located in Singapore UOB operates more than 500 branches and offices in Asia Pacific Europe and North America. It generates revenue from China (almost 10% of total revenue) Indonesia (some 5%) Malaysia (over 10%) and Thailand (around 10%) among others.

Financial Performance

The company's revenue increased to $10.0 billion in 2019 compared to $9.1 billion in the previous year. The increase was due to higher net interest income and net fee and commission income.

Net income increased by 8% to $4.3 billion compared to $4.0 million in the previous year.

Cash held by the company at the end of 2019 was $20.2 billion. Cash provided by operations was $8.3 billion while cash used for investing and financing activities were $500.1 million and $7.6 billion respectively. Main uses of cash were purchase of properties and other fixed assets and redemption of debts issued.

Strategy

UOB with its established Asian heritage and franchise is well positioned. The company connects its corporate clients to regional opportunities and provide financial solutions to our retail customers as their needs evolve with rising affluence.

UOB fulfill its purpose by pursuing a strategy based on the following pillars: deepening its regional connectivity through its network sector solutions and cross-border advisory capabilities; offering the complete customer experience with best-in-class products and services through its holistic omni-channel approach and Digital Bank; investing in people and technology for the long term; and being disciplined in risk and balance sheet management to navigate through economic cycles.

Company Background

UOB was founded in 1935 as the United Chinese Bank and catered mainly to the Fujian community in Singapore. The bank changed its name to United Overseas Bank in 1965.

Auditors: Ernst & Young LLP

LOCATIONS

HQ: United Overseas Bank Ltd. (Singapore)
80 Raffles Place, UOB Plaza, 048624
Phone: (65) 6222 2121   **Fax:** (65) 6534 2334
Web: www.uobgroup.com

2012 Sales

	% of sales
Singapore	58
Malaysia	15
Thailand	8
Indonesia	7
China	6
Other	6
Total	**100**

Selected Subsidiaries

Far Eastern Bank Limited (Singapore)
PT Bank UOB Indonesia
United Overseas Bank (China)
United Overseas Bank (Malaysia)
United Overseas Bank (Philippines)
United Overseas Bank (Thailand)
United Overseas Insurance Limited Singapore
UOB Australia Limited
UOB Capital Investments Pte Ltd Singapore
UOB Capital Management Pte Ltd Singapore
UOB Holdings Private Limited Singapore
UOB Insurance (H.K.) Limited Hong Kong
UOB International Investment Private Limited

PRODUCTS/OPERATIONS

2012 Sales

	% of total
Interest income	61
Fees & commission	23
Other non-interest income	16
Total	**100**

2012 Sales

	% of total
Retail	36
Wholesale	36
Global markets & investment mgmt.	19
Other	9
Total	**100**

COMPETITORS

AKBANK TURK ANONIM SIRKETI
Agricultural Bank of China Limited
BANK VTB PAO
Banco Bradesco S/A
China Merchants Bank Co. Ltd.
DBS GROUP HOLDINGS LTD
QATAR NATIONAL BANK (Q.P.S.C.)

Shinhan Financial Group Co. Ltd.
TURKIYE IS BANKASI ANONIM SIRKETI
The Bank of Nova Scotia
YAPI VE KREDI BANKASI ANONIM SIRKETI

HISTORICAL FINANCIALS

Company Type: Public

Income Statement   FYE: December 31

	ASSETS ($ mil.)	NET INCOME ($ mil.)	INCOME AS % OF ASSETS	EMPLOYEES
12/20	326,702	2,205	0.7%	0
12/19	300,580	3,228	1.1%	26,872
12/18	285,005	2,943	1.0%	0
12/17	268,425	2,537	0.9%	0
12/16	235,316	2,142	0.9%	0
Annual Growth	8.5%	0.7%	—	—

2020 Year-End Financials

Return on assets: 0.7%
Return on equity: 7.2%
Long-term debt ($ mil.): —
No. of shares (mil.): 1,672
Sales ($ mil): 9,731

Dividends
Yield: 4.8%
Payout: 135.6%
Market value ($ mil.): 57,160

	STOCK PRICE ($) FY Close	P/E High/Low	PER SHARE ($) Earnings	Dividends	Book Value
12/20	34.17	24 16	1.27	1.65	18.50
12/19	39.32	16 14	1.89	1.81	17.66
12/18	36.12	19 15	1.71	1.71	16.59
12/17	39.64	20 15	1.48	1.05	16.59
12/16	28.14	16 13	1.28	0.96	13.91
Annual Growth	5.0%	— —	(0.2%)	14.6%	7.4%

Vale SA

Brazilian mining company Vale is the world's top producer of metals such as iron ore iron ore pellets and nickel the key raw materials for steelmaking and stainless steel. Its Carajas mine in Northern Brazil boasts the highest grade iron ore anywhere in the world. With greenfield mineral exploration in six countries Rio de Janeiro-based Vale maintains a network integrating its mines with railroads ports and ships. Additionally it has a sustainable energy project in Brazil hydroelectric plants in Brazil Canada and Indonesia and pursues investments in energy and steel businesses through affiliates and joint ventures. About 60% of its revenue comes from China.

Operations

Vale reports three segments based on its products and operations ? ferrous minerals; base metals; and coal.

Ferrous minerals account for approximately 80% of annual sales the two leading products being iron ore and iron ore pellets. Vales operates four systems in Brazil for producing and distributing iron ore plus eleven pellet plants in Brazil and two in Oman. In addition it has approximately 50% stake in Samarco and some 25% stakes in two pellet companies in China. Vale also has ferroalloys and manganese mining operations through several subsidiaries. In addition its logistics infrastructure is top-notch with railroads maritime terminals distribution centers and ports. The company owns and charters dry bulk vessels to transport its own products.

Base Metal (about 20% of revenue) manages nickel mine production and processing as well as refining. The company also produces copper cobalt PGMs (platinum group metals) and other precious metals.

The company's coal operations are focused on metallurgical and thermal coal operations.

Geographic Reach

Based in Rio de Janeiro Brazil Vale produces ferrous metals copper and manganese in Brazil; nickel cobalt and platinum group metals in Canada; and coal in Mozambique.

In Brazil Vale divides its iron ore operations into four regional systems. The Northern and Southeastern regions are fully integrated containing mines railroads marine terminals and a port. The Southern system comprises two mining complexes and two maritime terminals. The company owns two railroads that connect production regions with export terminals the Vit ria a Minas and Caraj ́s railroads. Vale has about 10 pellet plants in Brazil (plus two in Oman).

Most of Vale's nickel production is in Canada but it has additional mining operations in Indonesia and New Caledonia and refineries in the UK Japan South Korea Taiwan and China.

Its products are sold across the world with China the leading market (about 60% of its annual sales) and followed by Europe (except Germany) and Asia (except Japan and China) each accounts nearly 10% of sales. Brazil Japan Germany Middle East Africa and Oceania the US and some other countries account for the remainder.

Sales and Marketing

The company sales copper concentrates from Sossego and Salobo under medium and long-term contracts to copper smelters in Europe India and Asia. It has medium-term copper supply agreements with domestic customer for part of the copper concentrates and copper matte produced in Sudbury which are also sold under long-term contracts in Europe and Asia. The sale of copper concentrates from Voisey's Bay under medium and long-term contracts to customers in Europe and electrowon copper cathodes from Sudbury and Long Harbour in North America.

Financial Performance

In 2020 company's net operating revenues were $40.0 billion 7% higher than the net operating revenues for the same period in 2019 which were $37.6 billion. The increase was mainly due to higher iron ore sales prices reflecting the increase in the market reference price.

Net income for fiscal 2020 was $4.5 billion compared with a net loss of $2.2 billion in the prior year.

Cash held by the company at the end of fiscal 2020 increased to $13.5 billion. Cash provided by operations was $14.3 billion while cash used for investing and financing activities were $4.7 billion and $2.7 billion respectively. Main cash uses were capital expenditures and payments of loans and borrowings from third-parties.

Strategy

In 2020 the company took important steps towards building a better Vale. Vale's goal is to be a company recognized by society for being: a benchmark in safety the best in class reliable operator a

talent-driven organization a leader in low-carbon mining and a reference in creating and sharing value. The company is dedicated to repairing Brumadinho and to transforming natural resources into prosperity and sustainable development based on the following main strategic pillars: safety and operational excellence; new pact with society; maximize flight-to-quality in iron ore; base metals transformation; and discipline in capital allocation.
Company Background

HISTORY

During the 1890s as land reforms opened the way for foreign investments in Brazil the mineral-rich state of Minas Gerais caught the attention of mining companies from Europe and the US. British engineers founded the Itabira Iron Ore Company and took over the Doce River Valley's Vit "ria-Minas Railroad. After Brazil's revolution (1930) Itabira was split up. One of the new companies Itabira Minera o began shipping iron ore in 1940.

A 1942 agreement prompted by the outbreak of WWII established iron export regulations from Brazil to the US and the UK. Later that year the Companhia Vale do Rio Doce (CVRD) was formed with the Brazilian government owning 80%. The new company received the assets of Itabira including Brazil's "iron mountain" Cau Peak. By the end of the 1940s 80% of Brazil's iron ore exports were mined by CVRD. During the 1950s CVRD invested in land holdings and shipping operations. The company set up a shipping and logistics subsidiary in 1962.

CVRD teamed up with US Steel in 1970 to mine iron ore at Caraj s in Amazonian Brazil; two years later the site was found to hold the world's largest iron ore reserves (18 billion tons). By 1975 CVRD had become the world's largest iron ore exporter. A year later the company finished doubling the tracks of the Vit "ria-Minas Railroad. It also set up a manganese mining company (Urucum Minera o) and an alumina production facility (Alumina do Norte do Brasil or Alunorte).

To support its Caraj s mining operations CVRD added the Estrada de Ferro de Caraj s railway (finished 1985) and a hydroelectric project. In all the giant Caraj s project involved investments from the US Japan France the European Economic Community and the World Bank. (The Caraj s area like many mining sites in Brazil has been the site of intense controversy because it attracts subsistence miners including children who work under dangerous circumstances.) By the late 1980s the company had become a major supplier of pelletized iron used as feed for steel mill blast furnaces.

In 1992 CVRD expanded into the production of chemicals (Rio Capim Qu mica now Par Pigmentos SA). The company acquired stakes in two steel mills — Sider rgica de Tubar o and A o Minas Gerais SA — in 1993. In 1996 it invested in gold finds in Par state. CVRD was privatized in 1997 and the next year set the sales record for a private Brazilian company.

The company listed ADR shares on the NYSE in 2000. Acquisitions that year included Brazilian iron ore companies SOCOIMEX and SAMITRI (73%). CVRD sold its 50% stake in pulp and paper group Bahia Sul to Suzano for $320 million in 2001. It also sold its 51% share of pulp maker Cenibra and its share of steelmaker Companhia Sider rgica Nacional (CSN).

In 2002 the Brazilian Treasury and the National Social and Economic Bank (BNDES) sold 33% of CVRD's shares further privatizing the company. CVRD disposed of its last gold mine (Fazenda Brasileiro) in 2003. It also exited the dry bulk-shipping business that year.

Under pressure from increasing globalization Vale had been forced to trim some of its operations (including its stake in CSN) to focus on mining and bulk transport. Those asset sales helped fund Vale's win over Australian mining giant BHP Billiton the world's #2 iron ore producer in a battle for Brazil's iron miner Caemi Minera o e Metalurgia #4 worldwide. (From 2001 through 2006 the company picked up stakes in Caemi until it owned it fully.) The deal for Inco trumped offers from Canadian miner Teck and US copper producer Phelps Dodge.

Toward the end of 2007 the company — then called Companhia Vale do Rio Doce — decided that it wanted a new brand identity and so ditched its longtime nickname CVRD in favor of Vale. Two years later it changed its name legally dropping the more formal Companhia Vale do Rio Doce.

EXECUTIVES

Independent Director, Isabella Saboya De Albuquerque
Director, Roger Downey
Executive Officer for Global Business Support, Alexandre Pereira
Executive Officer of Sustainability and Institutional Relations, Luiz Eduardo Osorio
Director of People, Marina Quental
Head of Investor Relations, Andre Figueiredo
Vice Chairman of the Board, Fernando Jorge Buso Gomes
Executive Officer for Ferrous Minerals, Marcello Spinelli
Director, Murilo Cesar Lemos dos Santos Passos
Director, Patricia G. M. De A. Bentes
Director, Jose Luciano Duarte Penido
Director, Eduardo De Oliveira Rodrigues Filho
Security and Excellence Operations Department, Carlos Medeiros
Auditors: PricewaterhouseCoopers Auditores Independentes

LOCATIONS

HQ: Vale SA
Praia de Botafogo, 186 offices 701 1901 Botafogo, Rio de Janeiro 22250-145
Phone: (55) 21 3485 5000   **Fax:** (55) 21 3814 9935
Web: www.vale.com

2018 Sales

	$ mil.	% of total
China	15,242	42
Europe (excl. Germany)	4,454	12
Brazil	3,248	9
Japan	2,743	7
Germany	1,653	5
Asia except Japan and China	3,666	10
Americas (excl. US and Brazil)	1,476	4
Middle East/Africa/Oceania	2,738	7
US	1,353	4
Total	**36,575**	**100**

PRODUCTS/OPERATIONS

2018 sales

	$ mil.	% of total
Ferrous minerals	27,933	76
Coal	1,643	5
Base metals	6,703	18
Others	296	1
Total	**36,575**	**100**

COMPETITORS

Adastra Labs Holdings Ltd	Niocan Inc
Alderon Iron Ore Corp	RIO TINTO LIMITED
BHP GROUP PLC	RIO TINTO PLC
CLEVELAND-CLIFFS INC.	SIBANYE UK LIMITED
FREEPORT-MCMORAN INC.	Ternium Mexico S.A. de C.V.
Galiano Gold Inc	Western Magnesium Corporation
Nexa Resources	

HISTORICAL FINANCIALS
Company Type: Public

Income Statement
FYE: December 31

	REVENUE ($ mil.)	NET INCOME ($ mil.)	NET PROFIT MARGIN	EMPLOYEES
12/20	40,018	4,881	12.2%	74,316
12/19	37,570	(1,683)	—	71,149
12/18	36,575	6,860	18.8%	70,270
12/17	33,967	5,507	16.2%	73,596
12/16	27,488	3,982	14.5%	73,062
Annual Growth	**9.8%**	**5.2%**	**—**	**0.4%**

2020 Year-End Financials

Debt ratio: 16.3%	No. of shares (mil.): —
Return on equity: 12.8%	Dividends
Cash ($ mil.): 13,487	Yield: 2.8%
Current ratio: 1.67	Payout: 65.4%
Long-term debt ($ mil.): 13,891	Market value ($ mil.): —

	STOCK PRICE ($) FY Close	P/E High/Low	PER SHARE ($) Earnings	Dividends	Book Value
12/20	16.76	18 7	0.95	0.62	6.97
12/19	13.20	— —	(0.33)	0.22	7.81
12/18	13.19	12 9	1.32	0.53	8.58
12/17	12.23	12 7	1.05	0.34	8.36
12/16	7.62	12 3	0.77	0.04	12.26
Annual Growth	**21.8% (13.2%)**	**— —**	**5.4%**	**97.5%**	

Valeo SE

Auditors: ERNST & YOUNG et Autres

LOCATIONS

HQ: Valeo SE
43, rue Bayen, Paris, Cedex 17 75017
Phone: (33) 1 40 55 20 20   **Fax:** (33) 1 40 55 21 71
Web: www.valeo.com

HISTORICAL FINANCIALS
Company Type: Public

Income Statement
FYE: December 31

	REVENUE ($ mil.)	NET INCOME ($ mil.)	NET PROFIT MARGIN	EMPLOYEES
12/20	19,830	(1,336)	—	110,300
12/19	21,602	351	1.6%	114,700
12/18	21,773	625	2.9%	113,600
12/17	22,263	1,062	4.8%	111,600
12/16	17,506	976	5.6%	91,800
Annual Growth	**3.2%**	**—**		**4.7%**

2020 Year-End Financials

Debt ratio: 40.5%	No. of shares (mil.): 240
Return on equity: (-27.6%)	Dividends
Cash ($ mil.): 3,621	Yield: 0.5%
Current ratio: 0.85	Payout: —
Long-term debt ($ mil.): 4,860	Market value ($ mil.): 4,709

	STOCK PRICE ($) FY Close	P/E High/Low	PER SHARE ($) Earnings	Dividends	Book Value
12/20	19.60	— —	(5.58)	0.11	16.48
12/19	17.54	16 10	1.47	0.70	21.74
12/18	14.58	17 6	2.61	0.73	22.06
12/17	37.34	11 9	4.41	0.75	22.24
12/16	28.60	19 5	4.08	0.53	18.27
Annual Growth	**(9.0%)**	**— —**		**(32.1%)**	**(2.5%)**

Valiant Holding Bern (Switzerland)

Banking with true valor Valiant Holding was formed in 2002 with the merger of regional Swiss banks Valiant Bank (retail banking) and Valiant Privatbank (asset management) with IRB Interregio Bank and Luzerner Regiobank. Today Valiant Bank serves German-speaking clients in Switzerland while Banque Romande Valiant serves the country's Francophone population. Together the two banks have more than 100 offices. Valiant Holding also owns Spar + Leihkasse Steffisburg a bank with two branches in Switzerland. The banks offer savings and investments mortgages and loans retirement planning and private banking services including asset management for retail and institutional investors.

EXECUTIVES

Independent Non-Executive Vice Chairman of the Board, Christoph Buehler
Member of the Management Board, Head of Corporate and Institutional Clients, Marc Praxmarer, $242,765 total compensation
Chief Financial Officer, Member of the Management Board, Hanspeter Kaspar, $286,421 total compensation
Non-Executive Independent Director, Franziska von Weissenfluh
Non-Executive Independent Director, Ronald Trachsel
Non-Executive Independent Director, Barbara Artmann
Non-Executive Independent Director, Jean-Baptiste Beuret
Non-Executive Chairman of the Board, Markus Gygax
Non-Executive Independent Director, Nicole Pauli
Chief Executive Officer, Member of the Management Board, Ewald Burgener, $398,221 total compensation
Non-Executive Independent Director, Maya Bundt
Member of the Management Board, Head of Customer Services and Channels, Christoph Wille, $242,765 total compensation
Member of the Management Board, Head of Private and Business Clients, Deputy Chief Executive Officer, Martin Vogler, $283,226 total compensation
Member of the Management Board, Head of Products and Operations, Stefan Gempeler, $239,571 total compensation
Auditors: PricewaterhouseCoopers AG

LOCATIONS

HQ: Valiant Holding Bern (Switzerland)
Pilatusstrasse 39, Lucerne 6003
Phone: (41) 31 310 71 11　　**Fax:** (41) 31 310 71 12
Web: www.valiant.ch

COMPETITORS

BGEO GROUP LIMITED	NATWEST GROUP PLC
CLOSE BROTHERS GROUP PLC	OM RESIDUAL UK LIMITED
HSBC HOLDINGS PLC	Vontobel Holding AG

HISTORICAL FINANCIALS
Company Type: Public

Income Statement　　　　　FYE: December 31

	ASSETS ($ mil.)	NET INCOME ($ mil.)	INCOME AS % OF ASSETS	EMPLOYEES
12/19	30,936	125	0.4%	1,045
12/18	27,836	122	0.4%	1,013
12/17	28,242	122	0.4%	1,000
12/16	25,635	115	0.5%	957
12/15	25,625	115	0.4%	926
Annual Growth	4.8%	2.1%		3.1%

2019 Year-End Financials

Return on assets: 0.4%	Dividends
Return on equity: 5.2%	Yield: —
Long-term debt ($ mil.): —	Payout: 65.1%
No. of shares (mil.): 15	Market value ($ mil.): —
Sales ($ mil): 499	

Veolia Environnement SA

Auditors: KPMG Audit

LOCATIONS

HQ: Veolia Environnement SA
21 rue La Boetie, Paris 75008
Phone: (33) 1 71 75 00 00
Web: www.veolia.com

HISTORICAL FINANCIALS
Company Type: Public

Income Statement　　　　　FYE: December 31

	REVENUE ($ mil.)	NET INCOME ($ mil.)	NET PROFIT MARGIN	EMPLOYEES
12/19	30,526	701	2.3%	178,021
12/18	29,673	503	1.7%	171,495
12/17	30,118	481	1.6%	168,800
12/16	25,753	404	1.6%	163,226
12/15	27,191	490	1.8%	173,959
Annual Growth	2.9%	9.4%	—	0.6%

2019 Year-End Financials

Debt ratio: 41.3%	No. of shares (mil.): 554
Return on equity: 10.4%	Dividends
Cash ($ mil.): 6,560	Yield: 3.8%
Current ratio: 0.90	Payout: 81.8%
Long-term debt ($ mil.): 10,516	Market value ($ mil.): 14,746

	STOCK PRICE ($) FY Close	P/E High/Low		PER SHARE ($) Earnings	Dividends	Book Value
12/19	26.58	25	18	1.26	1.03	12.01
12/18	20.41	37	28	0.74	0.99	12.39
12/17	25.50	43	30	0.70	0.98	16.36
12/16	16.95	44	30	0.60	0.78	14.92
12/15	23.59	36	22	0.75	0.79	16.53
Annual Growth	3.0%	—	—	13.7%	6.9%	(7.7%)

Vestas Wind Systems A/S

Vestas Wind Systems and its subsidiaries manufacture and sell land-based wind turbines used to produce electricity. In all Vestas has installed more than 77000 wind turbines in nearly 85 countries. Besides installation Vestas is the world's largest servicer of wind turbines and maintains more than 50000 turbines with a combined capacity of over 132000 GW. Vestas generates nearly half of its sales in the Americas. Its power solutions segment accounts for more than 85% of its total sales.

Operations
Vestas operates in the two business segments: Power Solutions accounts for more than 85% of sales and Service generates nearly 15%.

The Power Solutions segment contains sale of wind power plants wind turbines development sites etcThe Service segment contains sale of service contracts spare parts and related activities.

Geographic Reach
Headquartered in Denmark Vestas has sales and service centers located in Africa Asia Europe North and Latin America and Oceania; Production facilities in Asia Europe and North and Latin America; and research facilities in Asia and Europe.

Americas is the company's largest market representing nearly half of total sales. Other major markets include Europe Middle East and Africa generating over 35% and Asia/Pacific accounting for around 15%.

Financial Performance
Note: Growth rates may differ after conversion to US Dollars.

In 2020 revenue from Power Solutions amounted to EUR 12.8 billion continuing the strong growth in past years. This was primarily driven by high activity levels in the Americas and particularly the USA.

In 2020 the company had a net income of ?771 million a 10% increase from the previous year.

The company's cash at the end of 2020 was ?3.1 billion. Operating activities generated ?743 million while investing activities used ?659 million mainly for capital expenditures. Financing activities used another ?234 million mainly for dividends paid.

Strategy
The company's strategy consists of: Accelerating the deployment of renewable energy; Driving society-wide electrification; and Implementing solutions for non-electrifiable use.

Company Background
Vestas which began manufacturing wind turbines in 1979 traces its roots back to the 19th century.

EXECUTIVES

Executive Vice President, Chief Service Officer, Christian Venderby
Independent Director, Carsten Bjerg
Independent Deputy Chairman of the Board, Lars Josefsson
Independent Chairman of the Board, Bert Nordberg
President, Chief Executive Officer, Henrik Andersen, $229,651 total compensation
Chief Financial Officer, Executive Vice President, Marika Fredriksson, $149,273 total compensation
Independent Director, Jens Hesselberg Lund
Director, Employee Representative, Michael Abildgaard Lisbjerg

Executive Vice President, Chief Sales Officer,
Juan Araluce y Martinez de Azagra
Director, Employee Representative, Kim Hvid
Thomsen
Director, Employee Representative, Sussie Dvinge
Agerbo
Independent Director, Bruce Grant
Independent Director, Eva Soefelde Berneke
Independent Director, Helle Thorning-Schmidt
Auditors: PricewaterhouseCoopers Statsautoriseret
Revisionspartnerselskab

LOCATIONS

HQ: Vestas Wind Systems A/S
Hedeager 42, Aarhus N. 8200
Phone: (45) 97 30 00 00 **Fax:** (45) 97 30 00 01
Web: www.vestas.com

2018 sales

	%
Americas	44
Europe Middle East and Africa	42
Asia/Pacific	14
Total	**100**

PRODUCTS/OPERATIONS

2018 sales

	%
Power Solutions	84
Service	16
Total	**100**

2018 sales

	%
Supply-and-install	43
Supply only	33
Service	16
Turnkey	8
Total	**100**

COMPETITORS

Alpiq Holding SA
INOTIV INC.
PRODUCT
INSTITUTE OF GAS
TECHNOLOGY
IQVIA HOLDINGS INC.
NANOSTRING
TECHNOLOGIES INC.

ORIGIN ENERGY LIMITED
PHARMACEUTICAL

DEVELOPMENT LLC
PPD DEVELOPMENT L.P.
TPI COMPOSITES INC.
Uniper SE

HISTORICAL FINANCIALS

Company Type: Public

Income Statement				FYE: December 31
	REVENUE ($ mil.)	NET INCOME ($ mil.)	NET PROFIT MARGIN	EMPLOYEES
12/20	18,187	938	5.2%	29,378
12/19	13,638	790	5.8%	25,541
12/18	11,605	783	6.7%	24,648
12/17	11,931	1,071	9.0%	23,303
12/16	10,809	1,018	9.4%	21,824
Annual Growth	**13.9%**	**(2.0%)**	**—**	**7.7%**

2020 Year-End Financials

Debt ratio: 6.1%
Return on equity: 19.2%
Cash ($ mil.): 3,759
Current ratio: 1.09
Long-term debt ($ mil.): 516

No. of shares (mil.): 1,004
Dividends
Yield: 1.5%
Payout: 28.2%
Market value ($ mil.): 78,572

	STOCK PRICE ($) FY Close	P/E High/Low		PER SHARE ($) Earnings	Dividends	Book Value
12/20	78.23	104	34	0.95	0.24	5.69
12/19	33.67	48	34	0.80	0.23	3.79
12/18	25.18	39	29	0.78	0.32	3.59
12/17	23.08	40	23	1.01	0.32	3.66
12/16	21.72	30	20	0.93	0.20	3.15
Annual Growth	**37.8%**	**—**	**—**	**0.7%**	**4.5%**	**15.9%**

Vienna Insurance Group AG

Vienna Insurance Group (formerly known as Wiener St ¤dtische) has grown from being Austria's largest insurance group to cover much of Austria Central and Eastern Europe as well. The firm which traces its roots back to 1990 has expanded its network across more than 30 countries. Much of its international growth has come from acquisition and joint ventures with local insurers which are then often brought under the Vienna Insurance Group banner. Its offerings include the basics of life and property and casualty insurance. However it also offers private health insurance. Vienna Insurance Group was among the first Western European insurance companies to jump into Eastern Europe in the early 1990's. While Austria is still its single largest market about 75% of the company's insurance premiums come from international customers.

Operations

The around 50 VIG insurance companies operate in the following reporting segments: Austria Czech Republic Slovakia Poland Romania Baltic states Hungary Bulgaria Turkey/Georgia Remaining CEE Other Markets and Central Functions. About 75% of total premiums accounts in Austria and the remaining accounts the rest.

About 25% of premiums accounts in life-regular in business lines while another 15% accounts in MTPL and the remaining accounts in motor own damage health life- single premium and other property and casualty.

Geographic Reach

VIG insurance companies have branch offices in Germany France Italy Kosovo Slovenia the Baltic countries of Estonia Latvia and Lithuania and the Northern European countries of Sweden Norway and Denmark. Its headquarters is located in Vienna.

Financial Performance

Premiums written reached ?10.4 billion in 2019 representing a year-on-year increase of 8%. The significant increase was primarily the result of good growth in other property and casualty and motor own damage insurance and first-time consolidation of the insurance companies Wiener TU (formerly Gothaer TU) in Poland and Seesam in the Baltic states. Adjusted for the first-time consolidation effects the Group recorded organic growth of 5%.

Cash held by the company at the end of 2019 increased to ?1.4 billion compared to the prior year with ?1.3 billion. Cash provided by operations was ?1.3 billion while cash used for investing and financing activities were ?886.0 million and ?272.3 million respectively. Main use for cash was payments for the acquisition of available for sale securities.

Strategy

The strategy of the VIG Insurance Group is aimed at achieving sustainable profitable growth. It relies on diversity as a success factor. The wealth of different languages cultures and entrepreneurial approaches ensures the greatest possible proximity to customers and promotes innovation and creativity.

The Group focuses on Austria and the CEE region with the aim of exploiting growth opportunities particularly in Central and Eastern Europe. The economic and insurance-related differences between the markets also ensure broad risk diversification.

Mergers and Acquisitions

In 2020 Vienna Insurance Group acquires interest in ViveLaCar start-up Innovative car subscription platform provides flexible mobility. The company holds an interest of around 20% in the German start-up ViveLaCar GmbH which is headquartered in Stuttgart. The new mobility start-up is aimed at target groups that want to be mobile as easily as possible for a specific period of time. Vehicles are subscribed directly online from an authorised dealer for a monthly fixed price. VIG's acquisition of an interest will help ViveLaCar's planned expansion into Austria and Switzerland in spring 2020.

In 2019 Vienna Insurance Group (VIG) acquires 100 percent of the shares of Gothaer Towarzystwo Ubezpieczen (Gothaer TU). Gothaer TU offers non-life insurance products mainly through brokers and agents. The company generated a solid premium volume of around EUR 170 million in 2018. Gothaer TU serves more than 700.000 customers and manages more than two million insurance policies. It currently has 530 employees. With the acquisition of Gothaer TU VIG strengthens the market position in non-life in Poland. Together with Gothaer TU the market share in non-life will increase to around 9 percent.

EXECUTIVES

Independent First Deputy Chairman of the Supervisory Board, Rudolf Ertl
Member of the Managing Board, Gabor Lehel, $626,673 total compensation
Member of the Managing Board, Harald Riener, $626,673 total compensation
Member of the Managing Board, Peter Thirring, $622,115 total compensation
Independent Member of the Supervisory Board, Martina Dobringer
Chairwoman of the Management Board, General Manager, Elisabeth Stadler, $901,269 total compensation
Member of the Supervisory Board, Peter Mihok
Member of the Managing Board, Peter Hoefinger, $622,115 total compensation
Independent Member of the Supervisory Board, Gabriele Semmelrock-Werzer
Independent Member of the Supervisory Board, Gertrude Tumpel-Gugerell
Member of the Managing Board, Gerhard Lahner, $626,673 total compensation
Independent Member of the Supervisory Board, Heinz Oehler
Independent Second Deputy Chairman of the Supervisory Board, Georg Riedl
Independent Member of the Supervisory Board, Gerhard Fabisch
Independent Chairman of the Supervisory Board, Guenter Geyer
Independent Member of the Supervisory Board, Katarina Slezakova
Member of the Management Board, Hartwig Loeger

Chief Financial Officer, Member of the Management Board, Liane Hirner, $622,115 total compensation
Auditors: KPMG Austria GmbH Wirtschaftsprufungs- und Steuerberatungsgesellschaft

LOCATIONS

HQ: Vienna Insurance Group AG
    Schottenring 30, Vienna 1010
Phone: (43) 50 390 22000
Web: www.vig.com

PRODUCTS/OPERATIONS

Selected Subsidiaries
Bulstrad (Bulgaria)
Compensa (Poland)
Donau Versicherung (Austria)
InterRisk Versicherungen (Germany)
IRAO (Georgia)
Jupiter (Ukraine)
Kontinuita (Slovakia)
Kooperativa Bratislava (Slovakia)
Kupala (Belarus)
Kvarner (Croatia)
Pojištovna (Czech Republic Slovakia)
Union Biztosí;tó (Hungary)
RaySigorta (Turkey)
S-Versicherung (Austria)
Seesam (Estonia Latvia Lithuania)
Sigma (Macedonia)

COMPETITORS

ADMIRAL GROUP PLC	Baloise Holding AG
AEGON N.V.	KBC Groep
ASSICURAZIONI GENERALI	NN Group N.V.
SPA	Sampo Oyj
AVIVA PLC	TELEFONICA SA
Ageas	Zurich Insurance Group
Allianz SE	AG

HISTORICAL FINANCIALS

Company Type: Public

Income Statement   FYE: December 31

	REVENUE ($ mil.)	NET INCOME ($ mil.)	NET PROFIT MARGIN	EMPLOYEES
12/20	12,571	284	2.3%	25,680
12/19	11,813	371	3.1%	25,736
12/18	11,506	307	2.7%	25,947
12/17	11,748	356	3.0%	25,059
12/16	9,966	303	3.0%	24,601
Annual Growth	6.0%	(1.7%)	—	1.1%

2020 Year-End Financials

Debt ratio: —
Return on equity: 4.5%
Cash ($ mil.): 2,141
Current ratio: —
Long-term debt ($ mil.): —
No. of shares (mil.): 128
Dividends
    Yield: 3.1%
    Payout: —
Market value ($ mil.): 694

	STOCK PRICE ($) FY Close	P/E High/Low		PER SHARE ($) Earnings	Dividends	Book Value
12/20	5.42	4	2	2.22	0.17	49.50
12/19	5.81	2	2	2.91	0.14	44.51
12/18	4.38	3	2	2.34	0.13	40.69
12/17	6.34	3	2	2.67	0.12	45.25
12/16	4.37	2	2	2.28	0.08	37.65
Annual Growth	5.5%	—	—	(0.7%)	20.7%	7.1%

Vinci SA

Vinci operates two semi-connected businesses: Contracting which builds roads buildings and infrastructure; and Concessions which operates and maintains toll roads railways airports and more. Vinci seeks synergistic projects that allow its Construction arm to hand over completed projects for operation by its Concessions arm. Vinci is active in nearly 120 countries but does more than half its total business in France. Its primary businesses are Vinci Construction Eurovia (roads) Vinci Energies Vinci Autoroutes and Vinci Airports. It also has a property development business Vinci Immobilier. Vinci was founded in 1899 and is run by CEO and Chairman Xavier Huillard. About 55% of its revenue comes from France.

Operations

Vinci divides its business into two segments: Contracting and Concessions.

The Contracting business generates some 80% of Vinci's total sales and consists of three multi-billion euro businesses: VINCI Autoroutes VINCI Airports VINCI Highways VINCI Railways and VINCI Stadium.

Vinci Construction is the leading French building and civil engineering group. Its three units build major projects such as large bridges and tunnels and provide geotechnical engineering nuclear digital services for construction and green energy. It also has a local network of small-scale constructors in France. Vinci Construction generates more than 30% of Vinci's total revenue.

Vinci Energies is a leading electrical engineering and construction company consisting of 1800 companies in more than 55 countries. It is active in infrastructure industry the service sector and ICT. Vinci Energies has a presence in North America via PrimeLine Utility Services. The unit generates around 30% of Vinci's total revenue. Vinci's road-building unit Eurovia generates more than 20% of Vinci's revenue.

The Concessions segment consists of the management and operations of roads airports and stadia primarily in France. It generates nearly 15% of total revenue.

Vinci Immobilier the group's real estate unit accounts for less than5% of sales.

Geographic Reach

Across its many subsidiaries Vinci does business in almost all corners of the globe. Its home market of France generates some 55% of total sales. Other important markets for the firm include Germany and the UK. Beyond Western Europe the group is active in Central and Eastern Europe the Asia/Pacific region Africa the Americas and the Middle East.

Headquartered in France Vinci Construction operates in more than 100 countries in five continents. Vinci Energies ranks among the top players in Germany Switzerland Belgium Netherlands Portugal Romania Scandinavia and Morocco. Vinci Airports is active in 45 airports in more than 10 countries including Portugal France Cambodia the Dominican Republic Chile Costa Rica Serbia the US Japan the UK Sweden and Brazil.

Financial Performance

Note: Growth rates may differ after conversion to US Dollars.

Vinci's revenue has been growing strongly over the last few years but saw a decline in 2020 brought about by the consequences of the Covid-19 crisis. Net income has experienced the same trend in the same five-year period.

In 2020 the company's sales declined by 10% to ?43.9 billion after recording decline in both concessions and contracting businesses in both France

and international markets. Concessions revenue fell over 30% to ?5.8 billion and Contracting revenue totaled ?36.9 billion down by 5% from 2019.

Net income fell 62% to ?1.2 billion in 2020 compared to ?3.3 billion in 2019.

Cash provided by operating activities was ?6.7 billion in 2020 while investing activities used ?2.4 billion. Financing activities used another ?42 million. The company ended fiscal 2020 with ?11.4 billion in cash and cash equivalents.

Strategy

VINCI is committed on developing solutions by 2030 that will contribute to improving the living environment and mobility while managing and reducing the direct impact of its businesses. This goal covers three areas: climate change the circular economy and the natural environment. VINCI is committed on taking concrete action to reduce its greenhouse gas emissions (Scopes 1 and 2) in line with the 2Â°C scenario established in the Paris Climate Agreement. As a consequence the Group aims to reduce its direct emissions by 40% by 2030 (against its historic scope as at 2018).

As part of its long-term strategy VINCI Concessions is focused on long cycles high amounts of invested capital. It plans to renew and internationalize the concession portfolio and extend its average maturity. It also focuses on growth primarily on transport infrastructure and consider opportunities in renewable energies.

On the other hand in terms of energy and construction the company puts priority on margins over business volume and practice disciplined risk management. It also strengthens the group's presence in high value-added segments such as energy. Additionally Vinci plans to diversify the company's geographical spread of expertise through digital transformation and energy transition.

Mergers and Acquisitions

In 2020 VINCI Energies acquired some 20 companies representing full-year revenue of around ?400 million. The main acquisitions were: Transelec Common Inc. in Canada a Quebec-based provider of energy and telecoms network infrastructure services; Danske Sprinkler a Danish specialist in fire protection; EWE Offshore Services & Solutions a German company specializing in the development of projects for offshore wind farms as well as solutions for their operations and maintenance; Planus Informatica e Tecnologia a Brazilian provider of IT solutions; Novabase GTE a Portuguese specialist in data processing and business applications; and Sanitherm specializing in heating ventilation and air conditioning (HVAC) installation works in Western France.

VINCI Construction Terrassement acquired the Climent Travaux Publics (CTP) group based in Eastern France.

Company Background

HISTORY

VINCI's origins lie with French conglomerate Vivendi (now Vivendi Universal) which was founded in 1853 as Compagnie G n rale des Eaux. Its mission was to irrigate French farmland and supply water to towns. The company won contracts to serve Lyons (1853) Nantes (1854) Paris (1860) and Venice (1880). G n rale des Eaux moved into construction in 1972 building an office tower (and later hotels and houses) in Paris. The company also entered communications in the 1980s.

In 1988 G n rale des Eaux acquired control of construction and civil engineering giant Soci t G n rale d'Entreprises. SGE subsidiaries included Campenon Bernard SGE (part of G n rale des Eaux since 1981) Sogea Freyssinet Cochery Bourdin Chauss Saunier Duval Tunzini Lefort Francheteau and Wanner. SGE traces its construction roots to 1910. It became a subsidiary of Générale d'Electricité in 1966. Glassmaker Saint-Gobain acquired control of SGE in 1984. Under Générale des Eaux SGE enhanced its European profile through acquisitions including British builder Norwest Holst (1989) German road builder VBU (1991) and German pipe and duct maker MLTU (1992).

Générale des Eaux acquired publisher Havas in 1998 and took the name Vivendi — representing vivacity and mobility. Its purchase of USFilter in 1999 made Vivendi the world's largest water company. Vivendi's SGE unit (renamed VINCI) agreed to acquire the construction arm of rival conglomerate Suez's GTM unit in 2000.

Groupe GTM traces its roots to Société Lyonnaise des Eaux et de L'Eclairage a leading French water utility. Formed in 1880 Lyonnaise des Eaux built up its French and international operations to include water distribution as well as gas and electricity production and distribution. A century later the company had diversified into such businesses as heating (Cofreth) waste management (Sita) and communications acquiring a stake in Lyonnaise Communications (now Lyonnaise Câble) in 1986.

In 1990 Lyonnaise des Eaux acquired construction firm Dumez whose subsidiary GTM-Entrepose was France's largest car park manager. Four years later Dumez-GTM was formed to consolidate the construction and civil engineering businesses of Dumez and GTM-Entrepose. In 1997 Lyonnaise des Eaux and Compagnie de Suez merged to create a leading provider of private infrastructure services Suez Lyonnaise des Eaux (which shortened its name to SUEZ in 2001). Compagnie Universal du Canal Maritime de Suez the builder of the Suez Canal was founded in 1858 and became Financière de Suez in 1958. In 1967 Financière de Suez acquired control of Lyonnaise des Eaux.

SGE changed its name to VINCI in 2000. That year as part of their strategy to rationalize operations and focus on core businesses Vivendi and SUEZ agreed to a friendly takeover of GTM by VINCI. SUEZ emerged as the combined company's largest shareholder but by the following year both SUEZ and Vivendi Universal had exited most of VINCI's capital leaving no core stockholder.

To better control its car park management operations the company in 2001 created VINCI Park to operate as an umbrella of its VINCI Concessions unit. It expanded its concessions holdings even more in 2002 by hooking up with construction group Eiffage to grab a 17% stake in Europe's second-largest toll road operator ASF which was floated that year by the French government.

In 2003 the group won the contract to manage the restoration of the historic Hall of Mirrors. It also won the concession contract to operate along with joint venture partner Keolis the International Airport of Grenoble.

VINCI completed its acquisition of ASF in 2005. The deal was part of a government program to privatize motorway companies.

The company has had volatile internal struggles. There was unrest in the board room during 2006 as chairman Antoine Zacharias reportedly wanted to oust CEO Xavier Vuillard in favor of Nexity CEO Alain Dinin. Zacharias was the one who ended up resigning and at the end of 2006 Dinin resigned from VINCI's board.

In 2007 VINCI's top French construction businesses Sogea Construction and GTM Construction merged to create VINCI Construction France its domestic construction giant.

The company strengthened its position in the UK in 2008 when it bought British construction and facilities management firm Taylor Woodrow from Taylor Wimpey. The deal consolidated VINCI's position in UK facilities management and public-private partnership projects such as rail airports and energy infrastructure. In 2009 VINCI Construction acquired the troubled UK builder Haymills Group as that company teetered on the brink of collapse.

In 2008 Eurovia branched out from the road to the rails when it acquired rail infrastructure firm Vossloh Infrastructure Services (now ETF-Eurovia Travaux Ferroviaires) from Vossloh. The division specializes in rail track maintenance and installation.

EXECUTIVES

Chairman of the Board and Chief Executive Officer, Chairman of the Executive Committee and Chairman of the Management and Coordination Committee, Xavier Huillard, $1,367,287 total compensation

Chief Financial Officer, Executive Vice President, Member of the Executive Committee, Christian Labeyrie

Executive Vice President, Chairman of VINCI Autoroutes, Member of the Executive Committee, Pierre Coppey, $276,149 total compensation

Vice Chairman of the Board, Yves-Thibault de Silguy

General Counsel, VINCI, Secretary to the Board of Directors, Member of the Executive Committee, Patrick Richard

Executive Vice President, Member of the Executive Committee, Richard Francioli

Vice-President, Corporate Communications, VINCI, Member of the Executive Committee, Pierre Duprat

Independent Director, Michael Pragnell

Chairman of Vinci Construction, Chairman of Eurovia, Member of the Executive Committee, Pierre Anjolras

Vice President of Human Resources, Member of the Executive Committee, Jocelyne Vassoille

Chairman and Chief Executive Officer, VINCI Energies, Member of the Executive Committee, Arnaud Grison

Independent Director - Representative of Qatar Holding LLC, Abdullah Al Attiyah

Director, Employee Representative, Miloud Hakimi

Director, Employee Representative, Uwe Chlebos

Independent Director, Graziella Gavezotti

Lead Independent Director, Yannick Assouad

Independent Director, Marie-Christine Lombard

Director, Employee Shareholders Representative, Dominique Muller Joly-Pottuz

Independent Director, Caroline Gregoire Sainte Marie

Chief Executive Officer, VINCI Concessions, Member of the Executive Committee, Nicolas Notebaert

Vice-President, Business Development, VINCI, Member of the Executive Committee, Christophe Pelissie du Rausas

Independent Director, Rene Medori

Independent Director, Ana Pessoa

Director, Pascale Sourisse

Director, Robert Castaigne

Auditors: Deloitte & Associés

LOCATIONS

HQ: Vinci SA
1, cours Ferdinand-de-Lesseps, Rueil-Malmaison, Cedex 92851
Phone: (33) 1 47 16 35 00   **Fax:** (33) 1 47 51 91 02
Web: www.vinci.com

2018 Sales

	% of total
France	57
Germany	7
United Kingdom	5
Central and Eastern Europe	4
Benelux	3
Other European countries	7
North Americas	4
Central and South America	3
Africa	3
Russia Asia Pacific and Middle East	3
Oceania	3
Total	**100**

PRODUCTS/OPERATIONS

2018 Sales

	% of total
Contracting	
VINCI Construction	32
VINCI Energies	28
Eurovia	20
Concessions	
VINCI Autoroutes	12
VINCI Airports	4
Other Concessions	1
VINCI Immobilier	3
Total	**100**

Selected Subsidiaries

VINCI Construction
    CFE (12.11%; Benelux)
    VINCI Construction France
    VINCI PLC (UK)
    VINCI Construction Filiales Internationales (Germany Central Europe overseas France Africa)
    VINCI Construction Grands Projets
    Freyssinet (specialized civil engineering)
VINCI Concessions
VINCI Park
Eurovia
VINCI Energies
    Actemium (industry solutions)
    Axians (voice-data-image communication)
    Cité;os (urban lighting)
    Graniou (telecommunications infrastructure)
    Omexom (high-voltage power transmission)
    Opteor (maintenance)

COMPETITORS

ACS ACTIVIDADES DE CONSTRUCCION Y SERVICIOS SA
ARCADIS N.V.
BOUYGUES
Bilfinger SE
COLAS SA
ENGIE
FOMENTO DE CONSTRUCCIONES Y CONTRATAS SA
HOCHTIEF AG
STRABAG SE
WS ATKINS LIMITED

HISTORICAL FINANCIALS

Company Type: Public

Income Statement				FYE: December 31
	REVENUE ($ mil.)	NET INCOME ($ mil.)	NET PROFIT MARGIN	EMPLOYEES
12/20	53,966	1,524	2.8%	217,731
12/19	55,197	3,660	6.6%	222,397
12/18	50,894	3,416	6.7%	211,233
12/17	49,416	3,292	6.7%	194,428
12/16	40,912	2,644	6.5%	183,487
Annual Growth	**7.2%**	**(12.9%)**	**—**	**4.4%**

2020 Year-End Financials

Debt ratio: 41.1%
Return on equity: 6.0%
Cash ($ mil.): 14,439
Current ratio: 0.96
Long-term debt ($ mil.): 32,749

No. of shares (mil.): 562
Dividends
    Yield: 2.3%
    Payout: 14.4%
Market value ($ mil.): 14,007

STOCK PRICE ($)		P/E		PER SHARE ($)		
	FY Close	High/Low		Earnings	Dividends	Book Value
12/20	24.92	15	8	2.70	0.57	45.56
12/19	27.63	5	3	6.53	0.75	41.37
12/18	20.51	5	4	6.09	0.75	39.60
12/17	25.50	5	4	5.89	0.65	38.48
12/16	16.97	4	3	4.73	0.50	31.35
Annual Growth	10.1%	—		—(13.1%)	3.6%	9.8%

Vipshop Holdings Ltd

Auditors: Deloitte Touche Tohmatsu

LOCATIONS

HQ: Vipshop Holdings Ltd
128 Dingxin Road, Haizhu District, Guangzhou
510220
Phone: (86) 20 2233 0025   **Fax:** (86) 20 2233 0111
Web: www.vip.com

HISTORICAL FINANCIALS

Company Type: Public

Income Statement   FYE: December 31

	REVENUE ($ mil.)	NET INCOME ($ mil.)	NET PROFIT MARGIN	EMPLOYEES
12/20	15,574	903	5.8%	7,567
12/19	13,364	577	4.3%	20,442
12/18	12,288	309	2.5%	57,638
12/17	11,204	299	2.7%	58,702
12/16	8,149	293	3.6%	45,302
Annual Growth	17.6%	32.5%	—	(36.1%)

2020 Year-End Financials

Debt ratio: 0.2%
Return on equity: 23.4%
Cash ($ mil.): 1,834
Current ratio: 1.17
Long-term debt ($ mil.): —

No. of shares (mil.): 135
Dividends
    Yield: —
    Payout: —
Market value ($ mil.): 3,815

STOCK PRICE ($)		P/E		PER SHARE ($)		
	FY Close	High/Low		Earnings	Dividends	Book Value
12/20	28.11	1	0	6.54	0.00	32.10
12/19	14.17	0	0	4.25	0.00	23.39
12/18	5.46	1	0	2.27	0.00	18.88
12/17	11.72	1	0	2.45	0.00	16.74
12/16	11.01	1	1	2.43	0.00	7.08
Annual Growth	26.4%	—		—28.1%	—	45.9%

Vivendi SE

Vivendi is one of the world's biggest media companies offering music movies and TV games and more. Its Universal Music Group (UMG) is the world's biggest recorded music company featuring artists such Ariana Grande Post Malone Taylor Swift and the Rolling Stones. Canal+ Group is a pay-TV provider in France Africa Europe and Asia. It also is a major producer and distributor of motion pictures. The Vivendi property Havas is a global advertising and public relations agency. The Gameloft unit develops and produces video games

with an emphasis on mobile games such as Asphalt Minion Rush and Dragon Mania. France Vivendi's home country accounts for about 30% of revenue.

Operations

Universal Music Publishing Group (UMPG) is one of the world's largest music publishing companies acquiring the rights to musical compositions (as opposed to recordings) and licensing them for use in a variety of formats including films television advertisements video games concerts and other public performances. It also licenses compositions for use in sheet music and song portfolios. The division accounts for around 45% of revenue.

Canal+ Group (about a third) is a major player in television and cinema in France and abroad. It is a leader in the production bundling and distribution of first run movie and themed pay-TV channels in France Africa Europe and Asia (Vietnam and Myanmar). Through its Studiocanal subsidiary Canal+ Group is also the European leader in the production and distribution of feature films and TV series.

The Havas Group's (less than 15%) agencies belong to numerous professional associations and bodies providing a forum for consultations with industry stakeholders including peers customers suppliers regulators and consumers.

Editis is France's second-largest publishing group and a major player in the European book market. A leading operator among publishers authors bookstores and all sale outlets it offers stellar support and service on both paper and digital formats.

Gameloft is one of the French video game publisher flagships Gameloft enjoys world-renowned expertise with around 190 smartphone games developed in its over 15 studios.

Geographic Reach

Paris-based Vivendi has operations located in France (generates around 30% of total revenue) Americas (more than 30%) Rest of Europe (around 25% of revenue) Asia and Oceania (around 10% of revenue) and Africa (around 5%).

Sales and Marketing

With 8.7 million subscribers in mainland France Canal+ Group boasts the largest portfolio of pay-TV customers.

Interforum has been a key link in the publishing chain for more than forty years connecting publishers to sales outlets Broad and qualitative marketing is a means for Interforum to offer its partner publishers access to all sales outlets from bookstores to large cultural retailers hypermarkets supermarkets online sales specialized bookstores and export companies. Interforum has a total of over 15000 customers. Games are delivered through smartphone and tablet app stores such as the Apple App Store Google Play the Windows Store and Amazon Appstore.

Advertising costs amounted to ?393 million in 2020 (compared to ?416 million in 2019).

Financial Performance

In 2020 revenues were ?16.1 billion compared to ?15.9 billion in 2019. This increase of ?192 million (+1%) mainly resulted from the growth of Universal Music Group (UMG) (+?273 million) Canal+ Group (+?230 million) of which +?285 million related to M7 and Editis (+?38 million).

Earnings for fiscal 2020 decreased to ?1.4 billion compared from the prior year with ?1.6 billion.

Cash held by the group at the end of 2020 decreased to ?976 million. Cash provided by operations was ?1.2 billion while cash used for investing and financing activities were ?1.6 billion and ?675 million respectively. Main cash uses were investments and purchases of Vivendi SE's treasury shares.

Strategy

The Creation for the Future program is built around three pillars that provide perspective on the environmental societal and social impacts of the group's activities at all levels and set the first milestone for 2025.

This approach advocated by the group's most senior management is a powerful driver of performance and value creation that is the focal point of Vivendi's strategy. The approach relies on an organization to oversee the roadmap that applies each pillar to the various Vivendi business lines. It is shared with all employees who serve as its main ambassadors.

The strategic plan is implemented in accordance with a foundation of ethical values and a culture of integrity that underpin the way in which the group does business. They are reflected in the group's corporate compliance policy which contributes to maintaining relationships of trust with the group's numerous partners especially its clients.

Mergers and Acquisitions

In 2021 Vivendi completed its acquisition of Prisma Media France's number one magazine publishing group in print and digital with some 20 leading brands. The Prisma Media acquisition is part of Vivendi's development strategy in media to gain a foothold in an industry that strongly complements its existing businesses.

HISTORY

Authorized by an imperial decree Compagnie Generale des Eaux was founded in 1853 by investors such as the Rothschild family and Napoleon III's half-brother to irrigate French farmland and supply water to towns. It won contracts to serve Lyons (1853) Nantes (1854) Paris (1860) and Venice (1880).

A supplier of water and other basic services for most of its history the company that became Vivendi didn't move strongly into other areas until the 1980s when it made investments and acquisitions into telecommunications and then media and entertainment in the 1990s.

EXECUTIVES

Chief Operating Officer and Chairman and Chief Executive Officer of Gameloft, Member of the Management Board, Stephane Roussel, $1,139,406 total compensation
Group Chief Compliance Officer, Group General Counsel, Member of the Management Board, Frederic Crepin, $911,524 total compensation
Chairman of Vivendi Village and Senior Executive Vice President, Communications of Vivendi, Member of the Management Board, Simon Gillham, $854,554 total compensation
Independent Member of the Supervisory Board, Laurent Dassault
President of the Talent Unlimited international, Amandine Maudet
Member of the Supervisory Board, Employee Representative, Athina Vasilogiannaki
Chief Financial Officer, Member of the Management Board, Herve Philippe, $1,071,041 total compensation
Member of the Supervisory Board, Dominique Delport
Vice Chairman, Supervisory Board, Philippe Bénacin
Chairman of the Management Board, Chief Executive Officer, Arnaud Nicolas De Puyfontaine, $1,595,168 total compensation
Chairman of the Supervisory Board, Yannick Bollore
Member of the Supervisory Board, Cyrille Bollore

Senior Vice President in Charge for Inter-Group coordination, Member of the Management Board, Gilles Alix, $797,583 total compensation

Independent Member of the Supervisory Board, Aliza Jabes

Senior Vice President responsible for investor relations and inter - group financial communication, Member of the Management Board, Cedric De Bailliencourt, $455,762 total compensation

Member of the Supervisory Board Representing Employee Shareholders, Sandrine Le Bihan

Independent Member of the Supervisory Board, Michele Reiser

Independent Member of the Supervisory Board, Katie Jacobs Stanton

Independent Member of the Supervisory Board, Cathia Lawson-Hall

Member of the Supervisory Board, Employee Representative, Paulo Cardoso

Member of the Supervisory Board, Veronique Driot-Argentin

Auditors: Deloitte & Associes

LOCATIONS

HQ: Vivendi SE
42, avenue de Friedland, Paris, Cedex 08 75380
Phone: (33) 1 71 71 10 00   **Fax:** (33) 1 71 71 10 01
Web: www.vivendi.com

PRODUCTS/OPERATIONS

2018 Sales

	% of total
Universal Music Group	43
Canal+ Group	37
Havas	17
Gameloft	2
Vivendi Village	1
New Initiatives	-
Elimination	-
Intellectual Property Licensing	47
Subscription Services	32
Advertising Merchandising and Other	21
Total	**100**

COMPETITORS

AVESCO SERVICES LIMITED
Bertelsmann SE & Co. KGaA
Entertainment One Ltd
GAMES WORKSHOP GROUP PLC
IAC/INTERACTIVECORP
LAGARDERE SA
NEXT FIFTEEN COMMUNICATIONS GROUP PLC
ProSiebenSat.1 Media SE
TELEFONICA SA
TELEVISION FRANCAISE 1
UBISOFT ENTERTAINMENT

HISTORICAL FINANCIALS

Company Type: Public

Income Statement				FYE: December 31
	REVENUE ($ mil.)	NET INCOME ($ mil.)	NET PROFIT MARGIN	EMPLOYEES
12/20	19,725	1,767	9.0%	42,526
12/19	17,854	1,777	10.0%	44,641
12/18	15,962	145	0.9%	41,600
12/17	15,092	1,472	9.8%	33,200
12/16	11,423	1,326	11.6%	22,603
Annual Growth	14.6%	7.4%	—	17.1%

2020 Year-End Financials

Debt ratio: 20.5%	No. of shares (mil.): 1,092
Return on equity: 9.2%	Dividends
Cash ($ mil.): 1,197	Yield: 2.0%
Current ratio: 0.63	Payout: 47.3%
Long-term debt ($ mil.): 5,096	Market value ($ mil.): 35,080

	STOCK PRICE ($) FY Close	P/E High/Low	PER SHARE ($) Earnings	Dividends	Book Value
12/20	32.10	26 17	1.55	0.65	17.70
12/19	28.95	23 18	1.44	0.56	14.73
12/18	24.15	284 233	0.11	0.55	15.64
12/17	26.82	29 20	1.14	0.48	16.84
12/16	18.95	— —	1.00	0.00	16.25
Annual Growth	14.1%	— —	11.4%	—	2.2%

Vodafone Group Plc

Vodafone is one of the world's top wireless phone carriers with its more than half a billion subscribers (across some 25 countries) behind only China Mobile. A network of partnerships with other mobile networks extends its reach into another 45 countries. As well as telephony it has 27 million fixed broadband customers and more than 20 million TV customers. The company generates the majority of its business in Europe where it is a leader in the wireless markets in the UK and Germany. Vodafone increasingly serves callers in Africa the Middle East and Asia through subsidiaries and joint ventures. It holds a 45% stake in Vodafone Idea Limited the company formed by the merger of Vodafone India and local carrier Idea.

Operations

Vodafone's Consumer segment generates two-thirds of the company's revenue and provides the standard range of mobile services and fixed line services such as broadband TV and voice as well as other value-added services. Vodafone's Enterprise segment (almost 30% of sales) offers telephony services for corporations as well as cloud and hosting and Internet of Things services. Vodafone generates almost 10% of sales from renting capacity to mobile virtual operators.

Geographic Reach

Vodafone's geographic footprint is well-diversified and it holds #1 or #2 market positions in most of the markets in which it directly operates. The UK-based company operates in 22 countries and two geographic regions ? Europe and Rest of the world.

Europe is Vodafone's biggest market representing more than 75% of sales. Germany is its most lucrative country followed by Italy then its home territory of the UK Spain and others. It has almost 65 million mobile customers 25 million broadband customers 14 million TV customers and more than 7 million "converged" customers — those high-value customers that subscribe to all three product types.

Vodacom is Vodafone's African business which counts more than 100 million customers in South Africa Tanzania the DRC Mozambique Lesotho and Kenya. It brings in some 15% of sale.

Vodafone is also active in the Asia/Pacific region including India and the Middle East; the region also accounts for almost 10% of sales.

Sales and Marketing

Vodafone uses data analytics to support personalization and increase revenue per customer. Digital is increasingly becoming Vodafone's primary customer acquisition channel as well as its main customer support method. Chat bots and digital agents enhanced with AI will become Vodafone's primary customer interface.

Financial Performance

Note: Growth rates may differ after conversion to US Dollars.

Vodafone's revenue has fallen for consecutive financial years but grew in 2019.

In fiscal 2019 the company's sales rose 3% to 45 billion primarily due to the 6% growth in European Service Revenue. In 2019 the company significantly reduced their losses from 8 billion on 2018 tp 920 million.

Vodafone had 13.3 billion of cash and cash equivalents in its coffers. It had an inflow of 17.4 billion from operations. Vodafone had outflows of 8 billion and 9.4 billion from investing and financing activities respectively.

Strategy

Vodafone's strategy is focused on two scaled and differentiated regional platforms?Europe and Africa

Its priorities consists of: Deepening customer engagement; Accelerating digital transformation; Improving asset utilization; and Optimizing the portfolio.

Vodafone completed its sale of its New Zealand business for about $2.2 billion to New Zealand-based infrastructure investor Infratil and Canadian alternative asset management firm Brookfield Asset Management in an effort to reduce its debt.

Mergers and Acquisitions

Vodafone announces in mid-2020 that Vodafone Hutchison Australia Pty Limited (VHA) and TPG Telecom Limited (TPG) have completed their merger to establish a fully integrated telecommunications operator in Australia. The merged entity has been admitted to the Australian Securities Exchange (ASX) and will trade under the name TPG Telecom Limited. The new TPG Telecom will trade using a range of brands including Vodafone and TPG.

Vodafone Telecom Italia Group ("TIM") and INWIT completed the merger of Vodafone Italy's towers into INWIT in early 2020. INWIT is now Italy's largest tower operator and will focus on maximizing tower utilization which also supporting the deployment of TIM and Vodafone Italy's respective 5G networks. Vodafone and TIM intend to retain joint control but over time will consider jointly reducing their respective ownership levels to a minimum of 25.0%. On 31 March Vodafone will receive 360200000 ordinary INWIT shares and cash proceeds of ?2140 million which will be used to reduce net debt.

In mid-2019 Vodafone acquired German and Eastern European assets including Unitymedia from Liberty Global in a $18.4 billion deal. Vodafone Group CEO Nick Read said: "With the acquisition of Liberty's assets in Germany and CEE we have completed our transformation into Europe's leading converged operator. Not only have we reshaped our business becoming the owner of the largest gigabit-capable next generation network infrastructure in the region we are now able to play our part in realizing the digital society for millions of customers."

Company Background

Vodafone was formed in 1983 as a joint venture between Racal Electronics (a UK electronics firm) and Millicom (a US telecom company) and was granted one of two mobile phone licenses in the UK (the other was held by Cellnet). Its service launched in 1985. In 1988 Racal offered 20% of Vodafone to the public; three years later the rest of the firm was spun off to become Vodafone Group. It made a landmark acquisition of Mannesmann in Germany making it one of the country's largest carriers and began its partner networks business model in 2011. Vodafone sold its 45% stake in Verizon Wireless for $130 billion in 2013 one of the biggest ever corporate deals.

HISTORY

Vodafone was formed in 1983 as a joint venture between Racal Electronics (a UK electronics firm) and Millicom (a US telecom company) and was granted one of two mobile phone licenses in the UK. It launched service in 1985 as a Racal subsidiary. Vodafone and Cellnet the other licensee were swamped with demand. In 1988 Racal offered 20% of Vodafone to the public; three years later the rest of the firm was spun off to become Vodafone Group.

Vodafone moved beyond the UK in the 1990s. By 1993 it had interests in mobile phone networks in Australia Greece Hong Kong Malta and Scandinavia.

EXECUTIVES

Chief Executive Officer, Europe Cluster, Serpil Timuray
Chief Financial Officer and Director, Margherita Della Valle, $913,894 total compensation
Group General Counsel and Company Secretary, Rosemary Martin
CTO, Johan Wibergh
Chief Executive Officer, Vodafone Germany, Hannes Ametsreiter
Chief Executive Officer, Vodafone Italy, Aldo Bisio
CEO, Vodafone UK, Ahmed Essam
Chief Executive Officer, Vodacom Group, Shameel Joosub
Chief Commercial Officer, Alex Froment-Curtil
Chief Executive Officer and Director, Nick Read, $1,370,842 total compensation
Chief External and Corporate Affairs Officer, Joakim Reiter
Chief Human Resource Officer, Leanne Wood
Chief Executive Officer, Vodafone Business, Vinod Kumar
CEO, Vodafone Spain, Colman Deegan
Auditors: Ernst & Young LLP

LOCATIONS

HQ: Vodafone Group Plc
Vodafone House, The Connection, Newbury, Berkshire RG14 2FN
Phone: (44) 1635 33251
Web: www.vodafone.com

2018 Sales

	% of total
Europe	
Germany	23
UK	15
Italy	13
Spain	11
Other Europe	11
Africa Middle East and Asia Pacific (AMAP)	
Vodacom	12
Other AMAP	12
Common Functions	3
Total	**100**

PRODUCTS/OPERATIONS

2018 Sales

	% of total
Service revenue	88
Other revenue	12
Total	**100**

Countries of Operation (controlled interests)

Africa/the Middle East/Asia-Pacific
Australia
Democratic Republic of Congo
Egypt
Ghana
India
Lesotho
Mozambique
New Zealand
Qatar
South Africa
Tanzania
Europe
Albania
Czech Republic
Germany
Greece
Hungary
Ireland
Italy
Malta
Portugal
Romania
Spain
The Netherlands
Turkey
UK

COMPETITORS

Deutsche Telekom AG	VODAFONE ESPA 'A SAU
MTS PAO	VODAFONE IDEA LIMITED
Proximus	WIND TELECOMUNICAZIONI
Swisscom AG	SPA
TELECOM ITALIA SPA	

HISTORICAL FINANCIALS

Company Type: Public

Income Statement   FYE: March 31

	REVENUE ($ mil.)	NET INCOME ($ mil.)	NET PROFIT MARGIN	EMPLOYEES
03/21	51,390	131	0.3%	96,506
03/20	49,269	(1,007)	—	95,219
03/19	49,038	(9,006)	—	98,996
03/18	57,410	3,006	5.2%	106,135
03/17	50,888	(6,727)	—	111,556
Annual Growth	**0.2%**	**—**		**(3.6%)**

2021 Year-End Financials

Debt ratio: 40.6%	No. of shares (mil.): —
Return on equity: 0.1%	Dividends
Cash ($ mil.): 6,828	Yield: 5.7%
Current ratio: 0.94	Payout: 23,466.2%
Long-term debt ($ mil.): 57,905	Market value ($ mil.): —

	STOCK PRICE ($) FY Close	P/E High/Low		PER SHARE ($) Earnings	Dividends	Book Value
03/21	18.43	5045	3477	0.00	1.05	2.32
03/20	13.77	—	—	(0.03)	0.94	2.51
03/19	18.18	—	—	(0.33)	1.64	2.57
03/18	27.82	3843	12	0.11	1.88	3.13
03/17	26.43	—	—	(0.24)	1.50	2.90
Annual Growth	**(8.6%)**	—	—		**(8.5%)**	**(5.4%)**

voestalpine AG

The voestalpine is the world's leading steel and technology company and one of the leading partners to the automotive and consumer goods industries in Europe and to the oil and gas industry around the world. The company produces steel in various forms for the automotive railway aerospace and energy industries sold in 50 countries worldwide. Its metal engineering division serves the railway industry with the manufacture of rails wires and tubes used in rail systems. voestalpine also engineers and manufactures automotive components. The company's metal forming division makes sections custom-tailored special tubes and precision steel tubes. Begin as construction of an iron and steel factory in 1938 voestalpine gener-

ates about 55% of the total revenue from the European Union market.

Operations

voestalpine has five reportable segments: Steel Division (about 35% of total revenue); Metal Engineering Division (about 25%); Metal Forming Division (nearly 20%); High Performance Metals Division (approximately 20%); and Other.

The Steel Division produces advanced hot and cold rolled steel as well as electrogalvanized hot-dip galvanized and organically coated steel strip. Its other activities include electrical steel heavy plate a foundry and downstream sectors ? the Steel & Service Center and Logistics Service.

The Metal Engineering Division produces the world's widest range of premium rails and turnout systems high-quality wire rod and drawn wire ready-to-install seamless tubes medium and high-alloy welding consumables and welding machines. The division also possesses its own expertise in steel which ensures ultra-high-quality supplies of pre-materials throughout the division.

The Metal Forming Division is a leading global manufacturer of custom-tailored special tubes and sections and precision strip steel tubes pre-finished system components made from pressed punched and roll-profiled parts as well as storage system solutions which are of the highest quality.

The High Performance Metals Division is the global market leader for tool steel and a leading provider of high-speed steel valve steels and other products made from special steels as well as powder materials nickel-based alloys and titanium. It operates a global network of service centers with a focus on tool manufacturing offering component processing heat treatment and coating services besides warehousing and preprocessing of special steels. The division also offers a broad range of services including logistics distribution and processing especially for the oil and natural gas industry.

The company's two financing entities one raw materials purchasing companies as well as one personal services companies and the group-IT companies are included in the "Other" business segment. These companies are combined because their focus is on providing coordination services and support to the subsidiaries.

Geographic Reach

voestalpine which operates globally has around 500 Group companies and locations in more than 50 countries on all five continents. About 55% of the total revenue comes from the European Union (without Austria) followed by USMCA which accounts for about 15% another nearly 10% is from Asia Austria represents beyond 5% and South America brings in less than 5%. The rest of world accounts for the remainder.

The company is headquartered in Linz Austria.

Sales and Marketing

voestalpine serves a diverse array of industries including automotive consumer goods aerospace oil and gas railway systems and tool steel sectors among others.

More than 30% of the revenue comes from automotive market followed by railway systems with about 15% more than 10% is from energy approximately 10% from building/construction about 10% from mechanical engineering white goods/consumer goods represents some 5% and aerospace market contribute less than 5%. Other markets generate the remainder.

Financial Performance

The year-over-year decrease in reporting period revenue by 11% to ?11.3 billion compared to previous year's ?12.7 billion. The negative ramifications of the COVID-19 pandemic impacted the business year 2020/21 the most early on. The meltdown in revenue during the first quarter resulted directly from the measures that were put in place worldwide to contain the pandemic.

In 2021 the company had a net profit of ?216.5 million a ?248.2 million increase from the previous year.

The company's cash at the end of 2021 was ?1.2 billion. Operating activities generated ?1.6 billion while investing activities used ?665.8 million primarily for additions to other intangible assets property plant and equipment. Financing activities used another ?595.6 million primarily for repayment of non-current financial liabilities.

Strategy

At its core voestalpine's corporate strategy relies on leadership in innovation technology and quality. Hence research and development (R&D) as an integral part of the company's business model is rooted in that precept. The continuous development of both new products and new production processes is vital to any technology-driven company so that it can differentiate itself from the competition and remain successful in the market. Innovations are the key to voestalpine's future success.

Research expenditures have climbed continually in recent years. The expenditures were a bit lower in the business year 2020/21 due to the outbreak of the COVID-19 pandemic and measures such as short time work associated with it. But a budget of ?185 million for the business year 2021/22 reconnects the level of R&D activity to the multiyear rising trend and thus reflects the importance of R&D within the company.

Mergers and Acquisitions

In early 2020 voestalpine B¶hler Welding a leading global company in the field of welding technology and part of the technology group voestalpine has acquired a majority stake in the traditional Italian manufacturer for welding machines Selco s.r.l.. With this voestalpine B¶hler Welding is further expanding its market position after the successful launch of the welding machine series in its "B¶hler Welding" brand in mid-2019.

Company Background

Construction of an iron and steel factory begins in Linz Austria in 1938 as part of the German Nazi regime's war industry; its operations are launched incrementally starting in 1941.

EXECUTIVES

Chairman of the Management Board, Chief Executive Officer, Herbert Eibensteiner, $1,293,019 total compensation
Independent Deputy Chairman of the Supervisory Board, Heinrich Schaller
Independent Member of the Supervisory Board, Franz Gasselsberger, $1,007,960 total compensation
Independent Member of the Supervisory Board, Employee Representative, Gerhard Scheidreiter
Independent Member of the Supervisory Board, Employee Representative, Hans-Karl Schaller
Independent Member of the Supervisory Board, Employee Representative, Sandra Fritz
Independent Member of the Supervisory Board, Elisabeth Stadler
Member of the Management Board, Head of the Steel Division, Hubert Zajicek, $1,060,043 total compensation
Independent Member of the Supervisory Board, Maria Kubitschek
Independent Chairman of the Supervisory Board, Joachim Lemppenau
Member of the Supervisory Board, Wolfgang Eder, $500,088 total compensation
Independent Member of the Supervisory Board, Ingrid Joerg
Independent Member of the Supervisory Board, Florian Khol

Independent Member of the Supervisory Board, Employee Representative, Josef Gritz
Chief Financial Officer, Member of the Management Board, Robert Ottel, $1,060,043 total compensation
Member of the Management Board, Head of the High Performance Metals Division, Franz Rotter, $1,060,043 total compensation
Member of the Management Board, Head of the Metal Forming Division, Peter Schwab, $1,060,043 total compensation
Member of the Management Board, Head of the Metal Engineering Division, Franz Kainersdorfer, $1,106,638 total compensation
Auditors: Deloitte Audit Wirtschaftspruefungs GmbH

LOCATIONS

HQ: voestalpine AG
  Voestalpine Strasse 1, Linz 4020
Phone: (43) 70 50304 15 2090 **Fax:** (43) 70 50304 55 8981
Web: www.voestalpine.com

PRODUCTS/OPERATIONS

2016 Sales

	% of total
Steel	30
Metal Engineering Division	23
Special Steel Division	21
Metal Forming Division	18
Others	8
Total	**100**

COMPETITORS

ARKEMA
Aperam
BIOME TECHNOLOGIES PLC
BODYCOTE PLC
FERROGLOBE PLC
Orbia Advance Corporation S.A.B. de C.V.
Outokumpu Oyj
RENOLD PUBLIC LIMITED COMPANY
SEVERSTAL PAO
SSAB AB
thyssenkrupp AG

HISTORICAL FINANCIALS
Company Type: Public

Income Statement				FYE: March 31
	REVENUE ($ mil.)	NET INCOME ($ mil.)	NET PROFIT MARGIN	EMPLOYEES
03/21	13,216	49	0.4%	48,654
03/20	13,931	(243)	—	49,005
03/19	15,229	458	3.0%	50,102
03/18	15,899	955	6.0%	48,904
03/17	12,067	530	4.4%	47,186
Annual Growth	**2.3%**	**(44.8%)**	**—**	**0.8%**

2021 Year-End Financials

Debt ratio: 32.0%	No. of shares (mil.): 178
Return on equity: 0.7%	Dividends
Cash ($ mil.): 1,360	Yield: 0.0%
Current ratio: 1.31	Payout: 10.6%
Long-term debt ($ mil.): 3,338	Market value ($ mil.): 1,484

	STOCK PRICE ($) FY Close	P/E High/Low		PER SHARE ($) Earnings	Dividends	Book Value
03/21	8.32	35	17	0.28	0.03	36.30
03/20	3.87	—	—	(1.36)	0.15	33.62
03/19	6.09	5	2	2.59	0.20	41.17
03/18	10.54	3	2	5.42	0.17	44.65
03/17	8.27	3	2	3.03	0.14	35.70
Annual Growth	**0.1%**	—	—	**(44.8%)**	**(32.3%)**	**0.4%**

Volkswagen AG

Bolting together around 10 million vehicles each year Volkswagen AG (VW) tussles with Toyota for position as the world's most prolific auto manufacturer. The company produces cars motorbikes and commercial vehicles of all sizes under more than 10 independently operating brands including VW Audi SKODA SEAT Porsche Lamborghini and Scania. Volkswagen AG is the parent company of the Volkswagen Group. It develops vehicles and components for the Group's brands but also produces and sells vehicles in particular passenger cars and light commercial vehicles for the Volkswagen Passenger Cars and Volkswagen Commercial Vehicles brands. VW also offers leasing financing and fleet solutions for its corporate customers.

Operations

VW is divided into two business — Automotive and Financial Services.

The Automotive division generates some 85% of sales and comprises VW's passenger and commercial vehicle business as well as its Power Engineering unit. Its more than 10 independently operating brands are VW Audi SKODA SEAT (mass-market vehicles); Bentley Bugatti Lamborghini Porsche (luxury cars); Ducati (motorbikes); Volkswagen Commercial Vehicles Scania and MAN (commercial vehicles). By brand VW generates roughly a third of total group sales followed by Audi (about 20%) and Porsche (around 10%). Audi is its most profitable brand.

Power Engineering manufactures large-bore diesel engines turbomachinery special gear units propulsion components and testing systems.

The Financial Services segment (nearly 20% of sales) provides dealer and customer financing leasing banking and insurance activities fleet management and mobility offerings.

Geographic Reach

VW is based in Wolfsburg Germany a city that could reasonably be described as Volkswagenville and which grew upon the wealth generated by the auto manufacturer and its legions of employees. The city is home to the world's largest car manufacturing plant.

Outside Wolfsburg VW has more than 120 production sites in about 20 European countries and a dozen more in some 10 countries in the Americas the Asia/Pacific region and Africa. Europe accounts for about 60% of the company's total sales while the Americas and Asia each generate 20% each. Key markets include Western Europe China the US Brazil Russia Poland Turkey and Mexico.

Sales and Marketing

VW holds a global market share of more than 10%. The global economy recorded negative growth in fiscal year 2020 due to the impact of the Covid-19 pandemic. Global demand for vehicles was lower than in the previous year. Amid these challenging market conditions the Volkswagen Group delivered 9.3 million vehicles to customers.

In fiscal year 2020 the global market volume of passenger cars fell significantly below the prior-year level due to the Covid-19 pandemic decreasing to 67.7 million vehicles (?15.2%). This marked a decline for the third year in a row. All regions were affected by this slump. The overall markets of Western Europe South America and Africa recorded above-average losses while the decline in Asia-Pacific and the Middle East was smaller in percentage terms.

Financial Performance

Note: Growth rates may differ after conversion to US Dollars.

Sales revenue rose over the years between 2016 to 2019 but recorded a decline in the most recent fiscal year.

In the fiscal year 2020 VW generated sales revenue of ?222.9 billion. The year-on-year decrease of 11.8% was mainly attributable to falling volumes as a result of the Covid-19 pandemic as well as the negative effects of changes in exchange rates.

The company's net income increased by about 28% or ?1.4 billion to ?6.3 billion in 2020.

Cash held by the company at the end of 2020 increased ?9.1 billion to ?33.4 billion compared to ?24.3 billion in the prior year. Cash provided by operations was ?24.9 billion while cash used for investing was ?22.7 billion mainly for addition to capitalized development costs. Financing activities provided ?7.6 billion.

Strategy

The company's enhanced TOGETHER 2025+ Group strategy comprises consistent strategic decisions and specific modules aimed at safeguarding the long-term future of the Group and generating profitable growth. These modules are namely Best Governance Best Performance Best Brand Equity Software-enabled Car Company and Excellent Leadership.

The aim of the best performance module is to achieve a sustainable increase in its enterprise value by increasing efficiency productivity and profitability.

In the best brand equity module the focus is in realigning the brand portfolio making a significant increase in the value of brands by 2025.

In the Software-enabled Car Company module the company are working to make software development one of the Volkswagen Group's core competencies. To achieve this the company pooling existing expertise substantially strengthening their resources and establishing a dedicated organizational unit. By 2025 all new vehicle across the Group will be based on their own cross-brand software platform. This approach will enable us to leverage synergies between the individual brands and vehicle projects.

The excellent leadership module will accelerate the transformation to a more open more partnership-based and more value-based leadership.

Mergers and Acquisitions

In 2020 TRATON SE indirect subsidiary of VW agreed to acquire Navistar International Corporation (Navistar) a leading US truck manufacturer for approximately US$ 3.7billion. As of December 31 2020 TRATON already held a 16.7% interest in Navistar. The completion of the transaction through which TRATON will become Navistar's sole owner is intended for mid-2021.

HISTORY

Since the early 1920s auto engineer Ferdinand Porsche (whose son later founded the Porsche car company) had wanted to make a small car for the masses. He found no backers until he met Adolf Hitler in 1934. Hitler formed the Gesellschaft zur Vorbereitung des deutschen Volkswagen (Company for the Development of the German People's Car) in 1937 and built a factory in Wolfsburg Germany. No cars were delivered during WWII as the company produced military vehicles using the slave labor of Jews and Russian prisoners of war.

Following WWII British occupation forces oversaw the rebuilding of the bomb-damaged plant and initial production of the odd-looking "people's car" (1945). The British appointed Heinz Nordhoff to manage Volkswagen (1948) and then turned the company over to the German government (1949).

In the 1950s VW launched the Microbus and built foreign plants. Although US sales began slowly by the end of the decade acceptance of the

little car had increased. Advertising that coined the name "Beetle" helped carve VW's niche in the US.

VW sold stock to the German public in 1960. In 1966 it purchased Auto Union (AUDI) from Daimler-Benz. The Beetle became a counterculture symbol in the 1960s and US sales took off. By the time of Nordhoff's death in 1968 the Beetle had become the best-selling car in history.

EXECUTIVES

Chairman, Hans Pötsch, $341,821 total compensation

Deputy Chairman, Peter Mosch, $113,940 total compensation

Independent Member of the Supervisory Board, Hessa Sultan Al-Jaber, $113,940 total compensation

Independent Member of the Supervisory Board, Hussain Ali Al-Abdulla, $113,940 total compensation

Member of the Management Board, Responsible for Sport & Luxury brand Group, Oliver Blume

Deputy Chairman of the Supervisory Board, Employee Representative, Jorg Hofmann, $227,881 total compensation

Chairman, Herbert Diess

Member of the Management Board, Responsible for Integrity and Legal Affairs, Hiltrud Werner

Member of the Supervisory Board, Employee Representative, Conny Schoenhardt, $113,940 total compensation

Member of the Supervisory Board, Employee Representative, Werner Weresch, $113,940 total compensation

Independent Member of the Supervisory Board, Stephan Weil, $113,940 total compensation

Member of the Management Board, Human Resources and Truck and Bus, Gunnar Kilian

Member of the Supervisory Board, Employee Representative, Kai Bliesener, $60,452 total compensation

Auditors: Ernst & Young GmbH Wirtschaftpruefungsgesellschaft

LOCATIONS

HQ: Volkswagen AG
    Letterbox 1848, Wolfsburg 38436
Phone: (49) 5361 9 0   **Fax:** (49) 5361 928282
Web: www.volkswagen.com

2018 sales

	% of total
Europe/Other Markets	61
Asia/Pacific	18
North America	16
South America	4
Unallocated	1
Total	**100**

PRODUCTS/OPERATIONS

2018 sales

	% of total
Automotive	
Passenger Cars	68
Commercial Vehicles	16
Power Engineering	1
Financial Services	15
Total	**100**

2018 sales

	% of total
Vehicles	62
Leasing business	11
Genuine parts	7
Used vehicles and third-party products	5
Engines powertrains and parts deliveries	5
Other sales revenue	4
Interest and similar income	3
Power Engineering	2
Hedges sales revenue	1
Motorcycles	-
Total	**100**

Selected Brands

Audi
Bentley
Bugatti
Ducati
Lamborghini
MAN Commercial Vehicles
MAN Power Engineering
Porsche
Scania
SEAT
ŠKODA
Volkswagen
Volkswagen Commercial Vehicles

COMPETITORS

AUDI AG	MAHINDRA AND MAHINDRA
Bayerische Motoren	LIMITED
Werke AG	MITSUBISHI MOTORS
GENERAL MOTORS COMPANY	CORPORATION
GROUP LOTUS LIMITED	Mercedes-Benz Group AG
KIA CORPORATION	PEUGEOT SA

HISTORICAL FINANCIALS

Company Type: Public

Income Statement

	REVENUE ($ mil.)	NET INCOME ($ mil.)	NET PROFIT MARGIN	EMPLOYEES
12/20	273,543	10,228	3.7%	662,600
12/19	283,646	14,984	5.3%	671,200
12/18	270,093	13,544	5.0%	664,496
12/17	276,531	13,610	4.9%	642,292
12/16	229,408	5,431	2.4%	626,715
Annual Growth	**4.5%**	**17.1%**	**—**	**1.4%**

2020 Year-End Financials

Debt ratio: 48.9%	No. of shares (mil.): 295
Return on equity: 6.6%	Dividends
Cash ($ mil.): 41,616	Yield: 1.9%
Current ratio: 1.18	Payout: 1.8%
Long-term debt ($ mil.): 134,621	Market value ($ mil.): 6,153

	STOCK PRICE ($) FY Close	P/E High/Low		PER SHARE ($) Earnings	Dividends	Book Value
12/20	20.85	1	1	20.37	0.37	528.40
12/19	19.29	1	1	29.87	0.35	463.35
12/18	15.60	1	1	26.99	5.50	454.51
Annual Growth	**15.6%**	**—**		**(6.8%)**	**(49.1%)**	**3.8%**

Volvo AB

AB Volvo is one of the world's largest manufacturers of heavy-duty trucks construction equipment buses and heavy-duty combustion engines as well as a leading supplier of marine and industrial engines. It has production facilities in almost 20 countries and sales of products in more than 190 markets. It makes trucks under the ten brands including Volvo UD Trucks Prevost Renault Trucks and Mack. The company also provides financing services though Volvo Financial Services and it generates majority of sales from Europe. The company was founded in 1927.

Operations

The Volvo Group organizes itself into six main business segments: Trucks Construction Equipment Buses Volvo Penta Financial Services and Group functions & other.

The Trucks segment is the largest with around 60% of net sales and produces light- and heavy-duty trucks and provides maintenance and repair services as well as financing and leasing.

Construction Equipment (about 25% of sales) makes products for the construction extraction waste processing forestry and materials handling sectors and markets its vehicles under the Volvo SDLG and Terex Truck brands.

Other smaller units include Volvo Buses (more than 5% of sales) one of the world's largest manufacturers of buses coaches and bus chassis. Volvo Penta (less than 5%) which makes engines and power systems for leisure and commercial boats as well as for power generation and industrial off-road applications. The Financial Services segment provides flexible financing insurance and other services and represents almost 5% of net sales. The Group functions & other account for less than 5%.

Overall the company generates about 95% of sales from industrial operations and almost 5% from financial services.

Geographic Reach

Volvo headquartered in Gothenburg Sweden has production facilities in nearly 20 countries and sells its products and services in more than 190 markets worldwide. Europe accounts for some 40% of sales. Other major markets include North America and Asia which both accounts for nearly 25% each and South America and Africa and Oceania with over 10% combined.

Sales and Marketing

The Volvo Group's global network of dealers and service centers staffed by competent and service-oriented personnel are key factors for customer satisfaction and success. The brand organizations within the Volvo Group support customers via efficient dealer workshops and through service and maintenance agreements.

The company partners in alliances and joint ventures with SDLG Eicher and Dongfeng.

Financial Performance

During 2020 net sales decreased by 22% to SEK 338 billion. Adjusted for currency movements the decrease was 18%. Vehicle sales decreased by 23% adjusted for currency movements. Sales were lower in all business areas as a consequence of the measures to mitigate the Covid-19 pandemic affecting customer demand primarily in the spring.

In 2020 the company had a net income of SEK19.3 billion a 46% decrease from the previous year's net income of SEK35.9 billion.

The company's cash at the end of 2020 was SEK85.2 billion. Operating activities generated SEK30.6 billion while investing activities provided SEK20.7 billion.

Strategy

The strategic priorities were updated during 2020 with the intention of strengthening the areas where the company already performs well and adding new areas of importance for the future. The strategic priorities guide the company's decision-making and result in action but should not be seen as a detailed action plan in itself. The seven strategic priorities include: Transform the Volvo Group; Grow the Service Business; Secure a Desirable Sustainable Product and Service Portfolio; Grow in Asia and the US; Develop Robust Profitability; Selectively Capture and Scale-Up New Businesses; and Reinforce Value-based Leadership and Ways of Working.

Mergers and Acquisitions

In early 2021 Volvo Group has signed definitive agreements to acquire 60 percent of Designwerk Technologies AG an engineering company in Switzerland that develops and sells electromobility products and engineering services within electromobility eco-systems. By investing in Designwerk Technologies the Volvo Group will complement its current capabilities when it comes to niche products and solutions. Terms were not disclosed.

Also in 2021 Daimler Truck AG and the Volvo Group today completed the transaction to form the previously announced fuel-cell joint venture. The Volvo Group has acquired 50 percent of the partnership interests in the existing Daimler Truck Fuel Cell GmbH & Co. KG for approximately SEK 6.3 billion (approximately EUR 0.6 billion) on a cash and debt-free basis. The ambition is to make the new joint venture a leading global manufacturer of fuel-cells and thus help the world take a major step towards climate-neutral and sustainable transportation by 2050. Daimler Truck AG and the Volvo Group have agreed to rename the company cellcentric GmbH & Co. KG. The joint venture will develop produce and commercialize fuel-cell systems for use in heavy-duty trucks as the primary focus as well as other applications.

Company Background

Swedish ball bearing maker SKF formed Volvo (Latin for "I roll") as a subsidiary in 1915. Volvo began building cars in 1926 trucks in 1928 and bus chassis in 1932 in Gothenburg. Sweden's winters and icy roads made the company keenly attentive to engineering and safety. The Volvo Group sold its Volvo Cars division to Ford Motor Company in 1999; Volvo Cars was subsequently acquired by Chinese Zhejiang Geely Holding Group Co. Ltd in 2010.

EXECUTIVES

Executive Vice President Volvo Group and President Volvo Financial Services, Marcio Pedroso

Executive Vice President, Volvo Group and President Renault Trucks, Bruno Blin

Executive Vice President Volvo Group and President Mack Trucks, Martin Weissburg

EVP, Volvo Group and Chairman, UD Trucks, Joachim Rosenberg

Chairman, Carl-Henric Svanberg, $12,484 total compensation

EVP, Group Communication, Kina Wileke

EVP, Group Legal & Compliance and General Counsel, Sofia Frändberg

Deputy Chief Executive Officer, Jan Gurander, $854,503 total compensation

President and Chief Executive Officer, Martin Lundstedt, $1,576,016 total compensation

Executive Vice President Volvo Group Trucks Purchasing & Chief Purchasing Officer for Volvo Group, Andrea Fuder

EVP, Group Trucks Technology and CTO, Lars Stenqvist

Executive Vice President, Group Trucks Operations, Jens Holtinger

President and CEO, Arquus, Emmanuel Levacher

President, Volvo Penta, Helene Mellquist

Executive Vice President, Volvo Group and President, Volvo Construction Equipment, Melker Jernberg

Executive Vice President, Volvo Group and President, Volvo Trucks, Roger Alm

Chief Financial Officer, Jan Ytterberg

Executive Vice President and Chief Digital Officer, Volvo Group, Scott Rafkin

President, Volvo Autonomous Solutions, Nils Jaeger

President, Volvo Buses, Anna Westerberg,

Auditors: Deloitte AB

LOCATIONS

HQ: Volvo AB
Volvo Bergegaards v., Goeteborg SE-405 08
Phone: (46) 31 66 00 00   **Fax:** (46) 31 53 72 96
Web: www.volvogroup.com

2018 Sales

	% of total
Europe	41
North America	27
Asia	20
South America	5
Africa & Oceania	7
Total	**100**

PRODUCTS/OPERATIONS

2018 Sales

	% of total
Trucks	63
Construction Equipment	21
Buses	7
Volvo Penta	4
Group Functions & Other	2
Financial Services	3
Total	**100**

Selected Products & Brands

Volvo
Volvo Trucks
Volvo Buses
Volvo Construction Equipment
Volvo Penta
Volvo Penta Marine Leisure
Volvo Penta Marine Commercial
Volvo Penta Industrial
Terex Trucks
Renault Trucks
Prevost
Nova Bus Global
Mack Trucks
Arquus
Arrow Truck

COMPETITORS

ALLISON TRANSMISSION HOLDINGS INC.	MAHINDRA AND MAHINDRA LIMITED
ASSA ABLOY AB	MERITOR INC.
Atlas Copco AB	PEUGEOT MOTOR COMPANY PLC
CIE AUTOMOTIVE SA	
Clariant AG	SENIOR PLC
DANA INCORPORATED	SIG PLC
Dongfeng Motor Group Company Limited	SSAB AB
KION GROUP AG	TELETRAC NAVMAN (UK) LTD
LOOKERS PLC	

HISTORICAL FINANCIALS

Company Type: Public

Income Statement				FYE: December 31
	REVENUE ($ mil.)	**NET INCOME** ($ mil.)	**NET PROFIT MARGIN**	**EMPLOYEES**
12/20	41,423	2,364	5.7%	96,194
12/19	46,437	3,855	8.3%	103,985
12/18	43,662	2,781	6.4%	105,175
12/17	40,800	2,557	6.3%	99,488
12/16	33,307	1,450	4.4%	94,914
Annual Growth	5.6%	13.0%	—	0.3%

2020 Year-End Financials

Debt ratio: 3.6%	No. of shares (mil.): 2,033
Return on equity: 13.5%	Dividends
Cash ($ mil.): 10,428	Yield: 0.1%
Current ratio: 1.47	Payout: 157.8%
Long-term debt ($ mil.): 11,647	Market value ($ mil.): 47,481

	STOCK PRICE ($) FY Close	P/E High/Low		PER SHARE ($)		
				Earnings	Dividends	Book Value
12/20	23.35	3	1	1.16	1.84	8.75
12/19	16.61	1	1	1.90	1.08	7.33
12/18	13.03	2	1	1.37	0.50	6.78
12/17	18.49	2	1	1.26	0.39	6.42
12/16	11.60	2	1	0.71	0.33	5.22
Annual Growth	19.1%		—	13.0%	53.4%	13.8%

Vontobel Holding AG

Vontobel Holding wants your business if you're wealthy. The company owns Bank Vontobel one of the largest players in the famously private world of Swiss banking. Bank Vontobel and the company's other subsidiaries provide investment funds and other investment banking and asset management services for private and institutional clients primarily in Europe and North America. The family of former company chairman Hans-Dieter Vontobel (through various entities including the Vontobel Foundation) control the company which has more than $192 billion in assets under management.

EXECUTIVES

Independent Member of the Board of Directors, David Cole, $180,264 total compensation
Independent Member of the Board of Directors, Stefan Loacker, $158,969 total compensation
Member of the Group Executive Management, Chief Operating Officer, Felix Lenhard
Independent Member of the Board of Directors, Bruno Basler, $204,328 total compensation
Member of the Group Executive Management, Head of Asset Management, Axel Schwarzer
Independent Member of the Board of Directors, Clara Streit, $173,449 total compensation
Member of the Group Executive Management, Head of Wealth Management, Georg Schubiger
Member of the Board of Directors, Maja Baumann, $158,969 total compensation
Member of the Board of Directors, Bjoern Wettergren, $173,449 total compensation
Independent Member of the Board of Directors, Elisabeth Bourqui, $183,032 total compensation
Independent Chairman of the Board of Directors, Herbert Scheidt, $1,330,954 total compensation
Chief Executive Officer, Member of the Group Executive Management, Zeno Staub, $1,064,763 total compensation
Independent Vice Chairman of the Board of Directors, Frank Schnewlin, $201,559 total compensation
Chief Financial Officer, Member of the Group Executive Management, Thomas Heinzl
Auditors: Ernst & Young Ltd.

LOCATIONS

HQ: Vontobel Holding AG
Gotthardstrasse 43, Zurich CH-8022
Phone: (41) 58 283 59 00   **Fax:** (41) 58 283 75 00
Web: www.vontobel.com

COMPETITORS

ABRDN PLC
FLETCHER KING PLC
MERCHANT HOUSE GROUP PLC
OM RESIDUAL UK LIMITED

ROBERT W. BAIRD & CO. INCORPORATED
Sampo Oyj
THE ZS FUND L P

HISTORICAL FINANCIALS

Company Type: Public

Income Statement | | | | FYE: December 31

	ASSETS ($ mil.)	NET INCOME ($ mil.)	INCOME AS % OF ASSETS	EMPLOYEES
12/20	35,677	275	0.8%	2,094
12/19	27,144	259	1.0%	2,049
12/18	26,468	224	0.8%	2,079
12/17	23,467	207	0.9%	1,767
12/16	19,052	255	1.3%	1,756
Annual Growth	17.0%	1.9%	—	4.5%

2020 Year-End Financials

Return on assets: 0.8%	Dividends
Return on equity: 13.0%	Yield: —
Long-term debt ($ mil.): —	Payout: 52.9%
No. of shares (mil.): 55	Market value ($ mil.): —
Sales ($ mil): 1,838	

Wal-Mart de Mexico S.A.B. de C.V.

Wal-Mart de Mexico (operating as Wal-Mart de Mexico y Centroamerica) is the numero uno retailer in Mexico Costa Rica El Salvador Guatemala Honduras and Nicaragua with about 3000 stores. These include Bodega food and general merchandise stores and Superama supermarkets as well about 10 Medimart Farmacia de Walmart. It also runs Wal-Mart Supercenters SAM'S CLUB and ClubCo warehouse stores. Its stores are located in more than 500 cities throughout the region. Wal-Mart Stores formed a joint venture with Mexico's Cifra in 1991 and in 2000 acquired it and renamed it Wal-Mart de Mexico. Wal-Mex then added Wal-Mart's operations in Central America and became Wal-Mart de Mexico y Centroamerica in 2010.

Operations

In Mexico alone the company has 1719 Bodega Aurrera discount stores 256 Walmart hypermarkets 160 Sam's Club membership self-service wholesale stores 95 Superama supermarkets 10 Medimart pharmacies and 114 Suburbia apparel and accessories stores in Mexico. In addition it imports and sells goods; develops properties; and manages real estate companies.

In Costa Rica Guatemala Honduras Nicaragua and El Salvador Wal-Mart de Mexico y Centroamerica operates through 484 discount stores 99 supermarkets 102 discount warehouse stores 24 Walmart hypermarkets and 1 ClubCo membership self-service wholesale store.

Geographic Reach

Wal-Mart de Mexico y Centroamerica owns and operates self-service retail stores in Mexico and Central America.

It operates in Costa Rica (230 stores) El Salvador (88) Guatemala (217) Honduras (82) Mexico (2363) and Nicaragua (92).

Strategy

The company is focusing on growth it of its core assets by selling of some of its businesses. It has refocused on its stores after selling restaurants and a bank.

In 2016 it planned to invest 14.7 billion pesos ($822.6 million). Some 39% of the total would be earmarked to opening new stores 31% to remodeling and maintaining existing ones 24% to technology and e-commerce and the remaining 6% to logistical improvements.

In 2016 Wal-Mart de Mexico y Centroamerica agreed to sell its Suburbia clothing chain to El Puerto de Liverpool SAB Mexico's biggest department store chain operator in a deal valued at 19 billion pesos ($1.03 billion).

Banco Wal-Mart (launched in 2007) operates more than 260 branches located inside Bodega Aurrera Wal-Mart and SAM'S CLUB stores in some 30 cities and cater to a clientele that for the most part is new to banking. The bank has been losing money for its parent though. To cut its losses in late 2014 Wal-Mart de Mexico y Centroamerica sold the banking unit to a group of

buyers that includes Grupo Financiero Inbursa the financial services operations of billionaire Carlos Slim Hel . The deal was valued at MXN 3.6 billion ($247 million).

HISTORY

Spanish-born Jer nimo Arango Arias studied art and literature at several American universities without graduating. In his twenties he wandered around Spain Mexico and the US. He struck upon an idea after seeing a crowd waiting in line at the E. J. Korvette discount department store in New York City. Jer nimo called his two brothers Pl cido and Manuel and convinced them to join him in a new business venture.

Borrowing about $250000 from their father a Spanish immigrant to Mexico successful in textiles the three brothers opened their first Aurrer Bolivar discount store in downtown Mexico City in 1958. Offering goods and clothing well below manufacturers' list prices the store was an immediate hit with consumers but encountered hostility from competing Mexico City retailers. When local retailers threatened to boycott the Arangos' suppliers the company turned to suppliers in Guadalajara and Monterrey.

In 1965 the Arango brothers formed a joint venture with Jewel Cos. of Chicago to open new Aurrer stores. Jewel bought a 49% interest in the business a year later. Pl cido and Manuel left the business with their portion of the money but Jer nimo stayed as head of the company taking it public in 1976.

By 1981 almost a third of Jewel's earnings came from its operations in Mexico. But the next year the peso crashed obliterating its earnings there. American Stores took over Jewel in 1984 and Jer nimo bought back Jewel's stake in the company (which was renamed Cifra that year).

With the Mexican economy staggering from the peso devaluation weak oil markets and a huge debt crisis Jer nimo was taking a major risk. Although no new stores were opened none were closed. Employees were expected to work longer and those who left were not replaced. With Mexico's middle class hit hard Jer nimo emphasized the Bodega Aurrer no-frills warehouses which discounted all kinds of nonperishable merchandise from canned chili to VCRs.

Cifra and Wal-Mart Stores formed a joint venture in 1991 to open Club Aurrer membership clubs similar to Sam's Club outlets. The two companies expanded the venture the next year to include the development of Sam's Club and Wal-Mart Supercenters in Mexico.

Remodeling began on Cifra's stores in 1992. The work was completed two years later and the company was poised to take advantage of Mexico's much-improved economy.

However devaluation struck again late in 1994. The resulting contraction of credit and rise in prices hit Mexican consumers hard and Cifra's 1995 sales declined 15%. But again it kept on as many employees as possible transferring them to new stores that had been in development. Despite the hard times Cifra opened 27 new stores (including 15 restaurants). The company was able to withstand the difficulties in part because it stayed debt-free.

Wal-Mart consolidated its joint venture into Cifra in 1997 in exchange for about 34% of that company; Wal-Mart later raised its stake to 51%. The cost-conscious companies combined the joint venture stores and Cifra's separate stores under one umbrella. Cifra opened 11 stores and eight restaurants that year.

Cifra opened nine stores and 17 restaurants in 1998; the next year it opened about 20 stores and nearly 25 restaurants. In early 2000 Cifra was renamed Wal-Mart de Mexico. Shortly thereafter Wal-Mart upped its stake in Wal-Mart de Mexico to about 61%.

In 2001 all the Aurrer¨ stores were converted to either Wal-Mart Supercenters or Bodega stores.

Eduardo Castro-Wright was promoted in 2002 from COO to CEO of Wal-Mart de Mexico succeeding Cesareo Fernandez who retained the chairman's title. The retailer opened 50 new outlets that year.

In March 2003 Mexico's Federal Competition Commission closed an investigation of Wal-Mex's purchasing practices citing a lack of evidence that the retailer violated competition laws. Overall that year Wal-Mex entered nine new cities in Mexico and added 46 new outlets. In 2004 Mexico's largest retailer grew bigger adding 17 restaurants 23 Aurrer¨ stores eight SAM'S CLUBS six supercenters and four Superama stores.

In January 2005 Fernandez stepped down as chairman and was succeeded by Ernesto Vega. A month later Castro-Wright left Wal-Mex to become EVP and COO of the Wal-Mart Stores Division in the US. He was succeeded by Eduardo Solorzano formerly COO of Wal-Mex. Also that year Wal-Mex acquired the Mexican assets of French retailer Carrefour. Carrefour which operated 29 hypermarkets in Mexico restructured its operations and left the Mexican market.

In November 2006 Wal-Mex received a license from Mexico's Finance Ministry to organize and operate a bank there. Overall in 2006 the retailer opened 120 new locations including stores in Monterrey the country's most affluent city and throughout northern Mexico where its Texas rival H. E. Butt Grocery is well established. In November 2007 Wal-Mart Bank began operations with 16 branches in five Mexican states.

Wal-Mex inked a deal with Tobacco One in August 2008 to distribute the tobacco firm's Rojo cigarette line in about 140 supercenters and some 60 Superarma stores throughout Mexico.

In December 2009 Wal-Mex announced the acquisition of Walmart's operations in Central America from Walmart Stores and two minority partners. The transaction was completed in early 2010 and Wal-Mex became Walmart Mexico and Central America.

The company discontinued its Vips restaurant business in early 2014 with an agreement to sell the 360 restaurants to Alsea S.A.B. de C.V. for about $625 million.

EXECUTIVES

Director, Kirsten Evans
Independent Director, Adolfo Cerezo
Senior Vice President - Real Estate, Gaston Wainstein
Senior Vice President - Operations Mexico, Cristian Barrientos
Vice President - Internal Audit Mexico and Central America, Roque Velasco Ruiz
Vice President - Centralized Operations, Ivonne Montiel
Vice President - Superama, Lucas Somaschini
Vice President - Bodega Aurrera, Lilia Jaime
Vice President - Walmart Supercenter, Sergio Guillin
Vice President - Human Resources, Central America, Juan Carlos Alarcon
Vice President - Merchandising Fresh Food, Wine & Liquor, Juan Carlos Aja
Vice President - Legal Operations, Enrique Ponzanelli
Independent Director, Roberto Newell Garcia
Vice President - Merchandising, Basic & Processed Food, Edmundo Delgado
Independent Director, Blanca Trevino de Vega

Vice President - General Merchandising, Enrique Guzman
Chairman of the Board, Enrique Ostale Cambiaso
President, Chief Executive Officer, Director, Guilherme De Souza Macedo Loureriro
Auditors: Mancera, S.C. (member of Ernst & Young Global)

LOCATIONS

HQ: Wal-Mart de Mexico S.A.B. de C.V.
Blvd. Manuel Avila Camacho 647, Colonia Periodista, Alcaldia Miguel Hidalgo, Mexico City 11220
Phone: (52) 55 5283 0100   **Fax:** (52) 55 5328 3557
Web: www.walmex.mx

2015 Stores

	No.
Mexico	2,363
Costa Rica	230
Guatemala	217
El Salvador	88
Nicaragua	92
Honduras	82
Total	**3,072**

PRODUCTS/OPERATIONS

2015 Mexico Stores

	% of total
Bodega Aurrera Express	924
Bodega Aurrera	475
Mi Bodega Aurrera	324
Walmart Supercenter	256
Sam's Club	160
Suburbia	114
Superama	95
Medimart Farmacia de Walmart	10
Zona Suburbia	5
Total	**2,363**

Selected Operations

Bodegas & discount stores
  Bodega Aurrera
  Dispensa Familiar
  MAXI Bodega
  PALI
Hypermarkets
  Hiper Paiz
  Hiper Mas
  Walmart
Warehouse clubs
  Sam's Club
  ClubCo
Supermarkets
  La Union
  Mas por Menos
  Paiz
  Superama
Apparel Stores
  Suburbia
Restaurants
  El Porton
  VIPS

COMPETITORS

ALBERTSON'S LLC	Organizaci n Soriana
CARREFOUR	S.A.B. de C.V.
CASINO	RALLYE
GUICHARD-PERRACHON	Tengelmann
DELHAIZE AMERICA LLC	WALMART INC.

HISTORICAL FINANCIALS
Company Type: Public

Income Statement				FYE: December 31
	REVENUE ($ mil.)	NET INCOME ($ mil.)	NET PROFIT MARGIN	EMPLOYEES
12/20	35,317	1,682	4.8%	231,271
12/19	34,189	2,003	5.9%	238,972
12/18	31,372	1,869	6.0%	234,431
12/17	29,099	2,023	7.0%	237,055
12/16	25,729	1,611	6.3%	228,854
Annual Growth	8.2%	1.1%	—	0.3%

2020 Year-End Financials

Debt ratio: —	No. of shares (mil.): —
Return on equity: 19.7%	Dividends
Cash ($ mil.): 1,795	Yield: 5.8%
Current ratio: 0.99	Payout: —
Long-term debt ($ mil.): —	Market value ($ mil.): —

	STOCK PRICE ($) FY Close	P/E High/Low		PER SHARE ($)		
				Earnings	Dividends	Book Value
12/20	28.14	16	13	0.10	0.17	0.49
12/19	28.59	14	12	0.11	0.11	0.51
12/18	25.45	14	11	0.11	0.08	0.48
12/17	24.42	11	8	0.12	1.13	0.46
12/16	17.87	12	9	0.09	0.78	0.46
Annual Growth	12.0%	—	—	1.1%(32.0%)		1.3%

Weichai Power Co Ltd

Auditors: Ernst & Young Hua Ming LLP

LOCATIONS

HQ: Weichai Power Co Ltd
197, Section A, Fu Shou East Street, High Technology Industrial Development Zone, Weifang, Shandong Province 261061
Phone: (86) 536 819 7069   **Fax:** (86) 536 819 7073
Web: www.weichaipower.com

HISTORICAL FINANCIALS
Company Type: Public

Income Statement				FYE: December 31
	REVENUE ($ mil.)	NET INCOME ($ mil.)	NET PROFIT MARGIN	EMPLOYEES
12/20	30,196	1,407	4.7%	0
12/19	25,058	1,308	5.2%	0
12/18	23,153	1,258	5.4%	0
12/17	23,291	1,046	4.5%	0
12/16	13,419	351	2.6%	0
Annual Growth	22.5%	41.5%	—	—

2020 Year-End Financials

Debt ratio: 2.1%	No. of shares (mil.): —
Return on equity: 19.0%	Dividends
Cash ($ mil.): 9,512	Yield: 1.6%
Current ratio: 1.23	Payout: 150.0%
Long-term debt ($ mil.): 3,169	Market value ($ mil.): —

	STOCK PRICE ($) FY Close	P/E High/Low		PER SHARE ($)		
				Earnings	Dividends	Book Value
12/20	15.86	17	11	0.18	0.25	(0.00)
12/19	16.87	14	7	0.17	0.37	(0.00)
12/18	9.02	10	7	0.16	0.40	(0.00)
12/17	8.75	31	9	0.13	0.21	(0.00)
12/16	12.26	22	11	0.09	0.09	(0.00)
Annual Growth	6.6%	—	—	19.2%	29.8%	—

WESFARMERS Ltd.

Auditors: Ernst & Young

LOCATIONS

HQ: Wesfarmers Ltd.
Level 14, Brookfield Place Tower 2, 123 St Georges Terrace, Perth, Western Australia 6000
Phone: (61) 8 9327 4211   **Fax:** (61) 8 9327 4216
Web: www.wesfarmers.com.au

Income Statement				FYE: June 30
	REVENUE ($ mil.)	NET INCOME ($ mil.)	NET PROFIT MARGIN	EMPLOYEES
06/20	21,138	1,162	5.5%	107,000
06/19	19,561	3,860	19.7%	105,000
06/18	49,386	883	1.8%	217,000
06/17	52,588	2,207	4.2%	223,000
06/16	49,091	302	0.6%	220,000
Annual Growth	(19.0%)	40.0%	—	(16.5%)

2020 Year-End Financials

Debt ratio: 7.1%	No. of shares (mil.): 1,133
Return on equity: 17.5%	Dividends
Cash ($ mil.): 1,996	Yield: 2.7%
Current ratio: 1.11	Payout: 43.2%
Long-term debt ($ mil.): 1,475	Market value ($ mil.): 17,654

	STOCK PRICE ($) FY Close	P/E High/Low		PER SHARE ($) Earnings	Dividends	Book Value
06/20	15.57	11	7	1.03	0.43	5.65
06/19	12.61	4	2	3.41	5.44	6.16
06/18	18.26	17	14	0.78	0.72	14.82
06/17	15.38	7	6	1.95	0.66	16.22
06/16	14.98	46	38	0.27	0.64	15.16
Annual Growth	1.0% (21.9%)			— —	39.7%	(9.5%)

Weston (George) Ltd

George Weston Limited is a company based in Canada and offers services and products in: retail real estate and consumer goods. More than 90% of the company's sales come from its majority-owned Loblaw Companies Limited Canada's largest retailer with more than 2000 grocery stores markets and drug stores across the country. Its locations (both corporate-owned and franchised) operate under such banners as Loblaws Joe Fresh Shoppers Drug Mart and President's Choice Bank. Loblaw Companies also provides banking and other financial services through PC Financial. In addition George Weston owns Weston Foods with operations in Canada and the US which makes freshly baked bread rolls cupcakes donuts cookies cakes pies cones and wafers.

Operations

George Weston operates through three operating segments: Loblaw Choice Properties and Weston Foods.

The Loblaw operating segment accounts for more than 90% of company revenue and includes grocery and drug store chains as well as financial services through PC Financial. Its banners include Loblaws Joe Fresh President's Choice Bank and Shoppers Drug Mart.

Weston Foods is a leading food manufacturer in North America known for fresh and frozen bakery items (breads rolls cakes pies cones and wafers). Some of Weston foods brands include Wonder Casa Mendosa Ace Bakery Country Harvest and D' Italiano. This segment accounts for around 5% of George Weston's revenue.

Choice properties which accounts for less than 5% of George Weston's revenue is a large diversified owner manager and developer of real estate properties. It is comprised of retail properties predominantly leased to necessity-based tenants industrial office and residential assets concentrated in attractive markets and offers an impressive and substantial development pipeline.

Geographic Reach

Based in Toronto George Weston operates across Canada and generates more than 95% of its revenue. It has limited operations in the US through Weston Foods.

Sales and Marketing

George Weston serves retail customers through more than 2000 grocery stores markets and drug stores across Canada. Its Weston Foods segment serves retail and foodservice.

Financial Performance

George Weston's performance for five years has continued to have an increasing with 2020 as its highest-performing year.

In 2020 the company's revenue decreased by about 9.2% or $5.6 billion to $54.7 billion compared to $50.1 billion in 2019.

In 2020 net income increased by about $721 million to $963 million compared to $242 million in the previous year.

Cash at the end of fiscal 2020 amounted to about $2.6 billion. Cash from operations contributed $5.5 billion to the coffers while investing activities used $1.7 billion. Financing activities also used another $3 billion mainly for repayments of long-term debt.

Strategy

George Weston's three operating segments have their own strategy.

Loblaw's strategy is committed to delivering industry leading financial performance by leveraging data-driven insights and by delivering process and efficiency excellence. This model ultimately fuels truly customer-centric investments in Everyday Digital Retail Payments and Rewards and Connected Healthcare.

For Choice Properties its goal is to provide net asset value appreciation stable net operating income ("NOI") growth and capital preservation with a long-term focus.

Weston Foods is committed to offering superior products and services to its consumers and customers in an increasingly competitive environment.

Company Background

A baker's apprentice George Weston began delivering bread in Toronto with a single horse in 1882. He added the Model Bakery in 1896 and began making cookies and biscuits in 1908.

Upon George's death in 1924 his son Garfield gained control of the company and took it public as George Weston Limited in 1928.

During the 1940s the company made a number of acquisitions including papermaker E.B. Eddy (1943; sold 1998 to papermaker Domtar giving it a 20% stake in Domtar) Southern Biscuit (1944) Western Grocers (1944 its first distribution company) and William Neilson (1948 chocolate and dairy products).

In 1953 it acquired a controlling interest in Loblaw Groceterias Canada's largest grocery chain. George Weston continued its acquisitions during the 1950s and 1960s adding grocer National Tea and diversifying into packaging (Somerville Industries 1957) and fisheries (British Columbia Packers 1962; Conners Bros. 1967).

HISTORY

A baker's apprentice George Weston began delivering bread in Toronto with a single horse in 1882. He added the Model Bakery in 1896 and began making cookies and biscuits in 1908.

Upon George's death in 1924 his son Garfield gained control of the company and took it public as George Weston Limited in 1928. Having popularized the premium English biscuit in Canada Garfield acquired bakeries in the UK to make cheap biscuits (uncommon at the time). He grouped the bakeries as a separate public company called Allied Bakeries in 1935 (it later became Associated British Foods and is still controlled by the Weston family).

Expansion-minded Garfield led the company into the US with the purchase of Associated Biscuit in 1939. By the late 1930s George Weston was making cakes breads and almost 500 kinds of candy and biscuits.

During the 1940s the company made a number of acquisitions including papermaker E.B. Eddy (1943; sold 1998 to papermaker Domtar giving it a 20% stake in Domtar) Southern Biscuit (1944) Western Grocers (1944 its first distribution company) and William Neilson (1948 chocolate and dairy products).

In 1953 it acquired a controlling interest in Loblaw Groceterias Canada's largest grocery chain. George Weston continued its acquisitions during the 1950s and 1960s adding grocer National Tea and diversifying into packaging (Somerville Industries 1957) and fisheries (British Columbia Packers 1962; Conners Bros. 1967).

By 1970 when Garfield's son Galen became president the company's holdings were in disarray. Galen brought in new managers consolidated the food distribution and sales operations under Loblaw Companies Limited and cut back on National Tea (which shrank from over 900 stores in 1972 to 82 in 1993). When Garfield died in 1978 Galen became chairman.

Ever since Galen a polo-playing chum of Prince Charles was the target of a failed kidnapping attempt by the Irish Republican Army in 1983 the family has kept a low public profile.

George Weston became the #1 chocolate maker in Canada with its purchase of Cadbury Schweppes' Canadian assets in 1987. The 1980s concluded with a five-year price war in St. Louis among its National Tea stores Kroger and a local grocer. This ultimately proved fruitless and Loblaw sold its US supermarkets in 1995 ending its US retail presence. As part of its divestiture of underachieving subsidiaries the company sold its Neilson confectionery business back to Cadbury Schweppes in 1996 and sold its chocolate products company in 1998.

In early 1998 Loblaw set its sights on Quebec buying Montreal-based Provigo. Other George Weston acquisitions in the late 1990s included Oshawa Foods' 80-store Agora Foods franchise supermarket unit in eastern Canada and its Fieldfresh Farms dairy business the frozen-bagel business of Quaker Oats Pennsylvania-based Maier's Bakery and Bunge International's Australian meat processor Don Smallgoods. It also sold its British Columbia Packers fisheries unit.

Early in 2001 George Weston surprised analysts when it won Unilever's Bestfoods Baking Company (Entenmann's Oroweat) with a bid of $1.8 billion. The company reduced its stake in Loblaw by 2% and sold its Connors canned seafood business to fund the purchase which was completed in July 2001. To help pay down debt in early 2002 the company sold its Orowheat business in the western US to Mexican bread giant Grupo Bimbo for $610 million.

In 2003 Weston's food distribution business introduced about 1500 private label products. It sold its fisheries operations in Chile at a loss in 2004 for about $20 million. That September the company purchased Quebec-based Boulangerie Gadoua Lt e a family-owned baking business.

In 2005 the company sold its Heritage Salmon subsidiary thus exiting the unprofitable fisheries business entirely. The company also restructured its US biscuit operations and opened a new fresh bakery plant in Orlando Florida in 2005 as part of its push to increase its business in the southeastern US. A new bakery in the midwestern US began production of bread and English muffins in late 2006.

In early 2007 Weston's Loblaw subsidiary announced it was writing down its operations in Quebec to the tune of $768 million tied to its struggling Provigo grocery stores.

In December 2008 the company sold the Neilson dairy division of Weston Foods Canada to Saputo for some C$465 million in cash (about $373 million). It will use the money to pay down debt. In January 2009 it completed the sale of its fresh bread and baked goods business in the US. Later in the year Loblaw acquired T&T Supermarket Canada's largest retailer of Asian food.

In September 2010 George Weston through its Maplehurst Bakeries subsidiary acquired Keystone Bakery Holdings for approximately $185 million. Keystone is comprised of three operating companies: Freed's Bakery of Manchester New Hampshire a leading supplier of frozen thaw and sell iced cupcakes; Granny's Kitchens of Frankfort New York a leading supplier of both frozen pre-fried and frozen thaw and sell donuts; and Heartland Baking of DuQuoin Illinois a specialty supplier of frozen thaw and sell cookies. In November Weston Foods acquired artisan and European-style bread manufacturer ACE Bakery for C$110 million (US$108 million). Based in Toronto ACE was made a subsidiary of Weston Foods (Canada). Its breads are distributed in Canada and the US.

Chairman and president Galen Weston stepped down as the company's president in late 2011 but remained chairman.

EXECUTIVES

Executive Vice President, Chief Talent Officer, Rashid Wasti
Independent Director, Andrew Ferrier
Lead Independent Director, J. Robert Prichard
Chief Operating Officer of Loblaw, Robert Sawyer
Independent Director, Christianne Strauss
Independent Director, Nancy Lockhart
Executive Vice President, Chief Legal Officer, Gordon Currie, $522,677 total compensation
Chairman of the Board, Chief Executive Officer and Executive Chairman and President of Loblaw, Galen Weston, $894,944 total compensation
Director, Paviter Binning
Independent Director, Barbara Stymiest
Chief Strategy Officer, Khush Dadyburjor
President, Chief Financial Officer, Chief Financial Officer of Loblaw, Richard Dufresne, $699,175 total compensation
Independent Director, Sarabjit Marwah
Independent Director, Gordon Nixon
Auditors: KPMG LLP

LOCATIONS

HQ: Weston (George) Ltd
22 St. Clair Avenue East, Toronto, Ontario M4T 2S5
Phone: 416 922-2500
Web: www.weston.ca

2017 Sales

	% of total
Canada	97
US	3
Total	**100**

PRODUCTS/OPERATIONS

2017 Sales

	% of total
Loblaw	95
Weston Foods	5
Total	**100**

Selected Operations

Loblaw Companies Limited
Shoppers Drug Mart
Choice Properties REIT
President's Choice Financial
Weston Foods

COMPETITORS

ASSOCIATED BRITISH FOODS PLC	GENERAL MILLS INC.
BATLEYS LIMITED	METCASH LIMITED
BRAKE BROS LIMITED	SUPERVALU INC.
CAMPBELL SOUP COMPANY	THE CHEFS' WAREHOUSE INC
CONAGRA BRANDS INC.	

HISTORICAL FINANCIALS

Company Type: Public

Income Statement
FYE: December 31

	REVENUE ($ mil.)	NET INCOME ($ mil.)	NET PROFIT MARGIN	EMPLOYEES
12/20	42,964	756	1.8%	299
12/19	38,480	185	0.5%	194,000
12/18	35,664	421	1.2%	197,000
12/17	38,521	605	1.6%	198,000
12/16	35,616	408	1.1%	6,500
Annual Growth	**4.8%**	**16.7%**	**—**	**(53.7%)**

2020 Year-End Financials

Debt ratio: 25.9%	No. of shares (mil.): 152
Return on equity: 12.4%	Dividends
Cash ($ mil.): 2,027	Yield: 0.0%
Current ratio: 1.33	Payout: 35.6%
Long-term debt ($ mil.): 10,617	Market value ($ mil.): 11,395

	STOCK PRICE ($) FY Close	P/E High/Low	PER SHARE ($) Earnings	Dividends	Book Value
12/20	74.78	15 11	4.68	1.67	40.26
12/19	79.29	67 54	0.97	1.60	38.03
12/18	65.55	20 16	2.93	1.43	38.50
12/17	86.74	18 15	4.41	1.44	49.23
12/16	83.72	22 19	2.89	1.29	45.04
Annual Growth	**(2.8%)**	**— —**	**12.8%**	**6.6%**	**(2.8%)**

Westpac Banking Corp

Founded in 1817 and Australia's oldest bank and company Westpac Banking is a stalwart financial institution serving clients in Australia New Zealand and neighboring Pacific Islands. The company serves approximately 13 million customers through its key customer-facing divisions which operate a unique portfolio of brands including Westpac St.George Bank of Melbourne BankSA BT and RAMS. Westpac is one of the largest banks in Australia with a loan portfolio of around $700 million. It serves the financial needs of small businesses multi-national corporates institutional and government clients.

Operations

Westpac Banking operates six reporting segments: Consumer Bank Business Bank Westpac Institutional Bank Westpac New Zealand Specialist Business and Group Businesses.

The Consumer Bank contributes over 60% of revenue and serves consumer customers in Australia. It provides its services via several branded banks including its namesake Westpac Bank of Melbourne St George Bank SA and RAMS.

The Business Bank segment generates more than 15% of revenue by tending to the financial needs of its commercial small-to-medium enterprise and agribusiness customers. The Business Bank offers financial facilities up to $150 million. The segment provides services though all the same bank brands as its affiliate Consumer segment except RAMS.

The Westpac Institutional Bank provides services to commercial corporate institutional and government clients in Australia New Zealand the US UK and Asia. It is also responsible for Westpac Pacific a bank in Fiji and Papua New Guinea. The segment provides over 5% of total revenue.

The Westpac New Zealand segment addresses all customer types (including consumer business institutional etc.) across New Zealand. Westpac New Zealand account for nearly 15% of total revenue.

Specialists Business is responsible for sales and service of Auto and Vendor Finance Australian insurance products Superannuation Platforms and Investments.

Group Businesses segment houses its Treasury (which manages the company's balance sheet) technology strategy and architecture arm Group Technology and operational division Core Support.

Net interest income generates over 80% of Westpac's sales.

Geographic Reach

Westpac Banking's customers are supported through branches and subsidiaries located in Australia New Zealand Asia the United States and the United Kingdom. It has foreign offices in Shanghai Beijing Jakarta Mumbai London New York City Hong Kong and Singapore.

Sales and Marketing

Westpac Banking's business segment are promoted through its retail banking locations as well as through relationship managers wealth specialists business banking centers customer service channels and online. The institutional segment conducts sales through dedicated industry relationship and specialist product teams. Westpac's advertising expenses for 2020 and 2019 were A$95 million and A$245 million respectively.

Financial Performance

Note: Growth rates may differ after conversion to US dollars.

Westpac Banking's 2020 revenue dropped over 3% from the prior year. Its net interest income decrease A$211 million compared to 2019 predominantly due to decrease in net interest margin of 9 basis points to 2.03%. The movement in net interest income is attributable to the impact of lower charges for estimated customer refunds and payments than in 2019.

Its net income fluctuated with a major drop in 2019 towards 2020. Reported net profit in 2020 was A$2.3 billion down from A$6.8 billion in 2019 primarily due to increase in impairment charges due to economic impact of COVID-19 pandemic costs associated with the AUSTRAC proceedings asset impairment charges and revaluations and estimated customer refunds payments associated costs and litigation.

Cash and balances with central banks as at the end of 2020 totaled A$30.1 billion A$10.4 billion higher than the previous year. Operating activities generated A$7.2 billion. Investing and financing activities used A$19.5 billion and A$28.8 billion respectively. Main cash uses were purchase of investment securities purchase of intangible assets and redemption of debt issues.

Strategy

Westpac strategy seeks to deliver on this purpose by building deep and enduring customer relationships being a leader in the community being a place where the best people want to work and in so doing delivering superior returns for share-holders.

In delivering on its strategy Westpac is focused on its core markets of Australia and New Zealand where it provide a comprehensive range of financial products and services that assist them in meeting the financial services needs of customers. With its strong position in these markets and over 13 million customers its focus is on organic growth growing customer numbers in its chosen segments and building stronger and deeper relationships.

Westpac Banking has three strategic priorities for the year ahead:

Fix: Addressing its shortcomings by materially improving its management of risk and risk culture reducing customer pain points completing historical customer remediation program and reducing the complexity of its technology.

Simplify: Returning to its core businesses of banking in Australia and New Zealand including exiting some businesses and international locations. Rationalizing products and simplifying processes to make it easier for customers.

Perform: Improving performance by building customer loyalty and growth through service sharpening its focus on returns and resetting its cost base. A strong balance sheet and engaged workforce form the foundations of performance.

Mergers and Acquisitions
Company Background

Westpac Banking launched in 1817 as the Bank of New South Wales?the first bank established in the country. It changed its name to Westpac Banking Corporation in 1982 after it acquired the Commercial Bank of Australia. In 2011 it merged with St.George which then launched the Bank of Melbourne.

HISTORY

Westpac proudly calls itself Australia's "First Bank." But when predecessor Bank of New South Wales was founded in 1817 some 90% of the eponymous colony's inhabitants were convicts or their relatives. (The penal colony was established just 30 years before the bank.) The British challenged the bank's charter forcing it to become a joint-stock company.

New South Wales' parliament rechartered the company as a bank in 1850 amidst the country's first gold rushes. (Some bank branches consisted of tents in mining camps.) Heavy British investment and an influx of colonists kept the country growing. The bank's future partner Commercial Bank of Australia was founded in 1866 in Melbourne in the neighboring colony of Victoria. More than half of the country's banks disappeared in a panic at the end of the century when land speculation and a collapse in wool prices caused a depression.

Australia became a country with the onset of the 20th century and its government formed Commonwealth Bank a central bank. The Bank of New South Wales now known as "The Wales" helped finance Australia's WWI efforts. Along with the rest of the world the country and the bank rode up the Roaring '20s and down the Great Depression.

About 65% of the bank's male staff enlisted during WWII. Its New Guinea branches closed; others were hit by air raids. In 1947 the government moved to nationalize the prospering country's banks within the Commonwealth Bank but the courts helped the banks fend off the attack on their independence.

The Bank of New South Wales moved into the newly opened savings banking market in 1956. The next year it bought into Australian Guarantee Corporation (it bought the rest in 1988).

The bank expanded abroad and diversified operations in the 1970s. Battered by a lagging pro-

tectionist economy Australia moved to deregulate banking in the 1980s. As foreign banks hustled in Bank of New South Wales and Commercial Bank of Australia in 1982 made what was then the largest merger in Australia's history.

The new bank known as Westpac (for its Western Pacific market area) began building its non-teller-based banking networks in the early 1980s. The company developed an extensive ATM network and established telephone and computerized banking. Later that decade it bought a stake in London gold dealer Johnson Matthey (1986) and all of William E. Pollock Government Securities (1987).

In 1992 Australia's wealthiest man Kerry Packer took a 10% share in troubled Westpac gaining board seats for himself and friend "Chainsaw" Al Dunlap. Packer's power grab failed and he sold the stake in 1993.

After buying itself into the equities market in the mid-1980s Westpac sold its Ord Minnett brokerage division in 1993. The bank withdrew from Asia and expanded closer to home in the mid 1990s buying Western Australia's Challenge Bank in 1995 Trust Bank of New Zealand in 1996 and Victoria's Bank of Melbourne in 1997.

In 1998 the bank agreed to merge its back-office operations with those of ANZ Banking Group providing economies of scale while avoiding antitrust issues. The next year Westpac announced 3000 job cuts mainly through attrition to ready itself for increased competition from changes in Australian law. Pacific operations caused waves in 2000: Westpac said it would pull out of Kiribati in response to government action and a coup in Fiji prompted the bank to reduce employees' hours (a move that was criticized by the Fiji government). The next year however Westpac was strengthening ties to the Pacific market. It doubled its holdings in the Bank of Tonga (on the island of Tonga) and its share of Pacific Commercial Bank (on the island of Samoa).

In 2007 subsidiary Westpac Essential Services Trust formed a joint venture with another Australian firm to operate the Airport Link Company a rail-to-airport passenger service in Sydney. The trust was established so investors could invest in public-private partnership (PPP) assets.

Westpac's acquisition of St.George Bank in 2008 catapulted Westpac from fourth to second among Australia's leading banks. The combination set Westpac and its St.George subsidiary behind only the National Australia Bank in terms of assets.

Auditors: PricewaterhouseCoopers

LOCATIONS

HQ: Westpac Banking Corp
275 Kent Street, Sydney, New South Wales 2000
Phone: (61) 2 9374 7113   **Fax:** (61) 2 8253 4128
Web: www.westpac.com.au

2018 Sales

	% of total
Australia	86
New Zealand	11
Other countries	3
Total	**100**

PRODUCTS/OPERATIONS

2018 Sales by Segment

	% of total
Consumer Bank	39
Business Bank	24
BT Financial Group Australia	10
Westpac Institutional Bank	13
Westpac New Zealand	10
Group Businesses	4
Total	**100**

2018 Sales

	% of total
Net interest income	74
Non-interest income	26
Total	**100**

Selected Products and Services

Bank accounts
Home loans
Credit cards
Personal loans
Travel money card
Share trading
Insurance
Savings accounts
Credit cards
Business loans
Merchant services

COMPETITORS

AUSTRALIA AND NEW ZEALAND BANKING GROUP LIMITED
BANK OF CHINA LIMITED
COMMONWEALTH BANK OF AUSTRALIA
HSBC HOLDINGS PLC
NATIONAL AUSTRALIA BANK LIMITED
NATWEST GROUP PLC
Nordea Bank AB
QATAR NATIONAL BANK (Q.P.S.C.)
STANDARD CHARTERED PLC
STATE BANK OF INDIA
The Toronto-Dominion Bank

HISTORICAL FINANCIALS

Company Type: Public

Income Statement				FYE: September 30
	ASSETS ($ mil.)	NET INCOME ($ mil.)	INCOME AS % OF ASSETS	EMPLOYEES
09/21	673,339	3,926	0.6%	40,143
09/20	649,046	1,629	0.3%	36,849
09/19	612,561	4,583	0.7%	33,288
09/18	634,390	5,838	0.9%	35,029
09/17	667,716	6,262	0.9%	35,096
Annual Growth	0.2%	(11.0%)	—	3.4%

2021 Year-End Financials

Return on assets: 0.5%	Dividends
Return on equity: 7.7%	Yield: 3.6%
Long-term debt ($ mil.): —	Payout: 62.7%
No. of shares (mil.): —	Market value ($ mil.): —
Sales ($ mil): 20,084	

	STOCK PRICE ($) FY Close	P/E High/Low	PER SHARE ($) Earnings	Dividends	Book Value
09/21	18.53	13 8	0.99	0.68	14.13
09/20	12.04	33 16	0.45	0.57	13.40
09/19	19.99	10 8	1.28	1.33	12.67
09/18	20.01	10 8	1.66	1.34	13.55
09/17	25.22	12 10	1.80	1.45	14.16
Annual Growth	(7.4%)	—	— (13.8%)	(17.3%)	(0.1%)

WH Group Ltd

Auditors: Ernst & Young

LOCATIONS

HQ: WH Group Ltd
Unit 7602B-7604A, Level 76, International Commerce Centre, 1 Austin Road West, Kowloon,
Phone:
Web: www.wh-group.com

Income Statement				FYE: December 31
	REVENUE ($ mil.)	NET INCOME ($ mil.)	NET PROFIT MARGIN	EMPLOYEES
12/20	25,589	828	3.2%	107,000
12/19	24,103	1,465	6.1%	101,000
12/18	22,605	943	4.2%	112,000
12/17	22,379	1,133	5.1%	110,000
12/16	21,534	1,036	4.8%	104,000
Annual Growth	4.4%	(5.4%)	—	0.7%

2020 Year-End Financials

Debt ratio: 14.3%
Return on equity: 8.8%
Cash ($ mil.): 1,599
Current ratio: 1.93
Long-term debt ($ mil.): 1,840

No. of shares (mil.): —
Dividends
  Yield: 4.4%
  Payout: 1,334.6%
Market value ($ mil.): —

	STOCK PRICE ($) FY Close	P/E High/Low	PER SHARE ($)		
			Earnings	Dividends	Book Value
12/20	16.68	404272	0.06	0.75	0.68
12/19	20.60	246147	0.10	0.48	0.59
12/18	15.36	389214	0.06	0.76	0.53
12/17	22.60	294187	0.08	0.63	0.51
Annual Growth	(9.6%)	— —	(7.8%)	4.5%	7.5%

Wilmar International Ltd

Wilmar International is among Asia's largest agribusiness groups. The vertically integrated company's business activities include oil palm cultivation oilseed crushing edible oils refining sugar milling and refining among others. It crushes a wide range of oilseeds from soybeans rapeseeds and sunflower and sesame seeds and has expanded into flour and rice milling. Wilmar's consumer brands include China's market leader Arawana. It also owns over 230000 hectares of palm plantations; Wilmar processes the crops into palm oil specialty fats oleochemicals and biodiesel which it then packages and sells. It generates some 55% its revenue from China.

Operations

Wilmar International operates through four primary segments: Feed and Industrial Products (over 50% of sales) Food Products (about 45%) Plantation and Sugar Milling (about 5%) and others.

The Feed and Industrial Products segment comprises the processing merchandising and distribution of products which includes animal feeds non-edible palm and lauric products agricultural commodities oleochemicals gas oil and biodiesel.

The Food Products segment comprises the processing branding and distribution of a wide range of edible food products which includes vegetable oil produced from palm and oilseeds sugar flour rice noodles specialty fats snacks bakery and dairy products.

The Plantation and Sugar Milling segment comprises oil palm plantation and sugar milling activities which includes the cultivation and milling of palm oil and sugarcane.

Other segment includes logistics & jetty port services and investment activities.

Overall sales of agricultural commodities and consumable products accounts for almost all of its sales.

Geographic Reach

Headquartered in Singapore Wilmar International has marketing offices manufacturing facilities and distribution networks in more than 50 countries (primarily in China India and Indonesia).

China accounts for some 55% of total revenue with countries in Southeast Asia contributing another some 20%. Europe Africa Australia New Zealand and India bring in a combined around 15% of sales.

Financial Performance

The company's revenue totaled $50.5 billion in 2020 an 18% increase from the previous year's revenue of $42.6 billion. This was due to a higher sales of agricultural commodities and consumable products.

In 2020 the company had a net income of $2.3 billion a 36% increase from the previous year's net income of $1.7 billion.

The company's cash at the end of 2020 was $2.6 billion. Operating activities generated $552.8 million while investing activities used $1.8 billion mainly for capital expenditures. Financing activities provided another $1.8 billion.

Strategy

Wilmar's strategy of building an integrated agri and food business has proven its effectiveness in achieving long-term sustainable growth despite fluctuations from time to time. The company is continuing to build more plants in existing and new complexes in new locations and to develop new high growth and complementary businesses like central kitchen soy sauce vinegar and yeast. This will widen the company's range of food products and improve its distribution network. Wilmar sees good prospects in all its business segments and the economic prospects of the major countries it operates in.

Company Background

Wilmer International was founded in Singapore in 1991. Its first project was an oil palm plantation in Indonesia.

The company expanded both operationally and geographically over the following 15 years and went public in 2006.

EXECUTIVES

Group Technical Head, Matthew Morgenroth
Group Head - Oleochemicals and Biofuels, Rahul Kale
Chief Sustainability Officer, Jeremy Goon
Chief Financial Officer, Cheau Leong Loo
Non-Executive Director, Young Guy
Non-Executive Independent Director, Yoke Sin Chong
Non-Executive Independent Director, Gim Teik Soh
Chief Scientific Advisor, Nam-Hai Chua
Group Head - Sugar, Jean-Luc Bohbot
Executive Chairman of the Board, Chief Executive Officer, Khoon Hong Kuok, $788,516 total compensation
Group Head of Internal Audit, Soo Chay Tan
Executive Vice Chairman - China, Yankui Mu
Group Head of Shipping, Hang Chwee Beh
Executive Director, Group Legal Counsel and Company Secretary, La-Mei Teo, $476,437 total compensation
Country Head - Malaysia, Chek Toong Yee
Chief Operating Officer, Executive Director, Seck Guan Pua, $409,797 total compensation
Group Financial Controller, Miow Ching Sng
Non-Executive Independent Director, Kishore Mahbubani
Group Head - Edible Oils, Kim Guan Lim
Non-Executive Director, Khoon Hua Kuok

Non-Executive Director, Khoon Ean Kuok
Group Head - Human Resources, Kok Liann Tan
Non-Executive Independent Director, Kah Chye Tay
General Manager - China, Yu Xin Niu
Country Head, Indonesia, Darwin Indigo
Non-Executive Independent Director, Thiam Hock Kwah
Non-Executive Independent Director, Siong Seng Teo
Non- Executive and Lead Independent Director, Siong-Guan Lim
Chief Information Officer, Tan Kah Chai
Auditors: Ernst & Young LLP

LOCATIONS

HQ: Wilmar International Ltd
56 Neil Road, 088830
Phone: (65) 6216 0244   **Fax:** (65) 6536 2192
Web: www.wilmar-international.com

2017 Sales

	% of total
China	51
Southeast Asia	20
Europe	6
Africa	6
India	4
Australia/New Zealand	2
Other	11
Total	**100**

PRODUCTS/OPERATIONS

2017 Sales

	% of total
Oilseeds & grains	44
Tropical oils	40
Sugar	11
Other	5
Total	**100**

Selected Operations

Palm oil cultivation
Oilseed crushing
Edible oil refining
Sugar milling & refining
Grain processing
Fertilizer manufacturing

COMPETITORS

ARCHER-DANIELS-MIDLAND COMPANY
Alpek S.A.B. de C.V.
BP P.L.C.
BayWa AG
GLENCORE PLC
INGREDION INCORPORATED
KERRY GROUP PUBLIC LIMITED COMPANY
KIKKOMAN CORPORATION
Louis Dreyfus Holding B.V.
LyondellBasell Industries N.V.
OLAM INTERNATIONAL LIMITED
TOTALENERGIES SE
Ultrapar Participacoes S/A
WH Group Limited

HISTORICAL FINANCIALS
Company Type: Public

Income Statement				FYE: December 31
	REVENUE ($ mil.)	NET INCOME ($ mil.)	NET PROFIT MARGIN	EMPLOYEES
12/20	50,526	1,534	3.0%	100,000
12/19	42,640	1,293	3.0%	90,000
12/18	44,497	1,128	2.5%	90,000
12/17	43,846	1,219	2.8%	0
12/16	41,401	972	2.3%	90,000
Annual Growth	5.1%	12.1%	—	2.7%

Debt ratio: 45.3%
Return on equity: 8.5%
Cash ($ mil.): 2,706
Current ratio: 1.22
Long-term debt ($ mil.): 6,003

No. of shares (mil.): —
Dividends
  Yield: 2.5%
  Payout: 369.5%
Market value ($ mil.): —

	STOCK PRICE ($) FY Close	P/E High/Low	PER SHARE ($) Earnings	Dividends	Book Value
12/20	35.66	148 78	0.24	0.89	2.99
12/19	30.10	155108	0.20	0.65	2.64
12/18	23.42	139121	0.18	0.70	2.54
12/17	22.99	145117	0.19	0.45	2.52
12/16	24.61	179119	0.15	0.51	2.29
Annual Growth	9.7%	— —	11.8%	14.8%	6.9%

Wistron Corp

Wistron has manufactured by design since its founding in 2001. The company is one of the leading global technology service provider (TSP) supplying innovative information and communications technology (ICT) products solutions and systems to top branded companies worldwide. Its product service lines include PCs server and networking systems enterprise storage solutions professional display products and communication devices among others. Wistron is one of the world's largest producers of notebook computers. The company's largest market is the US with about 40% of total sales.

Operations

Wistron offers after-sales services and electronics scrap recycling as well as cloud and display vertical integrations solutions. With the development of cloud computing Wistron combines hardware devices and cloud data systems through software services to provide technical service platform and solutions to its customers. The company's major activities are the design manufacture and sale of information technology products. It operates through one reportable segment: research and manufacturing service department which accounts for about 90% of the company's total sales.

Overall Wistron's major product is computer communication and consumer electronics (3C Electronics).

Geographic Reach

Wistron is headquartered in Taiwan and has offices and operations in Asia North America and Europe. The company generates about 40% of total sales from the US nearly 30% from China and almost 20% from Europe.

Sales and Marketing

Wistron sells its products to international brand customers by delivery. The company often offers volume discounts to its customers based on aggregate sales as well as extended warranty. Its sells to OEM customers Hypermarket consumer electronic retailer and end consumers. Wistron generats more than half of total sales from its top four customers in 2019.

Financial Performance

Winstron enjoyed revenue growth in recent years beginning in 2016.

However in 2019 revenue slid 1% to NT$878.3 billion. Among product lines server display smart devices and component module businesses enjoyed growth while traditional compute products (notebook desktop PC) suffered lower demand.

Profit for the year was NT$6.8 billion. The rise in income was attributable to lower cost of sales and higher Other income.

Cash and cash equivalents at the end of the year were NT$47.4 billion. Cash generated from operating activities was NT$18.6 billion while investing and financing activities used NT$8.8 billion and NT$5.1 billion respectively. Main cash uses were for acquisition of financial assets and repayment of short-term loans.

Strategy

Winstron focuses on the effective execution of its operating strategies and continuous to focus on the five major operating directions which are as follows: Optimizing global footprints including the extension of manufacturing plants; Build technology services and innovative value: Aggressively invest develop and acquire key technologies: Make positive impact from digital transformation; and Pursue sustainable value for better engagement on ESG.

EXECUTIVES

General Manager-Wistron Smart Devices Global Manufacturing, James Chou
Independent Director, S.J. Chien
Independent Director, Christopher Chang
Deputy General Manager-Wistron Technologies Service Business Group, Peter Tung
Deputy General Manager-Wistron Technologies Computing Products Business Group, Felix Lai
General Manager-Wistron Technologies Computing Products Business Group, CL Lin
General Manager-Wistron Technologies Global Manufacturing, Jackie Lai
Chief Digital Officer, Kenny Wang
Deputy General Manager-Strategy Planning, KY Wang
Chief Financial Officer, Stone Shih
Vice Chairman of the Board, General Manager-New Business, Robert Hwang
General Manager-Wistron Technologies Enterprise Business Group, William Lin
Co-General Manager, Chief Executive Officer-Wistron Smart Devices, David Shen
Chief Staff Officer, Senior Deputy General Manager, F.C. Lin
Co-General Manager, Chief Executive Officer-Wistron Technologies, Jeff Lin
Director, Chin-Bing Peng
Director, Haydn Hsieh
Chairman of the Board, Chief Strategy Officer, Simon Lin
Chief Technology Officer, Donald Hwang
Deputy General Manager-Technical, Kelvin Chang
Independent Director, Peipei Yu
Independent Director, Yu-Liang Chen
Independent Director, Sam Lee
General Manager-Wistron Smarts Devices Component Business Group, Vincent Cho
Auditors: KPMG

LOCATIONS

HQ: Wistron Corp
No. 5, Xin'an Rd., East Dist., Hsinchu 30076
Phone: (886) 3 577 0707
Web: www.wistron.com

2013 Sales

	% of total
Asia/Pacific	
Taiwan	65
Other countries	17
Other regions	18
Total	**100**

PRODUCTS/OPERATIONS

Selected Products

Application PC
Desktop computers
Information appliance
Interface cards
LCD TVs
Mobile television
Monitors
Motherboards
Netbook computers
Network storage system
Notebook computers
Portable navigation devices
Printed circuit boards (PCBs)
Rugged mobile computers
Set-top boxes
Servers
Smartphone
Spare parts
Storage products
Tablet PC
Voice over Internet Protocol (VoIP) phones
Wireless data products
Workstations

Selected Services

Design and product development
Logistics
Outsourcing management
Prototyping
Repair
Safety and compliance testing
Supply chain management
Usability and reliability testing

COMPETITORS

ASTRONOVA INC.
CISCO SYSTEMS INC.
F5 INC.
IMMERSION CORPORATION
JUNIPER NETWORKS INC.
KEYSIGHT TECHNOLOGIES INC.
LITE-ON TECHNOLOGY CORPORATION

PEGATRON CORPORATION
SILICON GRAPHICS INTERNATIONAL CORP.
SKYWORKS SOLUTIONS INC.
TD SYNNEX CORPORATION

HISTORICAL FINANCIALS

Company Type: Public

Income Statement   FYE: December 31

	REVENUE ($ mil.)	NET INCOME ($ mil.)	NET PROFIT MARGIN	EMPLOYEES
12/20	30,069	308	1.0%	0
12/19	29,335	227	0.8%	0
12/18	29,084	160	0.6%	0
12/17	28,196	131	0.5%	0
12/16	20,397	91	0.4%	0
Annual Growth	10.2%	35.5%	—	—

2020 Year-End Financials

Debt ratio: 1.0%
Return on equity: 11.9%
Cash ($ mil.): 2,355
Current ratio: 1.15
Long-term debt ($ mil.): 901

No. of shares (mil.): —
Dividends
  Yield: —
  Payout: —
Market value ($ mil.): —

Woolworths Group Ltd

Woolworths Group (Woolworths) is a diversified retailer with about 3360 stores in Australia and New Zealand including more than 180 supermarkets under the Woolworths and Countdown banners. It also operates BWS and Dan Murphy's liquor stores. Woolworths' 179-odd general merchandise discount stores operate under the Big W name. Woolworths also operates upwards more than 334 hotels. The company was founded in 1924 by Percy Christmas. It generates almost 89% of sales in its home country.

Operations

Woolworths is consists of five main divisions: Australian Food New Zealand Food Endeavour Drinks BIG W and Hotels.

Australian Food generates more than 66% of Woolworths' revenue. It consists of around 1050 Woolworths supermarkets and Metro Food Stores.

New Zealand Food (more than 11%) consists of more than 182 stores in New Zealand.

Woolworths' Endeavour Drinks business brings in about 15% of annual sales through the sale of alcoholic drinks under four banners: Dan Murphy's and BWS (liquor stores) Cellarmasters (wine home delivery) and Langton's (wine auction).

The BIG W general merchandise chain generates more than 6% of Woolworths' revenue across almost 180 stores. The Hotels business ALH Hotels (less than 2% of sales) operates almost 335 hotels including bars dining gaming accommodation and venue hire operations. The company's revenue mainly comprises the sale of goods in-store (more than 90% of total sales) and online (around 5%) and leisure and hospitality services.

Geographic Reach

Australia accounts for nearly 90% of Sydney-based Woolworths' revenue; New Zealand generates the rest.

Sales and Marketing

Woolworths racks up around 14.2 million customer visits each week. The company serves 29 million customers every week.

Financial Performance

The company revenue for fiscal 2020 increased by 8% to $63.7 billion due to all businesses excluding hotels reported strong sales growth on the prior year.

Net profit for fiscal 2020 decreased by 1% to $1.6 billion compared from the prior year with $1.8 billion.

Cash held by the company at the end of fiscal 2020 increased to $2.1 billion. Cash provided by operations was $4.6 billion while cash used for investing and financing activities were $1.9 billion and $1.6 billion respectively. Main uses of cash were payments for property plant and equipment and intangible assets; and dividends paid.

Strategy

Woolworths Group's F20 strategy house consists of six key priorities that focus on the value drivers for the company. Good progress was made against each priority enabling the ongoing transformation of the company. The key priorities are: Better together recognition; Better rewards every day; Evolving the in-store experience; Evolve its Drinks Business; Unlock Value in its Portfolio; and Better for Customers Simpler and Safer for Stores and Support.

Following Woolworths Group's initial announcement in 2019 significant progress has been made on creating and transforming Endeavour Group. After gaining shareholder approval in December 2019 the restructure and merger of ALH and Endeavour Drinks to form Endeavour Group was completed in February.

Mergers and Acquisitions

In 2021 Woolworths Group Limited agreed to extend to its strategic partnership with PFD Food Service one of Australia's leading food service suppliers by acquiring a 65% equity interest in the business. Woolworths Group will also acquire 100% PFD Freehold properties that primarily comprise 26 distribution centers. Woolworths Group will initially invest $302 million in PFD to acquire a 65% equity interest. The transaction implies a multiple of 11x pre-AASB 16 EBITDA of $57 million assuming net debt of $157 million1. Woolworths Group will also acquire PFD's freehold distribution centre properties for $249 million which will be leased back to PFD.

Company Background

Woolworths was founded in 1924 by Percy Christmas as Woolworths Stupendous Bargain Basement touting its wide range of goods offered at cheap prices. It took its name from a US chain F.W. Woolworth which did not hold the copyright to the Woolworth name in Australia at the time. It entered New Zealand shortly after in 1929 and the next near-century was marked by steady organic and inorganic expansion and brand diversification. It began selling petrol in 1996 and liquor in 1998.

HISTORY

Harold Percival Christmas first tried a mail-order dress business before opening the popular Frock Salon retail store. Christmas and his partners opened a branch store in the Imperial Arcade in Sydney in 1924 renaming it "Woolworths Stupendous Bargain Basement" and luring customers with advertisements calling it "a handy place where good things are cheap ... you'll want to live at Woolworths." The company borrowed the name from Frank Woolworth's successful US chain after determining that chain had no plans to open stores in Australia. Woolworths was listed on the Australian stock exchange in 1924.

Food sales came more than 30 years later. Woolworths opened its first freestanding full-line supermarket in 1960 then diversified into specialty retail buying the Rockmans women's clothing store chain the next year (sold in 2000). It expanded into discounting with the Big W chain in 1976 and further diversified when it bought 60% of the Dick Smith Electronics store chain in 1981 (buying the remainder in 1983).

The purchase of the Safeway grocery chain (the Australian operations of the US-based chain) put Woolworths on the top of the supermarket heap in 1985. But the company was hurting (it lost $13 million in 1985-86) because of a restructuring in the early 1980s that had weakened management by bulking up the front offices and dividing responsibilities. Woolworths got a shot in the arm from Paul Simons who returned to the company in 1987 after running competitor Franklins. Simons cleaned house in the front offices closed unprofitable stores and began the successful "Fresh Food People" marketing strategy.

Industrial Equity Limited (IEL) bought the company in 1989; IEL then became part of the Adelaide Steamship group which spun off Woolworths as a public company in 1993. Career Woolworths manager Reg Clairs took over as CEO the following year following the untimely death (on a golf course) in 1993 of Harry Watts who was being groomed for the job. As a result the company has an unwritten rule of avoiding CEOs older than 60.

Clairs took the company in a variety of new directions. Woolworths began supplying fresh food to neighbor Asia in 1995. The company added Plus Petrol outlets adjacent to Woolworths Supermarkets in 1996. It also started a superstore concept for its Dick Smith Electronics chain (Power House) that year. In 1997 the company launched its Woolworths Metro store chain which targets commuters and other on-the-run shoppers in urban areas and it aggressively jumped into wholesaling to independent grocers.

Clairs (who was turning 60 in 1999) stepped down in late 1998 and Roger Corbett took over as CEO. Woolworths also began offering banking services to its customers and bought Dan Murphy a Victoria-based liquor chain in 1998. It divested its Chisholm Manufacturing meat plants in 2000.

In 2001 Woolworths acquired two liquor store chains (Liberty Liquor Booze Bros) more than 200 Tandy Electronics stores and 72 Franklins supermarkets from Hong Kong-based Dairy Farm International Holdings (most of which were later converted to the Woolworths and Food for Less banners). It sold its Crazy Prices general merchandise stores and began restructuring its liquor operations into four distinctive formats.

Woolworths exited the New Zealand market in 2002 when it sold its supermarkets group there to Foodland Associated for $690 million.

Supermarket division chief Bill Wavish resigned in May 2003 and was replaced by former chief general manager of supermarket operations Tom Flood. Wavish was considered one of the top candidates to replace CEO Corbett. Also in 2003 the company discontinued its Australian Independent Wholesalers (AIW) operations. Flood who like Wavish was considered a likely successor to Corbett resigned abruptly in August 2004.

The company acquired Australia's biggest pub owner Australian Leisure & Hospitality (ALH) in 2005. Woolworths operates ALH's retailing activities leaving the pubs and gaming operations to its partner in the purchase The Bruce Mathieson Group. (Previously the duo had acquired a 16% stake in ALH.) In mid-2005 the company acquired the New Zealand supermarkets of Foodland Associated and 22 Action stores in Western Australia Queensland and New South Wales for about $1.8 billion.

In September 2006 the company announced it had purchased a 10% stake in New Zealand's The Warehouse retail chain. Corbett retired as CEO in October. He was succeeded by Michael Luscombe the company's long-serving director of supermarkets.

Woolworths offered about $1.7 billion in 2008 to buy all of New Zealand's leading general merchandise retailer Warehouse Group. The purchase however which would have allowed Woolworths to expand from food into general merchandise in New Zealand was blocked by that country's competition regulator in mid-2008. An attempt to take over Australia's JB Hi-Fi an independent chain of home entertainment products also failed.

In February 2011 Woolworths acquired The Cellarmasters Group from Archer Capital for A$340 million ($346 million). In October Grant O'Brien was named CEO of the company.

EXECUTIVES

Independent Non-Executive Director, Jennifer Carr-Smith, $189,060 total compensation

Chief Executive Officer, Managing Director, Executive Director, Bradford Banducci, $1,965,411 total compensation

Independent Non-Executive Director, Scott Perkins, $262,589 total compensation

Managing Director - Woolworths Supermarkets, Natalie Davis, $500,722 total compensation

Group Head - Reputation, Government Relations and Industry Affairs, Christian Bennett

Chief People Officer, Caryn Katsikogianis

Chief Customer Transformation Officer, Von Ingram

Non-Executive Independent Director, Philip Chronican

Managing Director - Wooliesx, Amanda Bardwell

Format and Network Development Director, Rob Mccartney

Chief Information Officer, John Hunt

Chief Supply Chain Officer and Managing Director of Primary Connect, Paul Graham

Managing Director - B2B and Everyday Needs, Claire Peters, $255,573 total compensation

Independent Non-Executive Chairman of the Board, Gordon Cairns, $505,798 total compensation

Independent Non-Executive Director, Holly Kramer, $190,722 total compensation

Independent Non-Executive Director, Siobhan McKenna, $246,490 total compensation

Chief Risk Officer, David Walker

Managing Director - Woolworths Food Company and Metro, Guy Brent

Chief Financial Officer, Stephen Harrison, $642,601 total compensation

Chief Marketing Officer, Andrew Hicks

Chief Legal Officer, Bill Reid

Independent Non-Executive Director, Kathryn Tesija, $238,423 total compensation

Managing Director - Big W, Pejman Okhovat

Company Secretary, Michelle Hall

Group Company Secretary, Group Counsel, Kate Eastoe

Independent Non-Executive Director, Maxine Brenner, $143,776 total compensation

Managing Director - Woolworths New Zealand, Spencer Sonn

Chief Sustainability Officer, Alex Holt

Auditors: Deloitte Touche Tohmatsu

LOCATIONS

HQ: Woolworths Group Ltd
 1 Woolworths Way, Bella Vista, Sydney, New South Wales 2153
Phone: (61) 2 8885 0000
Web: www.woolworthsgroup.com.au

2016 Sales

	% of total
Australia	90
New Zealand	10
Total	**0**

PRODUCTS/OPERATIONS

2018 Sales

	% of total
Australian Food	66
New Zealand Food	10
Endeavour Drinks	14
BIG W	6
Hotels	3
Unallocated	1
Total	**100**

Selected Brands

Australian Food
Woolworths Supermarkets Caltex Woolworths
 Woolworths Rewards Financial Services & Insurance
New Zealand Food
Countdown
Endeavor Drinks
Dan Murphy's BWS Cellarmasters Langton's
 Portfolio
BIG W ALH Group

COMPETITORS

COSTCO WHOLESALE CORPORATION
DOLLAR GENERAL CORPORATION
EDEKA ZENTRALE Stiftung & Co. KG
J SAINSBURY PLC
SUPERVALU INC.
TARGET CORPORATION
THE GREAT ATLANTIC & PACIFIC TEA COMPANY INC.
THE KROGER CO
VILLAGE SUPER MARKET INC.

HISTORICAL FINANCIALS
Company Type: Public

Income Statement
FYE: June 28

	REVENUE ($ mil.)	NET INCOME ($ mil.)	NET PROFIT MARGIN	EMPLOYEES
06/20	43,768	800	1.8%	215,000
06/19	42,026	1,886	4.5%	196,000
06/18	42,307	1,280	3.0%	202,000
06/17	42,134	1,160	2.8%	202,000
06/16	43,244	(916)	—	205,000
Annual Growth	0.3%	—	—	1.2%

2020 Year-End Financials

Debt ratio: 7.0%
Return on equity: 12.2%
Cash ($ mil.): 1,421
Current ratio: 0.62
Long-term debt ($ mil.): 1,308

No. of shares (mil.): 1,258
Dividends
 Yield: —
 Payout: 101.9%
Market value ($ mil.): —

Woori Financial Group Inc

EXECUTIVES

Non-Executive Independent Director, Yin Seop Yoon

Non-Executive Independent Director, Yo Hwan Shin

Non-Executive Independent Director, Sang Yong Park

Non-Executive Independent Director, Ji Pyeong Jeon

Chairman of the Board, Chief Executive Officer, Tae Seung Son

Vice President, Dong Su Choi

Vice President, Seok Yeong Jung

Non-Executive Independent Director, Chan Hyeong Jung

Vice President, Jin Ho Noh

Vice President, Gyu Mok Hwang

Vice President, Seok Tae Lee

Auditors: Deloitte Anjin LLC

LOCATIONS

HQ: Woori Financial Group Inc
 51, Sogong-ro, Jung-gu, Seoul 04632
Phone: (82) 2 2125 2050   **Fax:** (82) 2 0505001 0451
Web: www.wooribank.com

HISTORICAL FINANCIALS
Company Type: Public

Income Statement
FYE: December 31

	ASSETS ($ mil.)	NET INCOME ($ mil.)	INCOME AS % OF ASSETS	EMPLOYEES
12/20	366,691	1,201	0.3%	14,893
12/19	313,507	1,621	0.5%	15,529
12/18	305,364	1,823	0.6%	15,085
12/17	296,681	1,418	0.5%	14,458
12/16	258,609	1,049	0.4%	15,534
Annual Growth	9.1%	3.4%	—	(1.0%)

2020 Year-End Financials

Return on assets: 0.3%
Return on equity: 5.8%
Long-term debt ($ mil.): —
No. of shares (mil.): 722
Sales ($ mil): 10,978

Dividends
 Yield: 6.3%
 Payout: 120.5%
Market value ($ mil.): 19,776

	STOCK PRICE ($) FY Close	P/E High/Low		PER SHARE ($) Earnings	Dividends	Book Value
12/20	27.38	0	0	1.60	1.73	29.33
12/19	30.26	0	0	2.36	0.61	25.79
Annual Growth	(9.5%)	—	—	(9.3%)	29.9%	3.3%

WPP Plc (New)

Once upon a time WPP sold wiring and plastics products but now it's the world's largest marketing and advertising agency. The company operates through more than 3000 offices in upwards of 112 countries and works with some 350 of the Fortune 500 Global Companies among others. Its advertising agency networks including Grey Worldwide JWT Ogilvy & Mather and Young & Rubicam offer creative campaign development and brand management services. WPP's holdings also include public relations firms media buying and planning agencies and many specialized marketing and communications units. In addition its Kantar Group division is one of the world's leading market research organizations.

Operations

WPP operates four business segments: Advertising and Media Investment Management (45% of total revenue); Data Investment Management (20%); Public Relations & Public Affairs (8%); and Branding Identity Healthcare and Specialist Communications (27%).

The Advertising segment produces advertising content across essentially all sectors such as television internet radio magazines and newspapers. The segment also includes GroupM which is WPP's media investment management operation and is the largest global player in its field; GroupM boasts that it serves one in three adverts globally. In 2019 the WPP agreed to sell a 60% stake in marketing data consultancy Kantar to Bain Capital for proceeds of about $3.1 billion.

WPP's Data Investment Management segment is organized under the Kantar Group umbrella which comprises 12 specialized operating brands that together aim to offer a complete view of consumers. Public Relations offers advice to clients looking to communicate to customers governmental bodies and other businesses. Lastly the Branding & Identity segment offers branding and design services; marketing solutions for healthcare firms; and a range of specialist and customer services including for sports youth and entertainment marketing.

The company's nine 'billion-dollar brands' include Ogilvy J. Walter Thompson Mindshare MEC MediaCom Y&R MillwardBrown TNS and Wunderman.

Geographic Reach

WPP has a worldwide reach and operates out of upwards of 3000 offices in 112 countries. North America (mostly the US) is the company's most valuable region by revenue at around 37% of total; the UK and Western Continental Europe pull in approximately 34%. The Asia-Pacific region Latin America the Middle East and North Africa and Eastern Europe make up the rest.

The company generated revenue of more than $1 billion in five markets: the US the UK Germany Australia/New Zealand and Greater China.

Financial Performance

Note: Growth rates may differ after conversion to US Dollars.

Total revenue in 2015 was up on prior year by 6% to 12.2 billion after taking into account headwinds from foreign currency movements - the strength of the pound against the euro detracted from revenue by 1.4%. This was the fifth consecutive year of record sales. The strongest growth was in the Advertising and Media Investment Management segment which grew by 400 million. The second-largest segment Branding & Identity brought in 3.3 billion. Factors behind the year's strong results include an industry-leading performance in winning new business and customer retention as well as greater focus on emerging markets.

By region North America generated sales of 4.5 billion - representing growth of around 15%. Western Continental Europe was the only region to see sales fall in 2015 down nearly 6% on prior year to 2.4 billion - this was due to a poor macroeconomic climate and unfavorable currency movements.

Net income was up to 1245 for the year. Factors in this include exceptional gains of 296 million in 2015 which came from the sale of Kantar's internet measurement business and WPP's stakes in e-Rewards and Chime Communications. On the other hand WPP incurred 106 million in restructuring costs almost half of which was severance-related from the Data Investment Management business in Western Continental Europe.

The company's cash flow from operating activities fell from 1703 million in 2014 to a still-considerable 1360 million.

Strategy

WPP strategy comprises four key tenets: 'horizontality' which means closer links between the various WPP businesses via global client leaders and regional sub-regional and country managers (there are 45 cross-group client teams today up from 10 in 2010); a concerted effort to increase emerging market revenue to 40-45% of total sales (currently at 19% up a point since 2010); a focus on expanding new media to 40-45% of revenue (currently at 38% up 9 points since 2010); and hold firm in the more measureable marketing services such as Data Investment Management at 50% of revenue.

WPP aims to increase flexibility in cost structure particularly in staffing costs in order to mitigate against WWP's vulnerability and overreliance on large clients (the company's 10 largest customers account for 16% of revenue in 2015) which can scale back marketing budgets at short notice.

Acquisitions are a big part of WPP strategy particularly as a means to access new markets. Of the 52 new acquisitions in 2015 18 were in new markets and 37 in quantitative and digital. This was in line with the company's drive to expand the share of revenue in the Asia-Pacific region Latin America Eastern Europe and the Middle East and Africa to 40-45% and in new media to 40-45% also.

Mergers and Acquisitions

WPP has long been exceptionally active on the acquisition front and 2015 was no exception - indeed it was among the industry's most prolific acquirer for the year. The group made 40 acquisitions to a sum of 693.1 million up 40% on 2014's 495 million (although down in number from 52). The most notable acquisition includes GroupM's purchase of a majority stake of Essence the world's largest independent buyer of digital media alongside a number of bolt-ons such as ABS Creative (?2.8 million revenue in 2015) Webling Interactive (A$4.4 million) and WANDA Digital ($3.4 million). Emerging market acquisitions include nudeJEH in Thailand and Ideal Group and J ssi Intention Marketing in Brazil.

HISTORY

WPP Group began as Wire and Plastic Products a maker of grocery baskets and other goods founded in 1958 by Gordon Sampson (who retired from the company in 2000). Investors led by former Saatchi & Saatchi advertising executive (and current WPP CEO) Martin Sorrell bought the company in 1985 and began acquiring marketing firms under the shortened name of WPP. In 1987 Sorrell used revenue from these businesses (and a sizable loan) to buy US advertising warhorse J. Walter Thompson (now JWT).

JWT was founded by William James Carlton as the Carlton & Smith agency in 1864. The New York City-based firm was bought by James Walter Thompson in 1877 and was later responsible for Prudential Insurance's Rock of Gibraltar symbol (1896). It began working for Ford (which is still a client) in 1943. JWT went public in 1969.

Following its acquisition of JWT WPP formed European agency Conquest in 1988. The company (and its debt) grew the next year when it bought the Ogilvy Group (founded by David Ogilvy in 1948) for $860 million making WPP the world's largest advertising company. But its acquisition frenzy also positioned the company for a fall in 1991 when depressed economies in the US and the UK slowed advertising spending. Saddled with debt WPP nearly went into receivership before recovering the next year.

WPP began a period of controlled growth with no major acquisitions in 1993. It expanded internationally in 1994 opening new offices in South America Europe the Middle East and Asia. Winning IBM's$500 million international advertising contract that year also aided WPP's financial recovery. However this led to the loss of business from IBM's rivals including AT&T Compaq's European division (Compaq was purchased by Hewlett-Packard in 2002) and Microsoft.

By 1997 the company was again ready to flex its acquisition muscle. The firm bought 21 companies that year including a stake in IBOPE (a market research firm in Latin America) and a share of Batey Holdings (the majority owner of Batey Ads a prominent ad agency in the Asia/Pacific region). That year WPP also created its media planning unit Mindshare.

More acquisitions followed in 1998 including a 20% stake in Asatsu (the #3 advertising agency in Japan). The next year the company bought Texas-based market research firm IntelliQuest Information Group which was merged with WPP's Millward Brown unit. Along with its acquisitions WPP snagged some significant new accounts in 1998 and 1999 lining up business with Kimberly-Clark Merrill Lynch and the embattled International Olympic Committee.

In 2000 the company bought US-based rival Young & Rubicam for about $4.7 billion — one of the largest advertising mergers ever. The move catapulted WPP to the top spot among the world's advertising firms. As if that wasn't enough its Mindshare unit later snagged the $700 million media planning account of consumer products giant Unilever. WPP also took a 49% stake in Uni-World Group the largest African-American-owned ad agency in the US.

Hamish Maxwell chairman since 1996 retired in 2001 and was replaced by Philip Lader the former US ambassador to the UK. That year however WPP's top ranking was stolen away by Interpublic Group following its acquisition of True North Communications. It later sparked a bidding war with Havas Advertising when it offered $630 million to buy UK media services firm Tempus Group. WPP grudgingly completed its acquisition of Tempus in 2002. The following year the company acquired Cordiant Communications.

WPP positioned itself for both short- and long-term growth in 2005 when it completed a $1.75 billion acquisition of US-based rival Grey Group beating out bids from private equity players (including Kohlberg Kravis Roberts & Co.) and rival advertising firm Havas.

WPP in 2007 expanded its digital marketing and advertising services by acquiring 24/7 Real Media. The company snatched up Blast Radius an interactive marketing agency a few months later and aligned Blast Radius with Wunderman a marketing communications unit of WPP's Young & Rubicam Brands division.

During the same year WPP signed a lucrative $4.5 billion three-year deal for providing advertising and marketing services to Dell. In an unconventional move WPP created a new agency Enfatico to cater to the computer giant during the three-year contract.

Throughout 2008 market research rival TNS rejected several unsolicited takeover bids from WPP (including a $2.1 billion offer in July). However TNS eventually acquiesced to the proposal when more than 60% of its shareholders accepted WPP's offer in October. The deal greatly enhanced WPP's Kantar operations and created a global market research juggernaut. In late 2008 WPP also shortened its legal name from WPP Group plc to WPP plc.

The next year WPP worked to streamline its operating structure when it integrated TNS Custom with its Research International subsidiary to create the world's largest custom research group. Throughout 2010 WPP focused on acquisitions and investments in the digital arena deriving from China Brazil Singapore the UK and the US.

EXECUTIVES

Chief Executive Officer and Director, Mark Read, $1,167,130 total compensation
Chief Operating Officer, Andrew Scott
Chief Financial Officer and Director, John Rogers, $824,686 total compensation
Global Chief Executive Officer, VMLY&R, Jon Cook
Global Chief Executive Officer, Hogarth, Richard Glasson
Global Chief Executive Officer, Grey, Michael Houston
Global Chief Executive Officer, Wavemaker, Toby Jenner
Chief Marketing and Growth Officer, Laurent Ezekiel
Global Chief Executive Officer, Wunderman Thompson, Mel Edwards
Global Chief Executive Officer, Burson Cohn & Wolfe, Donna Imperato
Chief Technology Officer, Stephan Pretorius
Chief Executive Officer, AKQA, Ajaz Ahmed
Non-Executive Director, Simon Dingemans
Chairman, Roberto Quarta
Chief Client Officer, Lindsay Pattison
Group Chief Counsel and Head Sustainability, Andrea Harris
Global Chief Executive Officer, GroupM, Christian Juhl
Global Chief People Officer, Jacqui Canney
Global CEO, Ogilvy, Andy Main
Global Chief Creative Officer, Rob Reilly
Auditors: Deloitte LLP

LOCATIONS

HQ: WPP Plc (New)
Sea Containers, 18 Upper Ground, London SE1 9GL
Phone: (44) 20 7282 4600
Web: www.wpp.com

22015 Sales

	% of total
North America	37
Asia-Pacific Latin America Africa & Middle East and Central & Eastern Europe	29
Western Continental Europe	20
United Kingdom	14
Total	**100**

PRODUCTS/OPERATIONS

2015 Sales

	% total
Advertising and Media Investment Management	45
Branding Identity Healthcare and Specialist Communications	27
Data Investment Management	20
Public Relations & Public Affairs	8
Total	**100**

Selected Operations

Advertising
  Asatsu-DK (21% Japan)
  Bates Asia (China)
  Diamond Ogilvy
  Direct.com (US)
  Gallagher Group (US)
  Grey Worldwide (US)
  JWT (US)
  Kinetic Worldwide
  Malone Advertising (US)
  Ogilvy & Mather Worldwide (US)
  Red Cell (US)
  Soho Square (US)
  Studio.com (US)
  Tarantula
  The Weinstein Company (US)
  The Voluntarily United Group of Creative Agencies
  Y&R (US)
  Rainey Kelly Campbell Roalfe / Y&R (UK)
  SicolaMartin (US)
Media services
  GroupM
  MAXUS
  MediaCom Worldwide (US)
  Mediaedge:cia
  The Digital Edge
  Outrider
  Wunderman Media (US)
  Mindshare
  Performance
  Portland Outdoor
Research information and consulting
  The Kantar Group (US)
  Added Value Group
  Cheskin Added Value
  ASI/Kantar Research
  BPRI
  Cannondale Associates (US)
  Center Partners (US)
  Everystone
  Fusion 5 (US)
  The Futures Company
  Glendinning Management Consultants
  IMRB International (India)
  KMR
  AGBNielsen Media Research (50%)
  BMRB International
  Mediafax (Puerto Rico)
  Lightspeed Research (US)
  MVI
  Mattson Jack Group (US)
  Millward Brown (US)
  Research International
  RMS Instore
  TNS
  Ziment (US)
  ohal
Public relations and public affairs
  ABC Public Relations (Denmark)
  BKSH (US)
  Blanc & Otus
  Buchanan Communications
  Bulletin International
  Burson-Marsteller (US)
  Chime Communications (21%)
  Clarion Communications
  Cohn & Wolfe (US)
  Federalist Group (US)
  Finsbury

Hill & Knowlton (US)
Blanc & Otus (US)
Wexler & Walker Public Policy Associates (US)
Impact Employee Communications (Australia)
IPR Asia Holdings (China)
Ogilvy Public Relations Worldwide (US)
Penn Schoen & Berland (US)
Quinn Gillespie (US)
Robinson Lerer & Montgomery (US)
Timmons & Company (US)
Wexler & Walker Public Policy Associates
Branding and corporate identity services
  Addison Corporate Marketing
  BDGMcColl
  BDGworkfutures
  The Brand Union
  Coley Porter Bell
  Dovetail
  Fitch (US)
  G2 Worldwide
  Lambie-Nairn
  Landor Associates (US)
  The Partners
  MJM Creative Services (US)
  WalkerGroup (US)
  Warwicks
Direct marketing promotions and relationship
  marketing
  A. Eicoff & Company (US)
  Bridge Worldwide
  Dialog Marketing
  Einson Freeman (US)
  EWA
  Good Technology
  G2
  G2 Branding & Design (US)
  G2 Direct & Digital (US)
  G2 Interactive (US)
  G2 Promotional Marketing (US)
  Headcount Worldwide Field Marketing
  High Co. (34% France)
  Imaginet (US)
  Mando Brand Assurance
  Maxx Marketing (China)
  OgilvyAction (formerly 141 Worldwide)
  OgilvyOne Worldwide (US)
  rmg:connect
  RTC Relationship Marketing (US)
  VML (US)
  Wunderman
  KBM Group (US)
Health care communications
  Grey Healthcare Group (US)
  Feinstein Kean Healthcare (US)
  Geoff Howe Marketing Communications (US)
  Ogilvy CommonHealth Worldwide (US)
  Sudler & Hennessey (US)
Specialized communications
  Alliance Agency (US)
  Banner Corporation
  The Bravo Group (US)
  The Farm Group
  The Food Group (US)
  Forward
  G WHIZ (US)
  The Geppetto Group (US)
  Global Sportnet (Germany)
  JWT Specialized Communications (US)
  Kang & Lee (US)
  MosaicaMD (US)
  Metro Group
  Ogilvy Primary Contact
  PACE (US)
  PCI Fitch
  Première Group
  PRISM Group
  Spafax
  UniWorld Group (49% US)
  WING Latino (US)

COMPETITORS

ADUX
DAVIS ZIFF INC
HEIDRICK & STRUGGLES INTERNATIONAL INC.
MONSTER WORLDWIDE INC.
NEXT FIFTEEN COMMUNICATIONS GROUP PLC
PUBLICIS GROUPE S.A.
SIZMEK INC.
THE MISSION GROUP PUBLIC LIMITED COMPANY
YUME INC.

HISTORICAL FINANCIALS
Company Type: Public

Income Statement
FYE: December 31

	REVENUE ($ mil.)	NET INCOME ($ mil.)	NET PROFIT MARGIN	EMPLOYEES
12/20	16,380	(4,049)	—	99,830
12/19	17,476	824	4.7%	106,786
12/18	19,920	1,357	6.8%	134,281
12/17	20,618	2,453	11.9%	134,413
12/16	17,700	1,722	9.7%	134,341
Annual Growth	(1.9%)	—		(7.2%)

2020 Year-End Financials

Debt ratio: 51.2%	No. of shares (mil.): 1,225
Return on equity: (-45.8%)	Dividends
Cash ($ mil.): 17,603	Yield: 1.2%
Current ratio: 1.04	Payout: —
Long-term debt ($ mil.): 6,790	Market value ($ mil.): 66,266

	STOCK PRICE ($) FY Close	P/E High/Low	PER SHARE ($) Earnings	Dividends	Book Value
12/20	54.08	— —	(3.31)	0.65	5.40
12/19	70.29	142 105	0.65	3.75	8.48
12/18	54.80	109 61	1.08	3.97	9.49
12/17	90.56	90 59	1.92	4.06	10.10
12/16	110.66	104 76	1.33	2.94	8.96
Annual Growth (11.9%)	(16.4%)	— —		—(31.4%)	

X5 Retail Group NV

Auditors: Ernst & Young Accountants LLP

LOCATIONS

HQ: X5 Retail Group NV
  Zuidplein 196, Amsterdam 1077 XV
Phone:
Web: www.vprok.ru

HISTORICAL FINANCIALS
Company Type: Public

Income Statement
FYE: December 31

	REVENUE ($ mil.)	NET INCOME ($ mil.)	NET PROFIT MARGIN	EMPLOYEES
12/20	26,442	378	1.4%	339,716
12/19	27,866	313	1.1%	307,444
12/18	21,989	410	1.9%	278,399
12/17	22,399	543	2.4%	250,874
12/16	16,881	364	2.2%	196,128
Annual Growth	11.9%	1.0%	—	14.7%

2020 Year-End Financials

Debt ratio: 0.3%	No. of shares (mil.): 67
Return on equity: 26.7%	Dividends
Cash ($ mil.): 267	Yield: —
Current ratio: 0.50	Payout: 36.6%
Long-term debt ($ mil.): 2,472	Market value ($ mil.): —

Xiamen C & D Inc

You name it — Xiamen C&D trades it. Abbreviated as C&D which stands for construction and development the company primarily imports and exports sundry light industry merchandise including apparel and accessories automobiles ceramics chemicals consumer electronics edible oils luggage medical equipment metals paper products plastics textiles and wine. It also provides real estate development and property leasing through subsidiary Lianfa Group. Among its prestigious projects it operates the Xiamen International Conference & Exhibition Center a property that provides exhibit conference and hotel facilities. Xiamen C&D was founded in 1998 and is owned by Xiamen C&D Corp.

EXECUTIVES

Vice Chairman of the Board, Wenzhou Huang
General Manager, Director, Mao Lin
Independent Director, Yiyi Dai
Chairman of the Board, Yongda Zheng
Director, Yanliu Ye
Deputy General Manager, Director, Dongxu Chen
Deputy General Manager, Secretary of the Board, Guizhi Jiang
Deputy General Manager, Zhibing Wang
Chief Financial Officer, Deputy General Manager, Jia'na Xu
Independent Director, Shoude Chen
Independent Director, Tao Lin
Director, Qin Wang
Auditors: Ascenda Certified Public Accountants Co., Ltd.

LOCATIONS

HQ: Xiamen C & D Inc
7/F., Seaside Building, No. 52, Lujiang Road, Xiamen, Fujian Province 361001
Phone: (86) 592 2132319   **Fax:** (86) 592 2112185
Web: www.chinacnd.com

COMPETITORS

C C INDUSTRIES INC.
COLUMBIA PIPE & SUPPLY LLC
China Minmetals Corporation
Guangzhou R&F Properties Co. Ltd.
HINES INTERESTS LIMITED PARTNERSHIP
INTEPLAST GROUP CORPORATION
LANKFORD & ASSOCIATES INC.
MARUBENI AMERICA CORPORATION
MATERION ADVANCED MATERIALS TECHNOLOGIES AND SERV
OKAYA & CO. LTD.
PANATTONI DEVELOPMENT COMPANY INC.
STANHOPE PLC
SUMITOMO CORPORATION OF AMERICAS
THE CONNELL COMPANY
TINGUE BROWN & CO.
TRITEC REAL ESTATE CO INC
Xiamen Itg Group Corp.Ltd

HISTORICAL FINANCIALS

Company Type: Public

Income Statement — FYE: December 31

	REVENUE ($ mil.)	NET INCOME ($ mil.)	NET PROFIT MARGIN	EMPLOYEES
12/20	66,197	688	1.0%	0
12/19	48,466	671	1.4%	0
12/18	40,763	679	1.7%	0
12/17	33,592	511	1.5%	0
12/15	19,722	406	2.1%	0
Annual Growth	27.4%	11.1%	—	—

2020 Year-End Financials

Debt ratio: 3.4%
Return on equity: 12.9%
Cash ($ mil.): 8,226
Current ratio: 1.64
Long-term debt ($ mil.): 10,977
No. of shares (mil.): —
Dividends
  Yield: —
  Payout: —
Market value ($ mil.): —

Xiamen International Trade Group Corp Ltd

Auditors: Ascenda Certified Public Accountants

LOCATIONS

HQ: Xiamen International Trade Group Corp Ltd
Level 16 - 18, International Trade Building, Hubin South Road, Xiamen, Fujian Province 361004
Phone: (86) 592 5161888   **Fax:** (86) 592 5160280
Web: www.itg.com.cn

HISTORICAL FINANCIALS

Company Type: Public

Income Statement — FYE: December 31

	REVENUE ($ mil.)	NET INCOME ($ mil.)	NET PROFIT MARGIN	EMPLOYEES
12/20	53,681	399	0.7%	0
12/19	31,336	331	1.1%	0
12/18	30,036	318	1.1%	0
12/17	25,301	293	1.2%	0
12/16	14,123	150	1.1%	0
Annual Growth	39.6%	27.7%		

2020 Year-End Financials

Debt ratio: 3.5%
Return on equity: 10.2%
Cash ($ mil.): 1,901
Current ratio: 1.48
Long-term debt ($ mil.): 2,134
No. of shares (mil.): —
Dividends
  Yield: —
  Payout: —
Market value ($ mil.): —

Xiamen Xiangyu Co Ltd

Auditors: Grant Thornton LLP

LOCATIONS

HQ: Xiamen Xiangyu Co Ltd
2F, Yinsheng Mansion, Xiangyu Bonded Area, Xiamen, Fujian Province 361006
Phone: (86) 592 6516003   **Fax:** (86) 592 5051631
Web: www.xiangyu.cn

HISTORICAL FINANCIALS

Company Type: Public

Income Statement — FYE: December 31

	REVENUE ($ mil.)	NET INCOME ($ mil.)	NET PROFIT MARGIN	EMPLOYEES
12/20	55,076	198	0.4%	0
12/19	39,149	158	0.4%	0
12/18	34,021	145	0.4%	0
12/17	31,239	109	0.4%	0
12/16	17,146	61	0.4%	0
Annual Growth	33.9%	34.1%		

Xiaomi Corp

Auditors: PricewaterhouseCoopers

LOCATIONS

HQ: Xiaomi Corp
Xiaomi Campus, Anningzhuang Road, Beijing, Haidian District
Phone:
Web: www.mi.com

HISTORICAL FINANCIALS

Company Type: Public

Income Statement — FYE: December 31

	REVENUE ($ mil.)	NET INCOME ($ mil.)	NET PROFIT MARGIN	EMPLOYEES
12/19	29,582	1,443	4.9%	18,170
12/18	25,430	1,970	7.7%	16,683
12/17	17,614	(6,734)		0
12/16	9,855	79	0.8%	0
12/15	10,287	(1,167)		0
Annual Growth	30.2%	—	—	—

2019 Year-End Financials

Debt ratio: 1.3%
Return on equity: 13.1%
Cash ($ mil.): 3,725
Current ratio: 1.49
Long-term debt ($ mil.): 687
No. of shares (mil.): —
Dividends
  Yield: —
  Payout: —
Market value ($ mil.): —

Xinjiang Zhongtai Chemical Co Ltd

EXECUTIVES

Deputy General Manager, Wenhan Lu
General Manager, Hong Liu
Director, Changhui Wang
Chief Financial Officer, Jiangling Peng
Director, Yifeng Zhou
Independent Director, Jipeng Li
Director, Liangfu Li
Independent Director, Jiejiang Wu
Director, Jun Xiao
Independent Director, Xinhua Wang
Deputy General Manager, Yunhua Li
Deputy General Manager, Yongzhong Ding
Independent Director, Zihao Wang
Independent Director, Fuling Han
Deputy General Manager, Kexiong Zhao
Deputy General Manager, Secretary of the Board, Ling Zhang
Director, Perhat Maimaitiyimin
Chief Engineer, Yaling Wang
Independent Director, Yimin Jia
Director, Deyun Bian
Director, Yajing Yu

2020 Year-End Financials (top middle column)

Debt ratio: 3.0%
Return on equity: 9.0%
Cash ($ mil.): 1,779
Current ratio: 1.37
Long-term debt ($ mil.): 1,111
No. of shares (mil.): —
Dividends
  Yield: —
  Payout: —
Market value ($ mil.): —

Chairman of the Board, Jianghong Yang
Deputy General Manager, Jianping Chen
Auditors: Shu Lun Pan Certified Public
  Accountants Co., Ltd.

LOCATIONS

HQ: Xinjiang Zhongtai Chemical Co Ltd
  No. 78, Xishan Road, Urumqi, Xinjiang Province
  830009
Phone: (86) 991 8751690   **Fax:** (86) 991 8751690
Web: www.zthx.com

HISTORICAL FINANCIALS

Company Type: Public

Income Statement   FYE: December 31

	REVENUE ($ mil.)	NET INCOME ($ mil.)	NET PROFIT MARGIN	EMPLOYEES
12/20	12,873	22	0.2%	0
12/19	11,945	49	0.4%	0
12/18	10,209	353	3.5%	0
12/17	6,309	369	5.9%	0
12/16	3,364	265	7.9%	0
Annual Growth	39.9%	(46.2%)	—	—

2020 Year-End Financials

Debt ratio: 4.8%   No. of shares (mil.): —
Return on equity: 0.7%   Dividends
Cash ($ mil.): 788   Yield: —
Current ratio: 0.65   Payout: —
Long-term debt ($ mil.): 1,360   Market value ($ mil.): —

Yamada Holdings Co Ltd

Yamada Denki is the #1 consumer electronics retailer in Japan and among the overall leading retailers in the country. The company's core products include appliances audio and video equipment personal computers smart phones and software. Yamada Denki's roughly 300 stores are located mainly in midsized and large cities throughout Japan; it also maintains a retail presence in China after entering the country in 2010. In addition to Yamada Denki stores the company operates retailer KOUJIRO which specializes in building and selling custom PCs under the Frontier brand. Its Daikuma discount department chain peddles food bicycles household goods and electronics. Yamada Denki was established in 1973.

EXECUTIVES

**Chairman of the Board, President, Chief
  Executive Officer, Representative Director,**
  Noboru Yamada
Executive Officer, Representative Director, Tatsuo
  Kobayashi
Executive Officer, Director, Akira Fukui
**Executive Officer, Manager of Solution Service
  Office in Main Segment Business Unit,** Junichi
  Suzuki
Independent Director, Tsukasa Tokuhira
Director, Takayuki Fukuda
**Executive Officer, Director of Environment
  Business Management, Director of Food
  Business,** Shigeaki Yamada
Executive Officer, Director, Megumi Kogure
Executive Officer, Director, Yoshitsugu Ueno

Executive Officer, Director, Atsushi Murasawa
Independent Director, Miki Mitsunari
Executive Officer, President of Subsidiary,
  Kenichi Koyano
Auditors: KPMG AZSA LLC

LOCATIONS

HQ: Yamada Holdings Co Ltd
  1-1 Sakae-cho, Takasaki, Gunma 370-0841
Phone: (81) 570 078 181
Web: www.yamada-denki.jp

PRODUCTS/OPERATIONS

2014

	%
Home electrical	59
Home Information	29
Other products	12
Total	100

COMPETITORS

EDION CORPORATION
FAST RETAILING CO. LTD.
FERROTEC HOLDINGS CORPORATION
H2O ASSET MANAGEMENT CO. LTD.
HUSSMANN INTERNATIONAL INC.
ISETAN MITSUKOSHI HOLDINGS LTD.
J.FRONT RETAILING CO.LTD.
KENWOOD APPLIANCES LIMITED
KEYMED (MEDICAL & INDUSTRIAL EQUIPMENT)
  LIMITED
MARUI GROUP CO.LTD.
Macintosh Retail Group N.V.
NIPPAN GROUP HOLDINGS INC.
P.C. RICHARD & SON INC.
ROBERT DYAS HOLDINGS LIMITED
SEVEN & I HOLDINGS CO. LTD.
SHOP VAC CORPORATION
SONY GROUP CORPORATION

HISTORICAL FINANCIALS

Company Type: Public

Income Statement   FYE: March 31

	REVENUE ($ mil.)	NET INCOME ($ mil.)	NET PROFIT MARGIN	EMPLOYEES
03/21	15,827	467	3.0%	33,558
03/20	14,846	226	1.5%	29,481
03/19	14,453	132	0.9%	28,373
03/18	14,821	280	1.9%	29,329
03/17	13,979	308	2.2%	28,908
Annual Growth	3.2%	10.9%	—	3.8%

2021 Year-End Financials

Debt ratio: 0.1%   No. of shares (mil.): 819
Return on equity: 8.0%   Dividends
Cash ($ mil.): 672   Yield: —
Current ratio: 1.72   Payout: 28.7%
Long-term debt ($ mil.): 1,226   Market value ($ mil.): —

Yamaha Motor Co Ltd

Best known for its extensive line of motorcycles Yamaha Motor also makes scooters electric-hybrid bicycles four-wheel ATVs leisure and fishing boats racing and golf carts and snowmobiles. Other products include engines swimming pools electric wheelchairs robots and helicopter drones used to spray agricultural crops. Motorcycles which make up about 65% of the company's sales includes in-

termediate parts for products knockdown parts for overseas production all-terrain vehicles recreational off-highway vehicles (ROVs) snowmobiles electrically power-assisted bicycles automobile engines and automobile components. Founded in 1955 Yamaha Motor and its some 135 subsidiaries and affiliates operate sales and manufacturing plants throughout the world. Musical instrument manufacturer Yamaha Corporation owns about 10% of the company. Majority of its sales were generated in Asia.

Operations

The company operates in four segments: Land Mobility (about 65% of sales) Marine Products (over 20%) Robotics (around 5%) and Financial Services (nearly 5%). Other products account for the rest.

The Land Mobility segment includes motorcycles intermediate parts for products knockdown parts for overseas production all-terrain vehicles recreational off-highway vehicles (ROVs) snowmobiles electrically power-assisted bicycles automobile engines and automobile components.

The Marine Products segment comprises outboard motors personal watercraft boats FRP pools fishing boats and utility boats.

The Robotics segment includes surface mounters semiconductor manufacturing equipment industrial robots and industrial-use unmanned helicopters.

The Financial segment includes sales finance and leasing related to the company's product.

Other products include golf cars generators multi-purpose engines small-sized snow blowers and electric wheelchairs.

Geographic Reach

Headquartered in Shizuoka Japan its products are offered in some 30 countries and regions and are sold in over 180 countries and regions worldwide. It also has some 135 subsidiaries in Europe Asia Americas and Oceania. Its Asian markets account for some 40% of sales followed by North America with nearly 25% Europe with about 15% and Japan and other countries account for around 10% each.

Sales and Marketing

The company offers retail and wholesale financing leasing and insurance packages for dealerships and customers through sales finance subsidiaries in the United States Canada Australia France Mexico Brazil and other market.

Financial Performance

Although sales increased in the Robotics and Financial Services segments unit sales fell in the motorcycle business of the Land Mobility segment as well as in the Marine Products segment due to the COVID-19 pandemic leading to a year-on-year decline in net sales of 193.5 billion to 1.5 trillion.

Net income attributable to owners of parent declined 22.7 billion year on year to 53.1 billion.

Cash held by the company at the end of fiscal 2020 increased to 267.2 billion. Cash provided by operations and financing activities were 110.5 billion and 83.7 billion respectively. Cash used for investing activities was 44.0 billion mainly for purchasing fixed assets.

Strategy

Yamaha Motor is promoting a digital transformation (DX) leveraging the latest digital technology and data in a strategic manner. Amid restrictions on going outdoors and difficulties in maintaining physical customer touchpoints the company are accelerating its DX efforts based on the understanding that using DX to capture customer needs rapidly and accurately is a pressing task.

With this in mind the company launched an online sales website for motorcycles in India in fiscal 2020. Everything from product selection to purchase can be completed entirely online and those making a purchase can also choose their preferred dealership as well as other options on the website. This service also addresses the needs of consumers wishing to avoid going outdoors by offering vehicle delivery right to their door.

HISTORY

The origins of Yamaha Motor can be traced back to WWII. During the war Nippon Gakki Co. — like most Japanese businesses — retooled to make products for Japan's war effort. Nippon Gakki which literally means "Japan musical instruments" switched from making pianos and organs to building propellers fuel tanks and wing parts for Japanese Zero fighter planes. This experience would later help Nippon Gakki (now called Yamaha Corporation) diversify into other industrial products during the years immediately after the war.

Nippon Gakki built its first motorcycle the 125 cubic centimeter (cc) YA-1 in 1955. Later that year Yamaha Motor was created. Nippon Gakki retained partial ownership of the new company.

Yamaha Motor built its first sailboat using fiberglass-reinforced plastic in 1960. The company's line of marine products soon expanded to include powerboats outboard motors fishing vessels and patrol boats for Japan's Maritime Safety Agency.

During the early 1960s Yamaha Motor (along with Honda and Suzuki) successfully penetrated the US market with a line of small inexpensive motorcycles. Prior to the introduction of Japanese imports the US motorcycle market had been dominated by heavy models built by the likes of Harley-Davidson and Triumph. Yamaha Motor's motorcycles also enjoyed success in Asian markets.

In 1966 Yamaha Motor provided the engine for Toyota's 2000GT sports car. By 1968 the company had introduced its first snowmobile (the SL350) and had opened its first overseas subsidiary Yamaha Motor Europe NV (the Netherlands).

The company continued to expand geographically as it established Yamaha Motor do Brasil (1970) and Yamaha Motor Canada (1973). Product lines also grew in 1973 to include racing karts and generators. Yamaha Motor began marketing its first line of golf carts two years later. In 1977 the company created Yamaha Corporation USA. The following year Yamaha Motor began marketing its first snow blower.

By 1981 the company had developed industrial assembly robots. Yamaha Motor introduced a four-wheel ATV in 1984. The following year the company entered into a development agreement with Ford for high-performance engines and by 1986 the company offered personal watercraft. Yamaha Motor entered new markets in 1987 — gas heat-pump (GHP) air conditioners (exited in 2000) and surface mounters for printed circuit boards.

Yamaha Motor started the Zhuzhou Nanfang Yamaha Motor Co. joint venture in China in 1993 for the production of motorcycles. The following year the company established two more joint ventures in China for the production of boats. Continuing to build upon its innovative traditions Yamaha Motor developed the world's first auxiliary electric power unit for wheelchairs in 1996 and the PAS MH Super electro-hybrid bicycle in 1998.

In 1999 the company began producing motorcycles in Vietnam. Yamaha Corporation decreased its stake in Yamaha Motor to about 28% in 2000 and Toyota Motor took a 5% stake in the company to become Yamaha Motor's second-largest shareholder. In early 2001 Yamaha Motor announced that it would pursue legal action against the manufacturers of counterfeit motorcycles bearing the Yamaha name made in China.

The following year in anticipation of its 50th anniversary in 2005 Yamaha announced its NEXT 50 mid-term management plan. The three-year plan increased net sales while strengthening Yamaha's position in China India and ASEAN (Southeast Asia) countries. In 2005 Yamaha launched a subsidiary in Russia Yamaha Motor CIS to sell Yamaha products at more than 80 dealers in that country. The same year it set up a subsidiary to sell motorcycles in India.

In 2006 the Japanese government filed a criminal complaint accusing Yamaha Motor of exporting unmanned helicopters to China in violation of regulations that forbid the unlicensed export of products that could have a military use.

EXECUTIVES

Independent Director, Yuko Tashiro
Independent Director, Tetsuji Ohashi
Chairman of the Board, Hiroyuki Yanagi
Executive President, President, Chief Executive Officer, Representative Director, Yoshihiro Hidaka
Managing Executive Officer, Director, Katsuhito Yamaji
Executive Vice President, Representative Director, Katsuaki Watanabe
Senior Executive Officer, Chief Director of Research & Technology, Director, Heiji Maruyama
Independent Director, Takuya Nakata
Independent Director, Takehiro Kamigama
Auditors: Ernst & Young ShinNihon LLC

LOCATIONS

HQ: Yamaha Motor Co Ltd
2500 Shingai, Iwata, Shizuoka 438-8501
Phone: (81) 538 32 1144
Web: www.yamaha-motor.co.jp

2015 Sales

	% of total
Asia	
Japan	10
Other countries	42
North America	22
Europe	13
Others	13
Total	**100**

PRODUCTS/OPERATIONS

2015 Sales

	% of total
Motorcycles	63
Marine products	19
Power products	10
Industrial machinery & robots	3
Other products	5
Total	**100**

Selected Products

Marine products
  Boats (power sail & utility)
  Diesel engines
  Outboard motors
  Personal watercraft
  Swimming pools
Motorcycles
  Motocrossers
  Road racers
  Scooters
  Sports bikes
  Trail bikes
Power products
  All-terrain vehicles (ATVs)
  Generators
  Golf carts
  Multi-purpose engines
  Racing kart engines
  Side-by-side vehicles
  Snowmobiles
  Snow throwers
Other products

Automotive components
Automotive engines
Electric wheelchairs
Electro-hybrid bicycles (PAS)
Industrial robots
Surface mounters
Unmanned helicopters

COMPETITORS

AUTOCAM CORPORATION	MITSUBISHI MOTORS
Bayerische Motoren	CORPORATION
Werke AG	NISSAN MOTOR CO.LTD.
CYCLING SPORTS GROUP	PACCAR INC
INC.	PIAGGIO & C. SPA
GENERAL MOTORS COMPANY	SUBARU CORPORATION
GKN LIMITED	SUZUKI MOTOR
Giant Manufacturing	CORPORATION
Co.Ltd.	TATA MOTORS LIMITED
HONDA MOTOR CO. LTD.	TOYOTA MOTOR
ISUZU MOTORS LIMITED	CORPORATION
LEHMAN TRIKES U.S.A.	YAMAHA MOTOR
INC.	CORPORATION U.S.A.

HISTORICAL FINANCIALS

Company Type: Public

Income Statement   FYE: December 31

	REVENUE ($ mil.)	NET INCOME ($ mil.)	NET PROFIT MARGIN	EMPLOYEES
12/20	14,274	514	3.6%	63,367
12/19	15,333	697	4.5%	68,164
12/18	15,214	849	5.6%	67,071
12/17	14,842	902	6.1%	64,180
12/16	12,849	539	4.2%	62,322
Annual Growth	**2.7%**	**(1.2%)**	**—**	**0.4%**

2020 Year-End Financials

Debt ratio: 0.2%	No. of shares (mil.): 349
Return on equity: 7.4%	Dividends
Cash ($ mil.): 2,642	Yield: —
Current ratio: 2.14	Payout: —
Long-term debt ($ mil.): 3,438	Market value ($ mil.): —

Yamanashi Chuo Bank, Ltd. (Japan)

The Yamanashi Chuo Bank serves customers primarily in the Yamanashi prefecture near Tokyo in Japan. The bank provides a range of standard banking services including lending savings and financial planning to the retail and commercial markets. Yamanashi Chuo Bank's other services include leasing and credit card services. The bank operates about 90 branch domestic branch locations and one office in Hong Kong.

EXECUTIVES

Manager of Yoshida Branch, Director, Takehiro Hirose
President, Representative Director, Nakaba Shindo
Managing Director, Director of Business Planning, Kimihisa Tanabe
Senior Managing Director, Mitsuyoshi Seki
Managing Director, Director of Main Office Sales, Masanobu Tanaka
Manager of Hachioji Branch, Director, Fumiaki Asakawa
Director of Financial Market, Director, Tatsuyuki Miyakae

Director of General Affairs, Director, Hisato Inoue
Senior Director of Business, Director, Masaaki
 Saito
Managing Director, Senior Director of Sales,
 Tadashi Kato
Manager of Tokyo Branch, Director, Masayuki
 Ogihara
Chairman of the Board, Representative Director,
 Toshihisa Ashizawa
Independent Director, Akio Hosoda
Auditors: Deloitte Touche Tohmastu LLC

LOCATIONS

HQ: Yamanashi Chuo Bank, Ltd. (Japan)
 1-20-8 Marunouchi, Kofu, Yamanashi 400-8601
Phone: (81) 55 233 2111
Web: www.yamanashibank.co.jp

COMPETITORS

EHIME BANK LTD. THE   NISHI-NIPPON
HACHIJUNI BANK LTD.   CITYBANKLTD.
 THE

HISTORICAL FINANCIALS

Company Type: Public

Income Statement				FYE: March 31
	ASSETS ($ mil.)	NET INCOME ($ mil.)	INCOME AS % OF ASSETS	EMPLOYEES
03/21	37,802	27	0.1%	2,316
03/20	32,348	34	0.1%	2,342
03/19	31,431	44	0.1%	2,394
03/18	31,138	46	0.1%	2,428
03/17	29,384	65	0.2%	2,353
Annual Growth	6.5%	(19.1%)	—	(0.4%)

2021 Year-End Financials

Return on assets: 0.0%	Dividends
Return on equity: 1.4%	Yield: —
Long-term debt ($ mil.): —	Payout: 36.2%
No. of shares (mil.): 31	Market value ($ mil.): —
Sales ($ mil): 448	

Yamato Holdings Co., Ltd.

The well-known black cat logo of express delivery giant Yamato Holdings crosses paths throughout Japan. The holding company's flagship unit Yamato Transport delivers billions of parcels and pieces of mail yearly from a network of thousands of delivery centers throughout Japan. Besides Yamato Transport and its signature next-day TA-Q-BIN (door-to-door parcel delivery) and Kuroneko Mail (document delivery) businesses Yamato Holdings' operations include B2B logistics information system development financial transaction processing fleet maintenance and household moving services. Yamato Transport accounts for the bulk of the holding company's annual revenue. The company has more than 60 subsidiaries

EXECUTIVES

Executive Vice President, Vice President,
 Representative Director, Kenichi Shibasaki
Director, Haruo Kanda
Chairman of the Board, Masaki Yamauchi

Independent Director, Masakatsu Mori
Independent Director, Yoichi Kobayashi
President, Executive President, Representative
 Director, Yutaka Nagao
Independent Director, Mariko Tokuno
Independent Director, Noriyuki Kuga
Independent Director, Shiro Sugata
Auditors: Deloitte Touche Tohmatsu LLC

LOCATIONS

HQ: Yamato Holdings Co., Ltd.
 2-16-10 Ginza, Chuo-ku, Tokyo 104-8125
Phone: (81) 3 3541 4141
Web: www.yamato-hd.co.jp

2016 Sales

	% of total
Japan	98
North America	1
Other	1
Total	100

PRODUCTS/OPERATIONS

2016 Sales

	% of total
Delivery	78
BIZ-Logistics	8
Financial	5
Home Convenience	3
e-Business	3
Autoworks	2
Other	1
Total	100

2016 Sales

	% of total
TA-Q-BIN	66
Kuroneko DM-Bin	6
Other	28
Total	100

COMPETITORS

ANA HOLDINGS INC.
CASTLETON TECHNOLOGY
 LIMITED
CEVA LOGISTICS LIMITED
DAI-ICHI LIFE HOLDINGS
 INC.
DIMENSION DATA
 HOLDINGS LTD
FAST RETAILING CO.
 LTD.
GEODIS
HIKARI TSUSHIN INC.
INTERSERVE PLC

JAPAN POST HOLDINGS
 CO.LTD.
MITSUI-SOKO HOLDINGS
 CO.LTD.
OFFICETEAM 2 GROUP
 LIMITED
PANTHER PREMIUM
 LOGISTICS INC.
SEVEN & I HOLDINGS CO.
 LTD.
THE DUCHOSSOIS GROUP
 INC
UNIGROUP INC.

HISTORICAL FINANCIALS

Company Type: Public

Income Statement				FYE: March 31
	REVENUE ($ mil.)	NET INCOME ($ mil.)	NET PROFIT MARGIN	EMPLOYEES
03/21	15,316	512	3.3%	223,191
03/20	15,017	205	1.4%	224,945
03/19	14,676	231	1.6%	225,125
03/18	14,491	171	1.2%	213,096
03/17	13,119	161	1.2%	201,784
Annual Growth	3.9%	33.4%	—	2.6%

2021 Year-End Financials

Debt ratio: 0.0%	No. of shares (mil.): 388
Return on equity: 10.0%	Dividends
Cash ($ mil.): 2,181	Yield: 0.0%
Current ratio: 1.36	Payout: —
Long-term debt ($ mil.): —	Market value ($ mil.): 10,339

STOCK PRICE ($)		P/E		PER SHARE ($)		
	FY Close	High/Low		Earnings	Dividends	Book Value
03/21	26.62	0	0	1.37	0.37	13.40
03/20	14.95	0	0	0.52	0.27	13.28
03/19	25.01	0	0	0.59	0.25	12.96
03/18	25.08	1	0	0.44	0.25	13.14
03/17	21.48	1	0	0.41	0.25	12.23
Annual Growth	5.5%	—	—	35.5%	10.6%	2.3%

Yankuang Energy Group Co Ltd

Yanzhou Coal Mining is helping fuel China's industrialization. The company is a controlled subsidiary of Yankuang Group. It is a leader in coal production in Eastern China where most of its coal is generated though Yanzhou also operates in Australia. The company produces about 106.4 million tons of raw coal and nearly 1.8 million tons of methanol; sold over 116.1 million tons of salable coal and around 1.8 million tons of methanol. Yanzhou Coal operates seven mines producing both thermal coal for electric generation and coking coal for metallurgical production. It also owns major rail transport assets. About three-fourths of it sales came from China.

Operations

Yanzhou Coal is engaged primarily in the mining business. It is also engaged in the coal railway transportation business. The company does not currently have direct export rights in the PRC and all of its export sales is made through China National Coal Industry Import and Export Corporation Minmetals Trading Co. Ltd. or Shanxi Coal Imp. & Exp. Group Corp. In addition to coal mining (accounts for about 95% of sales) its other principal activities include methanol electricity and heat supply (some 5%) coal railway and equipment manufacturing.

Geographic Reach

Most of Yanzhou Coal's sales are in China as well as Japan South Korea Singapore Australia and other countries. The company is located in Jining City Shandong Province of East China one of the most developed area of China and the frontal area for coal transferring from north to south. About 75% of the company's total sales were generated in China Australia accounts for roughly 5% and other countries account for the rest.

Sales and Marketing

The sales revenue attributable to the company's biggest customer is RMB 2.3 billion representing about 5% over the annual sale revenue. In addition the sales revenue attributable to the its top five customers is RMB 9.5 billion accounting for nearly 15% of total annual sales revenue; the sales revenue attributable to connected parties among the top five customers is RMB1.7 billion accounting for less than 5% of the total annual sales revenue.

Financial Performance

The Company's revenue in 2019 increased to RMB 67.8 billion compared to 2018 with RMB 67.4 billion. The increase was due to higher gross sales of coals.

Profit for the year 2019 was RMB 11.8 billion higher by RMB 504.1 million compared to the prior year.

Cash held by the Company at the end of 2019 decreased to RMB 22.8 billion. Cash provided by operations was RMB 16.4 billion while cash used for investing and financing activities were RMB 11.4 billion and RMB 9.9 billion respectively. Main uses for cash were payments for construction in progress and repayment of guaranteed notes.

Strategy

In 2019 the Company by seizing policy opportunities of supply-side structural reform and replacement of the old growth drives with new ones in coal industry has continuously improved the vitality and core competitiveness in various ways such as optimizing the industrial structure strengthening lean management and accelerating changes in operating mechanisms. The coal industry focused on an integrated growth with high efficiency and significant achievements on intelligent coal mine construction. A group of Smart Fully-Mechanized Caving Workfaces advanced at home and abroad was built and put into normal operations. The percentage of high value-added products had been increased continuously through devoting great energy to implementing the win by clean coal strategy.

Company Background

The company had been increasing its reach abroad with the purchase of a mine in Australia in 2004. Yanzhou Coal Mining began expanding the production capacity and upgrading the technology at the mine the next year and commenced coal production in 2006.

However the continuing industrialization of China has seen domestic sales take on greater importance to the company. By 2007 international sales had dipped below 10% of the company's total sales where they had accounted for as nearly half at the beginning of this decade.

Still and all the company joined other Chinese businesses with interest in the Australian minerals market when it bought coal miner Felix Resources for about A$3.3 billion ($2.7 billion US) in 2009. At the time the the deal was closed it was the largest direct investment in Australia by a Chinese corporation.

Yanzhou Coal formed an $830 million joint mining venture in 2011 with its parent company state-owned Yankuang Group.

EXECUTIVES

Staff Elected Director, Ruolin Wang
Deputy General Manager, Zhaohua Tian
Deputy General Manager, Chief Security Officer, Peng Wang
Chief Engineer, Chunyao Wang
Independent Director, Hui Tian
Deputy General Manager, Chuanchang Zhang
Joint Company Secretary, Wing Han Leung
Deputy General Manager, Weiqing Li
Chairman of the Board, Wei Li
Deputy General Manager, Zhijie Gong
Independent Director, Zhaoguo Pan
Chief Financial Officer, Director, Qingchun Zhao
General Manager, Director, Jian Liu
Director, Xiangqian Wu
Independent Director, Chang Cai
IR Contact Officer, Qingbin Jin
Independent Director, Limin Zhu
Chief Investment Officer, Lei Zhang
Auditors: SHINEWING (HK) CPA Limited

LOCATIONS

HQ: Yankuang Energy Group Co Ltd
298 Fushan South Road, Zoucheng, Shandong Province 273500
Phone: (86) 537 5382319   **Fax:** (86) 537 5383311
Web: www.yanzhoucoal.com.cn

PRODUCTS/OPERATIONS

2013 sales

	% of total
Coal mining revenue	97
Methanol electricity and heat supply revenue	3
Railway transportation revenue	1
Unallocated and eliminations (1)	
Total	**100**

COMPETITORS

ADANI ENTERPRISES LIMITED	NACCO INDUSTRIES INC.
CLOUD PEAK ENERGY INC.	PEABODY ENERGY CORPORATION
COAL INDIA LIMITED	PT. BUMI RESOURCES TBK
Compliance Energy Corporation	U.S. CHINA MINING GROUP INC.
L&L ENERGY INC.	WARRIOR MET COAL INC.

HISTORICAL FINANCIALS

Company Type: Public

Income Statement				FYE: December 31
	REVENUE ($ mil.)	NET INCOME ($ mil.)	NET PROFIT MARGIN	EMPLOYEES
12/20	32,872	1,088	3.3%	0
12/19	28,835	1,245	4.3%	0
12/18	23,698	1,149	4.9%	0
12/17	23,239	1,040	4.5%	0
12/16	4,791	237	5.0%	68,550
Annual Growth	61.8%	46.3%	—	—

2020 Year-End Financials

Debt ratio: 5.5%
Return on equity: 12.1%
Cash ($ mil.): 3,752
Current ratio: 0.57
Long-term debt ($ mil.): 9,308
No. of shares (mil.): —
Dividends
  Yield: 24.2%
  Payout: 332.8%
Market value ($ mil.): —

	STOCK PRICE ($) FY Close	P/E High/Low		PER SHARE ($) Earnings	Dividends	Book Value
12/20	7.90	7	5	0.22	1.92	(0.00)
12/19	9.00	6	4	0.25	1.92	(0.00)
12/18	7.94	11	5	0.23	0.80	(0.00)
12/17	11.70	9	5	0.21	0.15	(0.00)
12/16	6.68	23	10	0.05	0.01	1.28
Annual Growth	4.3%	—	—	46.1%	258.4%	—

Yapi Ve Kredi Bankasi AS

Yapi ve Kredi Bankasi (Yapi Kredi for short) boasts over $80 billion in assets making it Turkey's fourth-largest private bank. Yapi Kredi provides financial services — including retail corporate and private banking services — in Turkey through more than 1000 branches and about 4025 ATMs. It also operates in Bahrain and has subsidiary banks in Azerbaijan Germany the Netherlands and Russia. Yapi Kredi which launched Turkey's first credit card in 1988 now has 6 million cardholders. The bank also provides leasing factoring mutual funds insurance investment banking and brokerage services. Ko § Financial Services (KFS) jointly owned by UniCredit and Ko § Holding owns 82% of Yapi Kredi.

Operations

Yapi Kredi's operates three major business segments. Its Retail Banking segment serves individuals and small- to medium- enterprises (SMEs) with consumer loans (auto mortgage and general purpose) and commercial installment loans respectively. About 59% of its loans were corporate and commercial loans in 2014 while retail loans and credit card receivables made up 27% and 14% of its total portfolio. The Retail Banking segment also provides card payment systems investment accounts insurance products and payroll services.

Its Corporate & Commercial Banking segment has three subgroups: Corporate Banking for large-scale companies Commercial Banking for medium-sized companies and Multinational Companies Banking. Yapi Kredi's Private Banking and Wealth Management segment provides investment products to high net worth customers.

About 80% of Yapi Kredi's total revenue came from interest income (mostly from loans) in 2014 while another 14% came from fees and commissions income. The rest of its revenue came from trading gains (2%) and other miscellaneous income sources (4%).

Geographic Reach

Beyond its 1000 branches in Turkey Yapi Kredi has subsidiary-owned branches in Amsterdam Moscow Baku (in Azerbaijan) and an offshore branch in Bahrain.

Sales and Marketing

Yapi Kredi's retail banking arm serves individuals with up to T$500000 (roughly $170000) in financial assets and SMEs with annual turnovers of less than $10 million. Its commercial banking customers typically have annual turnover of more than $10 million while its corporate banking customers are businesses with turnover of more than $100 million. The bank served more than 10 million customers in 2014.

Financial Performance

Note: Growth rates may differ after conversion to US dollars. This analysis uses financials from the company's annual report.

Yapi Kredi's revenue jumped 21% to T$15.9 billion ($6.8 billion) in 2014 mostly from higher interest income as its loan assets swelled by 26% (compared to sector growth of 18%) with growth in TL company general purpose and SME loans during the year. Its fee and commission income grew by 10% despite new regulations while deposits rose by 22%.

Even with revenue growth the bank's net income fell 44% to T$2.06 billion ($887 million) mostly as its discontinued operations had generated some T$1.6 billion in 2013 but also because the bank incurred higher provisions for loan and other receivable impairments.

Yapi Kredi's operating cash levels jumped 72% with operations using T$1.13 billion ($486 million) — compared to T$3.97 billion ($1.86 billion) in 2013 — mostly thanks to favorable working capital changes and higher cash earnings.

Strategy

Yapi Kredi has been moving toward digital banking channels that are quickly taking the industry by storm allowing the bank to slow expensive branch-expansion plans and cut operating costs significantly while giving customers faster access to banking services.

To this end the bank in 2015 planned to continue boosting its mobile and internet banking customer base (which reached 1.2 million and 4.2 million users at the end of 2014 respectively). It also would continue to expand its ATM network and self-service banking corners implement video channel for digital banking customers increase IVR self service usage for its call center and divert more of its calls away from branches into a central location. Though its brick-and-mortar expansion plans have slowed compared to prior years Yapi Kredi still added 54 physical branches to its network in 2014 to grow its business.

Yapi Kredi's aggressive expansion over the years has been effective at growing its customer base and overall business. Indeed during 2014 the bank added 600000 new customers to its business growing its base about 2.7 times faster than in previous years and bringing its total customer count to 10.6 million.

The bank has been the market leader in credit card market share since 1988 and controlled nearly a 22% market share of the outstanding volume nearly 20% of the issuing volume and an 18% market share on the number of credit cards outstanding during 2014. Yapi Kredi was also the market leader in leasing and factoring and was number two in mutual funds and brokerage categories.

Company Background
Yapi Kredi was previously controlled by ukurova one of Turkey's largest business conglomerates. ukurova fell to near-collapse in the aftermath of Turkey's economic crisis in 2001 and the group sold Yapi Kredi to Ko §bank owner Ko § Financial Services (KFS) in 2005. The following year KFS merged Yapi Kredi and Ko §bank in what was the largest bank merger Turkey had seen. The combined group took the Yapi Kredi name.

Ko § Financial Services (KFS) which is jointly owned by UniCredit and Ko § Holding owns 82% of Yapi Kredi which was founded in 1944.

EXECUTIVES

Non-Executive Director, Ahmet Ashaboglu

Assistant General Manager – Compliance and Internal Control and Risk Management, Mehmet Ozdemir

Assistant General Manager - Alternative Delivery Channels, Yakup Dogan

Assistant General Manager - Legal Activities Management, Cemal Sanal

Non-Executive Director, Aykut Taftali

Assistant General Manager - Human Resources and Organization, Member of the Executive Committee, Hakan Alp

Non-Executive Independent Director, Ahmet Cimenoglu

Non-Executive Independent Director, Virma Sokmen

Assistant General Manager - Credits Management, Nurgun Eyuboglu

Non-Executive Director, Niccolo Ubertalli

Non-Executive Director, Levent Cakiroglu

Assistant General Manager - Retail Banking, Member of the Executive Committee, Serkan Ulgen

Chief Operating Officer, Akif Erdogan

Non-Executive Director, Wolfgang Schlik

Assistant General Manager - Financial Planning and Administration Management, Demir Karaaslan

Assistant General Manager - Treasury and Financial Institutions, Member of the Executive Committee, Saruhan Yucel

Assistant General Manager - Corporate and Commercial Banking, Member of the Executive Board, Erhan Adali

Non-Executive Chairman of the Board, Ali Koc

Chief Executive Officer, General Manager, Executive Director, Goekhan Eruen

Auditors: PwC Bagimsiz Denetim ve Serbest Muhasebeci Mali Musavirlik A.S.

LOCATIONS

HQ: Yapi Ve Kredi Bankasi AS
Yapi Kredi Plaza D Blok, Istanbul, Levent 34330
Phone: (90) 212 339 70 00   **Fax:** (90) 212 339 60 00
Web: www.yapikredi.com.tr

COMPETITORS

AKBANK TURK ANONIM SIRKETI	PT. BANK MANDIRI (PERSERO) TBK
AXIS BANK LIMITED	SHINSEI BANK LIMITED
PT. BANK CENTRAL ASIA TBK	UNITED OVERSEAS BANK LIMITED

HISTORICAL FINANCIALS
Company Type: Public

Income Statement				FYE: December 31
	ASSETS ($ mil.)	NET INCOME ($ mil.)	INCOME AS % OF ASSETS	EMPLOYEES
12/20	65,439	683	1.0%	16,938
12/19	69,101	604	0.9%	17,446
12/18	70,569	882	1.3%	18,448
12/17	84,625	955	1.1%	18,839
12/16	76,846	831	1.1%	19,419
Annual Growth	(3.9%)	(4.8%)	—	(3.4%)

2020 Year-End Financials

Return on assets: 1.1%	Dividends
Return on equity: 11.4%	Yield: —
Long-term debt ($ mil.): —	Payout: —
No. of shares (mil.): —	Market value ($ mil.): —
Sales ($ mil): 5,959	

Yorkshire Building Society

Yorkshire Building Society (YBS) provides mortgages savings personal loans and brokerage services. One of the UK's largest mutually owned financial institutions the group also offers insurance coverage including mortgage-payment policies and home and auto insurance. YBS's brands include the Chelsea Building Society the Norwich & Peterborough Building Society YBS Share Plans and other subsidiaries including Accord Mortgages. All together YBS operates more than 200 branches and agency offices in the UK and Northern Ireland. It has 3.1 million members and assets of more than 39 billion.

Operations
YBS is one of the largest building societies in the UK and as a mutual organization is owned by and run for the benefit of members. It has no external shareholders. Its YBS Share Plans unit has been administering share plans for more than 30 years.

Geographic Reach
YBS is based in Bradford in the North of England.

Financial Performance
Note: Growth rates may differ after conversion to US Dollars.

In fiscal 2015 interest income fell 4% to 1.3 billion. A few factors were behind the fall: a reduction in mortgage rates due to high industry competition and the continued availability of low-cost retail funding. Net interest income (interest income less interest payable) was also down by 3% to 534 mil-

lion. Similarly profit was down 6% to 144.6 million.

Strategy
YBS decided in 2015 to reduce its target lending volumes to avoid competing in over-heated parts of the market.

In 2016 the company re-jigged its brand portfolio retiring its Barnsley Building Society brand in 2016 and making Chelsea Building Society online and telephone only. Branches under the two brands were rebranded as Yorkshire Building Society. The change will allow customers of both brands access the wider YBS network of more than 250 branches and agencies across the UK. YBS also enacted a consolidation process whereby if it operated two or more brands in any given area the number of branches would be reduced to one.

Company Background
The society merged with Chelsea Building Society in 2010 and with Norwich & Peterborough Building Society the following year; the two institutions continue to operate under their own brands.

The company was established in 1864 as the Huddersfield Equitable Permanent Benefit Building Society.

Auditors: PricewaterhouseCoopers LLP

LOCATIONS

HQ: Yorkshire Building Society
Yorkshire House, Yorkshire Drive, Bradford BD5 8LJ
Phone:
Web: www.ybs.co.uk

PRODUCTS/OPERATIONS

2015 Sales

	% of total
Interest receivable and similar income	96
Fees and commissions receivable	3
Other operating income	1
Total	**100**

COMPETITORS

INTU PROPERTIES PLC
LIVERPOOL VICTORIA FRIENDLY SOCIETY LTD
Leeds Building Society
Nationwide Building Society
SILVERFLEET CAPITAL LIMITED
STANDARD CHARTERED PLC
WILLIS TOWERS WATSON PUBLIC LIMITED COMPANY

HISTORICAL FINANCIALS
Company Type: Public

Income Statement				FYE: December 31
	ASSETS ($ mil.)	NET INCOME ($ mil.)	INCOME AS % OF ASSETS	EMPLOYEES
12/19	58,471	170	0.3%	3,536
12/18	54,970	191	0.3%	3,906
12/17	56,792	168	0.3%	4,220
12/16	48,708	140	0.3%	4,542
12/15	56,637	205	0.4%	4,576
Annual Growth	0.8%	(4.6%)	—	(6.2%)

2019 Year-End Financials

Return on assets: 0.3%	Dividends
Return on equity: 0.3%	Yield: —
Long-term debt ($ mil.): —	Payout: —
No. of shares (mil.): —	Market value ($ mil.): —
Sales ($ mil): 1,339	

Yunnan Copper Co., Ltd.

Auditors: Ascenda Certified Public Accountants

LOCATIONS

HQ: Yunnan Copper Co., Ltd.
  No. 111, Renmin East Road, Kunming, Yunnan
  Province 650051
Phone: (86) 871 3106797
Web: www.yunnan-copper.com

HISTORICAL FINANCIALS

Company Type: Public

Income Statement   FYE: December 31

	REVENUE ($ mil.)	NET INCOME ($ mil.)	NET PROFIT MARGIN	EMPLOYEES
12/20	13,491	58	0.4%	0
12/19	9,095	96	1.1%	0
12/18	6,895	18	0.3%	0
12/17	8,808	34	0.4%	0
12/16	8,524	29	0.3%	0
Annual Growth	12.2%	18.6%	—	—

2020 Year-End Financials

Debt ratio: 8.0%
Return on equity: 4.5%
Cash ($ mil.): 319
Current ratio: 1.16
Long-term debt ($ mil.): 1,703

No. of shares (mil.): —
Dividends
  Yield: —
  Payout: —
Market value ($ mil.): —

Zhejiang Material Industrial Zhongda Yuantong Group Co., Ltd.

EXECUTIVES

Director, Qiang Xu
Independent Director, Shenglin Ben
General Manager, Director, Hongjiong Song
Independent Director, Jianlin Shen
Deputy General Manager, Bingxue Gao
Independent Director, Weiming Xie
Director, Zuoxue Zhang
Vice Chairman of the Board, Bo Zhang
Director, Weiqing Lin
Deputy General Manager, Zhenghong Yang
Chairman of the Board, Tingge Wang
Deputy General Manager, Lu'ning Wang
Director, Chao Yan
Auditors: Pan-China Certified Public Accountants
  Co., Ltd.

LOCATIONS

HQ: Zhejiang Material Industrial Zhongda Yuantong
  Group Co., Ltd.
  Tower A, Zhongda Plaza, Hangzhou, Zhejiang Province
  310003
Phone: (86) 571 85777029   **Fax:** (86) 571 85778008
Web: www.zhongda.com

HISTORICAL FINANCIALS

Company Type: Public

Income Statement   FYE: December 31

	REVENUE ($ mil.)	NET INCOME ($ mil.)	NET PROFIT MARGIN	EMPLOYEES
12/20	61,766	419	0.7%	0
12/19	51,582	392	0.8%	0
12/18	43,693	348	0.8%	0
12/17	42,508	343	0.8%	0
12/16	29,834	310	1.0%	0
Annual Growth	20.0%	7.9%	—	—

2020 Year-End Financials

Debt ratio: 2.3%
Return on equity: 10.5%
Cash ($ mil.): 2,347
Current ratio: 1.11
Long-term debt ($ mil.): 1,064

No. of shares (mil.): —
Dividends
  Yield: —
  Payout: —
Market value ($ mil.): —

Zhejiang Materials Development Co., Ltd.

Auditors: Carea Schinda Certified Public
  Accountants

LOCATIONS

HQ: Zhejiang Materials Development Co., Ltd.
  No. 235, Wuyi Avenue, Changsha, Hunan Province
  410011
Phone: (86) 731 4588358   **Fax:** (86) 731 4588490
Web: www.nfjc.com.cn

HISTORICAL FINANCIALS

Company Type: Public

Income Statement   FYE: December 31

	REVENUE ($ mil.)	NET INCOME ($ mil.)	NET PROFIT MARGIN	EMPLOYEES
12/20	16,662	84	0.5%	0
12/19	10,557	77	0.7%	0
12/18	9,201	44	0.5%	0
12/17	7,438	26	0.4%	0
12/16	4,748	18	0.4%	0
Annual Growth	36.9%	47.3%	—	—

2020 Year-End Financials

Debt ratio: 2.8%
Return on equity: 17.6%
Cash ($ mil.): 557
Current ratio: 1.20
Long-term debt ($ mil.): 11

No. of shares (mil.): —
Dividends
  Yield: —
  Payout: —
Market value ($ mil.): —

Zhongsheng Group Holdings Ltd.

Auditors: Ernst & Young

LOCATIONS

HQ: Zhongsheng Group Holdings Ltd.
  No. 20 Hequ Street, Shahekou District, Dalian
Phone: Fax: (852) 2803 5676
Web: www.zs-group.com.cn

HISTORICAL FINANCIALS

Company Type: Public

Income Statement   FYE: December 31

	REVENUE ($ mil.)	NET INCOME ($ mil.)	NET PROFIT MARGIN	EMPLOYEES
12/20	22,682	847	3.7%	31,460
12/19	17,826	646	3.6%	29,293
12/18	15,663	528	3.4%	26,969
12/17	13,260	514	3.9%	25,577
12/16	10,310	267	2.6%	19,878
Annual Growth	21.8%	33.3%	—	12.2%

2020 Year-End Financials

Debt ratio: 5.3%
Return on equity: 22.9%
Cash ($ mil.): 1,282
Current ratio: 1.19
Long-term debt ($ mil.): 1,097

No. of shares (mil.): —
Dividends
  Yield: 0.0%
  Payout: 158.9%
Market value ($ mil.): —

	STOCK PRICE ($) FY Close	P/E High/Low	PER SHARE ($) Earnings	Dividends	Book Value
12/20	66.68	27 17	0.36	0.57	1.77
12/19	30.55	16 13	0.28	0.42	1.38
12/18	34.00	20 13	0.23	0.38	1.17
12/17	17.30	12 12	0.23	0.35	1.08
12/16	10.18	11 6	0.12	0.05	0.82
Annual Growth	60.0%	— —	31.0%	80.7%	21.3%

Zijin Mining Group Co Ltd

Auditors: Ernst & Young Hua Ming LLP

LOCATIONS

HQ: Zijin Mining Group Co Ltd
  1 Zijin Road, Shanghang County, Longyan, Fujian
  Province 364200
Phone: (86) 592 2933662   **Fax:** (86) 592 2933580
Web: www.zjky.cn

HISTORICAL FINANCIALS

Company Type: Public

Income Statement   FYE: December 31

	REVENUE ($ mil.)	NET INCOME ($ mil.)	NET PROFIT MARGIN	EMPLOYEES
12/20	26,222	995	3.8%	0
12/19	19,559	615	3.1%	0
12/18	15,409	595	3.9%	0
12/17	14,529	539	3.7%	0
12/16	11,355	264	2.3%	0
Annual Growth	23.3%	39.2%	—	—

2020 Year-End Financials

Debt ratio: 5.5%
Return on equity: 12.0%
Cash ($ mil.): 1,827
Current ratio: 0.83
Long-term debt ($ mil.): 6,909

No. of shares (mil.): —
Dividends
  Yield: 1.2%
  Payout: —
Market value ($ mil.): —

Zte Corp.

ZTE Corporation is one of China's largest telecommunications manufacturers. The company offers a variety of telecom hardware including base stations phones and systems for switching optical transport videoconferencing power supply and monitoring. The company is a leading holder of intellectual property (patents) and one of the largest telecommunications equipment exporters in China. ZTE sells to more than 500 telecom carriers worldwide with customers that include AT&T China Mobile China Unicom and China Telecom. ZTE was founded in 1985 as Zhongxing Semiconductor Co. Ltd.

Operations
ZTE gets 57% of its revenue from carriers and another 32% from its consumer business. Sales to government and corporate customers accounts for the remainder. About 19% of revenue comes from one customer and ZTE's five biggest customers account for 43% of the company's revenue.

The company does its own manufacturing from major production facilities in Brazil China Sweden France Japan Canada and the US.

Geographic Reach
ZTE has been focusing on globalization introducing more of its products and services to international markets. Some 47%of sales come from customers outside of China. ZTE offers its products and services in 160 countries with customers in every region including Asia/Pacific South Asia Europe North America Latin America and Africa.

Financial Performance
ZTE rang up higher sales profit and cash flow in 2015 from 2014.

Revenue rose 16.6% to $15.5 billion in 2015 from 2014. It posted gains in all business and geographic segments emphasized by higher increases in its biggest business and market.

Profit followed revenue rising 11.5% in 2015 to $494 million from $428 million.

Cash poured in to the tune of $869 million in 2015 compared to $179 million in 2014.

Strategy
ZTE sees an opportunity for growth in the construction of mobile and wireline broadband networks where growth is being spurred by the mobile Internet and cloud computing. The company is looking to shift its focus from supply of products to integrated product offerings for the government enterprise and service market segments while continuing to offer more in-depth products to the traditional carrier segment.

EXECUTIVES

Executive Vice President, Executive Director, Junying Gu

Non-Executive Director, Weimin Zhu

Independent Non-Executive Director, Manli Cai

President, Executive Director, Ziyang Xu

Non-Executive Director, Rong Fang

Non-Executive Director, Buqing Li

Chief Financial Officer, Executive Vice President, Ying Li

Independent Non-Executive Director, Jundong Wu

Executive Vice President, Xiyu Wang

Chief Operating Officer, Executive Vice President, Junshi Xie

Secretary of the Board, Jianzhong Ding

Independent Non-Executive Director, Jiansheng Zhuang

Chairman of the Board, Executive Director, Zixue Li

Auditors: Ernst & Young Hua Ming LLP

LOCATIONS

HQ: Zte Corp.
ZTE Plaza, Keji Road South, Hi-Tech Industrial Park, Nanshan District, Shenzhen, Guangdong Province 518057
Phone: (86) 755 26770282   **Fax:** (86) 755 26770286
Web: www.zte.com.cn

PRODUCTS/OPERATIONS

2015 Sales

	% of total
Carriers' networks	57
Consumer business	32
Government and corporate business	11
Total	**100**

2015 Sales

	% of total
Asia	
PRC (People's Republic of China)	53
Other countries	15
Europe the Americas and Oceania	25
Africa	7
Total	**100**

COMPETITORS

3517667 Canada Inc	MAXLINEAR INC.
CALAMP CORP.	MRV COMMUNICATIONS
CLEARONE INC.	INC.
COMMSCOPE HOLDING	Quanta Computer Inc.
COMPANY INC.	STARHUB LTD.
Huawei Investment &	Samsung Electronics
Holding Co. Ltd.	Co. Ltd.
KVH INDUSTRIES INC.	UNIVERSAL ELECTRONICS
LG Electronics Inc.	INC.

HISTORICAL FINANCIALS
Company Type: Public

Income Statement
FYE: December 31

	REVENUE ($ mil.)	NET INCOME ($ mil.)	NET PROFIT MARGIN	EMPLOYEES
12/20	15,511	651	4.2%	0
12/19	13,040	739	5.7%	0
12/18	12,432	(1,015)	—	0
12/17	16,721	701	4.2%	0
12/16	14,578	(339)	—	0
Annual Growth	1.6%	—	—	—

2020 Year-End Financials

Debt ratio: 3.5%	No. of shares (mil.): —
Return on equity: 10.8%	Dividends
Cash ($ mil.): 5,452	Yield: 1.1%
Current ratio: 1.44	Payout: 34.3%
Long-term debt ($ mil.): 3,457	Market value ($ mil.): —

	STOCK PRICE ($) FY Close	P/E High/Low		PER SHARE ($) Earnings	Dividends	Book Value
12/20	4.95	10	5	0.14	0.03	(0.00)
12/19	6.04	5	3	0.18	0.00	(0.00)
12/18	3.69	—	—	(0.24)	0.00	(0.00)
12/17	7.50	8	3	0.17	0.00	(0.00)
12/16	3.35	—	—	(0.08)	0.06	(0.00)
Annual Growth	10.3%	—	—	—(16.3%)		—

Zurich Insurance Group AG

Active in nearly every country globally Zurich Insurance Group is a major global provider of property and casualty and life insurance. Serving customers that include individuals small businesses and mid-sized and large companies as well as multinational corporations the company provides a wide range of products and services in more than 215 countries and territories. Its life insurance division offers life and health insurance annuities endowments and other investment products. Zurich's Farmers Group business includes all reinsurance assumed from the Farmers Exchanges by the Group. Generates most of its sales from the North America the company was founded in 1872.

Operations
Zurich operates through five segments: Property & Casualty Life regions Farmers Group Functions and Operations and Non-Core Businesses.

The Farmers provides through Farmers Group Inc. (FGI) and its subsidiaries certain non-claims services and ancillary services to the Farmers Exchanges as attorney-in-fact. FGI receives fee income for providing services to the Farmers Exchanges which are owned by their policyholders and managed by Farmers Group Inc. a wholly owned subsidiary of the Group. This segment also includes all reinsurance assumed from the Farmers Exchanges by the Group. Farmers Exchanges are prominent writers of personal and small commercial lines of business in the US. In addition this segment includes the activities of Farmers Life a writer of individual life insurance business in the US.

Property & Casualty offers insurance and reinsurance in Europe Africa North America Latin America and the Asia Pacific region. It offers car home and commercial insurance and services to individuals and small to large businesses. The Life segment also operates globally offering comprehensive range of life and health insurance products for individuals and groups including annuities endowment and term insurance unit-linked and investment-oriented products as well as full private health supplemental health and long-term care insurance.

Group Functions and Operations comprise the group's Holding and financing. Certain alternative investment positions not allocated to business operating segments are included within Holding and Financing. In addition Group Functions and Operations includes operational technical governance activities relating to technology underwriting claims actuarial and pricing.

Non-Core Businesses include insurance and reinsurance businesses that the group does not consider core to its operations and that are therefore mostly managed to achieve a beneficial runoff. Non-Core Businesses are mainly situated in the US Bermuda and the UK.

Geographic Reach
Headquartered in Zurich Switzerland Zurich has a strong position in North America and Europe as a provider of insurance to individuals commercial operations and global corporate customers with growing positions in Asia Pacific and Latin America. It generates about 55% of sales from North America. Europe Middle East and Africa accounts for more than 30% Latin America brings in about 10% and Asia Pacific represents around 5%. The company provides a wide range of property and casualty and life insurance products and services in more than 215 countries and territories.

Sales and Marketing

All of Zurich's operating segments use a mixture of distribution channels to promote their products. The company has affiliated agents and it also uses independent brokers employee benefits consultants financial advisors bank representatives travel providers and car dealerships to promote its policies. Zurich markets its products to individual small businesses commercial and corporate customers.

Financial Performance

The company's revenue for fiscal 2020 decreased to $59.0 billion compared to $71.8 billion in the prior year.

Net income for fiscal 2020 decreased to $4.1 billion compared with $4.4 billion in the prior year.

Cash held by the company at the end of fiscal 2020 increased to $11.7 billion. Cash provided by operations was $5.7 billion while cash used for investing and financing activities were $496 million and $2.7 billion respectively. Main cash uses were additions to tangible and intangible assets; and Dividends paid.

Strategy

Zurich's strategic priorities focus on: Customers; Simplification; and Innovation.

Zurich increased the efficiency of its claims assessments through digital solutions for example an app in Spain enabled its adjusters to perform live claims assessments via a smartphone camera. This cut the entire assessment time to 15?30 minutes compared with 10?15 days previously.

To further simplify the experience of its customers during the COVID-19 pandemic the company also rolled out the use of digital signatures across its business.

Zurich reorganized its internal IT and Data functions and brought in an expert in the field ? Group Chief Information and Digital Officer Ericson Chan ? to lead its efforts.

Mergers and Acquisitions

In late 2020 Zurich agreed to acquire from the founders the digital health and wellbeing service providers HealthLogix based in Australia and HealthInsite based in South Africa to further expand its Zurich LiveWell health and wellbeing business. The companies jointly known as HLX offer customers a range of mobile applications and web-based health and wellbeing solutions for corporate employees and retail customers.

HISTORY

The roots of Zurich Financial Services stretch back to the 1872 founding of a reinsurer for Switzerland Transport Insurance. The company soon branched out into accident travel and workers' compensation insurance and in 1875 it changed its name to Transport and Accident Insurance plc Zurich to reflect the changes. It then expanded into Berlin (the jumping-off point for its expansion into Scandinavia and Russia) and Stuttgart Germany. The company exited marine lines in 1880; it later left the reinsurance business and expanded into liability insurance; in 1894 it changed its name to Zurich General Accident and Liability Insurance.

In 1912 Zurich crossed the Atlantic expanding operations into the US. It agreed in 1925 to provide insurance for Ford cars at favorable terms. Zurich's business was hard hit during the war years of the late 1930s and 1940s. In 1955 the company changed its name to Zurich Insurance.

Starting in the 1960s Zurich began buying other insurers including Alpina (1965 Switzerland) Agrippina (1969 Germany) and Maryland Casualty Group (1989 US). It also bought the property liability operations of American General.

The company shifted its strategy in the early 1990s expanding into what it deemed underrepresented markets in the UK and the US. Being big

wasn't enough; Zurich needed to find a focus. It also jettisoned such marginal or unprofitable business lines as commercial fire insurance in Germany.

In 1995 Zurich bought struggling Chicago-based asset manager Kemper and in 1997 bought lackluster mutual fund manager Scudder Stevens & Clark forming Scudder Kemper. That year it also bought failed Hong Kong investment bank Peregrine Investment Holdings.

Zurich merged in 1998 with the financial services businesses of B.A.T Industries formerly known as the British-American Tobacco Co. created in 1902 as a joint venture between UK-based Imperial Tobacco and American Tobacco. As public disapproval of smoking grew in the 1970s British-American Tobacco began diversifying; it changed its name to B.A.T Industries in 1976 and moved into insurance. In 1984 it rescued UK insurer Eagle Star from a hostile offer by German insurance giant Allianz. The next year it bought Hambro Life Assurance renaming it Allied Dunbar. Moving into the large US market in 1988 B.A.T bought Farmers Insurance Group.

While B.A.T battled the antismoking army of the 1990s the insurance industry struggled with stagnant growth. In 1997 Europe's largest insurance firms were named as defendants in class action lawsuits that sought recovery for unpaid claims on Holocaust-era insurance policies. In 1998 Zurich became a founding member of the International Commission on Holocaust Era Insurance Claims (ICHEIC).

Also in 1998 Zurich and B.A.T's insurance units merged to create Zurich Financial Services. The firm reshuffled some of its holdings and sold Eagle Star Reinsurance. In 1999 Zurich spun off its real estate holdings into PSP Swiss Property and at the turn of the century it focused on expansion buying the new business of insurer Abbey Life which it merged into Allied Dunbar. In 2000 the holding companies formed to own Zurich (Zurich Allied and Allied Zurich) were merged into the firm.

EXECUTIVES

CEO, Latin America, Member of the Executive Committee, Laurence Maurice
CEO, Asia Pacific, Member of the Executive Committee, Tulsi Naidu
CEO, North America and Member of the Executive Committee, Kristof Terryn
Group Chief Executive Officer and Director, Mario Greco, $1,810,097 total compensation
Group Chief Financial Officer, Member of the Executive Committee, George Quinn
Vice-Chairman, Christoph Franz, $232,916 total compensation
CEO Zurich Global Ventures and Member of the Executive Committee, Jack Howell
Member of the Executive Committee, Chief Executive Officer of Farmers Group, Inc., Jeffrey Dailey
CEO, EMEA and Bank Distribution and Member of the Executive Committee, Alison Martin
Chairman, Michel Lies, $998,215 total compensation
Group Chief Risk Officer and Group Chief Investment Officer ad interim and Member of the Executive Committee, Peter Giger
Group Chief Information and Digital Officer and Member of the Executive Committee, Ericson Chan
Auditors: PricewaterhouseCoopers AG

LOCATIONS

HQ: Zurich Insurance Group AG
Mythenquai 2, Zurich 8002
Phone: (41) 0 625 25 25   **Fax:** (41) 0 625 35 55
Web: www.zurich.com

PRODUCTS/OPERATIONS

Selected Subsidiaries

Farmers Group Inc. (property/casualty US)
  21st Century Insurance Company (property/casualty US)
  Farmers New World Life Insurance Company (life insurance US)
  Foremost Insurance Company (specialty insurance US)
  Bristol West Holdings Inc. (specialty insurance US)
  Zurich American Insurance Company (general insurance US)
Zurich Insurance plc (general insurance UK)
Zurich International Life Limited (life insurance UK)

COMPETITORS

AMERICAN INTERNATIONAL GROUP INC.	LIBERTY MUTUAL HOLDING COMPANY INC.
AVIVA PLC	RESOLUTION LIFE AAPH LIMITED
CNA FINANCIAL CORPORATION	Swiss Life Holding AG
GORDON BROTHERS GROUP LLC	THE TRAVELERS COMPANIES INC
GROUPE CRIT	WOODBURY FINANCIAL SERVICES INC.
Holcim AG	
ICAHN ENTERPRISES L.P.	

HISTORICAL FINANCIALS

Company Type: Public

Income Statement

FYE: December 31

	ASSETS ($ mil.)	NET INCOME ($ mil.)	INCOME AS % OF ASSETS	EMPLOYEES
12/20	439,299	3,834	0.9%	55,089
12/19	404,688	4,147	1.0%	55,369
12/18	395,342	3,716	0.9%	53,535
12/17	422,065	3,004	0.7%	53,146
12/16	382,679	3,211	0.8%	53,894
Annual Growth	3.5%	4.5%	—	0.5%

2020 Year-End Financials

Return on assets: 0.9%	Dividends
Return on equity: 10.4%	Yield: 0.3%
Long-term debt ($ mil.): —	Payout: 0.5%
No. of shares (mil.): 148	Market value ($ mil.): 6,270
Sales ($ mil): 59,000	

	STOCK PRICE ($) FY Close	P/E High/Low		Earnings	PER SHARE ($) Dividends	Book Value
12/20	42.22	2	1	25.56	0.13	257.77
12/19	41.00	1	1	27.69	1.90	236.42
12/18	29.81	1	1	24.83	1.86	205.00
12/17	30.41	2	1	19.90	1.68	220.14
12/16	27.57	1	1	21.36	1.75	205.22
Annual Growth	11.2%	—	—	4.6%	(47.7%)	5.9%

Hoover's Handbook of

World
Business

Executive index

Index of Executives

A

A.O, Genevieve Bell 135
Aamund, Marie-Louise 168
Aasheim, Hilde 363
Abadin, Antonio Abril 243
Abbott, Michael 30
Abdool-Samad, Tasneem 6
Abdrabbuh, Samir A. Al 422
Abdullah, Ahmad Sufian Che 128
Abdullah, Enick Jasani Bin 232
Abdullah, Mohd Suhail 307
Abe, Yasuyuki 459
Abe, Toshinori 491
Abel, Nir 253
Abelman, Jerome 93
Abgrall-Teslyk, Karine 290
Abou-Khalil, Nassib 359
Aboumrad, Daniel Hajj 28
Abraham, Joseph 134
Abramovich, Aharon 253
Achard, Stephane 341
Achten, Dominik von 222
Ackland, Michael 485
Acut, Sabino 83
Adachi, Tamaki 418
Adali, Erhan 540
Adam, Christos 188
Adamo, Emma 45
Adams, Paul 410
Adebowale, Victor 132
Adler, Reuven 253
Adt, Katrin 108
Advaithi, Revathi 197
Afaleq, Mohammed Al 407
Agassi, Ronen 64
Ageborg, Katarina 46
Agerbo, Sussie Dvinge 515
Agg, Andy 342
Agnefjaell, Peter 283
Agogue, Christophe 184
Agrawal, Saurabh 478
Agustin, Juan Pablo San 145
Ahlstrom, Jonas 446
Ahlund, Pontus 470
Ahmad, Abdul Rahman bin 128
ahmad, Mohd Nasir 128
Ahmad, Kamaludin 307
Ahmadjian, Christina 462
Ahmaine, Mohammed 395
Ahmed, Riaz 497
Ahmed, Ajaz 533
Ahn, Nadine 412
Ahn, Hyo Ryeol 438
Ai, Sachiko 369
Aiba, Tetsuya 255
Aijaz, Mufti Irshad Ahmed 64
Aila, Minna 346
Aizpiri, Arturo Gonzalo 400
Aja, Juan Carlos 525
Akbari, Homaira 61
Akerstroem, Carina 471
Akimoto, Toshiya 437
Akimoto, Nobuhide 494
Akimov, Andrei 385

Akita, Seiichiro 65
Akiya, Fumio 437
Akiyama, Katsusada 272
Akiyama, Satoru 272
Akiyama, Yasuji 288
Akiyama, Sakie 325
Akiyama, Sakie 373
Akkol, Ozgur 281
Akkus, Senar 504
Akseli, Ari 275
Aksyutin, Oleg 385
Akutagawa, Tomomi 36
Al-Abdulla, Hussein Ali 134
Al-Abdulla, Hussain Ali 522
Al-Anzi, Abdullah 423
Al-Awfi, Talal 334
Al-Azzawi, Moutaz 407
Al-bayat, Isam Bin Alwan 422
Al-bilaihed, Mohammed Bin
   Abdulrahman 422
Al-dosary, Mahdi Nasser 422
Al-Fadli, Abdulla Ahmed 134
Al-ghubaini, Humoud Bin Awdah 422
Al-gnoon, Khalid Bin Hamad 422
Al-Haffar, Maher 109
Al-hogail, Abdulmalik Bin Abdullah 422
Al-Jaber, Hessa Sultan 522
Al-jabr, Yehia Bin Ali 422
Al-Kaabi, Nasser 395
Al-khudair, Khaled Walid 407
Al-koraya, Nader 407
Al-lazzam, Faisal Bin Mohammed 422
Al-Mohannadi, Hamad 411
Al-Murshed, Ziad Thamer 422
Al-Nahas, Mohammed Talal 407
Al-Nahas, Mohammed Talal 422
Al-Naja, Mohammed Abo 407
Al-obayed, Abdulrahman Bin
   Mohammed 422
Al-Oraini, Abdullah Ali 407
Al-Otaibi, Mohammed 407
Al-Oudan, Abdulaziz 422
Al-Qudaibi, Talal 407
Al-Qurri, Walid Bin Sulaiman 64
Al-Rammah, Jamal 407
Al-sada, Ibrahim Bin Abdullah 423
Al-Sadhan, Tareq 407
Al-Saleh, Adel 95
Al-Saleh, Adel 163
Al-Shaikh, Ahmed 422
Al-sudairi, Fahad Bin Hussein 422
Al-thani, Jassim Bin 395
Al-twaijri, Sulaiman Bin Abdulaziz 422
Al-Wehibi, Nader Ibrahim 422
Al-yahya, Mohammed 407
Al-zahrani, Riyadh 407
Al-zahrani, Jamaan Bin Ali 422
Al-Zamil, Riyadh Bin Fahad 422
Alabbadi, Mohammed 423
Alaoudah, Emad 423
Alarcon, Juan Carlos 525
Alati, Jorge Perez 110
Albers, Martin 190
Albert, Barbara 190
Albert, Mario 239
Albi, Carlos 444

Albrecht, Felix 219
Albuquerque, Isabella Saboya De 513
Aldabbagh, Khalid Hashim 422
Aldott, Zoltan 333
Alekperov, Vagit 386
Alessandro, Gianpaolo 509
Alexanderson, Marcus 402
Alfaraj, Haithem 423
Alfonsi, Davide 251
Alghamdi, Ahmed 423
Alias, Abdul Farid 307
Alisov, Vladimir 208
Alix, Gilles 519
Alkanhl, Abdullah Abdulrahman 423
Allain, Bernard 90
Allaire, Martin 322
Allen, Ken 162
Allen, Jennifer 191
Allen, Steve 405
Allera, Marc 95
Alm, Roger 523
Almaguer, Everardo Elizondo 109
Almberg, Jeanette 446
Almeida, Edmar De 206
Almeida, Flavia Buarque De 506
Almirante, Paulo 184
Almog, Yael 63
Alnowaiser, Turqi 219
Alonazi, Riyad 423
Alonso, Joseph Anthony 70
Alonso, Mercedes 346
Alonso, Rudolfo Figueroa 381
Alp, Hakan 540
Alpen, Joachim 446
Alqueres, Jose Luiz 506
Alsuwaidi, Faisal 411
Althoff, Daniel 48
Althoff, Sven 218
Altintas, N. 21
Altmueller, Wolfgang 81
Altozano, Angel Manuel Garcia 9
Altozano, Angel Manuel Garcia 227
Alund, Petra 446
Alvarado, Rodrigo Huidobro 177
Alves, Herculano Anibal 309
Alves, Rodrigo 380
Alvez, Leo 417
Alymova, Natalya 424
Amado, Luis Filipe Marques 172
Amado, Nuno Manuel da Silva 172
Amano, Reiko 170
Amano, Hiromasa 268
Amaral, Decio de Sampaio 506
Amatayakul, Parnsiree 441
Amato, Paolo 391
Ambe, Kazushi 454
Amend, Michael 213
America, Carmine 294
Ametsreiter, Hannes 520
Ammann, Erich 425
Amore, John 189
Amorim, Paula Fernanda Ramos 206
Amoroso, Stefano 293
Amoudi, Omar Bin Abdullah Al 422
Amranand, Piyasvasti 270
Amsden, Mark 413

Amunategui, Domingo Cruzat 179
An, Zhiqiang 81
An, Cong Hui 208
Anami, Masaya 67
Anand, Dorai 395
Ananthothai, Thongchai 62
Anapa, Pinar 21
Anata, Kazuhisa 237
Ancira, Carlos Eduardo Aldrete 198
Andersen, Eric 35
Andersen, Jens 168
Andersen, Kim Krogh 484
Andersen, Nils 510
Andersen, Henrik 514
Anderson, Nicholas 53
Anderson, Troy 100
Anderson, Eric 102
Anderson, Magali 229
Anderson, Jeremy 391
Anderson, William 408
Anderson, William 465
Anderson, Claudia 480
Andersson, Johan 446
Ando, Haruhiko 17
Ando, Hiromichi 127
Ando, Yoshiko 264
Andorfer, Ludwig 367
Andrada, Noel 83
Andrade, Miguel Stilwell de 172
Andrade, Juan 189
Andrade, Lucio de Castro 506
Andre, Emmanuel 395
Andreotti, Lamberto 509
Andrew, Ewan 165
Andrieux, Nathalie 106
Andronikakis, Spyridon 27
Andronov, Sergey 503
Aneaknithi, Pipit 270
Ang, Pek-san 16
Ang, Janet 70
Ang, Ramon 417
Ang, John Paul 417
Angeletti, Paola 251
Angelini, Laura 156
Angkasith, Pongsak 113
Anjolras, Pierre 517
Antebi, Yadin 63
Antonio, Maria Carina 83
Antonov, Igor 208
Anuchitworawong, Chaiyarit 62
Aoki, Shuhei 339
Aoki, Shigeki 369
Aono, Asao 491
Aoyama, Yasuhiro 314
Apfalter, Guenther 306
Apotheker, Leo 427
Appel, Frank 162
Arai, Yuko 149
Arai, Satoshi 360
Arai, Fumio 437
Arakane, Kumi 286
Arakawa, Ryuji 23
Araki, Saburo 330
Aramichi, Yasuyuki 66
Aran, Hakan 504
Aranha, Brian 39

Girard, Isabelle 250
Girouard, Denis 341
Giroux, Marc 322
Girre, Xavier 175
Given, Mark 259
Giza, Helen 203
Glaser, Juergen 321
Glashauser, Renate 81
Glasson, Richard 533
Glebikowska-Michalak, Justyna 71
Glimcher, Laurie 210
Glimstrom, Anna-Karin 446
Glomnes, Einar 363
Gloor, Christoph 55
Gloria, Geneva 83
Gluskie, Kevin 222
Glynn, Martin 465
Gnardellis, Theodore 383
Go, Maria Cristina 70
Go, Jonathan 83
Go, Alvin 83
Go, Sonia Maribel 83
Go, Marilyn 83
Gobert, Wilfred 100
Godda, Abdul Sattar Abdul Karim Abou 395
Godfrey, Darren 250
Godfrey, John 291
Goeman, Danny 200
Goffaux, Denis 507
Goh, Derrick 155
Goh, Shirley 307
Goh, Ti Liang 376
Goh, Chin Yee 376
Goh, Euleen 434
Goitini, Elena 87
Goland, Anthony 35
Golodets, Olga 424
Gomes, Fernando Jorge Buso 513
Gomez, Eugenio Llorente 9
Gomez, Sylvia 61
Gomez, Frederic Mark 83
Goncalves, Rui Paulo da Costa Cunha e Silva 206
Gonda, Barbara Garza Laguera 198
Gonda, Mariana Garza Laguera 198
Gong, Zhijie 539
Gonzalez, Adrian Sada 22
Gonzalez, Cipriano Lopez 61
Gonzalez, Monica Jimenez 171
Gonzalez, Cristian Gonzalo Palacios 177
Gonzalez, Alberto Bailleres 198
Gonzalez, Bertha 198
Gonzalez, Carlos Crespo 243
Goodman, Laurie 40
Goodman, Nicholas 94
Goodman, Jesse 210
Goodman, Russell 322
Goon, Jeremy 529
Gopakumar, K. 64
Gopalan, Srini 163
Gordillo, Rodrigo Echenique 59
Gore, Stephen 261
Gori, Roy 308
Gori, Francesco 391
Gorriz, Michael 457
Gosa, Noluthando 335
Gossiaux, Paul 134
Goto, Teiichi 205
Goto, Yuichiro 279
Goto, Yasuhiro 418
Goto, Katsuhiro 430
Goto, Masao 450
Gottlieb, Tamar 64
Gottschling, Helena 412
Gotuaco, Joseph 83
Goudswaard, Robert 29
Goulet, Beverly 410
Goulet, Jacques 465
Gowland, Glen 69
Goyal, Vijay 39
Grabner, Alexandra 367
Graf, John 189
Graham, Ian 195
Graham, Anthony 389

Graham, Paul 531
Granata, Claudio 185
Granata, Matias 255
Grande, Maria Malaxechevarria 179
Grandi, Paolo 252
Grange, Pascal 90
Grange, Pascal 133
Granger, Alberto Consuegra 171
Granger, Karine 175
Granier, Jean-Laurent 43
Grant, Shane 152
Grant, Bruce 515
Grantham, Helen 132
Grasso, Filippo 293
Grau, Richard 83
Gray, Brian 399
Greco, Mario 543
Green, Gary 139
Green, John 396
Green, Michael 470
Greenberg, Ian 82
Greenberg, Evan 126
Gref, Herman 424
Gregg, Steven 30
Gregori, Nazzareno 144
Gregoriadi, Alice 188
Greiner, Doris 75
Greve, Bradley 53
Grevy, Brian 12
Grieco, Maria Patrizia 179
Griffin, Tim 156
Griffith, Brad 421
Griffiths, Jane 53
Griffiths, Anthony 191
Griffiths, Jane 266
Grimaldo, Aimee Sentmat de 61
Grisel, Johannes 491
Grishanin, Maksim 502
Grison, Arnaud 517
Grisoni, Constance 402
Gritz, Josef 521
Grobler, Fleetwood 421
Groebler, Gunnar 50
Groot, Jan de 283
Gros-Pietro, Gian Maria 251
Grose, Douglas 42
Grosset, Michele 174
Grote, Byron 456
Gruending, Colin 178
Grunewald, Barbara 190
Grynberg, Marc 507
Gu, Wenxian 83
Gu, Feng 209
Gu, Haoliang 431
Gu, Chaoyang 432
Gu, Junying 542
Guajardo, Pablo Roberto Gonzalez 28
Gualtieri, Giuseppina 511
Guan, Bingchun 236
Guan, Xueqing 244
Guan, Shan 434
Guay, Marc 322
Guell, Miguel Montes 57
Gueltekin, Ege 21
Guenard, Jean 174
Guenter, Ismail 21
Guerin, Nicolas 372
Guerra, Karen 93
Guerrero, Angel Alija 28
Guerrero, Pedro Guerrero 71
Guevarra, Lazaro Jerome 83
Guggenheimer, Steven 234
Gui, Sheng Yue 208
Guidi, Federica 294
Guido, Alfonso 251
Guilarte, Juan Sanchez Calero 179
Guillaume, Henri 278
Guillaume-Grabisch, Beatrice 348
Guillen, Federico 359
Guillin, Sergio 525
Guindani, Pietro 185
Guionnet, Francois 398
Guiony, Jean-Jacques 301
Gularte, Miguel 309
Gulich, Frank 166

Gulliver, Stuart 262
Gunderson, Kelsey 290
Gunn, Robert 191
Guo, Yimin 118
Guo, Guanghui 119
Guo, Shiqing 121
Guo, Zhaoxu 123
Guo, Shuzhan 214
Guo, Dexuan 442
Gupta, Jan 10
Gupta, Rajiv 37
Gupta, Sapan 40
Gupta, Samir 128
Gupta, Piyush 155
Gupta, Sanjeev 439
Gupta, Ashok 465
Gur, Sharon 64
Gurander, Jan 523
Gurdal, Hakan 222
Gursoy, Ozan 504
Gutierrez, Jaime Alberto Villegas 61
Gutierrez, Pedro Fernando Manrique 171
Gutierrez, Juan 444
Gutovic, Miljan 229
Guy, Young 529
Guzman, David Martinez 22
Guzman, David Martinez 57
Guzman, Jorge Andres Saieh 255
Guzman, Douglas 412
Guzman, Enrique 525
Gwon, Yeong Su 296
Gwon, Sun Hwang 297
Gygax, Markus 514

H

Ha, Eon Tae 238
Ha, Dae Ryong 388
Haag, Markus 187
Haas, Herbert 218
Haba, Kenzo 17
Habeler-Drabek, Alexandra 187
Haberhauer, Regina 187
Habu, Yuki 14
Haeberli, Gerard 72
Haefelfinger, John 75
Haentjens, Eric 133
Hagenauer, Florian 367
Hai, Yancey 474
Haj-Yehia, Samer 64
Hajjar, Karim 451
Hakimi, Miloud 517
Haley, Sean 448
Halfon, Jean-Michel 487
Halford, Andy 311
Halford, Andy 456
Hall, Michelle 532
Hallaker, Mikael 470
Halliday, Matthew 30
Halligan, Catherine 195
Hamada, Michiyo 21
Hamada, Masahiro 452
Hamaguchi, Daisuke 299
Hamamoto, Wataru 331
Hamid, Effendy 128
Hamid, Nazlee Abdul 307
Hamid, Zulkiflee Abbas bin Abdul 307
Hamilton, Jean 399
Han, Huihua 125
Han, Kwee Juan 155
Han, Fangming 194
Han, Geun Tae 296
Han, Fuling 535
Handa, Kimio 436
Handa, Tadashi 493
Handjinicolaou, George 383
Hanebeck, Paul 246
Haneef, Rafe 128
Hanegbi, Noam 63
Hankonen-Nybom, Raija-Leena 154
Hannasch, Brian 25
Hannigan, Deirdre 17
Hannoraseth, Puntipa 65

Hanprathueangsil, Saisunee 65
Hanratty, Paul 335
Hansen, Signhild Arnegard 446
Hanzawa, Junichi 330
Hao, Yibin 209
Hara, Takashi 23
Hara, Noriyuki 334
Harada, Yasuhide 127
Harada, Hiroki 356
Harada, Susumu 493
Haraguchi, Tsunekazu 21
Haraguchi, Tetsuji 332
Harashima, Akira 493
Hardaker-Jones, Emma 291
Hardegg, Maximilian 187
Harder, V. Peter 306
Hardwick, Elanor 27
Harings, Roland 50
Harings, Lothar 287
Harlow, Jo 259
Harmer, Peter 135
Harms, Gerhard von Borries 141
Harnacke, Ulrich 91
Harney, David 213
Harper, Katherine 421
Harris, John 197
Harris, Jason 396
Harris, Margaret 465
Harris, Andrea 533
Harrison, Marianne 308
Harrison, Stephen 532
Hart, Cees 't 18
Hart, Jeffrey 111
Harthy, Said Al 64
Harthy, Nasser Bin Mohammed Al 64
Harthy, Saif Bin Salim Al 64
Hartmann, Nathalie 87
Hartung, Michael 197
Hartz, Scott 308
Hartzband, Meryl 189
Harvey, Alex 304
Hasan, Aznan 307
Hasebe, Yoshihiro 270
Hasegawa, Nobuyoshi 68
Hasegawa, Takuro 317
Hasenfratz, Linda 193
Hashar, Walid Al 64
Hashim, Hasnita Binti Dato' 307
Hashimoto, Takayuki 127
Hashimoto, Hirofumi 148
Hashimoto, Kiyoshi 272
Hashimoto, Takayuki 324
Hashimoto, Takashi 339
Hashimoto, Eiji 395
Hashimoto, Yoshihiro 432
Hasimoglu, Ibrahim 281
Hassall, Bruce 199
Haswua, Kenji 367
Hata, Hiroyuki 67
Hata, Hideo 206
Hatchoji, Takashi 312
Hato, Hideo 461
Hattori, Satoru 68
Hattori, Nobumichi 192
Hattori, Rikiya 435
Haub, Christian 322
Haugetraa, Line 363
Haugland, Thor-Christian 454
Hauser, Wolfhart 45
Hawel, Thomas 2
Hayafune, Kazuya 350
Hayakawa, Shigeru 501
Hayashi, Noboru 17
Hayashi, Akio 17
Hayashi, Kingo 127
Hayashi, Masahiro 206
Hayashi, Nobuhide 269
Hayashi, Naomi 330
Hayata, Fumiaki 459
Hayo, Zeev 63
Haza, Rafael De la 179
He, Long 97
He, Zhi-qi 97
He, Qi 115
He, Biao 124

This Page left intentionally blank